FROM THE PUBLISHER

In this edition we have introduced two new sections: '*Trusts*' and '*Motor Insurance Fraud*'. We have also renamed the '*Fraud: Criminal*' section to '*Financial Crime*' to better reflect our coverage of this market.

We have continued to expand our coverage of Scotland, providing for the first time a '*Scottish Stars at the Bar*' and '*Scottish Stable Overviews*'.

Our editorial continues to provide greater depth in the commentaries on each ranked barrister. We describe the scope of their practice and their key strengths as identified by those who instruct them, providing examples of recent major work undertaken in the last twelve months.

Michael Chambers

Published by Chambers & Partners Publishing
39 Parker Street, London WC2B 5PQ
Tel 0207 606 8844
Fax 0207 831 5662
Email info@chambersandpartners.co.uk

Publisher Michael Chambers
Editor-in-Chief Rieta Ghosh

Editor Jonathan Rubin
Deputy Editors Bryony Hirsch, Georgina Watts, Deborah Lewis, Simon Christian and Steven Preston

Bar Editor James Cowdell
Deputy Bar Editor Jon Comlay

Advertising Manager Tom Hewitt
Co-ordinators Gemma Buckle, Gillian Reid, Ben Stevens

Production Jasper John, David Nobakht, Pete Polanyk

Business Development Director Brad Sirott

Orders to Chambers & Partners Publishing
39 Parker Street, London WC2B 5PQ

ISBN 978-0-85514-124-0

Chambers & Partners Legal Recruitment
0207 606 8844

Solicitors

SURVEYS AND COMMENTARY

Specialist areas

LEADING LAW FIRMS PROFILES

INDEXES

Chambers UK – The Bar

The Bar

England & Wales

Scotland

LEADERS AT THE BAR

INDEXES

Our Editorial Team

Here you can see our editors, deputy editors and researchers. They are all currently (October 2014) working full-time at our head office in central London. More biographical information can be found on the 'About Us' page of our website.

The Editors

The Editors are responsible for the overall content of their guides and for managing the research team.

Rieta Ghosh
Publishing Director. Graduated in Ancient History at Durham University. Former Client Information Manager with a European market research agency. Previously worked at a leading business advisory company.

Alex Marsh
Managing Editor, Chambers Confidential. Graduated with a First in English Literature from Manchester University. Also has an MA with Distinction in Contemporary Literature and Novel Writing. Has previously worked as a researcher with a City headhunting firm and at a business knowledge centre.

Andrés Jaramillo Mejía
Latin America Editor. Graduated in Law from the Pontificia Universidad Javeriana in Bogotá, Colombia, and holds a Masters (LLM) Cum Laude in European Intellectual Property Law from Stockholm University. He is a qualified lawyer in Colombia, with significant experience in media, entertainment and intellectual property law.

Antony Cooke
Student Editor. Graduated from Durham University in Russian & French. Taught English at St. Petersburg State University. Previously worked at Michelin, and at PricewaterhouseCoopers as an audit associate in Investment Management. Fluent in Russian and French.

Jonathan Rubin
UK Editor. Graduated with Honours in Law from the University of Kent in 2006. Completed the LPC at BPP College in London. Qualified as a solicitor in 2009, training with a top American firm in London and Dubai. Recently completed an LLM in Law and Political Justice at Birkbeck College, University of London.

Claire Oxborrow
Editor, Legal Practice Guides. Graduated with a First in Modern History from the University of St Andrews in 2005. During postgraduate studies at the LSE she worked as a visiting lecturer at the University of Roehampton. After completing the GDL and the LPC she spent time as a volunteer at the Brunel Museum.

Dee Sekar
Editor, Women in Law. Studied Law (LLB) at Queen Mary College, University of London, and completed the Legal Practice Course at BPP Law School. Trained at a City firm and worked as a Project Finance solicitor. Also has a background in events and international marketing.

Edward Shum
Editor for Africa, Canada, the Middle East, Caribbean and Global-wide sections. Studied Law at Magdalene College, Cambridge. Previously worked at a South London law firm.

James Cowdell
UK Bar Editor. Barrister. Read Modern History at The Queen's College, Oxford. Practised at the Criminal Bar for five years and was a fee earner in the family department of a leading London law firm.

Georgia Brooks
Europe Editor. Graduated with an MA in Ancient History from UCL and a BA Hons in Classics from the University of Warwick. Previously worked in marketing and as a freelance translator and travel writer. Speaks Arabic, French and Italian.

Ignacio Abella
Editor, In-house. BA (Hons) English, Universidad de Oriente, Cuba. Bilingual in English and Spanish. Extensive experience in market research, translation/ interpretation, and social media.

Laura Mills
USA Editor. Graduated with a BA in History and Middle Eastern Studies from the University of Pittsburgh and an MA in Middle Eastern Studies from the School of Oriental and African Studies, University of London. Has studied French, Arabic, Spanish and Turkish.

Shi-Ning Koay
Asia-Pacific Editor. Graduated in Law from the University of Manchester. Completed the Bar Vocational Course and was subsequently called to the Bar in 2005. Trained with a leading Malaysian law firm and was called to the Malaysian Bar in 2006.

The Deputy Editors

The Deputy Editors work with the Researchers and the Editor to ensure the rankings and commentary are a true reflection of the market.

Antonia-Joy Akoto
UK Deputy Editor. Graduated with a BA in English from Peterhouse, Cambridge, in 2013, with a focus on art in literature.

Bryony Hirsch
UK Deputy Editor. Graduated with an honours degree in History from the University of York. Completed a GDL at the College of Law in York and an LPC at the College of Law in Bloomsbury.

Catherine Treherne-Thomas
Latin America Deputy Editor. Graduated from King's College London with a BA in Hispanic Studies. Spent a year abroad teaching English in Madrid. Fluent in Spanish.

Christopher Teevan
USA Deputy Editor. Graduated from the University of Warwick in 2006 with Honours in English Literature. Also holds an MA in Creative Writing from Royal Holloway, University of London.

Deborah Lewis
UK Deputy Editor. Graduated from the University of Nottingham in 2009 with a BA in Law with Australian Law after spending a year abroad at the University of Melbourne. Subsequently completed an MA in Media Practice from the University of Sydney.

Dimitra Tennakoon
Latin America Deputy Editor. Graduated from Wadham College, University of Oxford in 2013 with a BA in Modern Languages (Spanish & Portuguese). Has previously lived and worked in Brazil, Argentina and Spain.

Francesca Lean
Europe Deputy Editor. Graduated from Newcastle University in 2008 with a BA in French and German, with Spanish. Has previously worked in multilingual financial recruitment. Speaks French and German.

Georgina Watts
UK Bar Deputy Editor. Read Classics at The Queen's College, Oxford. Completed the GDL at The City Law School as a Lincoln's Inn Bar scholar.

Graham Gilbert
Client Research Team Leader. Graduated in Ancient History from the University of Exeter in 2010. Subsequently converted to law by undertaking the GDL at City, where he also took the Bar exams.

Harriet Carter
Global Deputy Editor. Graduated with a First in English from the University of York. Completed an MA in Aberystwyth and a PhD in Creative and Critical Writing at the University of East Anglia. Taught English literature and creative writing at both school and undergraduate level, and has written two novels.

Indy Tsang
UK/US Assistant Editor. Graduated from Regent's Park College, Oxford, with a degree in English Literature. Was active in student drama and writes fiction in her spare time.

Jane Pasquali
USA Deputy Editor. Graduated with a First in Spanish and Italian from Exeter University in 2007. Has lived and taught in Madrid and Barcelona, and worked for three years in a financial spreadbetting company in London. Awarded a PGCE with Distinction in Primary Education and Spanish in 2011.

Jessica Bird
Confidential Deputy Editor. Graduated from the University of York in 2013 with a BA (First) in English and Related Literature. Has taught English in Kerala, India, is involved with a number of charity organisations and writes for several online publications in her spare time.

Joanna Haber
Global Deputy Editor. Graduated in Public Affairs and Management and International Development from Carleton University in Canada and holds a Postgraduate Diploma in Journalism from the London School of Journalism. Speaks French.

Joe Twomey
Europe Deputy Editor. Graduated with a degree in Modern Languages (French) from New College, Oxford. Previously taught English as a foreign language in Paris.

Jon Comlay
UK Bar Deputy Editor. Graduated in History from the University of York in 2005.

Katherine Hughes
Global Deputy Editor. Graduated from the University of Leeds in 2007 with a First in Latin and Italian. Previously worked as a tour guide in Rome. Speaks Italian.

Kimberley Staines
USA Deputy Editor. Graduated with a BA in English Literature, Film & Theatre from the University of Reading, before completing the Graduate Diploma in Law and Legal Practice Course at BPP Law School.

Lucy Craig
Europe Deputy Editor. Graduated from the University of Oxford in 2011 with a BA in French and German. Previously taught English as a foreign language in Germany. Speaks French and German, and is currently learning Russian. Oversees research in Germany.

Madalena Andrade
Latin America Deputy Editor. Graduated in English Literature with Publishing from Loughborough University. Previous experience includes teaching English as a foreign language and translating. Madalena is a Portuguese national.

Matthew James
Europe Assistant Editor. Graduated from Newcastle University with a First in History in 2008. Has previously worked in an IP firm in Australia and an investment bank.

Michael Perkin
USA Deputy Editor. Graduated in English Language and Linguistics from the University of Sheffield. Worked as a journalist for Hayters Press Agency and has had copy printed in a number of national newspapers, including The Daily Telegraph and the Mail on Sunday.

Nicolás Obregón Fox
Latin America Deputy Editor. Studied literature in Madrid before gaining substantial journalistic experience with a market-leading consumer magazine. Worked for three years as a researcher/writer for a travel magazine. Speaks fluent Spanish and intermediate French.

The Deputy Editors *continued*

Peter Whitfield
USA Deputy Editor. Gained an MA with Distinction in Philosophy at Birkbeck College, University of London, and is currently working towards a research degree in the subject at the same institution. Previously earned a BA in English Literature from the University of Newcastle-upon-Tyne.

Phil Roe
Deputy Editor of Chambers Associate. Joined Chambers & Partners in 2007 from a global executive search firm, where he advised private equity clients. Graduated with an MA in English from Oxford University, and is a theatre critic for London-based newspapers in his free time.

Sam Morris
Student/Associate Deputy Editor. Graduated from the University of Leiden, The Netherlands, with a First in Political Science in 2008 and from the London School of Economics with an MSc in Comparative Politics in 2009. Has worked for the Dutch Ministry of Foreign Affairs. Speaks Dutch and German.

Sara Veale
Student/Associate Deputy Editor. Graduated Magna Cum Laude from the University of North Carolina at Charlotte with degrees in English and Dance, and recently completed an MA in English at University College London. She is a published poet and currently freelances as a literary critic.

Sarah Kogan
Asia-Pacific Deputy Editor. Graduated from Oxford University in 2004 with a degree in English Language & Literature. Worked in the television industry for several years as a Researcher and Associate Producer. Subsequently completed the GDL in 2011 at the College of Law.

Simon Christian
UK Deputy Editor. Studied Law at University College London and has been called to the Bar at the Middle Temple.

Stefan Corre
USA Deputy Editor. Graduated from Leeds University with a degree in Philosophy. Subsequently attended the College of Law in London and qualified and worked as a solicitor in the West End of London.

Steven Preston
UK Deputy Editor. Graduated from University College London with an LLB.

Yvonne Berman
Asia-Pacific Deputy Editor. Having completed a law degree (at the University of North London) became a member of the Bar of England and Wales (non-practising) and spent several years in industry and private practice in IP, specialising in trade marks and copyright.

The Assistant Editors and Senior Researchers

The Assistant Editors and Senior Researchers are responsible for interviewing clients and lawyers, and for assisting with the rankings and commentary.

Alistair Faiers
UK/USA Senior Researcher. Graduated in 2012 from the University of Warwick with a BA in English and Latin Literature. Writes and directs plays for his theatre company in his spare time.

Anna Winter
Student/Associate Senior Researcher. Graduated with a BA in English Literature from Balliol College, Oxford. Took journalism qualifications following internships at The Observer and The New Statesman magazine.

Ben McCarthy
Student/Associate Senior Researcher. Graduated from the University of Reading with a First in History, and also presented a paper at the International Children of War Conference in 2011. Currently writes for a film review site in his spare time.

Cesare Omissi
UK/USA Senior Researcher. Graduated with a BA (Hons) in Ancient and Modern History from Corpus Christi College, Oxford, in 2010. Has previously worked in private practice in the field of intellectual property, specialising in trade mark matters throughout the world.

Chris Nicholson
UK/USA Senior Researcher. Completed BA and MA degrees in History at UCL, where he also submitted his PhD in History. Has co-edited two books on Central and Eastern Europe, and served on the editorial boards of two academic journals.

Claudia Solaro
Confidential Senior Researcher. Graduated with a First in French and Classics from the University of Reading. Fluent in French and Italian.

David Greaves
UK/USA Senior Researcher. Graduated in English and Creative Writing from the University of Warwick before obtaining an MLitt (Distinction) in Creative Writing from the University of Glasgow. Speaks Spanish.

David Watson
Asia Senior Researcher. Has a BA in Modern History from Keble College, Oxford, an MA in War Studies from King's College, London, and over 20 years' experience researching military historical matters for a Ministry of Defence Agency.

Felipe Goralski
Latin America Senior Researcher. Graduated with a BA (Hons) in Politics from UCL in 2006. Previously worked for a French medical assistance company in London. Studied the GDL and LPC at College of Law and obtained an LLB. Speaks Spanish and French.

The Assistant Editors and Senior Researchers *continued*

Fiona Wong
Confidential Senior Researcher. Holds a BA (First) and an MPhil in English from the Chinese University of Hong Kong, and a PhD in English and Comparative Literary Studies from the University of Warwick. Has been writing for publishing companies and an online magazine. Speaks Cantonese and Mandarin.

Francois Gill
UK Assistant Editor. Graduated with a First in History from University College London in 2006. Went on to complete a Master's in the subject at UCL. Speaks French.

Jack Torbet
Asia Senior Researcher. Graduated with an LLB (Hons) in Law and French from the University of Glasgow. Holds an LLM from SOAS in Human Rights, Conflict and Justice. Spent a year studying International Law at the Université de Strasbourg in France.

Jack Watkins
Student/Associate Senior Researcher. Graduated with a BA Honours degree in History from the University of Sheffield in 2010.

James Booth
UK/USA Assistant Editor. Graduated from the University of Manchester with a BA in History and completed the Graduate Diploma in Law at BPP Law School.

Jamie Yule
Europe Senior Researcher. Graduated with a degree in law from Oxford. Also holds an LLM with Distinction from Dundee University.

Jurgita Meskauskaite
Europe Assistant Editor. Graduated with an MA in Development Management from the University of Westminster in 2007. Fluent in Russian and Lithuanian.

Kielan Thompson
Confidential Assistant Editor. Graduated with a BA (First) in History and English in 2007, before completing an MRes in Russian Literature from the University of Keele in 2009.

Mandeep Sran
UK/US Senior Researcher. Graduated in Law from the School of Oriental and African Studies (SOAS) at the University of London, and completed the Legal Practice Course at the Nottingham Law School. Qualified as a solicitor in 2009 specialising in litigation.

Paul Rance
Student / Associate Assistant Editor. Graduated from Exeter University with a First in English Literature, and also spent a year abroad at the University of Toronto to read Canadian Literature. Completed an MA in English at UCL in 2010.

Ramani Rajaratnam
UK/USA Senior Researcher. Graduated from Nottingham University with a BA (Hons) in History in 2011. Recently completed the GDL at BPP Law School, London.

Raquel Holzmann
Latin America Assistant Editor. Graduated from UCL with a degree in European Social and Political Studies with French. Previously worked for the NHS and taught English as a foreign language in Brazil.

Rosie Seville
Global Senior Researcher. Graduated with a First in Chinese and French from the University of Leeds in 2012, and also studied at National Taiwan University.

Rupert Wilson
UK/USA Assistant Editor. Graduated from Trinity College, Cambridge, in 2010 with a BA (Hons) in History. Has since studied the GDL and BPTC at City Law School, London.

Samantha Steele
Asia Senior Researcher. Graduated from the University of Oxford with a BA in Jurisprudence. Has taught English in Australia and New Zealand.

Stella Heng
Global Assistant Editor. Graduated in Law from London School of Economics. Completed the Bar Vocational Course at the College of Law and was called to the Bar in 2010. Fluent in English and French, and also speaks Malay.

Talia Addleman
Europe Assistant Editor. Graduated from the University of Birmingham in 2008 with a BA in Ancient and Medieval History. Has completed the GDL and LPC at the College of Law.

Tobias Waters
Asia Assistant Editor. Graduated from the University of Kent with a BA in English and American Literature, and also holds an MA in English Literary Studies from the University of Durham.

Toby Eccleshall
UK/USA Senior Researcher. Graduated from the University of Birmingham with a BA in German and Russian Studies and subsequently completed the GDL at Brunel University. Has previously worked as an English teacher in Moscow

The Researchers

The Researchers are responsible for interviewing clients and lawyers, and for assembling the data needed for the rankings and commentary.

Adam Squibbs
Graduated from the University of Cambridge in 2013 with a BA in Law.

Aileen Devlin
Graduated in Law from Corpus Christi, Cambridge in 2013; spent 2011/12 studying Law at La Universidad Autonoma de Madrid.

Alexia Aradipiotis
Graduated from the University of Nottingham in 2012 with a degree in English and subsequently completed her GDL at BPP Law School. Speaks fluent Modern Greek.

Alice Saville
Graduated from Oxford University with a First in English, then completed an MA in Medieval and Renaissance Studies at UCL. Also writes theatre criticism and features for several arts publications.

Ben Nickson
Graduated with a BA in English Literature from Cambridge University in 2007, and has recently completed a GDL with BPP College in Bristol. Has also worked in the Civil Service, as a freelance copy-editor and writer.

Carlota Garcia-Patel
Graduated from Queen Mary, University Of London, with a BA in Hispanic Studies and Portuguese. Studied abroad in both Spain and Portugal.

Carly Minsky
Graduated from University of Nottingham with first class joint honours in Physics and Philosophy. Did her postgraduate BPhil in Philosophy at Balliol College, Oxford University. Has worked on development programmes in India and Sri Lanka. Continues to write articles about travel, art and culture in her spare time.

Charles Davies
Graduated in 2011 with a Master's degree in Modern Languages (French and Spanish) from the University of Manchester.

Charles Scherer
Studied Ancient History at the University of Bristol, and has previously worked as a copywriter.

Charlotte Baker
Graduated from the University of St Andrews with an MA (Hons) in English Literature before completing the Graduate Diploma in Law (University of Law) and the BPTC (Kaplan Law School). Denning scholar and member of Lincoln's Inn.

Chloe Kite
Graduated with an LLB in Law from the London School of Economics. Has spent time in China both working and studying Mandarin.

Daniel Fisher
Graduated from Queen Mary University of London with a degree in Film (BA) in 2012. Previously worked in video production.

Danielle Vidigal
Holds a bachelor's degree in Cinema. Has worked for the main broadcasting company in Brazil and as an interpreter for the NHS. Speaks Portuguese and Spanish, and is learning German.

Dennis Li
Graduated with an MA (Merit) in Publishing from University College London. Considerable editing and project management experience in publishing. Native Mandarin speaker and also speaks German.

Diana Statham
Graduated with a BA (Hons) in Russian and French from Murray Edwards College, Cambridge, in 2013. Spent one year at the St. Petersburg State Conservatory. Studying the cello.

Duncan Scott
Graduated from UCL in 2012 with a BA (Hons) in History, specifically focused on British, American and Caribbean Colonial History. Also completed the Graduate Diploma in Law (Commendation) at the University of Law, Bloomsbury in 2013.

Eden Palmer-O'Connor
Graduated from the University of Leeds with a 2:1 in Chinese Studies. Has spent time working in China.

Elaine Allaby
Graduated with a BA in English Literature from Warwick University in 2011. Has lived, studied and worked in Nepal and India.

Eleanor Burt
Graduated with a BA (Hons) in History from University College London in 2011, specialising in London history. Went on to complete the GDL and LPC, finishing in 2013.

Eleanor Veryard
Graduated in 2011 with a BA in History before completing an MA in Early Modern History from the University of Sheffield. While at University worked as Head of Research and then Editor-in-Chief for a monthly student magazine.

Elizabeth Court
Graduated with a BA (Hons) in English from the University of Cambridge and studied the GDL at BPP Law School (Distinction). Previously worked for MasterCard and interned at a pharmaceutical company in Geneva, Switzerland.

Ellen Davis-Walker
Graduated from the University of Cambridge in 2013 with a BA in Modern and Medieval Languages. Sits on the steering committee for a local film festival in her spare time. Speaks French and Italian.

Elzi Lewis
Graduated with a BA (Hons) in English from the University of Manchester before completing an MA in Literature & Politics at the University of Amsterdam. Has previously worked as an editor for a (Dutch) national magazine, and as a consultant for a London-based PR firm.

Emilia Halton-Hernandez
Graduated in 2013 from the University of Warwick with a BA in History. She has also spent some time studying Philosophy and Literature at the Universidad Complutense in Madrid and at UC Berkeley.

Emily Rainbow
Graduated with a BA (Hons) in English and Spanish from The Queen's College, Oxford, in 2013. Spent a year teaching English in Costa Rica and Argentina.

Felicity Allsop
Graduated from the School of Oriental and African Studies with a BA (Hons) in Politics before completing the Graduate Diploma in Law at BBP Law School.

The Researchers *continued*

Felix Turner
Graduated from UCL in 2012 with a BA in History. Speaks Spanish fluently.

Francois Le Grand
Graduated from Royal Holloway with a BA in Human Geography. Studied International Relations in Brazil for two years before becoming a full-time translator working in English, Spanish, French and Portuguese.

Georgia Stephens
Graduated in 2012 with a BA Hons in Politics and International Relations at the University of Sussex. Worked at the university as a news editor for its weekly newspaper.

Georgina Street
Graduated from the University of Liverpool with a degree in International Politics and Policy. Has completed research and communications-based internships with the British Red Cross and Giving Africa.

Geraint Biggs
Graduated from UCL in 2013 with an LLM in Jurisprudence and Legal Theory. Studied law for a year at Universitê Paul Cêzanne as part of the Erasmus programme and speaks French.

Guy Garrud
Graduated from Durham University with an MSci in Physics. Has previously worked as a quality control engineer and forensic scientist.

Hannah Hill
Graduated in 2013 from the University of Sheffield with a BA in German and Economics. Spent one year studying at the Humboldt-Universität zu Berlin.

Harry Dalton
Graduated from the University of Nottingham in 2012 with a BA in Politics. Received his NCTJ training qualification from the Press Association.

Harry Tuffs
Graduated from the University of Oxford in 2013 with a BA in English Literature, and recently completed his GDL at Oxford Brookes.

Ines Cortesao
Graduated from Nova University of Lisbon with a degree in English and Literature, and studied abroad at the University of Southampton for one semester. Portuguese is her first language.

Jessica Gray
Graduated from UCL with a BA in English Literature in 2012 and an MA in Modern Literature in 2013. Previous work experience includes internships with several publishing companies.

Jessica Jacobsen
Graduated in English Law and French Law from the University of Manchester in 2012. This included spending a year studying French Law and Language in Lyon, France. Previously worked in legal administration. Speaks French and Spanish.

Jonathan Karstadt
Graduated from the University of Sheffield with a BA in Modern Languages (Russian, German and Czech). Has travelled extensively in Europe and completed a study abroad period in Petrozavodsk, Russia, and a work placement in Vienna, Austria.

Julian Frazer
Graduated in 2013 from King's College London with an LLB in Law. Has previously lived in Hong Kong, Mexico and Germany, and has worked in Malta and Shanghai for a global wealth management practice.

Karl Read
Graduated in 2012 from Durham University with an LLB.

Katy Newson
Graduated from King's College London with an LLB in Law in 2012. Went on to complete a Master's degree at University College London in Law specialising in Human Rights Law.

Kristen McGachey
Originally from Los Angeles, CA, moved to the UK in 2008 and graduated from the University of Nottingham in 2011 with a BA degree in English Studies with Philosophy. Completed her Master's degree in Philosophy & Literature at the University of Warwick in 2012.

Kristina Tailor
Graduated from the University of Nottingham in 2013 with an LLB in Law with European Law.

Lara-Jane Ideo
Graduated with a BA (Hons) in English Literature from Homerton College, Cambridge. Previously interned as a script consultant. Speaks Italian and French and has lived in both countries.

Laura Valdez
Graduated in English Language & Literature (European) from the University of Leeds in 2013. Spent a year studying abroad in Valencia and will study the GDL and LPC from September 2014 at the University of Law.

Laurence Kilpatrick
Graduated from the University of Leeds in 2012 with a degree in English Literature before moving on to Pembroke College at the University of Oxford where he obtained a Master's in Victorian Literature, focusing in particular on Dickens and urban space. He is also the subeditor of a football publication which he co-founded with a friend.

Leena Taha
Graduated from LSE with a BA in International History. Previously worked in publishing, as a copywriter and creating online content. Fluent in Arabic.

Leslie Jaji
Graduated in 2013 from King's College London, with an LLB degree in Law. Has previously worked in the public sector.

Lucy Pether
Studied undergraduate law at London School of Economics and previously worked for a legal news website.

Lydia Malley
Graduated from University of Reading in 2013 with first class honours in History and Philosophy. An active participant in amateur dramatics and fundraising for charities.

Maria Spirova
Has an MSc in Criminology & Criminal Justice from Oxford University, and a BA in Cultural Studies from Sofia University, Bulgaria. Award-winning freelance journalist.

Mario Adamou
Graduated in July 2013 with a degree in Law (LLB) from King's College London.

Our Editorial Team

The Researchers *continued*

Marlene Hermann
Graduated from the University of Nottingham with a BA in English and History before completing an MA in Politics and Contemporary History. Speaks fluent German.

Matthew Juggins
Has a BA in History & Ancient History from the University of Exeter in 2012. Has worked in Hong Kong, China and Singapore. In his spare time is a writer and an artistic director of an amateur theatre company he co-founded.

Matthew Lewis
Graduated from King's College London in 2010 with a BA in Hispanic Studies with English and from University College London in 2012 with an MA in English Literature. Works as a book and film critic in his free time.

Megan Jones
Graduated from the University of Cambridge with a BA (Hons) in Law.

Natalia Davies
Graduated from Queen Mary University of London in 2012 with a BA Hons in English. Has spent six months working in Australia, and has experience in freelance copywriting.

Natalia Rossetti
Graduated with a First in English & Theatre Studies from Warwick in 2010, then went on to complete an MA in Text & Performance at the Royal Academy of Dramatic Art and an MPhil in Multi-Disciplinary Gender Studies at Cambridge University. In her spare time she collaborates as Associate Producer with a London-based theatre company. Bilingual Italian/English and fluent in French.

Quinta Chapman
Graduated from Newcastle University in 2012 with first class honours in Government and European Union Politics. Went on to complete the GDL at the University of Law, London.

Rachel Annandale
Graduated from UCL in 2014 with a degree in Linguistics. Speaks Spanish and is currently learning Arabic.

Rachel Laurenson
Graduated from Newcastle University with a First in Modern Languages (Spanish with Chinese). Completed an MA in Latin American Interdisciplinary Studies in 2011. Spent a year studying at the Universities of Shenzhen and Chongqing.

Rebecca Lodder
Graduated from the University of Exeter with a BA in English in 2013. Has previously edited and produced a student creative arts magazine and interned with several literary agencies.

Robert Li
Graduated in Modern Chinese Studies from Leeds University, later completing the CPE at Westminster University. Speaks Mandarin Chinese.

Roshiny Panchalingam
Graduated from King's College London with an LLB in Law in 2012. Previously worked in financial regulation. Speaks fluent Tamil and currently learning French.

Sara Heltai
Graduated with a BA (Hons) from UCL in European Social and Political Studies with a minor in Italian Language and Culture. Holds a double MA in Euroculture from Universidad de Deusto and Uniwersytet Jagiellonski. Speaks Hungarian, English, French and Italian.

Sehar Rasul
Graduated from Queen Mary, University of London, with a BA in Politics. Previously worked as a project finance journalist and has also edited student magazines.

Shanthi Sivakumaran
Graduated with an LLB (English and European Law) from the University of Leeds and Universite de Jean-Moulin, France, and with an LLM (Human Rights Law) from the School of Oriental and African Studies in 2010. Speaks French.

Shaun Tey
Graduated with an LLB (Law) from Queen Mary, University of London and subsequently completed the Bar Vocational Course at BPP Law School. Previously worked at the BBC.

Shereen Zaki
Graduated from King's College London with an LLB (Hons) in Law in 2011. She has experience in Competition Law and Property Law.

Soffi James
Graduated from the University of Exeter with a First in English Literature in 2012, before completing a Masters in English Studies with a focus on 21st century literature.

Tiffany Cox
Graduated from the University of Kent in 2013 with first class honours in Law (Hons), finishing fifth in her cohort. Loves to travel and learn about different cultures.

Vian Chowdhury
Graduated in 2011 with an MSc in Development Economics. Previously lived in Indonesia.

Virginia Santini
Graduated from King's College London in 2011 with a History BA and from Queen's University Belfast with an MA in Irish Politics in 2012. Speaks Italian and Spanish.

Zahra Damji
Graduated in Law from the University of Birmingham in 2014. Previous work experience at a national newspaper and as news editor for a student newspaper.

Direct Access to the Bar

Since 2004, significant changes to the law have ensured that there is greater direct access to the Bar. This comes in two forms.

(A) Licensed Access

Individuals or organisations with expertise in specialist areas of the law are able to apply to the Bar Standards Board to be licensed to instruct barristers directly via the licensed access scheme. If successful, the licence holder is permitted to instruct any member of the Bar for advice, and in certain circumstances representation, in areas relating to the licence holder's field of expertise. Potential licence holders must go before the Access to the Bar Committee in order to satisfy certain criteria. Matters which will be looked at include the type of work the body wishes to refer directly to a barrister, its expertise or experience, its familiarity with any relevant area of the law its ability to obtain and prepare information for the barrister.

(B) Public Access

Public access enables members of the public to directly instruct a barrister without having to first seek out a solicitor or other intermediary. Prior to the implementation of public access, clients were required to involve a solicitor or a recognised third party who would then instruct the barrister on the client's behalf.

The key benefits of public access for clients are financial; having removed the need to engage a solicitor, clients have public access to the Bar without the added legal expenditure of engaging a law firm.

Clients are able to make use of this new system across the full scope of work undertaken by barristers, with the notable exception of legal aid funded cases. Public access is designed principally for cases which are relatively straightforward in their nature, and clients are advised to carefully consider the differences between the services offered by barristers and solicitors before seeking to instruct a barrister through the scheme.

Barristers are expert advisers and advocates, and as such clients may use the scheme to garner specialist legal advice, to instruct a barrister to appear on their behalf in court, or to draft legal documents. A barrister is not permitted to issue legal proceedings upon a client's behalf, or to instruct an expert witness on a client's behalf.

Not all barristers are able to receive instructions through the public access scheme; in order to qualify they must have practised for a minimum of three years, and they must have attended a public access training course which has been approved by the Bar Standards Board. Clients are also advised that even barristers who are fully qualified for the scheme are not obliged to accept public access instructions.

For clients seeking assistance from the Bar who cannot afford to pay, there are certain circumstances where financial support can be obtained from the Bar Pro Bono Unit, a registered charity which helps to find free legal assistance from volunteer barristers. The Bar Pro Bono Unit is able to assist clients in receiving both advice and representation.

In this year's publication, those barristers who are authorised to accept instructions under the public access scheme appear in our tables and under their set profiles with an 'A' appended to their names.

Leading Sets by number of rankings

Sets by number of rankings

Ranked in 20 practice areas
Thirty Nine Essex Street

Ranked in 18 practice areas
Kings Chambers

Ranked in 17 practice areas
Blackstone Chambers

Ranked in 16 practice areas
No5 Chambers (Birmingham) (15)

Ranked in 15 practice areas
Doughty Street Chambers

Ranked in 14 practice areas
Brick Court Chambers
Matrix Chambers

Ranked in 12 practice areas
Maitland Chambers

Ranked in 11 practice areas
Fountain Court Chambers
Guildhall Chambers
Serle Court
St Philips Chambers

Ranked in 10 practice areas
Crown Office Chambers
Essex Court Chambers

Ranked in 9 practice areas
XXIV Old Buildings
Outer Temple Chambers
4 Pump Courts
St John's Chambers
Wilberforce Chambers

Ranked in 20 practice areas

Thirty Nine Essex Street

Thirty Nine Essex Street has gone from strength to strength since taking on 25 barristers from 4-5 Gray's Inn Square in 2013. Now boasting 40 silks and 83 juniors, the set has outgrown its current quarters in the Middle Temple and at the time of going to press is looking for new premises. Its rapid growth has allowed the set to deepen its expertise in its core areas and to develop new practice specialisms. Traditionally strong in public law, environment and regulatory matters, it acts for local authorities and central government, and is increasingly instructed on private sector development work. It also has a strong commercial law and construction offering, and is further noted for its capabilities in mental capacity cases, with one interviewee stating that "there's no doubt it is the stand out set for Court of Protection work by a long way." Barristers here also have significant expertise in human rights cases, and regularly represent claimants and defendant public bodies. Chambers is home to the "spectacularly experienced" Nigel Pleming QC and the "hugely impressive" Stuart Catchpole QC. They are but two of a number of "very well-known, big names and rising stars" at the set. The clerks, led by David Barnes, win praise for their strong client service and commitment to finding the right counsel at the appropriate level. "Whenever you call, you know you will get somebody who is very good," says one source. Another simply states: "In terms of client service Thirty Nine Essex Street has absolutely nailed it."

Ranked in 18 practice areas

Kings Chambers

Kings Chambers is "going from strength to strength," and "getting bigger by the day," whilst not losing any of its "uncompromising attitude to quality." It is a set that continues to satisfy even the most demanding of instructing solicitors and clients, and one that is noted for its careful investment in its juniors. Commentators say that it "really believes in pushing its younger members," a policy that has paid off in recent years as evidenced by the presence of a number of rising stars within its walls. The breadth of the practice is another key selling point for this chambers. Kings has the size and reach to provide coverage across a number of legal disciplines, and has come to dominate the Northern and North-Eastern Circuits in particular. It has offices in Manchester, Leeds and Birmingham, all of which are manned by high-calibre barristers who are assisted by a clerking team that "bends over backwards to help" instructing solicitors. Standout individuals at the set include the "truly exceptional" Lesley Anderson QC, the "simply top-class" Paul Chaisty QC and "intellectual heavyweight" David Casement QC.

Ranked in 17 practice areas

Blackstone Chambers

Blackstone Chambers is a modern, forward-thinking set, which is characterised by its "entrepreneurial" and "energetic" approach. Its "hard-working, responsive and client-friendly barristers" offer a "strategic, tactical approach" to so diverse a range of public law, commercial and regulatory cases that sources attest they "have no equal when it comes to breadth of experience and accessibility." The members receive effusive praise for their commerciality and approachability, qualities which are mirrored in the set's excellent clerking team: "The clerks are very responsive, very flexible and highly commercial. They make a huge difference." The chambers is a "first port of call for both silks and juniors for public law issues," as evidenced by its involvement in high-profile cases such as the Criminal Bar Association's challenge to the Legal Services Board's Quality Assurance Scheme for Advocates and the Prince of Wales's letters freedom of information appeal. Its barristers are also sought after to appear in commercial cases, with recent highlights including the Madoff litigation. This year, the set has added new ranking to its extensive collection of accolades on the back of its impressive work in the field of data protection law. In addition to its superlative stable of silks, such as "fearless advocate" Dinah Rose QC and Treasury Devil James Eadie QC, Blackstone Chambers is home to a multitude of "consistently good" juniors, including the "absolutely brilliant" Shaheed Fatima.

Ranked in 16 practice areas

No.5 Chambers

No.5 Chambers is one of the largest sets in the country, and has more than 230 members, including 26 silks. A market leader on the Midlands Circuit, it also has a strong presence in London, Bristol and Leicester. This broad geographical spread is allied to an impressive diversity of practice area specialisms, with members here undertaking clinical negligence, crime, company and commercial cases, as well as public law matters of every hue. The set is also top-rated for family law, and has matrimonial finance specialists who are "pre-eminent in Birmingham and very well regarded nationally." The "very efficient" clerking team is led by practice director Tony McDaid, who takes "a refreshingly modern-day attitude to communication and the negotiation of fees," a fact much appreciated by instructing solicitors. Leading practitioners at the set include Mark Anderson QC, a "real heavyweight" commercial litigator, and the "absolutely brilliant" Court of Protection specialist Nageena Khalique. They, along with the other members of the set, show "enthusiasm, ability and a genuine passion for the law."

Ranked in 15 practice areas

Doughty Street Chambers

Doughty Street Chambers attracts civil and criminal cases involving the highest-profile civil liberties issues and "stands out as a leader in actions against the police and human rights work." Its members are "at the forefront in terms of their ethos and the level of service they give to solicitors and clients" across a range of relevant practice areas, leading sources to comment: "They have incredible depth and some of the best barristers in the field. They can draw on resources to tackle any type of matter." In addition to its civil liberties, public law and crime expertise, the set has an impressive reputation for representing claimants in complex tort trials, including clinical negligence and product liability cases, and a niche specialism in defamation cases involving human rights issues. The set is characterised by the excellence of its clerking team, which is admired for its organised, collaborative approach, and by the consistent quality of its barristers, who "show dedication, commitment and professionalism." It fields a choice selection of pre-eminent silks, such as renowned human rights practitioner Ed Fitzgerald QC and highly respected terrorism specialist Tim Moloney QC. It is also noted for the calibre of its juniors, including Adam Straw, who has had a particularly good year appearing in both the Duggan and Litvinenko inquests.

Ranked in 14 practice areas

Brick Court Chambers

Brick Court's success is built on a strong foundation of star performers who have extensive expertise in all manner of commercial litigation cases. Instructing solicitors express unwavering confidence in the members, commenting that "everyone there is very bright. You know you'll be getting an exceptionally good lawyer whoever you instruct." Exceptional in all they do, they prove particularly strong on EU and competition law, where "they've created an incredible centre of excellence." They are also heavily involved in the banking and finance market and have had involvement in industry-critical litigation such as Deutsche Bank v Unitech and the Guardian Care Homes Libor test case. The members here are comfortable handling matters of great note and complexity, and benefit from the "charming and effective" clerking provided by Julian Hawes and Ian Moyler, two individuals who "really understand client service." Hawes and Moyler attend to a number of top silks at the Commercial Bar such as Mark Howard QC, a man known for his "exceptional advocacy and stunning practice." Juniors of note include the "formidably bright" Maya Lester, who is praised for her "supreme knowledge" of European and competition law, and further acclaimed for her specialist expertise on sanctions. With such an abundance of intellectual firepower, sources describe the set as "the Rolls-Royce of barristers."

Matrix Chambers

Matrix Chambers has built itself an outstanding reputation as "the first chambers to go to for complex or difficult litigation, especially where there are elements of international human rights." The quality of its civil liberties expertise runs through its practices in crime, public international law and employment, and is enhanced by its members' "progressive outlook." The set has enjoyed yet another highly successful year, attaining new rankings as a result of its growing excellence in inquests and inquiries, and data protection work. Matrix barristers are admired for their dedication to their cases and characterised as "very bright people, who are prepared to go the extra mile." Their number includes a raft of top-class silks, such as "intellectual giant" Clare Montgomery QC and "exceptional advocate" Ben Emmerson QC, in addition to a talented pool of up-and-coming juniors. The members are supported by a "super-quick," "super-responsive" clerking team, which receives high praise for its ability to accommodate urgent instructions: "They are beyond co-operative, and will go the extra mile when you are struggling against tight deadlines."

Ranked in 12 practice areas

Maitland Chambers

"A pre-eminent Chancery Commercial set," Maitland Chambers is known for its strength across a number of legal disciplines. The set demonstrates prowess in commercial disputes of all kinds, and is particularly noted for being "a first-rate civil fraud set." It houses a stellar cast of 66 silks and juniors, who are "dynamic and effective" practitioners "clearly in the premier league." "I have yet to come across a counsel in that set who disappoints," stated one interviewee. The most renowned barristers fielded by the set include the "extremely bright and tremendously experienced" Paul Girolami QC, the "street-fighting yet sophisticated silk" Anthony Trace QC and the eminent Christopher McCall QC, who "possesses an extraordinary breadth of knowledge." The outstanding service provided by the barristers is more than matched by the calibre of the clerking team, according to sources. John Wiggs leads the way and ensures that "things run like clockwork." His clerking team is "one of the best. They are so attentive and quick to respond."

Ranked in 11 practice areas

Fountain Court Chambers

Widely acknowledged as one of the strongest commercial sets in London, Fountain Court Chambers is "a magic circle set that is a go-to for those confronted with large, complex cases." First-class advocates abound here, with one solicitor remarking: "They're all good, and have CVs to die for. If I was offered any one of them today on a case I'd take them, as they're very strong from top to bottom." The talented individuals at the set receive high-profile instructions across an impressive breadth of practice areas, and prove particularly strong in aviation civil fraud and banking disputes. They "have their fingers in all the big litigation pies," and handle cases such as the recent BTA Bank v Ablyazov matter, where the members once again demonstrated that they have "a very deep understanding of civil fraud cases, and the strategic issues as well as substantive law issues that arise in them." Fountain Court is home to a plethora of high-quality silks, including the "absolutely stellar" David Railton QC, whose workload includes the widely reported Deutsche Bank v Sebastian Holdings case. The set is not short of impressive juniors either, and the "incredibly clever and very hard-working" Simon Atrill has enjoyed another fine year in the banking and finance market. Others to impress include Ben Valentin, who recently joined from South Square. The clerking team also comes in for its fair share of praise and lives up to the same standard of excellence as the "unfailingly smart and hard-working" counsel. Senior clerk Alex Taylor is considered to be "really commercial, and ahead of the rest in terms of client service."

Guildhall Chambers

A standout on the Western Circuit, Guildhall Chambers "can go head-to-head with the London sets," offering instructing solicitors "the same service you'd get in London at a fraction of the cost." The set specialises in civil litigation and commercial chancery, and has additional expertise in areas such as crime and personal injury. It has also "really carved out a niche in insolvency work," an area in which it is seen as being "a seriously top-quality chambers." A number of Guildhall barristers have further niche expertise in health and safety law, an area where they are said to be "streets ahead of other chambers" in the region. Commentators report that "the expertise of the barristers is matched by the quality of the clerks." The "very helpful" clerking team is led by Justin Emmett for civil law and Lucy Northeast for criminal, regulatory and sports cases. Winning plaudits for their "no-fuss approach," they "add real value and are a pleasure to work with." Star performers at this chambers include "phenomenal" commercial litigator Stephen Davies QC and the "unsurpassed" Richard Smith QC, who specialises in crime and sports law matters.

Serle Court
Serle Court is a market-leading chancery set that is particularly known for its handling of complex offshore litigation. It frequently handles cases in offshore jurisdiction such as Bermuda, the British Virgin Islands and the Cayman Islands, and is particularly known for its efforts in the Channel Islands. The set is "a powerhouse in the civil fraud space," and also enjoys high renown for its handling of restructuring and insolvency, real estate litigation and banking disputes. Its members include Philip Marshall QC, who was recently involved in the high-profile Constantin Medien v Ecclestone case involving allegations of bribery and conspiracy to undervalue Formula 1. Marshall is but one of a number of impressive barristers who are known for "their commercial and realistic approach to cases and their understanding of how to operate in the business world." Juniors of note include the "intellectually superb" Dakis Hagen, and the widely respected Justin Higgo. These individuals are supported by "incredibly user-friendly and helpful clerks," led by Steve Whitaker, who is known for his professionalism and for running "a very slick clerks' room."

St Philips Chambers
Having long been one of the leading sets on the Midlands Circuit, St Philips Chambers has been on a remarkable expansionist streak of late. A merger with Chancery House Chambers has established it in Leeds, whilst the opening of new premises in Bloomsbury has demonstrated its commitment to the London market. It has 175 barristers including 18 silks, making it "a big set with a broad range of work and some very strong individuals." Chancery and commercial matters form the backbone of the set's practice, with members specialising in insolvency, real estate litigation and company law. Chambers also possesses a well-regarded regulatory and public law team, as well as strong family and employment practitioners. Those instructing the set appreciate the "well-drilled clerks' room" led by Joe Wilson, which adds to the perception of St Philips as "a very good, slick commercial outfit." This strong service ethos extends to the barristers, with interviewees reporting that "all of them are really good with clients." Leading silks at St Philips include the "brilliant" insolvency specialist Avtar Khangure QC and eminent Midlands commercial litigator John Randall QC, who has "a brain the size of planet" according to instructing solicitors.

Ranked in 10 practice areas

Crown Office Chambers
Crown Office Chambers is distinguished by the quality of its members. From its outstanding silks down to its leading juniors, excellence runs through the set. Numerous interviewees attest to this fact, with one saying: "The secret of its success lies in the sheer strength and depth it has to offer." The set "doesn't just have one star but a collection of excellent, technical and client-focused advocates." Chambers has a broad range of expertise but is considered a market leader in health and safety, personal injury and property damage, whilst also excelling in product liability and construction-related international arbitration. Impressed solicitors note that "its counsel have a great depth and range of experience so you always know you're going to find someone who can cover the case however complex it is." It is difficult to single out individual barristers from its talented cohort but two in particular stand out. Roger ter Haar QC is an expert construction-focused silk and "is an exceptionally clever and very persuasive advocate," while Andrew Bartlett QC is considered "a formidable opponent and an experienced operator." The clerks, led by Andy Flanagan, are "extremely helpful and easy to deal with," and were described by one instructing solicitor as being "the best chambers in terms of responsiveness."

Essex Court Chambers
An outstanding set with broad capabilities in commercial, international and European law, Essex Court Chambers is considered "a go-to set for complex commercial litigation and arbitration. "Packed with superstars," its "superb barristers" offer expertise across a range of areas including the energy, insurance and shipping sectors. "Streets ahead of the majority of the competition," it is a set that has an impressive array of quality silks, backed up by juniors who also attract significant praise. One of the best of these is the "phenomenally bright" Edmund King, who excels in a range of areas, and has particular strength in complex banking disputes. A "striking advocate," his practice continues to go from strength to strength. The members here have the support of the clerks that their practices merit. David Grief and Joe Ferrigno lead a fine team of clerks who "understand the clients' needs, and are very helpful when it comes to recommending counsel."

Ranked in 9 practice areas

XXIV Old Buildings
XXIV Old Buildings is "an impressive set from top to bottom" with "heavyweight QCs and impressive juniors who are well versed in an array of areas." It is one of the leading chancery sets and pre-eminent in offshore work, with one interviewee saying: "They remain the market leader in that world." Expert at handling multi-jurisdictional issues, the members are "well known for tackling cross-border disputes, and are particularly strong on trust-related matters." The set's incredible array of excellent silks includes star at the Bar Alan Steinfeld QC. Sources say of him: "For high-value claims he is the one to go to. He's a masterful advocate and when he forms a view about something he sticks to it." The clerks are similarly impressive, with interviewees noting that they are "efficient at getting back to you and very accommodating. They bend over backwards to make something happen for you and always provide cover if necessary." Another impressed interviewee commented: "The clerking service is utterly excellent. What always impresses me is that the clerks are spot-on with giving and keeping to cost estimates, and could not be more helpful when it comes to setting up court hearings and liaising with the courts."

Outer Temple Chambers
Outer Temple Chambers is a well-regarded multidisciplinary set, which "offers a breadth of experience and a depth of knowledge which few can match." Its members have particular experience of personal injury and clinical negligence cases, and growing expertise in international personal injury law. The set is also called upon to handle commercial litigation, regulatory matters and criminal cases within the financial service sector, and is increasingly recognised for its investigations work. It is equally praised for the strength of its pensions and employment practices. The ability of its barristers is shored up by the excellence of its "completely reliable, super-friendly" clerking team, which is admired for its attention to detail and personal approach: "You really feel that they're on your side when trying to get something difficult sorted out."

4 Pump Court

4 Pump Court is a set that offers high-quality advice in a number of different areas. It has long been praised for its foresight in "building a brand as the go-to set for IT cases," but this only tells half the story. Its barristers have a wealth of knowledge in other areas and score highly for their efforts in construction, shipping, insurance, energy and professional negligence cases amongst others, many of which are international in nature. Instructing solicitors look favourably on this set's ethos: "The guys are very user-friendly, very focused and very commercial." The clerks have also made a good impression and have been variously described as being "truly outstanding" and "really switched-on." They "will go out of their way to try and assist," according to one interviewee. The set is home to 21 silks, including the "superb advocate" Nigel Tozzi QC and Sean Brannigan QC, who is "phenomenal on his feet."

St John's Chambers

St John's has a broad range of specialist areas and a deep bench of barristers. It is one of the leading chambers in the South West but such is its quality it "can match itself with London sets," according to commentators. The team is known for its ability across areas as diverse as real estate litigation, partnership and family law, and is "the first port of call for licensing and planning." It is also "head and shoulders above the other sets in Bristol when it comes to chancery work." Leslie Blohm QC is a standout silk here, with one interviewee noting: "He is excellent and extremely intelligent. He always gives clear advice in good time." The strength of the set's barristers is matched by its clerking team, with interviewees stating that "the clerks, led by practice manager Robert Bocock, are great and really helpful. They are efficient and have never fallen short of expectations."

Wilberforce Chambers

Wilberforce is a leading set across a range of practice areas, and is considered to be second to none in all aspects of traditional and commercial chancery law. Widely viewed as "pre-eminent in the pensions field," it is "some way ahead of other sets" in this field due to the presence of "tour de force QCs," who are also noted for the quality of their offshore work. Members at the set offer "practical and technical advice" and prove particularly effective on trust-related work. Solicitors view them as being "straightforward individuals, who provide an excellent service and are very personable to deal with." Prominent amongst them is Robert Ham QC, "a grandee and a nice guy with it," and Brian Green QC who is "commercial, incisive, assertive and always the cleverest person in the room. He's an exceptional asset to have on any case." The clerking at the set is also unquestionably excellent, with one impressed solicitor saying that the clerks "don't go overboard on fee negotiations, and value long-term relationships." "You can rely on them to deliver whatever they promise; if they say something will get done, it will get done." "The head clerk, Mark Rushton, is really interested in client service."

Sets with the most barrister rankings

The table shows the 50 sets that have achieved the highest number of barrister rankings in this edition. The number of rankings includes barristers ranked more than once. Where two or more sets gained the same number of rankings, the smaller one appears first in the table.

Position	Position Last Year	Set	Number of Rankings	Number of Barristers
1	1	Blackstone Chambers	210	91
2	2	Thirty Nine Essex Street	170	120
3	3	Brick Court Chambers	163	81
4	7	Matrix Chambers	150	77
5	5	Fountain Court Chambers	149	66
6	4	Doughty Street Chambers	146	119
7	6	Essex Court Chambers	135	83
8	12	No5 Chambers	122	246
9	9	Kings Chambers	118	100
10	8	3 Verulam Buildings	117	67
11	11	Maitland Chambers	112	67
12	15	11KBW	109	58
13=	13	Landmark Chambers	108	81
13=	10	One Essex Court	108	85
15	14	Serle Court	103	56
16	16	4 New Square	102	76
17	22=	Garden Court Chambers	99	193
18	17=	4 Pump Court	96	61
19	22=	St Philips Chambers	94	178
20=	24=	3 Raymond Buildings Barristers	93	49
20=	20=	Guildhall Chambers	93	79
22	17=	Wilberforce Chambers	88	53
23=	24=	XXIV Old Buildings	87	42
23=	19	Crown Office Chambers	87	91
25=	30	Monckton Chambers	86	51
25=	20=	Keating Chambers	86	57
27=	28	1 Crown Office Row	84	69
27=	27	Outer Temple Chambers	84	76
29	24=	Atkin Chambers	81	42
30=	29	South Square	72	41
30=	34	7 King's Bench Walk	72	51
32	33	St John's Chambers	67	81
33	35=	Serjeants' Inn Chambers	66	51
34	31	20 Essex Street	64	55
35=	37=	4 Stone Buildings	59	31
35=	32	Radcliffe Chambers	59	43
35=	35=	Quadrant Chambers	59	56
38	44=	Devereux	57	50
39	37=	Exchange Chambers	55	145
40=	42=	Cornerstone Barristers	54	54
40=	44=	2 Bedford Row	54	73
42–	39	Francis Taylor Building	52	53
42=	40	Old Square Chambers	52	75
44=	41	Enterprise Chambers	51	39
44=	48=	7BR	51	87
46	-	6KBW College Hill	50	52
47	42=	2 Hare Court	49	56
48	47	Littleton Chambers	48	53
49=	46	11 Stone Buildings	47	42
49=	48=	2TG - 2 Temple Gardens	47	52

Sets with the highest proportion of barrister rankings

This table measures the total number of barrister rankings as a proportion of the size of the set. The number of rankings includes barristers ranked more than once.

Position	Position Last Year	Set	Number of Rankings	Ranking of Barristers	Rankings as a % of size
1	2	Cloth Fair Chambers	22	7	314
2	3	Blackstone Chambers	210	91	230
3	1	Fountain Court Chambers	149	66	225
4	5	XXIV Old Buildings	87	42	207
5	4	Brick Court Chambers	163	81	201
6	12	Matrix Chambers	150	77	194
7	6=	Atkin Chambers	81	42	192
8	9	4 Stone Buildings	59	31	190
9	13	3 Raymond Buildings Barristers	93	49	189
10	11	11KBW	109	58	187
11	6=	Serle Court	103	56	183
12	8	South Square	72	41	175
13	10	3 Verulam Buildings	117	67	174
14	26	Monckton Chambers	86	51	168
15	16	Maitland Chambers	112	67	167
16	14	Wilberforce Chambers	88	53	166
17	18=	5 Stone Buildings	46	28	164
18	17	Essex Court Chambers	135	83	162
19	20=	4 Pump Court	96	61	157
20=	18=	Keating Chambers	86	57	150
20=	-	Field Court Tax Chambers	6	4	150
22=	23	Thirty Nine Essex Street	170	120	141
22=	35=	7 King's Bench Walk	72	51	141
24	20=	8 New Square	38	27	140
25=	22	Radcliffe Chambers	59	43	137
25=	24	Byrom Street Chambers	22	16	137
27=	15	Erskine Chambers	42	31	135
27=	33	One Brick Court	23	17	135
29	31	4 New Square	102	76	134
30	29=	Landmark Chambers	108	81	133
31	28	11 South Square	21	16	131
32	27	Enterprise Chambers	51	39	130
33	29=	Serjeants' Inn Chambers	66	51	129
34	25	One Essex Court	108	85	127
35	32	Doughty Street Chambers	146	119	122
36	-	1 Crown Office Row	84	69	121
37	39=	Kings Chambers	118	100	118
38	37	Guildhall Chambers	93	79	117
39	43	20 Essex Street	64	55	116
40	35=	Pump Court Tax Chambers	38	33	115
41	42	Civitas Law	24	21	114
42=	44	Devereux	57	50	113
42=	41	Falcon Chambers	42	37	113
44	39=	11 Stone Buildings	47	42	111
45	45=	Outer Temple Chambers	84	76	110
46	-	New Square Chambers	45	42	107
47	45=	Quadrant Chambers	59	56	105
48=	48	Cornerstone Barristers	54	54	100
48=	-	11 New Square	7	7	100
48=	-	48 Bedford Row (Partnership Counsel)	2	2	100

Stars at the Bar

The Stars at the Bar have proved their excellence across a range of practice areas.

Alan Boyle QC: Serle Court

Alan Boyle QC's "first-class legal brain" and "stellar intellect" find him the consistent recipient of noteworthy instructions in commercial, fraud and offshore disputes. His trusts work is undoubtedly the jewel in the crown of his practice, however, with sources advising that "if you want an authority on trusts, he is your man." His depth of experience and client-handling skills are recognised by peers, who commend him for "striking a perfect balance between being sympathetic with clients and utterly combative on their behalf in Court." He is also "utterly dedicated to the client's cause." Demonstrating his "sound commercial judgement," he recently acted in a series of disputes concerning the insolvency of a hot strip steel mill in South Wales. He is further praised for the speed at which he assimilates information, with one solicitor commenting that he is "astonishingly quick to develop a detailed understanding of a case and a client's needs." According to one interviewee, he is "fantastically focused and committed and always offers an excellent service," thus cementing him as a go-to silk in the eyes of market observers.

Alan Steinfeld QC: XXIV Old Buildings

Alan Steinfeld QC is widely seen as a "leading choice of silk" who is "outstanding in everything he does." He is lauded as an expert across countless disciplines and is praised for being "one of the stars of the Commercial Chancery Bar" and the "godfather of offshore work." Excellent on his feet, he is renowned as a "masterful advocate" who "commands the court." Steinfeld is an exceptional silk who marries his vast legal acumen with outstanding commercial sense. This means he can get to the heart of a matter in lightning quick time, a fact which is confirmed by interviewees, with one saying: "I have seen him master a brief so fast it's unbelievable." His caseload includes some of the most complex and high-profile matters, and he is "the go-to man for high-value claims," a fact illustrated by his continued work on a USD1 billion claim in Guernsey relating to the collapse of Carlyle Capital, a subsidiary of The Carlyle Group.

Ali Malek QC: 3 Verulam Buildings

"A strong punchy advocate with good instincts and good judgement," Ali Malek QC is highly celebrated for his track record in complex, high-stakes litigation. Considered "one of the outstanding practitioners in the banking area," he recently represented a Swedish pension fund in a substantial mis-selling case against BNY Mellon. "A strategic thinker and a formidable opponent," he is known for his command of a courtroom, with one instructing solicitor commenting that "he's a fierce cross-examiner but he doesn't do that as a bar-room brawler. Instead, he's elegant in how he deconstructs his opponents' cases." Widely respected as a "first-class super silk," he combines his commercial law expertise with a deep knowledge of regulatory issues. "He is excellent at guiding a client through a difficult regulatory problem, especially where there is a twin-track civil claim," reports one interviewee. Moreover, Malek is considered "a genuine leader in the field when it comes to fraud cases involving trusts and foundations," and is seen as "an excellent choice for matters requiring a high degree of product knowledge." On top of all this, he has a market-leading reputation at the International Arbitration Bar, and recently advised the government of Sri Lanka and a state-owned oil company in connection with litigation and arbitration relating to derivative contracts. "Thoroughly impressive," he is truly "at the top of his game and a superb advocate."

Antony Zacaroli QC: South Square

The "ferociously intelligent," Antony Zacaroli QC is widely acclaimed for his restructuring and insolvency expertise, and is "someone you expect to see in virtually every major insolvency case going." His recent highlights include advising the Co-operative bank in relation to its £1 billion restructuring. "Clearly one of the brightest silks at the Bar, he is unsurpassed in terms of his responsiveness and his ability to work seamlessly with other counsel and solicitors on a team." Much in demand, he has been instructed in numerous high-stakes banking disputes, including the highly publicised MF Global litigation. Those that engage him say: "He's extremely bright and commercial," and "he provides timely, pragmatic advice and instils confidence in clients." Further examples of his high-profile instructions include representation of the creditors of Lehmans post-administration. Interviewees say of him: "He is as good as it gets. As well as being technically superb and an impressive advocate, he is incredibly nice."

Bankim Thanki QC: Fountain Court Chambers

"Extremely technically able," Bankim Thanki QC is "really in a category of super silks, and his knowledge on privilege issues is market-leading." His practice is broad in scope, and he has tremendous experience in aviation disputes, banking litigation and civil fraud matters. Interviewees report: "He's steeped in financial litigation. A wise, calm, and measured individual, he's incredibly easy to work with." Recent case highlights include acting for China Southern Airlines in the Commercial Court, where he successfully defeated a variety of claims brought by Tigris. "A very powerful advocate," he is "someone whose manner in court is really terrific; it's soft and low key but very much to the point. He's just a very impressive advocate and has a complete mastery of his brief." Further examples of his abilities in high-value complex cases include appearing on behalf of BNP Paribas in a banking dispute with Anchorage Capital. He is also regularly instructed in international arbitration, insurance claims and professional negligence matters. Those that instruct him say that "for commercial litigation, he's really a number-one choice" as he is "a leader with a firm grasp of his subject matter who inspires confidence in the client."

Clare Montgomery QC: Matrix Chambers

The "extraordinarily brilliant" Clare Montgomery is recognised as one of the country's leading silks when it comes to criminal, regulatory and public law cases involving high profile human rights issues. Her sophisticated advocacy and formidable intellect make her a first choice practitioner for cutting-edge cases and she is frequently instructed to handle cross-jurisdictional matters, complex points of appeal and challenging corporate liability issues. She is regularly called upon to appear in cases attracting significant media attention, such as the Shrien Dewani extradition appeal, but is equally sought after by corporate clients to provide discreet advice on sensitive pre-charge matters. She is very much at home in the Administrative Court and recently represented a cross-party group of parliamentarians in a judicial review challenging the decision of the Home Secretary to exclude a dissident Iranian politician from entering the UK in order to discuss the state of human rights in Iran. Sources characterise her a "tenacious, fearless and incredibly focused" barrister, with an unparalleled command of the facts and the law.

David Mumford: Maitland Chambers

"Undoubtedly a rising star," David Mumford continues to be rightfully touted as one of the Bar's most impressive juniors, described by one observer as a "silk in junior's clothing." His approachable manner is identified as one of his many assets, with observers noting that "clients can't be in safer hands." His outstanding skill in the courtroom has also won him numerous admirers; he is marked out for his "excellent judgement and brilliant intellect," and described as "very clever and analytical" in his approach. His Chancery Commercial practice attracts myriad accolades, and he can be seen in some of the biggest cases both at home and abroad. A recent star turn saw him act as sole advocate for Cosmote in a dispute over contractual claims arising from the sale of a mobile phone operator in Macedonia. He is hugely popular with instructing solicitors, who say he is a "first-rate advocate whose written work is turned around with amazing speed," and "a match for many silks."

David Pannick QC: Blackstone Chambers

"Words fail me," says one of David Pannick QC's clients; "there's no doubt in my mind that he's one of the best barristers in the country." He is widely regarded as one of the leading public lawyers of his generation, and he has an impressively varied practice touching on EU law, media, sport and professional discipline matters: "He can really turn his hand to anything." He recently represented the Attorney General of Trinidad and Tobago in a human rights challenge to the legislature's retrospective revocation of a law imposing a ten-year time bar on prosecution for fraud. Another recent highlight saw him acting for the BBC in an application for judicial review of the Lord Chancellor's decision not to allow a journalist to record and broadcast an interview with a man who was detained pending extradition. With his much-lauded, elegantly persuasive advocacy and his facility for complex cases, instructing solicitors agree that he "lives up to his considerable reputation. He demonstrates legal and client-relation skills of the very highest order."

David Perry QC: 6KBW College Hill

David Perry QC is hailed as an "intellectual giant," who does "the absolutely highest level, top-notch work all the time" and has an undisputed reputation as "one of the best silks at the Bar." He is highly sought after to appear in the most challenging appellate cases on account of his "outstanding judgement" and the respect he commands from peers and judges: "He's hugely knowledgeable, very good on academic and technical questions, and he always has the trust of the court." He is no stranger to appearing in the Supreme Court and recently acted for the Ministry of Justice in response to the Nicklinson and Lamb assisted suicide appeal. His much-praised practice encompasses all manner of crime, extradition, confiscation and related public law matters, and he also handles an impressive array of corporate advisory work. He is regularly instructed in complex financial crime cases and is currently advising Barclays on SFO and FCA investigations into certain Qatari investments in the bank. Overseas work is another of his strengths, as evidenced by his selection to prosecute the former Premier of the Cayman Islands on charges of misconduct in public office.

Dinah Rose QC: Blackstone Chambers

Dinah Rose QC has an undisputed claim to being one of the greatest advocates of her generation. Sources wax lyrical about her precise and nuanced yet passionate advocacy, reporting that she "finds the killer argument and then charms the judges with it," mixing "charm and grit in equal measure to produce very persuasive results." Her "clear strategic leadership" is also praised by sources, who attest that "the way she sees a case makes her a cut above the rest." She is recognised as a master of many disciplines, and is particularly good on the overlapping spheres of public law, European law, employment and regulatory matters. Given her confirmed "superstar" status, it is no surprise that she has been instructed in a raft of high-profile cases over the past 12 months. Her recent work highlights include a judicial review of the Attorney General's decision regarding Prince Charles' letters and a case alleging the security services' complicity in the kidnap and rendition of Libyan dissidents to the Gaddafi regime for the purposes of torture. As befits her excellent reputation for handling cases arising in the telecommunications sector, she also acted for a number of interveners in the BT v Ofcom Ethernet case.

Hugo Keith QC: 3 Raymond Buildings Barristers

The "phenomenal and very user-friendly" Hugo Keith QC is an unfailingly popular choice for cases that straddle the divide between criminal and public law issues. He is known for giving "fantastic support on issues relating to Interpol and extradition," and has recently appeared in such high-profile matters as the Shrien Dewani case, in which he represented the Republic of South Africa. He is also sought after to act in high-level financial crime cases, judicial reviews and front-page inquests, as evidenced by his instruction by the Metropolitan Police in the inquest into the death of Mark Duggan. In addition to being a "charming and effective advocate," he is prized for his ability to combine knowledge, experience and creativity, with sources reporting that he is "great on the case law and good at looking at different angles." He is equally praised for his intellect, communication skills and gravitas: "He is incredibly bright, wonderfully articulate, a great team player and someone who is enormously respected by the judges."

James Eadie QC: Blackstone Chambers

James Eadie QC is "a brilliant advocate" who "commands the respect of the court." As First Treasury Counsel, he has become a go-to choice for the government's most high-profile and complex cases, demonstrating formidable skill in civil liberties and administrative and public law cases in particular. Recent instructions include an appearance for the government in the Court of Appeal regarding the extradition of Abu Qatada to Jordan. He also took the lead role for the government in a prisoner voting rights case relating to the European Parliament elections. He has an "unbelievably thorough approach," according to sources, who explain that "he is phenomenally well prepared," and that "he is able to get on top of a case in an unbelievably short amount of time." He is recognised for the impressive scope of his practice, and the "rare talent" required to have "an absolute mastery over every case that he does." Universally respected, he is known to instructing solicitors as a "really engaging" and "easy-to-use" silk, who is "very bright, but also someone who wears his knowledge lightly."

Joe Smouha QC: Essex Court Chambers

"One of the most complete QCs at the Bar," Joe Smouha QC is widely held to be "a star." He excels on his feet and sources particularly praise him for his "outstanding cross-examination skills." Another impressed interviewee told how "he gets to grip with the details of the case and is able to identify the weak spots in the other side's case in a very clever way." His legal acumen is matched by his client service, with interviewees acknowledging his "championing of his client's cause." He also excels when confronted with difficult clients with complex issues because "he is not intimidated by anybody and can help put the client in a position where they understand what can and cannot be done." His work on high-profile cases is demonstrated by his representation of Robert Tchenguiz in his multimillion-pound damages claim against the Serious Fraud Office relating to his arrest in 2011. He is also known as a master of international arbitrations and recently acted for Philip Morris in a dispute concerning the Australian government's decision to compel tobacco companies to package cigarettes in plain wrapping.

John Howell QC: Blackstone Chambers

John Howell QC is widely viewed as being "astonishingly clever." "One of the best brains at the Bar," he "completely knows his cases inside and out." He is "an excellent advocate" who is "well respected by courts" and who "often thinks of points nobody else has and then applies them brilliantly." Also an "excellent strategist," he has "a very strong command of public law" and is considered the go-to for the most difficult judicial reviews. "A real lawyer's lawyer," he excels at "clever points of statutory construction and technical matters of law." He recently acted for the local authority in Westminster City Council v SL, a noteworthy appeal in the Supreme Court, which saw him successfully argue that the Court of Appeal had erred in its interpretation of the National Assistance Act 1948. His mastery of civil liberties and human rights is well known and he regularly works with the Equality and Human Rights Commission. He recently advised the organisation on the Justice and Security Bill, looking at the compatibility of secret trials with Article 6 of the ECHR.

Jonathan Crow QC: 4 Stone Buildings

Renowned for his fantastic ability when on his feet, Jonathan Crow QC is commended as "someone you would go to when you want the judge to listen to what you've got say." Sources admire his "extraordinary breadth of expertise," which sees him instructed in a raft of high-profile commercial disputes including civil fraud and banking matters. "A heavyweight of the Chancery Commercial Bar," he recently acted for Fairfield Sentry, a Bernard L Madoff Investment Securities feeder fund, in a Privy Council appeal regarding the repayment of money received through investors' redemption of shares in the fund. Such marquee instructions confirm his reputation as "a great appellate lawyer," who is "authoritative and fast-thinking." His "elegant and succinct" style wins the admiration of peers, who acknowledge that "losing out to Jonathan Crow is never shameful." One interviewee confesses: "He's the barrister that everyone wants to be."

Laurence Rabinowitz QC: One Essex Court

The "absolutely outstanding" Laurence Rabinowitz QC has "an incredibly incisive analytical mind, coupled with hugely reassuring client-handling skills." He is "a great strategic thinker and someone with a very good feel for the court." One of the leading commercial and banking disputes silks at the Bar today, his practice also covers civil fraud, oil and gas litigation and international arbitration matters. He acted for one of the co-defendants in Pinchuk v Bogolyubov and Kolomoisky, a massive civil fraud claim in the High Court. This fiendishly complicated case turned on the claimant's allegation that the defendants misappropriated monies given to them for the purpose of buying a Ukrainian mining concern. An appearance before the Supreme Court in Benedetti v Sawiris saw him arguing a highly technical point on the quantum of restitutionary awards in cases of unjust enrichment. Clients cite "his ability to take an extremely complex point and be able to present it with such clarity" as one of the many reasons they choose him for these matters.

Mark Howard QC: Brick Court Chambers

Hugely sought after to act in some of the most high-profile commercial disputes in the market, "brilliant trial lawyer" Mark Howard QC also adroitly turns his hand to finance, professional negligence and insurance cases. He enjoys an outstanding reputation for his court skills, and is described by one source as "probably the most lethal cross-examiner at the Bar." He is also seen by observers as something of a strategic wizard, who can "easily turn a loss into a win," thanks to his "extreme gravitas and grasp of the issues." His formidable reputation leads to him being instructed in major civil fraud cases. By way of example, he acted in a Supreme Court case for VTB Bank against Nutritek, which concerned a USD200 million fraud. His success lies in his authoritative presence, according to interviewees, one of whom notes: "He has the respect of the court – they really listen to what he has to say." "He is in another class really," say peers, who declare him to be "undoubtedly one of the leaders of the Commercial Bar."

Michael Brindle QC: Fountain Court Chambers

Michael Brindle QC is a man of "vast experience and tremendous intellect," who is widely acclaimed for his "towering reputation" and impressive commercial practice. He is well versed in complex banking cases, and recently represented ARM Asset Backed Securities in a bond dispute with the FCA. "A colossus in this area, he is incredibly bright and robust, doesn't pull any punches and has the ear of the court," reports one source. Brindle is extensively praised for his courtroom manner, and commentators note that "he's a remarkable advocate, who is very thoughtful, careful, yet tenacious in his approach – he knows when to fight hard." In the financial services arena he is hailed as a star silk, and he has recently been instructed by the FSA in a high-profile judicial review brought by the British Bankers Association. He is also highly experienced in international arbitration and financial and commercial professional negligence matters. His distinguished career and superb skillset is lauded by both opposing counsel and instructing solicitors. Instructed in the long-running Fiona Trust litigation, he once again proved his skill in appellate matters and endorsed his reputation as "a bulldog of a litigator. You can send him in safe in the knowledge that he'll fight hard."

Nathalie Lieven QC: Landmark Chambers

Nathalie Lieven QC "is a force of nature," says one instructing solicitor. "She's irresistible on her feet, very direct and she quickly gets to the point." A public lawyer with a track record of representing often challenging clients, she is one of the top silks at the Planning and Environment Bar, and recently acted on the judicial review challenges to High Speed 2 and the Hinkley Point C new nuclear build. Again and again, interviewees praise her formidable skills as an advocate. Lieven is "just fantastic in court. She is very confident and the judges really like her." She recently acted for a jobseeker in a high-profile challenge to the government's 'workfare' policy, which had seen the geology graduate required to work in Poundland or face losing her unemployment benefits. Another recent instruction saw her argue an unusual habeas corpus application in the Supreme Court for a man then under US custody in Afghanistan, but who had originally been detained in Iraq by UK forces. Those who choose Lieven for tough cases like these do so because "the courts see her as someone who talks sense, and when she speaks, people listen."

Nigel Giffin QC: 11KBW

Nigel Giffin QC is a "phenomenal lawyer" and an "absolute star." He is noted for his exceptional technical ability, with one opponent emphasising his renowned strength in court: "I have had to sit there cringing as, step by step, he demolished my case." Another impressed source said: "He has appreciation for the commercial aspects of a matter, and delivers his case in the most effective fashion in court." His public law prowess is formidable and he is said to be a superstar barrister who is sought out for the most complex and high-value cases. Specific areas of expertise include education and administrative law, and he is "the first choice for all procurement work." The strength of his public sector work is demonstrated by his representation of the borough council in R (Buck) v Doncaster, where he successfully defended a claim that a directly elected mayor had acted unlawfully in refusing budget recommendations made by the council. He also successfully acted for Edexcel in its defence of a judicial review against its decision to raise the grade boundary for a 'C' in English GCSE.

Paul Chaisty QC: King's Chambers

A highly distinguished figure on the Northern Circuit, Paul Chaisty QC is "a real fighter" with "a no-nonsense approach to litigation." He is "sympathetic with the client and very user-friendly," and his skill in the courtroom is the envy of many. One source calls him "an unbelievably effective advocate who is best on his feet," adding that "his cross-examination can be devastating." Chaisty reportedly possesses "every legal argument a lawyer could possibly require," as well as a commanding presence in the courtroom. Such talent invariably generates high-profile instructions and Chaisty is no exception. He recently defended Wayne Rooney against claims relating to restraint of trade, and also acted in breach of contract claims against the footballer's wife, Coleen Rooney. "He's made being succinct an art form, and it's devastatingly effective," says an admiring observer.

Philip Jones QC: Serle Court

Acknowledged for the breadth of his practice, Philip Jones QC acts in commercial, partnership and tax disputes, among others, and is known for being "a superb all-rounder, who is lovely to deal with." Much is made of his prepossessing nature, with sources calling him "more user-friendly than most silks," and "a sophisticated, charming barrister," who is "wonderfully attentive to clients." Peers warn against underestimating his technical skills, revealing that they are more than equal to his charm – so much so that his "his name strikes fear into opponents' hearts." His "good tactical awareness" and "superb judgement" assisted him in his representation of BTA Bank in its headline-grabbing claim against Mukhtar Ablyazov and others. "He is calm and measured when handling high-pressure cases," says one source.

Pushpinder Saini QC: Blackstone Chambers

"Class act" Pushpinder Saini QC "is a star" and "a leading barrister who gets straight to what matters." He is noted for his "very wide-ranging practice" and he has in-depth expertise in both public and commercial law. A very effective cross-examiner, he is recommended for his clear and smooth manner in court. One commentator noted how in a hard-fought case, "he destroyed my witnesses one by one." Peers hold him in high esteem, with one saying: "He is brilliant. I am trying to emulate his practice." He also comes highly recommended by solicitors who say he is "extremely responsive and decisive. He stands back a little bit, takes a broad view of matters and gets right into the finer points as well." He recently advised Air Canada as a co-defendant in Virgin v Jet Airways, which saw the court reject attempts by English courts to review decisions of the European Patent Office.

Richard Drabble QC: Landmark Chambers

Richard Drabble QC is "one of the best advocates of his generation," according to his fellow practitioners. "You get a heavy heart when you know you're against him since his case always comes across well." His public law-focused practice encompasses judicial review, human rights and environment law as well as costs litigation and planning. He is best known for handling social security cases, and "for welfare and benefits he's head and shoulders above everyone else." In R (JS) v Secretary of State for Work and Pensions, he represented the Child Poverty Action Group as intervener in a challenge to the government's benefits cap and its effect on housing benefit. A consistent thread through Drabble's feedback was praise for his incisive ability to argue difficult points of law and statutory construction in a clear, direct and persuasive manner. Another member of the Bar says: "He's the person I would aspire to be in terms of advocacy skills and attention to detail. He has the ability to cut down a complicated matter to a single point which is really worthy of argument."

Robert Miles QC: 4 Stone Buildings

Bearing testament to the breadth of his practice, Robert Miles QC is described as "a polymath" by one source, who adds that he is "a very bright and very charming guy." He is "a real star of the Chancery Commercial Bar, and particularly good for complex matters with a financial services element." He is also widely acclaimed for his company law practice, and recently exhibited his "considerable gravitas and compendious knowledge of the law" in a directors' duties case, acting for the former directors of MWB Business Exchange. The matter concerned alleged breaches of duty relating to inter-company loans. He also picked up a high-profile instruction from Bernie Ecclestone defending bribery claims brought by Constantin Medien. Clients value his soaring intellect and brevity in court: "He speaks without ever wasting a word and you can see that everything he says is hitting the mark." He is also favoured for his ability to deliver creative advice and formulate winning strategies, with one interviewee calling him "intellectually brilliant and courageous in terms of what he proposes."

Robin Dicker QC: South Square

Robin Dicker QC "is absolutely top drawer and extremely clever. He has a wonderfully simple style of written and oral advocacy and is very convincing," according to sources. A go-to practitioner for heavyweight restructuring and insolvency matters, he is "an erudite and clever silk," who frequently handles high-profile litigation, as evidenced by his representation of Barclays Bank in the well-publicised Libor test case. His powerful and effective style is admired by peers, with one source reporting: "He is so incisive in his intellect, he can make complex ideas sound simple. It makes him a compelling advocate." Another commentator remarked: "He's a top-class advocate and excellent to have on your side in a punch-up concerning complex financial instruments." Dicker further enjoys a market leading reputation for his skill in company matters and offshore disputes. One interviewee noted: "He's superb and you would be very lucky to get him." Another added: "For anything really difficult and technical, I'd go to him." Recent case highlights include a dispute between Loreley and LBIE, involving allegations of fraudulent misrepresentation.

Tim Owen QC: Matrix Chambers

"Fantastic advocate" Tim Owen QC receives effusive praise for his "incredibly good manner with the court." Sources describe him as "a brilliant appellate advocate," commenting that "he's really easy to listen to, which makes him such a dangerous opponent." His outstanding advocacy skills are shored up by his experience, judgement and strategic prowess, leading peers to characterise him as a "wise tactician," with "a very long-standing reputation." His practice centres around the juncture between human rights and criminal law, with a particular focus on business crime cases. Last year, he successfully defended a former director of iSOFT, who was charged with market abuse following an FCA investigation. He is also experienced in judicial review proceedings and recently acted for an elderly peace campaigner in a judicial review successfully challenging the refusal of the police to remove his details from the National Domestic Extremism Database.

Client Service at the Bar

The following sets are particularly commended for their provision of quality client service.

Enterprise Chambers

Enterprise Chambers is heralded as "a very flexible and very modern chambers. They are not just 9 to 5 – they take a very businesslike approach, which is great for clients." This is reflected in the clerksroom, with instructing solicitors commenting: "The clerking is excellent – far more user-friendly than traditional clerking arrangements." The team is well known for its willingness "to get out and about, and out of London," with Joanne Caunt and Ellen Cockcroft in Leeds and Steve Walker in Newcastle recognised for their "superb service and clear fee estimates." Their proactivity regarding seminars and training is also a draw for clients. The clerking service in London is no less effective, with clients keen to endorse Antony Armstrong and his team: "The clerks are probably the best I have dealt with. You don't really have to think about the way in which chambers works; you go to them with your problem and it is sorted quickly." This collegiality is reflected at the upper echelons of the set where barristers are praised for their "collaborative and efficient approach."

Fountain Court Chambers

Fountain Court is a firm favourite with those looking for top-notch service at the upper end of the Bar: "You know you're getting quality from the second you speak to a clerk until the moment you walk out of trial," say instructing solicitors. Under the leadership of the vastly experienced Alex Taylor the team "goes well beyond what you might normally expect." In particular, the clerks' willingness to pick up the phone and talk through fees, and their ability to get barristers in front of clients was much commented upon. Big-name firms repeatedly turn to the set, but all manner of clients receive a dedicated service. One source enthused: "As a smaller client, we've felt a little unloved at other chambers, but at Fountain Court we feel looked after as much as the biggest client." The clerking team's prowess in customer service combined with its commercial ethos marks it out from the rest. These are people who are "very focused on getting what you need, when you need it."

Garden Court

Senior clerk Colin Cook's team is noted for its willingness to respond to out of hours requests and to recommend advocates at short notice. Time-sensitive requests are passed on to barristers who are "ready to step in and deal with urgent work." Senior crime clerk Keith Poynter comes particularly highly recommended, with one source commenting: "He's such a good clerk, and so responsive to what we need and what we are like as a client. He makes sure we're well looked after." The additional extras Garden Court offers clients are second to none, with the weekly immigration bulletin and Colin Yeo's Free Movement blog, described as "a finger-on-the-pulse resource for solicitors," earning particular praise. The facilities at chambers are of similarly high quality: "Their conference facilities are in a really nice location, and they are spacious and professional – you are treated really well." Rounding things off, the set also produces "outstanding seminars" and bespoke training sessions that are "immensely helpful."

Hailsham Chambers

Hailsham stands out in the client service arena for its efficient, businesslike approach and reasonable attitude towards billing. One commentator reports: "They have a costs management system where they will plug in the fees and try to keep tabs on things, which is a neat way of doing things." The clerking team is seen as "superb – they really look after us; nothing is too much trouble." Instructing solicitors note that Stephen Smith's tremendous experience ensures he has "a good appreciation of what the job of a solicitor is like – it makes for a good working relationship." Clients note: "Stephen Smith, Michael Kilbey and Richard Rodger are fantastic they don't fob you off – they are good at telling you if people are too busy or if something isn't someone's forte." The set is also commended for its excellent seminars, newsletters, podcasts and video-conferencing facilities. However, the reason why people return to Hailsham again and again is the fact that "you pick up the phone, speak to someone and things are done quickly."

Henderson Chambers

Henderson's repeated recommendations for client service often single out John White, who is unanimously praised as "one of the most personable, organised and charming chief clerks around." Instructing solicitors are happy to report that "others in his team are cut from the same cloth." The set goes out of its way to be proactive in finding the right barrister for a particular case, and clients value the opportunity to "talk about which barrister is most suitable and pick counsel based on the client's characteristics - I don't find that most other chambers are as switched on to that as them." Fees are described as "fair, transparent and quite flexible," and the set is renowned for never double-booking barristers. This common-sense approach continues at all levels: "The barristers don't patronise; they speak to you like a colleague. You can really work together as a team." Chambers is further noted for its value-added services, in particular its seminars. One source extolled their virtues, reporting: "The quality of handouts is brilliant; top of the league."

Landmark Chambers

"In terms of clerking, Landmark is a standout set," sources reveal. "The clerks are incredible, and give great client service. In particular, head clerk Jay Fullilove "is fantastic," say instructing solicitors. He heads a clerksroom that will "work very hard to get you access to your counsel of choice." Clients add: "I can trust their recommendation when my first choice is not available, and they are always open to discussion of fees." The set is also singled out by sources for its charitable efforts: "I commend their commitment to pro bono work – they don't treat it as second-rate work at all." Landmark is also noted for its provision of good-quality seminars and for having a "very professional set-up" with "brilliant conference facilities." One source summed up the team's strengths: "I think Landmark are the best set to instruct from the point of view of the clerks and the general assistance they give – they are very helpful and friendly, and take a lot of strain off you."

Maitland Chambers

Maitland Chambers is commended for offering an impressively efficient service: "The quality of service and the speed of response provided by the clerks, led by John Wiggs, is exemplary – if I had a concern, I'd phone them up and it would be dealt with in two minutes." The responsiveness of the barristers at the set is similarly lauded by satisfied clients, who line up to report: "They're incredibly speedy in their responses." The set's flexible approach to billing and willingness to negotiate delighted one instructing solicitor, who stated: "I've never had trouble with fees and we've had issues with other chambers. They are good at giving us the estimates which means we can get client approval. You can always trust Maitland to do the little things that really add value."

Monckton Chambers

The legal fraternity highlights clerking as a key factor in Monckton's success: "The set is very well clerked. David Hockney is very responsive and has a fantastic team. The clerks discuss things frankly and are never precious about giving you access to the barristers."

This ethos has led to instructing solicitors praising the "barristers' willingness to allow us direct access." The commercially minded team's well-cultivated relationships with the courts are also a boon when it comes to time-sensitive matters, as instructing solicitors note: "They have their ear to the ground when going to court – they always get applications in at the right time. They are very well informed." The team's willingness to negotiate and accept alternative fee arrangements makes for a "responsive and sensible approach," and the clerking team is able to "provide accurate fee estimates at the drop of a hat." One long-standing client summed up the reason for their continuing relationship: "The clerking at Monckton is outstanding – head and shoulders above the rest." Someone else said: "The set is very commercial and very focused, right from the clerks through to the QCs."

Old Square Chambers

Head clerk William Meade is "particularly good; he has an open ear to any concerns, and came to visit us recently to ask about service, which nobody else has done from other sets." He and his team are commended for "finding the best barrister for the case; they go out of their way to make sure they provide the right service." All of them are considered "extremely personable," "highly responsive and in-tune with client needs." They are also known for the commerciality of their thinking. Clients who use the set are appreciative of its seminars, training and mock trials and tribunals, which are considered "incredibly helpful." Instructing solicitors further value being kept apprised of developments in cases: "The clerks always find out whether the case is listed and the name of the judge the day before a hearing."

One Essex Court

One major corporate client revealed: "I use One Essex Court more than other commercial chambers largely because of their clerking team led by Darren Burrows. They don't overbook or double-book and will helpfully liaise with the court for us." Clients also highlight deputy senior clerk Jackie Ginty, stating: "She's always available to speak to and is unfailingly honest." The clerks have a track record for transparency and reliability, and win plaudits for their "modern and efficient" approach, and for the fact that they are "very switched-on, commercial and responsive." On the financial side, the set takes "a markedly sensible approach to fee negotiations." The set also holds regular seminars which are met with high acclaim.

6 Pump Court

6 Pump Court is revered for its "tip-top" clerking. Richard Constable heads the "absolutely fabulous" clerking team. His commitment to customer service led one client to report: "He always gives you the date you want, the time you want – Richard Constable's phone number is my number-one favourite phone number." This attentive approach continues throughout the team: "The clerks value each and every one of us as instructing solicitors and if there's something they can do to make it better for us they will go out of their way to do it." Smaller clients report the service is of the same calibre, noting: "6 Pump Court gives us the barristers that we want." The clerksroom's trusted recommendations and willingness to work alongside clients is described as "a very innovative approach; clerks will always find someone suitable and talk about how counsel will fit into the team structure." 6 Pump Court also delivers on the financial front: "Fees are competitive and clerks amenable to negotiation." One client elaborated: "They understand the pressures and issues that I and my clients are under, and because they are so understanding the system doesn't break down. I can have an open and frank dialogue with them about payment schedules."

Radcliffe Chambers

Radcliffe Chambers is commended for its responsive, approachable and client-centric ethos. The "brilliant clerks will respond the same day that you raise a query and they'll always come back and check if there's anything else you need," sources report. The set also runs warmly received seminars for clients. At the helm are highly experienced senior clerks Keith Nagle and John Clark, who run an efficient clerksroom and are "unfailingly attentive to clients' needs." Instructing solicitors report that good relationships are established "all the way down to the junior clerks." This is a chambers that is noted for its thoroughly modern approach, with clients praising counsel's accessibility: "You can often get through directly to counsel." One source reports: "At Radcliffe all the clerks are friendly and down-to-earth – the whole chambers is like that."

Tanfield Chambers

Tanfield's unwavering commitment to client service is demonstrated through its extensive seminar programme and its in-house training events. The clerks are respected for their open and transparent relationships with solicitors, and for the unprecedented access they allow. This pays dividends, as one instructing solicitor noted: "I have a fantastic relationship with the clerks and feel that I can be completely frank with them. They are reliable, highly professional and always contactable." A straightforward and flexible approach to fees is another key draw: "The clerks, Kevin Moore and Joanne Meah, are always willing to find ways of working within clients' budgets." Another commentator enthused: "Tanfield is very much our 'go to' set when it comes to most property disputes. You know that if you use a Tanfield barrister, you can expect an exceptional service."

Thirty Nine Essex Street

Thirty Nine Essex Street excels in the field of client service. Instructing solicitors commend the clerks for their responsiveness: "I can send work to the clerks knowing they will handle it quickly and incredibly reliably. They are so well organised that they can sort things out, regardless of the size of the crisis." All of them have deep knowledge of their barristers' expertise: "If I don't know who to use I can absolutely rely on the clerk's recommendation." They are regarded by the legal market as being amongst the best in the business because "they go the extra mile to find you the best person available for your case, and they take an interest in the way the case is developing." Their flexibility on fees also proves popular. As one solicitor commented: "They are always happy to talk about fees. You never feel like they're pushing for too much and they're always willing to negotiate."

2TG – 2 Temple Gardens

2 Temple Gardens goes above and beyond to deliver faultless client service, offering around 30 seminars a year, in-house training sessions and flexibility on fees and fee protocols. Instructing solicitors enthuse: "Lee Tyler runs a tight ship and he is always available to have a chat. He's really responsive and willing to negotiate on fees." The rest of the team is praised for being "approachable, modern and commercial in their outlook, which is always a nice surprise." The set's value-added services and physical resources are also top-of-the-tree, leading clients to report: "The conference facilities are excellent and they organise lots of high-quality seminars." The team reacts in a pinch, and always "thoroughly appreciates the urgency of matters."

RANKINGS AND COMMENTARY
ENGLAND & WALES

Contents:

LONDON

Administrative & Public Law London
Leading Sets
Band 1
Blackstone Chambers *
Band 2
Brick Court Chambers *
Doughty Street Chambers *
11KBW *
Matrix Chambers *
Band 3
1 Crown Office Row *
Thirty Nine Essex Street *
Landmark Chambers *
Monckton Chambers *
Band 4
Garden Court Chambers *
◊ *(ORL) = Other Ranked Lawyer.*
Alphabetical order within each band. Band 1 is highest.
🄰 *direct access (see p.18).*
* *Indicates set / individual with profile.*

Administrative & Public Law London	
Leading Silks	
Senior Statesmen	**de la Mare** Thomas *Blackstone Chambers*
Beloff Michael *Blackstone Chambers*	**Dutton** Timothy *Fountain Court Chambers (ORL)* ◊
Lester of Herne Hill Anthony *Blackstone Chambers*	**Elvin** David *Landmark Chambers*
Star Individuals	**Foster** Alison *Thirty Nine Essex Street*
Fordham Michael *Blackstone Chambers*	**Grodzinski** Sam *Blackstone Chambers*
Pannick David *Blackstone Chambers*	**Hoskins** Mark *Brick Court Chambers*
Rose Dinah *Blackstone Chambers*	**Johnson** Jeremy *5 Essex Court (ORL)* ◊ *
Band 1	**Knafler** Stephen *Garden Court Chambers*
Anderson David *Brick Court Chambers*	**Maclean** Alan *Blackstone Chambers*
Carss-Frisk Monica *Blackstone Chambers*	**Maurici** James *Landmark Chambers*
Chamberlain Martin *Brick Court Chambers*	**Morris** Fenella *Thirty Nine Essex Street*
Crow Jonathan *4 Stone Buildings (ORL)* ◊ *	**O'Neill** Aidan *Matrix Chambers*
Drabble Richard *Landmark Chambers*	**Shaw** Mark *Blackstone Chambers*
Eadie James *Blackstone Chambers*	**Stratford** Jemima *Brick Court Chambers*
Emmerson Ben *Matrix Chambers*	**Turner** Jon *Monckton Chambers* *
Fitzgerald Edward *Doughty Street Chambers*	**Westgate** Martin *Doughty Street Chambers*
Giffin Nigel *11KBW*	**Wolfe** David *Matrix Chambers* *
Gordon Richard *Brick Court Chambers*	**Band 4**
Havers Philip *1 Crown Office Row*	**Beer** Jason *5 Essex Court (ORL)* ◊ *
Howell John *Blackstone Chambers*	**Bowen** Paul *Brick Court Chambers*
Kaufmann Phillippa *Matrix Chambers*	**Brown** Paul *Landmark Chambers*
Lieven Nathalie *Landmark Chambers*	**Coppel** Philip *Landmark Chambers* 🄰
Perry David *6KBW College Hill (ORL)* ◊	**Cragg** Stephen *Doughty Street Chambers*
Pleming Nigel *Thirty Nine Essex Street*	**Demetriou** Marie *Brick Court Chambers*
Band 2	**Eicke** Tim *Essex Court Chambers (ORL)* ◊
Bailin Alex *Matrix Chambers* *	**Friedman** Danny *Matrix Chambers* *
Béar Charles *Fountain Court Chambers (ORL)* ◊ *	**Giovannetti** Lisa *Thirty Nine Essex Street*
Garnham Neil *1 Crown Office Row* *	**Guthrie** James *3 Hare Court (ORL)* ◊
Goudie James *11KBW* *	**Harrison** Stephanie *Garden Court Chambers*
Herberg Javan *Blackstone Chambers*	**Hermer** Richard *Matrix Chambers*
Husain Raza *Matrix Chambers*	**Knox** Peter *3 Hare Court (ORL)* ◊
Keith Hugo *3 Raymond Buildings Barristers (ORL)* ◊ *	**Kovats** Steven *Thirty Nine Essex Street*
Luba Jan *Garden Court Chambers*	**Pitt-Payne** Timothy *11KBW* *
McCullough Angus *1 Crown Office Row*	**Sheldon** Clive *11KBW*
Montgomery Clare *Matrix Chambers*	**Simor** Jessica *Matrix Chambers*
Mountfield Helen *Matrix Chambers* *	**Southey** Hugh *Matrix Chambers* *
Owen Tim *Matrix Chambers*	**Strachan** James *Thirty Nine Essex Street*
Richards Jenni *Thirty Nine Essex Street*	**Wise** Ian *Monckton Chambers* 🄰
Saini Pushpinder *Blackstone Chambers*	**New Silks**
Stilitz Daniel *11KBW* *	**Bacon** Kelyn *Brick Court Chambers*
Swift Jonathan *11KBW* *	**Bourne** Charles *11KBW* 🄰 *
Tam Robin *Temple Garden Chambers (ORL)* ◊ *	**Forsdick** David *Landmark Chambers*
Ward Tim *Monckton Chambers* 🄰 *	**Gallafent** Kate *Blackstone Chambers*
Band 3	**Hall** Jonathan *6KBW College Hill (ORL)* ◊
Clayton Richard *4-5 Gray's Inn Square (ORL)* ◊ *	**Pereira** James *Francis Taylor Building (ORL)* ◊ 🄰
Coppel Jason *11KBW* *	**Steyn** Karen *11KBW* *
Cory-Wright Charles *Thirty Nine Essex Street*	

Band 1

Blackstone Chambers

See profile on p.771

THE SET

Blackstone Chambers occupies a position of unparalleled excellence in matters of administrative and public law. Its ranks include a significant selection of the most accomplished, talented and experienced silks and juniors working in the field, who display equal skill when acting for claimants or defendants. The deep expertise offered by its members spans the full ambit of public law, and cases are undertaken for clients including individuals, government departments, corporate entities and regulatory bodies.

Client service: "The set is excellent – my first port of call for both silks and juniors for public law issues. And the clerking is very good and very smooth." Gary Oliver is the senior clerk.

SILKS

Michael Fordham QC Commands great respect for the force of his advocacy and his authoritative command of the principles of judicial review, on which subject he is the author of the leading text. He displays particular expertise in matters of human rights, immigration and environmental law. **Strengths:** "He is a fantastic oral advocate – a very powerful and compelling speaker, whether in the courtroom or presenting to a meeting." "He's phenomenal and has a brain like ten normal people's brains. A brilliant advocate and a brilliant lawyer." **Recent work:** Acted for the claimants in the high-profile case of Ali Zaki Mousa, addressing the question of the independence of a reconstituted investigation into the alleged mistreatment and deaths of a number of Iraqi citizens at the hands of British servicemen.

David Pannick QC Occupies a position of pre-eminence as a public law advocate, and attracts effusive praise for his expert and accomplished work in the field. His substantial experience includes handling matters of parliamentary privilege, constitutional and vires issues, freedom of information cases and commercial judicial reviews. **Strengths:** "He is one of the best advocates I've ever seen. He has a knack of making it seem like he's just having a chat with senior judges in the Supreme Court." "He demonstrates legal and client relation skills of the very highest order. He is able to distil even the most complex case into three or four apparently simple issues." **Recent work:** Represented Prudential in the Supreme Court in a judicial review addressing whether legal advice given on tax law by an accountant could fall under legal professional privilege.

Dinah Rose QC Enjoys an outstanding reputation as an advocate of the highest skill and energy, who applies a phenomenal standard of expertise and invention to any case she acts in. Her public law practice has seen her handle matters addressing discrimination, regulation, national security and competition issues, among others. **Strengths:** "A brilliant, fearless advocate. She is extremely authoritative and assured with clients, and gives clear strategic leadership." "She is exceptionally intelligent. She understands the

Administrative & Public Law London
Leading Juniors
Star individuals
Fatima Shaheed *Blackstone Chambers*
Jaffey Ben *Blackstone Chambers*
Band 1
Hickman Tom *Blackstone Chambers*
Hooper Ben *11KBW* *
O'Connor Andrew *Temple Garden Chambers (ORL)* ◊
Squires Daniel *Matrix Chambers*
Straw Adam *Doughty Street Chambers*
Band 2
Armstrong Nicholas *Matrix Chambers*
Auburn Jonathan *Thirty Nine Essex Street* [A] *
Buley Tim *Landmark Chambers*
Buttler Chris *Matrix Chambers* [A]
Gallagher Caoilfhionn *Doughty Street Chambers* [A]
Hill Henrietta *Doughty Street Chambers* [A]
Hyam Jeremy *1 Crown Office Row*
Lester Maya *Brick Court Chambers*
Moffett Jonathan *11KBW* [A] *
Proops Anya *11KBW* *
Band 3
Blundell David *Landmark Chambers*
Broach Stephen *Monckton Chambers*
Busch Lisa *Landmark Chambers*
Callaghan Catherine *Blackstone Chambers*
Clement Joanne *11KBW* *
Collier Jane *Blackstone Chambers*
Dobbin Clair *3 Raymond Buildings Barristers (ORL)* ◊ *
Facenna Gerry *Monckton Chambers* [A] *
Grange Kate *Thirty Nine Essex Street*
Harrop Griffiths Hilton *Field Court Chambers (ORL)* ◊
Kennelly Brian *Blackstone Chambers*
Kolinsky Daniel *Landmark Chambers* *
Rogers Amy *11KBW* *
Ruck Keene Alexander *Thirty Nine Essex Street* *
Sharland Andrew *11KBW* [A] *
Suterwalla Azeem *Monckton Chambers* *
Wakefield Victoria *Brick Court Chambers*
Watson Ben *3 Raymond Buildings Barristers (ORL)* ◊ [A] *
Band 4
Apps Katherine *Littleton Chambers (ORL)* ◊ *
Banner Charles *Landmark Chambers* *
Boyd Jessica *Blackstone Chambers*
Bretherton Kerry *Tanfield Chambers (ORL)* ◊ [A]
Broadfoot Samantha *Landmark Chambers*
Bunting Jude *Doughty Street Chambers*
Burton Jamie *Doughty Street Chambers*
Butler-Cole Victoria *Thirty Nine Essex Street*
Cumberland Melanie *6KBW College Hill (ORL)* ◊
Dixon Emma *Blackstone Chambers*
Emmerson Heather *11KBW* *
Hannett Sarah *Matrix Chambers* [A]
Jones Tristan *Blackstone Chambers*
Love Sarah *Brick Court Chambers*
Luh Shu Shin *Garden Court Chambers*
Mably Louis *6KBW College Hill (ORL)* ◊
Macdonald Alison *Matrix Chambers* *
McClelland James *Fountain Court Chambers (ORL)* ◊ *
McGurk Brendan *Monckton Chambers*
Palmer Robert *Monckton Chambers* [A] *
Patel Naina *Blackstone Chambers*
Patel Parishil *Thirty Nine Essex Street*
Pickup Alison *Doughty Street Chambers*
Rahman Shaheen *1 Crown Office Row*
Richards Tom *Blackstone Chambers*
Sandell Adam *Matrix Chambers*
Simblet Stephen *Garden Court Chambers*
Slater Matthew *3 Stone Buildings (ORL)* ◊ *
Steele Iain *Blackstone Chambers*
Street Amy *Serjeants' Inn Chambers (ORL)* ◊ *
Wheeler Marina *1 Crown Office Row*
Yeginsu Can *4 New Square (ORL)* ◊ *
Up-and-coming individuals
Beattie Kate *1 Crown Office Row*
Grubeck Nikolaus *Monckton Chambers*
Knight Christopher *11KBW* *
Lewis Gwion *Landmark Chambers*
◊ (ORL) = Other Ranked Lawyer.
[A] direct access (see p.11).
** Indicates individual with profile.*

judges and the best way to present a case, and the way she sees a case makes her a cut above the rest." **Recent work:** Represented a Guardian journalist in a high-profile judicial review of the decision of the Attorney General to overturn the Upper Tribunal's decision to require the publication of letters written by Prince Charles to government ministers.

Kate Gallafent QC Has taken silk this year following a career as an outstanding junior. She acts for individuals, regulatory bodies and government departments, and is strong on such issues as prison law and freedom of information. **Strengths:** "She prepares well, is effective and, although very pleasant, can be tough when she needs to be." **Recent work:** Acted on behalf of London Metropolitan University in a judicial review challenge to the decision of the UK Border Agency to revoke the university's status as a 'Highly Trusted Sponsor' and its licence in connection to overseas students.

Michael Beloff QC A widely respected advocate who has deep experience of handling public law matters and caters to a wide range of clients. **Strengths:** "He is pre-eminent in judicial reviews. His advocacy is beautifully balanced, and he expresses himself extremely felicitously." "I have no hesitation in recommending him for heavyweight public law matters. He is brilliant and streets ahead of the field." **Recent work:** Represented the London Metal Exchange in a judicial review challenging its decision to implement a new rule governing the delivery of metals to their approved warehouses.

James Eadie QC Hugely respected for his work as First Treasury Counsel, in which position he undertakes a diverse array of matters on behalf of the government. He is notably accomplished in matters of terrorism, freedom of information and privacy. **Strengths:** "He is a brilliant advocate. Like no one else, he is able to get on top of a case in an unbelievably short amount of time and present it in the most straightforward way." "He is phenomenally well prepared, and he's so quick. He is absolutely formidable, and evidently commands the respect of the court." **Recent work:** Acted for the government in the Court of Appeal case addressing the extradition of Abu Qatada to Jordan to face trial on terrorism charges.

Monica Carss-Frisk QC Maintains her reputation as a highly skilled advocate, and has experience in a diverse range of issues within public law. She is joint head of chambers and offers particularly adept representation in immigration and freedom of information matters. **Strengths:** "She is fantastic at dealing with clients. At quite a stressful time, her patience and client handling were first rate." "She is extremely impressive in front of judges – she has a calm and measured style that is very persuasive." **Recent work:** Acted for the appellants in a highly significant case in the Supreme Court establishing the right of judicial review of a decision of the Secretary of State for the Home Department to remove individuals to EU states under the Dublin II Regulation.

John Howell QC Very well regarded for his public law expertise and the depth of his knowledge in the field. He has a particular interest in constitutional, public obligations, and local government matters. **Strengths:** "He's probably the smartest person I've ever met, and he's really good to work with. He completely knows each case inside out, and the court really listens to him." "He is the man for a case that needs a very clever lawyer who's good at points of statutory construction and technical matters of law." **Recent work:** Intervened on behalf of the Law Society in a judicial review examining whether legal aid available to a child in private law family proceedings could extend so far as to cover the cost of an expert report.

Pushpinder Saini QC Acts primarily on behalf of government departments, regulatory bodies and applicant companies across a range of public law matters. He is particularly experienced in energy regulation, education and telecommunications issues. **Strengths:** "He is fiercely intelligent, and gets to grips with complex issues very quickly." **Recent work:** Acted for a group of aviation companies in a judicial review during the course of a major action concerning the legality of a decision by the European Patent Office.

Sam Grodzinski QC Represents both claimants and government departments in the course of his public law practice. He is notably accomplished in issues relating to the policing of protest, prison law and the energy industry. **Strengths:** "A concise, clear and persuasive advocate who is tax literate, commercial and who cuts straight through the issues." "He is excellent – very level-headed and straight with the court." **Recent work:** Represented the Parole Board in a case in the Supreme Court concerning the damages payable when prisoners' parole hearings are delayed.

Javan Herberg QC Experienced in public law matters in the context of financial services, commercial regulation and public procurement. He also has an interest in human rights and professional discipline issues. **Strengths:** "He is a developing star in the field. He has a broad practice, and he is excellent." "Very knowledgeable and switched on, particularly in relation to judicial reviews in financial services." **Recent work:** Acted for the BBC in successfully defending a claim for judicial review brought by listeners of its radio programme 'Jewish Hour' regarding the decision to take the show off the air.

Mark Shaw QC Maintains a well-respected public law practice, which typically deals with judicial reviews and statutory appeals on behalf of government bodies. He is notably experienced in the areas of professional discipline, extradition and human rights. **Strengths:** "He is very easy to work with, very approachable and open to suggestions from the client." **Recent work:** Represented the claimant in a judicial review that challenged the decision of the Home Secretary to order his extradition to Spain on historical criminal charges.

Alan Maclean QC Joins Blackstone this year, and has a well-regarded expertise in public law matters. He has a particular interest in aviation, healthcare and broadcasting issues. **Strengths:** "He is brilliant and entirely on top of the law. He's able to give advice concisely and in a client-friendly form." "He's a very precise silk. He is so good at getting to the only important lines in reams of paper, and knowing what matters." **Recent work:** Acted for the Human Fertilisation and Embryology Authority in a judicial review of its decision to introduce a new condition to its licences specifying a maximum for multiple birth rates for clinics.

Anthony Lester of Herne Hill QC Exceptionally well-regarded advocate who has over the course of his lengthy career helped develop and shape the field of public law. He remains a highly significant figure at the Bar with substantial influence.

Thomas de la Mare QC Maintains a well-respected practice in public law, and has expertise in EU and competition law. He has additional experience in human rights and advertising matters. **Strengths:** "He brings great verve to a case. He is very bright and is fantastic at seeing a clear strategic way forward in complex matters." "He's a good thinker, is very approachable and rolls up his sleeves when working on a task." **Recent work:** Acted on behalf of Sainsbury's in a judicial review contesting the decision of the ASA that Tesco was permitted to conduct price comparison schemes, even when compared products may not have been produced to the same ethical or environmental standards.

JUNIORS

Ben Jaffey Attracts the highest praise for his work in public law, which includes working for claimants and government defendants in a broad range of matters. His experience is especially pronounced in issues of national security, terrorism and torture, and prisoner rights. **Strengths:** "He is exceptionally bright, approachable, committed and hard-working." "An incredibly smart and wonderful advocate, with whom it is always a total joy to work." **Recent work:** Acted successfully for the claimants in the case of Belhaj, a high-profile matter addressing the practice of extraordinary rendition, in this instance allegedly of a Libyan national under the direction of a number of UK officials, including the then Foreign Secretary.

Shaheed Fatima Attracts great praise and respect for her practice in public law. She is a noted authority on the interface between international and domestic public law, and has expertise in the rights of women, arbitrary detention and fair trials. **Strengths:** "She is very articulate, and is the expert on using international law in a creative way in a domestic public law context." "She has a massive brain – the book she wrote on using international law in domestic courts is one of my bibles." **Recent work:** Acted for Afghan claimants challenging the lawfulness of their detention at Camp Bastion.

Tom Hickman Has a very well-regarded practice in public law, which spans a wide range of issues in the field. He acts for claimants and defendants in pursuing matters of national security, terrorism, regulation and competition. **Strengths:** "Fiercely intelligent, great to work with and very hard-working. He really is one of the stars." "He is superb. He's very proactive, incredibly bright, and does good paperwork." **Recent work:** Represented the appellants in a major case in the Court of Appeal that ruled on the jurisdiction of the Norwich Pharmacal principle in requesting documents from the UK Security Services on behalf of clients being held in Uganda.

Catherine Callaghan Focuses her work in public law on freedom of information, transport, human rights and advertising matters. She typically represents regulators, individuals and government departments. **Strengths:** "Her advocacy is impressive in its power and clarity." "She is very persuasive, and she argues points very strongly and firmly." **Recent work:** Acted for the Home Office as junior to James Eadie in defending a judicial review in the Supreme Court concerning the government's plan to introduce a mandatory work placement scheme for recipients of Jobseeker's Allowance.

Jane Collier Specialises in handling issues in the context of healthcare provision, social security, freedom of information and education. She has additional expertise in immigration and asylum matters. **Strengths:** "She is able to pick up relevant information very quickly, picking out the salient points and distilling them to neat grounds for judicial review. She has a good feeling for what the court and the judge are going to be interested in." **Recent work:** Acted for UCAS in an appeal to the First-tier Tribunal challenging a decision of the Information Commissioner regarding the ambit of the Freedom of Information Act.

Brian Kennelly Has expertise in handling EU and competition public law cases. He is also very strong in regulatory proceedings. **Strengths:** "He is probably the brainiest junior at the public law Bar, and is incredibly strong on European law issues." "He is excellent. His ability to explain things to clients in conference is fantastic." **Recent work:** Represented the government in the Supreme Court in an appeal against a favourable finding in the Court of Appeal that a UK insurance measure could be interpreted compatibly with EU law, contrary to an earlier ruling of the ECJ.

Emma Dixon Enters the listings this year on the back of the growing reputation of her public law practice. She has a particular interest in environmental, discrimination and human rights issues. **Strengths:** "She's first rate. Lovely to work with, she really knows her stuff and is always willing to go the extra mile." "She was really helpful and gave crucial, detailed analysis." **Recent work:** Appeared in the Supreme Court on behalf of ClientEarth in a case that successfully established that the UK is in breach of EU air quality limits with respect to nitrogen dioxide.

Naina Patel Has a burgeoning reputation in the administrative and public law world. She is notably accomplished in matters relating to immigration and asylum, religious freedoms and defence policy. **Strengths:** "She is a very skilled and able junior who's very pleasant to work with, but who has a trace of steely determination." "Her presentation in court is impressive, and she is a very fair opponent." **Recent work:** Represented the claimants in a Supreme Court case challenging the decision of the Registrar General not to register a chapel of the Church of Scientology as a 'place of worship.' The decision was overturned, with the court giving an important legal definition of religion in its ruling.

Jessica Boyd Has a broad practice in public law matters, with a particular emphasis on immigration law. She has further experience in matters touching on the conduct of the military. **Strengths:** "In a novel legal situation she wasn't fazed. She dealt with the work very thoroughly, and added value in a way that lots of counsel of her call wouldn't." **Recent work:** Acted for the claimant in a judicial review challenge to the decision of the Home Secretary to remove him to Uganda. The case turned on the question of whether such an action could be taken while civil proceedings against the Secretary were ongoing.

Iain Steele Attracts praise for his growing junior practice, which encompasses a diverse range of issues in public law. His areas of interest include matters relating to the powers of the police, prisoners' rights, education and local government. **Strengths:** "He is excellent. He's very good at distilling a large number of documents into concise, effective responses and is very friendly, personable and approachable." "He's brilliant, incredibly industrious and really good to have as part of the team." **Recent work:** Acted on behalf of Barnet London Borough Council in successfully defending a judicial review challenge of its decision to outsource the provision of key local services.

Tristan Jones Acts for government bodies, individuals, charities and corporate claimants in judicial reviews and public inquiries. He is experienced in handling regulatory, freedom of information and broadcasting matters. **Strengths:** "He works well as part of a team and is very approachable. He is excellent." "He's very dedicated and always on hand when you need him." **Recent work:** Acted for the government in a landmark Supreme Court case that determined that although the current legislation governing the rights of prisoners to vote is in breach of the ECHR, prisoners will not be allowed to vote until legislation is amended by Parliament.

Tom Richards Focuses on handling public law proceedings in relation to constitutional, EU and competition issues. He typically represents public bodies and corporate entities, as well as individual claimants. **Strengths:** "He is very quick but doesn't lose anything in the detail, and he provides the support you need." "He is bright and good value for money." **Recent work:** Represented the Attorney General of Trinidad and Tobago in a case challenging the decision to repeal a ten-year limitation period for the prosecution of criminal offences. The challenge was founded on the contention that the new legislation was unconstitutional.

Band 2

Brick Court Chambers

See profile on p.774

THE SET

The excellent reputation of Brick Court Chambers is founded in part on its deep expertise in public law matters in the context of EU and competition law. Its members appear with equal acuity on behalf of both claimants and defendants, and attract particularly strong praise for their advocacy in commercial public law proceedings. They are especially accomplished in challenges to the imposition of economic sanctions and in regulatory matters.

Client service: "Its members and the clerks are brilliant – when my favourite counsel aren't available, the clerks recommend someone different and then I have a new favourite."

SILKS

Martin Chamberlain QC Exceptionally talented counsel whose practice has gone from strength to strength since he took silk. His measured and expert advocacy is particularly well respected in relation to issues of human rights, torture, sanctions and freedom of expression. **Strengths:** "He's very impressive – he's charming, thoughtful and a pleasure to work with." "He is exceptionally intelligent and impressive in the clarity of his advice. He is also very user-friendly and hard-working." **Recent work:** Acted as leading counsel for the Foreign Secretary in the high-profile case of Sandiford, resisting an appeal for legal expenses on behalf of a British woman on death row in Bali.

David Anderson QC Enjoys an excellent reputation for his domestic public law practice, which focuses strongly on the interface with EU law. He regularly appears in the ECJ, as well as the High Court. **Strengths:** "A terrific, well-judged court advocate who is intelligent and commercial." "The top barrister for EU-related public law. A very good advocate who always makes his submissions appear reasonable." **Recent work:** Acted for Betfair, an interested party, in the challenge by William Hill of the decision by the Horseracing Levy Board to classify betting exchange customers as not being subject to betting levy.

Marie Demetriou QC Acts for both claimants and defendants in a broad range of public law issues, many of them EU law-related. She is also expert in competition issues. **Strengths:** "She is hugely clever and a very logical thinker who is very easy to work with." "She is very legally astute and knowledgeable, particularly in EU and human rights law, where she adds a lot of value." **Recent work:** Acted as lead counsel for the Secretary of State for Work and Pensions in a case determining whether the new housing benefit rules discriminate against those with mental health issues.

Richard Gordon QC Specialises in handling judicial review proceedings in the context of constitutional and regulatory matters. He is also highly accomplished in representing clients in cases dealing with local authority and environmental points. **Strengths:** "He is highly inventive, and can find an argument where some others can't." "With him you get the right answer and the best advice – you know where you are, both with him and the case." **Recent work:** Represented the Press Standards Board of Finance in a judicial review application to the Court of Appeal challenging a Privy Council decision to reject a petition for a Royal Charter for a self-regulatory body for the press industry.

Mark Hoskins QC Handles public law proceedings on behalf of both private claimants and governmental bodies, typically in relation to EU law. He is also a noted authority in the field of competition law. **Strengths:** "He is obviously very good indeed." **Recent work:** Acted on behalf of Heathrow Airport in defending a judicial review challenge to the charges it levies on airlines.

Jemima Stratford QC Maintains a diverse public law practice, with particular recent experience in matters relating to competition, regulation, data protection and the free movement of persons. **Strengths:** "She is excellent, and charming with it." "She's impressive, thorough and down to earth – a good team player." **Recent work:** Represented the Gambling Commission in a judicial review challenging its decision to classify the primary business activity on the claimant's property as being 'electronic gaming', rather than gambling.

Kelyn Bacon QC Focuses her practice in administrative and public law on issues relating to state aid, regulation and antitrust law. Her regulatory experience is particularly pronounced in the pharmaceutical sector. **Strengths:** "She is highly intelligent and grasps the key points quickly, while her advice is pragmatic and often takes account of the bigger picture." "She adds intellectual value without being difficult to work with." **Recent work:** Represented Aer Lingus in the judicial review of airline charges at Heathrow Airport.

Paul Bowen QC Centres his public law practice on matters relating to mental health, deaths in custody, and human rights obligations incumbent on public bodies. He is also expert in the rights of disabled people. **Strengths:** "He is very clever and effective, and a good tactician." "He's a very good advocate who's hard-working and bold. He can take cases which others would consider inarguable, and make good progress." **Recent work:** Acted for the claimant in a judicial review examining whether the current system of a Coroner's investigation following the death of a detained psychiatric patient is sufficient to discharge the duty for an independent investigation under Article 2 of the ECHR.

JUNIORS

Maya Lester Specialises in proceedings relating to targeted sanctions, competition and EU law, in which areas she enjoys a growing reputation. She has further strength in human rights and national security matters. **Strengths:** "She is fantastic, very bright and very hard-working. She's up there with the best juniors, and doesn't need to be led." "She is formidably bright, and is particularly good in EU public law cases." **Recent work:** Acted in a judicial review concerning the imposition by the Foreign and Commonwealth Office of a Marine Protection Zone around the Chagos Islands. The case raises a novel point of European law, addressing the meaning of provisions of the EC Treaty.

Victoria Wakefield Offers advice and representation in public law matters in the areas of competition, EU and commercial judicial review. She has further interest in immigration and healthcare matters. **Strengths:** "She is a delight to work with. She is extremely thorough and diligent in the advice she prepares, is extremely proactive and her advice is very solid." "She's clever, but accessible and happy to roll her sleeves up." **Recent work:** Acted for Eurostar in a regulatory appeals hearing before the Channel Tunnel Intergovernmental Commission seeking transparency in the charges levied by Eurotunnel for access to the tunnel.

Sarah Love Specialises in the commercial and competition elements of public law, her legal expertise being bolstered by a background as a professional economist. She represents individuals and charities as well as government bodies. **Strengths:** "She is very bright, very personable, commercially aware and responsive to client needs." "She is extremely clever." **Recent work:** Represented Transport for London in defending a judicial review challenging the policy to allow black cabs, but not minicabs, to use London's bus lanes.

Doughty Street Chambers

See profile on p.786

THE SET

Doughty Street Chambers enjoys an outstanding reputation for the quality of representation it offers to claimants in public law proceedings. Its incredibly strong counsel are renowned experts in pursuing actions on behalf of those who seek redress for having suffered injustice at the hands of the state and its agents, particularly in relation to fundamental issues of human rights. They are especially accomplished in handling matters in the context of immigration and asylum, terrorism, criminal justice, prison law, freedom of expression and mental health. **Client service:** "They have incredible depth and some of the best barristers in the field. They can draw on resources to tackle any type of matter."

SILKS

Edward Fitzgerald QC Revered advocate who enjoys significant recognition for his public law work in relation to criminal justice, and is particularly well known for bringing constitutional challenges to the death penalty. He is also highly expert in mental health, prisoner rights and extradition matters. **Strengths:** "He is irrepressible – he has an enormous energy, and he channels all that energy into every case he does." "He is an absolute gentleman, and very good for high-level constitutional law matters." **Recent work:** Represented Abu Qatada in the appeal by the Home Secretary against the Special Immigration Appeal Commission's decision that to deport him to Jordan would be a violation of his rights under Article 6 of the ECHR.

Martin Westgate QC Well respected for his expertise in a range of issues, including the rights of disabled people, social security and prisoners' rights. He is also notably expert in handling judicial reviews in relation to employment matters. **Strengths:** "He's a very committed and experienced public lawyer who's analytically very strong." "He is exceptionally gifted and very bright." **Recent work:** Acted for the claimants in a Divisional Court challenge to the 'bedroom tax,' on the grounds that it is discriminatory to disabled people and not in compliance with the public sector equality duty.

Stephen Cragg QC Acts on behalf of claimants in matters relating to prison law, mental health and the conduct of the police. He has a further interest in freedom of information. **Strengths:** "He is absolutely excellent, and has enormous amounts of knowledge. He really educates in his arguments, and reading them you feel completely outgunned." "The court are sympathetic to his low-key approach to deserving cases." **Recent work:** Represented the claimant in a test case addressing the issue of access to compensation for miscarriages of justice.

JUNIORS

Adam Straw Commands considerable respect for his practice in public law, which focuses on the interface with the criminal justice system. He is notably accomplished in inquests and the judicial review proceedings arising from them. **Strengths:** "He is very approachable, knowledgeable, extremely thorough and reliable, and a delight to work with." "He has an incredible legal mind – he really knows the law and has a sixth sense about what arguments will run in the Administrative Court." **Recent work:** Acted for Lindsay Sandiford in the challenge to the government's policy not to provide legal funding for British nationals held on death row abroad.

Caoilfhionn Gallagher Specialises in representing the interests of claimants in public law proceedings founded on human rights arguments. She is particularly proficient in prison law, community care and the rights of children. **Strengths:** "Her written work is impressive, clear and incisive." "She is tenacious, and a tireless worker." **Recent work:** Acted for the Media Lawyers' Association as an intervener in an appeal by the Metropolitan Police against the ruling that they were not entitled to rely on secret evidence or closed proceedings when applying for a Production Order against media organisations.

Alison Pickup Enjoys a growing reputation for her work in the areas of immigration and asylum and community care. She is also proficient in issues arising in the context of prison law. **Strengths:** "She is charming to work with, has good judgement and is increasingly instructed in test case litigation." "She's phenomenally hard-working and has superb judgement. Her confidence in her arguments is remarkable." **Recent work:** Acted for the claimant in a complex challenge to prison conditions, in which abuse of power was alleged due to the use of solitary confinement as a punishment, rather than as a security measure.

Jude Bunting Has a burgeoning practice in the field, which focuses particularly on prison law, open justice and challenging the conduct of the police. He is also proficient in terrorism matters. **Strengths:** "He's very bright, keen, approachable and willing to take on challenging and difficult cases." "He is a very strong advocate who is very inventive and creative." **Recent work:** Acted for the claimant in a judicial review appeal to the Supreme Court addressing the correct standard of procedural fairness to be applied for prisoners seeking to challenge their categorisation in detention of the highest security.

Henrietta Hill Experienced junior with a practice focusing on discrimination and bringing actions against the police. She is also expert at appearing in inquests. **Strengths:** "She is particularly strong on discrimination law, and is equally at home running points in that area in both public and private law contexts." "She is a very effective advocate, and a prodigious worker." **Recent work:** Represented Marina Litvinenko in her judicial review challenge to the decision of the Home Secretary not to order a public inquiry into the circumstances surrounding the death of her husband.

Jamie Burton Tackles judicial reviews on behalf of claimants in the areas of community and healthcare, the rights of children and social housing. Further experience includes bringing actions challenging cuts to the provision of public services. **Strengths:** "He is a tenacious advocate." **Recent work:** Appeared for the claimant in a judicial review concerning the rights of unwell residents of the European Economic Area to receive healthcare and housing in the UK.

11KBW

See profile on p.823

THE SET

11KBW offers representation of an extremely high standard across the full span of issues in administrative and public law. It is especially renowned for its expertise in acting for government departments in defending a diverse range of judicial review proceedings, while its members are also exceptionally adept at handling matters for individual and corporate claimants. They are particularly accomplished in the areas of education, local government, social security and the public equality duty.

Client service: "They offer a first-class service, and all the barristers are approachable and accommodating. Clerks are very flexible and calls are returned immediately, and followed up if necessary."

SILKS

Karen Steyn QC (see p.728) Took silk this year, having built on an excellent junior practice spanning a broad range of areas of expertise. She is especially accomplished in matters of national security, freedom of information and the extraterritorial application of human rights principles. **Strengths:** "She is in a league of her own. She is a superb lawyer who is ferociously hard-working, a brilliant writer and an excellent member of any team." "She is excellent. Immensely hard-working, and someone who always has a really in-depth understanding of the issues in the case." **Recent work:** Acted for the Secretary of State for Work and Pensions in a landmark judicial review of the government's controversial 'benefit cap' scheme.

Nigel Giffin QC Commands great respect for the depth of his expertise in public law matters, which is focused particularly on education issues. He has additional experience in proceedings relating to social services, housing and finance, and often handles commercial challenges to the decisions of public bodies. **Strengths:** "His written advice is clear, concise and accurate, and he is very good on his feet." "The ability he has to appreciate both the commercial aspects of the matter and how to present the case most effectively in court is of the highest possible standard." **Recent work:** Acted for the Legal Services Board in a judicial review challenging the implementation of the Quality Assurance Scheme for Advocates.

Jason Coppel QC (see p.578) Centres his public law practice on issues relating to public procurement, freedom of information and the interface with EU law. He acts for both central government and claimant NGOs. **Strengths:** "He is extremely good, feared as an opponent and a very welcome member of the team when an ally." "He is somebody who is extremely able and a very impressive opponent." **Recent work:** Acted for the Secretaries of State for the Home Department and for Justice, in a challenge to legislation requiring disclosure of convictions and cautions on criminal records checks.

Jonathan Swift QC (see p.733) An enormously well-regarded practitioner in public law with a tremendous depth of experience gained in part through his eight years spent as Treasury Devil. In that capacity he appeared for the government in issues relating to freedom of information, environmental, constitutional and regulatory law amongst others. **Strengths:** "He's a very compelling advocate, and has a brilliant legal mind." "He is hugely experienced in public law, and a very effective advocate." **Recent work:** Acted for the Foreign Secretary in significant litigation challenging his request for the UN Security Council to impose sanctions on an alleged terrorist. The case addressed important issues of admissibility of evidence possibly obtained through torture.

James Goudie QC (see p.612) Has a greatly respected practice in public law, which focuses particularly on matters relating to education and public financing. He is also interested in professional discipline and national security. **Strengths:** "His analysis is always brilliant, and the way he communicates it is great, because any non-lawyer who picks up his opinion clearly understands what the key issues are." "He's very authoritative. He makes it look simple and presents cases in a way that courts find helpful." **Recent work:** Represented Armagh City and District Council in a judicial review of a decision by the Northern Ireland Commissioner for Complaints in relation to the sale of a piece of land owned by the council. The primary argument concerned jurisdiction.

Timothy Pitt-Payne QC (see p.694) Centres his public law practice on information, employment and local government issues. He has additional experience in advising on state obligations. **Strengths:** "He is incredibly sharp, and very good in his advice – it's easy to understand what he's saying." "An authoritative expert on freedom of information law who gives excellent client service, whether paid or pro bono." **Recent work:** Acted for the Electoral Commission in a judicial review addressing what measures it should take under the Data Protection Act to protect electors' personal information being used for direct marketing purposes.

Daniel Stilitz QC (see p.729) Enjoys a strong reputation for the quality of his work in public law, which has a particular emphasis on commercial judicial review. He has additional experience in human rights and local government issues. **Strengths:** "He's very good. He's able to handle very complex questions and is never found out intellectually." **Recent work:** Represented the Post Office in a judicial review brought by a former sub-postmaster challenging a decision to terminate his contract, on the grounds that it was in breach of his rights under the ECHR.

Clive Sheldon QC Focuses on education, health and local government issues within the context of public law. He has further experience in handling matters relating to the powers of the police. **Strengths:** "He is capable, reasonable and a good opponent." **Recent work:** Acted for the London Borough of Haringey in successfully defending a judicial review challenge to its introduction of a Council Tax Reduction Scheme.

Charles Bourne QC (see p.553) New silk with a wealth of experience in immigration, prison law and mental health cases. He is also interested in community care and social security. **Strengths:** "He is very experienced in immigration and national security matters, is a very steady performer and is trusted with sensitive cases." "He's got a very solid practice in public law." **Recent work:** Represented the Department for Work and Pensions in resisting a challenge by way of judicial review of its policy on the retention of data on transgender claimants for benefits purposes. The case was brought on the grounds that the policy was irrational, and that it breached the rights of such benefits claimants under the ECHR.

JUNIORS

Ben Hooper (see p.630) A junior with an exceptionally accomplished public law practice. He focuses in particular on surveillance and national security, regulatory issues and proceedings relating to detention under the Mental Health Act. **Strengths:** "An intellectually strong and able advocate with the ability to simplify complex legal and factual issues." "He is brilliant at executing a strategy. Very smooth, he's persuasive with the court and very switched on." **Recent work:** Acted as a junior for the Secretary of State for Justice in judicial review proceedings brought by the Barclay brothers questioning a draft law amending the constitution of the island of Sark.

Anya Proops (see p.699) Focuses on information issues within the field of public law. She demonstrates particular prowess in handling proceedings in relation to freedom of information and the obligations of public bodies with respect to the handling of data. **Strengths:** "She's an excellent advocate who's very passionate about what she does." "An excellent, intelligent and robust oral advocate, who is always open to discussions on a case." **Recent work:** Represented the University of Leicester in a highly publicised judicial review challenge to the decision of the SSJ to grant a licence to inter the remains of Richard III at Leicester Cathedral.

Andrew Sharland (see p.718) Specialises in handling issues in the context of immigration, prison law and constitutional law. He acts for government and public bodies, as well as claimants. **Strengths:** "He is very good tactically – he advises on the law and also on what different approaches will work in court. He has expert knowledge of civil procedure rules." **Recent work:** Acted successfully for Worcestershire County Council in a challenge, on the grounds of consultation and public sector equality duty, to its scheme to set a maximum expenditure for adult community care services.

Jonathan Moffett (see p.675) Acts primarily for defendants by virtue of his position on the Attorney General's 'A' panel of counsel. He has a practical and academic interest in the principles of judicial review. **Strengths:** "He is absolutely excellent. He's very client-friendly, very accessible, and everyone is comfortable in him leading the case." **Recent work:** Acted for the London Fire and Emergency Planning Authority in the defence of a judicial review challenge brought by seven London Borough Councils to a decision to close fire stations across the capital.

Joanne Clement (see p.574) Acts for both claimants and defendants in proceedings dealing with human rights and commercial issues. She has further experience in the areas of community care, education and local government. **Strengths:** "She is super legally, very responsive and very approachable." "She is very, very competent in judicial review work." **Recent work:** Acted on behalf of the claimants in an expedited judicial review challenging the decision of the examination boards and Ofqual to move GCSE grade boundaries, resulting in a large numbers of children failing to achieve a 'C' grade.

Amy Rogers (see p.709) Focuses on the use of commercial judicial review to protect and further business interests. She also has experience in representing claimants and respondents in benefits matters. **Strengths:** "She is a great success in the making. She's super-talented, diligent, very clear thinking and drafts very well." "She's very clear, very sensible, incredibly hard-working and much in demand by QCs." **Recent work:** Acted on behalf of the claimant Iranian Bank in a landmark Supreme Court case that successfully challenged the UK's financial sanctions on Iran. The case was the first time the Supreme Court had admitted closed material in a hearing.

Heather Emmerson (see p.596) Maintains a broad practice in public law and has expertise in local government, education, housing and immigration matters. She regularly handles challenges to decisions relating to the provision of public services. **Strengths:** "She is a real rising star, and outstanding for her level of seniority. Her written work is excellent, and she is very personable." "She was very good and made an immediately good impression. She staggered everyone with the grasp she had of the case." **Recent work:** Acted for the University of Leicester in a high-profile judicial review brought by the Plantagenet Alliance challenging the granting of a licence to the university to reinter the remains of King Richard III in Leicester Cathedral.

Christopher Knight (see p.647) Has a growing reputation for his public law practice. He has pronounced experience in issues arising in the context of freedom of information and education. **Strengths:** "He is very sharp and adds a good deal of value in whatever role he's instructed." "He's very reliable and very dependable." **Recent work:** Appeared for two interveners in a highly significant Supreme Court case that addressed whether the right of freedom of expression under Article 10 ECHR includes a right of access to information, in the context of a Freedom of Information request.

Matrix Chambers

See profile on p.832

THE SET

Matrix Chambers maintains its extremely strong reputation for the diversity and quality of its advocacy across the full range of public law matters. Its highly accomplished members offer advice and representation to claimants including individuals, charities and corporate entities. They further act for local and central government bodies. Areas of special expertise include public law actions in relation to criminal justice, international law, commercial interests and EU law.

Client service: "The clerking is very good – they are beyond co-operative, and will go the extra mile when you are struggling against tight deadlines." Jason Housden is the senior practice manager.

SILKS

Helen Mountfield QC (see p.678) Maintains her highly respected practice focusing on education, community care, equality and discrimination issues. She is also expert in questions of the operation of human rights within public law. **Strengths:** "She is phenomenally gifted intellectually – she mixes really thorough analysis and high-level thinking with empathy for the defendant." "She is very approachable, and has an impressive ability to articulate very difficult arguments." **Recent work:** Represented the Equality and Human Rights Commission as interveners in a landmark case in the Supreme Court establishing that UK military personnel based abroad are within UK jurisdiction for the purposes of the Human Rights Act (HRA).

Danny Friedman QC (see p.604) Accomplished public law practitioner with a specialism in matters relating to national security and terrorism, particularly in relation to the activities of the military and intelligence services. He is also regularly instructed in public inquiries. **Strengths:** "He is absolutely superb. He has a dynamism and energy which is infectious for the whole legal team, and a complete command of detail." "He is able to put across complex and intricate arguments in a succinct and digestible way." **Recent work:** Acted for the claimant in a judicial review seeking to ban the MoD interrogation technique of 'challenging', previously known as 'harshing'.

Ben Emmerson QC Renowned advocate with substantial expertise in a wide range of public law matters. He is especially well regarded for his work in the context of criminal law and its interface with public law. **Strengths:** "He is incredibly good – he gives superb leadership and is an extremely powerful lawyer to have on one's side." "He is combative, argumentative and extremely good." **Recent work:** Represented the widow of Alexander Litvinenko in the inquest into his death.

Phillippa Kaufmann QC Exceptionally talented silk who maintains her outstanding reputation for her public law work, which has a strong emphasis on arguing fundamental points of human rights. She is especially experienced in handling judicial review proceedings on behalf of claimants. **Strengths:** "She is mellifluous, clever and very strategic." "She is just superb; she's incredibly bright, incredibly tenacious in court and produces really good paperwork." **Recent work:** Acted for the claimant in a judicial review test case addressing whether the Home Office guidance on the classification of historic victims of trafficking had failed to give effect to the UK's obligations under the Council of Europe Convention on Action Against Trafficking in Human Beings. The case successfully established that such historical victims are 'victims' pursuant to the Convention and are thus entitled to a certain standard of treatment.

Alex Bailin QC (see p.541) Expert criminal law practitioner whose practice in public law accordingly frequently involves arguments founded in criminal justice. He is experienced in handling public law proceedings relating to torture, rendition and terrorism legislation. **Strengths:** "He's a skilled practitioner, equally comfortable in the criminal and admin courts. He's incredibly good." **Recent work:** Represented JUSTICE as an intervener in a landmark case before the Supreme Court that established that the HRA applies to UK soldiers serving in foreign countries.

Raza Husain QC Attracts effusive praise for his authoritative advocacy in public law proceedings. He focuses particularly on issues in the context of immigration, asylum and extradition. **Strengths:** "He has made the law relating to unlawful detention his own, and continues to push boundaries." "He is the person to turn to for immigration issues in public law." **Recent work:** Acted for the appellants in a significant Supreme Court case establishing the correct application of the Dublin II Regulation for the transfer of an asylum seeker back to the EU state in which they first arrived, where it is claimed that such a removal would violate their rights under the ECHR.

Clare Montgomery QC Outstanding counsel in the fields of fraud, crime and extradition, which expertise informs her work in public law proceedings. She acts on behalf of both claimants and defendants. **Strengths:** "She is an excellent advocate who is incredibly quick and immensely knowledgeable. Right at the top for the overlap between public and criminal law." "She is extraordinarily brilliant and highly efficient." **Recent work:** Represented a cross-party group of parliamentarians in a judicial review challenging the decision of the Home Secretary to exclude a dissident Iranian politician from entering the UK in order to discuss the state of human rights in Iran.

Tim Owen QC Centres his practice on the overlap between criminal and public law, especially in relation to questions of human rights. He is notably accomplished in matters concerning the conduct of the military and in inquests. **Strengths:** "He has really good judgement, and in his public law advocacy he gets just the right tone for the courts." "He has an incredibly good manner with the court – he is really easy to listen to, which makes him such a dangerous opponent." **Recent work:** Acted for the claimant in a judicial review challenging the MoD's continuing policy of using an interrogation technique for foreign nationals known as 'challenging'. The challenge arose out of the report from the Baha Mousa Inquiry.

David Wolfe QC (see p.755) Typically represents claimants in public law matters concerning education, freedom of expression and environmental issues. He is also accomplished in handling proceedings addressing the rights of disabled people. **Strengths:** "He has a wonderful mixture of skills – he is an extremely impressive advocate, is fantastic with clients and is incredibly clear in his drafting." "One of the best, he produces clear, concise advice every time." **Recent work:** Represented the claimant in a judicial review that successfully established that North Somerset Council had failed to meet the Public Sector Equality Duty in cutting its budget for the provision of youth services.

Aidan O'Neill QC Informs his work in public law matters with his expertise in EU law. He has particular experience in discrimination and prisoners' rights. **Strengths:** "His advocacy skills are tremendous, he is intellectually impressive and he is prepared to take on extremely complex, difficult and notorious work." **Recent work:** Acted for London Christian Radio in a judicial review questioning whether a ban on political advertising on radio includes an advertisement calling for information on the marginalisation of Christians in the workplace. The Court of Appeal dismissed the claim, construing a wide interpretation of the meaning of 'political' in this context.

Hugh Southey QC (see p.725) Maintains a broad practice in public law, and has appeared on a number of occasions before the Supreme Court. He has noted expertise in mental health, prison law, immigration and criminal justice. **Strengths:** "He is a library of public law. He's more than willing to take on any difficult case, and he puts forward arguments strongly and eloquently." "He has an absolute command of the principles of public law, and is able to approach both cases and clients' situations in a way that solutions are found readily." **Recent work:** Acted for the appellant in a landmark Supreme Court case that established that a claim for damages for breach of rights under the ECHR need only show distress and not loss.

Richard Hermer QC Specialises in pursuing questions of human rights by means of public law proceedings. He has special expertise in issues arising in the context of the conduct of the military and the intelligence services, particularly in relation to allegations of torture. **Strengths:** "He's always there when I need him, and is exceptional in putting forward arguments in court." "He is pioneering, extremely hard-working and particularly good at simplifying the issues." **Recent work:** Represented the claimant in a challenge by judicial review of the policy of the UK for the detention of suspected Taliban militants in Afghanistan.

Jessica Simor QC Represents a broad range of clients from individuals to regulators and government bodies in a diverse array of public law matters. She has a particular interest in issues arising in the context of religious freedom, terrorism and refugees. **Strengths:** "She is very clever, works very hard and is unparalleled on issues relating to the ECHR." "Her taking silk was well deserved – she gives great drive and direction to cases." **Recent work:** Represented the United Sikh Association in Bradford in a challenge by judicial review of the decision of the local authority to grant planning permission for the building of a halal butchers next to a Sikh temple. The case addressed the tension between planning law and religious freedoms.

JUNIORS

Daniel Squires Commands a great deal of respect for his public law practice, which is founded particularly in actions relating to international human rights. He is also expert in terrorism and national security matters. **Strengths:** "He really is a class apart from most other juniors. He's forward-looking in what he can do, and is really good on paper and in court." "He's a pleasure to work with, and is very bright, very thoughtful and very helpful." **Recent work:** Acted for the claimant in a judicial review examining the right of a suspect detained under Schedule 7 of the Terrorism Act 2000 to access to a lawyer before being questioned. This was the first time this point had been raised before the court.

Nicholas Armstrong Enjoys a growing reputation for his claimant-centric practice in public law. He offers authoritative representation in cases concerning immigration, free movement of persons and false imprisonment. **Strengths:** "He is extremely bright and motivated." "His advocacy is great, he's very creative and is an easy person to talk through issues with." **Recent work:** Acted for the appellant in a judicial review case addressing whether the disclosure of cautions given in childhood is compliant with rights under Article 8 of the ECHR.

Adam Sandell A practising GP who attracts strong praise for his expertise in tackling public law proceedings turning on medical evidence. He also has a burgeoning practice in inquests. **Strengths:** "He is almost unique in the depth of his knowledge of medical issues and their overlap with the law." "He is an incredibly impressive, intelligent and dedicated lawyer." **Recent work:** Acted for the British Union for the Abolition of Vivisection in a case that established that it was permissible for a court to order pre-action disclosure of information for the purposes of determining whether to proceed with judicial review.

Alison Macdonald (see p.659) Focuses on human rights arguments within public law proceedings. She is well respected for her work in challenging the actions of the police, the retention of data and the rights of protesters. **Strengths:** "She is very, very clever and her drafting is immaculate. She's good at engaging in discussion with the judges and she doesn't get thrown by questions." "It's easy to work with her – she's lovely, highly intelligent and hard-working." **Recent work:** Represented Andrey Lugovoy in the inquest into the death of Alexander Litvinenko.

Sarah Hannett Acts for claimants and defendants in public law matters relating to education, local government and community care. She is also experienced in prison law issues. **Strengths:** "She's really efficient, very good with clients and expert on the crossover between public law and education." "She is excellent, hard-working and very thorough." **Recent work:** Intervened on behalf of the Fire Brigades Union in a judicial review challenging the decision to implement cuts to the budget for fire stations, fire engines and firefighters in London.

Band 3

1 Crown Office Row

See profile on p.784

THE SET

1 Crown Office Row maintains its excellent reputation for the work it undertakes on behalf of central government, as well as for its growing claimant client base. The specialism of many of its members is undoubtedly founded in healthcare and clinical negligence, in which field the set is pre-eminent, and, accordingly, many barristers here are often involved in major public law proceedings with a medical emphasis. Besides this area of outstanding accomplishment, the set offers expertise in matters relating to national security, terrorism, education, prison law and the provision of public services.

Client service: "They are very good and their rates are reasonable. The clerks are extremely efficient."

SILKS

Neil Garnham QC (see p.606) Focuses on healthcare provision, clinical negligence and personal injury issues within public law. He is also very well regarded for his expertise in highly significant inquests and public inquiries. **Strengths:** "He is absolutely excellent, and especially competent in service reconfiguration cases." "He is fantastic – he hones his submissions, and is a powerful advocate because he really thinks through what he's going to say." **Recent work:** Acted for the government in judicial review proceedings arising from the Litvinenko inquest.

Philip Havers QC Enjoys an excellent reputation for his deep experience in handling public law proceedings, typically addressing the function of human rights in the provision of healthcare. He has additional experience in matters relating to the conduct of the military and the obligation to conduct investigations. **Strengths:** "He is charming and hard-working, and has impeccable credentials." **Recent work:** Acted for the government in a high-profile challenge to the independence of an investigation into allegations of the abuse of Iraqis made against the British army.

Angus McCullough QC Specialises in appearing in closed proceedings in the capacity of special advocate, in which respect he is widely regarded as the leading figure. He is especially expert in issues relating to national security, torture, asset freezing and deportation. **Strengths:** "He is really, really good. He's calm, efficient and has exceptionally good judgement." "He is the special advocate's special advocate, and is the most successful in terms of winning cases." **Recent work:** Appeared as special advocate in a case challenging the Special Immigration Appeals Commission's upholding of a decision to deport an Ethiopian national to Ethiopia, in which it was held that the SIAC had erred in allowing for the Secretary of State to defer the question of the possible infringement of Article 3 of the ECHR to a later date.

JUNIORS

Jeremy Hyam Handles a variety of public law proceedings, with an emphasis on matters dealing with healthcare provision and the consultation duty incumbent on public bodies. He has further experience in environmental impact cases. **Strengths:** "He is very adept at quickly identifying the client's real concerns, and explaining their impact in practice and in context." **Recent work:** Acted for one of two claimants in successfully challenging the Secretary of State for Health's decision to close University Hospital Lewisham.

Shaheen Rahman Frequently instructed on behalf of claimants in judicial reviews challenging healthcare decisions. She is also expert in acting as special advocate and handling medical regulatory cases. **Strengths:** "She's very good, very effective, and has a forthright approach." "I have been impressed by her engagement with the issues in terrorist cases, in which she is often special advocate." **Recent work:**

Acted in a judicial review challenging the policy to refuse to provide Muslim prisoners methadone outside daylight hours during Ramadan.

Marina Wheeler Handles public law matters with an emphasis on human rights, particularly discrimination, mental health and the right to life. She typically acts for the government, local authorities and the NHS. **Strengths:** "She's very good – she's very thorough in her preparation and understands the issues of consultation and the obligations of health authorities very well." "She works hard and is really efficient." **Recent work:** Represented the MoD in a judicial review challenging the UK's policy of transferring prisoners to detention centres in Afghanistan. The challenge was founded on the assertion that the claimant's detention by UK armed forces was unlawful under both Afghan law and the HRA.

Kate Beattie Handles public law matters with an emphasis on human rights, particularly discrimination and the right to life. She has further experience in inquiries and matters relating to professional negligence. **Strengths:** "She is very impressive and very good on the crossover between public and healthcare law." **Recent work:** Acted for the claimant in a judicial review challenge to the GMC's implementation of new rules on registration of doctors trained overseas. The claim succeeded on the grounds that the GMC had breached the doctrine of legitimate expectation in that they had not made provisional arrangements for such doctors who had already embarked on courses.

Thirty Nine Essex Street

See profile on p.797

THE SET

Thirty Nine Essex Street boasts a deep bench of highly expert and accomplished counsel, experienced in handling judicial reviews arising from the decisions of governmental and regulatory bodies. Its members demonstrate particular proficiency in the areas of local government, education, environmental, regulatory and planning law, as well as in proceedings concerning torture, assisted dying, terrorism and miscarriages of justice. They are well versed in acting for government departments, regulatory bodies, local authorities, charities, NGOs and individual claimants.

Client service: "I can send work to the clerks knowing they will handle it quickly and incredibly reliably. They are so well organised that they can sort it out, regardless of the size of a crisis."

SILKS

Nigel Pleming QC Extremely well respected for the skill and learning he displays in the range of public law actions in which he is frequently instructed. He is especially authoritative in international proceedings in both commercial and human rights contexts. **Strengths:** "He's spectacularly experienced and his advocacy is very impressive. We couldn't ask for a better leader of a team." "He is an absolute pleasure to deal with and is so user-friendly." **Recent work:** Represented the claimant in a judicial review challenging the decision of the Foreign Secretary to impose a marine exclusion zone around the Chagos Islands.

Charles Cory-Wright QC Appears as a special advocate in matters related to terrorism. His public law work often sees him act before the Special Immigration Appeals Commission and the Administrative Court. **Strengths:** "He's a very sensible and well-prepared opponent."

Alison Foster QC Centres her public law practice on matters relating to tax disputes, constitutional and vires issues and professional discipline. She is experienced in acting in domestic and foreign jurisdictions. **Strengths:** "She is extremely generous with her time and expertise, and works extremely hard." **Recent work:** Acted for the Commissioners for Revenue & Customs in defending a judicial review challenging its decision to treat suppliers of pathology as exempt from VAT.

Fenella Morris QC Maintains a diverse practice, and has experience in handling issues arising in the context of commercial regulation, community care, and the detention of patients under the Mental Health Act. She is also well versed in professional discipline proceedings. **Strengths:** "She's very knowledgeable, explains things very well and really gets the issues very quickly in judicial reviews." "She gives pragmatic advice and is capable of getting to grips with intellectual arguments." **Recent work:** Acted for the Chartered Institute of Management Accountants in defending a judicial review challenging a finding that the claimant had been guilty of professional misconduct following a breach of confidentiality. The case addressed issues of the meaning of confidentiality in this context, and the influence of the right to free expression on it.

James Strachan QC Has a public law practice characterised by a focus on human rights issues. He is particularly experienced in matters relating to religious rights, the right to die, and miscarriages of justice. **Strengths:** "He has an incredible grasp of the law and the issues." "He's a very good lawyer and a smooth advocate." **Recent work:** Represented the Ministry of Justice in an extremely high-profile judicial review in the Supreme Court addressing the lawfulness of the prohibition on assisted suicide.

Lisa Giovannetti QC Acts for both government and individual claimants in the course of her varied public law practice. She is especially interested in questions of national security, asylum, immigration and broad human rights. **Strengths:** "She is a very effective advocate." "Her drafting is impeccable and she is a well-established practitioner." **Recent work:** Appeared for the Home Secretary in a case challenging the decision to revoke the claimant's British citizenship. He argued that the decision was taken as a precursor to his extraordinary rendition to the USA, and that it left him unlawfully stateless.

Steven Kovats QC Focuses on immigration, human rights and issues relating to the criminal justice system. He acts for central government, local authorities and private persons in judicial review proceedings. **Strengths:** "He is absolutely outstanding and a dream counsel. He is exceptionally bright and knowledgeable, and manages to produce beautiful written submissions in breathtakingly short amounts of time, while his advocacy is eloquent and inspires confidence." **Recent work:** Acted for the Foreign Secretary in a judicial review challenge of his imposition of a marine protection area around the Chagos Islands.

Jenni Richards QC Acts for claimants and defendants in high profile judicial review cases, often arising in the healthcare sector. She is admired by sources for her impressive intellect, incisive advocacy and ability to relate to vulnerable clients. **Strengths:** "She has a big brain and really gets behind the case. Her commitment is incredible. She represents with passion." "She is consistently brilliant, both on paper and in court." **Recent work:** Represented two fertility clinics in their judicial review of the Human Fertilisation and Embryology Authority's decision to add a condition to Dr Mohamed Taranissi's license which limited multiple births.

JUNIORS

Jonathan Auburn (see p.539) Offers advice and representation to government defendants and individual claimants in public law actions. He specialises particularly in questions of mental capacity, community care, education and service provision. **Strengths:** "He gives very good, practical advice that's easy to understand." "Clients like his practical attitude, his approachability and his flexibility." **Recent work:** Appeared for the Justice Secretary in a judicial review test case contesting, on human rights grounds, the decision to impose a levy on prisoners' earnings in order to fund services for victims.

Kate Grange Specialises in issues arising in the context of immigration, prison law, human rights and terrorism. She is also interested in matters relating to the environment. **Strengths:** "She is a really top-quality barrister, who is always on top of everything and knows everything in the papers." "She's very down to earth, is an incredibly practical lawyer and a delight to deal with." **Recent work:** Acted for the Defence Secretary in a high-profile judicial review seeking a public inquiry into the actions of British soldiers in Iraq. The claimants contended that soldiers had been responsible for the deaths and ill treatment of a number of Iraqi civilians.

Alexander Ruck Keene (see p.712) Has substantial experience in matters concerning damages for historical torture and serious assault, and the application of human rights principles in that context. He is also expert in issues of mental health and capacity. **Strengths:** "He has a phenomenal brain." "A very good opponent and an able junior." **Recent work:** Appeared for the applicant in a case before the ECHR contending that his seclusion at Ashworth Special Hospital violated Articles 3, 5, 8 and 14 of the ECHR. The court gave the first clarification to the circumstances under which a person may be deprived of their residual liberty in a psychiatric setting.

Victoria Butler-Cole Focuses on public law matters relating to healthcare, mental health and community care. She is especially knowledgeable on the application of ECHR rights to those areas. **Strengths:** "She's both intellectual and highly approachable." "She has a very sharp brain and turns round papers very quickly." **Recent work:** Acted for Shropshire Council in a number of related judicial review proceedings challenging the decision to close or transform day centres in the county. The cases addressed fundamental issues of the duty to consult and the operation of the public sector equality duty.

Parishil Patel Handles judicial reviews and statutory appeals on behalf of claimants and defendants. He is experienced in mental health and capacity, and local government issues. **Strengths:** "He will quite often drop everything at very short notice to help. Really responsive and really good at handling clients, he always gives great advice." "He's very good on his feet." **Recent work:** Represented the claimant in a judicial review of the decision of a police Chief Constable to refuse his security clearance. The court held that the Chief Constable was entitled to withhold documents underlying the decision on the basis that their disclosure would compromise intelligence sources.

Landmark Chambers
See profile on p.829

THE SET

Landmark Chambers' barristers are renowned experts in handling public law proceedings in the field of planning and the environment, in which areas they are undisputed leaders. They offer highly accomplished and learned representation in a range of further fields, including social security, education, immigration, health and housing, and are also strong on the general application of principles of the powers of public entities and regulatory bodies. Individuals here ably act on behalf of government, local authorities, NGOs, charities and individual claimants.

Client service: "Landmark is outstanding in its provision of service, and has a wide spectrum of experience in terms of areas of law as well as levels of counsel." Jay Fullilove is the senior clerk.

SILKS

Richard Drabble QC A renowned advocate with decades of experience of handling proceedings across the full range of public law issues. His particular areas of expertise include planning, environmental, social security and EU law. **Strengths:** "I've never seen the Court of Appeal take an advocate more seriously than him." "He is without a doubt the best social security advocate, and his knowledge of the principles of public law is encyclopaedic." **Recent work:** Represented the Mayor of London in the judicial review challenge to his decision to implement cuts to the budget for fire stations in the capital.

Nathalie Lieven QC Enjoys an excellent reputation for the quality of her representation in a diverse array of public law proceedings. She is a noted authority in appearing in cases relating to prison law, mental health, social security and community care. **Strengths:** "She is sensitive and articulate. The courts see her as someone who talks sense, and when she speaks, people listen." "She is a force of nature – she's irresistible on her feet, and very direct and quick to get to the point." **Recent work:** Acted for the claimants in a successful challenge in the Supreme Court to the government's controversial policy decision to require benefit claimants to work unpaid in order to be eligible for benefits, arguing the policy was ultra vires.

James Maurici QC Handles public law actions addressing education, planning, social security, local government and environmental issues. He is a noted expert in judicial review. **Strengths:** "He is a talented and very hard-working member of the Bar whose taking of silk recently was much deserved." "He's calming and gives you confidence, since he gives sensible advice, is impressive in court and is always organised." **Recent work:** Acted for the Environment Agency in a case before the Supreme Court that determined what the provision in the Aarhus Convention means when it says that bringing cases on environmental grounds must not be 'prohibitively expensive.'

David Forsdick QC Acts for claimants and defendants in public proceedings, typically relating to land and environmental matters. His land expertise encompasses issues in the context of the right to protest and national security provisions. **Strengths:** "He is very good. He's a nice person as well as being very tenacious." **Recent work:** Acted for the Secretary of State for Communities and Local Government in defending a judicial review challenging the decision of a planning inspector appointed by the defendant.

David Elvin QC Focuses on issues arising in the context of property, highways and local government. He is especially accomplished in human rights and EU arguments in those areas. **Strengths:** "He is very good, and has quite a forceful style." **Recent work:** Represented Blaby District Council in defending a judicial review brought by the Leicestershire Police Commissioner of its decision to grant planning permission for a substantial development near Leicester.

Philip Coppel QC Specialises in local government, licensing and employment judicial reviews. He has particular recent experience in challenges to the actions and decisions of the Treasury. **Strengths:** "He is a very good silk who is aggressive, will fight his client's corner and will go the extra mile to get the desired result. He's very focused on what can be achieved, and is very creative." "He is careful, quietly spoken and superbly well informed." **Recent work:** Acted on behalf of the claimant in a judicial review that sought quashing orders on two planning permissions and conservation area consents granted by the London Borough of Hackney.

Paul Brown QC Centres his public law practice on social housing, immigration and education matters. He is also expert in the expression of human rights principles in public law actions. **Strengths:** "He is a tremendously good advocate, who is very fluent, completely confident and always totally on top of things." "A very good advocate, who is persuasive, economical and scrupulously fair." **Recent work:** Acted for the appellant in a case that addressed whether a local authority is entitled to have regard to any additional assistance a homeless person may receive when deciding whether to classify them as 'vulnerable' under the provisions of the Housing Act.

JUNIORS

Tim Buley Enjoys a growing reputation in public law. He acts on behalf of individuals, charities, commercial entities and government, and has particular expertise in planning, immigration, social welfare and environmental law. **Strengths:** "He's very versatile and has a can-do attitude whatever we throw at him." "The judges listen to him with particular attention since he speaks with real authority." **Recent work:** Intervened on behalf of Child Poverty Action Group in a high-profile judicial review challenging the 'benefits cap' as it applies in the context of social housing.

Charles Banner (see p.542) Specialises in immigration, public services provision, education and planning matters. He is also expert in the principles and domestic application of EU law. **Strengths:** "He's a very good junior, and has been in a lot of good cases recently." **Recent work:** Acted for the HS2 Action Alliance in a significant challenge to the government's White Paper proposals for the building of a high-speed rail line from London to Birmingham.

Lisa Busch Handles judicial reviews on behalf of local authorities, government and individuals, typically with regard to environmental and planning matters. She has additional experience in appearing in planning inquiries. **Strengths:** "She is very impressive." **Recent work:** Acted for the Secretary of State for Work and Pensions in defending a judicial review challenge to the decision to close the Independent Living Fund.

Daniel Kolinsky (see p.648) Tackles cases in the areas of planning, environmental, non-domestic rating, and social security. He typically acts for individual and charitable claimants, and local and central government bodies. **Strengths:** "He relates to clients really well. He explains what is going to happen and what it means for them. In court he is very persuasive and doesn't let himself get carried away." **Recent work:** Acted for the claimants in a judicial review challenging the decision to grant planning permission for the building of a supermarket on the current site of the Bristol Rovers stadium.

Gwion Lewis Junior with a growing reputation for his work in planning, environmental and intellectual property law. He has further interests in the duties of reasonable adjustments and adequate consultation. **Strengths:** "He is adept at assimilating large amounts of information and separating the wheat from the chaff. He has a good manner with clients, listens to what others say and is a fearsome cross-examiner." "His pleadings are extremely effective." **Recent work:** Acted as sole counsel for the Welsh Language Commissioner in her judicial review challenge of the decision of National Savings & Investments to cease its Welsh language services for customers. It was the first judicial review in which a public body made submissions in Welsh.

Monckton Chambers
See profile on p.833

THE SET

Monckton Chambers has a strong reputation for its traditional focus in public law on EU, commercial, competition and regulatory matters, particularly in terms of utilities regulation. In addition to these specialist areas, its members have in recent years demonstrated additional prowess in handling matters in the areas of human rights, freedom of information and immigration. They are expert in acting in judicial reviews for government, commercial entities and pressure groups.

Client service: "The clerking at Monckton is outstanding – head and shoulders above the rest." David Hockney is the senior clerk.

SILKS

Tim Ward QC (see p.746) Specialises in representing commercial claimants in public law actions against regulatory bodies, in which respect he is very well regarded. He has further experience in appearing for defendants, particularly in the field of education. **Strengths:** "He is exceptional. He has a very good manner with clients and is passionate and enthusiastic. He is excellent at distilling a morass of information down to the nub of the issue." "A first choice for work concerning the crossover between public and competition law." **Recent work:** Acted for Akzo Nobel in a challenge to the efforts of the Competition Commission to exert control over the activities of a company taking place outside the UK, in a case raising significant questions of territorial jurisdiction in the context of regulation.

Jon Turner QC (see p.741) Centres his public law practice on commercial and regulatory actions, typically acting against regulatory bodies. He has additional expertise in issues arising in the context of environmental law. **Strengths:** "He is very impressive, and phenomenal in terms of his judgement and knowledge in the field of EU compliance." **Recent work:** Represented Ofwat in a judicial review challenge to its decision concerning the terms under which Welsh Water was required to give a bulk supply of water to a new market entrant. The case addressed the extent to which the regulator is entitled to discretionary exercise of statutory powers.

Ian Wise QC Maintains a diverse practice in the field, with a particular emphasis on healthcare and the rights of disabled people. He has additional experience in proceedings concerning the treatment of children and vulnerable adults. **Strengths:** "Undoubtedly a force to be reckoned with in public law litigation, he is tactically canny and has an encyclopaedic knowledge of decided cases." "A formidable opponent who develops a good line of argument in court." **Recent work:** Acted in Aintree University Hospital NHS Foundation Trust v James, the first case to reach the Supreme Court from the Court of Protection. The matter concerned the legal requirements for withholding and withdrawing treatment for critically ill patients.

JUNIORS

Brendan McGurk Represents government and regulatory bodies in judicial reviews and inquiries. He is particularly experienced in matters relating to the conduct of the military and national security. **Strengths:** "He is a supremely capable barrister whose public law practice is diverse and of a very high quality." **Recent work:** Acted for the Ministry of Justice in a case that sought a Declaration of Incompatibility in relation to the Gender Recognition Act.

Gerry Facenna (see p.598) Acts in judicial reviews for both the government, and commercial and traditional claimants. He is experienced in discrimination, equality law and regulatory challenges. **Strengths:** "He is an absolute engine in any case. He's a good advocate who is a very well-respected senior junior." **Recent work:** Acted for the Defence Secretary in a judicial review challenging the decision not to hold an inquiry into the deaths of six Royal Military Policemen in Iraq in 2003. The challenge follows a recent landmark case establishing the operation of the HRA in relation to soldiers serving abroad, and contends that this development is grounds for bringing a claim out of time.

Robert Palmer (see p.689) Maintains a broad public law practice that includes handling challenges to budget cuts, the imposition of financial sanctions and prison detention decisions. He is also accomplished in commercial and regulatory judicial reviews. **Strengths:** "He is an excellent public law junior whose written and oral advocacy often has the elegance and clarity of a QC." "He is excellent – he can do any area of public law." **Recent work:** Represented the Foreign Secretary in a judicial review seeking to overturn his decision to propose that five Iranian individuals be listed under EU sanctions.

Azeem Suterwalla (see p.732) Focuses his public law practice on immigration, asylum and children's rights matters. He has further experience in protecting the rights of prisoners. **Strengths:** "He fights tooth and nail for the client, the quality of his written work is very good and he has a very confident and assured courtroom manner." "He's a very nice opponent, but doesn't pull any punches and is effective." **Recent work:** Acted for the claimant in an age-dispute case at the Court of Appeal, in which the court issued important guidance as to the test to apply in such instances.

Stephen Broach Acts for claimants in public law proceedings relating to the rights of children and vulnerable adults. He also has an interest in regulatory matters, particularly in the context of the disclosure of adverse information. **Strengths:** "He's exceptionally bright and reliable." "Highly intelligent and has an excellent understanding of policy and the law." **Recent work:** Acted alone for the claimant in a successful judicial review challenging a decision to disclose certain information on Enhanced Criminal Record Certificates, on the basis it interfered with the subject's rights under Article 8 of the ECHR.

Nikolaus Grubeck Focuses on pursuing human rights arguments through public law proceedings. He has particular expertise in issues arising in the context of national security and the conduct of the military. **Strengths:** "He is incredibly competent and very accommodating. He seeks to push the boundaries of the law, yet always offers pragmatic and realistic advice." **Recent work:** Acted for the claimant in a high-profile and significant test case determining whether the UK military has a lawful power to detain terrorism suspects captured in Afghanistan.

Band 4

Garden Court Chambers

See profile on p.808

THE SET

Garden Court Chambers is very well respected for its work in public law on behalf of claimants seeking to challenge the decisions of central government and local authorities. Its members are highly accomplished in pursuing actions in the context of immigration, national security and social housing. They are also renowned for their prowess in appearing in inquests, particularly those touching on deaths following police contact.

Client service: "I have always found them really helpful and approachable."

SILKS

Jan Luba QC Centres his public law practice on matters relating to social housing and community care. He is also interested in questions of welfare benefits and human rights. **Strengths:** "He is very much a specialist in housing matters, and knows everything there is to know in that area." "He is a leading housing silk, but can turn his hand to anything." **Recent work:** Intervened on behalf of the Equality and Human Rights Commission in a judicial review of the assertion by Worcestershire County Council that it had no power to provide social care assistance to the disabled child of a travelling Romani showman under the Children Act.

Stephen Knafler QC Has a broad and diverse public law practice, encompassing community care, immigration and social housing matters. He is also experienced in pursuing judicial reviews challenging the decisions of local authorities. **Strengths:** "He gives composed and thoughtful addresses to the court, and has good tactical sense. Our first choice for social welfare judicial reviews." "Hard-working, intelligent and a good opponent." **Recent work:** Appeared for the Equality and Human Rights Commission in a test case concerning the prosecution of children who may have been victims of trafficking. The Court of Appeal gave guidance on the correct approach in such circumstances.

Stephanie Harrison QC Well respected for her work on behalf of claimants in bringing judicial review challenges to the policies and decisions of public bodies. She is especially proficient in the areas of unlawful detention, discrimination and the rights of minority groups. **Strengths:** "She is really on top of the issues, and is a great tactician." "A brilliant and personable barrister." **Recent work:** Acted for the claimant in a Court of Appeal case that successfully argued that new certification provisions introduced by way of the Justice and Security Act were ultra vires and thus invalid.

JUNIORS

Shu Shin Luh Focuses on pursuing public law actions seeking to protect the rights of children and vulnerable adults, particularly in the context of immigration. She is noted for her experience in matters relating to human trafficking. **Strengths:** "She really cares about the cases she does and always turns round work of a very high standard." "She is industrious and intelligent, and will only get better and better." **Recent work:** Acted for the claimant in a test case addressing whether the immigration detention of a child was in breach of the Home Secretary's own policy not to detain children, where she was under the mistaken belief that he was an adult.

Stephen Simblet Specialises in bringing actions against the police and other detaining authorities. He is well regarded for his expertise in inquests concerning deaths in custody. **Strengths:** "He is really on the ball with the law, really up to date, and knows answers off the top of his head." "His advocacy is superb, and I wouldn't like to be on the receiving end of his cross-examination." **Recent work:** Represented the claimant in a successful judicial review challenging the decision of the Coroner for Birmingham not to hold an inquest into a death from a Clostridium difficile infection.

Other Ranked Lawyers

Jeremy Johnson QC (see p.639) (5 Essex Court) Maintains a diverse public law practice with a strong emphasis on defending the police in judicial reviews. He is experienced in immigration, malfeasance and employment issues. **Strengths:** "He is a pleasant person to be against, and is phenomenally successful." **Recent work:** Acted for the Metropolitan Police in a judicial review addressing whether the police power to stop and search is in line with human rights principles.

Jason Beer QC (see p.547) (5 Essex Court) Highly experienced at appearing on behalf of the police in judicial review proceedings, in which regard he is highly respected. He is also well versed in acting in inquests and public inquiries. **Strengths:** "He's very thorough, a good technical lawyer and someone who is very easy to work with." "He is a very able, very intelligent advocate. He obviously has the skills." **Recent work:** Represented the Metropolitan Police in the judicial review brought by David Miranda.

Tim Eicke QC (Essex Court Chambers) Acts on behalf of the government and claimants in public law matters, particularly in relation to EU law, sanctions and national security. He is also interested in regulatory and welfare issues. **Strengths:** "Probably the government's leading lawyer for EU law, immigration or national security matters." "He is very authoritative in relation to EU and immigration law, and is the person the courts recognise as a true expert." **Recent work:** Acted for the government in the Supreme Court in the highly publicised case of Bank Mellat, addressing the lawfulness of economic sanctions on Iran and the use of closed material procedure.

Hilton Harrop Griffiths (Field Court Chambers) Specialises in the representation of local authorities in the area of social services provision. He is especially accomplished in matters relating to child immigrants and age assessments. **Strengths:** "An incredibly affable opponent who fights his client's corner, but who is very approachable and able to achieve good results by negotiating a good outcome." **Recent work:** Successfully represented two brothers from Ethiopia seeking a loan from the local authority that had housed them as children. They required the loan in order to study at university, and had been precluded from receiving a loan from the Student Loan Company following a change in legislation.

Charles Béar QC (see p.546) (Fountain Court Chambers) Well regarded for his advocacy skills, particularly in relation to commercial judicial reviews. He also handles employment and public procurement issues. **Strengths:** "He's very, very bright, and very hardworking – the silk I'd go to if I wanted someone to turn it on at court and also come up with the strategy behind the scenes." **Recent work:** Intervened on behalf of the Association of British Insurers in a significant judicial review challenging the government's decision to cut recoverable costs in relation to road traffic accident claims.

Timothy Dutton QC (Fountain Court Chambers) Handles regulatory, financial services and human rights matters, typically by way of judicial review proceedings. He is also well versed in handling inquiries founded on points of public law. **Strengths:** "He shows care and sensitivity when handling cases, and he is incredibly fair." **Recent work:** Acted on behalf of the Bar Standards Board in the judicial review challenge to the proposed introduction of the Quality Assurance Scheme for Advocates.

James McClelland (see p.667) (Fountain Court Chambers) Enjoys a growing reputation for his public law practice, which typically involves proceedings addressing commercial and regulatory issues. He is also experienced in education judicial reviews. **Strengths:** "Very, very bright, and my favourite junior for public law matters with a commercial flavour." "It's fair to say that he simply gets the law better than I get the law, and I appreciate that when I instruct a barrister." **Recent work:** Acted on behalf of the Home Secretary as an intervener in a Court of Appeal case addressing the jurisdiction in extraditing a British citizen to the USA, and whether such an action would violate his rights under the ECHR.

James Pereira QC (Francis Taylor Building) Maintains a public law practice characterised by his expertise in planning and environmental law. His expertise also includes questions of the powers of local authorities. **Strengths:** "He is very good on his feet, he has great empathy with clients, and is very prompt and courteous." **Recent work:** Acted for Forest of Dean Council in successfully defending a judicial review challenging its decision to implement a statutory development scheme that was in breach of the European Habitats Directive, particularly in relation to the impact of the development on bats.

Richard Clayton QC (see p.573) (4-5 Gray's Inn Square) Experienced advocate whose public law practice is founded on questions of discrimination, community care and freedom of information. He has additional expertise in local government and human rights issues. **Strengths:** "He is affable and has a mature approach." "Calm, reliable and consistent." "He has a very wide knowledge of the law." **Recent work:** Represented the claimant in the successful judicial review of the tribunal decision taken by the Chartered Institute of Management Accountants that the claimant had breached confidentiality by disclosing information.

James Guthrie QC (3 Hare Court) Handles constitutional law, human rights and judicial review cases, and regularly appears before the Privy Council in Commonwealth countries. He acts for governments, law officers, individuals and non-government institutions and is particularly known for his work in Mauritius and the Caribbean. **Strengths:** "He is totally capable. He knows how other jurisdictions work and he has significant experience in dealing with appeal courts." **Recent work:** Acted in Pfizer Limited v Medimpex Jamaica Ltd, NMF Pharmaceuticals Ltd & Lasco Distributors Ltd. This was a Privy Council case concerning two Jamaican suppliers of generic drugs facing a claim made against them by Pfizer regarding patent law.

Peter Knox QC (3 Hare Court) Has handled numerous appeals in the Privy Council concerning public law, constitutional and criminal matters. **Strengths:** "He really put the hours in and knows the case inside out. He is an advocate who is always polite but extremely effective." "His advocacy has a raconteur-like quality." **Recent work:** Acted in United Policyholders Group v Attorney General, a successful judicial review challenge to the government's proposed plan to compensate policyholders in a collapsed insurance company.

David Perry QC (6KBW College Hill) Extremely well-regarded advocate whose exemplary work in the areas of crime, fraud and extradition informs his practice in public law. He is a noted authority in human rights matters, particularly in relation to prisoner rights and assisted suicide. **Strengths:** "He's hugely knowledgeable, very good on academic and technical questions, and he always has the trust of the court." **Recent work:** Led for the Ministry of Justice in the Supreme Court case addressing the legal position on assisted suicide.

Jonathan Hall QC (6KBW College Hill) Appears on behalf of the government in public law proceedings arising from immigration, national security and the criminal justice system. He is also experienced in asset recovery cases. **Strengths:** "He's definitely going places. He's very good, very clever and full of energy." "He's enthusiastic, capable, incredibly down to earth and practical." **Recent work:** Acted for the Home Secretary in a case challenging the Terrorism Prevention and Investigation Measures applied against the claimant.

Melanie Cumberland (6KBW College Hill) Focuses on handling cases for the government that concern questions of national security and contempt. She has further experience in inquests and public inquiries. **Strengths:** "She is an absolutely first-rate public lawyer whose advocacy is very effective indeed." "She has a really effective manner. She's very relaxed, very conscientious and the judges trust her." **Recent work:** Acted alone on behalf of the Home Secretary in opposing an application for a protective costs order made by the widow of Alexander Litvinenko in relation to the inquest into his death.

Louis Mably (6KBW College Hill) Acts for the government in contempt, national security and terrorism-related matters. He is also expert in the powers of the police to stop and search, and to engage in coercive questioning. **Strengths:** "He is obviously a star in the making. I expect he will take silk soon." **Recent work:** Acted for the UK government in a high-profile case before the ECHR, in which it was ruled that whole-life tariffs for prisoners without the possibility of parole constitute a breach of their human rights.

Katherine Apps (see p.536) (Littleton Chambers) Acts on behalf of individual and trade union claimants, as well as government defendants, in judicial review proceedings. She is particularly interested in equality, EU and commercial law. **Strengths:** "An incredibly bright public lawyer who is very good with clients and gives solid advice." "She's appropriately cautious and is a pleasure to deal with." **Recent work:** Acted for the Work and Pensions Secretary in a judicial review challenging the assessment process for Employment and Support Allowance, on the basis that it discriminates against disabled people.

Can Yeginsu (see p.757) (4 New Square) Focuses on pursuing human rights and regulatory arguments through public law actions. He is particularly experienced in issues relating to freedom of expression and terrorism legislation. **Recent work:** Intervened on behalf of English PEN, Media Legal Defence Initiative and Article 19 in the Miranda judicial review.

Hugo Keith QC (see p.643) (3 Raymond Buildings Barristers) Centres his public law practice on matters arising in the context of the criminal justice system and extradition, in which areas he is well respected. He is also experienced in appearing in inquests. **Strengths:** "He's the first person I'd go to for a case with an overlap between public and criminal law. He is incredibly bright, wonderfully articulate, a great team player and someone who is enormously respected by the judges." **Recent work:** Acted for the claimant in a judicial review of the Metropolitan Police in relation to the issuing of search warrants against a person under suspicion of financing Zimbabwean politicians.

Clair Dobbin (see p.589) (3 Raymond Buildings Barristers) Specialises in public law proceedings relating to human rights, extradition and inquests. She acts on behalf of both claimants and defendants in judicial reviews and statutory appeals. **Strengths:** "She is fantastic, extremely clever and wonderful to work with." "She's great – very bright and very diligent." **Recent work:** Represented the Ministry of Justice in a judicial review challenging the policy of holding children in cells at adult courts, addressing whether the arrangement breached the Children and Young Persons Act.

Ben Watson (see p.747) (3 Raymond Buildings Barristers) Represents government and public bodies in proceedings typically relating to criminal, extradition and national security issues. He is also an experienced special advocate. **Strengths:** "He's in a different league to many juniors. He's extremely accessible and really good at giving advice." **Recent work:** Acted for the Metropolitan Police Service in the high-profile challenge by judicial review of the stopping of David Miranda at Heathrow Airport under Schedule 7 of the Terrorism Act.

Amy Street (see p.730) (Serjeants' Inn Chambers) Maintains a public law practice focusing on matters relating to human rights and incapacitated adults. She is especially well versed in questions of capacity in the context of the deprivation of liberty. **Strengths:** "A very diligent and focused practitioner." **Recent work:** Acted for the appellant in a landmark Supreme Court case addressing the extent to which disabled people in social care placements are entitled to liberty under the ECHR.

Matthew Slater (see p.722) (3 Stone Buildings) Experienced in handling proceedings for the government arising from national security, the conduct of the military and protester rights. He is also accomplished in questions of the rights of prisoners to hearings. **Strengths:** "He is a solid and confident performer who's popular with the Treasury Solicitor." **Recent work:** Acted for the Justice Secretary in a judicial review concerning the proper test to be applied in determining the exercise of discretion by the Ministry of Justice in deciding whether to convene an oral hearing.

Jonathan Crow QC (see p.582) (4 Stone Buildings) Commands considerable respect for his skilful advocacy across a diverse range of public law matters. He is particularly well regarded for his commercial public law litigation work, as well as his expertise in regulatory issues. **Strengths:** "Give him a good junior and that man can do anything – he is remarkably adept at turning his hand to new things." "He's really smooth and has excellent judgement." **Recent work:** Acted for the government in a high-profile judicial review seeking to compel the Home Secretary to order a public inquiry into the deaths of 24 civilians at Batang Kali in 1948. The case turned on the question of whether obligations arising under the Convention on the Protection of Human Rights applied to events occurring before its adoption.

Kerry Bretherton (Tanfield Chambers) Specialises in matters relating to community care and the funding of care homes. She has further expertise in issues arising in the context of immigration and education. **Strengths:** "She is a very strong and forceful advocate who will always explore all possible avenues and provide clear advice." "She is organised, determined and hard-working." **Recent work:** Acted for the claimant in a case contesting the decision of the Work and Pensions Secretary that a transgender woman who, due to her Christian faith, did not wish to divorce, and consequently could not acquire a Gender Recognition Certificate, should be assessed for a pension as a man.

Robin Tam QC (see p.733) (Temple Garden Chambers) Tackles public law actions on behalf of the government, particularly in the context of national security. He is also experienced in handling cases concerning immigration and asylum. **Strengths:** "He is very intellectual, rigorous and a classy advocate." **Recent work:** Acted as Advocate to the Court in the highly significant case of Bank Mellat, the first proceedings in which the Supreme Court relied in part on closed evidence in coming to its decision.

Andrew O'Connor (Temple Garden Chambers) Extremely well-regarded junior who focuses on representing the government in judicial review proceedings. His particular areas of expertise include terrorism, national security, control orders and the deprivation of citizenship. **Strengths:** "He is a star, and has a first-class practice in the field of national security." **Recent work:** Acted for the Foreign Secretary in a high-profile judicial review challenge to his decision to place the claimant on the United Nations Al-Qa'ida and Taliban sanctions list for suspected terrorists.

MIDLANDS

Administrative & Public Law Midlands
Leading Sets
Band 1
No5 Chambers *
St Philips Chambers *
Leading Silks
Band 1
Clayton Richard *Kings Chambers (ORL)* ◊ *
Dove Ian *No5 Chambers*
Leading Juniors
Band 1
Ahmad Mirza *St Philips Chambers* *
Khalique Nageena *No5 Chambers* 🄰
Mandalia Vinesh *No5 Chambers* 🄰
◊ (ORL) = Other Ranked Lawyer.
** Indicates set / individual with profile.*
🄰 direct access (see p.11).

Band 1

No5 Chambers

See profile on p.883

THE SET

No5 Chambers is one of the leading sets on the Midland Circuit for public law matters. Its members are especially expert in issues arising in the context of family, education, immigration, planning, prison law and mental health. Instructing solicitors praise them as being "very approachable as a set, but with a great rigour to their work."

Client service: "The clerks are very friendly, and are always co-operative and efficient."

SILKS

Ian Dove QC The leading administrative and public law silk practising on the Midland Circuit. His broad expertise in public law includes matters relating to immigration and planning. **Strengths:** "He is probably the most important public law practitioner in the Midlands. He has a brain the size of a planet." "He is a leading silk, and is very client-friendly and responsive." **Recent work:** Represented Birmingham City Council in resisting an application for a judicial review of the decision of the council to adopt the preliminary findings of a planning inspector in relation to two village green planning applications.

JUNIORS

Nageena Khalique Specialises in public law proceedings concerning social care, healthcare and mental capacity. She appears for public bodies and individuals in the High Court, Court of Appeal and Court of Protection. **Strengths:** "She is very, very good and has a very good reputation." **Recent work:** Acted for Staffordshire County Council on defending a judicial review challenging its decision to close a residential care home for learning disabled people. The case addressed the issue of whether judicial review is an appropriate recourse for adults lacking capacity.

Vinesh Mandalia Well-respected junior with a strong practice in administrative and public law. He specialises in matters relating to immigration, as well as having an interest in taxation and healthcare issues. **Strengths:** "He has been a key player in public law in the Midlands for a number of years." **Recent work:** Acted for the Home Secretary in a judicial review that established that decisions of the Secretary are construed on an objective basis, and clarifying the requirements for demonstrating a breach of legitimate expectation.

St Philips Chambers

See profile on p.886

THE SET

St Philips Chambers is respected as a public law set that informs its work in this area with its expertise in commercial matters, particularly in relation to housing, state aid and public procurement. Its members are also accomplished in handling public law proceedings concerning immigration, education and human rights.

Client service: "They are very good and very reliable. They are always able to provide someone with the right expertise within budget."

JUNIORS

Mirza Ahmad (see p.532) Offers expert representation in public law matters pertaining to local government, informed in part by his two decades of experience as an in-house counsel to local authorities. He focuses particularly on issues in employment and procurement. **Strengths:** "He is extremely knowledgeable in this area." **Recent work:** Acted for the claimant in an appeal against a strike-out decision regarding a challenge to the decision-making process for a public procurement contract.

Other Ranked Lawyers

Richard Clayton QC (Kings Chambers) Experienced advocate whose public law practice is founded on questions of discrimination, community care and freedom of information. He has additional expertise in local government and human rights issues. **Strengths:** "He is affable and has a mature approach." "Calm, reliable and consistent." "He has a very wide knowledge of the law." **Recent work:** Represented the claimant in the successful judicial review of the tribunal decision taken by the Chartered Institute of Management Accountants that the claimant had breached confidentiality by disclosing information.

NORTH EASTERN

Administrative & Public Law North Eastern
Leading Juniors
Band 1
Hussain Tasaddat *Broadway House (ORL)* ◊ *

Ranked Lawyers

Tasaddat Hussain (see p.634) (Broadway House) Maintains a well-respected public law practice heavily weighted towards his broader specialism in immigration matters. **Recent work:** Acted for the first appellant in a Court of Appeal challenge to country guidance on Iraq, in which it was argued that the increased risk of severe violence in the country affected the right to humanitarian protection and the appellants' refugee status.

NORTHERN

Administrative & Public Law Northern
Leading Sets
Band 1
Garden Court North
Kings Chambers *
Band 2
Doughty Street Chambers *
Leading Silks
Band 1
Weatherby Pete *Garden Court North*
Leading Juniors
Band 1
Fullwood Adam *Kings Chambers* *
Band 2
Burrows Simon *Kings Chambers* *
Cartwright Sophie *Deans Court Chambers (ORL)* ◊ *
Jagadesham Vijay *Garden Court North*
Karim Sam *Kings Chambers* *
Stanbury Matthew *Garden Court North*
Stone Kate *Garden Court North*
Band 3
Arshad Farrhat *Doughty Street Chambers* Ⓐ
Draycott Paul *Doughty Street Chambers*
Hunter John *Kings Chambers* *
McCormack Ben *Garden Court North*
Ponter Ian *Kings Chambers* *
Stockwell Matthew *St Johns Buildings (ORL)* ◊
◊ (ORL) = Other Ranked Lawyer.
Ⓐ direct access (see p.11).
** Indicates set / individual with profile.*

Band 1

Garden Court North

THE SET

Garden Court North is very well respected for the quality of the advice and representation it offers claimants in a wide range of public law matters. Its members are especially accomplished in handling proceedings relating to housing, community care, immigration and prison law.

Client service: "The clerking is exceptional – there is a good rapport between clerk and counsel, meaning work gets turned around quickly."

SILKS

Pete Weatherby QC Commands great respect as the leading silk for public law matters on the Northern Circuit. He has appeared in a number of the most high-profile public law cases concerning human rights and the rights of prisoners. **Strengths:** "He is a real force and very knowledgeable in public law." "He is the standout silk in public law in the North. He is very well regarded." **Recent work:** Acted for the claimant in a significant case addressing the issue of whether a failure to provide rehabilitative measures to prisoners constitutes arbitrary detention in violation of their rights under Article 5 ECHR.

JUNIORS

Vijay Jagadesham Enjoys a growing reputation for the quality of his public law practice. He focuses particularly on human rights issues arising in the context of prison law and immigration. **Strengths:** "He is a careful and effective advocate who commands trust and respect. He handles the complexities of cases very well and gives very helpful advice." **Recent work:** Successfully brought judicial review proceedings against the Justice Secretary in relation to a prisoner who had repeatedly been denied access to his children, despite the Secretary having previously conceded proceedings on the same issue.

Matthew Stanbury Focuses on handling public law actions on behalf of claimants, typically founded in the areas of prison law and the rights of women. He is particularly interested in equality and statutory construction issues. **Strengths:** "The standard of his work is excellent. He's very clear and concise in the arguments he puts forward, and anticipates and deals with contrary positions." "He is very dynamic and passionate about his work." **Recent work:** Acted for the claimant in a successful judicial review challenging the decision of the Justice Secretary not to award compensation to the claimant as a victim of a miscarriage of justice.

Kate Stone Specialises in appearing for claimants in prison law proceedings, particularly in challenges to decisions of the Parole Board and the Home Secretary. She is also experienced in inquests and matters concerning the actions of the police. **Strengths:** "She defended a complex case with discretion and vigour, and her pleadings were just brilliant." **Recent work:** Acted as junior counsel to 22 bereaved families in the Hillsborough Inquests.

Ben McCormack Centres his public law practice on matters concerning social housing, welfare rights and mental health. He is also interested in questions of discrimination. **Strengths:** "He is very approachable, and very good at explaining complex issues to lay clients." "He is a joy to work with, and is reliable and efficient on the papers." **Recent work:** Acted for the claimant in a judicial review challenging a decision of the Official Receiver to revoke a debt relief order. The case turned on the issue of whether the Receiver was bound by the public sector equality duty, on which the court held that her exercising of a judicial function meant this duty was not binding.

Kings Chambers

See profile on p.918

THE SET

The excellent reputation of Kings Chambers is founded on the high quality of advice and representation offered by its members to both claimants and defendants. The set's counsel are expert across the full range of public law issues, but are known to be especially accomplished in matters relating to planning disputes, social care, mental health, immigration and the decisions of local authorities.

Client service: "They are always extremely helpful, and proactive in terms of meeting deadlines."

JUNIORS

Adam Fullwood Centres his public law practice on issues arising in the context of immigration and asylum, social housing and human rights. He is also accomplished in matters relating to healthcare and the Court of Protection. **Strengths:** "He is very good – he's always well prepared, and is a good negotiator and advocate." "He is very reliable, and is able to provide solicitors with the confidence that the client will be well looked after." **Recent work:** Acted for the claimant in a judicial review application challenging a decision for community care support, in which it was found that where a previous application was stayed by consent, it may not be reinstated to challenge a subsequent decision.

Simon Burrows Specialises in social care and mental health issues. He is particularly interested in the tension between detention resulting from a lack of capacity and the rights surrounding the deprivation of liberty. **Strengths:** "He's excellent as an advocate, and is also helpful, approachable and available." **Recent work:** Acted for the appellant in a landmark case before the Supreme Court that addressed the ambit of Article 5 ECHR rights in relation to people in social care placements who lack capacity.

Sam Karim Represents the government, prison governors and the Parole Board in matters relating to immigration and prison law. Additional areas of expertise include healthcare and education. **Strengths:** "He is very good. He has a plenary style that is very logical and meticulous, and makes his points very well without annoying the judge." **Recent work:** Acted for the Home Secretary in successfully defending an application for judicial review of her decision to decline to examine an asylum application. The case turned on a disagreement as to the application of the Dublin II Regulation.

Ian Ponter Focuses on judicial reviews and inquiries into the planning decisions of local authorities. He has further experience in highways law and environmental matters. **Strengths:** "He's just very efficient, easy to work with, and a good team player." **Recent work:** Acted for the claimant in an application for a judicial review seeking to challenge the grant of planning permission for a large food retail shop in an out-of-town site.

John Hunter Focuses on handling judicial review proceedings on behalf of central government and local authorities. He is particularly experienced in issues relating to immigration, planning, prison law and education. **Strengths:** "His advocacy in court is relaxed, but very effective. He asks pertinent questions that cut through any line of defence." "He is bright, intellectual and enthusiastic." **Recent work:** Acted for East Sussex County Council in a successful appeal against a High Court ruling that its decision to register a tidal beach owned by the claimant as a village green was unlawful.

Band 2

Doughty Street Chambers
See profile on p.786

THE SET

Doughty Street Chambers is very well regarded for its work on behalf of claimants through a variety of public law proceedings. Its members on the Northern Circuit share the high reputation of their London colleagues for excellence in prison law matters, as well as demonstrating expertise in issues arising in the context of immigration.

JUNIORS

Paul Draycott Focuses his public law practice on issues relating to immigration and asylum, particularly by way of judicial review challenges. He has further experience in employment and equality matters. **Strengths:** "Paul Draycott is excellent – so determined, so hard-working." **Recent work:** Acted for the claimant in a judicial review before the Court of Appeal challenging the decision of the Home Secretary to refuse a work permit, despite the fact his asylum appeal had been outstanding for over 18 months. The case addressed the issues of compliance with the EU Reception Directive, and the claimant's right to a private life under Article 8 ECHR.

Farrhat Arshad Specialises in judicial reviews addressing issues in prison law and the criminal justice system. She is also expert in bringing actions challenging the conduct of the police. **Strengths:** "She is a good and sensible advocate." **Recent work:** Acted for the claimant in a successful judicial review challenging a Parole Board decision that had been based in part on a prejudicial statement not disclosed to the prisoner.

Other Ranked Lawyers

Sophie Cartwright (Deans Court Chambers) Acts on behalf of clinical commissioning groups, foundation trusts, local authorities and individual doctors in judicial review proceedings. She is also experienced in handling medical inquests. **Strengths:** "She is very confident, very competent and very knowledgeable. She's a very experienced advocate." **Recent work:** Represented a general practitioner in a judicial review challenging the finding of an inquest, in which the jury had recorded a verdict of unlawful killing as a result of the death of a patient from an overdose of prescription drugs. It was argued that the coroner had acted outside the scope of the inquest.

Matthew Stockwell (St Johns Buildings) Maintains a broad practice in judicial review proceedings, with a particular interest in health, social welfare, education, human rights and mental health issues. He acts for local authorities, government and individuals. **Strengths:** "He gives calm, assured and authoritative advice." **Recent work:** Acted in the Supreme Court for the appellant challenging the refusal of the Health Secretary to make a referral to the First-Tier Tribunal to review her detention under the Mental Health Act.

WALES & CHESTER

Administrative & Public Law Wales & Chester
Leading Silks
Band 1
Williams Rhodri *30 Park Place (ORL)* ◊ Ⓐ
Band 2
Henke Ruth *30 Park Place (ORL)* ◊
Leading Juniors
Band 1
Walters Graham *Civitas Law (ORL)* ◊ *
Band 2
Hillier Victoria *Civitas Law (ORL)* ◊ *
Up-and-coming individuals
Stickler Rebecca *30 Park Place (ORL)* ◊

Ranked Lawyers

Graham Walters (Civitas Law) Acts on behalf of government and local authorities in inquiries and hearings in the Administrative Court. He is particularly experienced in planning and highway matters. **Strengths:** "He's a long-standing practitioner of considerable experience and seniority, and is well respected." "He's a very experienced public law senior junior." **Recent work:** Represented the Welsh Ministers in a High Court challenge to the decision to grant planning permission for a wind farm.

Victoria Hillier (see p.628) (Civitas Law) Represents local authorities and the police in public law proceedings. She is particularly experienced in issues relating to unlawful imprisonment, housing and licensing. **Strengths:** "She is an excellent advocate – very bright, very thorough and approachable." **Recent work:** Acted for the Chief Constable of Gwent Police in an inquest into the death of a man arrested for domestic violence who went on to murder his wife and two of her colleagues. The inquest also looked into the death of his son, who had committed suicide after the event.

Rhodri Williams QC (30 Park Place) Specialises in the interface between domestic public law and EU public procurement principles. He is also a noted expert on constitutional issues in the context of Welsh devolution. **Strengths:** "He is a very bright and effective advocate." "He has a national reputation as a leading exponent of public procurement law." **Recent work:** Acted for Leeds City Council in defending a claim for breaches of the EU procurement regime, and in the tort of deceit.

Ruth Henke QC (30 Park Place) Specialises in public law proceedings arising from family law and childcare. She has further experience in appearing in the Administrative Court in relation to education and the rights of children and vulnerable adults to the provision of services.

Rebecca Stickler (30 Park Place) Acts primarily for local authorities in public law challenges to decisions in the context of education, licensing, and children and adult social services. **Strengths:** "She prepares cases to the nth degree, and she gets results." **Recent work:** Appeared in a hearing before the Supreme Court challenging the legislative competence of the Welsh National Assembly in respect to the first bill passed by the Assembly.

WESTERN

Administrative & Public Law Western
Leading Silks
Band 1
Blohm Leslie *St John's Chambers (ORL)* ◊
Leading Juniors
Band 1
Barker Kerry *Guildhall Chambers (ORL)* ◊
◊ (ORL) = Other Ranked Lawyer.
** Indicates set / individual with profile.*
Ⓐ direct access (see p.11).

Ranked Lawyers

Kerry Barker (Guildhall Chambers) Maintains a broad practice in public law, encompassing issues of human rights, education, social services and statutory interpretation. He acts on behalf of both local authorities and claimants in judicial reviews and statutory appeals.

Leslie Blohm QC (St John's Chambers) Anchors his public law practice around his wider areas of specialism, including chancery and commercial, property and agricultural matters. He is particularly interested in issues relating to the village green law.

Contents:

LONDON

Agriculture & Rural Affairs London
Leading Sets
Band 1
Falcon Chambers *
Band 2
Francis Taylor Building *
Landmark Chambers *
Maitland Chambers *
New Square Chambers *
Leading Silks
Band 1
Jourdan Stephen *Falcon Chambers* *
Laurence George *New Square Chambers* *
Massey William *Pump Court Tax Chambers (ORL)* ◊ *
Mercer Hugh *Essex Court Chambers (ORL)* ◊
Band 2
Chapman Vivian R *9 Stone Buildings (ORL)* ◊ *
Edwards Douglas *Francis Taylor Building* *
George Charles *Francis Taylor Building* Ⓐ
Band 3
Elvin David *Landmark Chambers*
Fancourt Timothy *Falcon Chambers* *
Gaunt Jonathan *Falcon Chambers* *
Karas Jonathan *Falcon Chambers* *
Morshead Timothy *Landmark Chambers*
Wonnacott Mark *Maitland Chambers*
Leading Juniors
Band 1
Crail Ross *New Square Chambers* *
Hutton Caroline *Enterprise Chambers (ORL)* ◊
Moss Joanne *Falcon Chambers*
Shea Caroline *Falcon Chambers*
Thomas Nigel *Maitland Chambers* *
Windsor Emily *Falcon Chambers*
Band 2
Healey Greville *Falcon Chambers*
Petchey Philip *Francis Taylor Building*
Taskis Catherine *Falcon Chambers* *
Band 3
Heywood Michael *Radcliffe Chambers (ORL)* ◊
Honey Richard *Francis Taylor Building* Ⓐ *
◊ (ORL) = Other Ranked Lawyer.
Ⓐ direct access (see p.11).
** Indicates firm / individual with profile.*

Band 1

Falcon Chambers

See profile on p.799

THE SET

This set continues to be regarded as a first point of reference for land and property matters within the agricultural sector. Its members boast significant expertise in agricultural landlord and tenancy cases, rent reviews and ownership disputes. They are further sought after for town and village green application cases and agricultural land diversification matters.

Client service: "The clerks are very efficient and get back to you quickly about things."

SILKS

Stephen Jourdan QC Handles a range of property-related disputes. He is an expert in agricultural property disputes, contentious partnership cases, succession claims and matters relating to rights of way. **Strengths:** "He's outstanding and does lots of this work; he's head and shoulders above the others." "He was really very efficient in what he did for us – he was great." **Recent work:** Successfully acted for the landlords in Wannop v Cartmell, opposing an application for succession to a farm tenancy.

Timothy Fancourt QC Landlord and tenant disputes remain a key area of activity, and his work includes cases relating to the termination of tenancies, land rights and agricultural property ownership. **Strengths:** "Although the matter was complex, his reasoning was clear and refreshingly unequivocal." **Recent work:** Recently acted for the landlord in Elveden Farms v Usher, a case concerning the rights to terminate the lease of shooting premises.

Jonathan Gaunt QC Handles contentious landlord and tenant cases, including many disputes in the agricultural sector. He is an expert on covenants, easements, rent reviews and land contracts and development agreements. **Strengths:** "I generally regard him as one of the best silks I've seen; he's formidable." "He's a very senior and well-respected silk with a very good practice in this area."

Jonathan Karas QC Acts for landowners and developers on matters relating to agricultural property and planning. He is also known for his expertise regarding the sale and development of agricultural land, tenancies and Agricultural Property Relief. **Strengths:** "He's a very experienced advocate, who makes complicated principles seem pretty straightforward, which is a great skill." "He's user-friendly and he gets back to you quickly; he's always on time. His written work is excellent and clients really like him." **Recent work:** Acted for the Church Commissioners in R (Church Commissioners) v Hampshire County Council, a case concerning the village green registration application pertaining to a large area of agricultural land.

JUNIORS

Joanne Moss Handles a range of matters relating to agriculture and rural affairs, and is particularly noted for her advisory work relating to agricultural holdings and tenancies. **Strengths:** "She has a broad-ranging agricultural practice and is always a first choice for matters in this area." "She is superb; she's very robust in her views and puts things across to the client very clearly."

Caroline Shea Acts on a variety of matters pertaining to agricultural land. She advises both landlord and tenants on disputes and is also an expert on agricultural holdings, boundary disputes and succession cases. **Strengths:** "Excellent, thorough and very good with clients. She's clever but personable, which is not as common a mixture as it perhaps should be." **Recent work:** Recently advised on a case concerning a tenant family's right to succession in relation to the Isle of Man Agricultural Holdings Act 1969.

Emily Windsor Has a strong practice encompassing matters ranging from agricultural holdings to rights of way and partnership disputes. **Strengths:** "She's very knowledgeable and very solid; she's an expert in her field who gives very clear opinions." "A star junior in my opinion." **Recent work:** Acted for the tenant in Cartmell v Wannop, an Agricultural Land Tribunal succession application.

Greville Healey Assists both landlords and tenants on a broad array of agricultural property-related matters. He advises on cases relating to tenancy disputes, rights of way, highways and other aspects of land law. **Strengths:** "He's very user-friendly and very approachable." "He's very thorough and responsive, and is happy to discuss matters over the telephone."

Catherine Taskis (see p.734) Advises primarily on landlord and tenant disputes in both the commercial and agricultural domains. She is also recognised for her expertise concerning farming partnership disputes and agricultural holdings tenancies. **Strengths:** "She's very approachable and very helpful. You can pick up the phone and shoot through problems with her – she's very good for that." "Very bright and intelligent, she's also practical and very easy to work with." **Recent work:** Acting in Wilkinson v Wilkinson, an arbitration case concerning the dissolution of a farming partnership.

Band 2

Francis Taylor Building

See profile on p.806

THE SET

This set is particularly strong on matters relating to town and village greens. Many members of chambers are instructed to act as inspectors in hearings, and also receive instructions on major contentious cases in this area of law. They are also particularly adept at planning and environmental law cases.

Client service: "The clerks at FTB are very good; I find them to be very efficient and friendly."

SILKS

Douglas Edwards QC (see p.594) A planning and environment barrister with significant expertise in agriculture and rural affairs. He is a recognised expert on cases concerning town and village greens, and frequently represents landowners. **Strengths:** "A true leader in relation to common land and town and village greens. He gives clear advice and is commercially astute." **Recent work:** Acted for Oxford City Council on opposing a town green registration application relating to land owned by it.

Charles George QC A pre-eminent barrister for town and village greens cases. His practice covers planning and environmental matters generally, and he undertakes a good deal of local government work. **Strengths:** "An experienced and respected advocate in this area; one of the kings of village greens work." "He's very thorough, very knowledgeable and has acted on lots of big cases." **Recent work:** Appeared for the landowner with regard to a town or village green application relating to Codnor Common.

JUNIORS

Philip Petchey His principal areas of focus are town and village greens, planning work, and the law relating to commons and footpaths. **Strengths:** "He has a deep understanding and academic knowledge of village greens and related property issues." "He's the junior to go to for complicated legal issues related to this area of law." **Recent work:** Appeared for an applicant seeking to register land around Blackbird Leys owned by Oxford City Council.

Richard Honey (see p.630) Enjoys an increasingly high profile for matters concerning commons and town and village greens. He acts as both advocate and inspector in cases relating to green registration applications, and also advises on highways, rights of way and other countryside matters. **Strengths:** "He clearly has a very comprehensive understanding of highways and footpaths and the law concerning rights of way." **Recent work:** Recently acted for Kent County Council as landowner in objecting to the application to register land proposed for development as a village green.

Landmark Chambers

See profile on p.829

THE SET

Landmark is an established set when it comes to property and planning cases with agricultural and rural aspects to them. Its barristers are recognised for their specialist knowledge in this area, and are regularly instructed in landlord and tenant disputes, as well as cases relating to highways and town and village green applications.

SILKS

David Elvin QC A highly respected practitioner who is particularly strong on planning issues relating to agricultural land. He advises on land and environmental law matters and is noted for his expert knowledge of EU law. **Strengths:** "He's amazingly good and is outstanding on this type of work." "He's a bright guy, who is very, very clever."

Timothy Morshead QC Has considerable experience of handling agricultural cases with public and planning law aspects. He is highly proficient at handling town and village green applications and is very good on the law relating to highways. **Strengths:** "He's incredibly clever and terrier-like in court." **Recent work:** Appeared in Dudley Metropolitan Borough Council v Dudley Muslim Association, a case concerning an agreement for the sale of some land as the site for an intended mosque.

Maitland Chambers

See profile on p.831

THE SET

Agricultural and rural affairs continues to be an area of strength for this commercial chancery set, and it is particularly good on cases with an agricultural property or land law slant. The expertise of its barristers covers disputes relating to agricultural tenancies, town and village green applications and matters concerning agricultural land diversification. Water law is also a niche area of expertise.

SILKS

Mark Wonnacott QC A strong all-round property litigator, who is recognised for his particular expertise in cases concerning rights of way, manorial rights and agricultural tenancies. **Strengths:** "A very meticulous exponent of the law, he is very good at whatever he gets involved in."

JUNIORS

Nigel Thomas His practice encompasses farming and agricultural disputes, water law and town and village green applications. **Strengths:** "He always does a cracking job. He's got fabulous experience and he can talk to the client in the right language." **Recent work:** Appeared in a case concerning a father and son's dispute over the dissolution of a multimillion-pound agricultural partnership.

New Square Chambers

See profile on p.837

THE SET

Barristers here are frequently instructed due to their expertise in countryside law, and prove highly adept at cases concerning commons and rights of way, and town and village green disputes. They also handle a good deal of work relating to agricultural landlords and tenants.

Client service: "The clerks at the set are perfectly nice and very easy to work with."

SILKS

George Laurence QC Has an outstanding reputation, most notably in connection with village greens work. He is also an expert on commons, rights of way and highways cases, and has regularly appeared in the Supreme Court. **Strengths:** "His strength is that he knows this area of the law like the back of his hand – he's just very, very experienced." "He's an exceptional barrister and an exceptional person. He possesses both great intellectual prowess and also extremely fine client-care skills." **Recent work:** Appeared for Newhaven Town Council in the Court of Appeal in R (Newhaven Port and Properties Ltd) v East Sussex County Council & another. The case concerned the registration of a beach as a village green.

JUNIORS

Ross Crail Represents clients in cases relating to commons, rights of way and highways, and also acts as an inspector in town or village green application hearings. **Strengths:** "She is an extremely intellectually able person, who has a good grasp of the more rarefied aspects of land law and rights of way." "She has this fantastic mind that can deal with very complex cases and she has the ability to look at things from a different angle." **Recent work:** Acted for Paddico in Paddico Ltd v Kirklees Metropolitan Council & Others, a case concerning the rectification of the Kirklees town and village green register.

Other Ranked Lawyers

Caroline Hutton (Enterprise Chambers) Highly regarded in this area and frequently instructed on agricultural landlord and tenant cases. **Strengths:** Offers "superb advocacy skills backed up by a strong intellect." "Her response time is fantastic, and the advice she provides is to the point and very practically oriented – she's brilliant." **Recent work:** Acted for the Ministry of Defence in an arbitration concerning one of its farm tenants.

Hugh Mercer QC (Essex Court Chambers) Receives praise from sources for his prowess on European Union law as it is applicable to agriculture cases. He is notably strong on cases concerning the Common Agricultural Policy and the Single Payment Scheme. **Strengths:** "He's first class and undoubtedly one of the top agriculture barristers in the country." "A classy operator; he's stunningly intellectual and a very experienced EU lawyer."

William Massey QC (see p.664) (Pump Court Tax Chambers) Much sought after for his expertise on taxation. His vast experience in this area covers matters relating to landed estates, trusts and succession planning. **Strengths:** "He has a phenomenal brain when it comes to rural and heritage matters." "He's well known and has a good reputation for his work dealing with agricultural property relief and tax matters."

Michael Heywood (Radcliffe Chambers) Acts for private clients and families on a range of matters linked to agriculture. He proves particularly strong when it comes to Agricultural Holdings Acts tenancies. **Strengths:** "A pleasure to work with, and someone who is both very knowledgeable and a team player." "Very good with clients; he speaks to them in a way that puts them at ease."

Vivian Chapman QC (see p.569) (9 Stone Buildings) Admired for his experience in cases concerning the registration of land as town and village greens. He receives instructions to appear as an advocate and to act as an inspector. **Strengths:** "Justifiably renowned in the world of village greens," he is a lawyer whose "opinions are very clear." **Recent work:** Appeared for Gloucester County Council as landowner of the Recreation Ground, Prestbury, concerning an application to register the land as a village green to prevent planned development work.

SOUTH EASTERN

Agriculture & Rural Affairs South Eastern
Leading Juniors
Band 1
Monnington Bruce *Fenners Chambers (ORL)* ◊
Band 2
Gore Andrew *Fenners Chambers (ORL)* ◊

Ranked Lawyers

Bruce Monnington (Fenners Chambers) Acts on a variety of agriculture and rural affairs matters. His experience covers a range of agricultural and land disputes, from landlord and tenant issues to restrictive covenants. **Strengths:** "He's user-friendly and pragmatic, which is what you really need from counsel."

Andrew Gore (Fenners Chambers) Handles a wide range of agricultural issues. His practice in this area encompasses restricted covenants, rights of way and diversification. He is also instructed to act as a mediator on agricultural disputes.

WALES & CHESTER

Agriculture & Rural Affairs Wales & Chester
Leading Juniors
Band 1
Lloyd Trefor *Linenhall Chambers (ORL)* ◊

Ranked Lawyers

Trefor Lloyd (Linenhall Chambers) Recommended for local agricultural tenancy disputes. He has a strong agricultural background and is also qualified as a chartered surveyor. He regularly advises landed estates in North Wales on property management, rights of way and estate planning. His practice also covers agricultural regulatory matters and farming partnership disputes.

WESTERN

Agriculture & Rural Affairs Western
Leading Silks
Band 1
Blohm Leslie *St John's Chambers (ORL)* ◊
Leading Juniors
Band 1
Batstone William *Guildhall Chambers (ORL)* ◊
Band 2
Newsom George *Guildhall Chambers (ORL)* ◊ *
◊ *(ORL) = Other Ranked Lawyer.*
* *Indicates firm / individual with profile.*

Ranked Lawyers

William Batstone (Guildhall Chambers) Agricultural expert who advises farmers, landowners and arbitrators on rural property and tenancy disputes. He has considerable experience of litigation arising under the Agricultural Holdings Act 1986 and also assists with land use regulation, sporting rights and access issues. He previously worked as a solicitor. **Strengths:** "He gives first-rate advice on option agreements and agricultural tenancies." "He is always comprehensive in his advice and has a good grasp of the commercial reality of the situation."

George Newsom (see p.682) (Guildhall Chambers) Leading authority on restrictive covenants who also represents clients in litigation concerning rural property issues. He has a broad practice covering trusts, proprietary claims and inheritance disputes. In addition he is a part-time judge for the Agriculture Land & Drainage Tribunal in the South West. **Strengths:** "He has a thorough grasp of the law and explains it extremely well before the court." "He has tremendous attention to detail and an enthusiasm for restrictive covenant cases and their complexities."

Leslie Blohm QC (St John's Chambers) Hugely respected advocate with a wide-ranging property and chancery practice. He has a particular interest in commons and village green cases, and sits as a village green inspector. He also acts for farmers and landowners in both succession and development disputes. **Strengths:** "He produces fiendishly clever advice presented in a readily understandable fashion." **Recent work:** He advised Bristol City Council on its opposition to a town and village green application for Stoke Lodge Playing Field.

ART AND CULTURAL PROPERTY LAW: An introduction

Contributed by Henry Legge QC and Jordan Holland 5 Stone Buildings

Art and cultural property as a distinct practice area has emerged only very recently. While law firms in the USA have promoted themselves as having 'art law' departments for some time, it is only in the last decade (with one or two exceptions) that English firms have begun to market themselves as having specialist departments in this area.

In that context, it may not be thought surprising that the emergence of this specialisation at the English Bar has come only very recently and in response to the increasing recognition of the practice area by English law firms together with the changing nature of the commercial art market. Nonetheless, the art and cultural property practice area is an extremely small field of highly specialised practice at the Bar, with the expertise and experience being concentrated across a narrow field of individual practitioners. This concentration, bringing as it does an unusual depth of knowledge, can be seen as one of the key reasons underpinning the development of the specialisation and, as such, this is unlikely to change in the foreseeable future.

The Current Landscape

The practice area of art and cultural property includes a diverse range of contentious and non-contentious legal work, the common thread of which is that the case will either be connected to the art market or have art or cultural property as its subject matter.

Disputes as to authenticity and attribution have received considerable attention over the last few years. As the value of works by desirable artists relative to other works has increased, so has the monetary value of such disputes. The increasing sophistication of forgers is another factor which will likely see the volume of such work increase, as will the growing importance of marketable provenance in the international art market. For precisely the same reasons, work involving professional negligence actions against art market professionals is continuing to gather pace.

Disputes as to ownership and title have always formed a significant part of the work in this specialism and they continue to do so. The related but distinct area of who is entitled to possession of any particular object, involving consideration of bailment and consignment issues (or lack thereof), continues to be a valuable source of work. The burden of domestic and international regulation has also seen a significant growth in the non-contentious element of such transactions, involving advising on the drafting of consignment and loan agreements, as well as the effect of various consumer protection measures.

There has also been an upsurge in restitutionary claims over the last decade. These fall into a number of categories, including those proceeding in the civil courts either on the footing of common law principles of restitution or on the basis of foreign statutory regimes. Claims concerning looted and stolen art, almost inevitably with a cross-border character, likewise continue to increase. Mention should also be made of the claims before the Spoliation Advisory Panel and cases involving the 1970 UNESCO Convention which, while fewer in number, are nonetheless an important feature of this area.

Taxation of art continues to be a largely non-contentious but important source of work. In particular, the acceptance in lieu scheme is likely to continue to expand as values increase. The globalisation of the art market has also brought to the fore the various taxation issues surrounding temporary or permanent import of art and cultural property.

It should be evident from the above that cases falling within this specialisation often include conflict of laws issues, both in relation to the correct forum for the resolution of the dispute as well as the governing law of the transaction in question. This is likely to remain the case with the increasingly international nature of many dealers, auction houses and other art market professionals. Contractual issues and disputes as to title, as well as looted art and restitution claims can raise particularly difficult and interesting issues in this regard. In common with other areas of practice, art and cultural property has seen an increase in disputed attempts at forum shopping. In themselves, such issues provide a growing stream of work.

The Future

As can easily be gleaned from the above, art and cultural property involves the assimilation and application of a diverse range of legal principles, some of which, such as the legislation relating to looted, stolen and spoliated art, are unique to this specialisation. However, many more are ordinary English law principles applied in the specific context of art and cultural property. This requires a detailed knowledge and understanding of the manner in which the art market operates. As the emergence of art and cultural property as a distinct practice areas continues to gather pace it is likely that such knowledge will become an even more integral part of the specialisation.

Looking ahead, there is every reason to suspect that the increase in art and cultural property work will continue. In particular, the increasing values of the best art and the growing trend in the investment of art as an asset class are likely to encourage growth in both contentious and non-contentious aspects of the art and cultural property practice area. The demands and expectations of increasingly sophisticated consumers and institutions should be expected to encourage the move towards growing specialisation which recognises and understands the unique nature and rapid expansion of the global art market.

LONDON

Contents:

Art and Cultural Property Law London
Leading Silks
Band 1
Legge Henry *5 Stone Buildings (ORL)* ◊ *
Palmer Norman E *3 Stone Buildings (ORL)* ◊ *
Band 2
Cooper Gilead *3 Stone Buildings (ORL)* ◊ *
Onslow Andrew *3 Verulam Buildings (ORL)* ◊
Smouha Joe *Essex Court Chambers (ORL)* ◊
Leading Juniors
Band 1
Edwards Richard *3 Verulam Buildings (ORL)* ◊
Harris Luke *3 Stone Buildings (ORL)* ◊ *
◊ (ORL) = Other Ranked Lawyer.
** Indicates set / individual with profile.*

Notable Practitioners

Joe Smouha QC (Essex Court Chambers) A highly renowned commercial litigator who has been instructed on significant cases involving cultural property. He has experience of tackling disputes covering the full range of art-related issues. **Strengths:** "He is a very good commercial litigator." "He is a person that you would want for any kind of dispute."

Norman Palmer QC (Hon) (see p.689) (3 Stone Buildings) A leading figure in the art law world, whose clients include a wide range of institutions, art dealers and collectors. He focuses primarily on advisory work, and is regularly instructed by the UK and foreign governments on the development of policy and legislation. **Strengths:** "What he doesn't know about art law isn't worth knowing." "He is a leader in his field: he has written several books on the subject and is highly respected." **Recent work:** He advised the Art Gallery of New South Wales on drafting and implementing legislation concerning the immunity from seizure of foreign art loans in Australia.

Gilead Cooper QC (3 Stone Buildings) Has a broad traditional chancery practice which encompasses cases involving art, antiquities and cultural property. He is consulted by national museums and galleries, and is noted for his knowledge of bailment issues. **Strengths:** "He is a very inventive barrister: he can analyse positions very quickly and then respond to them." "He is a very persuasive advocate and a brilliant speaker." **Recent work:** Recently acted for the Earl of Cardigan in a case concerning an attempt by estate trustees to sell Tottenham House, a Grade I listed building.

Luke Harris (see p.620) (3 Stone Buildings) Has significant expertise in handling traditional chancery cases involving art and antiques. He has acted in a range of title disputes over pieces of artwork and has handled a number of actions against auction houses. **Strengths:** "A go-to junior on arts matters, who is very client-friendly and who provides clear and concise advice on some of the most complex issues." "He is very personable, articulate and diligent." **Recent work:** Represented Selena Rendall in a claim against Sotheby's after the sale of a discarded painting by Winslow Homer, discovered during the filming of the 'Antiques Roadshow', was blocked by the descendants of the children in the painting.

Henry Legge QC (5 Stone Buildings) A heavyweight figure in the art law world. He has experience of handling a wide range of disputes, including spoliation of works of art during the Third Reich and claims against auction houses. **Strengths:** "You want him on your team in an art case." "He is a strong advocate, who has an excellent client manner." **Recent work:** Acting for the claimant in an action against Sotheby's over an alleged Caravaggio painting, which was sold as a copy.

Andrew Onslow QC (3 Verulam Buildings) Has acted in a number of high-profile art and cultural property cases. He regularly appears in matters concerning the sale of fine art, and, in particular, disputes involving auction houses. **Strengths:** "He is always willing to roll his sleeves up and drill down into the detail."

Richard Edwards (3 Verulam Buildings) Regularly handles a wide range of art and cultural property disputes, particularly those involving auction houses. He has particular specialist insight into the art world, having worked as a dealer prior to coming to the Bar. **Strengths:** "On his feet, he is very measured and he doesn't rise to the bait." **Recent work:** Defended Sotheby's in a case concerning the attribution of a painting, alleged to be by Caravaggio, which the auction house insisted was a copy.

AVIATION: An introduction

Contributed by Robert Lawson QC Quadrant Chambers

In relative terms aviation is a small field of specialist practice so far as the English Bar is concerned, with the expertise and workload being concentrated in a handful of sets.

As a practice area, 'aviation' describes the industry being served, i.e. which gives rise to disputes and the need for advice, as a particular area of law. In legal terms it covers a broad range of work. This includes a distinct body of legislation which regulates and governs aviation interests – aviation or air law – and is for the most part international in foundation and application. It also embraces work of a more general commercial and common law nature as it relates to the aviation industry, in particular concerning insurance and asset finance.

It is also, by its very nature, an area often producing work with an international dimension. As a result, the work done by the Bar frequently involves international arbitration and even litigation in overseas jurisdictions, in addition to litigation in the courts of England and Wales.

The volume of aviation work passing through the Bar at the current time is probably best described as steady rather than growing. This is in part because aviation law properly so called is relatively well defined in comparison to some other practice areas (particularly in terms of liability law), and safety standards of the industry are, thankfully, comparatively high. It is also so in part due to the downturn in aviation in the last few years of economic depression.

The work coming to the Bar continues to be of a diverse nature, as can be seen below.

Over the last year, our Senior Courts have given several significant decisions in aviation cases, including one by the Supreme Court in Stott v Thomas Cook Airlines concerning the rights of passengers with reduced mobility, in which strident comments were made by one member of the Court to the effect that the Montreal Convention 1999 is outdated.

In terms of regulatory activity and of attritional loss, the major concern of commercial air carriers at present lies in EC Regulation No. 261/2004 on 'compensation and assistance to passengers in the event of denied boarding and of cancellation or long delay of flights'. This is largely due to the impact of a steady diet of decisions on that regulation by the Court of Justice of the European Union. Many of these decisions have proved controversial in nature, especially the cases of Sturgeon and Nelson, which extend the compensation payable under that regulation to cases of long delay. This European jurisprudence has fed into an upsurge in claims against carriers as well as to associated regulatory issues of a compliance nature with national enforcement bodies – in England, the Civil Aviation Authority – both of which have been a source of work for the Bar.

For the more junior end of the Aviation Bar this development has meant a very considerable volume of claims for, or against, carriers in the Small Claims Courts. However, this year has also seen two important legal questions relating to Regulation 261 reach the Court of Appeal: Dawson, concerning the applicable time limit, and Huzar, concerning the scope of the 'extraordinary circumstances' defence. At the time of writing the outcome of these cases is not known. They may well have a bearing on the future flow of cases under this regulation.

Although revision of Regulation 261 has been under discussion in Brussels for some time, the progress is slow and there remains little prospect of any amendment to it reaching the statute book in the near future. It can therefore be expected that this stream of work will continue to be the bane of this sector for some time to come.

As the world continues to transition back towards economic health, the wave of work concerning aborted aircraft sales and/or lease-finance disputes coincident with the economic downturn appears to be receding. Nevertheless, some notable cases in this area have still hit the courts in the last year, such as the substantial Commercial Court case of Alpstream v PK Finance, concerning a mortgagee's powers and duties with regards to the sale of aircraft.

The general aviation sector remains dominated by cases involving fatalities or serious injuries sustained in accidents befalling light aircraft. The most significant legal development for this particular sector of the aviation market over the last year is the Court of Appeal's decision in Hoyle v Rogers, which confirmed the admissibility in civil proceedings of a report by the Air Accidents Investigation Branch outwith the scope of CPR Pt.35. It will be interesting to see the impact of this decision, and in particular whether and how it impacts upon the important work done by the AAIB.

Contents:

LONDON

Aviation London
Leading Sets
Band 1
Fountain Court Chambers *
Quadrant Chambers *
Band 2
Brick Court Chambers *
XXIV Old Buildings *
* *Indicates firm with profile.*
Alphabetical order within each band. Band 1 is highest.

Band 1

Fountain Court Chambers

See profile on p.804

THE SET

"A go-to set for complex commercial aviation litigation," Fountain Court is renowned for the depth of its practice and the superior experience and knowledge of its members. Individuals here are particularly active on claims relating to aviation incidents that result in serious injury or loss of life. They are also highly adept at aircraft repossession matters.

Client service: The clerks, led by Alex Taylor, "provide an excellent service" that "goes well beyond what you might normally expect." "They are of great assistance in getting costs assessed during the process," and are a good foil to their members, who are themselves "unfailingly smart, hard-working and fun to deal with."

SILKS

Michael Crane QC Widely recognised as the pre-eminent barrister for aviation, he is particularly noted for his work on complex commercial disputes and regulatory matters. Commentators are quick to praise him for his advocacy skills and outstanding specialist knowledge. **Strengths:** "Probably the best barrister for contentious aviation and regulatory work." "He is truly a big noise in the Commercial Bar generally and aviation is the jewel in his crown." **Recent work:** He successfully acted in Rogers v Hoyle before the Court of Appeal, a noteworthy case that changed the admissibility of Air Accidents Investigation Branch reports as evidence in civil proceedings.

Akhil Shah QC A market leader for aviation regulation matters, who is also noted for his skill in commercial litigation. He earns praise for his highly cerebral approach and commercial sensibility. **Strengths:** "A hugely intelligent and respected aviation counsel, who is very easy to communicate with and very strong in court." "He couples an unrivalled eye for forensic detail with a pragmatic, commercial approach. He's a reliable sounding board and a pleasure to work with." **Recent work:** Appeared for the lessors in HSH

Aviation London	
Leading Silks	
Star individuals	
Crane Michael	*Fountain Court Chambers*
Band 1	
Lawson Robert	*Quadrant Chambers* *
Shah Akhil	*Fountain Court Chambers* *
Shepherd Philip	*XXIV Old Buildings*
Thanki Bankim	*Fountain Court Chambers* *
Band 2	
Calver Neil	*Brick Court Chambers*
Kealey Gavin	*7 King's Bench Walk (ORL)* ◊
Lydiard Andrew	*Brick Court Chambers*
McLaren Michael	*Fountain Court Chambers* *
Moriarty Stephen	*Fountain Court Chambers* *
Band 3	
Steel John	*Thirty Nine Essex Street (ORL)* ◊ 🄰 *
Taylor John	*Fountain Court Chambers* *
Leading Juniors	
Band 1	
Kimbell John	*Quadrant Chambers*
Marland Timothy	*Quadrant Chambers*
Phelps Rosalind	*Fountain Court Chambers* *
Reeve Matthew	*Quadrant Chambers*
Shah Bajul	*XXIV Old Buildings*
Band 2	
Chambers Jonathan	*Quadrant Chambers*
Cutress James	*Fountain Court Chambers* *
Milner Alexander	*Fountain Court Chambers* *
Thompson Steven	*XXIV Old Buildings*
Band 3	
Cumming Edward	*XXIV Old Buildings*
Deal Katherine	*3 Hare Court (ORL)* ◊
Ghaffar Arshad	*XXIV Old Buildings*
Henton Paul	*Quadrant Chambers* *
Hilliard Emma	*7 King's Bench Walk (ORL)* ◊
Passmore John	*Quadrant Chambers*
Zellick Adam	*Fountain Court Chambers* *
Up-and-coming individuals	
Barrett Stephanie	*Quadrant Chambers*
🄰 *direct access (see p.11).*	
◊ *(ORL) = Other Ranked Lawyer.*	
* *Indicates firm / individual with profile.*	

Nordbank v Astra Worldwide, a leasing dispute resulting from the insolvency of Air Comet.

Bankim Thanki QC A commercial and banking law expert whose talents are regularly deployed in the aviation market. He is particularly adept at representing lessors in complex aviation finance matters. **Strengths:** "He is a class act – a very good advocate who is loved by clients." **Recent work:** Successfully defended China Southern Airlines in a case against Tigris concerning claims of conspiracy arising from the sale of six Airbus A300 jet airliners.

Michael McLaren QC Has cultivated a great reputation in the aviation market through his involvement in a variety of complex regulatory and commercial disputes. He takes a pragmatic approach to his cases and is a commercially minded advocate. **Strengths:** "He is punchy in court and always thoroughly prepared." "He is a team player, and considering he's a fairly senior silk, he has an enthusiasm and eagerness to get stuck in that is quite refreshing. He puts a lot of effort into helping us out in some urgent situations." **Recent work:** Assisted the National Police Air Service in obtaining necessary approvals from the Civil Aviation Authority (CAA) enabling it to operate its nationwide Helicopter Emergency Medical Service.

Stephen Moriarty QC Recently appointed as head of Fountain Court Chambers, he is well regarded for his courtroom skills by peers and instructing solicitors. He is well known for his expertise in aviation finance cases. **Strengths:** "In cross-examination he is amazing and really gets into the details." "He's very clever and very hands-on; solicitors and judges love him." **Recent work:** Appeared in the Commercial Court for PK Airfinance defending claims of conspiracy made by Alpstream, a consortium owned by business magnate Alexander Lebedev.

John Taylor QC Receives accolades from clients for his commercially geared advice. His practice encompasses a range of aviation matters including leasing and contractual disputes. **Strengths:** "Combines knowledge of the law with pragmatism and a commercial mindset." **Recent work:** Acted for Mitsubishi in the Commercial Court, handling a dispute with Virgin Atlantic Airways regarding the supply of aircraft seats.

JUNIORS

Rosalind Phelps A lawyer known for the strength of her advocacy, who is applauded for her finesse in resolving complex contractual disputes. She is further noted for her skill in regulatory work and has the CAA as a client. **Strengths:** "A number-one senior junior for knotty contractual disputes. Hard-working and bright," she is "a very good team player, who gets involved and is happy to discuss pertinent points. To the point, she doesn't mess around." **Recent work:** Instructed on behalf of Belfast International Airport in its dispute with Aer Lingus concerning the decision to terminate operations out of the airport before the completion of its contractual obligations.

James Cutress Commercially minded junior who offers expertise in a variety of aviation matters, including insurance and complex contractual disputes. **Strengths:** "A safe pair of hands for any complex aviation case," "he is very, very clever." **Recent work:** Acted in Virgin Atlantic v Koito and Mitsubishi, a dispute over allegedly falsified test results for seats.

Alexander Milner Attracts ample praise for his expertise in aviation cases and is known for being highly responsive to client needs. Sources were eager to highlight his language skills, particularly his fluency in Russian. **Strengths:** "A future star. He's bright, fast on turnaround and gives good, sensible advice." "Quietly spoken, he's cerebral and provides a very clear and precise understanding of the problem before him." **Recent work:** Acted in the case of Natixis v Islas Airways, a claim made against three guarantors of the defunct airline that sought to recover almost EUR30 million.

Adam Zellick Most notably active on complex commercial litigation cases, particularly disputes arising out of leasing complications. He is known for his pragmatic approach. **Strengths:** "A dogged advocate, who thinks laterally and constantly comes up with solutions." **Recent work:** Acted as counsel for Air France in litigation arising from the crash of Flight 447 in 2009, which resulted in the deaths of 228 people.

Quadrant Chambers

See profile on p.854

THE SET

Widely recognised in the market as a leading set for aviation insurance work, Quadrant Chambers is praised by commentators as being "excellent, not just in terms of the individuals it has but also due to the depth it has. If you cannot get the person you want, you can get someone equally as good straight away." One commentator noted that "the individuals have superlative intellectual abilities" and are well equipped to deal with any cases emanating from aviation incidents. Multiple members of the set have been instructed in high-profile cases that have had significant repercussions on aviation law.

Client service: "Quadrant as a set of chambers is great to work with; the facilities are excellent and the clerks most helpful." "The clerks, led by Gary Ventura and Simon Slattery, are always helpful in directing us to the right barrister with the necessary expertise." "They make a real effort to get to know us personally and are commercial when it comes to agreeing fees."

SILKS

Robert Lawson QC Highly sought after silk who is frequently instructed on sensitive cases that have a law-altering capacity. Commentators highlight his strong advocacy skills and note his years of experience in aviation law. **Strengths:** "He is extremely knowledgeable, responsive and good with clients. He also has a superb courtroom manner." **Recent work:** Successfully acted on behalf of Malaysian Airlines in the Court of Appeal in a dispute over injury caused by medical treatment administered in flight. This case has helped to further clarify the meaning and scope of 'accident' as applied by the Montreal Convention.

JUNIORS

John Kimbell Dual-qualified in England and Germany, he earns excellent praise for his abilities as an advocate and for his specialist aviation knowledge. He is regularly instructed on claimant cases and regularly acts on behalf of those affected by aviation incidents that have resulted in fatalities or serious injury. **Strengths:** "He shows exceptional ability when handling complex aviation cases, and has the drive to deliver successful strategies." "Charming, capable and clever; there isn't a hint of arrogance about him." **Recent work:** Acted in Coakely v Air France, representing one of the English families in a case concerning the crash of an Airbus A330 into the Atlantic Ocean in 2009.

Timothy Marland A leading junior who receives significant accolades for his work in aviation insurance. He also offers expertise in regulatory matters and lease disputes, and is frequently instructed by airlines to represent their interests in contentious litigation. **Strengths:** "He has an easy manner, and puts difficult issues in an easy-to-understand way. He's affable, charming and great at cross-examinations." "Represents the epitome of what we look for in a modern barrister; he doesn't just sit in chambers, but gets involved in cases and sees clients with you. His presentation is just fantastic." **Recent work:** Appeared in Samarsinghe v British Airways, successfully defending the airline against accusations of discrimination. This case involved interpretation of the Montreal Convention, and tested the territorial reach of the 2010 Equality Act.

Matthew Reeve Well regarded for his specialist regulatory and insurance knowledge, he receives praise for his analytical skills and strong advocacy. **Strengths:** "A proactive, hands-on senior junior who is both detailed and yet has sight of the bigger picture." "He shows great compassion and understanding with clients, and is excellent on complex quantum cases." **Recent work:** Acted in Cassley v GMP Securities and Sundance, a case arising from the fatal crash of a jet that occurred in the Democratic Republic of Congo in 2010.

Jonathan Chambers Noted by peers for his meticulous preparation, strong advocacy skills and easy manner with clients. He has a particular proficiency in aviation insurance matters. **Strengths:** "He has a brilliant touch with clients and with the court; they immediately get his intellect and he produces silky submissions." **Recent work:** Acted in Buckley v Monarch Airlines, representing the airline against a claim resulting from a drink spillage. The case involved a determination of what an 'accident' is under the Montreal Convention.

Stephanie Barrett Good at both commercial litigation and arbitration in the insurance market, she is praised by peers for her assertive advocacy. **Strengths:** "Bright, tenacious and happy to accommodate the client's needs." "A fearsome advocate with a first-rate intellect." **Recent work:** Acted on behalf of Malaysia Airlines in a case concerning negligent medical treatment aboard one of its aircraft.

John Passmore Although particularly noted for his expertise in aviation finance matters, he also offers significant experience on lease disputes. Commentators were keen to highlight the quality of his written material. **Strengths:** "He's meticulous in his preparation and advocacy."

Paul Henton (see p.625) An expert in matters relating to the sale of aircraft, lease disputes and cases arising from the maintenance of aircraft. Acts for a broad range of clients including airlines, insurers and aircraft maintenance firms. **Recent work:** Acted in Geodis Wilson v British Airways, a dispute over damage that occurred to medical testing equipment whilst being transported.

Band 2

Brick Court Chambers

See profile on p.774

THE SET

Acknowledged for its commercial focus, this set has a strong reputation for producing high-quality work in aviation insurance litigation. Commentators hail the chambers as a "quality all-rounder" in the aviation market. It is also recognised by sources for its work in financial leasing matters and the application of EU and competition law to the allocation of airport landing slots.

SILKS

Neil Calver QC Well regarded by peers, Calver maintains a reputation for his expertise in aviation insurance matters. He is frequently involved in international arbitrations representing the interests of insurers. **Strengths:** "A brilliant lawyer who is an automatic choice for insurance work."

Andrew Lydiard QC A strong presence in the market, who is strong on liability insurance and leasing disputes. His superior cross-examination skills were highlighted to researchers. **Strengths:** "He could probably handle anything, he is so bright. On insurance disputes he is first class." "He has been in aviation man and boy, and definitely knows his stuff."

XXIV Old Buildings

See profile on p.838

THE SET

A popular choice for aviation matters, held in particularly high regard for its expertise in commercial contractual disputes. The set's "extremely bright" collection of barristers are also well equipped to offer assistance with insurance claims, regulatory issues and product liability cases in an aviation context. Barristers here service a broad client base that includes airlines, lessors and maintenance firms.

SILKS

Philip Shepherd QC Has cultivated an excellent reputation for his commercial aviation work and is regularly instructed in contractual disputes. He also offers proficiency on insurance matters. **Strengths:** "He has bags of experience in the aviation sphere and is a fine courtroom performer." **Recent work:** Involved in Credit Suisse AB v Arabian Aircraft & Equipment, a case that arose from a default on a lease agreement.

JUNIORS

Bajul Shah Highly regarded by sources for his personable demeanour and excellent advocacy. He is frequently instructed on matters arising from contractual disputes, particularly those that have a multi-jurisdictional aspect. **Strengths:** "A very experienced junior with a wide and busy practice." "Clever, switched-on, and good with clients, he makes nice presentations in court." **Recent work:** Was instructed by claimants in a dispute with Kingfisher concerning breaches of lease agreements.

Steven Thompson Earns praise for his complex commercial litigation work. He is renowned for his proficiency in disputes that arise out of aircraft maintenance issues. **Strengths:** "He gives very good commercial advice, particularly in tricky circumstances, and has a very good courtroom manner." "A good advocate, who deals effectively with judges and fights his client's corner hard." **Recent work:** Instructed in Ryanair v Derry Airport, defending the airport against a contribution claim brought by the airline.

Edward Cumming A growing presence in the aviation market, who offers expertise in lease disputes and financing transactions. He is praised by commentators for his ethical integrity, intelligence and up-to-date knowledge of shifts in the aviation industry. **Strengths:** "He's really smart and works very hard; he's very proactive and good to have as part of the team." "A good, bold advocate, who fights for his clients very well and is emotionally intelligent." **Recent work:** Involved in the case of SmartLynx v Virgin Nigeria, a dispute emanating from the premature conclusion of a lease contract.

Arshad Ghaffar Frequently instructed on lease disputes, but also offers additional expertise in claimant cases arising from fatal aviation accidents. Commentators note his advocacy skills and his extensive knowledge of aviation matters in the Middle East. **Strengths:** "Very timely and responsive, and very efficient at identifying the legal issues in a case." "Careful and thoughtful, he's a strong advocate in court." **Recent work:** Appeared in Techdawn Aviation Consultants v Total Engineering Support, a dispute over unpaid commission.

Other Ranked Lawyers

John Steel QC (Thirty Nine Essex Street) An expert on aviation regulatory matters, who is particularly known for his knowledge of airspace and air traffic control matters. He regularly acts for airlines, airport operators and aircraft owners, amongst others. **Strengths:** "Incredibly professional and a vast resource of expertise." **Recent work:** Involved in a case that challenged the NATS on airspace changes made in Suffolk.

Katherine Deal (3 Hare Court) A personal injury specialist, who has significant technical aviation expertise. She is regularly instructed by claimants on matters resulting from fatal aviation incidents. **Strengths:** "She has good judgement and an excellent intellect, and is a good team player." **Recent work:** Instructed in Cunningham v MoD, a widely reported case concerning the death of a pilot as a result of a malfunctioning ejector seat.

Gavin Kealey QC (7 King's Bench Walk) Highly renowned for his work in insurance, he has developed a reputation for handling complex contentious litigation. He frequently represents aviation insurers and lessors. **Strengths:** "Spectacularly smart, he's a fantastic advocate and a masterful cross-examiner of witnesses."

Emma Hilliard (7 King's Bench Walk) Has a strong technical knowledge of the market and is particularly active in complex aviation insurance cases. **Strengths:** "She shows great attention to detail and is very good on the paperwork."

Contents:

LONDON

Banking & Finance London
Leading Sets
Band 1
Fountain Court Chambers *
3 Verulam Buildings *
Band 2
Brick Court Chambers *
One Essex Court *
Essex Court Chambers *
South Square *
Band 3
20 Essex Street *
Serle Court *
4 Stone Buildings *
* Indicates set / Individual with profile.
◊ (ORL) = Other Ranked Lawyer.
🄰 direct access (see p.11).
Alphabetical order within each band. Band 1 is highest.

Banking & Finance London	
Leading Silks	
Star individuals	Crow Jonathan *4 Stone Buildings* *
Brindle Michael *Fountain Court Chambers*	Dale Derrick *Fountain Court Chambers*
Dicker Robin *South Square* *	Davies Rhodri *One Essex Court*
Grabiner Anthony *One Essex Court*	de Garr Robinson Anthony *One Essex Court* *
Hapgood Mark *Brick Court Chambers*	Dohmann Barbara *Blackstone Chambers (ORL)* ◊
Howard Mark *Brick Court Chambers*	Downes Paul *2TG - 2 Temple Gardens (ORL)* ◊ 🄰
Milligan Iain *20 Essex Street*	Goldring Jeremy *South Square*
Rabinowitz Laurence *One Essex Court*	Hill Richard G *4 Stone Buildings*
Railton David *Fountain Court Chambers*	Kitchener Neil *One Essex Court*
Zacaroli Antony *South Square*	Lavender Nicholas *Serle Court* *
Band 1	Millett Richard *Essex Court Chambers*
Auld Stephen *One Essex Court*	Odgers John *3 Verulam Buildings*
Beltrami Adrian *3 Verulam Buildings*	Onslow Andrew *3 Verulam Buildings*
Foxton David *Essex Court Chambers*	Orr Craig *One Essex Court* *
Handyside Richard *Fountain Court Chambers* *	Saini Pushpinder *Blackstone Chambers (ORL)* ◊
Lord Tim *Brick Court Chambers*	**Band 4**
Malek Ali *3 Verulam Buildings*	Blayney David *Serle Court* *
McQuater Ewan *3 Verulam Buildings*	Butcher Christopher *7 King's Bench Walk (ORL)* ◊
Miles Robert *4 Stone Buildings*	Coleman Richard *Fountain Court Chambers* *
Salter Richard *3 Verulam Buildings*	Cousins Jeremy *11 Stone Buildings (ORL)* ◊ *
Thanki Bankim *Fountain Court Chambers* *	Davies-Jones Jonathan *3 Verulam Buildings*
Tolaney Sonia *3 Verulam Buildings*	Dhillon Jasbir *Brick Court Chambers*
Toledano Daniel *One Essex Court*	Gruder Jeffrey *Essex Court Chambers*
Wolfson David *One Essex Court*	Henshaw Andrew *Brick Court Chambers*
Band 2	Kimmins Charles *20 Essex Street*
Baker Andrew *20 Essex Street*	Malek Hodge M *Thirty Nine Essex Street (ORL)* ◊ *
Choo Choy Alain *One Essex Court*	Marshall Philip *Serle Court* *
Cox Raymond *Fountain Court Chambers* *	Quest David *3 Verulam Buildings*
Glick Ian *One Essex Court*	Robertson Patricia *Fountain Court Chambers* *
Howe Timothy *Fountain Court Chambers* *	Taylor John *Fountain Court Chambers* *
Mitchell Andrew *Fountain Court Chambers* *	Tregear Francis *XXIV Old Buildings (ORL)* ◊
Nash Jonathan *3 Verulam Buildings*	Trower William *South Square*
Smouha Joe *Essex Court Chambers*	Twigger Andrew M *3 Stone Buildings (ORL)* ◊ *
Snowden Richard *Erskine Chambers (ORL)* ◊	**New Silks**
Sutcliffe Andrew *3 Verulam Buildings*	Allison David *South Square* *
Waters Malcolm *Radcliffe Chambers (ORL)* ◊ *	Gibaud Catherine *3 Verulam Buildings*
Band 3	Goodall Patrick *Fountain Court Chambers* *
Boswood Anthony *Fountain Court Chambers*	Hardwick Matthew *3 Verulam Buildings*
Calver Neil *Brick Court Chambers*	Smith Tom *South Square* *
Chapman Jeffrey *Fountain Court Chambers* *	Strong Benjamin *One Essex Court* *

Band 1

Fountain Court Chambers
See profile on p.804

THE SET

Fountain Court Chambers is renowned for its deep bench of high-quality practitioners, and many of its barristers are at the top of their field. Its silks and juniors are universally praised for their excellence, with one source saying: "Their pleadings are fantastic, and it's a pleasure to go back and read their work." Members have been involved in the highest profile cases in the sector, such as Deutsche Bank v Unitech, Deutsche Bank v Khan and the Italian interest rate swaps litigation. This is "a terrific set of banking and finance specialists," and "a bastion of really good people, all of whom are of really high quality."

Client service: "Alex Taylor's team of clerks is wonderful. They're always on time, polite and approachable. The whole set-up is great. You know you're getting quality from the second you speak to a clerk to the moment you walk out of the trial."

SILKS

Michael Brindle QC A celebrated silk who is highly regarded for his deep experience in this field. He handles a broad range of contentious matters, and is celebrated for his international arbitration practice. **Strengths:** "He's a remarkable advocate, who is very thoughtful, careful yet tenacious in his approach – he knows when to fight hard." "He's got good courtroom presence and has a good intuitive feel for which points to run with and which points not to run with." **Recent work:** Acted for ARM Asset Backed Securities in a bond dispute with the FCA.

David Railton QC A standout QC who enjoys a stellar reputation. He is regularly sought out to act in high-profile, landmark cases. **Strengths:** "He always produces an exceptional service. Not many counsel have his ability to take very complex legal matters and produce clear and appropriate advice in no time at all. He consistently wows clients." "He's an extremely effective, careful and thoughtful lawyer. He has an excellent court style. He can disarm witnesses because they think they're getting a pussycat, but they're actually getting a tiger." **Recent work:** Acted for Deutsche Bank in a claim against Sebastian Holdings as part of the highly publicised dispute regarding equities trading and FX transactions.

Raymond Cox QC Has a far-reaching practice covering a broad range of banking issues, and he has recognised expertise in payments law. He also has a strong focus on derivatives disputes and notable strength in cases relating to debt-based securities. **Strengths:** "A cerebral, thoughtful silk who has an easy manner and is a pleasure to work with." "He has an impressive ability to assimilate volumes of information. He has a very measured, logical and persuasive style of advocacy." **Recent work:** Successfully represented Deutsche Bank in its dispute with the Khan family, winning a substantial loan repayment and defending the bank from a counterclaim alleging misrepresentation and mis-selling of structured products.

Richard Handyside QC A lawyer with a fine track record in high-profile international proceedings. Clients are impressed by his pragmatic advice and his tactical thinking. **Strengths:** "An absolute delight to work with, he's mild mannered and yet utterly tenacious." "A top choice. He's a lawyer with a relaxed and measured manner, who is at the same time both steely and forceful." **Recent work:** Acted for a syndi-

Banking & Finance London	
Leading Juniors	
Band 1	
Atrill Simon	*Fountain Court Chambers* *
King Edmund	*Essex Court Chambers*
Mumford David	*Maitland Chambers (ORL)* ◊ *
Valentin Ben	*Fountain Court Chambers* *
Band 2	
Birt Simon	*Brick Court Chambers*
Brent Richard	*3 Verulam Buildings*
John Laura	*3 Verulam Buildings*
King Henry	*Fountain Court Chambers* *
Phelps Rosalind	*Fountain Court Chambers* *
Polley Alexander	*One Essex Court* *
Zellick Adam	*Fountain Court Chambers* *
Band 3	
Bayfield Daniel	*South Square* *
Brown Hannah	*One Essex Court*
Cutress James	*Fountain Court Chambers* *
Duffy James	*Fountain Court Chambers* *
Hattan Simon	*Serle Court* *
Kenny Julian	*20 Essex Street*
Khan Farhaz	*Outer Temple Chambers (ORL)* ◊
Kramer Adam	*3 Verulam Buildings* *
Lazarus Michael	*3 Verulam Buildings*
MacDonald James	*3 Verulam Buildings* *
Midwinter Stephen	*Brick Court Chambers*
Parker Matthew	*3 Verulam Buildings* *
Pilbrow Fionn	*Brick Court Chambers*
Shivji Sharif	*4 Stone Buildings*
Wilson Ian	*3 Verulam Buildings*
Band 4	
Ayres Andrew	*Maitland Chambers (ORL)* ◊ *
Dawid Jonathan	*Brick Court Chambers*
Edwards William	*3 Verulam Buildings*
Forbes Smith Henry	*One Essex Court*
Hutton Louise	*Maitland Chambers (ORL)* ◊ *
Isaac Sebastian	*One Essex Court*
McClelland James	*Fountain Court Chambers* *
Morrison Craig	*Brick Court Chambers*
Mott Richard	*One Essex Court* *
Murray David	*Fountain Court Chambers* *
Oppenheimer Tamara	*Fountain Court Chambers*
Patton Conall	*One Essex Court* *
Pearce Luke	*20 Essex Street*
Pilling Benjamin	*4 Pump Court (ORL)* ◊ *
Raphael Thomas	*20 Essex Street*
Robins Stephen	*South Square* *
Sher Adam	*Fountain Court Chambers* *
Yeo Nik	*Fountain Court Chambers* *
** Indicates individual with profile.*	
◊ (ORL) = Other Ranked Lawyer.	

cate of banks seeking repayment of a substantial loan made to Unitech.

Bankim Thanki QC A polished performer, who has strong regulatory knowledge, Thanki is sought out for the most high-profile banking and finance and financial services cases. He often acts for major retail and investment banks, and frequently receives instructions to act both for and against the FCA. **Strengths:** "He's steeped in financial litigation. A wise, calm, and measured individual, he's incredibly easy to work with." "One to use on high-level cases. He has good judgement and a good feel for the case. He's very commercial and very experienced." **Recent work:** Brought a successful claim on behalf of BNP Paribas against multiple hedge funds managed by Anchorage Capital concerning the sale of subordinated private placement notes.

Timothy Howe QC Has an extensive litigation and international arbitration practice that sees him handling major cases worldwide. **Strengths:** "He works prodigiously hard, he's very commercial and he has excellent knowledge of complex financial products." "He's extremely user-friendly, very approachable, highly adaptable and he understands clients' needs." **Recent work:** Acted for Deutsche Bank in its landmark dispute with Unitech concerning the mis-selling of interest rate swaps and alleged Libor manipulation.

Andrew Mitchell QC Recognised for his experience in swaps cases. He represents a diverse range of retail banks in a significant number of claims arising from the alleged mis-selling of interest-rate hedging products. **Strengths:** "He's a very impressive advocate and is particularly good in cross-examination." "He's very commercial. He was able to distil points down into the information we needed. He's like a beacon in a sea of chaos." **Recent work:** Defended a multitude of banks including RBS in the highly publicised Green & Rowley case in the Court of Appeal.

John Taylor QC Acts both for claimants and for retail and investment banks in an array of mis-selling cases relating to PPI and interest rate swaps. His banking practice also crosses over into civil fraud. **Strengths:** "He has a top-quality brain and is absolutely superb on his feet. He has just the right level of aggression and displays very good judgement on how to pursue something." "His work ethic and attention to detail are superb." **Recent work:** Acted for the claimant, Metlife Seguros De Retiro, in its dispute with J.P. Morgan regarding bonds linked to the inflation rate in Argentina.

Anthony Boswood QC Offers a broad practice spanning banking, financial services, professional negligence and insurance cases. **Recent work:** Acted for the lenders, BMA Special Opportunity Hub, in its dispute with African Minerals Finance relating to the construction of a loan facility.

Jeffrey Chapman QC Experienced in a broad range of litigation including financial disputes, civil fraud and professional negligence cases. **Strengths:** "He's somebody we like a lot. He's very bright and has great common sense." **Recent work:** Acted for one of the defendants in the major multi-jurisdictional banking fraud case of BTA Bank v Ablyazov.

Derrick Dale QC Maintains a thriving banking practice, complemented by strength in professional negligence. He is well versed in mis-selling claims and litigation arising out of the sale of derivatives. **Strengths:** "A pragmatic silk who is very user-friendly." "He's bright and extremely responsive." **Recent work:** Defended the German bank IKB in a claim brought by RBS regarding the purchase of debt-based derivatives.

Richard Coleman QC Experienced in claims relating to the mis-selling of PPI and interest-rate hedging products. He has been instructed in some of the most high-profile and internationally significant cases in this sector of recent years. **Strengths:** "A silk who represents superb value, he is one of our first choices for banking disputes." "He is constructive in his thinking and good at finding answers in difficult cases. He's very hard-working." **Recent work:** Acted for Rabobank in relation to the international regulatory investigations into the manipulation of Libor.

Patricia Robertson QC Recognised for her expertise in claims rooted in the mis-selling of derivative products. She is experienced in an array of contentious domestic and international matters, and has a practice that further encompasses professional discipline, professional negligence and regulatory matters. **Strengths:** "A fount of knowledge when it comes to asset management, banking and regulation issues. She is extremely hard-working," and "absolutely all over the detail." **Recent work:** Defended the local authority of Florence against claims brought by numerous international banks regarding the enforceability of interest rate swaps.

Patrick Goodall QC A former solicitor at a top-ranking London firm who is lauded for his commercial approach. Numerous sources praise him for his succinct and easily digestible legal advice. **Strengths:** "A gentleman who is very efficient and careful with the details. He's client-friendly, fair and a nice opponent." "He's very bright and hard-working, and he produces good pleadings. He made himself available and fitted in as if he were a member of the team. He's very impressive indeed." **Recent work:** Led by Bankim Thanki in BNP Paribas' claim against Anchorage Group regarding the sale of subordinated private placement notes.

JUNIORS

Simon Atrill Recently instructed as sole counsel in the commercial court. Solicitors cite his engaging enthusiasm and the high quality of his oral advocacy as amongst his key strengths. **Strengths:** "He's very clever, very thorough and tremendously smooth. A very high-class operator." "His advocacy is phenomenal; it's clear, concise and gets to the heart of the issue very quickly. He has an eye for detail and doesn't miss anything in the documentation." **Recent work:** Led by Jeffrey Chapman, acting for one of the defendants in the high-profile BTA Bank v Ablyazov case.

Ben Valentin A leading senior junior with extensive experience of handling a range of commercial disputes. He also has expertise in civil fraud, and has a strong international arbitration practice. **Recent work:** Acted for Imcopa International on defending a claim brought by bondholders relating to restructuring consent payments.

James Duffy (see p.591) Instructed by major international banks in a number of landmark cases including the Unicredit litigation and UBS v City of Florence. He is noted for his expertise in litigation arising out of the sales of interest rate derivatives. **Strengths:** "He knows his stuff, he's very collaborative, he's quick to turn papers around and he's very sensible." "Clients really like him and have been really impressed with him. He's certainly made his mark and is doing really well." **Recent work:** Led by David Railton, he successfully brought a claim for Barclays against UniCredit. The case concerned the early termination of a securitisation transaction.

Henry King Dual-qualified as a barrister and chartered accountant, he is noted for his keen understanding of the finance sector. He is strong on both banking and financial services cases. **Strengths:** "He's exceptionally hard-working and has dogged determination." "He's excellent at getting to grips with the details and the numbers." **Recent work:** Led by Sonia Tolaney, he won a comprehensive victory for Deutsche Bank against Sebastian Holdings.

Rosalind Phelps Demonstrates skill in litigation concerning interest rate derivatives and asset financing. She regularly acts for major retail and investment banks in cases of significant reputational importance to them. **Strengths:** "She is extremely bright and efficient, and has a great understanding of financial products and markets and an innate ability to judge what clients want from junior counsel." "She's very effective at getting the job done well and with a minimum of fuss. She's very flexible and will drop stuff and help out when needed." **Recent work:** Acted in the high-profile dispute between Alpstream Aviation and PK AirFinance and GECAS concerning the enforceability of various debt obligations.

Nik Yeo A former solicitor at a high-level City firm, who has noteworthy strength in structured finance and derivatives-based litigation. He has been led by many high-quality banking silks and has also acted as sole counsel for a range of financial institutions. **Strengths:** "He is incredibly hard-working and approachable and combines impressive technical legal analytical abilities with a numeracy and familiarity with structured finance products which is rare at the Bar." "His written work is meticulous and thoughtful." **Recent work:** Acted in RMcGraw-Hill (Standard & Poor's rating agency) v RBS, representing the bank in a landmark case which held that a rating agency is liable to investors for its ratings.

James Cutress Maintains an impressively broad practice comprising banking, aviation, insurance and professional negligence cases. He has notable experience handling claims arising from the mis-selling of interest rate swaps. **Strengths:** "He's extremely bright and his attention to detail is first-class. He's very user-friendly and easy to get on with." "He's extremely good and has very sound judgement." **Recent work:** He acted for BMA Special Opportunity Hub in a claim against African Minerals Finance.

David Murray Gains instructions in big-ticket litigation and is led by some of the most high profile silks in the sector. Solicitors praise him for his determination and ability to maintain his good humour in difficult circumstances. **Strengths:** "His writing is fantastic. He's incredibly clever and willing to pick things up at the drop of a hat." "He has a friendly, co-operative approach." **Recent work:** Represented J.P. Morgan in a claim against BVG, the Berlin public transport authority. The case related to the purchase of CDOs.

Tamara Oppenheimer A highly reputable junior with a practice that is heavily freighted with banking and professional negligence cases. She has vast experience of handling high-profile derivatives claims. **Strengths:** "One of the cleverest people you'll ever meet, she is very easy to work with." "She is superb. She has fantastic attention to detail and is very commercial and sensible." **Recent work:** Acted for Nomura in a claim against Banca Monte dei Paschi di Siena. The case concerned the contractual validity of a set of high-value derivatives transactions.

Adam Zellick Demonstrates expertise in cases concerning a broad range of financial products, most often derivatives and debt-based securities. Clients praise his strategic insight and commercial manner. **Strengths:** "A star performer. His advocacy, his writing skills and his strategic input are extremely good. He's always positive and puts the client first at all times." "He's extremely clever; he thinks laterally about problems and comes up with inventive and practical solutions." **Recent work:** Acted for ten claimant banks in the high-profile proceedings of Deutsche Bank v Unitech.

Adam Sher (see p.719) A junior who has been instructed in many leading cases of late, often with regard to interest rate swaps, Libor manipulation and fraud. Solicitors praise him for his ability to reassure witnesses and connect with clients. **Strengths:** "He's exceptionally thorough and good at getting into the detail. He's wonderfully enthusiastic and has incredible stamina." "He's an extremely passionate, very talented lawyer. Because he cares so much he won't let something drop. He doesn't need to be led, prompted or pushed." **Recent work:** Acted for Deutsche Bank, with Mark Hapgood QC and Timothy Howe QC, in the bank's significant dispute with Unitech regarding allegations of Libor manipulation and the mis-selling of interest rate swaps.

James McClelland Celebrated for his intelligence and determination, he has been gaining increasing prominence in banking and finance circles of late. He has a strong banking practice and a keen interest in financial services regulation. **Strengths:** "His knowledge of detail and his precision are second to none. He never misses a trick and always considers things from every angle. He's also phenomenally bright." "After ten minutes of research, he seemingly understands the clients' products better than they do." **Recent work:** Won victory alongside Raymond Cox QC and Michael Pryor, acting for Deutsche Bank in its highly publicised dispute with the Khan family.

3 Verulam Buildings

See profile on p.875

THE SET

The barristers at 3 Verulam Buildings lead the way in appearing in high-profile banking and finance cases. They are active across the full range of disputes in this area, and a significant number of them have played key roles in mis-selling cases. By way of example, members were involved in the interest rate swaps litigation between various Italian municipalities and leading banks. Other landmark cases handled include Deutsche Bank v Sebastian Holdings, and the set has also had involvement in the litigation arising out of the insolvencies of the Icelandic banks. Sources hail 3VB as "one of the premier finance sets in the country, and a chambers that offers a universal service."

Client service: "I'd give Paul Cooklin's team ten out of ten. They really stand out in terms of the clerking they offer. They're good at recommending suitable people, they're commercial and they're realistic about pricing."

SILKS

Sonia Tolaney QC A barrister with an enviable reputation for her "very compelling and incredibly focused" advocacy. She is a go-to silk for numerous financial institutions and frequently receives instructions in the highest-profile cases in this area. **Strengths:** "She's determined, gets the judge's ear and fights tenaciously. She has an air of calm about her, is very clear in her thinking and is just a joy to watch." "She has the ability to speak beautifully in a way that's both incredibly persuasive and nuanced such that you don't realise you're on the receiving end of an incredible piece of advocacy. It's clear, crisp and powerful." **Recent work:** Won a decisive victory for Deutsche Bank in its high-profile dispute with Sebastian Holdings.

Adrian Beltrami QC A highly reputable silk with proven expertise in cases relating to structured products. He often represents major international retail and investment banks in cases of global importance. **Strengths:** "The complete package. He's highly intelligent, commercially astute, a great trial advocate and a very good team player." "He has an outstanding brain. He's incisive and highly effective in court. A calm and unflappable presence in the courtroom." **Recent work:** Instructed by Barclays in the landmark Libor test case against Graiseley Properties.

Ali Malek QC Applauded for his strategic thinking, he has recently demonstrated his skills acting for claimants in cases arising out of the mis-selling of financial derivatives. **Strengths:** "A very good advocate, who takes a big-picture view of the case. He's very receptive and has good judgement on how to handle the judge and the witnesses." "An excellent choice for matters requiring a high degree of product knowledge." **Recent work:** Acted for a collection of Portuguese public transport companies in claims against Santander relating to disputed derivatives contracts.

Ewan McQuater QC Recognised for his expertise in contentious restructuring and noteholder disputes. He is praised by solicitors for his direct dealing with clients. **Strengths:** "A number one choice for financial litigation and restructuring. He's good for those difficult, thorny questions, and clients appreciate his clarity of thought." "An excellent advocate, who gets on top of a lot of documents, carries out forensic examination of the case, and proves pretty brutal in cross-examination." **Recent work:** Led the team acting for the claimant, the Fortress Value Recovery Fund, in its dispute with the Blue Skye Special Opportunities Fund.

Richard Salter QC Highly effective on complex banking and insolvency cases. The quality of his advisory work was noted by interviewees, who also praised his ability to quickly produce drafts. **Strengths:** "For high-powered finance and insolvency advice he is just a god among barristers. His brainpower is certainly in the realms of genius." "He's superb at deconstructing complicated banking arrangements and identifying key legal issues in a case." **Recent work:** Acted for the bank in Standard Chartered Bank (Switzerland) SA v UBS (Bahamas) Ltd, a large Madoff-related case.

Jonathan Nash QC Peers draw attention to his "confidence-inspiring" approach and his "voluminous knowledge of banking law." He is recognised for his experience in cases relating to financial derivatives and structured products. **Strengths:** "He's very commercial and willing to get into the strategy side of it. He has a commendable crisp style, and he's someone who can express complex topics very simply." "A first-rate advocate with vast experience, particularly when it comes to complex financial structures. He's very calm in a storm." **Recent work:** Advised entities within the Lehman Brothers Group on the close-out disputes in the UK and the USA relating to structured products and derivatives.

Andrew Sutcliffe QC Acts for and against major banks, and has a practice heavily focused on cases where banking meets fraud. He is highlighted by solicitors for his willingness to be part of a team working directly with clients. **Strengths:** "He's a great team player, and an excellent technical lawyer, who is very supportive and encouraging of his juniors." "He's clear-thinking, wise and approachable." **Recent work:** Represented 220 timeshare clients in a group litigation against Clydesdale Financial Services. The claimants alleged fraudulent misrepresentation by the timeshare owners.

John Odgers QC An authority who is highly regarded for his deep understanding of financial products. He has ancillary strengths in financial services and civil fraud. **Strengths:** "It's in being meticulous and hard-working where he proves really extraordinary. He's also good at sitting back from things and giving that extra strategic input." "Excellent on all fronts. He's particularly responsive, a master of the detail and gives a high level of analysis. He's a massive asset to any team." **Recent work:** Represented Vervoer in its claim against Goldman Sachs Asset Management arising out of the significantly poor performance of Vervoer's funds managed by the defendant.

Andrew Onslow QC Recognised for his experience in asset-management disputes, particularly those with a fraud and professional negligence element. He has also demonstrated expertise in acting for claimants in a variety of mis-selling cases against major banks. **Strengths:** "Very hands-on and fiercely intellectual. He's a real team player, who is easy to work with." "He's tenacious and an excellent cross-examiner. He really rolls his sleeves up and gets stuck in." **Recent work:** Acted against the RBS for a group of claimants seeking compensation for losses arising out of an allegedly misleading prospectus pertaining to a rights issue.

Jonathan Davies-Jones QC Demonstrates strength in international litigation concerning complex derivatives. Sources are impressed by his courtroom style and technical ability. He acts both for and against major financial institutions. **Strengths:** "He's an outstanding leading counsel, who is highly intelligent, analytical and thorough. He's a pleasure to work with." "He's very bright and incisive." **Recent work:** Represented multiple Italian municipalities in disputes with a number of major banks concerning the enforceability of certain interest rate swaps.

David Quest QC A "hellishly bright" junior silk who frequently defends significant banks in substantial claims relating to derivatives and structured products. Sources routinely cite his intellectual capability. **Strengths:** "He's tenacious, analytical and quick minded in court. He's very good on fraud cases – he picks up the scent very quickly." "He's one of the go-to counsel on trade finance issues." "Very able, very bright, he has a good sense of judgement." **Recent work:** Defended Credit Suisse against allegations of mis-selling a structured investment product in a claim of approximately £20 million brought by Richard Desmond.

Catherine Gibaud QC A new silk noted for her expertise in cases rooted in the mis-selling of interest-rate hedging products. She has a broad practice with overlapping strengths in contractual disputes and insolvency. **Strengths:** "She's very strong in terms of identifying issues and getting to grips with the detail. She retains a good commercial view as well. She's considered in everything she does." **Recent work:** Successfully acted on behalf of the claimant in Första AP-Fonden v Bank of New York Mellon.

Matthew Hardwick QC An "absolutely brilliant new silk" praised for his courtroom advocacy. He has recently demonstrated expertise in a variety of cases for a diverse range of clients including banks, wealth management companies and stockbrokers. **Strengths:** "He's very effective as an advocate. He's good with detail and very forceful." "He's very good, very energetic, and he gets his teeth into things." **Recent work:** Defended stockbroker Teathers and its liquidator KPMG in Bieber & Ors v Teathers. The case concerned an allegedly unregulated collective investment scheme organised by the defendant to finance television programmes.

JUNIORS

Laura John Recognised for her superior written work, her reliability and her assurance in court. She is noted for her expertise in defending domestic and international banks against interest rate swap mis-selling claims. **Strengths:** "She's very responsive, on top of the material and a pleasure to work with. She also has very good client skills." "Extremely capable, she is absolutely fantastic for fraud and banking cases, and one of the brightest, most diligent barristers in practice at the moment." **Recent work:** Acted for African Minerals in its dispute with the BMA Special Opportunity Hub Fund over the enforcement of a prepayment fee.

Richard Brent Has recognised expertise in litigation arising out of debt-based securities transactions such as complex bond disputes. He is also experienced at acting for claimants in litigation concerning the mis-selling of swap products. **Strengths:** "He's very measured, has great attention to detail and is very calm." **Recent work:** Acted for a number of Portuguese public transport companies in claims against Santander relating to a series of derivative contracts.

Adam Kramer Receives praise from peers for the quality of his advocacy. He has notable experience in disputes concerning asset finance and interest rate hedging products. **Strengths:** "He's very bright, very personable, and has good team skills." "He shows great attention to detail and grasps key issues really early on." **Recent work:** Acted for over 75 institutional claimants in a dispute with the RBS concerning a misleading prospectus regarding the rights issue of spring 2008.

Michael Lazarus Possesses a broad commercial disputes practice, and has particular strengths in banking and fraud. Numerous sources highlighted his intellectual capability. **Strengths:** "A mild-mannered genius, who untangles problems with ease. He's a clear and effective advocate." "He's very able, particularly with regard to mortgage negligence." **Recent work:** Acted for a group of claimants seeking damages from the RBS following the publication of an allegedly misleading prospectus relating to a rights issue of 2008.

James MacDonald Experienced in significant international disputes concerning the trading of derivatives and equity-based assets. **Strengths:** "Understated but immensely hard-working, he has a huge hunger for the detail in a case and is exceptionally collegiate when working with solicitors. He's a star in the making." "He's good, hands-on, and has a sound knowledge of procedures." **Recent work:** Led by Sonia Tolaney QC in the successful representation of Deutsche Bank in its high-profile dispute with Sebastian Holdings.

Matthew Parker Acts for retail and investment banks in a diverse range of claims. His banking practice is complemented by strengths in fraud and professional negligence. **Strengths:** "A measured and powerful advocate, strong both on his feet and on paper." **Recent work:** Advised the claimant lender in a dispute with a major bank regarding a loan guarantee.

William Edwards Has a broad commercial practice and is often instructed in cases where banking meets fraud or insolvency. He also shows expertise in cases relating to debt-based securities and derivatives. **Strengths:** "He produces immaculate written opinions that are really logical, clear and concise." "He's extremely bright, has an enormous appetite for interesting cases, and has a very good armoury of legal knowledge. He's also very responsive." **Recent work:** Successfully acted for the claimant, Dubai Islamic Bank PJSC, in its dispute with PSI Energy Holding. The case involved a complex international trade receivables fraud.

Ian Wilson Recognised for his strength defending banks against claims relating to the mis-selling of PPI. His wide-ranging practice also includes commercial fraud and professional negligence cases. **Strengths:** "He has a calm and professional demeanour that can diffuse any tense situation." "I rate him very highly, particularly for being calm and unflappable in the most stressful circumstances. He has a good, balanced approach to casework." **Recent work:** Acted on appeal in the Supreme Court, led by Jonathan Crow QC, in Plevin v Paragon Finance, a leading case concerning the mis-selling of PPI.

Band 2

Brick Court Chambers

See profile on p.774

THE SET

A set with a strong reputation, that has been involved in numerous complex banking cases arising out of the global financial crisis. Its members deal with matters at the forefront of the market such as Deutsche Bank v Unitech, the Guardian Care Homes case, J.P. Morgan's dispute with the Berlin transport authority and UBS's case against the Leipzig waterworks. As well as gaining instructions from international retail and investment banks, many of its practitioners also act for claimants against major financial institutions. Solicitors regard the set highly for its "superb depth and breadth" and say "everyone there is very bright – you know you'll be getting an exceptionally good lawyer whoever you instruct."

Client service: "They're great to deal with. The clerks, led by Julian Hawes and Ian Moyler, are charming and effective. They're absolutely supportive and highly professional."

SILKS

Mark Hapgood QC A unanimously respected silk with laudable experience and great industry knowledge. He is described by numerous sources as a "banking litigation doyen" and "a go-to lead counsel" for banking, commercial fraud and professional negligence disputes. **Strengths:** "He is adept at cutting to the heart of complicated issues and presenting them simply and clearly. He provides practical, commercial and strategic advice and is a very persuasive advocate." "He is a widely respected advocate who shows incisive judgement in the most complex cases." **Recent work:** Represented Deutsche Bank in its significant case against Unitech regarding interest rate swaps and alleged Libor manipulation.

Mark Howard QC Maintains a strong commercial practice and has a reputation for being the man to instruct in complex cases. He has a wide-practice and often appears in cases with a fraud or professional negligence element. **Strengths:** "He is undoubtedly one of the leaders of the commercial Bar. He is absolutely excellent and has very good court skills." "Has the gravitas to command respect when handling large conferences." **Recent work:** Represented Andrew Caldwell, the independent valuer for Northern Rock, in his dispute with Harbinger Capital partners, following his decision not to award compensation to shareholders in Northern Rock.

Tim Lord QC Demonstrates particular strength when acting for claimants against investment banks in cases arising out of the financial crisis. He wins praise from instructing solicitors for his advocacy and relentless optimism. **Strengths:** "Without a doubt, a top choice for any party involved in a significant dispute with an investment bank. He's intelligent, tenacious and innovative. He handles teams brilliantly and inspires confidence in clients." "He has charisma, strategic nous and vision, and is a consummate cross-examiner." **Recent work:** Acted on behalf of the claimants in the widely reported Libor test case of Graiseley Properties v Barclays Bank.

Neil Calver QC A barrister praised by sources for the quality of his cross-examination, who is a great team player and "a challenging opponent for anyone." He has a broad practice with particular strengths in insurance, banking and aviation. **Strengths:** "He has a good rapport with the court. He is respectful and formal but conversational as well. He's always commercially minded and sensible."

Jasbir Dhillon QC A deeply experienced silk and former advocate at the New York Bar who was once with a top-quality Wall Street firm. He is highly regarded, particularly for his expertise in cases concerning complex financial products and derivatives. **Strengths:** "He's a safe pair of hands, who is commercial in his thinking and very friendly." "He's really confident and well-versed in ISDA documentation." **Recent work:** Acted for SNCB, the Belgian state railway, in a claim against UBS relating to a complex structured product.

Andrew Henshaw QC A former solicitor with a robust banking and commercial practice who has ancillary strength in regulatory matters. **Strengths:** "He's a brilliant man. He's clever and has really good judgement. When he speaks, he always says something intelligent. You get a first-class service from him – no point will be missed." **Recent work:** Defended HM Treasury against over 350 claimants seeking Francovich damages. The case concerned the failure of the (as was) FSA to prevent a firm from conducting unauthorised business at the expense of the claimants.

JUNIORS

Simon Birt A junior with a thriving reputation. Many sources draw attention to his intellectual prowess and he is lauded by peers for his written work and the quality of his analysis. **Strengths:** "He has an inner drive and confidence and provides superb technical analysis of legal issues." "He's extremely hard-working and incisive." **Recent work:** Led by Tim Lord QC, he acted for BVG, the Berlin transport authority, in bringing a counter claim against J.P. Morgan regarding the sale and alleged misrepresentation of CDO products.

Stephen Midwinter Continues to act in a range of areas including insurance, energy and fraud. He is experienced at acting on the claimant-side of proceedings against banks. **Strengths:** "He's exceptionally bright, efficient and a very good advocate. A first-class junior counsel, particularly for complex, civil fraud matters." "He is clever, incisive and gets to the point in a very concise way." **Recent work:** Acted for Leipzig-based water board KWL in its highly publicised dispute with UBS concerning the alleged fraudulent misrepresentation of debt-based derivatives.

Fionn Pilbrow The architect of a wide-reaching practice that takes in fraud and insurance cases amongst others. He acts both for and against banks. **Strengths:** "He's a very good lawyer and a good draftsman. He works well in a team, and is a very strong performer." "He's approachable, user-friendly and thorough." **Recent work:** Acted for the Co-operative Bank in four separate cases regarding the termination of hedging arrangements.

Craig Morrison Experienced in derivatives disputes and litigation relating to loan facilities. He impresses solicitors and peers alike with his analytical skill. **Strengths:** "He combines brilliant legal analysis with an easy manner, and is a pleasure to work with." "A good all-round barrister. He's good on the written side and he gets to the heart of problems." **Recent work:** Led by Tim Lord QC, he acted for KWL, the German water authority, in its dispute with UBS regarding the alleged fraudulent misrepresentation of CDOs by UBS.

Jonathan Dawid Has a practice heavy on banking, professional negligence and commercial fraud cases. Numerous sources draw attention to his technical skill. **Strengths:** "He is phenomenally bright and extremely hard-working. He's fantastic at drafting and putting complex concepts into words." "A real asset to the team and very good on tricky technical points of both law and fact." **Recent work:** Acted for UBS in a high-profile dispute with the German water authority KWL seeking the recovery of monies owed from CDO transactions.

One Essex Court

See profile on p.790

THE SET

This high-quality commercial set has a leading reputation in civil fraud claims and commercial dispute resolution generally. It has an extensive roster of barristers, many of whom are eminent figures in the financial sphere. Its silks and juniors have displayed substantial expertise in cases involving a number of complex financial products and derivatives such as CDOs and swaps of varying type. As well as many of the landmark swaps cases, they have also been involved in a variety of other standout cases involving Libor manipulation or matters arising from the fall out of Lehman Brothers' collapse.

Client service: "They're very good. I use One Essex more than other commercial chambers largely because of their clerking team led by Darren Burrows. They don't overbook or double-book and will helpfully liaise with the court for us."

SILKS

Anthony Grabiner QC An eminent silk with an impressive reputation and vast experience of handling complex and high-profile commercial cases. He is "a star class barrister who leads eye-catching cases." **Strengths:** "Has an unrivalled courtroom presence and an outstanding ability to focus both the clients and the court on the essentials of a case." "Utterly unflappable, he's incredibly robust and bullet-proof." **Recent work:** Successfully defeated Grupo Hotelero Urvasco's claim against Carey Value Added which concerned Carey's withholding of funds for the financing of a hotel and apartment complex on the Aldwych.

Laurence Rabinowitz QC A leading commercial barrister, who is praised for his advocacy and strategic advice. He is experienced in major banking cases and is also an expert in civil fraud matters. **Strengths:** "He has massive intellectual reserves, he's immensely charming, and judges have supreme confidence in him. He spots trouble a mile off and negotiates it well." **Recent work:** Represented J.P. Morgan in a claim against BVG, the Berlin public transport authority. This high-profile case relates to the recovery of debt arising from the purchase of CDOs.

Stephen Auld QC Regularly instructed by predominantly claimant firms against major financial institutions. He demonstrates key derivatives knowledge in cases related to interest rate swaps. **Strengths:** "He is a brilliant tactician and a very experienced, well-respected advocate. He has the ear of the most senior commercial judges." "He is brilliant at snatching victory from the jaws of defeat." **Recent work:** Acted for Graiseley Properties in a prominent Libor test case against Barclays Bank.

Daniel Toledano QC Maintains a broad-ranging practice encompassing banking, commercial dispute resolution, civil fraud and international arbitration cases. He is praised for his understanding of his clients' needs. **Strengths:** "He's really spectacular. He has sound judgement and is aware of the client's needs." "A clever man, who is fastidious about detail, he really understands what clients are trying to achieve. He's also an excellent advocate and a very good cross-examiner." **Recent work:** Obtained summary judgment for Merrill Lynch against Amorim Partners, in a case concerning the client investor's failure to pay for a share placement.

David Wolfson QC Highlighted for his expertise in complex multi-jurisdictional banking litigation. He is praised for his judgement and the attractive presentation of his cases. **Strengths:** "He's fearsomely bright and nothing seems too difficult for him. Having understood something of great complexity, he's able to distil it down and explain it in a comprehensive way." "An excellent, highly commercial advocate, who is a pleasure to work with." **Recent work:** Acted for Morgan Stanley in its dispute with Tael One Partners regarding the payment of a redemption premium.

Alain Choo Choy QC Possesses notable ability in complex financial disputes, and has corresponding strengths in civil fraud, jurisdiction and conflict of law matters. Instructing solicitors praise his technical ability and knowledge of derivatives. **Strengths:** "He has the most amazing attention to detail. He's extraordinarily hard-working, very precise and has great advocacy skills as well. He's a joy to watch." "He's very bright and he was quick on the uptake in terms of understanding where the pressure points in the case lay." **Recent work:** Represented UniCredit in its dispute with Barclays arising out of a complex transaction of cross-currency swaps.

Ian Glick QC Has a broad commercial practice and sits as a High Court judge in the Commercial Court and Chancery Division. **Strengths:** "He has an amazing eye for detail and is particularly good in cross-examination." "He's very quick to master the technical issues and see the next issue coming. He is very analytical in that respect." **Recent work:** Acted for RBS in a claim for breach of warranty against Winterthur UK Holdings.

Rhodri Davies QC Frequently advises on major financial cases, and has specialist strength in professional negligence with relation to accountants. He is adept at handling disputes involving financial products, bondholder rights and credit facility agreements. **Strengths:** "He's an extremely smooth advocate, who stands out as being very calm, and completely in control. There's something reassuring about his presence." **Recent work:** Advised a company on disputes arising out of the Lehman Brothers insolvency.

Anthony de Garr Robinson QC Oversees a diverse practice and is experienced in handling national and international disputes. He also sits as an arbitrator. **Recent work:** Represented a group of investment funds managed by Aberdeen Asset Management in a claim against Satyam Computer Services following the discovery that Satyam had been doctoring its accounts.

Neil Kitchener QC A robust silk with a strong following commensurate with his level of expertise. Peers and instructing solicitors praise his tenacity, intellect and strategic thinking. **Strengths:** "He is one of my favourite barristers. He's brilliant fun to work with and has absolutely fantastic judgement. He also has very high energy. He won't take 'no' for an answer but always injects humour into proceedings." "If you're going to get involved in a scrap, you definitely want him involved on your side. He's prepared to take points other silks won't take and make them forcefully. He'll put his neck on the line for other counsel and clients." **Recent work:** Acted for the Bank of Ireland in a claim of breach of fiduciary duty and bribery against a former senior executive.

Craig Orr QC Demonstrates capability handling multi-jurisdictional proceedings. He is well-versed in many aspects of commercial law and continues to gain high-profile instructions. **Recent work:** Acted for the liquidator of Blue Skye, a Luxembourg investment company whose hedge fund is in dispute with a hedge fund managed by Fortress Value.

Benjamin Strong QC A recent silk adept at handling complex international disputes involving derivatives. He is praised for his skill at case management. **Strengths:** "He's very practical, he gives good commercial advice and he's hands-on and responsive." "He's smart, very available and always willing to speak on the phone and meet up when necessary. His advocacy is excellent." **Recent work:** Acted for Stichting Vestia Groep in a prominent case against Credit Suisse regarding Vestia's losses arising out of trading of interest-rate derivatives.

JUNIORS

Hannah Brown Has a practice spanning banking, negligence, insurance and fraud. She also has specialist experience in international commercial arbitration. **Strengths:** "She's brilliant. She's very clever, fun to be around and good with clients."

Henry Forbes Smith A former capital markets lawyer at a New York firm, who is well-versed in a variety of securities and derivatives transactions. He is particularly well regarded for his experience in disputes concerning Russian law. **Strengths:** "He's a very impressive individual in terms of his knowledge of the law and his thoroughness. He works well with QCs, providing them with the ammunition to fight cases." "He's solid, responsive and cerebral." **Recent work:** Acted as sole counsel for a German company defending a claim brought by Lehman Brothers regarding its calculation of the close-out amount under ISDA.

Conall Patton A junior with a burgeoning reputation, who is involved in serious and complex cases of significant reputational importance. **Strengths:** "He's an all-rounder and a star of the future." "He's engaged, happy to help at all times and very responsive." **Recent work:** Acted as sole counsel for Stemcor, obtaining a summary judgment against GSHL in a dispute regarding loan arrangements.

Sebastian Isaac Acts as junior to some of the most eminent leaders in the field. He ably handles complex litigation involving a range of assets including complex bonds, RMBS and interest-rate derivatives. **Recent work:** Led by Laurence Rabinowitz QC in defending Prudential Insurance Assurance and one of its subsidiaries, against a claim made by fund managers Dominion. The case concerned the application by Prudential of market value reductions.

Richard Mott Well-regarded junior with a broad commercial practice that encompasses banking, civil fraud and commercial arbitration matters. He is particularly recommended for disputes regarding regulatory and consumer protection law. **Strengths:** "He's got an absolutely outstanding intellect and an amazing appetite for hard work." **Recent work:** Acted for the claimant, Richard Desmond, against Credit Suisse International in a £20 million claim arising from a complex CPPI swap contract.

Alexander Polley Proficient in multi-jurisdictional litigation and has experience in a number of high-profile cases. **Strengths:** "We rate him very highly, as he's extremely bright and works very hard. He has a common-sense, practical approach." "He's frighteningly good. He can absorb material and turn around a documented response in extraordinary time." **Recent work:** Acted for Banco Santander Totta against four Portuguese transport companies in a claim concerning the validity of snowball swaps transactions.

Essex Court Chambers

See profile on p.792

THE SET

The barristers at Essex Court Chambers have been involved in numerous landmark cases in this sector. They show particular strength in litigation arising out of capital markets transactions, and have been heavily involved in the recent swap mis-selling litigation. Some of the set's standout matters include Deutsche Bank v Sebastian Holdings, the litigation concerning the trading of foreign exchange options, and cases arising from transactions made by the now-insolvent Lehman Brothers. This is a set whose members can ably take on complex, high-value cases at a national and international level.

Client service: "The chambers provides an excellent service and David Grief's team of clerks are very much part of that service."

SILKS

David Foxton QC A widely respected silk, who is frequently instructed in landmark cases. He has a wide-ranging commercial litigation and international arbitration practice. **Strengths:** "He's the consummate professional. He's hugely bright, very hard-working and absolutely brilliant to deal with." "He's extremely able and well regarded in this field, and is super-analytical in his approach." **Recent work:** Successfully defended Deutsche Bank in the bank's internationally significant case against Sebastian Holdings.

Richard Millett QC Demonstrates expertise in a wide range of financial litigation, and has recently handled disputes regarding interest rate hedging products and debt and equity-backed securities. He is particularly experienced in international arbitration and offshore disputes. **Strengths:** "He's user-friendly and has a relaxed style. He's sharp, commercial and gives robust advice." "He's extremely on-the-ball, and very knowledgeable about derivative and insolvency-related matters. Responsive, helpful and friendly, he's a pleasure to deal with." **Recent work:** Represented three financial institutions in actions brought by Lehman Brothers Finance concerning terminated swaps and equity-linked notes.

Jeffrey Gruder QC Noted for his expertise in litigation arising out of transactions concerning securities and derivatives. He handles banking cases as part of his impressive commercial litigation practice. **Recent work:** Acted for Credit Suisse against Euro Asian Oil defending a claim to recover losses.

Joe Smouha QC A well-reputed silk who has a thriving domestic practice but is also strong on international arbitration and offshore work. **Strengths:** "He's fabulously clever, strategic and sensible, and has an extraordinary work rate." "A brilliant, clever and commercial advocate who is impressive with clients." **Recent work:** Acted for Robert Tchenguiz in his dispute with the SFO arising out of the SFO's investigation into Kaupthing Bank's financing of the Tchenguiz brothers' businesses.

JUNIORS

Edmund King Highly regarded for his expertise in bondholder disputes and litigation arising out of securitisation and structured finance transactions. He is frequently instructed in complex disputes of significant value. **Strengths:** "He's very astute and robust." "Very good to work with, he's extremely hard-working. He's excellent and his written advocacy is extremely good. He's a very smart guy." **Recent work:** Represented UniCredit in its dispute with Barclays regarding an early trade termination.

South Square

See profile on p.861

THE SET

South Square is a distinguished set with a well-deserved reputation for handling restructuring and insolvency cases that also has evident expertise in wider commercial and regulatory matters. Its members have handled a significant amount of litigation arising out of the financial crisis, and have proved their worth time and again when tackling the major cases of the day. Silks and juniors from the set have been involved in such cases as MF Global, the Graiseley Properties' dispute with Barclays, and matters concerning both insolvent Icelandic banks and Lehman Brothers. They are frequently instructed by market-leading firms in highly complex inter-jurisdictional cases that are often of global importance.

Client service: "Ron Barclay-Smith's team is excellent. The clerks are very easy to deal with, business-oriented and you can always get hold of them out of hours, which is very helpful."

SILKS

Antony Zacaroli QC A stellar QC with an impeccable reputation for his advocacy and intellect. He is accomplished in a great number of fields and has skill in insolvency law and financial services regulation. **Strengths:** "He's got a really well-honed bedside manner which gives both clients and instructing solicitors real confidence. He's good at mucking in and working as part of the team." "One of the best courtroom advocates around. He's very effective and can turn complex points into simple and obvious ones." **Recent work:** Advised the special bank administration of MF Global on many issues including client money, client classification and interpretation of GMRA repo transactions.

Robin Dicker QC A pre-eminent silk frequently instructed in some of the most significant landmark cases. Numerous sources highlight his intellect and efficacy, and praise him for his handling of litigation relating to complex structured products. **Strengths:** "He is so incisive in his intellect, he can make complex ideas sound simple. It makes him a compelling advocate." "Excellent to have on your side in a punch-up, and particularly good on cases concerning complex financial instruments." **Recent work:** Acted for Barclays in its highly publicised dispute with Graiseley Properties, a test case concerning allegations of Libor manipulation.

Jeremy Goldring QC Frequently instructed in cases of global significance. He has an impressive reputation and shows particular strength in cases where banking meets insolvency. **Strengths:** "As well as being bright and engaging, he has very sound judgement and great enthusiasm. He is not afraid to get his hands dirty when it comes to dealing with the details of a case." "He's frighteningly clever but also nice to deal with." **Recent work:** Acted on behalf of Barclays in a landmark Libor-related case against Graiseley Properties.

William Trower QC A silk with a growing reputation in the banking sector following his securing a series of high-profile instructions. He has a notable specialism in insolvency and company law. **Strengths:** "He inspires confidence from the outset. He has the ability to break down and explain the legal effect of complex transactions in a very lucid fashion and is extremely enjoyable to work with." "He's responsive, measured and sensible, and a go-to barrister for structured finance cases." **Recent work:** Represented Landsbanki, the insolvent Icelandic bank, in a close-out dispute with Rabobank.

David Allison QC A new silk who has undertaken a vast array of high-value structured finance litigation. He has experience acting in offshore and international jurisdictions. **Strengths:** "He has excellent judgement and is outstanding on paper." "He's enormously experienced and clever, and works prodigiously hard." **Recent work:** Acted for Bank of New York in its highly publicised case against Eurosail regarding the construction of the Eurosail CDO's terms.

Tom Smith QC Noted for his focus and expertise in cases covering the overlap of banking and insolvency. A recent silk, he is noted for his experience of tackling cases against silks. **Strengths:** "He's a pragmatic thinker in terms of finding solutions. He's extremely hard-working and has an impressive ability to turn work around." "Apart from providing thorough and well-considered advice, he is extremely responsive and pleasant to deal with. He has a good understanding of the needs of fund clients and is quick to grasp the issues in a deal." **Recent work:** Acted for claimants Grupo Hotelero Urvasco in a dispute with Carey Value Added regarding the breach of a loan agreement for the funding of a hotel on the Strand.

JUNIORS

Daniel Bayfield An eminently respectable insolvency barrister who has added expertise in banking litigation. He impresses instructing solicitors with his commercial approach. **Strengths:** "He's absolutely superb, extremely responsive, and a pleasure to deal with. He gives really good, concise opinions, both written and orally." "He's incredibly hard-working and clever." **Recent work:** Represented the joint administrators of Lehman Brothers International Europe as part of 'the Waterfall Application'.

Stephen Robins Frequently instructed in high-value proceedings in the Commercial Court and Chancery Division. He has specialist insolvency knowledge and expertise in civil fraud. **Strengths:** "He's an absolute delight to work with. He's really responsive, hugely proactive, he writes beautifully and he always produces first-rate opinions." "He's technically precise and he has massive energy and commitment – a real fighter and a winner." **Recent work:** Acted in an appeal to the Supreme Court appearing for Landsbanki Islands in its dispute with Heritable Bank.

Band 3

20 Essex Street

See profile on p.794

THE SET

A robust set that, whilst best known for its shipping and commodities work, has a broad commercial practice and acts in matters of the highest profile and value. It has appeared in a number of recent insolvency-related disputes, and its members have gained instructions in noteworthy cases relating to Lehman Brothers and the Icelandic bank Kaupthing. Other standout matters include involvement in the disputes between various major international investment banks and the local Italian authorities regarding swaps transactions. The set has further had involvement in the RBS shareholder litigation. 20 Essex Street's barristers show proficiency in multinational disputes and win praise for their compelling advocacy and the technical aptitude they display when handling cases concerning complex issues such as derivatives and structured products.

Client service: "The set is well organised and well clerked by Neil Palmer and Brian Lee's team."

SILKS

Iain Milligan QC A top-quality silk at the forefront of the commercial Bar. He is recognised for his involvement in various disputes arising out of the collapse of Lehman Brothers and for his expertise in international arbitration. **Strengths:** "Quite simply one of the best at the Bar, he has tremendous strength in financial services law and handles complex disputes." "He has a very crisp, clear way of thinking and presents his cases authoritatively." **Recent work:** Acted for the respondents in Cukurova v Alfa, a multi-jurisdictional dispute regarding the ownership of a telephone company.

Andrew Baker QC Focuses his practice on shipping and commodities law, but also earns praise for his technical skill when it comes to disputes arising out of derivatives transactions. **Strengths:** "A strong, black-letter technical lawyer. He has a strong economic grasp." **Recent work:** Acted for the claimant in Euro-Asian Oil v Abilo, a case concerning allegations of fraud and non-performance under sale contracts.

Charles Kimmins QC A highly reputable commercial silk with a recognised proficiency in banking, shipping and international arbitration. He also demonstrates technical expertise when it comes to derivatives matters and cases concerning the construction of ISDA 92. **Strengths:** "A barrister with an agile mind, who takes a ferociously determined approach." "He is very available and hands-on. He's very much a team player and has the intellect to do well." **Recent work:** Acted for a number of banks bringing claims against local Italian authorities with regard to the enforceability of certain swap contracts.

JUNIORS

Julian Kenny His recognised strength in banking law complements his notable expertise in shipping matters. He has earned his stripes in recent years acting in cases arising from the collapse of Lehman Brothers. **Strengths:** "He is thoughtful, thorough and user-friendly." **Recent work:** Led by Iain Milligan QC, he represented Lehman Brothers International Europe in a successful appeal against Lehman Brothers Finance.

Luke Pearce Covers a broad range of commercial disputes and is often called upon to handle very significant banking cases. He has regularly appeared in the High Court, the Court of Appeal and the Supreme Court. **Recent work:** Acted in a significant group action in a claim against RBS relating to an alleged misleading rights issue.

Thomas Raphael Has a strong commercial litigation practice that takes in shipping and insurance cases as well as banking matters. He is experienced in complex technical cases of substantial value. **Strengths:** "He can turn his hand to a lot of areas, and has a very good client manner." "He has a strong economic grasp." **Recent work:** Acted in Greenwood v RBS, a highly publicised multibillion-dollar shareholder group case.

Serle Court

See profile on p.860

THE SET

A set with solid market standing that handles heavyweight cases both domestically and in offshore jurisdictions such as the BVI. The silks and juniors here are involved in a variety of financial cases, including those relating to derivative mis-selling and financial fraud. They also have a growing reputation for their work in the financial services field.

SILKS

David Blayney QC Handles banking cases as part of his wide Commercial Chancery practice. He gains particular praise for his creativity, and is noted for bringing fresh ideas and solutions to cases. **Strengths:** "He's an out-of-the-box type thinker, who's not afraid to pose surprising questions." "He's very practical and he's intellectual in a very effective way. He found angles on problems no one else had come up with." **Recent work:** Acted for RBS in the £12 billion group litigation arising out of the bank's rights issue of 2008.

Philip Marshall QC A robust silk with a broad-based practice, who is praised by numerous sources for his tenacity in cross-examination. **Strengths:** "A really strong trial advocate, who's thick skinned and very thorough. He has a very good understanding of accounts and financial structures." "A superb advocate who balances aggression with excellent judgement. A first choice if the case requires the barrister to get across the detail." **Recent work:** Acted for BTA Bank in its high-profile dispute against Ablyazov.

Nicholas Lavender QC Has recognised financial market expertise and is praised for his commercial approach. **Strengths:** "He's very clever, a pleasure to work with and he shows good judgement." "He's fantastically good and very calm under pressure."

JUNIORS

Simon Hattan Recognised for his erudition and strong on highly technical cases. Sources acclaim him for his knowledge of financial structuring and his expertise in claims relating to interest-rate hedging. **Strengths:** "An excellent choice for regulated matters or those involving fraud. He gives robust advice and has the ability to identify the issues that must be resolved." "He offers sound commercial analysis, is very persuasive and doesn't sit on the fence."

4 Stone Buildings

See profile on p.865

THE SET

An illustrious chancery set that houses highly experienced banking and finance barristers. A number of its members are renowned for their knowledge of derivatives and structured finance and are further praised for their skill in handling financial services cases. As well as acting for major international investment banks, the individuals here have also handled matters on behalf of high net worth individuals and families. Notable cases undertaken include NAMA and AIB against Carey, JSC BTA Bank v Ablyazov and Al Khorafi v Bank Sarasin-Alpen.

Client service: "The clerking team, led by David Goddard, is good and responsive."

SILKS

Robert Miles QC Hugely experienced in large financial cases, he is particularly praised for his knowledge of structured products. **Strengths:** "A lawyer with a very sharp and analytical mind, who is not afraid to take a bold stance on issues when required. A reassuring presence for clients and solicitors alike, and someone with a calm, persuasive manner in court." "He's completely unflappable and speaks without ever wasting a word. You can see that everything he says is hitting the mark." **Recent work:** Acted for the receivers appointed by the court in the BTA Bank v Ablyazov fraud proceedings.

Jonathan Crow QC Regularly instructed in cases of great significance. His commercial practice is extensive and he is a noted expert in financial services matters. **Strengths:** "He's very easy to work with, and an excellent lawyer. He's commercial in his outlook." "He manages his time incredibly efficiently and he's a pleasure to work with." **Recent work:** Successfully acted in defence of NAMA which, alongside AIB, had claims brought against it by the Carey Group.

Richard Hill QC He is well-versed in disputes arising out of structured products transactions and debt capital markets. **Strengths:** "He's a clever guy and an excellent cross-examiner. Tactically brilliant, he knows how to keep points in reserve and is even-handed and fair. He's a great trial lawyer, who is comfortable on his feet." **Recent work:** Acted for Egyptian businessman Naguib Sawiris in his dispute with Alessandro Benedetti arising out of the LBO of an Italian telecoms company.

JUNIORS

Sharif Shivji A former derivatives trader with a growing reputation at the Bar, he is highly praised by solicitors for his technical aptitude. He demonstrates excellence in credit-crunch related litigation, and regularly acts for the FCA. **Strengths:** "He has a much better than average understanding of structured products. He is very proactive, incredibly responsive and really bright." "He's incredibly user-friendly and strategic." **Recent work:** Led by Richard Hill QC in acting for the claimants, the Al Khorafi family, in claims of structured product mis-selling against Bank Sarasin-Alpen.

Other Ranked Lawyers

Barbara Dohmann QC (Blackstone Chambers) A known expert in financial services cases, who has notable strength in cases concerning mis-selling, insolvency and fraud. She has a well-deserved reputation for the quality of her advocacy. **Strengths:** "She is superb and a total class act." "She is hugely efficient, extremely quick and brilliant when you need a hard hitter. Her advocacy is tenacious and forthright." **Recent work:** Defended multiple IFAs in the Keydata SLS Proceedings regarding claims of financial product mis-selling.

Pushpinder Saini QC (Blackstone Chambers) A silk with a far-reaching practice, who is particularly well reputed for his financial services work. He has been heavily involved in cases concerning the Madoff Ponzi scheme. **Strengths:** "An excellent advocate who has a talent for strategy and achieves commercial outcomes." "He is extremely decisive, user-friendly and quick to respond. He can stand back and get a good, broad view of the issues whilst also getting into the finer points as well." **Recent work:** Represented a Madoff trustee in Eurofinance v Rubin, a case concerning insolvency and claims of securities fraud.

Richard Snowden QC (Erskine Chambers) His robust banking practice runs alongside his recognised excellence in company law and insolvency disputes. **Strengths:** "Tough, creative and hardworking, he's one of the first ports of call for a serious corporate dispute." "He is direct and incisive, and has a formidable intellect." **Recent work:** Acted for the first representative respondent as part of MF Global's application regarding client money claims against an entity in administration.

Hodge Malek QC (Thirty Nine Essex Street) A market-leading silk in the financial regulatory field with an impressive reputation in banking disputes. He frequently acts in multi-jurisdictional proceedings for major banks and regulators. **Strengths:** "He is considered to be a market leader and is incredibly charismatic in front of clients. He's also an excellent team player." "He has such a depth of knowledge, not just legal knowledge but also tactics. He gives a really good insight into the industry." **Recent work:** Acted in the Supreme Court in Conlon v Black Horse, a case relating to the mis-selling of PPI.

Christopher Butcher QC (7 King's Bench Walk) Has a wide-ranging practice that covers insurance, professional negligence and commercial dispute resolution. **Strengths:** "His submissions are punchy and effective, and he's something of a force to be reckoned with." "He's very intelligent indeed." **Recent work:** Acted for Schahin Holding in a successful appeal against a summary judgement. The case concerned a substantial claim brought by CIMC Raffles Offshore.

David Mumford (Maitland Chambers) Highly regarded junior who frequently appears as sole advocate for banks facing well-reputed silks in the field. He has a range of expertise and is often instructed in high-profile banking cases. **Strengths:** "He has an amazing breadth of knowledge. He's extremely clever and an excellent advocate. He is a match for many silks and a junior barrister to watch." "He seems very capable and is very impressive." **Recent work:** Defended Kwik-Fit against claims of breach of warranty brought by Ageas. The case pertained to the appropriate accounting of a debt purchase facility.

Andrew Ayres (see p.540) (Maitland Chambers) A solid banking junior with corresponding strength in civil fraud. He is praised for his calmness in challenging circumstances and is regarded as a team player. **Strengths:** "He's excellent, very easy to work with and academically sound." "He has great emotional intelligence and a great radar for unspoken issues. He easily gets to grips with the personalities around the conference table. He shows commitment and has a team-player mentality." **Recent work:** Instructed by Lehman Brothers Bankhaus in claims against CMA CGM arising out of the settlement of a 2008 ISDA trade.

Louise Hutton (Maitland Chambers) Continues to gain instructions in prominent cases in the finance arena. She also displays impressive skill when it comes to civil fraud and chancery proceedings. **Recent work:** Acted for RBS in its dispute against Highland Financial Partners, including the application for an anti-suit injunction relating to fraud proceedings in Texas.

Francis Tregear QC (XXIV Old Buildings) Possesses notable expertise in acting for hedge funds in high-profile claims. He is also experienced in many other areas of the law, and regularly handles company, offshore and professional negligence cases. **Strengths:** "He has a very nice bedside manner, and is good to work with." "He's a very capable, very user-friendly barrister." **Recent work:** Acted for the claimant Torre Asset Funding in its highly publicised dispute with RBS concerning misrepresentation and breaches of obligation.

Farhaz Khan (Outer Temple Chambers) A junior with a growing reputation, who is particularly noted for his expertise in regulatory cases. **Strengths:** "A potential star in the making, who has really shone as a junior in high-profile cases." "He works hard, he knows his stuff and he's keen to impress." **Recent work:** Acted for the claimants, Graiseley Properties, in the Libor test case against Barclays Bank, regarding manipulation of the interbank offered rate.

Benjamin Pilling (4 Pump Court) Gains instructions in a range of retail banking cases, notable examples being the PPI mis-selling and the Bank Charges litigations. **Recent work:** Instructed by Bank Leumi in a dispute with Billimoria regarding a receivables financing agreement.

Malcolm Waters QC (Radcliffe Chambers) A consumer credit expert who impresses sources with his intellect and ability to distil complex technical detail. He is often called upon to give advice to major financial institutions. **Strengths:** "He has a very good reputation in the consumer finance market, and is very technically competent." "He's extremely helpful, very cerebral and gives very high-level advice in a short space of time. He always masters the underlying complex factual background to a case."

Andrew Twigger QC (3 Stone Buildings) Banking cases form part of his illustrious Chancery Commercial practice, and he is noted for his commerciality and client service. **Strengths:** "He is very bright, very user-friendly and very down to earth. He provides the client with complete confidence." "Clients really like him. He can be quite persistent and dogged. He doesn't give up easily and certainly fights your corner." **Recent work:** Instructed for the defendant in Bank of New York Mellon v Sterling Biotech, a case relating to a bond dispute after a repayment default.

Jeremy Cousins QC (11 Stone Buildings) He is often instructed by large building societies and also shows skill in cases relating to investment product mis-selling. **Strengths:** "He has tremendous judgement and is very reliable." "He's basically a dream to work with. He is incredibly knowledgeable and also very personable." **Recent work:** Acted for the claimant bank AIB alleging breach of trust in its dispute with Mark Redler.

Paul Downes QC (2TG – 2 Temple Gardens) Known for his experience acting for private individuals against major banks in high-profile disputes. He is recognised as an expert in Libor-related swaps claims. **Strengths:** "An energetic and tough fighter in courtroom battles." "Absolutely first rate. He's an aggressive litigator and a tough opponent."

NORTHERN

Banking & Finance Northern
Leading Sets
Band 1
Kings Chambers *
Leading Juniors
Band 1
Harper Mark *Kings Chambers* *
Temple Eleanor *Kings Chambers* *
* *Indicates set / individual with profile.*

Band 1

Kings Chambers

See profile on p.918

THE SET

Regarded as the go-to set on the Northern Circuit for banking and finance disputes, Kings Chambers is frequently sought out to act both for and against banks in high-value litigation. Its members are well versed in a broad range of banking matters, including enforcement of domestic and commercial securities, asset finance and breach of mandate claims. The strength of its banking practice is supplemented by its expertise in a wide array of related fields, including commercial dispute resolution, company law and professional negligence.

JUNIORS

Mark Harper A junior at the forefront of the market who possesses a broad commercial and chancery practice. He has notable expertise in cases involving security enforcement and asset finance. **Strengths:** "He's pragmatic and very user-friendly, and his advocacy is also excellent." **Recent work:** Acted for Trade Finance Partners on bringing a negligence claim against Barclays Bank for the bank's failure to freeze a customer's account.

Eleanor Temple A junior with a strong reputation in the finance space. She is noted for her strengths in insolvency, chancery, commercial disputes and company law. She also draws praise for her advocacy skills. **Strengths:** "She's a great court operator. Her legal knowledge is superb and she's good on the commercial side too." **Recent work:** Acted in Houlgrave v Houlgrave and Beaconsfield Footwear, a shareholder dispute concerning breach of fiduciary duty and fraud.

WESTERN

Banking & Finance Western
Leading Sets
Band 1
Guildhall Chambers *
Leading Silks
New Silks
Sims Hugh *Guildhall Chambers*
Leading Juniors
Band 1
Fentem Ross *Guildhall Chambers*
Levy Neil *Guildhall Chambers* *
McMeel Gerard *Guildhall Chambers*
Band 2
Ramel Stefan *Guildhall Chambers*
* *Indicates set / individual with profile.*

Band 1

Guildhall Chambers

See profile on p.890

THE SET

Guildhall Chambers is recognised as the go-to set on the Western Circuit for financial disputes. Its members act on behalf of a wide range of clients, including major financial institutions, insurance companies and investors. Its advocates are experienced in a broad array of disputes, including those concerning consumer credit, securities law, asset finance and mis-selling. Some of its members have been involved in landmark cases in the sector, including the disputes over the alleged manipulation of Libor and Forex. Guildhall Chambers' barristers are praised by peers and instructing solicitors for their cerebral approach and for the quality of their advocacy.

Client service: "Principal clerk Justin Emmett and his team are excellent. They're proactive and responsive, and create a good working relationship."

SILKS

Hugh Sims QC An impressive new silk who handles cases for and against banks as well as having notable experience in acting for lender clients. He is highly regarded by peers and instructing solicitors for his client management skills and his considerable experience. **Strengths:** "He makes fairly complex cases seem very easy, very effortless." "One of the most talented barristers at the Bristol Bar." **Recent work:** Successfully acted for the claimant lender, Platform Funding, in bringing a claim of professional negligence against solicitors Simon & Co.

JUNIORS

Ross Fentem Skilled in complex consumer credit and asset finance litigation. He is praised by instructing solicitors for his commercial and decisive advice. **Strengths:** "He's incredibly bright. He gets to the root of the problem incredibly quickly, he's very approachable and on his feet he's way ahead of the game." "He's bright and able to cut through complex cases and issues to summarise the points at the centre of the dispute. He's very easy to work with, even in a pressured timescale." **Recent work:** Successfully acted for the claimant Osteopathic Education and Research in its dispute with Purfleet Office Systems regarding misrepresentation and breach of contract.

Neil Levy Notable experience as an in-house lawyer in the banking sector informs his insolvency and payments law practice. He is praised by numerous sources for the quality of his written advocacy. **Strengths:** "He is an outstanding specialist in acting for banks and he has a good grasp of the commercial realities of the banking sector. His skill level makes him a top choice for heavyweight complex banking litigation." "He's a very solid, solicitor-friendly, and cost-effective advocate who has oceans of experience." **Recent work:** Acted for the claimants, Graiseley Properties, in the highly publicised Libor test case against Barclays.

Gerard McMeel Has a strong commercial banking practice complemented by strengths in financial services and commercial dispute resolution. He is highly regarded for his technical acumen, particularly in cases concerning EU regulation. **Strengths:** "He's excellent both on paper and on his feet, as well as with clients." "He's an expert in matters concerning commercial contracts and restitution." **Recent work:** Acts for a collection of more than 400 investors in a dispute with a US FX company that allegedly solicited millions of dollars of retail investors' money in breach of the Financial Services and Markets Act of 2000.

Stefan Ramel A talented junior with a focus on the financial sector. Instructing solicitors praise his commercial approach and describe him as a highly client-friendly counsel. **Strengths:** "He's excellent – very good on detail and very good on his feet." "He is very user-friendly and very sensible, and he's not afraid to give you an opinion. He's exceptional in his written submissions and he's always keen to deliver the desired commercial outcome. He understands the difference between the legal answer and the commercial one." **Recent work:** Acted on behalf of the Bank of Ireland in a bankruptcy petition.

CHANCERY: An Introduction

Contributed by Maitland Chambers

Traditional Chancery and 'Chancery: Commercial' work

Over the last decade or more, the work of chancery specialists has broadened from the more 'traditional' areas of probate, tax, property and private trusts to encompass a range of disputes with a business or commercial aspect. There has been an increasing demand for specialists with expertise in both commercial and chancery law, and a distinction has come to be drawn between traditional chancery work and what this guide describes as 'Chancery: Commercial' work.

Commercial chancery work is distinct from its traditional chancery cousin in that it arises in the commercial arena and to some extent overlaps with the work of the Commercial Court. It is, however, also distinct from 'pure' commercial litigation, in that it involves law deriving from equitable rather than common law principles, such as insolvency, companies, partnerships, fiduciary duties, constructive trusts and asset tracing. It is ever more common to find that cases cannot neatly be pigeon-holed as either 'chancery' or 'commercial', but rather call for a cross-disciplinary approach: thus a fraud claim will often raise issues as to the availability of proprietary remedies; a professional negligence claim may engage questions of corporate insolvency; a commercial joint venture dispute may turn on points of property law. Prominent examples of this phenomenon over recent years include Equitable Life, Lehmans, Berezovsky v Abramovich, Farepak and Madoff, in all of which advocates from the Chancery Bar appeared alongside those from commercial sets.

Review of 2013-14

Unsurprisingly, specialists in financial and business-related litigation and advice have found themselves busy in the continuing wake created by the economic downturn and 'credit crunch'. More recent controversies in the banking sector have contributed to this trend. The resulting disputes continue to work their way through the courts, but what is noteworthy is that the growth is not just in the obvious area of insolvency – civil fraud and asset recovery, professional negligence, shareholder and partnership disputes, claims against directors and other fiduciaries, and business-related litigation generally have all increased.

As before, disputes span a broad range of sectors, including energy and natural resources, financial services, retail, and property development and construction. Furthermore, the work of the Chancery Bar has an expanding international aspect. A large proportion of Chancery cases now derive, in terms of their parties or subject matter, from other jurisdictions. In the last year, as in previous years, Russia and the CIS have featured heavily (the Berezovsky, Ablyazov and Red October cases being notable Chancery Division examples) but, whilst that continues, Chancery practitioners are noticing a growing volume of work from both the Middle East (eg the ongoing DAAR litigation) and the Far Eastern jurisdictions of Hong Kong, Singapore and Malaysia (eg the litigation in Hong Kong over the estate of Henry Fok). This is particularly so with cases in the more traditional, private client sphere with a strong Chancery flavour – those which concern trusts, family companies and other structures holding private wealth. As many of those structures are established in tax havens, much of the related litigation inevitably takes place in offshore jurisdictions (notably Cayman and the BVI).

The moving of the Chancery Division and Commercial Court into shared premises in the Rolls Building in part reflected the increasing overlap between chancery and commercial work and, broadly, has been viewed by the profession as a success. This offers clients and litigators a modern, well-appointed and dedicated facility for the resolution of disputes across the business, financial and property spectrum. It remains to be seen to what extent it will lead to a greater harmonisation, or even merger, of the Chancery Division and Commercial Court.

So far as concerns more traditional chancery work, the tribunal system is now firmly established and is where a substantial proportion of tax and charity-related litigation now takes place.

Among important legal developments this year is the ruling by the Supreme Court in FHR European Ventures v Cedar Capital that – on grounds of principle, practicality and policy – a fiduciary's receipt of a bribe or secret commission gives rise to a proprietary claim in favour of the principal in addition to any personal claim for equitable compensation.

Looking ahead

A number of recent developments may have an impact on the Chancery Bar. First, new rules on litigation funding and budgeting, following the Jackson Review of Costs, have only just started to work their way through to live cases. Experience suggests that the 'menu' of more flexible case management techniques now available, particularly with respect to disclosure, has yet to be fully explored by judges.

Secondly, Chancery practitioners (like others at the Bar) are now able to participate in alternative business structures with other lawyers and indeed non-lawyers. So far there appears to have been limited take-up of these opportunities at the Chancery Bar, which is perhaps unsurprising given the specialist nature of the advocacy and advisory services which it offers. However, it remains to be seen whether this will change.

Thirdly, there is an increasing range of opportunities for Chancery practitioners to provide their services in developing legal jurisdictions abroad. The Chancery Bar, with its expertise in trusts and other wealth management structures, has a long history of working in traditional 'offshore' jurisdictions such as Cayman, Jersey and the BVI. However, new opportunities are emerging further afield, as jurisdictions such as Singapore seek to establish themselves as regional litigation hubs, and it is to be expected that Chancery specialists will have a prominent role to play there too.

Fourthly, as signs of economic recovery begin to emerge, one anticipates that there will be an increasing amount of transactional work. Whilst that will not immediately engage the Bar in a significant way, it would be surprising if there were not soon to be a greater number of disputes in the company and real property spheres which call for specialist Chancery advice and advocacy.

Contents:

LONDON Commercial

Chancery: Commercial London	
Leading Sets	
Band 1	South Square *
Maitland Chambers *	Wilberforce Chambers *
Serle Court *	**Band 3**
4 Stone Buildings *	Enterprise Chambers *
Band 2	New Square Chambers *
XXIV Old Buildings *	11 Stone Buildings *
Leading Silks	
Star individuals	**Wardell** John *Wilberforce Chambers*
Crow Jonathan *4 Stone Buildings* *	**Band 3**
Band 1	**Cousins** Jeremy *11 Stone Buildings* *
Beltrami Adrian *3 Verulam Buildings (ORL)* ◊	**Davis-White** Malcolm *XXIV Old Buildings*
Bompas George *4 Stone Buildings*	**Dowley** Dominic *Serle Court* *
Boyle Alan *Serle Court* *	**Gibbon** Michael *Maitland Chambers* *
Dicker Robin *South Square* *	**Hill** Richard G *4 Stone Buildings*
Girolami Paul *Maitland Chambers* *	**Hilliard** Lexa *11 Stone Buildings*
Jones Philip *Serle Court* *	**Machell** John *Serle Court* *
McQuater Ewan *3 Verulam Buildings (ORL)* ◊	**Malek** Ali *3 Verulam Buildings (ORL)* ◊
Miles Robert *4 Stone Buildings*	**Moverley Smith** Stephen *XXIV Old Buildings*
Moss Gabriel *South Square*	**Norbury** Hugh *Serle Court* *
Mowschenson Terence *Wilberforce Chambers*	**Phillips** Mark *South Square* *
Newman Catherine *Maitland Chambers* *	**Stallworthy** Nicolas *Outer Temple Chambers (ORL)* ◊
Smith Stephen *Erskine Chambers (ORL)* ◊ *	**Tipples** Amanda *Maitland Chambers* *
Steinfeld Alan *XXIV Old Buildings*	**Weatherill** Bernard *Enterprise Chambers*
Trace Anthony *Maitland Chambers* *	**Band 4**
Zacaroli Antony *South Square*	**Adkin** Jonathan *Serle Court* *
Band 2	**Ashworth** Lance *Serle Court* *
Arden Peter *Erskine Chambers (ORL)* ◊ *	**Blayney** David *Serle Court* *
Ayliffe James *Wilberforce Chambers*	**Caddick** Nicholas *Hogarth Chambers (ORL)* ◊
Bhaloo Zia *Enterprise Chambers*	**Cullen** Edmund *Maitland Chambers* *
Brisby John *4 Stone Buildings*	**Cunningham** Mark *Maitland Chambers* *
Brownbill David *XXIV Old Buildings*	**Goldring** Jeremy *South Square*
Cohen Lawrence *Wilberforce Chambers*	**Grant** Thomas *Maitland Chambers*
Collings Matthew *Maitland Chambers* *	**Levy** Robert *XXIV Old Buildings*
Croxford Ian *Wilberforce Chambers*	**McGrath** Paul *Essex Court Chambers (ORL)* ◊
de Garr Robinson Anthony *One Essex Court (ORL)* ◊ *	**Singh** Kuldip *Serle Court* *
Gourgey Alan *11 Stone Buildings* *	**Smith** Joanna *Wilberforce Chambers*
Jones Elizabeth *Serle Court* *	**Toube** Felicity *South Square* *
Marshall Philip *Serle Court* *	**New Silks**
Nicholls John *Maitland Chambers* *	**Aldridge** James *Maitland Chambers* *
Pymont Christopher *Maitland Chambers* *	**Allison** David *South Square* *
Rowley Keith *Radcliffe Chambers (ORL)* ◊	**Clutterbuck** Andrew *4 Stone Buildings* *
Tager Romie *Selborne Chambers (ORL)* ◊ *	**Moeran** Fenner *3 Stone Buildings (ORL)* ◊ *
Tolaney Sonia *3 Verulam Buildings (ORL)* ◊	**Reed** Rupert *Wilberforce Chambers*
Twigger Andrew M *3 Stone Buildings (ORL)* ◊ *	**Smith** Tom *South Square* *

◊ (ORL) = Other Ranked Lawyer.

[A] direct access (see p.11).

** Indicates set / individual with profile.*

Band 1

Maitland Chambers

See profile on p.831

THE SET

Members from this set continue to be instructed on some of the largest and most complex disputes heard in the Chancery Division. Its highly reputable silks and juniors have broad technical expertise and can handle all areas of chancery litigation. Testament to their standing in the market, they have been involved in a number of high-profile proceedings such as those relating to Berezovsky and Abramovich, and Guavadze and Patarkatsishvilie. They have also handled numerous Madoff-related cases and a number of disputes arising out of the collapse of Lehman Brothers. Recently, they have had involvement in the Anismov litigation.

SILKS

Paul Girolami QC Has an impressive domestic and international practice that spans a wide range of commercial chancery matters. He is a go-to figure for big-ticket company, civil fraud and insolvency matters. **Strengths:** "One of the top advocates at the Chancery Bar." "He is a total delight to work with as he's a decent human being, but also a fantastically capable lawyer."

Catherine Newman QC A standout figure at the Chancery Bar, who regularly handles some of the most complex and heavyweight disputes. She has historically been instructed on a diverse collection of commercial cases, ranging from shareholder disputes to civil fraud matters. **Strengths:** "She is a joy to work with and always delivers. Her ability to get to grips with complex issues and explain them in simple terms is second to none." "She is fantastically clever, intellectually very agile and someone who really adds value as a silk." **Recent work:** She acted for the private equity house Dunedin in a breach of warranty case over the sale of shares.

Anthony Trace QC Has a diverse commercial chancery practice and is routinely involved in major cases both domestically and in offshore jurisdictions. **Strengths:** "He is very bullish and can make a silk purse out of a pig's ear." **Recent work:** Acted in Aeroflot v Berezovsky in the Court of Appeal.

Matthew Collings QC A highly regarded advocate who specialises in company and insolvency litigation. He also has a solid reputation for fraud work. **Strengths:** "He is terrier-like in his commitment to the client's cause: he's really tenacious and fights hard." **Recent work:** Acted in a dispute regarding an Olympic gold medal-winning horse.

John Nicholls QC (see p.682) An accomplished commercial litigator who handles banking and financial services disputes, civil fraud matters and asset recovery cases. **Strengths:** "A self-effacing man, but a great advocate who leaves nothing to chance and covers all the angles."

Christopher Pymont QC A vastly experienced silk with a strong commercial practice. He is a popular choice for both traditional and commercial chancery cases, in particular those involving company and insolvency issues. **Strengths:** "He is just consistently excellent in all respects and great with clients." "He is completely unflappable." **Recent work:** Appeared in the Court of Appeal in FHR European Adventures v Mankarious, a dispute over an alleged breach of fiduciary duty.

Michael Gibbon QC Due to his background in investment banking prior to being called to the Bar, he is a go-to for any commercial disputes with significant banking or financial issues. **Strengths:** "He is bright, calm and approachable, and provides practical and swift solutions to challenging problems." "He invariably adds an insightful new dimension to the analysis of complex legal issues." **Recent work:** Acted in a £9 million contractual payment dispute over a failed tax avoidance scheme.

Chancery: Commercial London — Leading Juniors
Star individuals
Mumford David *Maitland Chambers* *
Band 1
Addy Catherine *Maitland Chambers* *
Bayfield Daniel *South Square* *
Denton-Cox Gregory *4 Stone Buildings* *
Hutton Louise *Maitland Chambers* *
Margolin Daniel *Maitland Chambers* *
Band 2
Adamyk Simon *New Square Chambers* *
Akkouh Tim *Erskine Chambers (ORL)* ◊ *
Barker James *Enterprise Chambers*
de Mestre Andrew *4 Stone Buildings* *
Eaton Turner David *New Square Chambers* *
Francis Edward *Enterprise Chambers*
Greenwood Paul *4 Stone Buildings*
Hagen Dakis *Serle Court* *
Harrison Christopher *4 Stone Buildings* *
Higgo Justin *Serle Court* *
King Edmund *Essex Court Chambers (ORL)* ◊
Lightman Daniel *Serle Court* *
Mold Andrew *Wilberforce Chambers* *
Penny Tim *11 Stone Buildings*
Pester Iain *11 Stone Buildings* *
Pickering James *Enterprise Chambers*
Richardson Giles *Serle Court* *
Shivji Sharif *4 Stone Buildings*
Winter Alexander *Maitland Chambers* *
Band 3
Bailey James *New Square Chambers* *
Boeddinghaus Hermann *4 Stone Buildings* *
Calland Timothy *Enterprise Chambers*
Cohen Edward *11 Stone Buildings* *
Drake David *Serle Court* *
Fisher Richard *South Square* *
Griffiths Peter *4 Stone Buildings*
Gunaratna Kavan *Enterprise Chambers*
Halkerston Graeme *Wilberforce Chambers*
Hattan Simon *Serle Court* *
Ife Linden *Enterprise Chambers*
John Benjamin *Maitland Chambers* *
Keller Ciaran *Maitland Chambers* *
Levy Juliette *Selborne Chambers (ORL)* ◊ *
Mallin Max *11 Stone Buildings*
Ohrenstein Dov *Radcliffe Chambers (ORL)* ◊ *
Ovey Elizabeth *Radcliffe Chambers (ORL)* ◊ *
Pay Adrian *New Square Chambers* *
Pringle Watson *New Square Chambers* *
Riley Jamie *11 Stone Buildings* *
Scott Tiffany *Wilberforce Chambers*
Singla Nikki *Wilberforce Chambers*
Staff Marcus *XXIV Old Buildings*
Staunton Ulick *Radcliffe Chambers (ORL)* ◊
Stephens John *XXIV Old Buildings*
Walton Alastair *Maitland Chambers* *
Weale James *3 Stone Buildings (ORL)* ◊ *
Band 4
Boardman Christopher *11 Stone Buildings*
Cloherty Adam *XXIV Old Buildings*
Collingwood Timothy *Serle Court* *
Foskett Rosanna *Maitland Chambers* *
Gavaghan Jonathan *Ten Old Square (ORL)* ◊ *
Gillett Emily *Erskine Chambers (ORL)* ◊ *
Graham Thomas *New Square Chambers* *
Hall Taylor Alex *4 New Square (ORL)* ◊ *
Harrison Nicholas *Serle Court* *
Hayman George *Maitland Chambers* *
Head Peter *11 Stone Buildings* *
Holtham den Besten Ruth *Serle Court* *
Hood Nigel *New Square Chambers* *
Hornett Stuart *Selborne Chambers (ORL)* ◊ [A] *
Hughes Jessica *XXIV Old Buildings*
Jeavons Anne *3 Verulam Buildings (ORL)* ◊
Kalfon Olivier *Enterprise Chambers*
Khan Farhaz *Outer Temple Chambers (ORL)* ◊
Kynoch Duncan *Selborne Chambers (ORL)* ◊ *
Majumdar Shantanu *Radcliffe Chambers (ORL)* ◊
Peters David *Essex Court Chambers (ORL)* ◊
Sawyer Edward *Wilberforce Chambers*
Sheehan James *Maitland Chambers* *
Shekerdemian Marcia *11 Stone Buildings*
Trompeter Nicholas *Selborne Chambers (ORL)* ◊ [A] *
Up-and-coming individuals
Gentleman Tom *4 Stone Buildings*
McCreath James *Wilberforce Chambers*
◊ (ORL) = Other Ranked Lawyer.
[A] direct access (see p.11).
* Indicates individual with profile.

Amanda Tipples QC Has a broad chancery practice, spanning both commercial and traditional matters. She is particularly active on disputes with partnership and company issues, and regularly handles cases involving asset tracing and fraud. **Strengths:** "She is a very bright and sensible counsel who doesn't take bad points." **Recent work:** Represented HMRC in appeals by charities against stamp duty land tax.

Thomas Grant QC A "powerful advocate" who tackles an impressive array of cases in the Chancery Division. His practice is commercial in nature, and he handles high-value, multiparty disputes. **Strengths:** "His technical and analytical skills are first-rate and his advice, whether technical or strategic, is commercial and pragmatic. Clients find him to be an impressive operator who instils great confidence." **Recent work:** Played a key role in Aeroflot v Berezovsky, a case concerning the airline's attempt to enforce a Russian judgment in relation to an alleged fraud.

Mark Cunningham QC (see p.582) Has an established commercial chancery practice and has handled a significant number of cases, both domestically and offshore. **Strengths:** "He is a top-rate advocate, able to deal with complex tax and fraud matters." "He is a no-nonsense, straight-talking practitioner with excellent advocacy skills."

Edmund Cullen QC Frequently instructed on high-profile commercial disputes across a wide range of sectors. He is particularly well known for assisting clients from the media and entertainment industry, and also handles a range of banking and fraud cases. **Strengths:** "He is a very good all-round lawyer who enthusiastically gets stuck into the detail."

James Aldridge QC (see p.533) An "impressive character" who acts on complex commercial conflicts, often involving contractual disputes and civil fraud. **Strengths:** "His technical and strategic analysis and advice is of a consistently high standard, and he is eminently approachable." "As an advocate, he is both charming and persuasive, and he always remains calm in sometimes challenging circumstances." **Recent work:** Defended National Express in a dispute over the alleged unlawful termination of a coach operator agreement.

JUNIORS

David Mumford A standout junior for commercial disputes both domestically and in offshore jurisdictions. He frequently litigates in high-profile and complex cases covering company, civil fraud and banking issues. **Strengths:** "Clients can't be in safer hands." "He has excellent judgement and a brilliant intellect." **Recent work:** Acted in a conspiracy claim concerning an outstanding debt owed by a Russian state-owned metallurgical business to a syndicate of international banks.

Catherine Addy A highly regarded advocate who is particularly involved in insolvency and company disputes in the Chancery Division. **Strengths:** "She is excellent in court and always seems to adopt the right tone with the bench." **Recent work:** Represented Landesbank Baden-Wurttemberg in a commercial dispute with UBS over a series of credit default derivative transactions.

Louise Hutton Typically instructed on chancery litigation that involves sophisticated banking and company issues. She receives particular plaudits for her expertise in civil fraud matters. **Strengths:** "She is a hard-working, dedicated and very supportive junior." "She is responsive, perceptive and very bright." **Recent work:** Appeared in litigation between RBS and Highland Financial Partners over a series of allegations of fraud.

Daniel Margolin Widely recognised for his real estate litigation practice within the Chancery Division, he is also frequently instructed on a broad spectrum of other commercial disputes, many of which include allegations of fraud. **Strengths:** "He is very calm and logical." "He gives thoroughly prepared and commercially sensible advice, and his analysis of the risks in a cases is always spot on, which allows the client to make a well-informed decision about how the case should be conducted." **Recent work:** Defended Deloitte against a £16 million claim for damages over a series of alleged misdealings.

Alexander Winter Impresses in chancery disputes, especially those with civil fraud and banking elements. He regularly acts in cases with significant multi-jurisdictional questions attached to them. **Strengths:** "He is right on the ball and very professional." "He is very intelligent, very responsive and a safe pair of hands." **Recent work:** Played a key role in a series of fraud claims worth USD11 million.

Benjamin John Maintains a diverse practice, and has noted expertise in fraud claims and asset tracing. He is often instructed on matters with considerable international components. **Strengths:** "He is very professional and brilliant with clients." "He is a hard-working and conscientious team player, who produces high-quality work." **Recent work:** Defended ETF Securities against a multimillion-pound claim by a former executive relating to share options.

Ciaran Keller A respected chancery junior with experience of handling commercial cases both domestically and in a number of offshore jurisdictions. **Strengths:** "He is very bright and user-friendly, and the type of junior barrister that clients look for." "He is a very measured and thorough individual." **Recent work:** Acted in a multimillion-pound dispute, defending a client against a series of claims relating to the demerger of two groups of companies and limited partnerships.

Alastair Walton (see p.745) A vastly experienced senior junior who devotes his practice to commercial and traditional chancery disputes. He receives particular praise for his written work. **Strengths:** "His written work is fantastically elegant, and he is one of the smartest guys you could come across."

George Hayman An accomplished litigator who acts in complex and high-value commercial disputes in the domestic and BVI courts. He is often instructed on civil fraud and insolvency cases. **Strengths:** "He is an incredibly hard-working chap, and a real team player, who turns papers around extremely quickly." "He is able to build a very good rapport with clients and will give them direct and firm advice." **Recent work:** He was involved in a £25 million contractual dispute between an internet television company and the Financial Times.

Rosanna Foskett (see p.602) One of the younger crop at the set of whom good things are expected in the future. She handles a broad range of chancery work and has acted unled on a number of cases. **Strengths:** "She is extremely personable and clearly does much work behind the scenes in her role as a junior in support of leading counsel." "She's extremely hard-working and a creative thinker." **Recent work:** Acted in Maloney & Others v Filtons/Mackay & Others v Ashwood, representing insolvency practitioners who were appointed receivers over a substantial block of flats near the Olympic Park.

James Sheehan (see p.719) Handles a number of major cases, and has a particular strength in fraud-related matters. He had a role in both the BTA v Ablyazov saga and the Berezovsky litigation. **Strengths:** "He works like there's no tomorrow" and gives "highly technical and extremely well thought-out advice." **Recent work:** Acted in Med Mining & Minerals Limited v Nusantara Energy Plc, a matter concerning the activities of an English mining company in Indonesia.

Serle Court

See profile on p.860

THE SET

Serle Court remains one of the leading sets for big-ticket disputes heard in the Chancery courts. It offers a critical mass of distinguished commercial litigators who are able to offer the breadth of expertise and experience that the most complex cases demand. **Client service:** "The clerks have always bent over backwards to help our clients. We can call them at short notice and know they will help us."

SILKS

Alan Boyle QC A distinguished heavyweight silk and a popular choice for the full range of commercial and traditional chancery disputes. He has notable strength across a wide range of legal sectors, and frequently appears in the most sophisticated cases. **Strengths:** "He is an impressive individual who takes a very analytical, logical approach to his cases." "He has a first-class legal brain and a stellar intellect." **Recent work:** He acted in a series of disputes arising from the insolvency of a hot strip steel mill in South Wales.

Philip Jones QC Has a stellar reputation for commercial litigation and regularly handles cases in the appellate courts of the Chancery Division. Noted for his experience in company law and insolvency matters, he is well placed to tackle disputes of any size, whether domestically or in offshore jurisdictions. **Strengths:** "He is very strong as an appellate advocate and expresses himself very clearly." "He is wonderfully attentive to clients."

Elizabeth Jones QC A renowned trial advocate who acts in commercial disputes in the domestic courts and offshore. Her prowess as a cross-examiner was regularly mentioned to our researchers. **Strengths:** "An advocate who leaves no stone unturned." "Her ability to chew through information and digest it is quite remarkable."

Philip Marshall QC A major force in a wide range of commercial disputes, who is particularly strong on international fraud matters. His practice also takes in insolvency, company and banking matters. **Strengths:** "He is combative, focused and multi-talented." "He is a bold cross-examiner and hugely experienced in fraud cases." **Recent work:** Represented Constantin Medien in a high-profile bribery case in the High Court against Formula One boss Bernie Ecclestone.

John Machell QC A formidable advocate with a highly regarded practice that encompasses fraud and partnership cases, to name but a few. He regularly handles cases with significant multi-jurisdictional elements. **Strengths:** "He is very measured, very intelligent, and will always make himself available." "Incredibly bright, hard-working and committed, he is particularly adept at dealing with the financial aspects of trust cases."

Dominic Dowley QC Has a thriving commercial dispute practice, and demonstrates particular mastery of banking and civil fraud issues. He also regularly represents clients on offshore matters. **Strengths:** "He displays excellent attention to detail; he finds all of the connections because he has such a good grasp of the detail." "He is a clear, incisive, quick-working advocate."

Hugh Norbury QC Highly regarded for his handling of complex and large-scale commercial disputes, he is typically instructed on matters with significant elements of fraud or which relate to fiduciary breaches. **Strengths:** "He is extraordinarily pleasant to deal with and a wonderful team player." **Recent work:** Acted in a case concerning the liquidation of a failed investment fund based in the Isle of Man with assets of approximately £40 million.

Jonathan Adkin QC A popular silk who has been involved in a number of the largest commercial cases heard in the Chancery Division. Particular areas of focus include offshore and civil fraud matters. **Strengths:** "He is combative, focused and has a fabulous knowledge of the jurisdictional issues." **Recent work:** Instructed in the billion-dollar dispute between the family of Badri Patarkatsishvili and Vasily Anisimov, a Russian oligarch.

David Blayney QC Frequently sought out for his significant insight into banking and financial issues, this forceful silk litigates in big-ticket commercial disputes across a wide range of industry sectors. **Strengths:** "He has immense brain power, and is focused and highly effective." **Recent work:** Defended RBS in a group litigation over a £12 billion rights issue.

Kuldip Singh QC A seasoned silk with years of experience of tackling large commercial cases on behalf of banks, corporations and individuals. He demonstrates particular proficiency in civil fraud matters. **Strengths:** "He takes control and is very forceful."

Lance Ashworth QC Specialises in commercial litigation with elements of civil fraud and insolvency, and enjoys a healthy reputation for the quality of his advocacy. He also sits as a mediator. **Strengths:** "He gets to grips with the issues very quickly and gives robust, practical and commercial advice." **Recent work:** Acted in UK Power Reserve v Read, a case concerning a breach of duty for dishonest assistance.

JUNIORS

Dakis Hagen A deeply respected junior who has developed a considerable commercial litigation practice. He is renowned for his expertise in offshore matters, particularly those concerning asset tracing and business disputes. **Strengths:** "He takes real pride in his work and is intellectually superb." "He is absolutely brilliant, totally committed and very strategic in his approach – he's the real deal." **Recent work:** Acted in Walker v Egerton-Vernon, defending a trust company against a claim alleging breach of trust and negligence.

Justin Higgo Eminently respected for his commercial chancery work, particularly in large-scale fraud cases. He has significant experience of handling high-profile domestic and international litigation. **Strengths:** "He is very bright, a real team player and a good thinker." "He is robust in court and doesn't throw punches."

Daniel Lightman Recognised for his experience in commercial litigation, and known for his skill at handling company law, insolvency and civil fraud cases. He also boasts a substantial international practice. **Strengths:** "He has a huge knowledge of the law and is immensely hard-working." "He is thoughtful, clever and astute – a great team player." **Recent work:** He acted for the shareholders of several offshore companies in a dispute over allegations of fraud, breaches of fiduciary duty, and negligence.

Giles Richardson His practice straddles commercial and traditional chancery matters. Owing to the strength of his offshore practice, he is frequently instructed on large-scale litigation with multi-jurisdictional legal questions. **Strengths:** "He is incredibly user friendly and hard-working." "Has excellent knowledge of the law and is good tactically. Clients love him." **Recent work:** He appeared in the Court of Appeal in a dispute claiming a breach of duty of care and wealth against a bank following the acquisition of a jet for its Russian clients.

David Drake Acts for corporate and public sector clients in high-value disputes heard in the Chancery courts. His practice encompasses civil fraud, insolvency and company matters. **Strengths:** "When confronted with the most esoteric legal problems, he finds the answer." "He is a super junior and a tremendously hard worker who has a real knowledge of the law." **Recent work:** He was instructed in a commercial dispute over profit shares relating to offshore oil exploration rights in Nigeria.

Simon Hattan Regularly appears in the Chancery Division in complex litigation. He is routinely instructed on matters involving breaches of fiduciary duty and civil fraud, and also has a thriving regulatory practice. **Strengths:** "He is pragmatic, decisive and brilliant." "He is a strong technical lawyer with a dogged advocacy style."

Timothy Collingwood A much praised practitioner with an extensive commercial chancery practice. He is particularly involved in company matters, especially shareholder disputes and matters concerning breaches of fiduciary duty by directors.

Strengths: "He is very good with clients and very commercial." **Recent work:** He acted in Re: LCM Wealth Management, a shareholder dispute surrounding accusations of breaches of duty.

Nicholas Harrison Frequently acts in commercial disputes domestically and in offshore jurisdictions. He enjoys a strong reputation for acting in sophisticated trust cases. **Strengths:** "He is a brilliant strategist on complex international trust and fraud disputes." "He is very bright and hard-working, and completely immerses himself in his cases."

Ruth Holtham den Besten Devotes her chancery practice to a wide range of commercial cases. Company law, insolvency and civil fraud matters are all key areas of expertise. **Strengths:** "She's such a good junior that she'll be a silk in no time." **Recent work:** She was involved in Bank of St Petersburg OJSC & Anor v Vitaly Arkhangelsky & Anor, a £50 million dispute.

4 Stone Buildings

See profile on p.865

THE SET

4 Stone Buildings continues to occupy a leading position in the market, and is noted for the consistently high quality of its members. Although smaller than some of its rivals, it has a concentration of talent few can hope to match. It offers expertise across the full range of relevant practice areas, and its members are frequently involved in the most significant and high-profile commercial cases in the Chancery Division. Recent cases handled by the members include both the MF Global and Fairfield Sentry sagas, and the high-profile Constantin Medien v Ecclestone.

Client service: "The clerks, led by David Goddard, are always very responsive, easy to use and approachable."

SILKS

Jonathan Crow QC A pre-eminent litigator with a proven track record at the Chancery Bar. He possesses a wealth of experience of tackling disputes across a wide range of practice areas, and is particularly strong on financial services and company law. He also regularly represents governmental departments in commercial disputes. **Strengths:** "He is a remarkable man and the best around; he is the barrister that everyone wants to be." "He has the ability to deal with a big caseload and focus on the main issues." **Recent work:** Acted in a Privy Council appeal concerning the repayment of money received from the redemption of shares by investors of Fairfield Sentry, a feeder fund for Bernard L Madoff Investment Securities.

George Bompas QC Has a strong chancery practice and is instructed by clients on a broad spectrum of domestic and overseas matters. Over the years he has handled many cases with complex financial elements to them. **Strengths:** "He is supremely accomplished, and his advocacy is extremely polished." **Recent work:** Active in Chemtrade v Fuchs Oil, a case in the British Virgin Islands (BVI) concerning a Middle East and North African joint venture.

Robert Miles QC A highly distinguished and "phenomenally bright" silk who handles the largest financial and company disputes. He is frequently instructed in the highest-value disputes. **Strengths:** "His advocacy is very clear and well structured, and the strength of his points speak for themselves." **Recent work:** Represented the court-appointed receivers, KPMG, in a large-scale fraud dispute between JSC BTA Bank and its former chairman, Mukhtar Ablyazov.

John Brisby QC A well-respected chancery practitioner with an outstanding reputation for company litigation, including shareholder disputes, asset recovery and directors' duties. **Strengths:** "He is a man who will always fight the client's corner." "He comes up with innovative arguments, is effective in court and has the respect of the Chancery Division judges." **Recent work:** Involved in a shareholder dispute regarding the technology company ATX Software.

Richard Hill QC A highly respected silk who is frequently instructed on cases involving insolvency, banking and company matters. **Strengths:** "Has every weapon he could possibly need to become a fantastic silk." **Recent work:** Acted for two of the defendants in Benedetti v Sawiris, a case heard in the Supreme Court concerning the acquisition of an Italian telecommunications company.

Andrew Clutterbuck QC (see p.574) Has a solid reputation for acting on a diverse range of matters in the Chancery Division and is building a strong silk's practice. **Strengths:** "He is a go-to for all chancery commercial matters as he is extremely hard-working and very knowledgeable." **Recent work:** Represented the claimant in Good v Onsette, a case regarding an offshore trust company and an attempt to recover an entrusted shareholding.

JUNIORS

Gregory Denton-Cox A highly regarded litigator across a wide range of commercial chancery cases. He has noted expertise in asset recovery, company and civil fraud claims. **Strengths:** "He is a very able junior who displays great legal awareness and maturity." "He has a very good drafting style and his pleasant and easy-going personality make him a pleasure to deal with." **Recent work:** Involved in litigation in the Court of Appeal over the ownership of the company that owned the Connaught, Berkeley and Claridges hotels.

Andrew de Mestre Features heavily in a vast array of complex chancery disputes, and has experience across insolvency, banking and company matters. **Strengths:** "He is a fantastically accomplished, natural advocate." "He has an encyclopaedic knowledge and is a fantastic sounding board for solicitors." **Recent work:** Acted for Global Energy Horizons Corporation in litigation concerning an alleged breach of fiduciary duty by the defendant.

Paul Greenwood Has an established commercial chancery practice with an emphasis on insolvency, company and general commercial issues. **Strengths:** "He has the ability to cut through a complicated problem" and regularly provides "incisive, clear and sensible advice." **Recent work:** Defended EPIC in litigation with Macquarie Infrastructure concerning a dispute over a sale of shares.

Christopher Harrison Renowned for his handling of shareholder disputes, but also has a broader commercial chancery practice. He has been instructed on a number of impressive big-ticket matters. **Strengths:** "He is a team player and a forensic and effective litigator." "He is a talented advocate who is very astute strategically, and extremely good with clients." **Recent work:** Acted in Richard Desmond v Credit Suisse International, a claim relating to investments in complex derivative transactions.

Sharif Shivji Has an impressive international practice, and possesses a superb reputation for financial services and company matters. **Strengths:** "Clever, intellectually curious and rigorous in his approach." **Recent work:** Acted in a dispute involving structured products, whereby Morgan Stanley were sued by in excess of 100 Irish investors.

Hermann Boeddinghaus (see p.552) Has a strong commercial chancery practice, and is regularly instructed on cases involving serious financial fraud. **Strengths:** "He is thorough, detail-oriented and very intellectually rigorous." "He is a brave advocate with a strong intellect." **Recent work:** Acted for Deloitte in a dispute arising from the liquidation of MK Airlines.

Peter Griffiths A well-established figure who is strong on the company and insolvency sides. He has particular experience in shareholder disputes. **Strengths:** "He is solid, both in terms of advocacy and legal knowledge, and always very well prepared." "He has the experience to anticipate the opponent's next move." **Recent work:** Instructed in a shareholder dispute concerning the acquisition by a joint venture of a port in Murmansk, Russia.

Tom Gentleman A lawyer who is building a strong reputation for himself. He focuses his practice on shareholder disputes, financial services and insolvency. **Strengths:** "He is a rising star who is beyond his years in terms of his legal knowledge and his drafting and communication abilities." "He is everything you want in a junior barrister: incredibly bright, hard-working and tenacious." **Recent work:** Represented the defendant in a case concerning an alleged breach of a joint venture agreement relating to a Bulgarian furniture company.

Band 2

XXIV Old Buildings

See profile on p.838

THE SET

A key player in the market for all areas of commercial chancery litigation, and a set that has a roster of experienced chancery silks and juniors. It is a popular choice for big-ticket litigation with an international element to it.

Client service: "The clerks are efficient at getting back to you and very accommodating. They bend over backwards to make something happen for you and to provide cover."

SILKS

Alan Steinfeld QC A leading silk for all types of chancery litigation who has a mightily impressive offshore practice. He has a wealth of experience of acting in the largest and most complicated commercial cases. **Strengths:** "He has a mega brain." "He has experience of appearing in every court imaginable."

David Brownbill QC A top-rate trusts specialist with an enviable reputation for handling the larger cases. He regularly appears in the Chancery courts, and is a constant in offshore jurisdictions. **Strengths:** "He is very thorough and leaves no stone unturned." "Extremely knowledgeable and commercial, he's a convincing advocate." **Recent work:** Involved in litigation in the BVI and Hong Kong relating to assets in the BVI.

Malcolm Davis-White QC Boasts a broad commercial chancery practice, and has deep expertise in company and insolvency matters. He is a go-to figure in the market for directors' duties cases. **Strengths:** "He is a very good advocate who really knows his stuff and has a really good manner." **Recent work:** He appeared in Richard Desmond v Bank of Scotland &

Uberior Investments, a case regarding the alleged mis-selling of financial products.

Stephen Moverley Smith QC A seasoned litigator who maintains a busy chancery practice. He is particularly strong on company and insolvency matters. **Strengths:** "He commands the respect of the court and is very thorough." **Recent work:** Was involved in a RUB1 billion dispute between a Russian bank and a controller of one of its customers over alleged fraudulent behaviour.

Robert Levy QC Has a large domestic and international practice, and frequently appears in the offshore courts. Civil fraud cases form a good part of his workload. **Strengths:** "He is very commercial and switched on, and doesn't lose sight of the big picture." "He's very precise and well prepared." **Recent work:** He acted in the BVI Commercial Court in a dispute relating to the exercising of options in shares for a Belize company.

JUNIORS

Marcus Staff Has extensive experience in the Chancery courts, acting, in particular, in insolvency and trust disputes. Cases on which he is instructed regularly have an international flavour. **Strengths:** "He has a remarkable intellect and a great breadth of knowledge." "He is very rewarding to work with because he is excellent at communicating ideas and recognising the interrelation of very complex matters." **Recent work:** Acted as junior in a Cayman Islands case concerning a Dubai investor who had brought a claim against his investment bank.

John Stephens A vastly experienced senior junior who acts in domestic and offshore disputes. He acts in the Chancery Division on a wide range of commercial matters. **Strengths:** "We very much value his support, his willingness to go the extra mile to be available, and his precise judgement." **Recent work:** Involved in Phillips v Symes, a multi-jurisdictional commercial dispute involving a French bank.

Jessica Hughes Has a broad traditional and commercial chancery practice, and acts in a wide range of disputes. She is well regarded for her trusts litigation involving businesses and individuals. **Strengths:** "She is a very good person to work with in difficult situations." **Recent work:** She drafted the grounds of appeal in Patel v Mirza.

Adam Cloherty Demonstrates strength in both traditional and commercial chancery work. He regularly appears in both domestic and offshore cases. **Strengths:** "Has an ability beyond his years of experience." **Recent work:** Acted as junior in a case representing the principal beneficiary with regard to a significant Nevis fund.

South Square

See profile on p.861

THE SET

This set enjoys an outstanding reputation for insolvency work, but has firmly secured itself a significant position in the market for handling broader commercial chancery disputes. Its members are experienced trial advocates with wide-ranging areas of expertise and commonly appear in the Chancery courts in complex financial, company and fraud litigation.

SILKS

Robin Dicker QC An "incredibly bright" silk who is universally recognised as one of the undoubted leaders at the Bar for insolvency cases. He is also instructed on a wide variety of other complex commercial disputes, and regularly handles matters involving banks and financial products. **Strengths:** "He combines meticulous preparation with razor-sharp cross-examination." **Recent work:** He acted in a dispute between Loreley and LBIE concerning an alleged fraudulent misrepresentation.

Gabriel Moss QC A heavyweight of the Chancery Bar, who has significant experience of litigating a broad range of commercial disputes. He is a highly regarded insolvency specialist and is frequently instructed on complex company cases.

Antony Zacaroli QC A renowned banking and insolvency expert with the ability to handle the most complex and high-value commercial chancery cases. He regularly appears in the largest domestic and international cases. **Strengths:** "He is everything you would look for in a forward-thinking, modern commercial chancery silk." "He is charming, user-friendly and has a very good client manner." **Recent work:** Acted for the administrators of MF Global, advising them on issues relating to special bank administration.

Mark Phillips QC A "masterful advocate" who acts in high-profile banking and insolvency disputes. He also demonstrates considerable expertise in commercial cases with a sports law crossover. **Strengths:** "He works as part of the team and takes a commercial, pragmatic approach." "Very academic, and a man with a very sharp brain – he looks at things laterally." **Recent work:** He represented Glasgow Rangers FC in a series of claims alleging fraudulent behaviour and a breach of solicitors' undertakings by Collyer Bristow. The case centred around the football club's takeover by Craig White.

Jeremy Goldring QC Has an impressive silk's practice, and regularly appears in major banking, insolvency and company disputes. **Strengths:** "Very clever in a most understated way, he is modest, thorough and impressive on his feet." **Recent work:** Instructed by Credit Suisse in a dispute with Stichting Vestia, a Dutch housing association, relating to credit rate swaps.

Felicity Toube QC Boasts a well-established commercial litigation practice, acting both domestically and in offshore jurisdictions. She acts in high-value disputes, often with complex insolvency and company questions attached to them. **Strengths:** "She is tremendous as she's super-bright, very user-friendly and able to handle clients very well." **Recent work:** Assisted in recovering assets misappropriated in the Rastogi metals trading fraud.

David Allison QC An in-demand new silk with a strong reputation for his commercial litigation practice. He is regularly instructed to act in the Chancery Division on company and finance matters. **Strengths:** "He is very commercial and provides a high level of technical competence." **Recent work:** Appeared in the Supreme Court in BNY Corporate Trustee Services Ltd v Eurosail, a dispute regarding centralised debt obligations.

Tom Smith QC Demonstrates notable prowess in commercial litigation, and acts for corporate and public sector clients across a wide range of areas. **Strengths:** "He is clever, approachable and down to earth." "He is particularly good in his written advocacy, and writes very compelling and impactful skeleton arguments." **Recent work:** He was involved in a dispute alleging a breach of directors' duties in relation to the collapse of the Dawnay Day group.

JUNIORS

Daniel Bayfield Tackles a broad range of cases across the commercial chancery spectrum, but has a strong focus on insolvency and banking disputes. **Strengths:** "A top-drawer advocate who is incredibly in demand and likes to be part of the team." **Recent work:** Has acted in a number of disputes related to the collapse of Lehman Brothers.

Richard Fisher Renowned for the quality of his work in large-scale commercial disputes. While insolvency is a key area of strength, he also demonstrates his capabilities in banking and civil fraud matters. **Strengths:** "He is very clever, very straightforward and gives good clear advice." "He is able to deliver quality results under time pressure." **Recent work:** Represented Snoras Bank in a EUR500 million claim alleging breach of duty and fraud against its former owner and chairman.

Wilberforce Chambers

See profile on p.876

THE SET

A go-to set for big-ticket traditional and commercial chancery matters that enjoys an outstanding reputation for its work on complex, multi-jurisdictional cases. It retains a large group of commercial litigation specialists who are able to offer a high-quality service. Its prestigious barristers have had a highly successful year acting in cases such as Accolade Wines v GJS and GJ4, a claim for over £100 million concerning defective premises, and Century Projects Ltd v Almacantar, a multimillion-pound dispute surrounding London's Centre Point building. Barristers at the set also handled Clutterbuck v Al Amoudi, a well-publicised case concerning a self-styled Saudi 'princess' who had been accused of lying her way to a £14 million property empire.

Client service: "The clerks there are very swift, efficient and well prepared." Mark Rushton is the head clerk.

SILKS

Terence Mowschenson QC A tenacious silk with a first-class commercial chancery practice. He possesses considerable experience in business disputes, and has an acute knowledge of company and financial services law. Commentators applaud him for his flourishing offshore practice. **Strengths:** "He is very clever, pleasant to deal with, and has a very easy manner." **Recent work:** Has frequently been instructed on cases arising from the Madoff investment fraud.

Lawrence Cohen QC A vastly experienced practitioner who is able to handle a wide variety of commercial cases in the Chancery courts. He frequently acts in offshore and international matters, particularly with regard to financial services and insolvency issues. **Strengths:** "He is very commercial, focused and thorough." "He is a terrific strategist who possesses great teamwork skills." **Recent work:** He defended Baker & McKenzie in claims relating to a EUR1.2 billion takeover.

James Ayliffe QC A popular silk with a well-established commercial chancery practice. He is a go-to figure for real estate and offshore disputes. **Strengths:** "He is efficient and effective." "He has an excellent ability to digest all the facts, and his turnaround time is very good." **Recent work:** He represented HMRC in a case concerning the recovery of £220 million owed in tax by a South African official.

Ian Croxford QC Has an impressive reputation for handling complex civil fraud and professional negligence matters. He is often instructed on cases with significant international elements. **Strengths:** "A very smooth and polished individual."

John Wardell QC A standout professional with years of experience of handling complex commercial fraud cases. His practice combines domestic and offshore work. **Strengths:** "He fights for his clients very well" and is "a tower of strength." "His advice has real clarity and strategic vision, and he always displays a strong tactical grip." **Recent work:** He acted for National Westminster Bank in a dispute regarding a Ponzi scheme operated by one of its customers.

Joanna Smith QC Praised by clients for her performances in professional negligence disputes and banking and finance litigation. **Strengths:** "She has expert knowledge and takes a pragmatic and commercial approach." "She has an excellent client service ethic." **Recent work:** Defended an ex-KPMG partner, an administrator for two companies, against allegations of fraudulently converting assets during liquidation.

Rupert Reed QC A much-praised new silk who regularly works on multiparty disputes, and is renowned for his abilities in real estate litigation. **Strengths:** "He quickly absorbs complex legal documentation and navigates his way through it." "He is efficient, smart and has good attention to detail." **Recent work:** Appeared in a multiparty, multi-jurisdictional dispute regarding the construction of the Pinnacle skyscraper.

JUNIORS

Andrew Mold (see p.675) An extremely capable junior with a broad chancery practice, who often appears in cases involving breaches of fiduciary duty and offshore matters. **Strengths:** "He is straight, clever and succinct." "He combines technical excellence with a user-friendly approach." **Recent work:** Acted in a case alleging conspiracy over the development of the luxury residential complex One Hyde Park.

Graeme Halkerston A "fantastic trial lawyer" who continues to impress in high-value commercial cases. He is regularly instructed on financial and insolvency matters, and possesses a substantial offshore practice. **Strengths:** "He is the complete package as he's very imaginative and highly focused." "He gives realistic advice, manages expectations and is very approachable." **Recent work:** Appeared on behalf of liquidators of a former investment fund based in Guernsey which had collapsed as a result of fraudulent behaviour by its principal.

Tiffany Scott A highly regarded junior who is able to tackle a wide variety of traditional and commercial chancery disputes. She is renowned for her real property work, as well as her efforts in civil fraud and trusts disputes. **Strengths:** "She is good to work with, clever and reliable." "She is a self assured advocate who is user-friendly and inspires confidence." **Recent work:** Was instructed in a claim by beneficiaries against a firm of financial advisers alleging negligent handling of trust investments.

Nikki Singla Tackles a full practice that focuses on contentious commercial matters, particularly those with offshore or company elements. **Strengths:** "He is a very intelligent lawyer who is able to get to the root cause of a conflict. He shows great empathy to the client and is able to translate a case to them such that it is understandable." **Recent work:** Acted for the Formula One rights holder for Spain in a breach of contract dispute resulting from the bankruptcy of Valencia.

Edward Sawyer Undertakes a wide range of commercial disputes domestically and in offshore jurisdictions. Many of these cases involve breaches of fiduciary duty and asset tracing. **Strengths:** "He is phenomenally hard-working and bright, and is willing to go that extra mile."

James McCreath Areas of expertise include contractual disputes, insolvency and company work. **Strengths:** "He has an excellent grasp of detail and is very user-friendly and available." **Recent work:** Acted as sole counsel in a contractual dispute over the sale of goods worth £1 million.

Band 3

Enterprise Chambers
See profile on p.788

THE SET

A set that offers comprehensive expertise in all areas of commercial chancery litigation, and possesses a fine pedigree in company, insolvency and property work in particular. Its barristers are frequently instructed in high-profile, complex litigation, and are noted for the commitment they show to each and every case they undertake. Solicitors favour them as "they really get stuck into every case and comprehend the commercial realities that are play in these disputes."

SILKS

Zia Bhaloo QC A popular and well-established figure in property litigation, whose practice also takes in wider commercial chancery work. A "forceful advocate," she is frequently involved in complex landlord and tenant disputes. **Strengths:** "A formidable force that you will always be happy to have on your side." "She is someone that exudes both calmness and confidence at the same time." **Recent work:** She acted for the trustees of the Meyrick Estate in a dispute with the Boscombe Partnership, in which she obtained forfeiture of a hotel.

Bernard Weatherill QC Has vast experience of acting in the Chancery courts in complex litigation. He has particular expertise in company law, and is frequently instructed on cases involving questions of directors' duties and shareholder disputes. **Strengths:** "He has a great courtroom presence and charms judges while luring witnesses into a false sense of security." **Recent work:** He was instructed to act for a former company director in claims against Mazars and Quiagen Manchester regarding alleged negligent handling of shares.

JUNIORS

James Barker Has a well-regarded chancery practice, focusing on insolvency, commercial contracts and directors' duties. He also regularly acts in mortgage and guarantee disputes. **Recent work:** Acted in Bank of Scotland v Ahmad, an appeal case concerning alleged breach of contract and negligence.

James Pickering Handles a wide variety of work in the Chancery courts, with an emphasis on insolvency and property disputes. **Strengths:** "A brilliant trial lawyer and very charming with it." **Recent work:** Acted as junior counsel in Matchbet Limited v Openbet Retail Limited, a £64 million breach of contract claim following a failed joint venture.

Edward Francis A specialist in real estate and wider chancery matters who is often involved in insolvency cases that arise from property disputes. **Strengths:** "He has excellent judgement and is first-rate intellectually." "Technically outstanding on property questions and highly persuasive on his feet." **Recent work:** Appeared in Bush & Baseline Properties Ltd v King, a dispute over alleged fraudulent misrepresentations regarding the sale of development land.

Kavan Gunaratna Has developed a strong commercial chancery practice and regularly acts for public and private sector clients in property and insolvency litigation. **Strengths:** "He is exceptionally user-friendly and good on his feet." "He is very clever, very thorough and knows how to obtain the ear of the court." **Recent work:** He acted for Network Rail in a number of disputes arising from its Thameslink Redevelopment Programme.

Linden Ife Has a wealth of experience of acting in company and insolvency litigation. Specialist areas include claims against directors and matters concerning dishonest assistance. **Strengths:** "A formidable advocate who is never intimidated and has no difficulty in arguing against silks." **Recent work:** She was instructed in a claim by a company's litigators concerning alleged director misfeasance and breaches of fiduciary duty.

Timothy Calland Has a broad litigation practice, and regularly handles insolvency, company and banking cases. **Strengths:** "A very good junior for commercial disputes of all types." **Recent work:** Appeared in Smeaton v Equifax, a matter looking at the duties owed by credit reference agencies to bankrupt individuals.

Olivier Kalfon Frequently acts in financial disputes both domestically and in offshore jurisdictions. His practice sees him tackling bankruptcy, property and professional negligence claims. **Strengths:** "He is very hard-working and clients like him."

New Square Chambers
See profile on p.837

THE SET

Although more closely associated with traditional chancery work, this set is also highly praised for its efforts on the commercial chancery front. Its members are well used to handling big-ticket disputes, and have handled a number of huge trusts, contract and fraud cases. They are further noted for their particular expertise in jurisdictional and conflict of laws disputes, and for the work they undertake in a number of Caribbean jurisdictions. Those that instruct the members here talk of the "good, collegiate working experience" they enjoy.

Client service: "The clerking team is very friendly, approachable and efficient. I trust Phil Reeves enough that if he recommends someone to me I'll use them."

JUNIORS

Simon Adamyk Partakes in a wide range of commercial chancery work, in particular cases involving civil fraud and company issues. He regularly gets involved in offshore matters and is called to the Bar in the BVI. **Recent work:** He was involved in a dispute between two investment funds, based in Jersey, and their former chairman over an alleged breach of fiduciary duty in relation to exit payments to former directors.

David Eaton Turner A highly experienced senior junior who often appears in company and insolvency disputes. He is frequently instructed to act in the Chancery Division and in offshore jurisdictions. **Strengths:** "He has a very wise head for complex disputes and provides considered, careful advice." **Recent work:** He defended Black Pearl Investments against Goldtrail liquidators in a matter dealing with allegations of dishonest assistance.

James Bailey A committed barrister who receives plaudits for his expertise across an impressive array of chancery matters. He is well known for company and insolvency disputes. **Strengths:** "He is enthusiastic, bright and increasingly impressive as he grows in maturity." **Recent work:** He was involved in UPMS v Fort Gilkicker, which concerned an alleged attempt by a company director to dishonestly divert business opportunities from the company to suit his own personal interests.

Adrian Pay (see p.690) Has a broad-based commercial chancery practice, and has experience of handling company, insolvency and real estate disputes. **Strengths:** "He is measured and accurate in his advice." "He is thorough, dilligent and extremely prepared."

Watson Pringle (see p.699) Focuses primarily on civil fraud and commercial matters heard in the Chancery courts. He also has a growing reputation for international insolvency work. **Strengths:** "He is extremely hard-working, has a fantastic eye for the detail and can ferret out the critical points in a case." **Recent work:** Played a key role in the Gudavadze v Anisimov litigation surrounding the proceeds of a Russian aluminium company.

Nigel Hood A go-to junior for civil fraud claims who regularly acts in complex commercial litigation involving breaches of fiduciary duty and misfeasance. **Strengths:** "Very straightforward in his approach." "He's been taking on and beating silks in big fraud cases in the past year." **Recent work:** Acted as sole counsel for the defendant in Group Seven Limited v Allied Investment Corporation & Nobre, a EUR100 million claim over allegations of cross-border fraud.

Thomas Graham (see p.613) A highly regarded senior junior with a renowned commercial chancery practice. He has a wealth of experience of acting in disputes involving company, insolvency and partnership elements. **Strengths:** "Clients love him as he is very easy to deal with and delivers the goods in court." "He is a fantastic advocate who has a very calm and collected approach but can turn up the heat when necessary. He's also very reactive and able to change his game plan when necessary." **Recent work:** Appeared in the Court of Appeal in Sohal v Suri, a case regarding the beneficial ownership of property.

11 Stone Buildings

See profile on p.868

THE SET

This set has a long history of appearing in high-end commercial disputes in the Chancery courts and is home to large number of specialists in this area. Praised for their accessibility, members exhibit enviable prowess in insolvency, company and civil fraud matters.

Client service: "The clerks are brilliant, from the junior clerks to the seniors. They always look at the dynamics to work out which barrister will best fit the case. The turnaround time is also excellent."

SILKS

Alan Gourgey QC Boasts significant expertise in numerous areas, including civil fraud and contractual disputes. He is a highly regarded silk who frequently appears in some of the largest cases in the Chancery Division. **Strengths:** "A very impressive cross-examiner who is completely on the ball and has all the facts at his fingertips." "He is very user-friendly and supportive, and displays a fine approach to dealing with both the people and the issues in a case." **Recent work:** Acted in Sharma v Sharma, a high-profile matter in the High Court involving an alleged breach of fiduciary duty.

Jeremy Cousins QC "A favourite for heavyweight litigation" who appears in the Chancery courts in complex cases. He is well renowned for his expertise in banking and finance disputes. **Strengths:** "A quite exceptional performer who is very intuitive and has a touch of genius about him." "Remarkably versatile and client-friendly. His encyclopaedic knowledge of the law and thorough preparation make him unbeatable."

Lexa Hilliard QC A well-known figure at the Chancery Bar whose commercial chancery practice centres on complex company, insolvency and civil fraud cases. **Strengths:** "She is practical and excellent with clients." "An extremely good lawyer, she is very well prepared and doesn't back down easily." **Recent work:** She appeared in E-Clear v Elia, a case regarding breaches of fiduciary duty and property claims.

JUNIORS

Tim Penny A large proportion of his work consists of matters with substantial elements of international fraud. He is a deeply experienced junior who acts in heavyweight commercial litigation. **Strengths:** "An extremely good advocate, he is imaginative and willing to be creative. The standard of what he does is consistently high." "He is extremely good on paper. He likes to knock ideas around, and generally gets good results." **Recent work:** He acted for the FCA in the High Court in a dispute alleging breaches of the Financial Services and Markets Act.

Iain Pester A highly rated junior who acts in a wide range of company and civil fraud disputes. He is frequently instructed in matters involving companies with a strong connection to the CIS. **Strengths:** "He is very bright and is someone that listens." **Recent work:** He was instructed as junior counsel in VTB Capital v Nutritek International, a USD200 million claim over alleged fraud regarding a Russian dairy business.

Edward Cohen (see p.575) Has a wealth of experience in the Chancery courts, and regularly handles partnership, company and insolvency disputes. **Strengths:** "He has good analytical skills and brings strong commercial understanding to a case." "He is very thorough, bright and quite formidable." **Recent work:** He was involved in a claim against former directors of ES Group, alleging breaches of duty relating to ventures connected with the Delhi Commonwealth Games and 2022 World Cup bid by Qatar.

Max Mallin Frequently instructed in commercial disputes with significant banking and finance elements. He also possesses company law expertise, and handles claims against directors and partnership disputes. **Strengths:** "He is brilliant at cutting through jargon." **Recent work:** Acted in a dispute over an alleged breach of joint venture relating to a restaurant business.

Jamie Riley He regularly acts in and advises on insolvency and banking disputes, and receives particular praise for his work on cases concerning breaches of fiduciary duty. **Strengths:** "He is proportionate, sendible, reassuring and calm." **Recent work:** Appeared in the High Court acting for the claimant in obtaining an emergency freezing order relating to a fraud and breach of trust claim.

Peter Head (see p.623) Has appeared in a wide range of matters ranging from contractual disputes to banking litigation. **Strengths:** "Exceptionally confident in court." "A rising star who is very commercial and turns round work well. He's a real team player." **Recent work:** Acted as junior counsel in Bank of Moscow v JFC Group, a matter concerning a director's liability for failing to comply with an international freezing order.

Marcia Shekerdemian A highly experienced practitioner who is well known for her prowess in company, insolvency and property related litigation. **Strengths:** "She is a very competent junior who has a good command of the detail." "She will always deliver good practical advice and tackle problems with vigour." **Recent work:** Acted in Brookwood Park v Guney and others, a large shareholder dispute alleging breaches of fiduciary duty and misapplication of company funds.

Christopher Boardman Has experience in a range of commercial chancery matters, but is best known for handling insolvency and company disputes. **Strengths:** "He is exceptional at advocacy as his cross-examination is fantastic and he identifies the pressure points in a case very early on." "He is very clear in his thinking and strategy." **Recent work:** Represented the defendants in a dispute arising from a failed joint venture.

Other Ranked Lawyers

Stephen Smith QC (Erskine Chambers) Has a long-standing reputation as one of the key figures at the Chancery Bar. He acts in the full range of commercial matters in both domestic and offshore courts. **Strengths:** "He is truly outstanding. On the ball, thorough and detailed, he really does have the ear of the court. He is hard-hitting but not in an aggressive manner." **Recent work:** He was instructed by the petitioner in Re Phoenix Partnership, a partnership dispute between the two founders of a company.

Peter Arden QC (Erskine Chambers) Praised by commentators for his prowess in company and insolvency disputes. He regularly appears in complex commercial cases in the Chancery courts. **Strengths:** "Very measured and effective in court." **Recent work:** Involved in the sale of law firm Cobbetts by way of pre-pack administration.

Tim Akkouh (Erskine Chambers) A junior whose particular areas of focus include civil fraud and asset recovery. He is also experienced in insolvency and company litigation. **Strengths:** "He is a very sharp advocate who marshals arguments very well in a clear and thorough manner." **Recent work:** He was lead junior acting for JSC BTA Bank of Kazakhstan in the high-profile Ablyazov litigation.

Emily Gillett (Erskine Chambers) A strong junior for company and insolvency work. **Strengths:** "She is impressive on her feet and very good at dealing with important points." **Recent work:** Was heavily involved in the Ablyazov litigation over JSC BTA Bank of Kazakhstan's attempts to recover USD5 billion from its former directors.

Anthony de Garr Robinson QC (One Essex Court) Highly regarded for his appellate work, he tackles a wide range of matters including civil fraud and banking disputes. **Strengths:** "He is incredibly bright and a master strategist." **Recent work:** He was instructed by the defendant in Antonio Gramsci Shipping v Recoletos, a big-ticket shipping fraud dispute.

Paul McGrath QC (Essex Court Chambers) A highly regarded civil fraud and asset recovery specialist who devotes a significant proportion of his practice to the Chancery Division. **Strengths:** "He is imaginative and someone you can really talk to and bounce ideas off." **Recent work:** He played a key role in Axiom v Schools, an alleged fraud of £120 million.

Edmund King (Essex Court Chambers) A distinguished junior with experience of acting in a wide range of commercial cases domestically and offshore. **Recent work:** He was instructed to act in Saltri v MD Mezzanine, a complex financial dispute which included questions relating to fiduciary duties.

David Peters (Essex Court Chambers) Handles civil fraud, company and insolvency disputes, and is often instructed on cases with multi-jurisdictional issues to them. **Strengths:** "He is an enormously impressive advocate. Cool and clear in his advice, he has a thorough grasp of the law." "A rising star whose quality of work is often beyond his level of call. He is able to distil complex facts into clear and concise arguments." **Recent work:** He was instructed to act for the claimant in Dar Al Arkan v Al-Refai, a dispute over alleged misuse of confidential information.

Nicholas Caddick QC (Hogarth Chambers) Undertakes a significant commercial chancery caseload. Historic areas of focus for this experienced silk include personal and corporate insolvency, and company disputes. **Strengths:** "He is very quick at picking up the salient facts." "Responsive, commercial, and his work is well thought out."

Alex Hall Taylor (4 New Square) Focuses primarily on financial and company disputes, and has a fine reputation for professional negligence cases. He often acts in litigation both domestically and offshore. **Strengths:** "Very conscientious and works hard." **Recent work:** He was involved in Langstone Leisure v Pannone, a large professional negligence case relating to advice given in wrongful trading proceedings.

Jonathan Gavaghan (Ten Old Square) Frequently acts on large-scale, multi-jurisdictional disputes heard in the Chancery courts. Partnership and property litigation are particular strengths of his. **Strengths:** "Quick, slick, and has a tremendous ability to grasp the real issues."

Nicolas Stallworthy QC (Outer Temple Chambers) Commands considerable respect for his commercial chancery practice and is renowned for his pension scheme expertise. **Strengths:** "He absolutely puts in the hours for his clients." **Recent work:** He acted in IBM v Dalgleish, a dispute regarding an alleged breach of duty of good faith with regard to the company's defined benefits pension plan.

Farhaz Khan (Outer Temple Chambers) Handles banking, pensions and financial services litigation, and commands considerable respect both from his clients and his peers. **Strengths:** "A junior with great commercial acumen." **Recent work:** He was instructed in Merrill Lynch v Amorim Partners, a contractual dispute regarding the sale of shares in Saipem SpA.

Keith Rowley QC (Radcliffe Chambers) A key figure at the Chancery Bar who is particularly good at pensions law but can turn his hand to all manner of commercial chancery work. Professional negligence and real estate disputes are other areas of focus for him. **Strengths:** "Provides clear and unequivocal advice."

Dov Ohrenstein (Radcliffe Chambers) Regularly involved in a wide range of commercial disputes heard in the Chancery courts. He mainly focuses on company, banking and professional negligence claims. **Strengths:** "Commercial and down to earth, he provides quick, practical, no-nonsense advice."

Elizabeth Ovey (Radcliffe Chambers) Has a chancery practice that straddles both commercial and traditional matters. She is frequently instructed on pensions and professional negligence claims. **Strengths:** "An excellent senior junior who has a great eye for detail and an outstanding grasp of the complexities of a case."

Ulick Staunton (Radcliffe Chambers) A highly experienced junior with a well-established domestic and international commercial practice. He appears in court and advises on a range of different areas of law, including professional negligence and partnership issues. **Strengths:** "A bullish advocate who has an excellent commercial approach that is appreciated by business and corporate clients."

Shantanu Majumdar (Radcliffe Chambers) An accomplished junior with a commercial chancery practice that spans insolvency, partnership and company matters. **Strengths:** "He is very bright, easy to work with, and what he provides is always to a top-level standard."

Romie Tager QC (Selborne Chambers) Noted for his broad commercial practice, this highly experienced silk is a fine all-rounder who is especially strong on real property litigation. **Strengths:** "A formidable advocate and a dominating courtroom presence." "He's always on top of the detail." **Recent work:** He has been heavily involved in Miller v Partridge, a fraudulent misrepresentation claim against the former chairman of an antiques dealership.

Juliette Levy (Selborne Chambers) Handles a wide range of commercial chancery cases and is highly regarded by instructing solicitors. **Strengths:** "Very hard-working and very approachable." **Recent work:** Acted in Abbar v Pinnacle Holdings, a multi-million fraud and breach of contract claim in relation to a property development.

Stuart Hornett (Selborne Chambers) A commercial litigator with an impressive chancery practice. A large amount of his practice is dedicated to company disputes, and he is also highly regarded for real estate litigation. **Strengths:** "A very measured advocate." **Recent work:** He acted in Levin v Tannenbaum, a case concerning guarantees of loans in relation to a Ponzi scheme.

Duncan Kynoch (see p.649) (Selborne Chambers) Experienced at handling insolvency and professional negligence cases, as well as contractual claims. **Strengths:** "He is straightforward to deal with and provides clear, crisp submissions."

Nicholas Trompeter (Selborne Chambers) A dynamic junior with a flourishing reputation whose practice encompasses insolvency, civil fraud and real estate disputes. **Strengths:** "He is very intelligent and has a good grasp of the law." **Recent work:** Was instructed in a claim against Clydesdale Bank alleging a breach of fiduciary duty with regard to overdraft facilities.

Andrew Twigger QC (3 Stone Buildings) Has a diverse chancery practice that is heavy on banking and finance and company disputes. He has a stellar market reputation and is praised for his courtroom advocacy. **Strengths:** "He has a first-class analytical mind." "He is very clever, cuts through the facts and gets down to what the legal position is very quickly." **Recent work:** He acted in Independent Trustee Services Limited v Morris, an asset tracing case concerning money fraudulently transferred from a pension fund.

Fenner Moeran QC (3 Stone Buildings) Has an extensive commercial and traditional chancery practice, and is a popular choice for a wide range of complex cases. He comes particularly highly regarded for his pensions and civil fraud work. **Strengths:** "Very good with clients and a great lateral thinker." "Extremely pragmatic and to the point, he's a pleasure to work with." **Recent work:** He acted in Konica Minolta v Applegate, a pensions dispute regarding rectification of a scheme's rules.

James Weale (see p.748) (3 Stone Buildings) Continues to make his mark in the chancery sphere, and has a blossoming practice. He concentrates on insolvency, professional negligence and contractual disputes. **Strengths:** "He is excellent at identifying the issues and pushing things forward." "In court he is incredibly competent and knowledgeable without coming across as arrogant." **Recent work:** He acted as junior in Earl of Cardigan v Cotton and Moore, an attempt by trustees of the family estate to sell Tottenham House, a Grade I listed building.

Adrian Beltrami QC (3 Verulam Buildings) A leading figure in the market for commercial chancery litigation who handles a range of high-value banking, insolvency and civil fraud disputes. He receives high praise for his advocacy skills. **Strengths:** "Hard-working, effective and knowledgeable." "His ability to produce work of great quality in incredibly short timescales is of particular note." **Recent work:** Acted in Benedetti v Sawiris, a share dispute involving an Italian telecoms company.

Ewan McQuater QC (3 Verulam Buildings) Possesses a chancery practice of great breadth. He is one of the leading figures at the Bar for banking, civil fraud and insolvency disputes, and regularly appears in some of the most significant cases in the Chancery Division. **Strengths:** "His advocacy skills are very good: he is direct, low key and extraordinarily precise." **Recent work:** He acted for the defendants in CF Partners v Barclays Bank, a claim arising out of a deal in the carbon credit sector.

Sonia Tolaney QC (3 Verulam Buildings) Has extensive knowledge of banking, civil fraud and insolvency law. **Strengths:** "Fantastically on the ball and someone with a very good client manner." **Recent work:** She acted for Deutsche Bank in a dispute with Kaupthing HF, arising from the Icelandic bank's collapse. The case concerned an attempt to recover EUR500 million.

Ali Malek QC (3 Verulam Buildings) Has a fantastic reputation for his handling of a wide range of commercial chancery work. He is a distinguished silk in the areas of banking, civil fraud and financial services litigation. **Strengths:** "Someone you want on your team on a difficult case." "A very stylish advocate who has incredible judgement." **Recent work:** He was instructed by the Saudi Economic and Development Company and a number of other defendants in a matter dealing with a share dispute over an Anguillan SPV.

Anne Jeavons (3 Verulam Buildings) Regularly undertakes insolvency, banking and civil fraud cases. **Strengths:** "She's bright, sensible and sound in her advice." **Recent work:** She was involved in Gudavadze v Anisimov, acting for the defendant in this high-profile dispute involving a wide range of allegations, including breach of contract and breach of fiduciary duty.

LONDON Traditional

Chancery: Traditional London
Leading Sets
Band 1
XXIV Old Buildings *
5 Stone Buildings *
Wilberforce Chambers *
Band 2
New Square Chambers *
Ten Old Square *
Radcliffe Chambers *
Serle Court *
Band 3
Maitland Chambers *
3 Stone Buildings *

Leading Silks
Star individuals
Green Brian *Wilberforce Chambers*
Taube Simon *Ten Old Square* *
Band 1
Barlow Francis *Ten Old Square* *
Boyle Alan *Serle Court* *
Brownbill David *XXIV Old Buildings*
Ham Robert *Wilberforce Chambers*
Herbert Mark *5 Stone Buildings* *
Hinks Frank *Serle Court* *
McCall Christopher *Maitland Chambers* *
Rajah Eason *Ten Old Square* *
Reed Penelope *5 Stone Buildings* *
Steinfeld Alan *XXIV Old Buildings*
Talbot Rice Elspeth *XXIV Old Buildings*
Warnock-Smith Shân *5 Stone Buildings* *
Band 2
Angus Tracey *5 Stone Buildings* *
Cooper Gilead *3 Stone Buildings* *
Furness Michael *Wilberforce Chambers*
Laurence George *New Square Chambers* *
Le Poidevin Nicholas *New Square Chambers* *
Legge Henry *5 Stone Buildings* *
Martin John *Wilberforce Chambers*
Tidmarsh Christopher *5 Stone Buildings* *
Band 3
Crampin Peter *3 Stone Buildings* *
Driscoll Michael *Maitland Chambers* *
Newman Catherine *Maitland Chambers* *
Pearce Robert *Radcliffe Chambers*
Rowley Keith *Radcliffe Chambers*
Russen Jonathan *Maitland Chambers* *
Tregear Francis *XXIV Old Buildings*
New Silks
Moeran Fenner *3 Stone Buildings* *

Leading Juniors
Star individuals
Henderson William *Serle Court* *
Tucker Lynton *New Square Chambers* *
Band 1
Dumont Thomas *Radcliffe Chambers*
King Michael *XXIV Old Buildings*
McDonnell Constance *3 Stone Buildings* *
Meadway Susannah *Ten Old Square* *
Rees David *5 Stone Buildings* *
Rich Barbara *5 Stone Buildings* *
Sartin Leon *5 Stone Buildings* *
Whitehouse Christopher *5 Stone Buildings* *
Wilson Richard *3 Stone Buildings* *
Band 2
Bedworth Georgia *Ten Old Square* *
Bryant Judith *Wilberforce Chambers*
Campbell Emily *Wilberforce Chambers*
Child Andrew J *3 Stone Buildings* *
Dew Richard *Ten Old Square* *
Feltham Piers *Radcliffe Chambers* *
Goldsmith Joseph *5 Stone Buildings* *
Hilliard Jonathan *Wilberforce Chambers*
Hubbard Mark *New Square Chambers* *
Learmonth Alexander *New Square Chambers* *
Shah Bajul *XXIV Old Buildings*
Studer Mark *Wilberforce Chambers* *
Weaver Elizabeth *XXIV Old Buildings*
Band 3
Brightwell James *New Square Chambers* *
Cloherty Adam *XXIV Old Buildings*
Crawford Grant *Radcliffe Chambers* *
Cumming Edward *XXIV Old Buildings*
Hagen Dakis *Serle Court* *
Holmes Justin *Radcliffe Chambers*
Hughes Jessica *XXIV Old Buildings*
McQuail Katherine *Radcliffe Chambers*
Moffett William *Radcliffe Chambers*
Mold Andrew *Wilberforce Chambers* *
Mullis Roger *Radcliffe Chambers*
Nurse Gordon *Radcliffe Chambers* *
Quint Francesca *Radcliffe Chambers*
Richardson Giles *Serle Court* *
Rowell David *9 Stone Buildings (ORL)* ◊ *
Staunton Ulick *Radcliffe Chambers*
West Mark *Radcliffe Chambers* *
Band 4
Allardice Miranda *5 Stone Buildings* *
Arkush Jonathan *11 Stone Buildings (ORL)* ◊ *
Arnfield Robert *Ten Old Square* *
Beasley Tom *Radcliffe Chambers*
Child John *Wilberforce Chambers*
Haren Sarah *5 Stone Buildings* *
Hill-Smith Alexander *New Square Chambers* *
Hochberg Daniel *Wilberforce Chambers*
Holbech Charles *New Square Chambers* *
Holden Andrew *XXIV Old Buildings*
O'Sullivan Michael *5 Stone Buildings* *
Ovey Elizabeth *Radcliffe Chambers* *
Scott Tiffany *Wilberforce Chambers*
Selway Kate *Radcliffe Chambers* *
Stewart Smith Rodney *New Square Chambers* *
Thomas Nigel *Maitland Chambers* *
Wells Nathan *Radcliffe Chambers* *
Up-and-coming individuals
Edge Charlotte *5 Stone Buildings* *
Ford Charlotte *New Square Chambers* *
◊ *(ORL) = Other Ranked Lawyer.*
* *Indicates set / individual with profile.*

Band 1

XXIV Old Buildings

See profile on p.838

THE SET A market-leading set for trusts work, XXIV Old Buildings continues to be instructed on the largest cases. The set's offshore firepower is evident and its highly respected barristers practise on an international scale in areas including trust insolvency and asset freezing. The set is a leader in jurisdictions such as the Cayman Islands and the BVI, but is also receiving a growing number of mandates from Asia and the Middle East.

Client service: "The clerks at XXIV Old Buildings, managed by Daniel Wilson and Paul Matthews, are always very good, quick and helpful. They will always try to get you what you want when you need it. "

SILKS

David Brownbill QC A high-calibre advocate who is widely recognised for his role in high-value, innovative international trust matters, including trust insolvency, fraud and asset recovery cases. **Strengths:** "He is fantastic, very bright and so well respected." "Intensely interested in and passionate about the law," he is "a very effective advocate who looks at things from every angle and then looks again." **Recent work:** Acted in Investec Trust v Glenalla Properties and others, a Guernsey-based trust case connected to the liquidation of Kaupthing Bank.

Alan Steinfeld QC A distinguished offshore trusts practitioner hailed for his assured understanding of complex disputes involving high net worth individuals and investment funds. His traditional chancery work is supported by significant expertise in professional negligence and pensions work. **Strengths:** "He has an ability to grasp and get to the nub of things and, more importantly, to both express the crucial issues and ask the right questions extraordinarily quickly." **Recent work:** Instructed in a high-value dispute involving a now defunct Carlyle Group spin-off investment bank.

Elspeth Talbot Rice QC A prominent presence in traditional chancery who focuses on proprietary estoppel and trusts litigation for clients ranging from private individuals to charities. She has specific knowledge of the law of mistake and offshore freezing injunctions. **Strengths:** "A very good, quick-minded advocate who gets to the core of complex scenarios, and is very pragmatic in terms of her solution." "She is one of those extraordinary barristers whose clarity of thought on difficult points is extremely welcome." **Recent work:** Appeared in Coward v MFP & others, a case concerning a claim on company assets held in trust for the applicant.

Francis Tregear QC Has a practice that draws together company law, asset tracing and professional negligence expertise. Many of his cases are international in scope and he is an expert on conflicts of law. **Strengths:** "He is extremely thoughtful, measured, intellectually very rigorous and has very good judgement. You want him on your side when you have a difficult technical matter and he's very good at being persuasive without being aggressive." **Recent work:** Instructed by the Joint Official Liquidators of a Cayman Islands trust in connection with allegations made against fund employees and issues concerning proof of debt.

JUNIORS

Michael King Offers high-quality advice in a number of traditional chancery areas. He is widely recognised for his depth of experience, which is routinely called on when he handles trusts and probate disputes. **Strengths:** "Has vast experience and is very good at getting to the critical issues." "He has a wonderful manner and is terrific to deal with." **Recent work:** Appeared in Illot v Richard Williams & others, a complex case concerning remuneration entitlement for a departing fund manager.

Elizabeth Weaver Prized for her skill in handling trusts, estates and wills litigation. She has a specialism in cases concerning conflicts of foreign laws, and she regularly acts for private clients, court-appointed receivers and trust protectors. **Strengths:** "She is fantastic as she's very sensible, clear and quite single-minded." "As an advocate she is very forward and always willing to interject." **Recent work:** Engaged in Pittas v Christou & Loizou, a probate case involving a challenge to a will made against the deceased's daughter by his adopted daughter, with alleged claims of forgery and lack of knowledge and approval.

Adam Cloherty Offshore trusts expert who provides counsel on both the contentious and non-contentious sides. He has a reputation for quality estates and wills planning and boasts an increasingly strong mediation practice. **Strengths:** "Extraordinarily intelligent, extremely responsive, and someone with a very wide range of knowledge." **Recent work:** Acted for multiple charitable beneficiaries in complex cross-border litigation involving jurisdictional challenge, the determination over whether English or US law governed capacity, and Inheritance Act issues.

Bajul Shah Has a highly rated trusts practice, and has deep expertise in trustee issues such as removal and costs. He couples this with knowledge of Beddoe applications and unlawful assistance, and is widely acknowledged for his excellent advocacy skills. **Strengths:** "First-rate. He's one of the first-choice barristers in a chambers full of talent." **Recent work:** Instructed by the trustee in a bankruptcy trial seeking recovery of funds secretly transferred by the defendant to offshore companies held by a family member.

Andrew Holden Increasingly a go-to advocate for solicitors faced with probate disputes and trust administration issues. His expertise in offshore work is bolstered by his knowledge of trust protectors and multi-territory structures. **Strengths:** "Technically excellent beyond his years and sees a clear way through knotty problems." **Recent work:** Acted in a dispute concerning the seeking of an order to allow the sale of discretionary will trust-owned property which was being challenged by one of the beneficiaries.

Edward Cumming Known for his comprehensive chancery practice, he is often retained on major trust disputes. He is very strong on proprietary estoppel and Inheritance Act matters. **Strengths:** "He's refreshingly robust in his advice and very good on his feet." "Extremely hard-working and diligent, he's a very fine tactician." **Recent work:** Appeared in Crociani v Crociani, an offshore dispute involving multi-jurisdictional proceedings relating to significant family trusts and assets.

Jessica Hughes Excels in both commercial and traditional chancery work, and has experience of handling disputes between trustees and families, particularly those concerning accusations of wrongful exercise of authority. She has significant expertise in the representation of minors and unborns, and is noted for handling trust applications including fund segregation and protector removal. **Recent work:** Represented three sisters in a dispute relating to Lord Lambton's estate.

5 Stone Buildings

See profile on p.866

THE SET

A set to be reckoned with, 5 Stone Buildings has an extensive roster of superlative advocates. It demonstrates outstanding expertise across the gamut of traditional chancery and has lawyers who can handle everything from probate and proprietary estoppel to pensions and offshore trusts. Continually extending their expertise, its members tackle niche areas such as art litigation, and trust-related matrimonial finance work.

Client service: "The clerks, led by Paul Jennings, are flexible, extremely responsive to a request and will go through available counsel with us so we can make an informed choice."

SILKS

Mark Herbert QC A highly regarded tax and trust expert renowned for his keen grasp of complex, sophisticated cases involving capital taxation and offshore matters. His multi-jurisdictional experience covers probate, breach of trust and family provision disputes. He also has a significant advisory practice and displays great expertise in trust drafting. **Strengths:** "Does a first-rate job." "Has a huge amount of experience and always has the ear of the court."

Penelope Reed QC An eminently popular and much-admired silk with a reputation for tackling highly technical probate matters. She couples this with a personable approach and is "widely seen to be at the top of the game." Also has a strong mediation practice. **Strengths:** "A very persuasive advocate who makes a real difference in court. She's very good on the detail and explains complex points clearly." "She's clear on strategy and a persuasive advocate who gets the judge's ear without bluster or fuss."

Shân Warnock-Smith QC Revered for her skills in UK trusts and estates matters, she also has distinct expertise in charitable wealth structuring for international families. In addition to her domestic practice, she offers litigation and advisory counsel from a Cayman Islands base, and is sought out for sensitive cases involving family companies and trust reconstruction. **Strengths:** "She is brilliant. A first-class lawyer who is very calm and understated." "She is a very canny strategist – I have seen her pull rabbits out of hats." **Recent work:** Instructed by Dr Winston Wong in a dispute against Bermuda over asset recovery of funds held in purpose trusts.

Tracey Angus QC A front runner in Inheritance Act cases who is also looked to for equity, land law and probate work. She exhibits further dynamism in Court of Protection and professional negligence work, and is highlighted for her formidable advocacy. **Strengths:** "She's fantastic and has an incredible capacity to absorb information at very short notice. She doesn't sit on the fence and is a brilliant advocate." "She has a meticulous approach and gives clear advice." **Recent work:** Appeared in a contentious probate case concerning artist Lucian Freud's estate and legality of trust issues.

Christopher Tidmarsh QC Acclaimed for his considerable strength in tax matters, but has a broader chancery practice that encompasses advisory and contentious work in domestic and offshore trusts. Also has notable knowledge of professional negligence in relation to pension schemes. **Strengths:** "He has tremendous drafting skills and is extremely bright."

Henry Legge QC Adroit chancery practitioner who focuses on high-profile, large-scale trusts and pensions disputes, both domestic and offshore. He is well respected for his ability to handle difficult, entangled matters, including asset recovery and breach of trust, and has specialist knowledge of cases involving art. **Strengths:** "An extremely good advocate who is very personable with clients." "He takes a very analytical approach to things, and judges like him. They will take advice from him and ask his opinion on things. He's a barrister with standing." **Recent work:** Successfully acted in Gorbunova v Berezovksy, a case seeking a multi-territory freezing injunction against Boris Berezovsky and associated parties.

JUNIORS

David Rees A greatly sought-after junior whose standout practice encompasses trusts and estates litigation. He couples this with mediation expertise and a strong advisory practice. **Strengths:** "A pre-eminent name for Court of Protection work." "He can give you a very clear opinion on difficult topics." **Recent work:** Engaged in Baker Tilly v Makar, a matter involving issues of capacity and the designation of a litigation friend.

Barbara Rich (see p.707) A noted trusts expert who is also known for her substantial Court of Protection expertise, particularly when it comes to cases concerning the Mental Capacity Act 2005. She takes a detailed, authoritative approach to complex, sensitive succession and power of attorney disputes. **Strengths:** "She fights her case very well and does a thoroughly good job." "Adept at dealing with complex Court of Protection work." **Recent work:** Instructed in a five-day Court of Protection hearing which involved issues such as permission to claim recovery of funds unlawfully paid to third parties, lifetime gift authorisation and statutory will matters.

Leon Sartin A prominent presence at the Chancery Bar hailed for the wide scope of his practice, which takes in traditional trusts and estates work as well as Court of Protection and professional negligence matters. **Strengths:** "Offers invaluable assistance on complex trust queries. He's always responsive and commercial, and a pleasure to work with." "He has a very good bedside manner with clients, and makes the complicated very straightforward."

Christopher Whitehouse A highly rated junior who carries a sterling reputation for tackling the full spectrum of trusts and private taxation work. He demonstrates further expertise in multi-territory domicile cases and the administrative aspects of wills and estate planning. **Strengths:** "Absolutely first-class, he grasps the issues extremely well and extremely quickly, is very practical in his advice, and the quality of his written work is faultless." "Very relaxed but very bright, he has this tremendous ability to take hard tax matters and make them simple."

Joseph Goldsmith Advises on property, capital taxation and proprietary estoppel related matters. He is well versed in Court of Protection mental capacity issues and has specific strength in professional negligence cases concerning ecclesiastical issues. **Strengths:** "Very bright, thorough and easy to work with. He can explain things very clearly and has a good courtroom manner." **Recent work:** Defended multiple parties against a claim brought by the Pensions Regulator in relation to 'pension liberation' and allegations of a sham trust.

Miranda Allardice An Inheritance Act authority who also has an excellent matrimonial finance practice. She is noted for being a tenacious advocate, but she also has an extensive and much in demand mediation practice. **Strengths:** "An extremely competent advocate." "She has an encyclopaedic knowledge and is very dogged." **Recent work:** Instructed in a long-running contested probate matter arising from Inheritance Act, company law and administration issues in relation to an estate consisting of a trading company.

Sarah Haren Brings substantial experience of trust taxation, wills and the 1975 Act to her well-regarded practice. She offers additional contentious and non-contentious expertise in Court of Protection cases. **Strengths:** "Provides clear, concise advice." "She's bright and very good on the details." **Recent work:** Successfully acted for the defendant in Bennett v Petit, a probate case where the validity of a will was maintained despite claims of want of knowledge and approval due to the deceased's illiteracy.

Michael O'Sullivan Acts for high-profile clients in prominent matters ranging from probate cases involving lack of capacity to statutory wills and property disputes concerning professional negligence and fraudulent misrepresentation. **Strengths:** "Great clarity and forthrightness of advice."

Charlotte Edge Fast-rising junior who is praised for her excellent written and oral advocacy and expertise in probate litigation. She appears in complex, multilateral cases that often involve claims of lack of capacity and incompetent trustee conduct. **Strengths:** "She is able to get on top of matters quickly and advise clients with ease, clarity and good commercial sense. A dynamic, firm and persuasive advocate." "She drafts beautifully, and is just a pleasure to deal with." **Recent work:** Appeared in Green v Astor, a case arising from the challenge by an estate's beneficiary against various actions by the executor, alleging improper conduct.

Wilberforce Chambers

See profile on p.876

THE SET

An outstanding set which maintains its widely acknowledged position as a leader in traditional chancery matters. It has an enviable depth of expertise, and its talented barristers are prominent in high-profile, high-value trusts and estates cases and pensions matters. They are also involved in trust-related work arising out of divorce proceedings.

Client service: "The clerks, headed by Mark Rushton, are helpful, proactive and serve the barristers well."

SILKS

Brian Green QC A powerhouse practitioner who offers almost unparalleled authority and expertise across the spectrum of traditional chancery work. He is acclaimed for his exceptional pensions knowledge and continues to counsel on high-profile, complex litigation involving trusts. **Strengths:** "He is up there in lights for everyone." "He has a very easy manner, superlative intelligence and the ability to keep innumerable balls in the air. He is an extraordinarily collaborative person and even if he is on the other side you can get things done."

Robert Ham QC Offers exemplary skill in major trust disputes on a domestic and international scale. He is further renowned for his knowledge of fiduciary principles, and tax avoidance limitations. **Strengths:** "Superb. He wears his intelligence and skills very lightly, and you know as soon as you are going to go see him you will get the answer." "He is a mine of information and a fount of authority, and has a really detailed, in-depth understanding of all the issues that arise in relation to chancery-type litigation. A very persuasive and powerful advocate."

Michael Furness QC Has a forte in contentious UK and offshore trust matters combined with extensive experience in tax litigation. He has a well-regarded practice in relation to Hong Kong and is a noted professional negligence lawyer. **Strengths:** "He has excellent insight and the ability to refine difficult intellectual points into a client-friendly form." "Has a huge intellect and a brain the size of a football." **Recent work:** Instructed in a case before the Court of Appeal concerning the Malcolm Arnold estate. This matter concerned power of attorney and interpretation of will issues.

John Martin QC Has a great track record across numerous areas of the traditional chancery field, from property and trusts work to charities-related matters. In addition to his contentious practice, he is also an acclaimed arbitrator and mediator, and further sits as a deputy High Court judge. **Strengths:** "A great court animal who is terrific on his feet." "An enormously impressive man, he has tremendous gravitas."

JUNIORS

Judith Bryant Devotes much of her time to trusts and related tax issues, handling both contentious and non-contentious cases. She is sought after by trustees in relation to additional powers and financial authority applications, and is expert in administrative matters concerning offshore trusts. **Strengths:** "Very pragmatic and measured in her advice." "Absolutely a safe pair of hands."

Emily Campbell Handles technically difficult and sophisticated litigious cases in relation to domestic and offshore trusts, taxation and pensions. She is also strong on the advisory side and has an admirable private client roster. **Strengths:** "She is great at getting to the root of the legal issue." "Astute and willing to take difficult points and run with them."

Jonathan Hilliard A prominent client list looks to him for assistance on major, high-value domestic and offshore trusts cases. He has considerable experience in matters concerning the capacity and limitations of UK court attempts to include overseas trusts in divorce cases. **Strengths:** "He is super-bright and displays a real energy and commitment to the case." "Self-effacing, down to earth, extremely bright, and really good to put before clients." **Recent work:** Defended law firm Ackerman against allegations of dishonesty in its management of a trust brought by Hassans, Line Trust Corporation and others.

Mark Studer Has an excellent advisory practice, and handles a wide scope of private client disputes. He has specialist knowledge of charity-related trust administration and matters concerning agricultural estates. **Strengths:** "Very experienced and very knowledgeable. He's always willing to help at short notice and his responsiveness is first-class."

Andrew Mold (see p.675) Has a notable chancery practice which is especially strong in relation to sensitive trust disputes and high-value divorce proceedings. He handles a wide range of chancery cases including pensions, partnership and property cases. **Strengths:** "Incredibly brainy and he goes out of his way to make life easy for the instructing solicitor and to find practical solutions for his clients." **Recent work:** Appeared in high-profile, multi-jurisdictional divorce case Rybolovleva v Rybolovlev, which concerned USD12 billion assets held in a Cypriot trust structure.

John Child A trust structuring expert who advises on cases concerning landed estates and major family trusts. He combines this with significant knowledge of revenue issues and has further niche expertise in matters concerning the Society of Lloyd's.

Daniel Hochberg Lauded for his expertise in trusts matters involving trading companies, many of which are overseas entities. He couples this with extensive work concerning employee benefit trusts. **Strengths:** "A trusts expert with a great deal of experience." **Recent work:** Engaged by Ennismore & Vistra in a successful defence against an employee claim for alleged breach of contract and trust in relation to an employment benefit trust.

Tiffany Scott Provides well-regarded advice for a diverse range of clients, including financial institutions and charities, as well as private individuals. She mainly concentrates on trusts and estates matters, both litigious and non-contentious, on a domestic and global scale. **Strengths:** "Offers straightforward, sensible and clear advice." **Recent work:** Appeared in Taylor v Peacock Financial Management, a matter involving beneficiary claims of trustee negligence, excessive remuneration and beneficiary bias.

Band 2

New Square Chambers

See profile on p.837

THE SET

New Square Chambers is a highly popular choice for solicitors due to its provision of excellent barristers who are well versed in trust matters. Individuals here are also strong on insolvency, tax and company law cases as well as many other traditional chancery areas. Commentators applaud the high calibre of the members and say that they are particularly good when it comes to handling sophisticated offshore matters and Court of Appeal cases.

Client service: "The clerks, led by Neil Garrett and Phil Reeves, are always very friendly, helpful and efficient at dealing with enquiries."

SILKS

Nicholas Le Poidevin QC A highly regarded advocate who specialises in contentious trusts and wills work, and has an excellent reputation for handling real property and professional negligence matters. He exhibits a skilful grasp of conflict of law issues and provides considered advice on cases concerning challenges to trustee authority, trust variation and Beddoe applications. **Strengths:** "Any superlative would not do him justice. His advice is superb, his drafting is elegant and he is tremendous in conference." "Learned but practical and able to take a commercial approach. Whatever he says about the law, you feel comfortable with, and he's very good at working with you and seeking out your ideas."

George Laurence QC Specialises in village green matters and rights of way, especially in relation to local authority land. His practice also extends to environmental and minor highways cases. **Strengths:** "A fabulous opponent who is hard-working, modest, effective and impressive." "He is amazing. Not only is he extremely clever, but he will always be able to see sense in any unformed thing you say." **Recent work:** Appeared in a case before the Court of Appeal in connection with the upholding of a judgment that a Newhaven beach could be registered as a village green.

JUNIORS

Lynton Tucker An outstanding performer who excels in domestic and offshore trust matters including trusteeship duties and breach of trust, self-dealing and applications for directions. He remains a standout practitioner on the non-contentious side, advising on estate planning and administration, wills and trust structuring. **Strengths:** "One of the best, not just of juniors but silks, who has an incredible knowledge of trust law."

Mark Hubbard Deemed especially knowledgeable on cases concerning the interplay between trusts and company law, he is noted for expertise in offshore disputes. His chancery practice is supported by considerable experience in the conflicts of laws area. **Strengths:** "A rising star who is first-class on quirky trust points." "Exceptionally brilliant in coming up with solutions to a case, he thinks creatively and comes up with ideas no one else has thought of." **Recent work:** Appeared in Mosley v Popely, a dispute alleging breach of trust through unlawful facilitation by an offshore trustee of a multi-aspect structure.

James Brightwell Highlighted for his strong trusts practice and noted tax expertise. He adroitly handles probate and Inheritance Act disputes and handles cases concerning requests for trustee removal. **Strengths:** "Very helpful and a very good tactician, he offers excellent advice throughout." "A good-quality person on tricky matters. He is good at explaining things in a user-friendly way, and wants to feel that you know the law and understand the practicalities." **Recent work:** Successfully acted for the claimants in a probate challenge seeking the invalidation of a will due to undue influence.

Alexander Learmonth (see p.653) An authority on wills who is an expert on the law of succession. He is sought out for major probate disputes, and also frequently advocates on real property matters. **Strengths:** "Erudite and affable." "He's very technically and tactically able."

Alexander Hill-Smith (see p.628) An excellent client list regularly instructs him on real property matters. He demonstrates further experience in professional negligence and cases involving freezing injunctions. **Strengths:** "Very bright and practical, he applies a lot of common sense to cases."

Charles Holbech (see p.629) Has a strong reputation for trust disputes and matters involving tax elements. He has additional strength in proprietary estoppel and administration of estate issues. **Strengths:** "Very succinct and very clear in his advice." "He brings detailed knowledge to a case." **Recent work:** Acted in Neale v Gresham Thompson, a dispute over the validity of a will involving claims and counterclaims concerning want of knowledge and approval, proprietary estoppel and codicil issues.

Rodney Stewart Smith (see p.728) Offers high-quality, broad-ranging advice on offshore and multi-jurisdictional trust cases. He is particularly good at advising on the structuring of trusts and variation of terms. **Strengths:** "Very good on technically difficult matters."

Charlotte Ford (see p.601) Has a high-profile trusts and contentious probate practice, and is particularly active in matters concerning disputed representation of estates, power of attorney, and complex Inheritance Act issues. **Strengths:** "She's very down to earth and her advocacy skills are excellent. She's particularly good when faced with challenging litigants in person." **Recent work:** Acted in Watts v Watts, a breach of trust case alleging undue influence in the procurement of trust interests.

Ten Old Square

See profile on p.839

THE SET

Ten Old Square offers authoritative advice to a host of leading private client solicitors' firms both at home and abroad. Its members take on an interesting spread of work, and prove particularly strong on trusts, contentious probate and wills cases. They also have an interest in charity law matters and Court of Protection cases. Commentators note that the members here have been involved in some of the most high-profile matters to hit the market in recent times. Examples include the Nina Wang, Schrader and Sheffield cases.

Client service: "The clerking, led by Keith Plowman, is very good. The clerks are engaged, pull out the stops and go the extra mile."

SILKS

Simon Taube QC Has an exemplary domestic and offshore trusts practice and deep knowledge of trust taxation and organisation. He excels in both contentious and advisory matters, and receives ample praise for the strength of his advocacy and excellence of his advice. **Strengths:** "Determination, massive intellect and a nose for his opponents' weaknesses make him both a brilliant advocate and adviser." "He's phenomenally bright, has impeccable judgement, and his advice is always concise and clear." **Recent work:** Appeared in Labrouche v Frey, a case concerning breach of trust, clandestine profits and unlawful investment by a Swiss trustee.

Francis Barlow QC Revered for the quality of his broad traditional chancery practice and his outstanding knowledge of trusts. He is highly respected for his expertise in the law of succession and also provides sought-after advice on estate administration and wills, proving especially strong on executorship law. **Strengths:** "He is someone who thinks about things a lot and comes up with clever solutions to difficult problems. If something worries you or if you want heavyweight opinion, he is the one you go to." "He has incredible, in-depth knowledge of the intricacies of trust law at his fingertips."

Eason Rajah QC Maintains his upward trajectory in the chancery field, and regularly takes on complex cross-border trust litigation. He is an authority on the role of executors, and works on tax and professional negligence issues in connection with wills. **Strengths:** "A superb QC who makes unbelievably complicated things look very easy." "A consummate problem solver, who is brilliant, personable and confidence-instilling." **Recent work:** Acted in multi-jurisdictional proceedings involving allegations of breach of trust. The claimant was seeking restitution of over USD100 million of trust property.

JUNIORS

Susannah Meadway (see p.670) A leading junior with consummate skill in estates and trusts work, who is expert at drafting, will rectification and the restructuring of funds. She has further experience in Court of Protection and charity law cases. **Strengths:** "Absolutely excellent in all respects. Very technically strong indeed, she gives very thorough advice." "She's excellent at untangling complicated trust structures."

Georgia Bedworth Looked to by private clients for trusts and probate work, notably in connection with real property. She has a further focus in related capital tax matters and contentious construction issues. **Strengths:** "On the ball and very user-friendly." "She's bright, practical and responsive." **Recent work:** Engaged in a matter before the Court of Appeal over the interpretation of 'benefit' rules in relation to inheritance tax and the application of that interpretation to a reversionary lease agreement.

Richard Dew (see p.587) Excels in traditional chancery work, especially in relation to professional negligence and taxation work. He couples this with considerable knowledge of capacity questions and inheritance tax matters and has notable expertise in Court of Protection cases. **Strengths:** "Very incisive and very clear in his advice." "He takes a pragmatic and commercial approach and has excellent client-handling skills." **Recent work:** Acted in Goodman v Goodman, a case concerning a considerable UK estate which involved an application for the removal of the estate's executors.

Robert Arnfield (see p.537) Rated for his internationally focused trusts and estates practice, he is an expert on issues of entailment, executor powers and variation. His broader chancery practice extends to insolvency, real property and professional negligence, as well as capital gains and inheritance tax. **Strengths:** "He has the ability to clearly communicate issues to lay clients and his advocacy is pragmatic, appropriately structured, and covers the key points incisively." **Recent work:** Acted for the executors in Starkey v Higham, a case brought before the High Court disputing the legitimacy of lifetime gifts.

Radcliffe Chambers

See profile on p.856

THE SET

Radcliffe Chambers has a deep focus on contentious and non-contentious traditional chancery work, and brims with practitioners who use their broad expertise to tackle high-value, prominent cases. The set is noted for its excellent private client representation, and commands respect for its ability to meld trusts, estates and probate work. It also has extensive experience of areas such as charity law, professional negligence, pensions and property.

Client service: "The clerks, headed by Keith Nagle and John Clark, are efficient, responsive and keep in touch with you. They are incredibly helpful and always find someone with the correct expertise."

SILKS

Robert Pearce QC Remains well respected for his trusts expertise, both contentious and non-contentious, and is good on tax-related issues. He is also experienced in Court of Protection cases and has strong in-depth professional liability knowledge. **Strengths:** "He is very approachable, very clear in explaining the issues and good at drafting." **Recent work:** Advised on a matter concerning familial disputes over the administration of parental estates.

Keith Rowley QC Particularly active in disputes concerning professional negligence claims and breaches of trust, he is one of the big names at the Chancery Bar. **Strengths:** "He's excellent on large trust matters." **Recent work:** Acted in litigation brought by a lender claiming breach of trust and unlawful assistance in relation to several back-to-back residential mortgages where the same solicitor represented connected buyers.

JUNIORS

Thomas Dumont A highly rated junior who is sought out for complicated, high-profile proceedings and sensitive cases involving minors as beneficiaries. He acts for a diverse range of clients and is renowned for the scope of his practice, which takes in contentious probate and trusts work. He has a noted specialism in advising charities on legacy matters. **Strengths:** "A heavyweight junior for the more complex cases, whose wealth of experience is invaluable in getting to the bottom of difficult technical questions." "He has a wonderful way with clients, can be relied on to keep them on the straight and narrow, and continues to attract very interesting cases." **Recent work:** Successfully acted for beneficiaries of minor age in a major variation of trusts application.

Piers Feltham Has experience of handling prominent chancery cases and an impressive pedigree in proprietary estoppel matters. He advises on estates and real property cases on a domestic and international scale, and has substantial expertise in matters concerning will rectification and undue influence. **Strengths:** "Highly skilled and knowledgeable in Court of Protection matters, he has an invaluable ability to keep clients focused." "He's very pragmatic, decisive and a good all-rounder." **Recent work:** Acted for the victims of Jimmy Savile against the Jimmy Savile Charitable Trust, seeking administrative efforts to preserve his estate for funding compensation claims.

William Moffett A probate, wills and trusts expert who garners notice for his work in want of capacity cases and Inheritance Act disputes. He has a niche specialism in the area of deathbed gifts and often acts in professional negligence-related chancery litigation. **Strengths:** "He has superb attention to detail and a charming manner with clients." "Practical, thorough, and building a strong reputation in chancery work." **Recent work:** Appeared in multiple proceedings concerning lack of testator capacity in terms of estate beneficiaries.

Grant Crawford (see p.580) Focuses on trusts and related tax implications, notably tax avoidance, together with property matters. He is adept at handling disputes relating to the validity of wills and breaches of duty, and further advises on estate administration. **Recent work:** Instructed in a matter concerning proprietary estoppel rights in relation to a sports club's occupation of property and grounds.

Katherine McQuail Has a broad traditional chancery practice and boasts excellent contentious probate expertise and specific knowledge of freezing injunctions and non-compliance related sanctions. She frequently appears in Inheritance Act cases, and retains her acclaimed standing in Court of Protection matters. **Strengths:** "She has great ability and is also a great team player." "As an advocate she is always well prepared." **Recent work:** Acted in an Inheritance Act dispute concerning a minor's entitlement to an estate amid claims of proprietary estoppel brought by the grandparents.

Roger Mullis A property disputes specialist who is also engaged in probate litigation. He has significant experience in questions of capacity and claims of forgery, and is strong on cases concerning the mishandling of estate assets. **Strengths:** "Quite understated but strong." "An excellent advocate who marries very significant academic ability with an innate practicality." **Recent work:** Appeared in a will trust and sub-trust dispute involving an equitable accounting claim and issues of entitlement to occupation rent and quantum.

Gordon Nurse (see p.683) An experienced and astute practitioner with a wide scope of traditional chancery expertise, who regularly handles Court of Protection work and cases involving professional negligence. **Recent work:** Acted in relation to a widow's efforts to settle claims against the estate of her deceased husband made by children from his first marriage, a matter made problematic by the existence of potential offshore assets.

Francesca Quint Renowned for her extensive advisory and charity law practice, she is frequently engaged on matters concerning will interpretation and charitable endowments. **Strengths:** "She is sound on legal principles and clear and practical in her advice." **Recent work:** Instructed by the governor of a hospital in relation to the terms and overseeing by a protector of a substantial gift made by his charitable foundation.

Ulick Staunton Has dual excellence in traditional and commercial chancery work, and handles everything from contentious probate and issues of capacity to negligence claims and conflicts of interest. **Strengths:** "An extremely effective strategist." "A tenacious advocate who is extremely quick on his feet in court."

Mark West Has substantial experience of trusts and estates cases, and handles work including will rectification and estate administration. He regularly advises on trustee duties and exercise of power issues. **Strengths:** "He's incredibly thorough, and leaves no angle unexamined." **Recent work:** Instructed by the beneficiary in relation to rectification issues surrounding a deed of appointment.

Tom Beasley Provides considered counsel to a range of clients, including beneficiaries, executors and creditors in relation to wills and estates. He complements this with a laudable professional negligence practice, and is noted for handling cases involving improper execution of wills. **Recent work:** Acted in a case concerning two wills signed on the same day, addressing the question of which will should take precedence.

Justin Holmes His traditional chancery practice continues to go from strength to strength, and encompasses Inheritance Act disputes, and cases concerning executor and trustee removal, want of capacity, and gifts of shares. He has specific experience in matters involving the application of foreign law to English assets, especially in relation to matrimonial disputes and the validity of overseas wills and codicils. **Strengths:** "His intellect is combined with a pragmatic approach to problem solving." "Enthusiastic, very approachable and well liked by clients." **Recent work:** Appeared in a contentious probate case concerning matters of authenticity, forgery and undue influence, where the will was apparently discovered in the street among the testator's rubbish and received by the claimant from an anonymous source.

Elizabeth Ovey Has a traditional chancery practice strong on wills, trusts and estates, and pensions cases. She is known for having a significant grasp of issues concerning trustee powers. **Strengths:** "She's calm, balanced and has a considered air about her. She is very good with clients, who find her reassuring, and she gives a fantastic written opinion." "Very conscientious, empathetic and user-friendly." **Recent work:** Engaged in Knox v Sharp Young and Pearce, a matter arising from the gift of a property by parents to a son which was undermined in tax terms when the mother unexpectedly died.

Kate Selway Has great ability in tax-related chancery work along with Court of Protection expertise and substantial knowledge of charitable trusts. She retains an accomplished contentious probate practice, tackling validity issues and questions of capacity, and is regularly instructed in cases addressing trustee powers of advancement. **Strengths:** "Always very enthusiastic, she's crystal clear on the issues and on the road map through them." **Recent work:** Appeared in a dispute over the capacity of the benefactor in relation to a substantial lifetime bequest.

Nathan Wells (see p.749) Advisory and contentious practice which encompasses a wide scope of traditional chancery work, from unlawful suppression of wills to litigious estate administration. He is particularly well regarded for his professional negligence work, especially in connection with misrepresentation and trust construction. **Strengths:** "His pleadings are absolutely brilliant, his skeleton arguments are par excellence and he is incredibly good at writing letters. He is extremely technically accomplished and clients like him. A lawyer with a very nice manner when on his feet, he forensically builds up a case." **Recent work:** Successfully defended an estate's sole beneficiary in a proprietary estoppel and Inheritance Act case which also featured questions of common intention constructive trust.

Serle Court

See profile on p.860

THE SET

Serle Court stands out due to the high calibre of counsel provided by its roster of "absolute stars." It has an impressive pedigree in traditional chancery, and a history of handling cases of note and major value, particularly in the offshore trusts area. Engaged by a distinguished client list, it is a highly popular choice with solicitors, and enjoys a sterling reputation, not least for its bench of acclaimed juniors.

Client service: "The clerking, with Steve Whitaker as Head Clerk, is great. They are co-operative, helpful and responsive."

SILKS

Alan Boyle QC An esteemed advocate who is widely acclaimed for his distinguished trusts and probate practice. He has a specific specialism in the trust elements of divorce proceedings and is further prized for his depth of expertise in offshore and multi-jurisdictional trust-related fraud. **Strengths:** "Highly impressive and astonishingly quick to develop a detailed understanding of a case and a client's needs." "Utterly dedicated to the client's cause, he's tirelessly hard-working, an imaginative problem solver and an outstanding advocate to have on side when cases reach court."

Frank Hinks QC An eminent silk who commands respect for his exceptional track record in trust litigation. He advises on high-value cases involving prominent clients and is an expert on validity issues surrounding offshore trusts and the judicial overview of trustee powers. **Strengths:** "Immensely reliable, learned and in the top flight of trust litigators and advisers." "He's a good collaborator, who is extremely good at turning the work around, very accessible and very much part of the team. He's at the top of his game."

JUNIORS

William Henderson An outstanding junior who is acclaimed for his leading probate and trusts expertise. He acts for a broad array of clients, from private individuals to HMRC, on chancery matters including estate administration and professional negligence. He also receives praise for his superb knowledge of charity law. **Strengths:** "A standout junior who is very highly regarded and operates at the level of a silk." "He's got very good judgement on the tactical side." **Recent work:** Appeared in Pitt v Holt, a case ultimately addressed in the Supreme Court concerning a settlement made by Mrs Pitt in her capacity as a Court of Protection receiver, which she carried out on the basis of seemingly proficient but actually incorrect counsel.

Dakis Hagen A trusts, estates and wills barrister with a practice that covers breach of trust and improper conduct, as well as offshore fund restructuring. He is highly rated for his grasp of trust matters in connection with matrimonial disputes, and offers quality counsel on fraud and asset tracing. **Strengths:** "He is absolutely fantastic as he's so clever and quick. You want him on your side. He's absolutely destined for greatness and is a practitioner of the highest quality." **Recent work:** Acted in Tchenguiz v Imerman, divorce proceedings with substantial trust aspects that included matters connected to offshore Beddoe proceedings.

Giles Richardson Has a distinct international aspect to his trusts work, and has strong company and insolvency law expertise. **Strengths:** "He's extremely helpful, user-friendly, and gets right to the issues." **Recent work:** Appeared in a matter regarding a Jersey foundation set up by a Russian businessman who was subsequently convicted of fraud in relation to a Russian state bank.

Band 3

Maitland Chambers

See profile on p.831

THE SET

Maitland Chambers draws on its impressive commercial background to offer vastly experienced counsel on chancery matters ranging from traditional trusts and estates cases to matters involving property, tax and company law. It has a bedrock of esteemed silks and a growing presence at junior level, and is particularly known for its adept handling of high-value offshore litigation.

Client service: "I was confident in the clerks' ability to correctly correspond with the barristers, and never had trouble getting hold of anyone. Led by John Wiggs they were also good at giving us estimates, which meant we could get client approval."

SILKS

Christopher McCall QC A dynamic trusts practitioner who devotes the majority of his practice to tax-related matters, and is further looked to for expertise in charity law. He offers much-admired counsel on domestic and offshore issues, and receives significant instructions in high-value cases stemming from Asia. **Strengths:** "Still impressive and much sought after." "Somebody who comes up with ideas I would never have thought of if I'd contemplated them for a year."

Michael Driscoll QC A barrister noted for the quality of his advocacy who is well respected for his work in contentious trusts, real property and professional negligence cases. **Strengths:** "A stalwart of the Bar." "An excellent advocate who is able to provide clear and focused advice."

Catherine Newman QC A highly regarded advocate who has an extensive track record of representing a diverse client base in matters in the highest courts. She has a deep understanding of trusts and company law, and also draws on substantial probate, insolvency and finance experience. **Strengths:** "She's able to very quickly digest a lot of complex information and give us a roadmap for the case." "A bright, forceful litigator."

Jonathan Russen QC An accomplished commercial litigator who tackles traditional chancery matters including offshore trusts and wills work. His practice is strengthened by his additional expertise in company law and financial services cases. **Strengths:** "A charming advocate." "One of the nicest people at the Bar and a man with a fierce intellect." **Recent work:** Instructed by the defendant in Liao v Liao, a case heard in the British Virgin Islands involving estate administration rights endowing corporate control of an extensive business empire in Asia and Europe.

JUNIORS

Nigel Thomas (see p.736) Has long-standing traditional chancery experience and a history of acting in major cases. He has a notable background in probate and Court of Protection cases addressing questions of capacity. Also boasts exemplary property law knowledge, particularly in matters involving agricultural land and drainage. **Strengths:** "A specialist in proprietary estoppel who is very user-friendly and practical." **Recent work:** Acted in Evans v Lloyd, a dispute over alleged undue influence and unconscionable bargain resulting in the entire bequest, without legal advice, of a farm worker's assets to his employer.

3 Stone Buildings

See profile on p.864

THE SET

Acclaimed traditional chancery set 3 Stone Buildings is renowned for its trusts and probate capability, and its expert knowledge of the extent to which foreign law can be applied to the establishment of trusts in England. Its eminently popular silks and juniors are hailed for their ability to tackle major cases, and are proficient at handling matters involving real property, tax and company law aspects. They further have distinct specialisms in areas such as cultural property and antiquities.

Client service: "The clerks, managed by senior clerk Andrew Palmer, will always help you and are very accommodating and efficient."

SILKS

Gilead Cooper QC Offers masterful guidance on trust and property litigation, and has an excellent track record in high-profile disputes. His practice has an increasingly global outlook, advising on complex offshore issues, and he has a notable specialism in matters involving art and antiquities. **Strengths:** "A first-rate lawyer with tremendous clout, he has acted in many of the leading cases over the past ten years." "A very knowledgeable, creative barrister, whose very fine advocacy is incisive and rapier-like." **Recent work:** Instructed by the Earl of Cardigan against an application by trustees Cotton and Moore to sell Grade I listed Tottenham House.

Peter Crampin QC Retains a widely acknowledged domestic and international trusts-focused practice. He has appeared in a number of prominent charity law cases, and also acts on major property cases for a wide-ranging client base.

Fenner Moeran QC A recent silk and a renowned trusts expert, who has a particularly effective real property practice. Commentators further note that he is an expert in highly sensitive family and matrimonial disputes. **Strengths:** "He is able to absorb large amounts of material quickly and effectively, cut through to the key issues in a case and come up with creative ways of achieving a client's aims." "He really throws himself into the tricky points of law and gets the right results." **Recent work:** Appeared in Christie v Christie, a case between trustees and a beneficiary concerning a family trust.

JUNIORS

Constance McDonnell A highly sought-after junior who frequently acts alone against silks on sophisticated cases. She handles a wide range of traditional chancery work, tackling trusts and probate work, as well as professional negligence, Court of Protection and Inheritance Act matters. **Strengths:** "A leading junior in the contentious probate world. She is very calm, very clear, and very good with the lay client, and really inspires confidence." "She is an excellent advocate and her preparatory skills are first-class. Takes a very good commercial approach." **Recent work:** Successfully acted for two national charities in a dispute over the validity of a will amid allegations of lack of capacity due to schizophrenia.

Richard Wilson A trusts authority whose tax consultancy experience is of great advantage on cases involving trust taxation and fraudulent and improper trustee conduct. He has appeared in key onshore and offshore cases, and has also maintained a strong advisory practice counselling landed estates and major institutional trustees. **Strengths:** "A team player who demonstrates a very high level of trust expertise and is not afraid to consider novel approaches to complex problems." "Has a good, relaxed, fluent style in court and bags of practical knowledge." **Recent work:** Engaged in Slutsker v Haron Investments, a case concerning high-value London property held by Cayman trustees and addressing previously unclear issues surrounding the interaction of Russian joint property laws and English land acquisition.

Andrew Child Noted for his acclaimed advocacy and ability to lead on cases against experienced silks. He acts for trustees and beneficiaries in disputes involving the interplay of private international law, fiduciary matters and breach of trust allegations, and has specific strength in trustee and executor dismissal. **Strengths:** "A fantastic advocate who is very robust but manages clients well. He's superb in mediation and a very versatile advocate." "One of those people with that personal gravitas. His opponents look worried when he shows up." **Recent work:** Acted in Greaves v Stolkin, a dispute involving a challenge to the validity of a deathbed codicil.

Other Ranked Lawyers

David Rowell (see p.711) (9 Stone Buildings) A seasoned chancery practitioner who has a particularly strong reputation for his private client work. He provides counsel on probate, Inheritance Act and tax issues, as well as charity law. He is also noted for his property law expertise, particularly when it comes to tenancy matters. **Recent work:** Appeared in a case addressing the issue of whether a testator can endorse his signature on a signed will that is not physically present but has been previously seen by witnesses.

Jonathan Arkush (11 Stone Buildings) Has a highly active contentious chancery practice that takes in trusts, estates and wills cases. He is also strong on testamentary capacity and asset recovery, and has a significant mediation practice. **Strengths:** "He's very sharp and able to instil a great amount of confidence in the clients." **Recent work:** Acted for the defendant in a probate dispute alleging undue influence and lack of capacity in relation to a parent's will.

MIDLANDS

Chancery Midlands
Leading Sets
Band 1
St Philips Chambers *
Band 2
No5 Chambers *
Leading Silks
Band 1
Randall John *St Philips Chambers* *
Leading Juniors
Band 1
Brennan John *St Philips Chambers* *
Burden Angus *St Philips Chambers* [A] *
Eyre Stephen *St Philips Chambers* *
Mitchell David *No5 Chambers* [A]
Morgan James *St Philips Chambers* *
Taylor David *No5 Chambers* [A]
Band 2
Charman Andrew *St Philips Chambers* [A] *
Maguire Andrew *St Philips Chambers* [A]
Preston Nicola *No5 Chambers*
Stockill David *St Philips Chambers*
[A] *direct access (see p.11).*
* *Indicates set / individual with profile.*

Band 1

St Philips Chambers
See profile on p.886
THE SET
St Philips has a national reputation and is home to some of the Midlands' most highly regarded chancery counsel at both silk and junior level. Its members are experts in both traditional and commercial chancery concerns, and receive regular instructions on insolvencies, property and shareholder disputes, and director disqualifications. The barristers at St Philips are particularly praised by instructing solicitors for their willingness to make themselves available at short notice, and the set's juniors are especially noted for their "incredible efficiency."
Client service: Chief clerk Joe Wilson presides over "a well-drilled clerks' room" which "is highly commercial in its approach."

SILKS
John Randall QC The pre-eminent chancery silk on the Midland circuit. He has a broad practice which encompasses commercial disputes, insolvency matters and property litigation. **Strengths:** "A user-friendly barrister with a great bedside manner who inspires client confidence and provides very clear opinions." **Recent work:** Instructed in a complex solicitors' negligence claim which concerned issues of tax avoidance, offshore trusts, company law and breach of fiduciary duty.

JUNIORS
Angus Burden (see p.560) One of the leading traditional chancery practitioners in Birmingham, Burden is principally noted for his expertise in probate disputes, and he is also praised for his advice in relation to drafting trusts and estate planning. **Strengths:** "His knowledge in this area is second to none in Birmingham." "He is straightforward and pragmatic in his approach, and can communicate well with clients." **Recent work:** Instructed on a case which concerned the exercise of a testamentary option over farmland in Warwickshire worth £5 million.

Stephen Eyre An accomplished chancery practitioner whose practice encompasses both commercial and traditional matters. He is noted for his expertise in contentious probate disputes, and is also regularly instructed to act as a mediator. **Strengths:** "He is very precise and thorough and has a very good commercial approach." "He is straightforward and practical, and swift when giving responses." **Recent work:** Instructed by the claimant in a dispute which concerned the enforcement of restrictive covenants on land.

James Morgan A commercial practitioner who is noted for his expertise in commercial disputes and insolvencies. His commercial chancery practice is focused on shareholder disputes and unfair prejudice petitions. **Strengths:** "He is tenacious, but understated – a quietly efficient and highly effective counsel." **Recent work:** Represented a defendant in a complex unfair prejudice petition concerning a multimillion-pound shareholders dispute.

Andrew Charman (see p.570) A highly rated commercial chancery specialist who is able to draw upon his previous experience as a corporate solicitor at a magic circle law firm. **Strengths:** "His advice is very practical and very pragmatic, and he is always accessible, which is essential on fast-moving work." "He is good at working in a team, and is a very astute and knowledgeable counsel." **Recent work:** He successfully represented the claimants in a claim for specific performance and damages in lieu relating to a property sale in the high-profile 'Cube' building in central Birmingham.

Andrew Maguire Recognised for his commercial chancery litigation work, which covers issues relating to mortgages, fiduciary obligation, breach of trust and negligence. **Strengths:** "He is extremely good with clients; having him on our doorstep here in Birmingham is great." **Recent work:** Successfully acted for the National Merchant Buying Society in a case where a former company director was found to be liable under a personal guarantee made to a creditor in relation to debts due by the company.

David Stockill Highly regarded senior junior with a broad practice which covers both traditional and commercial cases. He is noted for his expertise on disputes concerning breach of fiduciary duty. **Strengths:** "A very sensible counsel, who provides practical advice and is good with clients."

John Brennan Has a broad practice that encompasses both the commercial and traditional aspects of chancery work. **Strengths:** "He is a tenacious advocate who is extremely good on his feet; a good personable counsel." **Recent work:** Instructed in a breach of trust claim brought against a solicitor by a lender following on from a remortgage transaction.

Band 2

No5 Chambers
See profile on p.883
THE SET
No5 Chambers' chancery team undertakes a range of both traditional and commercial work, although market commentators principally recognise its strength on the commercial side.

JUNIORS
David Mitchell Focuses his practice on traditional chancery matters, and is highly regarded for his expertise on trusts and estates matters. **Strengths:** "He is a very good team player, highly receptive to both solicitors and clients, and always practical and pragmatic in his advice." **Recent work:** He represented Bloor Homes in relation to issues surrounding the property acquisition and planning permission for a development of 800 homes near a popular tourist destination in Stratford-upon-Avon.

David Taylor Has built a well-recognised chancery practice which covers both commercial and traditional work. He is especially noted for his expertise on property-related matters. **Strengths:** "He is very sharp, very user-friendly and on a high plane of intellectual activity."

Nicola Preston Focuses her practice on traditional chancery work, including wills, probate and trusts matters. Her practice covers both litigation and non-contentious advice. **Strengths:** "She brings knowledge and experience to bear on a case in a direct manner that retains the confidence of the lay client while communicating an informed professional and dogged determination to assert her client's case to a judge and in negotiations."

NORTH EASTERN

Chancery North Eastern	
Leading Sets	
Band 1	
St Philips Chambers *	
Enterprise Chambers *	
Band 2	
Trinity Chambers *	
Leading Silks	
New Silks	
Jory Hugh	*Enterprise Chambers*
Leading Juniors	
Band 1	
Harrison Sarah	*St Philips Chambers* *
Klein Jonathan	*Enterprise Chambers*
Band 2	
Griffin Margaret	*Enterprise Chambers*
Groves Hugo	*Enterprise Chambers*
Howd Stephen	*Zenith Chambers (ORL)* ◊
Kelly Sean	*St Philips Chambers* *
Roberts Stuart	*St Philips Chambers*
Band 3	
Goldberg Simon	*Trinity Chambers* *
Rodger Jonathan	*Enterprise Chambers*
Walker Bruce	*Exchange Chambers (ORL)* ◊
Up-and-coming individuals	
Crossley Dominic	*St Philips Chambers*
Heath Duncan	*Enterprise Chambers*
◊ (ORL) = Other Ranked Lawyer.	
** Indicates set / individual with profile.*	

Band 1

St Philips Chambers
See profile on p.886

THE SET

Following a merger with Birmingham-based powerhouse St Philips the Chancery House Chambers brand has been subsumed by its Midlands partner, yet the legacy set's individual experts remain in situ, and are now backed up by the resources of a considerably larger set. This new branch of St Philips Chambers is home to practitioners with expertise in traditional and commercial chancery work. Members of chambers have significant experience in complex contentious trust and probate cases as well as more niche specialisms such as interest rate swaps and contested Court of Protection applications. Strength across all years of call has earned the set a loyal following among solicitors who seek local counsel with a deep aptitude for chancery cases.

Client service: "The head clerk Colin Hedley is absolutely first-class. He will always find me the right person and he is always willing to talk about fees."

JUNIORS

Sarah Harrison (see p.621) Maintains a broad practice covering all areas of contentious trust and probate work. She is also experienced in offering advice on a full range of non-contentious matters including wills and the administration of trusts. **Strengths:** "She is able to marry being an exceptionally bright individual with offering a commercial and practical point of view." "She knows her subject backwards and is great in court." **Recent work:** On the non-contentious side of her practice, recently advised on the drafting of a will for an individual with assets of more than £30 million. The matter was complicated by the effect of a complex ancillary relief order.

Dominic Crossley Regularly advises clients across the gamut of traditional chancery issues. He is an expert in contentious trusts, contested wills and probate, and Court of Protection applications. **Strengths:** "As a former solicitor himself, he understands what is useful to the professional client." "He is tremendous on his feet. He is not given to grandiose gesturing or posturing; he very much sticks to the facts and that seems to impress judges." **Recent work:** Successfully represented the appellant in a case concerning a cohabiting couple who claimed to have an interest in properties as a result of constructive trusts and proprietary estoppel. The case also raised issues of company law as the court was asked to consider whether properties purchased by the second defendant were acquired subject to the claimant's equitable rights.

Sean Kelly (see p.644) Specialises in cases arising from the mis-selling of interest rate swaps and other financial products. He also has expertise in company law and partnership disputes as well as professional negligence claims arising from the sale of businesses and property. **Strengths:** "The written advice he gives is first-class. He is pragmatic and won't lead you down a particular route without awareness of the financial consequences." **Recent work:** Numerous multimillion-pound mis-selling claims related to interest rate swaps, fixed-rate loans and tailored business loans.

Stuart Roberts Focuses on traditional chancery work. He acts for clients across a broad spectrum of matters including Court of Protection applications, partnership disputes, trusts of land and Inheritance Act claims. **Strengths:** "He is just absolutely brilliant with clients. He is very charming and understands how to deal with clients in different emotional situations." "He is very experienced, practical and good on his feet." **Recent work:** Acted for four family members in a multimillion-pound Court of Protection dispute concerning a statutory will for a party who lacked capacity. Roberts secured a highly favourable result for his clients following a two-day trial.

Enterprise Chambers
See profile on p.788

THE SET

Members of Enterprise Chambers frequently act in some of the most significant chancery cases in the North East. The set is a long-established presence on the North Eastern Circuit and has maintained a particular focus on complex chancery work. Its bases in Leeds and Newcastle are supported by a strong presence in London, allowing clients to draw on the wider resources of a much larger set.

SILKS

Hugh Jory QC Highly regarded for contentious insolvency work as well as partnership disputes, shareholder disputes, derivative claims and commercial litigation. As a former merchant banker, he has a detailed knowledge of the financial world and remains sought after both locally and nationally for complex cases. **Strengths:** "I have seen him completely demolish people both inside and outside court. I would be very concerned if I was on the other side." "He is very confident and very self-assured but only because he is brilliant."

JUNIORS

Jonathan Klein Regularly represents individuals in high-value contentious trust and probate claims. His area of expertise extends to breach of fiduciary duty, 1975 Act claims and real estate disputes. **Strengths:** "If you have something horribly complicated then he can work it out." "He is very good on his feet and very thorough." **Recent work:** Acted for the claimant in a multimillion-pound breach of trust claim brought against the estate of a now deceased co-trustee. The case was complicated by additional claims brought against the deceased in respect of other trusts.

Hugo Groves Comes highly recommended for company and insolvency work. He brings over 30 years' experience to advising clients on a range of issues including substantial shareholder disputes, claims against directors and claims arising from failed tax avoidance schemes. **Strengths:** "He is very bright, pragmatic and commercial." "He is very user-friendly."

Margaret Griffin Acts in an array of probate and property claims. She has a particular expertise in will disputes and contentious Court of Protection applications. **Strengths:** "She is a bright and talented practitioner." "She is a very good and experienced chancery practitioner." **Recent work:** A complex challenge to a will raising issues of capacity and undue influence. The matter was complicated by the unusual accusation that the sole beneficiary had poisoned the mind of the testatrix to unjustly exclude the client from benefiting under the will.

Jonathan Rodger Experienced in handling high-value chancery work in the County Courts, High Court and Court of Appeal. He is skilled in tackling a wide variety of disputes including those related to commercial property, construction and breach of confidence. **Strengths:** "He is excellent on company law issues and also very approachable." **Recent work:** Successfully acted in the third of three actions between a vendor and purchaser concerning boundaries, rights of way and parking rights.

Duncan Heath An up-and-coming member of the North Eastern Bar with experience in both commercial and traditional chancery work. His practice encompasses claims under TOLATA 1996, breaches of trust and contentious probate actions. **Strengths:** "He's an extremely good advocate with an extremely good intellect."

Band 2

Trinity Chambers
See profile on p.927

THE SET

Solicitors view Trinity Chambers as a strong set for chancery work in Newcastle. Members have a broad range of expertise covering the entire spectrum of both contentious and non-contentious work. In particular, the group is skilled in handling probate disputes, real property claims, fraud cases and Court of Protection applications. Members of chambers are accustomed to dealing with cases of varying levels of complexity and have experience before a number of tribunals from the County Courts to the Supreme Court.

JUNIORS

Simon Goldberg Heads the set's commercial litigation team and maintains a broad chancery practice. He represents a range of clients from individuals to large plcs on high-value litigation in the Chancery Division. **Strengths:** "He is very approachable and very effective at what he does."

Other Ranked Lawyers

Bruce Walker (Exchange Chambers) Highly regarded for his chancery work on the North Eastern Circuit both in the High Court and in Court of Appeal. The long list of reported cases in which he has acted is evidence of his ability to handle some of the most high-profile and complex chancery matters. **Strengths:** "He is a tenacious advocate and won't let a point go unless he is satisfied." "He is very good academically as well as being very though and practical." **Recent work:** Sought an injunction to prevent demonstrators from blockading depots in ASDA v Farmers for Action.

Stephen Howd (Zenith Chambers) Frequently appears in the High Court as well as the Court of Appeal on high-value and complex chancery cases. He is experienced in handling a variety of disputes including those related to trusts, directors' duties and shareholder disputes. **Strengths:** "His advocacy is very strong and his cross-examination was superb." **Recent work:** Acted for the appellant developer in the reported Court of Appeal case of Urban I (Blonk Street) Ltd. v Ayres. The case set important guidance on the circumstances in which a contract for the sale of land can be terminated for delay.

NORTHERN

Chancery Northern
Leading Sets
Band 1
Kings Chambers *
Band 2
Exchange Chambers *
9 St John Street *
Leading Silks
Band 1
Anderson Lesley *Kings Chambers* *
Bartley Jones Edward *Exchange Chambers*
Casement David *Kings Chambers* *
Cawson Mark *Exchange Chambers*
Chaisty Paul *Kings Chambers* *
Band 2
Berkley David *St Johns Buildings (ORL)* ◊
Leading Juniors
Band 1
Berragan Neil *Kings Chambers* *
Harper Mark *Kings Chambers* *
Latimer Andrew *Kings Chambers* *
Band 2
Doyle Louis *Kings Chambers* *
Fryer-Spedding James *9 St John Street* *
Grantham Andrew *Kings Chambers* *
Halliwell Mark *Kings Chambers* *
Mohyuddin David *Exchange Chambers* *
Temple Eleanor *Kings Chambers* *
Terry Jeffrey *Kings Chambers* *
Vinson Andrew *Exchange Chambers*
Band 3
d'Arcy Eleanor *Kings Chambers* *
Gilchrist David *9 St John Street*
Green David *Atlantic Chambers (ORL)* ◊ *
Maynard-Connor Giles *Exchange Chambers* *
Price Richard *9 St John Street* *
◊ (ORL) = Other Ranked Lawyer.
* Indicates set / individual with profile.

Band 1

Kings Chambers

See profile on p.918

THE SET

Kings Chambers is one of the leading sets in the North of England, and is home to 39 commercial and chancery practitioners, including five silks. This depth of expert resources allows the set to deal with all matters pertaining to both traditional and commercial chancery work.

Client service: Chief clerk Colin Griffin ensures his team provide "efficient and user-friendly clerking."

SILKS

Lesley Anderson QC A deeply respected silk and accredited mediator who draws praise for her commercial chancery expertise. She is frequently instructed in complex insolvency, partnership and shareholder disputes, and commercial property matters. **Strengths:** "She's got a first-class mind. She's great with clients, solicitors and juniors." "She's probably one of the most respected silks in Manchester. She is a very punchy cross-examiner." **Recent work:** Acted for the liquidator of an investment company in relation to shares in the parent company that owns Hamleys Toy Store.

David Casement QC A leading commercial chancery silk who deals with complex, heavy-hitting cases. He focuses his practice on commercial litigation and arbitration, including shareholder disputes, insolvency procedures and contested trusts. **Strengths:** "He is superb; a good team player, thorough, reliable and his knowledge of this area of law is excellent. He takes a commercial view." **Recent work:** Instructed on a major shareholder dispute concerning allegations of breach of fiduciary duty by a provider of tax services towards accountancy firms.

Paul Chaisty QC A veteran silk dealing with big-name commercial chancery cases. He places particular emphasis on commercial property, and insolvency work, and also deals extensively with landlord and tenant and partnership disputes. **Strengths:** "He is very knowledgeable, very commercial, to the point, very clear, concise and user-friendly. We get a very high standard from every member of Kings Chambers we instruct but if I had to say who stood out it would be Paul Chaisty QC." **Recent work:** Instructed in a multimillion-pound damages claim concerning claims of breach of fiduciary duty and misrepresentation in the sale of shares.

JUNIORS

Neil Berragan Manages a practice built on complex commercial chancery work, dealing with fraud and insolvency claims, as well as pre-emptive and restraint injunctions. **Strengths:** "A senior junior with a very good advocacy style; he gets more done by saying less." "He's ferocious. He'll always put up a good fight." **Recent work:** Defended a claim brought by a former employer accusing a senior executive of tampering with the value of shares.

Louis Doyle A strong and imaginative barrister who focuses on all things commercial chancery. He is particularly noted for his expertise on insolvency cases and financial litigation. **Strengths:** "He's just everywhere. If you have a problem and you need some creativity, he's the man to see. Expect the unexpected." "He's just very persuasive. He will do his best to talk the judge around – the court can be against you on a point and he just makes arguments quite clearly. He doesn't back down." **Recent work:** Instructed by the claimant against a high-street bank which was accused of mis-selling interest rate swaps.

Mark Harper An experienced junior with a commercial slant to his practice. He is often instructed on matters pertaining to corporate insolvency and partnership disputes, and banking litigation. **Strengths:** "When you see that you're against him your heart sinks." "He's an astute tactician. He doesn't sugar the pill, and clients certainly appreciate that."

Andrew Latimer Maintains an extensive chancery practice focusing on commercial litigation. His caseload encompasses insolvency law, landlord and tenant disputes, partnership, shareholders' rights and breach of trust. **Recent work:** Acted for owners of a small plane who maintain a right of way to use an airfield owned by the defendants.

Andrew Grantham A senior junior recognised for his commercial litigation focus. He is frequently instructed on cases concerning professional negligence claims, fraud and asset recovery. **Strengths:** "He's a well-regarded chancery practitioner. You know you're in for a good and well-prepared fight." **Recent work:** Instructed on behalf of the defendant in a high-value claim relating to a contract determining the transfer of shares in a mineral mining company.

Jeffrey Terry A highly respected junior with a wealth of experience. He can turn his hand to traditional contested probates and estates administration equally as adeptly as he can to commercial litigation and corporate disputes. **Strengths:** "He's very experienced, a silk in all but name."

Mark Halliwell An experienced junior in the field of traditional chancery matters. He is frequently instructed in cases concerning contested trusts, charities' rights, and the administration of estates and associated contentious probates. **Recent work:** Instructed by a charity in regards to its claim to the title to numerous art installations that appear in the grounds of a country house.

Eleanor Temple Manages a flourishing commercial practice. Insolvency disputes form the mainstay of her practice, alongside corporate restructuring, partnership law and shareholders' rights. **Strengths:** "She knows her subject inside out and is very clear in her advice." **Recent work:** Instructed in an acrimonious shareholder dispute involving allegations of fraud and conspiracy.

Eleanor d'Arcy One of the Northern Circuit's rising stars. She manages a diverse chancery practice, receiving instruction in insolvency cases, property disputes and commercial dispute resolutions. **Strengths:** "She handled the case very well. The advocacy was succinct, to the point and perfectly judged."

Band 2

Exchange Chambers

See profile on p.910

THE SET

Exchange Chambers benefits from its broad Northern spread of offices, covering both Manchester and Liverpool, as well as Leeds on the North Eastern Circuit. Its team has a strong base of commercial litigation and insolvency specialisms, augmented by considerable expertise in traditional chancery work.

Client service: "The clerking is excellent because they are highly responsive and realistic on costs."

SILKS

Edward Bartley Jones QC Manages a practice which encompasses traditional as well as commercial chancery work, with extensive experience in the Court of Appeal. He has led prominent cases on such matters as commercial litigation, insolvency and property disputes. **Strengths:** "To my mind he is one of the best lawyers in the North of England. His ability to analyse issues and to get a grip on them is phenomenal. His ability as an advocate is massively impressive. The Court of Appeal can be a daunting place, but he is completely at ease." "He's a rare beast as a silk, in that he is good with his papers, and good on his feet also, both as an advocate and as a cross-examiner." **Recent work:** Represented a local authority in a case involving complex human rights considerations where a number of protestors were to be removed from their highway protest.

Mark Cawson QC An experienced silk and an accredited mediator who manages an expansive and market-leading chancery practice. Alongside his adeptness in ADR and property-related cases, he also deals with complex commercial and insolvency disputes. **Strengths:** "He's very measured, very bright, very careful in his approach. He always seems to get it right." "At the trial he is excellent on his feet and can give his opponent a good pummelling. His cross-examination is excellent. He's very measured and considered. He's very bright and sees things in cases that no one else has." **Recent work:** Represented a bank in a substantial guarantee claim levied against senior executives at a property development company.

JUNIORS

Andrew Vinson Maintains a wide-ranging chancery practice, with a particular focus on commercial work. He deals with many insolvency and banking cases, as well as associated property disputes and matters of commercial litigation. **Strengths:** "He is very good with clients and a very nice guy. He's very practical and gets matters resolved. He doesn't get lost in the law or make silly points." "He's always been very thorough in his preparation. He's a natural advocate. He's always been very measured and calm before the judiciary." **Recent work:** Acted successfully for a defendant who was accused of acquiring bank guarantees unfairly by imparting undue influence on the parties.

David Mohyuddin A senior junior with a strong chancery practice. He has developed a reputation for expertise in insolvency cases. He deals with a range of commercial matters, including company and shareholder disputes, asset recovery and commercial litigation. **Strengths:** "He is approachable, calm under pressure, professional, robust and an excellent advocate."

Giles Maynard-Connor A commercial specialist frequently instructed for high-value complex litigation. He is praised by his peers and solicitors alike for his expertise in all things insolvency-related. **Strengths:** "He gives robust advice to the client. There's no fence-sitting. He sets out strategy early. He is great because he'll get to it straight away, measuring risk and prospects. He's very calm, and strong in the way he presents his case."

9 St John Street

See profile on p.923

THE SET

9 St John Street covers the full range of commercial and traditional chancery work. It is home to nine specialist practitioners who receive instruction throughout the Northern Circuit and beyond, and the team is commended for its breadth of experience and its diligence in dealing with clients and solicitors alike.

Client service: "The clerking team, led by Tony Morrissey, are very good and down to earth. They are very accommodating, and more efficient than most. They're very quick at putting things under counsel's nose."

JUNIORS

James Fryer-Spedding Maintains a practice of exclusively commercial and chancery litigation cases for private individuals and corporations alike. He has a strong reputation for his work on contested wills, probate and trust litigation, while also advising on questions of insolvency and partnership disputes. **Strengths:** "He is an extremely sound lawyer. He deeply immerses himself in the cases that he is instructed in, and has a very client-friendly manner." "His skeleton arguments are excellent and well researched. He does his homework. He's not flamboyant in his questions, but he gets a thorough understanding of the case and presents it accordingly. He's very effective in his cross-examination." **Recent work:** Successfully represented adult children in an inheritance claim.

Richard Price (see p.699) Draws on his previous career as a senior property solicitor to augment a burgeoning chancery practice. Litigation is his strongest area of expertise, especially property and landlord and tenant disputes, and he also manages cases of associated professional negligence and the administration of estates. **Strengths:** "He's very good on his feet and is very concerned with making the points that will make a difference, rather than grandstanding. He gives good advice and he's meticulous in his preparation and pleadings." "He has a lot of experience in the law. That experience means he's very good at speaking with clients, which other barristers aren't always."

David Gilchrist An experienced junior with a focus on traditional chancery work. He handles questions on contested wills and trusts, and the administration of estates. **Strengths:** "He's understated when on his feet, but persistent. Which is a good thing. Commercial judges don't like theatrics. They can see the issues and they don't want a barrister who wastes their time." "He is very straight-talking and practical. Clients are very trusting of him because he talks down the line and will point out weaknesses in a case and speak very frankly." **Recent work:** Instructed by the defendants in a misrepresentation claim concerning the purchase of a house.

Other Ranked Lawyers

David Green (Atlantic Chambers) The leading chancery practitioner at this Liverpool-based set. He is experienced in matters of property litigation and landlord and tenant disputes.

David Berkley QC (St Johns Buildings) Works with the Northern business community on cases of shareholder and partnership disputes, and related commercial property and professional negligence. **Recent work:** Instructed in a case concerning corporate tax evasion.

WALES & CHESTER

Chancery Wales & Chester
Leading Juniors
Band 1
Hughes Gwydion *9 Park Place (ORL)* ◊ *
Walters Graham *Civitas Law (ORL)* ◊ *
Band 2
Davies Angharad *30 Park Place (ORL)* ◊ *
Jones Emyr *9 Park Place (ORL)* ◊
Kember Richard *9 Park Place (ORL)* ◊ *
Thomas-Symonds Nicklaus *Civitas Law (ORL)* ◊ *

Ranked Lawyers

Graham Walters (Civitas Law) Handles an extensive chancery practice related principally to property and public law work. This frequently includes inheritance, probate and ownership disputes. **Strengths:** "He can see the wood for the trees, and he can cut through it very quickly. Technically he's brilliant, and he commands perspectives very authoritatively. Younger barristers would ask witnesses or ask judges, but with Graham it's more like he's telling them what the law is. He doesn't do it patronisingly, but he has that gravitas." **Recent work:** Instructed for the defendant to oppose a claim by the executor for possession of farm land. The defendant's right to the land by proprietary estoppel was challenged when the claimant raised the conduct of the defendant as a ground to exclude relief.

Nicklaus Thomas-Symonds Civitas Law Receives instructions on inheritance and will disputes, and handles issues relating to the administration of complex estates. Contentious probate and property-based cases form a strong element of his practice. **Strengths:** "He always has his eye on the commercial aspect of the work – he cuts through the chaff and gets directly to what is necessary." "He is very pragmatic. He's an incredibly approachable guy, and he's very conscious and attuned to the clients' needs, and understanding of familial relationships. He balances everyone's needs. He knows it isn't black and white."

Gwydion Hughes (9 Park Place) Manages a diverse practice of all things chancery. Insolvency, trust, probate and planning disputes are all well within his ambit, and he also has an affinity for associated landlord and tenant enquiries. **Strengths:** "He's very strong in his cross-examination. He's confident in the way he presents himself and his case. He can see through the mire and pick out the best points." "He has great attention to detail and tremendous courtesy in court, which generates respect."

Emyr Jones (9 Park Place) Undertakes a broad range of both traditional and commercial chancery work, including boundary disputes, Inheritance Act claims and probate disputes to name but a few. He has particular expertise on issues relating to public rights of way, and is frequently consulted by local authorities on the subject. **Strengths:** "He is down to earth and approachable, and not afraid to engage with the client to make them feel at ease." **Recent work:** Successfully acted on behalf of the executor in establishing the validity of a contested will that had been executed by the testator only 12 hours before his passing.

Richard Kember (see p.644) (9 Park Place) Possesses a chancery practice which covers land and will, trusts and probate disputes. His contentious probate cases frequently cover issues relating to inheritance and family provisions. **Strengths:** "He has a very effective style in that he's not bombastic, but is calm and measured. That's what makes him appeal to judges. He's sensible and he's not hot-headed." **Recent work:** Represented the successful applicant in contested application for first registration of a property based on lost title deeds, where the respondent objected to the registration on the grounds of proprietary estoppel and adverse possession following an alleged verbal agreement by the applicant's deceased husband.

Angharad Davies (see p.583) (30 Park Place) A traditional chancery specialist, who focuses her practice on contentious probates, the interpretation of wills and property disputes. A great number of her cases are concerned with questions of undue influence, fraud and capacity of the testator. **Strengths:** "She's exactly what you want from counsel. She inspires confidence, but in no way comes across as aloof. She lets the clients talk, and makes them feel that they are being heard. She can simplify things and reassure clients." "She's very measured and very clear. She doesn't ramble. She gets straight to the point and everything she says is very relevant. She has the respect of the judge in front of her, without question."

WESTERN

Chancery Western
Leading Sets
Band 1
Guildhall Chambers *
St John's Chambers *
Leading Silks
Band 1
Blohm Leslie *St John's Chambers*
New Silks
Sims Hugh *Guildhall Chambers*
Leading Juniors
Band 1
Auld Charles *St John's Chambers*
Bamford Jeremy *Guildhall Chambers*
Sharples John *St John's Chambers* Ⓐ
Troup Alex *St John's Chambers* Ⓐ
Wales Matthew *Guildhall Chambers*
Band 2
Briggs Nicholas *Guildhall Chambers*
Dickinson John FH *St John's Chambers* Ⓐ *
Jones Christopher *St John's Chambers*
Paton Ewan *Guildhall Chambers*
Band 3
Berkley Michael *Magdalen Chambers (ORL)* ◊
Maher Martha *St John's Chambers* Ⓐ
Marsden Andrew *St John's Chambers* Ⓐ *
* *Indicates set / individual with profile.*
◊ *(ORL) = Other Ranked Lawyer.*
Ⓐ *direct access (see p.11).*

Band 1

Guildhall Chambers

See profile on p.890

THE SET

Guildhall Chambers maintains its position as one of the pre-eminent sets on the Western Circuit. It is home to a strong team of chancery practitioners who are frequently viewed as genuine competition for London-based counsel. Its members have considerable expertise in cases pertaining to property, insolvency and commercial litigation. Solicitors and private clients alike appreciate the user-friendly approach taken by all chambers' staff.

Client service: "The clerks, led by Justin Emmett, add real value and are a pleasure to work with."

SILKS

Hugh Sims QC Receives instructions in the South West and London on both traditional and commercial chancery matters. Disputes relating to trusts, real property, partnerships and insolvency form a large part of his caseload. **Strengths:** "What he does so well is he has a fresh curiosity about everything. He doesn't get stuck in conventional wisdoms. He adds fresh value to everything." "It is no mystery why he has been made up to silk this year; he is charming, clever and has a great mind."

JUNIORS

Jeremy Bamford Focuses on commercial chancery matters, and is especially noted for his expertise in cases concerning insolvency disputes. His caseload covers both private individual and corporate insolvency work, and he frequently provides representation in shareholder disputes. **Strengths:** "He's very understated. The test at the Bar is 'do you fear to be against someone?' He is someone you fear to be against." **Recent work:** Acted in a case relating to unauthorised investments paid into an investment scheme which was alleged to be unlawful under the terms of the Financial Services Act.

Matthew Wales Manages a chancery practice which is rooted predominantly in property law. He receives frequent instructions in property-related insolvency and professional negligence-related cases. **Strengths:** "He's very professional. He deals with things sensibly and realistically, and he doesn't pull any punches." "He won't be pushed over, by the judge or the opposition. He's quite robust, though he won't pursue a bad point." **Recent work:** Represented the executor in a dispute concerning how a neighbour had jointly acquired the family smallholding with the deceased.

Nicholas Briggs Maintains a chancery practice anchored in both contentious and non-contentious insolvency law. He has been involved in a number of complex insolvency cases relating to large corporations and investment banks. Cross-border insolvency disputes all fall within his ambit, and he frequently represents clients in the South West, the North West, and London. **Strengths:** "He's a people person. Clients love him because he understands how to convey ideas to clients, which comes from his past experience before coming to the Bar." "He's very popular with solicitors and very effective as an advocate. He's excellent at understanding what solicitors need and he can roll up his sleeves when he needs to." **Recent work:** Acted in a claim brought against senior executives of a company in liquidation where it was alleged that transactions had been made which were undervalued.

Ewan Paton Has forged a practice centred around traditional chancery and, in particular, real property work. He frequently acts in landlord and tenant disputes, and contested estates cases. **Strengths:** "A very impressive adviser and advocate." **Recent work:** Advised the trustees of a rugby club in a dispute concerning the ownership of land and other club assets.

St John's Chambers

See profile on p.893

THE SET

St John's Chambers is one of the largest sets on the Western Circuit. Traditional chancery is one of the cornerstones of its practice, and its members undertake a wide range of cases relating to contentious probate and property disputes.

Client service: "The clerks, led by practice manager Robert Bocock, are great and really helpful. The administration is very efficient. They have never fallen short of expectations."

SILKS

Leslie Blohm QC Has developed an extensive chancery practice that has seen him represent clients before the highest courts in the country. Property and commercial litigation are the mainstays of his work, and he is also well versed in probate and landlord disputes. **Strengths:** "He has a strong hand, and speaks fairly. He's not stuffy. Judges respect his authority, and he doesn't pull punches in his cross-examinations. He's rather firm and vigorous. He doesn't let a point go if he thinks he's got something." "I find his style of advocacy very measured and solid. He doesn't go in for theatrics. He's a man of substance." **Recent work:** Acted in a proprietary estoppel claim where the daughter was removed from her parents' wills and evicted from their property after many years working on their farm for little remuneration.

JUNIORS

Charles Auld Manages a diverse chancery practice focused principally on commercial litigation. He frequently represents clients in partnership and property disputes, and is also adept in related professional negligence claims and will challenges. **Strengths:** "He is knowledgeable in the law, but also has a pragmatic approach to cases, he can see a possible settlement that others might miss – and his advocacy is excellent." **Recent work:** Instructed in a case concerning allegations of undue influence where one sibling retained almost the entirety of the late mother's estate, leaving the other siblings with very little.

John Sharples Deals in all things real property, and is frequently instructed by large landowners, developers and public authorities. He is one of the Western Circuit's leaders in property litigation and is an authority on the subject of land licences. **Strengths:** "He's very easy to deal with. He's very down to earth, and very impressive at cross-examination." **Recent work:** Acted in a substantial claim concerning allegations of fraudulent misrepresentation in the sale of mobile homes.

Alex Troup Manages a strong chancery practice focusing on probate disputes. He has acquired a fantastic reputation for this type of work and is regularly instructed on contested probates, and associated trust and proprietary estoppel cases. **Strengths:** "He is very good at giving practical advice. He offers solutions where other barristers offer a glut of options." "He doesn't shirk away from telling it how it is, and when he's on his feet he is very authoritative. He's very sharp." **Recent work:** Acted in a dispute which hinged on whether the estate of the deceased retained any beneficial interest in a property and other monetary assets.

John Dickinson Instructed on a diverse range of chancery issues, often with a commercial background. His work includes partnership and shareholder disputes, insolvency claims, property litigation and contested probates. **Strengths:** "He provides really excellent advice and paperwork. He's very clear and quietly reassuring. He's first-class when before a judge. He's quietly persuasive."

Christopher Jones This junior manages a broad chancery practice which is largely focused on matters pertaining to trust litigation and advice. He is also frequently instructed on questions on probate and property disputes. **Strengths:** "He is just extremely popular. There are some barristers who can connect with clients and solicitors really well, and some really don't. He gets on extremely well with people and does extremely well." "He's very good with clients, very reassuring. He inspires confidence. When he's before a judge, he's very presentable and clear and cogent in his argument."

Martha Maher Maintains a strong commercial chancery practice with a particular focus on insolvency litigation and partnership disputes, an asset valued by peers and solicitors alike. **Strengths:** "She's very straightforward with clients; if a client has a good case she'll back them to the hilt. If they have a weak case, she'll tell them and try to convince them not to waste their money early on."

Andrew Marsden A commercially minded barrister whose practice encompasses company, shareholder and partnership disputes. **Strengths:** "He is an excellent communicator, and he challenges clients. He provides what he is meant to provide when he is meant to provide it. He's thoroughly commercial in his approach. He gives sensible commercial advice." **Recent work:** Instructed in a case concerning the enforcement of restrictive covenants in a partnership agreement.

Other Ranked Lawyers

Michael Berkley (Magdalen Chambers) The joint head of Magdalen Chambers, Berkley has particular expertise in commercial and property disputes, as well as contentious trust, probate and will cases. **Strengths:** "He is probably the leading practitioner for chancery work in Exeter."

Contents:

LONDON

Charities London	
Leading Sets	
Band 1	
Radcliffe Chambers *	
Band 2	
Maitland Chambers *	
Band 3	
Wilberforce Chambers *	
Leading Silks	
Senior Statesmen	
Picarda Hubert	*Chambers of Hubert Picarda QC (ORL)* ◊
Star individuals	
McCall Christopher	*Maitland Chambers* *
Pearce Robert	*Radcliffe Chambers*
Band 1	
Crampin Peter	*3 Stone Buildings (ORL)* ◊ *
Taube Simon	*Ten Old Square (ORL)* ◊ *
Band 2	
Furness Michael	*Wilberforce Chambers*
Herbert Mark	*5 Stone Buildings (ORL)* ◊ *
Kessler James	*Tax Chambers 15 Old Square (ORL)* ◊ *
Tipples Amanda	*Maitland Chambers* *
Warnock-Smith Shân	*5 Stone Buildings (ORL)* ◊ *
Leading Juniors	
Star individuals	
Quint Francesca	*Radcliffe Chambers*
Band 1	
Dumont Thomas	*Radcliffe Chambers*
Henderson William	*Serle Court (ORL)* ◊ *
Smith Matthew	*Maitland Chambers* *
Band 2	
King Michael	*XXIV Old Buildings (ORL)* ◊
Mullen Mark	*Radcliffe Chambers*
Studer Mark	*Wilberforce Chambers* *
Westwood Andrew	*Maitland Chambers* *
Band 3	
Lewison Josh	*Radcliffe Chambers* *
Winfield Joshua	*Radcliffe Chambers*
◊ (ORL) = Other Ranked Lawyer.	
** Indicates set / individual with profile.*	
Alphabetical order within each band. Band 1 is highest.	

Band 1

Radcliffe Chambers
See profile on p.856

THE SET

Radcliffe Chambers continues to sustain its reputation as the definitive leading charities set within the market. It has an unmatched concentration of charity law experts, who between them boast an impressive breadth of experience. They advise and appear on behalf of a host of third sector clients on issues ranging from charity formation and governance to acquisition and disposal of land, ecclesiastical law and taxation. Unsurprisingly, many of them are at the heart of the most high-profile cases within the sector, the Cup Trust case serving as a recent example.

Client service: One solicitor commented: "The clerks, headed jointly by Keith Nagle and John Clark, are incredibly efficient and responsive to queries. I came to them with quite an urgent query and they were able to explain all my options so that I was able to find the appropriate barrister quickly."

SILKS

Robert Pearce QC One of the most highly sought after silks at the Charity Bar, he frequently advises and acts for the Charity Commission, the Attorney General and various trustees on matters of a complex and delicate nature. **Strengths:** "His advice displays a breadth of vision and he has great experience. When he provides you with advice, you know it's good and will be pithy and to the point." "He's an extremely able and powerful opponent." **Recent work:** He has recently been acting for the University of London in a case concerning the legal status, governance and financing of the Warburg Institute.

JUNIORS

Francesca Quint Unquestionably one of the most distinguished juniors specialising in charity law. Her practice deals with a wide spectrum of chiefly non-contentious issues, and she regularly handles questions involving wills, trusts and tax, property and local authority governance. **Strengths:** "She knows her stuff and you can have complete confidence in her abilities. She pleasantly and professionally points out issues in a case and always comes up with helpful suggestions." "Her experience is unrivalled." **Recent work:** She appeared in Bangor Provident Trust Ltd and Victoria Housing Estates Limited, which was notable for being the first case to come before the Charity Tribunal of Northern Ireland and the first to be subsequently appealed to the High Court in Northern Ireland.

Thomas Dumont A highly sought-after junior, who represents high-profile national charities in contentious probate actions. Commentators note his "excellent grasp of trust and charity law." **Strengths:** "Clients feel very reassured when they hear him speak. He gets straight to the heart of the matter and provides firm advice." "He has a very nice style in court. He clearly understands his market and who he is dealing with, which allows him to give tailored advice." **Recent work:** Advised a national institution on ownership issues relating to its valuable Central London flagship headquarters.

Mark Mullen Advises and represents third sector clients in cases involving cy-près schemes, governance, mergers, disposal of property and duties of trustees. During his career, he has acted on behalf of the Attorney General and HMRC on significant cases within the sector. **Strengths:** "He's brilliant at working with the client and handles himself excellently before the tribunal." "He's ever so willing to make himself available to give off-the-cuff advice, and he's good on cases with complex issues." **Recent work:** He acted on behalf of six celebrated animal charities in a case concerning a question of donatio mortis causa.

Joshua Winfield Undertakes charity law as part of a strong chancery practice. He is particularly noted for his expertise in disputes involving religious charities and unincorporated associations. Also regularly advises local authorities that hold land as charitable trustees. **Strengths:** "His advice is thorough, easy to read and understandable." **Recent work:** He appeared in Marhawa v Singh, a case centring around an injunction to restrict the holding of elections to the management committee of a Sikh temple in Leicester.

Josh Lewison (see p.656) Handles a good deal of charity work as part of his broad chancery practice. **Strengths:** "He is personable and explains things clearly." "A capable junior who gives well thought-out, practical advice." **Recent work:** He advised the trustees of The Cup Trust during the early stages of its litigation.

Band 2

Maitland Chambers
See profile on p.831

THE SET

Maitland Chambers houses members who have been consistently involved in some of the most significant charity cases of the past decade. Its individuals also remain at the forefront of new legislative developments within the sector, and have key advisory roles in this respect.

Client service: "The members provide terrific value for money. I'm entirely happy with the quality of service and the speed of response provided by the clerks, led by John Wiggs. If I had a concern, I'd phone them up and it would be dealt with in two minutes."

SILKS

Christopher McCall QC One of the most venerated members of the Chancery Bar. Clients and peers concur that he is "synonymous with charities work." **Strengths:** "He possesses an extraordinary breadth of knowledge. He's a trust expert and a tax expert, and he has what I would describe as a Rolls-Royce brain. His clarity of thought and expression is truly unique." "He has a resourceful way of thinking and enormous depth of experience." **Recent work:** He was instructed on behalf of the trustees of the Henry Smith Charity in a case focusing on the charitable status of trusts seeking to benefit 'poor relations' and similar limited classes of beneficiaries.

Amanda Tipples QC Has considerable experience in general chancery and commercial litigation, and has continued to develop her charities practice. She has recently acted for both the Attorney General and HMRC on substantial charity law cases. **Strengths:** "She is excellent – concise, clear and rigorously on top of the paperwork." "A very thorough and hard-working individual." **Recent work:** She was instructed by the Attorney General in University of London v Prag & Attorney General, a dispute concerning the trust deed by which the university holds a library of great historical import.

JUNIORS

Matthew Smith (see p.724) Unanimously hailed by commentators as one of the pre-eminent juniors advising on charity law matters, so much so that one commentator stated: "It's difficult to find a charities case that he's not involved in." **Strengths:** "He is excellent at what he does and is very easy to deal with." "Young, imaginative and good on his feet, he is becoming involved in some of the biggest cases at the moment." **Recent work:** He acted on behalf of Mounstar in the widely publicised Mounstar v Charity Commission case. In this matter the appellant challenged the Commission's decision to open an inquiry into, and appoint an interim manager over, The Cup Trust.

Andrew Westwood (see p.749) Maintains an exceptional commercial chancery practice with a prominent focus on charity law issues. He has conducted litigation and advised a wide array of charitable clients and regulatory bodies, including the Attorney General and the Charity Commission. **Strengths:** "He has been consistently helpful, both in terms of drafting and in his presentation to ourselves and the clients." "He demonstrates sound judgement when deciding on the strategy in a case." **Recent work:** Acted on behalf of JUSTICE in relation to the appeal made by Human Dignity Trust against the Charity Commission's decision not to award the trust charitable status.

Band 3

Wilberforce Chambers

See profile on p.876

THE SET

A pre-eminent chancery set that fields a number of key charity law practitioners chiefly engaged in advisory work for prominent charities solicitors, housing charities and charitable trustees. They regularly handle cases concerning governance issues, charitable constitutions and objectives, and endowments. **Client service:** "As a chambers, they are a class outfit. The clerks, led by Mark Rushton, are able to accommodate clients at short notice and can swiftly offer alternatives when a particular barrister is already predisposed."

SILKS

Michael Furness QC Possesses considerable experience in all manner of trust-related matters and remains a respected figure in the charity law sector. Recently, he has significantly developed his practice in the areas of tax law and onshore and offshore trust litigation. **Strengths:** "Michael combines huge authority on tax matters with an in-depth knowledge of trust law." "We went to Michael because he's been involved in a number of charities cases before, and his name and reputation give us credence. He mastered the material very well and had a sympathetic approach to what we were trying to achieve." **Recent work:** He advised on the Preston Down case, which dealt with the charitable status of a religious charity and looked into questions concerning the notion of public benefit.

JUNIORS

Mark Studer (see p.731) Has cultivated a practice with a particular focus on trusts and estates, as well as charity law. He regularly advises trustees, local authorities and high-profile charitable clients on an array of issues, including governance, funding and contentious probate. **Strengths:** "Extremely personable and straight to the point. We were asking him to advise on some pretty arcane documents and we felt he rose to the challenge magnificently. He also answered questions we asked with great clarity and brevity."

Other Ranked Lawyers

Hubert Picarda QC (Chambers of Hubert Picarda QC) A long-standing specialist in the field who regularly provides invaluable advice to charitable clients. A number of commentators said that they are indebted to him for his outstanding publications dealing with charity law. **Strengths:** "You can be confident that he knows what he's talking about." "He has a very smooth and calm way of getting things across."

Michael King (XXIV Old Buildings) A reputable commercial and traditional chancery practitioner who has particular expertise in charity law and regularly advises charities solicitors in relation to probate disputes. He increasingly receives mandates to assist with mediations involving charities, and both represents clients at mediation hearings and serves as the appointed mediator. **Strengths:** "He is firm in his views and certainly knows his charity law."

Simon Taube QC (Ten Old Square) A highly respected silk who undertakes advisory work and litigation across the full spectrum of chancery law. He continues to receive frequent mandates in relation to charities cases, particularly those of a contentious nature. **Strengths:** "He got to grips with some very complicated issues in an extremely limited timescale." "An effective and able advocate who has a top practice." **Recent work:** While acting for the Secretary for Justice, he was able to successfully persuade the Hong Kong court that the late Nina Wang had left her HKD10 billion estate to charitable trusts.

William Henderson (Serle Court) Acts for private clients, trustees and trust companies across a range of chancery-related matters, such as trustee disputes or cases involving probate and the administration of estates. As junior counsel to the Treasury in charity matters, he frequently advises and represents the Attorney General with regard to contentious and non-contentious charity law matters. **Strengths:** "He has a very good detailed knowledge of the ins and outs of charity law. He's a genuine expert in the field." **Recent work:** Provided a reference for the Attorney General in the landmark case of Independent Schools Council v Charity Commission, which addressed the obligation independent schools have towards public benefit.

Peter Crampin QC (3 Stone Buildings) Possesses an exceptional understanding of charity law issues, developed in part from his stint as junior counsel to the Attorney General, during which time he appeared in a number of prominent charity cases. **Strengths:** "He is a very clever chap," who is "thorough and creative in the way he thinks about things." **Recent work:** He appeared in Helena Housing Ltd v Revenue & Customs Commissioners, a case which addressed issues concerning corporate tax, public benefit and charitable purpose.

Mark Herbert QC (5 Stone Buildings) A seasoned chancery practitioner who is held in high esteem due to his encyclopaedic knowledge of tax and trust law. His practice encompasses a number of legal issues that frequently overlap with charity law matters, including settlements, wills and trust litigation and occupational pension schemes. **Strengths:** "He's obviously very clever, as well as being a gentle and persuasive advocate." **Recent work:** Advised on the Wedgwood Museum Trust proceedings, which questioned whether or not personal endowments could belong to guarantee companies with exclusive charitable objectives.

Shân Warnock-Smith QC 5 Stone Buildings, has considerable experience of acting in litigious cases involving charities in offshore jurisdictions. She is especially well versed in matters involving private and commercial trusts and those cases concerning complex private and commercial wealth issues. **Strengths:** "She is a delightful person and is a well-known and respected silk at the Chancery Bar." **Recent work:** She acted in a case in Bermuda that questioned the validity of a Bermuda trust and a Swiss foundation holding billions of dollars.

James Kessler QC (see p.645) (Tax Chambers 15 Old Square) A leading practitioner who is an expert in taxation issues relating to foreign domiciliaries, offshore entities, charities, trusts and wills. **Strengths:** "He cuts so quickly to the nub of the issue. He's a very, very clever man who seems to hold the entirety of tax law in his head."

Contents:

LONDON

Civil Liberties & Human Rights London
Leading Sets
Band 1
Blackstone Chambers *
Doughty Street Chambers *
Matrix Chambers *
Band 2
Garden Court Chambers *
11KBW *
Band 3
Brick Court Chambers *
1 Crown Office Row *
Thirty Nine Essex Street *
Landmark Chambers *
* *Indicates set / individual with profile.*
◊ *(ORL) = Other Ranked Lawyer.*
[A] *direct access (see p.11).*

Civil Liberties & Human Rights London	
Leading Silks	
Senior Statesmen	
Lester of Herne Hill Anthony	*Blackstone Chambers*
Star individuals	
Eadie James	*Blackstone Chambers*
Emmerson Ben	*Matrix Chambers*
Fitzgerald Edward	*Doughty Street Chambers*
Fordham Michael	*Blackstone Chambers*
Pannick David	*Blackstone Chambers*
Rose Dinah	*Blackstone Chambers*
Band 1	
Howell John	*Blackstone Chambers*
Husain Raza	*Matrix Chambers*
Kaufmann Phillippa	*Matrix Chambers*
Lieven Nathalie	*Landmark Chambers*
Owen Tim	*Matrix Chambers*
Pleming Nigel	*Thirty Nine Essex Street*
Williams Heather	*Doughty Street Chambers*
Band 2	
Bailin Alex	*Matrix Chambers* *
Bowen Paul	*Brick Court Chambers*
Chamberlain Martin	*Brick Court Chambers*
Drabble Richard	*Landmark Chambers*
Friedman Danny	*Matrix Chambers* *
Giffin Nigel	*11KBW*
Grodzinski Sam	*Blackstone Chambers*
Havers Philip	*1 Crown Office Row*
Hermer Richard	*Matrix Chambers*
McCullough Angus	*1 Crown Office Row*
Monaghan Karon	*Matrix Chambers*
Montgomery Clare	*Matrix Chambers*
Mountfield Helen	*Matrix Chambers* *
O'Neill Aidan	*Matrix Chambers*
Otty Timothy	*Blackstone Chambers*
Saini Pushpinder	*Blackstone Chambers*
Southey Hugh	*Matrix Chambers* *
Swift Jonathan	*11KBW* *
Band 3	
Carss-Frisk Monica	*Blackstone Chambers*
Clayton Richard	*4-5 Gray's Inn Square (ORL)* ◊ *
Demetriou Marie	*Brick Court Chambers*
Eicke Tim	*Essex Court Chambers (ORL)* ◊
Farbey Judith	*Doughty Street Chambers* [A]
Gordon Richard	*Brick Court Chambers*
Knafler Stephen	*Garden Court Chambers*
Mansfield Michael	*Mansfield Chambers (ORL)* ◊
Maurici James	*Landmark Chambers*
Richards Jenni	*Thirty Nine Essex Street*
Ryder Matthew	*Matrix Chambers*
Simor Jessica	*Matrix Chambers*
Westgate Martin	*Doughty Street Chambers*
Wolfe David	*Matrix Chambers* *
Band 4	
Coppel Jason	*11KBW* *
Cragg Stephen	*Doughty Street Chambers*
de la Mare Thomas	*Blackstone Chambers*
Harrison Stephanie	*Garden Court Chambers*
Hill Mark	*Francis Taylor Building (ORL)* ◊ *
Morris Fenella	*Thirty Nine Essex Street*
Robertson Geoffrey	*Doughty Street Chambers*
Strachan James	*Thirty Nine Essex Street*
Stratford Jemima	*Brick Court Chambers*
Wise Ian	*Monckton Chambers (ORL)* ◊ [A]
New Silks	
Gallafent Kate	*Blackstone Chambers*
Steyn Karen	*11KBW* *
Thomas Leslie	*Garden Court Chambers*

Band 1

Blackstone Chambers

See profile on p.771

THE SET

Blackstone Chambers boasts in its ranks a large number of the finest silks and juniors working in the field of civil liberties and human rights. Its formidable array of exceptional advocates offer counsel across the full span of issues in the area, and act with equal skill for both claimants and defendants. The set's pre-eminence in public law matters means its capacity in that regard for questions of human rights is incomparable, and its members are also highly accomplished in acting in civil proceedings. They have especially pronounced expertise in national security, protest, extradition, religious rights and discrimination cases.

Client service: "Their barristers are without fail incredibly intelligent and incredibly experienced. They are a go-to set, since you know you'll get high quality."

SILKS

James Eadie QC Enjoys an exceptional reputation for his work undertaken in the capacity of the government Treasury Devil. His substantial expertise in human rights includes issues relating to terrorism, freedom of information and the actions of British troops abroad. **Strengths:** "He is just an incredible advocate – really, really brilliant." "He is very good, very authoritative and he has to be listened to." **Recent work:** Acted for the government in a Supreme Court case addressing the rights of prisoners to vote in elections to the European Parliament. The claimant argued that withholding the ability to participate in the elections was a breach of his rights under the ECHR.

Michael Fordham QC Maintains his outstanding practice in human rights, for which he is extremely well regarded. He employs his formidable advocacy in a range of areas within civil liberties, including the applicability of the ECHR to the actions of British troops in foreign countries, and immigration detention. **Strengths:** "He is fantastic – super-concise and effective in court. He is amazingly good at compressing a huge amount of material into a short amount of time." "He gets to grips with the minutiae of a case, and will stand up in court, having mastered all the papers, and be an incredibly powerful and compelling advocate." **Recent work:** Acted for the appellants in a case in the Supreme Court arguing that the decision of the Secretary of State for Foreign and Commonwealth Affairs not to establish an inquiry into the deaths of 26 people at the hands of British troops in Batang Kali in 1948 was in breach of Article 2 ECHR.

David Pannick QC Revered silk with a long-established position as a pre-eminent advocate in the spheres of public law and human rights. He acts both for claimants and for defendants across a broad span of matters, including in freedom of information, protestor rights and Parliamentary and legal privilege cases. **Strengths:** "He is the best silk in the country by a hundred miles. The judges listen to him in a different way to other silks – they write down every word he says." "He is incredibly industrious and applied. Superb in court, and can analyse issues with real acuity." **Recent work:** Acted in the ECHR for Mikhail Khodorkovsky in relation to his trial and detention in Russia.

Dinah Rose QC Commands resounding praise and respect from peers and those she represents alike for her formidable advocacy and expertise. She has appeared in a number of the most high-profile cases of recent years, and is accomplished in such areas as discrimination, rendition and torture, and freedom of religion. **Strengths:** "She is concise – she cuts to the chase, finds the killer argument and then charms the judges with it." "She is amazing. In terms of confidence in the Supreme Court, she just towered above the defendant counsel." **Recent work:** Represented the claimant in a high-profile case alleging complicity on the part of the British Security Services in the kidnap and rendition of Libyan dissidents to the Gaddafi regime for the purposes of torture.

John Howell QC Highly respected for his meticulous and inventive approach to human rights issues. His substantial expertise includes the compatibility of closed proceedings with the ECHR and the public

Civil Liberties & Human Rights London
Leading Juniors
Star individuals
Jaffey Ben *Blackstone Chambers*
Squires Daniel *Matrix Chambers*
Band 1
Buley Tim *Landmark Chambers*
Fatima Shaheed *Blackstone Chambers*
Hickman Tom *Blackstone Chambers*
Macdonald Alison *Matrix Chambers* *
Band 2
Brander Ruth *Doughty Street Chambers* Ⓐ
Bunting Jude *Doughty Street Chambers*
Gallagher Caoilfhionn *Doughty Street Chambers* Ⓐ
Gerry Alison *Doughty Street Chambers*
Hill Henrietta *Doughty Street Chambers* Ⓐ
Hooper Ben *11KBW* *
Straw Adam *Doughty Street Chambers*
Band 3
Buttler Chris *Matrix Chambers* Ⓐ
Dubinsky Laura *Doughty Street Chambers*
Finch Nadine *Garden Court Chambers*
Hyam Jeremy *1 Crown Office Row*
Kilroy Charlotte *Doughty Street Chambers*
Knights Samantha *Matrix Chambers*
Lester Maya *Brick Court Chambers*
Patel Naina *Blackstone Chambers*
Pickup Alison *Doughty Street Chambers*
Rahman Shaheen *1 Crown Office Row*
Sandell Adam *Matrix Chambers*
Simblet Stephen *Garden Court Chambers*
Steele Iain *Blackstone Chambers*
Wagner Adam *1 Crown Office Row*
Weston Amanda *Garden Court Chambers*
Band 4
Armstrong Nicholas *Matrix Chambers*
Chandran Parosha *1 Pump Court (ORL)* ◊ Ⓐ
Clement Joanne *11KBW* *
Crowther Sarah *3 Hare Court (ORL)* ◊
Gardner Piers *Monckton Chambers (ORL)* ◊ Ⓐ
Gask Alex *Doughty Street Chambers*
Grieves Edward *Garden Court Chambers*
Hemingway Sarah *Garden Court Chambers*
Hirst Leonie *Garden Court Chambers*
Law Helen *Matrix Chambers*
Morris Anna *Garden Court Chambers*
Pievsky David *Blackstone Chambers*
Poole Tom *3 Hare Court (ORL)* ◊
Prochaska Elizabeth *Matrix Chambers* *
Suterwalla Azeem *Monckton Chambers (ORL)* ◊ *
Watson Ben *3 Raymond Buildings Barristers (ORL)* ◊ Ⓐ *
Weereratne Aswini *Doughty Street Chambers* Ⓐ
* *Indicates individual with profile.*
◊ *(ORL) = Other Ranked Lawyer.*
Ⓐ *direct access (see p.11).*

sector equality duty. **Strengths:** "Very intelligent and good all round." "He provides very, very thorough written opinions." **Recent work:** Intervened on behalf of the Law Society in a judicial review examining whether legal aid available to a child in private law family proceedings could extend as far as to cover the cost of an expert report.

Timothy Otty QC Centres his human rights practice on the lawfulness of economic sanctions, detention on terrorism charges and the admissibility of evidence gained through torture. He has appeared in a number of fora, including the US Supreme Court, the Privy Council and the ECHR. **Strengths:** "He was very assured, and when we hit difficulties he was a very good reference point." **Recent work:** Acted for the appellant in a case before the Court of Appeal addressing the lawfulness of the UK's support for a UN designation of an individual for asset freezing where supporting evidence was obtained by torture.

Sam Grodzinski QC Specialises in the rights of prisoners and protestors, and in police powers of stop and search. He often acts for central and local government bodies, as well as for claimants. **Strengths:** "He's very user-friendly, very bright, great on paper and wonderful on his feet." "If I'm against Sam, I know I have a fight on my hands." **Recent work:** Acted for the claimant in a judicial review against the Independent Police Complaints Commission addressing the failure to investigate properly the circumstances of a man's death following his restraint by the police.

Pushpinder Saini QC Represents clients in human rights cases both domestically and internationally. He has a particularly strong reputation in the application of Convention arguments to asset freezing decisions, and in the right to freedom of movement within the EU. **Strengths:** "He is brilliant." **Recent work:** Acted for the appellants in a case before the Court of Appeal which argued that the process for valuation of shares in Northern Rock was not compatible with Article 1 of Protocol 1 of the ECHR.

Monica Carss-Frisk QC Acts for claimants and respondents in human rights actions, and has a broad-ranging practice in the field. She has pronounced expertise in the application of Article 3 to the Dublin Regulation, in issues arising from undercover policing and the Equality Act. **Strengths:** "She's brilliant – she's generous with her time, good in terms of communication, gives clear advice and is really great to work with." "She got up to speed really quickly, offered excellent arguments and was very impressive in court." **Recent work:** Acted for the Metropolitan Police in a test case concerning the use of undercover police officers, in which the claimants argued that their rights under Article 8 ECHR had been breached by their allegedly having been deceived into having sexual relationships with the officers.

Thomas de la Mare QC Attracts praise for his work on the interface between EU law and domestic human rights issues, and on the rights of commercial entities under the ECHR. He represents a diverse range of clients, from charities and suspected terrorists to multinational corporations. **Strengths:** "He brings a zest and enthusiasm to the case that one knows is founded on a very secure and in-depth knowledge of the applicable law." "He is very bright, writes well and is a good lateral thinker." **Recent work:** Acted for the claimants in a damages claim by 11 alleged members of the Libyan Islamic Fighting Group regarding the alleged complicity of the UK security services in their detention and questioning abroad.

Kate Gallafent QC Took silk this year and has an excellent reputation for handling civil liberties matters for a range of clients. Her practice in this area focuses on immigration detention, the rights of prisoners and freedom of information. **Strengths:** "Her paperwork is very strong, and she is a delight to work with." **Recent work:** Acted on behalf of the Justice Secretary in defending a series of challenges to decisions taken in relation to male prisoners in sexual relationships with other prisoners.

Anthony Lester QC Occupies a position of eminence in the field of human rights, having pursued cases at the forefront of the profession for more than four decades. **Recent work:** Acted for the claimants in a judicial review challenge to the decision of the Registrar General not to certify a chapel of the Church of Scientology as a place of worship. The Supreme Court ruled that the decision was discriminatory, providing in the process a legal definition of religion.

JUNIORS

Tom Hickman Attracts a great deal of praise and respect for his work in civil liberties and human rights. He has particular expertise in matters arising from national security, terrorism and freedom of information issues. **Strengths:** "He is the first choice for sensitive cases involving the state security services, and is able to turn around a high volume of complex and strategically challenging work." "He's really committed to paperwork and to the clients, and takes a real interest in all parts of the case. He sees arguments that others miss." **Recent work:** Acted for the claimant in a landmark Supreme Court case addressing the power of the Secretary of State for the Home Department to make an order for the deprivation of citizenship where such an order would leave its subject stateless.

Ben Jaffey Has an outstanding reputation as a junior of the highest calibre in the field of human rights. He is especially expert in cases dealing with issues of torture, rendition, prisoners' rights and religious freedoms. **Strengths:** "As well as having a really good legal brain, he also sees the big picture – he thinks about the political and media aspects of a case, too." "Ben Jaffey is superb – he's very bright and a very good advocate." **Recent work:** Acted for Privacy International in a claim in the Investigatory Powers Tribunal against PRISM and Tempora, the covert surveillance programmes operated by the NSA and GCHQ.

Shaheed Fatima Commands a great deal of respect for her civil liberties practice. She focuses on the interface between public international law and domestic human rights law, in which area she is an acknowledged expert. **Strengths:** "She is incredibly intelligent, and particularly strong on international law." "She is an excellent speaker." **Recent work:** Acted for the claimant in a challenge to the Secretary of State for the Home Department's decision not to hold an investigation into the killings of four people in Afghanistan by British special forces.

Iain Steele Specialises in police powers and duties, prisoners' rights and the law surrounding the right to protest. He also has experience in matters concerning the conduct of British troops. **Strengths:** "He was very good as he was very quick to respond to queries, and gave excellent written submissions. Our success was down to the hard work he put in." **Recent work:** Acted for the claimant in a landmark judicial review challenge to the police practice of requiring demonstrators to give their personal details and to be photographed before being allowed to leave a 'kettle'.

Naina Patel Represents clients in relation to immigration, asylum, constitutional matters and questions of religious freedoms. She also has experience in the applicability of human rights principles to the conduct of British troops in foreign jurisdictions. **Strengths:** "She is a very skilled and able junior who's very pleasant to work with, but who also has a steely determination." **Recent work:** Represented the claimant in a judicial review challenge to the lawfulness of the decision to detain him under immigration powers. It was held that the last four months of his detention were unlawful.

David Pievsky Centres his human rights practice on protest law, judicial review challenges to police policy and the extraterritorial application of the Human Rights Act. He also has an interest in issues arising from freedom of expression and of religion. **Recent work:** Represented the Metropolitan Police Commissioner in a case concerning the alleged sexual misconduct of police officers operating undercover.

Doughty Street Chambers

See profile on p.786

THE SET

Doughty Street Chambers is held in the highest regard as a set offering an outstanding quality of representation to claimants. Its accomplished members have acted in a significant number of landmark cases in the civil liberties field over the past decade, and are unafraid of pursuing actions of the greatest importance and political sensitivity. Claimants benefit from deep expertise and prowess in such areas as discrimination, freedom of sexual orientation, religious rights, mental health, immigration and prison detention, freedom of information and actions against the police.

Client service: "Their clerking is reliable and helpful, and they get back to me very quickly."

SILKS

Edward Fitzgerald QC A human rights advocate of significant renown, who has acted in a large number of landmark and pioneering cases over the past three decades. His exceptional reputation is founded particularly in the areas of extradition, prisoners' rights and international challenges to the death penalty. **Strengths:** "In cases with a strong moral argument, he'll give you one of the best, most passionate submissions you could hope for." "A charming and delightful person, he has an intellect that is second to none." **Recent work:** Acted for the claimant in an application to the ECHR that contended state immunity afforded to Saudi Arabia against civil actions alleging torture was in violation of Article 6 ECHR.

Heather Williams QC Commands considerable respect for her work in the field of civil liberties. She focuses in particular on judicial review challenges to the conduct of the police, discrimination cases and employment matters. **Strengths:** "She combines an exceptional intellect with a down-to-earth approach, and is involved with every aspect of the case down to the smallest detail." "She is so skilled as an advocate at trial – her advocacy is masterful, and she is brilliant to watch." **Recent work:** Acted for the claimant in a landmark case in which the Metropolitan Police were found liable for the first time for unlawful disability discrimination and a breach of Article 3 ECHR in respect of their treatment of a member of the public. The prolonged restraint of a severely autistic boy who had become fixated by the water at a swimming pool was found to constitute inhuman or degrading treatment.

Judith Farbey QC Focuses on human rights matters relating to immigration, asylum and nationality status. She also has experience of challenging decisions affecting the rights of prisoners. **Strengths:** "She is a very clever and competent lawyer." "Judith is very good at working out what is worth arguing. She is extremely sensible and reliable." **Recent work:** Acted in a judicial review challenge to the scope of the Home Office Destitution Domestic Violence Concession, a welfare benefit available to migrant victims of domestic violence.

Martin Westgate QC Offers expertise in a wide range of human rights issues, including right to life, freedom from arbitrary detention and disability rights. He is also experienced in matters arising from protest rights and the conduct of the police. **Strengths:** "He has taken well to silk. I was impressed by the way he selected the right points and ran with them in a tremendously complicated case." "He is a very clever and thorough man." **Recent work:** Represented Liberty as an intervener in an important case addressing the retention of data by the police on unproven allegations against an elderly protestor, in which it was found that such a practice was in contravention of his rights under Article 8 ECHR.

Stephen Cragg QC Centres his human rights practice on challenging the actions of the police, notably in terms of the retention and disclosure of information on members of the public. He is also noted for his expertise in prison law and mental health. **Strengths:** "He is very good with clients, and has good attention to detail in terms of the paperwork. Everything in his oral advocacy is well argued, too." **Recent work:** Acted for a Northern Irish teenager and her mother as litigation friend in a High Court case challenging the decision of the NHS not to provide free abortion services in England, after they had been denied those services under the stricter laws of Northern Ireland.

Geoffrey Robertson QC A significant figure in the field of domestic and international human rights, who has acted in many important cases in the area over the course of his career. He is particularly expert in issues of freedom of expression, torture and national security. **Strengths:** "He is an inspiration as a lawyer, and a figurehead in international law." "He thinks about the law in a novel and ingenious way." **Recent work:** Acted successfully on behalf of five students of the University of Sussex at a disciplinary hearing at which they were threatened with expulsion for taking part in a peaceful protest.

JUNIORS

Ruth Brander Enjoys a growing reputation for her work in the areas of protest law, and the rights of children and vulnerable adults. She is also experienced in representing bereaved families in inquests arising out of deaths in custody. **Strengths:** "She is brilliant – her written work is incredibly clear, and she is very good on her feet." "She is very down to earth, very experienced, and a legal expert on protest cases." **Recent work:** Acted for the claimant in a judicial review challenging the process by which the Metropolitan Police retain information on individuals who are charged but not prosecuted for an offence.

Caoilfhionn Gallagher Acts in a number of areas in the field of civil liberties and human rights. She is particularly expert in prison law and data protection, and in representing bereaved families at inquests. **Strengths:** "She has a phenomenal grasp of the law, is remarkably intelligent, and her preparation is extremely detailed." "She was excellent – she knew all the facts of the case, presented it very well and was very articulate." **Recent work:** Successfully challenged the policy of the Home Secretary to treat 17-year-olds in custody as adults in a landmark judicial review in the Divisional Court. Following a ruling that this approach was incompatible with Article 8 ECHR, the Home Secretary amended her policy.

Alison Gerry Focuses her human rights practice on bringing actions against the police and the prison service by way of judicial review and in civil proceedings. She also often acts in cases with a prominent mental health element, particularly on behalf of those detained under the Mental Health Act. **Strengths:** "She's brilliant with clients, since she's very good at explaining what are often complex legal matters in a way that puts them at ease." "She's approachable and has good instincts. She is noted for her fine drafting skills and for being good on her feet." **Recent work:** Acted for a claimant who had been kept as a domestic servant against her will in a case contending that the police had failed to meet their positive obligation to protect against slavery under Article 4 ECHR. As a result of the case, the investigation into the perpetrators was reopened, and they were convicted.

Henrietta Hill Frequently instructed in cases brought against the police and prison service, and has a particular specialism in matters arising from deaths in police shootings. She also has notable experience of acting on behalf of those who have suffered sexual orientation or race discrimination. **Strengths:** "She is very persuasive, and while being firm and strong in her arguments, she also manages to win over everyone's confidence." "She's not one to flinch from a battle – a real fighter." **Recent work:** Acted for the claimants in a high-profile case concerning a gay couple who had been turned away from a Christian-run hotel, which considered the tension between the right to freedom of religion and the right to freedom of sexual orientation.

Adam Straw Specialises in representing bereaved families at inquests and public inquiries, and in bringing actions against the police. He is also experienced in issues arising in the contexts of freedom of information and national security. **Strengths:** "He's excellent at sniffing out new arguments, and finding a path through a case – he has an incredible legal brain." "He always delivers fantastic written work that is very forensic and expresses the key points succinctly." **Recent work:** Represented the claimants in a judicial review into the failure of the Secretary of State for Justice to establish an inquiry into the high rate of deaths of people in custody aged 18–24.

Laura Dubinsky Offers representation in actions against the police and prison service, and in relation to the prohibition of torture. She is an exceptionally accomplished junior in the field of immigration law. **Strengths:** "She is innovative in the way she approaches the law, and leaves no stone unturned." "She is really cutting-edge – a class act." **Recent work:** Brought a judicial review challenge on behalf of the claimant to the Ministry of Justice's policy concerning Home Detention Curfews for prisoners and their compatibility with the ECHR.

Jude Bunting Focuses on pursuing actions arising from issues in the prison service and from the conduct of the police. He is also experienced in handling discrimination matters, and those arising from privacy and national security. **Strengths:** "He is very bright and very enthusiastic, and is creative in finding a way of arguing cases." "He writes beautifully and is brilliant on his feet for someone so young – he has an infectious enthusiasm that whips up the whole court." **Recent work:** Represented the claimants in a Supreme Court case that is the leading authority on the correct interpretation of the offence of aggravated trespass.

Charlotte Kilroy Specialises in handling cases relating to immigration, asylum and trafficking. She is also well versed in bringing human rights actions against the police and in connection with the security services. **Strengths:** "Her attention to detail is second to none." "She is excellent on the immigration side of civil liberties." **Recent work:** Acted for the appellants in a case addressing whether their Convention rights had been breached by officers engaging in sexual relationships with them for the purposes of gathering covert intelligence.

Alison Pickup Maintains a diverse practice that includes immigration, prison law and actions for unlawful detention. She is also accomplished in broader public law actions with human rights implications. **Strengths:** "She's firm but very pleasant to work with, and has a meticulous attention to detail." **Recent work:** Acted as junior counsel on a challenge to the proposed residence test for eligibility to civil legal aid. The challenge is founded on arguments of rights to equality of treatment and access to justice.

Aswini Weereratne Centres her human rights practice on questions of mental capacity and mental health, particularly in the context of the deprivation of liberty. She also has an interest in matters relating to torture and inhuman or degrading treatment.

Alex Gask Enjoys a growing reputation for his human rights practice, which focuses on public law challenges to the police and the prison service, and on behalf of vulnerable people. He also has noted experience in pursuing damages claims for historic abuse. **Strengths:** "Very bright and talented, he is easy to work with and spot-on in his analysis of legal issues." "He is a really hard-working, bright and incisive junior who is a pleasure to work with." **Recent work:** Acted for four claimants in the Mau Mau civil litigation against the Foreign & Commonwealth Office for torture and abuse suffered during an uprising in Kenya in the 1950s. The case resulted in compensation, and an apology being read in the House of Commons for the first time.

Matrix Chambers

See profile on p.832

THE SET

Matrix Chambers attracts effusive praise for the outstanding quality of its members and their work across the full range of concerns in human rights. Clients are able to call on a large number of exceptional advocates of all levels of seniority, who have phenomenal expertise in pursuing cases relating to such areas as immigration, the conduct of the police and the military, terrorism, public demonstrations and national security. The work of its members in this area is informed in part by their excellence in criminal and international law.

Client service: "They're definitely the first chambers to go to for complex or difficult litigation, especially where there are elements of international human rights, and any other project where we need a set with a progressive outlook."

SILKS

Ben Emmerson QC An exceptionally well-regarded advocate with decades of experience in acting on behalf of claimants and defendants in some of the most significant human rights cases. His substantial expertise includes questions of international law, crime, the right to protest and terrorism, the lattermost bolstered by his position as the UN Special Rapporteur on Counter-Terrorism and Human Rights. **Recent work:** Acted for the widow of Alexander Litvinenko in a judicial review challenging the decision of the Home Secretary not to set up a public inquiry into the death of her husband. After successful submissions, the decision was quashed in the High Court.

Raza Husain QC Commands great respect for his skill as an advocate and for his practice in human rights. His work in this area is typically centred around immigration, extradition and asylum issues. **Strengths:** "He is very good – a great enthusiast and very energetic." "He is committed and clever." **Recent work:** Acted for a cross-party group of Parliamentarians in a judicial review challenging the decision of the Home Secretary to exclude a prominent Iranian dissident politician from entering the UK for the purposes of discussing human rights in Iran.

Phillippa Kaufmann QC Maintains her exceptional reputation as an outstanding human rights advocate, and has a practice focused on prisoners' rights, actions against the police and protest law. She has recently developed expertise in actions arising from international human rights violations. **Strengths:** "She is one of a kind. She's down to earth, really practical, direct and straight, and has legal expertise that is second to none." "Her attention to detail is great, as is her drafting and client service – there's nothing to fault her on." **Recent work:** Represented two women who had been victims of multiple rapist John Worboys in a landmark case against the police for failing to pursue an effective investigation pursuant to Article 3 ECHR. The case has established clearer obligations on the police to investigate allegations of sexual assault.

Danny Friedman QC Attracts resounding praise for his human rights practice, which has a particular emphasis on issues related to national security and terrorism. He is also accomplished in acting in public inquiries into those areas. **Strengths:** "He is able to put across complex, intricate arguments in a succinct and digestible way." "He is phenomenally intelligent and incredibly committed with it." **Recent work:** Acted for survivors and relatives of those killed in a massacre in Batang Kali in 1948 in a case challenging the decision of the Foreign Secretary not to order a public inquiry into the incident.

Richard Hermer QC Has pronounced expertise in the areas of terrorism and torture, especially in cases where it is alleged that the security services have been complicit. He is equally comfortable handling domestic or international matters. **Strengths:** "He is a motivating and brilliant person to work with since he knows the law so well he can foresee the arguments before they arise." "He is very, very good and is doing the cutting-edge cases." **Recent work:** Brought a claim against Jack Straw on behalf of Abdul-Hakim Belhaj, a Libyan dissident who alleged that the former Foreign Secretary and MI6 colluded with Colonel Gaddafi to bring about his extraordinary rendition and torture.

Alex Bailin QC Has a practice in human rights that is strongly informed by his work in the criminal sphere. His cases in this area often involve challenges to the police and security services, or investigate the conduct of the military. **Strengths:** "Very organised, very generous with his time, and legally brilliant. He understands every aspect of the case, and every argument that can be run." **Recent work:** Acted for a consortium of media groups in the inquest into the death of Alexander Litvinenko, the former Russian intelligence agent killed by radioactive polonium in London.

Tim Owen QC Commands great respect for his civil liberties practice, which incorporates expertise in criminal and public law actions. He is also experienced in acting in high-profile inquests and in cases relating to data retention. **Strengths:** "He has a very long-standing reputation. He's written a number of textbooks in the area, has a deep knowledge of the subject and is a wise tactician." **Recent work:** Acted for an elderly peace campaigner in a judicial review successfully challenging the refusal of the police to remove his details from the National Domestic Extremism Database.

Karon Monaghan QC Very well regarded for her expertise in discrimination matters and in issues relating to the public sector equality duty. She represents claimants ranging from individuals to charities and NGOs. **Strengths:** "She wrote the book on equalities and is a very committed and knowledgeable adviser who works brilliantly in a team." "She has probably the most comprehensive discrimination expertise across the Bar." **Recent work:** Acted for the claimants in a case before the Supreme Court addressing whether there should be an exception in cases of domestic violence to the rule that police forces are immune to suits of negligence. The case was brought by the family of a woman killed after the police failed to respond to a 999 call detailing an immediate threat to her life.

Clare Montgomery QC Maintains a human rights practice informed by her work in crime, fraud and extradition, in which areas she is widely regarded as exceptional. **Strengths:** "She is tenacious and fearless, and incredibly focused – she just gets it." "She is someone with enormous spirit in her advocacy, who is incredibly effective on behalf of her client." **Recent work:** Represented the claimant in a case with significant implications for the serving of foreign criminal convictions, in which it was found that it was possible for the Home Secretary to decline to serve a conviction where the original proceedings did not meet Article 6 requirements for a fair trial.

Helen Mountfield QC Has a diverse practice in human rights, which is commonly founded in public law actions in the areas of terrorism, equality and education. She is also a special advocate and has appeared in that capacity in a number of closed proceedings. **Strengths:** "She is a brilliant strategic thinker and a highly persuasive advocate, who is very committed to her clients." "A go-to person for anything to do with the public sector equality duty. She gives sound, practical advice and is good on her feet." **Recent work:** Acted for the claimants in a case before the ECHR challenging the UK Tempora programme of generic interception of 'external communications' on the basis that it is incompatible with the ECHR convention.

Aidan O'Neill QC Frequently instructed in human rights cases with a strong element of EU law. He is also admitted to the Scottish Bar, and has additional expertise in matters of discrimination and religious freedom. **Strengths:** "The Supreme Court is his natural forum – he can more than hold his own in that environment, and is clearly well respected there." "He is extremely hard-working and incredibly diligent, as well as being willing to pursue novel arguments." **Recent work:** Acted for one of the claimants in a case before the Supreme Court arguing that the decision to deprive prisoners of the right to vote in European Parliament elections was a violation of their rights under the ECHR.

Hugh Southey QC Specialises in prisoners' rights, actions arising from police policy and mental health. He is also experienced in handling immigration and extradition matters. **Strengths:** "He is unflappable and not afraid to argue unpalatable points. It's difficult to think of another claimant barrister who currently has the same level of work that he does." "He's very good at problem solving and is brave in taking on complex and novel legal issues." **Recent work:** Acted successfully for the claimants in a landmark Supreme Court case that established that prisoners have a right to an oral hearing when their parole is being reviewed. The case also offered judicial guidance on the relation between the common law and the ECHR.

Jessica Simor QC Acts for both claimants and defendants on matters relating to religious freedom, terrorism and constitutional issues. She also has expertise in international human rights in the context of refugees. **Strengths:** "She's a very intelligent, responsive and able lawyer. A persuasive advocate, who's well prepared and very good on her feet." "She works very hard, is great with clients and has an exceptional talent for human rights cases." **Recent work:** Represented the claimants in a case before the Supreme Court that established that soldiers serving in Iraq are entitled to the protection of the Human Rights Act, since they are acting under the full authority and control of the UK.

David Wolfe QC Centres his human rights work on issues relating to freedom of expression. He also has extensive expertise in education and is an expert when it comes to the public sector equality duty. **Strengths:** "He has a very quick mind, is extremely efficient and is a good fighter." "He speedily grasps the crux of the argument, and is unassuming and generous with his time." **Recent work:** Represented the Equality & Human Rights Commission as interveners in a case before the Supreme Court, where it was found unanimously that the failure to consult a patient before placing a 'do not resuscitate' notice on her records breached her rights under Article 8 ECHR.

Matthew Ryder QC Enjoys a growing reputation for his practice in human rights, which includes handling cases in the context of national security and privacy. His work has a strong criminal element, especially as related to fraud and terrorism. **Strengths:** "Matthew finds solutions where no one else could – he is quite brilliant." "He is always extremely balanced, articulate and professional, and he reads courts very well." **Recent work:** Acted for David Miranda in his challenge to the use of powers under Schedule 7 of the Terrorism Act which were used to seize materials from him deriving from former NSA operative and whistle-blower Edward Snowden.

JUNIORS

Alison Macdonald Commands a great deal of respect for her human rights practice, which interleaves closely with her work in bringing actions against the police and the criminal justice system. She has a further interest in protestor rights and the retention of data. **Strengths:** "She is really adept at navigating the relationship between our policy position as clients, and the legal arguments of the case." "She has a fantastic, wonderful intellect and is a pleasant and approachable woman." **Recent work:** Represented Liberty as an intervener in David Miranda's challenge to the use of Schedule 7 powers.

Daniel Squires Attracts effusive praise for his work in civil liberties, and has a practice with a marked emphasis on international human rights issues. He has particular expertise in matters arising from terrorism charges, as well as prison law. **Strengths:** "He has a brilliant mind, is very committed and is easy to work with." "Dan is very good on international human rights issues, and good on his feet – he's not afraid to go for it." **Recent work:** Acted for the UK government in the ECHR in a case brought by Christians who argued that the UK was in breach of its duty to protect their religious freedoms. It has become a leading judgment on the right to religious freedoms in the workplace.

Chris Buttler Acts for children, vulnerable adults and victims of trafficking and torture as claimants in judicial reviews and damages claims. He has additional expertise in issues of mental capacity. **Strengths:** "He can be aggressive against the court when necessary, and is able to choose the right moments to do so." "He is tactically shrewd, and liked by the court." **Recent work:** Acted successfully for the claimants in a test case that established that the Home Secretary had failed to properly apply its own policy on the treatment of asylum seekers who were also victims of torture. The case also gave rise to a judicial definition of torture.

Samantha Knights Focuses her human rights practice on issues relating to immigration, refugee status and deportation. She is also interested in the expression of religious rights, and has written a textbook on the subject.

Nicholas Armstrong Acts primarily on behalf of claimants in bringing public law actions. He focuses largely on issues arising out of immigration, including deaths in immigration detention and false imprisonment. **Strengths:** "He is a really clever thinker and a problem solver." "He is great as an advocate – he always gets passionately involved in the cases and brings a lot of energy and enthusiasm to them." **Recent work:** Acted for the respondents in a Supreme Court appeal brought by the Home Secretary against an earlier Court of Appeal decision declaring the disclosure of childhood cautions to be incompatible with Article 8 ECHR.

Helen Law Has a mixed practice in criminal law and civil human rights, and her work in each informs the other. She is experienced in prison and police law, as well as in international public law. **Strengths:** "She is one of the most skilled juniors I've seen, and has a rare talent to be able to turn her hand to civil and criminal litigation with equal aplomb." "She is able to handle complex legal issues and offers excellent drafting."

Elizabeth Prochaska (see p.699) Offers representation in a diverse range of human rights issues, including prison law, education and freedom of information. She has a particular interest in the rights of women in childbirth. **Strengths:** "She's very strong, both as an advocate and in terms of her written advice – she clearly has a stellar future ahead of her." "She is technically very good, and displays keen attention to detail." **Recent work:** Acted as junior in a judicial review challenge to the granting of planning permission for a halal butcher to be built next to a Sikh temple, in a case addressing the interface between planning law and the right to religious freedoms.

Adam Sandell Frequently instructed in cases with a pronounced medical element, due in part to his being a practising doctor. He has extensive experience in inquest work, as well as in prison law. **Strengths:** "He's a very clever man who's great to work with, and a great street-fighting barrister who doesn't take any nonsense." "His being a GP is completely invaluable in that it's like having a barrister and an expert rolled up in one person." **Recent work:** Represented one of the claimants in the Supreme Court in a high-profile case considering whether there exists in law a right to assisted suicide without fear of prosecution. The Court of Appeal had previously decided that the DPP's policy constituted a breach of the claimant's Article 8 rights.

Band 2

Garden Court Chambers

See profile on p.808

THE SET

Garden Court Chambers continues to command respect for the skilful, knowledgeable and energetic manner in which it pursues actions on behalf of vulnerable clients seeking redress for ill-treatment suffered at the hands of public bodies. Members are notably accomplished in matters relating to immigration, community and social care, police misconduct and mental health. They are especially well regarded for their work in inquests into deaths in custody and from police shootings.

Client service: "The standard there is very high, and its members are very knowledgeable. The clerking is very good and very prompt."

SILKS

Stephen Knafler QC Specialises in representing a diverse range of clients, from individuals to regulators and local authorities, in matters relating to community care and immigration. He has further expertise in the fields of social housing and healthcare. **Strengths:** "His written work is outstanding. His arguments are always to the point and succinctly drafted." "Proves very comfortable on his feet in the Supreme Court." **Recent work:** Acted for the claimant in a judicial review that addressed the question of whether it was lawful to detain a child asylum seeker where the Home Secretary held a rational belief that the child was an adult, and where there was a policy not to detain children.

Stephanie Harrison QC Maintains a broad human rights practice, offering expertise in such diverse areas as immigration detention, freedom of expression and the right to protest, and discrimination. Her recent work also includes national security and terrorism-related matters. **Strengths:** "She's incredible on paper, and her arguments are flawless. Her advice is brilliant and really easy to digest." **Recent work:** Acted for the claimant in successfully opposing an application to strike out his claim for breach of statutory duty under the Gender Recognition Act and his rights under Article 8 ECHR. The case was transferred to the High Court as a result.

Leslie Thomas QC Takes silk this year against a background of a well-regarded practice in civil liberties as a junior characterised by actions against the police and appearances in inquests and inquiries on behalf of bereaved families. He has particular expertise in cases concerning deaths in custody, and fatalities as a result of police shootings. **Strengths:** "He is well respected for his calm, methodical case preparation, sound legal knowledge and good judgement.

Best of all is his fearless and at times devastating cross-examination." "He obviously holds the importance of understanding the client very dear." **Recent work:** Acted for the claimant in a test case that successfully brought about only the second inquiry into the near death of a child in state care. The child had suffered severe and persistent sexual abuse and had made suicide attempts over the course of four years.

JUNIORS

Nadine Finch Focuses on matters relating to immigration, family law and community care. She is a respected authority on the rights of child victims of human trafficking. **Recent work:** Represented the Children's Commissioner for England as intervener in a judicial review challenging the Home Secretary's policy on the use of force against children held in immigration detention. As a result of the challenge, the Secretary amended her policy to bring it into line with the UN Convention on the Rights of the Child.

Stephen Simblet Centres his civil liberties practice on claims for false imprisonment, misfeasance, assault and malicious prosecution brought against the police and detaining authorities. He is also expert in acting in inquests concerning deaths involving those bodies. **Strengths:** "He's fantastic – very committed, very bright, helpful and approachable." "He is a fine tactician and has really good instincts." **Recent work:** Acted for the claimant in a judicial review challenging the prohibition on near relatives of patients to apply for their discharge.

Amanda Weston Specialises in human rights issues arising from the fields of community care, mental health and immigration. Her expertise also includes bringing actions against the police and security services. **Strengths:** "She is very tenacious and known to be a fighter on behalf of her client." **Recent work:** Acted for the claimant in a renewed appeal against a decision of the Special Immigration Appeals Commission, which addressed issues of deprivation of citizenship and the powers of the Commission to render an individual stateless.

Edward Grieves Focuses on representing claimants in challenges to the imposition of control orders, and in appearances before the Special Immigration Appeals Commission. He is also experienced in challenging terrorist designations on asset freezing lists. **Recent work:** Acted for the claimant in a challenge to the imposition of a Terrorism Prevention & Investigation Measure on the basis that the decision of the Home Secretary was neither reasonable nor proportionate. The ruling relied on both an open and a closed judgment from a previous hearing.

Anna Morris Focuses her human rights practice on issues arising from the right to protest, and in challenging the actions of the police. She also has experience of appearing in inquests touching on deaths as a result of police contact. **Strengths:** "Very passionate about her cases, she will always go the extra mile, will plan her work well and will come up with creative arguments." "She is forensically analytical in her approach, and is a very human lawyer who is not pompous." **Recent work:** Acted for one of three defendants in a criminal prosecution for public nuisance, after they had displayed a protest banner on Tower Bridge. She achieved an acquittal following an argument based on the balance between the protection of the public and the right to individual freedom of expression.

Leonie Hirst Handles civil and public law challenges to detention in the context of immigration and prisons. She has a particular interest in protecting the rights of disabled prisoners. **Strengths:** "She gives competent, comprehensive advice and is a very client-focused barrister." "She is hard-working, much in demand and extremely effective both on her feet and on paper." **Recent work:** Acted for the claimant in a judicial review challenging a prison's treatment of a disabled inmate, in which it is alleged that ill-treatment by prison staff led to him being unable to wash or associate with other prisoners, amounting to a breach of his Article 3 rights.

Sarah Hemingway Offers representation in matters relating to mental health, the right to protest and data retention by public bodies. She is also experienced in inquests and public law challenges to detention in various contexts. **Strengths:** "She is a thoughtful barrister with a human touch."

11KBW

See profile on p.823

THE SET

11KBW regularly acts in human rights cases for central government, and also offers highly accomplished representation for a growing number of claimants. Advocates at the set are particularly expert in matters concerning freedom of information, the obligations of public bodies and national security. Commentators say the individuals here "are top notch and are in the premier league of counsel."

SILKS

Jonathan Swift QC (see p.733) An enormously experienced advocate who was until recently First Treasury Counsel. He is well versed in the full span of human rights issues, and has a particular interest in the imposition of sanctions on suspected terrorists. **Strengths:** "Jonathan is excellent – a very compelling advocate and a brilliant legal mind." "A very eminent and experienced barrister, who is at the top of his profession." **Recent work:** Acted for HM Treasury in a landmark case challenging the first use of powers under the Counter Terrorism Act to impose sanctions on an Iranian bank.

Jason Coppel QC (see p.578) Acts primarily, but not exclusively, for the government on domestic and international human rights matters. He is particularly well versed in information principles, and matters of detention. **Strengths:** "He is very, very sound, and very well liked by clients." "He is extremely able, and a very impressive opponent." **Recent work:** Represented the Equality and Human Rights Commission as interveners in a claim that the Justice Secretary was required to take steps to inform former detainees at Secure Training Centres that they had been unlawfully restrained, and were thus entitled to take legal action.

Nigel Giffin QC A well-regarded advocate who acts for the government on a range of human rights matters. He is noted for his proficiency in education, social services and environmental issues. **Strengths:** "He is very measured and very precise, and his drafting is excellent. His management of his own paperwork is masterly." "His style of advocacy is understated and devastating, and he has an incredible grasp of detail." **Recent work:** Acted for the Legal Services Board in a challenge to the introduction of the Quality Assurance Scheme for Advocates. It was found that the proposed scheme did not contravene European law, and nor did it fall outside the legitimate exercise of powers by the LSB.

Karen Steyn QC (see p.728) Appointed silk this year on the back of a highly successful career as a junior, which saw her acting for the government on a series of high-profile and significant matters. She has pronounced expertise in cases relating to the freedom of information, the intelligence services and the extraterritorial application of the Human Rights Act. **Strengths:** "Ferociously hard-working, a brilliant writer and a fine drafter, she is an excellent member of any team." "She is very good at client handling and at giving clear advice in difficult contexts." **Recent work:** Acted for the defendants in a case brought by Abdul-Hakim Belhaj against the former Foreign Secretary and UK intelligence services.

JUNIORS

Ben Hooper (see p.630) Focuses on privacy and surveillance issues for the government, particularly in relation to Article 8 ECHR. He has recently acted in a number of claims brought in the context of the Snowden revelations. **Strengths:** "He is very bright, and an extremely good and thoughtful lawyer." "An intellectually strong and able advocate who has the ability to simplify complex legal and factual issues." **Recent work:** Acted for the respondents in two hearings before the Investigatory Powers Tribunal in relation to the programme of communications interception operated by GCHQ and revealed by Edward Snowden.

Joanne Clement (see p.574) Represents both defendants and claimants in public law challenges on the basis of human rights arguments. Her expertise includes freedom of information, immigration and extradition issues, especially in the context of terrorism. **Strengths:** "She is experienced and has a good attitude." **Recent work:** Acted for the UK government in a case brought before the ECHR that examined the scope of the duty incumbent on a state to protect life. In the context of the facts of this case, no violation of Articles 2 or 8 ECHR was found.

Band 3

Brick Court Chambers

See profile on p.774

THE SET

Brick Court Chambers maintains its reputation as a set accomplished in providing representation to claimants and defendants across a wide span of issues in the field of human rights. Its members are experienced in handling matters arising in the context of deprivation of liberty, alleged state complicity in torture, economic sanctions, the transfer of asylum seekers between states where their rights might be infringed, and the rights of detained patients. They are well versed in acting in both domestic and international courts on behalf of their clients.

Client service: "The clerking at Brick Court is very good as it's flexible, friendly and responsive."

SILKS

Paul Bowen QC Maintains a strong reputation for his work in a diverse range of human rights issues. He is a noted expert in the areas of mental health, particularly in the context of detention in prison and under the Mental Health Act, and in protestor rights. **Strengths:** "He is extremely good, particularly in relation to mental health cases." **Recent work:** Intervened on behalf of the Equality & Human Rights Commission in a leading case on the meaning of deprivation of liberty in Article 5 ECHR in the context of two learning-disabled adults in restrictive care.

Martin Chamberlain QC Enjoys an excellent reputation among peers and clients for his measured and accomplished advocacy in human rights matters. He has expertise in a diverse range of issues within human rights and acts on behalf of clients ranging from individuals and NGOs to defendant governments. **Strengths:** "He is fabulous. He has the court eating out of his hand, and can manage to make anything sound reasonable." "A very polite and succinct advocate." **Recent work:** Acted as leading Special Advocate for Bank Mellat in the first ever closed hearing in the Supreme Court, in which financial restrictions imposed on the bank for the purpose of limiting Iranian nuclear proliferation were overturned.

Marie Demetriou QC Centres her civil liberties practice on the rights of refugees and asylum seekers, particularly in relation to discrimination on the grounds of sexual orientation, as well as the asset freezing of suspected terrorists. She is frequently instructed by the United Nations High Commissioner for Refugees. **Strengths:** "She is excellent and extremely easy to work with. She is very approachable, and pragmatic in coming to a solution that will make everybody happy." "Very easy-going and relaxed, but also very efficient in the way she goes about her work, and very sharp when it comes to European law." **Recent work:** Acted for the UNHCR in a hearing before the Supreme Court addressing whether the removal of asylum seekers to Italy under the Dublin II regulation would be in contravention of their human rights due to the risk of ill-treatment in the destination country.

Richard Gordon QC A noted authority in broader constitutional and public law principles, which expertise informs his work in civil liberties. His recent experience in this area includes issues of liberty in the context of incapacity, and of press freedom. **Strengths:** "He is quick to respond and collaborative, and his drafting is of the highest quality." "He has definitely got the ear of the court, and if you are instructing him, they will listen to what you have to say." **Recent work:** Acted for the Press Standards Board of Finance in a claim for judicial review challenging an order of the Privy Council rejecting the application for a Royal Charter for a recognition body for press self-regulators.

Jemima Stratford QC Incorporates expertise in EU law into her human rights practice, which is itself broad in nature. She has acted in significant cases concerning topics such as state immunity, child trafficking and control order hearings. **Strengths:** "She has very strong, clear and accessible ideas, and the ability to boil things down to the nub without making you feel stupid." **Recent work:** Acted on behalf of the Foreign Office in proceedings before the ECHR addressing the issue of immunity of foreign state agents against civil or criminal actions alleging torture.

JUNIORS

Maya Lester Focuses on targeted sanctions, particularly those imposed on the basis of allegations of terrorism. She also has experience in the interface between political activity and the designation of charitable status. **Strengths:** "She combines being incredibly clever with being modest, engaging and responsive." **Recent work:** Acted for Liberty in a test case challenging provisions in the Equality Act that prevented same-sex civil partners from benefiting from pensions that had accrued before the Act came into force.

1 Crown Office Row

See profile on p.784

THE SET

1 Crown Office Row continues to be respected for the exceptional standard of its work in the context of healthcare and clinical negligence. The majority of its human rights practice stems from this expertise, with members appearing in a number of significant cases addressing the right to life and to die. In addition to this, the set has a growing reputation in the area of national security and terrorism, particularly in relation to special advocacy in closed proceedings. **Client service:** "They're a very professional set, and the clerks are good."

SILKS

Angus McCullough QC Commands significant respect for his work as a leading special advocate in closed proceedings, typically dealing with allegations of terrorism. He is also expert in freedom of information and of the press, especially in relation to contempt. **Strengths:** "He is the premier silk for closed material procedures. He's taken a real interest in the broader development of the law, and is a genuinely well-respected voice in that area." **Recent work:** Acted as lead special advocate in a significant matter, in which it was decided that the existence of the Crime (International Co-operation) Act precluded the court from making an order for the release of material from an entity not party to foreign criminal proceedings under the Norwich Pharmacal principle.

Philip Havers QC Attracts considerable praise for his human rights practice, which is characterised by a concentration on the interaction between medical issues and fundamental rights. He also has an interest in regulatory matters. **Strengths:** "He's brilliant – very egalitarian and a pleasure to work with. He knows all there is to know about medical law, and his judgement is impeccable in terms of knowing how to put things to the courts." "He is an outstanding silk with years of experience whom the government often turns to." **Recent work:** Acted for the claimant in the Supreme Court case challenging the DPP policy on assisted suicide.

JUNIORS

Shaheen Rahman Enjoys a growing reputation for her work in civil liberties and human rights, which tends towards equality and discrimination issues. She is also a special advocate and has appeared in a number of significant cases dealing with allegations of terrorism. **Strengths:** "She's incredibly efficient and a fighter – when the chips are down she really sticks up for her client." **Recent work:** Represented the claimant in a challenge to the policy of refusing to provide methadone medication to prisoners outside daylight hours during Ramadan on the grounds that it violates their Article 9 rights.

Adam Wagner Strong on challenges to the circumstances of immigration and prison detention, as well as issues arising in the context of mental health. He has further experience of appearing in major public inquiries. **Strengths:** "He is a star in the making. He's extraordinarily literate and has a great understanding of human rights issues." **Recent work:** Instructed by the Treasury Solicitor in an Article 5 claim brought by a man wrongly committed to prison for failing to pay a debt.

Jeremy Hyam Focuses on human rights issues as they arise in the context of mental health, social care and community care. He also has an interest in environmental and local government law. **Strengths:** "He is a good, reliable and effective advocate." **Recent work:** Acted for the claimant in the judicial review successfully establishing that NHS trusts have a duty to consult before placing 'do not resuscitate' notices on patient records.

Thirty Nine Essex Street

See profile on p.797

THE SET

Thirty Nine Essex Street offers advice and representation to claimants and defendants in a diverse array of human rights matters. It boasts members with expertise in mental health, prisoners' rights, social care and the freedoms of expression, religion and sexual orientation. They have appeared in cases at all domestic levels, and in the European courts. **Client service:** "They are a go-to set for human rights cases. I see them as a very modern chambers, where even the most senior barristers are happy to converse by e-mail."

SILKS

Nigel Pleming QC An extremely well-regarded advocate with substantial expertise in a broad range of areas. His human rights work is characterised by issues arising from freedom of expression and of sexual orientation. **Strengths:** "An incredibly nice person and a very well-respected advocate – the court listens when he speaks." **Recent work:** Acted for the claimant in a third challenge to the decision of the Foreign Secretary to establish a marine protection zone around the Chagos Islands. This was the first case in the UK in which WikiLeaks material was admitted as evidence.

Jenni Richards QC Expert in human rights issues arising in the context of mental health, deprivation of liberty and freedom of information. She is also accomplished in the areas of local government and prison law. **Strengths:** "Her advocacy is brilliant – she's exceptionally hard-working and truly believes what she does, which really shines through." "She is a leading silk, particularly in relation to mental health issues." **Recent work:** Represented the claimant in a case against an NHS trust concerning the treatment it gave to a young boy with mental health problems and a severe hearing impediment. The case addressed whether a failure to provide adequate treatment can constitute a breach of Article 3 ECHR.

James Strachan QC Frequently instructed on behalf of the government in a diverse range of matters in the human rights sphere. He has appeared in the Supreme Court and the ECHR in cases addressing issues such as prisoners' rights, and the rights to die and to freedom of religion. **Strengths:** "He is very thoughtful, reliable, helpful and completely dedicated to providing us with the assistance we're looking for in each case." "He's very good, both on his feet and in his writing." **Recent work:** Acted for the Ministry of Justice in a high-profile case before the Supreme Court that considered the legal position on assisted suicide.

Fenella Morris QC Maintains a varied civil liberties practice typified by work in the areas of health and social care, and human rights in a commercial context. She is also experienced in matters concerning the Article 2 obligation to conduct independent investigations. **Strengths:** "She's a fearsome opponent, as she can come at things from so many different angles due to the depth of her knowledge." "She's very bright, very organised and enthusiastic." **Recent work:** Acted on behalf of the Official Solicitor in a test case before the Supreme Court addressing what constitutes a deprivation of liberty contrary to Article 5 ECHR in the context of the Mental Capacity Act.

Landmark Chambers

See profile on p.829

THE SET

The work of Landmark Chambers in civil liberties typically arises from its broader expertise in public law, in which wider field its members are noted authorities. They are highly experienced in applying those principles to human rights arguments, particularly in relation to detention, mental health, prisoners' rights, social security and the Geneva Convention. They are happy to accept instructions on a pro bono basis where necessary.

Client service: "The clerking there is very good and very professional. I also commend their commitment to pro bono work – they don't treat it as second-rate work at all."

SILKS

Nathalie Lieven QC Commands great respect for her skilful and formidable representation. She is especially expert in matters relating to mental health and capacity, prisoners' rights and torture. **Strengths:** "She is a force of nature. She is irresistible on her feet, and is very direct and quick to get to the point." "She is very impressive and very clear, and the court trusts her." **Recent work:** Acted for the claimant in the Supreme Court in an application for habeas corpus against the Foreign Secretary after the claimant had originally been detained by UK forces in Iraq before being transferred to US detention in Afghanistan.

Richard Drabble QC Has a strong practice in human rights that is informed by his expertise in public law, social housing and local government. He is particularly accomplished in handling social security matters founded on Convention arguments. **Strengths:** "His oral advocacy is excellent. He shines at explaining to a judge exactly how a complex point fits together." "He is very able, and has a very persuasive style of advocacy." **Recent work:** Acted for Child Poverty Action Group as an intervener in a challenge to the 'benefits cap' as it applies to housing benefit in the context of those re-housed in temporary accommodation due to domestic violence.

James Maurici QC Offers representation in cases turning on planning, environmental and road traffic safety issues. He also has experience in the extraterritorial application of the ECHR. **Strengths:** "His paperwork is always very thorough, and he's got a nice style since he always says enough but never overstates his position. He has a real knack of knowing where to draw the line on his arguments." **Recent work:** Acted for the claimants in the second judicial review of Ali Zaki Mousa, which sought a public inquiry into the deaths and mistreatment of Iraqi civilians at the hands of British troops.

JUNIORS

Tim Buley Enjoys an excellent reputation for his well-established practice in human rights. He acts for the full span of clients, from individuals to government departments, in such diverse areas as social security, disability discrimination and planning. **Strengths:** "He just continues to get better and better – as good as it gets as a junior counsel." "He is very smart and very good at strategic thinking. When discussing matters in conference, he is good at looking at what will work and what won't." **Recent work:** Represented the claimants in a test case before the Court of Appeal arguing that there is a duty on the Secretary of State to make reasonable adjustments in consulting medical advice before making decisions on Employment and Support Allowance for mentally disabled people.

Other Ranked Lawyers

Tim Eicke QC (Essex Court Chambers) Acts on behalf of claimants and defendants in cases addressing issues of transgender recognition, the legality of national security proceedings and extradition. He is also a noted authority on the relationship between EU and domestic law. **Strengths:** "He is a really excellent and efficient advocate, and very knowledgeable in the field of human rights." "He is a very competent counsel and understands the law very well." **Recent work:** Acted for HM Treasury in the first case in which the Supreme Court held a closed hearing.

Mark Hill QC (see p.627) (Francis Taylor Building) Specialises in questions of religious rights and freedoms, and how they interact with other fundamental rights. He is a noted authority in ecclesiastical law. **Recent work:** Acted for the appellants in a case concerning the ownership of two Sikh Gurdwaras, in which a central question was the alleged status of the Third Holy Saint as the leader of a sect in India. The court declined to rule on the spiritual issues on the basis of non-justiciability.

Richard Clayton QC (4-5 Gray's Inn Square) Demonstrates significant expertise in a wide range of issues in the field of human rights. He has represented claimants and defendants a number of times before the Supreme Court, most notably in relation to questions of police retention of data. **Strengths:** "He is extremely knowledgeable and a leading light in the field." **Recent work:** Acted for Media Legal Defence Initiative as intervener in a landmark Supreme Court case addressing whether the right to freedom of expression includes a right to access to information, and its interaction with the Freedom of Information Act.

Sarah Crowther (3 Hare Court Centres) Her human rights practice focuses on matters concerning discrimination and religious freedoms. She is particularly interested in the tension between religious expression and discrimination on the basis of sexual orientation. **Strengths:** "She is a very able advocate who wins the respect of the court, clients and opponents with her straightforward, friendly and common-sense approach." **Recent work:** Acted for the defendants in a case addressing whether Christian hoteliers had directly or indirectly discriminated against a gay couple in a civil partnership in refusing to provide them with a double room.

Tom Poole (3 Hare Court) Specialises in cases addressing issues of discrimination, immigration and asylum, and the right to a fair trial. He has particular experience of appearing before the Privy Council. **Recent work:** Acted for the Home Secretary in a judicial review challenging her decision that the claimant was not a victim of trafficking. The case established the principle that a person need not have been trafficked into the UK for them to be considered a victim pursuant to the Trafficking Convention.

Michael Mansfield QC (Mansfield Chambers) Acts for defendants in criminal trials, particularly those where questions of civil liberties and human rights are central to proceedings. He is also experienced in representing bereaved families in high-profile inquests and public inquiries. **Recent work:** Represented the family of Mark Duggan in the inquest into the circumstances of his death.

Ian Wise QC (Monckton Chambers) Offers representation in a range of issues, and has particular experience in cases concerning healthcare and police retention of data. He is also a noted authority in the area of children's rights. **Strengths:** "He is very approachable, really clear and not at all elitist in his approach. He has a broader constitutional picture in his mind at all times." **Recent work:** Acted for the claimant in a successful judicial review of the decision of the police to disclose unproven allegations against a nurse on her Enhanced Criminal Record Certificate. The Court of Appeal found that the decision was disproportionate and unlawful.

Piers Gardner (Monckton Chambers) An expert on international human rights law and its integration into domestic law. He is particularly experienced at handling predominantly commercial cases between nation states that are founded on human rights arguments. **Strengths:** "He is an excellent lawyer, who has a huge knowledge of human rights issues, and he does his utmost for his clients." "He is very hard-working and has wonderful insight into how everything works in the European Court." **Recent work:** Acted for YUKOS against Russia in the largest financial claim ever brought before the ECHR, which contested severe tax assessments that had led to the company's liquidation.

Azeem Suterwalla (Monckton Chambers) Has a human rights practice characterised by an emphasis on challenging policies on the retention and disclosure of data by the police. He also often brings actions on behalf of children and vulnerable adults. **Strengths:** "He is very capable and has a very good grasp of what is needed to assist the client." **Recent work:** Acted for the claimants in a judicial review successfully challenging the policy of the police to retain photographs of people arrested who are not subsequently convicted of any offence. The policy was declared incompatible with Article 8 ECHR.

Parosha Chandran (1 Pump Court) Focuses on cases arising in the context of human trafficking, in their public, civil and criminal law forms. She is a noted authority in this area, and has a particular interest in the law surrounding forced labour and trafficking for the purposes of sexual exploitation. **Recent work:** Acted for two defendants in a criminal case in which their convictions were quashed on the basis that their criminal actions had arisen as a consequence of their being trafficked.

Ben Watson (3 Raymond Buildings Barristers) Frequently instructed on behalf of the government and police, typically in cases concerning extradition or national security. He is also a special advocate, and has appeared a number of times on behalf of claimants in that capacity. **Strengths:** "He is extremely assiduous and very hard-working, and has a great eye for detail. A very reliable person to have on your team." **Recent work:** Acted for the Metropolitan Police in David Miranda's challenge to his being stopped at Heathrow Airport under Schedule 7 of the Terrorism Act.

MIDLANDS

Civil Liberties & Human Rights Midlands
Leading Silks
Band 1
Clayton Richard *Kings Chambers (ORL)* ◊ *
Leading Juniors
Band 1
Khalique Nageena *No5 Chambers (ORL)* ◊ 🄰
Tindal Jim *St Philips Chambers (ORL)* ◊ *

Ranked Lawyers

Richard Clayton QC (see p.573) (Kings Chambers) Well respected for his expertise in a wide range of human rights issues. He is especially accomplished in handling questions of police retention of data and freedom of expression. **Strengths:** "He is a very calm, unwavering, unmovable and consistently excellent counsel." **Recent work:** He represented the claimant in a judicial review challenging a disciplinary decision by the Chartered Institute of Management Accountants that he had breached an obligation of confidentiality. The claim succeeded on the basis that the information was not confidential, and thus that it did not violate the right for privacy given under Article 8 ECHR.

Nageena Khalique (No5 Chambers) Typically acts in matters relating to the provision of healthcare, capacity, and detention under the Mental Health Act. She has further experience of appearing in inquests. **Recent work:** She acted for Nottinghamshire Healthcare NHS Trust in a judicial review challenge brought by serving prisoners to the prescription policy for addictive neuropathic drugs in prison. The case turned on whether any disparity between the policy in prison and in the community was in breach of Articles 3 and 14 ECHR.

Jim Tindal (St Philips Chambers) Focuses his civil liberties practice on issues arising in the context of immigration, and the rights of children and of prisoners. He is noted for his expertise on employment issues in a human rights context. **Strengths:** "He's good – very approachable and incredibly fast at supplying an opinion." **Recent work:** He acted on behalf of Staffordshire & West Midlands Probation Trust in defending a judicial review application by a convicted sex offender to challenge the decision to release him on licence to a hostel, rather than into the community. The application was refused on paper as a result of the reasons given in defence.

NORTHERN

Civil Liberties & Human Rights Northern
Leading Sets
Band 1
Doughty Street Chambers *
Garden Court North
Kings Chambers *
Leading Silks
Band 1
Weatherby Pete *Garden Court North*
Leading Juniors
Band 1
Stanage Nick *Doughty Street Chambers* 🄰
Band 2
Arshad Farrhat *Doughty Street Chambers* 🄰
Butler Jonathan *Deans Court Chambers (ORL)* ◊
Fullwood Adam *Kings Chambers* *
Jagadesham Vijay *Garden Court North*
Karim Sam *Kings Chambers* *
Nicholson John *Kenworthy's Chambers (ORL)* ◊
Stanbury Matthew *Garden Court North*
◊ (ORL) = Other Ranked Lawyer.
🄰 direct access (see p.11).
* Indicates set / individual with profile.
Alphabetical order within each band. Band 1 is highest.

Band 1

Doughty Street Chambers

See profile on p.786

THE SET

Doughty Street Chambers acts for claimants on a diverse range of actions contesting points of civil liberties and human rights. Its members on the Northern Circuit offer expertise in protestor rights, prison law, actions questioning the conduct of the police, and human rights issues arising in the context of immigration.

JUNIORS

Nick Stanage Specialises in pursuing human rights arguments which concern the actions of the police through civil actions. He is also noted for his expertise in inquests into deaths in custody. His peers highlight his experience in cases concerning the policing of political protest and failures to investigate allegations of sexual assault. **Strengths:** "He's a brilliant lawyer; a formidable advocate who is great with clients." **Recent work:** He acted in a civil trial against the police in which a central question was whether Football Banning Orders violate the right to a private life under the ECHR.

Farrhat Arshad Focuses on civil liberties issues arising in a criminal context. She is noted for her expertise in the rights of protestors and of prisoners. **Strengths:** "She is extremely bright and one of the most tenacious practitioners in the North West. She has judges singing her praises."

Garden Court North

THE SET

Garden Court North is noted for its skilful and vigorous pursuit of human rights actions on behalf of claimants against detaining authorities and the police. Its members provide advice, training, and advocacy relating to the full range of human rights and civil liberties issues. Solicitors praise the set's "quick turnaround of work and no-nonsense approach to advice."

SILKS

Pete Weatherby QC Commands great respect for his expertise across a broad range of human rights issues. He is particularly experienced in matters concerning the rights of prisoners. **Strengths:** "He's really very involved with the issues, and capable of good, steady advocacy when presenting emotive issues. He gets his tone just right in court." **Recent work:** He acted successfully for the claimant in a landmark case in the ECHR, in which it was established that whole-life tariffs without review for prisoners constituted inhuman and degrading treatment, in violation of the ECHR convention.

JUNIORS

Vijay Jagadesham A public law specialist who has developed a strong practice in civil liberties and human rights work, assisted by his considerable expertise in prison and immigration law. He is also an expert in cases relating to religious freedom. **Strengths:** "He's very, very bright and a tenacious advocate." **Recent work:** He represented the two claimants in a significant Supreme Court case concerning the right of prisoners to an oral hearing when their sentence is reviewed by the Parole Board. The case established that not allowing prisoners a hearing was a violation of procedural fairness and their rights under the ECHR.

Matthew Stanbury Specialises in human rights actions relating to miscarriages of justice, the rights of prisoners and the representation of bereaved families at inquests. He has a further interest in points of discrimination and equality. **Strengths:** "He's very enthusiastic and is definitely an up-and-coming figure; he has a good reputation in prisoners' rights work." **Recent work:** He acted in a judicial review challenge to the Justice Secretary's policy on strip-searching female prisoners, founded on the contention that a failure to balance the risk to their mental health against security considerations breached their rights under Article 8 ECHR.

Kings Chambers

See profile on p.918

THE SET

Kings Chambers is well known for the acuity of its members in representing both claimants and defendants in a diverse range of human rights matters. The set is noted for its members' expertise in mental health, community care, immigration and prison law issues. **Client service:** "The clerking is good – they are very efficient, and pass on messages quickly."

JUNIORS

Adam Fullwood Focuses on matters concerning mental health and capacity, immigration, social care and prison law issues. He has further experience of appearing in inquests. **Strengths:** "He's very down to earth and an effective advocate." "He's very reliable in respect of deadlines and getting things to you." **Recent work:** He acted for the claimant in a challenge to a decision not to disclose records to a mother seeking contact with her daughter who had been adopted by way of a court order. The challenge was based on the contention that the decision violated her rights under Article 6 ECHR.

Sam Karim Acts for defendants and claimants in human rights matters arising in prison law, inquests, social welfare and questions of capacity. He is also experienced in cases relating to mental health and immigration. **Strengths:** "He's excellent, and used by all parties – he's very academic in his thought processes." **Recent work:** He acted for the Home Secretary in a judicial review challenging her decision to refuse indefinite leave to remain to an immigrant who had previously been granted a spousal visa. The claimant was found to be entitled to leave to remain as a victim of domestic violence.

Other Ranked Lawyers

Jonathan Butler (Deans Court Chambers) Specialises in issues arising in the context of mental health law. He is particularly experienced in questions of deprivation of liberty. **Strengths:** "His work is excellent, he's very punctual and he gives straightforward advice. He grasps the issues very quickly."

John Nicholson (Kenworthy's Chambers) Focuses on human rights matters in the context of immigration. He has further experience in the rights of children, particularly in relation to the right to a private and family life given under the ECHR.

CLINICAL NEGLIGENCE: An Introduction

Contributed by John de Bono QC of Serjeants' Inn Chambers

The clinical negligence world continues to be dominated by Jackson and Mitchell. In a Marvel comic there would be a superhero over the page, coming to the rescue of hard-pressed practitioners. Meanwhile, back on planet Earth…

Costs budgeting remains in its infancy but has cast a long shadow already. Huge amounts of time are spent preparing complicated budgets that have to deal with every eventuality. Foreseeability as a legal concept has moved from tort to budgeting as solicitors worry whether their cases might take an unpredicted twist. It remains to be seen whether all the extra effort and court time associated with budgeting actually reduces costs.

Mitchell remains a major issue. If Lord Justice Jackson wanted to bring the profession to heel then he has certainly done so, but at what cost? At the time of writing it remains to be seen whether a claimant would ever actually be deprived of his cause of action for non-compliance with a court order.

In that idyllic microclimate of the personal injury world inhabited by clinical negligence practitioners we have, for many years, been used to claimants and defendants working together in the best interests of their mutual clients. The odd exceptions know who they are. There have been hard battles but, in general, the principle has been observed that what goes around comes around. Thus, extensions were agreed by one party on the basis that the favour might be returned. Both sides have to manage busy experts for whom deadlines are not always a priority. Poor cases are abandoned, good cases are settled. The system was not perfect but it worked.

Mitchell has led to a climate of paranoia and fear. Mutual co-operation has been discouraged by the possibility of taking quick advantage at the merest hint of non-compliance and, indeed, the fear that not doing so might lead to allegations of professional negligence. There has been farce too as parties have had consent orders struck down and been obliged to cross-apply for relief from sanctions. What happens if both claim and defence are struck out? The introduction of the CPR in 2002 was a massive change but it worked because everyone could understand and buy into the overriding objective and its key concept of proportionality. The problem with Mitchell is that if you put a foot wrong you risk being nuked. That makes sensible litigation very difficult. If only our Right Honourable friend had walked home.

At least there is no shortage of work. Most clinical negligence lawyers work in the field because they love the medicine. If your real passion was civil procedure you would surely have done something else (worked for the MIB perhaps?). Successive changes in the NHS have apparently not led to a fall-off in claims. Indeed, the opposite is true. Therefore, in those spare moments between preparation of costs budgets and scanning diaries for deadline compliance, we still have real cases to work on.

Politically, we are now firmly in an era of holding doctors and other clinicians to account. Eighteen months on from Robert Francis QC's landmark inquiry there is still no statutory duty of candour but patients and their relatives are beginning to adopt a default position of questioning poor outcomes. We see no reduction in the volume of work any time soon.

Legal aid has almost disappeared. That will undoubtedly lead to some potential claimants missing out, particularly in the most complex cases. It remains to be seen whether the bigger firms will be able to 'self fund' cases which would previously have required legal aid for investigative help. Looking more widely, and particularly in the context of lower and mid-range cases, it looks as though the insurance market is stepping up to the plate. In the late nineties, when legal aid was withdrawn from most personal injury cases, some feared for the future. Predictions of doom were wide of the mark, though, as the involvement of the private sector led to a dramatic increase in the number of claims. We suspect this pattern will be repeated. Funding is not drying up. Uncertainty over future funding has also contributed to the recruitment merry-go-round, with practitioners wanting to ensure that they are in a 'safe place'.

The tsunami of pre 1st April 2013 cases still has to work its way through the system. In the next twelve months we will start to see the impact of QOCS. Will defendants fight more trials? We suspect that simple economics and the unpredictability of trial outcomes will continue to lead to the overwhelming majority of cases settling before trial.

As for black letter law there is little to report this year. In Meiklejohn v St George's Healthcare NHS Trust, the Court of Appeal took the opportunity to re-state the widely held view that Chester v Afshar was a narrow exception to the law of causation and should not be extended. They also took a swipe at the 'first instance' reasoning in Birch v University College Hospital NHS Trust, in which liability had been established on the basis of a failure to warn of the relative risks of alternative treatments. Causation remains heavily stacked in favour of claimants following Bailey v MoD, and there is no sign of a retreat from this high water mark.

Let's see what happens in 2015: more substance, we hope, and less satellite litigation.

Contents:

LONDON

Clinical Negligence London
Leading Sets
Band 1
1 Crown Office Row *
Band 2
7BR *
Hailsham Chambers *
Outer Temple Chambers *
Serjeants' Inn Chambers
Band 3
1 Chancery Lane
Cloisters *
Crown Office Chambers *
2TG - 2 Temple Gardens *
Band 4
42 Bedford Row *
Devereux *
Doughty Street Chambers *
Thirty Nine Essex Street *
9 Gough Square *
* *Indicates set / Individual with profile.*
◊ *(ORL) = Other Ranked Lawyer.*
[A] *direct access (see p.11).*
Alphabetical order within each band. Band 1 is highest.

Clinical Negligence London
Leading Silks
Star individuals
Maskrey Simeon *7BR*
Band 1
Badenoch James *1 Crown Office Row*
Block Neil *Thirty Nine Essex Street* *
Bowron Margaret *1 Crown Office Row*
Browne Benjamin *2TG - 2 Temple Gardens* *
Faulks Edward *1 Chancery Lane* *
Francis Robert *Serjeants' Inn Chambers* *
Gibson Christopher *Outer Temple Chambers*
Glancy Robert *Devereux* *
Gumbel Elizabeth-Anne *1 Crown Office Row*
Havers Philip *1 Crown Office Row*
Hopkins Adrian *Serjeants' Inn Chambers* *
Lambert Christina *1 Crown Office Row*
McCullough Angus *1 Crown Office Row*
Miller Stephen *1 Crown Office Row*
Moon Angus *Serjeants' Inn Chambers* *
Oppenheim Robin *Doughty Street Chambers*
Rees Paul *1 Crown Office Row*
Spencer Martin *Hailsham Chambers* [A] *
Taylor Simon W *Cloisters* *
Vaughan Jones Sarah *2TG - 2 Temple Gardens* *
Watson James *Serjeants' Inn Chambers* *
Weir Robert *Devereux* *
Westcott David *Outer Temple Chambers*
Band 2
Aldous Grahame *9 Gough Square* *
Bishop Edward *1 Chancery Lane* *
Burton Frank *12 King's Bench Walk (ORL)* ◊ *
Coonan Kieran *1 Crown Office Row*
de Navarro Michael *2TG - 2 Temple Gardens* [A]
Donovan Joel *Cloisters*
Evans David *1 Crown Office Row*
Forde Martin *1 Crown Office Row*
Hitchcock Patricia *Cloisters* *
Hutton Alexander *Hailsham Chambers* *
Johnston Christopher *Serjeants' Inn Chambers* *
Mylonas Michael *Serjeants' Inn Chambers* *
Post Andrew *Hailsham Chambers* *
Readhead Simon *1 Chancery Lane* *
Ritchie Andrew *9 Gough Square* *
Rodway Susan *Thirty Nine Essex Street*
Sweeting Derek *7BR* [A]
Whipple Philippa *1 Crown Office Row*
Whitting John *1 Crown Office Row* *
Wilson-Smith Christopher *Outer Temple Chambers* *
Band 3
Balcombe David *1 Crown Office Row*
Bebb Gordon *Outer Temple Chambers*
Booth Richard *1 Crown Office Row*
Coghlan Terence *1 Crown Office Row*
Edis William *1 Crown Office Row*
Harrison Caroline *2TG - 2 Temple Gardens* [A] *
Hart David *1 Crown Office Row*
Pittaway David *Hailsham Chambers* *
Porter Martin *2TG - 2 Temple Gardens* [A] *
Preston Hugh *7BR* [A] *
Smith Sally *1 Crown Office Row*
New Silks
Antelme Alexander *Crown Office Chambers*
de Bono John *Serjeants' Inn Chambers* *
Levy Jacob *9 Gough Square* *

Band 1

1 Crown Office Row
See profile on p.784

THE SET

1 Crown Office Row is an impressive set with a large number of highly experienced silks and juniors whose reputation ensures its place at the top of the London clinical negligence market. It acts for both private and publicly funded claimants, as well as numerous defendants including hospitals, NHS bodies and medical defence organisations. Members here show their stripes by also being adept at medical crime and disciplinary cases, and appearing in high-profile multiparty claims. Examples include the benzodiazepine litigation, the MMR litigation and the oral contraceptive litigation. They have also had roles in a number of leading public inquiries including those relating to Alder Hey and the Mid Staffordshire NHS Trust.

Client service: The clerking team is led by the highly respected Matthew Phipps. "The clerks are amazing; they always go out of their way to help, are really efficient and are very supportive."

SILKS

James Badenoch QC Has over 25 years of experience of handling clinical negligence and professional disciplinary cases. He is also well versed in medical law. **Strengths:** "He's brilliant on liability issues and he's fearless in his approach. He also makes clients feel very at ease and fills them with confidence." "A lawyer who's seen it all, done it all and is tremendously well respected, he is someone with exacting standards, who demands a lot from his instructing solicitor, but produces top-quality work." **Recent work:** Achieved a £5.7 million settlement for a claimant in a cerebral palsy birth injury case.

Margaret Bowron QC A silk with vast clinical negligence expertise, who is noted for her handling of high-value cases relating to brain damage sustained at birth. Familiar with complex liability and quantum issues, she acts for both claimants and defendants. **Strengths:** "She's very fair, sympathetic, approachable and pragmatic." "Calm and very considered in how she presents herself, she gives you confidence and clients like her non-aggressive style, which goes down well in the often sensitive cases that we're dealing with." **Recent work:** Acted for Sussex University Hospitals NHS Trust in defending a high-value cerebral palsy birth injury claim.

Kieran Coonan QC A well-respected silk with a wide range of clinical negligence experience, who acts for both claimants and defendants. His practice also sees him representing doctors and dentists in medical professional disciplinary proceedings. **Strengths:** "He is really clever and very thoughtful. He's a very good student of human nature and also knows how to run an argument. Furthermore he is truly kind to clients, many of whom are quite vulnerable and terrified of lawyers."

Martin Forde QC A silk of over 30 years' call, who is highly regarded for his broad knowledge of health law. He acts on clinical negligence cases of a complex and severe nature, and has particular expertise in cases relating to mental health. Forde acts for both claimants and defendants. **Strengths:** "He was exceptional. I'd never been in that sort of environment before and he was very knowledgeable and understanding of my situation. He took complete control, but was very down to earth and wanted to make sure he got me the best compensation he could."

Richard Booth QC A silk with a strong knowledge of regulatory law, who acts for both claimants and defendants on high-value clinical negligence cases. **Strengths:** "Richard is an exceptionally hardworking and dedicated barrister. Clients like the fact that he is understanding yet robust and thorough in his approach." "Very astute, he's able to describe in one page what others would take three or four pages to say." **Recent work:** Represented the claimant in a complex case involving allegations of haematological negligence on the part of St George's Healthcare Trust.

Terence Coghlan QC A barrister with a broad knowledge of medical matters, whose practice has a strong focus on clinical negligence cases. He regu-

Clinical Negligence London — Leading Juniors	
Star individuals	
Witcomb Henry	*1 Crown Office Row*
Band 1	
Boyle Gerard	*Serjeants' Inn Chambers* *
Cartwright Richard	*Devereux* *
Davidson Ranald	*Serjeants' Inn Chambers* *
Dyer Simon	*Cloisters* *
Ellis Peter	*7BR* [A] *
Furniss Richard	*42 Bedford Row*
Guthrie Cara	*Outer Temple Chambers*
Hallissey Caroline	*Serjeants' Inn Chambers*
Horne Michael	*Serjeants' Inn Chambers* *
Jackson Matthew	*Hailsham Chambers* *
Jones Charlotte	*Crown Office Chambers* *
Kennedy Andrew	*1 Crown Office Row*
Latimer-Sayer William	*Cloisters*
Mangat Tejina	*Hailsham Chambers*
Matthews Julian D	*7BR*
Mishcon Jane	*Hailsham Chambers* *
Neale Fiona	*Hailsham Chambers* *
Pendlebury Jeremy	*7BR*
Tracy Forster Jane	*Hailsham Chambers* *
Woolf Eliot	*Outer Temple Chambers* *
Band 2	
Baker Richard	*7BR* *
Bradley Clodagh	*1 Crown Office Row*
Carpenter Jamie	*Hailsham Chambers* *
Davy Neil	*Serjeants' Inn Chambers* *
Formby Emily	*Thirty Nine Essex Street* *
Gollop Katharine	*Serjeants' Inn Chambers* *
Holl-Allen Jonathan	*Serjeants' Inn Chambers* *
Hough Christopher	*Doughty Street Chambers*
Hyam Jeremy	*1 Crown Office Row*
Kemp Christopher	*Outer Temple Chambers*
Korn Adam	*7BR*
Lambert Sarah	*1 Crown Office Row* *
Martin Bradley	*2TG - 2 Temple Gardens* [A] *
Meakin Timothy	*7BR* [A]
Partridge Richard	*Serjeants' Inn Chambers* *
Price Clare	*Hailsham Chambers* *
Rahman Shaheen	*1 Crown Office Row*
Samuel Gerwyn	*Doughty Street Chambers*
Skelton Peter	*1 Crown Office Row*
Sparks Paula	*Doughty Street Chambers*
Sullivan Lisa	*Cloisters* *
Thomas Owain	*1 Crown Office Row*
Trusted Harry	*Outer Temple Chambers*
Utley Charles	*42 Bedford Row*
Vickers Rachel	*Outer Temple Chambers*
Band 3	
Aldridge James	*Outer Temple Chambers*
Begley Laura	*9 Gough Square*
Catford Gordon	*Crown Office Chambers*
Cridland Simon	*Serjeants' Inn Chambers* *
Dolan Bridget	*Serjeants' Inn Chambers* *
Goodwin Deirdre	*7BR* *
Hand Jonathan	*Outer Temple Chambers*
Jerram Harriet	*Outer Temple Chambers*
Johnson Laura	*1 Chancery Lane* [A] *
Keegan Leslie	*7BR*
Matthewson Scott	*42 Bedford Row*
Mauladad Farrah	*Crown Office Chambers*
Peacock Nicholas	*Hailsham Chambers* *
Stephenson Christopher	*9 Gough Square* *
Thomson David	*1 Chancery Lane* *
Toogood Claire	*Crown Office Chambers* *
Weitzman Adam	*7BR*
Band 4	
Barnes Matthew	*1 Crown Office Row*
Bertram Jonathan	*7BR* *
Bloom Margaret	*Hardwicke (ORL)* ◊
Bradley Ben	*Outer Temple Chambers*
Charles Henry	*12 King's Bench Walk (ORL)* ◊ *
Foster Charles	*Serjeants' Inn Chambers* *
Godfrey Hannah	*Cloisters* *
Harris Roger	*2TG - 2 Temple Gardens* [A]
Hill Matthew	*1 Crown Office Row*
Hockton Andrew	*Serjeants' Inn Chambers* *
Holwill Derek	*Hailsham Chambers* *
King Simon	*7BR*
Knight Heidi	*Serjeants' Inn Chambers* *
Mackinnon Lucy	*Hailsham Chambers* *
Manknell David	*1 Crown Office Row*
McLeish Martyn	*Cloisters*
Mortimer Sophie	*1 Chancery Lane* *
Myhill David	*Crown Office Chambers* *
Naughton Sebastian	*42 Bedford Row*
Powell Debra	*Serjeants' Inn Chambers* *
Rogerson Judith	*1 Crown Office Row*
Sheldon Neil	*1 Crown Office Row*
Tavares Nathan	*Outer Temple Chambers*
Walker Adam	*7BR* *
Up-and-coming individuals	
Dobie Lisa	*1 Chancery Lane* *
Wraight William	*2TG - 2 Temple Gardens* *

** Indicates individual with profile.*
◊ (ORL) = Other Ranked Lawyer.
[A] direct access (see p.11).

larly acts for health authorities and medical practitioners, and has experience of dealing with medical defence organisations. **Strengths:** Commentators praise Coghlan for being "fully au fait with the medicine side of affairs."

David Evans QC A clinical negligence specialist who frequently advises both claimants and defendants on high-value cases. He has notable expertise in brain and spinal injury cases, and he is also experienced at handling coroners' inquests and public inquiries. **Strengths:** "I think he's a class act. He's lovely to deal with, very laid back and totally in command of his brief."

Angus McCullough QC A well-respected advocate who has a wide-ranging practice and is a significant presence in the clinical negligence market. He has particular experience of cases concerning severe birth defects and those involving wrongful birth claims. **Strengths:** "He's one of those consummate QCs who's both authoritative but also really helpful and approachable." "He responds promptly and in terms of drafting his attention to detail is very good. He's very smart and dedicated, and has got a fantastic scientific background, which is a great asset in cases where the medical side is complicated." **Recent work:** Represented the claimants in a high-value wrongful birth case brought against Nottingham University Hospitals NHS Trust.

Elizabeth-Anne Gumbel QC Has substantial experience in the most severe clinical negligence cases including multiparty actions. She is especially well known for her expertise in cases involving children with birth injuries or brain damage. **Strengths:** "She's pretty remarkable really. Hugely committed, she understands the personal aspects of what we do, and is also shrewd and has sound judgement. She is a tough negotiator, is extremely hard-working and has produced remarkable results." "She stands out in her level of client care. She'll always go out to see clients and is not fazed by anything." **Recent work:** Heads the team that is receiving instructions from ten separate claimant firms regarding the breast cancer surgery claims being brought against Ian Paterson.

Philip Havers QC A highly skilled barrister who acts for both claimants and defendants and has a comprehensive understanding of clinical negligence issues. **Strengths:** "Philip goes through cases like a hot knife through butter. He's got the judgement and the intellectual courage to pare things down to what really matters." "He has the court's ear as he is an excellent advocate, prepares meticulously and has sound judgement. He has the capacity to take on huge quantities of work but always delivers." **Recent work:** Acted on behalf of the defendant in a high-value brain injury claim brought against the Royal Free Hospital.

Christina Lambert QC Acts on all types of complex, high-value clinical negligence claims, advising both claimants and defendants. She has particular knowledge of wrongful birth claims and professional healthcare regulation. **Strengths:** "She's a tough negotiator who has excellent judgement, great insight and a detailed knowledge of the field." "She's very easy to work with, really knows her stuff, and is superb in conference, both with experts and with clients."

Stephen Miller QC Has 25 years of experience of handling a variety of cases involving medical issues. He regularly acts for the NHS and frequently advises the NHSLA on birth injury claims. **Strengths:** "He's superbly authoritative on both the medicine and the law. The experts always like him because he really understands the law and he is very impressive in conference and in trial." **Recent work:** Acted on behalf of numerous private surgeons in connection with the PIP breast implants group litigation.

Paul Rees QC Has a wide medical and healthcare practice, and is particularly admired for his formidable negotiation skills when handling clinical negligence cases. He is seen by many as the authority on periodic payment type orders, and is noted for his technical expertise. **Strengths:** "He's very sharp, very on the ball and very good on the financial side of things." "Technically exact and extremely knowledgeable, he always has complete mastery of his brief." **Recent work:** Acted for the defendant in a matter where the claimant was rendered tetraplegic as a result of GP and hospital negligence.

Philippa Whipple QC A former solicitor, who has a breadth of experience of acting for both sides on clinical negligence matters. Many of her cases involve children with birth defects or those with brain damage. **Strengths:** "An excellent counsel, who is good for big, complex medical cases. She's good fun to work with and very, very bright." **Recent work:** Represented a claimant in bringing allegations against the Princess Alexandra Hospital concerning a delay in diagnosing meningitis, which caused a child to go deaf.

John Whitting QC (see p.751) Has vast experience of complex and high-value cases as part of a wider specialist professional negligence practice. His expertise also covers product liability in the healthcare sector and coronial law. **Strengths:** "Cool as a cucumber, he's incredibly calm and never misses a trick." "He's extremely user-friendly, in that he always answers e-mails and is happy to chat on the phone. Intellectually superior, he cuts to the quick and doesn't get sidetracked by irrelevant issues." **Recent work:** Acted as lead counsel to multiple defendant clinicians in a class action concerning unsatisfactory Isolagen therapy.

David Hart QC A silk with over 30 years of clinical negligence and medical law experience, who has, of late, handled both birth injury and paediatric claims. He is well known for his handling of major cerebral palsy cases. **Strengths:** "He's a very brainy guy, and also a thoughtful and conscientious man."

Sally Smith QC Acts for both claimants and defendants on a wide range of clinical negligence cases, and has a particular interest in class actions. Medical law has been one of her specialist areas for the past 15 years. **Strengths:** "Liaises effectively with clients, and has a calming influence and authoritative manner."

William Edis QC A QC with a comprehensive understanding of all aspects of healthcare law including clinical negligence cases and professional disciplinary proceedings. **Strengths:** "A sensible and tough opponent" who "is very good on quantum."

David Balcombe QC An experienced advocate whose practice is focused on clinical negligence and matrimonial finance work. **Strengths:** "He is a sound advocate who is calm under pressure, very responsive and down to earth." **Recent work:** Instructed in Ron Brown v Southend University NHS Trust, a high-value claim relating to a catastrophic brain injury caused by an untreated subarachnoid haemorrhage.

JUNIORS

Clodagh Bradley A junior with nearly 20 years of experience, who acts for both sides on a variety of complex clinical negligence claims. She has notable experience of handling obstetric claims such as ectopic pregnancies, issues relating to kidney transplant surgery, and GP negligence claims. **Strengths:** "She was so good with the clients and absolutely razor-sharp on the details. She had to master a vast brief and in conference she was absolutely on top of all the facts." "Every aspect of the work she does is done to a very high standard. She is very thorough and has a great eye for detail. Fantastic with clients, she's very direct but always very sensitive." **Recent work:** Acted for the claimants in a case regarding a negligent kidney transplant that ultimately led to the death of the recipient.

Jeremy Hyam A widely respected junior in the healthcare market, who has notable experience in clinical negligence cases and mental health law. **Strengths:** "Intellectually he's very creative, and understands a wide area of law. He's very careful and exceptionally responsive – a 24/7 person who's easy to talk to."

Sarah Lambert A highly regarded individual in the clinical negligence and healthcare fields, who is appreciated by sources for her efforts on behalf of both claimants and defendants. She has handled everything from small injury to extremely high-value obstetric claims. Also frequently appears at inquests and before the mental health review tribunal. **Strengths:** "I think she's got more emotional intelligence and reads situations better than anyone else I know. You get sound, valuable and pragmatic advice from her and she doesn't ask you to do the impossible. The clients love her and she likes them, and they feel that genuine interest coming across and they respond to that." **Recent work:** Acted for Medway NHS Foundation Trust in defending a liability claim regarding below-the-knee amputation.

David Manknell Advises claimants and defendants on all types of clinical negligence cases including many that are high-value and high-profile. His practice also covers best interests cases and mental health law. **Strengths:** "He's thorough, he understands the medicine as well as the law and he speaks to clients, as opposed to over them or at them. He's easy to work with and he's efficient – if he says he'll return something, he does, and the work is always worthwhile."

Matthew Hill A junior with a growing reputation in clinical negligence circles, who has appeared in several high-profile cases. He has represented both sides at jury and non-jury inquests, and also appeared for doctors at the Medical Practitioners Tribunal Service. **Strengths:** "He's very articulate, very on the ball, and doesn't miss a thing." "He's really hungry for the work. As clever as 16 cats, he's a fighter and he really works hard." **Recent work:** Acted on behalf of the claimant in a catastrophic brain injury claim brought against the Royal Cornwall Hospitals NHS Trust.

Henry Witcomb A leading junior barrister renowned for his work on difficult and complex clinical negligence cases involving catastrophic injuries. Acclaimed for his skill on quantum, he is particularly well known for handling cerebral palsy cases and high-value wrongful birth and death claims. **Strengths:** "He's absolutely top-drawer. Extremely bright, completely in command of the detail of a case, and a formidable opponent, he has a detailed medical and legal knowledge far above the average specialist." **Recent work:** Acted on behalf of a man and his daughter in an inquest into the death of a wife and mother in a psychiatric unit.

Peter Skelton Highly praised by market sources for his clinical negligence expertise, he has particular experience of high-value claims and multiparty actions. Has represented government departments and families at inquests, many relating to detention and medical or psychiatric treatment. **Strengths:** "He's phenomenally bright and incredibly popular. You can ask him anything about any part of the most complex cases and he knows it all." **Recent work:** Instructed in a multiparty action brought against the Department of Health and Castlebeck Care concerning abuse allegations at Winterbourne View Hospital.

Owain Thomas An active presence in the clinical negligence market, who is also an expert on public law relating to healthcare. He acts for both claimants and defendants, often on high-value birth injury claims, and regularly represents public authorities in complex inquests. **Strengths:** "He's great. He did a very difficult inquest for me and he was brilliant and completely on top of the medicine."

Judith Rogerson A well-respected individual with significant experience of obstetrics, gynaecology, orthopaedics and plastic surgery claims. Also praised for her work as junior counsel on several high-value brain injury cases involving both liability and quantum. **Strengths:** "She thinks things through properly and invariably gets the right answer."

Shaheen Rahman An active and well-regarded barrister in the medical negligence market, who whilst being equally adept at acting for both sides regularly appears for top claimant firms. She frequently advises on cases involving delayed diagnosis of cancer, stillbirths and plastic surgery. **Strengths:** "She was very good on her feet and fearless as an advocate – she really persevered in what was quite a difficult circumstance. She has a very nice way with clients, but she's pretty no-nonsense, which is a useful trait to have." **Recent work:** Acted on behalf of a hospital trust to defend allegations of negligent midwifery.

Neil Sheldon Enters the table this year following market praise for his work acting for both claimants and defendants in high-value clinical negligence cases. He also frequently appears at medical inquests. **Strengths:** "He's absolutely fantastic and his written work is beautiful." "He's exemplary as he's reliable and gets on very well with the clients." **Recent work:** Instructed on behalf of a GP and hospital trust to defend a claim alleging delayed diagnosis of intracranial hypertension which caused a young mother to go blind.

Matthew Barnes A rising star of this set, he is a clinical negligence specialist who acts for both claimants and defendants. He advises on cases ranging from high-value brain injury claims to cerebral palsy, and is also an expert on fatality cases. **Strengths:** "Incredibly pragmatic, he sifts through an argument very quickly to get to the nub of an issue. He really does avoid delays in cases by progressing them very quickly, and is excellent in round-table meetings. Very tenacious and quite punchy, he gets very good results." **Recent work:** Represented the North West London Hospitals NHS Trust in a fatal accident claim concerning the death of a mother of four after the hospital neglected to diagnose and remedy an arterial haemorrhage.

Andrew Kennedy Principally focuses on clinical negligence work, alongside regulatory and disciplinary law, and has experience of representing both claimants and defendants in complex and high-value claims. **Strengths:** "He's very responsive, very pragmatic and has a good courtroom presence." "In the case we undertook he was very good at getting the witnesses on board and getting them to provide evidence clearly – there were quite a few of them, some of whom were relatively junior and not in any way experienced in the world of courts and medical claims, and he really put them at ease." **Recent work:** Acted for a GP in defending of a clinical negligence claim alleging a delay in the diagnosis of skin cancer in a patient.

Band 2

7BR

See profile on p.772

THE SET

This set draws praise for the medical expertise and in-depth legal knowledge of its members, who possess a wealth of experience of handling complex cases for both claimants and medical defence organisations. Much of the set's practice is devoted to serious injury cases, including cauda equina and cerebral palsy, as well as fatal accidents claims. Two of its members sit as deputy coroners, and the team as a whole has significant expertise relating to medically complex inquests.

Client service: The clerking team is led by Rod McGurk and Paul Eeles. "The clerks are personable and very accessible, which makes for a very good working relationship. They are really geared up to dealing with the Jackson reforms – we were sending paperwork to them on an unprecedented scale and they processed it very impressively."

SILKS

Simeon Maskrey QC Head of chambers and universally held to be the leading practitioner in maximum severity clinical negligence matters. He is noted in particular for his unrivalled expertise in birth injury claims. His practice further extends to personal injury and product liability work. **Strengths:** "He is the standout at the chambers and the best silk I work with. An exceptional operator who can get straight to the heart of the issues in even the most complex matters." "He is a formidable advocate with brilliant analytical skills, who knows when to settle and achieves excellent results for his clients." **Recent work:** Represented a leading surgeon in connection with a £9 million claim arising from negligent surgery that resulted in spinal injury and tetraplegia.

Hugh Preston QC Concentrates on complex, high-value and maximum severity cases including a large number of birth injury and cerebral palsy claims. He possesses notable expertise in relation to claims arising from defective medical products. **Strengths:** "A fantastic advocate with great attention to detail, who is not only knowledgeable and in possession of good judgement, but also approachable, kind and genuinely concerned about his clients' predicament." **Recent work:** Instructed in a maximum severity birth injury claim, where the baby was born with severe cerebral palsy as a result of a mismanaged labour.

Derek Sweeting QC Acts mainly for claimants in matters concerning maximum severity injuries, medical product liability and fatal accidents claims. He is currently instructed by the Attorney General in connection with the ongoing Iraqi abuse in custody claims brought against the Ministry of Defence. **Strengths:** "He puts clients immediately at ease and makes them feel that their case is in safe hands. Fantastic to watch in court, he's one of the silks of choice for complex medical cases because of his ability to cut through the evidence to the important issues and ensure that all points are covered." "Clients like Derek Sweeting's calm approach, and his paperwork is first-rate." **Recent work:** Acted in connection with a claim arising from the misdiagnosis of meningitis.

JUNIORS

Peter Ellis (see p.595) Represents both claimants and defendants in a variety of high-value clinical negligence and personal injury matters. His ability to draw upon his experience as an assistant coroner and former hospital doctor is particularly valuable when it comes to coroners' inquests. **Strengths:** "His medical experience is very helpful and he really knows his law. He is able to analyse the evidence forensically and his pleadings can really make the difference between winning and losing a complex clinical negligence case." **Recent work:** Instructed on behalf of a claimant who suffered neurological damage as a result of a delay in diagnosing TB meningitis.

Richard Baker Specialises in handling clinical negligence and personal injury work for claimants, insurers and local authorities. Fatal accident claims and inquests are notable areas of focus for him. **Strengths:** "He's brilliant, very thorough, and very good on complex quantum issues." "He has a very good manner with clients, is on top of all the issues and has excellent advocacy skills. He's also a deputy coroner, so in addition to dealing with clinical negligence claims he is very good for complex inquest work." **Recent work:** Represented the claimant in a case concerning the failed diagnosis of a brain tumour which gave rise to serious physical and cognitive dysfunction.

Julian Matthews Acts on behalf of both claimants and defendants in high-value, complex clinical negligence cases. He is considered to be a leading authority on birth injury and other neurological damage claims, and possesses enviable expertise relating to orthopaedic and anaesthetic accidents and delayed diagnosis cases. **Strengths:** "Meticulous on the detail, authoritative, someone who instils the utmost confidence. His draftings and pleadings are excellent, and he is very contactable and willing to give ongoing advice throughout the case." **Recent work:** Acted on behalf of the claimant in a cerebral palsy birth injury claim, involving complex causation issues and questions about the possibility of a mismanaged labour.

Adam Korn Concentrates on claimant work concerning obstetric negligence, severe brain injury claims and orthopaedic matters. He is also commended for his representation of healthcare professionals in disciplinary proceedings. **Strengths:** "His advocacy is of the highest order. I think he's incredibly charming, both in the way he engages with clients and also in his cross-examination. He achieves incredible outcomes without at any point appearing to be threatening or overbearing."

Leslie Keegan Has a diverse caseload of clinical negligence matters, and receives instructions from numerous local authorities. As a former neurophysiologist, he has a wealth of knowledge pertaining to serious brain injury cases. **Strengths:** "He's quietly persuasive with the defendants. His medical background is a great asset and he is very approachable." **Recent work:** Represented a claimant who suffered bilateral below-knee amputations and loss of fingers as a consequence of failed treatment of abdominal sepsis.

Jeremy Pendlebury Acts primarily for claimants, and is particularly strong on obstetric and neonatal brain injury matters, along with other neurological damage claims. **Strengths:** "He's very committed, very enthusiastic and really very focused. Very good in conference and at round-table meetings, he's dependable, thorough, very approachable and knows the subject matter inside out." **Recent work:** Acted for a claimant who was left with cerebral palsy and severe cognitive and physical disabilities as a result of a mismanaged labour.

Adam Weitzman Maintains an almost exclusively claimant clinical negligence practice. He tackles a number of serious brain and spinal injury cases and has considerable experience of representing families at inquests. **Strengths:** "He's incredibly impressive – a great advocate who is very methodical and superb with clients." "He's very incisive, very pragmatic and intelligent, and impresses with his analysis of complex medical issues and with the empathy that he displays." **Recent work:** Represented the family of a 1-year-old child at the inquest into her death at Birmingham Children's Hospital following heart surgery.

Simon King Represents both claimants and defendants in clinical negligence and personal injury cases. He is especially interested in sports law and thus has developed notable expertise pertaining to claims arising from sporting injuries. **Strengths:** "He's an incredibly capable advocate." "He really knows his stuff, is happy to travel and tends to spot things that others might have missed." **Recent work:** Acted for a GP in defending allegations of failure to diagnose a spontaneous bowel lesion which resulted in sepsis and the death of a 40-year-old man.

Adam Walker (see p.744) Handles a broad range of clinical negligence matters for both claimants and defendants, including claims arising from iatrogenic injuries and delays in diagnosis. He frequently appears at inquests on behalf of families of the deceased. **Strengths:** "He's able to go the extra mile for the clients. He's very sensitive to the issues and has a very good working knowledge of the areas he works in." "Very forensic in taking us through each step of the case; he is very detailed and able to guide the experts." **Recent work:** Instructed in a claim arising from death as a result of medical negligence of a prisoner who had a congenital heart defect.

Jonathan Bertram (see p.549) Claimant lawyer who has been instructed in a number of matters arising from the delayed diagnosis of cancer, negligent surgery and dental negligence. **Strengths:** "He's very personable and very thorough. In conference with experts it's clear that he has a very good grasp of the medicine and he's very good at digesting pretty complex medical issues. I also think he's very aware of what the client's going through." **Recent work:** Represented a claimant who fell victim to surgical negligence during a hip replacement procedure and in consequence was left with considerable mobility difficulties.

Timothy Meakin Demonstrates far-reaching expertise in the field of clinical negligence, and has experience of handling severe neurological injury claims, obstetrics and significant orthopaedic matters. He acts for both claimants and defendants. **Strengths:** "Clients trust him and they feel at ease in his company. He's really detailed and thorough in his preparation, and always helpful and responsive with any issues that arise." **Recent work:** Instructed on behalf of the claimant in a case concerning a child left with serious brain injury as a result of negligent anaesthetic management in hospital.

Deirdre Goodwin (see p.611) A well-regarded individual with over 35 years of experience, who has developed a specialist practice in both clinical negligence and personal injury. Clients highlight her vast medical expertise, and note her particular skill in obstetric and perinatal asphyxial brain injury claims. **Strengths:** "She's got an encyclopaedic knowledge of human anatomy and medical issues. It makes dealing with doctors and opposing counsel much, much easier just because she has such a vast amount of knowledge and she's up to date with the latest research."

Hailsham Chambers

See profile on p.814

THE SET

Hailsham Chambers continues to develop an impressive reputation in the market and has members expert in both claimant and defendant work. Possessing a large number of barristers specialising in the clinical negligence field and two qualified doctors, the set regularly handles complex cases and multimillion-pound claims. Commentators say that this is a set with "impressive depth to the team – it has an efficient line-up from the senior end right down to the most junior member."

Client service: "The clerking team at Hailsham Chambers, led by Stephen Smith, is exceptionally good. I always find the clerks to be very polished in their approach, very polite, helpful and amenable." "The responsible clerking means that you always feel as though you're being prioritised."

SILKS

Martin Spencer QC (see p.726) Head of chambers, he has a diverse caseload that encompasses a broad range of clinical negligence matters. He acts for both claimants and defendants, and regularly handles cases with high-quantum issues. **Strengths:** "He is very affable, charismatic, thorough in his advice and a good advocate in court." "He's incredibly bright, very approachable, very kind and compassionate, but also firm and brave with the opposition." **Recent work:** Acted for the defendant in a maximum severity claim regarding brain injury sustained at birth by the claimant.

Alexander Hutton QC Undertakes a variety of high-value, medically complex clinical negligence cases on behalf of both claimants and defendants. In addition to being impressed by his work in this field, market sources laud his costs litigation practice. **Strengths:** "His star has been in the ascendancy for years and is continuing to ascend. He's very sensible, very fair and very, very bright." "He's always very well prepared, and is very impressive on the papers." **Recent work:** Represented the defendant in a maximum severity case involving a baby who sustained brain damage due to negligent midwifery.

Andrew Post QC Focuses on clinical negligence and costs law. He routinely represents claimants and defendants in complex claims arising from birth injuries and spinal cord damage. **Strengths:** "He is great and one of these very clever people who gets to the nub very quickly." "He's very personable, explains things well and has a nice manner with the clients." **Recent work:** Instructed on behalf of the claimants in a complex cerebral palsy case involving prematurely born twins who both suffered brain damage.

David Pittaway QC Has a wealth of experience pertaining to catastrophic injury claims. He provides regular counsel to NHS trusts and other medical defence bodies, and also acts for claimants. He is especially good at working on matters involving complex causation issues. **Strengths:** "He is user-friendly and he's very sensible. What we like about him is that he is pragmatic and doesn't over-intellectualise cases." "He's able to pick up something really big and complicated at a late stage and conduct a conference the next day with all the details in his mind." **Recent work:** Instructed on behalf of the defendant in relation to claims brought against Ian Paterson and Spire Health Care for negligent breast surgery.

JUNIORS

Jamie Carpenter An expert on professional negligence, medical law and costs litigation. His scientific background enables him to confidently tackle the most medically complex cases. **Strengths:** "Supremely intelligent and a man with an eye for detail, he's fantastic for complex cases and on quantum." "Excellent at drafting documents, excellent in conference, and excellent with witnesses and experts, he's very intelligent, very bright and highly tenacious." **Recent work:** Represented the claimant in a case brought against a GP alleging failure to refer the patient for suspected cancer.

Matthew Jackson Identified as a very popular choice for the NHSLA, Medical Protection Society and MDU when it comes to defending high-value clinical negligence claims. The majority of his cases concern brain and spinal injuries, but he is also experienced in orthopaedics, cardiology and oncology. **Strengths:** "Matthew has the ability to take on board and retain a large amount of information very quickly – you'll send him papers on Friday and on Monday morning he knows everything about that case." "He's very good on the detail and on tricky technical cases." **Recent work:** Instructed to defend allegations of brain damage caused by negligent surgery.

Tejina Mangat A former doctor, renowned for the medical expertise that she brings to bear in clinical negligence matters and coroners' inquests. Her recent work has included cauda equina, brain injury and wrongful birth claims. **Strengths:** "She's very impressive indeed on the higher-value cases. Her eye to detail is second to none and the quality of her pleadings and advocacy is there for all to see." "She combines exceptional legal know-how with medical knowledge, which really gives her the edge in cases involving complex medical issues." **Recent work:** Instructed in a joint claim for wrongful birth and birth injury brought about by GP negligence.

Jane Mishcon (see p.673) Has extensive experience of representing both claimants and defendants in high-value matters. The focus of her practice is on obstetrics claims. **Strengths:** "She's excellent, especially on difficult and sensitive cases, as she has a great approach to dealing with people. In meetings she's been able to show a great deal of empathy for the other side and talks in a human way – not necessarily a lawyer's way – while at the same time putting forward strong arguments."

Derek Holwill An expert in professional negligence and clinical negligence claims. In addition, he frequently provides counsel on general insurance policy issues. **Strengths:** "He's extremely nice and very sensible." "He's very sound both academically and practically."

Lucy Mackinnon (see p.660) Routinely instructed on behalf of both claimants and defendants in a wide range of clinical negligence matters. Her expertise extends from surgical negligence to mental health claims and cases concerning cosmetic procedures. **Strengths:** "Her responses are always very timely; she's very organised, and if there's ever a problem, which there often is with these cases, she is always accommodating. She has an innate ability to argue something in a very persuasive manner, and she's able to pull those 50/50 through to a successful conclusion." **Recent work:** Instructed in a case involving the death of a 2-year-old girl who was wrongly diagnosed as suffering from swine flu when, in fact, she had contracted septicaemia.

Fiona Neale Noted for her vast knowledge relating to perinatal injury claims, she receives instructions on behalf of claimants and various medical defence organisations. **Strengths:** "She's good, confident and quite fearless. I've seen her as junior counsel and she's quite happy to roll her sleeves up and take on QCs."

Jane Tracy Forster (see p.740) Singled out by market sources as an expert on birth-related injuries. She also possesses notable expertise in relation to claims arising from the delayed diagnosis of various cancers. Forster acts for both claimants and defendants. **Strengths:** "She's highly experienced and has real gravitas, because she's done every kind of case possible. The fact that she does both claimant and defendant work is a real strength of hers when it comes to the strategic side of things." "She has vast medical knowledge and is extremely good at managing experts." **Recent work:** Acted on behalf of the claimant in a strongly contested wrongful birth claim.

Clare Price A pre-eminent figure in the market, who is appreciated for her long-standing expertise in relation to complex, high-value clinical negligence matters, as well as professional disciplinary proceedings. **Strengths:** "Very well prepared and very thorough, she's able to put clients at ease but also able to talk about difficult issues sensitively. She's always turns around papers very quickly." **Recent work:** Represented a claimant who suffered neurological injuries at birth.

Nicholas Peacock Lauded by commentators for his work on dental claims. His additional areas of focus include regulatory and disciplinary matters, and general healthcare law. **Strengths:** "He's never fazed by the technical difficulty of a case. He turns things around quickly and is very thorough, responsive and approachable." **Recent work:** Acted for a GP in a trial concerning the alleged failure to refer a patient with suspected malaria.

Outer Temple Chambers

See profile on p.842

THE SET

Outer Temple Chambers is a strong set with a broad range of clinical negligence expertise and a vast amount of experience amongst its members. Its barristers continually impress clients on high-value cases and have handled a number of serious neurological and birth injuries claims. They have also had a key role in the De Puy hip replacement litigation. Claimant instructions come from top firms nationwide, and members also act for medical defence organisations and their panel firms. On the defence side new instructions have gone up 50% over the past year.

Client service: The clinical negligence and personal injury clerking team is led by Paul Barton. "The service provided by Outer Temple is excellent, particularly that of the clinical negligence clerking team. The clerks are completely reliable, super-friendly and fun to work with." "You really feel that they're on your side when trying to get something difficult sorted out."

SILKS

Christopher Gibson QC Highly knowledgeable when it comes to obstetrics, paediatrics and neurosurgical matters. He also possesses notable expertise regarding legal negligence claims relating to the healthcare sector. **Strengths:** "The most striking thing about him is his great courtroom manner. He has a beautiful way of connecting with the judge and tribunal, and a clear way of expressing arguments in court. He's totally authoritative and a good tactician, as well as being lovely to work with." **Recent work:** Instructed on behalf of the claimant in a high-profile fatal accident matter concerning the death of a woman due to negligent care in a Hong Kong hospital.

David Westcott QC Represents both claimants and defendants in multimillion-pound clinical negligence matters. His recent caseload has been weighted towards birth injury and surgical claims. **Strengths:** "A standout silk, particularly with regard to birth injury cases. He has a thorough command of the medical issues and is a first-class advocate with an incredible intellect."

Christopher Wilson-Smith QC Routinely instructed by claimant and defendant solicitors on high-value clinical negligence matters, especially those concerning babies injured at birth. His additional areas of focus include personal injury, crime and health and safety. **Strengths:** "He is always well prepared and his conduct of conferences with experts and joint settlement meetings is exceptional. He shows great skill in identifying the important and relevant issues." **Recent work:** Instructed on behalf of Western Sussex Hospitals NHS Trust to defend allegations of a delay in diagnosing cancer in a patient.

Gordon Bebb QC A specialist in catastrophic personal injury and birth injury cases, who is renowned for his knowledge of quantum. **Strengths:** "He's a QC but he's still very approachable, very helpful. Really imaginative, he finds a way of dealing with very difficult cases and moves matters forward. He's very responsive, and he'll never make you feel as if you're being a nuisance." **Recent work:** Acted for the claimant a high-value cerebral palsy claim brought against Mayday NHS Health Trust.

JUNIORS

Cara Guthrie Acts for claimants and for various medical defence organisations in connection with a range of clinical negligence claims, including cerebral palsy and spinal injury matters. **Strengths:** "A QC of the future, she's clever, robust and hard-working. Very user-friendly, she's good tactically and excellent in court." "She's great with numbers and phenomenally quick in conference." **Recent work:** Instructed on behalf of King's College Hospital to defend a claim arising out of a delay in diagnosing a brain tumour.

James Aldridge A predominantly claimant lawyer, with experience across the clinical negligence spectrum. His practice of late has focused upon claims concerning cerebral palsy, delays in diagnosis and negligent surgery. **Strengths:** "Very nice, very good and very fair." "He's extremely analytical and great for complex cases."

Christopher Kemp Represents both claimants and defendants in a broad variety of clinical negligence matters. He is singled out as an expert on Erb's palsy matters, but also has substantial expertise relating to other birth injury cases and claims brought against GPs. **Strengths:** "The clients love him as he's so approachable and down to earth. He always comes across as being quite laid back but when push comes to shove he's a really impressive fighter. Also possesses invaluable negotiating skills."

Jonathan Hand Instructed on behalf of both claimants and defendants, primarily in connection with complex, high-value clinical negligence matters. Catastrophic brain and spinal injury claims constitute a large part of his current caseload. **Strengths:** "He's calm, really responsive and helpful." "He is well organised and extremely helpful when finalising evidence. Always well prepared and on hand to advise when needed, he has a great manner when addressing clients and experts."

Harriet Jerram A claimant and defendant practitioner whose wide-ranging experience encompasses delayed diagnosis of cancer cases, surgical negligence claims and inquests. Sources highlight her specialist expertise relating to plastic surgery cases. **Strengths:** "She is fantastic with clients – her sympathetic demeanour means they feel she's completely on their side. She takes great interest and pride in the outcome of a case. You know she's got your back and it's very reassuring to have her involved." **Recent work:** Acted for the claimant in a complex inquest into the death of a patient suffering from aortic dissection.

Eliot Woolf Instructed by claimants and on behalf of the NHSLA in numerous high-value clinical negligence matters. He has considerable experience of cases relating to cardiology, vascular surgery and ophthalmology claims. **Strengths:** "Very good with clients and very astute, he's able to identify issues straight away and get straight to the point." "A very kind advocate who's clever, considered and patient." **Recent work:** Successfully represented the claimant in a trial regarding negligent ophthalmic retinal peel surgery.

Rachel Vickers Represents claimants and medical defence organisations in a range of high-value clinical negligence issues. She is appreciated for her work in relation to obstetrics claims, neurological injury cases and wrongful birth matters. **Strengths:** "Offers very thorough and trustworthy advice. She's quick-thinking, very committed and her trial preparation is excellent." "She brought a sense of calm to the proceedings which was second to none. Her forensic analysis on complex medical issues is extremely impressive."

Harry Trusted A prominent practitioner in the clinical negligence market who acts for both claimants and defendants. He has substantial experience of handling a variety of cancer, amputation and neurological damage claims. **Strengths:** "He's incredibly bright, very forward-thinking, and understands the issues very quickly. He puts clients at ease and is good at taking the lead." "Harry is intellectually bold and confident, and he makes really good judgement calls."

Nathan Tavares Receives the majority of his instructions on behalf of claimants, and handles a number of spinal cord injury cases, psychiatric claims and inquests. Commentators value the expert knowledge of mental health issues that he has gleaned from sitting as a judge of the Mental Health Tribunal. **Strengths:** "He is a very methodical and incredibly hard-working advocate. Very good with clients, he's excellent at fielding questions." **Recent work:** Represented the claimant in a case brought against Oxford University Hospitals NHS Trust concerning the delayed diagnosis of a spinal abscess.

Ben Bradley Represents both claimants and defendants, and has developed notable expertise in relation to catastrophic injury claims. Many of his recent instructions have involved birth injuries leading to cerebral palsy, neonatal deaths and damage to the spinal cord resulting in paralysis. **Strengths:** "He's incredibly experienced given his year of call. He does a lot of research, prepares very well and knows what he's talking about. If it's a case he hasn't come across before he'll go into every detail possible to make sure he knows it all." **Recent work:** Instructed in a claim arising out of a neonatal death due to a mismanaged home delivery.

Serjeants' Inn Chambers

THE SET

A set with members equally happy to handle both claimant and defendant work. The barristers here have experience of all manner of clinical negligence cases including complex multiparty product liability claims and claims relating to catastrophic injuries. One interviewee described them as being "clear, direct, focused, and people who act on instructions. They've made a name for themselves by getting results and they don't have to prove anything."

SILKS

Sir Robert Francis QC Widely praised by market sources for his work on high-profile medical negligence cases. He is regularly instructed on complex clinical negligence cases by leading claimant and defendant firms, as well as medical defence organisations. **Strengths:** "He's a very skilled advocate who's very easy to listen to in really difficult cases. So clever and so good with clients, he's utterly brilliant and one of the best-regarded silks around." **Recent work:** Instructed in a significant causation case arising from the suicide of a young woman following her untimely release from the psychiatric ward at Stepping Hill Hospital.

Adrian Hopkins QC Has specialised in the area for 28 years, and is frequently instructed on extremely severe injury cases and complex medical matters by both claimants and defendants. **Strengths:** "He's absolutely focused and always able to identify the issues that matter. He works extremely well with clients, solicitors and experts, and has a brilliant manner with doctors. Very intelligent, humane and astute, he never loses his cool." **Recent work:** Achieved a high-value settlement for a child who was left with cerebral palsy after suffering brain injury at birth.

Angus Moon QC A highly regarded figure in clinical negligence circles, who is mainly noted for his defence work but also acts on the claimant side. Market sources highlight his medical prowess, demonstrated by his position as editor of the Medical Law Reports for the last 14 years. **Strengths:** "His intellectual approach is very impressive. He's very bright, a very shrewd tactician and a solid negotiator. You know you'll get a good deal if he's on your side." **Recent work:** Defended a GP accused of negligent care that caused severe brain damage to a patient.

James Watson QC One of several fine silks at this set who is renowned for his appearances for both claimants and defendants. He has significant experience of advising on obstetric, wrongful birth and nervous shock cases, as well as those concerning brain injury sustained at birth. **Strengths:** "He's excellent and technically very sound." **Recent work:** Acted on behalf of the defendant in connection with a high-value cerebral palsy claim.

Christopher Johnston QC Head of the set's clinical negligence team, he regularly advises on complex and technically difficult cases, as well as class actions. **Strengths:** "He's extraordinarily good and very patient with clients – he debunks the mysteries associated with litigation, makes things understandable and puts them at ease." "He's exceptionally detailed. His preparation for conferences is second to none and you always know he'll have got to grips with everything." **Recent work:** Represented a claimant who was left permanently paralysed as a result of negligent spinal surgery.

Michael Mylonas QC Impresses with his knowledge of high-value, complex medical negligence matters. He has had significant success in several high-profile end-of-life cases. **Strengths:** "He's somebody who is utterly confident and inspires belief in solicitors and clients despite not having been in silk that long. He has exquisite judgement; he fights at the right time but knows how to position the case to achieve a settlement when that's what we need." "Conducts cases in a very charming but persuasive way." **Recent work:** Instructed on behalf of the claimant in a matter relating to obstetric negligence.

John de Bono QC A recently appointed silk with a growing reputation as a clinical negligence specialist. He is instructed by both claimants and defendants, and has particular experience in brain damage cases, including those involving cerebral palsy. **Strengths:** "He's very smart and very tactically focused. He impresses with his empathy as a person as well as with his legal acumen." **Recent work:** Instructed on behalf of the defendant in a matter relating to an alleged delay in diagnosing ovarian cancer.

JUNIORS

Gerard Boyle Routinely instructed by claimants and medical defence organisations on high-value clinical negligence cases, and he is particularly well known for his skilful cross-examination of experts. **Strengths:** "He's very punchy and very competent. He knows exactly what's going on and will fight his corner." "Experts have been very impressed by his understanding of the very complicated and technical medical aspects of cases." **Recent work:** Acted for a defendant with regard to a claim alleging delayed diagnosis of meningitis in a child.

Ranald Davidson (see p.583) Brings particularly strong medical expertise to bear, thanks to his training as a doctor before being called to the Bar. He has acted for both claimants and defendants on complex and high-value clinical negligence claims, including those relating to permanent physical and intellectual disabilities. **Strengths:** "He's methodical, knowledgeable and meticulous. Extremely good on his feet, he has a very nice manner in court, which is very reassuring for the clients." "His working knowledge of the law is very, very good and his ability to grasp complex medical issues is outstanding. In terms of his advocacy, he's very robust and confident." **Recent work:** Represented Chesterfield Royal Hospital NHS Trust in defence of allegations of negligent ophthalmic surgery and post-operative care.

Neil Davy (see p.585) Rising star of this set who has a broad range of expertise, and experience of representing both claimants and defendants. His comprehensive understanding of complex, high-value medical and dental cases continues to impress clients. **Strengths:** "He's extremely mature and he's single-minded in his approach – he never loses sight of the end goal but can adapt to situations, depending on what is thrown at him." **Recent work:** Defended Walsall Healthcare NHS Trust against allegations of negligent surgery.

Simon Cridland A well-regarded barrister with 15 years' experience of acting for both sides on matters concerning clinical and dental negligence. His knowledge and understanding of complex legal issues allows him to oppose silks on complex claims. **Strengths:** "He's exceptionally bright – the amount of information he can digest in a short space of time is quite amazing." "He's very helpful and offers a very comprehensive review and solid opinion that you can really use." **Recent work:** Instructed in connection with a claim arising from severe neurological damage caused to a patient during negligent surgery.

Bridget Dolan Admired for her wealth of experience in medical and mental health law, and someone who was a forensic psychologist prior to coming to the Bar. She has an interest in cases relating to psychiatric injury brought about by psychiatric negligence or through physical injury. She has additional experience in claims by secondary victims for nervous shock. **Strengths:** "Bridget conducts cases above her call and her attention to detail produces impressive results." "The minute she stands up in front of the coroners, they're on their best behaviour. She knows the law inside out and she knows how to work it in her favour and pull all the stops out for the family."

Charles Foster His widespread medical practice covers a wide range of areas, including consent to treatment, withdrawal of treatment and clinical negligence cases. **Strengths:** "He's incredibly quick and efficient. His legal knowledge is rock-solid and it's always current – he's very good at keeping us up to date with non-case-specific information too. He's delightful with clients and always gets the best out of the medical experts – he used to be a vet so he's very familiar with all the medical issues and terminology."

Caroline Hallissey An active presence in the clinical negligence market, and a lawyer with a primarily claimant-focused practice. Has experience in obstetrics, spinal injuries and birth brain injury claims, and is particularly admired for her comprehensive knowledge of medical law. **Strengths:** "She's very good on the medicine, particularly when it comes to to obstetric cases." "She develops a real rapport with the clients but can still be very straightforward and businesslike, which is a difficult balance to achieve."

Michael Horne (see p.631) An in-demand junior with over 20 years' experience at the Bar, who has developed an exclusively medical practice. He frequently appears as sole counsel opposite silks on high-value, complex cases involving birth injury or serious neurological injury. Market sources highlight his very good grasp of quantum. **Strengths:** "He's a really conscientious barrister. He's a very hard-working man and you'll always get his full attention. Good on his feet, he has a very sure grasp of the case and is genuinely helpful – nothing's too much trouble." **Recent work:** Represented the claimant in a matter regarding catastrophic brain injury sustained by a 1-year-old as a consequence of the delayed diagnosis of pneumococcal disease.

Katharine Gollop A highly respected junior who acts for both claimants and defendants in the areas of clinical negligence and professional discipline. Clients are impressed by her incredibly detailed preparation and impressive input into cases. **Strengths:** "A rising star – she's so efficient, so quick and so helpful." "Her advice is very well considered and she is always very well prepared in conferences." **Recent work:** Instructed on behalf of a claimant alleged to have suffered serious psychiatric injury as a result of a delay on the part of the Royal Free Hampstead NHS Trust in diagnosing hepatitis C.

Jonathan Holl-Allen Has enjoyed a nigh-on 25-year career at the Bar. Although equally adept at acting for both sides, he has particular experience defending medical and dental defence organisations and the NHSLA. He is known for his expertise in cases relating to the delayed diagnosis of cancer. **Strengths:** "He's incredibly nice and very thorough." **Recent work:** Defended a professor of gynaecology against a claim arising from bowel damage sustained by a patient during the allegedly substandard performance of a laparoscopic procedure.

Andrew Hockton Highly experienced, he has extensive knowledge of clinical negligence cases, and displays notable strength in high-value claims involving cerebral palsy and catastrophic injury. He regularly acts for both claimants and defendants.

Heidi Knight A rising star of this set, who enters the table this year following extensive praise from market sources for her increasing strength in clinical negligence. Her practice primarily focuses on claimant work, although she also represents several defence organisations. She has developed an interest in obstetrics and orthopaedic surgery cases. **Strengths:** "Her medical knowledge is excellent. She's seen a great number of these cases and has a lot of confidence." "We are very impressed with her accessibility and her attention to detail." **Recent work:** Represented a woman in a claim brought against the Doncaster & Bassetlaw Hospitals NHS Foundation Trust alleging clinical negligence that gave rise to an above-knee amputation.

Richard Partridge A doctor before being called to the Bar, he has extensive knowledge of complex medical issues which he applies to all manner of clinical negligence claims. He is admired by market sources for his vast knowledge and his real passion for the case at hand. **Strengths:** "He's very incisive on liability and very good on the medical aspects of a claim." "With Richard, you feel you're working in a real partnership. He's very responsive, very pragmatic and his attention to detail is excellent."

Debra Powell A junior who has handled a good deal of high-value, complex cases, including claims concerning HIV, and significant orthopaedic cases. She is also regularly instructed in medical treatment cases, often advising on end-of-life care. **Strengths:** "She's very approachable and you can have a sensible discussion about the issues in the case." **Recent work:** Instructed on behalf of the parents who suffered serious psychiatric injury after substandard obstetric care at Guy's & St Thomas' Hospital NHS Foundation Trust led to the stillbirth of their son.

Band 3

1 Chancery Lane

THE SET

1 Chancery Lane has long had strength in the clinical negligence sphere, and is noted for handling work for both claimants and defendants. Its members routinely receive instructions from large defence organisations and medical practitioners, as well as private individuals. They consistently offer advice of a very high standard on a range of clinical negligence matters, whether they be relatively modest cases or multimillion-pound claims.

Client service: The highly respected Clark Chessis is senior clerk at this set. "The clerks are very helpful and co-operative, and I never have any issues regarding fees. It's generally a very timely service and they're very approachable."

SILKS

Edward Faulks QC An esteemed silk who has been handling the most complex clinical negligence cases for many years. His wider practice covers professional negligence, police and public law cases. **Strengths:** "He's wonderfully client-friendly as he's terribly calm and measured. In fraught situations he creates an atmosphere of calm and confidence, and he must be one of the most charming and polite men on the earth – in negotiations he's never aggressive, just very clear, firm and incredibly clever." **Recent work:** Represented a defendant NHS hospital in a high-profile judicial review of a hospital's 'do not resuscitate' policy, where the preliminary issue decided in favour of the defendant.

Edward Bishop QC Admired for his breadth of experience in cases across all areas of the clinical negligence field. He is instructed by claimants and defendants on high-value matters, and has notable expertise in damages claims under the Human Rights Act. **Strengths:** "He's very experienced, very practical and very calm in conference with experts." "He's very fair and takes a sensible and pragmatic approach towards negotiating settlements. In complex cases he's able to narrow down the issues very quickly, and his drafting is excellent." **Recent work:** Successfully obtained a substantial sum by settlement for a claimant in a case concerning failure to suspect and treat cauda equina syndrome.

Simon Readhead QC A high-ranking silk with over 30 years' experience at the Bar, who specialises in clinical and other professional negligence claims. He has notable expertise in clinical liability cases, and has a particular interest in medico-legal issues. **Strengths:** "He has a very good eye for detail and excellent client care skills." "His preparation is very thorough and he is able to master all the facts of a case. He is also responsive and easy to work with." **Recent work:** Assisted a claimant who suffered brain damage and spinal injuries whilst in an Immigration Removal Centre.

JUNIORS

Laura Johnson A barrister who is regularly instructed, predominantly by claimants, in a variety of high-value cases. She has continued to advise on a number of fatal claims cases, and is also well versed in gynaecology and obstetric claims. **Strengths:** "A very bright and thorough barrister, and a tough negotiator. She has a super manner with the clients, and is also completely au fait with what the law says and what all the medical issues are." "She's very easy to deal with, very helpful, and her turnaround time is fast." **Recent work:** Advised a claimant on a case concerning a father of three young children who died of sepsis contracted in the post-operative phase.

David Thomson (see p.737) A lawyer with substantial medical expertise gleaned from his time as a junior surgeon and GP before coming to the Bar. He regularly advises both claimants and defendants on both complex causation and high-value quantum matters, and is especially knowledgeable on cases concerning catastrophic injury and cerebral palsy. **Strengths:** "His ability to communicate with members of the medical profession is amazing, but he is also good at explaining things in layman's terms, and is brilliant with difficult clients." **Recent work:** Reached settlement in a case on behalf of a claimant whose father had died following an NHS trust's failure to diagnose pancreatic cancer.

Lisa Dobie A new entrant to this year's table, whose caseload includes claims relating to failure to diagnose, infant deaths and cosmetic surgery. She predominantly acts for claimants, but is increasingly instructed by defendants as well. **Strengths:** "She's very client-focused and an excellent communicator. I have been impressed by her advocacy skills and by her ability to draw out the important issues in case."

Sophie Mortimer Applauded for her honest approach and clear advice, she handles both claimant and defendant cases. **Strengths:** "She grasps what's going on very quickly and her advice is always concise and direct." "Her legal knowledge is excellent and she's very good with clients, who appreciate her direct and realistic approach."

Cloisters

See profile on p.778

THE SET

A standout exclusively claimant set that is active nationally on cases of the utmost value and complexity. The size of the clinical negligence group here has grown in recent times, as has its reach. Members are now active not just in London but everywhere from the North East to the South West. Highly respected, they have appeared in a number of important claims such as A v Powys Local Health Board and Iqbal v Whipps Cross University Hospitals, and have further enhanced their credentials by contributing to papers and articles in the clinical negligence. Great solicitors' favourites, they also put on popular seminars for professional clients.

Client service: The clerks, led by Glenn Hudson, have "extremely high standards and are reliable." "I like that they're really part of the team when you get them on board on a case. They're always available on e-mail."

SILKS

Joel Donovan QC Routinely represents claimants in a range of high-value, complex clinical negligence matters. A large proportion of his cases concern damage to the spinal cord and secondary brain injuries. **Strengths:** "Joel has outstanding analytical skills and provides thorough advice and a realistic view." **Recent work:** Instructed in a complex claim brought against three GPs and one hospital trust concerning alleged failure to diagnose bleeding from a cerebral aneurysm which gave rise to serious disability.

Simon Taylor QC (see p.735) A qualified doctor who brings his former professional experience to bear when handling claims involving particularly medically complex challenges. **Strengths:** "He's a very impressive counsel who deals well with birth injury cases and the most complex claims." "A very strong negotiator," he is "a formidable opponent, who's very bright, persuasive and quite passionate." **Recent work:** Instructed in a serious brain injury claim arising from obstetric negligence.

Patricia Hitchcock QC Frequently represents claimants in maximum severity medical negligence cases involving spinal injuries and cancers. She is also singled out for the wealth of knowledge she possesses in relation to brain injury cases. **Strengths:** "She is absolutely meticulous, very warm and very good with clients." **Recent work:** Provided pro bono representation for the family at an inquest into the death of a man who had died as a result of negligent management of liver abscesses.

JUNIORS

Simon Dyer Renowned for his knowledge of spinal injury, obstetrics and cerebral palsy cases. Most commonly he receives instructions on behalf of the claimant. **Strengths:** "His advocacy style is subtle, courteous and very effective; he is nimble but surefooted when put in tight corners. He is very engaging and persuasive in settlement meetings."

William Latimer-Sayer Focuses on catastrophic personal injury and clinical negligence claims, and is universally admired for his quantum expertise. **Strengths:** "He's absolutely brilliant. He's very analytical, has excellent interpersonal skills and is very sympathetic with the clients. William understands the issues very quickly and is not afraid to push the boundaries. Although extremely busy, he always finds the time to respond." **Recent work:** Represented the claimant in a maximum severity complex cerebral palsy case, with a schedule of loss totalling in excess of £17 million.

Hannah Godfrey (see p.610) Acts in the main for claimants, and handles a broad variety of clinical negligence matters. She has substantial experience of handling oncology, ophthalmology and plastic surgery claims. **Strengths:** "She's very approachable, highly organised and always well prepared. Some of these cases are very complex and she's really good at explaining what's happening to the clients without using legal jargon." "A good problem solver in tricky scenarios."

Martyn McLeish Noted for his strength across the board in high-value clinical negligence cases, he regularly receives instructions concerning severe brain damage and spinal injury claims. **Strengths:** "He's very thorough, very helpful and will always give you time on the phone." **Recent work:** Instructed in relation to a claim arising from cervical cord injury sustained as a result of negligent surgery.

Lisa Sullivan (see p.731) Established clinical negligence and personal injury barrister who engages primarily in claimant work. She tackles a diverse caseload of high-value matters, including brain injury cases and claims arising from the delayed diagnosis of cauda equina and meningitis. **Strengths:** "She's fast, client-friendly and measured."

Crown Office Chambers

See profile on p.782

THE SET

Members are in high demand for both claimant and defendant work, and regularly receive instructions from individual claimants, as well as the NHS and other large medical defence organisations.

Client service: Andy Flanagan is the set's senior managing clerk, whilst Paul Hurst leads the personal injury, occupational diseases and clinical negligence teams. "The clerks are very efficient and very friendly. Everyone will be looked after, and you know it's going to work very well."

SILKS

Alexander Antelme QCA newly appointed silk who draws extensive praise from sources for his knowledge and experience of high-value complex cases. He acts for both claimants and defendants. **Strengths:** "Incredibly thorough and a real fighter, he has the ability to construct and hold an argument. He produces good, detailed advice and and manages his clients very well along the way." **Recent work:** Acted for the defendant in a case where the claimant died after suffering a stroke following heart surgery.

JUNIORS

Gordon Catford Rises in this year's rankings following praise from market sources for his superior knowledge and personable approach. He regularly acts on high-value claims and cases involving periodical payment orders. **Strengths:** "He's very thorough, his written work is excellent and he really knows his stuff." "From the client's point of view he is very user-friendly and provides clear advice."

Charlotte Jones (see p.639) A leading junior barrister with an exclusive clinical negligence practice, who is highly regarded by market sources due to her extensive experience and formidable prowess in the courtroom. She appears for both claimants and defendants, although she is increasingly acting for large defence organisations. Obstetric and birth injury cases are a specialism of hers. **Strengths:** "She's excellent at analysing expert evidence and fantastic at breaking down complicated case histories." "The complete package – she is tough when necessary but empathetic with clients. Her knowledge is great and she has an ability to get to the point. Her advice is always 100% sound and she is accessible and supportive."

Farrah Mauladad Works extensively on cases involving knowledge of psychology and psychiatry, and though experienced in acting for both sides, primarily acts for defendants. **Strengths:** "She's über-organised, exceptionally efficient, and always has the facts at her fingertips. She's really good with clients – they trust her implicitly."

David Myhill (see p.680) Praised for his medical knowledge, he regularly acts for both claimants and defendants, representing parties both at inquests as well as trial. He is particularly good on quantum issues. **Strengths:** "He's firm, intelligent and good to negotiate with. Mature and balanced, he is a lawyer who knows both his medicine and the law." **Recent work:** Acted in a claim against a GP relating to an alleged failure to diagnose ascending lymphangitis.

Claire Toogood (see p.739) A barrister with a rising profile who is developing her experience in cases of growing complexity and value. **Strengths:** "She's very assured, very robust and doesn't take any prisoners. At the same time she's very good with clients and sensitive to their concerns."

2TG – 2 Temple Gardens

See profile on p.873

THE SET

A chambers that handles a broad range of clinical negligence cases, many of which are of high value. Its members have significant knowledge of medical issues, and are noted for their proficiency in matters of an unusual or complex nature. Both claimants and defendants are represented and the set's clients include the NHSLA, the GMC, hospital trusts and individual claimants.

SILKS

Benjamin Browne QC Regularly advises both claimants and defendants in complex clinical negligence claims and personal injury cases. Catastrophic birth injury cases and claims of negligent diagnosis and/or treatment are a particular specialism. **Strengths:** "He's an exceptionally effective advocate." "He's very responsive – if you ask him to do something by a certain date, he does it."

Michael de Navarro QC Noted for his prowess in cases involving catastrophic disability as a result of cerebral palsy or brain and spinal damage. He mainly acts for defendants, but is also regularly instructed by claimants as well. **Strengths:** "He understands the medical issues on liability and he gets to the heart of a matter quickly, no matter how complex the issue." "He is a go-to barrister for multimillion-pound claims – particularly brain damage cases."

Sarah Vaughan Jones QC (see p.743) A high-ranking silk who has extensive medical knowledge and experience of handling complex, high-value clinical negligence cases. She is especially noted for her prowess in cases involving brain-injured babies. Her practice is primarily defendant-focused. **Strengths:** "She's got an incredible eye for detail and prepares the most amazing counter-schedules. At round-table meetings she is extremely impressive – she has it all in her head and is able to explain and pull out every one of those figures as and when she needs them."

Caroline Harrison QC (see p.621) A clinical negligence specialist who is known in the market for her compassionate nature and superior knowledge of medicine. She acts for both claimants and defendants, and regularly advises on high-value quantum claims. **Strengths:** "Caroline is intelligent, committed and very user-friendly. She is an excellent advocate and totally dedicated to her work and to her clients."

Martin Porter QC Mainly acts on complex claims for defendants, and is experienced in brain damage and psychiatric injury cases. **Strengths:** "He is speedy, precise and he understands what the clients' requirements are."

JUNIORS

Bradley Martin (see p.663) An experienced junior who has handled many high-value cases of maximum severity. His practice is broad and covers brain damage, spinal injury and amputation cases, for both claimants and defendants. **Strengths:** "He's a fantastic advocate – I would always prefer to have him on my side than on the other side." "His approach is careful and considered and he is particularly user-friendly. He puts clients and clinicians at ease."

Roger Harris High-value clinical negligence claims relating to catastrophic injuries at birth are a particular area of expertise for this barrister. He also has a wide personal injury practice. **Strengths:** "Technically brilliant, he's very clever and understands the law and its intricacies to a very high level."

William Wraight (see p.756) A barrister whose background as a surgeon provides him with a solid knowledge of the sector. He has advised on cases relating to delayed diagnosis and the mismanagement of cancer, obstetrics and gynaecology. **Strengths:** "He has an exceptionally good manner with witnesses. He's really easy to work with, his turnaround times are great and he's good on his feet."

Band 4

42 Bedford Row

See profile on p.769

THE SET

42 Bedford Row is an increasingly active player in the clinical negligence market. Its barristers have a wide-ranging skill set and undertake inquests, professional disciplinary proceedings, and personal injury claims, on top of their clinical negligence workload. Market sources appreciate the approachable atmosphere engendered by the set's clerking team and barristers, and are confident in the members' skill when acting for either claimants or defendants.

Client service: The clerks, led by the affable and highly co-operative Alan Brewer, are "very friendly and efficient, and know their barristers inside out."

JUNIORS

Richard Furniss A well-regarded clinical negligence and personal injury advocate, who is recognised by market sources for his approachable manner and technical skill. His practice covers both the claimant and defendant side and takes in cases relating to cerebral palsy and catastrophic injury. **Strengths:** "He can cut through a case, see what the main issues are and give you really practical solutions when you're trying to settle cases." "He's great with clients and really leads the way when it comes to round-table meetings."

Scott Matthewson Head of the set's clinical negligence group and a man whose practice focuses primarily on medical law. He has experience in a broad range of matters including high-value and complex cases concerning failures to diagnose. **Strengths:** "He has handled the various parties in conference skilfully, managing to explain the issues and the process clearly and simply, whilst at the same time drafting a comprehensive schedule of loss." **Recent work:** Assisted the family of a young mother who died of multi-organ failure after suffering empyema following an alleged failure to diagnose necrotising fasciitis.

Charles Utley Has handled numerous high-value, complex clinical negligence claims in his 35 years at the Bar. His practice covers both claimant and defendant work and is almost exclusively based in the field of clinical negligence. **Strengths:** "He's very experienced at handling high-value cases."

Sebastian Naughton Enters the rankings for the first time following positive feedback from a range of market sources, who particularly note his friendly approach to both clients and peers. His practice is predominantly claimant-focused and his recent caseload has included a number of amputation and fatal injuries claims. **Strengths:** "He's very meticulous and his attention to detail is very good. Very concise, he is able to pull out the relevant parts of the case and really get to grips with the key points."

Devereux

See profile on p.785

THE SET

The set really wins its spurs on high-value claimant cases, but its members are equally as experienced at acting for defendants, as evidenced by their representation of NHS trusts and health authorities. Interviewees stress the barristers' efficiency when it comes to complex clinical negligence issues, especially those relating to brain injury. Clients also highlight the efficiency of the clerking team, led by chambers director Vince Plant.

SILKS

Robert Glancy QC A highly respected silk with a top-level clinical negligence practice developed over 40 years at the Bar. He is regularly instructed on cases of high complexity and value, and is best known for representing claimants who have suffered catastrophic brain and spinal injury. He also has significant experience of acting for children with cerebral palsy. **Strengths:** "Robert is a fund of knowledge and experience." "A first choice for the more difficult cases, he brings a wealth of experience and is prepared to fight." **Recent work:** Acted for a claimant who brought a case following complications during the birth of a premature twin.

Robert Weir QC A widely respected silk with great expertise and a broad practice. He is especially noted for acting for claimants on cases where cerebral palsy has developed due to perinatal and neonatal negligence. **Strengths:** "He's a formidable intellect and has a very strong courtroom presence." "An extremely intelligent and able counsel, he's always on top of the detail and able to grasp really complex issues." **Recent work:** Represented a child claimant with cerebral palsy.

JUNIORS

Richard Cartwright A top-rated junior with 20 years' experience at the Bar, who is widely appreciated for his specialist clinical negligence and personal injury practice. A former chartered accountant, he is noted by market sources for his knowledge of quantum issues. **Strengths:** "Richard Cartwright has a 'can do' approach to everything. He thrives on complex cases and is tenacious in getting the best result for the client. He is an intelligent and caring barrister." **Recent work:** Acted for a wife in a dependency damages claim following the death of her husband. The husband had died from a haemorrhage after spinal surgery.

Doughty Street Chambers

See profile on p.786

THE SET

A well-respected chambers with a strong claimant-focused practice that takes in a range of healthcare law matters, including regulatory work and Human Rights Act cases. Members handle cases of every value and complexity, and have notable experience in claims concerning hospital-acquired infection, adult and child abuse, and product liability.

SILKS

Robin Oppenheim QC Specialises in high-value catastrophic brain and spinal injury claims, as well as meningococcal disease litigation. Commentators praise him for his far-reaching knowledge of the law and his expertise on questions of quantum. **Strengths:** "He's compassionate and astute, and his analysis of difficult causation arguments is almost unsurpassed. He presents a calm and confident air which gives clients great confidence in his ability."

JUNIORS

Christopher Hough Highly regarded claimant barrister who concentrates on high-value matters. Generally speaking his cases are complex in terms of questions of liability, causation and quantum. **Strengths:** "He's brilliant on the medicine side and very good at dealing with matters proactively and constructively." One client commented: "He is a really nice gentleman. I met him in my home and he was very professional and didn't make me feel inferior. I am glad I had him on my side." **Recent work:** Instructed in relation to a cerebral palsy claim arising from the mismanaged delivery of a child against North East Strategic Health Authority.

Gerwyn Samuel A highly knowledgeable claimant practitioner who is appreciated for his expert knowledge of quantum issues and noted for his inquest work. A large proportion of his cases concern brain and spinal cord injuries resulting from negligent surgery. **Strengths:** "An excellent senior junior who's thorough, tenacious and very accessible." **Recent work:** Assisted on a claim by a 68-year-old man who was left an incomplete paraplegic after undergoing negligent spinal surgery at Cardiff & Vale University Health Board.

Paula Sparks Acts for claimants on a wide range of high-value, complex clinical negligence matters. She is very strong on human rights issues, inquests and fatality claims. **Strengths:** "Paula has an excellent practical understanding of the medical issues. She gets to grips with the issues very quickly and is compassionate and understanding with clients."

Thirty Nine Essex Street

See profile on p.797

THE SET

The set's experienced silks and juniors are routinely called upon to advise on cases encompassing all manner of minor and severe injury claims, and fatalities. Sources admire them for the fact that they "always provide a great service." The set's client base consists of both claimants and defendants.

SILKS

Neil Block QC A standout defendant barrister who handles complex multimillion-pound claims, including birth trauma and spinal injury cases. He is singled out for his knowledge of quantum and for his experience of acting on behalf of high-profile insurers. **Strengths:** "Incredibly calm and efficient, he gets things done without any fuss, and brings immense gravitas to any team he works with." "He looks at a set of papers and knows exactly which issues you need to focus on. Very good at looking at the bigger picture, and he gives good, pragmatic advice." **Recent work:** Defended Great Ormond Street Hospital against a complex paediatric neurology claim.

Susan Rodway QC Specialising in catastrophic birth injury and other medically complex claims, she routinely represents both claimants and defendants. **Strengths:** "She is extraordinarily brave, will not be bullied and will not give in easily." "Good with the clients," she is "full of energy and determination."

JUNIORS

Emily Formby Undertakes a mixture of work for both claimants and defendants. She has significant courtroom experience and frequently appears at inquests. **Strengths:** "She is very understanding and very friendly in her approach. Someone who gives very practical advice, she talks to clients very clearly and is able to express complicated legal and medical terminology in a simple way."

9 Gough Square

See profile on p.812

THE SET

Barristers from this set are frequently instructed by both claimants and defendants on high-value cases including those relating to spinal, birth and dental injuries. Sources highlight the "professional but humane ethos" adopted by the set.

Client service: One solicitor commented: "The clerking there is, and I don't say this lightly, the best in the business. No call ever goes unanswered. Requests for costs budgeting data are invariably dealt with in full within an hour."

SILKS

Grahame Aldous QC (see p.533) Acts mainly for claimants on a variety of cases, but is best known for acting on the more complex, high-value claims. Of late he has handled matters relating to brain-damaged and severely injured claimants. **Strengths:** "Excellent and very pragmatic, he's focused on achieving the right the result and is not prone to getting bogged down in irrelevant detail."

Jacob Levy QC A newly appointed silk with a largely claimant-focused practice. Having been at the Bar for 30 years, this highly experienced barrister is well versed in high-value and complex clinical negligence claims, including matters relating to birth accidents, spinal and orthopaedic injuries, and ocular negligence. **Strengths:** "He's incredibly hard-working, totally in command of the facts, and absolutely committed. He's also personable and so kind to clients." "Meticulous to the nth degree, he will deal with anything – large or small – as though it's the most important thing he's doing."

Andrew Ritchie QC (see p.708) Head of chambers and a seasoned professional whose clinical negligence expertise includes cases relating to brain damage at birth and failure to diagnose. He's widely respected by market sources for his impressive knowledge of the sector and his detailed approach. **Strengths:** "He's good with clients, very much a team player and very forensic with experts." "He's very straight-talking, very detailed on the medicine side and someone who really gets to grips with the financial angle of a case." **Recent work:** Acted for a claimant who suffered as a result of failure to diagnose a transient ischaemic attack, which resulted in a stroke and severe brain damage.

JUNIORS

Christopher Stephenson A specialist claimant barrister who has particular experience of complex issues of causation. He has an extremely broad range of expertise, having advised on all manner of cases including those concerning wrongful birth, failure to diagnose and failed cosmetic surgery. **Strengths:** "He's very approachable and very balanced." **Recent work:** Assisted on an alleged misdiagnosis claim of an eye condition after a patient died of an aortic aneurysm.

Laura Begley An increasingly prominent junior who is developing a significant reputation in the clinical negligence sector. Her practice is broad and ranges from cosmetic and dental surgery matters to wrongful birth cases and claims arising out of hypoxia at birth. She is also widely acknowledged as an expert in Criminal Injuries Compensation Authority claims. **Strengths:** "Hugely knowledgeable, caring and professional, she's very thorough, considered and thoughtful, and has a lovely manner with clients."

Other Ranked Lawyers

Margaret Bloom (Hardwicke) Practised as a GP for 13 years prior to coming to the Bar. She enjoys a broad practice that encompasses orthopaedics, obstetric negligence and mental health cases, and has a particular focus on cerebral palsy claims. **Strengths:** "She's very sympathetic and very willing to explore difficult cases. She has that medical expertise, too, which makes it easier for her to challenge experts." **Recent work:** Acted for the claimant in a complex matter arising from delayed diagnosis of a bowel obstruction and subsequent negligent care which resulted in a baby being left with severe cerebral palsy.

Frank Burton QC (12 King's Bench Walk) Has an enviable reputation as both a clinical negligence and personal injury barrister. **Strengths:** "I was very impressed because he was always anticipating what the other side would do. He'd predict something and, sure enough, in 15 minutes they would do just that, and he'd always have a strategy to counter it. It was like watching an expert poker player." **Recent work:** Represented a claimant who suffered spinal injury due to a delayed hospital referral on the part of his GP.

Henry Charles (12 King's Bench Walk) Has an almost exclusively claimant clinical negligence practice. He possesses notable expertise in relation to orthopaedic negligence, and is also adept at spinal injuries and dental negligence cases, as well as claims arising from the delayed diagnosis of cancer. **Strengths:** "Henry's got very good judgement and a good feel for the merits of the case. He can spot where things may start to unravel on the evidence." "Tenacious and supportive, he is very compassionate with clients, extremely thorough and tries to get the best out of the experts." **Recent work:** Instructed in connection with a claim brought against the Royal National Orthopaedic Hospital, whose negligent care had led to incomplete tetraplegia in a patient.

MIDLANDS

Clinical Negligence Midlands
Leading Sets
Band 1
No5 Chambers *
Band 2
Ropewalk Chambers *
Leading Silks
Band 1
Hunjan Satinder *No5 Chambers*
Band 2
Bright Christopher *No5 Chambers* *
Jones Jonathan *No5 Chambers* *
Nolan Dominic *Ropewalk Chambers* *
Leading Juniors
Band 1
Fox Simon *No5 Chambers*
Michael Simon *No5 Chambers* *
Punt Jonathan *No5 Chambers*
Rochford Thomas *St Philips Chambers (ORL)* ◊ *
Band 2
Beard Simon *Ropewalk Chambers*
Brown Emma *No5 Chambers* *
Coughlan John *No5 Chambers* *
Cox Jason *Ropewalk Chambers* *
Evans Andrew *St Philips Chambers (ORL)* ◊ *
Hirst Karl *No5 Chambers*
Khalique Nageena *No5 Chambers* [A]
Pitchers Henry *No5 Chambers* *
Tyack David *No5 Chambers* *
Up-and-coming individuals
Gupta Mamta *No5 Chambers* *
◊ *(ORL) = Other Ranked Lawyer.*
[A] *direct access (see p.11).*
* *Indicates set / individual with profile.*

Band 1

No5 Chambers
See profile on p.883

THE SET

The outstanding clinical negligence set on the Midland Circuit, No5 Chambers has tremendous depth and breadth of expertise in this area, and is home to more than 30 expert clinical negligence practitioners. Its members receive regular instructions in a wide range of cases on behalf of NHS trusts, medical defence organisations, and private individuals.

Client service: "Administratively the clerking, led by Zoe Owen and Martin Hulbert, is really good. They're very amenable as to where we want conferences." "The clerking is very slick – they're always keen to please."

SILKS

Christopher Bright QC Handles complex cases which commonly have issues of causation and PCT/local authority funding. He is regarded as a specialist in catastrophic injury and cerebral palsy cases. **Strengths:** "He is very forensic in how he considers claims. He looks at them in their minutiae." "He has a very good bedside manner and a good way of explaining things to clients in easily comprehensible terms." **Recent work:** Advised on a multimillion-pound historical cerebral palsy case, in which breach of duty and causation were the central issues due to contentious evidence. A settlement of 75% of damages was secured.

Satinder Hunjan QC Heads the set's clinical negligence group, and is frequently instructed on cases of the utmost complexity. He often takes on catastrophic cases, and has developed a niche practice focusing on injuries acquired by sports professional. **Strengths:** "He is bold and tenacious, and has superb tactical awareness." "He is a really tough negotiator and very good during trial sessions."

Jonathan Jones QC Focuses mainly on brain damage cases and inquests, although he also undertakes birth injury and cosmetic surgery claims. **Strengths:** "He goes through the medicine in the minutiae of detail in conferences. This expands my knowledge and the client's knowledge." "He's excellent. He's got everything really: good people skills, he's very good technically, very good on difficult points of law, he's a very good negotiator and a very supportive barrister to work with." **Recent work:** Advised a claimant who suffered a brain injury at birth due to negligent mismanagement, helping to put together a claim for her loss of earning capacity.

JUNIORS

David Tyack (see p.742) Known for handling heavyweight cases, particularly birth and surgical negligence claims in addition to missed diagnoses, neurological issues and fatalities. A fifth of his practice also covers personal injury. **Strengths:** "Clinical negligence is a highly technical area, but he's very skilled at cutting through that." "He's very bright but also down to earth with clients and solicitors, which aids efficiency and achieves results." **Recent work:** Instructed on a complex case with unusual procedural aspects, regarding the cancer-related fatality of a man with dependants, whose GP failed to refer him for a screening test.

Emma Brown (see p.557) Has a broad clinical negligence practice acting for both claimants and defendants. She has an increasing number of catastrophic injury cases, and is acknowledged for her expertise in cases concerning gynaecology, obstetrics, oncology and ophthalmology. **Strengths:** "She's great with cases that have experts who need close scrutiny and clients that need attention. She has that good manner about her and isn't afraid of a tricky case." **Recent work:** Instructed in a case brought by the estate and dependants of an individual who died due to a brain tumour. It was argued that the GP failed to refer for assessment a mole which was later found to be malignant melanoma.

Simon Fox Has extensive experience across the board, including paediatric brain injury, ophthalmology, oncology, orthopaedics and anaesthetics, with a growing focus on negligence with a neurological element. His practice benefits from his medical background. **Strengths:** "He has a very good way with experts and clients." "Having Fox cross-examine really makes it possible to put together a robust claim." **Recent work:** Instructed on a case where toxic epidermal necrolysis led to death.

Simon Michael Specialises in fatal cases and those relating to cerebral palsy, paraplegia and stroke. He is currently working for a significant number of the claimants alleging negligence by a breast surgeon at an NHS trust. **Strengths:** "He's extremely experienced, and hugely knowledgeable on both medicine and the law." **Recent work:** Acted on a scientifically complex case where congenital hypothyroidism was not diagnosed, leading to significant brain damage.

Jonathan Punt A former paediatric neurosurgeon whose medical expertise is of real benefit on complex brain injury claims. His caseload includes inquests, alongside an increasing number of cerebral palsy and serious spinal injury cases. **Strengths:** "His medical expertise is a real asset and sets him apart from other counsel. His ability to analyse the medical evidence and attention to detail is second to none."

John Coughlan Instructed across the gamut of clinical negligence work. He predominantly acts for claimants, but is developing a strong defendant practice as well. **Strengths:** "He is fantastic; a safe pair of hands for any case of considerable complexity."

Karl Hirst Undertakes a wide range of clinical negligence work, including high-value, complex cases such as spinal and brain injury. His practice includes personal injury work. **Strengths:** "He is very good with clients and a very capable advocate." "He's just brilliant at coming up with innovative suggestions when you've got issues on a case."

Nageena Khalique Former hospital dentist who specialised in oral and maxillofacial surgery. She represents both claimants and public bodies, including clinical commissioning groups. **Strengths:** "She is very good with her clients, very hard-working and effective." **Recent work:** She was instructed on a highly sensitive case concerning the death of a newborn infant following obstetric negligence, which resulted in serious psychiatric injuries for the mother.

Henry Pitchers Maintains a strong clinical negligence practice focusing on high-value complex cases, including those relating to cerebral palsy and delayed diagnosis of cancer. **Strengths:** "He was thorough and well prepared, putting clients at ease very quickly."

Mamta Gupta (see p.616) A clinical negligence specialist whose practice focuses predominantly on representing claimants. She is noted for her work with female claimants on complex and sensitive cases. **Strengths:** "She has a really good eye for detail."

Band 2

Ropewalk Chambers
See profile on p.928

THE SET

Historically known as a defendant-focused set, Ropewalk Chambers has successfully expanded into claimant work and receives a roughly equal number of instructions from either side. Its barristers are regularly instructed on complex and high-value claims, and have expertise across a wide range of cases, including those concerning brain injury, clinical misdiagnosis and mental health.

Client service: "Other chambers are not as user-friendly, but with Ropewalk if you need something urgently, they will get in their cars and go to the client. And if the client is disabled you never have to worry about transport." "The clerks, led by Tony Hill, are amenable when negotiating fees. I've never had problems with availability of barristers or double booking."

SILKS

Dominic Nolan QC Splits his practice equally between clinical negligence and personal injury. He focuses mainly on high-value claims, including cases of GP negligence of late. **Strengths:** "He can crystallise even the most complex of cases into a client-friendly form." **Recent work:** Acted on several ophthalmic cases that were complex and also significant in value.

JUNIORS

Simon Beard Represents both claimants and defendants, and also undertakes inquest work for families that have suffered loss due to medical negligence. His practice also covers personal injury and disease claims. **Strengths:** "He is a safe pair of hands and a very experienced counsel."

Jason Cox Has an established clinical negligence practice which is principally focused on representing claimants. He is noted for his experience in cases concerning optometrist negligence. **Strengths:** "He is easy to engage with and knows the subject matter intimately."

Other Ranked Lawyers

Tom Rochford (St Philips Chambers) Focuses his practice on complex and high-value clinical negligence and personal injury claims, predominantly acting on behalf of claimants. **Strengths:** "He's very good at communicating in simple terms; a lot of clinical negligence work involves complicated medical jargon, and he has a knack for being able to make complicated things sound very simple."

Andrew Evans (see p.596) (St Philips Chambers) Principally a personal injury practitioner, Evans has built up a thriving clinical negligence practice and is regularly instructed on cases concerning medical negligence. **Strengths:** "His client care is second to none. I use him on cases with clients that are more difficult as he manages their expectation well." "He picks up on complex issues quickly."

NORTH EASTERN

Clinical Negligence North Eastern
Leading Silks
Band 1
Brown Stuart *Parklane Plowden (ORL)* ◊
Band 2
Wilby David *Parklane Plowden (ORL)* ◊
Leading Juniors
Band 1
Axon Andrew *Parklane Plowden (ORL)* ◊
Band 2
Elgot Howard *Parklane Plowden (ORL)* ◊
Hill Michael *Trinity Chambers (ORL)* ◊ *

Ranked Lawyers

Stuart Brown QC (Parklane Plowden) Acts for both claimants and defendants in cases of severe injury. He is noted for his considerable expertise on obstetric negligence issues. **Strengths:** "He's a highly experienced advocate who exhibits fantastic judgement."

David Wilby QC (Parklane Plowden) Undertakes a broad range of clinical negligence work, and is noted for his expertise on complex and high-value claims. **Strengths:** "He's an adroit advocate; extremely thorough in his preparation and great with clients."

Andrew Axon (Parklane Plowden) The head of chambers, Andrew Axon is also one of the set's leading clinical negligence practitioners. He is noted for his expertise on brain injury claims. **Strengths:** "He's an amazing advocate – when you've got him onside you want the case to go to court. It's almost worth paying the money just to watch him in action: he's fantastic, exudes confidence and knows the law inside out."

Howard Elgot (Parklane Plowden) Receives instructions from both claimants and defendants in clinical negligence cases, and is noted for his expertise in catastrophic brain and spinal injury cases. **Strengths:** "He is a tenacious advocate who is particularly skilled in his analysis of medical evidence."

Mike Hill (see p.627) (Trinity Chambers) Has a broad clinical negligence practice, and acts for both claimants and defendants. He is a former dental surgeon, and is particularly highly valued for his expertise in dental negligence cases. **Strengths:** "He is always willing to help, and he really simplifies complex dental cases. As a former dentist, he is an expert witness and a counsel rolled into one." **Recent work:** He advised in a dental claim involving the cosmetic dentist from the Channel 4 show 'Ten Years Younger'.

NORTHERN

Clinical Negligence Northern
Leading Sets
Band 1
Byrom Street Chambers *
Band 2
Kings Chambers *
Leading Silks
Band 1
Allan David *Byrom Street Chambers*
Brown Stuart *Parklane Plowden (ORL)* ◊
Grime Stephen *Deans Court Chambers (ORL)* ◊
Hatfield Sally *Byrom Street Chambers*
Heaton David *Byrom Street Chambers*
Melton Christopher *Byrom Street Chambers* *
Poole Nigel *Kings Chambers* *
Redfern Michael *St Johns Buildings (ORL)* ◊
Rowley James *Byrom Street Chambers* *
Band 2
Braslavsky Nicholas *Kings Chambers* *
Hunter Winston *Byrom Street Chambers* *
Machell Raymond *Byrom Street Chambers*
Martin Gerard *Exchange Chambers (ORL)* ◊
Yip Amanda *Exchange Chambers (ORL)* ◊
New Silks
Allen Darryl *Byrom Street Chambers* *
** Indicates set / individual with profile.*
◊ (ORL) = Other Ranked Lawyer.
Alphabetical order within each band. Band 1 is highest.

Clinical Negligence Northern
Leading Juniors
Band 1
Eccles David *Deans Court Chambers (ORL)* ◊
Feeny Charles *St Johns Buildings (ORL)* ◊
Forrest Alastair *18 St John Street (ORL)* ◊
Pearce Richard *Byrom Street Chambers*
Pritchard Sarah *Kings Chambers* *
Ruck Mary *Byrom Street Chambers* *
Band 2
Bridgman Andrew *St Johns Buildings (ORL)* ◊
Donovan Scott *Atlantic Chambers (ORL)* ◊
Limb Christopher *18 St John Street (ORL)* ◊ *
Maguire Stephen *Kings Chambers*
Mulholland Helen *Kings Chambers* *
Norton Richard *St Johns Buildings (ORL)* ◊
Owen Wendy *St Johns Buildings (ORL)* ◊
Roussak Jeremy *Kings Chambers* *
Ryder Timothy *Deans Court Chambers (ORL)* ◊
Smith Michael *Deans Court Chambers (ORL)* ◊
Steward Claire *Kings Chambers* *
Wright Alastair *St Johns Buildings (ORL)* ◊
Up-and-coming individuals
Law Charlotte *Kings Chambers* *
McNamara Stephen *Kings Chambers* *
Wells Jason *18 St John Street (ORL)* ◊ *

Band 1

Byrom Street Chambers

See profile on p.914

THE SET

This group of heavyweight silks and senior juniors covers the most complex and high-value cases, taking key roles in difficult catastrophic, misdiagnosis and birth injury cases. The set's clerking scores particularly highly, with interviewees impressed by the helpful and approachable attitude adopted by the clerksroom.

Client service: "The clerking system led by Terry Creathorn is great; they could not be any better. It's a thorough and personable service."

SILKS

James Rowley QC Covers a significant volume of heavyweight cases, and is roundly praised by solicitors who note that "he's able to view the case from a bird's eye view in terms of strategy, but also able to completely home in on the key details – this marvellous ability to do both at once makes him a great choice for a high-value claim." He is noted for his expertise in obstetric and neo-natal mismanagement claims. **Strengths:** "If you have a tricky case that needs pulling apart, take it to him. He's very analytical." "He is concise and cuts directly to the chase – what some counsel would achieve in four hours he'll do in two." **Recent work:** He was instructed by the claimant on a complicated case of steroid overdose which led to osteomyelitis and other medical difficulties.

Sally Hatfield QC A specialist clinical negligence practitioner whose practice is largely focused on representing claimants. She is frequently instructed on cases concerning injuries of maximum severity, and is noted for her considerable expertise in the psychiatric ramifications of breach of duty by healthcare staff. **Strengths:** "She has got a lot to offer as a barrister – she's intelligent and quick to get to the issues." "She has a phenomenal ability to devour documents and absorb the important points from them quickly." **Recent work:** She advised on a complicated obstetric and psychiatric secondary victim case for an individual who lost his wife and baby in labour. It was argued that the death of the baby was avoidable.

Christopher Melton QC Specialises in serious injury and maximum severity cases. A large volume of his caseload consists of cerebral palsy claims. **Strengths:** "He manages to gain the clients' confidence easily." "He's very bright and very much on the ball." **Recent work:** He was instructed in two claims on behalf of elderly patients with ankylosing spondylitis on the failed diagnosis of spinal fracture and spinal cord injury.

David Allan QC Frequently instructed in complex and high-value clinical negligence claims, especially those relating to birth injuries. **Strengths:** "He has great attention to detail, and conducts a forensic examination of the evidence; he's a go-to barrister for cerebral palsy cases." **Recent work:** He was instructed on a case concerning a four-week-old baby who suffered a brain haemorrhage after failing to receive the Vitamin K injection.

Winston Hunter QC Intellectual heavyweight whose practice encompasses the full range of clinical and medical negligence. He is particularly highly regarded for his expertise in claims concerning the failure of treatment or diagnosis, especially in accident and emergency medicine. **Strengths:** "He has a fabulous intellect, a wonderful manner with clients, and a phenomenal work rate." **Recent work:** He was instructed in a claim brought by a mother concerning the failure to advise on screening for Down's syndrome. The case concerned issues of causation and economic loss.

Raymond Machell QC A veteran silk whose considerable clinical negligence expertise makes him a top choice for cases concerning catastrophic injuries and high-value claims. **Strengths:** "He's an intimidating advocate who puts his huge brain to good use – his attention to detail is second to none." **Recent work:** He was instructed on a complex cerebral palsy case where the individual concerned had the most severe manifestations of the condition, including epilepsy, visual impairment and profound learning difficulties.

David Heaton QC Handles a wide range of clinical negligence issues, and is equally adroit in his representation of claimants and defendants. He is recognised for his expertise in cerebral palsy cases. **Strengths:** "Clients love him – he's incredibly well prepared, very patient, and not in any way pompous." **Recent work:** He handled a cerebral palsy case where causation was disputed due to the interpretation of the MRI scans.

Darryl Allen QC Frequently called upon by claimants to handle complex cases crossing a wide range of issues, including cases concerning catastrophic injury and failure to diagnose. Sources highlight his ability to build strong working relationships with clients. **Strengths:** "He is just absolutely brilliant; he really fights his client's corner, he is very down to earth, and he's great on a complex case." **Recent work:** He represented an elderly claimant in a case concerning the negligent administration of spinal anaesthesia, which resulted in a spinal cord injury.

JUNIORS

Richard Pearce Takes on a range of work, including misdiagnosed psychiatric injury, surgical mishaps, delayed cancer diagnosis and cerebral palsy. He represents both claimants and defendants. **Strengths:** "He is a friendly and down-to-earth person – he has a great manner with vulnerable clients, taking the time to put them at their ease rather than jumping straight into the case." **Recent work:** He represented a claimant who developed post-traumatic stress disorder after witnessing his mentally ill brother murder his father. It was argued that the claimant's brother had previously received negligent psychiatric care.

Mary Ruck (see p.712) Maintains a broad clinical negligence practice, and is frequently instructed on behalf of both defendants and claimants. She is noted for her expertise in brain injury claims. **Strengths:** "She really empathises with the client and becomes involved in the whole journey from an early stage." **Recent work:** She was instructed in a complex and highly sensitive case concerning the transmission of hepatitis A from a birth mother to her baby, and then onwards to the baby's adoptive mother.

Band 2

Kings Chambers

See profile on p.918

THE SET

A strong group of clinical negligence practitioners who are praised by solicitors for their "proactive and highly personable approach." The set handles a range of complex cases, including birth and catastrophic injury. It has a significant concentration of expertise in cosmetic surgery, fatalities and cases with a human rights element. Many of its members act for both claimants and defendants.

Client service: "They are just really responsive – the chief clerk Steve Loxton leads a team that will bend over backwards for you."

SILKS

Nicholas Braslavsky QC Praised for his considerable expertise in birth and brain injury work. He is highly experienced in dealing with cases concerning neuroradiology and obstetric management. **Strengths:** "He's a very impressive barrister who is approachable, hands-on, and a consummate advocate."

Nigel Poole QC A veteran advocate who leads the set's clinical negligence and personal injury teams. He undertakes a wide range of clinical negligence cases, and is particularly praised for his work on cosmetic surgery and oncology claims. **Strengths:** "He is very good with clients, providing advice in a sympathetic but clear manner." **Recent work:** He was successfully instructed on behalf of a claimant in a complex case where urogynaecological surgery had led to nerve injury and somatoform disorder.

JUNIORS

Helen Mulholland (see p.679) Has a special interest in obstetric and gynaecological cases, and is noted for her expertise in delayed diagnosis claims. She draws particular praise from instructing solicitors for her advocacy skills. **Strengths:** "She is brilliant on her feet, a really bright and quick thinker." "Her advocacy is just fantastic."

Sarah Pritchard (see p.699) Acts for both defendants and claimants in cases concerning maximum severity injuries. Her expertise covers the full breadth of clinical negligence issues, including birth damage, brain injuries, orthopaedics and ophthalmics. **Strengths:** "She possesses excellent advocacy skills – she's a formidable cross-examiner." "She is really patient, supportive and understanding of her clients' needs." **Recent work:** She acted for a NHS trust in a high-value claim that arose from an alleged delay in the diagnosis of a progressive neurological condition.

Jeremy Roussak (see p.711) An experienced advocate who focuses on cases concerning late diagnosis, mistreatment of cancer and cerebral palsy. His proficiency in the medico-legal realm is boosted by his background as a thoracic surgeon. **Strengths:** "He's quick and efficient in turning around papers." "One of his main skills is grasping the central medical issues of a case."

Claire Steward (see p.728) Has a broad clinical negligence practice, and is noted for her expertise on claims relating to plastic surgery. Sources comment that she has strong client management skills. **Strengths:** "She is incredibly thorough in preparation and has a lovely way with clients – she's very approachable."

Charlotte Law (see p.652) Maintains a broad clinical negligence practice covering areas such as delayed diagnosis, pharmaceutical and medical negligence. **Strengths:** "She's measured and thorough; her paperwork is a dream to read." "She is a very approachable and responsive barrister."

Stephen Maguire Works on both clinical negligence and personal injury cases. He is known for his strong advocacy skills, which he first began developing in his prior career as a solicitor. **Strengths:** "He's great on quantum, schedules and maximising damages." "He is adaptable and sympathetic, yet robust with clients when required." **Recent work:** He advised a claimant whose wife underwent bariatric surgery and did not receive the appropriate preventative treatment for the surgery's associated risks of a DVT and pulmonary embolism.

Stephen McNamara (see p.669) Acts mainly on behalf of claimants, with frequent involvement in high-value and negligent cosmetic surgery cases. He also specialises in claims of suicide arising from negligent psychiatric treatment, including those brought forward under the Human Rights Act 1998. **Strengths:** "He is very firm and clear with clients; he grapples with complex causation issues in a clear way during conference." "He is down to earth and highly intelligent."

Other Ranked Lawyers

Scott Donovan (Atlantic Chambers) Singled out by sources as one of the busiest clinical negligence barristers in Liverpool. He is a veteran practitioner who takes on complex and high-value cases. **Strengths:** "He is a very experienced pair of hands." "He is pretty formidable and takes on really challenging cases."

Stephen Grime QC (Deans Court Chambers) Veteran practitioner Stephen Grime QC has a heavyweight practice focusing on cerebral palsy and catastrophic injury cases. **Strengths:** "He is pragmatic

– he doesn't go round the houses, he cuts through all that and goes straight to the heart of the matter."

David Eccles (Deans Court Chambers) Handles both clinical negligence and personal injury work. He is praised by peers for his strong advocacy. **Strengths:** "He is very bright and very approachable – it makes him popular with the judges." "He has the technical ability, but is also very personable and knows what the client wants."

Timothy Ryder (Deans Court Chambers) Has an important focus on birth injury and infant brain damage cases. He is regularly instructed on claims concerning spinal injury, surgical negligence and misdiagnoses of cancer, in particular those of the breast and bladder. **Strengths:** "He has a very good and relaxed negotiating style that can really facilitate a favourable settlement." "He is amazing with statistics and very analytical."

Michael Smith (Deans Court Chambers) Frequently instructed on complex and high-value clinical negligence cases, predominantly on the claimant side. He is also experienced in handling substantial personal injury cases. **Strengths:** "He is good on technical applications such as interim payments." "He is particularly good analytically – if you've got a case with a tricky legal point, go to him." **Recent work:** He appeared on behalf of the defendant in a cosmetic surgery case that went to trial due to a dispute over informed consent.

Gerard Martin QC (Exchange Chambers) A specialist in brain damage cases involving both adults and children. He is also noted for his expertise in cases concerning pain and somatoform disorders, and amputations. **Strengths:** "He has the ability to completely demystify a highly complex area of the law."

Amanda Yip QC (Exchange Chambers) Divides her practice between clinical negligence and personal injury cases. Her strong reputation in the field derives from high-quality work in childbirth and neonatal claims. **Strengths:** "She is a quietly and calmly persuasive advocate."

Stuart Brown QC (Parklane Plowden) Has developed a niche clinical negligence practice focusing on cases concerning infants with cerebral palsy. He is instructed by both claimants and defendants. **Strengths:** "He is very sound in his judgement, and has a fantastic presence; if you go to trial the defendants will know they've got something to worry about."

Michael Redfern QC (St Johns Buildings) Has focused his clinical negligence practice on cerebral palsy cases. He has a mixed practice that includes personal injury cases, and often takes on pro bono work. **Strengths:** "He was fantastic – he is vastly experienced, thinks fast on his feet, and is exactly what you're looking for in an advocate."

Charles Feeny (St Johns Buildings) Principally represents defendants in cases concerning surgical negligence, particularly those involving vascular and cardiac issues. **Strengths:** "He is a go-to lawyer for heavy-duty brain damage cases." "He is personable and knows how to relate to clients, insurance companies and the opposition."

Andrew Bridgman (St Johns Buildings) A former dental surgeon, he is renowned for his work on dental negligence issues. He also covers general personal injury work. **Strengths:** "He is a robust advocate whose style really appeals to clients."

Richard Norton (St Johns Buildings) Has a mixed practice covering clinical negligence, personal injury and industrial disease. He is noted for his adroit handling of complex and high-value clinical negligence cases. **Strengths:** "He is a pragmatic and personable advocate, not frightened to pursue novel points at the same time as understanding the cost issues that surround doing so."

Wendy Owen (St Johns Buildings) Represents claimants across the full breadth of clinical negligence work. Her prior career as a defence solicitor has ensured that she has strong client-handling skills.

Alastair Wright (St Johns Buildings) Has an exclusively claimant-focused clinical negligence practice. He undertakes a wide range of cases, and is noted for his particular expertise on claims relating to cerebral palsy and surgical error. **Strengths:** "He is a strong advocate and approaches the case in a very impressive manner."

Alastair Forrest (18 St John Street) A prominent practitioner on the Northern Circuit for clinical negligence work. He also covers personal injury and professional negligence. **Strengths:** "He takes a firm grip on the case and eases his way through it."

Christopher Limb (see p.656) (18 St John Street) Recognised for his considerable expertise in cerebral palsy cases. He handles the full range of clinical negligence work, but is particularly adept at dealing with quantum issues. **Strengths:** "He is always thorough in his approach, and is willing to fight for a case." "He is good at looking at the case from different angles to find alternate avenues of attack that might benefit a claimant's case."

Jason Wells (see p.749) (18 St John Street) Well versed in the medical field due to his prior career as a urologist. He is beginning to utilise his medical expertise in inquests-related work. **Strengths:** "His medical background gives him fantastic insight."

WALES & CHESTER

Clinical Negligence Wales & Chester
Leading Sets
Band 1
Civitas Law *
Leading Silks
Band 1
Huckle Theodore *Civitas Law* *
Leading Juniors
Band 1
Brace Michael *Civitas Law* *
Jones Nicholas David *Civitas Law* *
Thomas Bryan *Civitas Law* *
* *Indicates set / individual with profile.*

Band 1

Civitas Law

See profile on p.894

THE SET

The leading set for clinical negligence matters in Wales. Its members receive regular instructions from both claimants and defendants, and are noted for the breadth of their clinical negligence expertise.

SILKS

Theodore Huckle QC A founder member of chambers, he maintains a broad practice that encompasses clinical negligence matters. He is well versed in complex spinal and brain injury cases. **Strengths:** "He very much represents the client's interests at all times, never losing focus on that. He doesn't mind arguing points that need to be argued robustly."

JUNIORS

Michael Brace Clinical negligence forms a key part of his practice and he specialises particularly in obstetric and birth problems. **Strengths:** "He cuts through the argument to present complex points succinctly – he is an excellent advocate."

Bryan Thomas Handles a heavy workload of both clinical negligence and personal injury matters. He is particularly commended by commentators for his client care skills.

Nicholas David Jones Acts for claimants across an extensive range of clinical negligence matters. Areas of strength include consent to treatment and missed cancer diagnosis claims. **Strengths:** "He just inspires confidence. He is very quietly and calmly authoritative. He is very good at interacting with clients."

WESTERN

Clinical Negligence Western
Leading Sets
Band 1
Guildhall Chambers *
St John's Chambers *
Band 2
3PB Barristers *
Leading Juniors
Star individuals
Fox Simon *No5 Chambers (ORL)* ◊
Plowden Selena *Guildhall Chambers*
Band 1
Dunlop Hamish *3PB Barristers*
Grice Timothy *St John's Chambers*
Leeper Tom *St John's Chambers* 🄰
Snell John *Guildhall Chambers*
Sowersby Robert *Guildhall Chambers*
Townsend James *Guildhall Chambers*
Band 2
Bennett Daniel *Doughty Street Chambers (ORL)* ◊
Dennis Rebecca *Queen Square Chambers (ORL)* ◊
Lomas Mark *3PB Barristers*
McKinlay Vanessa *St John's Chambers*
Regan David *St John's Chambers* 🄰
Stamp Abigail *Guildhall Chambers*
Weston Louis *3PB Barristers*
Zeb Emma *St John's Chambers* 🄰
Up-and-coming individuals
Beeby Gabriel *Guildhall Chambers*
Coventry Charles *St John's Chambers*
Holme Sophie *Guildhall Chambers*
◊ *(ORL) = Other Ranked Lawyer.*
🄰 *direct access (see p.11).*
* *Indicates set / individual with profile.*

Band 1

Guildhall Chambers

See profile on p.890

THE SET

Guildhall Chambers' clinical negligence practice is centred on the representation of claimants. The set has a number of experienced practitioners who frequently undertake complex cases of significant value, including claims concerning catastrophic and birth injuries. Its members also have niche expertise in areas such as sperm destruction and genital injuries.

Client service: "The clerking team are always responsive and helpful. If there's an issue with the availability of barristers, they will offer alternative suggestions." "The clerks, led by Heather Bidwell, are always more than happy to accommodate your needs."

JUNIORS

Selena Plowden Works on the most complex and high-value cases, including catastrophic, birth and surgical injuries. She also handles cases relating to missed cancer diagnoses, and claims concerning the management of chronic illnesses. **Strengths:** "She knows her onions when it comes to the medical issues, and is equally good at the quantum side of things." "She is very precise and hugely thorough." **Recent work:** She acted on an inquest into a child fatality, which was linked to the changing of a peg feeding tube. She represented the company to which the NHS outsourced enteral feeding services.

John Snell Focuses on high-value cases including cerebral palsy, spinal injury and obstetric issues. He represents both claimants and defendants. **Strengths:** "He's good on detail, particularly with paperwork and drafting." "He's thoroughly approachable and easy to work with." **Recent work:** He represented the defendant in a claim of alleged surgical negligence following an operation to remove a Morton's neuroma.

Robert Sowersby Handles a wide range of clinical negligence work, with noted niche expertise in male genital injuries and issues of the bowel. Although he has a national client base, a strong portion of his caseload originates from Wales. **Strengths:** "He is a dogged, tenacious advocate." "He's focused on client management and is particularly good with sensitive issues."

James Townsend Focuses his practice on representing claimants in high-value clinical negligence cases. He is developing a specialism in the new territory of sperm destruction. **Strengths:** "He can think on his feet and adapt when things come up that are unexpected." **Recent work:** He advised on issues of quantum for a case concerning the negligent storage of the patient's sperm.

Abigail Stamp Handles a range of clinical negligence work, including cases of a surgical and psychiatric nature. Solicitors praise her pragmatic and client-friendly approach to complex and high-value cases. **Strengths:** "She is excellent; a competitive advocate whose attention to detail is second to none, she is personable and flexible, able to ease her client through the trial process."

Gabriel Beeby Has focused his practice on cases concerning brain and obstetric injuries. He principally represents claimants, but has also acted for a number of health boards on the defendant side. **Strengths:** "He is a likeable advocate – calm, cool and very much in control." "He is very user-friendly and good with clients." **Recent work:** He advised in a group action of roughly 300 women claiming surgical negligence against a urogynaecologist at the Liverpool Women's Hospital.

Sophie Holme Heavily focused on clinical negligence, with a small portion of her practice consisting of personal injury work. She principally acts on behalf of claimants. **Strengths:** "She is a rising star, extremely good with clients, and her written advice is excellent."

St John's Chambers

See profile on p.893

THE SET

St John's Chambers acts for both claimants and defendants in clinical negligence cases, and has increased its market share this year with some notable new client wins. While the set has an important niche in dental negligence cases, its members are noted for their expertise across a wide range of clinical negligence issues, including cerebral palsy, oncology, surgical negligence and catastrophic injuries.

Client service: "The clerks, led by Annette Bushell, organise seminars for clinical negligence with other partners. They are active in the field of legal education." "It's a really organised and well-run clerksroom; they get things done and take responsibility."

JUNIORS

Tom Leeper A part-time coroner, his practice is focused solely on clinical negligence and inquests work. He represents a mixture of both claimants and defendants, and covers the gamut of clinical negligence work. **Strengths:** "He's very good at the detail and won't leave any stone unturned." "He has an appropriate way of dealing with people who have been through trauma."

Timothy Grice Handles a high volume of cerebral palsy and birth injury cases. A heavyweight advocate, his general clinical negligence practice is focused on high-value work. **Strengths:** "His knowledge of the law and his skill in court are outstanding." "He has an ability to process a lot of information and regurgitate it in a logical manner."

Vanessa McKinlay Leads the set's clinical negligence group, and benefits from her prior experience as a senior physiotherapist at the NHS. She is commended for her ability to swiftly grasp complex technical and medical concepts. **Strengths:** "She deals with issues in sensitive areas and has proven to be very good with clients." "She has a thorough and methodical approach. She can get very tough with experts in conference, but she is very well balanced." **Recent work:** Represented the claimant in relation to negligent laparoscopic surgery. The case proceeded to a four-day trial in the High Court.

David Regan Takes on work for both the claimant and defendant sides. Alongside clinical negligence, he also practises in the areas of personal injury and professional negligence. **Strengths:** "He is diligent and approachable. You use him because you know he will do a good job."

Emma Zeb Focuses on dental negligence and medical negligence work, particularly on those cases where breach of duty and causation are concerned. Her practice also comprises personal injury cases and inquests. **Strengths:** "She has a commonsensical approach – her ability to strip down complex matters and convey them in a user-friendly way is impressive." "She is good in conference and has a nice way of handling the client." **Recent work:** She acted for a claimant who suffers from spina bifida in a highly complex medical negligence case.

Charles Coventry Covers the full range of clinical negligence cases, specialising in dental negligence cases. He receives frequent instructions from both healthcare providers and patients. **Strengths:** "He is very thorough and very bright – a real up-and-coming star." **Recent work:** He successfully settled a complicated dental negligence case which had issues regarding liability, causation and quantum.

Band 2

3PB Barristers

See profile on p.846

THE SET

The chambers is praised for the high quality of its individual counsel, with whom solicitors enjoy strong working relationships. The set covers the full range of clinical negligence work, receiving frequent instructions on cases concerning complex injuries. 3PB's members act on behalf of a range of clients, including healthcare providers, individual medical practitioners and individual claimants.

Client service: "The clerks team, headed by Stephen Clark, are brilliant – you know they will look after you." "The clerks are tenacious; they always revisit issues. If there's someone that can't help with a case, they'll try someone else until they find the best fit for you."

JUNIORS

Hamish Dunlop Undertakes a wide range of work, with proficiency in cases relating to accommodation needs and lifetime care. In addition, he specialises in dependency claims brought forward by partners and children. **Strengths:** "He's extremely user-friendly and clicks very well with clients."

Mark Lomas Has a broad clinical negligence practice which includes dental and therapy work. The range of his work covers minor to catastrophic injuries, and fatalities. **Strengths:** "He is extremely thorough and works very hard." "He has a very good turnaround time and is highly responsive." **Recent work:** He successfully settled a case where the claimant acquired shoulder dystonia due to negligent medical care at birth.

Louis Weston Has established an interesting niche in veterinary surgery cases alongside his general clinical negligence caseload. He is chiefly noted in this area for his work on behalf of doctors, surgeons and other individual healthcare professionals. **Strengths:** "He is extremely able and extremely effective in everything that he does – he never disappoints."

Other Ranked Lawyers

Daniel Bennett (Doughty Street Chambers) Noted for his specialist expertise in claims concerning infection, disease and allergic reaction. He also deals with a large volume of abuse cases relating to elderly patients. **Strengths:** "He's more familiar than many barristers with the practicalities of dealing with multiple defendants and costs issues." "He was good on his feet and in terms of preparation." **Recent work:** Successfully settled a case at mediation involving the loss of the claimant's limb after a negligently administered injection caused infection. It was particularly unusual due to the prominent role played in the case of witness evidence by the claimant and his partner.

Simon Fox (No5 Chambers) Renowned for his varied caseload of high-quality work, he represents both claimants and defendants across a broad range of clinical negligence claims. Commentators note the added benefit of his previous career as a doctor, which has contributed towards his specialist knowledge of neurosurgical and neuroendocrine cases. **Strengths:** "He's very good at case strategy; with difficult cases he always sees a way through." "He's first-rate – a really top-level barrister."

Rebecca Dennis (Queen Square Chambers) Has established expertise in gynaecology and obstetrics. She splits her practice between clinical negligence and personal injury cases. **Strengths:** "She really gets to grip with the details of the case. She is a safe, reliable, good advocate to use." "She's very approachable and deals with experts in the right way."

Commercial Dispute Resolution

Contents:

LONDON

Commercial Dispute Resolution London
Leading Sets
Band 1
Brick Court Chambers *
One Essex Court *
Essex Court Chambers *
Fountain Court Chambers *
3 Verulam Buildings *
Band 2
Blackstone Chambers *
20 Essex Street *
Band 3
7 King's Bench Walk *
Maitland Chambers *
4 Pump Court *
Quadrant Chambers *
Serle Court *
Wilberforce Chambers *
* *Indicates set with profile.*
Alphabetical order within each band. Band 1 is highest.

Band 1

Brick Court Chambers

See profile on p.774

THE SET

Brick Court has long been regarded as a heavyweight chambers in commercial litigation work and remains a firm favourite with instructing solicitors. The instructions it receives are wide-ranging in nature, and include natural resources, banking, property and company disputes, as well as disputes originating in Russia and the CIS. The set is well stocked with leading silks and highly regarded juniors, and its members are consistently praised for their robust and intelligent advocacy. Sources say: "The barristers exhibit strong technical expertise and commercial awareness, and will always go the extra mile for the client."

Client service: "Superb on clerking. They are fantastically responsive. They are always transparent about diaries and what can be done, and you don't get problems with double-bookings." Ian Moyler and Julian Hawes serve as joint heads of a clerking team that is praised for its modern and commercial approach.

SILKS

Mark Howard QC A titan of the Commercial Bar, Howard is praised by instructing solicitors as "nothing short of superb" and by peers as "the person one would least like to find oneself against." His practice spans the commercial spectrum and features regular appearances in the Court of Appeal, the Supreme Court and the Privy Council on some of the most high-profile cases of recent years. **Strengths:** "Delivers decisive, clear commercial advice and is formidable in the courtroom." "A brilliant trial lawyer who combines an astute legal mind with an eye for strategy, and is a great team player." **Recent work:** Acted for the appellant in Benedetti v Sawiris, a dispute relating to the quantum meruit basis of remuneration.

Mark Hapgood QC A leading light in commercial litigation and regarded by instructing solicitors as an "outstanding commercial advocate" who "works like stink." He is a go-to silk for heavyweight and high-stakes disputes, and his recent cases have included fraud claims, insolvency-related disputes and professional negligence matters. **Strengths:** "Provides top-drawer oral advocacy and runs rings around the opposition." "He is particularly adept at cutting to the heart of complicated issues and presenting them simply and clearly. He provides practical commercial and strategic advice and is a very persuasive advocate." **Recent work:** Represented Cattles Group in its USD1.6 billion professional negligence claim against PwC, arising out of the collapse of the Welcome Financial Services group.

Charles Hollander QC A silk held in high esteem by solicitors, who has significant courtroom presence and intellectual ability and a reputation for being easy to work with. He is an acknowledged expert on questions of legal privilege. **Strengths:** "He is very good on his feet and very articulate. He always has the ear of the judge and is someone with an enormous amount of courtroom presence." "Highly intelligent, yet unassuming and very client-friendly." **Recent work:** Acted for FG Wilson (now Caterpillar NI) on two claims against John Holt relating to international sale of goods and retention of title clauses.

Helen Davies QC Joint head of chambers and an experienced silk, with an international practice spanning arbitration, energy and competition. She is held in high regard by instructing solicitors and is an established name at the Commercial Bar. **Strengths:** "Highly intelligent and a pleasure to work with." "A very good commercial advocate." **Recent work:** Represented telecom operator BMIC in its high-profile shareholder dispute with former investment partner Siva and Siva's chairman, Chinnakannan Sivasankaran.

Jonathan Hirst QC Joint head of chambers alongside Helen Davies QC. He is a seasoned advocate with experience in a range of commercial matters, including financial services disputes, shipping cases and arbitration. Sources name him as a "heavyweight" who "truly understands appellate courts." **Strengths:** "A leader in his field. He gives very clear advice and instils real confidence in the client." "He's excellent in every way." **Recent work:** Acted for International Oil and Gas Technology Fund in relation to a high-value contractual dispute with, and counterclaim against, QOGT.

Tim Lord QC Held in high regard by instructing solicitors for his engaging advocacy skills, as well as his user-friendliness. He handles heavyweight commercial matters, and has a particular focus on complex and high-profile banking and finance disputes. **Strengths:** "A genuine fighter who is capable of standing up to difficult points. He has a great rapport with the judge and is a very entertaining advocate. He's super-jolly and fun to work with." "His cross-examination was superb: it was very thorough, very carefully put and very thoughtful. He's a great strategist and he really understands client management." **Recent work:** Acted for CF Partners in its £75 million claim against Barclays Bank, alleging breach of confidence in relation to the Tricorona M&A deal.

Simon Salzedo QC An impressive recent silk who attracts praise from peers and instructing parties for his sound advice and high-calibre advocacy. His practice spans general commercial, financial services and professional negligence disputes as well as arbitration. **Strengths:** "A superb advocate who is very nimble on his feet and very easy to get on with." "A consummate performer and a brilliant advocate." **Recent work:** Acted for Erste on a conspiracy and tortious interference claim against Russian state entity Red October.

Neil Calver QC A bright and user-friendly advocate whom sources praise as a "strong all-rounder." His expertise encompasses insurance and reinsurance, banking and finance, and aviation law, and he also has a strong arbitration practice. **Strengths:** "Super-good with clients, he wins their confidence very quickly." "He has always been very much a hands-on silk, and he gives very good commercial, strategic advice." **Recent work:** Acted for Aspen on a Court of Appeal case relating to product liability under a product liability insurance policy.

Daniel Jowell QC A relatively recent silk who has notable experience in so-called 'oligarch' litigation arising in Russia and the CIS. Instructing solicitors hold him in high regard, praising him as a "brilliant up-and-coming all-rounder." **Strengths:** "Very bright and detailed, and a useful cross-examiner." "A real star in the making." **Recent work:** Instructed by Enyo Law to seek a conflict of interest injunction against White & Case, as a result of which the defendant was debarred from acting for Victor Pinchuk in his high-profile dispute with Gennadiy Bogolyubov and Igor Kolomoisky.

Harry Matovu QC Comes strongly recommended by instructing solicitors, who consistently highlight his charm and his ability in cross-examination. He maintains a diverse commercial practice which encompasses civil fraud, natural resources disputes, jurisdictional challenges and arbitration. **Strengths:** "Absolutely charming to work with and very good with clients. He produces really first-rate written work and is a very good cross-examiner. He works hard, is sensible and doesn't pursue duff arguments." "Some advocates bamboozle, bully or fight; he charms them all, and mauls witnesses with a smile." **Recent work:** Represented two of the three principal defendants to a USD1.1 billion fraud claim brought by Alliance Bank.

Michael Bools QC Has a strong commercial practice covering both arbitration and litigation, and regularly handles appellate work. He has notable experience in natural resources, energy and insurance

Commercial Dispute Resolution London

Leading Silks

Star individuals

- **Brindle** Michael *Fountain Court Chambers*
- **Gaisman** Jonathan *7 King's Bench Walk*
- **Grabiner** Anthony *One Essex Court*
- **Howard** Mark *Brick Court Chambers*
- **Milligan** Iain *20 Essex Street*
- **Rabinowitz** Laurence *One Essex Court*

Band 1

- **Crow** Jonathan *4 Stone Buildings (ORL)* ◊ *
- **Foxton** David *Essex Court Chambers*
- **Hapgood** Mark *Brick Court Chambers*
- **Hollander** Charles *Brick Court Chambers*
- **Malek** Ali *3 Verulam Buildings*
- **McCaughran** John *One Essex Court*
- **Miles** Robert *4 Stone Buildings (ORL)* ◊
- **Railton** David *Fountain Court Chambers*
- **Smith** Stephen *Erskine Chambers (ORL)* ◊ *
- **Smouha** Joe *Essex Court Chambers*
- **Thanki** Bankim *Fountain Court Chambers* *
- **Zacaroli** Antony *South Square (ORL)* ◊

Band 2

- **Auld** Stephen *One Essex Court*
- **Beltrami** Adrian *3 Verulam Buildings*
- **Butcher** Christopher *7 King's Bench Walk*
- **Cavender** David *One Essex Court*
- **Choo Choy** Alain *One Essex Court*
- **Crane** Michael *Fountain Court Chambers*
- **Davies** Helen *Brick Court Chambers*
- **Dicker** Robin *South Square (ORL)* ◊ *
- **Edey** Philip *20 Essex Street*
- **Flynn** Vernon *Essex Court Chambers*
- **Gourgey** Alan *11 Stone Buildings (ORL)* ◊ *
- **Handyside** Richard *Fountain Court Chambers* *
- **Hirst** Jonathan *Brick Court Chambers*
- **Jones** Philip *Serle Court* *
- **Kitchener** Neil *One Essex Court*
- **Lord** Tim *Brick Court Chambers*
- **MacLean** Kenneth *One Essex Court*
- **McQuater** Ewan *3 Verulam Buildings*
- **Mill** Ian *Blackstone Chambers*
- **Nash** Jonathan *3 Verulam Buildings*
- **Onions** Jeffery *One Essex Court*
- **Onslow** Andrew *3 Verulam Buildings*
- **Orr** Craig *One Essex Court* *
- **Salzedo** Simon *Brick Court Chambers*
- **Steinfeld** Alan *XXIV Old Buildings (ORL)* ◊
- **Tolaney** Sonia *3 Verulam Buildings*
- **Toledano** Daniel *One Essex Court*
- **Tozzi** Nigel *4 Pump Court* *
- **Trace** Anthony *Maitland Chambers* *
- **Wolfson** David *One Essex Court*

Band 3

- **Anderson** Robert *Blackstone Chambers*
- **Ashworth** Lance *Serle Court* *
- **Baker** Andrew *20 Essex Street*
- **Berry** Steven *Essex Court Chambers*
- **Bools** Michael *Brick Court Chambers*
- **Boyle** Alan *Serle Court* *
- **Calver** Neil *Brick Court Chambers*
- **Collings** Matthew *Maitland Chambers* *
- **Croxford** Ian *Wilberforce Chambers*
- **de Garr Robinson** Anthony *One Essex Court* *
- **Dunning** Graham *Essex Court Chambers*
- **Fenwick** Justin *4 New Square (ORL)* ◊ *
- **Freedman** Clive *7 King's Bench Walk*
- **Girolami** Paul *Maitland Chambers* *
- **Hochhauser** Andrew *Essex Court Chambers*
- **Howe** Robert *Blackstone Chambers*
- **Howe** Timothy *Fountain Court Chambers* *
- **Jacobs** Richard *Essex Court Chambers*
- **Jowell** Daniel *Brick Court Chambers*
- **Kealey** Gavin *7 King's Bench Walk*
- **Kinsky** Cyril *3 Verulam Buildings*
- **Lowenstein** Paul *3 Verulam Buildings*
- **Machell** John *Serle Court* *
- **Maclean** Alan *Blackstone Chambers*
- **Marshall** Philip *Serle Court* *
- **Matovu** Harry *Brick Court Chambers*
- **Matthews** Duncan *20 Essex Street*
- **Millett** Richard *Essex Court Chambers*
- **Odgers** John *3 Verulam Buildings*
- **Philipps** Guy *Fountain Court Chambers* *
- **Pollock** Gordon *Essex Court Chambers*
- **Rainey** Simon *Quadrant Chambers*
- **Ritchie** Stuart *Littleton Chambers (ORL)* ◊
- **Rubin** Stephen *Fountain Court Chambers* *
- **Saini** Pushpinder *Blackstone Chambers*
- **Snowden** Richard *Erskine Chambers (ORL)* ◊
- **Stanley** Paul *Essex Court Chambers*
- **Sutcliffe** Andrew *3 Verulam Buildings*
- **Tager** Romie *Selborne Chambers (ORL)* ◊ *

Band 4

- **Adam** Tom *Brick Court Chambers*
- **Adkin** Jonathan *Serle Court* *
- **Béar** Charles *Fountain Court Chambers* *
- **Blayney** David *Serle Court* *
- **Boulton** Richard *One Essex Court*
- **Brisby** John *4 Stone Buildings (ORL)* ◊
- **Chapman** Jeffrey *Fountain Court Chambers* *
- **Chivers** David *Erskine Chambers (ORL)* ◊ *
- **Cogley** Stephen *Quadrant Chambers*
- **Dale** Derrick *Fountain Court Chambers*
- **Davies** Rhodri *One Essex Court*
- **Day** Anneliese *4 New Square (ORL)* ◊ *
- **de la Mare** Thomas *Blackstone Chambers*
- **Dohmann** Barbara *Blackstone Chambers*
- **Douglas** Michael *4 Pump Court* *
- **Downes** Paul *2TG - 2 Temple Gardens (ORL)* ◊ [A]
- **Gee** Steven *Stone Chambers (ORL)* ◊
- **Gillis** Richard *One Essex Court* *
- **Glick** Ian *One Essex Court*
- **Graham** Charles *One Essex Court* *
- **Hill** Richard G *4 Stone Buildings (ORL)* ◊
- **Hossain** Sa'ad *One Essex Court*
- **Hunter** Andrew *Blackstone Chambers*
- **Lavender** Nicholas *Serle Court* *
- **Malek** Hodge M *Thirty Nine Essex Street (ORL)* ◊ *
- **McGrath** Paul *Essex Court Chambers*
- **McLaren** Michael *Fountain Court Chambers* *
- **Mitchell** Andrew *Fountain Court Chambers* *
- **Moriarty** Stephen *Fountain Court Chambers* *
- **Norbury** Hugh *Serle Court* *
- **Robertson** Patricia *Fountain Court Chambers* *
- **Rowley** Keith *Radcliffe Chambers (ORL)* ◊
- **Russen** Jonathan *Maitland Chambers* *
- **Sabben-Clare** Rebecca *7 King's Bench Walk* *
- **Salter** Richard *3 Verulam Buildings*
- **Samek** Charles *11 Stone Buildings (ORL)* ◊ *
- **Swainston** Michael *Brick Court Chambers*
- **Talbot Rice** Elspeth *XXIV Old Buildings (ORL)* ◊
- **Wardell** John *Wilberforce Chambers*
- **White** Antony *Matrix Chambers (ORL)* ◊ *

Band 5

- **Bingham** Camilla *One Essex Court*
- **Blanchard** Claire *Essex Court Chambers*
- **Bompas** George *4 Stone Buildings (ORL)* ◊
- **Collins** James *Essex Court Chambers*
- **Cullen** Edmund *Maitland Chambers* *
- **Davies** Huw *Essex Court Chambers*
- **Davies-Jones** Jonathan *3 Verulam Buildings*
- **Dhillon** Jasbir *Brick Court Chambers*
- **Doctor** Brian *Fountain Court Chambers* *
- **Dougherty** Charles *2TG - 2 Temple Gardens (ORL)* ◊ *
- **Elkington** Ben *4 New Square (ORL)* ◊ *
- **Fletcher** Andrew *3 Verulam Buildings*
- **Goldring** Jeremy *South Square (ORL)* ◊
- **Gruder** Jeffrey *Essex Court Chambers*
- **Gunning** Alexander *4 Pump Court* *
- **Henshaw** Andrew *Brick Court Chambers*
- **Houseman** Stephen *Essex Court Chambers*
- **Jarvis** John *3 Verulam Buildings*
- **Jones** Elizabeth *Serle Court* *
- **Key** Paul *Essex Court Chambers*
- **Kimmins** Charles *20 Essex Street*
- **Kirby** PJ *Hardwicke (ORL)* ◊ [A] *
- **Levy** Robert *XXIV Old Buildings (ORL)* ◊
- **Lockey** John *Essex Court Chambers*
- **Masefield** Roger *Brick Court Chambers*
- **McGhee** John *Maitland Chambers* *
- **Mitchell** Gregory *3 Verulam Buildings*
- **Moger** Christopher *4 Pump Court* *
- **Morgan** Richard *Maitland Chambers* *
- **Mowschenson** Terence *Wilberforce Chambers*
- **Oudkerk** Daniel *Essex Court Chambers* *
- **Potts** James *Erskine Chambers (ORL)* ◊ *
- **Quest** David *3 Verulam Buildings*
- **Slade** Richard *Brick Court Chambers*
- **Symons** Christopher *3 Verulam Buildings*
- **Taylor** John *Fountain Court Chambers* *
- **ter Haar** Roger *Crown Office Chambers (ORL)* ◊
- **Tregear** Francis *XXIV Old Buildings (ORL)* ◊
- **Twigger** Andrew M *3 Stone Buildings (ORL)* ◊ *

New Silks

- **Allison** David *South Square (ORL)* ◊ *
- **Blackwood** Andrew Guy *Quadrant Chambers*
- **Fealy** Michael *One Essex Court*
- **Goodall** Patrick *Fountain Court Chambers* *
- **Hardwick** Matthew *3 Verulam Buildings*
- **Lewis** David *20 Essex Street*
- **O'Sullivan** Sean *4 Pump Court* *
- **Smith** Tom *South Square (ORL)* ◊ *
- **Strong** Benjamin *One Essex Court* *
- **Weisselberg** Tom *Blackstone Chambers*

◊ (ORL) = Other Ranked Lawyer.

[A] direct access (see p.11).

** Indicates individual with profile.*

Alphabetical order within each band. Band 1 is highest.

Commercial Dispute Resolution London	
Leading Juniors	
Band 1	
Goldsmith Jamie	*One Essex Court* *
Lazarus Michael	*3 Verulam Buildings*
Mumford David	*Maitland Chambers* *
Band 2	
Birt Simon	*Brick Court Chambers*
Boase Anna	*One Essex Court*
George Andrew	*Blackstone Chambers*
Gledhill Orlando	*One Essex Court* *
Lightman Daniel	*Serle Court* *
MacDonald James	*3 Verulam Buildings* *
Midwinter Stephen	*Brick Court Chambers*
Nambisan Deepak	*Fountain Court Chambers* *
Patton Conall	*One Essex Court* *
Pilbrow Fionn	*Brick Court Chambers*
Polley Alexander	*One Essex Court* *
Scorey David	*Essex Court Chambers*
Valentin Ben	*Fountain Court Chambers* *
Willan James	*Essex Court Chambers*
Band 3	
Adamyk Simon	*New Square Chambers (ORL)* ◊ *
Brocklebank James	*7 King's Bench Walk*
Colton Simon	*One Essex Court* *
Cutress James	*Fountain Court Chambers* *
Dilnot Anna	*Essex Court Chambers*
Haydon Alec	*Brick Court Chambers*
Higgo Justin	*Serle Court* *
Isaac Sebastian	*One Essex Court*
John Laura	*3 Verulam Buildings*
Keller Ciaran	*Maitland Chambers* *
King Edmund	*Essex Court Chambers*
Kramer Adam	*3 Verulam Buildings* *
Levey Edward	*Fountain Court Chambers*
Milner Alexander	*Fountain Court Chambers* *
Oppenheimer Tamara	*Fountain Court Chambers*
Pilling Benjamin	*4 Pump Court* *
Pillow Nathan	*Essex Court Chambers*
Ratcliffe Peter	*3 Verulam Buildings*
Sinclair Paul	*Fountain Court Chambers*
Singla Tony	*Brick Court Chambers*
Weekes Robert	*Blackstone Chambers*
Zellick Adam	*Fountain Court Chambers* *
Band 4	
Akkouh Tim	*Erskine Chambers (ORL)* ◊ *
Barker James	*Enterprise Chambers (ORL)* ◊
Brown Edward	*Essex Court Chambers*
Cohen Jonathan	*Littleton Chambers (ORL)* ◊
Cook Matthew	*One Essex Court*
Craig Nicholas	*3 Verulam Buildings* *
Cumming Edward	*XXIV Old Buildings (ORL)* ◊
Davies David	*Essex Court Chambers*
Dawid Jonathan	*Brick Court Chambers*
Elliott Steven	*One Essex Court* *
Head David	*3 Verulam Buildings*
Holtham den Besten Ruth	*Serle Court* *
Ife Linden	*Enterprise Chambers (ORL)* ◊
John Benjamin	*Maitland Chambers* *
Jones Oliver	*Brick Court Chambers*
Lascelles David	*Littleton Chambers (ORL)* ◊ *
Mallin Max	*11 Stone Buildings (ORL)* ◊
Mott Richard	*One Essex Court* *
Parker Matthew	*3 Verulam Buildings* *
Phelps Rosalind	*Fountain Court Chambers* *
Pillai Rajesh	*3 Verulam Buildings* *
Power Richard	*Fountain Court Chambers* *
Ramsden James	*Thirty Nine Essex Street (ORL)* ◊ [A]
Raphael Thomas	*20 Essex Street*
Reffin Clare	*One Essex Court* [A]
Staunton Ulick	*Radcliffe Chambers (ORL)* ◊
Temmink Robert-Jan	*Quadrant Chambers*
West Colin	*Brick Court Chambers*
Band 5	
Abram Sarah	*Brick Court Chambers*
Allen Rupert	*Fountain Court Chambers* *
Atrill Simon	*Fountain Court Chambers* *
Blakeley Richard	*Brick Court Chambers*
Brier Jeremy	*Essex Court Chambers*
de Verneuil Smith Peter	*3 Verulam Buildings* *
Diwan Ricky	*Essex Court Chambers*
Emmett Laurence	*One Essex Court*
Fatima Shaheed	*Blackstone Chambers*
Harris Christopher	*3 Verulam Buildings* *
Hobson Fred	*Brick Court Chambers*
Hubbard Daniel	*One Essex Court*
Jackson Hugh	*Selborne Chambers (ORL)* ◊ *
Jeavons Anne	*3 Verulam Buildings*
Lewis David	*Hardwicke (ORL)* ◊ [A] *
Lidington Gary	*11 Stone Buildings (ORL)* ◊ *
Lynch Ben	*Devereux (ORL)* ◊ *
Majumdar Shantanu	*Radcliffe Chambers (ORL)* ◊
Marshall Paul	*No5 Chambers (ORL)* ◊
McClelland James	*Fountain Court Chambers* *
Mills Simon	*Five Paper (ORL)* ◊ [A] *
Morgan Gemma	*Quadrant Chambers*
Murray David	*Fountain Court Chambers* *
Ohrenstein Dov	*Radcliffe Chambers (ORL)* ◊ *
O'Leary Sam	*One Essex Court* *
Phipps Sandy	*3 Verulam Buildings*
Plewman SC Thomas	*Brick Court Chambers*
Riches Philip	*Stone Chambers (ORL)* ◊ *
Richmond Jeremy	*Quadrant Chambers*
Rothschild Gerard	*Brick Court Chambers*
Shekerdemian Marcia	*11 Stone Buildings (ORL)* ◊
Spalton George	*4 New Square (ORL)* ◊ *
Stephens John	*XXIV Old Buildings (ORL)* ◊
Vinall Mark	*Blackstone Chambers*
Wood Emily	*Essex Court Chambers*
Wygas Luke	*4 Pump Court* *
Up-and-coming individuals	
Sloboda Nicholas	*One Essex Court* *

◊ (ORL) = Other Ranked Lawyer.

[A] direct access (see p.11).

* Indicates individual with profile.

cases. **Strengths:** "He is meticulous in his attention to detail, and is incredibly bright, fantastically user-friendly and highly accessible." **Recent work:** Acted with Mark Hapgood QC for Bambino Holdings, Bernie Ecclestone's family trust company, in relation to a USD140 million fraud claim brought by Constantin Medien.

Tom Adam QC Highly regarded by instructing parties and peers alike, with one source naming him as "undoubtedly one of the most brilliant legal minds of his generation." His practice covers a range of commercial matters, and he has particular expertise in insurance and professional negligence matters. **Strengths:** "Commercial, user-friendly and a delight to work with. He has terrific judgement and is an accomplished advocate." "Clearly had a grasp of the detail that was second to none. A very good advocate who was very good on cross-examination; he knew where he was going tactically." **Recent work:** Acted for a syndicate of investors bringing high-value claims of fraudulent misrepresentation and breach of fiduciary duties against Dr Balwinder Sidhu and others. The case concerned a Bulgarian land investment venture.

Richard Slade QC A well-liked silk with a broad commercial practice. His recent cases include disputes in the banking, financial services and international trade sectors. **Strengths:** "Excellent at cutting to the heart of the matter and very user-friendly." "He was very accessible to the client, which was great." **Recent work:** Acted for UBS in relation to its USD100 million claim against the Leipzig water authority, Kommunale Wasserwerke Leipzig.

Michael Swainston QC Held in high regard by instructing solicitors, and has a high-profile, international caseload. He is particularly well regarded in respect of civil fraud matters and 'oligarch' litigation arising in Russia and the CIS. **Strengths:** "Exceptionally bright. A leader that you would not want to see appearing for the other side. Devastatingly effective in cross-examination, he's strongly recommended for civil fraud and CIS disputes." **Recent work:** Acted for JKX Oil & Gas on a dispute with Eclairs Group and Glengary over the validity of voting and transfer restriction notices.

Jasbir Dhillon QC A silk with a strong reputation in the commercial market, particularly for complex banking and finance disputes. **Strengths:** "He is very good with the client, and will do all he can to work with the material he is given." "Impressive in the more complex disputes, particularly banking and company law matters." **Recent work:** Acted for FG Wilson (now Caterpillar NI) on its USD13 million claim against Holt for generators, other goods and services, as well as in defence of a USD50 million claim brought against FG Wilson by Holt.

Andrew Henshaw QC Negotiates a broad commercial litigation and arbitration practice, and has particular experience in oligarch disputes. He is also noted for his handling of jurisdictional challenges, and for his expertise in European and public law. **Strengths:** "Very good on the paperwork, and a real brain." **Recent work:** Acted for Linton Capital in relation to claims brought by QOGT over the management of an investment fund.

Roger Masefield QC A junior silk with a strong reputation in the commercial market, who acts on complex and high-stakes litigation and arbitrations. He has a practice covering civil fraud, energy and insurance, and has particular experience in banking and finance matters. **Strengths:** "A very creative, lateral thinker who has a tremendous depth of legal knowledge that he has acquired through his involvement in massively complex cases. He is a very clear-thinking lawyer in terms of strategy and has a very good manner with clients, whose commercial objectives he understands." **Recent work:** Acted for Standard Bank on the defence of a claim by Sabre relating to the sale of an oil company investing in an offshore oil field.

JUNIORS

Simon Birt Receives consistently high praise from instructing solicitors and has a strong reputation at the Commercial Bar. His practice is wide-ranging, and he tackles financial services, insurance, professional negligence and shipping cases, to name but a few. **Strengths:** "An extraordinarily thoughtful, bright barrister whose drafting is excellent. A very,

very smart guy who has great advocacy skills." "Unbelievably hard-working, he was a pleasure to work with on a super-stressful case." **Recent work:** Acted alongside Tim Lord QC and Simon Salzedo QC for J.P. Morgan on a complex CDO claim against the Berlin transport authority.

Fionn Pilbrow An active junior who attracts a range of high-end instructions, and has particular experience in energy and natural resources disputes. Instructing solicitors consider him to be "very good on his feet," and he often acts as sole advocate. **Strengths:** "His advice is clear and logical." "Incisive and commercial in his approach, he's a force for the future." **Recent work:** Represented Energy Venture Partners, with Mark Howard QC, in its successful recovery of an approximately USD110 million commission payment from Malabu Oil & Gas following the sale of a Nigerian oil licence.

Stephen Midwinter A darling of the junior Bar who attracts praise from peers and instructing solicitors alike. He appears, led and unled, in both general commercial disputes and international arbitrations. **Strengths:** "Exceptionally bright, efficient and also a very good advocate. He is a first-choice junior counsel, particularly on complex civil fraud matters." "A very, very able advocate, he really did wipe the floor with the opposition." **Recent work:** Led by Mark Howard QC in Goldman Sachs' defence of a EUR200 million professional negligence claim brought by Pensionenfonds Vervoer.

Jonathan Dawid Has a strong reputation for representing major financial institutions, accountancy firms and investment managers. He has particular expertise in the application of EU law to the financial services sector. **Strengths:** "A real asset to the team and very good with tricky technical points of both law and fact." **Recent work:** Represented UBS in a claim against the Leipzig water authority for sums owed under a CDO. He also acted for UBS Global Asset Management in defence of professional negligence claims relating to the management of the CDO portfolio.

Alec Haydon Senior junior with a broad commercial practice that covers shareholder, professional negligence, insurance and banking disputes. He is particularly valued by instructing solicitors for his strategic input. **Strengths:** "Incredibly good at devising strategy, getting to the key issues and finding a way through them that meets clients' commercial objectives." "He's very good on fraud and careful to find a proportionate strategy." **Recent work:** Led by Mark Howard QC for Gennadiy Bogolyubov in relation to his high-profile dispute with Victor Pinchuk.

Tony Singla An impressive and active junior, with a broad practice encompassing insurance, energy, civil fraud and professional negligence cases. Solicitors appreciate his user-friendliness and strong work ethic. **Strengths:** "Tony is very approachable, good on his feet, and excellent if you require practical and commercial advice." "He has a very good grasp of the issues and puts a lot of effort into knowing everything about the case. Very easy to work with, he has no airs and graces." **Recent work:** Led by Mark Howard QC on the 'Alexandros T' Supreme Court case, regarding the operation of Articles 27 and 28 of the Brussels Regulation.

Colin West A bright and reliable junior, with a practice spanning a range of commercial litigation and arbitration cases. Insurance, civil fraud and shipping cases are a particular focus, and he is strong on contractual disputes. **Strengths:** "Very bright, good on the detail and excellent tactically." "Really calm, really sound and obviously going places." **Recent work:** Acted for African Minerals in defence of a significant fee claim by Renaissance Capital.

Oliver Jones A dynamic junior who has impressed with his work rate and intellectual ability. He appears in a number of heavyweight commercial cases. **Strengths:** "He has a fantastically rigorous intellect." "A total glutton for work and someone who is wise beyond his years." **Recent work:** Led by Tom Linden QC for Group Lotus in relation to an unfair dismissal claim by its former CEO and a counterclaim concerning the same's conduct during his tenure as CEO.

Thomas Plewman SC A well-regarded advocate with particular experience in financial services, banking, professional negligence, intellectual property and mining law. His heavyweight presence in the London market follows on from his success as a commercial silk in South Africa. **Strengths:** "Extraordinarily good." "Pugnacious, straightforward and straight-talking." **Recent work:** Appeared in Cattles v PricewaterhouseCoopers, a USD1.6 billion professional negligence dispute over the collapse of the Welcome Financial Services group.

Sarah Abram Has a strong commercial litigation and arbitration practice, and has expertise in EU and competition law. **Recent work:** Appeared unled for BAE Systems in defence of a fee claim by two former agents.

Richard Blakeley A well-regarded junior with an enviable and high-profile recent caseload. **Strengths:** "Incredibly hard-working and very smart, he punches above his weight. On his feet, he is very confident and very effective, and he shows good judgement." **Recent work:** Led by Michael Swainston QC for API in defending claims for declaration of liability to indemnify British American Tobacco for the cost of the Fox River cleanup.

Fred Hobson An active junior with a practice spanning energy, banking and civil fraud disputes. His recent work has included high-profile oligarch litigation. **Strengths:** "Very easy to deal with and very fair." **Recent work:** Appeared with Mark Howard QC and Alec Haydon for Gennadiy Bogolyubov in relation to the high-profile dispute with Victor Pinchuk over an iron ore mining company.

Gerard Rothschild A well-regarded junior with a practice that takes in commercial, competition and public law cases. **Recent work:** Instructed as sole counsel by Archimedes Pharma in relation to a breach of contract and compensation for loss claim against Recipharm.

One Essex Court

See profile on p.790

THE SET

With stellar silks and sought-after juniors, One Essex Court remains a first-choice set for those faced with complex, high-value commercial litigation. Its members handle energy, banking, company, insurance and civil fraud disputes, among others, and together constitute "a consistently strong group of barristers." According to market commentators, this is "a very high-quality set, from top to bottom."

Client service: Darren Burrows leads the clerking team at One Essex Court. "The clerks there are absolutely superb. They're first-class, and look after us and our clients very well."

SILKS

Anthony Grabiner QC A confirmed star of the Commercial Bar who draws praise from across the market for his superlative advocacy, masterful courtroom presence and strategic intelligence. Instructing solicitors are particularly complimentary of his client-facing skills. He practises across a broad range of commercial cases, particularly those with banking, finance, oil and gas, civil fraud, competition and company elements. **Strengths:** "A force of nature. The clients absolutely love him and he has natural authority." "Has an outstanding ability to focus both clients and the court on the essentials of the case." **Recent work:** Represented Victor Pinchuk in high-profile Commercial Court claims against Gennadiy Bogolyubov and Igor Kolomoisky, relating to the ownership of an iron ore company.

Laurence Rabinowitz QC A leading light at the Commercial Bar, with high-level expertise in a slew of practice areas. He receives glowing reviews from peers and instructing parties alike, and is identified as client-friendly, "formidably bright" and "a go-to advocate for any bet-the-bank commercial litigation or arbitration." **Strengths:** "He has the full package of intellectual prowess, commercial sense, and the ability to get on with clients and speak to them in a way that they like to be spoken to." "A polymath, he handles everything from tax through to energy, and is able to distil complex legal concepts almost into words of one syllable." **Recent work:** Appeared in Benedetti v Sawiris and others.

Stephen Auld QC A favourite with many instructing solicitors due to his collaborative approach, client-friendliness and "terrific" cross-examination skills. His practice spans commercial and chancery cases, and he has a particular focus on banking and finance, civil fraud and contractual disputes. **Strengths:** "He is good with clients and a powerful advocate who is a great cross-examiner. He's a silk of choice for financial litigation." "A workhorse and a real fighter. He is someone I would look to work with if I had a really tough bit of litigation that needed to be dealt with urgently." **Recent work:** Acted for Derek Quinlan as respondent to an unfair prejudice petition concerning Coroin, which owns Claridge's, The Connaught and The Berkeley hotels.

Alain Choo Choy QC Sought-after silk especially for commercial cases with a strong financial services flavour. Sources appreciate his intellectual ability and technical excellence. **Strengths:** "A top-end silk who is very bright, a joy to work with, and someone who listens." "Incredibly intelligent but also client-friendly."

Neil Kitchener QC Receives widespread praise from market commentators for his robust and tenacious advocacy, as well as his inclusive, collaborative approach to cases. His commercial practice is diverse, and spans banking and finance litigation, civil fraud, company law and energy disputes. **Strengths:** "Makes the complicated look very simple." "A tremendously good lawyer and a fantastic fighter who has great human intelligence and intuitively knows the client's needs." **Recent work:** Acted in Marathon v Hosking, a significant fraud and 'team move' claim relating to a City investment management firm.

John McCaughran QC A well-liked and highly regarded silk renowned for handling energy sector litigation and contractual disputes. He has a loyal following of instructing solicitors who praise his intellectual rigour, commerciality and user-friendliness. **Strengths:** "He thinks of points and ways round that no one else really can, and presents his case in a way that seems entirely logical. He's extremely calm under pressure, and very good at dealing with the pressured environment you get when tackling a heavy commercial dispute." **Recent work:** Represented BHP Billiton in a dispute with E.ON regarding the termination of a gas sales agreement.

Jeffery Onions QC A highly regarded silk whom sources identify as "a natural advocate" and "a man for the most difficult cases." His practice is wide-ranging, and he handles banking, insolvency, insurance, oil and gas, and sports and media cases among others. **Strengths:** "Fantastically hands-on for such a senior leading counsel." "When he speaks, you listen. He has got a captivating style." **Recent work:** Represented Sir Frederick and Sir David Barclay in relation to the high-profile ownership dispute with Patrick McKillen over Coroin, which owns Claridge's, The Connaught and The Berkeley hotels.

Daniel Toledano QC Highly regarded advocate with a broad commercial practice. Sources consistently praise him for being bright, user-friendly and in command of the details of a case. **Strengths:** "Incredibly bright, very technically proficient and a details man. It is difficult to think of someone who could be more polished." **Recent work:** Appeared before the Court of Appeal in Les Laboratoires Servier v Apotex, in which the ambit of the ex turpi causa rule was considered.

David Wolfson QC Handles commercial disputes and arbitration, and is particularly well known for his skill at banking litigation. He is held in high regard by instructing parties, who appreciate his robust and engaging style of advocacy. **Strengths:** "A go-to person for any difficult cross-border issues." "Has an exceptional intellect and great commercial awareness." **Recent work:** Acted for UniCredit in a dispute with Barclays.

David Cavender QC Highly regarded as an advocate, and praised by sources for his courtroom presentation and technical skill. His commercial practice covers a wide range of matters, including banking and finance, company law, insurance and civil fraud matters. **Strengths:** "Robust, practical and commercial." "He is a brilliant advocate who works his socks off, and knows every document in a case like the back of his hand." **Recent work:** Represented Ravi Chilukuri in defending a deceit claim brought by RP Explorer Master Fund relating to USD18 million of global depository receipts.

Ian Glick QC A very well-regarded silk with a diverse commercial practice who regularly handles energy, and banking and finance disputes. **Strengths:** "Very quick to master the technical issues and see the next issue coming." **Recent work:** Acted for HSBC in relation to a claim against HMRC for the recovery of stamp duty reserve tax paid on the issue of shares following the acquisition of Crédit Commercial de France.

Kenneth MacLean QC Receives complex, heavyweight commercial instructions from top litigation law firms. Sources particularly appreciate his sound commercial judgement. **Strengths:** "He gives sensible, no-nonsense and sound commercial advice." "Very easy to work with and a good cross-examiner." **Recent work:** Represented Cukurova Finance International in its high-profile and long-running dispute with Alfa Group over control of Turkish phone company Turkcell.

Craig Orr QC Active on some of the most high-profile and substantial commercial disputes of the day, he receives instructions from magic circle and top-tier litigation firms. He is recognised for his expertise in commercial, insurance, and banking and finance matters. **Strengths:** "Absolutely fantastic" and "a pleasure to work with." **Recent work:** Acted for Kroll Associates in defending a significant breach of confidence claim brought by Dar Al Arkan and Bank Alkhair.

Rhodri Davies QC Well regarded in the commercial, banking and financial spheres, and a lawyer who has further noted expertise in energy and accountant's negligence cases. **Strengths:** "A good academic lawyer who is very robust at dealing with difficult opponents." "A very good, understated advocate who is very good with clients and thoroughly charming." **Recent work:** Acted for Alfa in obtaining an interim injunction application preventing the enforcement of an early termination of a loan agreement with Deutsche Bank.

Anthony de Garr Robinson QC Manages a diverse commercial practice encompassing company, banking and finance, and civil fraud cases. He is particularly noted for his experience in offshore litigation and is admitted to the Bar in the Bahamas and the British Virgin Islands. He is also registered as an advocate in the Dubai International Financial Centre Courts. **Strengths:** "Delivers practical advice." **Recent work:** Acted for the defendants to a claim brought by Geoffrey Logue, the purchaser of an apartment in the One Hyde Park, alleging unlawful means conspiracy to prevent the completion of the purchase.

Richard Gillis QC Well regarded for commercial disputes with company and insolvency elements. He also handles civil fraud, professional negligence and natural resources cases. **Strengths:** "Extremely personable and user-friendly. He is methodical and diligent, and has excellent intuition for how a point will play out before an arbitrator. He interacts very well with clients and experts." **Recent work:** Represented the unsecured banking creditors of Kaupthing Singer & Friedlander who are challenging the creation and/or operation of a trust fund account which was established immediately before the bank went into administration.

Charles Graham QC (see p.613) A popular silk who has a practice strong on banking disputes, professional negligence cases and litigation in the energy sector. He is praised by solicitors for his user-friendliness and client skills, with one source recommending him for cases "where clients feel a bit overwhelmed and need to feel they're being looked after." **Strengths:** "He's immensely hard-working and has a phenomenal memory, which is an advantage in dealing with fact-intensive cases." **Recent work:** Appeared for North Sea Energy in a dispute with Ithaca Energy relating to the interpretation of a joint venture agreement for offshore drilling.

Camilla Bingham QC Has a strong reputation for civil fraud work, and handles both domestic and international litigation. **Strengths:** "Excellent with clients, robust and fearless." **Recent work:** Acted for Victor Pinchuk in his high-profile dispute with Gennadiy Bogolyubov and Igor Kolomoisky, relating to the ownership of an iron ore company.

Sa'ad Hossain QC Praised by instructing solicitors for his approachability, charm and good judgement. He handles top-notch commercial litigation and international arbitration work. **Strengths:** "Absolutely charming and very clever." "He has a mighty intellect." **Recent work:** Acted for Landprop Holdings defending a claim for losses brought by Dorchester Project Management, in relation to the purchase of a site near the Olympic grounds in Stratford.

Richard Boulton QC Wins praise from peers and instructing solicitors for his work in financial disputes, civil fraud investigations and damages claims. Instructing solicitors say his background in accountancy represents an asset to them. **Strengths:** "Recommended for his tenacity, hard work, unfailing good humour and willingness to roll up his sleeves." "He is very easy-going and easy to work with, and is also very thorough." **Recent work:** Acted for Quayle on a professional negligence claim against chartered accountants Rothman Pantall & Co concerning tax advice.

Benjamin Strong QC Became silk in 2014, an appointment regarded by market commentators as being thoroughly deserved. He handles substantial and often document-heavy commercial cases with a focus on matters relating to financial institutions and investment. **Strengths:** "Hands-on and practical, he provides good commercial advice without beating around the bush." "Always spots the really good points." **Recent work:** Acted for Hammonds as defendant to a claim brought by Sun Capital Partners IV in connection with the acquisition of companies which had large and unexpected liabilities.

Michael Fealy QC Took silk in 2014. He has a broad commercial practice, covering company law, contractual disputes, energy and natural resources, and civil fraud matters. **Strengths:** "An iron fist in a silk glove when in court." "He's fantastic at seeing the wood for the trees and being able to navigate all of the complexities in a case. He makes matters simple so that both the client and judge understand his position." **Recent work:** Acted for a respondent resisting the enforcement of a loan agreement which was non-compliant with the Consumer Credit Act.

JUNIORS

Jamie Goldsmith (see p.610) An impressive and sought-after junior who wins instructions from top City law firms. He is particularly recognised for his client-friendly approach, intellectual skills and ability to handle labour-intensive cases. **Strengths:** "Very composed and very polished. His written advocacy is first-rate." "He is brilliant in terms of his ability to digest enormous amounts of complicated material. If you have thousands of documents, he will pick out the five that will determine the dispute." **Recent work:** Acted for Sabre in a claim against Standard Bank in relation to an oil and gas project.

Conall Patton Recognised for his expertise in energy and natural resources, competition law, and banking and finance, he is held in high regard by peers and solicitors alike. **Strengths:** "One of the brightest commercial juniors at the Bar. He has a ready ability to assimilate huge amounts of factual information, digest it, and then present it in a fashion that clients can understand and make commercial decisions from." **Recent work:** Appeared as sole counsel in a dispute between Kenrick Santana and Priory Land, relating to an oral agreement for commission on the sale of land.

Alexander Polley Senior junior praised for his intellectual ability and experience in complex litigation. He has particular expertise in civil fraud and banking and finance matters. **Strengths:** "Absolutely superb. An excellent lawyer who has very good judgement and is incredibly hard-working and very user-friendly." "A real team player." **Recent work:**

Polley was part of the team representing the Candy brothers and associated companies in relation to a claim of unlawful means conspiracy brought by the purchaser of a One Hyde Park apartment.

Anna Boase A hard-working and technically accomplished junior who peers say is "unflappable" when on her feet. **Strengths:** "Bright and hard-working, she has a winning manner both with clients and in court." "Clever, but also incredibly obliging and productive." **Recent work:** Led by Tim Lord QC, she acted for HSBC in enforcement action against Ahmad Hamad Algosaibi and Brothers and individual partners, following the withdrawal of their defence at trial.

Orlando Gledhill Held in high regard by instructing solicitors and praised by peers as being "bright and easy to work with." His practice spans a range of commercial disputes, and he is particularly good at energy and natural resources and civil fraud matters. **Strengths:** "Prepared to stand up to judges, he's a tough, no-nonsense barrister. He's very meticulous and a great trial advocate who is understated but effective." "An outstanding draftsman." **Recent work:** Represented Deutsche Bank as sole counsel in relation to significant claims against Total Global Steel.

Sebastian Isaac Experienced at handling heavy commercial cases and arbitrations. He is particularly noted for his expertise in banking and finance disputes. **Strengths:** "He is the man for big complicated cases requiring the ability to crunch through a huge amount of material. He can stay at the coalface for long periods of time whilst producing high-quality work." "He takes a considered view. If he drafts an opinion, you can be confident that he has thought about every angle." **Recent work:** Led by Daniel Toledano QC, he acted for Centrica in claims against Medway power station relating to a 'take or pay' gas supply contract and the issue of whether or not power outages at the plant were outside of the plant operator's control.

Simon Colton (see p.576) Handles significant commercial litigation and is particularly active in terms of international and cross-border cases. He is a go-to junior for magic circle and top-tier litigation firms. **Strengths:** "He is phenomenally clever and incredibly easy to deal with, as well as astoundingly quick at turning around documents. He has got good tactical nous and is very willing to muck in and help his solicitors out." **Recent work:** Acted as leading junior for the SFO in defence of high-profile compensation claims brought by the Tchenguiz brothers.

Steven Elliott Highly regarded for his work on a raft of commercial disputes, many of which have a fraud aspect to them. He acts as both junior and sole advocate, and is admitted to the Bar in the British Virgin Islands. **Strengths:** "Highly intelligent and someone who produces very detailed and persuasive paperwork." "Very thorough and very calm to work with, he's good at taking on complex issues and good at dealing with the detail." **Recent work:** Represented Littlewoods Retail in connection with restitution claims against HMRC for £1.2 billion of overpaid VAT.

Richard Mott (see p.678) A well-regarded junior with particular expertise in civil fraud and banking and finance matters. **Strengths:** "A smart guy with excellent drafting skills." **Recent work:** Appeared before the Court of Appeal as sole counsel to one of the defendants in a fraud and negligence claim relating to the collapsed Weavering Capital hedge fund.

Clare Reffin A respected senior junior with a broad commercial practice that spans commercial contracts, commodities, banking and finance, company law and jurisdictional disputes. **Strengths:** "Very proactive, thorough and also personable." **Recent work:** Acted for Fern Advisors on bringing a claim of fraudulent misappropriation of assets against its former CEO, Adrian Burford.

Matthew Cook A senior junior who regularly handles major commercial cases and international arbitrations, he is particularly strong on the energy side. Sources praise him for his intellectual ability and user-friendliness. **Strengths:** "Extremely bright and exceptionally numerate." "He's a good, experienced junior who gives quick, clear advice, is very user-friendly and is almost always available to talk." **Recent work:** Led by Jeffrey Onions QC, he acted for Topland Group on defending allegations of fraud and bribery in connection with property transactions.

Daniel Hubbard Experienced in litigation and arbitration relating to contractual disputes, company law and the energy sector. He also has expertise in freezing injunctions. **Strengths:** "A smart cookie. He knows what he's doing; he's good on his feet, good on paper and highly responsive." **Recent work:** Represented Jean-Claude Pierre Ferdinand Gunther Andre and Jane Ellis Andre in a substantial claim against Clydesdale Bank for breach of bailment in respect of a trunk said to contain, among other things, valuable Treskilling Yellow stamps.

Laurence Emmett A well-regarded junior who has particular expertise in energy and natural resources and banking and finance matters. **Strengths:** "He leaves no stone unturned, is very charming and very hard-working. He's got excellent attention to detail and a forensic mind. He's a very good fresh pair of eyes on any case." "He is tireless in his approach and won't give up." **Recent work:** Appeared with Anthony de Garr Robinson QC in Antonio Gramsci Shipping v Recoletos, a case heard before the Court of Appeal which concerned the application of jurisdiction agreements to individuals standing behind companies.

Sam O'Leary Experienced in both commercial litigation and arbitration, and someone with a particular interest in banking and finance work. **Recent work:** Acted for the majority owners of Charterhouse Capital Partners in relation to an unfair prejudice petition brought by its second largest shareholder.

Nicholas Sloboda (see p.722) A well-regarded junior with experience in both commercial litigation and arbitration. He has particular expertise in banking and finance cases. **Strengths:** "Punchy and very practical, he's a hands-on counsel." **Recent work:** Led by Craig Orr QC for Kroll Associates, defending a significant breach of confidence claim brought by Dar Al Arkan and Bank Alkhair.

Essex Court Chambers

See profile on p.792

THE SET

Essex Court has long been regarded as being in the front rank of sets handling complex commercial litigation and arbitration. Members are routinely instructed in high-value and high-profile disputes in a variety of areas, including the energy, natural resources and financial services sectors. Oligarch litigation has proved a fertile source of instructions in recent times, and Essex Court barristers have had a stake in the majority of the headline-grabbing cases. Market commentators say of this chambers: "As a set, Essex Court is in the premier league for arbitration and general commercial work. Its members are renowned for handling these cases, and have an intuitive, collegiate way of working."

Client service: "The clerking team, led by David Grief, is friendly, proactive and helpful."

SILKS

David Foxton QC A heavyweight of the Commercial Bar and "an intellectual powerhouse." He is held in high esteem by solicitors and peers alike due to the quality of his commercial litigation and arbitration appearances. **Strengths:** "Very cerebral and very approachable." "A polymath and a terribly nice guy. He's a fantastic lawyer and a very polished advocate."

Joe Smouha QC An impressive and strategically astute advocate who receives top commercial instructions. His work spans the financial, energy and media sectors, and he is particularly known for his experience in arbitration. **Strengths:** "His reputation at the Bar is very powerful." "He has an easy style and is quick-witted and humorous. He has always read his papers and can be relied upon." **Recent work:** Acted for Robert Tchenguiz in an approximately £100 million claim against the SFO for business losses sustained following dawn raids on the Tchenguiz brothers' homes and offices.

Vernon Flynn QC A highly rated silk with an active international practice and a reputation for user-friendliness among solicitors, who praise him for his "dynamic enthusiasm." His commercial dispute portfolio is diverse, with energy sector and entertainment matters, arbitral award disputes and jurisdictional challenges all featuring. **Strengths:** "He has a brilliant courtroom manner and is hugely impressive in predicting judicial instincts." "He knows his way around all the leading arbitration cases and is personable and very easy to deal with." **Recent work:** Represented Taaleem, a UAE private school operator, in relation to its dispute with National Bonds Corporation and Deeyar Development over a 33% share in a luxury residential complex.

Andrew Hochhauser QC A powerful advocate and adviser, with a wide-ranging commercial practice. He is particularly known for his handling of success fee and bonus-related disputes. **Strengths:** "An awesome cross-examiner." "The consummate court advocate, he's brilliant at making submissions, brilliant at cross-examination and great on the detail."

Gordon Pollock QC An extremely well-known name at the Commercial Bar, whose work spans civil fraud, international trade, media and entertainment, and financial services cases among others. **Recent work:** Acted for Yukos Capital in relation to various disputes with Roseneft Oil following the break-up and renationalisation of Yukos.

Steven Berry QC A well-regarded silk who has experience in a range of international and domestic commercial disputes. He has particular expertise in shipping, commodities and insurance. **Strengths:** "He commands the attention of judges" and is "a very impressive performer." **Recent work:** Acted for Russian financial group Otkritie Securities on its high-profile fraud claim against George Uromov and others.

Graham Dunning QC Co-head of chambers and an experienced commercial advocate with a reputation for having excellent cross-examination skills. He has a practice that is international in scope, and has particular expertise in civil fraud cases and jurisdictional challenges. **Strengths:** "A careful and considered advocate who is capable of pulling rabbits out of hats when it's most needed." "Graham is extremely commercial in his approach and able to get into the depth of the argument very quickly." **Recent work:** Acted for Isle of Man subsidiaries of Kyrgyz Mobile in relation to a fraud dispute with Bitel.

Richard Jacobs QC A well-regarded silk, particularly known for his insurance and shipping work. **Strengths:** "A terribly nice, affable opponent who knows insurance law inside-out." "He has a first-class mind and has a good practical sense of what to do in a case. He is really good with clients and gives them a realistic view." **Recent work:** Acted for Howden North America in relation to a dispute with Ace European and others. In this case the claimants sought negative declaration of liabilities for US asbestos claims.

Richard Millett QC A highly regarded silk whose practice spans banking and financial services, insolvency, energy, and media and entertainment disputes. He has particular expertise in insurer insolvency. **Strengths:** "He has an extraordinary ability to cut through all the detail and see the bigger picture. He is extremely good at bouncing ideas off." "A class act who is excellent with clients."

Paul Stanley QC An impressive advocate who remains a popular choice with solicitors. He has a wide-ranging practice that covers insurance and reinsurance, financial services, civil fraud, contractual disputes and jurisdictional issues. **Strengths:** "Clients like his style of advocacy and his incisiveness." "A very bright guy who's willing to consider all the arguments in difficult cases."

Paul McGrath QC An "extremely clever" silk with a practice focused on chancery, commercial and civil fraud cases, particularly claims involving constructive trusts, knowing receipt and asset tracing. **Strengths:** "A brilliant tactician and a team player." "Excellent with clients; he has a laid-back style and is very user-friendly."

Claire Blanchard QC Maintains an active commercial practice, with shipping, international trade, energy and insurance matters being especially to the fore. She appears at all levels in the English courts, and has significant experience in international arbitration. **Recent work:** Appeared in Perca Shipping v Cargill, a case in which the trading house sought an extension of time to commence arbitration.

James Collins QC An active silk with a practice spanning international trade, shipping, insurance, civil fraud and transactional finance disputes. **Strengths:** "He is very easy to work with." "He is an extremely impressive barrister with an extremely sharp mind, who has extensive knowledge of the Bermuda Form." **Recent work:** Acted for Ocean Capital on a claim against HIG Capital for misuse of confidential information.

Huw Davies QC Has a broad international practice and is particularly known for his expertise in aviation disputes. **Strengths:** "Very, very able and incredibly user-friendly."

Jeffrey Gruder QC A highly experienced silk praised by instructing solicitors both for his user-friendliness and his advocacy skills. He has handled a significant number of commercial cases and arbitrations, both domestically and internationally. **Strengths:** "A very clear thinker. He manages to explain even the most complicated legal arguments in a clear and practical way, which clients appreciate. He's very hard-working and a pleasure to deal with." "He produces sublime pleadings." **Recent work:** Instructed by Hong Kong billionaire Samuel Tak Lee in relation to allegations of forgery of financial documents and attempting to pervert the course of justice made by his son's ex-wife, Florence Tsang.

John Lockey QC Acts for financial institutions, insurance and reinsurance companies, energy companies and accountancy firms, and has a practice focused on international and multi-jurisdictional disputes. **Strengths:** "A really enjoyable guy to work with. He has a great brain and a wonderful sense of humour." **Recent work:** Acted in British-American Insurance Co v Matelec, in which the Commercial Court ruled that a London arbitration clause was binding.

Daniel Oudkerk QC Known for handling both commercial and employment disputes, he counts investment banks and financial institutions as well as Lloyd's brokers and insurers as being among his clients. **Strengths:** "He's very user-friendly and very good at working in a team. He is strategically, commercially and legally very astute, and brilliant on his feet." "Simplifies complex matters and knows how to get results." **Recent work:** Acted for Kirill Stein in a high-profile breach of contract claim against Patokh Chodiev, Alexander Machkevitch and Alijan Ibragimov, founding shareholders of ENRC.

Stephen Houseman QC A well-regarded silk with a practice covering banking and finance, energy and natural resources, insurance and reinsurance, and technology cases. He is particularly adept at handling complex, multi-jurisdictional disputes. **Strengths:** "I needed a very tricky bit of advice and he turned it around very quickly. He gave punchy advice that got to the point." **Recent work:** Acted for Kaspersky Lab in relation to significant fee and damages claims brought by ServiceSource following the termination of a service sales management agreement.

Paul Key QC His practice covers a wide range of commercial disputes, including those involving conflict of laws, international trade, energy, telecoms, shipping and foreign investment. **Strengths:** "Produces compelling written work." **Recent work:** Instructed by National Iranian Oil Company in relation to the defence of breach of obligation claims brought by Sharjah-headquartered Crescent Petroleum and Crescent Gas.

JUNIORS

David Scorey A popular junior with an active commercial practice. He is known for his expertise in insurance, reinsurance and shipping, and is also strong on banking and civil fraud litigation. **Strengths:** "Quick, concise and commercial in his advice."

Edmund King A barrister with a broad practice, whose caseload includes insurance, shipping, commodities, banking, shareholder dispute and arbitration matters. **Strengths:** "Modern, approachable, intelligent and a quick thinker." **Recent work:** Acted on Saltri v MD Mezzanine, a dispute between mezzanine and senior lenders over the right to buy a German autopart supply company.

Nathan Pillow Well regarded by instructing solicitors for both his advisory and advocacy work on domestic and international disputes. He is known for his expertise in civil fraud cases. **Strengths:** "He has a very nice manner with clients and he is very good on his feet." **Recent work:** Instructed by ExxonMobil in relation to its Commercial Court claim alleging overcharging by logistics supplier TDG UK.

James Willan An exceptionally well-regarded junior whom instructing solicitors regard as operating well above his year of call. He has handled High Court, Court of Appeal and arbitration matters, and has been admitted as an ad hoc advocate in the Isle of Man. **Strengths:** "Outstandingly committed and already firmly established at the Commercial Bar, he's a brilliantly analytical and fast-thinking advocate." "He has a brain the size of Jupiter, is tenacious, polite and very good on his feet." **Recent work:** Acted for NNPC, the Nigerian state-owned oil company, in a long-running and high-value dispute with IPCO over an oil terminal project.

Edward Brown Has a wide-ranging commercial practice which spans financial services, banking, civil fraud, company law, and media and entertainment cases. Sources praise him for being hard-working and client-friendly. **Strengths:** "Very hard-working and collegiate in his approach." **Recent work:** Instructed by Standard Bank to handle banking fraud claims brought against nine defendants.

David Davies A sought-after junior with wide-ranging commercial experience in both litigation and arbitration. Much of his work is cross-border or international in scope, and he is increasingly instructed as a sole advocate. **Strengths:** "One of the first choices on the team sheet for a substantial case." "He shows excellent judgement for someone who is still relatively junior." **Recent work:** Acted for Carl Sax on a claim against Lev Tchernoy relating to a deal to develop a Sardinian property into a luxury hotel.

Anna Dilnot A dynamic and experienced junior whom sources regard as "going places." Her practice is international in nature and has a particular focus on civil fraud cases. **Strengths:** "Very intelligent and quick to get to the issues. He's a real fighter and can be trusted with serious cases." "Good on her feet and gave good advice in meetings." **Recent work:** Acted for Burger King in proceedings brought against its former Cypriot franchisee. She achieved termination of the Cypriot franchise agreements and secured mandatory injunctions forcing closure of restaurants and the removal of livery.

Ricky Diwan Admitted to the Bar in both New York and England, and has experience in both commercial litigation and arbitration. His practice spans commodities and international trade, energy, telecoms and company law.

Jeremy Brier A junior with a strong commercial practice who often appears in cases unled. He handles high-profile, complex cases, including arbitrations, and regularly appears in shipping, technology and contractual disputes. **Strengths:** "Drafts very well indeed." **Recent work:** Led by Graham Dunning QC for Scott Law as a successful respondent in RBS v Highland and Others, a Court of Appeal fraud case involving the denial of an anti-suit injunction on the basis of 'unclean hands'.

Emily Wood Maintains an active caseload in both the Commercial Court and Chancery Division, and has particular expertise in jurisdictional challenges. She is experienced beyond her year of call and increasingly acts as sole advocate. **Recent work:** Acted as sole counsel for Mauritius Commercial Bank in its EUR15 million dispute with Hestia Holdings.

Fountain Court Chambers

See profile on p.804

THE SET

An elite set boasting a strong bench of counsel at all levels of seniority. Members have handled some of the most high-profile commercial cases of recent years, and are consistently praised for their work ethic, client-friendliness and effective advocacy. Market commentators say: "Fountain Court barristers are very easy to work with and incredibly rigorous."

Client service: "Fountain Court as a whole, including the clerking team, is a very smooth operation." Alex Taylor leads the clerking team, which instructing solicitors praise for being proactive and responsive.

Michael Brindle QC Highly experienced senior silk with a raft of big-ticket commercial cases under his belt. He is held in very high regard by peers and instructing solicitors alike for his assured advocacy, strategic awareness and reliability in handling high-stakes disputes. **Strengths:** "He's a bulldog of a litigator. You can send him in safe in the knowledge that he'll fight hard." "Extremely bright, client-friendly and provides good leadership." **Recent work:** Acted in the Court of Appeal on behalf of appellant Novoship in a dispute over ownership and status of assets. The case arose out of the long-running Fiona Trust litigation concerning alleged bribery, corruption and civil fraud in a Russian shipping business.

David Railton QC Has recognised expertise in banking and finance disputes, particularly those relating to complex financial products. Solicitors appreciate his user-friendliness and further instruct him in insurance and professional negligence cases among others. **Strengths:** "He's incredibly able, and produces very succinct, very structured submissions. He has you following him every step of the way, and he uses cold, clinical logic to obtain the result he wants." "His performance was sensational; he pushed all the right buttons in cross-examination." **Recent work:** Represented Depfa Bank in a dispute with UBS and the Leipzig water authority relating to credit default swaps referencing collateralised debt obligations.

Michael Crane QC Receives strong market approval for his excellent advocacy, legal knowledge and interpersonal skills. His practice focuses on oil and gas disputes, contentious aviation matters, and insurance and reinsurance cases. **Strengths:** "Outstanding" and "a well-established expert." **Recent work:** Acted for Texas Keystone in the successful defence of an approximately USD1.7 billion claim brought by Excalibur Ventures concerning oil and gas concessions in Iraqi Kurdistan.

Bankim Thanki QC Highly rated in both commercial litigation and arbitration, he handles banking and finance, civil fraud, aviation, insurance, professional negligence and offshore cases. He is an accomplished advocate with "great intellectual firepower." **Strengths:** "A very wise, calm and measured individual. He's incredibly easy to work with, and very hands-on." **Recent work:** Represented Sonera and TeliaSonera in a multi-jurisdictional ownership dispute with Alfa Group and Cukurova Telecoms concerning a Turkish telecoms company.

Richard Handyside QC (see p.618) A tremendously well-regarded silk with a reputation among solicitors both for his tactical acumen and for being "very easy to work with but incredibly rigorous in his approach." He is particularly noted for his handling of disputes in the financial and banking sectors. **Strengths:** "Generally superb. He's a delight to work with and is, obviously, fearsomely clever. When handling cases he has always approached even the darkest hours with a great sense of humour and has shown a real willingness to address any difficulties that have arisen." "He's a complete delight to work with." **Recent work:** Acted for Deutsche Bank seeking declarations that the bank did not act as adviser or fiduciary when dealing with Norwegian oil and gas company Petromena's attempts to restructure indebtedness and raise new finance.

Timothy Howe QC Has a wide-ranging commercial practice, and experience in insurance, banking and finance, telecoms, professional negligence and international arbitration matters. Market sources highlight his commerciality, tactical awareness and hard-working approach. **Strengths:** "A favourite who has never let us down." "He is fantastic to work with." **Recent work:** Represented Deutsche Bank in its high-profile litigation with Unitech relating to the legal consequences of alleged Libor manipulation.

Guy Philipps QC Praised by market commentators for his intellect, high-quality advocacy and ability to handle complex disputes. His practice covers commercial disputes, professional negligence cases and financial services litigation. **Strengths:** "He is very helpful and puts in a lot of effort. He is very intelligent indeed and very able, and he adapts to different sorts of cases." **Recent work:** Acted for Anglo American South Africa in challenging the jurisdiction of English courts over personal injury damages claims brought by South African gold miners. The case raised questions of the 'England-domiciled' status of foreign subsidiaries of multinational companies which have group headquarters in London.

Stephen Rubin QC Well regarded by sources for his robust advocacy and his skill in cross-examination. He is particularly well known for civil fraud and telecoms disputes. **Strengths:** "A pugnacious performer who is admired by the court and clients alike for his voracious appetite for detail when handling complex cases." "He was utterly ferocious, which was exactly what the client wanted." **Recent work:** Acted for Qatari prince Sheikh Mohammed Al-Thani in the defence of a USD22 million claim by US auctioneers AH Baldwin & Sons. The matter concerned the alleged purchase of rare coins at a New York auction.

Jeffrey Chapman QC A favourite with instructing solicitors due to his user-friendliness, responsiveness and collaborative approach to his cases. He is particularly active in banking and finance disputes and civil fraud cases. **Strengths:** "Meticulous, concise, and a man with an effective and persuasive style of advocacy." "He is commercial and hard-working, and has got a disarming, unassuming manner. He just gets people to agree with him." **Recent work:** Represented Group Seven in claims brought against Allied Investment Corporation and others relating to an alleged EUR100 million fraud.

Derrick Dale QC Noted for his user-friendliness, pragmatism, and the clarity of his advice. He handles domestic and international disputes in the commercial, professional negligence, and banking and finance fields. **Strengths:** "Exceptionally hard-working and good with clients." "He's insightful, responsive and on top of the facts." **Recent work:** Appeared in Samara v MBI Partners UK, a dispute over the existence of and rights under two contracts between the parties.

Michael McLaren QC A hard-working and proactive silk who has strong advocacy skills. His practice focuses on commercial and professional discipline cases, and he is particularly well known for his handling of aviation cases. **Strengths:** "Fantastically responsive. He goes the extra mile and isn't afraid of giving you and the client feedback on the case, warts and all. He gives you a reality check but also does his best to plot paths through the obstacles you will face." **Recent work:** Acted for Monde Petroleum on a claim against LeeLanes solicitors for turnkey contract commission fees held in an escrow account.

Andrew Mitchell QC An experienced advocate with a broad practice that covers insurance, banking and financial services matters among others. Sources praise him for his robust advocacy and for the clarity of his advice. **Strengths:** "He has gravitas, is respected by tribunals and is very good on his feet." "Superb and very knowledgeable."

Stephen Moriarty QC Head of chambers and an accomplished silk, noted for his cerebral approach. His experience is wide-ranging, and he has handled a good deal of appellate work over the years. He is a recognised expert in aviation cases. **Strengths:** "Outstanding." "He's very cerebral and suitable for cases that are hugely complex and need a lot of thought." **Recent work:** Represented Cayman Island investment advisers Pioneer Alternative Investments in relation to claims brought by Primeo Fund arising out of funds put into Bernard L Madoff Investments.

Patricia Robertson QC Particularly well regarded for her skill in financial sector, professional negligence and professional discipline disputes. She is noted for expertise in financial services regulation and is often instructed on cases involving mis-selling, investment losses and complex financial products. **Strengths:** "Extremely thorough and impressive in front of clients." **Recent work:** Acted for Plurimi Capital in a USD27 million claim brought by an ultra high net worth Saudi investor for losses sustained on a structured products portfolio during the financial crisis.

Charles Béar QC An impressive and accomplished advocate, with a practice devoted to both commercial litigation and administrative and public law. **Strengths:** "He's supremely clever and extremely good with clients. He is a good leader, who is able to roll up his sleeves, get stuck in and assert himself." "He was on the other side and as soon as he opened his mouth I thought, 'We're going to get creamed.'"

Brian Doctor QC (see p.589) Has a broad practice with a particular focus on international commercial disputes and conflicts of law cases. **Strengths:** "Very effective" and "hugely experienced." **Recent work:** Appeared for the defendants in Access Bank v Rofos Navigation Limited and Capital Oil, seeking to resist an 'unless order' pursuant to an anti-suit injunction obtained in London by the claimant.

John Taylor QC (see p.734) A recent silk who has already gained a loyal following in the litigation departments of top-flight firms. He is particularly noted for his work on banking and finance cases and aviation disputes. **Strengths:** "He is really responsive, is very quick in turning around papers and offers excellent advice." "First on my list for anything difficult. A fantastic advocate whose work ethic and attention to detail are superb." **Recent work:** Instructed by Mitsubishi as defendant in a dispute over the quality of aircraft seats.

Patrick Goodall QC Took silk in 2014, having long been regarded as one of the stars of the junior Bar. He is a favourite of magic circle solicitors, and has a practice covering banking and finance, civil fraud, insurance and professional negligence. **Strengths:** "Responsive, extremely intelligent, and adds a lot of value." "He is very bright, hard-working, and he produces good pleadings." **Recent work:** Led by Laurence Rabinowitz QC in representing Igor

Kolomoisky in a high-profile dispute with Victor Pinchuk over the ownership of an iron ore company.

JUNIORS

Deepak Nambisan A popular junior with a diverse commercial practice covering media and entertainment work, as well as international arbitration and civil fraud cases. He is particularly noted for his user-friendliness and ability to handle labour-intensive cases. **Strengths:** "Very thoughtful, diligent and hard-working, he's someone you can really rely on." **Recent work:** Acted for ITV2 in defence of a claim brought by Mr H TV (formerly Can Associates TV) over the termination of production agreements for three reality TV shows featuring, separately, Kerry Katona and Peter Andre. ITV2 alleges that the production company acted in breach of contract, pursuant to which the production agreements were terminated.

Ben Valentin Joined Fountain Court from South Square Chambers in 2014. He is well regarded for commercial litigation in the banking and financial industries, and is experienced in representing offshore clients in the BVI and the Cayman Islands. **Strengths:** "Provides sound advice combined with solid drafting and hard-hitting, persuasive advocacy." "Very user-friendly and approachable, he's a good team player and a smart lawyer." **Recent work:** Acted as sole counsel for the defendants in Weavering Macros Fixed Income Fund v Peterson & Ekstrom. In this matter the liquidators of a hedge fund brought claims for damages for breach of duty and wilful neglect or default against former non-executive directors.

James Cutress Has a broad commercial practice focusing on banking and finance disputes, aviation and insurance. Sources consistently praise him for his sound judgement and his client-facing skills. **Strengths:** "Incredibly reliable and hugely talented. He's a confident advocate who always receives good reviews from clients." **Recent work:** Acted as sole counsel for DVB Bank in a contested application in respect of loans made to IRISL subsidiaries.

Paul Sinclair A senior junior praised for his economical advisory style and strong advocacy skills. He has an international practice focusing on commercial disputes, and he frequently appears as sole counsel. **Strengths:** "He quickly picks up the issues and gets straight to the key points – he's good at stripping away anything that's irrelevant. Judges trust what he's saying, respect him and find it easy to agree with his arguments. He presents things very attractively." **Recent work:** Acted for Glengary in relation to its high-profile shareholder dispute with JKX Oil & Gas.

Adam Zellick Sought-after junior who is praised for both his advocacy and his drafting abilities. He handles civil fraud and aviation cases, and has a strong reputation for banking and finance disputes. **Strengths:** "Procedurally brilliant" and "a very good 'details man.'" **Recent work:** Acting as sole counsel for NatWest in relation to a multiparty dispute over approximately £40 million transferred to the bank during the partition of India in the late 1940s.

Edward Levey Senior junior with a wide-ranging international practice that takes in banking and finance, civil fraud and insurance disputes. Sources say he is "extremely bright" and "amazingly thorough." **Strengths:** "An extremely good cross-examiner." "He has a very relaxed and engaging manner, and judges seem to love him." **Recent work:** Acted with David Railton QC and Richard Power for Depfa Bank in a dispute with UBS and the Leipzig water authority relating to credit default swaps referencing collateralised debt obligations.

Alexander Milner (see p.673) A fluent Russian speaker and rising star, who has significant experience in cases involving Russia and the CIS. His practice covers commercial litigation, civil fraud and banking disputes, and he is particularly recognised for his expertise in aviation. **Strengths:** "Calm, efficient and a man with a no-nonsense approach." "He's easy to deal with and his advocacy and advice are both excellent." **Recent work:** Instructed by Vis Trading in an appeal to the Court of Appeal against a USD27 million judgment in favour of Nazarov. The dispute is governed entirely by Russian law.

Richard Power (see p.698) A well-regarded junior with a practice focusing on energy disputes and banking and finance cases. Sources praise him for his intellectual ability and user-friendliness. **Strengths:** "Very charming, mild and genial. He writes very well." **Recent work:** Led by David Railton QC for Depfa Bank in a dispute with UBS and the Leipzig water authority relating to credit default swaps referencing collateralised debt obligations.

David Murray (see p.679) A sought-after junior attracting instructions from top City law firms, particularly in the banking and finance field. He is praised for his ability to handle heavy, work-intensive disputes. **Strengths:** "Obviously very, very clever. He is a great team player and it's enormously helpful to have someone so affable on your team. He was happy to be phoned at any time." **Recent work:** Acted for Qatari prince Sheikh Mohammed Al-Thani in defence of claims by AH Baldwin & Sons and Bonhams relating to unpaid auction debts.

Rosalind Phelps A highly regarded junior with a busy commercial practice. She is particularly known for handling aviation, banking and finance, and civil fraud cases, and has growing expertise in cases with Russian and CIS elements. **Strengths:** "Very bright, very user-friendly and no-nonsense." **Recent work:** Represented Vincent Tchenguiz in significant compensation claims against the SFO arising from raids on his home and business premises which were declared unlawful by judicial review.

Rupert Allen Praised by instructing solicitors for his intellectual ability, approachability and responsiveness. His busy practice takes in insurance, telecoms and professional discipline matters among others. **Strengths:** "Extremely bright, he has a real eye for detail, and prepares for everything incredibly well so he's never taken by surprise. He knows the law inside-out and is extremely hard-working." **Recent work:** Acted for Kermas on claims against Merlin Mineral Resources alleging misuse of confidential information, disclosed during litigation between the parties in 2011, for the purpose of harming Kermas's commercial interests in the Republic of Burundi.

Simon Atrill A well-regarded junior with an international practice heavily focused on civil fraud and financial services disputes. **Strengths:** "His attention to detail was very impressive, as was the speed of his turnaround of papers." "Extremely reliable and responsive, he's able to provide confident, first-class advice." **Recent work:** Defended African Barrick Gold against claims brought by gold mining companies and their English parent company relating to injuries inflicted on a number of Tanzanian villagers.

Tamara Oppenheimer Hard-working and well liked by instructing solicitors, who consistently highlight her intellectual abilities and great attention to detail. Her practice covers, inter alia, professional negligence cases, and banking and finance disputes. **Strengths:** "A very hard worker who has a very can-do, pleasant attitude and a sense of humour." "Always produces quality work product, and she will tell you if she disagrees with you." **Recent work:** Acted for Texas Keystone in successfully defending a high-value claim concerning oil and gas concessions in Iraqi Kurdistan brought by Excalibur Ventures.

James McClelland Consistently attracts praise from instructing solicitors, who highlight his intellectual ability and excellent drafting skills. He is involved in heavyweight commercial cases, and wins instructions from top litigation law firms. **Strengths:** "Excellent on FCA contentious regulatory work. He's very diligent and a solid black letter lawyer whom it's a delight to work with as he produces a very polished work product." **Recent work:** Advised the successful principal defendant in the Supreme Court case of VTB Capital v Nutritek International & Malofeev.

3 Verulam Buildings

See profile on p.875

THE SET

3 Verulam Buildings is one of the capital's elite sets for commercial disputes, and houses an impressive array of practitioners at both silk and junior levels. Particularly known for banking work in the commercial litigation sphere, it has members who have handled some of the most high-profile and influential disputes of recent times in the financial services sector. Solicitors name the set as "one of the go-to chambers for high-level commercial and banking matters," and say: "It has the necessary strength and depth to assist us and our clients ably at every level." **Client service:** The clerking team, led by Paul Cooklin, is praised for its proactivity, responsiveness and commercial outlook. "The clerks are very good, very efficient, and good at getting back to you."

SILKS

Ali Malek QC A highly sought-after and impressive silk who handles both litigation and international arbitration. He is instructed on high-profile and high-value commercial disputes, and has particular experience in cases originating in Russia and the CIS. **Strengths:** "A fantastic barrister who is easy to work with, commercially astute and tactically very sound." "Very effective in cross-examination." **Recent work:** Represented Vasily Anisimov in the defence of a USD1.5 billion claim by the Patarkatsishvili family relating to the Metalloinvest mining company.

Ewan McQuater QC Highly experienced advocate with expertise in banking, restructuring and insolvency, and civil fraud. His commercial practice sees him attract weighty cases from magic and silver circle solicitors' firms, many of which have international elements. **Strengths:** "Focused, effective and clinical." "A specialist fraud operator whose forensic skills are of the highest quality." **Recent work:** Represented Fortress Value Recovery Fund in its case against Blue Skye Special Opportunities Fund and others. The case concerned an allegation of conspiracy in relation to an investment structure.

Adrian Beltrami QC Highly regarded by peers and instructing solicitors, particularly for financial sector and civil fraud work. Beltrami is as equally praised for his considered advice as he is for his assured advocacy. **Strengths:** "His understated approach can take the wind out of almost any opponent's sails." "His written work is always first-class and he is an extraordinarily powerful advocate. People recognise the force of his arguments." **Recent work:** Acted for RBS in its successful defence of claims by Torre Asset Funding relating to the bank's obligations under a syndicated loan agreement.

Jonathan Nash QC A popular choice for instructing solicitors, particularly for professional negligence disputes and cases involving insurance and the financial services. Sources consistently highlight his calm and client-friendly manner, and note the quality of his work for overseas clients. **Strengths:** "He is unflappable and always remains calm under any sort of pressure. I have never seen him rattled by anything." "He is very smooth and very good with clients. He's an affable individual with real skills." **Recent work:** Acted for Nigerian National Petroleum Corporation on the enforcement of a significant arbitral award arising out of the construction of a Niger Delta oil terminal.

Andrew Onslow QC Has an impressive international practice, handling both litigation and arbitration in a range of commercial sectors. As well as financial services matters, his recent work has included construction and renewable energy disputes. **Strengths:** "A very persuasive advocate with a nice, easy-going style, who interacts well with the judge." "Bright, approachable and extremely good in court. He takes seriously the importance of meeting or bettering the expectations of both professional and lay clients." **Recent work:** Represented several defendants in PJSC VAB v Makisomov & Others, a dispute over share ownership in a Ukrainian company.

Sonia Tolaney QC A respected and experienced advocate with particular expertise in representing banking clients. She is regularly instructed by top City firms on complex financial litigation. **Strengths:** "A serious presence at the Bar and a great strategist to have on your side." "She quickly earns the respect of solicitors and clients alike." **Recent work:** Acted for Deutsche Bank in its high-profile Commercial Court battle with Sebastian Holdings, which resulted in the dismissal of the latter's USD8 billion compensation claim and the award of substantial costs to Deutsche Bank.

Cyril Kinsky QC Active in civil fraud and professional negligence cases among others, and has notable experience in disputes arising in Russia and the CIS. He is highly regarded by instructing solicitors, who particularly appreciate his collaborative approach. **Strengths:** "He's very bright and gets stuck in. He's a fantastic team player." "Extremely able and very user-friendly." **Recent work:** Acted for Usarel Investments, as a defendant, in the BTA v Ablyazov litigation.

Paul Lowenstein QC A popular silk with instructing solicitors, particularly for commercial contract, banking and civil fraud disputes. He is regularly called upon for high-profile cases and significant international arbitrations. **Strengths:** "Very forensic, good in court, very good with clients and extremely commercial. An excellent QC." "He instils confidence and is a real team player." **Recent work:** Represented Baglan Zhunus in defence of a £100 million fraud claim made by Kazakhstan Kagazy.

Richard Salter QC Active in a range of commercial disputes, and is particularly noted for his banking and civil fraud work. Commentators praise him for his technical ability and superior knowledge of the law. **Recent work:** Acted for Tempo Group in a shareholder dispute over control of a Cayman Island company.

Andrew Sutcliffe QC A well-regarded silk with a broad commercial practice that encompasses banking, media, civil fraud and company disputes. Sources appreciate his collaborative approach, as well as his persuasive advocacy. **Strengths:** "He shows dedication to the case and is a real team player." "He manages his juniors very well, and is very personable." **Recent work:** Acted for multiple investors in a failed airport project in relation to the recovery of sums paid to solicitors in escrow.

John Odgers QC Active in financial services, professional negligence and civil fraud disputes. Sources are impressed by his user-friendliness and consistently praise him as being "very bright." **Strengths:** "Forensic and thorough, he has good judgement and a nice style in court. He's quietly insistent and persuasive." "Excellent on the detail – which he grasps incredibly quickly – very hands-on, practical and responsive." **Recent work:** Acted for Dutch Institutional Pension Fund on its EUR500 million damages claim against Goldman Sachs for alleged negligent management of funds.

Christopher Symons QC Handles a range of commercial disputes, and has particular experience in professional negligence, insurance and arbitration matters. **Recent work:** Acted on a claim brought by shipowners and their insurers against ship surveyors, which arose out of a shipyard fire.

Andrew Fletcher QC Handles a range of commercial disputes, with his recent work covering arbitrations, civil fraud cases and freezing injunctions. He has particular expertise in the shipping industry. **Strengths:** "He is very responsive and works very hard." "He has good judgement and is very conscientious." **Recent work:** Acted for a German bank on a freezing injunction application and arbitration in relation to the enforcement of its claims under a group of ten bareboat charters.

John Jarvis QC A well-regarded silk with an international commercial practice. Banking and arbitration are particular areas of strength, and he has recently received instructions originating in European, Asian, Middle Eastern and US jurisdictions. **Strengths:** "He is very able technically, he's perceptive, and he's good at assessing witness evidence. He has a quick turnaround, is very bright and obviously very knowledgeable." **Recent work:** Acted for a failed Icelandic bank on claims relating to derivatives contracts brought against a well-known bank.

Gregory Mitchell QC Acts on an extensive range of commercial disputes, including those with banking and finance, insurance, insolvency and civil fraud elements. **Strengths:** "He's very effective and very good at working with the team to get the right outcome." "He's technical but also shows good commerciality."

Jonathan Davies-Jones QC A relatively new silk whom instructing solicitors praise for his user-friendliness and intelligence. He is particularly active in banking disputes as well as general commercial matters. **Strengths:** "He is already establishing himself as an outstanding leading counsel. Highly intelligent, analytical and thorough; he's a pleasure to work with." "An excellent general commercial and banking lawyer." **Recent work:** Represented GDF SUEZ in relation to its approximately £100 million breach of warranty claim against Teesside Power following the sale and purchase of a power station.

David Quest QC Active in a range of commercial litigation matters and well regarded for civil fraud, professional negligence and financial services disputes. **Recent work:** Represented Dutch steel manufacturer Mercon in an approximately EUR30 million dispute with Bluewater over the construction of an offshore mooring system.

Matthew Hardwick QC A popular advocate with instructing solicitors, who has particular expertise in financial sector disputes, insolvency and company law. **Strengths:** "Well regarded and very easy to work with. He's very good with clients." "Both user-friendly and client-friendly." **Recent work:** Acted for Ennismore Management in defence of an approximately £3 million claim by a former employee. The dispute raised novel questions of rights to bonus sums managed by third-party trustees and of the clawing back of bonuses in the event of subsequent investment losses.

JUNIORS

Michael Lazarus Lauded by peers and instructing solicitors alike, who regard him as a "phenomenal" and "absolutely outstanding" senior junior. He is active in a range of commercial fields, and handles both domestic and international disputes. **Strengths:** "Very methodical, calm and easy to work with considering quite how clever he is. He is great on his feet." "He is just such a great academic lawyer." **Recent work:** Acted for Merchant International on an enforcement action against Naftogaz, following a Ukrainian court judgment and statutory suspension of enforcement in Ukraine.

Adam Kramer Acts on a range of commercial instructions, including banking, civil fraud and energy disputes. He is well regarded by both peers and instructing solicitors. **Recent work:** Led by Adrian Beltrami QC, he represented the second and third defendants in Benedetti v Sawiris. The claim related to a substantial commission arising out of an Italian telecoms deal.

James MacDonald (see p.659) A well-regarded and busy junior with a practice encompassing general commercial banking and finance, and arbitration matters. **Strengths:** "His advice was extremely accurate and his performance in court was exceptional." **Recent work:** Acted with Sonya Tolaney QC and David Foxton QC for Deutsche Bank in its successful and high-profile Commercial Court battle with Sebastian Holdings.

Laura John A bright and accomplished junior with a practice spanning commercial litigation, arbitration and financial services disputes. **Strengths:** "Has an excellent courtroom manner and delivers polished and thorough cross-examinations. Her work is structured and she is a good team player." "Good technical lawyer and a great advocate." **Recent work:** Acted for Ipsos Mori in relation to its software licensing claim against Aegis, arising out of the sale and purchase of shares in certain former Aegis companies.

Rajesh Pillai A well-known name in both litigation and arbitration, with particular expertise in banking, finance and civil fraud disputes. **Recent work:** Represented derivatives investors in an approximately EUR100 million fraud claim against spread-betting and contracts for difference provider IG Markets.

Peter Ratcliffe A highly regarded junior with a focus on media, professional negligence, banking and financial services disputes. **Strengths:** "A star of the junior Commercial Bar who is good on his feet." **Recent work:** Represented Tiku in relation to a Commercial Court claim by Diorite, arising out of the sale of energy and mineral commodities in Kazakhstan and Tajikistan.

Nicholas Craig An experienced advocate who has particular expertise in jurisdictional disputes, freezing orders and arbitration. **Strengths:** "Solid, proactive and commercial." **Recent work:** Acted for Desarrollo in an action seeking to enforce an Arizona court judgment against Kader Holdings in England.

David Head A popular and client-friendly junior with expertise in a range of commercial areas, including civil fraud, professional negligence, financial services and international arbitration. He has been particularly active in cases arising in, or involving parties in, the CIS. **Strengths:** "Provides good input on complicated professional negligence issues." "He has a very good manner with lay clients." **Recent work:** Acted as sole advocate for Ukrainian state oil and gas company Naftogaz in relation to its resistance of a USD20 million third-party debt order arising out of a bond issue.

Matthew Parker Robust and highly regarded junior, with a wide-ranging commercial practice. His instructions have included general commercial, financial services, civil fraud, energy and offshore disputes, as well as arbitrations. **Strengths:** "An impressive up-and-coming junior member of the Bar and an excellent advocate." "Very thorough and assured with clients." **Recent work:** Acted as sole advocate defending AllProperty Media in respect of an unsuccessful claim by Alegro Capital for payment of a corporate finance consultancy fee.

Peter de Verneuil Smith (see p.586) A very well-regarded junior, noted for his advocacy and intellectual ability. His practice encompasses general commercial litigation and arbitration. Financial services, insurance, civil fraud and company law matters all contribute to his caseload. **Strengths:** "Creative, responsive and smart." **Recent work:** Acted, with Ali Malek QC, on Gennadiy Bogolyubov's defence of claims brought by his former Rabbi, relating to whether or not two valuable properties fell under an alleged profit-sharing agreement.

Christopher Harris Maintains a robust domestic and international practice, and has particular experience in commercial contracts disputes, energy cases and arbitration. **Recent work:** Represented oil trading company Orlen Lietuva in a dispute with Proton relating to an abortive oil purchase transaction.

Sandy Phipps A popular junior with experience in banking and financial services disputes, as well as so-called 'oligarch' litigation. **Recent work:** Led by Ali Malek QC and Sonia Tolaney QC for Vasily Anisimov on the defence of allegations that he, along with Arkadi Patarkatsishvili, entered into an agreement to invest USD600 million in mining company MGOK.

Anne Jeavons An up-and-coming junior with a growing following of instructing solicitors. Her practice covers a range of commercial disputes, and she acts both as sole counsel and as a junior to silks. "Her submissions were concise and accurate, and she dealt well with things when on her feet. Quite understated, but everything she said was brilliant." **Recent work:** Acted as sole counsel for Ting on claims brought against Remedy Research alleging fraud, misrepresentation and breach of contract.

Band 2

Blackstone Chambers

See profile on p.771

THE SET

Blackstone boasts a strong bench of sought-after commercial counsel at both silk and junior level. Solicitors comment that the set has "some absolutely outstanding barristers" and note that the "juniors in chambers are consistently good." They appreciate not only the technical skill of members of chambers but also "their strategic, tactical approach and strong client service." Blackstone handles a wide variety of instructions including civil fraud cases, shareholder disputes, insurance claims and commercial contract matters. The set also has complementary expertise in regulatory matters, public law and the financial services sector.

Client service: "The clerking is very responsive, very flexible and highly commercial, and it makes a huge difference. Part of the reason I have worked with them so much is the effective clerking." Gary Oliver leads the team.

SILKS

Ian Mill QC A highly regarded silk noted for his robust advocacy and user-friendliness. Although known for his stellar reputation for media and entertainment work, he has a wide-ranging practice that covers sport, civil fraud, IP and partnership disputes. **Strengths:** "An intellectual bruiser who is good fun to work with and fantastic with clients." "You wouldn't want to be against him as he's a really, really clever operator who is incredibly bright and can think outside the box." **Recent work:** Acted for representative members of the UK record industry in claims against the major UK internet providers, requiring them to block subscriber access to BitTorrent tracker site The Pirate Bay.

Robert Anderson QC A popular silk with a busy practice spanning sports and media and entertainment disputes, among others. He is particularly noted for his expertise in civil fraud matters. **Strengths:** "Bright, thoughtful and unfailingly courteous." **Recent work:** Represented HSBC Securities Services defending claims brought by Interretire alleging mismanagement of an offshore pension scheme.

Barbara Dohmann QC A highly respected and experienced silk who is particularly highly regarded for her financial services and civil fraud cases. She has noted expertise in offshore disputes. **Strengths:** "She is hugely efficient and extremely quick. She is a hard-hitter who makes the case well and is very, very firm." "One of the most formidable advocates of recent generations." **Recent work:** Appeared in Blyumkin v Risc Management, a dispute concerning allegations of computer hacking and misuse of confidential information.

Robert Howe QC A respected silk known for his strong advocacy skills and ability to handle high-level, complex litigation. He is particularly noted for his media and entertainment sector expertise, as well as his work in civil fraud, employment and sport cases. **Strengths:** "He's incredibly bright and a real strategic thinker." "He's commanding in court." **Recent work:** Represented Cuccolini in a jurisdiction dispute with Elcan Industries, arising out of proceedings concerning the termination of a distribution agreement.

Pushpinder Saini QC A "class act" with a wide-ranging practice, spanning sport, civil fraud, media and entertainment, financial services and telecoms disputes. He is also highly regarded in the fields of administrative and public law and competition law. **Strengths:** "Thorough and positive, forthright and clear." "He is particularly good and knowledgeable in the regulatory field." **Recent work:** Appeared before the Court of Appeal in Harbinger Capital Partners v Caldwell, which concerned public law errors in relation to the valuation of Northern Rock.

Alan Maclean QC This well-regarded silk joins Blackstone from Brick Court Chambers. He wins praise from market commentators for both his cross-examination and client-facing skills. In addition to commercial litigation, he is experienced in administrative and public law. **Strengths:** "A clever and formidable junior silk who is particularly effective on fraud cases. Combines excellent client skills with robust and effective advocacy." **Recent work:** Represented mobile phone company Three in relation to a dispute with Huawei over contractual arrangements for network maintenance and development.

Thomas de la Mare QC A recent silk held in high regard by market commentators, who highlight his intellectual ability and creative approach. His practice spans media and entertainment, competition and public law cases, among others. **Strengths:** "He has an amazingly flexible mind, and is very good at producing creative solutions." "A thoroughly nice guy with a real presence about him. You can just tell when you speak to him that his mind is sparkling." **Recent work:** Represented a group of over 400 clients seeking compensation from BA for overcharging, following the air cargo cartel investigation.

Andrew Hunter QC Wins praise from peers and instructing parties for his assured advocacy and tactical ability. He is active across the banking and finance, financial services, and media and entertainment sectors, and has particular expertise in civil fraud cases. **Strengths:** "He is very good on his feet – he floats like a butterfly and stings like a bee." "He's hugely understated and massively effective. Judges just want to buy into his arguments." **Recent work:** Acted for London Capital Group as defendant in a contractual dispute over web-based ForEx trading.

Tom Weisselberg QC Took silk in 2014, having long been considered a leading junior for both commercial and media and entertainment work. He is held in high regard by market commentators for his strong advocacy skills. **Strengths:** "Very good and very smart." "He's thoroughly charming and extremely bright." **Recent work:** Represented the producer of 'Monty Python and the Holy Grail' in a dispute with Python (Monty) Pictures, concerning spin-off royalties for the musical 'Spamalot'.

JUNIORS

Andrew George He is particularly well regarded for financial services cases, and has a growing reputation in the civil fraud arena. Solicitors appreciate his user-friendliness, and praise him for being "hugely supportive." **Strengths:** "A very good team player who gives clear and succinct advice." "Good with clients, he really rolls his sleeves up and gets involved." **Recent work:** Represented MPL Homes in a multi-jurisdictional licensing dispute with Gordon Ramsay over 'Gordon Ramsay' branded merchandise.

Robert Weekes A well-regarded junior with a busy practice spanning commercial litigation, banking and finance disputes, and civil fraud cases. **Recent work:** Acted for Mongolian copper producer Erdenet Mining defending an accessory liability claim brought by Standard Bank in respect of loan transactions to The Just Group.

Shaheed Fatima An impressive junior with a strong international practice. She has a wide commercial litigation practice and particular expertise in conflicts of law cases. **Strengths:** "Absolutely brilliant." **Recent work:** Acted for Kader Holdings resisting the recognition and enforcement of a US judgment in England.

Mark Vinall Handles a diverse mix of commercial cases, and has particular expertise in banking and finance, and media and entertainment disputes. **Strengths:** "Fiendishly intelligent and extremely hard-working." "He's hugely experienced in financial services cases." **Recent work:** Led by Tom Weisselberg QC acting for the producer of 'Monty Python and the Holy Grail' in a dispute over spin-off royalties for the musical 'Spamalot'.

20 Essex Street

See profile on p.794

THE SET

Although traditionally known for its insurance, shipping and commodities work, 20 Essex Street has solidified its reputation in recent years as a serious player in the commercial litigation market. Members of chambers are regularly instructed on high-profile litigation and high-value international arbitrations. Recent instructions have originated in sectors as diverse as banking, telecoms, sports and aviation.

Client service: "The clerks were helpful and a good source of advice." Neil Palmer and Brian Lee lead the team.

SILKS

Iain Milligan QC Has a stellar reputation and is regarded as one of the leading silks in commercial litigation and arbitration. Sources consistently highlight his intellectual ability and outstanding advocacy skills. **Strengths:** "Hugely effective, fiercely clever, and clear and concise in court." "He is an absolute legal genius." **Recent work:** Appeared before the Supreme Court acting in the matter of 'Alexandros T', which concerned the operation of Articles 27 and 28 of the Brussels Regulation.

Andrew Baker QC Well regarded for his broad commercial practice, which spans banking and finance, and shipping and commodities work. **Strengths:** "Someone who puts in a huge amount of work, and proves utterly compelling in court." **Recent work:** Represented Cargill International in arbitration and at appeal. The case concerned a dispute with NYK Bulkship (Atlantic) relating to the construction of a common off-hire clause and the scope of an employment clause in a common time charter form.

Philip Edey QC A very highly regarded silk with a strong reputation for handling insurance, shipping and commodities cases. His is praised by market commentators for his assured and engaging advocacy. **Strengths:** "He is incredibly able" and has an "enormous reputation for his appellate and Supreme Court work. He is a very, very superior advocate." **Recent work:** Represented Hut Group in its claim for breach of warranty arising out of a business sale and purchase transaction.

Duncan Matthews QC A silk who continues to impress market commentators with his quick understanding and robust advocacy skills. He is particularly noted for his work in shipping, commodities and civil fraud cases. **Strengths:** "He's a very strong advocate who has a very, very good understanding of arbitration tribunals. He's a very smooth performer." "He works very hard and is just fantastic – there are no chinks in his armour." **Recent work:** Represented Mukhtar Ablyazov in relation to a high-profile fraud dispute with BTA Bank.

Charles Kimmins QC An impressive recent silk with a strong reputation for his work in shipping and commodities cases, who also handles banking and finance cases. **Strengths:** "He is extremely bright, very hands-on and very much a team player." **Recent work:** Acted for RMA in relation to a claim for breach of agency agreement in respect of logistics services in Afghanistan.

David Lewis QC Took silk in 2014, an appointment widely supported by market commentators. He is particularly recommended for his expertise in shipping and commodities cases, and is known for the strength of his international arbitration practice. **Strengths:** "An advocate who displays effortless charm." "Very good with the clients, he's supportive and really does make you feel like he's fighting your corner." **Recent work:** Acted for Addax Energy in its claim against Fueltrade relating to non-performance of a crude oil sale contract.

JUNIORS

Thomas Raphael Highly regarded for his cerebral and knowledgeable approach to substantial commercial cases, particularly those in the financial sector. His practice also covers shipping and commodities disputes. **Strengths:** "Outstandingly bright and always seems to be a couple of steps ahead of everyone. His paperwork is outstandingly good." **Recent work:** Acted for ATTL, an arm of Alfa, on its multi-jurisdictional dispute with Cukurova over the ownership of Turkcell.

Band 3

7 King's Bench Walk

See profile on p.827

THE SET

7KBW is traditionally known for its shipping and insurance work, but has established its reputation in the commercial market generally as a result of the high quality of its silks. Commodities, insurance and professional negligence cases remain the bedrock of its practice, and the set has also received recent instructions on energy, shareholder, fraud and financial products disputes.

Client service: "The clerking there is very good. The clerks take the time to get to know you and the way you work, and their recommendations have always been good. That really influences my purchasing decisions as a solicitor." Bernie Hyatt and Greg Leyden serve as joint senior clerks.

SILKS

Jonathan Gaisman QC Ascends to star status in the rankings on the back of his involvement in some of the most high-profile and heavyweight commercial instructions of the past year. He has an outstanding reputation among instructing solicitors, who say he is a "tremendously bright, energetic and hard-working" advocate who "cross-examines like a bulldozer." **Strengths:** "Terrifyingly clever. He's an utterly fantastic lawyer; an enormously impressive guy with a really supreme mind." "He is completely on top of the detail and has a style which is robust and gets to the heart of the issue." **Recent work:** Instructed for RBS and four directors, in relation to the defence of significant shareholder claims arising out of a £12 billion rights issue.

Christopher Butcher QC Widely respected in the market, particularly for his specialist shipping and insurance practice. He is also well versed in banking and finance cases. **Strengths:** "He is unsurpassed in terms of his knowledge of reinsurance. He exudes confidence, knows the cases and is easy to work with." **Recent work:** Acted for Equitas in a claim against brokers Walsham Brothers for monies which had been received under contracts of insurance but had not been passed on.

Gavin Kealey QC Highly regarded in the commercial litigation and arbitration worlds, especially for his work on insurance disputes and aviation cases. Sources highlight his thorough, hands-on approach to litigation. **Strengths:** "His presentation is absolutely superb." "He is spectacularly smart, a fantastic advocate and a masterful examiner of witnesses. He works very hard and is very well prepared." **Recent work:** Led for British American Tobacco in a claim against Windward Prospects and Appleton Papers for indemnity against potential liabilities arising out of the pollution of the Fox and Kalamazoo rivers.

Rebecca Sabben-Clare QC A silk with a particularly strong reputation in insurance work. Market commentators praise her for being client-friendly and extremely hard-working. **Strengths:** "She is extremely bright and gives commercial and forthright advice. She works very hard and is a pleasure to have on a team." **Recent work:** Was part of the team acting for Cattles in its £1.6 billion claim against PwC for negligence in respect of its 2006 and 2007 financial statements audits.

Clive Freedman QC A well-regarded and tenacious advocate who wins praise for his "dedication to cases," which sources describe as being "second to none." His practice covers both commercial and civil fraud cases. **Strengths:** "He has a very impressive intellect and is extremely good in court." "He's bright, has good knowledge of the law, and is great at devising a strategy." **Recent work:** Appeared for Daad Sharab in his successful claim against a Saudi prince for commission relating to the sale of an aircraft.

JUNIORS

James Brocklebank A highly regarded senior junior who wins praise for his expertise in insurance and professional negligence cases. **Strengths:** "Phenomenally intelligent." **Recent work:** Acted for Primary Capital in its professional negligence claim against Ernst & Young, arising out of a financial due diligence exercise.

Maitland Chambers

See profile on p.831

THE SET

Maitland Chambers continues to win significant, cross-border and high-value commercial instructions from international and City firms. The set's long-standing reputation for chancery and offshore work is well known, and it proves very good on cases which are cross-disciplinary in nature. Members of this chambers are praised for their thorough preparation and persuasive advocacy.

SILKS

Paul Girolami QC A highly regarded silk, known for his expertise in company law, restructuring and insolvency, offshore and civil fraud matters. **Strengths:** "He is a very attractive advocate who has a knack for putting points in the most appealing way possible."

Anthony Trace QC A popular silk with a longstanding reputation in commercial and chancery cases. **Strengths:** "He has a very disarming courtroom manner. He's conversational but, at the same time, very compelling. He's a joy to listen to." **Recent work:** Instructed by investment bank Bank Alkhair and property development company Dar Al Arkan in a high-profile conspiracy claim against Al Refai, Kroll Associates UK and FTI Consulting Group.

Matthew Collings QC Particularly noted for his expertise in commercial chancery work generally, including company law and civil fraud cases. He is well regarded among instructing solicitors, who praise him for his robust style of advocacy. **Strengths:** "Bright and always fun to work with." "He has a knack for finding creative but practical solutions to complex legal issues." **Recent work:** Appeared in a dispute between Office Depot Inc and Office Depot (Israel) over a share purchase agreement.

Jonathan Russen QC A well-regarded silk with a reputation for user-friendliness among instructing solicitors. His practice is broad in nature, and he is particularly celebrated for his financial services work. **Strengths:** "Provided clear, concise advice on a dispute with a complex matrix of facts. He is able to see woods for the trees." "He is so thoughtful and considerate of clients' personal needs during the course of difficult litigation. People really feel safe with him." **Recent work:** Acted for Mountain Sky Resources in a claim concerning the dilution of its shareholdings in a Hong Kong public company.

Edmund Cullen QC Recent silk with a diverse commercial practice and a reputation for the high quality of his written work. He is particularly noted for his expertise in IP cases relating to the media and entertainment industries. **Strengths:** "Shows meticulous attention to detail and has an unflinching determination to get to the right result. He works exceptionally hard and provides tremendous value for money." **Recent work:** Acted for Banwaitt in a fraud claim against Dewji, relating to a Cambodian hotel development joint venture.

John McGhee QC Attracts praise from peers and instructing parties alike for his intellectual ability and clear, commercial advice. He has particular expertise in relation to property and insolvency matters. **Strengths:** "Hugely impressive. He has incredible gravitas and can crunch through volumes of material with great speed and clarity of thought." "A fantastic lawyer who is very clever, very sensible and very quick." **Recent work:** Acted in a dispute between the seller, purchaser and dealer of a painting, which involved proceedings in England and New York.

Richard Morgan QC Has a strong reputation among instructing solicitors for his user-friendliness and his firm advocacy style. He is particularly well regarded for his work in relation to civil fraud matters. **Strengths:** "Very good with clients, and very good at delivering a hard message in a way that they will accept. He also has solid analytical skills, and you come away feeling confident about the advice he's given." "A freezing order specialist, with an encyclopaedic knowledge and grasp of the technicalities and procedure in this field." **Recent work:** Represented HSBC in a debt enforcement claim in the Isle of Man.

JUNIORS

David Mumford A leading commercial chancery junior, consistently tipped as "a rising star" by market commentators. He is a favourite of instructing solicitors and senior barristers for a range of commercial work, including civil fraud and banking and finance cases. **Strengths:** "Very clever and analytical, he has excellent judgement and a calm manner." "Extremely bright, client-friendly and approachable." **Recent work:** Acted as sole advocate for Cosmote in defence of contractual claims brought by Telekom Slovenije relating to the sale of a mobile phone business operating in Macedonia.

Ciaran Keller An impressive junior praised by market commentators for being client-friendly, diligent and "one to watch." **Strengths:** "Very bright and client-friendly, he turns papers round quickly." "He has excellent judgement and is user-friendly." **Recent work:** Led by Joe Smouha QC for Noble, in defence of substantial claims brought by Barnsley for breach of contract, misrepresentation, deceit and breach of duty arising out of the demerger of the two groups of companies.

Benjamin John A popular junior for all manner of commercial chancery cases. Sources particularly appreciate his high-quality written work. **Strengths:** "A hard-working, analytical team player who produces high-quality work." **Recent work:** Part of the team acting in the high-profile conspiracy claim brought by Bank Alkhair and property development company Dar Al Arkan against Al Refai, Kroll Associates UK and FTI Consulting Group.

4 Pump Court

See profile on p.849

THE SET

4 Pump Court's growing commercial disputes practice sees it enter the rankings this year. It undertakes a string of substantial and international cases, and has barristers who have an excellent reputation for handling technology, professional negligence, construction and energy disputes, to name but a few. Its wealth of experience in these areas ensures that it represents an attractive prospect to instructing solicitors.

Client service: "You get great clerking from them that really makes a difference." "The clerks are always very switched-on and supportive." Carl Wall and Stewart Gibbs lead the clerking team.

SILKS

Nigel Tozzi QC An impressive silk with a strong and diverse practice that takes in insurance, shipping, energy, IT and professional negligence cases. Sources praise his effective advocacy style and instructing solicitors consider him "a gifted QC." **Strengths:** "He is good on his feet and keeps the submissions going at a good clip. He is not the sort of guy that loses the interest of the judge, and he's very good at cross-examination." "You've got to make sure your armour is up when you're against him." **Recent work:** Represented energy trader Vitol in claims against Sterling for breach of contract in respect of an oil sale agreement.

Michael Douglas QC Particularly noted for his specialism in technology and professional negligence cases, he has a reputation for adopting a collaborative approach and being highly user-friendly. **Strengths:** "Had the ear of the court and retained a sense of humour even in the most trying times." "He was very good, very focused, very efficient and concise in the submissions he made." **Recent work:** Acted for the defendant in connection with claims by the government of Brazil concerning the proceeds of frauds committed by the former mayor of São Paulo.

Christopher Moger QC An experienced advocate who handles numerous commercial cases, and proves particularly strong on insurance work. He is particularly recognised for his expertise in professional negligence cases. **Recent work:** Appeared in Alpha Construction v Barclays Wealth Trustees (Guernsey), a substantial claim in which the defendants are alleged to have been negligent in respect of the administration services provided to an offshore group of companies.

Alexander Gunning QC A silk with a broad-based practice that takes in shipping and commodities, and energy and natural resources cases. He regularly handles a wide range of international arbitrations, and is well regarded by peers and instructing solicitors alike. **Recent work:** Acted for Russian-owned Vis in connection with fraud claims brought against Ansol and its director, Avaz Nazarov.

Sean O'Sullivan QC Took silk in 2014, having established an excellent reputation as a junior for his handling of energy, shipping and commodities industries. He is also particularly noted for his international arbitration practice. **Strengths:** "He is 'Mr Sensible' and keeps everyone grounded. The advice he gives is very good and commercial." "He is technically outstanding, responsive and very user-friendly. His bedside manner with clients is also excellent." **Recent work:** Appeared in Wuhan v Emporiki Bank, a case relating to the operation of a shipbuilding payment guarantee.

JUNIORS

Benjamin Pilling A popular senior junior noted for his expertise in construction and professional negligence matters, as well as IT disputes. Sources consistently highlight the quality of his drafting. **Strengths:** "He is very good on paper, and has a clear and crisp writing style. He has a very clear way of viewing things and is excellent at expressing those views." **Recent work:** Acted for Simmons & Simmons in a substantial claim to recover fees brought against a former client.

Luke Wygas A well-regarded junior who handles a variety of commercial cases. He has a background in construction and sources appreciate his "good technical understanding" in this area. **Recent work:** Appeared at first instance and before the Court of Appeal in the 'punt wars' dispute, a case concerning the right to punt on the River Cam.

Quadrant Chambers

See profile on p.854

THE SET

Quadrant has an excellent reputation and a loyal following of leading instructing solicitors. Its superlative shipping, travel and aviation expertise serves it well, and it proves particularly strong on contractual disputes and multi-jurisdictional cases. Sources particularly appreciate the set's progressive and co-ordinated approach to client service, saying: "There's a lot of cohesion between counsel and clerk, and they present themselves as a team."

Client service: "They 'get' customer service. They always seem to make counsel available to us, and hold conferences at our lay clients' offices. The level of assistance from Gary Ventura, Simon Slattery and the rest of the clerking team is key to maintaining our relationship with the set."

SILKS

Simon Rainey QC Maintains a strong reputation in the market for his commercial work, and has particular expertise in shipping, commodities and energy-related matters. Sources praise him for being highly knowledgeable and user-friendly. **Strengths:** "A strong player" who "doesn't sit on the fence. He takes a view and justifies it with ease." **Recent work:** Acted for Archer Daniels Midland in a claim against Tarif Akhras, a prominent member of Bashar Al Assad's family, relating to grain importation into Syria.

Stephen Cogley QC Well regarded for commercial and insurance-related disputes, and has experience in insolvency, civil fraud, shipping and commodities cases. His practice covers both domestic and international cases. **Strengths:** "An unrelenting advocate who is perfect for the most difficult and challenging cases." "A determined advocate who is client-friendly and accessible." **Recent work:** Appeared in Integral Petroleum v SCU Finanz, an oil trading dispute.

Guy Blackwood QC Took silk in 2014. Sources praise him as a responsive and effective counsel, with particular experience in commercial, shipping and insurance cases. **Recent work:** Acted for Taurus Petroleum on its claim against the State Oil Ministry of Iraq, a case which reduces the scope of the state immunity in the context of commodities trading.

JUNIORS

Jeremy Richmond Well regarded by instructing solicitors, he has a strong commercial chancery practice. **Strengths:** "Impressive with clients and really sharp in terms of his work – it's hard to think how he could be better as a litigator. He's excellent on his feet and good tactically." "He's not afraid of a fight when handling cases that are difficult to get off the ground, and is good at dealing with aggressive counsel on the other side." **Recent work:** Acted in a dispute between FG Wilson (now Caterpillar NI) and John Holt, relating to international sale of goods and retention of title clauses.

Robert-Jan Temmink An impressive senior junior with a broad commercial practice, covering both litigation and arbitration. Sources particularly praise him for his assured advocacy and strong courtroom presence. **Strengths:** "He has a very nice presentational style and judges listen to him." "He is very tidy on the paperwork, very inclusive, and has a very modern way of working." **Recent work:** Acted for a partner of a well-known law firm in defence of allegations of conspiracy and fraud pertaining to an arbitration in the shipping industry.

Gemma Morgan A bright and hard-working up-and-comer, noted for her commercial expertise and particular interest in shipping cases. **Recent work:** Acted for the owners of a vessel on a product liability claim against Renold Power Transmission, arising out of damage caused when chains inside the vessel's engine broke.

Serle Court

See profile on p.860

THE SET

Has a superb reputation in general commercial chancery, offshore and civil fraud cases, and remains a go-to set for the most complicated corporate and commercial disputes. The set has a substantial bench of respected and well-liked barristers at all levels of seniority. Sources say: "This is a fantastic chancery commercial set, with a real strength in fraud work."

Client service: "The clerks are always very, very helpful." "I was looking for a particular specialism and they went to a lot of effort to find the right people for me." Steve Whitaker heads the clerking team.

SILKS

Alan Boyle QC Commands a strong reputation in the market for his company and commercial work, and has a particular focus on offshore and trusts cases. He remains a firm favourite among instructing solicitors. **Strengths:** "He is fantastically focused and committed and always offers an excellent service, striking a perfect balance between being sympathetic with clients and utterly combative on their behalf in court." "Has vast experience and provides clear, authoritative advocacy." **Recent work:** Appeared in disputes arising out of the high-profile Madoff fraud.

Philip Jones QC A highly regarded commercial chancery practitioner whose practice encompasses tax, restructuring and insolvency, civil fraud and professional negligence cases. **Strengths:** "He has a calm and confident manner, and is very good at drawing out the most significant points of an argument. He puts the lay client at ease and commands the attention of the court." "He has superb judgement and is bright, hard-working and accessible." **Recent work:** Represented BTA Bank in its high-profile claim against Mukhtar Ablyazov and others.

Philip Marshall QC Known for his robust advocacy and effective cross-examining. His practice spans company, civil fraud, and restructuring and insolvency cases. Much of his work is done offshore. **Strengths:** "He's goal-oriented in terms of understanding what the client is looking to achieve, and will take robust decisions and find nuanced, calculated means of achieving those aims. He will use his immense legal knowledge to get you the practical result you're looking for." "Spots the weakness in the other side's position and goes on the attack. Watching him cross-examine a witness – it's like they do it in the films." **Recent work:** Acted for Constantin Medien in its high-profile claim against Bernie Ecclestone, alleging conspiracy and bribery in the context of its sale.

Lance Ashworth QC (see p.538) A popular silk with a broad commercial chancery practice who is highlighted for his strong advocacy skills. **Strengths:** "He's a joy to work with and thinks outside the box." "He has very good attention to detail and is very solicitor-friendly." **Recent work:** Acted for Merlin Associates in successfully resisting a claim for injunctive relief seeking to prohibit the opening of Chessington World of Adventures.

Nicholas Lavender QC (see p.652) An intellectual silk praised for his technical ability and capacity for handling complex cases. His practice spans both commercial and chancery work, and he has a particular focus on banking and finance disputes. **Strengths:** "Enormously intelligent and extremely hard-working, he shows exquisite judgement." "Lovely to deal with, and very much a details person." **Recent work:** Acted for Constant Capital Markets & Securities defending claims brought by a Nigerian bank for restitution and/or enforcement of repo agreements.

John Machell QC A very highly regarded silk with a strong commercial chancery practice, who is a recognised expert on partnership cases. **Strengths:** "Offers commercial and pragmatic advice, and always integrates himself into the team." "A hugely impressive operator, he is a hard-working barrister with razor-sharp intelligence and an incisive eye for detail." **Recent work:** Acted on a joint venture dispute between Hitchcox and Handelsman relating to a property development at St Pancras station.

Hugh Norbury QC A popular recent silk who has particular expertise in civil fraud cases. Sources particularly appreciate him for his user-friendliness. **Recent work:** Represented Macquarie in a substantial dispute with EPIC relating to whether or not an investment adviser's fee is properly payable under an investment agreement.

Elizabeth Jones QC Attracts praise from peers and instructing parties alike for her assured advocacy and command of the details of a case. She is particularly known for her experience in offshore matters. **Strengths:** "Extremely well respected." "I was able to go down and see her and explain the intricacies of my market, and she soaked everything up. She was also seemingly available any time of day or night." **Recent work:** Advised a Middle Eastern company in relation to a dispute with a car manufacturer.

Jonathan Adkin QC An up-and-coming recent silk with a strong reputation for commercial chancery work, who is very active offshore. **Strengths:** "He's a brilliant advocate who offers good judgement and good analysis. Judges like him and he pitches the case just right." "He inspires confidence at every turn and is able to cut through the most complex disputes with ease." **Recent work:** Appeared in Patarkatsishvili v Anisimov, acting for SFR Solutions, respondent to a third-party disclosure application.

David Blayney QC Attracts praise from peers and instructing parties alike for the quality of his commercial chancery work. His practice spans company, partnership, and banking and finance cases among others. **Strengths:** "He is an incredibly clever technical lawyer who is very understated but quite brilliant. He says little, but when he speaks he always says something that adds a new dimension to the way one is thinking about things." "Extremely bright and a pleasure to work with." **Recent work:** Acted for Constantin Medien in its high-profile claim against Bernie Ecclestone, alleging conspiracy and bribery in the context of its sale.

JUNIORS

Daniel Lightman A bright and innovative junior with an excellent reputation for company law and restructuring and insolvency in particular. **Strengths:** "Bright, enthusiastic and insightful." "He has an outstanding brain, is tremendously hard-working and likes to be very involved in every aspect of the case." **Recent work:** Acted for Yasmin Prest in a Supreme Court case concerning whether family courts can pierce the corporate veil to access beneficially owned assets in divorce proceedings.

Justin Higgo A highly regarded and personable senior junior, known for his robust advocacy style and user-friendliness. He has a good reputation for commercial chancery work, and is particularly recognised for his expertise in civil fraud cases. **Strengths:** "Extraordinarily focused and talented, as well as great fun to work with." "He's scarily clever." **Recent work:** Appeared in Bank of St Petersburg v Arkhangelsky, a dispute concerning allegedly forged bank guarantees.

Ruth Holtham den Besten A well-known commercial chancery barrister who is strong on civil fraud cases. Sources stress her intellectual ability and robust advocacy. **Strengths:** "Bright, incisive and approachable." **Recent work:** Represented Patrick Mc-

Killen in a high-profile dispute concerning Coroin, which owns Claridge's, The Connaught and The Berkeley hotels.

Wilberforce Chambers
See profile on p.876
THE SET
Wilberforce is "a really strong set with some very powerful people in it." Its members have extensive experience in international disputes and cases heard in foreign jurisdictions, and are particularly well versed in civil fraud and professional negligence matters.
Client service: "Very professional and very easy to deal with, the clerks adopt a team approach. When talking about fees, I get a straightforward answer." Mark Rushton heads the clerking team here.

SILKS
Ian Croxford QC A seasoned silk with a strong reputation for commercial chancrey work generally, and civil fraud and professional negligence disputes in particular. **Strengths:** "A classic trial advocate who is absolutely superb on his feet."

Terence Mowschenson QC A well-regarded silk in commercial chancery disputes. **Strengths:** "Very user-friendly and a very persuasive, charming and forceful advocate." **Recent work:** Acted for Crédit Agricole in its successful appeal of a ruling on the enforceability of a Greek judgment in Gibraltar. The case arose out of allegations by the Michailidis family that the bank received proceeds of misappropriated monies.

John Wardell QC Has a strong reputation in civil fraud and professional negligence cases. Market commentators praise him for his tenacious advocacy and his strategic ability. **Strengths:** "An outstanding advocate who is highly skilled at cross-examination. He is able to digest large volumes of information quickly and impresses clients with his commercial knowledge." "He's a very clever tactician." **Recent work:** Acted for the defendants in a high-profile shareholder dispute over FiCall, in which Prince Abdulaziz and other Global Torch shareholders faced allegations of gross misconduct made by a Jordanian business partner.

Other Ranked Lawyers

Roger ter Haar QC (Crown Office Chambers) A sought-after silk with a substantial international practice. He is known for his forceful and effective advocacy, and is highly regarded for handling construction and professional negligence matters. **Strengths:** "His principal strengths lie in his penetrating, versatile and at times devastating cross-examining skills, his ability to marshal facts, and his facility for knowing the brief better than the witnesses put before him." **Recent work:** Appeared in Dhanani v Crasnianski, a case concerning the formation of a private equity fund.

Ben Lynch (Devereux) A popular junior with instructing solicitors, who consistently praise him for being hard-working and client-friendly. He has a broad commercial practice that spans telecoms, insurance and professional negligence disputes. **Strengths:** "Approachable and client-friendly, he is an excellent communicator and a man with a sharp mind."

James Barker (Enterprise Chambers) An impressive senior junior with a strong reputation in banking and real estate litigation. Sources appreciate his ability to communicate equally well in court and with lay clients. **Strengths:** "A strong and capable counsel." **Recent work:** Acted for Bank of Scotland in a claim against a partnership for the recovery of an outstanding loan.

Linden Ife (Enterprise Chambers) A well-regarded senior junior with significant courtroom experience. Sources consistently highlight her effective and forceful advocacy. **Strengths:** "A formidable advocate who is never intimidated and has no difficulty arguing against silks. She's very robust, shows great judgement, and is very quick with papers." **Recent work:** Appeared for two defendants to damages claims brought by over 400 owners and lessees of defective TX4 taxis.

Stephen Smith QC (Erskine Chambers) Highly regarded for his commercial chancery work, he has a reputation as a leading silk in the field of civil fraud. He wins praise from market commentators for his ability to handle the most challenging of briefs. **Strengths:** "He works hard and the Court of Appeal just loves him." **Recent work:** Appeared as lead counsel for BTA Bank in relation to its high-profile fraud dispute with former members of its senior management, in which it sought to recover USD5 billion.

Richard Snowden QC (Erskine Chambers) A well-regarded silk with a strong commercial practice, who has a stellar reputation with regard to company and insolvency cases, and further significant expertise in banking and finance disputes. **Strengths:** "Tough, creative and hard-working. He's very bright and one of the first ports of call for a serious corporate dispute." **Recent work:** Acted for RBS defending claims relating to the alleged sale at undervalue of Liverpool FC.

David Chivers QC (Erskine Chambers) An accomplished and authoritative advocate with an excellent reputation for handling company and insolvency cases. **Strengths:** "He has this wonderful ability to distil the essence of a case and present it with real force and elegance." "He's eye-wateringly bright." **Recent work:** Acted for New England Sports Ventures, the current owners of Liverpool FC, in relation to the high-profile dispute over the club's sale.

James Potts QC (Erskine Chambers) Has an excellent reputation among instructing parties for his technical ability, efficiency and high-quality drafting. He focuses on company and commercial disputes, and is an expert on matters relating to fiduciary duties, partnership, restructuring and insolvency, joint ventures and professional negligence. **Strengths:** "Simply first-class." "He's an excellent advocate, who is easy to work with." **Recent work:** Appeared before the Court of Appeal in a dispute between Clearwell International and MSL Group Holdings, concerning a claim for unpaid fees.

Tim Akkouh (Erskine Chambers) Wins praise from market sources for his strong advocacy skills and approachability. His practice spans the full range of commercial and chancery matters, including civil fraud cases. **Strengths:** "His advocacy was brilliant and his cross-examination was masterful. He has an easy-going, confident manner with clients, and gives comfort to them without affording them unrealistic expectations." **Recent work:** Appeared in the dispute between Glencore and Clarendon Alumina Production Resources and Noble Resources, relating to contracts for the delivery of alumina.

Hodge Malek QC (Thirty Nine Essex Street) A well-known name at the Commercial Bar, particularly in relation to financial services, professional discipline and civil fraud cases. Sources praise him for being an assured advocate and a good team player. **Strengths:** "He is supremely diligent and a top-class litigator." "When it comes to dealing with freezing injunctions and matters pertaining to the Middle East there's no need to look any further than him." **Recent work:** Instructed in Harrison v Black Horse, a case relating to payment protection insurance in the context of the Consumer Credit Act.

James Ramsden (Thirty Nine Essex Street) Highly regarded for his commercial, client-friendly advice and known for his ability in civil fraud proceedings. Solicitors and peers alike consider him to be an accomplished advocate. **Strengths:** "Very charming and technically strong. He tells it like it is." "He's very good with clients and very commercially focused." **Recent work:** Acted as sole counsel for Konstantin Kagalovsky and Wilcox Ventures in relation to proceedings in the Commercial Court in Kyiv and the Commercial Court in London, seeking the recovery of ownership of the independent Ukrainian media outlet TVi.

PJ Kirby QC (Hardwicke) A respected and experienced recent silk known for his expertise in professional negligence cases, commercial employment cases and costs litigation. **Strengths:** "Provides excellent strategic and legal advice," and is "very user-friendly. He gives clear commercial advice." **Recent work:** Acted in a dispute between Starlight Shipping and its former solicitors, in which a former partner of the defendant law firm is admitted to have doctored hearings transcripts prior to their supply to Starlight Shipping.

David Lewis (see p.655) (Hardwicke) A respected senior junior with significant advocacy experience and a collaborative, client-friendly approach. He has strength in civil fraud cases, and is particularly strong on restrictive covenants injunction and commercial agency cases. **Strengths:** "Great to work with, very sharp and very responsive." **Recent work:** Advised litigation funder Buttonwood Legal Capital on the merits of a claim it was funding. The withdrawal of funding was subsequently upheld in High Court proceedings.

Stuart Ritchie QC (Littleton Chambers) Widely praised for his pragmatism, client-friendliness, and technical and strategic ability. His practice covers a raft of commercial areas, including partnership disputes and civil fraud cases. **Strengths:** "Brilliant both as an advocate and as a technical lawyer." "He gets on very well with clients and other members of the team, and is incredibly impressive." **Recent work:** Acted for Al Refai defending conspiracy and breach of confidence claims brought by Saudi Arabian property development Dar Al Arkan.

Jonathan Cohen (Littleton Chambers) A well-regarded senior junior with notable experience in international commercial disputes, particularly those with Russian and CIS elements. He is also noted for having considerable expertise and experience in employment cases. **Recent work:** Acted for Kazakh mining company ENRC in its high-profile dispute with Sir Paul Judge. ENRC alleged that the former director leaked confidential information and attempted to undermine the company's commercial reputation.

David Lascelles (Littleton Chambers) A hard-working, thorough and technically accomplished junior with considerable experience as a sole advocate. He has a robust corporate and commercial practice, and has particular expertise in contractual litigation, shareholder disputes and civil fraud cases. **Strengths:** "Very hard-working and has a nice manner. He's very easy to deal with and considers everything very thoroughly." "He has an excellent grasp of legal issues, is incredibly diligent and has good client skills." **Recent work:** Acted for healthcare staffing provider Medacs Healthcare in defence of claims brought by Acolyte Resource Group alleging engagement in a contract and subsequent wrongful termination.

Antony White QC (Matrix Chambers) Consistently receives praise from market commentators for his "ability to turn his hand to pretty much anything." Instructing solicitors routinely entrust him with complex and challenging cases, particularly those with data privacy dimensions. **Strengths:** "He is a very high-quality commercial silk who is extremely thorough and who always provides excellent commercial advice. He is extremely bright and always sees the bigger picture. In addition, he is always a pleasure to work with." **Recent work:** Appeared in Orb and others v Ruhan, a high-value dispute over commercial property.

Justin Fenwick QC (4 New Square) A leading silk with a broad commercial practice encompassing construction, insurance, product liability, civil fraud and offshore disputes. He attracts praise for his tactical acumen and robust advocacy, and is particularly known for his prowess in professional negligence cases. **Strengths:** "Calm in a crisis and a clear thinker." "He's excellent on the strategy and tactics of a case, and he is good at looking ahead." **Recent work:** Appeared in the high-profile and high-value dispute between Cattles and PwC in which the claimant sought £1.4 billion in damages for alleged negligence in the auditing of the Welcome Financial Services group.

Anneliese Day QC (4 New Square) Wins widespread praise from market commentators for her thorough and collaborative approach, strong work ethic and excellent client-facing skills. She is particularly experienced in disputes with construction and professional negligence elements. **Strengths:** "Hard-working, very bright and a pleasure to deal with, she's tough and impressive on her feet." "She reassured our clients and made insightful comments on their position from an early stage." **Recent work:** Acted for the Port of Sheerness in a dispute with Vestas Offshore UK concerning an option agreement which the latter sought to terminate.

Ben Elkington QC (4 New Square) A popular and client-friendly silk known for his expertise in commercial disputes, including professional negligence matters and insurance cases. **Strengths:** "An exceptionally able, persuasive and always reliable commercial silk." "He understands what commercial clients need, and can speak their language in a non-patronising way. His attention to detail is excellent and he comes up with curveball ideas that actually work." **Recent work:** Acted for estate agent Spicerhaart on defending a contractual claim brought by Tesco concerning a failed joint venture to launch an online estate agency.

George Spalton (4 New Square) Wins praise from market commentators for being hard-working and user-friendly. He is widely regarded as a strong junior counsel, particularly in the fields of commercial arbitration, professional negligence and professional discipline. **Strengths:** "He's very client-friendly and has a relaxed, easy manner about him. He was well briefed, knew his stuff and was incredibly responsive. He anticipated issues very well and proved a real team player." **Recent work:** Acted for Central Bank of Trinidad and Tobago in relation to significant claims brought by the bank and CLICO Insurance against CLICO's former chairman and former financial executive.

Simon Adamyk (New Square Chambers) An experienced junior with an international practice that spans company, commercial and chancery disputes. **Strengths:** "A man with a formidable legal intellect." **Recent work:** Advised on and appeared as sole counsel in relation to several sets of proceedings in the high-profile dispute between BTA Bank and various defendants, including Mukhtar Ablyazov.

Paul Marshall (No5 Chambers) An experienced senior junior with an international commercial practice, who has particular expertise in financial services matters. **Strengths:** "He's a very thorough, dogged and determined lawyer who is both inventive and courageous." "He's very conscientious, his attention to detail is excellent, and he thinks outside the box." **Recent work:** Acted in an appeal concerning the basis for evaluation of damages arising out of a wrongly granted freezing order.

Alan Steinfeld QC (XXIV Old Buildings) A seasoned and highly respected chancery commercial silk with an outstanding reputation in offshore company and trusts disputes. He has notable expertise in civil fraud, partnership, pensions and professional negligence matters. **Strengths:** "A good communicator who is enormously talented and a real pleasure to deal with. I've seen that man master a brief so fast it's unbelievable." **Recent work:** Appeared in the dispute between Carlyle Capital and Conway heard in Guernsey, relating to a failed investment fund. The case involved complex jurisdictional issues.

Elspeth Talbot Rice QC (XXIV Old Buildings) Held in high regard by market commentators for her incisive and robust advocacy. She has "a voracious work appetite" and notable experience in offshore trusts and traditional chancery matters. **Strengths:** "Ferocious when on her feet." "She's superb on complex matters and very good with clients." **Recent work:** Appeared in a case concerning software IP rights in the context of the dissolution of a partnership.

Robert Levy QC (XXIV Old Buildings) Handles a range of commercial disputes, and has particular experience in offshore cases. **Strengths:** "An impressive counsel who puts the client at ease with his calm, assured approach." **Recent work:** Appeared in a dispute between Puritan International Fund (in liquidation) and Active Fund Services and others, that arose out of the failure of an investment fund.

Francis Tregear QC (XXIV Old Buildings) Maintains a broad company and commercial practice, and has expertise in banking and finance, professional negligence and offshore disputes. Sources praise him for being user-friendly and approachable. **Recent work:** Instructed by the liquidator of a Bahamian bank in relation to claims of breach of fiduciary duties and misapplication of securities brought against the bank's directors.

Edward Cumming (XXIV Old Buildings) An impressive junior whose "superb advocacy skills and sound judgement" win widespread approval from instructing solicitors. His practice sees him regularly handle civil fraud and aviation disputes, and he routinely undertakes offshore cases. **Strengths:** "Quick, calm, thorough, responsive; he's a pleasure to deal with." "Approachable, down-to-earth and measured in conference; he's extremely user-friendly. He's also good at drafting." **Recent work:** Instructed as sole counsel for six property investment companies in relation to an action to recover approximately £30 million of company funds from a former director.

John Stephens (XXIV Old Buildings) An experienced senior junior who has particular expertise in onshore and offshore trusts. **Strengths:** "We very much value his input. and his willingness to go the extra mile and make himself available." "He's a great strategic thinker and a real problem solver." **Recent work:** Acted for the claimant in multi-jurisdictional recovery proceedings against the Gibraltar branch of a French bank.

Simon Mills (see p.673) (Five Paper) Highly regarded for his advice and advocacy in relation to commercial and finance matters. He is active in the field of freezing injunctions and has a recognised specialism in invoice discounting and trade factoring. **Strengths:** "He is technically brilliant and is a master tactician. In court, he is a fighter, and he's a barrister you always want on your side, rather than against you." **Recent work:** Acted for Bilimoria Holdings, the holding company of Cobra Beer, in relation to claims that an administration charge by Leumi constitutes an unlawful penalty.

Keith Rowley QC (Radcliffe Chambers) A well-regarded commercial and chancery silk who is a favourite among instructing solicitors for both pensions and professional negligence cases. **Strengths:** "Incisive, courageous and someone with excellent judgement." "He is a highly tenacious advocate who gives clear and robust advice."

Ulick Staunton (Radcliffe Chambers) Known for his tenacious and forceful courtroom style, he has a broad commercial chancery practice and extensive advocacy experience. **Strengths:** "Clear, concise and to the point which, from a commercial client's perspective, is exactly what you want. He takes a very direct approach in both his written and oral advice, which always finds favour with commercial clients looking to cut to the chase."

Shantanu Majumdar (Radcliffe Chambers) An approachable and responsive junior, with a wide-ranging and international commercial practice. He handles insolvency, partnership, civil fraud, engineering and energy disputes. **Strengths:** "He gave very good practical advice, then advocated very well for us and won. He was always available – he could answer your question on the same day if you e-mailed at 8 at night." **Recent work:** Acted for DCD Factors in its successful £20 million fraud, warranty and guarantee claim against Ramada Trading.

Dov Ohrenstein (see p.684) (Radcliffe Chambers) A well-regarded junior with a broad commercial chancery practice. Solicitors particularly appreciate his approachable manner and the commerciality of his advice. **Strengths:** "Very commercial and responsive, ≠≠with an excellent grasp of legal issues." "Very good on paper, in conference and as an advocate."

Romie Tager QC (Selborne Chambers) Well regarded for his work in commercial chancery disputes, and particularly well known for handling real estate litigation. Sources consistently highlight his robust advocacy style. **Strengths:** "He has a great capacity for detail and constructs winning arguments." **Recent work:** Acted for the Right Honourable David Mellor QC in a case before the Court of Appeal, seeking to restore claims against the former chairman and sales director of Partridge Fine Arts which had previously been struck out.

Hugh Jackson (Selborne Chambers) Particularly well regarded for professional negligence cases, and highlighted by sources for his user-friendliness and ability to master the details of a case. **Strengths:** "He is very firm in his opinions, extremely thorough and has the ear of the judge. He took the judge through it in a methodical way and put us in the best position to get us the result we wanted." **Recent work:** Advised on a professional negligence claim relating to the estate of a bankrupt involved in a complex dispute.

Antony Zacaroli QC (South Square) Well liked and well respected by market commentators, he has a heavyweight reputation in banking and finance, company and insolvency matters. **Strengths:** "He cross-examines like an assassin, in a way that doesn't make witnesses realise they are giving anything away. Incisive in his questions, there's no wastage with him at all. He's very effective and a charming person to deal with." **Recent work:** Appeared in Pineway & Tecsbaco v London Mining Company, a dispute relating to royalties on sales of iron ore.

Robin Dicker QC (South Square) A leading silk in company, banking and finance, and insolvency cases, who has notable expertise in offshore disputes. Sources praise him for being an assured and cerebral advocate. **Strengths:** "You go to him for anything really difficult and technical." "Robin prepares cases from all angles, dealing not only with the legal arguments but the merits of a case too. He is able to identify key issues and arguments quickly, and his manner in court is understated and assured." **Recent work:** Acted for Barclays Bank in its high-profile derivatives dispute with Graiseley Properties. This was considered a test case for Libor-related derivatives disputes but settled shortly before trial.

Jeremy Goldring QC (South Square) A "bright" and "level-headed" silk with a strong commercial, company, and banking and finance practice. He has notable experience in high-profile, offshore litigation. **Strengths:** "Able to get to the heart of the matter, he has a no-nonsense, no-fuss approach in terms of his written work. He has a very relaxed style of advocacy but it proves very effective." **Recent work:** Acted for Barclays Bank in its high-profile derivatives dispute with Graiseley Properties, which settled shortly before trial.

David Allison QC (South Square) Took silk in 2014, having built a strong reputation at the junior Bar for his handling of restructuring and insolvency, banking disputes and financial services cases. **Strengths:** "Very impressive and very smooth." "He was an exceptional leading junior who even then was a match for many of the leading insolvency silks." **Recent work:** Instructed by US Bank Trustees as defendant to a claim brought by Omicron Investment Management relating to an investment advisory agreement.

Tom Smith QC (South Square) Took silk in 2014, an appointment widely endorsed by market commentators, who had long regarded him as a go-to junior, particularly for insolvency and restructuring matters. His practice also encompasses banking and finance and company law matters. **Strengths:** "Enormously committed and responsive, he is a man of great intellect." **Recent work:** Acted for Grupo Hotelero Urvasco in its approximately £60 million damages claim against Carey Value Added, concerning the collapse of a project to construct a hotel on the Strand.

Andrew Twigger QC (see p.742) (3 Stone Buildings) A popular silk building a loyal following of instructing solicitors due to his work in commercial chancery mattters, especially banking and finance cases. **Strengths:** "There is a real air of authority about him." "He's someone who is always very user-friendly and approachable, and his written work, in particular, is superb. He has a first-class analytical mind." **Recent work:** Represented Mr Benedetti in his dispute with Mr Sawiris regarding the acquisition of an Italian telecoms company.

Jonathan Crow QC (4 Stone Buildings) A "superb advocate" and "a great legal mind." He is a supremely gifted advocate who is exceptional whether handling commercial or public law cases. **Strengths:** "Decisive and easy to work with, he's great with lay clients and is a pleasure to work with." "A heavyweight of the Commercial Chancery Bar, who has an extraordinary breadth of expertise." **Recent work:** Acted for Sonja Kohn and a corporate defendant in relation to fraud claims following the collapse of Madoff Securities. He secured the discharge of a freezing order and obtained indemnity costs.

Robert Miles QC (4 Stone Buildings) Held in the highest regard by market commentators, not least because of his exceptional advocacy. He maintains a top-flight practice in commercial litigation and arbitration, and regularly handles banking and finance, company law, restructuring and insolvency, and civil fraud cases. **Strengths:** "He is a polymath, and a very bright and very charming guy." "His advice is robust and creative, and is delivered in measured tones." **Recent work:** Acted for Bernie Ecclestone defending high-profile bribery claims brought by Constantin Medien.

John Brisby QC (4 Stone Buildings) An experienced and effective trial lawyer famed for his skill at cross-examination. His practice spans company, civil fraud, and restructuring and insolvency matters. **Strengths:** "He is popular with clients due to his raw ability, straight-talking approach and ability to get results. He also has an impressive eye for detail, and retains and recalls the smallest points on a case at just the right time." "Fun to work with and one of the best cross-examiners in the business." **Recent work:** Acted for Clive Christian Perfume in the successful defence of a claim brought by its Italian distributor. He also represented the company with regard to its successful counterclaim for unpaid invoices and repudiatory breach of contract.

Richard Hill QC (4 Stone Buildings) An impressive recent silk with a very fine reputation in banking and finance, company and civil fraud cases. **Strengths:** "Very diligent and good to have on your side." **Recent work:** Represented the first and fourth defendants in the appeal of Benedetti v Sawiris. The dispute centred on questions of quantum meruit arising out of an Italian telecoms deal.

George Bompas QC (4 Stone Buildings) A recognised expert in company law and corporate guidance, who is particularly well regarded for his technical knowledge and ability. **Strengths:** "An exceptional chancery lawyer who is highly responsive and has outstanding client-handling skills." "If you want an analysis of a complex point of law, particularly if there is a company law element, then he is an ideal choice." **Recent work:** Involved in Chemtrade v Fuchs Oil Middle East, a dispute concerning a Middle East and North Africa joint venture heard before the Court of Appeal of the Eastern Caribbean.

Alan Gourgey QC (11 Stone Buildings) A popular silk among instructing solicitors known for his intellectual agility and strong advocacy skills. He has notable expertise in civil fraud and IT cases. **Strengths:** "Has an excellent brain and provides clear advice even on the most complex of cases." "He is an excellent advocate both orally and on paper, and his turnaround time for high-quality written work is impressive." **Recent work:** Appeared for the respondent in Sharma v Sharma before the Court of Appeal, a dispute which raised the question of whether silence could amount to fully informed consent in the context of a claim for breach of fiduciary duty.

Charles Samek QC (11 Stone Buildings) An accomplished advocate favoured by instructing solicitors for commercial cases generally and civil fraud cases in particular. Sources appreciate his hands-on, collaborative approach. **Strengths:** "He is very, very user-friendly, very hard-working, very good at being part of a team and a very effective advocate. He's particularly strong on injunctions." "Fantastically hands-on and a talented advocate." **Recent work:** Acted for Provincia di Crotone in defence of a misrepresentation claim brought by Dexia Crediop relating to interest rate swaps.

Max Mallin (11 Stone Buildings) A well-regarded senior junior with a background in investment banking and a reputation for providing accessible, commercial advice. He wins praise from market commentators for his client-facing skills. **Strengths:** "Very commercially focused, he takes a no-nonsense and direct approach, and furnishes high-quality advice." "He has a commercial background and so is fluent in investment banking cases." **Recent work:** Appeared in DIB v PSI & Others, a substantial claim for fraud and/or breach of contract.

Gary Lidington (11 Stone Buildings) Recognised for his broad commercial practice and particularly his real estate litigation expertise. Sources praise him for his client skills and his approachable manner. **Strengths:** "He's practical and very good with the client."

Marcia Shekerdemian (11 Stone Buildings) Highly regarded for her efforts in commercial chancery cases, particularly those involving restructuring and insolvency issues. She is consistently praised for her user-friendliness and robust advice. **Recent work:** Led by Lexa Hilliard QC for NGM Sustainable Developments in relation to its claim against Lizzano and others for fraudulent misrepresentation and unlawful expropriation of a patent for the construction of floating or floating-enabled buildings.

Steven Gee QC (Stone Chambers) A well-regarded silk with a broad commercial practice that covers civil fraud, shipping and commodities matters among others. **Strengths:** "The leading light on worldwide freezing orders. He is hugely useful on complex litigation." **Recent work:** Appeared for Lloyd's market insurers in relation to the 'Alexandros T' Supreme Court case, which concerned the operation of Articles 27 and 28 of the Brussels Regulation.

Philip Riches (Stone Chambers) Praised by market commentators as a bright, hard-working and creative junior. He is particularly recommended for his handling of shipping and commodities disputes. **Strengths:** "Someone who really rolls up their sleeves and provides invaluable support both to his leader and his solicitor." "He's bright, responsive and commercial." **Recent work:** Acted for Gui Hui Dong and other Chinese nationals seeking to discharge freezing orders obtained against them by the Serious Organised Crime Agency.

Paul Downes QC (2TG – 2 Temple Gardens) A tenacious and assured advocate favoured for hard-fought cases. He has notable expertise in banking and finance matters, but also handles general commercial disputes. **Strengths:** "Isolates the core issues from a mass of complex material and explains them in clear terms." "He speaks the language that clients like and never gives up." **Recent work:** Acted for Mir Steel UK in defence of an approximately EUR50 million claim brought by Lictor Anstalt concerning the ownership of a hot strip steel mill. The dispute arose out of the sale of the mill following insolvency.

Charles Dougherty QC (2TG – 2 Temple Gardens) A popular recent silk who attracts consistent praise from market commentators for his intellectual ability and user-friendliness. He handles a broad range of matters, ranging from insurance, product liability and professional negligence matters to cases involving civil fraud and directors' duties. **Strengths:** "He's really good on his feet and would often win applications we thought were unachievable – he could somehow always persuade the judge. He just always nails what the issues are and is very impressive." **Recent work:** Acted for ship operator Novoship in its USD150 million bribery and breach of fiduciary duty claim against former directors and others.

MIDLANDS

Commercial Dispute Resolution Midlands
Leading Sets
Band 1
St Philips Chamber *
Band 2
No.5 Chambers *
Leading Silks
Star individuals
Randall John *St Philips Chambers* *
Band 1
Anderson Mark *No5 Chambers* [A] *
Khangure Avtar *St Philips Chambers*
Pepperall Edward *St Philips Chambers*
Zaman Mohammed *St Philips Chambers*
Band 2
Jones Richard *No5 Chambers*
Leading Juniors
Band 1
Brennan John *St Philips Chambers* *
Charman Andrew *St Philips Chambers* [A] *
Clegg Simon *St Philips Chambers* [A] *
Eyre Stephen *St Philips Chambers* *
Maguire Andrew *St Philips Chambers* [A]
Morgan James *St Philips Chambers* *
Taylor David *No5 Chambers* [A]
Band 2
Beever Edmund *St Philips Chambers* *
Beresford Stephen *Ropewalk Chambers (ORL)* ◊ *
Bristoll Sandra *St Philips Chambers*
Brown Marc *St Philips Chambers* *
Chaffin-Laird Olivia *No5 Chambers*
Garvie Carl *St Philips Chambers*
Joseph Paul *No5 Chambers* *
Reed Steven *No5 Chambers* *
Willetts Glenn *No5 Chambers*
** Indicates set / individual with profile.*
◊ (ORL) = Other Ranked Lawyer.
[A] direct access (see p.11).

Band 1

St Philips Chambers

See profile on p.886

THE SET

St Philips is widely recognised as the pre-eminent commercial dispute resolution set on the Midland Circuit. It draws instructions from a number of leading solicitors' firms both within and outside the region and its members draw praise for their user-friendly approach. The size of the set allows for a broad coverage of commercial disputes, with particular expertise in commercial contract and finance disputes.

Client service: "The clerks, led by chief clerk Joe Wilson, are really, really good. They have a flexible approach and really value the relationship."

SILKS

John Randall QC The leading commercial disputes silk on the Midland Circuit. His broad practice ranges from commercial contract disputes to professional negligence work. **Strengths:** "He is one of the standout silks in Birmingham. He seems to be able to deal with anything and be knowledgeable in so many areas." "You would use him for top, multimillion-pound stuff because he is at the top of his game." **Recent work:** He acted for the claimant in a restitution claim for the entire purchase price of a piece of Egyptian land.

Edward Pepperall QC Recommended for high-profile and high-value commercial litigation. He has significant expertise in commercial contract disputes and also specialises in professional negligence cases. **Strengths:** "He is a top choice for disputes involving business sales." "He is very commanding in court and has a polished presence." **Recent work:** He was instructed in a £2.5 million breach of warranty claim regarding the multimillion-pound purchase of a manufacturing company.

Avtar Khangure QC Maintains his reputation as a leading commercial litigator who can turn his hand to an impressively wide range of disputes. He is particularly known for his expertise in shareholder and company disputes, often with international elements. **Strengths:** "He is very slick and has no rough edges. He got the case well and truly kicked into touch."

Mohammed Zaman QC Continues to work on a range of commercial disputes, including company and civil fraud matters. He is consistently praised for his advocacy skills and international work. **Strengths:** "He is absolutely superb on his feet and has a great mastery of the documents." "He was the dominant force in the room and the star performer."

JUNIORS

Andrew Maguire Has a complex caseload with a focus on finance and contract disputes. He is particularly praised for his abilities in managing clients. **Strengths:** "He has an affable manner, both in advocacy and in conferences." "He takes a commercial approach to preparation and delivery." **Recent work:** He was instructed to act for a defendant in a claim brought by two former shareholders for £1.5 million each.

John Brennan (see p.556) An experienced chancery and commercial junior. His caseload is varied and covers a wide range of general commercial disputes. **Strengths:** "He is robust on his advice and he is very thorough and good as an advocate." "He is not someone who will back down or give guarded opinions and is very good with difficult cases." **Recent work:** He acted on a complex claim brought against the insurers of a firm of solicitors. The case centred on the meaning and effect of the aggregation clause.

Andrew Charman (see p.570) A noted junior whose instructions cover general commercial disputes as well as professional negligence and company and trusts disputes. He is widely praised for his user-friendly approach, which many sources attribute to his prior career as a solicitor at a magic circle law firm. **Strengths:** "He really is a heavyweight; he can cut through the murky facts and provide clearly thought-out solutions." **Recent work:** He acted on behalf of house-building firm Bovis Homes, successfully defending a claim for commission by a land agent.

Simon Clegg (see p.573) Has a strong reputation for handling general commercial cases, often with a financial or property aspect. He is well-respected in the market as a highly experienced junior. **Strengths:** "He is a good advocate, clear and very experienced. He has good client-handling skills." **Recent work:** He was instructed to act in a claim valued in excess of £750,000 which concerned the possession of property held as security.

Stephen Eyre Maintains a loyal following for commercial, chancery and insolvency work. He also sits as a recorder and has a reputation as a methodical and pragmatic practitioner. **Strengths:** "He is very good at providing advice that is accessible for clients and is commercially driven." **Recent work:** He acted in a series of applications for Chinese company Shenyang Brilliant Elevator regarding the recovery of funds from solicitors and liquidators.

James Morgan Has considerable commercial, chancery and company dispute resolution expertise. He continues to be recognised as one of the leading juniors on the Midland Circuit. **Strengths:** "You could put any work with him and it would be safe. He provides everything you need for really big litigation." "He has great paperwork and drafting skills and is very calm with a good bedside manner." **Recent work:** He acted for the claimant in a £1 million damages action brought against Homebase for the breach of a supply contract.

Edmund Beever (see p.547) Strong commercial junior with considerable experience in insurance, insolvency and directors' duties disputes. He is known in the market as a reliable and clear advocate. **Strengths:** "He is meticulously organised and an absorbing advocate, with a significant flair for detail." "He is very good at explaining a complex issue and is an excellent advocate." **Recent work:** He acted as the junior in a High Court claim against three defendants involving fraudulent director activity and breach of fiduciary duties.

Sandra Bristoll Specialises in commercial issues with an insolvency angle. She is known for her eye for detail. **Strengths:** "She has a great attention to detail and the sheer ability to pull out what is important." "She is personable, helpful, and you always feel like you have her attention."

Carl Garvie Combines commercial skills from his previous career as a solicitor with a confident and effective style of advocacy. Instructing solicitors are impressed by both his technical ability and his user-friendly nature. **Strengths:** "He combines the skill set of being very able technically with being a key commercial litigator." "He strikes up a good rapport with clients. He is especially user-friendly and a good man for a spot of rough-and-tumble litigation."

Marc Brown Swiftly becoming an important player at the Commercial Bar. He is known for insolvency work as well as general commercial disputes. **Strengths:** "He is a very clever guy and is always used by silks, which tells you a lot about his quality." "He is absolutely excellent on paperwork and with clients." **Recent work:** He was instructed to act for the claimant finance company on the recovery of monies due on the security of a bill of sale.

Band 2

No5 Chambers
See profile on p.883
THE SET
This set once again impresses the market with the quality and breadth of the commercial work undertaken. The high-quality clerking and the efficiency and flexibility of the set are all praised by instructing solicitors. No5 has a growing reputation as one of the strongest commercial dispute groups in the Midlands. Instructions come from across the spectrum of commercial matters and the set displays particular strength in company and construction disputes. **Client service:** "We go to No5 because we find the clerks, led by James Parks, are approachable as the first port of call."

SILKS
Mark Anderson QC Has a consistently complex caseload involving high-value matters. His recent work has included claims concerning breach of distribution and commercial agreements, share sale disputes and claims concerning breach of warranty. **Strengths:** "He is a real heavyweight, sees the issue from all sides, and is very commercial and experienced." "He is very effective and has a hint of the Rottweiler about him when he's on his feet in court." **Recent work:** He acted in a multimillion-pound claim on behalf of 200 clients against a Cypriot bank in relation to alleged negligent financial planning advice.

Richard Jones QC Experienced silk with a strong reputation on the Midland Circuit. He heads the chancery and commercial group at No5 and his commercial practice focuses on financial services disputes. **Strengths:** "He has provided good advice and is very approachable." **Recent work:** He acted on behalf of Midlands Regen in a high-profile fraud claim valued at £1.7 million in relation to a construction project.

JUNIORS
David Taylor Veteran junior with experience of handling commercial disputes in the County Court, High Court and Court of Appeal. He has an extensive experience in commercial contract and property disputes, as well as professional negligence claims. **Strengths:** "His cross-examination is a pleasure to watch because he is very probing and precise." "He has amazing attention to detail and a brilliant ability to reduce all the information into the important points."

Steven Reed (see p.706) Covers a wide spectrum of commercial disputes. He is regularly instructed on contractual matters, as well as disputes with IP or media aspects. **Strengths:** "He is accessible and flexible, has great business sense and provides sensible advice." **Recent work:** He was instructed to act for the claimant as sole counsel in a breach of contract claim worth £1.2 million. The case involved allegedly misappropriated metal.

Glenn Willetts A junior with a broad commercial litigation practice. He scores highly with solicitors, who praise his advocacy skills. **Strengths:** "He is a really, really good all-rounder." "Clients like him because they know he bats really hard for them."

Olivia Chaffin-Laird A well-respected commercial disputes junior. She has particular expertise in financial services matters. **Strengths:** "She performed very well on her feet and prepares very thoroughly." "She takes a very assertive and robust approach." **Recent work:** She represented defendant Bostik in a matter concerning its allegedly defective product which had actually been used by another defendant to formulate a different product.

Paul Joseph (see p.641) A former solicitor who has established a solid reputation at the Commercial Bar. He is recognised for his focus on costs disputes. **Strengths:** "He is really well prepared and has an excellent skill for communicating with clients." "He is very approachable and can clearly explain the law and the practicalities of a case."

Other Ranked Lawyers

Stephen Beresford (see p.548) (Ropewalk Chambers) A well-established junior with experience in a wide variety of commercial disputes. He is a vastly experienced practitioner who solicitors describe as "a junior with a silk's quality." **Strengths:** "He is very calm, collected and balanced, and gives advice and opinions in plain English."

NORTH EASTERN

Commercial Dispute Resolution North Eastern
Leading Sets
Band 1
Enterprise Chambers *
Kings Chambers *
Band 2
Trinity Chambers *
Leading Silks
New Silks
Jory Hugh *Enterprise Chambers*
Leading Juniors
Band 1
Groves Hugo *Enterprise Chambers*
Latimer Andrew *Kings Chambers* *
Pipe Gregory *St Philips Chambers (ORL)* ◊
Band 2
Goldberg Simon *Trinity Chambers* *
Klein Jonathan *Enterprise Chambers*
Rodger Jonathan *Enterprise Chambers*
Temple Eleanor *Kings Chambers* *
Band 3
Buck William *St Philips Chambers (ORL)* ◊ *
Holland Charles *Trinity Chambers* *
◊ *(ORL) = Other Ranked Lawyer.*
* *Indicates set / individual with profile.*
Alphabetical order within each band. Band 1 is highest.

Band 1

Enterprise Chambers
See profile on p.788
THE SET
One of the leading sets on the North Eastern Circuit, Enterprise Chambers' members are instructed on complex, high-value business disputes. Individuals are well versed in court and tribunal appearances, arbitration and mediation. The set covers a wide range of commercial law, and is recognised for its focus on insolvency and professional negligence matters in particular.

SILKS
Hugh Jory QC Newly appointed silk with a practice spanning insolvency work, shareholder disputes and contract work. He has a deep knowledge of financial matters, in which he is instructed by both regional and national firms. **Strengths:** "He's good with clients, and is not fazed by anything. He's experienced, and gives you confidence that you are in good hands." "He's excellent at cross-examining, particularly with experts."

JUNIORS
Jonathan Klein Has a broad and highly regarded commercial disputes practice. He has considerable experience in property matters and commercial fraud, arising from his focus on trusts and probate cases. **Strengths:** "He is very popular with judges. He's absolutely thorough and detailed in his preparation." **Recent work:** He acted for the claimant in a £2.9 million breach of trust claim brought against the estate of the claimant's deceased co-trustee. The claim concerns complex issues of trust management.

Hugo Groves Maintains a broad commercial disputes practice which encompasses warranty claims, partnership disputes, and company and insolvency matters. He has experience in bringing claims against directors, and also handling litigation with an international element. **Strengths:** "He is universally liked, very good with clients, and he has the ear of the Bench."

Jonathan Rodger Established barrister handling high-value and complex disputes in the chancery, property and insolvency areas. A highly experienced practitioner, he has handled cases before the High Court and the Court of Appeal. **Strengths:** "He is very commercial, and gives clients sensible and practical advice." **Recent work:** He acted in a dispute worth £1 million related to the misappropriation of confidential information by previous employees.

Kings Chambers
See profile on p.918

THE SET

Kings Chambers has an incredible wealth of talented commercial litigators to call upon. Its members are instructed on a broad range of contract disputes, shareholder and partnership disputes, and banking-related claims. The set has accrued an impressive client list and garners instructions from a number of high-profile institutions, companies and high net worth individuals.

Client service: "Its clerking system is second to none. They are very reliable and approachable."

JUNIORS

Andrew Latimer (see p.651) Has a comprehensive commercial and chancery practice, which covers partnership and shareholder disputes, commercial property and professional negligence. He is a favourite with solicitors, who value his "fantastically bright, can-do attitude." **Strengths:** "He is very hard-working. He's not only academic, but able to get into detail in a practical sense too." **Recent work:** He defended an arms dealer based in the North of England against two company claims, one in the Companies Court in London, and the other at the Royal Court of Justice.

Eleanor Temple Focuses her practice on commercial disputes, with particular expertise in insolvency, shareholder, and banking and finance disputes. She is noted for her expertise in cases with an international element. **Strengths:** "She is a popular advocate – she is not just easy to deal with, but a highly skilled tactician." **Recent work:** She acted in a complex £80 million claim concerning allegations of fraud and conspiracy relating to a company and shareholder dispute involving Hotter Shoes. This nine-week case involved 30 witnesses giving evidence in the High Court of Justice.

Band 2

Trinity Chambers
See profile on p.927

THE SET

Trinity Chambers' business law team handles a wide range of both contentious and non-contentious matters for a variety of clients, including SMEs, local authorities and individual professionals. The set is able to cover the full range of commercial litigation, including disputes relating to insolvency, construction and engineering.

Client service: "The clerks are really excellent and responsive."

JUNIORS

Simon Goldberg Has a broad commercial and chancery practice noted for its focus on shareholder disputes and directors' duties. A veteran advocate, he has considerable experience of litigating in the Chancery and Queen's Bench Divisions of the High Court. **Strengths:** "He combines good analytical skills with a firm grasp of the commercial realities of the client's situation." **Recent work:** He acted in a dispute between Big Communications and Opia, successfully defending against a claim of breach of contract concerning an online racing game.

Charles Holland Has a strong commercial and chancery practice focused on business and property matters. He is noted for his considerable expertise in the leisure sector. **Strengths:** "He is absolutely first-class. His paperwork is thorough, and his attention to detail on drafting is excellent." **Recent work:** He acted in a High Court claim and a subsequent £20 million counterclaim related to monies invested in the Dubai property market.

Other Ranked Lawyers

Gregory Pipe (St Philips Chambers) Focuses his commercial practice on company and property-related disputes. He is a strong advocate and a client-friendly counsel, and regularly appears in cases before the High Court in both Leeds and London. **Strengths:** "He is a forceful advocate. He prepares very thoroughly and he has a good delivery. He has a good way of extracting things from witnesses."

William Buck (see p.559) (St Philips Chambers) A commercial specialist whose practice is focused on finance disputes and banking litigation. He is noted for his pragmatic and commercial advice. **Strengths:** "He knows what judges are looking for in skeleton arguments." "He is very practical and commercial, and clients like that." **Recent work:** He acted for major lenders including Lombard in proceedings to recover 900 vehicles from third parties, following the collapse of Drive Asset.

NORTHERN

Commercial Dispute Resolution Northern	
Leading Sets	
Band 1	
Exchange Chambers *	
Kings Chambers *	
Leading Silks	
Band 1	
Anderson Lesley	*Kings Chambers* *
Casement David	*Kings Chambers* *
Cawson Mark	*Exchange Chambers*
Chaisty Paul	*Kings Chambers* *
Band 2	
Bartley Jones Edward	*Exchange Chambers*

* *Indicates set / individual with profile.*
◊ *(ORL) = Other Ranked Lawyer.*
Alphabetical order within each band. Band 1 is highest.

Commercial Dispute Resolution Northern	
Leading Juniors	
Band 1	
Berragan Neil	*Kings Chambers* *
Harper Mark	*Kings Chambers* *
Band 2	
Chapman Richard	*18 St John Street (ORL)* ◊ *
Fryer-Spedding James	*9 St John Street (ORL)* ◊ *
Grantham Andrew	*Kings Chambers* *
Pennifer Kelly	*Kings Chambers* *
Sandbach Carly	*Exchange Chambers* *
Terry Jeffrey	*Kings Chambers* *
Vinson Andrew	*Exchange Chambers*
Band 3	
Connolly Stephen	*Exchange Chambers*
Cook Christopher	*Exchange Chambers*
Gilchrist David	*9 St John Street (ORL)* ◊
Halliwell Mark	*Kings Chambers* *
Rañales-Cotos Tina	*Kings Chambers* *
Up-and-coming individuals	
Dainty Cheryl	*Kings Chambers* *
Harding Ben	*Kings Chambers* *

Band 1

Exchange Chambers
See profile on p.910

THE SET

Exchange Chambers has offices in Manchester, Leeds and Liverpool, and is one of the North of England's leading commercial sets. The set attracts a broad range of high-value commercial instructions relating to property, finance and professional negligence.

Client service: "There's a common theme in the set – they are good people to work with, and very approachable. They are happy to help you out and answer any question, no matter what it is!"

SILKS

Edward Bartley Jones QC Liverpool-based barrister with a broad commercial dispute caseload covering professional negligence and insurance claims, as well as experience in judicial reviews. He is regularly seen in the Court of Appeal, and his court performances have earned him praise from peers. **Strengths:** "He is well thought of and has a very distinctive and very effective style of advocacy." "He is a very accomplished advocate. He has the command of the court."

Mark Cawson QC A veteran commercial litigator who also sits as a Deputy High Court Judge. He is a specialist in insolvency matters, and is increasingly noted for his work in professional negligence claims. **Strengths:** "One of the top silks in Manchester in chancery and commercial work. He is of great stature." "He is quiet and unflappable, and his work is very thorough."

JUNIORS

Christopher Cook A qualified engineer as well as a barrister, he has a mastery of complex technical matters. **Strengths:** "He is exceptionally user-friendly – very practical, sensible and easy to work with."

Andrew Vinson Has a broad practice in commercial litigation, with extensive experience in insolvency and property dispute matters. His work portfolio encompasses regular instructions relating to injunctive relief, and the enforcement of restrictive covenants. **Strengths:** "He is a very smart chap – a good lawyer, with great ability."

Carly Sandbach Has a broad commercial and chancery practice, and is regularly instructed on insolvency, contractual and trusts-related disputes. **Strengths:** "She fights her cases with vigour. She is proactive, and brings a commercial view to cases."

Stephen Connolly Handles a wide spectrum of commercial dispute matters, and has a particular specialism in property disputes. His developing practice sees him regularly handle high-value claims involving solicitor negligence and civil fraud. **Strengths:** "He takes a good strategic view of cases – he's very commercial." "He has proven to be a very effective and reliable junior counsel."

Kings Chambers

See profile on p.918

THE SET

One of the largest sets in the country, Kings Chambers' members are instructed across England and Wales, and increasingly in international jurisdictions. The set is a go-to for the gamut of commercial matters, such as professional negligence, corporate and contractual disputes. It represents a wide range of clients, from large institutions to high net worth individuals.

Client service: "Kings Chambers are a good set to deal with – amenable and accessible."

SILKS

Lesley Anderson QC Unanimously praised for her capacity to handle big-ticket commercial disputes. Her practice encompasses a wide range of commercial work, including partnership disputes, professional negligence and mediation. **Strengths:** "She is very, very strong in everything she does. She's excellent." "Lesley Anderson has a fantastic and well-earned reputation." **Recent work:** Acted in the Court of Appeal and Supreme Court in a matter related to an FSA winding-up petition.

David Casement QC Has a broad commercial practice, acting for an array of high-profile clients. He is noted for his work on high-value commercial and sports disputes, and is also well versed in civil fraud and restructuring. **Strengths:** "He is a very strong, robust and respected advocate." **Recent work:** Acted for the former director of Magpie, defending a £15 million claim for alleged breach of confidentiality and misuse of information.

Paul Chaisty QC Represents high-profile individuals and clients in high-value disputes. He is also noted for his skill in commercial arbitrations. **Strengths:** "He's a real fighter." "He takes a no-nonsense approach to litigation. He quickly cuts through the chaff to get to the salient issues and provides the lay client with confident authoritative advice." **Recent work:** Defended against claims related to restraint of trade in a dispute between Wayne Rooney and his former management company, Proactive. Successful in the Court of Appeal in the well-publicised matter.

JUNIORS

Jeffrey Terry (see p.735) A seasoned junior in high demand among a number of prominent clients, including banks, local authorities and large corporations. **Strengths:** "Not only does he have a high level of technical ability, but he has the confidence of the client. His mastery of the issues in the case, and the detail, is most impressive." **Recent work:** Acted in a dispute based on the alleged liability of Safeways for the flooding of a residential home and a children's nursery.

Mark Harper Praised as an impressive litigator who offers succinct and definitive counsel. He provides representation and advice in commercial litigation, partnership and shareholder disputes. **Strengths:** "He is quietly and efficiently effective." **Recent work:** Acted for QCR Motors in its claim against Biffa, ADT and Zicam relating to the damage of cables which resulted in a fire on the claimant's premises. The claim is worth over £1 million.

Ben Harding (see p.619) Has a strong reputation for handling high-value commercial cases. He represents a range of clients, including financial institutions, corporate clients and private individuals. **Strengths:** "He is an exceptional intellect and a skilled advocate." **Recent work:** Successfully acted for a claimant seeking £450,000 for services provided outside of a construction contract.

Mark Halliwell A chancery and commercial specialist whose broad commercial practice encompasses a wide range of contractual disputes and commercial arbitrations. **Recent work:** Instructed in a claim for £1 million in damages in a joint venture dispute between a solicitor and claims management company. The matter involved allegations of fraudulent misrepresentation and negligence.

Tina Rañales-Cotos (see p.703) Covers a wide range of commercial dispute resolution, and is particularly noted for her expertise in trade mark infringement and business restraint matters. **Strengths:** "She is on the ball, able to assimilate a lot of detailed information very quickly, and has a good grasp of the minutiae." **Recent work:** Defended an ex-employee client against claims by the ex-employer concerning alleged fraud and breach of fiduciary duties, worth over £1 million.

Cheryl Dainty (see p.582) Praised for the high calibre of her advocacy, she has become a go-to for high-value and technical cases. Her experience in company, contract and insolvency disputes has led to her involvement in high-stakes matters before the Court of Appeal. **Strengths:** "She's an excellent advocate. She's very much in demand." **Recent work:** Advised the liquidator of a company in an action against the previous director, who had made significant payments from the company towards his own personal liabilities and a property in France. The liquidator was awarded £75,000 and a 50% interest in the property.

Neil Berragan Has a practice covering a wide range of commercial matters, including commercial fraud and shareholder disputes. **Strengths:** "He can turn his hand to anything. He saves the day at the last minute, keeping things calm and pulling out all the stops." **Recent work:** Instructed in a claim for arrears due under a claim referral agreement.

Andrew Grantham (see p.614) Receives instructions on a broad range of general commercial dispute matters, acting on behalf of banks, public companies and professional firms. **Strengths:** "He is very intelligent and good on detail – a most determined opponent." **Recent work:** Acted for a claimant who sought £2.5 million under policy insurance for fire damage.

Kelly Pennifer Has a broad commercial practice, and is noted for her work on disputes relating to construction law and professional negligence. **Strengths:** "She's extremely good – fantastic in court, good with clients, calm; she's just very impressive." "She has a razor-sharp mind with a fantastic eye for detail." **Recent work:** Represented an individual in a claim against DWF solicitors for damages of around £5.8 million. The claim concerned alleged professional negligence related to a share purchase transaction.

Other Ranked Lawyers

James Fryer-Spedding (see p.604) (9 St John Street) Chancery and commercial specialist who is noted for the breadth of his expertise. He is frequently instructed in property, insolvency and contractual disputes. **Strengths:** "He's very highly regarded, and highly technical in his approach." "He offers value for money, is very good with clients, and is able to explain and offer practical solutions which are well received by both clients and solicitors."

David Gilchrist (9 St John Street) Has a broad commercial practice which covers property, construction, franchise and insolvency disputes. **Strengths:** "He has an immense knowledge of the law." **Recent work:** Acted for the claimant in the Technology and Construction Court, in a claim brought against Mercury Forecourts concerning alleged nuisance on the grounds of contamination of land caused by the neighbouring petrol station.

Richard Chapman (see p.569) (18 St John Street) Practises in a wide range of commercial matters, including on property, contractual, insolvency and professional negligence disputes. **Strengths:** "He is a very good opponent. He's very straightforward and intelligent, and he does a good job for his client." "He is a very strong practitioner who is very well prepared."

SOUTH EASTERN

Commercial Dispute Resolution South Eastern
Leading Sets
Band 1
Crown Office Row *
3PB Barristers *
Leading Juniors
Band 1
Ashwell Paul *Crown Office Row*
Clargo John *3PB Barristers*
Band 2
Davies James *3PB Barristers*
Sheriff Andrew *3PB Barristers*
Wright Stuart *Crown Office Row*
Up-and-coming individuals
Godfrey Lauren *Crown Office Row*

Band 1

Crown Office Row

See profile on p.888

THE SET

Crown Office Row in Brighton has a strong reputation across a range of areas including contract, misrepresentation and partnership disputes. It is one of the South Eastern Circuit's premier sets and its practitioners are well equipped to handle the full spectrum of commercial disputes. The team is highly regarded for its core expertise in property law and continues to attract a significant number of instructions from local clients.

Client service: "The clerks, led by David Bingham, are very good at looking after you. They're always very prompt whenever you need help and they've got good systems in place so nothing gets overlooked."

JUNIORS

Paul Ashwell Handles a range of property and commercial disputes. His areas of expertise include construction, insolvency and contract disputes. **Strengths:** "He's able to advise on very complex matters and break them down so they are easy for clients to understand." "His legal knowledge is truly encyclopaedic."

Lauren Godfrey Acts for a range of clients including company directors, banks and local authorities. He demonstrates particular expertise in employment-flavoured disputes such as restraint of trade and data protection. **Strengths:** "He throws everything into the case and leaves no stone unturned." "He takes a good, common-sense approach informed by his understanding of his clients' situation." **Recent work:** He advised on a claim by Crown United Group relating to professional duties when pleading fraud, tax issues, negligence, insolvency and breach of fiduciary duties.

Stuart Wright Deals with commercial and contract disputes. He has particular expertise in property law and specialises in sensitive cases concerning vulnerable tenants. **Strengths:** "He's very thorough, charming and persuasive." "He's a good all-round junior. He has an impressive court presence and persuasively articulates legal arguments on his feet. "

3PB Barristers

See profile on p.846

THE SET

Oxford-based 3PB is one of the leading sets on the South Eastern Circuit for commercial litigation. It is well regarded for its advisory and advocacy work on a range of matters including commercial property, construction and insolvency disputes. Recent highlights for the set include advising on a claim in respect of defective works to a League One football pitch.

Client service: "The clerks, led by Russell Porter, are really helpful, both with specific queries and making recommendations."

JUNIORS

John Clargo Focuses his practice on property disputes for commercial and residential clients. His areas of expertise include the enforcement of covenants and disputes concerning the construction, assignment and termination of leases. **Strengths:** "For any particularly tricky matters, he is a great person to call – he's very good on his feet, always well prepared, very user-friendly, and he provides commercially driven advice." **Recent work:** He represented the defendants in a claim to recover a £2 million house in Oxford.

James Davies Highly sought after for all kind of business disputes. He has particular expertise in relation to franchises, partnerships and guarantees. **Strengths:** "He's brilliant on detail. He's particularly good where there's a debate over figures or where there's issues over deals involving complex transactions." "He is thorough, well prepared, accessible and always successful!" **Recent work:** He has acted for a defendant in a multiparty property partnership dispute.

Andrew Sheriff Deals with a range of disputes including contract, property, landlord and tenant, and defamation. **Strengths:** "He's extremely thorough: he doesn't miss a trick. He is very bold in picking up the issues, gives very commercially oriented advice and leaves no stone unturned." "He's very good on his feet, has good client handling skills and is easy to deal with." **Recent work:** He acted for the claimant in a dispute concerning the appropriate time for valuing gold following a loan.

WALES & CHESTER

Commercial Dispute Resolution Wales & Chester
Leading Juniors
Band 1
Jones Emyr *9 Park Place (ORL)* ◊
Vines Anthony *Civitas Law (ORL)* ◊ *
Walters Graham *Civitas Law (ORL)* ◊ *
Band 2
Hughes Gwydion *9 Park Place (ORL)* ◊ *
Thomas-Symonds Nicklaus *Civitas Law (ORL)* ◊ *
* *Indicates set / individual with profile.*
Alphabetical order within each band. Band 1 is highest.
◊ *(ORL) = Other Ranked Lawyer.*

Ranked Lawyers

Anthony Vines (Civitas Law) Acts for both businesses and individuals in a range of commercial disputes. He regularly advises and represents in consumer protection matters, contract and lending disputes, and company disputes. **Strengths:** "He goes above and beyond his role to help the case progress." "He's very approachable and very understanding of the position of the client."

Graham Walters (see p.745) (Civitas Law) Combines his commercial and chancery expertise with a considerable public law practice. He focuses on property, planning, and public and administrative law, and handles a variety of commercial disputes, including business tenancy disputes, contract matters and property disputes. **Strengths:** "He gives simple solutions to complex problems: he's an effective and cost-effective counsel." **Recent work:** Acted on a case concerning the proper interpretation of the Public Passenger Vehicles Act 1981.

Nicklaus Thomas-Symonds (see p.736) (Civitas Law) Has a substantial chancery and commercial practice. He focuses on contract and construction disputes, and regularly takes instructions relating to large-scale public sector projects and high-value disputes between large companies. **Strengths:** "He has very good soft skills." "He's very knowledgeable, and as a trained mediator he has an extra perspective on things." **Recent work:** Acted for a private client in an unjust enrichment dispute involving mortgage payments.

Emyr Jones (9 Park Place) Has a broad chancery and commercial practice. He is noted for his expertise in property and land disputes, and increasingly handles contract and construction matters. **Strengths:** "He's obviously a very clever stick and his advocacy was fantastic." "He handles judges very well: he has the first-hand knowledge of what they think, what they're looking for, what will keep them happy and what will annoy them, and I value that." **Recent work:** Acted on a vehicular right of way dispute over a municipal park in Barry.

Gwydion Hughes (see p.633) (9 Park Place) Handles a variety of commercial and business disputes. His areas of expertise include commercial property, professional negligence, insolvency and company law. **Strengths:** "He's a quite formidable jury advocate."

WESTERN

Commercial Dispute Resolution Western
Leading Sets
Band 1
Guildhall Chambers *
Band 2
St John's Chambers *
Leading Silks
Band 1
Blohm Leslie *St John's Chambers*
Davies Stephen *Guildhall Chambers*
Palmer Adrian *Guildhall Chambers*
New Silks
Sims Hugh *Guildhall Chambers*
Leading Juniors
Band 1
Briggs Nicholas *Guildhall Chambers*
Dickinson John FH *St John's Chambers* [A] *
Levy Neil *Guildhall Chambers* *
Marsden Andrew *St John's Chambers* [A] *
McMeel Gerard *Guildhall Chambers*
Pearce-Smith James *St John's Chambers*
Virgo John *Guildhall Chambers*
Band 2
Adams Guy *St John's Chambers* [A]
Ascroft Richard *Guildhall Chambers* *
Bamford Jeremy *Guildhall Chambers*
Fentem Ross *Guildhall Chambers*
Maher Martha *St John's Chambers* [A]
Ramel Stefan *Guildhall Chambers*
Stead Richard *St John's Chambers* [A]
Troup Alex *St John's Chambers* [A]
Up-and-coming individuals
Pointon Nicholas *St John's Chambers*
[A] *direct access (see p.11).*
* *Indicates set / individual with profile.*

Band 1

Guildhall Chambers

See profile on p.890

THE SET

Guildhall Chambers maintains its standing as the leading set for commercial dispute resolution on the Western Circuit. Its members provide advice and advocacy on all areas of commercial law, including partnership and joint ventures, corporate and shareholder disputes, and professional negligence. The team has strong expertise in a variety of sectors, including construction, energy, accountancy and technology. Recent highlights for the set include acting on the first reported case concerning the mis-selling of interest rate swaps.

Client service: "The clerks, led by Mike Norton, are excellent in terms of receiving high-volume and complex documents and updating counsel with a full brief within a matter of hours. It's their adaptability and flexibility in terms of being able to react to our demands."

SILKS

Stephen Davies QC An insolvency specialist with a strong track record in high-profile insolvencies. He specialises in failed PFI/PPP projects, sports insolvencies, cross-border issues and clawback claims. **Strengths:** "One of the joys of working with him is you're part of the team: he pulls you in and gets you involved, and it's a delight." **Recent work:** Acted for several claimants in the first test case on Libor manipulation.

Adrian Palmer QC Specialises in contract, sale of goods, insurance and professional negligence matters. He has advised and acted on numerous substantial investment cases on behalf of high-profile clients. **Strengths:** "He is remorseless in his preparation: if there's something he doesn't understand then he damn well makes sure he does." **Recent work:** Acted on a claim against Credit Suisse over the mis-selling of investments into the AIG Enhanced Variable Rate fund.

Hugh Sims QC Acts on a range of complex and substantial commercial matters, receiving instructions from local and national solicitors. **Strengths:** "He's an absolutely stellar lawyer but a terrific chap as well. It's quite rare to combine the two and he does it effortlessly." "He's a very able advocate, is immensely practical and commercial, and has courage in his conviction." **Recent work:** Acted for John Grimes Partnership in a professional negligence claim against a construction engineer relating to a residential development in Cornwall.

JUNIORS

John Virgo Has extensive experience in banking and finance and professional negligence. He focuses his practice on financial product mis-selling and has acted on a number of the leading mis-selling cases. **Strengths:** "He is an extremely experienced barrister who gives straightforward advice." "He's energetic, thorough and commercial. He brings immense focus to a case." **Recent work:** Acted on the first case in a series of actions over the mis-selling of AIG bonds.

Nicholas Briggs Has a broad practice centred on insolvency, commercial disputes, professional negligence and indemnity. His litigation and advisory experience includes enforcing proprietary and commercial securities, sale of goods disputes and breach of warranty claims. **Strengths:** "He's fantastic. He tends to throw in some fantastic practical advice as he's seen it from the other side when sitting as a judge, so his experience is second to none." "He's got a gravitas that serves him well. He's a very good advocate and a good analyst too." **Recent work:** Acted on a breach of contract and negligence dispute against Mercedes in relation to the supply and fit out of ambulances for the Welsh Ambulance Services NHS Trust.

Ross Fentem Handles a range of commercial and property disputes. He frequently handles banking and finance matters, and has particular experience of the asset finance sector. **Strengths:** "He's able to quickly grasp the full details of a case and get through to the commercial outcome with lightning speed. He's right at the end of the game before everyone else has got to square one." **Recent work:** Successfully represented Osteopathic Education and Research in a dispute against Purfleet Office System relating to a series of asset finance agreements for office equipment.

Neil Levy Undertakes a variety of commercial disputes, including general contract disputes, credit sales, asset finance, shareholder agreements and warranty claims. He specialises in banking disputes and has particular experience of domestic banking transactions. **Strengths:** "He's pragmatic and sensible. He provides very clear advice and is a good strategist." "He's very commercial and very helpful – a good guy to just pick up the phone to." **Recent work:** Acted for Lloyds Bank in a £900,000 claim arising out of an asset sale agreement.

Gerard McMeel Has a broad commercial practice with a heavy focus on financial service matters. He has appeared in a variety of courts and forums, and regularly advises and acts on cases with an international element. **Strengths:** "He is extremely pleasant to work with, very quick and diligent, and very likeable. He is an intellectual giant." "He is very knowledgeable and very pleasant to deal with." **Recent work:** Acted for hundreds of investors in a dispute against Gain Capital LLC, a US foreign exchange company, for breach of the Financial Services and Markets Act 2000.

Jeremy Bamford Handles a range of commercial, matters including breach of warranty disputes, restraint of trade and freezing injunctions. He has particular expertise in dealing with live company work, directors disqualification proceedings and professional negligence claims. **Strengths:** "He's a very good advocate, very user-friendly with very detailed legal knowledge."

Richard Ascroft Specialises in company law, insolvency law and commercial litigation. He has particular expertise in claims involving breaches of warranty and misrepresentation, interference with goods, employment restrictive covenants and professional negligence. **Strengths:** "He has an extremely impressive ability to get to grips with quite substantial facts, specific topic areas and the legal issues as well." "He's very calm and very good on strategy." **Recent work:** Successfully represented the purchaser of an accountancy practice in a breach of warranty dispute against the vendor.

Stefan Ramel Acts on a broad range of commercial disputes. He litigates regularly in the High Court and has appeared in the Court of Appeal on several occasions. **Strengths:** "He seems to pick up the nub of the matter very quickly." "He is a very determined and confident advocate." **Recent work:** Acted on behalf of the claimant in a fraudulent misrepresentation claim arising out of the sale of a parcel of land.

Band 2

St John's Chambers

See profile on p.893

THE SET

St John's Chambers handles claims on behalf of clients from a broad range of industries and businesses. Members of the set frequently appear in the commercial courts, including the Mercantile Courts in Bristol and Cardiff, as well as representing clients in various forms of ADR. Recent highlights for the set include acting for Airbus in a £1 million bribery, secret profits and conspiracy dispute against several individuals.

Client service: "The clerks, led by Robert Bocock, are very thorough – everything works seamlessly."

SILKS

Leslie Blohm QC Joint deputy head of chambers and head of the chancery and commercial practice group. He is noted for handling disputes with a property flavour, including development and overage agreements, town and village green applications, and commercial landlord and tenant disputes. **Strengths:**

"He is a standout in terms of both advice and advocacy." **Recent work:** Acted on a dispute between three former solicitors concerning their leasehold interest of their office premises, held as part of their pension fund.

JUNIORS

John Dickinson Has particular expertise in company and banking disputes. His commercial practice also covers breach of contract, consumer credit, restraint of trade and sale of goods, fraud, injunctions and freezing orders. **Strengths:** "He is extremely able, very pragmatic, commercial and responsive." "He is willing to listen, and has a good analytical mind. He can get to the heart of a matter quite easily."

Andrew Marsden Specialises in corporate, partnership and commercial law, with a particular interest in commercial agency. He has particular experience in contractual disputes, including those related to restraint to trade, sale of goods and services, and the breakdown of business relations. **Strengths:** "He's thoroughly commercial in his approach. He gives sensible, commercial advice." "He is a very clever man and very knowledgeable; he rarely misses anything." **Recent work:** Acted in a dispute arising out of a catering services contract in relation to Llanelli RFC's stadium.

James Pearce-Smith Specialises in large commercial disputes and professional negligence claims. He has additional experience in the construction and engineering sector, and has represented independent builders, employers and national house builders. **Strengths:** "He's very thorough, very good with clients and very user-friendly." "He's able to turn matters round very quickly. He has a very logical mind and is very bright." **Recent work:** Acting for Airbus in a £1 million bribery, secret profits and conspiracy dispute against several individuals.

Alex Troup Has strong expertise in probate, trust and property disputes. **Strengths:** "He's extremely forthright – really punchy, to the point where on occasion you almost feel sorry for the other side. He just doesn't let up." "He immediately builds rapport with clients, quickly identifies the key issues, and gives practical, no-nonsense advice."

Guy Adams Deals with a broad range of commercial and chancery disputes. His experience includes handling shareholder disputes, commercial contract matters and disputes following the break-up of a professional partnership. **Strengths:** "He really gets his teeth stuck into things." "If you have a difficult case Guy is good at diffusing tricky situations." **Recent work:** Acted for Subway Realty in a dispute concerning leasehold arrangements with a franchisee.

Martha Maher Has significant experience of handling contract and corporate disputes, civil fraud and claims concerning a breach of fiduciary duty. She also acts for clients in professions such as medicine and accountancy in relation to partnership disputes. **Strengths:** "She isn't afraid to pick something up and delve into it." "She has a very keen eye for detail, and she's very proactive: she likes to maintain a dialogue. Some barristers you use will eventually send you an opinion and that's it, but she keeps in touch, and really takes the time to understand your issue." **Recent work:** Acting on a dispute for alleged multi-handed procurement fraud/secret commission in connection with a gasworks installation in a development site in the Midlands.

Richard Stead Head of chambers and one of the set's most experienced commercial litigators. He has particular experience in commercial agency, product liability, sale of goods, insurance and property damage. **Strengths:** "You get exactly what you expect – he's a mature, experienced, calm, heavyweight counsel. And he's extremely efficient as well." "He is very approachable, intelligent and good at getting to the issues quickly." **Recent work:** Acted on a reported decision concerning the duty of a landowner to take reasonable steps to prevent natural occurrences on a landowner's property from causing damage to neighbouring property.

Nicholas Pointon Specialises in cases with an international or cross-border dimension. He has acted on cases concerning numerous European jurisdictions and regularly advises on issues of jurisdiction and the enforceability of foreign judgments. **Strengths:** "He is very good at getting to grips with highly complex matters extremely quickly; he's very astute, methodical and good with detail." "He provided a very measured, thoughtful and clear analysis." **Recent work:** Successfully defended Mitsubishi UK in a misrepresentation and sale of goods dispute in relation to Evolution X, the company's flagship performance car.

Contents:

LONDON

Community Care London
Leading Silks
Band 1
Giffin Nigel *11KBW (ORL)* ◊
Howell John *Blackstone Chambers (ORL)* ◊
Knafler Stephen *Garden Court Chambers (ORL)* ◊
McGuire Bryan *Cornerstone Barristers (ORL)* ◊
Richards Jenni *Thirty Nine Essex Street (ORL)* ◊
Band 2
Bowen Paul *Brick Court Chambers (ORL)* ◊
Cragg Stephen *Doughty Street Chambers (ORL)* ◊
Morris Fenella *Thirty Nine Essex Street (ORL)* ◊
Rutledge Kelvin *Cornerstone Barristers (ORL)* ◊
Wise Ian *Monckton Chambers (ORL)* ◊ [A]
Wolfe David *Matrix Chambers (ORL)* ◊ *
Leading Juniors
Band 1
Armstrong Nicholas *Matrix Chambers (ORL)* ◊
Auburn Jonathan *Thirty Nine Essex Street (ORL)* ◊ [A] *
Broach Stephen *Monckton Chambers (ORL)* ◊
Buley Tim *Landmark Chambers (ORL)* ◊
Buttler Chris *Matrix Chambers (ORL)* ◊ [A]
Harrop-Griffiths Hilton *Field Court Chambers (ORL)* ◊
Band 2
Butler-Cole Victoria *Thirty Nine Essex Street (ORL)* ◊
Clement Joanne *11KBW (ORL)* ◊ *
Gallagher Caoilfhionn *Doughty Street Chambers (ORL)* ◊ [A]
Greaney Nicola *Thirty Nine Essex Street (ORL)* ◊ *
Luh Shu Shin *Garden Court Chambers (ORL)* ◊
Sharland Andrew *11KBW (ORL)* ◊ [A] *
Suterwalla Azeem *Monckton Chambers (ORL)* ◊ *
Band 3
Baldwin Timothy *Garden Court Chambers (ORL)* ◊
Davies Sian *Cornerstone Barristers (ORL)* ◊ *
Hannett Sarah *Matrix Chambers (ORL)* ◊ [A]
Hirst Leonie *Garden Court Chambers (ORL)* ◊
Williams Felicity *Garden Court Chambers (ORL)* ◊
Up-and-coming individuals
Amraoui Thomas *Thirty Nine Essex Street (ORL)* ◊
◊ (ORL) = Other Ranked Lawyer.
[A] direct access (see p.11).
** Indicates individual with profile.*
Alphabetical order within each band. Band 1 is highest.

Ranked Lawyers

John Howell QC (Blackstone Chambers) Community care and public law heavyweight briefed by public bodies to lead on major, law-defining matters. He has been a deputy High Court judge since 2008. **Strengths:** "Genuinely a superstar." **Recent work:** Made an appeal to the Supreme Court on behalf of Westminster City Council regarding the meaning of "care and attention" under Section 21 of the National Assistance Act 1948.

Paul Bowen QC (Brick Court Chambers) Recommended community care practitioner especially well regarded for his work on the claimant side. He has particular expertise in human rights and mental health as it relates to community care. **Strengths:** "He's not afraid to take challenging points and he shows real vision in the cases he takes." "He grasps the detail and the urgency of the situation clearly, and responds accordingly with great tactical awareness." **Recent work:** Led a successful appeal for a client, overturning the assessment that she lacked capacity to decide to continue a marital relationship with her husband following his release from prison.

Bryan McGuire QC (Cornerstone Barristers) Well-liked silk who focuses his practice on providing representation to defendant local authorities. He receives praise for his tactful manner in highly contentious cases. **Strengths:** "He's absolutely phenomenal at anything related to judicial review, and obviously his experience is right up there." "Very knowledgeable, straight, and a reasonable and affable opponent." **Recent work:** Secured a victory for Solihull Council in a case which clarified when local authorities are required to provide college fees funding to foreign students in the UK.

Kelvin Rutledge QC (Cornerstone Barristers) Leading defendant practitioner highlighted for his substantial experience of representing local authorities. He wins plaudits for his staunch advocacy. **Strengths:** "His delivery on his feet and his technical interpretation of the law are just faultless." "He's hugely knowledgeable in this area and very experienced." **Recent work:** Successfully represented the London Borough of Southwark in a major case which determined that local authorities may take into account existing third-party support when deciding which homeless individuals should receive priority for housing assistance.

Sian Davies (Cornerstone Barristers) Noted practitioner with particular knowledge and understanding of migrant eligibility for community care services. She is aided by parallel expertise in social housing. **Recent work:** Successfully defended the London Borough of Tower Hamlets, led by Kelvin Rutledge QC, in an appeal against its decision to pay less money to foster carers related to the children they foster than to those who are not related.

Stephen Cragg QC (Doughty Street Chambers) Highly regarded silk who is particularly well known for claimant work. He is praised for his creativity, as well as his reassuring manner with clients. **Strengths:** "He's very intelligent and hard-working, has a wealth of expertise in the field of community care and possesses humility, kindness and a charismatic personality. His advice is succinct and very convincing." "I call on him for trickier community care and healthcare issues because he's creative and not afraid to try novel points." **Recent work:** Represented a Northern Irish teenager and her mother in a challenge to the NHS over its failure to provide abortions to women denied abortions in Northern Ireland.

Caoilfhionn Gallagher (Doughty Street Chambers) Holds a strong reputation at the Bar, and is valued for her tenacity in the courtroom. Her community care work benefits from her crossover expertise in prison law and children's law. **Strengths:** "She's quick and energetic, and sees her points early and clearly. She's an effective advocate and will fight doggedly for the claimant." "She's very persistent and good analytically."

Jenni Richards QC (Thirty Nine Essex Street) A go-to practitioner for instructing solicitors on both the defendant and claimant side of community care cases. She is considered a first choice barrister for complex and high-profile work. **Strengths:** "She's fantastic – she has a huge knowledge of this field, is a very persuasive advocate and is well-rounded and versatile." "She's very good to work with, invariably pleasant with opponents, but also has a steely core, and is extremely robust in defence of her clients' interests."

Fenella Morris QC (Thirty Nine Essex Street) Handles a range of significant community care matters, and has a particular focus on aftercare under the Mental Health Act. She demonstrates an outstanding breadth of knowledge on a wide range of community care and related public law matters. **Strengths:** "She's really excellent as she's approachable, intelligent, good humoured and willing to get involved. She'll still get you a response very quickly even if the question's quite mundane for a QC." "An extremely good lawyer and a very clear advocate."

Jonathan Auburn (Thirty Nine Essex Street) Talented junior in the community care area, who is experienced in representing both applicants and defendants. He produces the set's highly regarded newsletter on community care law and recently co-authored the OUP textbook on judicial review. **Strengths:** "He's very practical, approachable in his style and very flexible." "Good on his feet, he knows the field inside out, and has the extra advantage of experience acting for both claimants and local authorities." **Recent work:** Appeared in a key test case which considered who is entitled to social care and in what circumstances a person receiving social care is also entitled to accommodation.

Victoria Butler-Cole (Thirty Nine Essex Street) Star junior of the field, who takes on significant cases for local authority as well as claimant clients. Her broad public law practice has a particular focus on the overlap between community care and Court of Protection cases. **Strengths:** "She's excellent, as she's really approachable and highly intellectual." "She turns the work around very quickly, is easy to talk to and can quickly grasp issues." **Recent work:** Defended Shropshire Council against challenges to the proposed closure of several of its day care centres.

Nicola Greaney (Thirty Nine Essex Street) Conducts an impressive public law practice with a significant community care component. She has a particular focus on mental health issues as they relate to community care law. **Strengths:** "She's extremely clear and authoritative; the court listens to her particularly attentively." "She manages to be very direct and very good at focusing parties in on the issues."

Thomas Amraoui (Thirty Nine Essex Street) Up-and-coming junior with a growing presence in the community care arena. He bases his practice on local authority representation, but also has experience in acting for claimants. **Strengths:** "He's very knowledgeable and good at getting back to you. He's always willing to discuss how he thinks the law's changing and where it's relevant." "I know that if I go to Tom I will get something very quickly, so I often ask for him first on an urgent case. His drafting is precise and very quick." **Recent work:** Successfully defended the London Borough of Hackney against a challenge to its assessment that a migrant family who had overstayed their visa were not 'in need' as defined by Section 17 of the Children's Act 1989.

Hilton Harrop-Griffiths (Field Court Chambers) Established junior with long-standing experience of acting on the defendant side in community care cases. He receives commendations for his measured approach when handling sensitive matters. **Strengths:** "He's very approachable, very knowledgeable, and technically very sound on the law." "He has very sound judgement, spots points well, and solicitors feel comfortable instructing him as he sees the issues and identifies the arguments." **Recent work:** Led by John Howell QC in representing Westminster County Council in a Supreme Court case over whether a suicidal failed asylum seeker's need to have his mental condition monitored by a social worker required the council to provide him with funded accommodation.

Stephen Knafler QC (Garden Court Chambers) Outstanding community care silk and the general editor of the community care law reports. He acts for both defendants and claimants, and has a particular focus on migrant issues. **Strengths:** "An exceptionally bright and intuitive lawyer who comes out with new points nobody's seen before." "An excellent, first-rate barrister who's almost single-handedly pushed the boundaries of Section 21." **Recent work:** Represented the claimant in a recent case which considered what support an authority is required to provide under the National Assistance Act 1948.

Shu Shin Luh (Garden Court Chambers) Rising junior with a broad community care practice, who receives praise for her tenacious approach. She specialises in the overlap between children's law and complex immigration matters. **Strengths:** "A highly intelligent barrister with a really impressive approach to finding new ways to push the boundaries of the law." "Very knowledgeable and approachable, she gets good results and really cares about the outcome for the client." **Recent work:** Acted for a migrant child and her mother in a challenge to a local authority's decision to withhold support and shelter, successfully arguing that they had a duty to provide support under Section 17 of the Children's Act 1989.

Timothy Baldwin (Garden Court Chambers) Experienced junior noted for his expertise in relation to mental health, whose community care practice dovetails with his social housing expertise. He is an editor of the community care law reports. **Strengths:** "Highly regarded for his mental health work." "One of the most industrious members of the successful Garden Court community care team."

Leonie Hirst (Garden Court Chambers) Well-regarded community care barrister noted for her parallel strengths in Court of Protection and immigration work. She has a particular focus on mental health and those cases involving support for those leaving either hospital or detention. **Strengths:** "She's passionate and very hard-working, and gives very, very clear advice. She gets her point across in court very succinctly, and is also very good in negotiation." "She's excellent, hard-working and committed." **Recent work:** Led a successful challenge on behalf of a man who was hospitalised following a stroke and subsequently released without a Section 47 assessment of his needs, leading to him being placed in unsuitable accommodation.

Felicity Williams (Garden Court Chambers) Noted community care junior with a focus on judicial review. She has a particular interest in handling cases relating to aftercare for those leaving prison. **Strengths:** "She has an outstanding and impressive range of public law knowledge. She is emerging as a key barrister for clients with disabilities." "Approachable and a pleasure to work with, she responds speedily, is extremely passionate and is fully committed to the clients." **Recent work:** Represented a young man in a case which examined whether his social care needs had been adequately assessed by his local authority following his release from prison.

Nigel Giffin QC (11KBW) Pre-eminent silk with a fantastic reputation across the board on public law and community care matters. He is frequently instructed in the most complex and high-profile proceedings. **Strengths:** "He's in that category of barristers who are flown in to act in important cases."

Joanne Clement (see p.574) (11KBW) Leading junior in public law who appears on community care cases for both adults and children. She draws praise for her client-friendly demeanour and powerful advocacy. **Strengths:** "She definitely knows her stuff and is approachable, accessible, sensitive and understanding. She's able to identify the key issues very quickly at short notice." "She's sensible and has very good judgment." **Recent work:** Acted in a case concerning the question of whether, in certain circumstances, judicial review claims can be amended in the course of community care proceedings.

Andrew Sharland (see p.718) (11KBW) Strong junior whose broad public law practice includes a strong community care component. He is particularly well known for representing government bodies, and is noted for his parallel expertise in judicial review. **Strengths:** "Fantastic, very thorough and able to focus people's minds on what is required." "A very good lawyer generally and a good bet for a local authority that wants representation." **Recent work:** Successfully defended a challenge to Worcestershire County Council's policy of setting a financial limit to the amount that can be spent on community care services for adults.

Tim Buley (Landmark Chambers) Singled out as a future star of the community care field. He frequently appears on high-profile cases and is renowned for his knowledge of the crossover between community care and immigration law. **Strengths:** "He's really bright and technically able, and is very good on the strategy of a case." "He's got a very good legal brain and is good at cutting through all the issues and looking at things from a novel point of view." **Recent work:** Represented the Secretary of State for Health in a case which considered whether a local authority could take into account existing resources in assessing the need for publicly funded service provision.

David Wolfe QC (Matrix Chambers) Heavyweight of the public law sphere, frequently chosen to appear in high-profile and complex community care cases. He wins plaudits for his creative approach and strong analytical skills. **Strengths:** "Excellent – he's very sharp and quick, and will put up a good fight." "If you want creative lawyering delivered with verve and panache, you can't beat him." **Recent work:** Represented a group of five disabled claimants in a leading case which successfully challenged the government's proposed closure of the Independent Living Fund, which provides support to 19,000 individuals to enable them to live independently in their community.

Nicholas Armstrong (Matrix Chambers) High flying community care junior who has a broad claimant-based practice. He is singled out for his expertise in migrant rights and disability law. **Strengths:** "An exceptionally bright, quick and energetic lawyer who specialises in immigration issues relating to community care." "His input is always invaluable. He's very bright and he covers so many areas; he's got his finger on the pulse." **Recent work:** Represented the father in a case which examined the extent to which Article 8 of the ECHR can be used as a basis for arguing that vulnerable adults should remain living within the family.

Chris Buttler (Matrix Chambers) Highly lauded for his human rights-focused community care work, which ties in with his noted Court of Protection practice. He receives particular praise for his tenacity and ability to think laterally and produce novel arguments. **Strengths:** "He's very intelligent, hard-working and willing to help, and his advice is succinct and convincing." "He's very industrious, very quick, and is very good at spotting points and running with them." **Recent work:** Successfully brought a claim on behalf of a psychiatric patient who was detained in demeaning conditions in a hospital.

Sarah Hannett (Matrix Chambers) Valued practitioner with substantial experience of handling judicial review applications, and someone who has lectured in public law and human rights. She also has a noted education practice which complements her community care work. **Strengths:** "Her oral advocacy and written submissions are both excellent. She can be relied on to turn work around on time, and fully address all the issues." "She's instructed on the more complex cases as she's got a lot of community care experience. She'll pick up on the main issues very quickly, even at short notice, and her drafting is excellent." **Recent work:** Acted for the London Probation Trust in bringing an application for a judicial review over the lack of accommodation provision by the responsible local authority for a man leaving prison.

Ian Wise QC (Monckton Chambers) Prolific silk who focuses heavily on claimant representation. He is popular amongst instructing solicitors for his knowledge of children's rights law, and is also particularly experienced in acting for charities. **Strengths:** "Undoubtedly a force to be reckoned with in public law litigation. He has an encyclopaedic knowledge of decided cases and stays completely up to date with developments in all aspects of public law." "A tenacious lawyer who has incredible insight into the Convention on the Rights of the Child and how it should be developed." **Recent work:** Appeared in a case which considered whether a local authority had engaged in sufficient discussions before implementing a tax reduction scheme.

Stephen Broach (Monckton Chambers) High flyer of the administrative public law and community care fields. He is particularly valued for his public policy background and his understanding of children's rights law. **Strengths:** "Very good and also very easy to work with. He's really impressive in terms of his skills and in terms of children's rights, and is a first choice for the most complex cases." "He knows the area of children's law backwards. His drafting style is brilliant and he is really committed." **Recent work:** Led by Ian Wise QC on a Supreme Court case which considered whether individuals who lacked capacity and were receiving local authority funded care were being deprived of their liberty under the ECHR.

Azeem Suterwalla (see p.732) (Monckton Chambers) Highly recommended junior with an active community care practice. He receives particular acclaim for his work relating to age assessment cases and care leavers. **Strengths:** "Extremely engaged and a very good tactician." "Really bright and pleasant to deal with." **Recent work:** Acted for a woman who was a failed asylum seeker and mother of a young child in making a successful claim for local authority support under the Children's Act 1989.

COMPANY: An introduction

Contributed by Michael Todd QC of Erskine Chambers

It doesn't seem too long ago that there appeared to be almost an irreversible exodus of companies from London to far-off and "offshore" destinations, as they sought perhaps more sympathetic, and certainly different, markets and regulatory regimes better suited to their businesses. By way of example, the large insurers migrated, almost in one wave, to Bermuda; the gaming industry migrated to other offshore jurisdictions, such as Gibraltar. Fortunately, that exodus didn't result in any dramatic downturn in work for the corporate lawyer. After all, most migrations were effected by means of a court sanctioned Scheme of Arrangement, which involved imposing a new foreign holding company on top of the existing group as the group's new parent. The effect of such schemes was to move the group's head office function abroad, but to leave the heart of the business beating in the UK.

Now there is further migration afoot. In recent years we have become used to hearing about multimillion-pound businesses operating in the UK, making large profits out of those operations, yet contributing very little to the UK Treasury. Corporate transactional lawyers can expect a flurry of work if the government ever gets round to doing something about the way those companies manage largely to insulate themselves from our corporation tax regime!

More recently, however, it is our corporation tax regime which has attracted businesses from elsewhere. It is reported that so called "Tax Inversions" (buying or merging with businesses in another jurisdiction with a lower tax rate, thereby reducing the overall tax rate) is currently the driver for some 60% of proposed US outward migrations.

Inversions are apparently good for business in the pharma sector, as AbbVie's acquisition of Ireland-based Shire shows. That Inversion, it is said, could slash the business's corporate tax rate from 22% to 13%. Earlier this year, Pfizer's courtship of AstraZeneca was rebuffed, with its price tag of £69.4 billion rejected as inadequate. Since then AstraZeneca's share price has languished well below the £55 per share offered by Pfizer and the market has watched closely whether AstraZeneca's management could pull something out of the hat to match that bid price. Speculation of a renewed bid is rife.

The Cross-border Merger Regulations continue to be a useful tool for pan-European cross-border merger activity, whilst increased demand for advice on restructurings and on financial assistance issues strongly suggests that the domestic market is showing encouraging signs of life.

The financial crisis (accompanied as it was by mis-selling claims, Libor fixing and Foreign Exchange rate fixing, and the division of the responsibilities of the former FSA between the Financial Conduct Authority and the Prudential Regulation Authority) has brought into sharper focus the scope for regulatory expertise. As part of the government's response to the financial crisis of 2008, the long-awaited Financial Services (Banking Reform) Act 2013 has introduced a requirement for certain UK banking groups to "ring-fence" core banking services that are critical to retail customers and SME clients. Ring Fencing Transfer Schemes should, at least in the short term, provide even more work for those versed in Banking and Insurance Business Transfer Schemes.

At the heart of most joint venture and shareholder disputes are issues and principles which require the expertise of the corporate lawyer. Whilst in recent years litigation has tended to settle before trial, there have been some notable exceptions in the past year.

In Charterhouse Capital, the founder and former director of a successful private equity business (in which he retained nearly 10% of the shares) failed in his attempt to prevent the exercise of a drag-along provision in articles of association which had been recently adopted by those who wished to accept an offer from a company controlled by the majority.

There are signs that the courts are becoming more robust when dealing with fraudulent conduct. In the ongoing JSC BTA Bank litigation the Commercial Court directed disclosure by solicitors employed by Mr Ablyazov (the former chairman of the bank) of communications between Mr Ablyazov and the solicitors, finding that those documents were outside the normal scope of the solicitors' professional engagement on the basis of Mr Ablyazov's iniquitous conduct, and therefore could not attract legal professional privilege.

Following the relatively recent litigation in Ultraframe v Fielding and in Wilkinson v West Coast Capital (concerning the Gadget Shop), you may be forgiven for thinking that the law concerning conflicts of duty and interest under the Companies Act was fairly well settled. In fact, however, that is not the case, as is demonstrated by the recent Court of Appeal decision in Sharma v Sharma.

In the near future, we can also look forward to further consideration of the law relating to the exercise of fiduciary powers and improper purpose by the Supreme Court, when it hears the appeal from the Court of Appeal's recent decision in JKX Oil & Gas v Eclairs Group.

Contents:

LONDON

Company London	
Leading Sets	
Band 1	
Erskine Chambers *	
Band 2	
4 Stone Buildings *	
Band 3	
Maitland Chambers *	
New Square Chambers *	
XXIV Old Buildings *	
Serle Court *	
South Square *	
Band 4	
Enterprise Chambers *	
11 Stone Buildings *	
Leading Silks	
Star individuals	
Chivers David	*Erskine Chambers* *
Crow Jonathan	*4 Stone Buildings* *
Hollington Robin	*New Square Chambers* *
Miles Robert	*4 Stone Buildings*
Moore Martin	*Erskine Chambers* *
Snowden Richard	*Erskine Chambers*
Todd Michael	*Erskine Chambers* *
Band 1	
Bompas George	*4 Stone Buildings*
Davis-White Malcolm	*XXIV Old Buildings*
Dicker Robin	*South Square* *
Girolami Paul	*Maitland Chambers* *
Mabb David	*Erskine Chambers*
Marshall Philip	*Serle Court* *
Mowschenson Terence	*Wilberforce Chambers (ORL)* ◊
Steinfeld Alan	*XXIV Old Buildings*
Trower William	*South Square*
Zacaroli Antony	*South Square*
Band 2	
Arden Peter	*Erskine Chambers* *
Boyle Alan	*Serle Court* *
Brisby John	*4 Stone Buildings*
Collings Matthew	*Maitland Chambers* *
Gibbon Michael	*Maitland Chambers* *
Green Michael	*Fountain Court Chambers (ORL)* ◊ *
Hill Richard G	*4 Stone Buildings*
Hilliard Lexa	*11 Stone Buildings*
Jones Philip	*Serle Court* *
Moss Gabriel	*South Square*
Moverley Smith Stephen	*XXIV Old Buildings*
Newman Catherine	*Maitland Chambers* *
Potts James	*Erskine Chambers* *
Stubbs Rebecca	*Maitland Chambers* *
Trace Anthony	*Maitland Chambers* *
Tregear Francis	*XXIV Old Buildings*
Band 3	
Blayney David	*Serle Court* *
de Garr Robinson Anthony	*One Essex Court (ORL)* ◊ *
Goldring Jeremy	*South Square*
Toube Felicity	*South Square* *
New Silks	
Allison David	*South Square* *
Smith Tom	*South Square* *
Thompson Andrew	*Erskine Chambers* *

* *Indicates set / individual with profile.*
◊ *(ORL) = Other Ranked Lawyer.*

Company London	
Leading Juniors	
Star individuals	
Thornton Andrew	*Erskine Chambers* *
Band 1	
Davies Edward	*Erskine Chambers* *
Lightman Daniel	*Serle Court* *
Band 2	
Banner Gregory	*Maitland Chambers* *
Collingwood Timothy	*Serle Court* *
Cone John	*Erskine Chambers* *
Denton-Cox Gregory	*4 Stone Buildings* *
Dougherty Nigel	*Erskine Chambers* *
Eaton Turner David	*New Square Chambers* *
Gillyon Philip	*Erskine Chambers* *
Greenwood Paul	*4 Stone Buildings*
Griffiths Ben	*Erskine Chambers*
Harrison Christopher	*4 Stone Buildings* *
Horan Stephen	*Erskine Chambers*
Mumford David	*Maitland Chambers* *
Prentis Sebastian	*New Square Chambers* *
Ritchie Richard	*XXIV Old Buildings*
Roberts Catherine	*Erskine Chambers* *
Shaw Benjamin	*Erskine Chambers* *
Shekerdemian Marcia	*11 Stone Buildings*
Shivji Sharif	*4 Stone Buildings*
Stokes Mary	*Erskine Chambers* *
Stonefrost Hilary	*South Square*
Band 3	
Adair Stuart	*XXIV Old Buildings*
Adamyk Simon	*New Square Chambers* *
Addy Catherine	*Maitland Chambers* *
Bailey James	*New Square Chambers* *
Barden Alex	*Erskine Chambers* *
Cumming Edward	*XXIV Old Buildings*
Griffiths Peter	*4 Stone Buildings*
Holtham den Besten Ruth	*Serle Court* *
Ife Linden	*Enterprise Chambers*
Knott James	*4 Stone Buildings*
Kyriakides Tina	*11 Stone Buildings*
Lascelles David	*Littleton Chambers (ORL)* ◊ *
McCulloch Niall	*Enterprise Chambers*
Nourse Edmund	*One Essex Court (ORL)* ◊ *
O'Leary Sam	*One Essex Court (ORL)* ◊ *
Tomson Alastair	*4 Stone Buildings*
Zelin Geoffrey	*Enterprise Chambers*

Band 1

Erskine Chambers

See profile on p.789

THE SET

Erskine Chambers is the undisputed king of company law sets. It is particularly adept at advisory work such as schemes of arrangement, but also possesses enviable and increasing strength in contentious matters. It continues to be the choice of many of the leading City firms and fields members in the majority of the leading company law cases of the day. Sources say that it is "the best corporate set: heavyweight and authoritative, yet also approachable and practical."

Client service: "The clerking is very efficient and prompt, and they give good advice." The senior clerk is Mike Hannibal.

SILKS

David Chivers QC A name at the top of many solicitors' lists, with exceptional experience in both litigation and non-contentious company work. He is consistently praised for the quality and clarity of his advice as well as his wholly authoritative advocacy. **Strengths:** "A compelling heavyweight barrister. He listens, discusses and then gives completely clear advice." "He has truly expert knowledge of his areas of practice and offers cutting-edge advice." **Recent work:** Acted on the proposed scheme of arrangement relating to return of value regarding the sale by Vodafone of USD84 billion shares in Verizon.

Martin Moore QC (see p.675) An adviser of the highest quality on company matters, who is regularly instructed on some of the largest and most complicated takeovers and transactions. He is noted for his outstanding diligence and for the practicality of his advice. **Strengths:** "He has this enormous fund of common sense. If he thinks something isn't quite right, he'll tell you it won't fly and give you reasons why." **Recent work:** Advised Verizon on the proposed scheme of arrangement for Vodafone's sale of USD84 billion Verizon shares.

Richard Snowden QC A highly respected practitioner who receives particular praise for his advocacy. He is also active on a range of advisory matters. **Strengths:** "Probably Erskine's best litigator in what is a highly competitive field." **Recent work:** Instructed in a case concerning the estate of Henry Fok and various companies owned by the Fok family.

Michael Todd QC A superb practitioner with vast experience and a reputation matched by few in the market. He acts on a wide range of disputes, including directors' duties and shareholder issues, and also advises on M&A. **Strengths:** "A first choice for anything really tricky." "Very good if you want heavy-hitting advice." **Recent work:** Acted on a Bermudian case on appeal to the Privy Council alleging fraud arising from a complex insurance and reinsurance scheme.

David Mabb QC Has a wealth of experience on a wide range of company law matters, and is a true leader in court as well as in an advisory capacity. Sources are quick to point out his technical strengths. **Strengths:** "A very experienced lawyer who is excellent on the technical side of things."

Peter Arden QC Highly regarded and experienced QC who acts across a broad spectrum of company and insolvency matters. Sources note his measured but effective manner in court. **Strengths:** "Very analytical and very knowledgeable." "He's really smart."

James Potts QC A young silk with a broad commercial, company and insolvency practice, who impresses commentators with his analytical prowess and drafting skills. He regularly appears in significant disputes in the High Court. **Strengths:** "He's got great intellectual firepower, and sees things other people don't." "Excellent with clients, he understands the issues and finds solutions to problems." **Recent work:** Represented Marylebone Cricket Club in resisting an injunction to restrain the holding of the club annual general meeting.

Andrew Thompson QC (see p.736) A new silk who receives consistent praise for his intelligence and legal ability. His practice encompasses a variety of company and insolvency law matters. **Strengths:** "Very personable and very reliable academically." "One of the smartest lawyers around." **Recent work:** Assisted David Chivers QC for the petitioner in an unfair prejudice petition against Charterhouse Capital.

JUNIORS

Andrew Thornton (see p.737) Stands head and shoulders above other juniors when it comes to schemes of arrangement, according to sources. His practice focuses largely on advisory matters relating to corporate transactions. **Strengths:** "Very pragmatic and commercial, and amazingly responsive." **Recent work:** Advised on the proposed merger of Sharp Electronica España, Sociedad Unipersonal and Sharp Electronics (Europe).

Edward Davies (see p.584) A pragmatic and experienced junior whose practice takes in a mix of insolvency and company work. Sources are full of praise for both his advocacy and his advisory work. **Strengths:** "Excellent on corporate advisory matters and, in particular, unfair prejudice claims." "He is very user-friendly, very responsive and very commercial." **Recent work:** Acted as junior to David Chivers QC acting for Nat Rothschild on the proposition of an unfair prejudice petition relating to Bumi Resources.

Catherine Roberts (see p.709) A knowledgeable and technically strong barrister who acts for clients both in the UK and in offshore jurisdictions. She has a broad base of experience in company and insolvency matters. **Strengths:** "Offers practical and effective advice on difficult legal questions." "Technically first-class." **Recent work:** Advised on the compulsory acquisition of Alpha Group Jersey from shareholders.

John Cone (see p.576) A seasoned junior who has decades of experience in company law. His practice now focuses almost purely on advisory matters, and he has particular proficiency at drafting schemes of arrangement. **Strengths:** "A man with years of experience who is very commercial and user-friendly."

Nigel Dougherty (see p.589) Has gained a strong reputation as a proficient junior, who handles a wide array of company disputes. He is instructed across a range of minority shareholder disputes, and also handles unfair prejudice petitions and acts as an adviser on transactional matters. **Strengths:** "Sound and in control on every case." **Recent work:** Acted as junior for claimant Eclairs Group in a complex company case concerning directors' conduct.

Philip Gillyon (see p.608) Veteran senior junior who is highly rated by sources for the strength of his company and insolvency practice. Appears as leader and junior on a range of disputes. **Strengths:** "He's very bright and incisive, and gives good strategic commercial advice. He's user-friendly as well – clients like him." **Recent work:** Assisted Appleby on company issues in a case concerning alleged breach of fiduciary duty.

Ben Griffiths An insolvency and company practitioner who has a strong reputation with peers and clients alike for his litigation-based practice. He has appeared in a number of reported cases in the High Court and Court of Appeal. **Strengths:** "He is diligent, thorough and willing to get his hands dirty." "Technically very strong." **Recent work:** Instructed as junior to Gavin Kealey QC and Andrew Thompson QC in a case between BAT Industries and Windward Prospects concerning issues around the latter's insolvency.

Stephen Horan A senior junior able to bring his experience as a former City solicitor to bear on a range of company matters, most notably on schemes of arrangements concerning potential mergers and takeovers in the energy sector. **Strengths:** "A delightful opponent – very thoughtful and intelligent." "A provider of refreshingly clear and commercial advice." **Recent work:** Assisted oil exploration company Rockhopper with the drafting of a scheme of arrangement and additional reduction of capital.

Benjamin Shaw (see p.718) Has a strong practice finely balanced between advisory work and litigation. Noted for his in-depth knowledge of company law and his expertise in M&A matters. **Strengths:** "Provides responsive and pragmatic advice on technical company law issues." **Recent work:** Acted as lead company junior for Petrodel Resources against Prest in the Supreme Court.

Mary Stokes (see p.729) Highly regarded by sources due to the quality of her written work and her advocacy. She regularly handles company disputes. **Strengths:** "She knows company law inside-out." "Superb at providing detailed technical advice on unusual structures." **Recent work:** Contributed written advice in the case of Smithton Ltd v Naggar and others, heard before the Chancery Division of the High Court.

Alex Barden (see p.543) An emerging presence at the Company Bar, who is noted by sources for the tenacity of his advocacy. **Strengths:** "Concise and to the point, he gives a very quick response and provides the answers you require." "He gives very prompt and commercially astute advice, shot through with technical analysis." **Recent work:** Acted in Magri Builders, representing Pattinson as petitioner in an unfair prejudice shareholders petition under S994 of the Companies Act 2006.

Band 2

4 Stone Buildings
See profile on p.865

THE SET

Company law forms the main staple of 4 Stone Buildings' work, with nearly all of its barristers having a solid foundation in the area. As a result, it remains a go-to set for clients needing high-quality and considered advice and representation in all manner of company or insolvency matters.

Client service: "The clerks there were very helpful. They explained the situation to the client and there were never any issues regarding fees." David Goddard heads up the clerking team.

SILKS

Robert Miles QC One of the leading barristers currently at the Commercial Chancery Bar, who has a wide-ranging practice encompassing company, insolvency and commercial dispute resolution. Regarded as one of the top litigators around, and a man with exceptional technical skills. **Strengths:** "He is outstanding and has such a winning way in court." "A delight to work with. You don't get something very academic from him – you get practical, sensible advice." **Recent work:** Acted in a directors' duties case brought against sometime directors of MWB Business Exchange.

Jonathan Crow QC Has established a reputation as one of the very finest practitioners working in company law, and has pre-eminent status in several other practice areas. Sources are quick to point out his strengths in advocacy which make him one of the first choices for a major chancery case. **Strengths:** "An absolute delight to work with, even when he's on the other side. He's a really good lawyer." **Recent work:** Successfully defended Sonja Kohn and another defendant in a civil fraud trial resulting from the Madoff scandal. The case involved complex company aspects.

George Bompas QC Another of 4 Stone Building's multi-talented QCs, Bompas is instructed on a variety of commercial chancery matters, with company law being one of them. He has 20 years as a silk to his name, and there are few more experienced company practitioners around. **Strengths:** "He anticipates the implications of the point before most people have even grasped it." "He's exceptional and has great knowledge of the law." **Recent work:** Represented Fuchs Oil Middle East in a trial against Chemtrade in the British Virgin Islands (BVI), relating to a cross-border joint venture.

John Brisby QC Described as a "big-hitter" by sources who are quick to point out his formidable strength in the courtroom. He has a wide-ranging practice with expertise in civil fraud, financial services and insolvency matters, as well as his obvious strengths in company law. **Strengths:** "He's everything you want in a QC – he really fights the tough battles. His cross-examination is known to be fearsome." "A strong advocate who will fight a case creatively and with the client's interests at heart. He has a tigerish determination." **Recent work:** Representing John and Frank Partridge in defence of a case concerning the sale of Partridge Fine Arts.

Richard Hill QC Focuses his practice on litigation in company and other commercial chancery matters. He has developed a strong practice as a junior silk, and is known for his outstanding work rate. **Strengths:** "He has every weapon he could possibly need to become a fantastic silk and a great leader." "He is a very diligent and thorough barrister." **Recent work:** Instructed as part of a high-powered litigation team to represent the former owners of Liverpool FC in its dispute against RBS.

JUNIORS

Paul Greenwood An experienced junior highly rated among peers for the strength of his company law practice. He regularly appears in significant disputes, often acting as sole counsel. **Strengths:** "He provides clear and focused advice, and his sense of humour is a real asset when you're working as a team on a difficult case." **Recent work:** Acted in an unfair prejudice petition relating to a clothes retailer.

Gregory Denton-Cox Credited by sources as a talented senior junior who is recognised for his strong work ethic. He has a broad-based commercial and chancery practice. **Strengths:** "A workhorse and a generally excellent lawyer." **Recent work:** Instructed as junior to Lord Goldsmith QC, Richard Hill QC and Philip Marshall QC in litigation in the Court of Appeal concerning a company that owns three famous London hotels.

Christopher Harrison A veteran senior junior who has a great deal of experience in company, civil fraud and other commercial chancery matters. He is regularly instructed as lead or sole counsel in a range of complex disputes. **Strengths:** "Very easy to use and willing to roll up his sleeves and get stuck in. He has a commercially realistic approach." **Recent work:** Represented Premier Telecom Communications Group in a Court of Appeal hearing concerning an expert share valuation.

Sharif Shivji A quality senior junior who is particularly recognised for his ability in financial matters. He has previous experience as a derivatives trader and economist. **Strengths:** "Offers great analysis of a case and provides good commercial advice." **Recent work:** Instructed as junior to Richard Hill QC in Nasser Kazeminy v Kamal Siddiqi, a case concerning an investor claiming shares in a research and development company.

Peter Griffiths A highly experienced senior junior of some 37 years' call, who is noted for his advocacy skills. He often appears as sole counsel in a variety of chancery cases. **Strengths:** "Peter was very, very good. He obviously gets to grip with issues very quickly and he has a quite aggressive approach, which means he doesn't let any point go that's important to the case." **Recent work:** Appeared for two defendants in Blindley Heath Investments v Bass, a significant recent case in the Chancery Division concerning rectification of the register following a share transfer.

Alastair Tomson A well-regarded junior who primarily practises in company disputes, but also has expertise in civil fraud, insolvency and other chancery matters. **Strengths:** "A rising star who can hold his own against silks." "He's extremely personable, calm under extreme pressure, and an articulate advocate."

James Knott An emerging name in chancery law, who has a strong reputation for his company law capabilities. He is particularly credited for his drafting skills. **Strengths:** "Very diligent and very thorough." "He's really great on the documents and the detail." **Recent work:** Acted as junior to Jonathan Crow QC in the defence of Sonja Kohn against fraud claims arising from the Madoff scandal.

Band 3

Maitland Chambers

See profile on p.831

THE SET

A formidable commercial chancery set with a large number of barristers who undertake a significant amount of company work. Its members are often instructed on major company cases, including those involving directors' duties and shareholders' disputes. Sources are quick to point out Maitland Chambers' depth in the area, saying: "At the junior end of the practice, the people are all of such a high quality. They've got some amazing young blood as well as some great silks."

Client service: "The clerks are commercial and user-friendly." "They know exactly what you want and get things done with a minimum of fuss."

SILKS

Paul Girolami QC Sources are full of praise for Girolami's company law practice, and he is regularly instructed on significant matters in the UK and abroad, both from an advisory standpoint and in court. **Strengths:** "Hugely impressive, he gets on top of papers and has a sound knowledge of the law."

Matthew Collings QC An experienced and adept QC who has appeared in a plethora of reported cases across the Chancery Bar. Commentators count his strategic ability and client-handling skills among his many strengths. **Strengths:** "Wonderful with clients and a great advocate." "What you get with him is a great deal of experience and an extremely user-friendly barrister." **Recent work:** Instructed on a shareholder dispute for a number of claimants against Union Zone Management, a BVI company.

Michael Gibbon QC A highly regarded silk who undertakes a range of company law litigation, and has particular expertise in cases touching on tax issues. He gains plaudits for his advocacy skills and user-friendly approach.

Catherine Newman QC A vastly experienced silk who is able to put her wider commercial chancery skills to use in an array of company matters. Sources highlight her exceptional advocacy as a key strength. **Strengths:** "Whenever a question comes up, she's already thought of it. She's just so thorough; it's quite incredible." "She's great – she gives good, pragmatic advice and tends not to sit on the fence." **Recent work:** Acted in a case concerning a company takeover and alleged breach of warranty leading to significant liability for damages.

Anthony Trace QC A respected and experienced silk who has a superb reputation for his advocacy prowess. He is instructed on important company cases, and has handled a number of matters on behalf of the late Russian oligarch Boris Berezovsky. **Strengths:** "Aggressive when he needs to be but charming with clients." **Recent work:** Represented the late Boris Berezovsky in a case concerning a without-notice interim freezing injunction obtained against him.

Rebecca Stubbs QC She has an emerging silk's practice which primarily sees her instructed on company and insolvency matters. Among her other areas of expertise are financial services and banking matters. **Strengths:** "Excellent and destined for great things."

JUNIORS

David Mumford A top-notch junior who has developed an excellent reputation for company work as part of his wider commercial chancery practice. Sources are quick to praise his excellent legal mind. **Strengths:** "Really cool, calm and collected. He's an extremely thorough and really steely sort of guy. Very approachable to the client, but a man of steel to the opposition." **Recent work:** Acted for Bumi with regard to a shareholder-initiated unfair prejudice petition.

Gregory Banner (see p.542) Acts for clients in cases involving energy and natural resources and is known for his work on matters involving Russian interests. He has some 25 years' experience of working in company cases. **Strengths:** "He's a good advocate, who is very measured and picks up the temperature of the court. Clients enjoy working with him." **Recent work:** Represented Ludsin Overseas in a damages claim resulting from an investment in real estate which failed.

Catherine Addy She is primarily known for her work in insolvency and company matters and her reputation has led to her being appointed to the Treasury A-panel. Addy acts on a broad range of work, including directors' disqualification cases. **Strengths:** "She's very punchy in her style and always very busy." **Recent work:** Acted as junior to Mark Cunningham QC for the Secretary of State for Business, Innovation and Skills in a directors' disqualification case against six defendants.

New Square Chambers

See profile on p.837

THE SET

Company law forms a significant part of New Square Chambers' expertise and its members act in cases for domestic and international clients on a range of matters, both contentious and non-contentious in nature. Sources highlight it as "a very good set that provides a collegiate working experience for those that instruct it."

SILKS

Robin Hollington QC One of the leading practitioners on all manner of shareholder disputes. His 35 years at the Bar have made him a hugely experienced and respected lawyer who is one of the first ports of call for complex company cases. **Strengths:** "He is Mr Shareholder Disputes." "He turned around the instructions very quickly and provided very thorough advice." **Recent work:** Represented Caldero Trading as petitioner in a shareholders' dispute seeking to wind up defendant Beppler & Jacobson.

JUNIORS

David Eaton Turner A senior junior of 30 years' call whom sources praise for his abilities in company and insolvency matters. He regularly receives instructions in shareholder disputes and on issues involving directors' duties. **Strengths:** "He's a very bright guy, who is very reliable and thoughtful." **Recent work:** Represented Black Pearl Investments in an insolvency case involving travel company Goldtrail.

Sebastian Prentis An experienced junior who is often instructed on shareholder disputes and other company law cases. He is an approachable and responsive barrister who is building a strong and effective practice in the area. **Strengths:** "He is incredibly clever, sensible and approachable, and a good team member." **Recent work:** Represented a shareholder in Apollo Ventures in a case in the Turks and Caicos Islands alleging unfair prejudice.

Simon Adamyk (see p.531) He is instructed on a variety of company and insolvency matters, and regularly appears for clients in offshore jurisdictions including the BVI and the Bahamas. **Strengths:** "A pleasure to be against as he is both professional and courteous." **Recent work:** Acted for the ex-chairman of the board of two offshore investment funds in Jersey in defence of claims for breach of fiduciary duty.

James Bailey A well-regarded barrister whose practice encompasses company and insolvency cases, and is heavily freighted with unfair prejudice petitions and directors' duties cases. He acts for clients internationally, including in offshore jurisdictions such as the Cayman Islands. **Strengths:** "He is really easy to deal with," "thorough, responsive and very knowledgeable." **Recent work:** Acted for UPMS in its action against Fort Gilkicker, a significant case involving multiple derivative actions following alleged dishonest conduct by a company director.

XXIV Old Buildings

See profile on p.838

THE SET

A good number of the members of XXIV Old Buildings specialise in company law, and it forms one of the set's core areas. It has a splendid reputation for

offshore work and is a go-to set for company cases in jurisdictions including the Channel Islands and the BVI.
Client service: "The clerks have always been very easy to work with and very proactive. They go out of their way to look after you."

SILKS
Alan Steinfeld QC A titan of the Bar, with more than 45 years' experience as a barrister and some 27 as a silk handling company cases. He regularly appears in offshore jurisdictions. **Strengths:** "You bring him in when you want the definitive, punchy view of things. He's very incisive." "He's an exceptional talent who cuts to the chase." **Recent work:** Assisted with Carlyle Capital v Conway, a massive suit alleging mismanagement and breach of fiduciary duty in relation to a failed investment fund.

Malcolm Davis-White QC He concentrates a substantial part of his practice on company law, and regularly acts on cases with an offshore element. He has a superb reputation, and is praised for his intellect and detail-oriented approach. **Strengths:** "He's on top of the law and very practical in applying it." "The man to go to on directors' disqualification – he literally wrote the book." **Recent work:** Successfully defended a client in directors' disqualification proceedings following the insolvency of several companies.

Stephen Moverley Smith QC Has developed a strong practice, and has particular strength in company and offshore work. He is an experienced figure of nearly 30 years' call. **Strengths:** "He takes a robust, definitive view of things, but also has a good beside manner and is user-friendly." **Recent work:** Instructed in a case in the BVI alleging fraud relating to an attempted liquidation of a BVI company.

Francis Tregear QC An accomplished silk who is recognised by sources for his proficiency in complex shareholder disputes and other company matters. He is regularly instructed on international cases, including those in offshore jurisdictions. **Strengths:** "He's great with clients as he explains things very well, is completely receptive to client needs and can very quickly gain people's confidence." "He has a very broad range of experience and can draw upon it effectively." **Recent work:** Represented a client in relation to an application for termination of liquidation of a BVI company. The application was brought by a shareholder and director.

JUNIORS
Richard Ritchie A hugely experienced junior who is noted for his work in offshore jurisdictions including, of late, the Channel Islands and the Isle of Man. **Strengths:** "He unravels complicated factual scenarios and his legal analysis is top of the tree." "His advice is thorough and clear." **Recent work:** Instructed on a breach of warranty claim concerning a shareholders' agreement.

Stuart Adair He focuses his practice on contentious company and insolvency matters, and is strong on unfair prejudice petitions and other shareholder disputes. Sources are "very impressed" with the clarity of his advice. **Strengths:** "He was very user-friendly and able to speak in layman's terms." "He is very thoughtful and his drafting is of the highest order." **Recent work:** Defended clients in an unfair prejudice petition relating to a technology company.

Edward Cumming A "very sharp" junior praised for his client-handling skills. He has a wide-ranging commercial and chancery practice and is making a name for himself in several areas of specialism. **Strengths:** "He's got tremendous legal knowledge and he's dedicated, has a great work ethic and is a great team player." **Recent work:** Represented six property investment firms in a case concerning service of proceedings without seeking the court's permission.

Serle Court
See profile on p.860

THE SET
Many barristers at the set feature company law as part of their practice and numerous members of chambers have written authoritatively on company law matters. The set has good strength and skill at both junior and senior levels.
Client service: "They are one of the best-clerked chambers around. Really professional and a very slick machine." "They've been excellent at managing diaries and getting back to us quickly."

SILKS
Philip Marshall QC A leading company and commercial silk who is called upon to litigate in some of the top cases around. He is noted for his robust advocacy and is a formidable opponent. **Strengths:** "A very effective advocate – judges always listen to him." "Excellent if you need a weighty opinion." **Recent work:** Acted for Hobart Capital Markets in its case against Naggar and others concerning directors' duties.

Alan Boyle QC An immensely experienced figure, who has spent over 40 years working in commercial chancery. Sources are quick to comment on his very strong reputation in company matters. **Strengths:** "Calm, unflappable under pressure and someone with sound commercial judgement." **Recent work:** Acted in Lictor Anstalt v Mir Steel, a case involving the insolvency of a company that owned a steel mill.

Philip Jones QC A multi-talented silk who practises across the full range of commercial and chancery work. Although his practice is primarily litigious, he also increasingly acts on non-contentious matters. **Strengths:** "A superb all-rounder, who is lovely to deal with. He has superb judgement, and is bright, hard-working and accessible. A really outstanding guy." **Recent work:** Instructed in an Isle of Man claim against directors resulting from the failure of hedge fund Heather.

David Blayney QC Has developed a sound practice as a junior silk in commercial and company work. Sources point out his clear-thinking approach and his grasp of the law as key strengths. **Strengths:** "An incredibly clever technical lawyer, who is very understated but quite brilliant." **Recent work:** Instructed in multiple cases involving Lehman Brothers International (Europe), currently in administration.

JUNIORS
Daniel Lightman A skilled and highly regarded junior, who is credited by sources for his creativity and for knowing the law inside out. **Strengths:** "He's got a brilliant mind and is always thinking of a new angle. He surprises me with innovative ideas in a way that no one else I've worked with does." **Recent work:** He recently appeared as leader for three respondents in the Court of Appeal in Sukhoruchkin v van Bekestein, a case concerning alleged breaches of fiduciary duty, amongst other issues.

Timothy Collingwood (see p.575) A senior junior with a strong practice in company law, who is regularly instructed in shareholder disputes and unfair prejudice petitions. Sources say he is a popular figure in the area, who is easy to deal with. **Strengths:** "His knowledge of S994 petitions is really deep. He has great experience." **Recent work:** Acted for the petitioner on an unfair prejudice petition against LCM Wealth Management.

Ruth Holtham den Besten Has a strong practice across a wide range of commercial chancery matters, and regularly handles company law and insolvency cases. She regularly appears in winding-up petitions and commercial disputes. **Strengths:** "She's a tough and tenacious litigator, who fights through to the end." **Recent work:** Acted for a funder of bookmaker BetVictor in a winding-up petition and shareholder disputes.

South Square
See profile on p.861

THE SET
South Square has a very strong bench of company practitioners, including a raft of high-profile silks. The set is known as one of the best for non-contentious company work, including schemes of arrangement, but is also very strong in litigation, particularly in matters that touch on insolvency.
Client service: "The clerks are great, and try very hard to help." "They are good, flexible and responsive." Ashley Carr is the senior clerk.

SILKS
Robin Dicker QC A leading silk for company disputes, who regularly appears in significant cases in the Court of Appeal and Supreme Court. **Strengths:** "A very smooth advocate, who is an excellent cross-examiner and very detailed in his approach."

William Trower QC A top practitioner in matters involving company and insolvency law, who has acted on some of the leading recent cases in the area. He is also head of chambers. **Strengths:** "He's a very smart guy, who is very thoughtful." **Recent work:** Advised hibu on schemes of arrangement for the company, formerly known as Yell Group.

Antony Zacaroli QC An experienced figure, with over 25 years at the Bar. He has a wide-ranging, top-notch chancery practice, that sees him making forays into company law cases. **Strengths:** "Technically excellent, calm under pressure and very user-friendly." **Recent work:** Acted for creditors in a case concerning the insolvency of Lehman Brothers International Europe.

Gabriel Moss QC A barrister with 40 years' experience, who focuses his practice on insolvency and company work. He is a regular fixture in the senior courts, and has handled a number of recent cases in the Court of Appeal and Supreme Court. **Strengths:** "A man with a very lofty intellect."

Felicity Toube QC A regular in major insolvency and company matters, who acts internationally, including in cases in the Cayman Islands. She is praised by sources for her ability to handle clients and for her strong advocacy. **Strengths:** "She is tremendous as she's super-bright and very, very user-friendly." **Recent work:** Acted for the joint provisional liquidators of ARM Asset Backed Securities.

Tom Smith QC A new silk who is recommended for both the strength of his skill on paper and his abilities on his feet. **Strengths:** "His advocacy was just superb; very measured and persuasive." "Really, really impressive and extremely good technically." **Recent work:** Represented Travelodge in the company's restructuring.

David Allison QC One of South Square's crop of new QCs, who had a fantastic career as a junior. He is highly regarded in company matters, and is experienced in drafting schemes of arrangement and litigating shareholders' agreements and directors' duties cases. **Strengths:** "He's incredibly user-friendly and as smart as anyone at the Bar. He's always impeccably prepared and has an excellent manner in court." **Recent work:** Acted for Fitness First in a group and company restructuring.

Jeremy Goldring QC Acts across a range of matters, including company law cases, as well as banking and finance matters. Part of his practice involves acting on offshore cases.

JUNIORS

Hilary Stonefrost An experienced junior who has an impressive track record in working in company and insolvency matters. She has acted on numerous cases involving challenged schemes of arrangement. **Strengths:** "She's very measured and thoughtful in her submissions."

Band 4

Enterprise Chambers

See profile on p.788

THE SET

A set with both insolvency and company lawyers that is instructed on the full range of company matters. It is a smaller offering than many of its rivals but nevertheless has quality to spare and is capable of fielding excellent barristers in the major company law cases. **Client service:** "My overall impression is of a very well-organised chambers that provides a really smooth service." "It is a very welcoming and friendly chambers."

JUNIORS

Linden Ife A junior with more than 30 years' experience of working in company law. She is a passionate litigator who focuses on matters such as shareholder disputes and unfair prejudice petitions. **Strengths:** "A formidable advocate who is never intimidated and has no difficulty arguing against silks. She has great judgement and is very quick with papers." "Linden is incisive and clear-thinking, and quickly gets to the nub of an issue." **Recent work:** Acted for a company alleging breach of fiduciary duty against former directors.

Niall McCulloch A proficient company lawyer who represents clients in the UK and offshore, and has particular expertise in matters relating to the BVI. Sources note his advocacy prowess as a particular strength. **Strengths:** "He is incredibly bright, excellent on his feet and very approachable." "He is excellent in terms of his technical ability and he has great personal skills." **Recent work:** Represented Aiteal (Commercial and Project Management) in a High Court dispute concerning directors' duties and alleged breach of fiduciary duty.

Geoffrey Zelin A senior junior with a wealth of experience in all manner of company and insolvency work. He is noted for the toughness of his advocacy. **Strengths:** "A very creative thinker, who is very clever, works hard and really takes ownership of the case." **Recent work:** Acted on a dispute concerning transfer of shares in Tannhauser.

11 Stone Buildings

See profile on p.868

THE SET

11 Stone Buildings houses a number of highly capable company practitioners able to undertake the gamut of work, both advisory and litigious. Its barristers are regularly sighted in the senior courts, including on significant appeals. **Client service:** "The clerks were very friendly and approachable. They were helpful in trying to arrange conferences and very flexible in arranging them outside working hours."

SILKS

Lexa Hilliard QC A highly rated silk who is particularly known for her abilities in company and insolvency cases. Sources comment favourably on her client-handling skills. **Strengths:** "I was massively impressed by her advocacy skills. She certainly put her arguments across eloquently." "She gave very clear advice and was very approachable and very pragmatic in her approach to a problem." **Recent work:** Represented the appellant in a Court of Appeal case concerning the interpretation of part of the Companies Act 2006.

JUNIORS

Marcia Shekerdemian A seasoned junior who undertakes a significant amount of company and insolvency litigation. She is often instructed on matters including shareholder disputes and cases involving company liquidation. **Strengths:** "A straightforward and punchy advocate." "She's brilliant, and gives robust, first-class advice. A quality professional." **Recent work:** Acted for the shareholders and directors of a dissolved company in a dispute concerning a petition for restoration.

Tina Kyriakides An experienced junior known for her professionalism and knowledge of company matters. She also acts on matters involving insolvency. **Strengths:** "Diligent, calm and thorough, she always seems to find an answer to a difficult position."

Other Ranked Lawyers

Anthony de Garr Robinson QC (One Essex Court) A skilled and experienced practitioner across a broad spectrum of commercial and chancery areas, including company law. He practises on an international basis and acts in matters in the Bahamas and BVI. **Strengths:** "Very thorough, very smart and good to work with." **Recent work:** Acted for a respondent in an unfair prejudice petition, which subsequently settled.

Edmund Nourse (see p.683) (One Essex Court) An experienced junior who tackles company cases as part of his wider commercial practice. He has received numerous instructions in significant cases, including civil fraud trials. **Strengths:** "A fantastic operator who always gets results." **Recent work:** Acted as junior to Lord Grabiner QC and, separately, Ken Maclean QC in actions relating to the Barclay Brothers' ownership of three major London hotels.

Sam O'Leary (see p.685) (One Essex Court) An emerging talent who undertakes a range of commercial and company cases. Sources are impressed by his proactivity and persistence, as well as his obvious technical skills. **Strengths:** "He is very flexible and adaptable, and also good at coming up with novel ideas and solutions." **Recent work:** Acted as junior to Kenneth MacLean QC and James Potts QC for the majority shareholders of Charterhouse Capital in an unfair prejudice petition brought by a minority owner.

Michael Green QC (Fountain Court Chambers) Rated by sources for the strength of his commercial and chancery practice, he receives regular instructions on company matters. Commentators say he is "intelligent and good to work with." **Strengths:** "It was incredible how destructive he was in his cross-examination." **Recent work:** Acted for Partners Group on a winding-up petition brought in the Cayman Islands against Cybernaut Growth Fund.

David Lascelles (see p.651) (Littleton Chambers) Has a strong reputation for his work in contentious company disputes, including shareholder disputes, issues around share transfers and directors' duties. **Strengths:** "On top of all the detail and possessed of extremely strong analytical skills." "He has a massive brain and an extremely incisive way of getting to the facts and issues." **Recent work:** Acted as junior to Charles Samek QC in a dispute concerning directors' duties in the sale of the Somerfield chain.

Terence Mowschenson QC (Wilberforce Chambers) A highly respected practitioner who remains among the leading barristers at the Company Bar. He has acted on a number of disputes involving offshore jurisdictions. **Strengths:** "A very persuasive, charming and forceful advocate, who is one of London's finest commercial and chancery silks." **Recent work:** Acted in one of the many cases arising from the Madoff fraud, concerning Herald Fund SPC, which was a feeder fund into the fraudulent scheme.

MIDLANDS

Company Midlands
Leading Sets
Band 1
No5 Chambers *
St Philips Chambers *
Leading Silks
Band 1
Anderson Mark *No5 Chambers* A *
Khangure Avtar *St Philips Chambers*
Pepperall Edward *St Philips Chambers*
Leading Juniors
Band 1
Mitchell David *No5 Chambers* A
Najib Shakil *St Philips Chambers* *

Band 1

No5 Chambers

See profile on p.883

THE SET

No5 Chambers is held in high regard for the breadth of expertise it is able to offer in the field of company law. Its members are known for handling work for SMEs from an array of industry sectors, and often advise on partnership disputes, claims of prejudice, restructurings and LLP formations.

Client service: "They are well clerked, agreeable and efficient."

SILKS

Mark Anderson QC Demonstrates particular strength in handing matters involving management disputes and the enforcement of duties and liabilities. **Strengths:** "What distinguishes him is that he is very good in trial and great at cross-examination." "He is very thorough, sensible and pragmatic, and has commercial acumen." **Recent work:** Acted in Safetynet Security Ltd v Coppage, a case concerning a claim against a company director for breach of fiduciary duty.

JUNIORS

David Mitchell Frequently instructed on behalf of Midlands-based SMEs on a wide range of company law matters. He often acts as lead counsel. **Strengths:** "He has a great reputation and knows his law well." **Recent work:** Acted in Yorke v Chambers, a case concerning a dispute arising from the death of the owner of one half of the shares in a number of companies.

St Philips Chambers

See profile on p.886

THE SET

The company law team at St Philips Chambers has established an excellent reputation for the expertise it offers across a range of contentious and advisory work. Its members regularly handle shareholder and director disputes, and demonstrate particular strength in matters concerning unfair prejudice and breach of fiduciary duty.

Client service: "The clerks are very commercial in their approach and good fee negotiators."

SILKS

Avtar Khangure QC Widely regarded as one of the region's foremost company law specialists. He handles a broad range of matters, including those concerning shareholder disputes, breach of duties, and restructurings. **Strengths:** "He is great with clients: he really understands what they are after."

Edward Pepperall QC Offers a wealth of experience in matters arising from shareholder disputes. He is also an authority in the field of restrictive covenants.

JUNIORS

Shakil Najib Handles a wide range of matters in the field of company law, including those arising from partnership disputes. He is an authority on contract law and insolvency, and has experience of acting as lead counsel. **Recent work:** Represented the defendant in Carpet World (Midlands) Limited v Mohammed Imran. The case included a claim against the defendant alleging breach of fiduciary duty, and a petition by the defendant claiming unfair prejudice.

NORTHERN

Company Northern
Leading Sets
Band 1
Kings Chambers *
Leading Silks
Band 1
Casement David *Kings Chambers* *
Chaisty Paul *Kings Chambers* *
A direct access (see p.11).
** Indicates set / individual with profile.*
Alphabetical order within each band. Band 1 is highest.

Band 1

Kings Chambers

See profile on p.918

THE SET

Kings Chambers has established an outstanding reputation on the Northern Circuit for its proficiency in the field of company law. It is home to what interviewees describe as a "good portfolio of top-quality barristers, from silks through to juniors." These individuals regularly handle partnership and shareholder disputes, and matters relating to breach of fiduciary duty and unfair prejudice.

Client service: "They are a very user-friendly set, very commercially focused, with good clerks led by Colin Griffin."

SILKS

David Casement QC Has extensive experience in litigation and arbitration relating to company and insolvency matters. He is highly regarded for his expertise in the field of shareholder disputes, corporate governance and derivative actions. **Strengths:** "He is completely cool, calm and collected and totally unflappable. He is extremely focused on the strategy and commerciality of the case." "He is an excellent advocate – superb – with a confident style in court." **Recent work:** Acted in Bragg v Riddiford, a shareholder dispute and Part 7 claim.

Paul Chaisty QC One of the region's foremost authorities on company law matters. He has a particular interest in cases involving unfair prejudice, and is experienced in all levels of commercial and chancery litigation. **Strengths:** "He is simply top-class: commercial and pragmatic, and tactically very astute. He is a very tough advocate yet sympathetic with the client and very user-friendly." "He is an excellent advocate. He is very sharp and really has the judge's ear." **Recent work:** Acted in a case concerning unfair prejudice claims. The claims related to an alleged breach of fiduciary duty by Swift Fire & Security Group.

WESTERN

Company Western
Leading Sets
Band 1
St John's Chambers *
Band 2
Guildhall Chambers *
Leading Silks
New Silks
Sims Hugh *Guildhall Chambers*
Leading Juniors
Band 1
Ascroft Richard *Guildhall Chambers* *
Marsden Andrew *St John's Chambers* [A] *
Band 2
Dickinson John FH *St John's Chambers* [A] *
Pearce-Smith James *St John's Chambers*
[A] *direct access (see p.11).*
* *Indicates set / individual with profile.*
Alphabetical order within each band. Band 1 is highest.

Band 1

St John's Chambers
See profile on p.893

THE SET

St John's Chambers is renowned on the Western Circuit for the expertise it offers in a range of matters relating to shareholders' disputes. Its members are particularly adept at handling claims involving breach of directors' duties and unfair prejudice, and are known for acting for SMEs from a range of backgrounds, including the manufacturing, energy and healthcare sectors.

Client service: "The clerks, led by Robert Bocock, are good at trying to accommodate you on budget."

JUNIORS

Andrew Marsden Focuses on handling a range of shareholders' disputes, including cases of unfair prejudice and breach of directors' duties. **Strengths:** "He is thoroughly commercial in his approach." "He is very knowledgeable and rarely misses anything."

John Dickinson Handles claims relating to the performance of terms in shareholders' agreements. He is a qualified chartered accountant. **Strengths:** "He ascertains the issues very quickly and deals precisely with what is needed for a hearing at very short notice." "I was so impressed at the care with which he dealt with the case, and the thoroughness of his preparation."

James Pearce-Smith Assists clients with a wide range of shareholder disputes. He represents individuals who are both directors and shareholders of companies. **Strengths:** "His drafting is very clever, absolutely novel and very clear." "He does more than is asked of him." **Recent work:** Represented two shareholders/directors of a manufacturing company in an unfair prejudice claim.

Band 2

Guildhall Chambers
See profile on p.890

THE SET

Guildhall Chambers is able to offer advice and representation across a wide range of contentious company law matters, including those involving unfair prejudice claims, schemes of arrangement and the removal of directors. Its members often represent clients from the technology, financial services and sport sectors.

Client service: "The clerks, led by Mike Norton, are very good, very helpful and very easy to work with."

SILKS

Hugh Sims QC Offers advice and representation across a range of company law matters. He often works on cases involving schemes of arrangement, and is experienced in working with clients with backgrounds in sport and financial services. **Strengths:** "He always thinks of the wider picture." "He is equally good at drafting and advocacy."

JUNIORS

Richard Ascroft Acts for claimants and defendants in unfair prejudice petitions and claims involving misuse of company monies. He is particularly well known for his expertise in proceedings concerning breach of directors' duties and the removal of directors. **Strengths:** "His written advice is very clear and very succinct." "He is a very good technical lawyer."

Competition

Contents:

LONDON

Competition Law London	
Leading Sets	
Band 1	
Brick Court Chambers *	
Monckton Chambers *	
Band 2	
Blackstone Chambers *	
Band 3	
One Essex Court *	
Senior Statesmen	
Senior Statesmen	
Vaughan David	*Brick Court Chambers*
Leading Silks	
Star individuals	
Turner Jon	*Monckton Chambers* *
Band 1	
Beard Daniel	*Monckton Chambers* *
Brealey Mark	*Brick Court Chambers*
Davies Helen	*Brick Court Chambers*
Flynn James	*Brick Court Chambers*
Hoskins Mark	*Brick Court Chambers*
Morris Stephen	*20 Essex Street (ORL)* ◊
Robertson Aidan	*Brick Court Chambers*
Rose Dinah	*Blackstone Chambers*
Sharpe Thomas	*One Essex Court*
Thompson Rhodri	*Matrix Chambers (ORL)* ◊ *
Ward Tim	*Monckton Chambers* [A] *
Band 2	
Carss-Frisk Monica	*Blackstone Chambers*
de la Mare Thomas	*Blackstone Chambers*
Demetriou Marie	*Brick Court Chambers*
Harris Paul	*Monckton Chambers*
Howard Mark	*Brick Court Chambers*
Jowell Daniel	*Brick Court Chambers*
Lasok Paul	*Monckton Chambers* [A] *
Quigley Conor	*Serle Court (ORL)* ◊
Saini Pushpinder	*Blackstone Chambers*
Smith Kassie	*Monckton Chambers*
Stratford Jemima	*Brick Court Chambers*
New Silks	
Bacon Kelyn	*Brick Court Chambers*

◊ (ORL) = Other Ranked Lawyer.

[A] direct access (see p.11).

** Indicates set / individual with profile.*

Competition Law London	
Leading Juniors	
Star individuals	
Holmes Josh	*Monckton Chambers* *
Kennelly Brian	*Blackstone Chambers*
Pickford Meredith	*Monckton Chambers* [A]
Band 1	
Kreisberger Ronit	*Monckton Chambers* *
Lester Maya	*Brick Court Chambers*
Band 2	
Ford Sarah	*Brick Court Chambers*
Gregory Julian	*Monckton Chambers*
Howard Anneli	*Monckton Chambers* [A]
Lask Ben	*Monckton Chambers* [A]
Lindsay Alistair	*Monckton Chambers* [A]
O'Donoghue Robert	*Brick Court Chambers*
Patton Conall	*One Essex Court* *
Peretz George	*Monckton Chambers*
Piccinin Daniel	*Brick Court Chambers*
Quirk Iain	*Essex Court Chambers (ORL)* ◊
Rayment Ben	*Monckton Chambers* [A]
Singla Tony	*Brick Court Chambers*
Band 3	
Abram Sarah	*Brick Court Chambers*
Bates Alan	*Monckton Chambers* [A]
Berridge Alison	*Monckton Chambers* *
Boyd Jessica	*Blackstone Chambers*
Brown Christopher	*Matrix Chambers (ORL)* ◊ *
Cook Matthew	*One Essex Court*
Draper Owain	*One Essex Court*
Jones Tristan	*Blackstone Chambers*
Lee Sarah	*Brick Court Chambers*
Love Sarah	*Brick Court Chambers*
Scannell David	*Brick Court Chambers*
Spitz Derek	*One Essex Court*
Wakefield Victoria	*Brick Court Chambers*
Williams Rob	*Monckton Chambers*
Woolfe Philip	*Monckton Chambers* *
Up-and-coming individuals	
Bailey David	*Brick Court Chambers*
Blackwood Anneliese	*Monckton Chambers*
Gibson Nicholas	*Matrix Chambers (ORL)* ◊
John Laura Elizabeth	*Monckton Chambers* *

Band 1

Brick Court Chambers

See profile on p.774

THE SET

Brick Court houses a plethora of top-quality barristers with deep experience, who can offer assistance in all areas of competition law. Offering a uniformity of quality at both silk and junior level, it is able to tackle the majority of the leading cases of the field, however complex or challenging. As commentators note: "There is a benefit to the way that the practitioners work there. The set is a competition litigation hothouse, and members are able to bounce ideas off each other." Acting for a wide array of clients, including the government and the EC, the set has handled a number of recent interesting cases, including the BMI Healthcare litigation, Sainsbury's v MasterCard, and the Lafarge cement case. **Client service:** Joint senior clerks Julian Hawes and Ian Moyler lead the team. Clients say: "Their clerking is extremely organised and ensures you get the best out of the chambers."

SILKS

Mark Brealey QC A host of loyal clients seek out a silk at the top of his game. He is particularly adept at handling competition damages cases and is noted for his strength in cartel work. **Strengths:** "Unflappable, calm and measured in his approach, he just wins cases." "A very user-friendly, down-to-earth and responsive guy." **Recent work:** Acted for Sainsbury's in the MasterCard interchange fee litigation.

Helen Davies QC A first choice for many, she has wide experience of commercial law generally in addition to her specific competition law knowledge. She is a regular in leading competition cases such as FAPL v Ofcom. **Strengths:** "Sensationally good with clients and someone with an incredibly incisive mind." "She always gets results." **Recent work:** Represented Foundem in a damages claim brought against Google. The case alleged abuse of dominance by the search provider relating to vertical search services.

James Flynn QC A former solicitor in both Brussels and the City, as well as a référendaire at the ECJ, he is a highly esteemed lawyer who has regularly appeared before the Competition Appeal Tribunal (CAT) and the ECJ. He handles all areas of competition law, being an expert in everything from abuse of dominance and market investigations to criminal law cases. **Strengths:** "A highly accomplished advocate and adviser who is very easy to work with and puts clients at ease." "He has one of the finest analytical minds at the Competition Bar." **Recent work:** Represented Air Lingus in Ryanair v CC and Aer Lingus, a case concerning the interaction between UK and EU merger control procedures.

Mark Hoskins QC The toast of many a client due to his excellent legal analysis and accessibility, Hoskins is singled out for his advocacy skills as well as his strong competition law focus. A veteran of more than 80 cases before the ECJ and Court of First Instance, he has also been a regular before the CAT, acting for both public bodies and private clients. **Strengths:** "Incredibly clever, quick, user-friendly and accessible. He is light years ahead of virtually everyone else." "He is commercially very sound and produces succinct, forensic paperwork and crystal-clear arguments." **Recent work:** Acted for Panasonic in Panasonic v Commission before the General Court. This was an appeal against the largest ever aggregate cartel fine imposed by the EC.

Aidan Robertson QC Recognised for his role in many ground-breaking cases, he is well regarded for both his litigation and his advisory work. He is particularly strong on cartel claims, and recently acted for a number of firms in the huge OFT investigation into the construction industry. **Strengths:** "He is ever willing to discuss a brain teaser with you, even if he is not actually working on an active case on your behalf. He's a very friendly person to work with." **Recent work:** Acted for the British Retail Consortium, intervening in MasterCard's appeal to the ECJ regarding inte rchange fees.

Marie Demetriou QC A silk with experience of both competition law and wider EU law matters. She has been particularly active of late in private damages claims. **Strengths:** "Absolutely outstanding." "She is very easy to work with and very responsive." **Recent work:** Represented Morgan Crucible in an appeal to the Supreme Court regarding time limits for bringing a follow-on damages claim in the CAT.

Mark Howard QC Noted for his wide commercial experience and portfolio of highly impressive clients, he is "undeniably one of the top silks at the Commercial Bar." He has particular experience in the Supreme Court and the Court of Appeal. **Strengths:** "Stunning in his presentation, he can easily turn a loss into a win." "An immensely clever man and a highly able advocate," such is his reputation as a leading commercial silk that "when you put him before the CAT it's like putting a really large shark into a small sea." **Recent work:** Appeared in Lafarge Tarmac v Competition Commission.

Daniel Jowell QC As well as being a highly regarded competition law silk, he is a noted commercial litigator who has recently been working on Russian oligarch cases. On the competition law front he has handled a number of precedent-setting cartel damages actions involving the likes of ExxonMobil and Dow Chemical. **Strengths:** "A super-bright barrister with an excellent level of responsiveness." "Daniel Jowell is very thorough and very forensic in his approach. He leaves no stone unturned." **Recent work:** Represented Visa Europe in defending a damages action brought by major retailers in relation to interchange fees.

Kelyn Bacon QC A new silk, who has recently been involved in numerous high-profile cases relating to cartels, abuse of dominance and private damages. **Strengths:** "A very effective operator. She has the ability to arrive at the correct result and has excellent forensic skills." One peer commented: "She's a devastatingly effective advocate – I don't like being on the opposite side to her." **Recent work:** Acted as lead counsel for Teva in a follow-on damages claim brought against Reckitt Benckiser concerning abuse of dominance.

Jemima Stratford QC Has a broad practice that encompasses EU law, competition law, public law and human rights. She has been active of late on several cases concerning the interplay between patents and competition law. **Strengths:** "Impressive, thorough and down to earth. She's a good team player." **Recent work:** Appeared as lead counsel for Nokia in Nokia v HTC.

David Vaughan QC An immediately recognisable name within this field, with extensive experience of appearing before both national and EU courts. He regularly appears for private enterprises seeking to challenge EU decisions. **Strengths:** "Terrifically good at what he does," he is "tenacious and hard-working." **Recent work:** Advised Cathay Pacific Airways in relation to the air cargo cartel investigation.

JUNIORS

Maya Lester A hugely gifted public and competition law expert who receives consistent praise for both her advocacy skills and her thoughtful and creative approach to cases. Over the years she has acted in a number of headline cases, including the dairy cartel affair and the Premier League pay-TV affair. **Strengths:** "She is very measured and persuasive on her feet, managing to clearly cut through a case to its core issues." "A real team player who rolls up her sleeves." **Recent work:** Represented Foundem in the High Court in a case concerning alleged anti-competitive practices with regard to internet search results.

Sarah Ford A strong junior barrister who continues to advance her reputation and standing in this area. She handles a broad range of competition law work and has lately been busy working on a number of damages claims. **Strengths:** "One of the calmest and technically most able lawyers, who is a pleasure to work with." "Excellent – she's hard-working and efficient." **Recent work:** Led by Mark Brealey QC, she represented the bank in the high-profile case of Dahabshiil Transfer Services Ltd v Barclays Bank Plc, concerning abuse of dominance claims.

Robert O'Donoghue Praised for his excellent advocacy skills, and singled out by many as one to watch. He has previous experience as a solicitor in Brussels and also worked at DG Competition. His clients have included the likes of Samsung, British Airways, Google and Glencore. **Strengths:** "A really top-class litigator." "He was so involved that it felt as if he was part of the team, and was just working in the office next to us." **Recent work:** Acted for Google in the widely reported damages action Foundem v Google.

Daniel Piccinin A man on the march at the Bar, who receives excellent commendation from peers and clients alike. A former solicitor, he is noted for his ability to understand the commercial perspective of those that instruct him. **Strengths:** "Commercially and legally extremely sound, he is a pleasure to have on the team." "Intellectually very gifted, he is going to be a huge success." **Recent work:** Led by Kelyn Bacon QC, he is representing Teva in a follow-on damages claim against Reckitt Benckiser following the OFT's decision that Reckitt Benckiser abused its dominant position.

Tony Singla Tipped as a future star, he is already gaining significant recognition from top clients. In addition to competition law, he has wider experience in commercial litigation. **Strengths:** "Frustratingly brilliant," "he is also a very nice man" who is "very highly thought of by many people senior to him." **Recent work:** Defended MasterCard in a private damages claim for over £1 billion.

Sarah Lee A well-regarded practitioner who has experience in wider EU and public law, as well as the competition sphere. She is singled out as having particular expertise in the telecoms sector. **Strengths:** "Incredibly hard-working and conscientious." **Recent work:** Represented BT in the CAT, appealing a decision made by Ofcom.

Sarah Love Her background in economics is a real asset to those that instruct her. Over the years she has built up a strong reputation, having been part of the OFT's counsel team in the 'bank charges' test case, and having appeared in the headline-grabbing Ryanair litigation. **Strengths:** "She grasps the issues very quickly, and is also very user-friendly and excellent to work with." "A sensible practitioner, who is very clever."

Victoria Wakefield Receives significant praise from clients and peers alike. In addition to competition law, her practice spans commercial, public and European law. **Strengths:** "She has inexhaustible supplies of energy and is very, very good." **Recent work:** Represented Electrical Waste Recycling Group in a private damages action against Recolight in the High Court.

Sarah Abram Enters the table this year on the back of a consistent level of praise from the market. She is particularly singled out for her client service and advocacy skills. **Strengths:** "She was very, very good and excellent with the client." "She is beyond where she should be in terms of her litigation skills and decision making for one of her call." **Recent work:** Led by Mark Hoskins QC, she represented Panasonic in an appeal being heard at the General Court against the Commission's finding of a cartel in the market for cathode ray tubes.

David Bailey A client favourite who has a strong focus on EU and competition law. Before coming to the Bar, he was a senior référendaire at the CAT, and a lawyer at Linklaters. **Strengths:** "He is impressive and is gaining an excellent reputation at the Bar." **Recent work:** Led by Nicholas Green QC and Maya Lester, he represented Streetmap in a case against Google in the High Court. Streetmap alleges that Google has engaged in anti-competitive behaviour by favouring its own maps over competitors' in searches.

David Scannell Noted for his competition expertise, and his knowledge of European law more generally. He regularly appears before the ECJ and General Court on cases covering all aspects of EU law. **Strengths:** "Diligent, professional and responsive – nothing is too much trouble for him." **Recent work:** He has had a long-running role in the BSkyB v Ofcom pay-TV case.

Monckton Chambers

See profile on p.833

THE SET

Monckton Chambers offers a wealth of both experienced practitioners and up-and-coming stars. Clients and instructing solicitors regularly return to it due to the excellent advocacy skills and superior expert knowledge to be found at the set. A true market leader, it has members who regularly appear before the High Court, the CAT and the European courts on significant cases such as Lafarge, Eurotunnel and Global Holdings. Individuals at this chambers have been involved in the majority of the follow-on damages actions currently proceeding through the courts. They are further praised by market commentators for having set up a dedicated merger control group, which provides solicitors with teams of counsel who have specialist knowledge of merger work.

Client service: "The clerks, led by David Hockney, are on the ball and very responsive, and take the time to get to know you. They provide a really good service."

SILKS

Jon Turner QC A standout leader in the field, with a wealth of experience to his name. He excels at advocacy and receives consistent praise for the unfathomable depths of his competition law knowledge. **Strengths:** "He works incredibly hard and leaves nothing to chance." "A gold standard barrister, he's a superb advocate who masters the detail and gives himself absolutely to the case." **Recent work:** Lead counsel for National Grid in National Grid Electricity Transmission plc v ABB Limited and Others. The case concerned a damages claim for £500 million.

Daniel Beard QC Very much in vogue, Beard is in high demand and is marked out as the one to watch by all who have seen him in action. Owing to his remarkable body of case experience, his reputation precedes him as one of the best young silks around. **Strengths:** "A fearless advocate who really holds his own in court." "He's extremely clever, very insightful and also very user-friendly." **Recent work:** Acted for ExxonMobil in a multimillion-pound damages claim concerning an alleged aviation fuel cartel in Italy.

Tim Ward QC Receives a wealth of praise for his excellent advocacy and user-friendly attitude to clients. He has been particularly active of late in private damages actions. **Strengths:** "He is incredibly quick and someone who gets to the point." "Very approachable, accessible and hands-on, he's both a sensible and a persuasive advocate." **Recent work:** Represented Akzo Nobel in a judicial review against the Competition Commission. The case turned on whether the UK regulator can block a merger carried out by a company based outside the UK.

Paul Harris QC Combines knowledge of both sports law and competition law, making him a highly attractive option where the two interact. Beyond this, he has a very strong general competition practice and has appeared before all of the major forums. Of late he has proved himself to be particularly strong on follow-on damages actions. **Strengths:** "Like a one-man commando unit, he's highly forceful in court." "A great leader who is excellent on his feet; it's always impressive to see him in action." **Recent work:** Acted for two claimants in the private damages action Department of Health and Others v Reckitt Benckiser, which involved the medicine Gaviscon and raised the issue of exemplary damages.

Paul Lasok QC Noted for both his competition and wider European knowledge, he is a user-friendly barrister who advises and represents private clients and government departments in litigation before the English and European courts, and regularly appears before regulatory authorities. **Strengths:** "He's very good at boiling matters down to the issues that really affect the clients' commercial interests. He can also explain matters to them at a level which is understandable." **Recent work:** Represented the claimant in Secretary of State for Health v Reckitt Benckiser Group Plc, a damages action relating to the supply of certain pharmaceuticals to the NHS.

Kassie Smith QC A young silk popular with top clients, who gains particular praise for her cross-examination and advocacy skills. She has been active of late in a number of matters, ranging from market investigations to private enforcement actions. **Strengths:** "She knows her stuff and has a good head on her shoulders." "She stands her ground and thinks hard about questions." **Recent work:** Acted for the Competition Commission in its market investigation into the private healthcare sector.

JUNIORS

Josh Holmes An outstanding young barrister with an excellent knowledge of competition law and an impressive list of case highlights. Clients sing his praise, whilst peers envy him for the quality of his practice. **Strengths:** "He is a superstar; clients use him as an alternative to a silk." "Absolutely first-rate, he's responsive, switched-on, pragmatic and very easy to use." **Recent work:** Represented Google in a damages claim brought by Streetmap alleging that Google engaged in anti-competitive conduct in the way it compiled search results.

Ronit Kreisberger (see p.648) Regularly instructed by the best law firms in the business, she is respected by peers and clients alike. Kreisberger has a strong private client base, and also acts for government bodies and the regulator. **Strengths:** "A fearless advocate." "She is very helpful, clear and commercial, and is able to advise on new legal developments." **Recent work:** Represented Cathay Pacific Airways as junior counsel in its appeal against the EC's decision to impose fines in relation to the air cargo cartel.

Anneli Howard A former Freshfields lawyer who came to the Bar ten years ago, Howard has built up a very strong reputation, especially amongst private sector clients. Testament to her standing, she is Standing Counsel to the Civil Aviation Authority. **Strengths:** "She's very responsive and shows great attention to detail." "She's fantastic, knows the law inside and out and is intellectually very gifted." **Recent work:** Led by Stephen Morris QC and Daniel Jowell QC, she has been representing Visa Europe in 12 sets of proceedings brought against it for competition law damages regarding interchange fees.

Julian Gregory Has a strong focus on competition and regulatory matters. He has been particularly active of late in competition cases concerning telecoms companies. **Strengths:** "He is very approachable and combines a down-to-earth attitude with strong intellectual ability." **Recent work:** Worked on the case of Competition Commission v Sky, regarding pay-TV.

Ben Lask A well-regarded junior with a fast-growing profile. Within competition law he has a particular focus on telecommunications, broadcasting and environmental cases. **Strengths:** "He's very easy to work with and always keeps you informed." "You can rely on him completely." **Recent work:** Advised the OFT with regard to the payday lending market investigation.

Alistair Lindsay Specialises in competition law exclusively and has previous experience as a competition law solicitor. He is particularly recognised for his knowledge of merger control. **Strengths:** "Working with him is an absolute pleasure," as "he's incredibly approachable and patient to a large degree, and puts in hard work behind the scenes." **Recent work:** Assisted AG Barr in gaining unconditional approval from the Competition Commission for its proposed merger with Britvic.

Alan Bates Specialises in competition, procurement, EU, and public and administrative law. He moves up in the rankings this year due to an array of positive reviews from clients. **Strengths:** "He is very knowledgeable and always extremely well prepared." "He speaks plain English and gives incredibly clear advice." **Recent work:** Instructed as sole counsel by the EC to represent it in an appeal brought by British Airways. The appeal relates to a EUR104 million cartel fine concerning freight charges.

Anneliese Blackwood Represents clients in EU, commercial and procurement law matters, as well as competition law cases. Private clients such as Microsoft and Rolex have retained her, as have government clients such as the OFT and Ofgem. **Strengths:** "She is very good and undoubtedly a star of the future." "Her work is completed to a high standard and she really gets stuck in." **Recent work:** Instructed by Dualit in the case of Nestec SA and Others v Dualit Limited and Others, which involved the interaction between competition law and IP rights.

Laura Elizabeth John A favourite of both law firms and regulators, she is no stranger to the big stage and appeared in the first competition case to reach the Supreme Court, BCL Old v BASF. **Strengths:** "An excellent lawyer who is very poised in court." "Extremely hard-working, she puts in unsociable hours to get the job done." **Recent work:** Represented Welsh NHS claimants in the case of Welsh Ministers and Others v Reckitt Benckiser. Reckitt Benckiser has been accused of abuse of dominance in relation to the Gaviscon brand.

Meredith Pickford A star junior, who regularly receives rave reviews. Noted for his background in economics, he is selected for the most complex cases and has appeared unled in the Court of Appeal, High Court and CAT. **Strengths:** "Very incisive and user-friendly." "If you had a competition regulatory question on pricing, he'd be every competition silk's choice." **Recent work:** Represented the defendant in Albion v Dŵr Cymru (Welsh Water), a follow-on damages action for compensatory and exemplary damages.

George Peretz Advises on all areas of competition law, including state aid. He has been active in an array of competition law matters of late, including cases relating to abuse of dominance, anti-competitive agreements and damages. **Strengths:** "Absolutely brilliant on paper and someone who has had great success in court recently." **Recent work:** Represented AbbVie in the High Court and the Court of Appeal in Chemistree v AbbVie. The case regarded abuse of dominance.

Ben Rayment A former legal secretary to the Competition Commission/CAT, who has built up a strong practice at the Bar. He has, of late, been involved in numerous high-profile cases. **Strengths:** "He clearly knows this area of law extremely well." "He is proactive, gets stuck into a matter, and is a real team player." **Recent work:** Represented Arriva in Arriva The Shires Limited v London Luton Airport Operations Limited. The case concerned a claim for abuse of dominance.

Philip Woolfe Focuses on competition law and telecommunications. He is an increasingly strong presence in the market and moves up in the rankings this year, having earned positive client feedback. **Strengths:** "His advocacy is good, and he has the ability to see through a problem and find a way to solve it." **Recent work:** Involved in the case of Capital Meters v National Grid, a follow-on action for damages being heard in the CAT.

Rob Williams A promising competition law junior, who is also expert in wider commercial litigation, public procurement and public law cases. **Strengths:** "A joy to work with, he's extremely accessible and easy to get hold of despite being in high demand." "I have been really pleased how he has got stuck into the issues." **Recent work:** Led by Daniel Beard QC, Williams represented the Competition Commission in the case of Akzo Nobel NV v Competition Commission, regarding the Competition Commission's decision to block Akzo Nobel's acquisition of Metlac.

Alison Berridge (see p.548) A former solicitor who, since coming to the Bar in 2011, has built up a decent practice consisting of complex merger cases and high-profile competition litigation. **Strengths:** "She is very bright, gets across all the material in a case and really mucks in with the client team, which makes a huge difference." **Recent work:** She is acting as junior to Daniel Beard QC in defending the Competition Commission against Ryanair's challenge to the Commission's decision requiring the airline to reduce its stake in Aer Lingus.

Band 2

Blackstone Chambers

See profile on p.771

THE SET

In the past few years public law superset Blackstone Chambers has done a very good job of making its mark in the competition law market. Whilst still some way behind the big two sets in this field, it can justifiably claim to be affording them stiff competition, and it has had notable involvement in a number of leading competition law cases. Its members regularly appear on behalf of household-name companies, government bodies and competition authorities at home and abroad. **Client service:** The clerking team is headed by senior clerk Gary Oliver. Clients say: "The clerks are very easy to deal with. We always get the service we require. They find the right barristers quickly and are very focused on what we need."

SILKS

Dinah Rose QC A barrister who regularly gains matchless praise for her performances, regardless of the practice area she is handling. Although not an out-and-out competition specialist, she is a formidable opponent, who is particularly recognised for her exceptional advocacy skills. **Strengths:** "Dinah is a superstar." "She's a brilliant advocate who regularly wipes the floor with the opposition." **Recent work:** Represented the claimants in the case of Cooper Tire and Others v Dow and Others. This was a follow-on damages action relating to the rubber cartel.

Monica Carss-Frisk QC Recognised by peers and clients alike for her skill in a wide range of practice areas, competition law being one of them. Sources praise her positive attitude towards clients and her evident legal skills. **Strengths:** "She's extremely bright and gets to the point quickly." "She drafts well and is easy to deal with." **Recent work:** Represented numerous claimants in the case of Recall Support Services Ltd v Secretary of State for Culture, Media and Sport. This damages claim heard in the High Court regarded failure to supply and an allegation of an abuse of dominance.

Thomas de la Mare QC Has a broad practice which encompasses competition law cases. He has been particularly active of late on damages claims. **Strengths:** "Very engaging and easy to work with, he's full of flair and new ideas." "He knows the law better than anyone I know." **Recent work:** Acted for a group of more than 400 clients seeking compensation from British Airways for overcharging.

Pushpinder Saini QC A silk with a strong reputation and wide commercial and public law knowledge. He is particularly noted for his knowledge of the telecoms sector. **Strengths:** "A very thoughtful barrister," who is "rated very highly by clients." **Recent work:** Represented Ofcom in the Court of Appeal case of British Telecommunications plc v Office of Communications. This was an appeal of Ofcom's finding that BT engaged in anti-competitive conduct.

JUNIORS

Tristan Jones Moves up in the rankings this year and is seen as one to watch for the future. **Strengths:** "Universally excellent," he is "a very calm, sensible and personable junior." **Recent work:** Appeared in Ryanair v Competition Commission, the most significant UK merger case of 2014.

Brian Kennelly Gains a star ranking this year due to his appearance in numerous high-profile cases. **Strengths:** "A very impressive barrister with a real depth of competition knowledge." "He has excellent client skills and is very highly regarded." **Recent work:** Represented Visa in the case of New Look Retailers and Others v Visa Inc and Others. This was a damages claim alleging anti-competitive behaviour.

Jessica Boyd The architect of a broad practice, who receives particularly strong praise from clients. She has recently handled a number of appeals. **Strengths:** "She's extremely bright and gets to the point quickly." "A great team player and a barrister with excellent drafting skills." **Recent work:** Represented Somerfield in a judicial review brought against the OFT regarding the tobacco cartel case.

Band 3

One Essex Court

See profile on p.790

THE SET

One Essex Court is a leading commercial set that has barristers of proven worth at all levels, who have handled cases of great complexity and importance over many years. Its involvement in competition law is limited but marked by the same reputation for excellence that the set brings to all its cases. Members here can advise on the gamut of competition law matters, including abuse of dominance cases, cartel proceedings and mergers. They regularly appear in cases involving the IT and telecoms, energy and utilities, and transport sectors, to name but a few.

Client service: Senior clerk Darren Burrows leads a clerking team that is described as being "modern and efficient."

SILKS

Thomas Sharpe QC A regular before the Competition Commission and CAT, Sharpe regularly acts for clients challenging decisions of the regulator. His background in economics adds a further string to his bow. **Strengths:** "Robust, reliable and quick to react, he's good on his feet." "Very clear and straightforward, he's an excellent practitioner." **Recent work:** Acted for MasterCard in the high-profile damages case brought by various retailers relating to interchange fees.

JUNIORS

Matthew Cook Handles both competition law and wider commercial and company litigation. He has been active of late in a number of high-profile cases, such as the MasterCard litigation. **Strengths:** "Outstandingly bright, he is a highly capable litigator." **Recent work:** Represented Albion Water in the case of Albion Water v Dŵr Cymru Cyfyngedig, heard in the CAT. The case was a follow-on damages action regarding a water supply agreement.

Conall Patton A commercial barrister who receives significant praise for his work in this area. He moves up in the rankings this year due to excellent reviews from clients. **Strengths:** "First-class in every way." "He's quick on his feet, extremely accessible and a very nice guy to work with." **Recent work:** Represented British Airways in the case of Emerald and Others v British Airways, a follow-on damages action being heard in the High Court.

Derek Spitz A barrister who is advancing his reputation within the competition law field due to his work on high-profile cases. He has particular experience in competition law damages actions. **Strengths:** "He is very bright and he drafts well." "A fantastically calm presence in court and a strong technical lawyer." **Recent work:** Led by Mark Brealey QC, Spitz has been representing Sainsbury's as the claimant in a follow-on and standalone case against MasterCard regarding interchange fees.

Owain Draper Has handled a number of matters relating to competition investigations, and has recently represented two major pharmaceutical companies in abuse of dominance claims in the High Court. **Strengths:** "Very client-friendly and responsive. He's able and really delivers what you need." "He's extremely approachable and very helpful." **Recent work:** Worked on the Kerry Foods/Headland Foods merger, which was ultimately cleared by the Competition Commission. Prior to the merger the companies were the two largest suppliers in the UK of frozen ready meals.

Other Ranked Lawyers

Iain Quirk (Essex Court Chambers) Has a broad commercial practice that encompasses competition law cases. He has particular expertise within the energy, financial and construction sectors. **Strengths:** "Fantastically clever and not afraid to be brave with his advice. He is also brilliant with the detail and never loses sight of the big picture."

Stephen Morris QC (20 Essex Street) Has a practice that takes in competition law, EU law and commercial law. He has recently been active in numerous high-profile cases. **Strengths:** "He is very good with clients and grasps the issues very quickly." "He takes a broad view of matters and can spot things which others may not have." **Recent work:** Appeared on behalf of HCA International in relation to a Competition Commission inquiry into the private healthcare sector.

Rhodri Thompson QC (Matrix Chambers) Particularly known for practising competition, public and sports law. He has handled a number of high-profile cases and market investigations. **Strengths:** "A great advocate who instils confidence." "He is responsive, efficient and persuasive." **Recent work:** Instructed by HSBC as an interested party in the case of MasterCard v Commission.

Christopher Brown (see p.557) (Matrix Chambers) Has recently been particularly active in regulatory appeals. He also has experience in EU law and human rights law. **Strengths:** "He is exactly what you want in a junior. He has a really thorough understanding of competition law and is always on top of the detail." **Recent work:** Successfully acted for Somerfield in an application for permission to appeal to the CAT against the OFT's tobacco decision.

Nicholas Gibson (Matrix Chambers) A former solicitor, who advises both public and privates sector clients on the whole range of competition law matters. **Strengths:** "Very clever, energetic and hardworking." "He has a first-class mind for detail and is fabulous to have on a case." **Recent work:** Acted in a case concerning a complaint from Thus and Gamma Telecom against BT, alleging margin squeeze in wholesale call pricing.

Conor Quigley QC (Serle Court) Has 25 years' experience in competition law and has built up a reputation for himself as a specialist in state aid, who regularly appears in cases and writes extensively on the subject. His clients include the likes of International Air Transport Association and British Airways, and he has also acted for the Treasury Solicitor and HMRC **Strengths:** "He found a very simple, very elegant and robust solution to our problem." **Recent work:** Represented ALRO, the largest Romanian aluminium producer, in the General Court against a decision of the EC to open an investigation into alleged state aid.

Contents:

LONDON

Construction London
Leading Sets
Band 1
Atkin Chambers *
Keating Chambers *
Band 2
4 Pump Court *
Band 3
Crown Office Chambers *
Thirty Nine Essex Street *
Band 4
4 New Square *
Band 5
Hardwicke *
◊ (ORL) = Other Ranked Lawyer.
[A] direct access (see p.11).
** Indicates set / individual with profile.*
Alphabetical order within each band. Band 1 is highest.

Construction London	
Leading Silks	
Star individuals	**Band 3**
Brannigan Sean *4 Pump Court* *	**Bowdery** Martin *Atkin Chambers*
Catchpole Stuart *Thirty Nine Essex Street*	**Cross** James *4 Pump Court* *
Streatfeild-James David *Atkin Chambers*	**Fenwick** Justin *4 New Square* *
Taverner Marcus *Keating Chambers* *	**Goddard** Andrew *Atkin Chambers* *
White Andrew *Atkin Chambers* *	**Hughes** Adrian *Thirty Nine Essex Street*
Band 1	**McCall** Duncan *4 Pump Court*
Bartlett Andrew *Crown Office Chambers* *	**Moran** Vincent *Keating Chambers* *
Barwise Stephanie *Atkin Chambers* *	**Patten** Ben *4 New Square* *
Darling Paul *Keating Chambers* *	**Rigney** Andrew *Crown Office Chambers* *
Dennison Stephen *Atkin Chambers* *	**Rowlands** Marc *Keating Chambers* *
Dennys Nicholas *Atkin Chambers*	**Sinclair** Fiona *4 New Square* *
Furst Stephen *Keating Chambers* *	**Smith** Joanna *Wilberforce Chambers (ORL)* ◊
McMullan Manus *Atkin Chambers* *	**Speaight** Anthony *4 Pump Court* *
Nissen Alexander *Keating Chambers* *	**Stansfield** Piers *Keating Chambers* *
Sears David *Crown Office Chambers*	**Walker** Steven *Atkin Chambers* *
ter Haar Roger *Crown Office Chambers*	**Wilken** Sean *Thirty Nine Essex Street*
Thomas David *Keating Chambers* *	**Band 4**
Williamson Adrian *Keating Chambers* *	**Black** Michael *XXIV Old Buildings (ORL)* ◊
Wilmot-Smith Richard *Thirty Nine Essex Street*	**Bowsher** Michael *Monckton Chambers (ORL)* ◊ [A] *
Band 2	**Cannon** Mark *4 New Square* *
Acton Davis Jonathan *Atkin Chambers* *	**Curtis** Michael *Crown Office Chambers*
Baatz Nicholas *Atkin Chambers*	**Hannaford** Sarah *Keating Chambers* *
Boulding Philip *Keating Chambers* *	**Hughes** Simon *Keating Chambers* *
Constable Adam *Keating Chambers* *	**Jefford** Nerys *Keating Chambers* *
Day Anneliese *4 New Square* *	**Jones** Nigel *Hardwicke* [A] *
Doerries Chantal-Aimée *Atkin Chambers* *	**Lofthouse** Simon *Atkin Chambers* *
Elliott Timothy *Keating Chambers* *	**McCredie** Fionnuala *Keating Chambers* *
Fernyhough Richard *Keating Chambers* *	**Parkin** Fiona *Atkin Chambers*
Fraser Peter D *Atkin Chambers* *	**Rawley** Dominique *Atkin Chambers* *
Friedman David *4 Pump Court* *	**Reed** Paul *Hardwicke* [A] *
Harding Richard *Keating Chambers* *	**New Silks**
Hargreaves Simon *Keating Chambers* *	**Ansell** Rachel *4 Pump Court* *
Marrin John *Keating Chambers* *	**Chapman** Graham *4 New Square* *
Nicholson Jeremy *4 Pump Court* *	**Howells** James *Atkin Chambers* *
O'Farrell Finola *Keating Chambers* *	**Mort** Justin *Keating Chambers* *
Soole Michael *4 New Square* *	**Quiney** Ben *Crown Office Chambers* *
Stewart Roger *4 New Square* *	

Band 1

Atkin Chambers

See profile on p.762

THE SET

Atkin Chambers continues to be the first port of call for many in the construction industry, and its members are experienced in acting on high-profile and high-value domestic and international cases. Commentators note the set is "fully geared up to deal with the construction industry" and praise it for having good strength and depth. One solicitor commented: "Whoever you instruct at this set you can be guaranteed that they know what they are doing."

Client service: The clerks, led by Justin Wilson, have "always found somebody suitable even at short notice." "They are particularly good, as they are accessible and do what they say they will do. They are approachable, and offer a very high level of service." "They approached me unbidden during the case on a couple of occasions to check that I was happy with the service I was receiving."

SILKS

David Streatfeild-James QC A leading light with a wealth of experience in construction matters. He frequently acts for governments, employers and contractors in high-value litigation both domestically and internationally. **Strengths:** "Highly skilled and knowledgeable when it comes to the complex technical aspects of construction cases." "Intellectually outstanding, he's a brilliant orator and very astute tactically." **Recent work:** He acted for the Danish claimant in MT Højgaard A/S v E.ON, a TCC action concerning the design of an offshore wind farm.

Andrew White QC Best known for his experience in international arbitrations and mediations. He is regarded as "a big hitter" by market commentators, and specialises in civil engineering, shipbuilding and energy project disputes. **Strengths:** "His performance was superb." "He is very professional, he has an impressive grasp of the law and can master an enormous amount of technical detail."

Stephanie Barwise QC (see p.544) Acts in construction and engineering cases, specialising in contract disputes and professional negligence claims. She is praised by market commentators for being "hard-working" and "very sound." **Strengths:** "Very responsive and commercial." "She adopts a very sensible approach, takes the big points and has a good rapport with the judge." "She's very confident and very decisive." **Recent work:** She acted for the contractor in McGee Group v Heathfield, a claim in the TCC for a declaration of the wrongful repudiation of a contract to construct a multistorey car park.

Nicholas Dennys QC A prominent advocate and adviser. He is instructed on a wide range of cases, including those relating to construction-based engineering and infrastructure. **Strengths:** "Strategic and highly persuasive. He also shows excellent judgement." **Recent work:** Acted in Sabic UK Petrochemicals v Punj Lloyd, a dispute concerning issues around bond and termination performance.

Manus McMullan QC A leading construction barrister who is held in high regard by the market. He has a broad practice which incorporates engineering, construction and infrastructure disputes. **Strengths:** "Astute and thorough, he's a pleasure to deal with." "He will give good clear advice and doesn't beat about the bush." **Recent work:** He appeared in Grupo Unidos v Panama Canal Authority, a case relating to cost overruns and delays in the USD5 billion project to widen the Panama Canal.

Jonathan Acton Davis QC (see p.531) Specialises in construction, engineering and energy-related arbitration and litigation. He is often instructed in high-profile cases, both domestically and overseas. **Strengths:** "Very good on his feet. Excellent with the clients, he's quite charming and able to engage readily." "He is very commercial and easy to get on with." **Recent work:** Instructed by Transport for Greater Manchester in a TCC case relating to the extension of a tram system and the supply of a tram operating system.

Nicholas Baatz QC Has significant expertise in high-value and complex construction, engineering and transport disputes. He advises professional ad-

Construction London — Leading Juniors
Band 1
Henderson Simon *4 Pump Court* *
Hickey Alexander *4 Pump Court* *
Lewis Christopher *Atkin Chambers* *
Pilling Benjamin *4 Pump Court* *
Band 2
Bowling James *4 Pump Court* *
Chennells Mark *Atkin Chambers*
Coplin Richard *Keating Chambers* *
Garrett Lucy *Keating Chambers* *
Ghaly Karim *Thirty Nine Essex Street* *
Grange Kate *Thirty Nine Essex Street*
Hussain Riaz *Atkin Chambers* *
Lamont Calum *Keating Chambers* *
Leabeater James *4 Pump Court* *
Lemon Jane *Keating Chambers* *
Livesey Kate *4 Pump Court* *
McCafferty Lynne *4 Pump Court* *
Pimlott Charles *Crown Office Chambers* *
Pliener David *Hardwicke* [A] *
Robb Adam *Thirty Nine Essex Street*
Selby Jonathan *Keating Chambers* *
Slow Camille *Atkin Chambers* *
Band 3
Buckingham Paul *Keating Chambers* *
Chambers Gaynor *Keating Chambers* *
Cheng Serena *Atkin Chambers* *
Chern Cyril *Crown Office Chambers* *
Clarke Patrick *Atkin Chambers* *
Clay Robert *Atkin Chambers* *
Collings Nicholas *Atkin Chambers* *
Franklin Kim *Crown Office Chambers*
Gillies Jennie *4 Pump Court* *
Laney Anna *Crown Office Chambers*
Lee Jonathan *Keating Chambers* *
Lewis Jonathan *4 Pump Court* *
Medd James *Crown Office Chambers*
Montagu-Smith Tom *XXIV Old Buildings (ORL)* ◊
Packman Claire *4 Pump Court* *
Pigott Frances *Atkin Chambers* *
Shaw Annabel *4 New Square* *
Sims Alice *Keating Chambers* *
Smith Marion *Thirty Nine Essex Street*
Stephens Jessica *Keating Chambers* *
Townend Samuel *Keating Chambers* *
Webb William *Keating Chambers* *
Wheater Michael *Hardwicke* *
Winser Crispin *Crown Office Chambers* *
Band 4
Bodnar Alexandra *Thirty Nine Essex Street* *
Briggs Lucie *Atkin Chambers*
Connors Jess *Thirty Nine Essex Street* *
Crangle Thomas *4 Pump Court* *
Evans Robert *Keating Chambers* *
Fenn Andrew *Atkin Chambers* *
Gough Karen *Thirty Nine Essex Street* *
Hanna Ronan *Atkin Chambers* *
Jinadu Abdul *Keating Chambers* *
Jones Jennifer *Atkin Chambers* *
Kennedy Stuart *3PB Barristers (ORL)* ◊
Khayum Zulfikar *Atkin Chambers* *
Lazur Thomas *Keating Chambers* *
Lee Krista *Keating Chambers* *
McCann Sarah *Hardwicke* [A] *
O'Hagan Rachael *Thirty Nine Essex Street* *
Piercy Catherine *Hardwicke* *
Powell Katie *4 New Square* *
Scott Holland Gideon *Keating Chambers* *
Taylor Rebecca *Crown Office Chambers*
Up-and-coming individuals
Crawshaw Simon *Atkin Chambers* *
Neuberger Edmund *Atkin Chambers* *
Thompson James *Keating Chambers* *

* *Indicates individual with profile.*
◊ *(ORL) = Other Ranked Lawyer.*
[A] *direct access* *(see p.11).*

visers, suppliers, contractors and employers. Sources consistently praise him for his intellectual and technical ability. **Strengths:** "A real brainbox, who is very knowledgeable." "He's very good on the detail and very bright." **Recent work:** He acted for a piling subcontractor in Accolade Wines v Volker Fitzpatrick and others, a multiparty TCC litigation which raised questions about contract formation and design liability.

Martin Bowdery QC Frequently acts in cases in the High Court and Court of Appeal. He is well regarded as an advocate, adjudicator, mediator and arbitrator. **Strengths:** "Very innovative." "Very sharp and he knows his onions." **Recent work:** Acted in GDF SUEZ International Holdings v Teesside Power Holdings, representing a purchaser in a high-value breach of warranties claim against a seller.

Stephen Dennison QC An experienced silk who is often instructed in High Court cases as well as domestic and international arbitrations. He handles work from the transport, utilities and energy sectors amongst others. **Strengths:** "An extremely able leading counsel. His judgement is excellent, and his advice is very clear and commercial." "He's nothing short of impressive." **Recent work:** He acted in Doosan Babcock v MABE, a dispute regarding performance bonds.

Chantal-Aimée Doerries QC A well-regarded silk instructed on high-value domestic and international cases. She speaks French and German, and she has been instructed in cases in Europe, the Middle East, South America and Asia. **Strengths:** "She is absolutely excellent and really commercial. She got to grips with the paperwork very quickly and was very good at flagging up the risks." "Her language skills are extremely helpful in dealing with clients." **Recent work:** Instructed in a dispute before the TCC, concerning a subcontract for reinforced concrete frames in the construction of certain buildings in the London Olympic Athletes' Village.

Peter Fraser QC A popular silk who is instructed by governments, employers, contractors and professional advisers. He handles domestic and international litigation, as well as arbitration proceedings. **Strengths:** "He's very easy to get on with, insightful and very thorough. For a QC, he is easily accessible." "His preparation is second to none and he always delivers clear advice in a no-nonsense manner that is easy to understand." **Recent work:** Appeared in BAM Nuttall v AmeyCespa, a dispute concerning design failures at a waste recycling plant in Cambridgeshire.

Andrew Goddard QC A well-regarded silk who focuses on construction and engineering disputes with commercial or professional negligence elements. He is particularly active advising contractors, subcontractors, employers and governments. **Strengths:** "A creative thinker." "He's very easy to work with and very responsive – nothing is too much trouble – and he has excellent drafting skills."

Simon Lofthouse QC A well-rounded silk who acts on a range of construction-related professional negligence, energy and infrastructure disputes. He has a strong international practice, and experience in cases arising in Europe, Africa, the Middle East and the Caribbean. **Strengths:** "Very down to earth, frank and open, he gets to the point very quickly. Excellent in front of clients, he's wonderful on his feet and a brilliant draftsman." "He has an immense capacity for hard work." **Recent work:** Acted as lead counsel on Cuddy Civil Engineering v Liberty Mercian, a TCC case concerning issues of mistake and rectification surrounding a large retail construction.

Fiona Parkin QC Held in high regard by instructing solicitors, who say she "shows real grit when handling difficult disputes." She advises a range of stakeholders in domestic and international cases, and is particularly active on disputes arising out of infrastructure projects. **Strengths:** "Very thorough, hard-working and very bright indeed." **Recent work:** Advised the government of Gibraltar on a £30 million dispute arising out of redevelopment work carried out at Gibraltar airport.

Dominique Rawley QC An "extremely impressive advocate" with considerable experience in construction and engineering disputes, particularly those concerning infrastructure projects. Her expertise also covers litigation relating to PPP/PFI, energy and waste projects, as well as fire issues. **Strengths:** "Client-friendly, creative and fast in her response times." "A highly talented advocate who is not afraid to get stuck into the detail." **Recent work:** Acted for ADT as defendant to a claim brought by QCR Motors for damages arising out of a fire at a business premises.

Steven Walker QC A "very impressive and very clever" advocate, who handles TCC and Court of Appeal cases. He focuses on a diverse range of contractual disputes including those relating to the construction of buildings, oil and gas instillations, and ships. **Strengths:** "Very user-friendly and great at analysing the facts. He's very cool and calm under pressure." **Recent work:** Acted for Lend Lease in a dispute against a subcontractor.

James Howells QC A new silk with a wealth of experience in construction law matters. He has broad ADR experience, and particular expertise in international arbitration. **Strengths:** "Very bright and offers good commercial advice. He's hard-working and quick to turn things around." "A sensible, down-to-earth chap." **Recent work:** Advised Cardiff University in a dispute concerning the design and construction of laboratories at its medical research school.

JUNIORS

Christopher Lewis A leading junior whom it is a "great pleasure to work with," according to instructing solicitors. He advises on construction-related energy, engineering and infrastructure disputes, as well as arbitrations and adjudications. **Strengths:** "Extremely bright, very thorough and someone who considers every eventuality." "He's technically very good, and masters complex issues very quickly." **Recent work:** Appeared in Secretary of State for Transport v Balfour Beatty, a dispute concerning alleged professional negligence in the design of the pavement layers of a motorway in the North of England.

Riaz Hussain A well-regarded barrister who acts on high-value construction and engineering disputes. Sources appreciate his client-friendliness, collaborative approach and assured advocacy. **Strengths:** "He is readily accessible and he researches his cases well." "He has handled high-quality work well above his years of qualification." **Recent work:** Instructed in Anglo Holt v Oakrock and Others, defending the contractor against claims of defective and incomplete works at a hotel.

Camille Slow Has a broad commercial disputes practice, and has particular expertise in construction and engineering cases, as well as related professional negligence matters. She is experienced in arbitration, mediation and adjudication, and handles both domestic and international disputes. **Strengths:** "She provides well-considered, timely and effective advice." **Recent work:** She acted in Transport for Greater Manchester v Thales Transport and Security, a dispute connected to the upgrading of the Manchester Metrolink tram system.

Serena Cheng (see p.570) Acts for employers and suppliers on construction disputes in the transport, infrastructure, energy and utilities sectors. Sources consistently praise her for being hard-working and "technically excellent." **Strengths:** "Her preparation was immaculate and her presentation was brilliant." **Recent work:** Acted in Geophysical Service Centre v Dowell Schlumberger (Middle East), a dispute concerning an alleged breach of a co-operation agreement.

Mark Chennells A specialist in construction and technology disputes. He has a significant international practice and often acts on cases in Europe and the Far East. **Strengths:** "He is very good and a pleasure to work with. He is very personable and bright." **Recent work:** Instructed by Atkins in defence of a £6 million claim brought by the Secretary of State for Transport, alleging professional negligence in connection with the reconfiguration of a motorway junction.

Patrick Clarke (see p.573) An experienced junior with a specialism in project disputes involving construction, infrastructure and logistics issues. He handles both domestic and international litigation. **Strengths:** "He is very good, very down to earth and very responsive." "He's perfectly lucid, intellectually gifted, and has a very nice manner with clients." **Recent work:** He acted in Zuetina v Hunt Thermal Technologies, a £5 million dispute relating to a Libyan LNG plant.

Nicholas Collings An expert in construction-related commercial litigation and arbitration. He acts for a range of clients including employers, contractors and insurers. **Strengths:** "You can't fault the quality of his work. Everything is so meticulously drafted, and he employs arguments others wouldn't ever think of." **Recent work:** Acted for the employers in National Express v Smith's, a multiparty TCC litigation. The claim was in connection to the failure of the contractors to identify and remove asbestos.

Frances Pigott (see p.693) Acts as both an adviser and an advocate, and regularly appears in TCC and Court of Appeal cases. He advises on construction disputes and professional negligence claims, as well as on the drafting of construction and telecoms contracts. **Strengths:** "Very intellectually sound. She's good at drafting, she's a good strategist and she works well with other leading counsel." **Recent work:** Acted in CIP Property (AIPT) v Galliford Try Infrastructure, a multimillion-pound dispute concerning design and construction defects at a mixed-use development.

Lucie Briggs Acts for contractors, employers and professional advisers on a range of construction, engineering and energy sector disputes. She is also experienced in handling arbitrations, both in the UK and internationally. **Strengths:** "Incredibly bright." **Recent work:** Advised on AKD Engineering v Cyclotech, a misrepresentation and breach of contract claim relating to the design and manufacture of water treatment units.

Robert Clay (see p.573) Frequently instructed on construction and professional negligence disputes in the TCC. He also acts in major international arbitrations concerning construction, engineering and shipbuilding-related issues. **Strengths:** "Extremely thorough, scholarly in his approach and a lawyer who has a lovely way with the clients." **Recent work:** Acted on court proceedings and an adjudication in Metnor v Wates, a dispute relating to a retail and residential development in central London.

Jennifer Jones (see p.640) Frequently acts as sole counsel on construction and engineering disputes, and also handles professional negligence claims. She has particular expertise in jurisdictional challenges and issues relating to bonds and guarantees. **Strengths:** "Has a very good technical knowledge of construction law. She provides straightforward and pragmatic advice," and is "super with clients." **Recent work:** Instructed by McKay Securities in its claim against Galliford Try and Try Construction for the cost of repair works to defective cladding.

Zulfikar Khayum (see p.645) A well-rounded practitioner who handles litigation, arbitrations, adjudications and mediations. He has represented clients across the full construction spectrum, appearing both led and unled. **Strengths:** "He is very hard-working and bright." "He demonstrates a good understanding of both technical matters and the law." **Recent work:** He acted in Carillion JM v Warrington Collegiate Institute, a final account dispute which centred around issues of defects and variations.

Andrew Fenn (see p.599) A well-regarded up-and-comer, with experience in domestic and international cases. Sources particularly praise his user-friendliness and "amazing people skills." **Strengths:** "Very easy to deal with and responsive." "I would recommend him particularly for any issues relating to delays. These can be fiercely complicated cases and he is very good at them." **Recent work:** Appeared in a dispute relating to the construction of an international airport.

Ronan Hanna He handles construction and engineering disputes, and acts for a wide range of clients, including suppliers and purchasers. **Strengths:** "Pragmatic and easy to contact." "He has a very good brain on him and is hugely industrious." **Recent work:** Acted on RWE npower Renewables v JN Bentley, advising the employer on a multimillion-pound final account dispute concerning variations and delays in the construction of a hydropower station in Scotland.

Simon Crawshaw (see p.581) Advises professionals, employers and contractors on all forms of dispute resolution. He has particular expertise pertaining to contractual matters. **Strengths:** "Thorough, hard-working and very responsive," he is "always in demand." **Recent work:** Instructed in RWE npower Renewables v JN Bentley, acting for the claimant developer in relation to issues of contractual interpretation.

Edmund Neuberger (see p.681) Acts in construction disputes and also handles professional negligence claims. He benefits from his background in engineering, and acts as both junior and sole counsel in the TCC and other forums. **Strengths:** "He has a very mature style for his year of call and is very impressive. He's really good on the detail and great with clients." **Recent work:** Appeared as sole counsel in Reilly v Marshall, Marshall and Marshall, a dispute concerning allegations of defective workmanship and contamination surrounding the construction of an equestrian training ring.

Keating Chambers

See profile on p.824

THE SET

Keating Chambers is a pre-eminent set in the construction field. The practice is noted for having "talented and highly knowledgeable counsel" who deal with the largest matters and "aren't fazed when dealing with volumes of documents." Its practitioners have a wealth of experience relating to construction law and advise a range of clients, including employers, suppliers, insurers and funders, on the full range of disputes.

Client service: "The clerks are easy to deal with and very helpful and I have had a very positive experience with all of them." "They are helpful, prompt and knowledgeable," and "they understand the concept of budgeting." Chris Sunderland is the senior practice manager at the set.

SILKS

Marcus Taverner QC Regularly instructed in high-value domestic and international cases. He handles all manner of construction-related claims including professional negligence claims and energy project disputes. **Strengths:** "A commanding advocate, who is second to none in the construction field." "He is always effective and strategically astute."

Paul Darling QC An expert in construction, energy and commercial cases. He is frequently instructed in international cases. **Strengths:** "He is extremely good, very practical and very down to earth." "As a QC he just commands enormous gravitas and the very best respect for his advice and opinions." **Recent work:** "He is extremely good, very practical and very down to earth." "As a QC he just commands enormous gravitas and the very best respect for his advice and opinions."

Stephen Furst QC Acts for developers, contractors and governments in complex construction cases. He is a well-regarded practitioner who also acts as an arbitrator. **Strengths:** "Very bright and persuasive, he's extremely quick to understand cases and grapples with the issues contained in them well." **Recent work:** Acted in Robbins v Bexley LBC, successfully representing the claimant in a case concerning property damage caused by trees.

John Marrin QC Specialises in construction law, and handles major cases relating to the engineering, energy and technology sectors. **Strengths:** "An absolutely first-class arbitrator." "He has a real ability to zero in on the important stuff." **Recent work:** Acted for E.ON in a dispute with a subcontractor concerning the construction of a wind farm in Scotland.

Alexander Nissen QC He is frequently involved in engineering, energy and professional negligence-related construction disputes amongst others.

Strengths: "Very thorough and conscientious, he shows great attention to detail." "A go-to silk with a calm and reassuring manner, who is very commercial in his advice." **Recent work:** He acted in Rendlesham Estates & Others v Barr, representing 90 apartment holders in a £22 million defects claim.

David Thomas QC Regularly acts in high-value and complex disputes, both nationally and internationally. He has experience of appearing in cases in the TCC, Court of Appeal and Dubai World Tribunal. **Strengths:** "Provides thoughtful, clear advice, and is very approachable and easy to work with." "He's user-friendly, responsive and effective." **Recent work:** Successfully acted for Hackney Empire Theatre in a claim for money owed in relation to a performance bond.

Adrian Williamson QC A seasoned professional who routinely handles contractor and professional negligence claims. **Strengths:** "Outstanding; he gets straight to the heart of any case and is a brilliant advocate." **Recent work:** Acted in WCC v Mitie, a pensions dispute arising from construction contracts.

Philip Boulding QC A barrister with a solid grounding in construction law, who regularly handles international cases. He frequently advises governments and private companies on matters in the Far East. **Strengths:** "Bright and very hard-working, he gets results."

Adam Constable QC An experienced litigator and arbitrator, who handles engineering, construction and professional negligence disputes. **Strengths:** "He is extremely user-friendly and a very skilful advocate in terms of both his written skills and his advocacy. He is absolutely first-rate." **Recent work:** Acted in Serco v Fender Care, a TCC case concerning a claim for wrongful termination of contract.

Timothy Elliott QC (see p.595) A skilled barrister who has over 35 years' experience of construction, energy and engineering matters. **Strengths:** "A very careful lawyer who shows great attention to detail."

Richard Fernyhough QC A prominent practitioner who specialises in construction and engineering law. He is often instructed in project-related claims in the energy, leisure and transport sectors. **Strengths:** "Very solid, and his excellent reputation is well deserved."

Richard Harding QC Acts for a range of stakeholders, including governments, employers and contractors. He is well regarded for his work in the Middle East. **Strengths:** "Has a fantastic profile for Middle East work." **Recent work:** Acted for the contractor in Construction Delivery Group v Nakheel, a USD30 million claim in the Dubai World Tribunal relating to payment for facilities management services at villas on the Palm Jumeirah.

Simon Hargreaves QC Instructed on a range of matters including cases arising from fires and energy project-related matters. He also handles adjudications and arbitrations both domestically and internationally. **Strengths:** "He's very easy to deal with and has a very good work ethic. He turns things around quickly." **Recent work:** Acted for a defendant in Greenwich Millennium Village v Essex Services Group and HS Environmental Services and Others, a case involving issues of liability, professional negligence and quantum.

Finola O'Farrell QC Specialises in construction and engineering disputes, and regularly handles international arbitrations. Her broad practice includes cases relating to health and safety, insurance and shipbuilding. **Strengths:** "Very meticulous and a pleasure to work with." **Recent work:** Instructed in Hamid v Barnfield & Others, a claim in the TCC relating to the design and construction of retaining walls.

Sarah Hannaford QC Often acts in construction, engineering and energy matters, and has a strong interest in procurement cases. Her expertise also covers party walls and rights of light issues. **Strengths:** "She's responsive, analytical and hard-working." **Recent work:** She was instructed in S Tyrimos v Moortown and Others, acting for the claimant in breach of contract and negligence claims concerning structural damage to commercial and residential properties.

Simon Hughes QC (see p.633) A talented practitioner, instructed in high-profile and complex construction disputes, who acts on both a domestic and international stage. **Strengths:** "He is just excellent. He is very approachable and very user-friendly." **Recent work:** Acted for the claimants in Co-operative Group v Birse and Others, a multimillion-pound claim concerning defects in a distribution centre.

Nerys Jefford QC (see p.637) Handles all manner of construction cases, and has handled a number of disputes arising from the construction of substantial commercial, residential and public developments. She also deals with matters relating to major engineering and infrastructure projects. **Strengths:** "She very quickly grasps the most essential elements of cases involving complex facts and difficult legal arguments. She is clear-thinking and highly persuasive."

Vincent Moran QC Acts in a range of construction disputes, and also has a substantial construction-related professional negligence practice. **Strengths:** "He gives commercial and insightful advice."

Marc Rowlands QC (see p.711) A specialist in rail infrastructure cases, who further acts in a diverse range of complex and high-value domestic and international construction cases. **Strengths:** "A high-quality advocate with good client skills." **Recent work:** Acted in Balfour Beatty and Carillion Joint Venture v Transport for London, a £700 million dispute concerning the design and construction of the East London Line.

Piers Stansfield QC (see p.727) A formidable advocate, instructed by employers and suppliers alike in complex disputes. **Strengths:** "He produces first-class written work and gives well-considered and measured advice." **Recent work:** He defended the contractor in J Reddington v Galliford Try Construction. This was a £7 million claim brought by a subcontractor.

Justin Mort QC A sought-after silk with extensive construction law expertise. He has appeared in a host of cases in the TCC, and has also handled a range of domestic and international arbitrations and adjudications. **Strengths:** "He is very thorough and very good at getting to the heart of the problem." **Recent work:** Acted in Cooper v Kiani, a final account dispute involving claims of fraud against a contractor.

Fionnuala McCredie QC A highly sought-after silk who is active in a range of domestic and international cases. She has strong expertise in procurement law. **Strengths:** "Really helpful even in the most difficult circumstances. She has a good eye for a case and can anticipate the opposition's next move." **Recent work:** Acted in a dispute relating to the construction of the headquarters of a major international concern.

JUNIORS

Richard Coplin Frequently acts in cases in the TCC, and is experienced in professional negligence claims involving engineers, architects and surveyors. **Strengths:** "Down to earth, willing to roll up his sleeves, and very practical. His engineering background proves very helpful in construction disputes." **Recent work:** He acted in 199 Knightsbridge Development v WSP UK, a dispute over water damage at a high-rise development.

Lucy Garrett A well-regarded junior whose broad practice spans construction, energy and shipbuilding cases. She is experienced in litigation, adjudications and arbitrations. **Strengths:** "She's very enthusiastic" and "instantly masters the facts and the expert evidence in a case." **Recent work:** She acted for Amec in an £8 million dispute concerning defects in the Malmaison Hotel in Liverpool.

Jane Lemon Specialises in litigation and ADR in the construction, engineering and energy sectors. She has recently been active in a number of international cases, including matters in Jamaica, Australia and Nigeria. **Strengths:** "Very bright, friendly and approachable, she gives sound, commercial advice." **Recent work:** She acted in Hills Contractors v Struth, a final account dispute in relation to work done at a domestic residence.

Jonathan Selby (see p.716) Has a broad practice that takes in many and varied energy and construction disputes, including professional negligence claims. **Strengths:** "He has a super attitude, is great with clients and has an original mind." **Recent work:** Acted in BAM v Donarbon Waste Management, a claim concerning a waste treatment complex in Cambridge.

Paul Buckingham Handles international project-related disputes, and is assisted by the fact that he has a background as a chartered engineer. **Strengths:** "He is incredibly bright on the law and very practical." **Recent work:** Appeared in an international arbitration relating to the construction of a power plant.

Gaynor Chambers An experienced litigator and adjudicator. She is often instructed in cases concerning the energy and utilities sector. **Strengths:** "She is excellent and produces nice, well-reasoned opinions."

Calum Lamont Acts in a range of matters including matters arising out of infrastructure projects and offshore/marine developments. He is regularly instructed in cases in the UK and the Middle East. **Strengths:** "He is very bright, very practical and hands-on. He delivers advice very economically." **Recent work:** Acted in SCS v AGR, a multimillion-dollar TCC case concerning delayed and disrupted drilling operations off the coast of Guinea.

Jonathan Lee (see p.653) A construction dispute expert, who focuses on commercial and contractual disputes. **Strengths:** "Measured, effective, reliable and trustworthy." **Recent work:** He acted in National Museums and Galleries on Merseyside Board of Trustees (National Museum of Liverpool) v AEW v Pihl Galliford Try JV, a case connected to the design and construction of architectural steps and amphitheatres at the museum.

Alice Sims (see p.721) A talented junior who has been instructed in some high-profile disputes. She is particularly active in cases in the TCC and international arbitrations. **Strengths:** "Her ability to distil complex technical details into concise pleadings when under high levels of pressure is very impressive." **Recent work:** Acted in New Ireland Assurance Company v AMEC Construction, a TCC case concerning defects in a commercial building in Manchester.

Jessica Stephens (see p.728) Regularly handles litigation, adjudications and arbitrations. Her broad practice takes in construction, engineering and shipbuilding. **Strengths:** "She is practical and effective in her approach, and presents well before the tribunal." **Recent work:** She acted for the architect in Browns Hotel v Probyn Miers, a £1.5 million High Court claim concerning the alleged negligent design of bathrooms at a five-star hotel.

Samuel Townend (see p.739) An experienced barrister who has significant experience in construction, engineering and infrastructure disputes. He appears in cases both in the UK and internationally. **Strengths:** "Very pragmatic and clear-cut in his advice."

Robert Evans Handles construction and construction-related professional negligence claims at home and abroad. He is also frequently appointed as an arbitrator and adjudicator. **Strengths:** "He's hugely sensible and really knows his stuff." **Recent work:** Acted in Paradigm Housing Group v Planning Design Development, a £3 million claim by a housing association alleging a breach of contract.

Abdul Jinadu (see p.638) He acts on a range of construction disputes and is often instructed on cases in the Court of Appeal. **Strengths:** "He showed himself to be incredibly responsive to the client, and was always available to respond to queries." **Recent work:** Acted for the claimant in Mr Peter Newton T/A Newton Associates and as Eurocad v T Clarke, a final account claim in the TCC.

Krista Lee (see p.653) She focuses on engineering and construction disputes, and can handle the most complex technical matters. **Strengths:** "She's knowledgeable and gives highly detailed advice."

Gideon Scott Holland (see p.716) An experienced barrister with a broad practice, who appears in the TCC and Court of Appeal, and has handled a number of ICC arbitrations. **Strengths:** "He's very thorough, tactically astute and good with both clients and solicitors." **Recent work:** He acted in BAM Nuttall v AMEC, a £40 million damages claim concerning a flue gas desulphurisation project at a power station.

William Webb (see p.748) A construction law specialist who is regularly instructed by a range of purchasers and suppliers. **Strengths:** "Thorough and more experienced than his year of call would lead you to believe. He's also unflappable." **Recent work:** Successfully acted for the claimants in Hunt & Others v (1) Optima and (2) Strutt & Parker, a defects claim against builders and architects.

James Thompson (see p.737) A respected barrister, active in domestic construction cases and ICC arbitrations. He acts for a range of clients including individuals, contractors and employers. **Strengths:** "User-friendly and not afraid to carry out long, tedious tasks essential for the preparation of a construction case." **Recent work:** Instructed by Taylor Wimpey in multiparty litigation in the TCC. The case concerned claims of defective workmanship and design.

Thomas Lazur Focuses on construction law, often involved in construction-related shipbuilding and energy claims. **Strengths:** "Gives honest, realistic advice and is a pleasure to deal with even in the most highly pressured circumstances." **Recent work:** He acted in Erith v Barco, a £2 million final account claim concerning a demolition subcontract.

Band 2

4 Pump Court

See profile on p.849

THE SET

4 Pump Court is a well-rounded set that has significant expertise in both the domestic and international construction markets. Its talented barristers are "good value for money," according to commentators. Its practitioners are regularly instructed by construction law solicitors firms, government bodies and in-house teams at industry-leading companies. They handle the full spectrum of construction law-related matters.

Client service: "The clerks are really responsive, and are good at finding the right barrister for a particular job." Carolyn McCombe is the head of the clerking team.

SILKS

Sean Brannigan QC A highly respected practitioner who handles substantial international disputes. He frequently handles matters concerning the oil, gas and water sectors. **Strengths:** "One of the best silks at the Bar as a whole." "He's very accessible, user-friendly and highly commercial." "He is able to grasp things extremely quickly, gets straight to the issues and gives clear, robust advice that is easy to understand." **Recent work:** He acted in John Sisk & Sons v Shangri-La Hotels, a complex dispute concerning the construction of a hotel at the Shard.

David Friedman QC A leading silk whose practice covers the full spectrum of construction and engineering disputes. He has a particular focus on professional negligence cases. **Strengths:** "A charming and deeply intellectual barrister whom clients adore. He brings insightful analysis to any complex, large-value dispute." **Recent work:** Acted in Millharbour Management & Others v Weston Homes & Others, appearing for the developer in a claim concerning defects in a residential building.

Jeremy Nicholson QC An expert on construction disputes who handles domestic and international matters. He's adept at handling complex and technical claims, and acts both as an advocate and arbitrator. **Strengths:** "He puts a lot of thought into his cases and you can have complete confidence in what he is telling you. He also has a great sense of humour." **Recent work:** Acted in Countryside Properties (London & Thames Gateway) v Malden Drywall, a claim in the TCC arising out of a fire at a new block of flats.

James Cross QC Acts for a range of clients including insurance companies, employers and contractors in complex domestic and international disputes. He also handles adjudications and arbitrations. **Strengths:** "A highly organised barrister who is a polished performer." "Takes a highly technical and detailed approach." **Recent work:** Appeared in Leeds City Council v Arla Foods, a case concerning the collapse of a highway embankment above a distribution centre in Leeds.

Duncan McCall QC Specialises in construction disputes, and appears on matters involving professional negligence, project finance and infrastructure issues. **Strengths:** "A great, commercially minded barrister who has good business acumen."

Rachel Ansell QC Handles construction disputes in the UK, the Middle East and elsewhere. She has appeared in several high-value arbitrations of late. **Strengths:** "Hugely committed and very client-friendly." "Her attention to detail is second to none."

Anthony Speaight QC (see p.725) Has a broad practice which incorporates construction-related disputes concerning infrastructure projects, the energy sector and residential developments. He also acts as a mediator and adjudicator. **Strengths:** "Precise and unequivocal in his advice, he turns work around with speed." **Recent work:** Instructed by BT in Liberata UK v British Telecommunications, a £50 million claim brought by a subcontractor.

JUNIORS

Simon Henderson A talented and experienced senior junior who is instructed on the full spectrum of construction disputes. He acts for and against developers, suppliers and professionals. **Strengths:** "Very good with the client. His advocacy is smooth and he gets on top of the information in a case very quickly." **Recent work:** He was instructed by Cleveland Bridge in a dispute concerning the construction of the Shard.

Alexander Hickey A go-to junior with a strong domestic practice, who is also increasingly active in international disputes. He has recently handled a number of cases involving bulk containers, pipelines and power stations. **Strengths:** "He has very good client management skills" and is "an exceptionally good cross-examiner." **Recent work:** Acted in Prater v Galliford Try, a final account dispute brought by a cladding contractor concerning work done at the 2012 Olympic Athletes' Village.

Benjamin Pilling Has significant experience of handling high-value offshore and onshore project disputes. He predominantly acts on cases overseas. **Strengths:** "Technically gifted and always well prepared." **Recent work:** He acted for the defendant in Tyco Holdings v Ultra Electronics, a case concerning alleged defective works.

James Bowling (see p.554) Often acts as sole counsel in high-profile cases. He has a growing international practice, and has recently been involved in disputes in Hong Kong, Ghana and Nigeria. **Strengths:** "A good fighter who is very confident and robust." **Recent work:** He acted in Jeffrey v Ingleton Wood Architects, a dispute centred around claims of professional negligence.

James Leabeater A specialist in construction law who acts on a range of domestic and international disputes, and specialises in offshore construction issues, including shipbuilding disputes. **Strengths:** "A very impressive and highly articulate advocate." **Recent work:** He acted in National Trust v Haycock Associates, representing the Trust in a dispute over the design of a bridge.

Kate Livesey Acts on domestic construction disputes, often defending professionals. She has a growing international practice, and is instructed on major disputes and arbitrations. **Strengths:** "Very pleasant and very competent." **Recent work:** She acted for the engineers in Galliford Try v Clancy Consulting & IGI, a claim in the TCC relating to specialist ground improvement works undertaken at a sports and leisure complex.

Lynne McCafferty A popular barrister with a wide-ranging practice. She appears in domestic and international cases concerning infrastructure projects and commercial developments. **Strengths:** "Bright and very user-friendly." **Recent work:** Acted in Sainsbury's v Interserve Projects Services & Others, a multiparty TCC claim relating to defects in the design and construction of a distribution centre.

Jennie Gillies (see p.608) Frequently instructed in construction-related professional negligence cases. She also handles adjudications, and is well versed in adjudication enforcement. **Strengths:** "Very comprehensive and thorough." **Recent work:** She acted in Ace Liftaway v (1) WF Browne (2) Snashalls Steel, a £2 million defects claim brought against engineers and steel fabricators.

Thomas Crangle (see p.580) Has a solid domestic practice, and also has an interest in international arbitration work. He is increasingly active in construction-related energy disputes. **Strengths:** "His mastery of the facts and law is impressive, and he's an old head on young shoulders. He's very proactive and clients like him." **Recent work:** Acted in AMEC v Mitie Floorings, a multimillion-pound dispute concerning the design and construction of a car park.

Jonathan Lewis (see p.655) A busy junior who is an expert on construction-related insolvency cases. He has recently handled several substantial domestic disputes. **Strengths:** "An excellent and thoroughly approachable advocate who has a stinging intellect. He is able to precisely dissect the most complex case and reduce it to its bare essentials." **Recent work:** Acted in Network Rail v Hatfield Colliery & Others, a £40 million TCC case arising out of the collapse of a coal mine.

Claire Packman (see p.688) Regularly acts in high-value litigation and arbitration matters. She is instructed by a range of entities on both domestic and international work. **Strengths:** "Good, bright, determined and resilient." **Recent work:** She acted in Sainsbury's v Capita Symonds, which involved allegations of negligence in relation to the design of a car park.

Band 3

Crown Office Chambers
See profile on p.782

THE SET

Crown Office Chambers has a fine reputation for handling construction disputes. Its members have extensive expertise relating to construction law and regularly act, on behalf of a range of clients, in high-value and complex domestic and international disputes. Commentators say that the set has a "good attitude and clever people" and they particularly note the fact that "there are some very good senior silks on board here."

Client service: "The clerks are a friendly bunch and I have not had any issues. Their pricing is realistic." Simon Wigley is the senior clerk for this practice area.

SILKS

Andrew Bartlett QC A highly regarded practitioner who has considerable expertise of acting as an advocate, arbitrator and adjudicator on construction-related disputes. **Strengths:** "Very bright and strong," he is "very, very thorough."

Roger ter Haar QC A distinguished and respected silk who is instructed on the full range of construction disputes. He also acts as an arbitrator and adjudicator. **Strengths:** "He is completely unflappable in every situation. He knows his stuff well, and it's hard to outwit him." **Recent work:** Acted in a £5 million claim concerning flooding caused by the failure of pipework at Greenwich Millennium Village.

David Sears QC Experienced at handling disputes involving all manner of engineering and construction projects, he regularly tackles cases concerning breach of contract and delay. **Strengths:** "We were very impressed with his strong, consistent and clear advice, and his calm and thorough approach to the litigation." **Recent work:** He appeared in Cowlin Construction v Cwm Taf Local Health Board, a contractual dispute centred around the construction of a hospital.

Andrew Rigney QC A busy silk who is frequently instructed in substantial construction disputes involving energy and infrastructure projects. He has a broad international practice, and has recently been acting in matters in the Middle East and Asia. **Strengths:** "He has an encyclopaedic knowledge of the law and he's got a good analytical mind."

Michael Curtis QC Has a wide-ranging practice, and regularly handles insurance-related construction matters as well as professional negligence and property damage cases. **Strengths:** "He has a fantastic eye for detail when handling document-heavy cases." **Recent work:** Instructed by Volkerfitzpatrick in a £2 million claim against a French subcontractor concerning negligent design.

Ben Quiney QC Handles disputes in the TCC, adjudications and domestic and international arbitrations. He appears for employers and contractors, amongst others. **Strengths:** "Very nice and very capable." "He is exceptionally user-friendly and easy to work with. He is is very calm at all times and breaks cases down well." **Recent work:** Acted for the defendant engineer in a multimillion-pound professional negligence claim in the TCC concerning the construction of a leisure centre in Warrington, in Cheshire.

JUNIORS

Charles Pimlott Acts in a range of matters including construction-related disputes concerning infrastructure and energy projects. **Strengths:** "Very good and highly dedicated." **Recent work:** Acted for Thameside Construction in an adjudication enforcement concerning works undertaken at a residential property.

Cyril Chern An experienced practitioner who focuses on international engineering and construction disputes. He also sits as a mediator, arbitrator and adjudicator. **Strengths:** "Exceptionally well versed in both domestic and international matters."

Kim Franklin Acts for employers, contractors and consultants. She advises on complex international disputes and arbitrations. **Strengths:** "She is a measured and powerful advocate who is extremely convincing." **Recent work:** Appeared in PJ Livsey v SR Cladding, a dispute relating to damage to a penthouse at a residential development caused by the wind.

Anna Laney Advises on traditional construction disputes as well as insurance-related matters. **Strengths:** "A helpful team player who is decisive and very clear in her advice." **Recent work:** She acted in Littledene and Others v Yellowbox, a dispute relating to the construction of a block of flats.

James Medd Has a broad practice and regularly appears in insurance, property damage and construction-related disputes. **Strengths:** "Technically able, and gets into the detail of the case early." **Recent work:** Instructed by Penne to defend a claim brought by the Co-operative Group alleging the installation of defective vibropiling to the foundations of a supermarket.

Crispin Winser (see p.754) Specialises in construction-related insurance and professional negligence claims. He acts on domestic and international cases. **Strengths:** "Very pleasant and competent." **Recent work:** He acted for the purchasers in Rohan & Others v Daman Real Estate Capital Partners, a £2 million claim in the Dubai International Financial Centre Court relating to delays in completion of several high-end apartments.

Rebecca Taylor Experienced in domestic and international cases. She also handles adjudications and international arbitrations. **Strengths:** "She has a good advocacy style. She's relaxed and confident, and can adapt well when circumstances change in a case."

Thirty Nine Essex Street
See profile on p.797

THE SET

Thirty Nine Essex Street is "a good alternative to the older-established construction sets" and has "some very good-quality juniors" who are "diligent and hard-working," as well as some notable silks. The set has a range of barristers who act for a broad client base in domestic and international construction disputes arising in, amongst others, the oil and gas, engineering and telecommunication sectors.

Client service: The clerking team, led by senior practice manager Owen Lawrence, has been "helpful when agreeing terms and fees." "The clerks are very service-oriented, have rapid response times, and adopt a can-do attitude."

SILKS

Stuart Catchpole QC A highly regarded silk who is recognised as a leading practitioner for domestic and international litigation and arbitration. He handles cases concerning energy, infrastructure and construction projects. **Strengths:** "Frighteningly clever and a very hard worker who has the ability to run rings around the opposition's QC and their experts."

Richard Wilmot-Smith QC A specialist in construction and engineering disputes who handles matters on a domestic and international level. He has substantial experience of cases involving issues relating to performance bonds and guarantees. **Strengths:** "Very solid, very able and very persuasive." **Recent work:** Acted in Harrison v Maison Blanc, a claim brought following injuries caused by a falling shop sign.

Adrian Hughes QC An expert on construction-related disputes who often appears in arbitrations in Dubai and Singapore. He has a strong domestic practice, and has handled a number of cases in the TCC. **Strengths:** "Exudes gravitas," and "is always very much on top of the detail in a case." "His advice is very thorough and he is very approachable."

Sean Wilken QC A fine choice for high-value, complex international construction disputes. He is also strong on energy and finance matters. **Strengths:** "He is very, very quick in terms of his turnaround of papers and he gives very pragmatic advice." "He gets to the heart of the issue instantly, and it doesn't take him long at all to figure what a case is all about."

JUNIORS

Karim Ghaly A sought-after junior who has handled some of the most high-profile cases to come before the TCC. He further handles arbitrations and adjudications. **Strengths:** "Has a razor-sharp mind, and is very commercial in his approach." "He's a good team player, who is responsive and whose drafting and advocacy are both extremely good." **Recent work:** Acted for HS Environmental in a multiparty dispute concerning the flooding of residential flats caused by damaged pipework.

Kate Grange Has a broad practice and advises a range of clients on construction-related litigations, adjudications and mediations. **Strengths:** "Very approachable, very pleasant, and she has a sharp mind too. She is very willing and keen to get into the detail." **Recent work:** She acted for CAIB in a multiparty TCC dispute concerning damage caused to a bridge following the derailment of a train.

Adam Robb An experienced advocate who handles complex construction, engineering and infrastructure disputes. He also has considerable expertise in handling professional negligence-related cases. **Strengths:** "He's very confident, clear in his advice and tenacious in his approach." **Recent work:** He acted in Oakapple v DTR and Others, an £11 million professional negligence claim arising out of a fire at a residential and retail development.

Marion Smith Focuses on large-scale construction disputes, and frequently handles cases relating to the engineering and telecommunications sectors. **Strengths:** "She is knowledgeable, very thorough, and good at communicating with clients, particularly those in the public sector." **Recent work:** Advised in RWE npower Renewables v J N Bentley.

Alexandra Bodnar (see p.552) A talented junior who is instructed in domestic and international construction disputes. **Strengths:** "Bright and dedicated." **Recent work:** She acted for Unite Integrated Solutions in a dispute regarding the design and commissioning of a heating and hot water system at a student accommodation building in Leeds.

Jess Connors (see p.577) Regularly handles substantial litigation, arbitration and adjudication matters. She acts in both domestic and international cases. **Strengths:** "One of the most hard-working barristers you could come across, she is incredibly thorough."

Karen Gough (see p.612) Has considerable expertise in construction-related contractual disputes. **Strengths:** "Very experienced and very approachable." **Recent work:** She acted in Terna v Bin Kamils, a share purchase and shareholder agreement dispute regarding the construction of a cement plant in the UAE.

Rachael O'Hagan (see p.684) A popular choice for governments, employers and individuals, who has specific expertise in matters relating to nuclear and energy projects. **Strengths:** "Displays great attention to detail, is very hard-working and is also accessible and user-friendly."

Band 4

4 New Square
See profile on p.835

THE SET

4 New Square handles a wide range of construction cases, and is particularly highlighted for its expertise on disputes with an insurance background. Its practitioners are "very good on the professional negligence side" and are instructed by many of the leading solicitors in the field. The set has recently acted in several high-profile cases including Co-operative Group v Birse Developments.

Client service: The clerks are "helpful, responsive and they get back to me quickly." "They do listen properly and if someone isn't available then sensible suggestions are made as to who is available."

SILKS

Michael Soole QC A highly experienced silk who has significant experience of construction-related professional negligence and insurance issues. **Strengths:** "He was very good, he got a good grasp of the brief and gave clear advice. He was very user-friendly." **Recent work:** Acted in Millharbour Management v Weston Homes, Whitecode Design Associates & Others, a claim concerning allegations of excessive heat and inadequate air conditioning at a residential development.

Roger Stewart QC An expert in construction law, who is often instructed in high-value and complex disputes. He is also an experienced arbitrator, and frequently handles cases in the Middle East. **Strengths:** "A great choice for heavyweight matters," "he's very bright and very user-friendly." **Recent work:** Acted for Pinsent Masons in a claim alleging negligence in the drafting of contracts.

Anneliese Day QC A highly sought-after silk who handles high-profile, substantial cases. She has significant expertise in construction disputes and international arbitrations. **Strengths:** "Highly capable, she has a great eye for detail." She provides "pragmatic, commercial advice." **Recent work:** Appeared for ABB in a £60 million claim against BAM Nuttall relating to the design and construction of a bulk supply point on the London Underground.

Justin Fenwick QC A popular silk who handles a range of construction-related insurance disputes. He is also hugely experienced in professional liability matters. **Strengths:** "He provides pithy and highly cogent advice." **Recent work:** Acted in London Underground v Freshfields and Herbert Smith, a dispute concerning the drafting of a failed PFI contract.

Ben Patten QC A well-rounded practitioner who specialises in advising a range of stakeholders on construction-related professional indemnity cases. **Strengths:** "Technically he's one of the best around. He is also highly responsive." **Recent work:** Acted for the claimant in L&K v Time and Tide Developments, a case concerning the design and construction of commercial premises.

Mark Cannon QC An experienced practitioner with a broad practice that encompasses insurance, construction and professional liability cases. He is instructed in a range of disputes involving contractors, subcontractors and employers. **Strengths:** "He's very, very clever and is afforded huge respect." **Recent work:** Successfully acted in RPS v Follett, a case involving a claim for unpaid fees and a counterclaim for negligence.

Fiona Sinclair QC A recent silk who often acts in TCC, Court of Appeal and international arbitration cases. She has considerable experience of handling multiparty construction disputes. **Strengths:** "She's very bright, very persuasive and very amiable." **Recent work:** Acted in BMG (Mansfield) v (1) Galliford Try Construction and (2) Aedas Architects, instructed by the defendant contractor in a claim resulting from a fire at a designer shopping outlet.

Graham Chapman QC Advises both claimants and defendants in construction disputes, professional liability claims and commercial cases. He regularly acts on international matters. **Strengths:** "He's never afraid to make a decision and he's well able to lead a devastating forensic attack on his opponent's case." **Recent work:** He was instructed by the defendants in West Bromwich v Donaldsons, a multimillion-pound case in the TCC concerning commercial property valuation.

JUNIORS

Annabel Shaw (see p.718) Specialises in construction and technology disputes, and regularly handles domestic and international arbitrations. **Strengths:** "A dedicated practitioner." "She works incredibly hard and retains facts well." **Recent work:** Appeared in Carillion JM v Portscene, a claim against a subcontractor relating to works carried out at a medical centre in Oldham.

Katie Powell Has a strong domestic practice, and is especially strong on construction disputes involving issues of professional liability. **Strengths:** "We use her for the more cerebral cases as she's phenomenally bright. Her research skills and ability to reduce complicated legal points into digestible prose are really impressive." **Recent work:** Acted in Martyn Bramwich Associates v Mr M Busra, Pegasus UK, a claim against architects which involved issues concerning the scope of retainer.

Band 5

Hardwicke
See profile on p.816

THE SET

Hardwicke continues to act on high-profile and complex construction disputes. Its members are often instructed by leading law firms and appear for a host of well-known players in the construction sphere. Alongside domestic matters, they frequently act in substantial international disputes, and are praised for being "very approachable, practical and down to earth."

Client service: "Hardwicke represents a breath of fresh air in the way it operates." "Enlightened in its approach, it understands what instructing solicitors and clients want." Amanda Illing is the practice director.

SILKS

Nigel Jones QC Frequently handles complex construction disputes, and acts for a range of clients including housing associations and contractors. **Strengths:** "He takes a very pragmatic approach to his advice, and always offers value for money." **Recent work:** He acted in Heart of England (t/a Orbit) v Stratford District Council, appearing on behalf of a housing association in a £12 million claim against a local authority, relating to construction defects in 6,000 properties that were transferred to the claimant.

Paul Reed QC Regularly instructed in high-profile TCC and major international disputes. He has recently been active on matters in the Caribbean and Dubai. **Strengths:** "Methodical, commercial, and someone with great advocacy skills." "He's very diligent and hard-working." **Recent work:** He appeared in Grosvenor Street Partnership v Carillion & Others, a £20 million claim concerning the negligent design and construction of a new development which caused damage to adjoining properties.

JUNIORS

David Pliener Acts for contractors, property developers and insurers. He is experienced in domestic and international cases, and regularly handles arbitration and adjudication work. **Strengths:** "A very commercial problem solver, who is brilliant with lay clients and an active part of the legal team." "He's very thorough and doesn't miss any points." **Recent work:** He acted in Dalata v Litton, a case concerning a substantial water leak at a new hotel in Cardiff.

Michael Wheater (see p.750) Well regarded for his efforts in insurance-related constructed cases. He is experienced in issues relating to policy coverage and liability. **Strengths:** "Down to earth and gains a quick understanding of the issues." "Commercial, user-friendly and helpful." **Recent work:** Appeared for construction consultants in a claim resulting from the alleged defective design of a country estate in Essex.

Sarah McCann Experienced in high-profile and high-value disputes, she has a broad practice which covers construction, professional negligence and property damage matters. **Strengths:** "She is very quick and will always give a definite opinion." **Recent work:** She acted for the defendants in Lloyds TSB Bank v McBains Cooper, a case brought by Lloyds claiming that the defendants had breached the terms of their appointment.

Catherine Piercy (see p.693) Frequently instructed in significant TCC cases, she acts for a range of employers, contractors and insurers. **Strengths:** "Hard-working and good to bounce ideas around with; she gives good, practical advice." "She's phenomenally hard-working, bright and down to earth." **Recent work:** She acted for the engineers in Aldersgate v Robinson, a case concerning a breach of contract and negligence claim.

Other Ranked Lawyers

Michael Bowsher QC (Monckton Chambers) He has a wealth of experience in construction law matters, and is a specialist in procurement and tendering disputes. **Strengths:** "Technically astute and able to quickly grasp the issues at hand." **Recent work:** He acted for the developers in Nucom UK v Sandwell Homes, a case concerning public housing maintenance arrangements.

Michael Black QC (XXIV Old Buildings) A well-regarded silk who is best known for handling international construction disputes, including arbitrations. **Strengths:** "Very affable, and a man with a brain the size of a planet."

Tom Montagu-Smith (XXIV Old Buildings) A favourite of construction solicitors who is particularly active in the Middle East. **Strengths:** "He is a superb advocate and he has superb judgement. He is very good on the law."

Stuart Kennedy (3PB Barristers) A well-regarded practitioner who heads the technology and construction group at the set. Also a chartered quantity surveyor, he acts in domestic and international litigation and arbitrations. **Strengths:** "He has a very practical approach and understands the nature of the construction industry and the difficulties associated with it."

Joanna Smith QC (Wilberforce Chambers) Often instructed in TCC cases, and also handles adjudications and arbitrations. She has a broad practice which also incorporates professional negligence and general commercial matters. **Strengths:** "Charming, persuasive and able." "She is well prepared and a really good performer." **Recent work:** She acted in Aldersgate Estates v Ham Construction & Robinson Consulting, defending a firm of structural engineers.

MIDLANDS

Construction Midlands
Leading Sets
Band 1
No5 Chambers *
Leading Juniors
Band 1
Barrett Kevin *No5 Chambers* Ⓐ
Ensaff Omar *No5 Chambers*
Pye Derek *3PB Barristers (ORL)* ◊
◊ (ORL) = Other Ranked Lawyer.
Ⓐ direct access (see p.11).
** Indicates set / individual with profile.*

Band 1

No5 Chambers

See profile on p.883

THE SET

No5 Chambers is unanimously recognised as the pre-eminent chambers for construction matters on the Midland Circuit. The set's technology and construction group receives instructions from a wide range of clients, including developers, contractors, subcontractors and construction companies. Its members draw praise for their commercial and client-friendly approach to litigation, arbitration and mediation.

Client service: "The clerks, led by James Parks, are very good. They are very easy to contact, form good working relationships, and are very cost-effective."

JUNIORS

Kevin Barrett Focuses purely on construction matters and attracts instructions on defect and payment delay claims. He is a former solicitor who also acts in arbitrations, adjudications and mediations. **Strengths:** "His communication style is extremely client-friendly and he is a pleasure to work with." **Recent work:** Acted for the defendant in a damages claim resulting from the freezing of air conditioning pipe work. The case also involved insurance issues.

Omar Ensaff Has a strong reputation for technical construction cases, as well as insolvency and commercial disputes. He represents a wide range of clients in construction matters, including builders, contractors and subcontractors. **Strengths:** "He gets to the heart of the matter very quickly and gives robust advice." **Recent work:** Recently instructed in a complex Birmingham TCC case concerning a defective barn conversion with very minimal contract documentation.

Other Ranked Lawyers

Derek Pye (3PB Barristers) A vastly experienced construction specialist who is also a qualified chartered quantity surveyor. **Recent work:** Advised an international mechanical engineering group on performance damages liability.

NORTH EASTERN

Construction North Eastern	
Leading Juniors	
Band 1	
Singer Andrew	*Kings Chambers (ORL)* ◊ *
Band 2	
Edwards Anthony	*St Philips Chambers (ORL)* ◊ *
Pennifer Kelly	*Kings Chambers (ORL)* ◊ *

Ranked Lawyers

Andrew Singer (see p.721) (Kings Chambers) Has developed a significant and well-regarded construction practice in the North East. He also deals with associated professional negligence cases and is highly experienced in TCC litigation, as well as in arbitrations, adjudications and mediations. **Strengths:** "He is just a master of his brief. He has an excellent relationship with the lay client, is very practical and has good technical knowledge of the construction industry."

Kelly Pennifer (see p.691) (Kings Chambers) Recognised for her expertise in TCC and Mercantile Court matters. She works on both residential and commercial construction matters. **Strengths:** "She is absolutely superb. She reviews the papers very quickly and gives clear, practical and pragmatic advice on the merits and tactics of the case." **Recent work:** Defended a claim for summary judgment brought by Smith Group against Lewis's Liverpool LLP in relation to sums allegedly due under a guarantee given by Lewis's in respect of the £5.5 million refurbishment of the Lewis's building in Liverpool.

Anthony Edwards (see p.593) (St Philips Chambers) Acts on a range of construction and engineering cases, including petrochemical and power station matters, and has a surveying background which is appreciated by sources. He also has a growing international arbitration practice. **Strengths:** "He understands what the client wants to achieve." "He is particularly good in arguments over value and defects."

WESTERN

Construction Western	
Leading Sets	
Band 1	
St John's Chambers *	
Leading Juniors	
Band 1	
Kearney Andrew	*St John's Chambers*
Band 2	
Stead Richard	*St John's Chambers* Ⓐ
Taylor Rebecca	*St John's Chambers*
Ⓐ direct access (see p.11).	
◊ (ORL) = Other Ranked Lawyer.	
** Indicates set / individual with profile.*	
Alphabetical order within each band. Band 1 is highest.	

Band 1

St John's Chambers
See profile on p.893

THE SET

St John's Chambers is the dominant construction set on the Western Circuit. The set is home to a number of highly regarded juniors who attract instructions on complex cases from a number of heavyweight firms, including actions for contractors and on behalf of public bodies. The set is also handling an increasing amount of work from instructing solicitors based in Wales.

Client service: "The clerking team, led by Robert Bocock, are a lot more hands-on than some other chambers. They liaise with courts and save a lot of time and hassle."

JUNIORS

Andrew Kearney Continues to be known as one of the go-to construction and engineering barristers outside of London. He has a range of expertise, with recent experience in waste from energy matters, property damage cases and professional negligence-related construction disputes. **Strengths:** "He is a great intellect, an excellent tactician and tenacious as a litigator." "It was like watching Muhammad Ali – the witness was left reeling." **Recent work:** Acted for defendant Dwr Cymru (Welsh Water) in defence of a property damage claim arising from subsidence.

Richard Stead Has a well-regarded construction practice, often focusing on cases with a professional negligence strand. Property damage and insurance-related cases also feature in his workload. **Strengths:** "He's very approachable, firm in his views, certainly user-friendly, and provides clear, succinct advice. He is very easy to work with." **Recent work:** Instructed on behalf of Cornwall Council to defend a claim following the flooding of a holiday park.

Rebecca Taylor Continues to impress instructing solicitors with her confident and conscientious handling of cases. She is attracting an increasing construction caseload in her own right. **Strengths:** "She has a calm, controlled advocacy style and does not get flustered." "She has an ability to strip away the chaff and get to the nub of the issue, and to present it in a confident manner in the court." **Recent work:** Instructed at short notice to appear in a four-day trial defending a contractor in a defective works claim.

CONSUMER LAW: An introduction

Contributed by Miles Bennett and Denis Barry at 5 Paper Buildings.

Background

'Consumer law' is a title that covers a multitude of areas, and a multitude of sins. Out of date food, pricing, product safety, descriptions of products, consumer credit, 'transactional decisions'... the list is almost endless. All these aspects of consumer law affect our daily lives. The 'Horsegate' scandal was an indication of the increase in the profits to be made from, and the damaging commercial impact on major retailers of, food fraud.

The Torfaen County Borough Council v Douglas Willis Limited [2013] UKSC 59 case (possession for sale of frozen food past its sell by date) demonstrated that seemingly even the most modest case can end up in the Supreme Court.

Yet it is an area that, in the past, has seldom been given the recognition it deserves. With traditional legislation (such as the Trade Descriptions Act) being replaced by more and more EC Directives with their "purposive approach," and the impending Consumer Rights Act, this is changing and will change dramatically in the near future.

Courts, lawyers and businesses will all have to adapt to these changes. This is an area that is likely to become more regulated, not less.

The future

Costs

These changes, past, present and future in the area of criminal enforcement are set against the impact of dramatic changes to Defence Costs orders post-October 2012.

With companies unable to recover their costs from central funds and with individuals capped at recovering their costs at legal aid rates (where legal aid is available) we see an increasing number of applications for wasted costs under Section 19 of the Prosecution of Offences Act 1985.

Furthermore, if recent decisions are anything to go by (see R (Singh) v Ealing Magistrates Court & Anor [2014] EWHC 1443 (Admin)) there may be a far greater willingness of courts to award costs against prosecutors than has previously been the case. Prosecutors will have to choose their prosecutions and their defendants with care.

Jurisdiction

Some local authorities have been keen to push the boundaries of their jurisdiction to bring any proceedings to the very limits. In spite of Section 222 LGA 1970 having been around for over 40 years, it still appears to cause confusion to many.

R v Tesco Stores Ltd, a prosecution under Regulation 5 of the Consumer Protection from Unfair Trading Regulations by Birmingham City Council, is a case in point. A judge at first instance agreed with Birmingham CC's proposition that they could prosecute for offences "anywhere in England and Wales." The effect of this ruling was that Tesco was prosecuted in relation to a nationwide price promotion on strawberries, with a turnover of some £6 million.

It is hoped that clause 43(1) of the Draft Consumer Rights Bill will bring some degree of clarity to this difficult area, although if local authorities really can bring proceedings anywhere, one wonders why Parliament felt the need to draft a provision that a local weights and measures authority "may bring proceedings for a consumer offence allegedly committed in a part of England or Wales which is outside that authority's area."

Powers

The Draft Consumer Rights Bill also seeks to clarify and widen powers of enforcers to request information (see Schedule 5, Part 2 Investigatory powers). This will allow 'enforcers' to seek information and, upon refusal or non-compliance, seek a court order from either the High Court or the County Court.

It will be interesting to see how, if enacted, this works in practice. To protect the right against self-incrimination the fruits of such a request cannot be used against that person in criminal proceedings, nor can any question be asked by the prosecution relating to that information (clauses 16-19).

The Protection of Freedoms Act 2012

Concerns over local authority 'snooping' led to the introduction of this Act. Some local authorities have embraced these changes better than others. Some practitioners appear unaware that the legislation even exists.

An example of just one important change is that applications for directed surveillance by a local authority now need to be made to a magistrates' court. Some level of judicial scrutiny is to be encouraged to prevent abuse. This will only work effectively if local authorities fully disclose all relevant material to the court in each application and courts do not simply accept what they are told without question. Historically, this has not always been the case (see R (Vuciterni and Alsat UK Ltd) v Brent Magistrates' Court & Brent and Harrow Trading Standards Service [2012] EWCA 2140 (Admin)).

Food

At the time of writing there is considerable debate as to whether 'Best Before' labelling will be scrapped in an attempt to reduce the extraordinary (and unnecessary) levels of food waste

Summary

The year ahead will be a challenging one for consumer lawyers and their clients, whether they are enforcers or businesses. Consumers will be given a greater voice. There will be significant changes that will affect us all. As they say, "Watch this space!"

LONDON

Contents:

Consumer Law London
Leading Sets
Band 1
Gough Square Chambers *
Band 2
Henderson Chambers *
Band 3
5 Paper Buildings *
Leading Silks
Band 1
de Haan Kevin *Francis Taylor Building (ORL)* ◊ [A]
Kirk Jonathan *Gough Square Chambers* *
Travers David *6 Pump Court (ORL)* ◊ *
Waters Malcolm *Radcliffe Chambers (ORL)* ◊ *
Band 2
Mawrey Richard *Henderson Chambers* [A] *
New Silks
Hough Jonathan *4 New Square (ORL)* ◊ *
Leading Juniors
Star individuals
Philpott Fred *Gough Square Chambers*
Band 1
Andrews Claire *Gough Square Chambers*
Antrobus Simon *Crown Office Chambers (ORL)* ◊ *
Bennett Miles *5 Paper Buildings* *
Goulding Jonathan *Gough Square Chambers* *
Hibbert William *Henderson Chambers* *
Lomnicka Eva *4 New Square (ORL)* ◊ *
MacDonald Iain *Gough Square Chambers*
Popplewell Simon *Gough Square Chambers* *
Smith Julia *Henderson Chambers* *
Watson Mark *6 Pump Court (ORL)* ◊
Band 2
Barry Denis *5 Paper Buildings* *
Douglas-Jones Ben *5 Paper Buildings* *
Falkowski Damian *Thirty Nine Essex Street (ORL)* ◊ [A]
Heller Richard *Dyers Chambers (ORL)* ◊
Rich Jonathan *Five Paper (ORL)* ◊ *
Rosenthal Dennis *Henderson Chambers* *
Say Bradley *Gough Square Chambers*
Urell Kate *Gough Square Chambers* *
Williams Benjamin *4 New Square (ORL)* ◊
Band 3
Bala Ruth *Gough Square Chambers* *
Crowe Cameron *36 Bedford Row (ORL)* ◊ *
Glassbrook Alex *Temple Garden Chambers (ORL)* ◊ *
Gun Cuninghame Julian *Gough Square Chambers* *
Neville Stephen *Gough Square Chambers* *
Ovey Elizabeth *Radcliffe Chambers (ORL)* ◊ *
Riley-Smith Toby *Henderson Chambers* [A] *
Sumnall Charlene *5 Paper Buildings* *
Up-and-coming individuals
Ross James *Gough Square Chambers* *
** Indicates set / individual with profile.*
◊ (ORL) = Other Ranked Lawyer.
[A] direct access (see p.11).
Alphabetical order within each band. Band 1 is highest.

Band 1

Gough Square Chambers

See profile on p.811

THE SET

The set has a long history of commitment to consumer law. A true pioneer in the field, it has been involved longer than any other set, and enjoys a very strong reputation. It undertakes a broad range of matters, and proves particularly strong on the consumer credit front. The number of bodies it can throw at the sector is unmatched by any other set, and its capabilities at the junior end are there for all to see. Solicitors view it as a top pick: "This chambers is at the very top of its game."

Client service: "They never let us down. The clerks, led by Bob Weekes, are not just good business managers, but have a good understanding of the nature of the work too."

SILKS

Jonathan Kirk QC (see p.646) Particularly known for his expertise in food law, pricing issues and Trading Standards investigations. He is commended for his strong advocacy and noted for his superior communication skills when dealing with clients, judges and opponents. **Strengths:** "He gives very pragmatic, commercial advice. He sets out the risks and offers practical solutions." "Always well prepared and on top of the case." **Recent work:** Acted for Tesco Stores in a high-profile mis-selling scandal. The company was alleged to have misled consumers when selling strawberries at half price.

JUNIORS

Fred Philpott Has an enviable reputation in consumer credit and trading standards work, and has been practising exclusively in this area for longer than anyone else. He covers a range of areas, and has been involved in key cases affecting the retail and banking industries. **Strengths:** "Tremendous and trusted by some of the biggest names in the world." "He's seen it all and gets to the nub of the issue quickly." "A complete master of consumer credit law." **Recent work:** Instructed in a three-day hearing before an OFT Adjudicator concerning the consumer credit licences of HFO Capital, HFO Services and Roxburghe.

Claire Andrews Head of chambers and a barrister with a particular focus on unfair trading and food-related cases. She also acts as a specialist representative to importers. **Strengths:** "She is an excellent barrister, particularly when it comes to technical issues." "Good for the nitty-gritty cases because she makes the complex simple." **Recent work:** Advised on a case involving Iceland Foods concerning the horsemeat scandal.

Jonathan Goulding (see p.612) Has a strong consumer protection and trading standards practice, and also handles other regulatory work such as food and product safety. He acts for both claimants and defendants. **Strengths:** "He is very commercial, pragmatic and tactically astute." "He's calm at all times and really knows his stuff." **Recent work:** Advised the prosecution on a significant case regarding market traders who sold counterfeit training shoes and clothes.

Iain MacDonald Has a wide-ranging practice that takes in consumer credit, trading and food law cases. He frequently represents high-street retailers and major consumer lenders. **Strengths:** "He's very personable and probably the strongest technical lawyer." "A very good advocate who is always impressive to the clients." **Recent work:** Appeared in the Supreme Court successfully appealing a decision regarding the sale of food after its 'use by' date. He acted for the prosecution, Torfaen County Borough Council.

Simon Popplewell (see p.696) Acts for lenders in court, and advises both corporations and comparatively small traders on regulatory matters. He is an expert in complex consumer credit issues, and regularly drafts consumer credit agreements and advises on consumer credit licensing. **Strengths:** "Very thorough and highly approachable." "He's very responsive and clearly a bright chap." **Recent work:** Appeared in a three-day hearing before an OFT Adjudicator regarding the consumer credit licences of HFO Capital, HFO Services and Roxburghe.

Bradley Say The majority of his practice is angled towards consumer credit issues. He frequently represents debtors in both the secondary and non-status lending markets. **Recent work:** Worked on a case to ascertain whether a creditor complied with Section 77 of the Consumer Credit Act 1974.

Kate Urell (see p.742) Specialises in finance-related consumer matters, in particular consumer credit litigation. She has represented a number of high-profile clients in trials concerning the mis-selling of payment protection insurance. **Strengths:** "She's very cool and very clever." "All the judges like her and respond to her. She gets fantastic results." **Recent work:** Advised on complex consumer credit aspects of the government's energy efficiency scheme known as the Green Deal. Her clients included the Green Investment Bank, Green Deal Finance and British Gas.

Ruth Bala (see p.542) Handles the full spectrum of consumer credit issues for financial institutions, and regularly handles cases concerning unfair relationships and PPI mis-selling. **Strengths:** "She's very bright and very sharp." "She has her finger on the pulse." **Recent work:** Acted on a case, which also involved a product safety violation, regarding the sale of both counterfeit and illicit cigarettes.

Stephen Neville (see p.681) His expertise lies in consumer credit, contract law and financial services work, and he has acted for a number of major entities. He has a history of advising on many of the largest portfolio and business sales in the consumer lending sector. **Strengths:** "A good man for the bigger ticket matters." **Recent work:** Advised a major acquirer of consumer debt on due diligence issues pertaining to the sale of his business.

Julian Gun Cuninghame (see p.616) Predominantly advises on consumer credit matters, usually for clients with a claim against a bank. **Strengths:** "He is very assured and highly experienced." **Recent work:** Advised the debtors of Barons Finance and related entities in 15 cases. These cases concerned loans by unlicensed lenders to borrowers that had moved to the UK from the African continent.

James Ross (see p.711) Frequently represents both high street and secondary lending companies in consumer credit litigation. Mis-sold investments, mortgage repossessions and debt claims are all areas of interest to him. **Strengths:** "He's good at digesting information quickly and getting into the detail, which enables him to put forward succinct and appropriate arguments." "The hot pick in consumer law is unfair relationships, and he's at the cutting edge when it comes to that."

Band 2

Henderson Chambers

See profile on p.820

THE SET

Henderson Chambers' practice is tilted towards trading standards cases such as product recalls. Practitioners also conduct a significant amount of food safety work. The set often deals with cross-border issues and has a number of international clients both inside and outside the EU, including some within China.

Client service: "John White, the head clerk, is always very keen to help."

SILKS

Richard Mawrey QC A weighty player in the field who acts for a broad range of clients, including banks, building societies, finance companies and the Finance and Leasing Association. He has recently advised on the hand-over from the FSA and OFT regulators to the single FCA. **Strengths:** "He is very independent minded and very clear thinking." "He provides a practical and commercial view." **Recent work:** Involved in a case regarding unauthorised collective investment initiatives. The matter resulted from the FSA's pursuit of several property investment clubs.

JUNIORS

William Hibbert (see p.626) Specialises in consumer credit litigation, and is an expert in consumer protection. He is commended by his peers for his astute handling of complex cases that have wide-ranging implications for the area. **Strengths:** "Technically excellent." "He's incredibly bright and very good academically." **Recent work:** Advised GE Home Lending on a number of claims, including those relating to unfair relationships and mis-sold PPI.

Julia Smith Primarily deals with issues of consumer credit and unfair terms, and has an interest in FCA regulation and unfair commercial practice. She advises regulators and financial institutions, as well as retailers. **Strengths:** "SHe's very pithy and very precise, and sees things clearly." **Recent work:** Instructed by the Department for Energy & Climate Change in matters relating to the Green Deal.

Toby Riley-Smith Has a general consumer law practice and is an expert on cases regarding medical products, including breast implants and metal-on-metal implants. He also conducts works with the OFT on consumer finance issues. **Strengths:** "He's commercially oriented and puts energy and commitment into getting the best result for the client." **Recent work:** Involved in a case brought by Dorchester Hotel against Foodspeed. The claimant was seeking damages for compensation it made to guests who had suffered salmonella poisoning.

Dennis Rosenthal (see p.710) Handles a mixed practice but is particularly strong on consumer credit law. Other areas of focus include data protection and fraud protection. **Strengths:** "He's so sharp. He knows his stuff and is totally brilliant."

Band 3

5 Paper Buildings

See profile on p.844

THE SET

The set's team, comprised of renowned juniors, is best known for its criminal and regulatory work. It has a strong reputation for trading standards work, particularly on the prosecution side, and is instructed on a regular basis by a number of local authorities and county councils. On the defence side its client base includes a number of motor retailers and supermarkets. Market sources say: "The set is good in terms of both its clerking and the quality and performance of its barristers."

JUNIORS

Miles Bennett (see p.547) Both prosecutes and defends, and has acted for the OFT, local authorities, F.A.C.T, and a number of major plcs in the retail sector. **Strengths:** "A phenomenal jury advocate who is very technical and good on points of law." "Charming and personable, he's very passionate about every case he's involved in and fizzes with ideas."

Ben Douglas-Jones A key figure who frequently handles criminal cases that cross over into consumer law. He undertakes a large number of cases involving local authorities. **Strengths:** "He knows his stuff and knows the way around the legislation."

Denis Barry (see p.544) Entrusted with a vast number of criminal consumer matters, and has handled a number of unfair trading cases. He frequently handles difficult proceedings relating to novel legal points, and is an expert on the Enterprise Act 2002. **Strengths:** "I find him accessible, approachable and attentive." **Recent work:** Involved in a case regarding the use of European and foreign decoder cards for viewing Premiership football.

Charlene Sumnall (see p.732) Conducted work on a significant case regarding counterfeit pornography. She is commended for her skills in dealing with procedural and evidential issues. **Strengths:** "She's a very good advocate, who is very thorough and down to earth with clients." **Recent work:** Represented Kwik-Fit in a case concerning the supply of an unroadworthy vehicle that caused a multi-vehicle collision.

Other Ranked Lawyers

Cameron Crowe (see p.582) (36 Bedford Row) Represents both claimants and defendants in a range of cases relating to trading standards. He often works on matters arising from Part 8 of the Enterprise Act, and also has a growing practice dealing with offences under the Trade Marks Act. **Strengths:** "Cool as a cucumber. He's not fazed in a conflict setting, and in conference he's very knowledgeable and easy to speak to." **Recent work:** Involved in a case brought against a 'rogue trader' who fraudulently gained £300,000 from vulnerable individuals for construction that was found to be unnecessary.

Simon Antrobus (Crown Office Chambers) A high-quality criminal barrister who exclusively acts for the defence. He has represented a range of large food and clothes retailers. **Strengths:** "He really knows this area of the law inside out. He's very user-friendly and doesn't stand on ceremony." **Recent work:** Acted on behalf of a hotel chain after an outbreak of campylobacter at a wedding reception in one of its hotels caused food poisoning.

Richard Heller (Dyers Chambers) Has a practice overwhelmingly made up of regulatory and consumer law cases. He is frequently used by local authorities on complicated and large-scale matters. **Strengths:** "He has carved out a niche in the local authority world and is very good on complex rules and regulations." **Recent work:** Involved in a case brought against Primark Store concerning a breach of General Product Safety Regulations resulting from selling hazardous Christmas decorations.

Damian Falkowski (Thirty Nine Essex Street) Specialises in cases relating to consumer credit and mortgages. **Strengths:** "A real street fighter and someone who is tactically astute." "He's an excellent advocate who is very firm. He doesn't get bullied or intimidated by any level of the judiciary." **Recent work:** Represented ING Lease (UK) in a case brought against Garry O'Connor, the footballer, concerning the repossession of two cars bought on finance. A central issue was the Consumer Credit Act 2006 'high net worth' exemption.

Kevin de Haan QC (Francis Taylor Building) Has a mixed regulatory practice which, in addition to consumer law, comprises environmental, health and safety and licensing cases. **Strengths:** "He is a very bright man who is excellent on both domestic and EU regulatory matters."

Jonathan Hough QC (4 New Square) An expert in consumer credit and credit hire matters. He has recently appeared before the Court of Appeal handling significant cases on behalf of motor insurers. **Strengths:** "If anything is a bit out of the ordinary or tricky, he is the man to go to. He has an ability to get to the root of issues." "A steady hand and someone who is incredibly hard-working." **Recent work:** Involved in a professional liability case surrounding the question of whether consumer credit agreements were negligently prepared by solicitors.

Eva Lomnicka (4 New Square) Predominantly undertakes advisory work and is one of the country's leading experts on financial services, and in particular consumer credit. She has been involved in the field since the formation of the relevant law. **Strengths:** "She is very good and highly academic." "She has produced some excellent written work on the area."

Benjamin Williams (4 New Square) Has a strong reputation for his handling of major credit hire matters. He is also experienced in other areas of consumer law such as distance selling and marketing, and doorstep selling. **Strengths:** "He is known for the depth of his research and his ability to come at things from a fresh angle. He always adds something to a case." "His paperwork is very lucid and compelling." **Recent work:** Appeared in Salut v Baratis, a Court of Appeal case considering the legality and construction of the Doorstep Selling Regulations.

Jonathan Rich (see p.707) (Five Paper) Specialises in consumer and property law matters. He acts for both landlords and tenants, and is recognised for his extensive expertise on regulatory issues.

David Travers QC (6 Pump Court) Widely respected in the regulatory community for his performance on complex cases. He works on the gamut of cases in the field, and regularly provides consumer law advice to leading businesses. **Strengths:** "He is without a doubt one of the most outstanding performers in the field. The advice he gives is concise and accurate." **Recent work:** Represented a food wholesaler over claims that undeclared allergens were present in its food items.

Mark Watson (6 Pump Court) A consumer law veteran, who is especially good on food law and trading standards cases. He frequently receives instructions from the Food Standards Agency regarding enforcement. **Strengths:** "He conducts the most effective pieces of cross-examination I have ever seen of experts." "He's ferociously hard-working. He has superb judgement and real dogged determination." **Recent work:** Acted for the FSA in the prosecution against Selfridges and a farmer, regarding the sale of raw milk through vending machines.

Malcolm Waters QC (see p.747) (Radcliffe Chambers) Undertakes work for financial institutions involved in the consumer credit market. He has recently advised on changes to the regulatory system overseeing retail financial products. **Strengths:** "He knows his stuff absolutely backwards." "He's a very measured and skilled advocate."

Elizabeth Ovey (Radcliffe Chambers) An expert in regulatory matters. She receives consumer credit instructions from banks, building societies and other institutions. **Strengths:** "She is very solid and highly approachable."

Alex Glassbrook (see p.609) (Temple Garden Chambers) Approaches consumer law from the civil angle. He is frequently instructed in credit hire matters, particularly by insurers. **Strengths:** "He has a deep understanding of all the issues, and is good for a tricky case."

MIDLANDS

Consumer Law Midlands
Leading Juniors
Band 1
Berlin Barry *St Philips Chambers (ORL)* ◊ *
Band 2
Mills Ben *St Philips Chambers (ORL)* ◊ 🄰 *
Thorogood Bernard *No5 Chambers (ORL)* ◊ *
* *Indicates individual with profile.*
◊ (ORL) = Other Ranked Lawyer.
🄰 *direct access (see p.11).*
Alphabetical order within each band. Band 1 is highest.

Ranked Lawyers

Bernard Thorogood (No5 Chambers) Has a mixed practice combining regulatory, consumer and health and safety work. **Strengths:** "He is very well organised, analytical and an authoritative advocate."

Barry Berlin (see p.548) (St Philips Chambers) Covers a broad range of regulatory and consumer work. He deals with heavyweight matters, and is frequently instructed in prosecutions relating to fatal accidents. **Strengths:** "He is a very thorough practitioner and a great all-round advocate." **Recent work:** Instructed on a case concerning an alleged serious conspiracy by four brothers, including a police official, to make fraudulent sales of insurance for mobile phones.

Ben Mills (see p.672) (St Philips Chambers) A criminal practitioner who is active in the regulatory space. He has extensive experience in cases relating to consumer credit licensing matters. **Strengths:** "He is a very approachable barrister whose talent belies his year of call, which is relatively recent." **Recent work:** Acted for the prosecution against a family that was allegedly running a substantial counterfeiting factory.

COSTS LITIGATION: An Introduction

Contributed by Temple Garden Chambers

Reports of the death of costs litigation are greatly exaggerated. Control of costs is central to the changes introduced in April 2013 and all practitioners need to be able properly to understand costs. No client can be properly advised, nor judge competently addressed, without careful consideration of costs issues.

Case management decisions should only be made with regard to the cost implications of each option considered, and budgets set at the first case management conference are of great importance to each side. Practitioners experienced in detailed assessments now find themselves brought in at the outset of litigation to advise on and argue at costs management hearings. Those unfamiliar with Bills of Costs find Precedent H unfamiliar territory and the Costs Bar can help solicitors achieve the best results for them and their clients.

The deficiencies in the Costs Budgeting process are becoming apparent with experience. Otherwise straightforward directions hearings are now greatly extended by time spent reviewing budgets. The rules' exhortation for parties to discuss and, if possible, agree all or part of each other's budget in advance is rarely observed. Even those mindful of the Mitchell necessity to lodge budgets on time still serve revised budgets (one or more) in the last few days' flurry of activity before the Costs Management Hearing.

Every eventuality has to be considered and budgeted, even if unlikely to materialise, leading to budgets that cost for a perhaps improbable worst case scenario. Too often the party that believes it is likely to end up paying costs succumbs to the understandable temptation to challenge all parts of a budget as this is their best shot at saving some money in the long term. It remains to be seen how effective the costs budgeting process proves to be in limiting the challenges made on assessment at the conclusion of a case. If nothing else, the difficulties of comparing what has been allowed for the stages identified on a Precedent H budget with a detailed bill of costs will be apparent.

Meanwhile, legal practitioners and legal expenses insurers are busy developing new business models and products designed for the changed legal costs and funding landscape. Costs litigation's propensity for acronyms – what with CFAs and ATE – is now enhanced by QOWCS, DBAs and ABSs. Whilst Damages Based Agreements remain unfamiliar and unexploited, the opportunities created by Alternative Business Structures are hoped to be fertile ground for those seeking to generate new business and new ways for providing services to clients. The Costs Bar is in the vanguard, providing expert assistance to those seeking to get to grips with this brave new world.

Contents:

LONDON

Costs Litigation London
Leading Sets
Band 1
Hailsham Chambers *
4 New Square *
Band 2
Thirty Nine Essex Street *
Temple Garden Chambers *
Leading Silks
Band 1
Bacon Nicholas *4 New Square* *
Band 2
Browne Simon P *Temple Garden Chambers*
Hutton Alexander *Hailsham Chambers* *
Band 3
Drabble Richard *Landmark Chambers (ORL)* ◊
Holland David *Landmark Chambers (ORL)* ◊
Kirby PJ *Hardwicke (ORL)* ◊ [A] *
Post Andrew *Hailsham Chambers* *
Leading Juniors
Star individuals
Mallalieu Roger *4 New Square* *
Band 1
Williams Benjamin *4 New Square*
Band 2
Ayling Judith *Thirty Nine Essex Street*
Carpenter Jamie *Hailsham Chambers* *
Marven Robert *4 New Square* *
Band 3
Brown Simon J *Crown Office Chambers (ORL)* ◊
Edwards Simon *Thirty Nine Essex Street*
James Mark *Temple Garden Chambers*
Laughland James *Temple Garden Chambers* *
Sachdeva Vikram *Thirty Nine Essex Street* *
Band 4
Lambert Sarah *1 Crown Office Row (ORL)* ◊ *
McDonald George *4 New Square* *
Munro Joshua *Hailsham Chambers* [A] *
Saoul Daniel *4 New Square* *
Scott Katharine *Thirty Nine Essex Street*
Stacey Dan *Hailsham Chambers* *
Wignall Gordon *No5 Chambers (ORL)* ◊ [A]
Wilkinson Richard *Temple Garden Chambers* *
* *Indicates set / individual with profile.*
◊ *(ORL) = Other Ranked Lawyer.*
[A] *direct access (see p.11).*
Alphabetical order within each band. Band 1 is highest.

Band 1

Hailsham Chambers
See profile on p.814

THE SET

A top set with a highly regarded team of costs counsel. Members are in high demand for their advice and representation on a range of costs matters, and handle everything from drafting CFAs to handling disputes in the Senior Courts Cost Office (SCCO). Members of the set have appeared in some of the largest and most high-profile cost disputes of late, including Flatman v Germany, a matter that established the limits of solicitors' liability for adverse costs. Sources say of the individuals here: "They're good because they keep the advice practical and they get straight to the point. I get on and off the phone within ten minutes."

Client service: "I have always found the clerks to be very helpful and good at finding me someone at short notice. They're very reasonable regarding fees."

SILKS

Alexander Hutton QC Acts for both claimants and defendants, often on important points of costs law. He appears in both between-the-parties and solicitor/own-client costs disputes, and provides advice to solicitors on retainers and CFAs. **Strengths:** "He has a phenomenal command of costs law, and is adept at assimilating huge amounts of information. He has excellent client-handling skills and is extremely collaborative when working with instructing solicitors." "He's got a very smooth and easy manner in court." **Recent work:** Acted in BGC Capital v Rees and Tullett Prebon, an assessment of costs in a dispute between City institutions accused of illegally poaching each other's traders.

Andrew Post QC (see p.697) Acts in and advises on major costs litigation and appeals. He is frequently instructed in relation to retainers and solicitor/client disputes. **Strengths:** "He's risen to the challenge since taking silk." "He's a really nice chap – a true gentleman who's also very bright." **Recent work:** Acted for DLA Piper in a £1.8 million solicitor/client dispute in the SCCO.

JUNIORS

Jamie Carpenter A popular choice for City firms. He has particular experience of acting on disputes relating to wasted and non-party costs orders. **Strengths:** "He's authoritative, his advice has optimum clarity and he's a tough advocate." "He's good at persuading the judges to move towards his way of thinking." **Recent work:** Acted in Flatman v Germany; Weddall v Barchester Healthcare, a case concerning the limits of solicitors' potential liability to pay the other side's costs when they act for an impecunious client under a CFA, but with no after-the-event (ATE) insurance.

Joshua Munro (see p.679) Has handled a range of cost d isputes in courts of all levels. His experience includes acting in the SCCO and House of Lords on matters such as group actions and CFA success fees. **Strengths:** "He's got a very quick mind and speedily assesses how to deal with and head off the issues in a case." **Recent work:** Acted in Pfizer Inc v Gubbay, a case concerning preliminary issues relating to the costs of a claim for conspiracy to trade in fake Viagra.

Dan Stacey (see p.727) Acts on a broad range of costs cases, from CFA disputes to issues relating to fast-track costs. His non-contentious practice includes drafting CFAs and advising on damages-based agreements. **Strengths:** "His preparation skills are so thorough. He's good at identifying areas of potential risk, which he then closes off." "A very determined advocate." **Recent work:** Acted in ASN v Dartford v Gravesham Hospital Trust, one of the first costs budgeting hearings under the new regime.

4 New Square
See profile on p.835

THE SET

A market-leading set of costs specialists offering strength and depth in terms of both costs litigation and advisory work. Members have been involved in a number of high-profile and precedent-setting cases in recent years including the seminal case of Mitchell v Newsgroup. Members of the set were also retained by Boris Berezovsky in a multimillion-pound costs claim following the Abramovich litigation. Market commentators are full of praise for this chambers: "It has a strong team of specialists in this area and is certainly a go-to set."

Client service: "The clerks, led by Lizzy Stewart, are really helpful and very personable. I like the personal touch that they offer. They're clearly running a large and diverse set but I still feel like our work is always really valued."

SILKS

Nicholas Bacon QC (see p.540) Head of the costs team and a barrister who is frequently instructed on the leading cases in the field. He dominates this market and has a host of high-profile cases to his name, many of which have been reported. **Strengths:** "If you want an absolute costs specialist silk then there's only Nick Bacon." "His strength above everything else, lies in his ability to identify what success means in a job and ensuring that he achieves it. He's very down to earth, extremely easy to work with and, for somebody who is a leader in the field, he's also very accessible." **Recent work:** Acted in Andrew Mitchell v Newsgroup Newspapers, the leading Court of Appeal case on the application of costs budgeting and relief from sanctions under the Jackson reforms.

JUNIORS

Roger Mallalieu (see p.661) A popular choice for instructing solicitors. His costs practice includes advising and representing clients in relation to third-party costs, solicitor/own client disputes and CFA compliance matters. He is regularly instructed on appellate work and often handles test cases. **Strengths:** "He really is something else. The clear leader in the field now on the junior side. He knows the area so incredibly well but he's never overbearing with that knowledge. His approach is really helpful and his strength is when he's on his feet: he's a fantastic advocate." **Recent work:** Successfully acted without a leader in the Court of Appeal in Bartkauskaite v Tasleem, a case concerning an important point of practice relating to Part 8 proceedings.

Benjamin Williams Highly regarded by instructing solicitors and peers alike. He acts on a lot of group actions and has appeared in a number of major costs cases in the Court of Appeal in recent years. **Strengths:** "In terms of technical ability, he's as good as it comes. If you're looking for somebody who'll get to the heart of an issue at warp speed, he's your man." "Legally he's without compare, and he's also shrewd and is a very determined advocate." **Recent work:** Acted in the Sonae Group Litigation, the largest ever

UK group claim for compensation. The case involved costs claims in the region of £60 million.

Robert Marven (see p.664) Acts for a range of clients including solicitors, insurers, claims management companies and public bodies. His broad costs practice takes in issues relating to CFAs, costs budgets and estimates and non-party costs orders. **Strengths:** "The nice thing about working with him is he gives you confidence in what you're doing. He always comes out and expresses his opinion." "He's a courteous advocate. He's very much the iron fist in the velvet glove." **Recent work:** Acted in Bartkauskaite v Bartkauskiene, a Court of Appeal case concerning the operation of the fixed costs regime upon issue of a default costs certificate.

Daniel Saoul Has broad experience of both sides of the profession, having previously worked as a solicitor advocate in a City firm. He is frequently instructed by defendants in high-value costs disputes. **Strengths:** "He delivers a seamless service to clients. Good, bright and can put his hand to almost anything." "He's one of my favourite juniors at the moment because when a junior has worked as a solicitor and then gone on to the Bar, they're worth their weight in gold." **Recent work:** Acted for Welsh Water in a dispute brought by Albion Water concerning an issues-based costs order.

George McDonald (see p.667) Focuses his practice on costs law. He has acted on a number of reported cases concerning issues of significant importance to solicitors. **Strengths:** One solicitor commented: "George is immensely clever: he has an intellect that far outstretches my own on cases that I've had for a while. He'll always come in with a fresh thought." "A very pleasant and very likeable chap." **Recent work:** Acted in Elvanite Full Circle Limited v AMEC Earth & Environmental, the seminal case on costs budgets under the new costs management regime.

Band 2

Thirty Nine Essex Street
See profile on p.797

THE SET

The set boasts a good range of talent at the junior level, and its members frequently appear in the appellate courts and the SCCO on a range of costs disputes. Members of the set complement their practice with expertise in other areas including personal injury, clinical negligence and insurance litigation. The team undertakes all aspects of costs work and has particular expertise in advising on potential funding arrangements and in drafting costs documentation.

Client service: "The clerks are very responsive. Their recommendations are absolutely spot-on."

JUNIORS

Judith Ayling Acts for both paying and receiving parties and has particular experience in solicitor/own-client disputes. She handles the full range of cost issues, from group litigation to detailed assessment hearings in the SCCO. **Strengths:** "She's exceptional and she really knows her stuff." "She is very bright, marshals the arguments very well and gives very good advice." **Recent work:** Acted in a detailed assessment hearing where the claimant challenged the hourly rates and ATE premium incurred after moving firms at a late stage.

Vikram Sachdeva Has a wide costs practice, and acts for companies, individuals and public bodies on a range of costs disputes. He has particular expertise in cases concerning criminal costs, commercial costs and CFAs. **Strengths:** "He's very sharp and picks things up really quickly." "He's quite thorough and very determined." **Recent work:** Acted in Heron v TNT, a Court of Appeal case concerning third-party costs orders.

Simon Edwards Has extensive experience of handling a range of costs matters. He frequently appears at the SCCO, drafts solicitors' retainers and advises on third-party funding agreements. **Strengths:** "He's excellent. He has a lot of experience and is very sensible." "He's just very measured: he's the type of person who, if he tells you something, you have complete faith in him." **Recent work:** Acted for the paying party in a dispute concerning ATE premium and appropriate hourly rates following a personal injury trial.

Katharine Scott Advises and represents both claimants and defendants on the full gamut of costs litigation. Her experience includes acting on solicitor/own-client disputes and on party and party disputes. **Strengths:** "Thorough, committed and someone with excellent judgement." **Recent work:** Acted for the solicitor in a solicitor/own-client dispute concerning costs estimates and the nature and extent of the retainer.

Temple Garden Chambers
See profile on p.872

THE SET

A set with barristers equipped to handle all aspects of costs litigation. Members have been instructed in numerous costs budgeting hearings, and are often sought out for their advisory and drafting work. Some of the most high-profile cases in the market have been undertaken by individuals at Temple Garden Chambers. By way of example, tenants here successfully represented the claimant in Mitchell v News Group Newspapers. Market commentators say: "They are a good set of chambers. I see them as the new boys on the block: they are very ambitious and have a lot of drive. They have strength at the top, at the middle and some good new people coming through."

SILKS

Simon Browne QC A popular choice for costs disputes in heavy commercial and group litigation. He has appeared on a number of leading cases in the Court of Appeal in recent years, and was recently invited to sit on the Costs Committee of the Civil Justice Council. **Strengths:** "He's really come on since he's taken silk. He's solid, knowledgeable and so good at presenting a case." **Recent work:** Represented the claimant in Andrew Mitchell MP v News Group Newspapers, a Court of Appeal case concerning the application of costs budgeting and relief from sanctions under the Jackson reforms.

JUNIORS

Mark James Focuses his practice on appellate advocacy before the High Court and Court of Appeal. He undertakes a range of non-contentious advisory work and is frequently instructed to draft private retainers and CFAs. **Strengths:** "Very nice, very approachable and very quick." "He provides a very good service because of the speed in which he turns papers round and the clarity of the notes that he provides." **Recent work:** Acted in Stone Brewer LLP v Just Costs, a dispute concerning the applicability of the one-fifth rule in S70(9) of the Solicitors Act 1974 in relation to solicitor/client assessment.

James Laughland Acts and advises on a wide range of costs matters. He regularly appears in the SCCO, representing solicitors, legal expenses insurers and clients. **Strengths:** "He has a great ability to think on his feet." **Recent work:** Acted in Laux v Stewart, successfully arguing that the opponent party had unreasonably incurred all the costs subsequent to his client's pre-issue offers.

Richard Wilkinson Frequently appears in the Court of Appeal and SCCO on a range of costs disputes. He has particular experience in CFA funding issues and is particularly sought after for his advice and drafting. **Strengths:** "He comes across as very knowledgeable and very approachable, and gives good, sensible advice." "He has a great knowledge of costs law and is both steady and meticulous, exactly the skills we are looking for in a costs specialist." **Recent work:** Acted as junior counsel to Simon Browne QC in Mitchell v News Group Newspapers.

Other Ranked Lawyers

Simon Brown (Crown Office Chambers) Has a broad common law practice with a particular focus on costs. He deals with a lot of solicitor/client assessments and does mostly advisory work. **Strengths:** "Technically very good and a pleasure to work with." **Recent work:** Acted in Bentine v Bentine, a dispute concerning whether costs that are disallowed for want of a retainer should factor in the calculation of the one-fifth rule.

Sarah Lambert (see p.650) (1 Crown Office Row) Regularly appears in the SCCO and in the Court of Appeal. Her broad costs practice includes CFA compliance, wasted costs cases, costs capping and personal liability claims against experts. **Strengths:** "Impressive on her feet; her cross-examination is really incisive." "She's also really knowledgeable." **Recent work:** Acted in Walter Hall v Thomas and Others, a costs capping application by the defendant where the claimant's costs are estimated to be in excess of £1 million.

PJ Kirby QC (see p.646) (Hardwicke) As well as handling costs litigation, he is also a Bar Council-appointed High Court costs assessor and sits as a deputy district judge. **Strengths:** "I've always found him to be accurate in what he says. His role as a part-time judge helps give him that insight into the judicial approach to various arguments." "He's very careful with his preparation and picks up on points that opponents would miss." **Recent work:** Acted in Hussain v Chartis Insurance, a successful High Court appeal concerning whether causation of damage was an issue to be determined by the court's judge when considering an increase in the success fee of a settled personal injury claim.

Richard Drabble QC (Landmark Chambers) Acts on costs disputes in the context of his public law and planning practice. He is often instructed to act for and intervene on behalf of the Law Society. **Strengths:** "A brilliant man" who "always goes down well with judges." **Recent work:** Intervened for the Law Society in a case concerning obligations arising from the Legal Expenses Directives.

David Holland QC (Landmark Chambers) Has experience of handling a range of costs disputes in various courts including the SCCO. He is regularly briefed to advise and act for the Law Society. **Strengths:** "A very experienced practitioner with a very attractive advocacy style." "He's a bit of a whirlwind: he moves quickly. A likeable man and someone who is extremely good at identifying the nub of the case." **Recent work:** Acted in Flatman v Germany, a Court of Appeal case concerning the extent to which a solicitor can fund a client's disbursements whilst acting on a CFA.

Gordon Wignall (No5 Chambers) Splits his practice between London, Birmingham and Bristol. His costs experience includes handling multiparty actions and insurance funding disputes. **Strengths:** "A great barrister who is really commercially minded, very bright and good with clients." **Recent work:** Acted in Adlington v Els, a case concerning major relief from sanctions.

MIDLANDS

Costs Litigation Midlands
Leading Juniors
Band 1
Hogan Andrew *Ropewalk Chambers (ORL)* ◊

Ranked Lawyers

Andrew Hogan (Ropewalk Chambers) Receives instructions on the full range of costs work. He handles solicitor and own-client disputes, and costs disputes in the context of various tribunals, and frequently acts in detailed assessment hearings. **Strengths:** "He is a very good practitioner with a good costs practice." **Recent work:** He acted in a £700,000 detailed assessments hearing in the Senior Courts Cost Office.

NORTHERN

Costs Litigation Northern
Leading Sets
Band 1
Kings Chambers *
Leading Juniors
Band 1
Friston Mark *Kings Chambers*
Hughes Paul *Kings Chambers* *
Ralph Craig *Kings Chambers* *
Band 2
Latham Kevin *Kings Chambers* *
McDonald Margaret *Kenworthy's Chambers (ORL)* ◊
Smith Matthew *Kings Chambers* *
Up-and-coming individuals
Bedford Erica *Kings Chambers* *
◊ (ORL) = Other Ranked Lawyer.
** Indicates set / individual with profile.*
Alphabetical order within each band. Band 1 is highest.

Band 1

Kings Chambers
See profile on p.918

THE SET

The set has a strong team of costs specialists able to cater to clients' needs when it comes to all aspects of costs litigation, from drafting of retainers and specific funding agreements to appearances in the Court of Appeal. Its members act for both paying and receiving parties, and are highly sought after for their advocacy and advisory work. Market commentators say: "They are the go-to chambers for costs," and "they can cover London, Manchester and everywhere in between, and they have a range of experience so you can have any case covered in terms of value and complexity."

Client service: "The clerks, led by Colin Griffin, do an excellent job and are very good at getting hold of counsel when you need them."

JUNIORS

Craig Ralph (see p.703) Focuses his practice exclusively on the law of costs. He is frequently instructed in solicitor/own-client matters and disputes concerning 'broken retainer' allegations. **Strengths:** "He's a tenacious advocate, pragmatic with his advice and realistic in his outcome." **Recent work:** He acted in Uttamar Kaur Bhatti v Primark Stores, a Court of Appeal case concerning the presumption as to costs under a pre-action disclosure application.

Mark Friston Head of the costs team at the set. As well as appellate advocacy, he is regularly instructed to provide non-contentious business advisory work such as drafting detailed retainers regarding new legislation and group litigation orders. **Strengths:** "He's a really safe pair of hands, a great choice for any costs case, regardless of size, value or complexity." "He really is an expert in the field. His knowledge of the law is second to none." **Recent work:** He acted in Brown-Quinn v Equity Red Star, a Court of Appeal case concerning BTE insurance, European law and points of policy.

Matthew Smith (see p.724) Handles a range of cost matters, including group litigation, applications for security for costs and issues concerning success fees. He is particularly sought after for his experience in non-contentious costs and issues concerning contracts of retainer. **Strengths:** "He consistently impresses with his analytical skills; he is clearly capable of reacting to developing scenarios in litigation and then addressing these effectively." **Recent work:** He acted in Blankley v Central Manchester and Manchester Children's University Hospitals NHS Trust, an appeal concerning whether subsequent incapacity of a client automatically determines a retainer.

Paul Hughes (see p.633) Practises exclusively in costs law. He is regularly instructed on sizeable detailed assessments and appeals as well as being sought after for his advisory work. **Strengths:** "He's an exceptional advocate, always very well organised and prepared, and very persuasive." **Recent work:** He acted in a dispute relating to the detailed assessment of eight sample bills of costs totalling £700,000.

Kevin Latham (see p.651) Sought after for his experience in solicitor/own-client disputes and detailed assessments. His considerable expertise in this field is informed by his prior experience working at a firm of costs draftsmen and as an in-house advocate for a national law firm. **Strengths:** "He's very able, very calm and very measured, and never takes any bad points – he's just a pleasure to deal with." "He is very quick to digest the issues, even on a fairly complex case." **Recent work:** He acted for the defendant in a detailed assessment hearing following the conclusion of a catastrophic injury claim, successfully reducing the claimant solicitor's costs after securing a finding that they were disproportionate.

Erica Bedford (see p.546) Represents paying and receiving parties in actions up to £500,000 and frequently attends in the Supreme Court Costs Office. She has previous experience of costs litigation as a solicitor, and has developed considerable expertise in issues of misconduct, non-standard disclosure and claims where statements of costs for trial are exceeded. **Strengths:** "She's got experience beyond her years of call. You get a lot more than you paid for, and she also gives the impression that she will work her hind legs off for you." "She's incredibly well prepared, very willing to help and excellent on her feet. She argues your corner until she's blue in the face." **Recent work:** She acted for the paying party in a dispute where issues of misconduct were alleged in respect of the date of enactment of the CFA.

Other Ranked Lawyers

Margaret McDonald (Kenworthy's Chambers) Head of the personal injury and costs team at Kenworthy's Chambers. She specialises in costs litigation, particularly high-value bills in catastrophic personal injury, group actions and construction litigation, and is regularly instructed at costs appeals, detailed assessments and oral hearings following provisional assessments. **Strengths:** "She is very reliable, user-friendly and knowledgeable."

WESTERN

Costs Litigation Western
Leading Juniors
Band 1
Moore Oliver *Guildhall Chambers (ORL)* ◊
◊ (ORL) = Other Ranked Lawyer.

Ranked Lawyers

Oliver Moore (Guildhall Chambers) Heads the costs and litigation funding team at Guildhall Chambers. He represents paying and receiving parties in all civil costs matters, and is frequently instructed on costs appeals, appearing before costs judges and the Supreme Court Costs Office (SCCO). **Recent work:** He acted for a defendant in respect to the claimant's appeal from the SCCO relating to the applicable success fee to a personal injury claim.

COURT OF PROTECTION: An Introduction

Contributed by Malcolm Chisholm, One Garden Court Family Law Chambers

The Court of Protection, in its recreated guise, is now into its eighth year. The volume of work dealt with by the court continues to increase. Cases typically involve the court in making difficult decisions about where a relative, young or old, who has lost decision-making capacity should live, or how that relative's often significant finances should be managed: wills, trusts and other complex financial arrangements lie at the heart of the vast bulk of the Court of Protection's both contentious and non-contentious work.

The more complex welfare cases involving, for example, end-of-life decision making and capacity to consent to termination of pregnancy continue to be transferred to High Court judges of the Family Division for final and often urgent determination; they have 'dual tickets' as judges of the Court of Protection. The out-of-hours system for emergency orders is working smoothly, and already in 2014 there is a high ratio among the reported cases of occasions when High Court judges, exercising the jurisdiction of the Court of Protection, have sat late into the night to consider applications for orders to facilitate urgent medical treatment, for example caesarean sections.

The Regional Courts continue to be busy with both welfare and financial matters. There continues to be huge frustration that all cases must still be issued in London, even if their centre of gravity is Newcastle or Penzance – but moves are afoot to afford the facility of local issuing, which will facilitate early local case management by judges who are likely to remain involved throughout. In London, the Court of Protection now finds its (hopefully permanent) home in the building shared with the Central Family Court in Holborn, having moved from its previous temporary lodgings in the Thomas More Building at the Royal Courts of Justice.

Likewise, there is a greater willingness among judges to conduct hearings in a 'borrowed' court closer to P's home or even, in appropriate cases, in P's care home. This flexibility is surely welcome, as is the trend towards hearing directly from P in the courtroom, often by ensuring that he or she can talk to the judge without the formal constraints of formal, sworn evidence. There is a divergence of opinion about whether P's voice should be heard directly when the 'only' issue is best interests. Some practitioners think that P should, where possible, be present at all stages of the process; the point is forcefully made by others, however, that the court must concentrate on its core task of choosing between available options and that little is to be gained by hearing from P when the issue of capacity has already been put beyond doubt and when P's wishes and feelings can be reported by a litigation friend. Either way, the debate illustrates the healthy level of debate among committed and energetic practitioners.

The key development this year so far in the case law has been as a result of the seminal decision of the Supreme Court in Cheshire West on the proper definition of deprivation of liberty; the Court of Protection has as a result experienced an exponential rise in applications for court authorisations of deprivation of liberty, and indeed a similar rise in applications by P to challenge the deprivation of their liberty under s. 21A of the Mental Capacity Act 2005. Lady Hale's "acid test" that P must be under "continuous supervision and control" and "not free to leave" the establishment where he or she lives, combined with her rejection of Munby P's comparator of 'relative normality' has resulted in a significant increase in the number of incapacitated adults who are now likely to be deprived of their liberty.

The decision caused a degree of understandable anxiety for those tasked with organising services which fall outside the formal deprivation of liberty regime, as well as those within it. In light of the significant increase in potential applications to the court to authorise a deprivation of liberty, over two days in early June 2014 Munby P heard from a multiplicity of represented local authorities, the Official Solicitor and other interested parties to determine whether the procedure for court authorisation of a deprivation of liberty could be streamlined while nevertheless remaining Article 5 and 6 compliant. The outcome of the hearing is keenly awaited, not least by Directors of Social Services, who will be wondering how best to allocate scarce resources to ensure compliance with the law.

There has been a large increase of reported decision in the Court of Appeal since publication of Munby P's guidance on transparency in January 2014. The guidance applies to all judgments in the Court of Protection delivered by the Senior Judge, nominated circuit judges and High Court judges. A vast majority of those judgments are being anonymised in accordance with the guidance.

The recent decision in North Somerset Council v LW amounts to a cautionary tale for parties who consider that they do not need to comply with orders of the court. The party who failed to attend, having been directed to do so, was ordered to pay half of the local authority's costs. The case makes it clear, if it was not already, that when an issue of capacity is raised, the requirements of the MCA and Code of Practice must be diligently followed.

Also of keen interest to media-watchers is Re G: the media had made an application to be joined as a party to Court of Protection proceedings involving concerns about P's carers' influence over her, her property and her finances. The application was dismissed, but the case demarcates a clear line between, on the one hand, the desirability of increased transparency within Court of Protection proceedings and, on the other, the very limited role of the media in assisting the Court of Protection coming to a determination about P's communication with the press.

The flurry of reported cases appearing on the Bailii website and elsewhere illustrates that the jurisprudence of the Court of Protection is still in its relative infancy; the core elements of its substantive jurisprudence, as well as practice and procedure, continue to undergo rapid development.

Contents:

ALL CIRCUITS Health & Welfare

Court of Protection: Health & Welfare All Circuits
Leading Sets
Band 1
Thirty Nine Essex Street *
Band 2
Doughty Street Chambers *
Serjeants' Inn Chambers
Band 3
Garden Court Chambers *
1 Garden Court Family Law Chambers *
Hardwicke *
No5 Chambers *
St Johns Buildings *
Leading Silks
Band 1
Bowen Paul *Brick Court Chambers*
McGuire Bryan *Cornerstone Barristers (ORL)* ◊
Morris Fenella *Thirty Nine Essex Street*
Richards Jenni *Thirty Nine Essex Street*
Band 2
Johnston Christopher *Serjeants' Inn Chambers* *
Lock David *Landmark Chambers (ORL)* ◊ [A]
Mylonas Michael *Serjeants' Inn Chambers* *
* *Indicates set / individual with profile.*
◊ *(ORL) = Other Ranked Lawyer.*
[A] *direct access (see p.11)*

Court of Protection: Health & Welfare All Circuits	
Leading Juniors	
Star individuals	**Greatorex** Paul *11KBW (ORL)* ◊ [A] *
O'Brien Joseph *St Johns Buildings*	**Hirst** Leonie *Garden Court Chambers*
Band 1	**Lopez** Paul *St Ives Chambers (ORL)* ◊
Bagchi Andrew *1 Garden Court Family Law Chambers* *	**Powell** Debra *Serjeants' Inn Chambers* *
Burrows Simon *Kings Chambers (ORL)* ◊ *	**Pratley** Michelle *Thirty Nine Essex Street* [A] *
Butler-Cole Victoria *Thirty Nine Essex Street*	**Reeder** Stephen *Doughty Street Chambers*
Chisholm Malcolm *1 Garden Court Family Law Chambers* *	**Scott** Katharine *Thirty Nine Essex Street*
Dolan Bridget *Serjeants' Inn Chambers* *	**Weston** Amanda *Garden Court Chambers*
Greaney Nicola *Thirty Nine Essex Street* *	**Band 3**
Hewson Barbara *1 Gray's Inn Square (ORL)* ◊ [A]	**Allen** Neil *Thirty Nine Essex Street* *
Khalique Nageena *No5 Chambers* [A]	**Harris** Bethan *Garden Court Chambers*
McKendrick John *Outer Temple Chambers (ORL)* ◊	**Hearnden** Alexis *Thirty Nine Essex Street*
Patel Parishil *Thirty Nine Essex Street*	**Karim** Sam *Kings Chambers (ORL)* ◊ *
Ruck Keene Alexander *Thirty Nine Essex Street* *	**Lattimer** Justine *St Ives Chambers (ORL)* ◊ *
Sachdeva Vikram *Thirty Nine Essex Street* *	**Meacher** Alison *Hardwicke*
Street Amy *Serjeants' Inn Chambers* *	**Mullins** Mark *Outer Temple Chambers (ORL)* ◊
Weereratne Aswini *Doughty Street Chambers* [A]	**Oscroft** Jennifer *Cornerstone Barristers (ORL)* ◊
Band 2	**Paterson** Fiona *Serjeants' Inn Chambers* *
Bretherton Kerry *Tanfield Chambers (ORL)* ◊ [A]	**Rickard** Susanna *Serjeants' Inn Chambers* *
Burnham Ulele *Doughty Street Chambers*	**Scolding** Fiona *Outer Temple Chambers (ORL)* ◊ [A] *
Buttler Chris *Matrix Chambers (ORL)* ◊ [A]	**Stockwell** Matthew *St Johns Buildings*
Cavanagh Lorraine *St Johns Buildings*	**Up-and-coming individuals**
Davidson Laura *No5 Chambers* [A]	**Dobson** Catherine *Thirty Nine Essex Street*
Fullwood Adam *Kings Chambers (ORL)* ◊ *	**Mant** Peter *Thirty Nine Essex Street*

Band 1

Thirty Nine Essex Street
See profile on p.797

THE SET

Widely regarded as the leading chambers for Court of Protection health and welfare work across the UK, it represents a broad range of public sector and private clients in complex and high-profile matters. Such is its standing that a number of the set's tenants have appeared in the few Court of Protection cases to have been heard in the Supreme Court. Members here edit the Court of Protection Law Reports and contribute leading textbooks such as 'Heywood and Massey: Court of Protection Practice' and Jordan's 'Court of Protection Practice'.

Client service: "The clerking is really impressive; they are so responsive."

SILKS

Fenella Morris QC Renowned for her formidable advocacy, she is experienced at handling a wide range of Court of Protection matters, and has particular expertise in cases with a sexual element attached to them. **Strengths:** "She's incredibly focused and knows exactly when to draw blood. She's incredibly well prepared and knows the law inside out." "She's extremely sharp, very focused and very knowledgeable. She is a fearsome opponent, because she can come at things from so many different angles."

Jenni Richards QC A silk often chosen to appear on the most high-profile cases and a go-to advocate for both claimants and defendants. Her strong understanding of the law in relation to mental capacity and deprivation of liberty sets her apart. **Strengths:** "One of the best around, who is both extremely clever and pragmatic; she understands capacity law inside out." "Her advocacy is brilliant; she's exceptionally hard-working and truly believes in what she does."

JUNIORS

Nicola Greaney Highly recommended junior with a broad public law practice who regularly handles Court of Protection matters. She is on the Attorney General's A Panel. **Strengths:** "Extremely good with difficult litigants in person. She keeps her eye on the ball and has a very good knowledge of the law and the remedies we can apply for." "Very thorough and knowledgeable on complex sexual relations cases."

Parishil Patel Demonstrates substantial expertise in relation to medical treatment judgements. His Court of Protection practice benefits from his broad administrative and public law and human rights experience. **Strengths:** "An excellent advocate and an extremely adept cross-examiner. His knowledge of the law and relevant developments is always completely up to date, and he has first-rate intellectual and analytical skills." "Unflappable, very in command and very calm." **Recent work:** Represented the Official Solicitor in a case reviewing whether the wishes expressed in a letter purportedly written by a woman prior to her loss of capacity were in the woman's best interests.

Victoria Butler-Cole Highlighted for her outstanding knowledge of Court of Protection law, she is an editor of 'Heywood and Massey: Court of Protection Practice' and the Court of Protection law reports. **Strengths:** "Superb – she's a very good advocate with really good delivery, who is clear, extremely thorough, efficient and hard-working. She inspires complete confidence." "Very quick to get to the answer, she's persistent in holding her line." **Recent work:** Appeared for the interveners in a landmark Supreme Court case which considered whether it was lawful for an NHS trust to refrain from providing life-sustaining treatment to a patient.

Alexander Ruck Keene (see p.712) A stellar junior with an encyclopaedic knowledge of Court of Protection law, who has specialist expertise on jurisdictional points. He co-authors the set's Court of Protection newsletter and was selected to provide evidence to the House of Lords Select Committee on the Mental Capacity Act 2005. **Strengths:** "Brilliant – he's a thoughtful academic, and a fine practitioner as well. Great on cases where raw law meets advocacy, he's an intellectual force." "Very responsive, and really at the cutting edge of legal practice development." **Recent work:** Acted for the clinical intervener groups in a ground-breaking case relating to end of life treatment. This was the first case heard in the Supreme Court to consider the Mental Capacity Act 2005.

Vikram Sachdeva Celebrated Court of Protection junior, who has a standout practice in complex medical treatment cases. He is highly sought after by instructing solicitors not least because of his medical background and training. **Strengths:** "Very personable, astute and exceptionally skilled in medical cases." "Gives one great confidence as he understands the intricacies of the medical input into these cases, is very passionate and enthusiastic, and has a prodigious work rate." **Recent work:** Represented Aintree NHS Trust as the respondent in a Supreme Court case which considered the application by the family of a hospital patient that the patient be aggressively resuscitated if his health were to deteriorate.

Michelle Pratley A practitioner who impresses instructing solicitors and opponents alike with her calm and effective courtroom presence. **Strengths:** "Really brilliant – she's so clear-thinking she can win round even the most aggressive opponent with her focus. She works very hard and just makes dry concepts quite straightforward." "Excellent, a voice of calm in troubled waters, who produces incredibly impressive advocacy and written work." **Recent work:** Acted for the local council in Sandwell Metropolitan Borough Council v RG & Ors, a case which clarified the law in relation to marriage for incapacitated adults.

Katharine Scott Highly regarded junior who is well versed in Mental Health Act and healthcare law in relation to the Court of Protection. She receives particular praise for her pragmatic approach and reassuring manner with vulnerable clients who lack capacity. **Strengths:** "She's very intelligent and always has a practical solution for everything. She's brilliant with clients." "A bit of a force of nature: she's very thorough, and her written work is very good. She's a tough advocate and is very pleasant to work with."

Alexis Hearnden An admired barrister with a growing presence in the Court of Protection world. Her Court of Protection work is just part of her strong administrative and public law and human rights practice. **Strengths:** "Always very well prepared and ready to take on more senior counsel." "Very highly regarded and often instructed by the Official Solicitor."

Neil Allen (see p.534) Holds a strong reputation for his work on Court of Protection cases relating to deprivation of liberty and welfare under the Mental Health Act. He is a part-time lecturer in law at Manchester University. **Strengths:** "Intelligent and thorough, he offers an academic but accessible rights-based approach to complex welfare cases. He's an excellent communicator." "Very academic and extremely learned on the history of the law and its development. He is also fantastically approachable." **Recent work:** Acted for the local authorities in the landmark deprivation of liberty case P v Cheshire West and Cheshire Council.

Catherine Dobson Up-and-comer in the field who wins plaudits for her empathetic representation of clients. She has a particular focus on cases concerning sexual relations and reproductive rights issues for women. **Strengths:** "Razor sharp and extremely compassionate, she can pick up a case very quickly and get to the heart of the issues. She gives clients confidence, and has an extremely good rapport with judges." "Her skeleton arguments are excellently constructed and she has empathy and understanding for those in difficult circumstances."

Peter Mant Junior with a rising profile and notable recent experience of matters concerning deprivation of liberty and capacity to consent to marriage and sexual relations. He has a focus on safeguarding cases. **Strengths:** "Technically excellent, he has a persuasive manner in court, and is calm and quietly confident." "He has a quiet but authoritative manner, is very measured and calm but is absolutely on the ball and able to put his foot down when necessary." **Recent work:** Led by Jenni Richards QC on behalf of the local authorities in the high-profile deprivation of liberty case Cheshire West v P.

Band 2

Doughty Street Chambers

See profile on p.786

THE SET

An admired team with a strong human rights background that provides solid counsel and representation on the gamut of Court of Protection health and welfare proceedings. Members have appeared in two significant Supreme Court cases, and are appreciated for their crossover expertise in public and community care law.

JUNIORS

Aswini Weereratne Draws from a background in mental health to offer expert counsel on cases that touch on the overlap between the Mental Health Act and the Mental Capacity Act. **Strengths:** "She is a thoughtful, dynamic lawyer and a formidable advocate. Her attention to the detail of a case is second to none." "As astute as they come. Her ability to cut through the issues to the heart of complex and difficult cases is remarkable, as is her ability to turn around large volumes of work in sometimes the very shortest periods of time. The safest of safe hands."

Ulele Burnham Popular Court of Protection junior who regularly appears in high-profile and controversial medical treatment cases. **Strengths:** "Extremely impressive. She is quick to identify and grasp the issues in a case, and is able to rapidly absorb large amounts of material. She is highly respected by clients, who swiftly warm to her and trust her." "The quality of her written work is nothing short of tremendous and she has the all too rare ability to explain the most complex issues with perfect, penetrable clarity."

Stephen Reeder A talented practitioner with a focus on issues relating to dementia, who regularly advises the media on Court of Protection cases. Instructing solicitors appreciate his excellent client relationship skills and his ADR capabilities. **Strengths:** "He's got very good client care skills and has the ability to calm people down and get them focused. A lot of cases have a housing component to them, and because he sits on a housing tribunal he has that experience as well. He's very highly rated." "He has real empathy and a warmth of personality." **Recent work:** Acted for the successful local authority in a case determining where a mentally incapacitated individual should reside on reaching adulthood.

Serjeants' Inn Chambers

THE SET

The pre-eminent set for medical treatment decisions made in the Court of Protection, it advises NHS trusts and local authorities as well as the family members of protected parties and the Official Solicitor. One client remarked: "They are my first choice for deprivation of liberty cases and judicial reviews on funding. The members have diverse expertise and a very good knowledge of the landscape; they understand the repercussions that may arise for bodies."

SILKS

Christopher Johnston QC Has specialist expertise in medical treatment decision cases, and close to two decades' experience in the area. He is frequently instructed by the Official Solicitor on related matters. **Strengths:** "Very approachable, very collaborative, and quick to respond. He produces drafting of a high quality." "The Official Solicitor's counsel of choice for withdrawal of artificial nutrition cases." **Recent work:** Represented the Official Solicitor in a widely reported case in which it was determined that an anorexic woman who expressed a desire to die should continue to receive life-sustaining treatment.

Michael Mylonas QC Head of the set's Court of Protection team and experienced in providing representation on medical treatment cases. He was chosen to provide evidence to the House of Lords Select Committee in relation to the Mental Capacity Act. **Strengths:** "Continues to impress and be in demand. He is meticulous when it comes to preparation, and tenacious in court. He remains a very skilled and intelligent advocate with fantastic client relationship skills." "A quiet, calm, very effective case runner." **Recent work:** Represented a hospitalised patient who was brain injured and also suffering from dementia, whose family insisted that he should be aggressively resuscitated.

JUNIORS

Bridget Dolan (see p.589) Demonstrates striking expertise in cases relating to the Mental Health Act and Mental Capacity Act, and is noted for her expertise on matters concerning capacity to consent to sexual relations. A former forensic psychologist, she sits as a part-time mental health judge. **Strengths:** "Passionate about her work, she's a thorough and utterly reliable counsel, who is able to deliver digestible advice in tricky cases." "She is utterly dependable and has a keen eye for important details missed by others." **Recent work:** Acted for an NHS trust on successfully opposing an application by the parents of a 21-year-old woman with Down's syndrome that she be subjected to non-therapeutic sterilisation.

Amy Street (see p.730) Star of the medical Court of Protection sphere, she is often instructed in ground-breaking cases. She has a particular focus on human rights and deprivation of liberty cases. **Strengths:** "She's really clever and understatedly so. Her drafting is brilliant, her advice, both written and oral, is really thorough, and she has very good knowledge of all of the elements of Court of Protection cases." "She's appropriately persistent in court, and particularly good with intricate legal complexities." **Recent work:** Represented the Official Solicitor in the Supreme Court in P v Cheshire West, a landmark case on deprivation of liberty.

Debra Powell (see p.697) Valued for her knowledge of the crossover between Court of Protection and health matters. She is a contributing author to the textbook, 'Medical Treatment Decisions & The Law'. **Strengths:** "She's very sensible in court and she will definitely keep pushing a point if she thinks it's important. She's pragmatic, easy to work with and very responsive." "Good with clients, she offers good advice on overall strategy in complex cases." **Recent work:** Appeared for the Official Solicitor as litigation friend to a man detained under the Mental Health Act, who was resisting a potentially life-saving amputation to an infected leg.

Susanna Rickard (see p.707) Has particular knowledge in the areas of withdrawal of medical treatment and deprivation of liberty for hospital patients. **Strengths:** "Exceptionally insightful and effective, she cuts through to the real issues." "A favourite of the Official Solicitor, who is very highly regarded and gets cases above her call because of that." **Recent work:** Led by Christopher Johnston QC in representing the Official Solicitor in the widely reported case of E, in which the court determined it was in the best interests of an anorexic patient to continue to receive medical treatment against her wishes.

Fiona Paterson (see p.690) Highly recommended junior whose Court of Protection work has a medical treatment and human rights focus. She gained substantial experience in the medical law sphere in her eight years spent as a medical solicitor before joining the Bar. **Strengths:** "A newcomer into the Court of Protection arena and an advocate to watch. She is slowly but surely making her name and mark." **Re-**

cent work: Represented the hospital in a case which considered whether an asylum seeker patient detained under the Mental Health Act could lawfully be force-fed.

Band 3

Garden Court Chambers
See profile on p.808

THE SET

Boosted by the arrival of two former Tooks tenants, this noted team undertakes the full spectrum of Court of Protection work on the health and welfare side. Members draw on their specialisms in mental health, community care and social welfare to provide wide-ranging advice on all welfare matters overseen by the court.

JUNIORS

Leonie Hirst Wins plaudits for her deft handling of complex cases, and for her strong client relationship skills. She has corresponding expertise in immigration law and substantial experience of deprivation of liberty matters. **Strengths:** "She gives incredible advice on tricky cases, and is very supportive and very bright." "Packages her cases very effectively. She's tough but nice, and a very disarming opponent." **Recent work:** Led a successful challenge to an assessment that a woman placed in a nursing home under Deprivation of Liberty Safeguards lacked capacity.

Amanda Weston Highly experienced in handling cases that involve the interplay between the Court of Protection and judicial review. Her powerful advocacy is singled out for praise. **Strengths:** "One of the world's street fighters. If you were backed into a corner and wanted somebody to fight for you, Amanda would be the best one. She fights and she's clever."

Bethan Harris Frequently chosen to represent the Official Solicitor and family members, and able to draw from parallel social housing expertise when handling Court of Protection cases. Her recent work includes leading on sensitive matters relating to medical treatment and best interests determinations. **Strengths:** "Very organised and highly responsive. She has a particularly good style when dealing with matters that are very sensitive."

1 Garden Court Family Law Chambers
See profile on p.810

THE SET

Members of this well-regarded set benefit from a strong family law background, which complements their Court of Protection work in related cases. They have notable expertise in the areas of capacity to consent to marriage and sexual relations, and deprivation of liberty under the Mental Health Act 2005.

JUNIORS

Andrew Bagchi Acclaimed Court of Protection junior who brings his family law background to the table on related cases. He has particular expertise in overseeing cases relating to capacity to consent to marriage and sexual relations. **Strengths:** "He's hugely knowledgeable and has good judgement combined with really strong technical ability." "At the top of the list for instructions. Very pragmatic, he can get on top of issues very quickly. He's super-approachable and really responsive."

Malcolm Chisholm (see p.571) Distinguishes himself due to his conciliatory and grounded approach to highly fraught and complex cases. He has a particular specialism in the crossover between the Mental Capacity Act and the Mental Health Act. **Strengths:** "He has a sensitive manner with family members and is also realistic and sensible in his advice. He pursues cases with vigour and enthusiasm." "He has an almost fatherly oversight when handling cases. He really steadies the ship and calms everything down."

Hardwicke
See profile on p.816

THE SET

Esteemed set whose members are well versed in jurisdiction proceedings and have a strong grounding in cases concerning the Mental Capacity Act 2005. The team has strength in community care, social housing, public law and education law, all of which assists both claimant and local authority clients in related Court of Protection cases.

Client service: "Hardwicke barristers are a very friendly group, and their clerks are always helpful."

JUNIORS

Alison Meacher An impressive junior whose social housing background is highly valued by instructing solicitors. She acts for claimants and family members as well as local authorities, and is particularly good on questions concerning capacity to litigate and deprivation of liberty. **Strengths:** "A firecracker, who knows the area incredibly well, gets to the heart of the matter and gets on really well with clients and opponents alike." "The crossover with her social housing law knowledge is really good. She's a really good advocate and always tries to find a solution."

No5 Chambers
See profile on p.883

THE SET

Tenants of this noted chambers have key mental health expertise, and are strong on cases concerning Deprivation of Liberty Safeguards. They are also effective when dealing with residence and contact best interest decisions. The team is often instructed by the Official Solicitor as well as health trusts, and has particular strength in cases involving complex medical evidence considerations.

JUNIORS

Nageena Khalique Popular amongst instructing solicitors and peers at the Bar due to her medical background and expert knowledge of the law in relation to THE Court of Protection. She regularly advises clinical commissioning groups (CCGs) and NHS trusts, and also receives instructions from the Official Solicitor. **Strengths:** "She has a brilliant knowledge of very complex Court of Protection issues. She's both sensitive and extremely competent at getting down to the issues and being practical and pragmatic." "A very good advocate who is very tenacious in putting the client's case forward." **Recent work:** Appeared in a case relating to a woman with severe learning difficulties and a history of sexual abuse.

Laura Davidson Noted junior who is highly valued for both her strong commitment to cases and her academic background. She recently spent several months in Rwanda advising the government on the drafting of its first mental health law. **Strengths:** "It is difficult to find someone as grounded as Laura in mental capacity and mental health law, or as practical or positive. She is incredibly hard-working, dedicated and entirely approachable." "She's very energetic and will go the extra mile." **Recent work:** Appeared for the applicant in a delicate case regarding a young woman lacking capacity who made allegations of abuse against close family members.

St Johns Buildings
See profile on p.921

THE SET

Established Northern set with an expanding Court of Protection team and increasing national presence. Individuals handle the spectrum of welfare matters, taking on medical treatment and deprivation of liberty issues for both applicant and defendant clients.

JUNIORS

Joseph O'Brien A true star of the Court of Protection Bar and a first choice for the Official Solicitor on sensitive cases. He is instructed on landmark cases throughout the country. **Strengths:** "The king of the CoP, he is supremely knowledgeable. He is a fine orator and a dedicated advocate who can always be relied upon to make the best of a case." "Despite his entirely deserved position at the top of the Court of Protection tree, he retains a down-to-earth personality." **Recent work:** Acted in ground-breaking deprivation of liberty case Cheshire West v P.

Lorraine Cavanagh Tenacious junior singled out for her strong work ethic and energetic representation of claimant clients. Instructing solicitors appreciate her parallel expertise in family and human rights law. **Strengths:** "A tenacious and fearless advocate. She is capable of turning around the seemingly most hopeless cases and never loses sight of the client at the centre of the matter." "She is adept at mediating between parties to achieve resolutions, but once in court her oratory skills are exceptional." **Recent work:** Appeared in a contested hearing concerning a wife and mother who was deemed to lack capacity to consent to sexual relations and marriage and was faced with the removal of her child.

Matthew Stockwell Respected junior on the Northern Circuit noted for his skill in handling deprivation of liberty cases on behalf of the vulnerable adult. He has particular knowledge of cases stemming from acquired brain injury. **Strengths:** "Delivers very passionate, well-balanced arguments." **Recent work:** Acted for the applicant in bringing a successful appeal before the Supreme Court to have an elderly woman with complex medical treatment needs released from a care home.

Other Ranked Lawyers

Paul Bowen QC (Brick Court Chambers) Prominent and highly respected silk who conducts an impressive Court of Protection practice. He is sought after for highly sensitive and complex cases, and has particular experience in matters relating to medical treatment. **Strengths:** "A standout choice for difficult medical treatment cases." "He has a pretty encyclopaedic knowledge of cases relating to human rights and mental capacity, and is very thorough, approachable and very detailed." **Recent work:** Appeared for a local authority successfully seeking a judgment from the Court of Protection that it could administer medical treatment to a woman with advanced anorexia.

Bryan McGuire QC (Cornerstone Barristers) Esteemed barrister with substantial Court of Protection experience and a niche practice representing local authorities in sensitive matters. **Strengths:**

"He's hard work to be against in a good sense. He fights hard for his clients and is very good." **Recent work:** Acted for Brighton and Hove Council in a test case to determine whether the Deprivation of Liberty Safeguards procedures can lawfully be used to stop an alcoholic from drinking.

Jennifer Oscroft (Cornerstone Barristers) Rising Court of Protection junior whose practice focuses on the representation of local government bodies. She has particular knowledge of proceedings that relate to the Mental Health Act and Mental Capacity Act. **Strengths:** "Her advice is cogent and thorough, and she is very accessible." "She knows this area of law incredibly well, and is both approachable and down to earth. She is as good at explaining matters to the court as she is to the client." **Recent work:** Acted for a local authority in a case which examined the extent to which disclosure rules can be applied in a case dealing with a mother's desire to see documents relating to her biological daughter.

Barbara Hewson (1 Gray's Inn Square) Recommended for her staunch advocacy in cases relating to Deprivation of Liberty Safeguards and best interests. Her Court of Protection work forms a significant part of her wider public law practice. **Strengths:** "A no-nonsense barrister who is able to assimilate a lot of information very quickly at short notice, and get clients to focus on the relevant issues. If I need somebody who's really going to stand their ground, I'll go to Barbara." "Brilliant and fantastic to work with. She has a good rapport with the client, and there is nothing she can't answer." **Recent work:** Appeared in a case which considered whether it was in the best interests of a woman who had lost capacity to allow her estranged family to re-establish contact.

Paul Greatorex (11KBW) Has a strong reputation for Court of Protection work, which ties in with his general public law and human rights practice. He is a member of the Court of Protection user group and frequently lectures on mental capacity matters. **Strengths:** "His advice, his knowledge and the way he can focus people in on the issues is impressive." "He's very thorough and engaging."

Simon Burrows (see p.561) (Kings Chambers) Admired junior who has significant experience of handling Court of Protection cases relating to best interests, deprivation of liberty and the Mental Health Act. He is a Mental Health Tribunal judge. **Strengths:** "Very knowledgeable, logical and to the point." "Incisive, responsive and a commanding figure during difficult negotiations. He inspires confidence in the client." **Recent work:** Represented P through the Official Solicitor in Supreme Court case P & Q v Cheshire West & Chester Council, the leading case on deprivation of liberty.

Adam Fullwood (Kings Chambers) Leading light for Court of Protection matters in the North of England, who has wide-ranging experience of mental capacity, social care and asylum support cases. He is a committee member of the Court of Protection Practitioners Association. **Strengths:** "His knowledge base and his confidence in his work are second to none. He is pragmatic, realistic and an extremely compelling advocate." "Excellent all-round legal and client skills. He not offers only great advocacy but is also reliable and reassuring." **Recent work:** Appeared in a challenge to a local authority's decision to withhold the social care records of an incapacitated girl from her biological mother, who wished to re-establish contact.

Sam Karim (see p.642) (Kings Chambers) Demonstrates impressive expertise in highly sensitive matters relating to end of life medical treatment withdrawal. He has a particular focus on deprivation of liberty as it relates to people with autism. **Strengths:** "Thorough, responsive and thoughtful, he has all the qualities you need in a barrister working in this complex area. He is also very good on his feet and gains the confidence of the court very quickly." "He is charismatic, engaging and a strong advocate."

David Lock QC (Landmark Chambers) Star of the Midlands Public Law Bar whose expertise in healthcare law comes to play in his Court of Protection work. He has further notable experience of handling deprivation of liberty cases concerning children. **Strengths:** "Excellent and a standout barrister in this area." "A brilliant and very approachable practitioner."

Chris Buttler (Matrix Chambers) Standout junior on the rise, who is frequently instructed by the Official Solicitor on cases with parallel human rights and administrative law elements. **Strengths:** "He's extremely capable, particularly when it comes to the interface between the Mental Health Act and the Mental Capacity Act." "He's very tenacious and very decisive, and doesn't shy away from taking a firm stand for his client." **Recent work:** Represented the CCG responsible for a man with Prader-Willi syndrome, who had been deprived of his liberty to prevent him from over-eating. The case examined best interests and considered the validity of the psychiatric evidence available.

John McKendrick (Outer Temple Chambers) A strong junior who is often instructed by the Official Solicitor and is also chosen to represent local authorities. **Strengths:** "He has a tenacious, no-nonsense approach, and is very persuasive and articulate, and first rate with clients." "Exceptionally bright, he can just take instructions and come up with a plan the next morning. He's a bit of a magician in that way, and he's brilliant to work with." **Recent work:** Represented a local authority in a high-profile case that involved the sterilisation of a learning-disabled man who had expressed a desire to have no more children, but was not able to reliably use contraception and lacked the capacity to consent to the sterilisation operation.

Mark Mullins (Outer Temple Chambers) A seasoned practitioner with a wealth of experience in social welfare law. He has a particular knowledge of Court of Protection cases relating to the Mental Health Act. **Strengths:** "Very experienced, extremely down to earth, wise and persuasive." **Recent work:** Acted for the Health Board and a psychiatrist in a high-profile case considering whether it was in the best interests of a woman who was hospitalised with anorexia to continue to receive medical treatment against her wishes.

Fiona Scolding (Outer Temple Chambers) A noted junior who appears in challenging best interest cases, acting for family members and the Official Solicitor. Also acts for public bodies on landmark rulings regarding funding obligations. **Strengths:** "She's an absolute pleasure to work with, and incredibly conscientious. She often gets given difficult cases and she's not fazed by dealing with tough issues." "She's very pragmatic and sensible, wonderfully warm, fantastic with clients, and just has a way of cutting through a case so quickly." **Recent work:** Acted for the Ministry of Justice and the Legal Aid Agency in key proceedings examining when and how these bodies are required to fund a Court of Protection case.

Paul Lopez (St Ives Chambers) Well-regarded junior whose Court of Protection work is bolstered by his family and children law expertise. He is experienced in acting for local authorities as well as families and their children. **Strengths:** "An excellent advocate." "He's very well established in both the family law and the Court of Protection spheres."

Justine Lattimer (see p.651) (St Ives Chambers) Esteemed practitioner with a background in children protection, criminal and family law. Solicitors praise her for keeping the best interests of the child at the heart of Court of Protection cases relating to children. **Strengths:** "She picks up on the issues very quickly, and is very approachable and very good with clients." "She's very experienced and very sensible, and deals well with urgent and complicated Court of Protection cases."

Kerry Bretherton (Tanfield Chambers) Highly esteemed and experienced Court of Protection junior who has been appointed to the Attorney General's A Panel. **Strengths:** "Very experienced, very knowledgeable, and willing to put her head above the parapet. She is able to balance risks and make judgements very quickly and comfortably." "She has a very good grasp of the Mental Capacity Act and recent case law, and her advice to the client is pretty spot on." **Recent work:** Appeared in an application which raised the question of whether an individual's misunderstanding of facts meant that he lacked capacity in regard to decision making.

ALL CIRCUITS Property & Affairs

Court of Protection: Property & Affairs All Circuits
Leading Sets
Band 1
5 Stone Buildings *
Band 2
Radcliffe Chambers *
Leading Silks
Band 1
Rajah Eason *Ten Old Square (ORL)* ◊ *
Reed Penelope *5 Stone Buildings* *
Band 2
Angus Tracey *5 Stone Buildings* *
Leading Juniors
Star individuals
Rees David *5 Stone Buildings* *
Rich Barbara *5 Stone Buildings* *
Band 1
Feltham Piers *Radcliffe Chambers* *
Goldsmith Joseph *5 Stone Buildings* *
Holmes Justin *Radcliffe Chambers*
Mullen Mark *Radcliffe Chambers*
Band 2
Baxter Mark *5 Stone Buildings* *
Haren Sarah *5 Stone Buildings* *
Hughes Ruth *5 Stone Buildings* *
McQuail Katherine *Radcliffe Chambers*
O'Sullivan Michael *5 Stone Buildings* *
Sartin Leon *5 Stone Buildings* *
Smith Howard *Radcliffe Chambers*
Band 3
Bedworth Georgia *Ten Old Square (ORL)* ◊ *
East William *5 Stone Buildings* *
McDonnell Constance *3 Stone Buildings (ORL)* ◊ *
Staunton Ulick *Radcliffe Chambers*
Up-and-coming individuals
Edge Charlotte *5 Stone Buildings* *
Holland Jordan *5 Stone Buildings* *
◊ (ORL) = Other Ranked Lawyer.
* Indicates set / individual with profile.

Band 1

5 Stone Buildings
See profile on p.866

THE SET

Widely recognised as being top in the country for property and affairs matters in the Court of Protection, this is "a chambers you can't really find fault with," according to one impressed commentator. Its members receive frequent instructions from the Official Solicitor and several are contributors to the leading textbook, 'Heywood and Massey: Court of Protection Practice'. Areas of focus include statutory will applications, trusts and probate dispute resolution, landlord and tenant cases and professional negligence matters.

Client service: "The clerks are brilliant; they couldn't be easier to deal with and always find you somebody." The senior clerk is Paul Jennings.

SILKS

Penelope Reed QC Highly regarded silk valued by instructing solicitors for her wealth of experience in handling the full range of finance-related Court of Protection matters. Her practice has a strong emphasis on trusts and wills disputes. **Strengths:** "Outstanding: she makes difficult problems seem simple. She'll fight when she has to fight but is always in favour of finding a mediated solution. And she's very clear." "Incredibly reliable and very experienced – you can't bring anything to her she hasn't worked on before."

Tracey Angus QC (see p.536) An admired silk who wins plaudits for her expertise in trusts and probates disputes. She has additional experience in handling professional negligence matters as they relate to the Court of Protection. **Strengths:** "She's very pragmatic and always tries to find a sensible solution."

JUNIORS

David Rees (see p.706) A pre-eminent junior recommended for his technical abilities and his sweeping knowledge of the law relating to the Court of Protection. He is particularly noted for his expertise in advising on cross-jurisdictional matters. **Strengths:** "He's a very good adviser and a strong advocate. People stop and listen when he speaks." "A real tour de force; he's very meticulous and extremely impressive in presenting arguments."

Barbara Rich (see p.707) A leading light who has a strong focus on property and affairs disputes relating to the Mental Capacity Act. She is an experienced mediator and an editor of 'Heywood & Massey: Court of Protection Practice'. **Strengths:** "Her specialist knowledge of all things Court of Protection is overwhelming and I always feel like I have a safe pair of hands on board when she is involved." "Brilliant: she's got a very academic bent to how she does things, so you get a very, very detailed and highly intelligently argued result." **Recent work:** Appeared in a multifaceted five-day hearing in the Court of Protection involving a claim for the retrieval of money which had allegedly been unlawfully transferred to a third party.

Joseph Goldsmith An acclaimed junior in the Court of Protection and a go-to practitioner for the Official Solicitor. He distinguishes himself through his strong understanding of the Mental Capacity Act and the Inheritance Act. **Strengths:** "One of those people with a towering intellect, who's just able to verbalise things so well. He's got an excellent grasp of Court of Protection work and is in great demand." "He's able to go through a lot of evidence, cut to the chase and come up with a sensible compromise."

Ruth Hughes (see p.633) Singled out for her specialist expertise in financial matters, she has a practice with a strong focus on deputyship conflicts and statutory will applications. Clients appreciate her ability to simplify and explain complex legal matters. **Strengths:** "Very knowledgeable and thorough." "She has very good knowledge of the Mental Capacity Act in this area, and her written work is of a very high standard."

Mark Baxter (see p.545) Demonstrates particular expertise in contentious probate matters in the Court of Protection. He receives particular commendation for his strong but measured advocacy. **Strengths:** "He's enthusiastic and keen to find solutions to family issues. He also has a fantastic eye for detail, and is able to see the bigger picture." "He's extremely thorough and very personable."

Sarah Haren (see p.619) Standout junior highlighted for her responsiveness and ability to draw out the key issues at the heart of complex cases. She often acts for the Official Solicitor in statutory will applications. **Strengths:** "She's quick and clear, gets to the heart of the matter and gives you a definitive view." "She is excellent on her feet, has a really calm style, and her written work is always very concise and clear."

Michael O'Sullivan (see p.687) Noted practitioner whose parallel expertise in property-related professional negligence complements his Court of Protection work. He receives praise for his succinct and articulate arguments and written opinions. **Strengths:** "A commanding presence – he's a man of few words but what he says is worth its weight in gold." "A good advocate with a breadth of experience in this area."

Leon Sartin Lauded junior whose traditional chancery practice has a key focus on Court of Protection matters. He has particular experience in handling trusts disputes and is noted for his skills as an advocate. **Strengths:** "He's very dogged and will do the best for his client; he's a superb advocate."

William East (see p.593) Negotiates a broad Court of Protection practice encompassing contested probate and landlord and tenant disputes. He has significant recent experience of handling statutory will and gift applications. **Strengths:** "His advocacy and his written work are very good; his arguments are detailed and show an excellent understanding of the law in this area." "He provides, clear, practical advice on very complex cases."

Charlotte Edge (see p.593) A junior with a rising reputation who is endorsed enthusiastically by instructing solicitors for her strategic approach to cases and her impressive advocacy. She has notable recent experience of handling statutory will applications under the Court of Protection. **Strengths:** "A steel fist in a velvet glove. She's very good on strategy, extremely personable and a real fighter for her client." "She reads the dynamics of a tricky situation very well, and is very good at communicating her client's point of view to the court."

Jordan Holland (see p.630) Often led in complex statutory will applications. He has a growing practice handling cross-jurisdictional disputes. **Strengths:** "I go to him for tricky CoP matters: he's very approachable and very bright." "He has an encyclopaedic knowledge of this area of the law."

Band 2

Radcliffe Chambers
See profile on p.856

THE SET

An acclaimed set for all property and affairs cases that fall under the jurisdiction of the Court of Protection. Sources highlight the chambers' "friendly and down-to-earth" character, and are in no doubt as to the quality of its practitioners, with one saying: "I would feel comfortable and confident dropping anything their way at short notice and they'd be able to pick it up very quickly." One of the Official Solicitor's favoured sets, it has strength across the board, and is particularly strong on deputyship disputes, contentious trusts cases, and statutory will and gift applications.

Client service: "The clerking is faultless: the invoices come in on time, the terms and conditions are straightforward, and the clerks themselves are very client-focused."

JUNIORS

Justin Holmes A talented practitioner who wins plaudits for his firm but measured courtroom style. He is experienced in managing statutory will applications and deputyship disputes. **Strengths:** "His opinions are excellent; he turns them around very quickly, and gets the right balance between understanding the law and giving practical advice." "His advocacy is very good. He's charming but firm; he's not aggressive but he gets results."

Piers Feltham (see p.599) Handles Court of Protection work as part of a strong chancery practice. He has particular strength in cross-jurisdictional property disputes. **Strengths:** "He's very creative and empathetic in his approach. He is well regarded in the Court of Protection as he's completely on top of his papers, has a great intellect, and always delivers." "He's always prepared to go the extra mile, is very proactive and is a real team player."

Mark Mullen An accomplished practitioner with wide-ranging Court of Protection expertise. He is experienced in taking on deputyship applications and disputes, as well as issues arising from the mismanagement of personal injury trust funds. **Strengths:** "He's very good at drafting and has a good grasp of the issues."

Katherine McQuail Draws high praise for her grounded and constructive approach to court proceedings. As well as handling core financial Court of Protection work, she also has strength in the related areas of professional negligence and partnership disputes. **Strengths:** "Excellent and very approachable, she's good at understanding the human factors in a case and taking them into account." "She focuses on practical outcomes, is very accessible and always delivers to deadlines."

Howard Smith Respected counsel, who is commended for his affable yet authoritative manner. A property law specialist, he is highly experienced in related professional negligence disputes that come before the Court of Protection. **Strengths:** "Marvellous. He's very staunch about what he's saying on behalf of his client but nevertheless very easy to deal with."

Ulick Staunton Seasoned barrister whose noted chancery practice contains a large Court of Protection element. He is noted for being particularly strong in terms of his advice with regard to statutory will applications with complex tax aspects. **Strengths:** "Exceptionally good with the client, and he handles negotiations very well."

Other Ranked Lawyers

Eason Rajah QC (Ten Old Square) Masterful silk who is adept at handling highly complex Court of Protection work. He has over two decades' experience in the area and is an editor of the Court of Protection law reports. **Strengths:** "At the top of the tree for CoP, he can press home a point on behalf of a client in a very particular and persuasive way. His approach is unparalleled, and he's very good with clients." "He gives very clear and detailed advice, which gives you confidence that he's really got into the case and looked at it from every angle."

Georgia Bedworth (see p.546) (Ten Old Square) Impressive junior skilled in handling both the contentious and non-contentious aspects of Court of Protection work. She has particular expertise in inheritance tax planning cases. **Strengths:** "Her quiet manner is misleading as she goes into court and does a fantastic job for the client. She's very clever." "She responds quickly, and with clarity and practicality."

Constance McDonnell (see p.667) (3 Stone Buildings) Admired for her strategic vision and potent advocacy in complex and heavily contested Court of Protection cases. Contentious trusts and probate matters form a key component of her practice. **Strengths:** "A superb advocate who completely sticks to her guns and fights her client's corner." "She combines an impressive knowledge of the law with a calm but persuasive manner."

CRIME: An introduction

Contributed by 2 Bedford Row

We do not feel that it would be overstating the position to say that this year has seen many substantial and unprecedented issues affecting those who practise in crime.

There are the obvious ones, those that have attracted much press attention. The Criminal Bar has been engaged in a well-documented dispute with the Ministry of Justice over fees. That has seen days of action and the widespread adoption of the "no returns" policy. Fortunately, and in particular after the Court of Appeal's ruling in R v Crawley and others (Operation Cotton), there appears to be have been the beginnings of progress in reaching a solution to the circumstances which have led to the vast majority of members of the Criminal Bar refusing to sign VHCC contracts.

These are the events which have most occupied the media but it is our view that as significant a development has gathered pace this year, and one which may have a longer term impact on practitioners than arguments over Very High Cost Cases.

The ability of the public to instruct counsel without a solicitor in contentious matters has become the big story of the year. The importance of directories such as this one and the access for most people to chambers' and personal websites has spawned a new breed of potential client. That client is a discerning individual, perhaps a member of the family of a convicted defendant or someone facing an allegation themselves who has, at their fingertips, the opportunity to effectively "shop" for an advocate. That shopping is likely to be sufficiently focused such that it centres on particular expertise, experience and seniority. Going hand in hand with that focus is the acceptance that there is an appropriate level of remuneration for the job in hand and that there is an element of competition on price between different prospective advocates. This personal sourcing by the public of advocates is, in our view, something which is here to stay and the profile of an advocate, and a particular set housing that advocate, will become increasingly important in the selection of representation in criminal cases.

This should not be interpreted as any form of reflection on the traditional system of instruction via a solicitor. That, in our view, and in particular for the more serious and longer cases, still very much has its place. There is room for both but the fact that both co-exist now is unlikely to change in the foreseeable future. With the deep cuts in legal aid we have already started to see a shift in the way in which criminal cases are funded by defendants.

There is a growing perception of there being a two-tier system. Many clients now decide to pay privately and have a barrister of their choice rather than pay high legal aid contributions and have far less choice in who represents them. Family members are also increasingly funding defendants in criminal cases despite the inability to retrieve the vast majority of the cost. A value judgement is clearly being made and the public seem to have accepted that they may not necessarily be able to get the best – or in some cases even adequate – representation via public funding. As regards the type of cases that have dominated the criminal world this year, they have very much centred on allegations of different types against well-known individuals.

The lengthy and complex trial into "phone hacking" at the News of the World has caught the public imagination. The combination of these allegations with the consequences of the findings by the Leveson Inquiry have led to differing attitudes to the press by the public. The relationship between members of the press and the police, in particular during high-profile investigations, has been laid bare by a case lasting around ten months.

Whatever the effect of these proceedings on public opinion and the attitudes towards the press in the future, the interest in criminal law has never been greater.

The other area which has dominated the criminal law and practice during the last year is the litigation of historical sexual abuse. Whilst there have been many cases involving household names, practitioners will have noticed that there has been an increase in how many cases of this type are being prosecuted. It is another example of how closely the issues of public interest and criminal litigation are linked.

It is fair to say that many of those who practise in the criminal courts have faced extensive challenges this year. However, if there has ever been a year which has highlighted the importance of having a strong and independent Bar to both prosecute and defend it has been this one.

This year we saw the first televised hearing of an appeal at the Court of Appeal. We have to presume that now the Rubicon has been crossed there will be more to come. Whilst we all agree that justice should be open we cannot help but to have some reservations. Some of us would of course love nothing more than to become 'celebrity counsel' but there is a danger of the cases becoming more soap opera than forensic inquiry. We only have to look at the Pistorius trial to see how bad things can get when television ratings take over. As a corollary to this we have also seen an increase in the presence of, for example, the DPP on our screens often delivering a well-organised and strategic message. Are we moving to the US style of criminal litigation where the sound bite is as important as the evidence in the case? The answer is not yet but nevertheless we must be vigilant to prevent sleepwalking into that type of system.

LONDON

Crime London
Leading Sets
Band 1
2 Bedford Row *
2 Hare Court *
6KBW College Hill
QEB Hollis Whiteman *
3 Raymond Buildings Barristers *
Band 2
25 Bedford Row *
Cloth Fair Chambers
Doughty Street Chambers *
23 Essex Street *
Matrix Chambers *
Band 3
9-12 Bell Yard
Carmelite Chambers *
Garden Court Chambers *
Red Lion Chambers
Band 4
9 Bedford Row *
7BR *
Charter Chambers *
Furnival Chambers
5 King's Bench Walk
5 Paper Buildings *
3 Temple Gardens
Band 5
Dyers Chambers
187 Fleet Street *
Goldsmith Chambers
* *Indicates set with profile.*
Alphabetical order within each band. Band 1 is highest.

Band 1

2 Bedford Row

See profile on p.763

THE SET

2 Bedford Row is praised for the consistent excellence of its performance in high-profile criminal cases. Its members are sought after to act in complex matters, such as murder, terrorism and child exploitation cases, with recent instructions including the Private Lee Rigby murder trial, the Hyde Park bombing prosecution and the Oxford sex grooming case. The set is known for having an "abundance of quality advocates who are in high demand," leading one instructing solicitor to comment: "When I instruct a barrister at the chambers I can be sure I will get someone who knows what they are doing and will really fight for my client."

Client service: The clerking team is led by the "brilliant" John Grimmer, whom sources describe as "a guru when it comes to finding the right counsel for difficult matters." He runs an efficient team, which is praised for being "on the ball."

SILKS

Richard Whittam QC Prosecutes some of the highest profile cases in the criminal courts, including significant Islamic terrorism cases. He was recently appointed First Senior Treasury Counsel. **Strengths:** "He's got one of the heaviest prosecution practices in the country and is a hugely impressive and hugely able prosecutor." **Recent work:** Prosecuted both individuals accused of murdering and attempting to decapitate Private Lee Rigby in Woolwich.

Brian Altman QC (see p.535) Regularly instructed to prosecute significant criminal cases, including terrorism and murder trials involving sensitive political issues. **Strengths:** "He is very thorough, very detailed and very focused; he is a top lawyer." "He has amazing style in proving his point." **Recent work:** Acted for the Crown in the prosecution of John Downey, who was alleged to have carried out the IRA bombing in Hyde Park in 1982.

William Clegg QC Highly sought after to defend in heavyweight criminal trials and appellate matters, often involving novel points of law. **Strengths:** "He is incredibly bright, passionate and persuasive." "He's at the top of his game. He's very classy and he seems to be able to persuade judges of his case with the minimum amount of fuss." **Recent work:** Represented the former head of security at News International, who was charged with conspiracy to pervert the course of justice after allegations that he had colluded with others to conceal evidence during the police investigation into the media group.

Mark Milliken-Smith QC Has an impressive breadth of expertise, encompassing murder, sex and fraud trials, in addition to appellate cases. He is frequently instructed to act in highly publicised cases. **Strengths:** "He has great client care skills and he knows the briefs inside out immediately." "He has a brilliant brain and he's charming." **Recent work:** Acted for the defence in a case concerning a child exploitation ring in Oxford, which groomed vulnerable girls for sex.

Jim Sturman QC Frequently instructed to act for high-profile individuals, including politicians and sportsmen. He has wide-ranging experience, and has handled murder, GBH and sex cases, in addition to a broad variety of white-collar matters. **Strengths:** "He has the ability to deal with clients in a very straightforward way. He boils issues down and talks to clients on a normal level." **Recent work:** Represented a wealthy businessman who was acquitted of murder following a trial concerning the death of an individual at a 'V Festival' after party.

Michael Wolkind QC Highly regarded criminal barrister with outstanding strength in murder cases. **Strengths:** "He will assimilate an opponent's point and deliver a withering repost in the same moment." **Recent work:** Acted for the first defendant in a nine-handed murder trial concerning an alleged revenge killing.

Nigel Lithman QC Handles complex criminal matters, including murder, abduction and section 18 cases. He is chair of the Criminal Bar Association. **Recent work:** Acted for an individual with Asperger's syndrome, appealing against his conviction as a teenager for the murder of a ten-year-old child.

Peter Lodder QC Frequently instructed in sensitive cases, including murder trials involving young defendants and diminished responsibility defences. He is also called upon to represent high-profile clients accused of motoring offences. **Strengths:** "He is exceptionally hard-working and a great cross-examiner." **Recent work:** Represented the defendant in a complex murder trial involving multiple expert witnesses, including psychologists and psychiatrists.

JUNIORS

Christine Agnew (see p.532) Has considerable expertise in cases involving violent crime, such as homicide, robbery and sexual offences. **Strengths:** "She really is first class. She's sympathetic and hard-working, and clients love her, but she's not a soft touch." **Recent work:** Defended an individual charged with aggravated burglary in a case involving a bad character application.

Craig Rush Has extensive experience of murder and drugs cases, and has handled a number of blackmail cases. He is often instructed in trials concerning organised crime. **Recent work:** Acted for the defendant in proceedings concerning the possession of two tonnes of cocaine.

Contents:

2 Hare Court

See profile on p.818

THE SET

2 Hare Court has an outstanding reputation for prosecuting and defending the most serious criminal cases. It receives high-profile instructions in a broad range of matters, including murder, terrorism and sex cases. The chambers is increasingly instructed by professional clients, in cases such as the News International phone hacking trial and the prosecution of Christopher Huhne and Vicky Pryce for perverting the course of justice. Instructing solicitors describe it as "a real blue-chip set," and admire the consistently high quality of its members, from silk to junior lev el.

Client service: Julian Campbell is director of clerking at the set and is said to lead a "fantastic" team, which "understands customer service and is really progressive." Ben Heaviside is the senior practice clerk and a popular figure amongst instructing solicitors.

SILKS

Jonathan Laidlaw QC An outstanding advocate, who is regularly instructed in headline-grabbing cases. He is also eminently well equipped to advise significant individuals on sensitive matters involving reputational issues. **Strengths:** "He is fantastic. He's the hardest-working individual I have ever come across. The work he does is phenomenal. He is top drawer." **Recent work:** Successfully defended Rebekah Brooks in the News International phone hacking trial.

Sallie Bennett-Jenkins QC (see p.547) Acts for defendants in heavyweight criminal trials, including gang murder and sexual offences cases. She has additional experience of securing privacy injunctions for clients subject to media attention. **Strengths:** "She is very good at cross-examining in any case where there is expert evidence, and she has stunning ability in the cross-examination of pathologists." "She is great to work with. She just gets on with it and doesn't take any nonsense from judges." **Recent work:** Secured the acquittal of a defendant alleged to have been involved in a gang-related murder, in which the victim was selected at random.

Jonathan Rees QC Regularly prosecutes complex and sensitive criminal cases as Senior Treasury Counsel. He has expertise in trials involving a scientific element such as DNA evidence. **Strengths:** "He is a real star and quite outstanding. He has the

Crime
London
Leading Silks

Star individuals

- Emmerson Ben *Matrix Chambers*
- Fitzgerald Edward *Doughty Street Chambers*
- Gibbs Patrick *3 Raymond Buildings Barristers* [A] *
- Kelsey-Fry John *Cloth Fair Chambers* *
- Laidlaw Jonathan *2 Hare Court* *
- Montgomery Clare *Matrix Chambers*
- Perry David *6KBW College Hill*
- Pownall Orlando *2 Hare Court* *
- Purnell Nicholas *Cloth Fair Chambers* *
- Winter Ian *Cloth Fair Chambers* *

Band 1

- Altman Brian *2 Bedford Row* *
- Aylett Crispin *QEB Hollis Whiteman*
- Blaxland Henry *Garden Court Chambers*
- Blunt Oliver *Furnival Chambers* *
- Boyce William *QEB Hollis Whiteman*
- Burke Trevor *3 Raymond Buildings Barristers* [A] *
- Cameron Alexander *3 Raymond Buildings Barristers* [A]
- Carter-Stephenson George *25 Bedford Row*
- Chawla Mukul *9-12 Bell Yard* [A] *
- Clegg William *2 Bedford Row* *
- Dein Jeremy *25 Bedford Row* *
- Dennis Mark *6KBW College Hill*
- Edis Andrew *2 Hare Court*
- Ellison Mark *QEB Hollis Whiteman* *
- Etherington David *Red Lion Chambers* *
- Griffiths Courtenay *25 Bedford Row*
- Heywood Mark *5 King's Bench Walk*
- Horwell Richard *3 Raymond Buildings Barristers*
- Jafferjee Aftab *Atkinson Bevan Chambers, (ORL)* ◊ [A]
- Kamlish Stephen *Garden Court Chambers*
- Keith Hugo *3 Raymond Buildings Barristers* *
- Lakha Abbas *9 Bedford Row* [A] *
- Langdale Timothy *Cloth Fair Chambers* *
- Lewis James *3 Raymond Buildings Barristers* [A]
- Mansfield Michael *Mansfield Chambers (ORL)* ◊
- Mendelle Paul *25 Bedford Row*
- Milliken-Smith Mark *2 Bedford Row* *
- Moloney Tim *Doughty Street Chambers*
- Owen Tim *Matrix Chambers*
- Rees Jonathan *2 Hare Court*
- Rumfitt Nigel *7BR*
- Sturman Jim *2 Bedford Row* *
- Whittam Richard *2 Bedford Row*
- Wood James *Doughty Street Chambers* [A]
- Wright Peter *2 Hare Court* *

Band 2

- Bajwa Ali Naseem *Garden Court Chambers*
- Bennathan Joel *Doughty Street Chambers*
- Bennett-Jenkins Sallie *2 Hare Court* *
- Berry Anthony *9 Bedford Row* *
- Borrelli Michael *3 Raymond Buildings Barristers* *
- Bromley-Martin Michael *3 Raymond Buildings Barristers* [A]
- Brown Edward *QEB Hollis Whiteman* *
- Campbell-Tiech Andrew *Dyers Chambers* *
- Caplan Jonathan *5 Paper Buildings* *
- Darbishire Adrian *QEB Hollis Whiteman*
- Farrell Simon *3 Raymond Buildings Barristers* [A]
- Fisher David *6KBW College Hill*
- Hicks Martin *2 Hare Court* *
- Hill Max *Red Lion Chambers* *
- Howker David *No5 Chambers (ORL)* ◊
- Kelly Brendan *2 Hare Court* *
- Khan Judy *Garden Court Chambers*
- Latham Richard *7BR*
- Lithman Nigel *2 Bedford Row*
- Lodder Peter *2 Bedford Row*
- Mayo Simon *187 Fleet Street* [A] *
- Moore Miranda *5 Paper Buildings* *
- O'Neill Brian *2 Hare Court* *
- O'Neill Sally *Furnival Chambers* [A] *
- Rees Edward *Doughty Street Chambers*
- Russell Flint Simon *23 Essex Street*
- Ryder John *6KBW College Hill*
- Ryder Matthew *Matrix Chambers*
- Sallon Christopher *Doughty Street Chambers* [A]
- Spencer Timothy *7BR* [A]
- Spens David *QEB Hollis Whiteman*
- Trembath Graham *5 Paper Buildings* *
- Turner Michael *Garden Court Chambers*
- Wass Sasha *6KBW College Hill*
- Wolkind Michael *2 Bedford Row*

Band 3

- Bailin Alex *Matrix Chambers* *
- Barnes Timothy *7BR*
- Bott Charles *Carmelite Chambers* *
- Carlile of Berriew Alex *9-12 Bell Yard* *
- Christie Richard *187 Fleet Street* *
- Christopher Julian *5 Paper Buildings* *
- Coffey John *3 Temple Gardens* *
- Cottage Rosina *Red Lion Chambers* *
- Davies Hugh *3 Raymond Buildings Barristers* [A]
- Denison Simon *6KBW College Hill* *
- Forshall Isabella *Doughty Street Chambers*
- Forshaw Sarah *5 King's Bench Walk*
- Friedman Danny *Matrix Chambers* *
- Hall Andrew *Doughty Street Chambers*
- Healy Alexandra *9-12 Bell Yard* [A] *
- Heslop Martin S *2 Hare Court* *
- Humphryes Jane *3 Raymond Buildings Barristers* *
- Keleher Paul *25 Bedford Row*
- Kent Alan *23 Essex Street*
- Knowles Julian *Matrix Chambers*
- Larkin Sean *QEB Hollis Whiteman* *
- Laws Eleanor *6 Pump Court (ORL)* ◊ [A] *
- Lovell-Pank Dorian *6KBW College Hill*
- Nathan David *5 St Andrew's Hill (ORL)* ◊ *
- Price John *23 Essex Street*
- Scobie James *Garden Court Chambers*
- Shaw Antony *Red Lion Chambers* *
- Sidhu Jo *25 Bedford Row*
- Stern Ian *2 Bedford Row*
- Trollope Andrew *187 Fleet Street* *
- Trowler Rebecca *Doughty Street Chambers* [A] *
- Vaughan Kieran *Garden Court Chambers*

Band 4

- Ayling Tracy *2 Bedford Row* *
- Benson Jeremy *Red Lion Chambers* *
- Bogan Paul *23 Essex Street*
- Bourne Ian *Charter Chambers* [A] *
- Carter Peter *Red Lion Chambers* *
- Davis Adam *3 Temple Gardens* *
- FitzGibbon Francis *Doughty Street Chambers* [A]
- Godfrey Howard *2 Bedford Row*
- Grunwald Henry *Charter Chambers* [A] *
- Harbage William *36 Bedford Row (ORL)* ◊ *
- Hislop David *Doughty Street Chambers* [A]
- Jefferies Andrew *Dyers Chambers*
- Jeremy David *QEB Hollis Whiteman*
- Johnson Zoe *QEB Hollis Whiteman* *
- Kovalevsky Richard *2 Bedford Row* *
- Lambert Nigel *Carmelite Chambers* [A] *
- Malcolm Helen *3 Raymond Buildings Barristers* [A]
- Malik Amjad *36 Bedford Row (ORL)* ◊
- McAtasney Philippa *Furnival Chambers* *
- Metzer Anthony *Goldsmith Chambers*
- Orchard Anthony *Carmelite Chambers* [A] *
- Peart Icah *Garden Court Chambers*
- Rhodes Nicholas *Charter Chambers* [A] *
- Saxby Oliver *6 Pump Court (ORL)* ◊ [A]
- Stein Sam *Dyers Chambers*
- Swift Malcolm *2 Hare Court* *
- Turner Jonathan *6KBW College Hill* *

Band 5

- Arlidge Anthony *Red Lion Chambers* *
- Baker Maureen *7BR* [A]
- Bickerstaff Jane *9 Bedford Row* *
- Birnbaum Michael *9-12 Bell Yard* [A]
- Brimelow Kirsty *Doughty Street Chambers* [A]
- Carey-Hughes Richard J *9 Bedford Row* *
- Cooper John *25 Bedford Row*
- Fortson Rudi *25 Bedford Row*
- Glen Ian *5 King's Bench Walk*
- Higgs Jonathan *5 King's Bench Walk*
- Hughes William *9-12 Bell Yard* *
- Hynes Paul *25 Bedford Row*
- Jory Richard *9-12 Bell Yard* *
- Lynch Jerome *Charter Chambers* [A] *
- Matthews Richard *2 Bedford Row*
- Menon Rajiv *Garden Court Chambers*
- Nicholls Clive *3 Raymond Buildings Barristers* [A]
- O'Connor Patrick *Doughty Street Chambers* [A]
- Oldham Frances *36 Bedford Row (ORL)* ◊
- Plaschkes Sarah *QEB Hollis Whiteman*
- Power Lewis *Lamb Building (ORL)* ◊ *
- Radford Nadine *187 Fleet Street* [A] *
- Richmond Bernard *Lamb Building (ORL)* ◊
- Solley Stephen *Charter Chambers* [A] *
- Wilcock Peter *Garden Court Chambers*

Band 6

- Bentley David *Doughty Street Chambers* [A]
- Brompton Michael *5 Paper Buildings* *
- Cheema Bobbie *2 Hare Court* *
- Chinn Antony *9 Bedford Row* [A] *
- de Silva Desmond *Goldsmith Chambers*
- Goldberg Jonathan *North Square Chambers (ORL)* ◊ *
- Jones Alun *Great James Street Chambers (ORL)* ◊
- Magarian Michael *Dyers Chambers* *
- Waterman Adrian *Doughty Street Chambers*
- Whitfield Jonathan *Doughty Street Chambers*

New Silks

- Armstrong Dean *2 Bedford Row* *
- Bryant-Heron Mark *9-12 Bell Yard* [A] *
- Coltart Christopher *2 Hare Court* *
- Elliott Sarah *Doughty Street Chambers* *
- Fenhalls Mark *23 Essex Street*
- Henry Annette *Furnival Chambers* *
- Penny Duncan *6KBW College Hill*
- Smith Tyrone *25 Bedford Row*
- Summers Mark *Matrix Chambers* *
- Vullo Stephen *2 Bedford Row*
- Whitehouse Sarah *6KBW College Hill* *
- Wilding Lisa *Furnival Chambers* *

* *Indicates individual with profile.*

◊ *(ORL) = Other Ranked Lawyer.*

[A] *direct access* *(see p.11).*

Crime
London
Leading Juniors

Star individuals

- **Saunders** Neil *3 Raymond Buildings Barristers* 🄰 *

Band 1

- **Atkinson** Duncan *6KBW College Hill* *
- **Barnard** Jonathan *Cloth Fair Chambers* *
- **Byrnes** Aisling *25 Bedford Row*
- **Dempster** Jennifer *Red Lion Chambers* *
- **Emlyn Jones** William *3 Raymond Buildings Barristers*
- **Ferguson** Craig *2 Hare Court* *
- **Glasgow** Oliver *2 Hare Court* *
- **Hines** James *3 Raymond Buildings Barristers* 🄰 *
- **Morgan** Alison *6KBW College Hill*
- **Sibson** Clare *Cloth Fair Chambers* *
- **Williamson** Alisdair *3 Raymond Buildings Barristers* 🄰 *

Band 2

- **Agnew** Christine *2 Bedford Row* *
- **Allen** Tom *5 Paper Buildings* *
- **Eissa** Adrian *25 Bedford Row*
- **Forster** Tom *Red Lion Chambers* *
- **Hill** Miranda *6KBW College Hill*
- **Hughes** David *9 Bedford Row* *
- **Jones** Gillian *Red Lion Chambers* *
- **Ledward** Jocelyn *QEB Hollis Whiteman*
- **Little** Tom *9 Gough Square (ORL)* ◊ *
- **Mably** Louis *6KBW College Hill*
- **Maguire** Benn *QEB Hollis Whiteman*
- **Naqshbandi** Saba *3 Raymond Buildings Barristers* 🄰
- **Pople** Alison *Cloth Fair Chambers* *
- **Rush** Craig *2 Bedford Row*
- **Whittaker** David *2 Hare Court* *
- **Wormald** Richard *3 Raymond Buildings Barristers* 🄰

Band 3

- **Ahmad** Zubair *2 Hare Court* *
- **Aylott** Colin *Carmelite Chambers* 🄰 *
- **Buchanan** James *2 Hare Court* *
- **Butt** Matthew *3 Raymond Buildings Barristers* 🄰 *
- **Chalk** Alex *6KBW College Hill*
- **Cole** Justin *5 Paper Buildings*
- **Corsellis** Nicholas *QEB Hollis Whiteman* *
- **Cray** Timothy *6KBW College Hill*
- **Dineen** Maria *2 Bedford Row* *
- **Evans** Julian *QEB Hollis Whiteman*
- **Evans** Philip *QEB Hollis Whiteman* *
- **FitzGerald** Ben *QEB Hollis Whiteman* *
- **Hallam** Jacob *6KBW College Hill* *
- **Henry** Edward *QEB Hollis Whiteman* *
- **Jarvis** Paul *6KBW College Hill*
- **Kendal** Timothy *2 Bedford Row*
- **Lownds** Peter *2 Hare Court* 🄰 *
- **Lumsdon** Kate *23 Essex Street*
- **Moses** Stephen *Furnival Chambers* 🄰 *
- **Munyard** Terry *Garden Court Chambers*
- **Mylvaganam** Paul *Goldsmith Chambers*
- **Pardoe** Rupert *23 Essex Street*
- **Patterson** Gareth *6KBW College Hill*
- **Phillips** Paul *Charter Chambers* 🄰 *
- **Piercy** Arlette *25 Bedford Row*
- **Price** Roderick *187 Fleet Street* *
- **Ray** Simon *6KBW College Hill*
- **Rowlands** Peter *Garden Court Chambers*
- **Smitten** Ben *25 Bedford Row*
- **Strudwick** Linda *QEB Hollis Whiteman* *
- **Taylor** Paul *Doughty Street Chambers*
- **Ward** Alexandra *9-12 Bell Yard* 🄰 *
- **Yeo** Nicholas *3 Raymond Buildings Barristers* 🄰

Band 4

- **Cammerman** Gideon *187 Fleet Street* *
- **Causer** John *23 Essex Street*
- **Cockings** Giles *Furnival Chambers* *
- **Connolly** Dominic *5 St Andrew's Hill (ORL)* ◊ *
- **Conway** Charles *2 Bedford Row*
- **Cooper** Danielle *Chambers of Miss Danielle Cooper (ORL)* ◊
- **England** William *Carmelite Chambers* *
- **Fisher** Richard *Doughty Street Chambers* 🄰
- **Flanagan** Julia *Charter Chambers* *
- **Forte** Timothy *3 Temple Gardens* *
- **George** Dean *2 Bedford Row*
- **Harries** Mark *Carmelite Chambers* 🄰 *
- **Henley** Christopher *Carmelite Chambers* *
- **Howard** Nicola *25 Bedford Row*
- **Hunter** Timothy *Atkinson Bevan Chambers, (ORL)* ◊ 🄰
- **Jaffa** Ronald *25 Bedford Row*
- **Khan** Ashraf *2 Bedford Row* *
- **Khan** Zarif *Dyers Chambers* *
- **Lloyd** Ben *6KBW College Hill*
- **Macdonald** Alison *Matrix Chambers* *
- **Magee** Samuel *2 Bedford Row* *
- **Mann** Jonathan *Doughty Street Chambers*
- **Nelson** Michelle *Red Lion Chambers* *
- **Newton** Benjamin *Doughty Street Chambers*
- **Ratliff** Peter *6KBW College Hill*
- **Rodham** Susan *5 King's Bench Walk*
- **Rose** Alex *Garden Court Chambers*
- **Schutzer-Weissmann** Esther *6KBW College Hill*
- **Sheratt** Matthew *Carmelite Chambers* 🄰 *
- **Sherborn** Natalie *25 Bedford Row* *
- **Soertsz** Lauren *Doughty Street Chambers*
- **Swain** Jon *Furnival Chambers* 🄰 *
- **Thomas** Richard *Doughty Street Chambers*
- **Wakerley** Paul *QEB Hollis Whiteman*

Band 5

- **Aylett** Ken *9 Bedford Row*
- **Baker** Simon *Goldsmith Chambers*
- **Bex** Kate *2 Hare Court* *
- **Campbell** Brenda *Garden Court Chambers*
- **Carter-Manning** Jennifer *7BR* 🄰
- **Charbit** Valerie *2 Bedford Row* *
- **Cotter** Mark *5 St Andrew's Hill (ORL)* ◊ *
- **Cumberland** Melanie *6KBW College Hill*
- **Darlow** Annabel *6KBW College Hill*
- **D'Cruz** Rufus *Red Lion Chambers* *
- **Galvin** Kieran *Furnival Chambers* *
- **Gardiner** Sebastian *25 Bedford Row*
- **Goldring** Jenny *5 St Andrew's Hill (ORL)* ◊ *
- **Haughey** Caroline *Furnival Chambers* 🄰 *
- **Heer** Deanna *5 Paper Buildings* *
- **Higgins** Nichola *Doughty Street Chambers* *
- **Horlick** Fiona *Outer Temple Chambers (ORL)* ◊
- **Huntley** Clare *9-12 Bell Yard* *
- **Ivill** Scott *2 Hare Court* *
- **Jobling** Ian *23 Essex Street*
- **Kenyon** Flavia *3 Temple Gardens* *
- **Lewis** Anya *Garden Court Chambers*
- **Martin** James *5 King's Bench Walk*
- **Millett** Kenneth *2 Hare Court*
- **Morrell** Roxanne *Carmelite Chambers* *
- **Osman** Osman *25 Bedford Row* *
- **Poku** Mary *9-12 Bell Yard* *
- **Polnay** Jonathan *5 King's Bench Walk*
- **Ponte** Luke *3 Raymond Buildings Barristers*
- **Power** Alexia *Furnival Chambers* 🄰 *
- **Rhodes** David *Doughty Street Chambers*
- **Ritchie** Shauna *2 Bedford Row* *
- **Selby** Lawrence *9 Bedford Row* *
- **Smaller** Elizabeth *9-12 Bell Yard* *
- **Weekes** Mark *6KBW College Hill*
- **Wilkinson** Kate *6KBW College Hill* *

Band 6

- **Alfred** Stephan *9-12 Bell Yard*
- **Bunyan** Angus *2 Hare Court* *
- **Carr** Jamie *4 Breams Buildings (ORL)* ◊
- **Cohen** Samantha *9 Bedford Row* *
- **Corre** Neil *Redbourne Chambers (ORL)* ◊
- **Duncan** Hannah *Atkinson Bevan Chambers, (ORL)* ◊ *
- **Ferguson** Stephen Michael *2 Bedford Row*
- **Forgan** Hugh *23 Essex Street*
- **Goodall** Emma *Dyers Chambers*
- **Gottlieb** David *Thomas More Chambers (ORL)* ◊ *
- **Goudie** Martin *Charter Chambers* 🄰 *
- **Hill** Rina-Marie *1 Pump Court (ORL)* ◊
- **Hossain** Ahmed *23 Essex Street*
- **James** Grahame *Carmelite Chambers* *
- **Ladenburg** Guy *3 Raymond Buildings Barristers* *
- **Langley** Charles *2 Bedford Row* *
- **Levinson** Jemma *1 Mitre Court Buildings (ORL)* ◊
- **Mian** Naeem *2 Hare Court* *
- **Modgil** Sangita *Carmelite Chambers* *
- **Nathwani** Rishi *5 King's Bench Walk*
- **Paley** Ruth *23 Essex Street* *
- **Przybylska** Sarah *2 Hare Court* *
- **Reiz** Stan *Carmelite Chambers* *
- **Rollin** Aron *Carmelite Chambers* *
- **Spiro** Dafna *Garden Court Chambers*
- **Sweet** Louise *Carmelite Chambers* *
- **Tanchel** Vivienne *2 Hare Court* *
- **Taylor** Martin *Carmelite Chambers* *
- **Warrington** John *5 St Andrew's Hill (ORL)* ◊ *

Up-and-coming individuals

- **Alexis** Fallon *QEB Hollis Whiteman* *
- **Oliver** Heather *3 Raymond Buildings Barristers* *
- **Zahir** Hossein *Garden Court Chambers*

* *Indicates individual with profile.*

◊ *(ORL) = Other Ranked Lawyer.*

🄰 *direct access* *(see p.11).*

most wonderful courtroom manner." **Recent work:** Prosecuted a defendant alleged to have murdered his girlfriend in 1995 and concealed her body.

Orlando Pownall QC Frequently called upon to appear for defendants in highly publicised criminal trials. His recent caseload includes significant terrorism and murder cases. **Strengths:** "He's a very able advocate and a star performer." **Recent work:** Secured the acquittal of an individual charged with two counts of murder, four counts of attempted murder, possession of a firearm with intent and assisting an offender. The case concerned the shooting of two soldiers in Antrim in 2009.

Andrew Edis QC A go-to prosecutor for the CPS and SFO, appearing in their biggest cases. He has an excellent practice, befitting a barrister of his standing. **Recent work:** Prosecuted Stuart Hazell, the murderer of his partner's 12-year-old granddaughter, Tia Sharp.

Crime: International Criminal Law London

Leading Silks	
Ellis Diana	*25 Bedford Row*
Emmerson Ben	*Matrix Chambers*
Griffiths Courtenay	*25 Bedford Row*
Haynes Peter	*St Philips Chambers (ORL)* ◊
Hooper David	*25 Bedford Row*
Jones John	*Doughty Street Chambers* Ⓐ
Kay Steven	*9 Bedford Row* *
Khan Karim	*Temple Garden Chambers (ORL)* ◊

Leading Juniors	
Ashraph Sareta	*Garden Court Chambers*
Butler Michelle	*Matrix Chambers* *
Dixon Rod	*Temple Garden Chambers (ORL)* ◊
Harvey Richard	*Garden Court Chambers*
Higgins Gillian	*9 Bedford Row* Ⓐ *
Reynolds Richard	*Garden Court Chambers*
Young David	*9 Bedford Row* *

◊ (ORL) = Other Ranked Lawyer.
Ⓐ direct access (see p.11).
** Indicates individual with profile.*

Peter Wright QC (see p.756) Defends and prosecutes serious criminal cases, often involving offences such as murder, financial crime and terrorism. **Recent work:** Prosecuted former Metropolitan Police Commander Ali Dizaei for misconduct in public office.

Brendan Kelly QC His broad criminal defence expertise includes significant experience in handling murder cases involving terrorist activity. He is regularly instructed to appear in trials in Northern Ireland. **Recent work:** Acted for the defendant in the much-publicised trial of Mark Bridger, who was found guilty of abducting and murdering five-year-old April Jones in Wales in 2012.

Martin Hicks QC Acts for defendants on a wide range of criminal cases, including those involving homicide, serious violence, blackmail and money laundering. **Strengths:** "He is very robust in advocating his case, but he never takes a bad point." **Recent work:** Instructed in R v Ahmed Shah, an extremely high-profile drug importation and money laundering case.

Brian O'Neill QC (see p.686) Prosecutes and defends in cases involving serious and organised crime. His recent instructions include murder, terrorism and sexual assault trials, in addition to a number of financial crime cases. **Recent work:** Acted for one of nine defendants accused of conspiring to cause explosions at multiple locations, including the London Stock Exchange.

JUNIORS

Craig Ferguson Acts for defendants on complex criminal matters, including attempted murder, blackmail and drugs cases. He is experienced in handling sensitive trials involving extensive psychiatric evidence. **Strengths:** "Juries just like him. They sit up and listen because they know he is a good advocate. He is an absolute class act." **Recent work:** Defended a businesswoman charged with blackmail, who was alleged to have used false personae to threaten her lesbian lover with revealing her sexuality.

David Whittaker Has an impressive breadth of experience in handling all manner of criminal matters, whether it be motoring offences or complex drugs trials. **Recent work:** Represented music teacher Michael Crombie, who was accused of committing a series of sexual offences against young girls over a period of 30 years.

Oliver Glasgow (see p.609) Handles criminal cases of a serious nature, as well as related regulatory matters. He is Junior Treasury Counsel. **Strengths:** "He is a brilliant prosecutor and unbelievably hard-working." **Recent work:** Acted for the Ministry of Defence in relation to the alleged battlefield murder of an Afghan insurgent at the hands of three Royal Marine Commandos.

6KBW College Hill

THE SET

6KBW is noted for the "impressively high standard of its 'house style'," with instructing solicitors attesting that its members are uniformly "robust, independent and tireless in all their dealings, while at the same time they maintain a relaxed, courteous and friendly manner." The set is recognised for its involvement in serious and high-profile prosecution work, including the 'Marine A' murder trial and the Rolf Harris sexual assault case. It is also instructed in substantial defence work and, increasingly, advises corporate clients on business-sensitive investigations and compliance matters.

Client service: "The clerks are helpful and professional and, in the event of unavoidable returns, will always ensure any case is dealt with by a barrister of equivalent or higher grade than the one originally instructed." The "exceptional" clerking team is headed by Andrew Barnes.

SILKS

David Perry QC Held in the highest esteem for his excellent appellate practice. He is also engaged in sophisticated trial and advisory work, and is regularly instructed in cases heard in international jurisdictions. **Strengths:** "David Perry is a genius. He just does absolute top-level, top-notch work all the time." "He has outstanding judgement and you can entirely trust his advice." **Recent work:** Instructed to prosecute the former Premier of the Cayman Islands on charges of misconduct in public office.

David Fisher QC Has a highly regarded practice, which ranges from heavyweight murder trials to sensitive advisory work. **Strengths:** "He is always calm but incredibly effective." "He is a joy to watch in court." **Recent work:** Acted for a defendant charged with murder and attempted murder, who was alleged to have tortured the deceased in front of his brother before attempting to take the latter's life as well.

Mark Dennis QC Has a wealth of experience in jury trials and appellate matters. He is regularly instructed in murder cases, and also advises corporations on large-scale criminal investigations. **Strengths:** "He is incredibly bright, he anticipates everything and everybody respects him. He is very measured in what he says and he really has charisma." **Recent work:** Advised News Corporation and News International in relation to police investigations arising out of the phone hacking scandal.

John Ryder QC Sought after to act in complex, document-heavy murder trials, in addition to fraud and corruption cases. He is also well versed in related human rights and regulatory issues. **Strengths:** "He has a very good court manner and is a superb jury advocate." "He has an amazing connection with a jury." **Recent work:** Acted for one of multiple defendants in a challenging joint enterprise murder case involving issues concerning the admissibility of evidence.

Sasha Wass QC Has had a highly successful year handling high-profile prosecution and defence work. She is freqently sought after to appear in trials involving complex and sensitive evidential issues, such as shaken baby and sexual offences cases. **Strengths:** "She is one of the leading practitioners in many areas of crime, and particularly in cases involving sexual offences and violence." **Recent work:** Secured the conviction of entertainer Rolf Harris for multiple historic sex crimes.

JUNIORS

Duncan Atkinson (see p.539) Has a good reputation for defending and prosecuting high-profile criminal cases, including a number of significant homicide trials. **Strengths:** "I think he is the perfect prosecutor. He has got a dozen cases going on in his head, but he manages to stay abreast of all of them and his work is unbelievably good." **Recent work:** Acted as junior counsel for the CPS in a complex trial concerning the murder of oil executive Carole Waugh.

Alison Morgan An excellent choice for high-profile matters involving sensitive issues. She has considerable experience in police misconduct and terrorism cases. **Strengths:** "She is extremely good. She has intellect of the highest calibre and the common sense to apply it. She identifies the right issues." **Recent work:** Appointed by the Home Secretary to act as junior counsel in the Stephen Lawrence Independent Review considering issues surrounding police corruption and undercover policing.

Louis Mably Handles a wide variety of criminal cases, from high-value international bribery cases to complex murders involving significant mental health aspects. **Strengths:** "He is fantastic and really bright." **Recent work:** Prosecuted a mentally ill woman for the murder of another woman in a public place. The defendant had recently been released from psychiatric care following the manslaughter of her mother.

Miranda Hill Acts for both prosecution and defence in a wide range of cases, including those concerning homicides, serious sexual offences and serious violent offences. **Strengths:** "She is a really conscientious barrister; her written submissions are fantastic, she's a great junior and she is a really good advocate." **Recent work:** Advised the Regulatory Investigations Committee of Barclays on criminal aspects of the SFO and FCA investigations into the circumstances of the Qatari investments in Barclays in 2008.

QEB Hollis Whiteman

See profile on p.853

THE SET

The concentration of talent on offer at this set has earned QEB Hollis Whiteman a longstanding reputation as a go-to destination for solicitors with heavyweight criminal cases. It receives extensive praise for the quality of its prosecution and defence work, and for its "fantastic" range of experience. Its members are sought after to handle serious criminal cases at trial and appellate level, with recent high-profile instructions including the News International phone hacking trial, issues arising from Plebgate and a number of gang murders.

Client service: The set's well-regarded clerking team is led by Chris Emmings.

SILKS

Crispin Aylett QC Highly sought after to prosecute and defend criminal cases attracting considerable media attention. He has recently been instructed in a number of significant murder and sexual offences cases. **Strengths:** "He is a real class act." **Recent work:** Secured the conviction of a defendant accused of murdering his sister, Gemma McCluskie, who was known for appearing in television soap 'Eastenders'.

Mark Ellison QC Regularly instructed to advise on high-profile cases, often involving politically sensitive issues. His practice places a heavy emphasis on financial crime matters. **Strengths:** "He is wonderfully user-friendly and is just streets ahead of everyone else intellectually." "He is an exceptionally bright and talented QC, who is fun to work with." **Recent work:** Advised the CPS in relation to possible criminal charges arising out of the Plebgate scandal.

William Boyce QC Has an excellent reputation for handling heavyweight trials, including complex fraud, murder and war crimes cases. He has significant expertise in financial crime matters. **Strengths:** "You will not find anybody more eloquent, and he has the most charming way of addressing the court. He is a superb lawyer."

Edward Brown QC (see p.557) Recognised as a leading prosecutor of headline-grabbing cases. He has recently acted for the CPS in a number of high-profile homicide matters, including cases involving gangland shootings and infanticide. **Recent work:** Acted for the prosecution in a case concerning the murder of a millionaire socialite at the hands of his former financial adviser.

Adrian Darbishire QC Called upon to defend professionals accused of financial crime and misconduct. He has considerable experience of advising businesses on corporate liability. **Strengths:** "He is very bright and charming with clients. He has a pleasant manner."

David Spens QC Has a strong reputation for appearing in murder trials and other significant criminal cases. **Strengths:** "He is a very stylish advocate, whom juries like because of his down-to-earth approach." "He is charming and clever, and has superb analysis. He's also second to none as a tactician." **Recent work:** Represented Clive Goodman in the News International phone hacking trial.

JUNIORS

Jocelyn Ledward Has experience of handling substantial criminal cases, including long-running murder and fraud trials. Her practice places an increasing emphasis on white-collar matters. **Recent work:** Acted as junior counsel for the prosecution in the Tia Sharp murder trial, a case concerning the killing of a 12-year-old girl by her grandmother's partner, Stuart Hazell.

Benn Maguire Both prosecutes and defends across a wide range of high-profile and complex criminal matters. **Recent work:** Acted for former News of the World royal editor Clive Goodman in the phone hacking trial.

3 Raymond Buildings Barristers

See profile on p.857

THE SET

3 Raymond Buildings is celebrated for providing outstanding advocacy and advisory services in high-end criminal matters. Its members are characterised by their "strength across the board" and are described as "high-calibre, quality advocates, who are a step ahead of many of their competitors." In addition to its market-leading fraud and extradition practices, the set is instructed in numerous heavyweight crime cases, such as the Operation Weeting phone hacking investigation and the Max Clifford indecent assault trial.

Client service: Eddie Holland is the senior clerk at chambers and the first point of contact for all criminal matters. Sources are full of praise for the clerking team, reporting that "they provide first-class clerking and a fantastic service. There is top to bottom quality."

SILKS

Alexander Cameron QC Highly sought after to handle serious criminal matters, including high-profile murder trials. He is a first-choice silk for all manner of cases, but is increasingly instructed in financial crime matters. **Strengths:** "He is intelligent, and has a commanding and persuasive courtroom manner." "He is a great jury advocate and a wonderful speech-maker." **Recent work:** He defended Nicholas Kutner, who was alleged to have killed businesswoman Carole Waugh and stolen her assets.

Patrick Gibbs QC Frequently called upon to defend and prosecute important cases, including murder and manslaughter trials. He is recognised for his ability to deal with sensitive and complex issues during criminal proceedings and related inquests. **Strengths:** "He is a star silk. His manner, ability and understated style are very effective." "He is charming, hard-working and frighteningly intelligent."

Trevor Burke QC Often instructed in high-stakes criminal cases involving prominent defendants and international elements. He is increasingly focused on financial crime defence and advisory work. **Strengths:** "His tactical reading of a case is of the highest order. He is held in high regard by professional and lay clients, and is a first-rate advocate." "He is very avuncular, very accessible and immensely skilled." **Recent work:** Represented the personal assistant of Rebekah Brooks, who was accused of perverting the course of justice in relation to the phone hacking investigation.

Richard Horwell QC Has notable expertise in cases that straddle the divide between criminal law and human rights. His impressive experience encompasses terrorism, drugs, murder and historic sexual abuse cases. **Strengths:** "He is one of the top QCs in general crime, and has huge amounts of experience and skills which he brings to cases." **Recent work:** Defended Max Clifford against indecent assault charges in a highly publicised trial.

Hugo Keith QC Has significant experience of handling cases involving terrorism. His practice places a heavy emphasis on financial crime, extradition and inquests involving potential criminal ramifications. **Strengths:** "He is a great authority in and out of court. He is clever and hard-working, and has a strategic approach."

James Lewis QC Regularly appears in complex cases, with a particular focus on matters involving multi-jurisdictional aspects, such as extradition and universal jurisdiction cases. **Strengths:** "He is very able and user-friendly, and has a very good brain and good client skills too. Clients love him." "He is fantastically good and knowledgeable – one of the few experts in the field of international criminal law." **Recent work:** He is instructed in a universal jurisdiction case involving allegations of torture in Nepal.

Michael Bromley-Martin QC Has a strong reputation for handling heavyweight cases, including sex, murder and drugs trials. He has particular experience of representing police officers charged with criminal offences. **Strengths:** "He is a fine and engaging barrister who is able to put defendants at their ease and draw out the information he requires with compassion and understanding." "He is one of the best silks I've ever worked with in terms of the quality of his advocacy, and the way he looks after clients and papers. It gives you great confidence just being near him." **Recent work:** Secured the acquittal of an ex-gang member charged with murder on the basis of self-defence.

Michael Borrelli QC (see p.553) Admired for his advocacy in a broad range of serious criminal cases, including multiple homicide trials. He is noted for his adept handling of expert evidence. **Strengths:** "He is an extremely persuasive jury advocate, and he is good on the law. He has fantastic forensic cross-examining skills and brings everything together beautifully in his closing speeches: a class act." **Recent work:** He represented a gunman charged with murder in a case involving issues of mistaken identity.

Simon Farrell QC A veteran advocate whose practice covers a wide range of serious criminal cases. **Strengths:** "He is very strong on complex legal arguments and can handle high-profile cases to a very high standard."

JUNIORS

Neil Saunders An outstanding criminal junior with an excellent reputation for prosecuting and defending significant cases. He has notable experience of complex assault, sexual offences and drugs cases, and is also celebrated for his financial crime expertise. **Strengths:** "He has an unequalled practice and his knowledge of the law and presentation of legal arguments is universally respected by judges and fellow counsel alike. His breadth of practice attests to his versatility." "He is a great diplomat, and a calming and reassuring presence when things get difficult." **Recent work:** Represented Charlie Brooks, who was charged with perverting the course of justice, in relation to the News International phone hacking investigation.

William Emlyn Jones Well versed in handling high-profile matters, including murder, serious organised crime and misconduct in public office cases. He is highly sought after to act as prosecution and defence counsel. **Strengths:** "He has a lovely manner, he is excellent on technical points and he is down to earth. Clients like him and judges like him." "He's hard-working and very straightforward, and produces precise legal arguments." **Recent work:** He represented the defendant in a murder trial involving complex issues relating to mental health and expert evidence.

James Hines Has wide-ranging criminal expertise, with a focus on financial crime and offences committed while acting in a professional capacity. His practice often includes cases with international elements. **Strengths:** "He is a very smooth, graceful advocate with a naughty sense of humour, which wins over clients and the courts." **Recent work:** Advised private investigator Glenn Mulcaire in relation to the News International phone hacking investigation.

Alisdair Williamson (see p.753) Regularly instructed as a leading defence junior in significant sexual offences and drugs trials. He also has experience of prosecuting cases involving misconduct in public office. **Strengths:** "He is a brilliant cross-examiner and an excellent jury advocate. He's very understated, but he's an experienced tactician and very good at making clients feel comfortable." "He is very good with all aspects of the process. He grasps what the client needs and what the strong points of the defence are, and liaises with the police well." **Recent work:** Successfully defended actor Michael Le Vell against allegations of child rape.

Richard Wormald Has extensive experience of heavyweight criminal cases, including murder, people trafficking and police corruption cases. He is regularly called upon to prosecute and defend. **Recent work:** Instructed as junior defence counsel in the Chris Huhne trial regarding perverting the course of justice.

Saba Naqshbandi Defends professional clients in complex cases, many of which involve issues relating to mental health, exclusion of evidence and international elements. She has notable experience of handling inquests relating to criminal proceedings. **Strengths:** "She has good judgement, is an effective advocate and is great with the client." **Recent work:** Acted for Tetrapak billionaire Hans Rausing in the inquest and criminal proceedings arising from his wife's death.

Band 2

25 Bedford Row

See profile on p.766

THE SET

25 Bedford Row fields "excellent silks and juniors" who defend clients accused of serious criminal offences, including murder, sexual offences and drugs importation. Its members have recently been instructed in a number of high-profile homicide trials, including the murder of former 'Eastenders' actress Gemma McCluskie and the PC Blakelock case, which arose out of the killing of a police officer during the Broadwater Farm riots in 1985. Instructing solicitors praise the depth of quality at the set, commenting that its advocates are "very polished, very thorough and very well prepared, and do the job to a very high standard."

Client service: Guy Williams heads a team of clerks who are praised for being "excellent communicators."

SILKS

George Carter-Stephenson QC A much-praised defence practitioner, with particular expertise in financial crime and murder cases. He has experience of handling cases involving human rights issues, and of working with vulnerable defendants. **Strengths:** "If I need someone with the stamina to do a long trial, I go to him. He is relentless. He cross-examines so methodically." **Recent work:** Appeared for the defence in a murder trial involving a shooting arising from gang warfare in South East London.

Jeremy Dein QC (see p.586) Frequently instructed in Old Bailey trials, including numerous murder cases. He is also called upon to appear in appellate matters. **Strengths:** "He is very polished, his judgement is very good, he is hard-working and he is very good with clients. He is top drawer." **Recent work:** Represented the first defendant in a nine-handed murder trial, in which the defendants were also charged with conspiring to pervert the course of justice.

Courtenay Griffiths QC Has a good reputation for representing defendants in domestic and international criminal cases. He has extensive experience of significant murder and terrorism cases. **Recent work:** Secured the acquittal of Nicky Jacobs, who was charged with the murder of PC Blakelock during the Broadwater Farm riots in 1985.

Paul Mendelle QC Recognised for his talent in defending serious criminal charges, including murder, sexual assault and drug trafficking. **Strengths:** "He is very smooth, and knows how to get on side with the judge. He has a lovely manner about him and he is very calm." **Recent work:** Acted for the defence in a murder trial involving issues of self defence.

Diana Ellis QC Well versed in handling cases involving war crimes, crimes against humanity and genocide. **Strengths:** "She has an extremely detailed knowledge of international jurisdiction. She is amazingly hard-working, a very good communicator and extremely thorough." **Recent work:** Acted in the Cambodian Court for a defendant accused of involvement in genocide and war crimes committed by Pol Pot's government.

David Hooper QC Regularly appears in key cases in the International Criminal Court. He has particular expertise in cases arising from war crimes and crimes against humanity committed in Africa. **Strengths:** "He is a very fine courtroom tactician with great experience of handling African cases." **Recent work:** Acted for Brigadier General Germain Katanga in the International Criminal Court in a case concerning war crimes and crimes against humanity in Eastern Congo.

JUNIORS

Aisling Byrnes Sought after to act for the defence in notable criminal cases, often involving challenging tactical decisions. She has an active appellate practice, and is also experienced at handling judicial review proceedings arising out of criminal law matters. **Recent work:** Secured acquittal for the defendant in the retrial of a rape case.

Adrian Eissa Frequently instructed as a leading junior on a range of complex criminal cases. He is noted for his work on cases involving money laundering, drug conspiracies and serious violence. **Strengths:** "He is great with clients, and pure class in court." **Recent work:** Instructed in R v Peter Lloyd, a well-publicised bigamy case.

Cloth Fair Chambers

THE SET

Cloth Fair Chambers is a boutique criminal set, whose members are highly sought after to appear in the most complex trials, and who offer discreet advice on sensitive pre-charge issues. The set is regularly instructed in the most high-profile cases, as evidenced by its involvement in the News International phone hacking trial. It is pre-eminent in the field of financial crime and corporate advisory work.

Client service: Nick Newman is the "highly affable and extremely well clued-up" senior clerk at the set.

SILKS

John Kelsey-Fry QC An excellent choice for business-sensitive criminal matters, including those in which his advice is sought in advance of charges being brought. He has impressive experience of handling financial crime cases. **Strengths:** "He brings an exceptional logical, strategic analysis to the cases we do." "He has clear and well thought-out views, and is a great pleasure to deal with."

Nicholas Purnell QC Has an outstanding reputation for advising professionals and corporations on issues of criminal liability. He is regularly called upon to advise pre-charge on investigations and compliance matters. **Strengths:** "He has seen everything and he brings unparalleled experience." "He's smooth as silk."

Ian Winter QC A highly skilled criminal advocate, with experience of defending clients accused of murder, sexual offences and financial wrongdoing. He also has a significant advisory practice. **Strengths:** "He is extremely intelligent and aggressive but not in a negative sense. You can trust his analysis and judgement." "He is charismatic, charming and clever. He makes the practice of law look easy." **Recent work:** Successfully defended an individual charged with murder and armed robbery in Gibraltar.

Timothy Langdale QC Highly sought after to defend high-profile clients in complex criminal trials. He has significant expertise in lengthy fraud cases. **Recent work:** Acted for Andy Coulson in the News International phone hacking trial.

JUNIORS

Jonathan Barnard Regularly called upon to act in heavyweight criminal matters, including sexual offences cases. He is also sought after to advise on corporate liability. **Strengths:** "He is fantastic in court and brilliant with clients, especially in difficult cases." **Recent work:** Defended former media magnate Eddie Shah against historic rape allegations.

Clare Sibson Much-praised criminal junior, with considerable experience of document-heavy, high-profile cases. She has particular strength in financial crime matters. **Recent work:** Defended Rebekah Brooks against charges of conspiracy to commit misconduct in public office and conspiracy to pervert the course of justice, in the much-publicised News International phone hacking trial.

Alison Pople Instructed by blue-chip crime firms in significant criminal cases. Her practice places an emphasis on high-value fraud cases. **Strengths:** "She is very measured, has very good judgement of the tone to adopt and is very responsive, even when under huge time pressures. She is very impressive." **Recent work:** Acted as junior defence counsel for Andy Coulson in the News International phone hacking trial.

Doughty Street Chambers

See profile on p.786

THE SET

Doughty Street Chambers is known for offering "an extensive range of astute and experienced counsel in criminal, human rights and international law," and is consequently called upon to handle numerous terrorism cases, including the territorial army barracks bomb plot trial and a case involving an alleged member of a Jihadi group who was charged with the kidnap and false imprisonment of two journalists in Syria. Its members have wide-ranging criminal defence experience, and regularly handle murder, sexual offences and drugs cases. They are often instructed to appear in appellate cases.

Client service: Graham Briggs runs the set's highly efficient clerking team.

SILKS

Tim Moloney QC Recognised for his achievements in high-profile and legally complex cases, often at appellate level. He has notable expertise in cases involving terrorism, murder and sexual offences. **Strengths:** "He's one of the foremost terrorist lawyers in the country and is highly respected internationally." **Recent work:** Represented a defendant in a murder case involving the alleged shooting of a teenager in gang-related circumstances.

Joel Bennathan QC Has extensive experience of representing defendants in murder and terrorism trials. He is also noted for his appellate practice. **Strengths:** "Joel is a first-class lawyer and advocate, who commands immense respect from the senior judiciary." **Recent work:** Acted for a defendant in a joint enterprise murder trial involving complex evidence and legal issues.

Edward Fitzgerald QC Well placed to advise on serious criminal cases involving international law and human rights elements. He has significant experience of challenging sentences. **Strengths:** "He is one of the most brilliant appellate advocates in the business." **Recent work:** Represented a convicted murderer in a challenge to the whole-life tariff that had been imposed on him.

Christopher Sallon QC Has a broad practice, which ranges from heavyweight murder trials to sensitive corruption cases. He has particular experience of handling cases with international aspects. **Recent work:** Defended a woman accused of planning and executing the murder of a garage owner with a number of accomplices.

James Wood QC Instructed at trial and appellate level in cases pertaining to murder, rape and terrorism offences. He is known for handling cases involving miscarriages of justice. **Strengths:** "He is experienced, thorough and reliable." "I recommend him for his ability to hold the attention of a court." **Recent work:** He defended the former defence editor of the Sun newspaper, who was charged with conspiracy to commit misconduct in public office as a result of the findings of Operation Elveden.

Edward Rees QC Highly skilled at handling cases concerning public order, homicide and fraud offences. He has considerable experience of appearing in matters involving mental health issues and vulnerable defendants. **Strengths:** "He is a brilliant trial advocate and one of the most tenacious and robust cross-examiners, especially when taking on police officers and those in the establishment." "He has a superb analytical mind." **Recent work:** Secured the acquittal of a client accused of carrying out a gang-related stabbing in North London.

John Jones QC Regularly called upon to appear in cases involving war crimes and crimes against humanity, as well as extradition hearings and challenges to INTERPOL red notices. **Recent work:** Instructed to act for Saif Gaddafi, son of the former Libyan dictator, in admissibility proceedings in the International Criminal Court, relating to allegations that he committed crimes against humanity.

23 Essex Street

See profile on p.795

THE SET

23 Essex Street provides high-calibre counsel who defend and prosecute in heavyweight criminal cases, including those involving gang murder, terrorism and human trafficking. Its members are also experienced in sexual offences and drugs trials, with recent instructions including an Operation Yewtree prosecution and a 15-defendant drugs supply case involving two organised crime groups. Sources associate the set with "high-quality advocates who prepare their cases well and keep their solicitors and clients updated regularly."

Client service: Instructing solicitors report that "the set is brilliantly clerked by Richard Fowler" and commend it for its "excellent approach to customer care." Richard Heatley, the service manager for prosecutions, is also singled out for praise, with sources asserting that "he is always available to assist and is of great benefit in making sure that you get the right counsel for your case."

SILKS

Simon Russell Flint QC Regularly instructed for the defence in notable murder cases, including those arising out of gang violence. He is admired for his skills as a jury advocate. **Strengths:** "Simon's cross-examination stands out. He just has this lovely manner about him and he is a very good tactician." **Recent work:** Defended a solicitor charged with multiple counts of rape in the context of human trafficking.

Matrix Chambers

See profile on p.832

THE SET

Matrix Chambers is eminently well equipped to provide "excellent criminal practitioners" in specialist cases, many of which involve sophisticated human rights and international law elements. Its members are frequently instructed in matters that attract significant media attention, and their recent briefs include advising David Miranda in relation to his arrest under anti-terrorism legislation. They are also active in appellate cases, including those in other jurisdictions. By way of example, members acted in a recent trial in the Hong Kong Court of Final Appeal, which involved a barrister accused of perverting the course of justice.

Client service: The highly capable and very experienced Paul Venables is the practice manager for this area of the law.

SILKS

Ben Emmerson QC A strong choice for criminal cases involving civil liberties. He also appears in inquests and inquiries arising from potential criminal wrongdoing. **Strengths:** "He is an exceptional advocate in court." "He's extremely bright and very good at getting his teeth into things."

Clare Montgomery QC A celebrated criminal, regulatory and public law silk. She is highly sought after to appear in cases involving international elements and those requiring the most complex legal analysis. **Strengths:** "She is fantastic on the law." "She argues well and effectively, and is completely in control of the facts and the law." **Recent work:** Appeared in the Hong Kong Court of Final Appeal, acting for a barrister who was subsequently cleared of perverting the course of justice.

Tim Owen QC Has a wealth of experience in handling serious crime cases, including human trafficking and sensitive fraud and corruption matters. His practice has a notably international outlook. **Strengths:** "He is a very clever lawyer and a brilliant appellate advocate." **Recent work:** Acted for the DPP in response to an appeal brought by certain alleged victims of child trafficking, who claimed that they had been prosecuted in contravention of the Convention on Trafficking.

Matthew Ryder QC Has impressive experience of terrorism and fraud trials, in addition to cases in the International Criminal Court. His practice straddles the divide between civil and criminal law. **Strengths:** "His ability to connect with the jury makes him stand out as someone who is good in cases where the defendant has received negative publicity." "He is superb and very approachable."

JUNIORS

Michelle Butler (see p.562) Has impressive experience of ICC cases. She is building a strong international practice and was recently appointed to the Attorney General's Public International Law panel. **Strengths:** "She is a rising practitioner in the area of international criminal law." "She performs very well under difficult circumstances, and navigates obstacles to access to documents and pressing deadlines in exemplary fashion." **Recent work:** Instructed as counsel to Libya in the cases against Saif Al-Islam Gaddafi and Abdullah Al-Senussi, which involve allegations of murder and persecution during the Libyan revolution.

Band 3

9-12 Bell Yard

THE SET

9-12 Bell Yard is briefed in a broad range of criminal cases, including those involving murder, section 18 offences and rape. Its recent high-profile work includes the Tia Sharp murder trial, the News International phone hacking trial and a significant arms dealing case. Its members are equally experienced in handling defence and prosecution instructions.

Client service: Angela May is the senior clerk at the set.

SILKS

Mukul Chawla QC Defends and prosecutes in large-scale criminal cases, including landmark fraud investigations. He also has extensive experience of acting for police officers accused of homicide offences and perverting the course of justice. **Strengths:** "He is an excellent advocate and he always has the ear of the court." **Recent work:** Acted for the Crown in a case concerning an international arms dealer alleged to have brokered the sale of automatic machine guns, pistols and ammunition from China to Nigeria.

Carmelite Chambers

See profile on p.775

THE SET

Carmelite Chambers has expertise in a wide variety of criminal defence work, including serious organised crime and complex fraud cases. Its members have recently been instructed in a number of sex cases, including the Oxford sex grooming trial, as well as multiple high-profile homicide cases, such as the trials of Dale Cregan, who was convicted of killing two police officers, and Michael Philpott, who was found guilty of the manslaughter of six children in a house fire in Derby.

Client service: Marc King leads the set's clerking team and is known as "a man who makes things happen."

Garden Court Chambers

See profile on p.808

THE SET

Garden Court Chambers is known for being "a significant set, which regularly conducts cases at the highest levels." It is a good choice for instructing solicitors seeking well-clerked, quality counsel for heavyweight criminal matters, including those relating to sexual offences, terrorism and gang murder. The set also has a notable international crime practice and has been involved in a number of significant cases at the Hague.

Client service: Instructing solicitors highlight the "excellent clerking of Colin Cook and his team." Senior crime clerk Keith Poynter is also singled out for praise, with one source commenting: "He's such a good clerk, and so responsive to what we need and what we are like as a client. He makes sure we're well looked after."

SILKS

Henry Blaxland QC Praised for his erudition and unflappability when handling complex criminal cases. He focuses on defending clients accused of fraud and terrorism offences, and is also a strong appellate lawyer. **Strengths:** "He is just fantastic. Calm, measured and knowledgeable, he's someone judges listen to." **Recent work:** Defended an individual charged with multiple historic sex offences alleged to have taken place in the 1960s and 1970s.

Stephen Kamlish QC Has a good reputation for defending clients accused of terrorism offences and gang-related murder. He is also instructed in significant inquiries arising out of criminal cases. **Strengths:** "He is a brilliant advocate, who is exceptionally hard-working and has strong client care." "He is generally recognised as one of the best cross-examiners in practice. He is very easy to work with, super bright and a fantastic tactician." **Recent work:** Instructed on appeal to represent an individual convicted of conspiracy to cause explosions as part of the failed 21/7 bomb plot.

Judy Khan QC Called upon to act for the defence in heavyweight cases, including homicide and sex trials. She has considerable experience of representing vulnerable offenders. **Strengths:** "She is a ferocious advocate, who is totally dedicated to clients." **Recent work:** Represented one of five defendants in a murder trial involving a gang of drug dealers who carried out a stabbing as revenge against an individual they thought had robbed them.

Michael Turner QC Has particular expertise in shaken-baby cases and significant murder trials. He has a highly regarded appellate practice. **Strengths:** "He is a tenacious lawyer, who is dedicated and incredibly hard-working."

Ali Naseem Bajwa QC Recognised for his expertise in representing defendants in high-profile homicide and terrorism cases. **Strengths:** "He is a very polished silk; a sound advocate who is much sought after." **Recent work:** Instructed in R v Artur Okrutny, the first 'crash for cash' manslaughter prosecution.

JUNIORS

Sareta Ashraph Regularly instructed by the United Nations to monitor potential breaches of international law as conflicts unfold. **Recent work:** Acted as senior legal analyst for the United Nations Commission of Inquiry on the Syrian Arab Republic, drafting speeches and briefings on human rights violations in the context of the ongoing civil war.

Richard Harvey Focuses his practice on international crime and human rights issues. He handles cases involving war crimes, crimes against humanity and ECHR matters as they apply to individuals accused of criminal conduct. **Recent work:** Instructed by the International Criminal Tribunal for the former Yugoslavia to prepare the case against Radovan Karadzic, the former president of Republika Srpska, who is accused of war crimes and crimes against humanity.

Richard Reynolds Well placed to act on international criminal matters involving human rights and public law considerations. He has notable experience of cases before overseas tribunals. **Strengths:** "He's a very bright lawyer and a future star." **Recent work:** Acted as part of the defence team in the appeal of Justin Mugenzi, the Minister of Trade in the Interim Government of Rwanda, whose conviction for involvement in the Rwandan genocide was overturned by the Appeals Chamber of the International Criminal Tribunal for Rwanda.

Red Lion Chambers

THE SET

Red Lion Chambers provides defence and prosecution counsel for complex matters, such as historic murder, organised sexual offences and terrorism cases. Its recent high-profile instructions include the Max Clifford indecent assault trial, the territorial army barracks bomb plot trial and an eight-handed rape and human trafficking case. The set is also called upon to handle high-value fraud cases.

Client service: Mark Bennett is the set's practice director.

SILKS

David Etherington QC A highly regarded criminal silk, with extensive experience of appearing in high-profile murder cases. He is also well versed in handling complex fraud matters. **Strengths:** "He is skilful, subtle and good with juries." **Recent work:** Defended a taxi driver accused of murdering his mistress in 1995.

Max Hill QC (see p.627) Sought after to defend and prosecute individuals accused of murder and terrorism offences. **Recent work:** Instructed by the Treasury Solicitor in a case concerning the violent murder of a Ladbrokes duty manager, which was carried out to enable the defendant to steal money from the till.

JUNIORS

Jennifer Dempster (see p.586) Recognised for her experience in handling serious criminal cases, including those involving rape, human trafficking and murder. She has particular expertise in working with vulnerable defendants and witnesses. **Strengths:** "She is a true heavyweight junior, a great jury advocate and a team player." "She has excellent client care skills and jury advocacy." **Recent work:** She acted for a former Metropolitan Police Officer accused of perverting the course of justice.

Tom Forster Defends and prosecutes in complex trials, many of which relate to organised crime. His expertise includes drugs, sexual offences, homicide and people trafficking cases. **Recent work:** Prosecuted a criminal gang charged with conspiracy to supply class A drugs as a result of the findings of a cross-border SOCA investigation.

Gillian Jones Handles a broad range of criminal cases, including those involving sexual offences, drug importation, murder and financial crime. In addition to her defence work, she is regularly instructed by the CPS, SFO and FCA. **Recent work:** Instructed to act as junior counsel for the defence in a joint enterprise murder trial concerning a pensioner whose decomposing body was found in the cellar of the supermarket in which the defendant was employed as a butcher.

Other Ranked Lawyers

Aftab Jafferjee QC (Atkinson Bevan Chambers) Called upon to prosecute heavyweight criminal trials, including cases involving gross negligence manslaughter, murder and terrorism. He also has a notable defence and advisory practice. **Strengths:** "He is fantastic. He's really clever and a really elegant prosecutor."

Abbas Lakha QC (see p.649) (9 Bedford Row) Has an excellent reputation for acting as defence counsel in murder and terrorism trials attracting significant media attention. He has considerable expertise in cases involving gangland killings. **Strengths:** "He is a top silk and is very good at investigating the early stages of a case." "He is an impressive advocate." **Recent work:** Represented Michael Adebowale, one of two Islamic fundamentalists convicted of murdering Private Lee Rigby in Woolwich.

Anthony Berry QC (see p.548) (9 Bedford Row) Regularly instructed in murder trials, often involving gang violence. He is also experienced in fraud and corruption cases. **Strengths:** "He is a really polished performer. He has got many years of experience and it shows; he gets to his feet and people sit up and listen." "He is just brilliant at cross-examination and fantastic with clients." **Recent work:** Defended a British marine charged with murdering an Afghan insurgent in Helmand.

Steven Kay QC (see p.642) (9 Bedford Row) Has significant experience before the International Criminal Court in matters involving crimes against humanity and war crimes. He is also sought after to counsel governments, corporations and membership organisations on best practice and compliance matters. **Strengths:** "He has a stellar international crime law practice and he is great in court." **Recent work:** Defended President Kenyatta of Kenya, who was charged with crimes against humanity for his alleged role in violence following the 2007 national elections in Kenya.

David Hughes (see p.633) (9 Bedford Row) Has broad experience of defending clients accused of serious criminal offences, including terrorism, murder and drugs importation, in addition to fraud. He has notable expertise in cutting-edge computer fraud cases. **Strengths:** "His practice covers the full spectrum of crime and he always manages to find an arguable point."

David Young (see p.757) (9 Bedford Row) Has impressive experience of international criminal litigation, particularly in cases relating to the Middle East and Africa. He has particular expertise in cases involving terrorism. **Recent work:** Defended an individual in the Special Tribunal for Lebanon at the Hague, who was charged with homicide, attempted homicide and conspiracy to commit an act of terrorism in relation to assassination of the former Lebanese prime minister.

Gillian Higgins (see p.626) (9 Bedford Row) Called upon to handle significant international crime cases, and has a particular focus on Africa-related matters. **Strengths:** "She has a great practice and is great in court." **Recent work:** Acted as junior counsel for President Kenyatta of Kenya, who was charged with crimes against humanity for his alleged role in violence following the 2007 national elections in Kenya.

Nigel Rumfitt QC (7BR) Has an impressive track record of prosecuting and defending high-profile murder cases. He has additional expertise in corporate manslaughter cases.

Richard Latham QC (7BR) Highly regarded for his prosecution and defence expertise. His practice places an emphasis on fraud and regulatory matters, and he also handles cases involving violent crime. **Recent work:** Acted for the CPS in a joint enterprise murder trial concerning the killing by arson of a family of four in Leicester.

Timothy Spencer QC (7BR) Recognised for his extensive experience of appearing in murder trials. He is also instructed in cases involving indecent images and sexual offences. **Recent work:** Represented the defendant in a case concerning the distribution of indecent images.

Andrew Campbell-Tiech QC (Dyers Chambers) A highly experienced criminal advocate whose practice covers a broad range of criminal matters. He is also the head of Dyers Chambers. **Strengths:** "He is enormously intelligent, and is a fierce proponent of his client's cause through compelling and persuasive advocacy." **Recent work:** Acted in R (Virgin Media) v Zinga, a case concerning whether private companies are permitted to conduct confiscation proceedings and claim compensation for themselves.

Simon Mayo QC (187 Fleet Street) Acts for both defence and prosecution on high-profile and complex criminal cases. He is particularly noted for his considerable expertise in homicide cases. **Strengths:** "He is a very hard-working and impressive advocate."

Oliver Blunt QC (see p.551) (Furnival Chambers) A first-class silk for heavyweight criminal trials, such as murder and drugs cases. He is also instructed in appellate matters. **Strengths:** "He's always very good. He's so experienced and laid back." **Recent work:** Acted for one of ten defendants in a murder trial concerning a revenge killing over the theft of a mobile phone.

Sally O'Neill QC (see p.686) (Furnival Chambers) Known for appearing in complex and sensitive matters, including baby shaking cases and serious sexual and violent crime cases. **Recent work:** Defended a young father accused of killing his four-month-old baby in a case involving detailed medical evidence.

Tom Little (9 Gough Square) Highly sought after to prosecute the most serious offences, including murder, sexual abuse and terrorism. His role as Treasury Counsel befits his high-profile prosecution experience. **Strengths:** "He takes it on the chin and is completely unflappable. He has fantastic judgement and instincts, and an incisive intellect." "He is superb. He is incredibly hard-working and exceptionally able." **Recent work:** Instructed by the CPS in the prosecution of publicist Max Clifford for historic sexual offences.

Mark Heywood QC (5 King's Bench) Walk Highly sought after to prosecute the most serious and sensitive cases, including significant murder trials. He is Senior Treasury Counsel at the Central Criminal Court. **Strengths:** "He has an encyclopaedic knowledge of the law and procedure, and he is immensely talented. He gets the right results because of his ability. Added to this he is very fair and he manages the whole thing beautifully to a satisfactory conclusion." "He has a brain the size of a planet and is a formidable opponent." **Recent work:** Prosecuted a woman who stabbed her victim to death shortly after having been released from a psychiatric hospital.

Michael Mansfield QC (Mansfield Chambers) Has distinguished himself as a pre-eminent criminal silk, with extensive experience of appearing in the most high-profile cases. **Strengths:** "He is a master of his game and can contextualise a trial in the history of the past 30 years."

David Howker QC (No5 Chambers) A veteran criminal advocate whose practice covers a wide range of serious criminal work. **Recent work:** Instructed in R v Kaleema, a high-profile gang-related murder in North London.

Miranda Moore QC (see p.676) (5 Paper Buildings) Called upon to act for the prosecution and defence in a variety of cases, including murder, sexual matters and fraud trials. She has particular expertise in mercy killing cases. **Strengths:** "She has the ability to take on board instructions from young defendants and put their defence concisely to the jury with robust logic." "She is fabulous with the clients and very good with the jury. She's also entirely fearless with the judge, and quite happy to stand her ground and fight her point." **Recent work:** Prosecuted Dave Lee Travis in the first trial to arise out of historic sex allegations investigated in Operation Yewtree.

Jonathan Caplan QC (5 Paper Buildings) A highly distinguished criminal silk, with experience of representing clients in high-profile cases and inquiries. He is also noted for the strength of his fraud practice. **Recent work:** Represented the former managing editor of the News of the World in the News International phone hacking trial.

Graham Trembath QC (see p.740) (5 Paper Buildings) Has wide-ranging experience of defending clients accused of a variety of crimes, including murder and violent robbery offences. **Strengths:** "He is a fantastic jury advocate." **Recent work:** Acted in a complex four-month trial for the first of three defendants charged with conspiracy to commit robbery.

Tom Allen (5 Paper Buildings) Has a broad practice covering a wide range of criminal matters, including corruption, fraud and homicide. **Strengths:** "He is a real jury advocate with an excellent feel for what appeals to a jury and what does not." "He is an incredibly hard-working leading junior, whose ability to identify the core issues against a morass of evidence is unrivalled." **Recent work:** Acted in R v Rumsey, a notable share selling fraud originating from Madrid which concerned the sale of USD100 million shares.

Peter Haynes QC (St Philips Chambers) A significant presence at the Hague, he has impressive experience in defending individuals accused of war crimes.

Karim Khan QC (Temple Garden Chambers) Has a strong reputation for handling international crime matters, and particular experience in cases involving war crimes and crimes against humanity committed in Africa and Eastern Europe. **Recent work:** Defended the deputy president of Kenya, William Ruto, who was charged with crimes against humanity for his alleged role in violence following the 2007 national elections in Kenya.

Rod Dixon (Temple Garden Chambers) Recommended for his practice in international criminal litigation. He has experience in representing politicians and governments. **Recent work:** Acted for President Morsi and his government in an International Criminal Court complaint relating to the 2013 military takeover in Egypt.

MIDLANDS

Crime Midlands	
Leading Sets	
Band 1	
No5 Chambers *	
St Philips Chambers *	
Band 2	
36 Bedford Row *	
7BR *	
Citadel Chambers	
No.1 High Pavement	
St Ives Chambers *	
Band 3	
KCH Garden Square	
Leading Silks	
Star individuals	
Crigman David	*St Philips Chambers* *
Band 1	
Joyce Peter	*No.1 High Pavement*
Oldham Frances	*36 Bedford Row*
Wall Mark	*Citadel Chambers*
Band 2	
Atkins Richard	*St Philips Chambers* [A] *
Brand Rachel	*Citadel Chambers*
Fisher Andrew	*Citadel Chambers*
Hotten Christopher	*No5 Chambers* [A]
Keeling Adrian	*No5 Chambers* [A] *
Malik Amjad	*36 Bedford Row*
Mann Paul	*No.1 High Pavement*
Mason David	*No5 Chambers*
Millington Christopher	*St Philips Chambers*
Smith Andrew	*St Philips Chambers* [A] *
Smith Shaun	*No.1 High Pavement*
Spencer Timothy	*7BR* [A]
Tedd Rex	*No5 Chambers*
Band 3	
Burrows Michael	*No5 Chambers* *
Donnellan Christopher	*36 Bedford Row* *
Duck Michael	*No5 Chambers* [A]
Hankin Jonas	*St Philips Chambers*
Harbage William	*36 Bedford Row* *
Heywood Mark	*No5 Chambers* [A] *
Laird Francis	*St Philips Chambers* *
Lloyd-Jones John	*36 Bedford Row* *
Lockhart Andrew	*St Philips Chambers* [A]
Montgomery Kristina	*St Philips Chambers*
New Silks	
Evans Michael	*No.1 High Pavement*
Gerry Felicity	*36 Bedford Row*
Lucking Adrienne	*36 Bedford Row* *

** Indicates set / individual with profile.*
[A] direct access (see p.11).
Alphabetical order within each band. Band 1 is highest.

Crime Midlands	
Leading Juniors	
Band 1	
Egbuna Robert	*No.1 High Pavement*
Jackson Andrew	*St Philips Chambers* *
Way Ian	*KCH Garden Square*
Band 2	
Bradley Phillip	*No5 Chambers*
Dean Brian	*No5 Chambers* [A]
Gilchrist Naomi	*St Philips Chambers* [A] *
Hannam Timothy	*Citadel Chambers*
Langdale Adrian	*7BR*
Liddiard Martin	*No5 Chambers* [A]
Reynolds Adrian	*No.1 High Pavement*
Band 3	
Bright David	*Citadel Chambers*
Cooper Peter	*St Ives Chambers* *
Garcha Gurdeep	*Citadel Chambers*
Heeley Michelle	*No5 Chambers* [A]
Jackson David	*St Ives Chambers* *
Kubik Heidi	*St Philips Chambers* *
Mills Ben	*St Philips Chambers* [A] *
Morse Malcolm	*St Philips Chambers* *
Pole Tim	*No5 Chambers* *
Sandhu Harpreet Singh	*No5 Chambers* [A]
Saunders Kevin	*St Ives Chambers* *
Singh Talbir	*No5 Chambers* [A]
Van der Zwart Mark	*KCH Garden Square*
Weetman Gareth	*7BR* *

Band 1

No5 Chambers
See profile on p.883

THE SET

No5 Chambers is one of the biggest sets on the Midland Circuit, with the strength and depth to cover a large variety of criminal cases. The set provides excellent counsel for all manner of criminal offences including serious violence and sexual offences but it has achieved particular renown for its white-collar crime work. Its advocates are said to display "enthusiasm, ability and a genuine passion for the law."

Client service: The senior practice manager of the crime team, Andrew Trotter, is described as "an extremely capable and efficient clerk, who is always willing to assist when required." He leads a "proactive clerking team that provides a high-class service."

SILKS

Christopher Hotten QC Prosecutes and defends across the circuit, undertaking a wide range of serious criminal cases. He is very well known for his expertise in homicide cases, and is also recognised for his expertise in criminal fraud cases.

Adrian Keeling QC Highly regarded for his prosecution and defence work in heavyweight criminal cases. He is regularly instructed in complex cases including drug cases, large-scale frauds, and multi-defendant murder cases. **Recent work:** Acted in R v Cosford and Falloon, a high-profile case where two prison officers were convicted of misconduct in public office.

Michael Burrows QC (see p.561) Has a broad criminal practice which covers offences such as sexual offences, drug conspiracies and frauds. He is highly regarded for his ability as both a prosecutor and a defence counsel.

Michael Duck QC Focuses on the prosecution and defence of serious organised crime. He is particularly noted for his expertise in complex and high-profile homicide and drug conspiracies. **Strengths:** "His empathy with the client is brilliant, as is his ability to grasp complex and unusual areas of law." **Recent work:** Acted for the defendant in R v Ward, a much-publicised case concerning the fatal stabbing of two Big Issue sellers in the centre of Birmingham at rush hour.

Mark Heywood QC (see p.626) Has a broad criminal practice, and is noted for his experience of murder and perjury cases. **Strengths:** "He is extremely thorough and has the forensic skills to scrutinise the evidence in detail."

David Mason QC Vastly experienced in all areas of serious crime, with regular instructions in cases relating to money laundering, drugs offences and sexual offences. **Strengths:** "He is approachable with the clients but a formidable advocate." **Recent work:** Acted in R v Dunkley, a gruesome case concerning the murder of a paraplegic former boxing champion by his carer.

Rex Tedd QC Has a varied practice that includes instructions in all major criminal and regulatory offences. Specific praise has been drawn from market commentators for his skill in engaging the jury.

JUNIORS

Phillip Bradley Has a particularly strong prosecution practice but has also been known to act for the defendant in serious criminal cases, including white-collar crime and sexual offences. **Recent work:** Acted for the defendants, alleged gang members, who set fire to a pub outside Birmingham city centre with the intention of luring the police away from rioting in the centre of the city.

Brian Dean Both prosecutes and defends a range of serious criminal cases, including gang-related crime, large drug conspiracies and high-value frauds. He also has a significant regulatory practice and is noted for his representation of the Police Federation of England and Wales. **Strengths:** "He is a robust advocate, who is very bright and works really hard." "Whilst being a strong and imposing figure, he also has great empathy and understanding."

Martin Liddiard Prosecutes and defends a vast range of criminal offences, including drugs conspiracies and violent crime. He also has considerable experience of handling firearms offences.

Harpreet Singh Sandhu Strongly commended by market commentators for his handling of serious sexual offences and violent criminal cases as well as regulatory and road traffic infractions. **Strengths:** "He is an exceptional speaker – his closing speeches are excellent and his speeches in mitigation are incredibly good." **Recent work:** Acted successfully for the defendant in R v Pollock, a murder case concerning a fatal stabbing. The defendant was acquitted of murder and convicted of manslaughter.

Talbir Singh An experienced barrister handling sexual offences, homicides and organised crime matters on a regular basis. He is a skilled advocate, and is noted for his successes on behalf of both the defence and the prosecution.

Michelle Heeley Defends and prosecutes in both the Magistrates' and Crown Courts. As a Grade 4 CPS prosecutor, she takes on complex frauds, cases of sexual abuse and large drugs supply cases. **Strengths:** "She is very bright, extremely enthusiastic and clearly dedicated to getting a good result for the client."

Tim Pole (see p.695) Receives regular instructions for both defence and prosecution in all areas of serious crime, from violent crime to fraud. He also has a strong regulatory practice, and acts in environmental offences. **Strengths:** "He is very commercially aware. He understands the commercial implications of charges against businesses."

St Philips Chambers
See profile on p.886

THE SET

With 12 silks and 47 juniors, St Philips Chambers has advocates prepared for all types of cases at all levels of call. Its members prosecute and defend on all major criminal offences, including homicide, sexual offences and business crime. It is also home to a significant regulatory practice, and advocates regularly take on cases of corporate manslaughter and other regulatory infringements.

Client service: The criminal clerking team is led by Phil Jones, whom sources describe as "a superb criminal clerk. He does everything you ask of him and is very informative." "His team goes the extra mile to rearrange hearings and makes sure that everything we need doing is covered."

SILKS

David Crigman QC (see p.581) Leads the Midland Circuit in terms of the complexity and profile of cases he undertakes. He prosecutes and defends in a practice that includes most heavyweight crime matters but is particularly focused on homicide cases. **Strengths:** "He has a devastating mind. He can cross-examine anyone and take them apart in a manner that is phenomenal to watch." **Recent work:** Acted for the defendant in R v Faure, a violent prison murder.

Richard Atkins QC (see p.539) Heads the set's criminal team and also sits as a Crown Court Recorder. He is a highly experienced advocate and is admired for his serious crime practice, which features both prosecution and defence work, in cases ranging from murder to fraud. **Strengths:** "He is a very intelligent and very sharp advocate." **Recent work:** Instructed in R v Howarth, a case concerning an alleged conspiracy to cheat the public revenue out of £1.2 million via income and corporation tax evasion.

Andrew Smith QC (see p.723) Undertakes a range of serious crime, fraud and complex business crime matters. His wider criminal practice includes homicide cases and money laundering offences. **Strengths:** "He is very clever and will find something that no one else picks up. His knowledge, skill and analytical ability are exceptional." **Recent work:** Instructed for the prosecution in R v Delves, a case concerning a father's manslaughter of his 9-week-old baby daughter through shaking.

Christopher Millington QC Praised for his expertise across a range of serious criminal cases, including drugs offences, sexual offences and financial crime. He is particularly highly regarded for his work in homicide cases, including gross negligence manslaughter. **Recent work:** Acted in R v Flynn, where he represented one of the eight defendants accused of the infamous Winson Green deaths during the Birmingham riots of 2011.

Francis Laird QC (see p.649) Well regarded for his heavyweight crime practice. He has significant experience in handling difficult fraud and money laundering offences, and receives regular instructions in homicide cases. **Strengths:** "He really fights hard for his clients."

Kristina Montgomery QC Focuses her practice on serious sexual offences and violent criminal cases as part of a wider criminal practice that strongly caters for privately paying clients. **Recent work:** Successfully defended in R v Perue, where an allegation of conspiracy to kill was made.

Andrew Lockhart QC Noted for his expertise in gang-related criminal cases, including murder and drugs offences. Instructing solicitors praise him for his exhaustive preparation of cases. **Recent work:** Engaged in R v Taft, a case concerning a gang-related nail-bombing campaign.

Jonas Hankin QC Prosecutes and defends across the full range of serious criminal offences. He is noted for his expertise in homicide cases which concern the deaths of minors. **Strengths:** "He is extremely talented, energetic and hard-working. He is an astute tactician and a tenacious cross-examiner, and is scrupulously fair." **Recent work:** Acted in R v Krezolek and Luczak, a high-profile case concerning the murder of 4-year-old Polish toddler Daniel Pelka by his mother and stepfather.

JUNIORS

Andrew Jackson (see p.636) Has a broad criminal practice covering a vast array of criminal offences. As a Grade 4 CPS prosecutor, he acts on cases of serious sexual assaults and violent crime. He also regularly appears on behalf of the defence. **Strengths:** "He is good with all areas of criminal defence work."

Naomi Gilchrist A former solicitor whose heavyweight crime practice is highlighted by solicitors due to her exemplary client care skills. She defends and prosecutes in cases ranging from white-collar crime to regulatory offences. **Strengths:** "She is a bright, enthusiastic and persuasive advocate." **Recent work:** Defended in R v Farooq & Others, representing Farooq, the head of a large-scale conspiracy to import heroin to the UK from Pakistan.

Heidi Kubik (see p.648) An expert in serious sexual offences. She also prosecutes and defends in a variety of serious violence and homicide cases. **Strengths:** "She is extremely able and can be trusted with anything, particularly cross-examinations of vulnerable witnesses in a sensitive manner." **Recent work:** Acted for the defendant in R v Blake, a case concerning the manslaughter of a pensioner in the course of a robbery. The defendant had long-standing mental health issues.

Ben Mills (see p.672) Has a criminal practice which encompasses offences including blackmail, money laundering and offences against the person. **Strengths:** "He is a very hard-working junior, who is very meticulous with his preparation." **Recent work:** Junior counsel for the defence in the case of R v Southerton and Shuttleworth. He acted for Southerton, who was jointly accused with his girlfriend of the murder of her 2-year-old son.

Malcolm Morse (see p.677) A Crown Court Recorder with a highly respected prosecution practice that includes frauds and sexual offences. **Strengths:** "He is an outstanding advocate and wordsmith; he is always a formidable opponent." "He is renowned for his forensic approach and his intellectual ability." **Recent work:** Instructed in R v Ali, a case concerning an illegal immigration scheme.

Band 2

36 Bedford Row
See profile on p.768

THE SET

36 Bedford Row's criminal team focuses on business crime, serious and organised crime, homicide and serious sexual offences. The set has a strong roster of silks, and its members both prosecute and defend across the Midland Circuit.

Client service: The criminal clerking team, led by Michelle Simpson, is described as "fantastic and very efficient."

SILKS

Amjad Malik QC Well regarded for a broad criminal practice focused on complex homicides and drugs conspiracies. He is particularly experienced in the area of white-collar crime. **Strengths:** "He is articulate and surgical in his advocacy, and the way he digests information and gives advice is amazing." "He prepares his cases fantastically thoroughly." **Recent work:** Instructed in R v Parker, a case concerning a murder committed in the course of an armed robbery.

John Lloyd-Jones QC (see p.657) Heads the set's criminal team. He defends and prosecutes on some of the highest-profile cases on the Midland Circuit, receiving regular instructions in business crime, fatal motoring incidents and murders. **Strengths:** "He works extremely hard and is particularly thorough, displaying forensic analysis." "His client care is outstanding and the strength of his preparation marks him out." **Recent work:** Acted in R v Padley, a death by dangerous driving case where the use of technical information from the car's airbag was contentious.

Adrienne Lucking QC (see p.658) A crime practitioner with particular expertise in serious sexual offences. She acts for both the defence and the prosecution, and draws particular praise for her ability to instil confidence in vulnerable clients. **Strengths:** "She had total command of the court, inspiring confidence from her knowledge and presentation of the case." **Recent work:** Prosecuted R v Pasierbek, a case concerning the brutal murder of an elderly woman by her son, who was also her carer.

Frances Oldham QC Widely acknowledged as one of the leading names on circuit when it comes to serious sexual offences and homicides. Sources extol her ability in cases where children and vulnerable witnesses are involved whilst also noting the authority she brings with her to the courtroom. **Strengths:** "She is a particularly engaging advocate, she gains the attention of the whole court, is very measured in her approach, and has judges and juries eating out of her hand."

Christopher Donnellan QC (see p.589) Has a broad practice which covers everything from road traffic offences and historic sexual offences to homicide and regulatory criminal offences. He is praised for his tactical ability, and acts for both prosecution and defence. **Strengths:** "His cross-examination is imaginative and incisive." **Recent work:** Acted in R v McMurray, defending the owner of a transport firm charged with manslaughter after one of the haulage drivers was killed in an RTA.

William Harbage QC (see p.619) Has a robust crime practice focused on serious criminal cases including kidnap, terrorism and financial crime. He is the joint head of chambers, and is particularly noted for his expertise in criminal cases with a medical element. **Strengths:** "He is a very calm advocate and a safe pair of hands." **Recent work:** Prosecuted in the high-profile murder case of R v Anxiang Du, concerning the murders of a family of four.

Felicity Gerry QC A vastly experienced advocate noted for her expertise in serious sexual offences, homicides and complex frauds. Commentators note her bold style of advocacy and her skill in dealing with young and vulnerable defendants. **Recent work:**

Acted on Ambrose Clifton's appeal against a conviction for the rape of a 6-year-old child who was too traumatised to give evidence.

7BR

See profile on p.772

THE SET

7BR is home to a number of excellent prosecution and defence barristers. This London-based set has a strong presence on the Midland Circuit, and takes significant instructions in business and regulatory crime, and also has advocates prepared to take on a wide range of criminal offences, including drugs offences, terrorism-related cases and violent offences against the person.

SILKS

Timothy Spencer QC An expert in acting for both prosecution and defence in areas including gang-related crime, firearms offences and terrorism cases, as well as the traditional silk staples of murder and high-value frauds.

JUNIORS

Adrian Langdale Specialises in heavyweight criminal matters, and is regularly engaged in cases concerning financial crime, serious organised crime and sexual offences. **Strengths:** "He is utterly tenacious, and gets exemplary end results with clear and focused thinking." **Recent work:** Successfully defended in R v Krali & Others, a case concerning a large-scale drug conspiracy.

Gareth Weetman (see p.748) A vastly experienced criminal practitioner whose work includes fraud, homicide and drugs supply cases. He prosecutes and defends across the Midland Circuit. **Strengths:** "He is extremely good, very thorough, his pleadings are excellent, his attention to detail is superb, and he's got a very nice demeanour in court and with clients."

Citadel Chambers

THE SET

Crime is one of Citadel Chambers' core focuses. Its experienced advocates cover a broad range of cases, including road traffic offences, firearms offences, serious sexual assaults and organised crime.

Client service: Senior clerk Rodney Neeld heads a clerking team that is "very reasonable and very easy to work with." Market commentators also note that the clerks are "very approachable and very efficient."

SILKS

Mark Wall QC Has a high-profile practice which covers serious organised crime matters as well as homicide, serious sexual offences, and white-collar crime. His considerable standing is underlined by his role as the leader of the Midland Circuit. **Strengths:** "He is an extremely approachable individual with a bright mind and clear, strong advocacy." "He is able to project the warm personality that juries like and he can do it without losing any of his gravitas."

Rachel Brand QC Defends and prosecutes in heavyweight crime matters, including firearms offences, serious sexual offences and armed robbery. She is particularly highlighted for her experience in representing vulnerable defendants, and those with a history of mental illness.

Andrew Fisher QC An experienced advocate who has leveraged the experience gained in his career in banking to develop a strong practice in business and financial crime. His wider criminal practice covers organised crime and gang-related offences, including drugs and homicide. **Strengths:** "He is an excellent advocate with an excellent client manner, who gets results."

JUNIORS

Timothy Hannam Has considerable experience of financial crime, and is frequently instructed on significant VAT frauds and money laundering cases. He prosecutes and defends across the circuit and is a standing counsel to the HMRC prosecutions office.

Gurdeep Garcha An experienced criminal practitioner recognised for his strong defence practice. He is noted for his work on drug importation cases and difficult frauds.

David Bright A criminal practitioner whose caseload covers a range of serious criminal and motoring offences. He regularly prosecutes and defends in cases of rape, serious frauds and serious offences against the person, including murder. **Strengths:** "He gets to grip with paperwork exceptionally well, making him a strong choice for the complex cases."

No.1 High Pavement

THE SET

No.1 High Pavement is an East Midlands-based set focused on providing high-quality criminal advocacy in complex cases ranging from drugs importation to serious violent crime. The set's members are adept in acting for both prosecution and defence.

SILKS

Peter Joyce QC Prosecutes and defends across a wide range of criminal cases, including serious sexual offences, fraud, drug cases and money laundering.

Michael Evans QC Highly rated for a consistently strong criminal practice. He regularly receives instructions in high-value frauds and complex homicide cases. **Strengths:** "He does violence, sex abuse and complex drugs cases very well." "He is a bright man and has a very personable manner. He is thus a great jury advocate."

Shaun Smith QC A highly experienced advocate whose prosecution and defence practice includes homicides, serious sexual offences and serious fraud. **Strengths:** "He is incredibly well prepared, thorough and very prompt with his advice."

Paul Mann QC Has a broad practice incorporating a mixture of serious criminal offences, including murder and sexual abuse, as well as road traffic offences and proceeds of crime cases.

JUNIORS

Robert Egbuna A popular advocate whose serious crime practice covers serious sexual offences, gang-related crime and white-collar criminal cases. **Strengths:** "He is a very likeable and approachable advocate, and that helps when engaging the juries." "He is an expert rape and sexual offences lawyer."

Adrian Reynolds Has a robust criminal practice focused on the defence of heavyweight crime matters. He handles offences ranging from murder to high-value financial crime, and is also noted for his substantial regulatory practice, where he regularly prosecutes on behalf of governmental agencies.

St Ives Chambers

See profile on p.885

THE SET

St Ives Chambers is home to 22 experienced criminal advocates who act on the full range of criminal offences, including fraud cases, serious sexual assaults and homicides.

JUNIORS

Peter Cooper (see p.578) Defends and prosecutes a broad range of criminal cases, including serious sexual offences, trafficking, drugs importation investigations and historic child sexual abuse cases. He is particularly highly regarded for his expertise in defending serious motoring offences such as death by dangerous driving. **Strengths:** "He is organised and efficient." **Recent work:** Acted in R v Card, a case concerning a conspiracy to import drugs. The case hinged on the use of telephone intercept evidence.

Kevin Saunders (see p.714) Defends clients in cases ranging from violent crime to serious sexual offences. He also conducts regulatory work, prosecuting and defending on matters including licensing and food infractions. **Recent work:** Acted in R v MacDonald, a case concerning a conspiracy to assist offenders in escaping custody.

David Jackson (see p.636) A Grade 4 CPS prosecutor who also has a robust defence practice. He is particularly experienced in handling crimes of dishonesty and sexual abuse cases. Commentators note his approachable manner and his personable character. **Strengths:** "He is a brilliant advocate; he can trip defendants up without being nasty and sneering." **Recent work:** Defended in R v Jones, where the defendant was charged with sexual assault on a teenager.

Band 3

KCH Garden Square

THE SET

Covering all courts from the Magistrates' Court to courts martial, this Nottingham-based set has a number of experienced advocates able to prosecute and defend on a range of criminal and regulatory matters. Particular areas of proficiency include RSPCA prosecutions, trading standards investigations and crimes of public disorder.

JUNIORS

Ian Way A distinguished advocate who both defends and prosecutes across a wide range of criminal offences. Particular areas of experience include drugs conspiracies, serious sexual offences and gun crime.

Mark Van der Zwart The head of chambers and a Grade 4 CPS prosecutor with particular expertise in cases of child deaths. His wider criminal practice sees regular instructions in cases of sexual offences and drugs importation cases. **Strengths:** "His communication is outstanding; nothing is too much trouble for him."

NORTH EASTERN

Crime North Eastern
Leading Sets
Band 1
No.6 Barristers Chambers
New Park Court Chambers
Band 2
Bank House Chambers
Sovereign Chambers *
Trinity Chambers *
Wilberforce Chambers
Leading Silks
Star individuals
Smith Robert *New Park Court Chambers*
Band 1
Greaney Paul *New Park Court Chambers* *
Swift Malcolm *Wilberforce Chambers*
Band 2
Hedworth Toby *Trinity Chambers* *
MacDonald Alistair *New Park Court Chambers*
Moulson Peter *No.6 Barristers Chambers*
Wright Richard *No.6 Barristers Chambers*
Band 3
Elvidge John *Dere Street Barristers (ORL)* ◊ *
Khan Tahir *Broadway House (ORL)* ◊
Stubbs Andrew *St Pauls Chambers (ORL)* ◊
Woodcock Robert *Dere Street Barristers (ORL)* ◊
Leading Juniors
Band 1
Drake Sophie *Broadway House (ORL)* ◊
Knox Christopher *Trinity Chambers* *
McKone Mark D *Sovereign Chambers* *
Murray Anil *Wilberforce Chambers*
Thackray John *Wilberforce Chambers*
Band 2
Brooke David *KBW (ORL)* ◊
de la Poer Nicholas *New Park Court Chambers*
Dixon David S *Sovereign Chambers*
Goddard Katherine L *Bank House Chambers*
Goldsack Ian *St Johns Buildings (ORL)* ◊
Hussain Gul Nawaz Mahboob *Bank House Chambers*
Makepeace Peter *Dere Street Barristers (ORL)* ◊ *
Melly Kama *No.6 Barristers Chambers*
Palmer Patrick *Sovereign Chambers*
Smith Andrew *Bank House Chambers*
Storey Tom *Zenith Chambers (ORL)* ◊
Band 3
Collins Michael *No.6 Barristers Chambers*
Horne James *Bank House Chambers*
Silverton Catherine *Sovereign Chambers* *
Smith Julian *New Park Court Chambers*
◊ (ORL) = Other Ranked Lawyer.
** Indicates set / individual with profile.*
Alphabetical order within each band. Band 1 is highest.

Band 1

No.6 Barristers Chambers

THE SET

No.6 Barristers Chambers' members act on all matters involving criminal law. With a substantial number of Grade 4 prosecutors, the set is renowned for handling complex and serious criminal cases. Expertise ranges from murder and child sex offences to large-scale fraud and drugs conspiracies.

Client service: Senior criminal clerk Richard Sadler runs a team regarded as "excellent" and "the benchmark for where other chambers should be aiming."

SILKS

Peter Moulson QC Handles a range of serious criminal work for prosecution and defence. He is well regarded for complex murder, drugs conspiracy and fraud cases. **Strengths:** "He is enormously hardworking, well prepared and in command of the detail; he is also superb at communicating with the client." **Recent work:** Advised an elite group of prosecutors in Nigeria on how to investigate and present counter-terrorism cases.

Richard Wright QC Defends and prosecutes the full range of serious crime. He is noted for his expertise in murder cases, particularly those with a joint enterprise element. **Strengths:** "After taking silk he has continued to deal with serious cases, applying his usual intellect and attention to detail." **Recent work:** Defended ex-army officer Jeremy Green, who was convicted of the murder of two women in York.

JUNIORS

Kama Melly Acts in heavyweight crime cases as prosecutor and defender. She is highly recommended in cases involving serious sexual offences, including child sex crimes. **Strengths:** "She has a very successful practice and a nice courtroom manner."

Michael Collins Advises clients in serious crime, road traffic offences and white-collar criminal matters. He regularly presents and defends in Police Disciplinary Tribunals. **Strengths:** "He has a good practice, a very good courtroom manner and a good personality."

New Park Court Chambers

THE SET

New Park Court Chambers maintains its standing as the pre-eminent criminal set in the North East. Members act for prosecution and defence on a wide range of criminal law matters. Cases include murder, sexual offences, serious violence and white-collar crime. A number of members are on the Attorney General's regulatory list and frequently prosecute for government departments.

SILKS

Robert Smith QC Prosecutes and defends the full range of criminal law cases. **Strengths:** "He is peerless; he would be head tutor on the silks masterclass." "He is an extremely busy silk – gold standard." **Recent work:** Prosecuted a nursery nurse, and her corporate employer, after the death of a minor on a slide. The corporate employer was successfully convicted under the Health and Safety Act.

Paul Greaney QC Handles serious, complex and high-profile criminal matters for both prosecution and defence. He is noted for his expertise in serious offences such as murder and drugs conspiracies. **Strengths:** "His attention to detail is second to none; he is very methodical in the way he approaches cases." "He's the best; if you can get him you're lucky because there will be no one else in the courtroom who knows the case as well as him." **Recent work:** Prosecuted Amanda Hutton, who was charged with starving her child to death and keeping his body in her bedroom.

Alistair MacDonald QC Defends and prosecutes in all criminal law matters, including murder and white-collar crime. He is recommended for complex cases with a scientific element due to his background as a biochemist. **Strengths:** "He is a very good and very persistent advocate." **Recent work:** Defended a joint enterprise murder where the victim was tortured and killed and his body burnt.

JUNIORS

Nicholas de la Poer Handles all criminal cases including blackmail, abduction and death by dangerous driving. His work extends to civil applications such as 'gang-bos' which are used to break up gang activity. **Strengths:** "He is a phenomenal barrister." **Recent work:** Acted for a man who abducted a teenage girl, leading to a national manhunt.

Julian Smith Acts as a Grade 4 prosecutor for serious sexual offences, and defends a multitude of criminal law matters. He is recommended for his knowledge in murder cases. **Strengths:** "He gets on well with solicitors; he really gets stuck in and rolls his sleeves up." **Recent work:** Prosecuted a complex murder and fraud case whereby the defendants then disposed of the deceased's estate.

Band 2

Bank House Chambers

THE SET

Bank House Chambers acts for clients in all aspects of criminal law. Its members defend and prosecute in high-profile serious crime cases. They offer additional expertise in regulatory offences and fraud.

Client service: "The clerks, led by Wayne Digby, are very helpful, they're generally approachable, and when the nominated barrister is not available they are always in a position to find an acceptable return."

JUNIORS

Andrew Smith Acts for clients on the full range of criminal law matters, including drugs conspiracies, manslaughter and fraud. He is recommended for his expertise in historic sex offences, particularly those with child witnesses. **Recent work:** Defended a client accused of a murder which involved issues of homophobia and disability discrimination.

Katherine Goddard Handles a variety of criminal law matters for the prosecution and the defence. She demonstrates particular expertise in cases concerning sex crimes and vulnerable individuals. **Recent work:** Defended a man accused of burglary who posed as a police officer to gain access to elderly people's homes.

Gul Nawaz Mahboob Hussain Advises clients on criminal law including robbery, conspiracy and manslaughter. He is noted for his capabilities in defending complex criminal matters such as organised crime. **Recent work:** Successfully appealed the sentence of a man accused of armed robbery, achieving a reduction in the sentence from 12 years to nine years.

James Horne Criminal defence barrister acting in historic sex offences, murder and serious violence. His capabilities extend to youth crimes and organised crime. **Recent work:** Defended maths teacher Mark Haywood, who was charged with sexual offences against students.

Sovereign Chambers

See profile on p.908

THE SET

Sovereign Chambers is recognised for its strength in criminal law matters. Its members prosecute and defend for privately and publicly funded individuals. Its barristers are recommended for serious and high-profile offences, particularly sex offences and violent offences.

Client service: "The clerks, led by Madeleine Gray, are very helpful – they always come back with answers to questions very quickly and they keep you up to date with issues around counsel."

JUNIORS

Mark McKone (see p.668) Handles the full remit of criminal law issues, including white-collar crime. He regularly prosecutes and defends on rape and serious sexual offences cases. **Strengths:** "He is efficient, with excellent attention to detail and an excellent manner towards clients." **Recent work:** Prosecuted a man accused of the rape of his stepchildren.

Patrick Palmer Acts for the prosecution and the defence in all criminal law matters. He has particular expertise in serious sex offences, murder and drugs conspiracy.

David Dixon Advises publicly and privately funded individuals in a wide range of criminal law cases. He demonstrates particular expertise in serious sexual offences and violent offences.

Catherine Silverton (see p.720) Prosecutes and defends on all criminal matters, most notably on sex crimes. She is recommended for her expertise in dealing with vulnerable and young defendants. **Strengths:** "She is very good with vulnerable people and sexual offences; she is also extremely thorough and has great attention to detail." **Recent work:** Defended Javed Robinson, who was accused of three counts of rape of a minor.

Trinity Chambers

See profile on p.927

THE SET

Trinity Chambers is highly regarded for its criminal law expertise. Members act for the prosecution and the defence in high-profile and complex criminal cases, in all courts including the appellate courts. They are recommended for their expertise in serious crime, regulatory crime and financial crime.

SILKS

Toby Hedworth QC (see p.624) Covers the entirety of criminal law. He is particularly noted for his expertise in drugs conspiracies, murders and gangland executions. **Strengths:** "He has superb advocacy and client care skills." **Recent work:** Defended Stephen Seddon, who was convicted of the execution-style killing of his parents.

JUNIORS

Christopher Knox Advises clients in complex criminal defence cases. He is recommended for his capabilities in serious sex offences and cases involving informants. **Recent work:** Successfully prosecuted members of a sex attack gang who groomed underage girls.

Wilberforce Chambers

THE SET

Wilberforce Chambers is recommended for its criminal law practice. The set offers expertise at all levels, from junior juniors to silks. These barristers act on cases ranging from complex crime to serious fraud. Members are praised for their jury advocacy skills.

SILKS

Malcolm Swift QC Acts for the prosecution and defence in high-profile and heavyweight criminal cases. He is noted for his expertise in murder, drugs conspiracies and complex fraud. **Strengths:** "He is a real jury advocate." "He is a heavy hitter."

JUNIORS

Anil Murray Handles a variety of criminal law matters for both the prosecution and the defence. He is a Grade 4 prosecutor for the CPS.

John Thackray Advises the defence and the prosecution on criminal law issues, including murder and trafficking. He regularly represents clients in the Crown Court and the Court of Appeal.

Other Ranked Lawyers

Tahir Khan QC (Broadway House) Handles the full remit of criminal law matters for the prosecution and the defence. His capabilities extend to serious and complex crime, including murder, drugs conspiracy and terrorism. **Strengths:** "He is a hard-working and very good advocate."

Sophie Drake (Broadway House) Advises clients on all criminal law matters. She has notable expertise in acting in sex crime cases and matters involving vulnerable individuals.

John Elvidge QC (see p.595) (Dere Street Barristers) Both prosecutes and defends a wide range of high-profile criminal matters, including murders, serious sexual offences and drugs conspiracies. He is the head of Dere Street Barristers, and also the leader of the North Eastern Circuit. **Recent work:** Acted in R v John Miller, a violent murder case where a father killed his partner and one of their daughters in the family home.

Robert Woodcock QC (Dere Street Barristers) Handles a variety of criminal law matters for the prosecution and the defence. He demonstrates particular expertise in murder and drugs conspiracy cases. **Strengths:** "He is an old-fashioned orator." **Recent work:** Secured the acquittal of Ronald Douglas, who was accused of the murder of a pensioner whose body was stored in a freezer while his bank accounts were emptied.

Peter Makepeace (see p.661) (Dere Street Barristers) Heads the set's criminal team. He acts on serious and complex crime including murder, drugs conspiracies and fraud. He is particularly recommended for complicated multiparty conspiracies. **Strengths:** "He takes time out to prepare; he works very thoroughly and is an engaging barrister who gets on with people." **Recent work:** Prosecuted seven individuals accused of a nationwide blackmail conspiracy, which lasted a year and concerned severe threats and multiple complaints.

David Brooke (KBW) Prosecutes and defends the full range of heavyweight crime. He is recommended for cases involving proceeds of crime, serious organised crime and environmental crime. **Strengths:** "He puts together excellent summaries and explains them to juries; he's an excellent advocate and argues his corner very well." "He is brilliant; forensic and thorough and extremely easy to work with." **Recent work:** Prosecuted a multiparty case for the Environment Agency concerning the illegal dumping of waste.

Ian Goldsack (St Johns Buildings) Acts for clients on a range of criminal law cases, including drugs conspiracy and high-value fraud. He is a Grade 4 prosecutor and a rape panel advocate. **Recent work:** Defended a man accused of supplying large quantities of Class A drugs.

Andrew Stubbs QC (St Pauls Chambers) Advises clients on serious crime matters. He is recommended for murder, historic sex offences and complex fraud cases.

Tom Storey (Zenith Chambers) Acts on firearms matters, violent crimes and health and safety prosecutions. He is recommended in cases with vulnerable or child defendants. **Strengths:** "He's very thorough, he communicates well and his advice is timely." **Recent work:** Defended a man charged with wounding with intent after he attacked a neighbour with a hunting knife.

NORTHERN

Crime Northern	
Leading Sets	
Band 1	
Deans Court Chambers *	
23 Essex Street *	
Exchange Chambers *	
7 Harrington St Chambers *	
Kenworthy's Chambers *	
Lincoln House Chambers *	
St Johns Buildings *	
Leading Silks	
Band 1	
Riordan Stephen	*7 Harrington St Chambers*
Wright Peter	*Lincoln House Chambers*
Band 2	
Denney Stuart	*Deans Court Chambers* [A]
Goddard Suzanne	*Lincoln House Chambers*
O'Byrne Andrew	*St Johns Buildings*
Samuels Jeffrey K	*St Johns Buildings*
Unsworth Ian	*7 Harrington St Chambers*
Band 3	
Blackwell Kate	*Lincoln House Chambers*
Fish David	*Deans Court Chambers* [A]
George Mark	*Garden Court North (ORL)* ◊
Johnson Nicholas	*7 Harrington St Chambers*
Pratt Richard	*7 Harrington St Chambers*
Weatherby Pete	*Garden Court North (ORL)* ◊
New Silks	
Myers Benjamin	*Exchange Chambers*
Leading Juniors	
Band 1	
Ainsworth Mark	*Exchange Chambers*
Curran Philip	*Lincoln House Chambers*
Grennan Barry	*Kenworthy's Chambers* [A]
Nolan Damian	*Exchange Chambers*
Simons Richard	*Lincoln House Chambers*
Band 2	
Berkson Simon	*Exchange Chambers*
Cassidy Patrick	*Kenworthy's Chambers* [A]
Harris Ian	*Exchange Chambers*
Harrison Keith	*St Johns Buildings*
McMeekin Ian	*Lincoln House Chambers*
Metcalfe Ian	*Cobden House Chambers (ORL)* ◊
Nuttall Andrew	*Lincoln House Chambers*
Parry Philip	*Exchange Chambers*
Roberts Lisa	*Lincoln House Chambers*
Savill Mark	*Deans Court Chambers* [A]
Thompson Patrick	*23 Essex Street*
Band 3	
Andrews Philip	*St Johns Buildings*
Arshad Farrhat	*Doughty Street Chambers (ORL)* ◊ [A]
Bennett Emma	*Exchange Chambers*
Duffy Jonathan	*7 Harrington St Chambers*
Farrow Adrian	*Exchange Chambers*
Grant Chudi	*Kenworthy's Chambers* [A]
Grattage Stephen	*Exchange Chambers*
Greenhalgh Jane	*23 Essex Street* *
Hart Joseph	*Deans Court Chambers* *
Judge Lisa	*Deans Court Chambers* [A]
Lavery Michael	*Exchange Chambers*
McKee Hugh	*23 Essex Street*
Penni Sally	*Kenworthy's Chambers* [A]
Riding Henry	*7 Harrington St Chambers*
Sastry Bob	*23 Essex Street*
Whitehurst Ian	*7 Harrington St Chambers*

◊ (ORL) = Other Ranked Lawyer.
[A] direct access (see p.11).

Band 1

Deans Court Chambers
See profile on p.915

THE SET

Manchester-based Deans Court Chambers maintains its standing as one of the pre-eminent sets for criminal work on the Northern Circuit. Its members act for the prosecution and the defence in all criminal law matters, including serious crime and complex fraud. They offer notable expertise in complex and high-profile cases.

Client service: "The clerks, led by Peter Kelly, keep the clients informed from the outset and have a very good diary system."

SILKS

Stuart Denney QC Advises clients on all aspects of general crime and regulatory work. His areas of specialism include serious sexual offences, homicide and prison law.

David Fish QC Handles a wide range of criminal law issues. He is regularly instructed in high-profile cases, including homicide, complex fraud and drugs conspiracies.

JUNIORS

Mark Savill Acts on all general crime matters. He is recommended for his expertise in defending sexual abuse allegations. **Strengths:** "His advocacy skills are outstanding."

Joseph Hart Acts primarily as a criminal defence advocate. He has considerable expertise in serious sexual offences, violent crimes and fraud. **Strengths:** "He has a practice that belies his relatively junior year of call – he punches well beyond his weight." **Recent work:** Successfully defended a man charged with inciting riots via Facebook.

Lisa Judge Handles a wide range of criminal law matters. She specialises in rape and sexual offences. **Strengths:** "She is an excellent advocate; she is down to earth and very approachable, and has good client care skills."

23 Essex Street
See profile on p.795

THE SET

23 Essex Street is recommended for the depth and breadth of its criminal law practice. Members act on heavyweight crime cases and are regularly seen in the Crown Court. They offer unrivalled expertise in handling multiparty serious crime and high-profile cases.

Client service: "Senior clerk Sean Hulston is excellent and runs a professional and efficient department."

JUNIORS

Patrick Thompson Acts for the defence in serious crime, fraud and regulatory matters. He is recommended for his knowledge of murder and violent offences. **Strengths:** "He is a very good jury advocate who charms the socks off people." "He is a great jury man, easy-going with clients and easy to work with." **Recent work:** Defended Cornelius Brown, who was charged with murder after stabbing his ex-girlfriend over 70 times.

Jane Greenhalgh (see p.615) Handles general crime matters for both the prosecution and the defence. Her expertise extends to multiparty conspiracies and organised crime. **Strengths:** "She is really pleasant with clients, and there is a real dialogue with her and solicitors; she's easy to work with, down to earth and she prepares masterfully." **Recent work:** Defended a man in a multi-handed drugs conspiracy involving concealing Class A drugs in the wheels of HGV trailers.

Hugh McKee Acts for the prosecution and the defence on criminal law issues. He regularly acts on cases involving carousel fraud, serious violence and drugs conspiracy. **Strengths:** "His preparation and presentation are excellent and he is also exceptionally amenable and easy to approach in relation to instructions and witnesses." "He is very bright and very good with clients, and has a very strong presence in court." **Recent work:** Defended a man accused of grievous bodily harm after he stamped on the victim's head causing permanent brain damage.

Bob Sastry Defends and prosecutes serious crime. He is noted for his expertise in drugs conspiracy cases and sexual assault matters. **Strengths:** "He has a very easy-going personality but he is never asked a question that he can't answer." "His paperwork is really good, he has good attention to detail and his cross-examination is extremely thorough." **Recent work:** Instructed in R v Mohammed Zafar Yasin, acting for the main defendant accused of importing heroin by post.

Exchange Chambers
See profile on p.910

THE SET

Exchange Chambers is one of the strongest sets on the Northern Circuit. It offers unrivalled expertise at all levels, with members acting for the prosecution and the defence on the full spectrum of criminal law. Its barristers are renowned for their work on serious and complex crime, including murder, trafficking, sexual offences and fraud.

Client service: "Their systems and procedures are exceptional; they're very professional and their administration is fantastic."

SILKS

Benjamin Myers QC Advises clients on general crime, with cases ranging from murder to high-value confiscation under the Proceeds of Crime Act. He is recommended for complex murder cases and appeals. **Strengths:** "He is a very impressive counsel who can handle difficult clients in very serious cases extremely well." **Recent work:** Acted on a complex joint enterprise case concerning a murder in a nightclub.

JUNIORS

Damian Nolan Represents The Crown and the defence in serious crime cases. He is recommended in cases where sensitivity is required, such as youth crimes or disputes between different cultural communities. **Strengths:** "He combines intellectual ability and interpersonal skills, and he's also very good in court." "He is a strong advocate who takes a firm approach with clients but is also very approachable and easy to work with."

Mark Ainsworth Acts as a criminal defence barrister and a Grade 4 prosecutor. He prosecutes rape and sexual offences across the Northern Circuit.

Ian Harris Regularly acts as lead junior in complex criminal cases. He is recommended for matters involving drugs conspiracies and murder. **Strengths:** "He is a senior junior who comes with the gravitas you would expect. He's not fazed by any particular issue and has a good eye for detail." "He is thorough and conscientious, presents brilliantly in court, and has a lovely way with the jury." **Recent work:** Defended a severely disabled individual accused of murder.

Simon Berkson Handles criminal defence and prosecution work. He is recommended for serious crime such as murder and sexual offences. **Recent work:** Successfully defended a man accused of murder where the body of the alleged deceased was never discovered.

Stephen Grattage Acts for the prosecution and the defence in serious sexual offences and white-collar crime matters. He is also noted for his expertise in computer-related crime. **Strengths:** "He is dedicated and driven, with an ability beyond his call." "He is renowned for his care and attention to detail." **Recent work:** Successfully defended a man accused of the rape of his girlfriend.

Philip Parry Defends and prosecutes the full range of criminal law matters. He regularly acts on violent crimes, sexual offences and complex fraud. **Strengths:** "He's excellent, very clear in his advice and very personable." "Tactically he's very good and he's very good on his feet as well; he's top-notch at dealing with serious issues." **Recent work:** Successfully acted as the sole defence counsel in the appeal against Lynette Banfield's murder conviction.

Emma Bennett Acts for The Crown and the defence on all criminal law cases, including very high cost case work. She is recommended for complex and high-value fraud. **Strengths:** "A go-to barrister, she loves a scrap and she usually wins!" **Recent work:** Secured an acquittal for George Walker, who was accused of a £20 million mortgage fraud.

Michael Lavery Handles the full range of heavyweight criminal law matters. His expertise extends to complex crime, including drugs conspiracies and murder. **Strengths:** "He is somebody who deals with things quickly; he's very efficient and gives good strong advice from the outset." "He is very professional, he goes over and above for the call of duty for the client, and he's very sensitive with the client, which is important." **Recent work:** Represented Dale Cregan's mother, Anita, who was accused of aiding and abetting misconduct in public office.

Adrian Farrow Instructed on behalf of the defence and the prosecution in a wide range of criminal cases. He is particularly experienced in murder, drugs and serious sexual offences matters.

7 Harrington St Chambers

See profile on p.912

THE SET

7 Harrington St maintains its ranking as one of the leading criminal law sets on the Northern Circuit. Its barristers offer universally high-calibre advocacy at all levels of seniority for the prosecution and the defence in complex and high-profile crime matters. Members regularly act on murder, drugs conspiracy and violent crimes.

SILKS

Stephen Riordan QC Prosecutes and defends serious, heavyweight crime. He is recommended for high-profile criminal cases ranging from murder to misconduct in public office. **Strengths:** "Juries like him. He's very good, he knows the law and he's articulate – you would be happy with him on your side." **Recent work:** Defended a drug dealer accused of beating and stabbing one of his underlings to death.

Richard Pratt QC Handles serious crime matters for the defence and the prosecution. He demonstrates particular expertise in high-profile and sensitive criminal law cases. **Recent work:** Defended a man accused of playing a part in the masked fatal shooting of a businessman.

Ian Unsworth QC Advises on a variety of criminal law matters for the defence and the prosecution, acting for regulatory bodies, prosecuting agencies, police forces and professional sportsmen. He is recommended for serious and complex cases. **Strengths:** "He is very thorough, very well prepared, and puts up a bloody good fight in court."

Nicholas Johnson QC An experienced criminal specialist noted for his expertise in homicide cases and large-scale conspiracies to import or distribute drugs. **Recent work:** Acted for a defendant accused of murdering another man who had suffered a brain haemorrhage following an unprovoked assault.

JUNIORS

Henry Riding Acts for the prosecution and the defence across the full remit of general crime matters. He is particularly adroit in handling high-profile murder cases. **Recent work:** Acted on the prosecution of Iftikhar Ahmed and Farzana Ahmed for the high-profile murder of their daughter Shafilea.

Ian Whitehurst Acts as a Grade 4 prosecutor and criminal defence advocate. He specialises in cases concerning sexual offences and attempted murder. **Strengths:** "He is a real fighter but smart with it." **Recent work:** Defended a woman accused of the attempted murder of her husband's pregnant ex-lover.

Jonathan Duffy Focuses primarily on defending cases in both the Crown Court and Court of Appeal. His experience covers cases relating to drug importation and distribution, serious sexual offences and homicides. **Recent work:** Successfully represented a defendant who had been charged with a murder committed in the course of a burglary at the home of an elderly individual.

Kenworthy's Chambers

See profile on p.917

THE SET

Kenworthy's Chambers is recommended for the breadth of its criminal law practice. Members act for the CPS and the defence on serious and complex crime, with cases ranging from murder to complex fraud operations. Its barristers are known for their committed appeals team, which regularly advises clients after conviction and sentence.

JUNIORS

Barry Grennan Handles serious and complex crime as well as regulatory matters and claims against the police. He is recommended for high-profile murder cases and sexual offences. **Recent work:** Defended clients accused of a gangland murder at a nightclub in Rochdale.

Patrick Cassidy Acts on a wide range of criminal law matters. He is noted for his expertise in gangland crime, drugs conspiracies and gross negligent manslaughter.

Chudi Grant Act for both The Crown and the defence on the full spectrum of criminal law issues. His specialisms include murder, drugs conspiracies and sexual offences, and he is particularly noted for his expertise in multi-handed cases.

Sally Penni Prosecutes and defends violent crimes and serious sexual offences. She specialises in complex and sensitive issues such as incest, male rape and gang crime. **Recent work:** Defended a man accused of playing a part in a multi-handed robbery.

Lincoln House Chambers

See profile on p.920

THE SET

Lincoln House Chambers' criminal advocates offer experienced representation for both the prosecution and the defence. Members act on the full remit of general crime, including murder, sexual offences and fraud. Its barristers are highly regarded for gangland crimes and terrorism cases.

Client service: David Wright's team attracts praise from market sources, who comment that "it is a great set that gives great service."

SILKS

Kate Blackwell QC Prosecutes and defends serious and white-collar criminal cases. She is recommended for her expertise in murder cases, in particular those with a multiparty element. **Strengths:** "She is an absolutely fantastic advocate."

Peter Wright QC Acts for the prosecution and defence in complex and serious criminal cases. He is noted for his expertise in murder and terrorism matters, having spent a number of years prosecuting terrorism cases for the Treasury. **Strengths:** "His preparation is always meticulous, his client manner is very assured without being arrogant, and his advocacy skills are second to none." "A QC of the highest calibre."

Suzanne Goddard QC Advises on serious criminal matters for the prosecution and the defence. She regularly acts on complex cases, including contract killings and gangland murders. **Strengths:** "She's well organised, has good client relationships and is a good advocate." "She is one of those people who can weigh you up with a stare and she very quickly gets to grips with what the case is about."

JUNIORS

Philip Curran Handles criminal defence and prosecution work. He is noted for his work prosecuting serious and high-profile cases such as attempted murders and gangland murders.

Richard Simons Primarily defends serious and organised criminal cases. He is highly regarded for his knowledge of gangland executions. **Strengths:** "He is brilliant before a jury and is an excellent tactician."

Andrew Nuttall A specialist in fraud and serious crime who acts for both The Crown and the defence. He is recommended for his expertise in cases relating to gangland crimes. **Strengths:** "He is hugely experienced and has a superb manner with lay clients." "He has an ability to find the central issues in complex matters where others might miss the point altogether."

Ian McMeekin Acts for clients on the full scope of criminal law matters. He is noted for his expertise in drugs offences, organised crime and homicides.

Lisa Roberts Handles serious crime and complex fraud for both the prosecution and the defence. She regularly acts for the Police Federation in the Crown

Court. **Strengths:** "She is a tremendous lawyer who is a silk in waiting."

St Johns Buildings

See profile on p.921

THE SET

St Johns Buildings is one of the Northern Circuit's pre-eminent sets. Its members regularly act on some of the most serious cases in the Crown Court for both The Crown and the defence. Its members are particularly noted for their expertise in high-profile murder cases.

Client service: "The clerks, led by Mark Heald, are excellent; they bend over backwards to make sure we get what we want."

SILKS

Jeffrey Samuels QC Handles the full breadth of criminal law and regulatory work. He is noted for his knowledge of high-profile murder cases.

Andrew O'Byrne QC The leader of the Northern Circuit, he defends and prosecutes on complex serious crime matters. He demonstrates particular expertise in murder and sex offences. **Strengths:** "He is the circuit leader. He's formidable – an excellent advocate with great judgement." "He's not only meticulously well organised and prepared, but also incredibly personable and very easy to work with." **Recent work:** Secured a life sentence in prosecuting a man accused of the Chester Park murder.

JUNIORS

Keith Harrison Prosecutes and defends the full range of general and serious crime matters. He regularly acts on cases involving drugs conspiracies and violent crimes. **Recent work:** Defended in one of Merseyside's biggest drug gang trials. The case involved an extensive police investigation and millions of pounds' worth of drugs.

Philip Andrews Handles serious crime work for the defence. He is recommended in cases involving serious sexual offences which include kidnapping. **Strengths:** "Literally nothing is too much trouble for him, and his ability in court is second to none." "He is masterful with a jury." **Recent work:** Successfully defended a taxi driver accused of detaining and sexually assaulting a female passenger.

Other Ranked Lawyers

Ian Metcalfe (Cobden House Chambers) Heads the criminal department at Cobden House Chambers. His expertise covers murder, sexual assault and violent crimes. **Strengths:** "He has a fantastic mastery of a brief, knowledge of the law and rapport with clients."

Farrhat Arshad (Doughty Street Chambers) Handles the full range of serious crime and complex fraud matters. She specialises in sexual offences, particularly historic sex offences.

Mark George QC (Garden Court North) Acts for clients on the full range of general crime work. He regularly acts on cases involving sexual offences and murder. **Strengths:** "He is very thorough and prepared to fight for the client."

Pete Weatherby QC (Garden Court North) A criminal defence advocate acting on cases ranging from murder to fraud. He is noted for his strong appellate practice and for his expertise in miscarriage of justice cases. **Strengths:** "He has a good way with clients and inspires confidence with his incisive intelligence."

SOUTH EASTERN

Crime South Eastern
Leading Sets
Band 1
Octagon House Chambers
One Paper Buildings *
Red Lion Chambers
Westgate Chambers
Leading Silks
Band 1
Khalil Karim *One Paper Buildings* *
Band 2
Christie Richard *187 Fleet Street (ORL)* ◊ *
Coffey John *3 Temple Gardens (ORL)* ◊ *
Laws Eleanor *6 Pump Court (ORL)* ◊ [A] *
Band 3
Barraclough Richard *6 Pump Court (ORL)* ◊ [A]
Power Lewis *Lamb Building (ORL)* ◊ *
Saxby Oliver *6 Pump Court (ORL)* ◊ [A]
Spence Simon *Red Lion Chambers* *
New Silks
Gerry Felicity *36 Bedford Row (ORL)* ◊
◊ (ORL) = Other Ranked Lawyer.
[A] direct access (see p.11).
* Indicates set / individual with profile.

Crime South Eastern
Leading Juniors
Band 1
Clare Michael *Octagon House Chambers*
Meredith Philip *Westgate Chambers*
Band 2
Barton Richard *Westgate Chambers*
Carter William *One Paper Buildings* *
Cherrill Beverly *Westgate Chambers*
Hamblin Nicholas *Westgate Chambers*
James Ian *Octagon House Chambers*
Lamb Jeffrey *Westgate Chambers*
Morgans John *Octagon House Chambers*
Shay Stephen *23 Essex Street (ORL)* ◊
Thompson Andrew *Red Lion Chambers* *
Upton Rebecca *Sussex Chambers (ORL)* ◊
Band 3
Ayers Guy *Octagon House Chambers*
Daly Nigel *Cornwall Street Chambers (ORL)* ◊
Dyble Steven *Red Lion Chambers* *
Gibbs Georgina *36 Bedford Row (ORL)* ◊ *
Jenkins Rowan *Crown Office Row (ORL)* ◊
Magee Mike *Fenners Chambers (ORL)* ◊
Matthews Claire *One Paper Buildings* *
O'Higgins John *6 Pump Court (ORL)* ◊
Perrins Gregory *One Paper Buildings* *
Rafferty Angela *One Paper Buildings* *
Sadler Rhiannon *9 Bedford Row (ORL)* ◊ *
Shaw Andrew *One Paper Buildings* *
Spence Stephen *One Paper Buildings* *
Stephens Andrew *Westgate Chambers*
Taylor Simon *6 Pump Court (ORL)* ◊
Band 4
Brady Jane *Cornwall Street Chambers (ORL)* ◊ *
Edwards Jennifer *Cornwall Street Chambers (ORL)* ◊
Farmer John *One Paper Buildings* *
Gardner Alan *23 Essex Street (ORL)* ◊
Gowen Matthew *Red Lion Chambers* *
Gray Jennifer *Lamb Building (ORL)* ◊
James Rhodri *Lamb Building (ORL)* ◊
Krolick Ivan *Lamb Building (ORL)* ◊
Lindop Sarah *Westgate Chambers*
Paxton Chris *Red Lion Chambers* *
Up-and-coming individuals
Harris Caroline *1 King's Bench Walk (ORL)* ◊ *

Band 1

Octagon House Chambers

THE SET

Based in Norwich, Octagon House is home to a team of high-quality advocates who command the respect of both their peers and the Bench. They prosecute and defend across the full range of criminal offences.

JUNIORS

Michael Clare A veteran advocate whose practice covers the full range of criminal offences. **Strengths:** "He is very charming and captivates the judges and juries." "He has a wealth of experience and is very impressive."

Ian James Has a substantial crime practice supplemented by vast experience in trading standards prosecutions, regulatory frauds and large-scale historic sexual abuse cases. **Strengths:** "He is a tough advocate. He's one of the few barristers who is requested by the clients before we have even told them about him."

John Morgans Has prosecuted and defended cases across the full range of criminal matters, although he is particularly noted for his expertise in homicides. **Strengths:** "He has excellent interpersonal skills. He is able to put clients at ease." "He thinks on his feet and is thus very effective in court."

Guy Ayers Sits as a recorder in addition to operating a busy prosecution and defence practice. His expertise covers a wide range of criminal law matters, from fraud to firearms offences.

One Paper Buildings

See profile on p.841

THE SET

An East Anglia-based set that prosecutes and defends on criminal offences ranging from drugs, homicides and serious sexual offences to motoring and regulatory crime matters. Members have the breadth and depth of expertise to ensure coverage in all areas of criminal law.

Client service: Mark Cornell's clerking team "are

very personable and will always try to accommodate the needs of those instructing them."

SILKS

Karim Khalil QC (see p.645) Has a presence and authority enhanced by his time sitting as a recorder at the Old Bailey. His highly respected practice encompasses the full range of serious criminal offences, including fraud and murder. He both prosecutes and defends. **Recent work:** Instructed for the defence of a foreign national charged with murder and rape.

JUNIORS

William Carter (see p.566) A Grade 4 CPS prosecutor who also acts for the defence. He acts on a wide range of criminal cases, from fraud to historic sex abuse allegations. **Strengths:** "He has a brilliant mind and is meticulous in his trial preparation." "He is incredibly thorough and his ability to deal with large volumes of complex paperwork is second to none." **Recent work:** Prosecuted a defendant alleged to have manufactured machine guns for sale on the 'deep web'.

Claire Matthews (see p.665) Has a broad general crime practice, and is particularly highly regarded for her expertise on cases concerning serious sexual offences. She prosecutes and defends across the whole of the South Eastern Circuit. **Strengths:** "She is extremely intelligent, very good with the clients and very tactically astute." **Recent work:** Prosecuted a Military Police Officer for the abduction and rape of a 12-year-old girl, and defended in a case of armed robbery of a petrol station.

Gregory Perrins (see p.691) A Grade 4 CPS prosecutor whose mixed practice covers the most serious criminal offences across the circuit. He both prosecutes and defends. **Strengths:** "He is very good at putting clients at ease and is meticulous in his preparation work." **Recent work:** Defended the former chief executive of a high-profile charity from fraud allegations.

Angela Rafferty (see p.702) Highly regarded in the area of serious crime, noted for her adroit handling of both prosecution and defence. **Strengths:** "She has an excellent knowledge of the law and is tactically brilliant." **Recent work:** Instructions include a joint enterprise murder of a homeless man, allegations of multi-handed child prostitution and the murder and rape of a woman involving complex pathological evidence.

Stephen Spence (see p.726) Has a wide-ranging practice that includes serious crime. He is a former RAF pilot and has developed a specialist aviation regulatory practice. **Recent work:** Has acted in defence of an assistant bank manager charged with theft, in defence of a priest accused of abusing children, and in a modern day slavery trial.

John Farmer (see p.598) A specialist serious crime practitioner with considerable experience of proceeds of crime cases and regulatory offences. He both prosecutes and defends across the circuit. **Recent work:** Instructions include a large multi-handed kidnap and a false imprisonment case.

Andrew Shaw (see p.718) Acts for both prosecution and defence on a wide range of criminal cases, including serious sexual offences, drug trafficking and homicides. **Recent work:** Acted for the defence in a case concerning a major conspiracy to supply class A drugs and money laundering.

Red Lion Chambers

THE SET

Red Lion Chambers has vastly experienced barristers in all areas of criminal law. From its Chelmsford base, the set's barristers both prosecute and defend on a range of complex cases, including high-profile frauds and murders. It is one of the largest sets on circuit, and instructing solicitors note that it always has quality advocates ready to take on a challenging case.

SILKS

Simon Spence QC (see p.726) Defends and prosecutes high-profile serious crime cases. His practice covers the full spectrum of criminal cases, including serious sexual offences, murders and drugs conspiracies. **Recent work:** Defended in a multi-handed murder case where the victim was stabbed, beaten and hit by a car.

JUNIORS

Andrew Thompson (see p.736) Principally recognised for his specialist focus on cases involving serious sexual offences, although his practice does encompass a range of other serious criminal cases, including drugs importation. **Strengths:** "He has a wealth of experience and is a very impressive advocate." **Recent work:** Acted in the case of R v Lourenz, Luitjen and Others, which concerned the importation of 80kg of Class A drugs.

Steven Dyble (see p.592) Retains a strong presence on the South Eastern Circuit. He defends in cases covering homicide, fraud and sexual offences, but has the experience to handle a wider range of criminal cases. **Strengths:** "He is a strong character, forthright and fierce in court." **Recent work:** Instructed in a drugs conspiracy case involving a large quantity of Class A drugs, believed to possess a street value of £3 million.

Chris Paxton (see p.690) Defends and prosecutes in large-scale frauds, homicides and drugs cases. His criminal practice is supplemented by a strong regulatory practice focused on the road transport and haulage sector. **Strengths:** "He is technically brilliant and will work tirelessly throughout the case. He is an excellent advocate and an absolutely superb barrister." **Recent work:** Acted in R v Fletcher, a death by dangerous driving case involving a suspect who was under the influence of drugs.

Matthew Gowen (see p.613) A general crime specialist whose practice covers the full range of serious criminal and regulatory offences. He acts for both prosecution and defence. **Strengths:** "The breadth of work he can do is exceptional." "He is the type of barrister who clients are really refreshed to meet."

Westgate Chambers

THE SET

From its Lewes base, Westgate Chambers provides counsel for both prosecution and defence across Surrey and Sussex. Its members are recognised for having the depth of expertise to cater for the full range of criminal work, including serious sexual offences and fraud.

JUNIORS

Philip Meredith A Grade 4 CPS prosecutor who has also acted for the defence. He is instructed on a range of cases, including murders, drugs conspiracies, rape and fraud. **Strengths:** "He has a staggering amount of experience and thus an assured touch in court." "He is a very good jury advocate and very good at cross-examination."

Richard Barton Takes on high-profile heavyweight crime cases, and draws praise from market commentators for his prosecution work. **Recent work:** Prosecuted R v Forrest, a high-profile case where a teacher abducted a teenage girl before being caught in Bordeaux.

Beverley Cherrill Has a wide practice encompassing theft, murder and drugs conspiracies, although she is best recognised for her expertise in serious sexual offences. **Strengths:** "Her style is charming and well measured." "Cross-examination is a difficult art and she judges it very well."

Nicholas Hamblin A recognised fraud expert with tremendous experience of both prosecuting and defending cases in areas ranging from firearms offences to sexual offences. **Strengths:** "He is meticulous, and a good advocate for complex work." **Recent work:** Defended in the case of R v Brown, concerning more than 170 women who had been trafficked to the UK to work in the sex trade.

Jeffrey Lamb The joint head of Westgate Chambers. His practice in heavyweight crime commands the respect of market commentators, who note his fraud expertise as a particular highlight. **Recent work:** Acted in a murder case, where an 81-year-old was killed in the course of a burglary.

Andrew Stephens A specialist defence barrister whose practice covers a variety of criminal cases, ranging from sexual offences to conspiracy to defraud. His strong work ethic draws praise from instructing solicitors.

Sarah Lindop Held in high regard for her work for both prosecution and defence, particularly on serious sexual offences.

Other Ranked Lawyers

Rhiannon Sadler (see p.713) (9 Bedford Row) Receives instructions from both defence and prosecution across the full range of criminal offences, including serious frauds. **Strengths:** "She is hardworking, diligent and very intelligent." "She is very personable and juries believe that they can trust her."

Felicity Gerry QC (36 Bedford Row) A noted expert in serious sexual offences who is also regularly instructed in complex homicide and fraud cases. **Recent work:** Prosecuted in the appeal of Ambrose Clifton, a complex case concerning the rape of a six-year-old child who was unable to give evidence in court.

Georgina Gibbs (see p.607) (36 Bedford Row) Focuses her practice on serious sexual offences, including rape and child abuse cases. **Strengths:** "She is a fabulous advocate. She is completely unflustered and unfazed by the greatest difficulties that can arise on cases."

Jennifer Edwards (Cornwall Street Chambers) Predominantly acts for defendants in cases relating to serious sexual offences. **Strengths:** "She is an exceptional cross-examiner; she has a subtle and gentle style that slowly and surely draws out the inconsistencies in testimony."

Nigel Daly (Cornwall Street Chambers) Covers a wide range of heavyweight crime cases, including serious sexual offences and homicides. **Strengths:** "He is absolutely thorough and provides fantastic written advice."

Jane Brady (see p.555) (Cornwall Street Chambers) Has a broad criminal practice that encompasses everything from drugs conspiracies and fraud cases to serious violent crimes and proceeds of crime litigation. **Strengths:** "She is an excellent barrister, extremely hard-working. She really goes the extra mile, and digs around in the unused material to find the details that the other advocates would miss."

Rowan Jenkins (Crown Office Row) Prosecutes and defends in a range of criminal and regulatory crime cases. He is known as a specialist in serious sexual offences, including rape. **Strengths:** "He is thoroughly reliable and very confident, and he provides a high level of client service." "He is extremely conscientious and excellent on his feet in court." **Recent work:** Defended in R v Sellu, acting on behalf of a surgeon accused of gross negligence manslaughter.

Stephen Shay (23 Essex Street) Focuses his practice on complex crime cases, including homicide, organised crime, serious sexual offences and domestic extremism. **Strengths:** "He just has a profoundly good knowledge of law." "He is extremely fair and conducts himself well in court."

Alan Gardner (23 Essex Street) Prosecutes and defends across the full spectrum of criminal cases, and is particularly noted for his expertise in cases involving serious sexual offences. **Strengths:** "He is tall and imposing but gentle in his delivery; he has one of those personas that means the juries in trials really listen to him."

Mike Magee (Fenners Chambers) Serious crime specialist who is noted for his expertise in serious violent crimes. He has also been instructed in cases involving charges of indecent assault and other serious sexual offences, including rape. **Strengths:** "He is very good with clients, excellent on his feet in court, and genuinely quite fun to work with."

Richard Christie QC (see p.571) (187 Fleet Street) A veteran criminal silk whose practice encompasses a wide range of cases, including drugs importation, gang-related murder and fraud.

Caroline Harris (see p.620) (1 King's Bench Walk) A criminal all-rounder whose experience covers a vast range of offences, including assaults, road traffic offences and fraud. **Strengths:** "She is good with the clients, and a hugely safe pair of hands."

Lewis Power QC (see p.698) (Lamb Building) Focuses on defending serious criminal cases such as murders, high-value frauds, forced labour and serious sexual offences. **Strengths:** "He is very impressive with the clients. They like the fact that he is tactically strong and very robust in his advocacy." **Recent work:** Defended a multi-handed gang murder at the Old Bailey.

Jennifer Gray (Lamb Building) Widely praised for her sensitive handling of cases involving vulnerable clients. Her superb client care skills ensure she is highly recommended for rape and serious sexual offences cases. **Strengths:** "She is very astute when working out the nature of the difficulty the client has." "She has a lot of experience in handling cases where the client has a mental disorder. She is a top choice in such cases."

Rhodri James (Lamb Building) Has a diverse practice covering a broad range of criminal cases. He has particular expertise in handling cases relating to smuggling, violent disorder and aggravated burglary.

Ivan Krolick (Lamb Building) Has significant experience of acting for financial institutions, which has translated into a significant white-collar crime practice. He is noted for his expertise in fraud and money laundering cases, and has also taken on cases relating to terrorism and corruption.

Eleanor Laws QC (see p.652) (6 Pump Court) Renowned for her expertise in cases involving serious sexual offences. Her broader criminal practice includes serious violent crime and drugs importation cases. **Strengths:** "She is very well prepared and a very good strategist." "She has a calm manner that radiates power." **Recent work:** Defended in R v Presley, a case concerning a young man murdered in a gang-related stabbing.

Richard Barraclough QC (6 Pump Court) Has a broad practice covering some high-profile homicides, serious violent crimes and serious sexual offences. **Strengths:** "He has a very commanding presence in court that the jury could not fail to notice." "He is an outstanding barrister. He makes clients believe that he is on their side and that he is there for them." **Recent work:** Has defended in the complex historic sex abuse cases of R v Etheridge and R v Breedon.

Oliver Saxby QC (6 Pump Court) Has a strong reputation for acting in high-profile serious crimes, in particular acting for the defence in homicide cases. He has also been instructed on a number of high-profile serious sexual offences and drug-related crimes. **Strengths:** "He gets right to the heart of the case at a very early stage, allowing us to instruct the right experts immediately." "He is calm, succinct and quietly persuasive." **Recent work:** Defended in R v Farrow, a complex and high-profile double murder case.

John O'Higgins (6 Pump Court) Has particular expertise in sexual assault and rape proceedings, and is also regularly instructed in serious violence and homicide cases as well as fraud prosecutions. **Strengths:** "He is an intense advocate who certainly gets the jury's attention." "He is an individual with acute intelligence, who is passionately committed to his clients and works incredibly hard for them." **Recent work:** Prosecuted in the case of R v Rawling, where complex medical evidence was adduced to explain serious injuries found on a month-old baby.

Simon Taylor (6 Pump Court) Both defends and prosecutes across the full range of criminal offences. He is noted for his expertise in sexual offences and offences against the person, and also undertakes fraud and money laundering cases. **Strengths:** "He has an excellent client manner that bears dividends with difficult and vulnerable clients." "He provides detailed timely advice, with clear and realistic instructions." **Recent work:** Prosecuted in the evidentially complex murder case of R v H & P.

Rebecca Upton (Sussex Chambers) A Grade 3 CPS prosecutor recognised for her specialist defence practice, which includes instructions in cases concerning serious sexual assaults and rapes, GBH, homicide and fraud. She has considerable experience of dealing with vulnerable clients, particularly where the defendants have learning difficulties and other mental health issues. **Recent work:** Defended a man charged with GBH for branding his partner.

John Coffey QC (see p.574) (3 Temple Gardens) Has a practice encompassing the full range of serious criminal offences, including fraud and homicide cases. Market commentators praise him for his ability to command the attention of the jury.

WALES & CHESTER

Band 1

Apex Chambers

THE SET

Apex Chambers is lauded by instructing solicitors as an "excellent set" for criminal law. Members act on the full range of criminal law cases, from murder to fraud, for both the prosecution and the defence.

Client service: Craig Mansfield heads an "extremely helpful clerking team" which has "tremendous clerking abilities."

JUNIORS

Susan Ferrier Defends and prosecutes all general and serious crime matters. She is recommended for her expertise in sexual offences cases, and for her handling of vulnerable clients and witnesses.

Timothy Evans Acts as a Grade 4 prosecutor and a criminal defence advocate. He is highly regarded for complex fraud and money laundering cases.

Jonathan Rees Advises clients on complex fraud, regulatory crime and professional disciplinary matters. He is noted for his experience in acting for the police in professional misconduct hearings. **Strengths:** "He is very thorough; a measured and considered advocate who does his research." "He is a solid and dependable advocate with strength in depth and great attention to detail."

Farrar's Building

See profile on p.800

THE SET

Farrar's Building is regarded as an "incredibly strong" criminal law set. Its members act on general crime cases on the Wales & Chester Circuit for both the Crown and the defence. They offer unrivalled expertise in high-profile murder cases.

Client service: Alan Kilbey MBE leads a "friendly clerking team."

SILKS

Patrick Harrington QC Advises the defence and the prosecution on heavyweight and high-profile criminal law matters. He is recommended for his expertise on murder cases and complex fraud matters. **Strengths:** "He provides a very attentive service and you never have any problem with him returning calls or e-mails." **Recent work:** Acted for the defence in R v Mills, a highly publicised case where the defendant was accused of triple murder by arson.

Ian Murphy QC Acts for the Crown and the defence across the full remit of serious crime cases. He is recommended for his expertise in high-profile murder trials. **Recent work:** Prosecuted Matthew

Crime Wales & Chester
Leading Sets
Band 1
Apex Chambers
Farrar's Building *
Iscoed Chambers
9 Park Place
30 Park Place *
Leading Silks
Band 1
Harrington Patrick *Farrar's Building*
Murphy Ian *Farrar's Building*
Rees John Charles *The Chambers of Mr J C Rees QC (ORL)* ◊
Band 2
Clee Christopher *Angel Chambers (ORL)* ◊
Evans Elwen Mair *Iscoed Chambers*
Lewis Paul *Farrar's Building* *
Mather-Lees Michael *Farrar's Building*
Leading Juniors
Band 1
Elias David *9 Park Place*
Ferrier Susan *Apex Chambers*
Lewis Marian *30 Park Place*
Rees Caroline *30 Park Place*
Rees Jonathan *Apex Chambers*
Richards Catherine *Iscoed Chambers*
Band 2
Edwards Heath *9 Park Place* *
Griffiths Roger *9 Park Place*
Pearson Elizabeth *9 Park Place*
Band 3
Evans Timothy *Apex Chambers*
Jeary Stephen *30 Park Place*
Waters Sarah *30 Park Place*
* *Indicates set / individual with profile.*
◊ *(ORL) = Other Ranked Lawyer.*
Alphabetical order within each band. Band 1 is highest.

Tvrdon for murder and 13 counts of attempted murder after he went on a rampage in his van.

Paul Lewis QC (see p.655) Handles serious crime work for the defence and prosecution. He is highly regarded for his expertise in high-profile cases, including sex offences and murder. **Recent work:** Acted on the high-profile defence of Rebecca Shuttleworth, who was accused of the murder of her two-year-old child.

Michael Mather-Lees QC Primarily prosecutes complex criminal law cases. He is recommended in matters where there is significant medical evidence, such as murder and violent crimes. **Recent work:** Successfully used a large volume of forensic evidence to prosecute a man accused of the murder of a baby.

Iscoed Chambers

THE SET

Iscoed Chambers is one of the leading criminal law sets on the Wales & Chester Circuit. It offers expertise at all levels of seniority. Members regularly act on complex and heavyweight crime matters for both the prosecution and the defence.

SILKS

Elwen Mair Evans QC Advises the prosecution and the defence on criminal law matters. She is recommended for serious and complex cases.

JUNIORS

Catherine Richards Acts as a Grade 3 prosecutor and a criminal defence advocate. She is noted for her expertise in violent crimes, sexual offences and drugs cases.

9 Park Place

THE SET

9 Park Place is one of the strongest criminal sets on the Wales & Chester Circuit. Members cater to both the defence and the prosecution, regularly working on serious crime, complex fraud and regulatory matters. Cases range from murder and drugs conspiracy to fraud and professional disciplinary proceedings. **Client service:** "The clerks, led by Nigel East, are excellent, on top of what's going on, and reasonable on fees."

JUNIORS

David Elias Handles serious crime and regulatory crime for the prosecution and the defence. He regularly defends individuals in cases brought against them by the Environment Agency.

Roger Griffiths Acts as a Grade 4 prosecutor, handling serious and complex criminal cases. He is noted for his expertise in high-profile drugs prosecutions. **Strengths:** "He is a good, thorough and approachable advocate."

Heath Edwards (see p.594) Advises on the full remit of general crime work for both prosecution and defence. He is well regarded for his expertise in white-collar crime, including cases relating to fraud and blackmail. **Strengths:** "He is very good with clients: he is approachable and speaks to them in a common-sense manner. He is also a thorough advocate." "He is very good with clients, a genial person; he puts them immediately at ease." **Recent work:** Prosecuted a solicitor who was accused of stealing from clients in order to fund the purchase of his own firm.

Elizabeth Pearson Handles serious crime work for the defence and the prosecution. She is highly regarded for her expertise in sex crimes, and for her skilled handling of vulnerable clients or witnesses. **Strengths:** "She is robust and forthright in the cases she handles."

30 Park Place

See profile on p.895

THE SET

30 Park Place maintains its standing as one of the pre-eminent sets on the Wales & Chester Circuit for criminal law. Its members act for both the CPS and the defence in the most complex and demanding cases from the lower courts through the appellate system. They are renowned for offering unrivalled expertise in sexual offence cases, particularly those involving vulnerable complainants and witnesses. **Client service:** "The clerks, led by Tony Naylon, are excellent. There is always a great chain of communication and they're progressive in trying to make sure the client is put first."

JUNIORS

Marian Lewis Handles the full range of criminal law matters for the prosecution and the defence. She regularly acts on serious sex offence cases and is recommended for her expertise in dealing with vulnerable individuals. **Strengths:** "She is always very personable with the clients. She is competent and capable, and has a lot of expertise." "She is an excellent advocate who has good rapport with clients."

Caroline Rees Acts as both a Grade 4 prosecutor and a criminal defence advocate. She is noted for her expertise in complex sexual abuse claims with vulnerable witnesses. **Strengths:** "She is a calm, firm advocate who doesn't let anything phase her."

Sarah Waters Represents clients in all criminal defence matters. She is recommended for cases involving serious sexual assault and rape. **Strengths:** "She is very good – she is detailed and analytical about the work and is a very strong advocate." "She is friendly and approachable, and can communicate with clients on their level. She is also fearless and will tackle anything." **Recent work:** Acted as junior defence counsel representing a client charged with murder following a fight in an Abergavenny pub.

Stephen Jeary Acts for the defence across all serious criminal law matters. He is highly regarded for his ability to handle complex historic sex abuse cases. **Strengths:** "He's very thorough, with a fine eye for every minor detail, and his advocacy is excellent." "He is experienced and respected by judges and calm in the way he approaches things in cross-examination – he is persuasive and effective."

Other Ranked Lawyers

Christopher Clee QC (Angel Chambers) Acts for clients on heavyweight criminal law cases. He is noted for his expertise in high-profile cases. **Strengths:** "His advocacy and his paperwork are top drawer."

John Charles Rees QC (The Chambers of Mr J C Rees QC) Advises individuals in serious crime and complex fraud cases. His capabilities extend to high-profile murder cases.

WESTERN

Crime Western
Leading Sets
Band 1
Albion Chambers *
Guildhall Chambers *
3PB Barristers *
Band 2
One Paper Buildings *
Pump Court Chambers *
Leading Silks
Star individuals
Langdon Andrew *Guildhall Chambers*
Smith Richard *Guildhall Chambers*
Band 1
Dunkels Paul *Walnut House (ORL)* ◊
Fitton Michael *Albion Chambers*
Lickley Nigel *3PB Barristers*
Meeke Martin *Colleton Chambers (ORL)* ◊
Band 2
Laws Simon *Walnut House (ORL)* ◊
Pascoe Nigel *Pump Court Chambers*
Quinlan Christopher *Guildhall Chambers*
Band 3
Hughes Ignatius *Albion Chambers* 🄰
Lawrie Ian *3PB Barristers*
Malcolm Alastair R *One Paper Buildings* *
Mott Philip *Outer Temple Chambers (ORL)* ◊
Parroy Michael *3PB Barristers*
◊ (ORL) = Other Ranked Lawyer.
🄰 direct access (see p.11).
* Indicates set / individual with profile.

Crime Western
Leading Juniors
Band 1
Brunner Kate *Albion Chambers* 🄰
Burgess Edward *Albion Chambers*
Collins Rosaleen *Guildhall Chambers*
Duval Robert *Albion Chambers*
Mooney Stephen *Albion Chambers* 🄰
Morgan Simon *St John's Chambers (ORL)* ◊
Row Charles *Queen Square Chambers (ORL)* ◊
Tully Ray *Guildhall Chambers*
Band 2
Feest Adam *3PB Barristers*
Gerasimidis Nicolas *Guildhall Chambers*
Jewell Matthew *One Paper Buildings* *
Lamb Maria *One Paper Buildings* *
Lowe Rupert *Guildhall Chambers*
Newton-Price James *Pump Court Chambers* *
Onslow Richard *3PB Barristers*
Pakrooh Ramin *Guildhall Chambers*
Band 3
Bagley Louisa *One Paper Buildings* *
Beal Jason *Devon Chambers (ORL)* ◊
Bennett James *Guildhall Chambers*
Bradbury Timothy *3PB Barristers*
Brown Anne *Pump Court Chambers* *
Bryan Robert *One Paper Buildings* *
Evans David *Walnut House (ORL)* ◊
Gohil Pushpanjali *Guildhall Chambers*
Grey Robert *3PB Barristers*
Haskell James *Guildhall Chambers*
Jones Sarah *Pump Court Chambers*
Linford Robert *Colleton Chambers (ORL)* ◊
McCarthy Mary *Walnut House (ORL)* ◊
Nelson Giles *Albion Chambers*
Reid David *3PB Barristers*
Rowland Nicholas *3PB Barristers*
Vigars Anna *Guildhall Chambers*
Worsley Mark *Guildhall Chambers*
Up-and-coming individuals
Horder Tom *3PB Barristers*
Jones Samuel *Guildhall Chambers*

Band 1

Albion Chambers

See profile on p.889

THE SET

One of the largest sets on the Western Circuit, Albion Chambers has assembled an experienced team of criminal advocates. Its Bristol base allows it to prosecute and defend across the circuit on the full range of criminal matters.

Client service:

"They have a breadth of good-quality practitioners, at all levels of experience, who score very highly across the board in terms of their user-friendly approach. Their internal structure allows them to provide a great service."

SILKS

Michael Fitton QC The head of Albion Chambers and a vastly experienced defender, who prosecutes in the most serious homicide and rape cases. **Strengths:** "He really is great with the jury; he is hard-working and is unfazed by anything."

Ignatius Hughes QC Has a broad criminal practice focused on the most serious and complex cases, such as multi-handed murders, serious sexual offences, and drugs and firearms conspiracies.

JUNIORS

Kate Brunner Maintains a wide-ranging practice covering serious crime, regulatory work and inquests. **Strengths:** "She's just extremely efficient, and she's a tough practitioner – you don't want to be against her if you can help it."

Edward Burgess Prosecutes and defends across the full range of serious criminal cases. He is a Grade 4 CPS prosecutor, and is also a member of the CPS' specialist rape panel. **Strengths:** "He would rate amongst the top barristers in the region." "He is a very measured, very well-prepared, and very reassuring advocate."

Robert Duval Specialist criminal advocate whose caseload covers the full breadth of serious crime. He both prosecutes and defends, and undertakes cases relating to homicides, serious sexual offences and conspiracies to supply drugs.

Stephen Mooney A specialist in heavyweight criminal cases who also defends and prosecutes in regulatory crime matters. **Strengths:** "He is a robust advocate who clients know is really fighting for them."

Giles Nelson Handles a range of criminal cases for both prosecution and defence. His practice is notable for its breadth, covering areas ranging from serious violent and sexual crimes to drugs conspiracies.

Guildhall Chambers

See profile on p.890

THE SET

The highly rated Guildhall Chambers has continued to receive significant praise from market commentators for its expertise in criminal matters. This Bristol-based set has the strength and depth needed to provide a comprehensive service, and is particularly noted for its "exceptional silks," who prosecute and defend across the Circuit.

SILKS

Andrew Langdon QC The leader of the Western Circuit. He is a heavyweight crime specialist who garners universal acclaim for his masterful prosecution and defence in heavyweight murder cases and frauds. **Strengths:** "He thinks through the problems in a case in a clear-sighted, analytical way, with an eye on where he wants the case to go." "He stands out as a silk. He makes the job look effortless. He really is superb." **Recent work:** Instructed in the high-profile murder case of R v James and Norris, where a man wrongly suspected of paedophilia was killed and set alight.

Richard Smith QC Prosecutes and defends in high-profile and complex criminal cases involving allegations of murder, manslaughter and serious sexual offences. **Strengths:** "He is a supreme tactician who thinks about a case through all 360 degrees. You would be hard pressed to find a silk in practice with greater murder experience." **Recent work:** He acted in the cases of R v Lagwinowicz and R v Vince, two high-profile murder cases.

Christopher Quinlan QC A veteran trial advocate who prosecutes and defends in complex criminal cases. His caseload includes high-profile homicides and serious sexual offences. **Strengths:** "He is an exceptionally hard-working silk." **Recent work:** Instructed in the murder cases of R v Stephens & Vince, R v Cox and R v Boult, as well as the slavery trial of R v Connors.

JUNIORS

Rosaleen Collins Has considerable experience across the full range of serious criminal cases. She is noted for her excellent client care skills, particularly with vulnerable or traumatised clients. **Recent work:** Instructed in R v T and Others, a multi-handed, gang-related attempted murder case.

James Bennett Covers the whole range of serious criminal offences. His practice is predominantly focused on criminal breaches of health and safety regulations.

Ray Tully Both prosecutes and defends in complex criminal matters such as homicides, money laundering and drug-related cases. **Strengths:** "His case preparation is impressively meticulous and he is very, very good with clients." **Recent work:** Instructed in R v Lagwinowicz, concerning a high-profile plot to commit murder for financial gain.

Nicolas Gerasimidis Prosecutes and defends in heavyweight criminal cases concerning murder, manslaughter and serious sexual offences. He is praised by commentators for his skilled handling of complex cases and for his ability to work with sensitive and vulnerable clients. **Recent work:** Instructed in R v Zakaria, a highly complex case featuring ten defendants and allegations of exploitation, rape and trafficking of women and girls by a Somali gang.

Rupert Lowe A Grade 4 CPS prosecutor whose substantial defence practice is focused on serious criminal cases. He has particular expertise in cases involving serious sexual offences. **Strengths:** "He is a credit to his set." **Recent work:** Instructed in R v Kathleen Boyle & Ors, a complex multi-handed conspiracy by union officials to steal union funds.

Ramin Pakrooh A defence specialist with considerable expertise in violent crime cases. He is also noted for his expertise in high-profile drugs and firearms cases. **Strengths:** "He has a seductive way with the jury." **Recent work:** Defended in an armed robbery and a case of Section 18 GBH.

Samuel Jones Prosecutes and defends in a broad range of criminal offences, including in cases concerning serious violence, serious sexual offences and drugs.

Mark Worsley Has a strong practice in all areas of criminal work, including fraud, money laundering and drugs cases. He acts for the defence, and is also a Grade 4 CPS prosecutor and a member of the CPS's specialist rape panel. **Recent work:** Instructed in a serious rape case, a multi-handed fraud, an attempted murder defence for a paranoid schizophrenic and a violent armed robbery involving the theft of £5,000 and the assault of a 77-year-old man.

James Haskell A specialist crime advocate who has represented prisoners in parole hearings and professionals in disciplinary proceedings. **Recent work:** Prosecuted in R v Lelliot, a fraud case where more than £100,000 was stolen.

Anna Vigars Noted for her expertise in relation to serious sexual offences. She acts for both the prosecution and the defence, and is also frequently instructed on homicides and cases concerning serious violence. **Strengths:** "She is down to earth and trusted by juries." **Recent work:** Acted in cases involving child sexual exploitation by a group of men, familial child abuse and a multi-handed murder involving evidential complexities.

Anjali Gohil Impresses market commentators with her work in serious criminal cases, including homicides, frauds and serious violence cases as well as sexual offences and financial crime. She is a CPS Grade 3 prosecutor and is a member of the CPS' rape panel. **Strengths:** "She is technically and procedurally astute." "She is a passionate, bright, articulate and robust advocate with fantastic client care skills."

3PB Barristers

See profile on p.846

THE SET

3PB has continued to provide the breadth and quality of service that impresses market commentators, "getting almost impossible results time after time." The number of high-quality advocates means that they are able to prosecute and defend on matters across the board from the set's bases in Bournemouth, Bristol and Winchester.

Client service: "The team of clerks, led by Stephen Clark, are very proactive and keep in contact very well. They also get to know the solicitors and always provide the substitutions that they know would be acceptable to us."

SILKS

Nigel Lickley QC Highly regarded for his experience and expertise across the full range of serious crime. He prosecutes and defends on the most challenging and high-profile cases on the Western Circuit. **Strengths:** "He is the full package – he's super-clever, relates to the jury well, and is exceptionally good face to face with clients, particularly with vulnerable clients." **Recent work:** Defended in R v Dennehy, a high-profile triple murder and double attempted murder case.

Ian Lawrie QC A criminal and regulatory specialist noted for his expertise in cases relating to the marine sector, including collision cases and pollution work. **Strengths:** "He is a great jury advocate, admired for his expertise on both prosecution and defence." **Recent work:** Instructed to represent Torbulk at an inquest in connection with the sinking of the vessel 'Swanland' and the loss of the majority of her crew.

Michael Parroy QC Has a broad criminal practice covering a wide range of serious crime, including homicides, serious sexual offences and financial fraud cases. **Strengths:** "He is a tireless worker with great attention to detail."

JUNIORS

Adam Feest Prosecutes and defends in cases ranging from fraud and theft to money laundering and drugs importation. He is widely praised for his expertise in cases concerning the ill treatment or neglect of vulnerable adults. **Strengths:** "He has excellent analytical abilities and is always calm under pressure." **Recent work:** Instructed in a complex four-handed cut-throat murder which involved torture of the victim, and the disposal and burning of the body.

Richard Onslow Has a smooth style of advocacy, a tenacious approach and vast experience, which has won him a significant following of instructing solicitors. He both defends and prosecutes, and is particularly visible in serious heavyweight crime cases. **Strengths:** "He directs cross-examination in a way that pulls juries with him. He is excellent in front of the jury." **Recent work:** Prosecuted two serving police officers for rape and misconduct.

Robert Grey Both prosecutes and defends a wide range of criminal cases, including those relating to serious sexual offences, drugs and fraud. **Strengths:** "He is a great problem solver and a reliable professional. He creates a lot of confidence in his clients with his ability to make everything seem effortless." "He knows what is in the client's best interests and is not afraid to fight for it." **Recent work:** Instructed in a multi-handed mortgage fraud.

Nicholas Rowland A Grade 4 CPS prosecutor, he both prosecutes and defends across a wide range of criminal offences. **Strengths:** "He is a very calm and client-friendly barrister."

Timothy Bradbury Has a mixed prosecution and defence practice with particular expertise in fraud, drugs conspiracy cases and violent crime. **Strengths:** "He is a great advocate, well suited to top-end, serious cases." **Recent work:** Successfully prosecuted an arms dealer arranging the export of a multimillion-pound shipment of munitions from North Korea to Azerbaijan, in breach of the 2008 export control order.

David Reid Has extensive experience across the full breadth of serious crime work. His caseload regularly includes cases relating to homicides, serious sexual offences and GBH. **Strengths:** "He has a great presence in court." "He grasps the technical aspects of the case very quickly." **Recent work:** Successfully prosecuted in a multimillion-pound Ponzi fraud and throughout the subsequent confiscation proceedings.

Tom Horder Covers the full range of criminal offences, and is best recognised for his expertise in regulatory criminal cases. He receives regular instructions from local authorities, government bodies and insurers in relation to cases concerning health and safety, trading standards, environmental, aviation and maritime issues. **Strengths:** "His advocacy is very good and he impresses with his knowledge of legislation and case law in niche areas." **Recent work:** He defended a hospital doctor accused of sexual assault.

Band 2

One Paper Buildings

See profile on p.841

THE SET

Under senior clerk Mark Cornell, One Paper Buildings has built a reputation as a set that delivers a high quality of service. With numerous standout performers and a user-friendly ethos, they prosecute and defend across the Circuit on all criminal matters.

SILKS

Alastair Malcolm QC (see p.661) Has a broad practice covering the full range of serious criminal cases, including homicides, serious sexual offences and armed robberies.

JUNIORS

Maria Lamb (see p.649) An expert in cases involving sexual offences. She prosecutes and defends in a range of serious criminal cases, including murder, serious violent offences and high-profile drugs matters. **Strengths:** "She is particularly strong in sexual offence cases and cases involving young defendants. She is very good in front of a jury and judge." **Recent work:** Successfully defended in R v Hunt, a 'baby shaking' murder case.

Matthew Jewell (see p.638) Recognised for his high-quality prosecution work across the Circuit. He has also proven to be equally adept in acting for the defence, and is particularly praised for his work in drugs conspiracy cases. **Recent work:** Instructed in R v Phillips, where it was alleged that a rape was facilitated by the use of 'legal highs'.

Robert Bryan (see p.559) Prosecutes and defends a range of criminal cases, including complex fraud cases and cases concerning historic sexual abuse allegations. **Recent work:** Has been instructed in a case concerning the £1.3 million defrauding of a government agency.

Pump Court Chambers

See profile on p.851

THE SET

Under the stewardship of "intelligent and forward-thinking" chief clerk David Barber, Pump Court Chambers has developed an impressive reputation for quality client care. The set covers the full range of criminal cases, and has high-calibre barristers at all levels of experience.

SILKS

Nigel Pascoe QC A former leader of the Western Circuit with a high-profile practice focused on serious criminal cases. He has acted in more than

100 murder cases, and is one of the Circuit's leading homicide experts. **Strengths:** "He's a great jury advocate – he can really tell them the story of the case." "He has a great court presence and that comes from years of experience." **Recent work:** Instructed in R v Addo, where a Bournemouth student was slashed to death before being beheaded and disembowelled by a suspected schizophrenic.

JUNIORS

James Newton-Price (see p.682) Market commentators highlight his expertise in rape and serious sexual offences cases. He both prosecutes and defends, and is praised by sources for his skill in dealing with sensitive clients. **Strengths:** "He is calm and direct with the jury, and also manages to deal with the victims in a lovely way." **Recent work:** Prosecuted in R v Last and Others, where a gang stole up to £540,000 worth of goods through a series of burglaries.

Sarah Jones Has a broad criminal practice but is best known for her defence work in cases involving historic sexual offences. **Strengths:** "She is an excellent advocate when it comes to sexual offences. She is very thorough, very hard-working and very tenacious. She has a sympathetic manner, which allows clients to trust and open up to her."

Anne Brown (see p.557) Prosecutes and defends in cases involving serious sexual violence and allegations of child abuse. **Strengths:** "She is very empathetic and is able to form relationships with vulnerable clients, which allows her to give decent instructions." "She is a very skilled and practical lawyer who gets to the heart of the matter." **Recent work:** Prosecuted R v Khan and Khan, a case concerning the grooming and sexual exploitation of teenage girls.

Other Ranked Lawyers

Martin Meeke QC (Colleton Chambers) Has a strong criminal practice focused on the most serious offences. He has built a reputation as a fearsome prosecutor, but also defends in the most serious murder, regulatory crime and sexual offences cases.

Robert Linford (Colleton Chambers) Joined Colleton Chambers in September 2013 from Devon Chambers, where he was previously head of chambers. He has vast experience of both prosecuting and defending across the spectrum of serious crime and regulatory work.

Jason Beal (Devon Chambers) The head of Devon Chambers. He is praised by commentators for his advocacy skills, which he uses to both defend and prosecute the most complex criminal cases. **Strengths:** "He is excellent on all case types, but particularly on proceeds of crime matters. He also has exceptional client care skills."

Philip Mott QC (Outer Temple Chambers) Has a broad criminal practice encompassing gross negligence manslaughter and major frauds.

Charles Row (Queen Square Chambers) Instructed across the range of serious criminal offences, including homicides, fraud, sexual offences and regulatory cases. **Strengths:** "He is very authoritative and conscientious, never flustered, and respected by judges."

Simon Morgan (St John's Chambers) A highly experienced advocate who both prosecutes and defends in serious crime cases. His previous instructions cover a wide range of cases, including child abuse allegations, homicides and serious sexual offences.

Paul Dunkels QC (Walnut House) Practises across the full range of serious heavyweight crime, including in homicide, fraud and drugs conspiracy cases. **Strengths:** "He is a high-quality advocate whom juries trust." **Recent work:** Instructed in R v Wilson, a case concerning a mother who was suspected of causing the death of her 11-month-old child.

Simon Laws QC (Walnut House) The head of chambers at Walnut House. He prosecutes and defends across a wide range of serious crime, including in homicides, sexual offences and drug-related cases. **Strengths:** "He has the ability to explain himself and the proposed course of action in a clear and simple manner to a wide variety of investigators and experts in a case, tailoring his style to suit the audience." **Recent work:** Acted in the matricide case of R v Cane.

David Evans (Walnut House) Highly experienced in a wide range of criminal cases, from drugs conspiracies to murders. He prosecutes and defends primarily across the Western Circuit. **Strengths:** "He is capable of doing highly complicated cases. He has the ability to absorb huge amounts of detail."

Mary McCarthy (Walnut House) Has substantial experience of acting in serious criminal matters, including murder, rape and fraud, amongst many others. **Strengths:** "She is a formidable advocate with great attention to detail and a great presence in court." **Recent work:** Instructed in R v Singer, a case where the defendant was charged with the murder of his girlfriend.

Contents:

LONDON

Data Protection London
Leading Sets
Band 1
11KBW *
Band 2
Blackstone Chambers *
One Brick Court *
Thirty Nine Essex Street *
Matrix Chambers *
Monckton Chambers *
Leading Silks
Star individuals
Coppel Philip *Landmark Chambers (ORL)* ◊ Ⓐ
Pitt-Payne Timothy *11KBW* *
Band 1
Caldecott Andrew *One Brick Court* *
Grey Eleanor *Thirty Nine Essex Street*
Spearman Richard *Thirty Nine Essex Street* *
Tomlinson Hugh *Matrix Chambers*
Band 2
Eadie James *Blackstone Chambers*
Swift Jonathan *11KBW* *
Band 3
Coppel Jason *11KBW* *
Shaw Mark *Blackstone Chambers*
White Antony *Matrix Chambers* *
Williams Rhodri *Henderson Chambers (ORL)* ◊ Ⓐ *
New Silks
Gallafent Kate *Blackstone Chambers*
Steyn Karen *11KBW* *
Leading Juniors
Star individuals
Proops Anya *11KBW* *
Band 1
Facenna Gerry *Monckton Chambers* Ⓐ *
Hooper Ben *11KBW* *
Hopkins Robin *11KBW* *
Band 2
Dunlop Rory *Thirty Nine Essex Street* *
Eardley Aidan *One Brick Court* *
Evans Catrin *One Brick Court* *
Skinner Lorna *Matrix Chambers*
Stout Holly *11KBW* *
Band 3
Choudhury Akhlaq *11KBW* *
Cornwell James *11KBW* *
Cross Tom *11KBW* *
Glen David *One Brick Court* *
John Laura Elizabeth *Monckton Chambers* *
Kamm Rachel *11KBW* *
Lask Ben *Monckton Chambers* Ⓐ
Milford Julian *11KBW* *
Sanders Oliver *1 Crown Office Row (ORL)* ◊
Scherbel-Ball Jonathan *One Brick Court* *
Sharland Andrew *11KBW* Ⓐ *
Welfare Damien *Cornerstone Barristers (ORL)* ◊ *
Up-and-coming individuals
Blackwood Anneliese *Monckton Chambers*
Knight Christopher *11KBW* *
* *Indicates set / individual with profile.*
◊ *(ORL) = Other Ranked Lawyer.*
Ⓐ *direct access (see p.11).*
Alphabetical order within each band. Band 1 is highest.

Band 1

11KBW

See profile on p.823

THE SET

11KBW is a set whose information and data protection law offering is unrivalled. Not only does it have the requisite members schooled in this discipline, but it also provides much-appreciated ancillary services to solicitors. By way of example, it hosts an annual conference on data protection, and produces a much-lauded blog on the subject called 'Panopticon', of which one happy solicitor commented: "Most of us have it bookmarked; it's excellently written and researched. They do themselves out of work because it's so good!" The set is the chief port of call for the Information Commissioner's Office (ICO) and other public authorities, and its barristers appear in the vast majority of important cases in the field. Recent matters handled include Kennedy v Charity Commission and Others, and Evans v Information Commissioner, the judicial review of the veto over disclosure of the Prince of Wales's correspondence with ministers. In discussing the set, one observer stated: "I think you can take it as read that anyone in a chambers of that quality will be bright and hard-working."

Client service: Lucy Barbet and Mark Dann are 11KBW's joint senior clerks. "I have only good things to say about 11KBW in terms of fee negotiation and the availability of counsel," noted one impressed client, adding: "The clerks are amazing to deal with. They not only provide a quick service, but have been prepared to go the extra mile when a matter is being heard."

SILKS

Timothy Pitt-Payne QC "In a league of his own," he has long led the way in the data protection field. Capitalising on the intersection between his three specialisms of information law, public/local government law and employment law, he handles leading cases for public and private clients, and has regularly appeared both for and against the ICO. **Strengths:** "Tim is an outstanding data privacy and FOIA specialist – he always provides responsive and practical advice and has an encyclopaedic knowledge of the area." "If I had to name one silk in this area, it would be him. He really stole a march specialising in this area before anyone else." **Recent work:** Acted for Oxford University in Deer v University of Oxford, a case concerning an individual's alleged right of access to personal information held by the university.

Jonathan Swift QC (see p.733) First Treasury Counsel, who handles this type of work as part of his widespread government representation. He has been particularly active in the Freedom of Information Act (FOIA) and Environmental Information Regulations (EIR) spheres lately. **Strengths:** "An extremely robust advocate, with the thick skin you need to be a government advocate." "He has masses of experience in the FOIA area." **Recent work:** Acted for the Attorney General in a judicial review challenge concerning the potential application of the FOIA to the sealing of Royal wills.

Jason Coppel QC (see p.578) Has broad-based knowledge of information law, and regularly acts for central and local government bodies and the ICO. He wins wide acclaim for his EU legal knowledge and drafting capabilities, and has a wealth of experience in heavyweight cases. **Strengths:** "He's crisp, to the point and doesn't go on. He's sophisticated on information systems, and delivers a seamless service." "He has a detailed understanding of information law, as well as an ability to provide clear strategic advice. You can have confidence in his judgement." **Recent work:** Acted for the Home Secretary and Justice Secretary on challenging legislation on criminal records checks disclosure of all convictions and cautions.

Karen Steyn QC (see p.728) A newly appointed silk, who is recognised for her concise opinions and strong drafting skills. She acts for public bodies and regulators, central and local government bodies, and individuals, across a diverse range of public and human rights law matters. **Strengths:** "She comes across well on paper and is concise in her advocacy." **Recent work:** Acted for the Charity Commission and the Secretary of State for Justice in Kennedy v Charity Commission and Ministry of Justice.

JUNIORS

James Cornwell (see p.578) Data protection and information rights, employment, education and local government law all fall within the remit of Cornwell's practice. He makes regular appearances before the First-tier Tribunal (Information Rights), Upper Tribunal and Administrative Court. **Strengths:** "He's calm, measured and reasonable in everything he does, and clear and precise in his language." **Recent work:** Appeared for the Department for Work & Pensions in a case against the Information Commissioner concerning the refusal by DWP of a request for information from a journalist about absent parents with the highest levels of child support arrears.

Akhlaq Choudhury (see p.571) An expert in information law both domestically and internationally, he was recently appointed to the A-Panel of the Treasury Counsel. His other strengths include employment, business protection and public law generally. **Strengths:** "He picks things up really quickly, provides straightforward, clear advice and is very calm." "He's very effective and is a strong performer." **Recent work:** Instructed by the NUT in resisting an appeal against an ICO judgment on FOI requests surrounding proposed free schools. The case was called National Union of Teachers v Department of Education.

Anya Proops Frequently appears in cutting-edge information and data protection cases, including the first ever appeal against an ICO monetary penalty notice. She is repeatedly described as a "standout junior" due to her freedom of information (FOI) and EIR work and general pragmatism, and is co-founder of 11KBW's highly regarded 'Panopticon' blog. **Strengths:** "Anya's greatest strength is her forensic mind when it comes to understanding a case. She is a powerhouse of knowledge and energy, and her advocacy is first class." "She's just got a litany of really good cases and she's excellent. She's a silk in junior's clothing basically." **Recent work:** Acted for the Information Commissioner in Central London Community Healthcare Trust v Information Commissioner (Upper Tribunal), an appeal against a data breach fine issued by the Commissioner under the Data Protection Act.

Robin Hopkins (see p.631) Covers the gamut of data protection matters, including Data Protection Act (DPA), FOI, data breaches and monetary penalties. He represents both public and private clients, and regularly acts for and against the Information Commissioner. He also speaks and writes extensively on information law. **Strengths:** "Very easy to deal with and switched-on – you can cut straight to the chase with him. He's immersed in the work on a daily basis, and is very responsive and experienced, despite being a junior." "I needed sensitive advice on a data protection matter and he turned it round quickly, and intuitively knew what was needed, with only brief instruction. He was sensitive and thorough – I really couldn't fault him." **Recent work:** Represented the Information Commissioner in Edem v Information Commissioner and Financial Conduct Authority, an appeal with widespread significance on the definition of 'personal data'.

Ben Hooper (see p.630) Leading information rights junior, with a practice covering conventional data protection matters, Article 8 privacy rights, and Regulation of Investigatory Powers Act work. He acts for both public and private clients, and recently appeared in the Supreme Court for the Information Commissioner (as intervener) in the high-profile Kennedy v Charity Commission case. **Strengths:** "Excellent and very measured in his approach. He's a great gentleman, who is very proper and good to be against." "A pleasant opponent, who is clear in his written and oral communications." **Recent work:** Acted for the Information Commissioner in Browning v IC and the Department for Business, Innovation and Skills. The case concerned FOIA requests made for the names of companies that sought export licences for trade with Iran.

Holly Stout (see p.730) Practises in diverse areas, including information and data protection, public, commercial, education and employment law. She has acted for numerous authority bodies recently, including the Information Commissioner, Cabinet Office and Electoral Commission. **Strengths:** "Good at getting to grips with a brief." "Concise and good on paper" **Recent work:** Advised the ICO in Peninsula Business Services Ltd v Information Commissioner and Ministry of Justice, a case concerning rights of access to court records.

Tom Cross Well established in data protection and information law, and has made a number of appearances before First-tier and Upper Tribunals (Information Rights) and the High Court. He has been particularly active in sensitive matters over the past year, including cases regarding disclosure of personal data in the context of gender reassignment. "Thoughtful and effective – that more or less sums him up," said one recent source. **Strengths:** "He's very willing to help, responsive and accessible. A clear thinker, who is legally right on the ball." "Very well prepared, he was familiar with the facts of our case in a short space of time, and the advice he's given has been excellent." **Recent work:** Acted for the ICO in Roberts v Information Commissioner and Cabinet Office, which concerned the question of disclosure of correspondence between the Prime Minister and the Archbishop of Canterbury.

Andrew Sharland (see p.718) Has a broad practice strong on media-related data protection issues. **Strengths:** "He's done some substantial work in the Supreme Court and he's been very good. Produces a very good end product." **Recent work:** Shared advocacy for Mr Kennedy and the Times Newspapers in Kennedy v Charity Commission and Ministry of Justice. The case concerned FOI exemptions in relation to Article 10 ECHR (right to freedom of expression).

Christopher Knight (see p.647) Prolific author, editor and contributor to data protection and information law publications, he is also a lawyer with a strong practice in the area. He handles FOI and data protection cases, including in the Upper Tribunal. **Strengths:** "He has an 'older than his years' way about him, and is one to watch." "I'd give enormous credit to his conference contributions for someone his age. His blogs on FOI are also full of sensible contributions." **Recent work:** Appeared for the ICO in Matthews v Information Commissioner, which concerned questions of procedural principle in the First-tier Tribunal (Information Rights).

Julian Milford (see p.672) Mainly acts for the government, particularly in high-profile FOI request cases. He garners consistent praise in the market for his acuity, accurate representation of his clients' needs, and the clarity of his advice. **Strengths:** "Julian is especially good at understanding sensitivities and concerns. He's honest and forthright with issues and problems, and will lay the legal issues out, and explain the best option to go forward." "His manner in conference is beautiful. He's approachable, articulate and very good at dealing with clients and understanding their perspectives." **Recent work:** Represented the Attorney General and seven government departments in a case concerning a journalist's FOI request for letters between the Prince of Wales and various ministers.

Rachel Kamm Has a comprehensive public law practice encompassing information, education, community care and local government law. She continues to build on her experience acting for public bodies, and has received recent instructions from the Charity Commission and Ministry of Justice in Kennedy v Charity Commission and Ministry of Justice. **Strengths:** "She's always on the ball and able to master a frightening number of bundles." **Recent work:** Acted for the local authority in Information Commissioner v Dransfield and Devon County Council, an Upper Tribunal appeal concerning public authority approaches to determine the potentially 'vexatious' or 'manifestly unreasonable' nature of FOI requests.

Band 2

Blackstone Chambers

See profile on p.771

THE SET

Very experienced in ICO cases, Blackstone Chambers is well regarded for its prowess in the data protection field generally, and proves particularly strong on those cases with a human rights element to them. Barristers from the set have been involved in a number of high-stakes data protection cases recently, including Noor Khan v Secretary for State for Foreign and Commonwealth Affairs, and the Court of Appeal case revoking the Prince of Wales's right to veto successful journalistic FOI requests concerning his letters to the government. The "tactical advice" and "brilliant performances" provided by Blackstone members were consistently commented upon by interviewees.

Client service: "The set offers good conferences and is very impressive all-round. I would have no hesitation in using them as they are absolutely first-class." Senior clerk Gary Oliver heads up the clerking team.

SILKS

Mark Shaw QC Has a broad information rights practice, and has recently represented the GMC, particularly in a disclosure capacity. Shaw often acts for regulators, and has regularly advised the Metropolitan Police Authority. **Strengths:** "A first-rate lawyer, especially when it comes to FOI and information regulations. He's good tactically and as an advocate." "He has a razor-sharp mind and takes a pragmatic and extremely effective approach." **Recent work:** Acted for 19 water companies in Fish Legal v Information Commissioner, a case concerning requests to disclose environmental information.

Kate Gallafent QC Undertakes extensive data protection work for the BBC, amongst others, as part of a wider public law practice. Commended for her "tactical advice," she has been particularly active in the FOIA space of late. **Strengths:** "Kate was really good in her written work and advocacy. She knew the law without needing to look it up, was very assured, and had really good judgement; things generally played out the way she said they would. I had total confidence in her." **Recent work:** Represented the Nursing & Midwifery Council in Stuart Syvret v Nursing & Midwifery Council, resisting FOIA and DPA requests from a former Jersey senator.

James Eadie QC As First Treasury Counsel he has undertaken a number of highly sensitive data protection matters for various government departments, including the Foreign & Commonwealth Office (FCO), GCHQ and the Department of Health. **Strengths:** "Really engaging, easy to use and likeable. He's also very bright, but wears his knowledge lightly." **Recent work:** Acted for the FCO in Foreign & Commonwealth Office v ICO (Plowden). This concerned a request for conversation notes between Tony Blair and George Bush prior to the Iraq War.

One Brick Court

See profile on p.773

THE SET

A set well used to appearing for applicants and defendants in the First-tier Tribunal (Information Rights), the County Court and the High Court. Its impressive roll call of clients includes the BBC and various national health trusts, and it also has experience of representing the government as it has a number of juniors on the Treasury Solicitor's Panel of Counsel.

SILKS

Andrew Caldecott QC Extremely strong defamation and media silk who is fully au fait with data protection and information rights cases. He has handled a number of high-profile FOIA cases and matters concerning journalistic ethics. **Strengths:** "A barrister who produces extremely high-quality pleadings." "He is dazzling." **Recent work:** Appeared as leading counsel for claimants in the formal arbitration proceedings for damage claims arising from the conduct of News International. The case concerned phone hacking, unlawful surveillance and related breaches of privacy and data protection rights.

JUNIORS

Catrin Evans A member of the Attorney-General's 'A-list' of counsel, she advises the government on information law matters, whilst simultaneously undertaking work on behalf of media organisations. **Strengths:** "Clever, efficient" and "a great strategic thinker." "I've been very impressed with her client handling when faced with a difficult claimant." **Recent work:** Appeared as junior counsel for Google in Vidal-Hall v Google Inc, a high-profile case concerning the application of data protection and privacy law when looking at Google's use of cookies to analyse users' browsing habits.

Aidan Eardley A widely acknowledged expert in high-profile FOI and data protection-related media matters. His recent conspicuous cases include appearing for Katie Price in a data protection claim against her former management company, and acting for The Guardian on successfully overturning the veto on disclosure of the Prince of Wales' correspondence with the government. **Strengths:** "Aidan has a modest, unassuming and understated presence, which works well in a tribunal environment, but he is also robust and knows the points he wants to argue." **Recent work:** Represented Guardian journalist Ian Cobain in Home Office v ICO and Ian Cobain. This was an appeal against the ICO decision requiring disclosure of the names of a number of individuals deprived of citizenship on counter-terrorism grounds.

Jonathan Scherbel-Ball Has experience as a former media solicitor and public body FOI request reviewer. He specialises in work with public bodies, counting various NHS trusts and the BBC amongst his eminent clients. **Strengths:** "He's really diligent, committed, responsive and engaged. He bounces with ideas, and has masses of enthusiasm." **Recent work:** Junior counsel for the BBC in the First-tier Tribunal (Information Rights), successfully defending journalistic exemptions to FOIA requests surrounding an environmental training seminar.

David Glen Noted for his representation of private and public figures in data protection matters, he has extensive experience of acting for News International phone-hacking victims. He also provides regulatory advice for Ofcom. **Strengths:** "He marshals his arguments well and presents them coherently." **Recent work:** Represented the BBC in Gee v Information Commissioner and BBC in a series of appeals before the Information Tribunals upholding significant rulings on the BBC's journalistic exemptions from the FOIA.

Thirty Nine Essex Street

See profile on p.797

THE SET

Thirty Nine Essex boasts broad data protection and FOIA proficiency. Its members make frequent appearances before the First-tier Tribunal (Information Rights), and are strong on cases with EIR, Regulation of Investigatory Powers Act, privacy and confidentiality issues attached to them. The set boasts a number of top silks in this area as well as a growing band of juniors. Sources say: "The set has a number of people with a good footing in the FOI world. Members' experience of big, complex government cases leaves them well placed to do well in this field." Chambers' provision of a monthly newsletter relating to data protection issues is a welcome boon to those that instruct it.

Client service: David Barnes is the well-respected chief executive and director of clerking at the set. His team includes Alastair Davidson and Michael Kaplan, both of whom are senior clerks.

SILKS

Eleanor Grey QC A barrister who has been on the Attorney General's Panel of FOIA Counsel for some years now. She has extensive experience of both advising on and litigating data protection and data access cases, and does a good deal of work for public authorities, amongst others. **Strengths:** "A super-steady pair of hands, she's measured, calm and really good." "She combines good technical knowledge with a level-headed style of advocacy. She impresses the court by being sensible, pragmatic, balanced, rational and reasonable." **Recent work:** Successfully acted for Leeds City Council in Snee v ICO and Leeds City Council, resisting an appeal against a request for full database content release previously denied by the ICO.

Richard Spearman QC Very highly regarded for any case with data protection, privacy, libel and confidentiality issues. One of the big names at the Bar, he frequently acts for high-profile commercial clients. **Strengths:** "A man with outstanding intellect, who is brilliant with clients and almost always wins." **Recent work:** Continues to advise News Group Newspapers, publishers of The Sun and The Sun on Sunday, on various information law points.

JUNIORS

Rory Dunlop Specialises in representing public authorities in FOIA cases before the First-tier and Upper Tribunals, and has been appointed to the Attorney General's FOIA Panel. He has recently acted in numerous appeals, for the likes of the Department of Health, the Department for Work & Pensions and the Department for Education. **Strengths:** "A good advocate and a sensible opponent. He has a fine working knowledge of FOIA and the DPA." "He managed a difficult case in a sensible, reasonable and attractive way, against a hostile tribunal. He was calm under pressure and came through very well." **Recent work:** Acted for NHS England in Cllr Illingworth v IC & NHS England.

Matrix Chambers

See profile on p.832

THE SET

Matrix has a strong media and information law group that adds lustre to the set's heavyweight reputation in other areas. Members here regularly act on data interception matters in particular, as evidenced by their representation of Big Brother Watch and their involvement in the Mobile Telephone Voicemail Interception Litigation. Notable too for their recent involvement in the highly publicised Construction Industry Blacklisting Litigation, they are seen as being "very much on the up in the world of privacy and information law."

Client service: Cliff Holland is practice manager of Team M, the employment, media and information, and commercial law team at Matrix. Sources say he and his group are "polite and friendly on the client-handling front."

SILKS

Hugh Tomlinson QC Noted for his strength in handling the data protection elements of privacy and defamation cases, he has a wealth of experience. His recent matters include cases relating to phone hacking and the employment 'blacklisting' of trade union activists. **Strengths:** "Hugh really knows his stuff. He is also an extremely decent individual, which shows in his advocacy; he gets the court on side." **Recent work:** Represented the claimant in Tinglan Hong v Associated Newspapers, a claim alleging misuse of private information.

Antony White QC Well practised in privacy and data protection cases, and particularly strong on misuse of private information cases. He has had key roles in both the Leveson Inquiry and the Google/Safari litigation. **Strengths:** "Antony is very erudite, and when you want a solution to a problem, and a clever argument, he will find a way." "Very presentable in front of clients, he brings weight and gravitas to cases, but is also very happy to muck in and get his hands dirty." **Recent work:** Acted in Imerman v Tchenguiz and Others, a case concerning the use of private information in matrimonial finance disputes.

JUNIORS

Lorna Skinner Media and information law specialist with extensive experience of appearing in the High Court. "Very good, detailed and thorough," she has acted on numerous high-profile cases of late, including Vidal-Hall v Google. **Strengths:** "She was tactically strong, very involved and very hands-on, helping directly in a way that meant we were always two steps ahead of our opponents." "She cuts to the point rather than setting out the scene." **Recent work:** Advised Vivian Imerman on a misuse of private information point in Imerman v Tchenguiz. Also appeared for Balfour Beatty in the widely reported construction blacklisting case.

Monckton Chambers

See profile on p.833

THE SET

Monckton is well capable of handling all manner of FOIA, data protection and EIR cases. It is well known for having a strong EU information law practice, and is expert on matters under the Aarhus Convention. Its client base includes the ICO, diverse local and central government bodies, NGOs, commercial organisations and private individuals. Ongoing judicial review challenges and FOI requests in a public procurement context are particular specialisms of the team here.

Client service: Senior clerk David Hockney heads up the team at Monckton. Sources note: "In terms of fee negotiation and ensuring the availability of counsel they are very good. They not only provide a quick service, but have been prepared to go the extra mile when a matter is being heard."

JUNIORS

Gerry Facenna The architect of an extensive public and EU law practice, he acts extensively for the Information Commissioner, public authorities and private information requesters. Peers view him as being "a shrewd litigator, who is a professional and worthy opponent." **Strengths:** "Gerry has an impressive understanding of the area and has shown an amazing grasp of detail in cases dealing with large amounts of highly technical information. He is also a highly effective and cordial cross-examiner." "He takes an appropriately robust approach." **Recent work:** Acted for the Environment Agency in a case where the ICO decided to uphold a refusal to disclose confidential information on financial guarantee arrangements for landfill sites. This followed an appeal from Swansea Friends of the Earth.

Laura Elizabeth John (see p.638) Regularly appears in the First-tier (Information Rights) and Upper Tribunals, she has particular strength in data protection cases concerning the environment and competition law. She often appears in the Court of Appeal, sometimes in a pro bono capacity for environmental requesters. **Strengths:** "She has made big strides in the data protection area, and is particularly strong in the environmental field." **Recent work:** Represented the ICO against Eastleigh Borough Council in a First-tier Tribunal case surrounding potential disclosure of preferred sites for strategic development.

Anneliese Blackwood Has broad DPA and FOIA experience, with additional competition, EU, procurement, commercial and human rights law expertise. She is routinely instructed by public authorities and the ICO. **Strengths:** "She can think on her feet and is incisive in her cross-examination of witnesses." **Recent work:** Successfully acted for Transport for London on resisting a vexatious FOI request concerning a conviction for an offence under Section 5 of the Regulation of Railways Act 1889.

Ben Lask Highly rated junior in the data protection, telecoms and EU competition spheres, who makes frequent appearances in the First-tier Tribunal (Information Rights), particularly on behalf of public authorities. **Strengths:** "Very nice to work with, responsive and accessible." **Recent work:** Acted for the Department for Work & Pensions in DWP v Information Commissioner. The case concerned a state benefits medical assessment appeal, and considered the definition of 'personal data' under the DPA and EU Data Protection Directive.

Other Ranked Lawyers

Damien Welfare (see p.748) (Cornerstone Barristers) Handles a good deal of work for public authorities, including on the information law front. He has a background in domestic and European policy proposal and legislation, and has particular expertise in FOIA matters. **Strengths:** "He offers excellent command of the subject area, clarity of advice with prompt delivery, and meticulous attention to detail." "He's very pleasant and sympathetic when dealing with public authority clients." **Recent work:** Represented Wirral MBC in a successful appeal against an ICO-ordered disclosure of procurement report drafts, e-mails and background papers.

Oliver Sanders (1 Crown Office Row) Frequently acts in FOIA appeals to the Information Commissioner, acting on behalf of various public bodies. He recently represented the Home Office and a number of NHS trusts. **Strengths:** "He's very experienced, has a good calm tribunal manner, and is measured in putting together tricky cases." "An important contributor to the FOI field, he knows his stuff." **Recent work:** Acted for the Home Office in Home Office v Information Commissioner & Cobain, a case concerning disclosure on deprivation of citizenship orders.

Rhodri Williams QC (Henderson Chambers) EU, local government, and administrative and regulatory law form the backbone of Williams' practice. He has displayed particular prowess of late in cases concerning Subject Access Requests. **Strengths:** "He reads the court really well, and has very good judgement when it comes to predicting outcomes or the path that things are going to go down." "He's thorough, incisive and client-focused."

Philip Coppel QC (Landmark Chambers) An eminent name in the field, who is recognised for his "considerable depth of knowledge" and for being the author of a definitive data protection text, 'Information Rights: Law and Practice'. He is a very strong trial lawyer, who is "both personable and a great advocate." **Strengths:** "He is excellent, user-friendly and willing to look at innovative ways of making data protection law work for clients." **Recent work:** Acted for Kennedy and the Times Newspapers in Kennedy v Charity Commission and Ministry of Justice, a case concerning FOI exemptions in relation to Article 10 ECHR (right to freedom of expression).

Contents:

LONDON

Defamation/Privacy London
Leading Sets
Band 1
One Brick Court *
5RB *
Band 2
Matrix Chambers *
Band 3
Doughty Street Chambers *
Ely Place Chambers *
Leading Silks
Star individuals
Caldecott Andrew *One Brick Court* *
Band 1
Barca Manuel *One Brick Court* *
Browne Desmond *5RB*
Millar Gavin *Doughty Street Chambers*
Page Adrienne *5RB*
Price James *5RB*
Rampton Richard *One Brick Court* *
Rogers Heather *Doughty Street Chambers*
Spearman Richard *Thirty Nine Essex Street (ORL)* ◊ *
Tomlinson Hugh *Matrix Chambers*
White Antony *Matrix Chambers* *
Band 2
Bailin Alex *Matrix Chambers* *
Garnier Edward *One Brick Court* *
McCormick William *Ely Place Chambers* *
Nicklin Matthew *5RB*
Rushbrooke Justin *5RB*
Ryder Matthew *Matrix Chambers*
Thwaites Ronald *Ely Place Chambers* *
◊ (ORL) = Other Ranked Lawyer.
** Indicates set / individual with profile.*
[A] direct access (see p.11).
Alphabetical order within each band. Band 1 is highest.

Defamation/Privacy London – Leading Juniors	
Star individuals	**Band 3**
Evans Catrin *One Brick Court* *	**Addy** Caroline *One Brick Court* *
Sherborne David *5RB*	**Jolliffe** Victoria *5RB*
Band 1	**Munden** Richard *5RB*
Bennett William *5RB*	**Palin** Sarah *One Brick Court* *
Dean Jacob *5RB*	**Reed** Jeremy *Hogarth Chambers (ORL)* ◊ [A]
Eardley Aidan *One Brick Court* *	**Starte** Harvey *One Brick Court* *
Hudson Anthony *Matrix Chambers*	**Wilson** Kate *One Brick Court*
Marzec Alexandra *5RB*	**Band 4**
Speker Adam *5RB*	**Atkinson** Timothy *One Brick Court* *
Wolanski Adam *5RB*	**Hirst** David *5RB*
Band 2	**Michalos** Christina *5RB*
Barnes Jonathan *5RB*	**Samson** John *Ely Place Chambers* *
Busuttil Godwin *5RB* *	**Scherbel-Ball** Jonathan *One Brick Court* *
Glen David *One Brick Court* *	**Shore** Victoria *5RB*
Helme Ian *One Brick Court* *	**Up-and-coming individuals**
Mansoori Sara *Matrix Chambers*	**Craven** Edward *Matrix Chambers* *
Phillips Jane *One Brick Court* *	**Kissin** Clare *One Brick Court* *
Skinner Lorna *Matrix Chambers*	**Ready** Hannah *One Brick Court* *
Vassall-Adams Guy *Matrix Chambers* [A]	**Silverstone** Ben *Matrix Chambers*
	Takatsuki Yuli *5RB*

Band 1

One Brick Court
See profile on p.773

THE SET

Consistently recommended as a market-leading set housing some of London's finest and most experienced defamation and privacy experts. From silk to junior, the quality of its barristers is consistently high. One commentator says of the individuals here: "We find them extremely helpful and have faith in everyone whom we instruct."

Client service: "Senior clerk David Mace is very good; he runs a tight ship. There always seems to be a unity of purpose." He is assisted by Melvin Warner, who "takes a down-to-earth, no-nonsense approach and is very easy to work with."

SILKS

Andrew Caldecott QC (see p.562) A true leader in the marketplace, he routinely acts on landmark cases representing broadcasters, celebrities and government departments. Commentators consistently name him the "best silk at the Libel Bar." **Strengths:** "He has a brilliant mind, and is a bit of a phenomenon really." "He is a shrewd lateral thinker, a very good team player and a forensically astute advocate." **Recent work:** Acted on the well-documented Makudi v Triesman case, which involved an appeal by the head of the Thai Football Association to the denial of his libel action against the former head of the English FA. Caldecott aided in the successful rejection of this appeal.

Richard Rampton QC (see p.703) Admired by solicitors for his confidence in court and his ability to effortlessly persuade a judge and jury of his case. He is a dominant presence in the defamation, privacy and data protection arenas, and has acted in some of the most prominent cases of recent times. He often appears in the Court of Appeal. **Strengths:** "He's hugely experienced and really engages in the case on behalf of the client." "Supremely confident and reassuring." **Recent work:** Acted as leading counsel for the defendants in the ongoing Cruddas v Calvert & Others case regarding a libel claim made against the Sunday Times by the former co-treasurer of the Conservative Party.

Manuel Barca QC A trusted adviser and advocate, who handles the full range of defamation and privacy cases. Clients praise him for his easy style and formidable advocacy skills. **Strengths:** "Tremendously good at gauging what the court needs." "His advocacy is very direct but it's also calibrated towards his audience. He's good at pitching it at the right level." **Recent work:** Led an application for an injunction to prevent the publication by The Times and the Oxford Mail of an arrested individual's name. The arrest had been made in relation to an investigation into child sex offences.

Sir Edward Garnier QC (see p.606) A highly revered and respected politician-barrister, Sir Edward Garnier is fully active in the marketplace following his retirement from his role as Solicitor General. Peers note that he has "got both feet firmly back in chambers." **Strengths:** "He's a very competent guy and very down to earth." **Recent work:** Represented the publishers of Belfast News Letter in the defence of a claim brought by Northern Ireland Civil Service's former head.

JUNIORS

Catrin Evans (see p.597) Has a superb reputation and is consistently engaged on the most significant and contentious cases in defamation and privacy law. Clients know her for her determination and tactical approach to cases. **Strengths:** "She shows very good attention to detail, is level-headed and is good with clients." "Very calm, assured and analytical." **Recent work:** Acted as junior for Associated Newspapers in an action brought against it by Paul Weller. The case concerned the publication of images and misinformed content published about his children.

Aidan Eardley (see p.592) Has acted in cases of substantial weight and significance in the defamation field in the last year. Solicitors instruct him not only for his impeccable legal knowledge but also for his affable manner when dealing with clients. **Strengths:** "Superb knowledge of the law." "He has an exceptional brain combined with a first-class work ethic. His advice is commercial yet carefully measured." **Recent work:** Represented singer Tulisa Contostavlos and footballer Danny Simpson in relation to a libel action brought against three newspapers and numerous websites owned by News Group Newspapers.

David Glen (see p.609) Has expertise in defamation law, and is a well-known name in the media and entertainment sector. Has acted on myriad high-profile cases that have been making waves in the industry in recent times. **Strengths:** "He's good at seeing the wood for the trees and giving very clear advice." "Exceptionally bright, he's someone you would want fighting your corner." **Recent work:** Acted as counsel for Guardian News & Media in relation to a claim brought by Sheikh Nasser bin Al-Shathri, a cleric and theologian, who insisted an article had presented him in a denigrating light.

Jane Phillips (see p.692) A strong performer, recognised for her dedication and her enthusiasm for her work, who has been involved in the phone hacking cases that have stirred up the media industry in the recent past. She often provides pre-publication advice to major newspapers and magazines. **Strengths:** "She's highly personable, approachable, responsive, helpful and knowledgeable." "She's very effective and provides great strategic insight." **Recent work:** She successfully acted on behalf of the BBC in defending a defamation claim made by an international geologist. The case has been held up in Parliament as an indicator as to the need for libel law change in Northern Ireland.

Harvey Starte (see p.727) Co-author of a seminal defamation law textbook, he is very good on black letter law but also a gifted advocate. In parallel with his litigious work he often advises magazines and newspapers on pre-publication legal requirements. **Strengths:** "Incredibly analytical in terms of examining how a claim looks and how a defence looks. Very good on heavy-duty technical issues." **Recent work:** Acted for a GP in a libel claim concerning an article published by the Daily Mail which quoted a patient accusing him of misdiagnosis.

Caroline Addy (see p.531) Has particular expertise in harassment cases, specifically those protecting the privacy of families and individuals. She acts both as claimant and as defender in an extensive range of defamation and privacy cases. **Strengths:** "She's very good at demystifying technical, complicated law, and has great empathy with clients." **Recent work:** Acted for the claimant in the case of Evans & Others v Ritch, which involved allegations of privacy invasion, harassment and defamation in the form of publications on the internet.

Ian Helme (see p.624) A strong player in the field, who has acted in a number of cutting-edge media cases in recent times. He represented the late Lord McAlpine of West Green in relation to the airing of false allegations about him. **Strengths:** "Outstanding, very reliable and easy to deal with, he has a calm and measured advocacy style." "He thinks very carefully; he's a good tactician." **Recent work:** Acted for the claimant in Waterson v Lloyd & Another, which involved an allegation of libel with regard to pamphlets containing content about the Eastbourne Liberal Democrat MP's expenses claims.

Sarah Palin (see p.688) Enjoys a strong reputation, and is instructed by solicitors for her detailed knowledge of the newspaper industry and her ability to tackle heavyweight disputes. **Strengths:** "Her advice will always take into account the realities of what in-house lawyers do." "She's reliable and produces good drafting and clear advice." **Recent work:** Represented the Daily Mail as defendant to a claim brought by author JK Rowling regarding material published about her life before the Harry Potter series was written.

Kate Wilson Distinguishing herself as an up-and-coming barrister in the market, who is recognised as having experience and knowledge beyond her year of call. **Strengths:** "She has the ability to deliver even the most difficult arguments with charm." "She shows bags of confidence when on her feet." **Recent work:** Acted as junior counsel in the Lord McAlpine of West Green and Sally Bercow case concerning a defamatory remark made on Twitter by Bercow. Specialist knowledge was needed due to the social media aspects of the case.

Jonathan Scherbel-Ball (see p.715) Has specialist expertise in media restrictions and political extremism cases. He is dual-qualified as he is called to the Bar in Northern Ireland. **Strengths:** "He was at the BBC – because of his background he really understands what the clients want." **Recent work:** Acted as second junior counsel for the BBC in the well-documented Morrice v BBC case in Northern Ireland.

Timothy Atkinson (see p.539) Has a sweeping client base that takes in claimants and defendants from many areas, including the education, defence and political sectors. He also has a strong international practice, and represents clients from Hong Kong to Turkey. **Strengths:** "He's very good with clients, and is conscientious, sensitive and also very open about the pros and cons of a case." **Recent work:** Appeared in the Court of Appeal representing the claimant in Cammish v Hughes. This matter involved decisions which relied on precedents set in the pivotal Jameel abuse of process case.

Hannah Ready (see p.705) Has quickly become a rising star in the sector since her 2010 call, and has built up a substantial client base. Peers predict she will be a market-leading barrister in the future. **Strengths:** "She's marvellous, as she's careful and clear in her delivery." "She's very good, quick to respond, and quite firm in her advice." **Recent work:** Recently worked as junior counsel acting for the claimant in PNM v Times Newspapers.

Clare Kissin (see p.647) Clients praise her confident advocacy and technical knowledge. Sources report that she punches above her weight and experience, and displays a charming attitude in court. Reporting restrictions cases are a particular specialism. **Strengths:** "Very personable and easy to deal with, she's receptive to different ideas, grasps details quickly and provides succinct and decisive advice." "She truly is a force to be reckoned with. Very bright and very effective, she is a really courageous advocate." **Recent work:** Acted alone for a media publication that wanted to release a video and names of three marines who allegedly murdered an insurgent in Afghanistan. She was successful in lifting anonymity of the individuals and the video was in the most part released.

5RB

See profile on p.858

THE SET

5RB has long been at the forefront of the defamation area. Not content to sit on its laurels though, it is "a classic example of a set that's looking to the future," as evidenced by its recent recruitment of three barristers from 25 Bedford Row. "A smart and slickly run chambers," it has members at every level who are well capable of handling all areas of the market, including defamation, reputation management, privacy, confidence and harassment.

Client service: "Very business-oriented and very commercially minded, the barristers understand their clients' needs very well."

SILKS

Desmond Browne QC Joint head of chambers at 5RB, he has handled many of the most high-profile cases that have affected the media in recent times. **Strengths:** "He comes without need for a recommendation." "He has an exceptional grasp of the bigger picture but never loses sight of the finer details in a case." "He is a tenacious advocate, who is extremely good with clients and who always takes a sound, commercial approach." **Recent work:** He obtained £180,000 in damages for former Conservative Party co-treasurer Peter Cruddas, in the much-reported Cruddas v Times matter.

Adrienne Page QC A highly respected practitioner, who is particularly known for her work in cases concerning online media. **Strengths:** "A wise and very sensible source of advice in areas of media law. She is a joy to work with." "She really knows her way around defamation, malicious falsehood, breach of confidence and privacy." **Recent work:** Acted for Kate and Gerry McCann in relation to Tony Bennett's defamatory allegations of their responsibility for the death of their daughter, Madeleine. Bennett was sentenced to three months in prison.

James Price QC Highly recommended for his depth of experience and expertise in defamation law. He is instructed on high-profile and high-quality actions, and consistently achieves successful results. **Strengths:** "He is fantastic in terms of both his court manner and his preparation." "A super all-round advocate" who is "extremely learned and knowledgeable." **Recent work:** Acted for the claimant in the well-chronicled Flood v Times case. In this matter a police officer was awarded £60,000 in damages from the newspaper after it had published an article making allegations of corruption.

Matthew Nicklin QC Has made a smooth transition into silk following his appointment in 2013. He represents both claimants and defendants in complicated defamation and privacy cases, and is admired for his ability to build strong relationships with clients. **Strengths:** "He is a very thorough lawyer and his enthusiastic commitment to a case is infectious." "He's got an exuberance to him and shows flair in his advocacy." "The real deal, he is skilled on paper and demonstrates excellent judgement on the big issues."

Justin Rushbrooke QC Has represented many famous names and often acts in cases for and against the country's major newspapers. **Strengths:** "Knowledgeable beyond belief," he is "a proactive, enthusiastic and commercially minded barrister." "He is both extremely bright and commercial, and adopts a hands-on approach."

JUNIORS

David Sherborne An outstanding junior and a favourite for many solicitors in the City. He is admired for his ability to connect with a jury, and is highly regarded for his pre-publication injunction practice. Also very strong on reputation management issues. **Strengths:** "He has good strategic vision, is great with clients and is unrivalled in respect of his knowledge of how the media operates." "Probably everyone's first port of call for celebrity privacy and harassment work." **Recent work:** Represented the claimants in the high-profile case of Weller v Associated Newspapers Limited, concerning the unpermitted publication of photographs and incorrect content describing the images.

William Bennett Regularly acts as sole counsel opposite some of London's most experienced QCs. Clients go to him due to the measured approach he takes to heavyweight cases. **Strengths:** "He's diligent, thoughtful and very good in court." "He is a good advocate, who is calm and very articulate." **Recent work:** Acted in the case of Asghar & Mujahid v Nawa-i-Jang, successfully securing damages of £45,000 each for claimants who had been wrongly accused of involvement in financial scandals.

Jacob Dean Offers the full range of defamation and privacy advice, and acts successfully for both claimants and defendants. He acts for all manner of media concerns, including television channels, magazine publishers and theatre producers. **Strengths:** "Good on paper and an authoritative advocate." "He's an outstanding adviser, who is excellent with clients."

Recent work: Represented a Serbian claimant in a libel case against a Montenegrin journalist arising out of a piece in a Balkan language publication.

Alexandra Marzec A leader in the defamation and privacy field who has recently been advising on and drawing up draft arbitration service rules arising from the Leveson Report. **Strengths:** "A very experienced and very capable senior junior." "She possesses both intellect and commitment." "She's uncompromising; if you want an advocate who is going to fight your corner she's able to do that for you."

Adam Speker Has been practising defamation and privacy law at 5RB for 25 years. In what has been a strong year, he has been instructed by claimants and defendants alike in relation to major newspaper scandals. **Strengths:** "He is always assured in his approach to advice and very clear about the goals that the client needs to achieve and how to achieve them." "He is clear and concise, and finds points others don't necessarily find." **Recent work:** Successfully acted for Carmarthenshire County Council and its director in a case concerning a libellous claim made by a blogger.

Adam Wolanski A specialist in media and entertainment law, who is particularly strong on privacy matters. Peers and solicitors alike say he is a popular choice due to his user-friendly approach and technical ability. **Strengths:** "He's brilliant, and both extremely combative and tenacious." "A very adept counsel who is flexible and fast in providing urgent advice to newspaper clients; he's very much trusted by in-house lawyers." **Recent work:** Acted on the high-profile Andrew Mitchell MP v News Group Newspaper case regarding the 'plebgate' libel matter.

Jonathan Barnes A solid barrister, who is strong on privacy, defamation and confidence cases, and who has 25 years at the Bar under his belt. He has been instructed on numerous high-value libel cases. **Strengths:** "He's a pure blue-chip defamation counsel; he knows it backwards." "He's got a very precise drafting style; he's very tight. He has an encyclopaedic knowledge of the relevant cases." **Recent work:** Successfully acted for the claimant, former Secretary of State the Rt Hon Dr Liam Fox, in the case of Fox v Boulter. The claim surrounded an interview about him aired on Sky News.

Godwin Busuttil (see p.562) Instructed equally by claimants and defendants with regard to media and entertainment cases. He is well known for representing author JK Rowling in the significant privacy case of Murray v Big Pictures. Since that matter in 2008 he has worked on similar noteworthy cases. **Strengths:** "A defamation expert with a particular specialism in UK/US cross-jurisdiction issues. He's concise, pragmatic and user-friendly." "He doesn't miss a trick."

Victoria Jolliffe Continues to build a strong practice in defamation law and is consistently instructed on privacy, malicious falsehood and data protection cases. She also provides pre-publication advice to newspapers. **Strengths:** "She's quick and conscientious, and has good judgement." "She cuts to the heart of the issue very quickly and is very responsive."

Christina Michalos Has niche expertise in cases pertaining to privacy and libel issues arising from social networking sites and other internet user-generated content. **Strengths:** "A furiously hard worker who fights for her clients. She makes a real impact in privacy cases by thinking outside the box and utilising her many legal skills."

David Hirst Widely known for his work in technology-related media cases and highly respected for the advice he gives to journalists on publishing laws. **Strengths:** "Very good, very confident and charming with clients."

Richard Munden An expert on defamation and privacy cases, whose practice has recently focused on malicious falsehood, harassment and copyright claims. **Strengths:** "He's cool, calm and collected." "Very down to earth," "he's a good advocate who is really coming into his own." **Recent work:** Acted for the claimant in the matter of Dar Al Arkan Real Estate Co v Al Refai, a case concerning conspiracy, breach of contract and malicious falsehood.

Victoria Shore Regularly instructed on work relating to defamation and privacy issues in the media and entertainment sector. She has acted for public figures and financial institutions in both the claimant and defendant capacity. **Strengths:** "She understands our needs, tailors her advice for us and is particularly user-friendly." "I trust her on judgement cases; her advice is very clear and sensible." **Recent work:** She recently assisted the adjudicator of the Voicemail Interception Compensation Scheme case in determining the victims of the phone-hacking scandal.

Yuli Takatsuki Acts for a wide variety of clients, both claimants and defendants. She regularly offers pre-publication advice for leading publishing houses in the UK. **Strengths:** "She's good on data protection, and has a very good legal mind." "She's excellent and extremely bright. She's in high demand from those at the top end." **Recent work:** Represented Google UK in relation to a breach of privacy claim concerning the publication of certain Streetview images.

Band 2

Matrix Chambers

See profile on p.832

THE SET

A team on the rise, with a significant number of proven barristers known for their key roles in ground-breaking matters in the media. It is praised for its contemporary set-up with regards to clerking and fee structuring, and includes barristers who are often selected for the more complex and unprecedented cases. This year has seen the set take on cases relating to criminal surveillance, social media and freedom of information. Members have represented A-list celebrities and major daily newspapers.

Client service: "Very professional. They've got a different set-up to traditional chambers in that they have dedicated clerking teams depending on the practice area. This system works well." Cliff Holland ably leads the clerks in this practice area.

SILKS

Hugh Tomlinson QC A distinguished privacy practitioner, with an excellent reputation for being an innovative thinker and an articulate advocate. His practice covers the full spectrum of media law matters, and he has handled a spate of privacy cases in recent times. Cases of note include the phone hacking saga and matters regarding Google's use of personal data. **Strengths:** "Accessible, hands-on and able to think outside of the box, Hugh has a brilliant legal mind and is very approachable." "The go-to man for privacy injunctions and arguably the most influential lawyer in this area through his leadership of the unparalleled Inform blog." **Recent work:** Acted in Tinglan Hong v Associated Newspapers, a case concerning published photographs and content in the Daily Mail relating to the claimant's relationship with Hugh Grant.

Antony White QC A leading silk who has enjoyed another busy year in the field. He is widely known for his representation of News International in the Leveson Inquiry, and for his involvement in Vidal-Hall v Google. He is regularly instructed in privacy and data protection matters. Clients praise him for his superlative archive of landmark phone hacking cases, and for his ability to take on heavyweight disputes. **Strengths:** "An extremely good lawyer, who is absolutely at the tip-top of his trade." "He's extremely knowledgeable and has in-depth understanding of privacy law." **Recent work:** Had an important role in the Karpov v Browder libel case, which generated much coverage in the press.

Matthew Ryder QC Increasingly active in the field of privacy law. He regularly represents clients in criminal cases arising out of harassment and invasion of privacy. **Strengths:** "He keeps the confidence of the court while powerfully putting over his position." **Recent work:** Known as a key figure in the landmark Trimingham v Associated Newspaper case.

Alex Bailin QC An expert on cases where criminal law and privacy law converge. He acts for a number of major daily newspapers, and is able to advise on the more esoteric media-related issues. **Strengths:** "A good communicator." "One of the things he is superb on is reporting restrictions. He's absolutely second to none when it comes to contempt of court and publication rules." **Recent work:** Has been representing myriad newspapers and publications in the Litvinenko Inquest.

JUNIORS

Anthony Hudson In popular demand by City solicitors for work relating to defamation and privacy law. His clients include major media publications, and public figures involved in cases relating to harassment, contempt and data protection. He has played a key role in the disputes arising from the phone hacking scandal. **Strengths:** "Absolutely on top of his brief, he shows good judgement and is incisive." "He takes a very practical approach. He doesn't waste words or time, and obviously knows his stuff." **Recent work:** Acted as junior counsel for Times Newspaper in relation to a case concerning a piece in the Sunday Times naming David Hunt as the leader of a crime network.

Sara Mansoori A genuine defamation specialist, who has particular expertise in litigation relating to phone hacking. She enjoys a growing reputation in the area and often represents celebrities and public figures in high-profile libel and defamation cases. Commentators applaud her for her work in relation to the Leveson Inquiry. **Strengths:** "Bright, practical and extremely user-friendly." "She's someone who has really come to fruition in recent years. She has a visceral instinct for what's important in a privacy case." **Recent work:** Worked as junior counsel on the David Hunt v Times Newspaper matter, appearing for the defence. The judge ruled that the matter had been reported responsibly.

Lorna Skinner A popular barrister who is strong in the areas of misuse of private information and freedom of expression. She is a senior junior who clients say always adds gravitas. **Strengths:** "She is very comfortable with cases concerning the interplay between defamation, the Human Rights Act and data protection." "She has authority beyond her year of calling, and feels more like a leader than a junior." **Recent work:** Acted for the claimant in Layne Norton v Jason Blaha, which involved an allegation of drug-taking brought against bodybuilder and power lifter Layne Norton.

Guy Vassall-Adams Has a defendant-led practice, and generally represents media tycoons and conglomerates in actions brought against them. He is known for his work on cases such as Jameel v Wall Street Journal. **Strengths:** "He's very knowledgeable on reporting restrictions and in the defamation field generally." "He often does applications from groups of media organisations, and is very pleasant to be against. He knows his stuff, gets on with the job and does it well." **Recent work:** Works as counsel for the Voicemail Interception Compensation Scheme, established by News Group Newspapers, which aids victims of phone hacking seeking compensation.

Edward Craven (see p.580) Moving rapidly into the spotlight as an up-and-coming individual in the field due to his work for claimants in the phone hacking litigation, as well as his efforts in High Court libel cases. He is an acknowledged expert on media law and frequently publishes commentary on the industry. **Strengths:** "He's one to watch for the future. A very, very bright and intelligent guy. He's got an instant grasp of the facts." "You can see he's the sort of person who's going to be very successful." **Recent work:** Provides ongoing pre-publication and broadcast advice to major publishing and broadcasting groups such as BBC News, The Guardian, The Observer and The Times.

Ben Silverstone Acts for a balanced clientele of claimants and defendants. He is regularly instructed on defamation and privacy cases, and has recently handled a number of claims relating to misuse of private information arising out of the voicemail interception litigation. **Strengths:** "He produces very good oral advocacy and his self-confidence is apparent. He's a pleasure to work with." **Recent work:** Junior counsel for the defendants in Lucy Adams v Michelle Stanistreet & National Union of Journalists. The case related to a claim brought against NUJ regarding a comment concerning Ms Adams on its website.

Band 3

Doughty Street Chambers

See profile on p.786

THE SET

Doughty Street Chambers is home to two of the market's most experienced and renowned silks practising in privacy and defamation law. Recent matters dealt with include libel trials on behalf of the defendant, and cases concerning the refutation of malicious falsehood claims. Members have also been engaged on providing a good deal of pre-publication advice. They often act in cases where human rights and media law meet.

SILKS

Gavin Millar QC A distinguished barrister who is "going from strength to strength." Solicitors instruct him due to his extensive knowledge of the field and his ability to connect with a judge and jury. **Strengths:** "A driving force at the Defamation Bar, who has a punchy style and an encyclopaedic knowledge of police procedures." "Offers great analysis and is trusted by the Bench." **Recent work:** Acted in the inquest into the death of Mark Duggan. He represented the BBC in resisting a summons requiring the corporation to lift the anonymity of a witness of the shooting.

Heather Rogers QC Lauded by clients and solicitors for her detailed knowledge of the field and her affable and professional approach to client service. She continues to appear in some of the most contentious and high-profile cases of the day. **Strengths:** "She has great tactical nous and is a strong lateral thinker." "Intellectual acumen personified, she is a barrister with superb legal ability." "She has formidable forensic skills, and provides cogent advice." **Recent work:** Acted for the defendants and appellants in Cruddas v Times Newspaper, concerning a claim for libel and malicious falsehood.

Ely Place Chambers

See profile on p.787

THE SET

A close-knit team of experienced and dedicated defamation and privacy barristers that handles high-profile cases and offers pre-publication advice to local and national publishers. The barristers here are supported by clerks who are noted for their rapid response times and eagerness to build relationships with clients.

Client service: The clerks, led by Chris Drury, are "very down to earth and very approachable."

SILKS

William McCormick QC (see p.667) Noted for his quick-thinking and practical approach to matters, he is a strong player in the market. Clients and solicitors applaud him for his tactical acumen and for his dogged approach in the courtroom. He has appeared in many of the most significant and pivotal trials of recent times. **Strengths:** "Tenacious – he gets stuck into hard-fought cases." "He's very persuasive and doesn't stand any nonsense." **Recent work:** Acted in Ecclestone v Khyami & Others, a case concerning harassment, privacy and conversion claims.

Ronald Thwaites QC Well known for his bullish cross-examination style and ability to sway a jury. He has an impressive number of successes under his belt and is accordingly instructed by high-profile individuals in defamation trials. **Strengths:** "Use him if you want to take someone down in court; he's a beautiful speech maker." "He's stunning with juries." **Recent work:** Successfully acted for author Sara Thornton in a claim concerning an article by Lynn Barber that appeared in The Daily Telegraph.

JUNIORS

John Samson (see p.713) Has a strong background in broadcasting and often acts on freedom of information and data protection matters. He regularly provides advice on reputation management. **Strengths:** "A hard worker who is seemingly inexhaustible. He looks at a problem from every angle." "He really cares about the cases, and about winning for the client. Quite theatrical on his feet, he explains things well."

Other Ranked Lawyers

Richard Spearman QC (Thirty Nine Essex Street) Has a defendant-led practice and years of experience in privacy matters. An authority on privacy law, he has an extensive portfolio of reported cases, including those relating to freezing injunctions, disclosure and confidence. **Strengths:** "An outstanding intellect and a preferred choice for complex claims involving privacy, particularly those concerning injunction applications. He is excellent with clients and understands how to present his advice in the right way." "An advocate with real gravitas – he knows the world of privacy and defamation like very few others at the Bar." **Recent work:** Acted in the well-documented Tesla v BBC case. This concerned claims of libel and malicious falsehood brought against BBC show 'Top Gear' following its review of the Tesla Roadster electric sports car.

Jeremy Reed (Hogarth Chambers) Has had a role in the phone hacking litigation from its inception. He has also been instructed on other media cases of late, and is known for his superior knowledge of privacy law. **Strengths:** "He always has a fantastic grasp of the facts, the law and the procedure." "It's very clear the court has a lot of respect for him."

Contents:

LONDON

Education London	
Leading Sets	
Band 1	
11KBW *	
Band 2	
Thirty Nine Essex Street *	
Hardwicke *	
Matrix Chambers *	
Leading Silks	
Band 1	
Giffin Nigel	*11KBW*
Mountfield Helen	*Matrix Chambers* *
Oldham Peter	*11KBW* *
Band 2	
Beloff Michael	*Blackstone Chambers (ORL)* ◊
Bowen Nicholas	*Doughty Street Chambers (ORL)* ◊ [A]
Goudie James	*11KBW* *
Grodzinski Sam	*Blackstone Chambers (ORL)* ◊
Kerr Tim	*11KBW* *
Sheldon Clive	*11KBW*
Wolfe David	*Matrix Chambers* *
Band 3	
Morris Fenella	*Thirty Nine Essex Street*
Pearce Robert	*Radcliffe Chambers (ORL)* ◊
Warnock Andrew	*1 Chancery Lane (ORL)* ◊ [A] *
Wise Ian	*Monckton Chambers (ORL)* ◊ [A]

◊ (ORL) = Other Ranked Lawyer.

[A] direct access (see p.11).

* Indicates set / individual with profile.

Education London	
Leading Juniors	
Band 1	
Lawson David	*Hardwicke* [A]
Moffett Jonathan	*11KBW* [A] *
Stout Holly	*11KBW* *
Band 2	
Cornwell James	*11KBW* *
Friel John	*Hardwicke* [A] *
Hannett Sarah	*Matrix Chambers* [A]
Hyams Oliver	*Devereux (ORL)* ◊ *
McKendrick John	*Outer Temple Chambers (ORL)* ◊
Oldham Jane	*11KBW* *
Rawlings Clive	*Hardwicke* [A]
Scolding Fiona	*Outer Temple Chambers (ORL)* ◊ [A] *
Sharland Andrew	*11KBW* [A] *
Squires Daniel	*Matrix Chambers*
Band 3	
Armstrong Nicholas	*Matrix Chambers*
Auburn Jonathan	*Thirty Nine Essex Street* [A] *
Bicarregui Anna	*Thirty Nine Essex Street* [A]
Clement Joanne	*11KBW* *
Edwards Denis	*Francis Taylor Building (ORL)* ◊ [A]
Greatorex Paul	*11KBW* [A] *
Hay Deborah	*Deborah Hay (ORL)* ◊
McColgan Aileen	*Matrix Chambers*
Purchase Mathew	*Matrix Chambers* *
Ward Galina	*Landmark Chambers (ORL)* ◊
Band 4	
Broach Stephen	*Monckton Chambers (ORL)* ◊
Cross Tom	*11KBW* *
Darwin Claire	*Matrix Chambers* *
Kamm Rachel	*11KBW* *
Lawrence Anne	*4-5 Gray's Inn Square (ORL)* ◊ *
Luh Shu Shin	*Garden Court Chambers (ORL)* ◊
Pratley Michelle	*Thirty Nine Essex Street* [A] *
Sackman Sarah	*Francis Taylor Building (ORL)* ◊
Walker Amelia	*1 Crown Office Row* *
White Gemma	*Blackstone Chambers (ORL)* ◊
Up-and-coming individuals	
Amraoui Thomas	*Thirty Nine Essex Street*
Anderson Jack	*Thirty Nine Essex Street*
Eddy Katherine	*11KBW* *

Band 1

11KBW
See profile on p.823

THE SET

11KBW is routinely identified as the leading chambers for education law. Its unrivalled team of silks and juniors acts for clients across the gamut of education cases, and regularly handles matters relating to special education needs, admissions and exclusions. Recent instructions include Winstanley v Leeds University, which raised questions as to whether academic judgment is outside the jurisdiction of the court, and R (Governing Body of Uplands Junior School) v Leicester City Council; a matter concerning the power of local authorities to be able to step in and run a school. Commentators say that "this extremely knowledgeable group of barristers delivers a top-quality and cost-effective service." Sources praise the set for offering "a bedrock of intellectual rigour. The barristers know their stuff, are very happy to share their knowledge, and frequently put on very good seminars."

Client service: The clerks, led by Lucy Barbet and Mark Dann, are "very efficient, on the ball and on top of things." "They are personable and always keep you informed in terms of fees." "Very responsive and obliging."

SILKS

Nigel Giffin QC A leading public law practitioner, who handles education cases as part of his hugely impressive practice. **Strengths:** "A top-class advocate." "He was superb and managed to win on a point that was almost unwinnable. He's very, very accomplished."

Peter Oldham QC A highly regarded advocate, who handles the full spectrum of education law cases, including admission, exclusion and special educational needs (SEN) matters. **Strengths:** "A superb tactician. He gives advice based on the outcome you want to achieve, and is commercial, responsive and very user-friendly." "He's extremely easy to deal with and very pragmatic." **Recent work:** He acted for the Secretary of State in a case that challenged the legality of the exclusions system.

James Goudie QC (see p.612) A well-respected silk with considerable expertise in the field. He has recently handled cases for universities and local authorities. **Strengths:** "A hard hitter, who always makes eminently sensible contributions to a case."

Tim Kerr QC A well-regarded barrister in the education arena, who regularly advises local authorities. **Strengths:** "A real pleasure to work with. He's well prepared and ready with an answer for everything." **Recent work:** He acted for the North Tyneside Council, challenging the formation of an academy.

Clive Sheldon QC A long-standing practitioner who has acted in a variety of education matters, including disability discrimination and exclusion cases. **Strengths:** "His advice is invariably clear and comprehensive." "Friendly, helpful and easy to work with." **Recent work:** He represented the Governing Body of Uplands Schools in defending a judicial review challenge.

JUNIORS

Jonathan Moffett (see p.675) Acts for individuals, local authorities, schools and higher education institutions on contentious matters. He also frequently advises on non-contentious issues. **Strengths:** "Very bright and very approachable, he knows his stuff." "He has a passion for the field." **Recent work:** He acted for the British government in AW v United Kingdom; a case concerning an application made by a pupil with SEN to the European Court of Human Rights.

Holly Stout (see p.730) Has a wide-ranging education practice, and acts for a range of clients in admissions, exclusions and duty to provide education cases. **Strengths:** "Sharp, user-friendly and good on her feet." "Incredibly clever – she just exudes intelligence." **Recent work:** She acted for the claimant in Fearnley v Imperial College London; a case concerning an alleged breach of contract.

Jane Oldham (see p.684) Frequently handles cases involving academy, further and higher education issues. **Strengths:** "Meticulous to the ninth degree and very sympathetic with clients." **Recent work:** She acted in R (Hunt) v North Somerset Council, which concerned an allegation that the council had failed to comply with the Education Act 1996.

Andrew Sharland (see p.718) He has a well-rounded practice and appears in admission, exclusion, academy and employment cases. **Strengths:** "He is an excellent barrister, who is always prepared for any meeting. He can analyse information very well and provide advice in a practical way." **Recent work:** He acted in Professor Stewart-Brown v Warwick University; a sex discrimination claim.

James Cornwell (see p.578) He is a highly experienced practitioner, particularly in matters concerning schools and further and higher education institutions. He is well versed in disability discrimination, admissions, exclusions and immigration issues. **Strengths:** "Precise and to the point, he focuses on the key facts and issues." **Recent work:** He represented Newcastle University in a case brought by a clinical medical student who was alleging a breach of contract.

Paul Greatorex Has a solid grounding in a range of education law matters. He has recently been active in several SEN cases, and has represented a number of local authorities. **Strengths:** "He is excellent. His advice covers a lot of areas and there is a breadth to his expertise, which is uncommon. The quality of his advice is fantastic – he thinks outside the box." **Recent work:** He acted for the appellant in R (Burger) v Office of the Independent Adjudicator for Higher Education.

Joanne Clement (see p.574) She has a broad public law practice with a strong emphasis on education cases. She is experienced in cases concerning exclusions, admissions, SEN and reorganisations. **Strengths:** "Very user-friendly and proactive," she is "a very reasonable and measured opponent." **Recent work:** She acted for the university in Richardson v University of Manchester, which concerned a claim of disability discrimination, breach of contract and negligence.

Tom Cross Acts for a range of clients, including parents, local authorities and government departments. He is experienced in cases relating to academies, exclusions and SEN. **Strengths:** "He's very pleasant, down to earth, easy to understand and practical." **Recent work:** He acted in Manchester City Council v Ingleby, representing the local authority in an Upper Tribunal appeal.

Rachel Kamm (see p.641) Frequently acts for panels, local authorities and education bodies on a broad range of matters. **Strengths:** "Impressive because she is very measured." **Recent work:** Advised the council in B v Oxfordshire County Council; an appeal in the First Tier Tribunal concerning a child with SEN.

Katherine Eddy (see p.593) She is experienced in SEN and disability cases in the First Tier Tribunal. She has recently acted for schools and universities. **Strengths:** "A phenomenal advocate who is very assured and instils confidence."

Band 2

Thirty Nine Essex Street

See profile on p.797

THE SET

Thirty Nine Essex Street has a range of established barristers who are experienced in handling the gamut of education law. Its members represent individuals, schools and higher education institutes, and advise on cases relating to educational negligence, employment and human rights, among others.

Client service: "The clerks there are excellent. They always help us out." "They're very approachable and they get back to you quickly."

SILKS

Fenella Morris QC She concentrates on higher education cases, including breach of contract and discrimination claims. **Strengths:** "She acts like one of our team." "She's excellent with clients, is very clear on the issues, and works hard to get a good result."

JUNIORS

Jonathan Auburn Has recently acted in several high-profile parent disputes. He acts for individuals, schools and higher education institutes. **Strengths:** "Extremely knowledgeable, easy to deal with and very friendly." **Recent work:** Appeared in Shalom v Newham College; a case involving claims of race and religious discrimination.

Anna Bicarregui Experienced in admissions cases, she specialises in SEN work and related judicial reviews. **Strengths:** "She is fantastic as she is very passionate, extremely approachable and very clever." **Recent work:** Bicarregui acted for the claimant in Luke Dansey v Havering; a case concerning a child with severe special educational needs.

Jack Anderson Often represents individuals and local authorities in SENDIST matters in the First Tier Tribunal. **Strengths:** "Really impressive in the way he conducts himself. He's very sharp and gets the legal points."

Michelle Pratley (see p.698) She focuses on SEN cases in the First Tier Tribunal and Upper Tribunals. Her practice also covers discrimination and breach of contract claims. **Strengths:** "She is great and clients absolutely love her. She is very reassuring."

Thomas Amraoui Experienced in SEN cases, and also handles admission and exclusion matters. **Strengths:** "He is very approachable and is concise when summing up messy situations." "He brings new ideas to the table, and is very responsive to changes in circumstances." **Recent work:** He acted in R (JR) v Royal Borough of Greenwich, representing the claimant in a judicial review challenge concerning the authority's failure to provide an adequate education provision to a child with special needs and behavioural difficulties.

Hardwicke

See profile on p.816

THE SET

This set has a well-rounded offering and is especially well regarded for its members' expertise in SEN cases. Individuals act for a wide range of clients and are regularly instructed to represent individuals, local authorities, schools and universities. Those that instruct the set are pleased not only by the quality of barrister on offer, but also by the added extras that the set provides. By way of example, "their seminars are very good and up to date in terms of content and relevance."

Client service: "The clerks are good and cover all bases." "Very efficient and responsive. There are never any delays or problems."

JUNIORS

David Lawson Acts on a broad range of matters in court and in an advisory role. He was recently active in a judicial review relating to the new exclusion regime. **Strengths:** "He takes a thorough, analytical approach to cases, and is skilful and creative in presenting difficult arguments." **Recent work:** Acted in Z v B University, appearing on behalf of the claimant in a race and discrimination claim.

John Friel (see p.604) A highly experienced barrister, who has recently been active in the Court of Appeal. He specialises in SEN and discrimination cases. **Strengths:** "A superb advocate, who is very approachable and always well prepared." "He is a specialist in the field, and he wins." **Recent work:** He successfully acted for the respondent in Slough Borough Council v The Special Educational Needs and Disability Tribunal & Others at the Court of Appeal.

Clive Rawlings Represents defendants and claimants, frequently appearing in the Court of Appeal and Upper Tribunal. He focuses on cases concerning SEN, exclusions and academy conversions. **Strengths:** "A very experienced advocate with a keen eye for detail, who is an expert at dealing with the most complex cases, in particular those concerning comparative costings and funding arrangements for specialist education placements." **Recent work:** He acted in Abukar v LB Barnet and Bishop Douglas School.

Matrix Chambers

See profile on p.832

THE SET

Matrix Chambers' members are experienced in a wide range of public law-related cases, including those relating to exclusions, admissions and SEN. They are also expert in matters involving academies and free schools. Sources say that this is a fine team with "very bright people, who are prepared to go the extra mile."

Client service: "Very responsive and efficient, the clerks are keen to provide a spread of people to cover the work." "It doesn't matter who you are talking to, they all know what's going on and are very responsive." Jason Housden runs the clerking team for this area of the law.

SILKS

Helen Mountfield QC A distinguished practitioner, who is an expert in education cases relating to public law. She acts on a range of high-profile matters. **Strengths:** "Specialises in equality act claims and is a leader in her field." "She's really impressive in court." **Recent work:** She acted in R (Kebede) v Secretary of State for Education, representing the claimant in a challenge to the state's decision to remove access to student finance.

David Wolfe QC A well-recognised and respected barrister who acts for claimants on a range of matters, including admissions, exclusions and SEN cases. **Strengths:** "Remarkably tenacious and very creative even in the bleakest circumstances." **Recent work:** He successfully acted in SA v London Borough of Camden & Ors, representing a teenager in a judicial review challenging the decision to uphold his exclusion.

JUNIORS

Nicholas Armstrong A well-regarded junior, who acts for individuals and institutions. He focuses on SEN and disability discrimination matters. **Strengths:** "Great at handling cases concerning maintained schools and academies." "He's very dependable and provides clear, sound advice."

Sarah Hannett Instructed on the full spectrum of education law cases. She represents individuals, institutes and local authorities. **Strengths:** "She inspires confidence and has the ability to turn papers around quickly." "She's very approachable and knowledgeable, and has a lot of sympathy for the client." **Recent work:** She acted in R (Arogundade) v Secretary of State for Business, Innovation and Skills.

Mathew Purchase Has a broad practice, which incorporates public, employment and community care law work as well as education cases. He has recently been active on unfair dismissal and discrimination cases. **Strengths:** "Very bright and hard-working, with very good judgement." **Recent work:** He acted in Fraser v University and College Union, an employment tribunal case centred around the alleged harassment of a Jewish lecturer.

Daniel Squires Experienced in SEN, admissions and educational negligence cases. He acts for claimants and defendants. **Strengths:** "The quality of his written work is fantastic. He has a brilliant mind and is incredibly user-friendly."

Claire Darwin Frequently acts in high-profile cases. Her areas of expertise include SEN, discrimination and admissions. **Strengths:** "An impressive advocate on special educational needs cases for appellants. She is confident and assertive, and takes a proactive approach to case strategy."

Aileen McColgan She has expertise in SEN and disability cases in the First Tier Tribunal and is also experienced in representing claimants and defendants in judicial review proceedings. **Strengths:** "She is attentive, client-friendly, extremely thorough and straight-talking." **Recent work:** Acted in Hunt v North Somerset CC; a case concerning the lawfulness of cuts to youth services.

Other Ranked Lawyers

Michael Beloff QC (Blackstone Chambers) A legendary barrister whose work in the education law sphere sees him acting for central government bodies and individuals. **Strengths:** "A wise and brilliant lawyer, who is an outstanding advocate." **Recent work:** He has advised the Department of Education on matters such as academies and free school lunches.

Sam Grodzinski QC (Blackstone Chambers) He predominantly represents claimants against educational institutions, and is highlighted for his human rights expertise. **Strengths:** "He is a beacon of excellence when it comes to pubic law." **Recent work:** He successfully represented the Office of the Independent Adjudicator (OIA) for students in higher education in a judicial review relating to the rejection of a student's complaint regarding King's College London's marking process.

Gemma White (Blackstone Chambers) Acts for individuals and institutions on a range of work, and is particularly well versed in SEN issues. **Strengths:** "She is very diligent and hard-working, and makes sure she's on top of everything." "Good at dealing with very vulnerable clients." **Recent work:** Acted for a student in the Court of Appeal in relation to a judge's refusal to judicially review an OIA decision.

Andrew Warnock QC (1 Chancery Lane) A well-regarded barrister with a wide-ranging public law practice. He acts for schools and further and higher education institutions, especially in negligence cases. **Strengths:** "He's particularly strong on failure to educate cases." "Clearly a formidable opponent, he's very persuasive in court." **Recent work:** Represented the school in Ghadimi v European School; a case concerning an allegation that the school had failed to prevent bullying.

Amelia Walker (see p.744) (1 Crown Office Row) Frequently acts for local authorities and parents in cases regarding SEN and disability discrimination. **Strengths:** "She always strikes me as being very knowledgeable, very responsive and willing to go the extra mile in terms of giving her view on how we can strengthen our position." **Recent work:** She acted in TB v Essex CC; an appeal case regarding the interpretation of the word 'school' under the 1996 Education Act.

Deborah Hay (Deborah Hay) Noted for her strength in SEN cases, she caters to an almost exclusively private client base. **Strengths:** "She doesn't waste time at all, asks the right questions and is highly efficient."

Oliver Hyams (see p.635) (Devereux) Highly regarded practitioner with a practice that spans the full spectrum of education law. He is an expert in employment matters and is frequently instructed in judicial reviews and appeals. **Strengths:** "He provides incisive, clear and timely advice, and has proved himself to be of invaluable assistance to the team." **Recent work:** He acted in Lam v St Mary's School Cambridge; a case concerning a claim of breach of contract relating to the failure of the school to provide an adequate duty of care to a new pupil.

Nicholas Bowen QC (Doughty Street Chambers) Has a broad public law practice and significant experience in the education law field. He primarily acts for claimants, often at the High Court and Supreme Court level. **Strengths:** "A very inventive, creative barrister." "He is the champion of lost causes." **Recent work:** He acted in R (otao) Dunham v Southend County Council, successfully bringing a judicial review concerning a funding package for the claimant.

Denis Edwards (Francis Taylor Building) A public law generalist with a strong interest in education law. **Strengths:** "Reasonable, affable and measured in his tones. He has a good grasp of the law and a good understanding of SEN cases." **Recent work:** He acted in R (P and M) v Hounslow LBC, which raised several important issues, including the definition of the word 'home' in relation to the council's home-to-school transport obligations.

Sarah Sackman (Francis Taylor Building) Has an extensive public law practice with a solid grounding in education law. She specialises in cases relating to exclusions, SEN and higher education. **Strengths:** "She responds rapidly and is well prepared. She's a great advocate."

Shu Shin Luh (Garden Court Chambers) Experienced in education matters relating to public and community care law. She is particularly strong on cases concerning disabled children and SEN. **Strengths:** "Very committed and hard-working, she is always approachable and gives good practical advice." **Recent work:** She acted in R (Elisa Nfuni) v Solihull MBC, a judicial review claim centred around the scope of the local authorities' obligations for a failed asylum seeker.

Anne Lawrence (see p.652) (4-5 Gray's Inn Square) Has a solid grounding in SEN cases, and focuses on SENDIST matters. She also has added expertise in cases relating to admissions and exclusions. **Strengths:** "Obtains excellent results in tribunal and other cases. She's reliable in terms of her turnaround of papers, and is exceptionally good at putting clients at ease."

Galina Ward (Landmark Chambers) She focuses on administrative and public law, and has recently been instructed on cases relating to education negligence and teacher-pupil relationships. **Strengths:** "She's very sympathetic with clients who have difficult issues, and really fights for her clients." **Recent work:** Acted in Disclosure & Barring Service v PH, a Court of Appeal case concerning the decision of the Upper Tribunal to allow an appeal by a teacher who had been barred as a result of assaulting a pupil.

Ian Wise QC (Monckton Chambers) Has extensive experience at the High Court, Court of Appeal and Supreme Court level. He frequently acts for claimants in public law cases involving children. **Strengths:** "A very pragmatic advocate, who works very quickly and is good on his feet. He's very clear and is a leader on the issue of children's rights." **Recent work:** He acted in R (Brooks) v Essex County Council, representing the claimant in a challenge to the council's decision to close down all of its children's homes.

Stephen Broach (Monckton Chambers) Focuses on children's rights and primarily advises individuals. He is well regarded for his expertise in disability matters. **Strengths:** "He provides clear advice and is approachable. His knowledge of community care issues proves useful." **Recent work:** Acted in R (O) v Hammersmith and Fulham, a case concerning the placement of a child with autism at a residential special school.

John McKendrick (Outer Temple Chambers) A well-respected practitioner, who is highlighted for his SEN expertise. **Strengths:** "A very good lawyer and advocate, who can assimilate large amounts of material and obtain excellent results."

Fiona Scolding (see p.715) (Outer Temple Chambers) Well versed in cases relating to the Equality Act 2010 and SEN. She represents individuals and authorities in First Tier Tribunal and Upper Tribunal cases, and regularly handles judicial reviews. **Strengths:** "Quick thinking when on her feet. She is a brilliant advocate, who is valued by clients for her straight-talking approach and unrivalled knowledge of the SEN sector." **Recent work:** She acted in K v A School, successfully representing the school in a Court of Appeal case relating to an alleged breach of the Equality Act and the Human Rights Act.

Robert Pearce QC (Radcliffe Chambers) Well known for his expertise in charity law, he is praised in the education law world for his work with trusts and independent schools. **Strengths:** "He is very good technically, and is also very good at explaining things to the client."

EMPLOYMENT: An Introduction

Contributed by Seán Jones QC and Harini Iyengar of 11KBW

The Impact of Fees

"Access to justice" has been the watchword across many legal sectors this year, with employment law no exception. The introduction of fees for the Employment Tribunal and the Employment Appeal Tribunal with effect from 29 July 2013 has had a dramatic effect upon employment litigation. Across the tribunal regions the number of individual claims commenced each month has fallen, on average, by significantly more than 50% when compared to previous years. A first judicial review of the regulations introducing the fees, sponsored by Unison, was rejected. An appeal is expected. The concern that the fees regime has restricted access to justice is real and widespread.

Although the system put in place for remission of tribunal fees is dauntingly complicated, there has, as yet, been little satellite litigation. That may be because those worst affected lack the personal and financial resources required to bring legal challenges. Some litigants are choosing to bring claims such as wrongful dismissal, protection against harassment and equal pay in the civil courts instead of the employment tribunals, because of the lower fees and different costs regime.

The new ACAS early conciliation system has had a mixed reception. Some claimants relish the opportunity to extend the limitation period whilst others genuinely engage in very early attempts at settlement; employers' attitudes likewise vary between enthusiasm and calling the employee's bluff until the fee is paid. Increased judicial mediation has also had a mixed reception, its main attraction being the reduced cost compared to private mediation and its main downfall being the parties' inability to request a particular mediator.

Popular Claims

Employees with the sheer numbers or union support to bring multiple claims, and those on the highest earnings seeking uncapped compensation, continue to proceed to full hearings and to appeals on issues such as holiday pay, whistle-blowing, discrimination and parental rights.

Holiday pay is expected to remain a busy area because of the high value of the claims, including issues of backdating, and large number of affected employees. Repercussions follow the CJEU's judgment in Lock v British Gas that commission payments fall within the concept of normal remuneration and the Employment Appeal Tribunal will consider a set of consolidated holiday pay cases in Neal v Freightliner principally focused on the question as to whether voluntary overtime should also be included in the calculation.

Whistle-blowing remains a popular jurisdiction. The Enterprise and Regulatory Reform Act 2013 addressed the longstanding complaint that there was no requirement that an employee should reasonably believe that their disclosure was in the public interest whilst demoting the requirement that a disclosure should be made in good faith to a factor affecting only compensation. It also plugged the hole found to exist in NHS Manchester v Fecitt by making employers vicariously liable where their employees subject the whistle-blower to a detriment.

The same piece of legislation modified the cap on unfair dismissal compensatory awards so that it is now the lower of £76,574 or one year's gross pay. While that might be good news for employers, less welcome will be the introduction with effect from 6 April 2014 of a tribunal power to penalise employers found to have breached employment legislation. Where an employer is found to have breached an employee's statutory rights and the breach is found to have one or more "aggravating features", the tribunal may now impose a penalty of between £100 and £5,000 on the employer. The money goes to the Treasury and not to the claimant.

The 2013 Act also introduced a "day one" right not to be dismissed for a reason which relates to one's political opinions or affiliations. The amendment was intended to remedy the shortcoming in domestic law identified by the European Court of Human Rights in Redfearn v UK.

Sex, race and age discrimination remain attractive claims for those with the resources to litigate, and sexual orientation claims appear to be a particular growth area. While the mass equal pay claims of a few years ago seem to have ceased, individual equal pay claims remain worthwhile for high earners and for those raising untested issues, such as men bringing novel claims. Liability for third party harassment has been abolished along with the much-valued questionnaire procedure.

The extension of the right to request flexible working to all employees may provoke further novel discrimination claims, as employers try to balance the needs of parents of both sexes and non-parents. Similarly, despite the low take up of additional paternity leave, the introduction of shared parental leave may trigger claims of discrimination from fathers.

As usual, the appeal courts have been busy. The Supreme Court has decided that LLP partners are "workers" (Clyde & Co LLP and another v Bates van Winkelhof) with all the consequent implications for entitlement to a range of statutory rights. In Jessemey v Rowstock Ltd the Court of Appeal confirmed to little surprise, but general relief, that despite some poor wording, s. 108(7) of the Equality Act 2010 does not have the effect of making post-dismissal victimisation lawful. As we go to press the CJEU is deciding whether obesity is a disability for the purposes of the Framework Directive.

Anticipated Legislation

The Government now proposes to require "prescribed persons" to report annually on public interest disclosures received, to fine employers who do not pay tribunal awards or settlement sums, to limit the number of postponement applications which a party may make to the tribunal, to increase the financial penalty for underpayment of the minimum wage, to render exclusivity clauses in zero hours contracts unenforceable, and to require public sector employees and office-holders to repay exit payments when re-employed in the public sector.

LONDON

Contents:

Employment London	
Leading Sets	
Band 1	Devereux *
Blackstone Chambers *	Essex Court Chambers *
11KBW *	Matrix Chambers *
Littleton Chambers *	Old Square Chambers *
Band 2	**Band 3**
Cloisters *	Outer Temple Chambers *
Leading Silks	
Star individuals	**Brown** Damian *Littleton Chambers*
Bowers John *Littleton Chambers*	**Devonshire** Simon *11KBW* *
Cavanagh John *11KBW* *	**Ellenbogen** Naomi *Littleton Chambers* *
Goulding Paul *Blackstone Chambers*	**Goudie** James *11KBW* *
Hochhauser Andrew *Essex Court Chambers*	**Lynch** Adrian *11KBW* *
Jeans Christopher *11KBW* *	**Mansfield** Gavin *Littleton Chambers* *
Linden Thomas *Matrix Chambers*	**McKie** Suzanne *Littleton Chambers*
Rose Dinah *Blackstone Chambers*	**Randall** Nicholas *Devereux* *
Band 1	**Ritchie** Stuart *Littleton Chambers*
Allen Robin *Cloisters* *	**Segal** Oliver *Old Square Chambers* *
Bloch Selwyn *Littleton Chambers* *	**Sheldon** Clive *11KBW*
Carr Bruce *Devereux* *	**Sutton** Mark *Old Square Chambers*
Clarke Andrew *Littleton Chambers* *	**Williams** Heather *Doughty Street Chambers (ORL)* ◊
Epstein Paul *Cloisters* *	**Band 4**
Hendy John *Old Square Chambers* *	**Bryant** Keith *Outer Temple Chambers*
Laddie James *Matrix Chambers*	**Carss-Frisk** Monica *Blackstone Chambers*
McNeill Jane *Old Square Chambers* *	**Ford** Michael *Old Square Chambers*
Oudkerk Daniel *Essex Court Chambers* *	**Gott** Paul *Fountain Court Chambers (ORL)* ◊ *
Reade David *Littleton Chambers* *	**Green** Patrick *Henderson Chambers (ORL)* ◊ 🄰 *
Band 2	**Howe** Robert *Blackstone Chambers*
Glyn Caspar *Cloisters* *	**Millar** Gavin *Doughty Street Chambers (ORL)* ◊
Griffiths Martin *Essex Court Chambers*	**Mountfield** Helen *Matrix Chambers* *
Jones Seán *11KBW* *	**Pitt-Payne** Timothy *11KBW* *
Monaghan Karon *Matrix Chambers*	**Romney** Daphne *Cloisters* *
Nicholls Paul *11KBW* *	**New Silks**
Short Andrew *Outer Temple Chambers*	**Ciumei** Charles *Essex Court Chambers*
Stilitz Daniel *11KBW* *	**Duggan** Michael *Littleton Chambers* *
White Antony *Matrix Chambers* *	**Galbraith-Marten** Jason *Cloisters* *
Band 3	**Gallafent** Kate *Blackstone Chambers*
Algazy Jacques *Cloisters* *	**Mulcahy** Jane *Blackstone Chambers*
Brennan Timothy *Devereux* *	**Tolley** Adam *Fountain Court Chambers (ORL)* ◊ *
◊ (ORL) = Other Ranked Lawyer.	
🄰 direct access (see p.11).	
* Indicates set / individual with profile.	

Band 1

Blackstone Chambers

See profile on p.771

THE SET

Blackstone is known for its strength across the employment spectrum. Its barristers are equally at home covering high-profile discrimination cases as they are advising on discreet corporate matters. The team contains an array of outstanding silks who are complemented by a group of fantastic juniors. Barristers at the set are at the forefront of the law and regularly push the boundaries of the law through their handling of complex and precedent-setting cases.

Client service: "They are very hard-working, responsive and client-friendly barristers. The clerks are also always helpful and very good at getting back to you quickly." "The clerking is very transparent and you can actually have a conversation, fees-wise, with them." Gary Oliver leads the team.

SILKS

Monica Carss-Frisk QC Represents claimants and employees in a broad range of employment matters, and has notable expertise in discrimination claims. **Strengths:** "A very good and very confident silk who knows her arguments." "She's exceptionally calm and persuasive."

Paul Goulding QC A highly skilled barrister who is considered an authority on restrictive covenants. He inspires confidence in clients who recommend him for 'bet the company' cases. A very good all-rounder, he is one of the very best employment silks in the market. **Strengths:** "The go-to person for post-termination covenants." "Superbly clever and particularly good on restrictive covenants, and cases concerning confidential information." **Recent work:** Acted for BlueBay Asset Management in a case involving the forfeiture of stock by a former employee.

Kate Gallafent QC An expert on the crossover between human rights law and employment. Her general employment practice is broad and encompasses everything from TUPE to discrimination matters. **Strengths:** "She is effective at communicating strategy and tactful when dealing with clients." **Recent work:** Advised Dentons in relation to a claim of sex discrimination lodged by a former trainee.

Dinah Rose QC A pre-eminent silk who is well known for her superior advocacy in the Supreme Court. She is a star of the Employment Bar and is highly sought after for her experience in handling the most complex and high-profile cases. **Strengths:** "She regularly does high-profile and complex legal cases in the discrimination arena." "What is most impressive about her is that she is the master of so many disciplines." **Recent work:** Acted for the appellant in the Supreme Court case of President of the Methodist Conference v Preston. She successfully argued that the respondent could not claim unfair dismissal because a Methodist minister was not an employee.

Robert Howe QC Has a commercial focus to his employment practice and mainly operates at the High Court level. His recent work includes cases concerning high-value team moves and post-termination restraint of trade. **Strengths:** "He is fabulously able, and someone you always want on your side." **Recent work:** Acted for the employer in Kaplan Financial v Locke, which concerned an application for a freezing injunction relating to breach of contract.

Jane Mulcahy QC Has a wide-ranging employment practice and is noted as an outstanding advocate. She is praised for her tribunal work but she also has a significant practice in the higher courts. Her client service is of a high standard and she is highly personable in difficult situations. **Strengths:** "She is very hands-on and effective." "She does a very good job of cross-examining" and is "an effective fighter who is a great person to work with."

JUNIORS

Thomas Croxford A pre-eminent senior junior who "you can use for QC-level matters." He is highly recommended for a broad range of work, including discrimination and restraint of trade cases. **Strengths:** "He is good on complicated discrimination cases and an excellent cross-examiner." "An expert on restrictive covenants who provides pragmatic advice." **Recent work:** Acted for the employer in Seldon v Clarkson Wright & Jakes, a long-running case concerning justified direct age discrimination.

Nick De Marco Has a diverse employment practice, and handles significant amounts of work in the tribunal and at the High Court. His recent work is broad and includes whistle-blowing claims as well as matters involving team moves and restraint of trade. **Strengths:** "He has a great knowledge of the law and is also very creative." "He has good judgement and is good at seeing the wood from the trees." **Recent work:** Acted for a number of the defendants in CEF Holdings v Mundey, which concerned the circumstances in which restrictive covenants and springboard injunctions can be enforced.

Catherine Callaghan Advises both senior employees and employers, and regularly appears in the Employment Tribunal, Employment Appeals Tribu-

Employment
London
Leading Juniors

Star individuals	**Mehrzad** John *Littleton Chambers* *	**Davies** Charlotte *Littleton Chambers* *
Craig David *Essex Court Chambers*	**Milsom** Chris *Cloisters* *	**Davies** Jonathan *Old Square Chambers* *
Leiper Richard *11KBW* *	**Proops** Anya *11KBW* *	**Dobbie** Olivia-Faith *Cloisters* *
Band 1	**Sendall** Antony *Littleton Chambers*	**Donnelly** Kathleen *Henderson Chambers (ORL)* ◊ [A] *
Burns Andrew *Devereux* *	**Stone** Judy *11KBW* *	**Dyal** Daniel *Cloisters* *
Cohen Jonathan *Littleton Chambers*	**Tuck** Rebecca *Old Square Chambers* *	**Genn** Yvette *Cloisters*
Cooper Ben *Old Square Chambers* *	**Windle** Victoria *Blackstone Chambers*	**Kemp** Edward *Littleton Chambers* *
Crasnow Rachel *Cloisters* *	**Band 4**	**Massarella** David *Cloisters* *
Croxford Thomas *Blackstone Chambers*	**Afeeva** Mark *Matrix Chambers*	**Mayhew** Alice *Devereux* *
Kibling Thomas *Matrix Chambers*	**Barnett** Daniel *Outer Temple Chambers*	**Milford** Julian *11KBW* *
McCafferty Jane *11KBW* *	**Beale** Anna *Cloisters* *	**Mitchell** David *Ely Place Chambers (ORL)* ◊ *
Nawbatt Akash *Devereux* *	**Blake** Andrew *11KBW* *	**Mitchell** Jack *3PB Barristers (ORL)* ◊
Quinn Chris *Littleton Chambers* *	**Collins** Ben *Old Square Chambers* *	**Musgrave** Caroline *Cloisters* *
Sethi Mohinderpal *Littleton Chambers*	**Darwin** Claire *Matrix Chambers* *	**Prince** Laura *Matrix Chambers* *
Band 2	**Edwards** Peter *Devereux* *	**Rajgopaul** Craig *Littleton Chambers* *
Cheetham Simon *Old Square Chambers* *	**Fodder** Martin *Littleton Chambers* *	**Rayner** Catherine *7BR (ORL)* ◊ *
Choudhury Akhlaq *11KBW* *	**Gardiner** Bruce *2TG - 2 Temple Gardens (ORL)* ◊ [A]	**Reindorf** Akua *Cloisters* *
De Marco Nick *Blackstone Chambers*	**Halliday** Patrick *11KBW* *	**Robson** Alexander *Littleton Chambers*
Edge Andrew *11KBW* *	**Hare** Ivan *Blackstone Chambers*	**Scott** Ian *Old Square Chambers* *
Forshaw Simon *11KBW* *	**Harris** Lucinda *Devereux* *	**Seymour** Lydia *Outer Temple Chambers*
McCann Claire *Cloisters* *	**Ling** Naomi *Outer Temple Chambers*	**Shiu** Ming-Yee *Littleton Chambers* [A] *
Michell Paul *Cloisters* *	**Masters** Dee *Cloisters* *	**Smith** Andrew *Matrix Chambers* *
Neaman Sam *Littleton Chambers* *	**Melville** Elizabeth *Old Square Chambers* *	**Toms** Nick *Doughty Street Chambers (ORL)* ◊
Newton Katharine *Old Square Chambers* *	**Misra** Eleena *Littleton Chambers* *	**von Wachter** Victoria *5 Essex Court (ORL)* ◊ *
O'Dempsey Declan *Cloisters* *	**Motraghi** Nadia *Old Square Chambers* *	**Williams** Ed *Cloisters* *
Pilgerstorfer Marcus *11KBW* *	**Omambala** Ijeoma *Old Square Chambers* *	**Wilson** Julian *11KBW* *
Rogers Amy *11KBW* *	**Panesar** Deshpal *Old Square Chambers* *	**Winstone** Hilary *Old Square Chambers* *
Sen Gupta Diya *Blackstone Chambers*	**Pritchard** Simon *Blackstone Chambers*	**Wynne** James *Littleton Chambers* *
Solomon Adam *Littleton Chambers*	**Purchase** Mathew *Matrix Chambers* *	**Up-and-coming individuals**
Tatton-Brown Daniel *Littleton Chambers*	**Shepherd** Jude *42 Bedford Row (ORL)* ◊	**Balmer** Kate *Devereux* *
Band 3	**Sheridan** Matthew *Littleton Chambers* *	**Banerjee** Lydia *Littleton Chambers* *
Belgrove Sophie *Devereux* *	**Stout** Holly *11KBW* *	**Barsam** Talia *Devereux* *
Bone Lucy *Littleton Chambers* *	**Tabachnik** Andrew *Thirty Nine Essex Street (ORL)* ◊	**Bell** Laura *Devereux* *
Brittenden Stuart *Old Square Chambers* *	**Tether** Melanie *Old Square Chambers* *	**Bickford Smith** James *Littleton Chambers* *
Brown Edward *Essex Court Chambers*	**White** Robin *Old Square Chambers* *	**Cordrey** Thomas *Devereux* *
Callaghan Catherine *Blackstone Chambers*	**Band 5**	**Fraser Butlin** Sarah *Cloisters* *
Chudleigh Louise *Old Square Chambers* *	**Allen** Andrew *Outer Temple Chambers*	**Holloway** Orlando *42 Bedford Row (ORL)* ◊
Clarke Gerard *Blackstone Chambers*	**Brook** David *Henderson Chambers (ORL)* ◊ [A]	**Lee** Michael *11KBW* *
Coghlin Thomas *Cloisters* *	**Brown** Thomas *Cloisters* *	**McNair-Wilson** Laura *Matrix Chambers*
Davis Carol *Littleton Chambers* *	**Burgher** Benjimin *Outer Temple Chambers* *	**Mussa** Hanif *Blackstone Chambers*
de Silva Niran *Littleton Chambers*	**Casserley** Catherine *Cloisters* *	**Omeri** Sheryn *Cloisters*
Hill Henrietta *Doughty Street Chambers (ORL)* ◊ [A]	**Chan** Susan *42 Bedford Row (ORL)* ◊	**Russell** Jane *Essex Court Chambers*
Jolly Schona *Cloisters* *	**Criddle** Betsan *Old Square Chambers* *	**Stone** Christopher *Devereux* *
Lewis Jeremy *Littleton Chambers*	**Cross** Tom *11KBW* *	
Martin Dale *Littleton Chambers* *	**Cunningham** Naomi *Outer Temple Chambers*	

◊ (ORL) = Other Ranked Lawyer.
[A] direct access (see p.11).
* Indicates individual with profile.

nal and higher courts. Her practice is broad and she is regularly instructed in all areas of employment law. **Recent work:** Acted for the respondent in Olotin v Sumitomo Mitsui Banking Corporation, succeeding in getting claims of victimisation and race discrimination struck out.

Gerard Clarke A number of sources recommend him for his advice on restrictive covenants, but he is more generally known for the strength of his High Court practice. Recent highlights include advising employers on cases involving trade unions. **Strengths:** "Never seen a better advocate – he works the judge well, is exceptionally intelligent and fights with passion." **Recent work:** Advised a number of the respondents in CEF Holdings v Mundey in opposing restrictive covenants and a springboard injunction.

Diya Sen Gupta Widely seen as one of the leading employment juniors, she counts prominent City-based law firms among her dedicated client following. She is experienced at both tribunal and High Court level, and is adept at advising on all aspects of employment law. **Strengths:** "Very sharp and hard-working, she is nobody's fool. Good with clients, she's enjoyable to work with." "A good all-round litigator, particularly on whistle-blowing cases." **Recent work:** Acted for RBS in defending a claim of wrongful dismissal and unfair dismissal brought by a former CDO trader.

Ivan Hare Excels in both employment and professional discipline cases, and is regularly called upon to advise clients where these two areas overlap. His pure employment practice is broad, but he is especially well known for the strength of his work on discrimination issues. **Strengths:** "He is very good on philosophical belief cases." **Recent work:** Acted in Weeks v Newham College, an appeal case concerning the Employment Tribunal's dismissal of victimisation and harassment claims.

Victoria Windle Widely praised for her all-round employment expertise, she regularly acts for claimants and respondents in the higher courts as well as the Employment Tribunals. **Strengths:** "She is very responsive and full of common sense." "Her analysis and appraisal of relevant points in the employment sphere is extremely helpful and spot on." **Recent work:** Acted for the BBC in successfully defending unfair dismissal and whistle-blowing claims brought by a former freelancer. The case also involved questions as to the redundancy payments a freelancer could expect.

Simon Pritchard Has recent experience spanning all areas of employment law. He has advised employers in the financial services sector on High Court actions and also worked with employees on unfair dismissal cases. **Strengths:** "He is responsive and thorough." **Recent work:** Acted in Mortimer v King, a dispute in the High Court relating to a team move and alleged breach of restrictive covenants.

Hanif Mussa Has a growing reputation for his broad employment expertise. He is equally at home advising on complex discrimination claims as he is on High Court breach of contract claims. He stands out because of the strength of his tribunal work. **Strengths:** "He's completely unfussy and totally modern in his approach to the instructing solicitor. You get top-quality advice delivered in a really helpful way." **Recent work:** Advised the employer in Bodimeade v Bam Nuttall, defending a number of claims including harassment and disability discrimination.

11KBW

See profile on p.823

THE SET

11KBW is renowned for the breadth and depth of its employment team, and has excellent barristers at all levels, from its leading silks through to its baby juniors. One impressed solicitor says: "I would feel comfortable using anyone at the set who I had not used before as I would be very confident that that person would be of high quality." Clients range from claimants with straightforward cases right up to global companies facing complex issues. The members here are used to appearing in the highest courts in the land.

Client service: "We find the set particularly impressive both in terms of the barristers but also the clerking." "All here have a reputation for working very hard and preparing matters very thoroughly." Lucy Barbet and Mark Dann are the joint senior clerks.

SILKS

John Cavanagh QC (see p.567) Widely viewed as one of the leading employment law silks, he is recommended for his work on heavyweight cases. His recent caseload has been broad, and he has handled a number of high-profile bonus disputes and industrial relations cases. **Strengths:** "He is extraordinarily good, he has an encyclopaedic knowledge of the law and he is happy to roll up his sleeves." "A first port of call if you need to instruct top-drawer leading counsel." "He is able to reel cases off the top of his head, and is very commercial. He's absolutely fantastic in terms of his legal analysis and judgement." **Recent work:** Advised Ineos on a high-profile industrial dispute at the Grangemouth oil and chemical refinery.

Christopher Jeans QC A leading employment silk who is cited as being "the best employment lawyer at the Bar" by a number of interviewees. He is well known for his expertise on the crossover between employment, EU and human rights law, and a number of his cases have an international dimension. **Strengths:** "His disarming modesty hides his razor-sharp intellect." "Great at grasping the detail but never losing sight of the bigger picture." **Recent work:** Advised UNISON on a high-profile racial discrimination claim brought by an Israeli academic. The claim arose due to an alleged boycott of a speaking engagement.

Seán Jones QC A go-to barrister for many of the top employment solicitors. His work covers all aspects of employment law and he is adept at both tribunal and High Court litigation. He is well regarded for his sports-related work. **Strengths:** "He has outstanding analytical ability, is highly polished and is clear in all his communications." "He's very sharp and has an impressive knowledge of all areas of employment law." **Recent work:** Advised the respondent in Neal v Freightliner, a case establishing that holiday pay calculations should take overtime payments into account.

Daniel Stilitz QC (see p.729) A "formidable advocate" who is singled out for the strength of his cross-examination. Solicitors see him as a highly commercial barrister and go to him for advice on all aspects of employment law, including complex discrimination and whistle-blowing claims. **Strengths:** "A pragmatic, commercial and technically able employment expert with practical skill in large-scale bonus and incentive claims in the finance sector." "He's very good on TUPE and in tribunal generally, as he's commercially and strategically astute." "He is very good, very calm and very clever, and can destroy people in cross-examination when he wants to." **Recent work:** Advised the claimant in Skipper v BP, in which a senior in-house lawyer claimed age discrimination, alleging he had been passed over for promotion because of his age.

James Goudie QC (see p.612) Regularly advises public sector groups including local councils and police forces, and is recommended for his work on sector-important TUPE cases. In addition to this, he regularly works with private sector organisations on all aspects of employment law. **Strengths:** "He stands out due to his technical knowledge and years of experience of handling highly sensitive issues of public interest."

Adrian Lynch QC (see p.659) Has a broad employment practice but is widely recognised as an expert on TUPE and equal pay. As well as the two aforementioned areas, his recent caseload has included work on discrimination and breach of contract claims. **Strengths:** "A very clever guy who is exceptionally nice to work with. I value an opinion from him on very tricky points." **Recent work:** Appeared for the respondent before the ECJ in Alemo-Herron v Parkwood. This important ruling clarified the relationship between collective agreements and TUPE transfers.

Paul Nicholls QC (see p.682) Well known for his work on High Court breach of contract claims, as well as those relating to restrictive covenants. He also regularly advises employers on pre-litigation matters and is particularly valued because of his commercial approach. **Strengths:** "A great advocate who does not sit on the fence." "He always does a fantastic job, especially on restrictive covenants." **Recent work:** Advised the respondent in Conneely v Irish Bank Resolution Corporation on the strike-out of a claim for breach of contract.

Clive Sheldon QC Focuses on discrimination claims and has recently advised on some of the most high-profile cases, such as Dizaei v Metropolitan Police Authority. He regularly acts in both racial and disability discrimination cases. **Strengths:** "A fighter and an intellectual. He displays great attention to detail and puts in the hours. He's great to have on your side in a scrap." **Recent work:** Assisted Cardiff University on the defence of a disability discrimination claim brought by a lecturer.

Simon Devonshire QC (see p.587) Widely viewed by both barristers and solicitors as one of the leading silks for advice on business protection, and a go-to barrister for cases involving restraint of trade. He is also recommended for his work on whistle-blowing claims. **Strengths:** "He is somebody who relishes rolling up his sleeves and he really mucks in." "He is a star beyond belief, and is intellectually brilliant and commercially astute."

Timothy Pitt-Payne QC (see p.694) Has a broad practice which encompasses all aspects of employment law. He is considered a star performer in the area of data protection and is well reputed for his advice on the intersection of information and employment law. **Recent work:** Advised Arthur Scargill on his dispute with the National Union of Mineworkers relating to post-retirement benefits including a flat in London's Barbican Centre.

JUNIORS

Andrew Blake (see p.551) Has an all-encompassing practice and regularly advises on discrimination, whistle-blowing and TUPE claims. He assists both employers and individuals, and is recommended for his work on equal pay cases. **Strengths:** "Very user-friendly, he shows a genuine interest in what he is dealing with and the client's point of view." "Extremely bright and very skilled at explaining things to businesspeople. He leaves clients feeling they are in the safest hands." **Recent work:** Advised the claimant in Rooney v West London Mental Health Trust, a constructive dismissal claim.

Richard Leiper (see p.654) Widely viewed as one of the leading juniors at the Employment Bar. His practice is broad and he is praised for his work in multiple areas. He is, however, most noted for his work on bonus disputes, restrictive covenants and other High Court litigation. **Strengths:** "He is very impressive, very robust and also client-friendly." **Recent work:** Advised the respondent in Clements v Lloyds in its defence of high-profile claims of age discrimination and whistle-blowing brought by its former head of business continuity.

Akhlaq Choudhury (see p.571) Has a varied employment practice and is well known for his High Court work. He advises both claimants and respondents on issues surrounding restraint of trade and bonus claims. **Strengths:** "He's very easy to work with and always an integral part of the team. He will go out of his way to help." "A very good advocate who gets good results for clients, and is very sensitive to clients' needs." **Recent work:** Advised Matt Nixson, the Sun's former head of features, after he was summarily dismissed.

Jane McCafferty (see p.666) A skilful advocate who excels at both tribunal and High Court work. She is noted for her experience in advising clients in the financial services sector, in which regard she has handled a number of recent cases for employers and senior executives. **Strengths:** "A super-brain, who is exceptionally brilliant on financial services matters because she really understands the sector."

Marcus Pilgerstorfer (see p.693) Receives praise for his work on complicated TUPE matters, and is widely viewed as a rising star of the junior Employment Bar. His expertise is wide and he is regularly sought out for advice on discrimination, whistle-blowing and bonus claims. **Strengths:** "He has a highly effective, intellectual approach and delivers results." "You can have complete confidence in his technical ability and clients like him very much." **Recent work:** Advised the claimant in Hainsworth v Ministry of Defence, a test case which sought to clarify whether an employer had a duty to make reasonable adjustment for a person who cares for another who is disabled.

Amy Rogers (see p.709) Widely reputed as being a first-class junior for complex tribunal and High

Court work, especially those matters with a commercial angle. Her recent caseload has been broad and has included high-profile bonus disputes as well as sensitive issues relating to blacklisting. **Strengths:** "So hard-working and so efficient, she just does not drop the ball." "She is very good with clients and gets the measure of the situation very quickly. Clients really feel she is fighting for them." **Recent work:** Led by Daniel Oudkerk QC, she acted for the claimant in Bahar v Group Lotus, an unfair dismissal claim brought by a former CEO.

Anya Proops (see p.699) Impresses with the strength of her employment practice, and is particularly good at handling high-profile whistle-blowing claims. She is adept at handling a broad range of matters. **Strengths:** "A silk in junior's clothing. She has great intellectual capacity and has appeared in the Supreme Court without a leader."

Andrew Edge (see p.593) A skilled advocate, especially on complicated matters. His recent work includes sex and race discrimination cases, and he has also handled a number of high-profile whistle-blowing claims. **Strengths:** "Very impressive and well prepared, he really covers all the bases in terms of legal position and case law." **Recent work:** Advised Banco do Brasil on a whistle-blowing claim brought by a former employee.

Simon Forshaw (see p.602) A rising star in the employment field who is a leading tribunal advocate. He is praised for his "pure charm and cogent, logical arguments." **Strengths:** "A stylish advocate." **Recent work:** Acted for the respondent in Chapman v Chief Constable of the Essex Police, which concerned allegations of discrimination made by a transgender police officer.

Judy Stone (see p.729) Has a diverse employment practice and is "a rising star of the reasonably priced Bar." She represents both employers and employees, and works with clients in the public and private sectors. **Strengths:** "She is immensely bright, and has a very good sense of how to tactically play a case in an employment tribunal. She knows which points are worth pursuing." **Recent work:** Acted as sole counsel to Imperial College London in defending a claim alleging discrimination and whistle-blowing relating to alleged cheating.

Patrick Halliday (see p.617) Has a diverse employment practice and regularly advises clients on a full range of matters. His recent work includes notable whistle-blowing and discrimination claims. **Strengths:** "He is very good and knows his cases inside out. He is a very strong junior." **Recent work:** Led by Christopher Jeans QC, he advised ASDA on an equal pay claim lodged by female shop workers who argued they should be paid the same as their male counterparts working in warehouses.

Holly Stout (see p.730) Has a broad employment practice and is adept at advising on a diverse range of issues, including unfair dismissal, discrimination and restraint of trade. She advises both claimants and respondents, and is noted for her work with public sector clients. **Strengths:** "Clients value her because she is brilliant and hard-working, and she really masters her brief." **Recent work:** Advised Invideous on its claim for contractual breach and breach of director's duties against a former shareholder and director.

Julian Milford (see p.672) A well-rounded employment practitioner with noted expertise in complex discrimination claims. He receives praise for his commercial focus and for his meticulous preparation of cases. **Strengths:** "He's very good on his feet, and has an excellent grasp of detail and a sharp intellect." **Recent work:** Continues to advise Northumberland County Council in relation to thousands of equal pay claims brought by female workers.

Julian Wilson (see p.753) Noted for his work on disputes with a corporate and commercial dimension, this former litigation solicitor is in particularly high demand for City cases. In this respect he has represented a number of clients in high-profile bonus, dismissal and whistle-blowing cases. **Strengths:** "Approachable, very knowledgeable and an incredibly proactive barrister."

Tom Cross (see p.581) An impressive cross-examiner, who is praised for his work in the employment tribunal. He advises both employees and employers, and has a burgeoning High Court practice. **Strengths:** "Persuasive but not obviously so. He's quietly confident and you naturally trust him." **Recent work:** Advised London and South Eastern Railways on a disability discrimination claim after an employee was allegedly fired for being incapable of performing his role.

Michael Lee (see p.654) Well known for his experience of advising financial services and education sector clients. He is renowned for his skill as a tribunal advocate, and sources note that he is "unflappable." **Strengths:** "His style is not overbearing, which we find works well with tribunal claims. He is warm and friendly, and gets the job done in terms of cross-examination." "A shrewd and knowledgeable lawyer." **Recent work:** Advised the respondents in White v Lloyds, where the claimant alleged unfair dismissal and disability discrimination. The case raised questions regarding an employer's duty to take positive steps to accommodate disabled employees during restructurings.

Littleton Chambers
See profile on p.830

THE SET

An outstanding set with an impressive history of involvement in difficult and precedent-setting cases. Its team is composed of standout barristers at both senior and junior level who regularly take on work at all levels of the court system. Individuals here are particularly well known for their expertise on employment law issues with a commercial dimension. Recent cases handled by the members include Preston v President Methodist Conference, an important matter concerning the employment status of the clergy, and Dr S Verma v Barts and the London NHS Trust, the leading case on the meaning of pay protection for doctors within the NHS.

Client service: "The clerks are responsive and give you straight answers which is key; we find them to be no-nonsense." "They are very commercial. I can speak very straight with them and they will not mess me about with fees and questions of who is or who isn't available." Alistair Coyne is the senior managing clerk.

SILKS

John Bowers QC A go-to lawyer for TUPE, whistle-blowing and industrial relations. His broad expertise makes him a highly sought-after silk for the most complicated cases. **Strengths:** "Effusive in his arguments, he is a charming but firm opponent." "He's incredibly responsive and realistic about what can be achieved." "An at-times fierce advocate, who can gain admissions from the most sophisticated and intelligent of witnesses he is cross-examining." **Recent work:** Acted for the appellant in the EAT case of Sharp v Worcester Diocesan Board, in which a vicar successfully claimed he was an employee or a worker.

Selwyn Bloch QC (see p.551) Specialises in advising clients on High Court litigation, and is considered to be a first choice for restrictive covenants. **Strengths:** "Delightful, charming and particularly good on restrictive covenants." **Recent work:** Advised the main defendant in BMS v TigerRisk, a claim relating to a team move.

Andrew Clarke QC (see p.572) Has "a brain the size of a planet" and is recommended for his "attention to detail and great advocacy skills. " He offers high-level advice relating to industrial relations, restrictive covenants and TUPE, and is widely considered to be one of the leading silks in those areas. **Strengths:** "He has got a wonderful gravitas about him, and can make a bad argument sound authoritative." "He has got a lot of tribunal experience and is really good at complex tribunal litigation." **Recent work:** Advised the Royal Mail on threatened strike action by the CWU in the run-up to the postal services privatisation.

David Reade QC (see p.705) A silk of choice for some of the leading City employment practices. He regularly advises on all aspects of employment law and is widely praised for his commercial and client-focused approach. **Strengths:** "Very knowledgeable on trade union issues and really good at holding a client's hand through industrial disputes." "He's very practical and has a good manner with clients; he will give you a view and stick to it." "His legal knowledge is second to none, and he manages to balance intellect with personability." **Recent work:** Acted for the owners of Crystal Palace FC in the Court of Appeal, defeating claims that they were liable for staff dismissed by administrators through the operation of TUPE.

Damian Brown QC A pre-eminent employment barrister with extensive experience of advising on industrial relations matters. He works with both employers and unions in the area and often appears on their most complex matters. He is also recommended for his work on business protection, and routinely advises on team moves and restrictive covenants. **Strengths:** "A creative thinker who establishes a rapport with the client quickly." "He has a strong background in labour relations law." "Really good on team moves, he's a good tactician." **Recent work:** Advised the respondent in Smith v Carillion, a high-profile union blacklisting claim.

Naomi Ellenbogen QC (see p.594) Excels at advising on multiparty equal pay claims, and is sought out by public sector clients such as NHS trusts and local councils. She also acts for private sector clients on a range of matters, including discrimination and whistle-blowing. **Strengths:** "She is absolutely fantastic and brilliant on her feet. She has a great eye for detail but does not get lost in it." **Recent work:** Acted for the respondent in Balmer v Darlington Borough Council, proving successful in having all claims struck out.

Suzanne McKie QC A superb cross-examiner who is very effective in tribunal. She is recommended for her commercial and client-focused approach and is considered a go-to for partnership disputes. She also has expertise in sex discrimination cases and notable knowledge on equal pay. **Strengths:** "Her advice is very clear and she is able to look at the case from a number of different angles." "Her strategy and how quickly she got to grips with the facts is impressive. She was extremely helpful at getting us on the front foot in the case." **Recent work:** Acted for Deloitte in defending high-value age discrimination claims lodged by partners within the firm.

Stuart Ritchie QC Advises clients on both employment and general commercial matters, and is noted for his work on cases which involve both disciplines. He is regularly instructed in High Court cases, acting for both individuals and employers, and has recently handled matters relating to team moves. **Strengths:** "He has a good way of cutting through sensitive issues and he manages to deliver difficult and sensitive messages in a way that does not upset people." "His technical ability and knowledge are fantastic." **Recent work:** Advised a defendant in Marathon Asset Management v Seddon, a case where the employer was claiming damages relating to an alleged team move to a competitor.

Gavin Mansfield QC (see p.662) Continues to impress with his work on restrictive covenants and team moves. He also regularly works on difficult discrimination claims. **Strengths:** "Clients like him because he is to the point and good at explaining the practical steps that need to be taken." "Tenacious in the fight but straightforward and down to earth with clients, he is very good at client handling." "Very calm and cool, he's an effective cross-examiner." **Recent work:** Acted for a defendant in Marathon Asset Management v Seddon, which involved allegations of an unlawful team move.

Michael Duggan QC (see p.591) Stands out for his expertise in complex High Court litigation, including cases relating to restrictive covenants and team moves. He is an expert on all areas of employment law and is particularly strong on wrongful dismissal and discrimination claims. **Strengths:** "Good for appellant and high-level work." "He is very client-friendly. He gives clear opinions in the cases he is working on and provides tremendous support." **Recent work:** Advised the claimant in Shiret v Credit Suisse, a multimillion-pound age discrimination claim in which the bank was found to be liable.

JUNIORS

Jonathan Cohen Sources hail him as one of the leading barrister at the junior Bar. He is well versed in City disputes, and represents both claimants and respondents in the High Court. He also excels in the employment tribunal and has an established reputation for his strength across the board. **Strengths:** "A brave and able litigator who is able to hold his own against silks." "Very persuasive, he is just so good and makes all the right points." "He's highly commercial, extremely able and excellent with clients." **Recent work:** Acted for the respondent in Kearns v Glencore, where the claimant alleged he had been wrongfully dismissed and, in the process, lost shares worth upwards of £8 million.

Lucy Bone (see p.552) An acclaimed senior junior who is praised for her grasp of detail and understanding of commercial reality. She also regularly advises on High Court disputes, and has particular skill in obtaining injunctions. Recently, she has impressed with her work on complex whistle-blowing and multiparty TUPE claims. **Strengths:** "A dogged and brave advocate, she will press points even if the judge may not be with her in the beginning." "She does not overcomplicate things, and is good at being straightforward and presenting things in a straightforward way." **Recent work:** Acted for Whitmar Publications in its ground-breaking application for injunctive relief relating to a breach of confidence claim for the misuse of social networks post-termination.

Carol Davis (see p.584) A well thought-of senior junior with a diverse employment practice. Her client-friendly and hard-working approach is emphasised, as is her skill at cross-examination. She has a wealth of experience of advising on whistle-blowing and discrimination claims in tribunal, and also has a substantial High Court practice. **Strengths:** "She is magnificent, superb in the tribunal and excellent with the judge." **Recent work:** Acted for the claimant, a former chief executive of the Barking and Dagenham Primary Care Trust, in his £700,000 plus wrongful dismissal claim.

Niran de Silva Applauded for his extremely commercial approach to instructions. He is singled out for his work on cases involving social media issues, and is also well known for advising both claimants and respondents on City-based claims. **Strengths:** "Excellent, he shows steely determination and is great on his feet." "He understands the commercial realities and does not get strung up on the law." **Recent work:** Acted as junior to David Reade in the Supreme Court case of Hounga v Allen & Allen, which concerned common law illegality and whether this could be a bar to a claim for racial discrimination.

Charlotte Davies (see p.583) Has a diverse practice, and noted strength in the Employment Tribunal and EAT. She is praised for her ability to handle difficult opponents, and recommended for her knowledge of discrimination law. She has a growing High Court practice and is also sought out to advise on internal disciplinary disputes. **Strengths:** "She has first-class presentation in the Employment Tribunal; her cross-examination and her submissions are fantastic." "Clients love her down-to-earth manner and superb advocacy." **Recent work:** Led by Adam Solomon in advising the appellant in Engel v Patrol, where the court found that potentially discriminatory acts performed in the capacity of judicial office holder were subject to judicial immunity.

Lydia Banerjee (see p.542) A junior whose skills and expertise far exceed her year of call, she comes highly recommended by those who have worked with her. **Strengths:** "She is good on discrimination cases, very commercial, and has a good client manner." "She provides advice beyond her years of call, has fantastic technical knowledge, and her performances on her feet are second to none for someone at her level." **Recent work:** Led by Stuart Ritchie QC, she advised an individual who was alleged to have been part of an unlawful team move from BMS to Tigerrisk.

James Bickford Smith (see p.549) Displays confidence beyond his years, according to impressed sources. He is praised for his grasp of legal principles, with numerous interviewees commenting on his standout academic strength. His practice is diverse and takes in an array of High Court work. **Strengths:** "Sensible, pragmatic and very pleasant to deal with." **Recent work:** Acted for a former trader at Morgan Stanley who claimed he was unfairly dismissed after asking the bank to match the salary offer made by a competitor.

Chris Quinn (see p.701) Widely regarded as a go-to barrister for those cases which require robust advocacy. He is widely praised for his work representing City-based claimants and respondents. High Court matters are his forte but he is equally adept at advising on proceedings before the tribunals. **Strengths:** "He was fantastic in giving robust and confident advice. His speed of response was first-class and his grasp of detail impressive." "He has got a good sense of what is needed in the courtroom and what needs to be shown." "A good guy to have on your side in a fist fight, and someone who is good on cross-examination." **Recent work:** Led by Andrew Stafford in the Supreme Court, he advised the respondents in the high-profile and precedent-setting case of Clyde & Co v Van Winkelhof.

Sam Neaman (see p.681) A renowned senior junior recommended for matters with complicated factual circumstances. He receives widespread praise for his ability to step into difficult cases at short notice as well as for the strength of his High Court work. **Strengths:** "Tenacious and good humoured, he's always a pleasure to deal with." **Recent work:** Acted for Semsysco in having TUPE-related breach of contract claims struck out. The case is notable because of the conflict of laws issues it posed.

Adam Solomon An excellent senior junior who is noted for fighting hard for his clients. He has a thriving practice in the High Court, with recent highlights including cases involving restrictive covenants and breach of confidential information. **Strengths:** "He's intelligent and helpful, and instils confidence in his clients." **Recent work:** Acted for the appellant in Engel v Patrol, where the court found that potentially discriminatory acts performed in the capacity of judicial office holder were subject to judicial immunity.

Daniel Tatton-Brown An excellent advocate who is noted for his client service. He receives praise for his work on restrictive covenants in the High Court, and for his handling of complex tribunal matters. He is also adept at leading appellate cases in the EAT and Court of Appeal. **Strengths:** "Good in terms of legal analysis and very user-friendly." "He has a belts and braces approach and is very methodical in putting his arguments across." **Recent work:** Acted for the employer in JM Finn v Holliday, securing a one-year period of garden leave for a departing stockbroker.

Antony Sendall Gets to grips with complex issues very quickly and is recommended for his work on significant High Court litigation. An accredited mediator, he handles a number of City-based mediations. **Strengths:** "A clever lawyer who is great in court, and a great person to work with." "He's a good and pragmatic advocate."

Jeremy Lewis He is recommended for his knowledge on how to set up complex cases in tribunal. Considered a straight-talking barrister, he is noted for his work in diverse areas such as whistle-blowing, restrictive covenants and injunctions. **Strengths:** "He is able to handle complex matters and offers superb case analysis." "He's the sort of barrister you immediately pay attention to as soon as he starts speaking."

Dale Martin (see p.664) Has a diverse employment practice and regularly appears in the Employment Tribunal, in the High Court and at appellate level. He is considered a leading individual for equal pay claims, and is highlighted for his tactical nous in this area. **Strengths:** "Personable and approachable, he is easy to get along with." "A great tactician who is on top of the detail." **Recent work:** Advised the defendants in Romero Insurance v Templeton, which concerned the enforceability of a 12-month non-solicitation of clients restrictive covenant.

Eleena Misra (see p.673) Has a great deal of recent experience of advising NHS trusts on issues as diverse as religious discrimination, agency worker regulations and whistle-blowing. She also has a thriving practice representing private sector groups on the full range of employment law. **Strengths:** "Very good at establishing a rapport with clients. She is also excellent at preparing clients for tribunal." "Detailed and thorough in her preparation, she can digest a large number of documents quickly, and she can really get to the nub of an issue." **Recent work:** Acted for the respondents in Lokhova v Sberbank, a multimillion-pound sexual discrimination claim.

Martin Fodder (see p.601) A senior junior with wide-ranging expertise, who is able to provide advice across the employment law spectrum. He is regularly instructed by groups in the public sector, and his recent work has included significant TUPE cases. **Strengths:** "He researches well and his cross-examination is devastating." **Recent work:** Advised the defendant in GMB v Birtley Building Products, which concerned the duty to inform and consult in TUPE.

John Mehrzad Excellent at injunction work and recommended for his handling of restrictive covenant cases. He is renowned for his employment work in a sporting context, and is regularly instructed by the Football Association. **Strengths:** "He has a really good manner with clients but is also tenacious. He punches above his weight." **Recent work:** Advised the respondent in Edohen v The FA, successfully defending a claim of sex discrimination.

Matthew Sheridan (see p.719) Has impressed with his work on restrictive covenants and is widely praised as a hard-working and diligent barrister. His employment practice spans the tribunals and High Court, and he is adept at providing advice on all aspects of employment law. **Strengths:** "He has gravitas, but he also adopts a friendly and approachable demeanour." "A talented and robust advocate who can pick through the detail to get to good points, which he is then able to put across in cross-examination."

Craig Rajgopaul (see p.703) An up-and-coming junior, whose employment practice is going from strength to strength. He is a former solicitor and is praised for his commercial outlook and keen understanding of the pressures facing those that instruct him. His recent work includes high-profile discrimination claims in the Employment Tribunal and breach of contract and team move matters in the High Court. **Strengths:** "Commercial, responsive and practical. He used to be a solicitor and really understands the environment in which we operate." "A rising star, he's quick and sharp, and gets stuff done." **Recent work:** Advised the claimant in Masson v Commission of the Metropolis, which involved a claim for religious and disability discrimination and whistle-blowing.

Alexander Robson Has a broad practice and regularly acts for claimants and respondents. He also has a thriving appellate practice, and routinely appears before the EAT. He has handled a number of matters for clients in the financial services sector, and has proved himself an expert on restrictive covenants. **Strengths:** "Delivers clear and concise advice and has a good grasp of commercial and business realities/pressures. He also has an excellent manner when dealing with lay witnesses." **Recent work:** Advised a former trader at RBS in a claim for unfair dismissal after he was sacked for alleged Libor rigging.

Edward Kemp (see p.644) Advises across the full range of employment law, and has standout expertise in discrimination cases. He routinely argues cases in front of the tribunals and higher courts, and has recently appeared in the Supreme Court. **Strengths:** "He deals with complex and challenging cases with grace and determination." **Recent work:** Advised the respondent in Golonka v Elizabeth Arden, a sex discrimination claim.

Ming-Yee Shiu (see p.720) Focuses on employment matters with a commercial crossover and is recommended for her work on restrictive covenants and injunctions. She is praised for her knowledge of the law and for her efficacy as an advocate. **Recent work:** Advised the applicant in BFCA v Ahmad Tanveer But, a case where an injunction was sought after former employees set up a competing business.

James Wynne (see p.756) Has notable expertise in working with employers on their industrial relations issues in both an advisory and contentious context. He is adept at handling cases with complex factual backgrounds and has recent experience of advising on English law disputes in Dubai. **Strengths:** "His advocacy is excellent, and he manages to tie down slippery witnesses with his cross-examination." **Recent work:** Advised the claimants in Hana Al Herz v Dubai International Financial Centre Authority, which concerned unfair dismissal in the emirate.

Mohinderpal Sethi Has built a strong, commercially focused employment practice and is regularly instructed on business protection cases. He is singled out for his high-profile work on diplomatic and state immunity and is widely viewed as an expert on cases involving these issues. **Strengths:** "He is good with clients because he is very personable. As you would expect he is on top of the law and good on cross-examination." "Provides excellent service and addresses difficult questions well." **Recent work:** Advised the respondent in Reyes v Al Malki, a high-profile and complex diplomatic immunity case.

Band 2

Cloisters
See profile on p.778

THE SET

Cloisters is a set with a great history in employment. Although traditionally associated with claimant work, it also regularly acts for respondents and counts leading law firms, NGOs and trade unions among its clients. It handles the full spread of employment work but is particularly known for acting for employees bringing litigation against law firms and for its efforts in equal pay cases. Its members have appeared in numerous key equality appellate cases including O'Brien v Ministry of Justice, and Abdulla v Birmingham.

Client service: "The clerks, led by Glenn Hudson, are friendly and reliable." "It is a good-quality set and competitive on prices."

SILKS

Robin Allen QC (see p.534) Considered one of the big hitters in the field, he routinely acts at appellate and European level and is ever present in the Supreme Court. He is considered a go-to person for heavyweight discrimination and equal pay claims. **Strengths:** "Well known for taking on cases at the cutting edge of employment law." "He does not put costs first and he really takes cases that are interesting." **Recent work:** Acted in the high-profile case of O'Brien v Ministry of Justice in both the Supreme Court and ECJ.

Paul Epstein QC (see p.596) Stands out for his work on complex cases. He is considered a formidable opponent by peers, and is a recognised expert on equal pay claims. His clients include both employers and employees, and he regularly handles regular work for City-based senior executives. **Strengths:** "A lawyer with a good tactical brain and someone you feel confident having on your side." **Recent work:** Acted for Birmingham City Council in a number of high-profile equal pay claims, including the precedent-setting Birmingham v Abdulla.

Caspar Glyn QC A masterful courtroom lawyer who excels when handling difficult litigation. He is a tenacious advocate and offers superb client service. His recent work has included a number of high-profile and high-value claims. **Strengths:** "He gets stuck in and likes to be in complete control of a case." "A great cross-examiner who is great with clients." "He is such a great trial lawyer that right from the outset the advice is focused on obtaining a favourable outcome." **Recent work:** Defended the BBC in a high-profile whistle-blowing claim lodged by its former Director of Personnel.

Daphne Romney QC (see p.710) Lauded for her discrimination expertise and recognised as being at the forefront of recent equal pay litigation. She regularly works on cases which push the boundary of the law. **Strengths:** "She is incredibly versatile and can adapt her style to her audience." "She is brilliant, especially on difficult legal points." **Recent work:** Advised the respondent in Singh v Urban Treat, where an injunction was sought to stop the poaching of staff. The case settled.

Jacques Algazy QC (see p.534) An extremely incisive barrister, he is known to be strong on his feet, and has an utterly charming style. His core expertise is in cases involving jurisdictional issues but his practice has a far broader scope and he is adept at advising on all aspects of employment law. **Strengths:** "Very good on technical points of law and very good at understanding how to get around them." **Recent work:** Acted for the respondent in Walker v Church Mission Society, a case which involved disputed jurisdiction owing to the claimant mainly working in Sudan.

Jason Galbraith-Marten QC (see p.605) An employment law expert with a track record of advising both claimants and respondents on all aspects of employment law. His talent for dealing with industrial relations was stressed by interviewees, and he has a wealth of experience of advising clients in the transport sector on these issues. **Strengths:** "Clients have been pleased with his level of preparation on complex cases and also his handling of them in court." "He impresses because of his attention to detail." "A man with a towering intellect who speaks with authority. He is charming and persuasive when dealing with both clients and judges." "In cross-examination, he is courteous and impressive; if there's ammunition to dismantle someone, he will use it." **Recent work:** Acted for the respondent in Turner v East Midlands Trains, where the claimant sought to challenge the test for unfair dismissal using human rights law.

JUNIORS

Rachel Crasnow (see p.580) Recommended for her work on complex discrimination cases, she is a tough and impressive opponent who is a talented advocate skilled at providing tactical advice. She has a broad client following and is regularly instructed by City-based firms as well as claimant and trade union-focused practices. **Strengths:** "She's unflappable, and has an easy manner in front of the tribunal." **Recent work:** Acted as junior counsel for the claimant in

O'Brien v Ministry of Justice.

Schona Jolly (see p.639) Renowned for her work on high-profile disputes, and has handled a number of recent complex discrimination cases. She regularly undertakes TUPE and whistle-blowing matters, and is particularly well known for her strength in equal pay cases. **Strengths:** "A very strong litigator and advocate, she is not intimidated by the other side." "Excellent on high-profile cases, she is really bright and good with clients." "We go to her for difficult cases, as she is very commercial and legally excellent. She is always willing to take on difficult cases." **Recent work:** Advised PC Carol Howard, a member of the Met Police's Diplomatic Protection Group on her successful, high-profile claim for sex and race discrimination.

Thomas Coghlin (see p.574) A multi-talented barrister who impresses with his ability to handle the most complex and significant employment disputes. He advises individuals including City-based employees and partners, and also regularly works with respondents in both the public and private sectors. **Strengths:** "His ability to cut through masses of paperwork and present his case is great." "A very good lawyer and advocate, he commands respect and is very good in tribunals." **Recent work:** Advised the appellant in the EAT and Court of Appeal case of Fox v British Airways, where the family of a deceased man successfully claimed for his full death in service benefit which had been lost when he was unfairly dismissed.

Anna Beale (see p.546) An employment law specialist who is well respected for her work on cutting-edge discrimination cases. She has notable experience in equal pay cases, having acted as junior counsel on a number of major claims in the past few years. **Strengths:** "Personable and intelligent, she has a practical attitude and can really progress a case." **Recent work:** Acted for the claimant in Austin v The Furniture Barn, where allegations of harassment, victimisation and discrimination on the grounds of pregnancy were made.

Catherine Casserley (see p.567) A discrimination expert who is especially good on disability discrimination matters. Her instructions come from a range of sources including City law firms, law centres and the Equality and Human Rights Commission. **Strengths:** "She has an in-depth knowledge of discrimination matters." **Recent work:** Acted on a disability discrimination claim for the claimant in Foster v Cardiff University.

Olivia-Faith Dobbie (see p.588) Has a burgeoning employment practice and is well beyond her years of call in terms of expertise. She is acclaimed for her client-focused and commercial outlook, and has a broad employment practice that has seen her handling work at the appellate level. **Strengths:** "Her work is at a high level and she always goes the extra mile." "Approachable, commercial and able to turn around complex instructions in a short timescale."

Daniel Dyal (see p.592) An employment and discrimination expert who also advises clients in other areas, including commercial and personal injury. His practice is broad and his caseload includes a range of matters in the EAT. **Strengths:** "He is very good on his feet. He did not have an easy run with the judge but he was persistent and well prepared." **Recent work:** Acted for EY and the National Audit Office in defending a TUPE claim relating to a large-scale transfer from the public to the private sector.

Yvette Genn Highly rated for her knowledge of discrimination law and has standout recent expertise in equal pay claims. She is experienced in acting for and against public sector bodies and is particularly strong on the tactical and strategic approach necessary in such cases. **Strengths:** "Brilliant at sifting through irrelevancies, she really gets to the nub of claims without getting distracted by background detail." **Recent work:** Acted for the respondents in Wolfe v North Middlesex NHS Trust, a disability discrimination claim where the claimant's disability was contested.

David Massarella (see p.664) A masterful advocate who is praised for his excellent tribunal manner. He advises on all aspects of employment and discrimination law and is instructed by a wide range of groups, including City law firms, claimant-focused practices and regional employment teams. **Strengths:** "Provides excellent client care and is good to work with. He is a brilliant advocate." **Recent work:** Acted for the claimant in Gabriel-Abraham v Sports Direct, where zero-hour contracts were challenged as constituting indirect sex discrimination.

Sarah Fraser Butlin (see p.604) A popular choice for NHS trusts, which instruct her on cases dealing with all aspects of employment and discrimination law. As well as handling work in the Employment Tribunal, she routinely appears at appellate level and also has a strong advisory practice. **Recent work:** Acted for the appellant in Cam v Matrix Service Development and Training, a race and disability discrimination claim where explicit racist language was used in general conversation.

Claire McCann (see p.666) A go-to advocate for tricky cases. She is noted for her work on difficult whistle-blowing and discrimination cases, and has recent experience of advising on equal pay matters. Her work with in-house legal teams stands out and she counts the likes of HSBC and Virgin Atlantic among her dedicated client base. **Strengths:** "Practical and commercial, she is very good at coming up with a resolution that suits everybody." "She's very hands-on and becomes part of the team." **Recent work:** Advised the respondents in Gill v Virgin Atlantic Airways, where the claimant argued disability discrimination due to an alleged failure to make reasonable adjustments.

Paul Michell (see p.671) Covers a wide range of expertise but is particularly recommended for his work on restrictive covenants. He has a noted command of equality and discrimination law, and regularly handles high-profile work for claimants and respondents. **Recent work:** Led by Christopher Jeans QC in the Supreme Court case of X v Mid-Sussex CAB, which concerned the application of discrimination law to the voluntary sector.

Declan O'Dempsey (see p.684) A multi-talented barrister who has masterful knowledge of employment and discrimination law and human rights cases. He is sought out for his experience of and expertise in complex and high-profile matters. **Strengths:** "Experienced on the crossover between employment, discrimination and human rights law." **Recent work:** Intervened on behalf of Age UK in the Supreme Court case Seldon v Clarkson Wright & Jakes.

Chris Milsom (see p.673) A sought-after employment and discrimination law expert, with a flourishing appellate practice. He also has personal injury expertise and is notable for his work on those matters which straddle personal injury and employment, such as stress at work cases. **Strengths:** "A very good advocate who shreds his opponents because he is straightforward and precise." "He produces excellent written work, and is a very enthusiastic and committed barrister." **Recent work:** Intervened in Jessemey v Rowstock on behalf of the Equality and Human Rights Commission, on the issue of post-termination victimisation.

Dee Masters (see p.664) Acknowledged for her impressive client service, she is praised for stringently fighting her client's corner. She is very experienced in acting on complex and high-profile cases, and regularly advises on a diverse range of subjects including TUPE and all forms of discrimination. **Strengths:** "Very on the ball, she thinks outside the box." "She's thorough and grasps the papers quickly. She's also user-friendly and clients like her." **Recent work:** Acted for the claimant in Amanda Pollard v CQC, a whistle-blowing claim linked with the Mid Staffordshire scandal.

Caroline Musgrave (see p.680) Identified as an impressive young barrister who is capable of turning her hand to all areas of employment law. She has recently developed her expertise in disability discrimination by undertaking a research project at Harvard University. **Strengths:** "Methodical and good at analysing a case." "Really personable and great with clients, she's reassuring and calm, and does not get into a flap." **Recent work:** Acted for the claimant in Williams v MOD, a high-profile sex discrimination claim brought by the RAF's most senior serving nurse.

Akua Reindorf (see p.706) A respected barrister, highly rated for her employment and discrimination practice. She has a diverse practice, and regularly works with both claimants and respondents in the Employment Tribunal and at appellate level. Her respondent practice includes instructions from private practice solicitors as well as multinational companies and public sector bodies. **Strengths:** "She has gravitas which means you can put her in front of senior businesspeople. She is good with witnesses and judges." **Recent work:** Advised Reading Borough Council in a long-running race discrimination case brought by the headteacher of a primary school who alleged there had been a racist campaign to have her removed from her job.

Ed Williams (see p.752) A notable employment and discrimination specialist. His client following is broad, and he regularly works with NHS trusts, local councils and unions. He also advises claimants and has undertaken recent work in the High Court on their behalf in breach of contract claims. **Strengths:** "His view on discrimination on political grounds is very good; he is invaluable for that." "A very able junior who gets to the heart of a brief quickly and is well liked by clients." **Recent work:** Advised the respondents in Moran v Ideal Cleaning Services, an important case which clarified the application of the Agency Worker Regulations.

Sheryn Omeri An employment and discrimination specialist who has niche expertise in matters with a personal injury crossover, including recent experience of stress at work cases. Her practice also has an international dimension, and she has appeared before the European Court of Human Rights on cases with employment elements. **Strengths:** "If she has a legal point she is like a dog with a bone." **Recent work:** Acted for the claimant in Bates v Southend University Hospital NHS Foundation Trust, a claim brought by an employee who had been on long-term sick leave.

Thomas Brown (see p.558) An expert in complex discrimination claims who has recently handled a number of matters involving major City banks. **Strengths:** "Intuitive and thoughtful and a lawyer whose written work is first-class." "He's calm and conscientious" and "does a masterful job." **Recent work:** Acted for the successful respondent in Donelien v Liberata UK Ltd, a whistle-blowing claim.

Devereux

See profile on p.785

THE SET

A strong set with experts who handle all aspects of employment law. Members of the team are regularly instructed in complex and high-profile cases involving issues as diverse as TUPE, equal pay and whistle-blowing. Its client list is broad and includes trade unions, large companies and public sector bodies.

Client service: "The clerks are very good. They are approachable and commercial, and there are never any issues with double booking." "They are client-friendly, personable and approachable. The barristers' rates are good too." Vince Plant is chambers director.

SILKS

Bruce Carr QC (see p.566) A pre-eminent employment and discrimination expert who has unrivalled experience and expertise on issues relating to industrial relations. He is highly sought after for his union expertise, and has handled significant work for employers in high-profile cases. He is singled out for his courtroom presence and is widely viewed as one of the leading advocates in the business. **Strengths:** "He is innovative and has clever ideas about how to tactically deal with situations." "Unflappable, he has a very cool head, and is very calm and authoritative." "Terrier-like, he's a difficult opponent in court but totally charming outside of it." **Recent work:** Acted for Lloyds in defending a multi-claimant indirect discrimination and equal pay claim relating to an attempt to harmonise terms and conditions after the bank's acquisition of HBOS.

Timothy Brennan QC Singled out for his unique blend of employment and tax expertise, he undertakes a large volume of advisory work for City-based employers. **Strengths:** "He has good technical knowledge which he can practically apply to the day-to-day down-in-the-gutter activity clients are involved in." "He is the person you think about for tax crossover cases."

Nicholas Randall QC Regularly advises clients in the financial services sector on their most high-value and business-sensitive matters. He has further carved out a niche advising sporting figures on their employment issues. **Strengths:** "He is a great advocate" who "is impressive with clients and works hard to get good results." "He's the real deal – if you've got a nasty, difficult problem he can come in and put people at ease." **Recent work:** Advised Credit Suisse on a high-value whistle-blowing and discrimination claim.

JUNIORS

Andrew Burns Considered the go-to junior barrister for industrial relations advice and litigation. He focuses on advising employers and regularly works for household-name companies with large unionised workforces. **Strengths:** "He's very clever and at the same time great with clients." "He's the go-to person for industrial relations advice." **Recent work:** Acted in Allen v TRW systems, a case concerning enhanced redundancy payments due to the implicit inclusion of redundancy policy into an employment contract.

Sophie Belgrove (see p.547) A well-seasoned litigator and a good all-rounder who regularly advises on all aspects of employment and discrimination law. She is praised for her innovation and noted for her ability to think outside the box. She specialises in advising clients in the financial services sector. **Strengths:** "She is a very strong advocate who is rightfully highly regarded." **Recent work:** Advised Laing O'Rourke in a series of cases relating to a high-value breach of contract claim where a former employee claimed commission payments and an equity stake in the company.

Peter Edwards A skilled personal injury and employment specialist who is part of a select group of barristers singled out for cases that straddle the two areas. He is also renowned for his experience in trade union issues, and he regularly represents some of the largest unions in their most critical employment issues. **Strengths:** "Engaging, energetic and hard-working, he is adept at marshalling huge amounts of information very quickly." "He gets right to the heart of the issue, explains things very quickly and clearly, and comes down on one side or the other." **Recent work:** Advised TFL on an appeal against an earlier decision in the EAT, centring on the test for a postponement application owing to ill health.

Lucinda Harris (see p.620) Has a thriving employment practice and is considered by one impressed interviewee to be one of the better barristers the set has to offer. She is particularly adept at advising on discrimination cases and has written widely on the subject. Her clients include market-leading firms and brand-name multinationals. **Strengths:** "She's brilliant, her written work is very good and she is personable and good with clients." **Recent work:** Advised IAG and BA on the defence of a claim brought by pilots who argued there had been a TUPE transfer to BA following its disposal of Baby BMI to IAG.

Alice Mayhew (see p.665) Has a diverse employment practice, and regularly appears in the High Court, at appellate level and before the Employment Tribunal. She regularly works with market-leading private practice firms as well as in-house teams from large companies. **Strengths:** "Very good with witnesses, she puts them at ease and speaks to them on their level." **Recent work:** Advised the GMB union in relation to proposed changes to terms and conditions by Brighton and Hove City Council and on threatened strike action by cleaning staff.

Taila Barsam (see p.544) An excellent employment junior recommended for her tough cross-examination and ease with witnesses. She has impressed with her work on high-value and complex discrimination claims, and has noted expertise in disability discrimination. **Strengths:** "She is good under pressure, calm under fire and great to work with." **Recent work:** Advised the respondent in Lefebvre v British Airways, a disability discrimination claim lodged by a member of cabin crew with obsessive compulsive disorder.

Laura Bell (see p.547) Has a wide-ranging employment practice and regularly advises on everything from whistle-blowing to breach of contract. She is known as a fearless litigator who is adept at thinking on her feet. She is also praised for putting clients at ease, with her client-friendly manner making her a trusted adviser. **Strengths:** "I really think cross-examination is one of her strengths because she can be very tenacious."

Thomas Cordrey (see p.578) An up-and-coming employment barrister with complementary expertise in personal injury and commercial law. He acts at all levels, and has undertaken significant work in the High Court and EAT. **Strengths:** "He's very gentle, which is good with clients." "He is very clear about his analysis of things, and when necessary he will go away and sift evidence. He's very organised in his approach." **Recent work:** Advised the appellant in Northbert Dentressangle v Hutton, a case concerning the limitation period for bringing an unfair dismissal claim.

Kate Balmer (see p.542) A baby junior who is widely considered to be able well beyond her years of call. She has standout expertise on the crossover between employment and tax. **Strengths:** "Absolutely fantastic and very tenacious in cross-examination." "She produces Rolls-Royce witness statements, has a very nice style with witnesses and judges, and always delivers."

Akash Nawbatt Comes highly praised for his tactical acumen and is recommended for particularly difficult cases. He is highly rated for his work across the board, and has notable recent experience in the High Court advising on multimillion-pound breach of contract claims as well as team moves.

Christopher Stone Has a growing reputation for the strength of his employment practice. Peers praise his handling of complicated multi-week whistle-blowing claims, and clients note his impressive and robust advocacy. He is a barrister of choice for many of the leading employment solicitors. **Strengths:** "He is completely unflappable and does not feel the pressure at all, even when he's handling complicated matters. His legal knowledge is second to none and he's regularly filling in the judges on points of law they may have missed." "Good with clients, he's more commercial than the average barrister." **Recent work:** Acted for the London Borough of Hammersmith and Fulham in defending a whistle-blowing and unfair discrimination claim.

Essex Court Chambers

See profile on p.792

THE SET The team excels at those employment cases with a commercial dimension and handles high-profile bonus claims, breach of contract and restrictive covenant cases. Members of the set are considered experts on High Court litigation but have also been at the forefront of the move towards arbitration as a means of settling employment disputes.

Client service: "I go to them for complicated areas of law because they have commercial experience." "The clerks at Essex Court are stellar." David Grief and Joe Ferrigno are two of the most respected clerks at the Bar.

SILKS

Andrew Hochhauser QC A standout employment silk and a go-to for high-level employment disputes. Fearsome on his feet, he is a tenacious and robust advocate with a much-admired talent for cross-examination. **Strengths:** "An unbelievable advocate in the sense of his critical analysis of a case and his cross-examination of witnesses." "He is the consummate court advocate, as he's brilliant at making submissions, and in cross-examination." **Recent work:** Acted for 21 former banking employees of Dresdner Kleinwort in a high-profile, high-value bonus claim.

Daniel Oudkerk QC (see p.688) A leading silk who specialises in employment matters with a commercial bent. He is a QC of choice for High Court cases involving restrictive covenants and applications for injunctions. One impressed source notes that, despite being a relatively junior silk, he is already considered a go-to for commercial matters. **Strengths:** "He always manages to imbue a sense of confidence. You know he will fight your client's corner tooth and nail." "He is a class act who is very bright and very personable. He really gets to grips with the issues." **Recent work:** Acted for the former CEO of Lotus in his multimillion-pound wrongful dismissal claim against the company.

Martin Griffiths QC A leading silk for commercial and City-based cases. As well as his work on high-value litigation, he also regularly provides counsel in an advisory capacity. **Strengths:** "He has a grasp of detail and a nice manner with solicitors and clients which always goes down well. He's very clever and tenacious." "He's a superb tactician as well as a brilliant court performer."

Charles Ciumei QC Stands out for his work with clients in the financial services sector, and regularly represents global banks, alternative asset managers and insurance companies. He is known for his advice on high-value business protection issues. **Strengths:** "Forthright and experienced, he gives 110% effort. He is also practical and explains matters in a user-friendly fashion." **Recent work:** Acted for McGinley Support Services in a claim for breach of confidence and restrictive covenant relating to a team move.

JUNIORS

David Craig A distinguished senior junior who is indisputably one of the very best at the Employment Bar. He is the complete package as he is a good advocate and a very effective cross-examiner, and has fantastic client service skills. **Strengths:** "Absolutely top-notch, he is incredibly user-friendly and works ferociously hard." "As a junior he is exceptional; you really feel he is fighting your corner in court."

Edward Brown Has a wealth of experience of handling High Court employment litigation, and is highly experienced on business protection issues. He also regularly works on high-value cases before the Employment Tribunal, focusing on assisting clients in the financial services sector. **Strengths:** "He has a fantastic intellect and is extremely client-friendly." **Recent work:** Acted as junior to Charles Ciumei QC advising McGinley Support Services on restrictive covenant and breach of confidence issues following a team move.

Jane Russell Has an extremely diverse employment practice and noted expertise in both commercially focused employment matters and discrimination work. She is praised for providing definitive advice, with one source noting that "she tells clients what they need to hear rather than what they want to hear." **Strengths:** "Unfailingly responsive and good under pressure. Her manner with clients is exemplary, whether she be dealing with vulnerable individuals or corporate executives who are not used to being told no."

Matrix Chambers

See profile on p.832

THE SET

Matrix Chambers has an exemplary employment team with a broad range of expertise. Barristers at the set are regularly involved in high-profile and high-value cases as well as those which push the boundaries of the law. The team continues to grow its High Court practice, and has recently handled a number of notable injunction cases and bonus disputes. Members act for both employers and employees, and have crossover expertise in areas such as public law and human rights.

Client service: "The fees are competitive and the clerks are always willing to discuss them." "Matrix has a compact team and is reliable, responsive and of good quality."

SILKS

Thomas Linden QC One of the pre-eminent silks in the area and a man very much in vogue over the past year. Market-leading City-based firms flock to him, and he is regularly instructed in high-profile and groundbreaking cases. He is "a real all-rounder and first-class appellate silk." **Strengths:** "He has the intellectual authority you really want. If difficult issues arise you will find that he will guide the judge with authority." "He really understands the commercial world in which most of us live, doesn't have the rarefied air some do at the Bar, and is very much an advocate for the 21st century." **Recent work:** Acted for the appellant in van Winklehof v Clyde & Co, a groundbreaking Supreme Court case in which it was established that equity partners are workers for the purpose of whistle-blowing legislation.

James Laddie QC A very fine advocate who is highly sought after by heavyweight financial services institutions. His cross-examination is praisedj as is his work on complex High Court cases. **Strengths:** "He puts an argument better than anyone I've seen – the client thinks they've met a superstar. He can summarise something so perfectly." "He's really effective at winning High Court battles, and has that talent for making arguments seem disarmingly simple." **Recent work:** Acted for the employer in Pan v Portigon, a harassment and race discrimination claim involving 28 separate allegations.

Antony White QC (see p.750) Has extensive experience in areas as diverse as contractual disputes, high-profile discrimination claims and issues affecting trade unions. He has, of late, handled a number of precedent-setting cases. **Strengths:** "Stands out for his creativity and lateral thinking." **Recent work:** Successfully defended UCU in an Employment Tribunal claim brought by a former lecturer who alleged institutional anti-Semitism.

Helen Mountfield QC Her work in this area predominantly focuses on equality and discrimination matters. She is highly rated for her work in this area, especially on matters with a public law crossover. Cases with an international element are another strength and she is well versed in European law. **Strengths:** "She's both a high-level thinker, and someone who has empathy with the client." **Recent work:** Assisted the Equality and Human Rights Commission on its intervention in Bracking v Secretary of State for Work & Pensions. The case concerned the impact of international law on UK equality law.

Karon Monaghan QC A pre-eminent silk who handles difficult discrimination cases. She acts for individuals but also regularly works with trade unions, charities and non-government organisations. **Strengths:** "One of our go-to people for big discrimination cases. Clients take to her and she is a very punchy litigator." "A delight to work with, she is exceptional on all counts, and will blaze a trail through any case I instruct her on." **Recent work:** Acted for the appellant in Barts and London NHS Trust v Verma, a significant claim concerning pay protection for doctors.

JUNIORS

Thomas Kibling Regularly works on the most complex employment matters. He is noted for his discrimination expertise, and has produced some standout work on equal pay cases. **Strengths:** "A really good advocate who is not aggressive but gets what he needs to get." "He understands the law well and breaks it down for clients in a way they understand." **Recent work:** Advised two board members of Brighton & Sussex NHS Trust on the defence of race discrimination claims.

Mark Afeeva Experienced in both employment and sports law, and highly sought after for those matters that require expert knowledge on both. His pure employment practice is wide-ranging and he is capable of advising on all aspects of the area. **Strengths:** "A very capable barrister who is particularly good on sports-related employment matters."

Claire Darwin (see p.583) Regularly instructed by some of the market-leading solicitors, her practice spans all levels of employment law, and she undertakes a significant amount of appellate work. She is well known for the strength of her advice on TUPE and discrimination cases. **Strengths:** "A very quick thinker on her feet, she is a rising star at the set." "A really strong advocate, she knows when and when not to be aggressive." "She is down to earth and clear in her explanations." **Recent work:** Acted for the appellant in the EAT case of Rhijnsburger v Rynda.

Mathew Purchase (see p.701) Advises on the full range of employment and discrimination law for unions, employees and employers. He is noted for his thorough and impressive cross-examinations, and for his personable nature. In addition to his work in the Employment Tribunal, he has undertaken significant work in the EAT and Court of Appeal. **Strengths:** "Technically brilliant and good on his feet." "He's good at getting to grips with the detail of a case." **Recent work:** Acted for the respondent in Kemeh v Ministry of Defence in the Court of Appeal. The case concerned potential liability for a subcontractor's employee's discriminatory conduct.

Andrew Smith (see p.723) Praised for his encyclopaedic knowledge of case law and the quality of his cross-examinations. He advises on all aspects of employment law with a focus on cases in the Employment Tribunal. **Strengths:** "He is one of our go-to juniors, who performs significantly beyond his level of experience." "Impressive on his feet, he has a lovely manner and is very engaging and persuasive." "Very hands-on, he really feels like a member of the team." **Recent work:** Acted for Tradition Securities in defending a high-profile claim for constructive dismissal and race discrimination brought by a former employee.

Laura Prince (see p.699) Has broad employment experience and has appeared, both led and unled, in the Court of Appeal. She regularly works in the Employment Tribunal and EAT, and has a wide client following including City employment teams, unions and NGOs. **Strengths:** "She shows good attention to detail, is very thorough and does not miss a point." **Recent work:** Appeared in the ECJ, led by Thomas Linden QC, in Alemo Herron v Parkwood Leisure. She acted for UNISON in relation to the interpretation of the Transfer of Undertakings Regulations.

Laura McNair-Wilson Considered a strong junior by market commentators, she advises on a wide range of employment issues and is sought out for advice on everything from high-value City claims and High Court matters to complex discrimination issues. **Strengths:** "She is very good with clients and is able to instil confidence." "She has a calm and incisive approach, and a confidence born out of the fact that she knows her case backwards." **Recent work:** She successfully defended Reading University against multiple claims made by a faculty professor.

Old Square Chambers

See profile on p.891

THE SET

This team does standout work for both respondents and claimants, and regularly works with both sides on the full range of employment matters, including City-related disputes. Employment law within the public sector is another key area of expertise and the set is also known for its handling of claims in the healthcare sector. Cases concerning trade unions and industrial relations also form a main staple of the practice.

Client service: "The clerks are responsive and flexible." "The set is a very well-oiled machine, and you know exactly which clerk to go to on which issues. I have e-mailed on the weekend and received phone calls the same day. They are highly responsive and in tune with client needs."

SILKS

John Hendy QC A major figure in cases involving industrial relations, and a go-to barrister for a number of unions. He is well known for his work on high-profile, precedent-setting cases, and is an expert on injunctive restraints to industrial relations. **Strengths:** "He is an incredibly calm advocate who is very creative in looking at cases and taking them to the appellate level." **Recent work:** Acted for the RMT in its challenge to the UK's ban on secondary action before the ECHR.

Mark Sutton QC Focuses on employment cases in the professional discipline field, and regularly advises NHS trusts on employment issues arising from disciplinary hearings. He also advises on straight employment matters, and has handled a number of bonus disputes. **Strengths:** "His knowledge of difficult doctors' cases is second to none." **Recent work:** Appeared before the Supreme Court in Chhabra v West London Mental Health Trust. The case considered the High Court's power to use injunctions to regulate internal disciplinary hearings.

Oliver Segal QC (see p.716) Advises on all aspects of employment and discrimination law, and regularly advises on some of the most high-profile cases. He specialises in collective disputes, including trade union-related matters. **Strengths:** "He just masters detail and puts forward convincing presentations." "Clients appreciate the fact that his advice is straight and direct. He tells them exactly what he thinks, so they can understand the risks in a case." **Recent work:** Appeared for the appellant in Abercrombie v AGA Rangemaster, a case which concerned guarantee payments in the context of a mutual agreement to temporarily reduce working hours.

Michael Ford QC An employment law expert who is well known for his work on high-profile test cases, and who has recently handled cases in the ECHR and ECJ. He is instructed by a range of clients including unions, NGOs and claimant-focused law firms. **Strengths:** "He is extraordinarily good and incredibly knowledgeable of the law and international conventions." **Recent work:** Acted for the applicant in Lock v British Gas, in which the ECJ found that calculations of holiday pay should include commission.

Jane McNeill QC (see p.669) Has a broad employment practice and regularly handles discrimination matters and cases with a medical element. **Strengths:** "A star for any case with a personal injury edge to it." **Recent work:** Acted for John Yapp, the former High Commissioner to Belize, in a claim against the Foreign and Commonwealth Office concerning employer's liability.

JUNIORS

Katharine Newton (see p.682) Stands out for her work in the Employment Tribunal. Her clients are drawn from a range of areas, including the media, financial services and healthcare sectors. **Strengths:** "She has great client-handling skills, and is personable and robust." **Recent work:** Acted for Citibank in a £1.4 million sex and pregnancy discrimination claim brought by a former vice president of the bank.

Rebecca Tuck (see p.741) Regularly works for both employers and employees on all aspects of employment and discrimination law. She regularly acts as an adviser to disciplinary panels and has expertise in employment cases with a personal injury bent. **Strengths:** "She does not mince her words and does not sit on the fence. She always fights the client's corner very hard." **Recent work:** Acted for the Public and Commercial Services Union in its successful defence of race discrimination and harassment claims brought by a current employee.

Ben Cooper (see p.577) His practice is broad and includes notable work on claims involving trade unions and industrial action. Recent highlights include cases involving blacklisting. **Strengths:** "Not just clever but also very accessible. Clients comment on how reassured they feel in his presence." "He's excellent on his feet, and is very clear and calm. Logical and persuasive, he is a very unemotional and extremely able advocate." **Recent work:** Advised Blake Lapthorn in a claim brought by a former solicitor who alleged unfair dismissal and also made a whistle-blowing claim.

Simon Cheetham (see p.570) Advises both claimants and respondents on all aspects of employment law. He has a focus on cases involving restrictive covenants and discrimination claims. **Strengths:** "He is very responsive and practical even when under significant time pressure." **Recent work:** Led by Michael Ford QC in Lock v British Gas, in which the ECJ found that calculations of holiday pay should include commission.

Louise Chudleigh (see p.572) An experienced senior junior with broad expertise. She has undertaken a range of work recently, including equal pay claims and matters involving union issues. Her practice is especially notable for its professional discipline crossover and she regularly advises on cases involving doctors and the NHS. **Strengths:** "She is able to digest a huge amount of documentation and give clear and prompt advice when discussing the approach to claims." **Recent work:** Acted for the appellant in West London Mental Health NHS Trust v Chhabra. The case confirmed that a court can intervene to stop an internal disciplinary procedure.

Deshpal Panesar (see p.689) Specialises in this area and tackles cases in the Employment Tribunal, in the High Court, and at appellate level. He has a wealth of recent experience of advising both claimants and respondents on disputes involving collective agreements. **Strengths:** "Very good if you need a robust advocate." **Recent work:** Led by John Hendy QC in George v Ministry of Justice, a dispute involving the incorporation of collective agreements into employment contracts.

Elizabeth Melville (see p.671) Represents clients in the education and financial service sectors. She regularly advises both claimants and respondents on all aspects of employment and discrimination law. **Strengths:** "Won an unwinnable legal argument through hard work, preparation and by taking a less than obvious approach to it." **Recent work:** Acted for the respondent in Westwood v Oxford University NHS Trust, a whistle-blowing claim brought by a senior midwife.

Melanie Tether (see p.735) Has a broad client base that includes unions, local authorities and individuals. Her practice is wide-ranging and she has recently handled equal pay disputes and claims involving breach of confidential information. **Strengths:** "Very demanding of herself, she goes through everything in meticulous detail. Her submissions are amazingly succinct, and when up against silks she's more than a match for them." **Recent work:** Acted in Kelly v Hesley Group, a case concerning collective redundancies and the duty to consult.

Nadia Motraghi (see p.678) In addition to her standout litigation work, she also acts as a trusted adviser on non-contentious matters. Her practice is broad but incorporates a good deal of work on cases involving issues relating to trade unions. **Strengths:** "She is a good and user-friendly barrister" who "has done extremely well in discrimination claims and has an excellent manner with clients." **Recent work:** Acted for the claimant in Kelly v Wightlink, a dispute in which it was alleged the claimants had been dismissed for union activity.

Ijeoma Omambala (see p.685) A senior junior sought out for her discrimination expertise. She also has notable High Court experience and regularly works on cases involving breach of contract claims and restrictive covenants. **Strengths:** "She is excellent as she's very good with clients, experienced and confident." **Recent work:** Acted for the appellant in McKinnon v London Borough of Redbridge, a case concerning the rights of park police to claim unfair dismissal and whether they were barred from doing so.

Stuart Brittenden (see p.556) A highly regarded practitioner who regularly handles discrimination cases, trade union issues and injunctive work. He acts for both claimants and respondents. **Strengths:** "He's excellent with clients and he's always extremely well prepared." "He combines technical and practical expertise with excellent client relationship skills." **Recent work:** Appeared in Anserson v London Fire & Emergency Planning Authority, representing more than 300 claimants in a claim for unlawful deductions from wages.

Ben Collins (see p.576) An experienced employment law specialist who is well known for appearing for clients in the public sector. He is regularly instructed in cases involving NHS trusts, and has a great deal of recent experience of handling discrimination and whistle-blowing claims. **Strengths:** "A feisty and incisive advocate who impresses clients with his grasp of detail." "He's exceptionally good, personable with witnesses and able to have a joke and a laugh." **Recent work:** Acted in Sheldon v Care

Quality Commission, a whistle-blowing claim linked to the Mid Staffs inquiry.

Ian Scott (see p.715) Has a broad employment practice and regularly handles noteworthy discrimination claims. He acts for employees, employers and trade unions, and is noted for his work on industrial relations issues. **Recent work:** Acted in Moran v Ideal Cleaning Services, a case involving the interpretation of the agency worker regulations.

Robin White (see p.750) Has an extensive employment and discrimination practice and is widely viewed as the leading barrister for cases involving discrimination against transgender people. Her recent work has included cases with difficult contractual issues and claims involving multiple grounds of discrimination. **Strengths:** "The go-to person for cases with transgender discrimination issues." **Recent work:** Acted for the claimant in Pietzka v PwC, a claim by a male employee who had faced difficulties with flexible working.

Betsan Criddle (see p.581) Regularly acts for claimants and respondents in a range of sectors, including healthcare and financial services. He is notable for his work with both NHS trusts and doctors in litigation and internal disciplinary hearings. **Strengths:** "She was determined, dogged and good at putting her point across forcefully without intimidating the client." "She is on top of cases involving multiple claims and multiple parties." **Recent work:** Led by Mark Sutton in Chhabra v West London Mental Health Trust, where the court considered the High Court's power to use injunctions to regulate internal disciplinary hearings.

Hilary Winstone (see p.754) Advises on all aspects of employment law, and handles a significant amount of appellate work. Her clients include groups in the private sector as well as public sector organisations such as NHS trusts. **Strengths:** "Excellent and extremely client-friendly, she's completely on top of the law and a rottweiler in the ET." "A creative and clever lawyer." **Recent work:** Assisted the respondents in Waterhouse v UKAEA, a long-running whistle-blowing claim.

Jonathan Davies (see p.584) Has a wide-ranging practice with recent experience of handling high-profile restrictive covenant cases. He also has complementary expertise in pensions law. **Strengths:** "He has good technical ability, and is cool and calculated when cross-examining."

Band 3

Outer Temple Chambers

See profile on p.842

THE SET

A leading team for cases where pensions and employment law cross over, the set also has expertise in the financial services sector, and is especially good on issues with a regulatory element. Although the team advises on all aspects of employment law, it has built up an especially strong reputation for handling equal pay claims due to its success in high-profile cases in this area.

Client service: "The clerking is very good. You get attention to detail and a very personal approach."

SILKS

Andrew Short QC An expert in both employment and pensions law who is highly sought after for his expertise in equal pay group claims. **Strengths:** "Nice to work with, he will roll his sleeves up and work with you." "He's just so incisive, so clever and great with clients. He's also confident that he's right." **Recent work:** Acted for approximately 130 part-time judges in Miller v Ministry of Justice, a high-value pensions case.

Keith Bryant QC Has expertise in employment and discrimination cases as well as pensions law. He is especially notable for his work on matters with a national security element. **Strengths:** "He is thoughtful and measured and has great experience in both pensions and employment law." **Recent work:** Acted for the employer in Rahman v Commissioner of Police of the Metropolis, a case where a police officer brought a discrimination claim after his security clearance was removed over alleged links to terrorist groups.

JUNIORS

Daniel Barnett A commercial, pragmatic barrister with a specialist knowledge of employment and discrimination law. He mainly represents employers but also has a thriving employee-focused practice. **Strengths:** "Absolutely outstanding. He's extremely responsive, and really keeps on top of client management." **Recent work:** Acted for Gwyn Williams, the former technical director of Leeds United, in his £250,000 breach of contract claim relating to his dismissal for gross misconduct.

Naomi Ling A strong junior with great client-handling skills, who undertakes a broad range of work. She has recently handled a number of groundbreaking equal pay claims and cases involving union issues. **Strengths:** "She is intellectually fearsome whilst also being personable and accessible – it's a crucial mix at the modern Bar." "One of her big strengths is her ability to cut through a large amount of information to sift out what's relevant." **Recent work:** Led by Andrew Short QC in the landmark Abdulla case concerning equal pay.

Lydia Seymour Sits as a fee-paid employment judge and is praised for her ability to bring that experience to her clients' cases. She is well known for her work on difficult discrimination cases and has also recently undertaken significant whistle-blowing cases. **Strengths:** "Very collegiate and always willing to put herself out." "She has really good insight into how to present a case effectively, and is very calm even in the most tense situations." **Recent work:** Assisted the claimant in Weerasinghe v Basildon & Thurrock University NHS Trust, a whistle-blowing claim lodged by a cardiothoracic surgeon relating to the death of a patient.

Andrew Allen Focuses on discrimination claims in both an employment and non-employment context. He regularly advises both employees and employers, and has a number of public sector clients. **Strengths:** "He is excellent, very sensible and has a good sense of humour." **Recent work:** Acted for the respondents in Mukhadam v London Underground, a disability discrimination claim.

Benjimin Burgher (see p.560) Has a wide employment and discrimination practice and impresses with his cross-examination. One source states: "He knows when to give the witness enough rope to hang themselves." **Strengths:** "He's a very measured, clinical and forensic barrister who clients love because he's able to break complex questions down to simple base factors." "He's excellent, very thorough and always gives a good service." **Recent work:** Advised the claimants in Butterworth v EL AL Airways, a multi-part sex and age discrimination claim.

Naomi Cunningham Advises on all aspects of employment and discrimination law, and has notable recent experience of advising on claims relating to agency worker regulations. **Recent work:** Acted in Engel v Transport & Environment Committee of London Councils, which concerned a compulsory retirement age of 70 and whether this could be justified age discrimination.

Other Ranked Lawyers

Jude Shepherd (42 Bedford Row) Focuses on advising respondents, and has particular strength in discrimination law. She is especially good on disability discrimination matters, and has tackled a number of recent cases in the Employment Tribunal and at the EAT. **Strengths:** "She is exceptional. Her rapport with clients, her preparation and her advocacy skills are second to none." "She always responds well to clients." **Recent work:** Successfully defended the respondents in Braithwaite v London Borough of Croydon against claims of disability discrimination and unfair dismissal.

Susan Chan (42 Bedford Row) Handles all areas of employment and discrimination law. She mainly works for the government and is a member of the Attorney General's A panel. **Strengths:** "If you're in a pickle she's really good as she's very supportive and instils confidence." "She's not fazed by anything."

Orlando Holloway (42 Bedford Row) Advises on all aspects of employment law for both employees and employers. In addition to his tribunal-focused work, he also undertakes High Court cases relating to restraint of business. **Strengths:** "He's down to earth and has very good technical ability." **Recent work:** Acted for the respondents in Felix v TFL, a disability discrimination claim concerning a failure to make reasonable adjustments.

Catherine Rayner (see p.704) (7BR) Works for both claimants and respondents, and has a practice with a strong focus on discrimination law. Her expertise in that field is broad, and she has niche expertise in disability discrimination claims relating to mental health. **Strengths:** "She is very impressive because of how tirelessly she works." **Recent work:** Acted for the respondents in Allied Irish Bank v Fletcher, an appeal against the tribunal's finding that the claimants had experienced an unlawful deduction in wages.

Heather Williams QC (Doughty Street Chambers) Handles employment and discrimination law matters as part of a wider practice. She is especially notable for her work on cases involving an employment and human rights crossover. **Recent work:** Acted for the claimant in Turner v East Midlands Trains, a human rights law-focused challenge to a test used for unfair dismissal.

Gavin Millar QC (Doughty Street Chambers) Focuses his employment work on representing trade unions on all aspects of employment law. He regularly acts on cases involving discrimination, particularly equal pay matters. **Strengths:** "Translates complex legal concepts in a user-friendly way to clients."

Henrietta Hill (Doughty Street Chambers) She is very strong on the law relating to discrimination and handles claims in both an employment and non-employment context. **Strengths:** "She is a master cross-examiner who knows exactly how to read the tribunal."

Nick Toms (Doughty Street Chambers) Handles employment and discrimination law, and mainly acts for claimants, especially those backed by unions. **Strengths:** "He has a real feel for trade unions and how they operate." **Recent work:** Acted for the claimant in Medcraft v Cubic Transportation Systems, which concerned health and safety-related unfair dismissal.

David Mitchell (see p.674) (Ely Place Chambers) Has a varied practice that takes in public law, libel and employment cases. As a member of the Attorney General's B panel, he regularly advises the government. **Strengths:** "He's very good on his feet and has a can-do attitude." **Recent work:** Acted for the claimant in Clinical Direct v Cheetham, obtaining an injunction stopping the defendant from using confidential information.

Victoria von Wachter (see p.744) (5 Essex Court) Advises on the full range of employment and discrimination matters, and has a wealth of experience of advising various public sector clients, especially police forces. She regularly works on cases in the Court of Appeal. **Strengths:** "The clients love her and the way she interacts with them. She has a concise grasp of the law and is able to get things across to them." "Her advice is of consistently high quality." **Recent work:** Acted for the Civil Nuclear Police Authority in responding to an appeal against the Employment Tribunal's decision to strike out a disability discrimination claim.

Andrew Tabachnik (Thirty Nine Essex Street) Regularly advises on discrimination claims, and has a number of NHS trust clients. He also works with private sector clients, and handles claims relating to the City. **Recent work:** Advised the defendants in Space Airconditioning v Guy & Smith Brothers where an injunction was sought because of alleged theft of trade secrets.

Paul Gott QC (see p.612) (Fountain Court Chambers) A member of the Attorney General's A panel and, as such, frequently advises the government on the full range of employment law issues. He also advises private sector clients, and has notable experience of cases concerning industrial relations. **Strengths:** "He's always very responsive and nothing is ever too much trouble for him." "He is great at very complicated industrial disputes." **Recent work:** Advised Crossrail following allegations of blacklisting by its subcontractors.

Adam Tolley QC (see p.738) (Fountain Court Chambers) Advises on all aspects of employment law and acts for both employers and employees. He routinely acts in both the Employment Tribunal and High Court and is also routinely instructed by the government. **Strengths:** "Good on cases involving a banking crossover." "He is calm, considered and extremely bright." "He grasps matters quickly, and is also extremely personable and very client-friendly." **Recent work:** Appeared in Tuil v W Partners, a whistle-blowing claim brought by an equity partner of the respondent.

Patrick Green QC (see p.615) (Henderson Chambers) An expert on employee status issues, having appeared in the leading cases in the area. He undertakes niche work on the crossover between IP and employment law, and also has experience of large class-action claims. **Strengths:** "Brilliant with clients; they have complete trust in him. He gets to the issues very quickly and he'll fight your corner." **Recent work:** Appeared in Pan v Portigon, a case which challenged the procedures of the EAT.

David Brook (Henderson Chambers) Has broad expertise and regularly provides advice on redundancies, contractual issues and restrictive covenants. **Strengths:** "I go to him for tricky issues because of his standing in the market and the gravitas he brings." **Recent work:** Advised the claimant in Ferris v Jubilee Markets, an age discrimination claim.

Kathleen Donnelly (see p.589) (Henderson Chambers) Regularly advises on difficult discrimination cases. She is described as a dogged opponent by impressed peers who note her skill in managing large-scale litigation. **Strengths:** "Good with clients in conference, she is very reassuring. She's also very thorough in her preparation." **Recent work:** Acted in Flexman v BG Group, a disciplinary matter relating to social media.

Jack Mitchell (3PB Barristers) Renowned for his work on high-value, high-profile whistle-blowing claims. He has a notable High Court practice and regularly acts for claimants and respondents in relation to restrictive covenants. **Strengths:** "He's got such an amazing command of the courtroom and control over witnesses. He has very strong knowledge of employment law cases, particularly whistle-blowing claims." "Very able and pleasant, he's a decent cross-examiner who knows his law."

Bruce Gardiner (2TG – 2 Temple Gardens) Advises on all areas of employment law, including TUPE, discrimination and stress at work cases. He regularly works with both claimants and respondents. **Recent work:** Acted for Barclays in successfully deflecting a £12.5 million occupational stress claim.

MIDLANDS

Employment Midlands	
Leading Sets	
Band 1	
No5 Chambers *	
St Philips Chambers *	
Leading Silks	
Band 1	
Pepperall Edward *St Philips Chambers*	
* Indicates set / individual with profile.	
◊ (ORL) = Other Ranked Lawyer.	
Ⓐ direct access (see p.11).	

Leading Juniors	
Band 1	Korn Anthony *No5 Chambers* Ⓐ *
Barney Helen *No5 Chambers* Ⓐ *	Maxwell David *St Philips Chambers* *
Beever Edmund *St Philips Chambers* *	McGrath Andrew *No5 Chambers* Ⓐ
Hignett Richard *No5 Chambers* Ⓐ	Meichen Jonathan *St Philips Chambers* Ⓐ *
Band 2	Powell Richard *River Chambers (ORL)* ◊
Cooksey Nick *River Chambers (ORL)* ◊	Sadiq Tariq *St Philips Chambers* Ⓐ *
Crow Charles *No5 Chambers* Ⓐ *	Sheppard Tim *No5 Chambers* Ⓐ
George Sarah *St Philips Chambers* *	Tindal Jim *St Philips Chambers* *
Gidney Jonathan *St Philips Chambers* *	**Up-and-coming individuals**
Hodgetts Elizabeth *St Philips Chambers* *	Roberts Gemma *No5 Chambers* *
Islam-Chowdhury Mugni *No5 Chambers*	

Band 1

No5 Chambers

See profile on p.883

THE SET

No5 Chambers retains its position as a leading employment set on the Midland Circuit. It attracts instructions on a range of matters arising in the public and private sectors, and offers particular expertise in proceedings involving health, retail and fashion. Where appropriate, members of the set who are authorised to do so will accept instructions directly from clients.

Client service: "The barristers at No5 are very easy to work with, well prepared, their advice is usually spot on, and they are very good at building a rapport with the clients. The employment clerks, led by Martin Ellis, work closely with us. They are very responsive and more than happy to try and accommodate any particular request we have."

JUNIORS

Helen Barney (see p.543) Deputy head of the set's employment practice. She is particularly adept at handling matters involving discrimination, and often represents local authorities and NHS trusts. **Strengths:** "She is a highly skilled and extremely intelligent advocate. She is detailed and thorough in her approach but also pragmatic." "I would be happy to instruct Helen on a range of issues. She displays attention to detail, tenacity and a willingness to drive hard for the interests of the clients."

Tim Sheppard Acts for respondents and claimants. He demonstrates particular expertise in cases concerning discrimination, unfair dismissal and breach of covenants. **Strengths:** "He has a very good manner with clients and is thorough in his preparation of cases. He is excellent in his cross-examination and in his summation of the issues in a case." "He doesn't see problems, he sees solutions. He knows the law and is a really good advocate." **Recent work:** Acted for an NHS trust in a high-profile, multi-day hearing in defence of claims brought by a consultant heart surgeon. The surgeon claimed that he was discriminated against on the grounds of disability, and unfairly dismissed as a result of whistle-blowing.

Richard Hignett Head of the set's employment practice. He offers particular strength in cases involving the retail and fashion industry, and is well regarded for his proficiency in proceedings concerning discrimination. **Strengths:** "He is very good at cross-examination and you feel he is in control." "He communicates well with clients. They find him straightforward to deal with and he always understands what they want to achieve." **Recent work:** Represented Walsall NHS Trust in defence of a claim brought by a nurse who was dismissed following the death of a patient. The patient had collapsed outside the hospital after having allegedly been neglected by NHS staff.

Charles Crow (see p.581) Focuses on cases involving dismissals and discrimination. He has a particular interest in cases involving discrimination against individuals for their religion or belief, and he acts for both claimants and respondents. **Strengths:** "He is a real battler. He is very sharp and thinks quickly. He goes the extra mile and wants to get the right result." "He is superb in court and has great arguments. He challenges and has sound judgement regarding the prospects of a case." **Recent work:** Acted for a claimant, a waste management adviser, who was dismissed by the respondent as a result of a negative Environment Agency report. The case concerned issues related to whistle-blowing and unfair dismissal.

Anthony Korn (see p.648) Acts for both claimants and respondents. He is an authority on the quantification of employment tribunal claims, and is experienced in the handling of matters involving whistle-blowing and equal pay claims. **Strengths:** "He is very good at grappling with complex issues and is very thorough and methodical." "He has a very clear understanding of the application of the law." **Recent work:** Represented the respondent in a case brought by Unison relating to the obligation to provide information to agency workers.

Andrew McGrath Represents claimants and respondents in complex discrimination claims and TUPE matters. He is particularly well versed in representing clients from the public sector, including local authorities and NHS trusts. **Strengths:** "He is a very experienced and pragmatic advocate." "He is a tried and tested employment lawyer." **Recent work:** Acted for 45 claimants in the High Court who alleged that their union and their union's solicitors had acted negligently and breached contract. The allegations related to an equal pay complaint.

Gemma Roberts (see p.709) Acts for multinational organisations, NHS trusts and local authorities. She is experienced in a broad range of employment law and discrimination matters, and is an authority on claims relating to employment agencies. **Strengths:** "She is very clever and witty. She understands employment law really well, gives good grass-roots advice and communicates well with clients." "She is competent beyond her year of call." **Recent work:** Successfully defended at the EAT a claim brought against Adecco by an employee who was dismissed after allegations of immigration and visa-related impropriety were broadcast on BBC2's 'Newsnight'.

Mugni Islam-Chowdhury Focuses on complex matters concerning discrimination and whistleblowing. He often acts for employers. **Strengths:** "He is a very robust and fearless cross-examiner. He inspires confidence in witnesses, who are happy to work with him." "He is always very good on his feet, thoroughly prepared, technically very good and easy to work with." **Recent work:** Successfully represented South Warwickshire NHS Trust in a race discrimination claim. The claim was brought by a dismissed finance director.

St Philips Chambers

See profile on p.886

THE SET

St Philips Chambers is able to offer counsel capable of handling a broad range of employment matters. Its members often act for respondents on matters arising in the public and private sector, and will also act for claimants. They often appear at the employment tribunal, the High Court and the Court of Appeal.

Client service: "The clerks, led by Joe Wilson, are very good and very helpful. They respond promptly, they are flexible on fees and they don't switch your barrister."

SILKS

Edward Pepperall QC Handles a broad range of matters, predominantly for employers. His areas of expertise include injunctions, the enforcement of restrictive covenants, the dismissal of senior executives, complex Employment Tribunals, and race discrimination proceedings. **Strengths:** "He is recognised as a specialist employment silk." "He is very good and responsive, and has an eye on what the client wants to achieve. He has a pragmatic approach." **Recent work:** Represented Birmingham City Council in a 28-day Employment Tribunal involving multiple allegations relating to race discrimination, unfair dismissal, victimisation and whistle-blowing. The claimant abandoned their case after lengthy cross-examination.

JUNIORS

Edmund Beever (see p.547) Handles commercial employment disputes for claimants and respondents. He is admired for his handling of complex matters concerning discrimination, restrictive covenants and senior director disputes. **Strengths:** "He has extremely good advocacy skills and is also very good with the clients. He builds a rapport and is very approachable." "He is good at communicating advice to clients in a way that makes the legal issues clear, and he sees the strengths and weaknesses of a case." **Recent work:** Acted for Birmingham City Council in defence of a complex race discrimination claim, a whistle-blowing claim and a case concerning allegations of sexual impropriety.

Tariq Sadiq Acts for claimants and respondents. He often handles employment matters that draw on his expertise in the fields of sport and professional conduct, and he offers additional expertise in dealing with cases involving questions of national security. **Strengths:** "He is very good, thorough and committed." "I think very highly of him and his capability with discrimination issues." **Recent work:** Represented a claimant in an unfair dismissal claim, the evidence for which could not be revealed in public as it presented a risk to national security. Mr Sadiq acted as a Special Advocate for the claimant at closed hearing proceedings.

Jonathan Gidney (see p.608) Appears predominantly on the respondent side of claims for local authorities, NHS trusts and private sector clients. He is a qualified mediator. **Strengths:** "He is very well organised and prepared, takes time to understand the bundle and has a very good manner with clients." "He is excellent on very technical issues – he flourishes when making difficult technical legal arguments." **Recent work:** Successfully defended Sainsbury's in a claim for unfair dismissal. The claimant was accused of gross misconduct after abusing employee discount arrangements.

Elizabeth Hodgetts (see p.629) Handles a wide range of discrimination matters. She is often instructed in cases involving public sector organisations. **Strengths:** "She has extremely good advocacy skills and a good level of expertise in public sector work, and is able to build a strong rapport with all of our clients." "She is technically fantastic." **Recent work:** Represented Birmingham City Council in an unfair dismissal claim arising from whistle-blowing and accusations of racial victimisation.

David Maxwell (see p.665) Represents both public and private sector clients at the employment tribunal, the High Court and the Court of Appeal. He is experienced in handling disciplinary matters. **Strengths:** "He is thorough and methodical – he works well to prepare the case for hearing and goes through everything step by step from beginning to end." **Recent work:** Acted for the West Midlands Fire & Rescue Service in defence of race discrimination claims brought by a senior officer.

Jim Tindal (see p.738) Handles a broad range of employment matters, often related to discrimination and personal injury. He acts solely for claimants. **Strengths:** "His level of advice and technically ability is fantastic." "He puts up an excellent fight." **Recent work:** Acted against the Cabinet Office in an EAT test case concerning the legality of national public sector pay freezes.

Jonathan Meichen (see p.670) Handles a broad range of employment matters. He is particularly adept at complex discrimination cases and carries out a large amount of work for local government. **Strengths:** "He produces very good opinions and is very persuasive at hearings." "He has a good manner with clients and comes well prepared." **Recent work:** Represented Birmingham City Council in an unfair dismissal case brought by a teacher.

Sarah George (see p.607) Specialises in handling employment matters involving discrimination. She acts for claimants and respondents from the public and private sectors. **Strengths:** "The quiet confidence with which she proceeds impresses me." "She is phenomenal and able to take on large cases."

Other Ranked Lawyers

Nick Cooksey (River Chambers) Handles employment cases arising in both the public and private sectors. He often appears at the Court of Appeal. **Strengths:** "He offers a model of how to handle a case professionally and competently." "He is client-friendly and well prepared, does not sit on the fence and is good on his feet."

Richard Powell (River Chambers) Specialises in handling commercial employment cases. He acts for some of the largest private employers in the UK. **Strengths:** "He has excellent client-management skills and a very good court presence."

NORTH EASTERN

Employment North Eastern
Leading Juniors
Star individuals
Sweeney Seamus *Parklane Plowden (ORL)* ◊
Band 1
Callan Jane *Trinity Chambers (ORL)* ◊ *
Sugarman Andrew *Parklane Plowden (ORL)* ◊
Band 2
Bayne Dominic *Parklane Plowden (ORL)* ◊
Bourne Colin *Kings Chambers (ORL)* ◊ *
Goldberg Simon *Trinity Chambers (ORL)* ◊ *
Jeram Kirti *Parklane Plowden (ORL)* ◊
Legard Edward *Dere Street Barristers (ORL)* ◊ *
Serr Ashley *Exchange Chambers (ORL)* ◊
Stubbs Richard *Trinity Chambers (ORL)* ◊ *
Band 3
Kirtley Paul *Exchange Chambers (ORL)* ◊
Morgan Jamie *Trinity Chambers (ORL)* ◊ *
Widdett Ceri *Exchange Chambers (ORL)* ◊
Wilson Paul *Broadway House (ORL)* ◊
* *Indicates individual with profile.*
◊ *(ORL) = Other Ranked Lawyer.*
Alphabetical order within each band. Band 1 is highest.

Ranked Lawyers

Paul Wilson (Broadway House) Heads the set's employment team. He handles a broad range of matters for claimants and respondents, and is an authority on cases concerning whistle-blowing and disability discrimination. **Strengths:** "He is well known on the Circuit as an extremely capable and experienced individual. I would trust him with any employment work."

Edward Legard (see p.654) (Dere Street Barristers) Handles a wide variety of matters regarding employment and equality law. He has a particular interest in discrimination and TUPE issues. **Strengths:** "He is rightly rated as one of the leading employment barristers on the North Eastern Circuit. He is a good advocate, really thorough, with a good manner about him in tribunal and a sensible approach outside." **Recent work:** He successfully appealed the findings of a tribunal concerning the victimisation of a trainee pharmacist due to her religious belief.

Ashley Serr (Exchange Chambers) Advises on a wide variety of employment law issues. He is particularly adept at handling matters involving principles of public law, and is most frequently instructed by local authorities and national firms on proceedings concerning TUPE, equal pay, discrimination and restrictive covenants. **Strengths:** "He is technically very able and a solid, capable performer."

Paul Kirtley (Exchange Chambers) Handles a wide range of employment advocacy matters. He demonstrates particular strength in proceedings involving trade unions, TUPE, redundancy, discrimination and equal pay issues. **Strengths:** "He is an experienced barrister with an easy manner. He knows the law and the clients are always happy with him. Because of his abilities he is in really high demand."

Ceri Widdett (Exchange Chambers) Focuses on proceedings relating to discrimination issues. She frequently acts for health authorities. **Strengths:** "She is able to adapt her style and approach. She is prompt and very able in any issue."

Colin Bourne (see p.553) (Kings Chambers) Often involved in complex TUPE cases. He represents both claimants and respondents from the public and private sectors. **Strengths:** "He is a very experienced barrister in knotty discrimination cases. He is an excellent strategist, always four steps ahead." "He is a seasoned pro who knows the law inside out. He is very comfortable in employment advocacy; it's his subject area. He is a true specialist and I have the highest regard for him." **Recent work:** Advised the Cleveland Police Authority on multiple claims and appeals brought to determine whether alleged disability discrimination may be said to amount to victimisation.

Seamus Sweeney (Parklane Plowden) A leading light in employment law on the North Eastern Circuit. He focuses on handling respondent work for local government and NHS trusts, and is an authority on matters concerning equal pay litigation. He also handles claimant work. **Strengths:** "He is an exceptional barrister. He is not stuffy, clients love him and he is willing to roll up his sleeves. Behind that friendly behaviour lies a killer cross-examiner, which is exactly what you want." "He is always excellent and is quite well known as being one of the best in the region. If I have a high-value claim locally, he is my first port of call." **Recent work:** Acted for Lord Alan Sugar's company, Amshold, on an unfair constructive dismissal and whistle-blowing claim brought by winner of 'The Apprentice', Stella English. The claims were dismissed.

Andrew Sugarman (Parklane Plowden) Represents commercial and public sector employers, charitable bodies, trade unions and their members. **Strengths:** "He is the calm port in the storm. He looks at things objectively and thinks well on his feet." **Recent work:** Instructed to act for BUPA Dental Services on an unfair dismissal and victimisation claim under the Equality Act. The issue succeeded before the ET and an appeal has been lodged at the EAT.

Dominic Bayne (Parklane Plowden) Handles respondent work for public clients and receives instructions from government in his position as regional treasury counsel. He also handles important claimant matters relating to discrimination, equal pay, unfair dismissals, TUPE, redundancy and whistle-blowing issues. **Strengths:** "His manner is very considered and belies the fact that he is extremely effective as an advocate and gets into the details really deeply." **Recent work:** Acted for Hartlepool BC on a 12-day whistle-blowing and unfair dismissal case.

Kirti Jeram (Parkland Plowden) Handles a broad range of employment matters. She is well known for her experience in proceedings relating to discrimination and unfair dismissal. **Strengths:** "She is very tenacious at tribunal and outstanding with clients." "She is terrific and incredibly bright."

Jane Callan (see p.563) (Trinity Chambers) Heads the set's employment practice. She regularly advises public sector respondents, and demonstrates particular expertise in discrimination and equal pay matters. She also handles claimant work relating to trade union activities and disability claims. **Strengths:** "She has incredible attention to detail and is completely thorough. She works really hard, doesn't miss a thing and you know that she is going to go all out for you."

Simon Goldberg (see p.610) (Trinity Chambers) Acts regularly in the ET, EAT and High Court. He is well regarded for his expertise in proceedings involving discrimination and equal pay. **Strengths:** "He is an excellent, extremely clear and very forceful yet absolutely fair advocate. He does an extremely good job for his client." "He is sharp and shrewd." **Recent work:** Advised Newcastle City Council on a four-day race discrimination and unfair dismissal hearing at the ET.

Richard Stubbs (see p.731) (Trinity Chambers) Regularly instructed on multi-day hearings of high value. He handles complex equal pay, TUPE and discrimination claims, and acts for individuals, local government, and NHS trusts. **Strengths:** "He is highly intelligent, hard-working, extremely level-headed and very much a team player. He is a clear and compelling advocate who copes extremely well with pressure, and if the situation demands he is also able to work very quickly. He is a delightful person to work with." "He is brilliant. He is going to be a real star in the future." **Recent work:** Represented the claimant in a GMF defence test case against the Doncaster & South Humber NHS Foundation Trust.

Jamie Morgan (see p.676) (Trinity Chambers) Regularly offers advice and representation to claimants in discrimination cases and TUPE-related dismissals. He is particularly experienced in matters concerning equal pay litigation. **Strengths:** "He provides excellent client care, he is able to think on his feet and is willing to engage in a two-way exchange of ideas, which is extremely important for effective advocacy." **Recent work:** Successfully represented claimants against St Helens MBC in an equal pay claim.

NORTHERN

Employment Northern	
Leading Sets	
Band 1	
9 St John Street *	
Band 2	
St Johns Buildings *	
Band 3	
Atlantic Chambers	
Kings Chambers *	
Leading Silks	
Band 1	
Gilroy Paul	*9 St John Street* *
Band 2	
Gorton Simon	*Atlantic Chambers*
Leading Juniors	
Band 1	
Boyd James	*Kings Chambers*
Brochwicz-Lewinski Stefan	*9 St John Street*
Connolly Joanne	*9 St John Street* *
Gumbs Annette P	*St Johns Buildings*
Morgan Edward	*9 St John Street*
Siddall Nicholas	*Littleton Chambers (ORL)* ◊ *
Wedderspoon Rachel	*9 St John Street*
Woodward Joanne	*9 St John Street*
Band 2	
Ali Kashif	*St Johns Buildings*
Barry Kirsten	*9 St John Street*
Draycott Paul	*Doughty Street Chambers (ORL)* ◊
Eeley Rebecca	*9 St John Street*
Gorasia Paras	*Kings Chambers* *
Grundy Nigel	*9 St John Street*
Mahmood Ghazan	*St Johns Buildings*
McCluggage Brian	*9 St John Street* *
McNerney Kevin	*St Johns Buildings*
Northall Daniel	*Littleton Chambers (ORL)* ◊
Quigley Louise	*St Johns Buildings*
Searle Jason	*St Johns Buildings*
Smith Kerry	*Garden Court North (ORL)* ◊
Snarr Matthew	*9 St John Street*
Up-and-coming Individuals	
Trotter Helen	*Kings Chambers* *
◊ (ORL) = Other Ranked Lawyer.	
** Indicates set / individual with profile.*	
Alphabetical order within each band. Band 1 is highest.	

Band 1

9 St John Street

See profile on p.923

THE SET

9 St John Street is not just one of the Northern Circuit's leading employment law sets, but is also celebrated for its strong national presence. It acts on demanding and complex cases for individuals, large corporations and trade unions in both the public and private arenas. It is particularly strong in handling unfair dismissals, discrimination and equal opportunities cases.

Client service: The clerks, led by Tony Morrissey, are praised for being flexible and approachable: "The clerks are so friendly it can feel like they are your colleagues; it is a great relationship. They also always make an effort to be flexible on fees."

SILKS

Paul Gilroy QC Handles high-value and high-profile cases, including wrongful dismissal, professional discipline and profile public inquiries. He is especially acclaimed for his substantial work in the sports and healthcare industries. He works on the largest, most high-profile and market-leading cases. **Strengths:** "He is an excellent advocate who has the gravitas to deal with complex tribunals." "He is very thorough and focused."

JUNIORS

Stefan Brochwicz-Lewinski Regularly instructed on particularly complex cases concerning whistle-blowing and unfair dismissals. He frequently works with clients in the retail, construction and healthcare industries. **Strengths:** "He is excellent – totally prepared at all times and good with clients."

Joanne Connolly (see p.577) Has a broad range of expertise, which includes excellent work in whistle-blowing and retirement cases. She appears regularly in tribunals, High Courts and County Courts. **Strengths:** "She is an excellent and experienced advocate who is clever and approachable. She also has excellent client skills."

Edward Morgan Receives auspicious feedback for his high level of work in the public sector. He also acts on complex and innovative cases concerning discriminations and restrictive covenants. The majority of his practice is devoted to claimant work. **Strengths:** "He is acutely intelligent and a brilliant advocate who excels with clients – he is one of the best."

Rachel Wedderspoon Impresses with her broad expertise, which encompasses all areas of employment law such as unfair dismissal, maternity/paternity rights and equal pay. Her experience as an employment judge aids her practice. **Strengths:** "She is very responsive, and very good with clients." "She is an extremely personable, thorough barrister who establishes good relationships with clients and has excellent advocacy skills. "

Joanne Woodward A tribunal judge and an exceptional litigator. Her experience of the employment market is considerable, and she is particularly specialised in handling discrimination cases. **Strengths:** "She is extremely cool under pressure – you will never see her flustered; she is a smart operator who is also smooth." "She is very sharp and very good. She is very quick to get to the point." **Recent work:** Acted for the University of Manchester against a constructive dismissal and public interest disclosure.

Nigel Grundy Renowned for his cross-departmental practice, which includes a long-standing presence in employment law. He also works consistently in regulatory proceedings. **Strengths:** "He is very well thought of and popular with solicitors."

Kirsten Barry Noted for her broad employment law practice, which emphasises matters such as dismissals, sexual harassment and redundancies.

Rebecca Eeley Instructed on complex cases in both the public and private sectors in areas such as TUPE, dismissals and redundancies. She is also an acclaimed mediator. **Strengths:** "She is an excellent lawyer who is always thoroughly prepared and good with clients – an excellent advocate."

Brian McCluggage Praised for his skills in handling disability discrimination cases. He is also renowned for his work in personal injury and property damage claims. **Strengths:** "He's a favourite because he gets results."

Matthew Snarr Noted for his work on complex race discrimination and unfair dismissal claims. He is also known for handling negotiations and settlement agreements.

Band 2

St Johns Buildings

See profile on p.921

THE SET

St Johns Building is host to some exceptional lawyers who have the capacity to cover all areas of employment law. It is regularly instructed in cases before the Employment Tribunal, the EAT, and both County and High Courts.

JUNIORS

Annette Gumbs Has a practice which spans all aspects of employment law, with a focus on whistle-blowing and discrimination cases. **Strengths:** "She is a very good advocate, both clever and approachable." **Recent work:** Successfully represented the Managing Director of BPP University College Manchester in her unfair dismissal claim against the college.

Kashif Ali Acts for both claimants and respondents across the full spectrum of employment law matters, including unfair dismissal and race and religious discrimination. **Recent work:** Represented a paralegal in his claim for unfair dismissal due to discrimination brought against Linklaters.

Ghazan Mahmood Best known for his work on discrimination claims, although this is but part of a much broader employment practice. He is particularly noted for his representation of healthcare professionals in both internal disciplinary matters and GMC proceedings. **Strengths:** "He's a very realistic and understated opponent – in the tribunal you need someone who will engage witnesses, and he is very good at cross-examination. He is highly thought of in the marketplace." **Recent work:** Successfully defended the Greater Manchester Probation Trust against claims of race discrimination and unfair dismissal.

Kevin McNerney Has far-reaching expertise in the healthcare sector and works exceedingly well in national minimum wage and TUPE cases. **Recent work:** Acted on an appeal concerning the purpose of the national minimum wage regarding 'on-call' duties.

Louise Quigley Handles complex cases with an emphasis on discrimination claims. She is instructed by both claimants and respondents, including local authorities, multinational corporations and high-profile individuals. **Recent work:** Successfully defended the University of Central Lancashire against a claim of constructive dismissal and victimisation.

Jason Searle A very talented barrister who works most prominently in the healthcare industry, with great success acting for claimants in complex discrimination cases. He is very well versed in handling cases involving social media in the workplace. **Recent work:** Represented the claimant in a sexual harassment case against the Aprite Nissan car dealership.

Band 3

Atlantic Chambers

THE SET

Liverpool-based Atlantic Chambers is noted for its excellent employment law expertise. Its members work across a range of discrimination cases, wrongful dismissals and restrictive covenants. The set also covers TUPE cases and breach of contract claims.

SILKS

Simon Gorton QC Has a broad employment law practice covering discrimination, equal pay and whistle-blowing cases. He receives instructions from a range of clients, including trade unions, public bodies, NHS trusts and medical professionals. **Strengths:** "He's a good all-rounder – practical, robust and a good jury advocate."

Kings Chambers

See profile on p.918

THE SET

Kings Chambers is home to a strong employment group with the capacity to represent both respondents and claimants across the full range of employment matters. Its employment team works with a range of clients, including NHS trusts, leading corporations, major unions, and also individual claimants.

Client service: "The clerks, led by Colin Griffin, are very helpful; they get back to you quickly and are always keen to assist." "It is a user-friendly and commercial set."

JUNIORS

James Boyd Proficient in all employment law areas, including matters such as unfair or wrongful dismissal, discrimination and TUPE cases. He primarily acts for respondents and operates on a national level. **Strengths:** "He is approachable and very helpful, and also very clear, concise and sharp – clients find him very impressive." "He is great with clients and really puts witnesses at ease." **Recent work:** Defended DHL against an unfair dismissal claim worth over half a million pounds.

Paras Gorasia (see p.612) A skilled advocate who has developed a far-reaching employment law practice. He often acts for government bodies in employment disputes. **Strengths:** "He is very good with the clients; a modern barrister with very good technical abilities." "He is very commercial and savvy." **Recent work:** Represented Tesco Stores against claims of race discrimination and unfair dismissal.

Helen Trotter (see p.740) An employment specialist focused on cases concerning discrimination, harassment and unfair dismissals. She receives instructions from a broad range of clients, including education providers, government departments, airlines and local authorities. **Strengths:** "She has a strong presence in tribunals and a good bedside manner with clients." "She is extremely good – client-focused, robust, personable, knows her stuff really well, and delivers great results." **Recent work:** Represented HMRC in an unfair dismissal and disability discrimination case concerning the implications of the Civil Service Management Code.

Other Ranked Lawyers

Paul Draycott (Doughty Street Chambers) Specialises in discrimination cases, immigration and public law. He is frequently instructed in matters pertaining to human rights on an international scale. **Strengths:** "He is excellent and will fight to the nth degree."

Kerry Smith (Garden Court North) Represents individuals and trade unions in a wide variety of matters before employment tribunals, the EAT and the County Court. She is best known for handling unfair dismissals, redundancy claims and TUPE matters. **Recent work:** Successfully represented the claimant in a third party harassment claim.

Nicholas Siddall (see p.720) (Littleton Chambers) An outstanding employment law barrister noted for his expertise in front of the High Court and tribunals. He handles the gamut of employment matters. **Strengths:** "He is a thorough and very well-prepared advocate."

Daniel Northall (Littleton Chambers) A well-regarded barrister who works consistently on unfair dismissal cases and contractual matters. **Strengths:** "He is very good with the witnesses, presenting information in a way in which witnesses can understand – he is very good like that. He is also clearly well informed. He makes you feel very confident."

SOUTH EASTERN

Employment South Eastern
Leading Juniors
Band 1
Ashley Neil *Octagon House Chambers (ORL)* ◊
Menzies Gordon *6 Pump Court (ORL)* ◊
Up-and-coming individuals
Cullen Grace *6 Pump Court (ORL)* ◊
Godfrey Lauren *Crown Office Row (ORL)* ◊
* *Indicates individual with profile.*
◊ *(ORL) = Other Ranked Lawyer.*

Ranked Lawyers

Lauren Godfrey (Crown Office Row) Acts for a wide range of clients, including financial institutions, trade unions, company directors and non-profit entities. He has particular expertise in chancery, commercial and discrimination law. **Strengths:** "He's very timely with paperwork, first class as an advocate, and his advice is always incredibly detailed and accurate." **Recent work:** Represented a local authority in a matter concerning equal pay issues.

Neil Ashley (Octagon House Chambers) Acts predominantly for large private companies and local authorities, as well as for individual claimants. His areas of expertise include discrimination claims, restructuring and equal pay class actions. **Strengths:** "He's very good at getting to grips with matters very quickly, and I like his advocacy – it's good to watch." **Recent work:** Defended over 200 TUPE claims arising from the collapse of the Connaught Group.

Gordon Menzies (6 Pump Court) Represents both claimants and respondents. He is an expert in constructive dismissal cases and procedural HR issues. **Strengths:** "He is consistently reliable, expertly informed and provides insightful advice and support." "In his field he's a thoroughly good thinker – he thinks a few steps ahead." **Recent work:** Acted for the respondent in a race discrimination claim involving allegations of specific and institutional racism.

Grace Cullen (6 Pump Court) Acts for individual claimants, local authorities, schools and public companies. She demonstrates particular expertise in unfair dismissal and discrimination claims. **Strengths:** "She has helped us to obtain very good results, employing novel and innovative arguments." **Recent work:** Acted for the respondent in an unfair dismissal and discrimination claim concerning the extent to which a genuinely held but offensive philosophical belief may be considered deserving of protection.

WALES & CHESTER

Employment Wales & Chester
Leading Juniors
Band 1
Walters Jonathan *Civitas Law (ORL)* ◊
Band 2
Howells Chris *Civitas Law (ORL)* ◊ *
Band 3
Vernon Robert *9 Park Place (ORL)* ◊ *
Vines Anthony *Civitas Law (ORL)* ◊ *

Ranked Lawyers

Jonathan Walters (Civitas Law) Regularly acts for city councils, large corporations and individuals. His wide-ranging employment practice covers claims relating to discrimination, whistle-blowing and disciplinary investigations. **Strengths:** "He is extremely practical and clear – a true leader of the Welsh market." "He is always a safe pair of hands." **Recent work:** Acted for Gwent Police on a six-figure remedy hearing in a whistle-blowing case.

Chris Howells (see p.632) (Civitas Law) Has a nationwide practice that covers the full range of employment law. He acts for both individuals and city councils on matters such as unfair dismissals and grievances. **Strengths:** "He is an excellent lawyer who is extremely personable." "He is well prepared and very pleasant to work with." **Recent work:** Acted for Swansea County Council in a disability discrimination claim, professing dismissal as a result of protected disclosures.

Anthony Vines (see p.744) (Civitas Law) Acts for both respondents and claimants on matters such as TUPE, unfair dismissal and whistle-blowing. **Strengths:** "He is very approachable and gives excellent advice."

Robert Vernon (see p.743) (9 Park Place) Advises local authorities, solicitors and national corporations on the gamut of employment matters. He also acts as an employment judge for the East Midlands region. **Strengths:** "He is excellent with clients – you can leave him to it. You can build a good rapport with him and he has a nice style about him." **Recent work:** He defended the respondent against multiple claims including unfair dismissal and age and racial discrimination.

WESTERN

Employment Western
Leading Sets
Band 1
Guildhall Chambers *
Old Square Chambers *
Band 2
3PB Barristers *
Pump Court Chambers *
Band 3
Albion Chambers *
Leading Silks
Band 1
Ford Michael *Old Square Chambers*
Leading Juniors
Band 1
Grennan Debbie *Guildhall Chambers*
Smith Nicholas G *Guildhall Chambers*
Band 2
Allsop Julian *Guildhall Chambers* *
Cunningham Elizabeth *Albion Chambers* [A]
Dracass Timothy *Pump Court Chambers*
Keen Spencer *Old Square Chambers*
Kempster Toby *Old Square Chambers*
Mitchell Jack *3PB Barristers*
Self Gary *Pump Court Chambers* *
Tether Melanie *Old Square Chambers* *
White Matthew *St John's Chambers (ORL)* ◊ [A]
Winstone Hilary *Old Square Chambers* *
Band 3
Currie Fergus *Unity Street Chambers (ORL)* ◊
Dawson James *3PB Barristers*
Gower Helen *Old Square Chambers*
Leach Douglas *Guildhall Chambers*
Midgley Andrew *Old Square Chambers* *
Platt Heather *Pump Court Chambers* *
Roberts Stephen *Albion Chambers*
Watson Graham *Colleton Chambers (ORL)* ◊
Whitcombe Mark *Old Square Chambers*
Up-and-coming individuals
Fear-Davies Harriet *3PB Barristers*
Graham Gareth *3PB Barristers*
Macphail Andrew *3PB Barristers*
Roberts Allan *Guildhall Chambers* *
Tibbitts Simon *3PB Barristers*
Wyeth Stephen *3PB Barristers*
* *Indicates set / individual with profile.*
◊ *(ORL) = Other Ranked Lawyer.*
[A] *direct access (see p.11).*

Band 1

Guildhall Chambers

See profile on p.890

THE SET

A highly regarded Bristol-based employment set with vast experience of representing both national and regional firms, local authorities and government departments, in high-end disputes. Its barristers are well versed in complex appellate work, and are recognised for taking a highly commercial approach to both disputes and advice.

Client service: "The clerking is good – efficient, approachable and friendly."

JUNIORS

Debbie Grennan One of the Western Circuit's leading employment barristers, with vast NHS and local authority-related experience. She is noted for the breadth of her practice, which covers discrimination, whistle-blowing, TUPE and equal pay-related claims. **Strengths:** "She is incredibly intuitive in terms of knowing what you want to achieve and finding the quickest way to get you there. If you ask her to do something you know it will be done quickly, but you can also be safe in the knowledge that everything is going to be done properly." "She is an excellent advocate, clear and concise in the advice which she provides." **Recent work:** Represented Newport City Council as the respondent in a case at the Court of Appeal concerning a complex disability discrimination issue.

Nicholas Smith A leading junior with vast experience across all manner of employment disputes, from tribunal hearings to prominent High Court litigation. He has had particular success in whistle-blowing actions both for and against public sector clients. **Strengths:** "He is incredibly commercial, and talks in English rather than legalese. His written advice is very succinct and clear." "He is a very experienced advocate who gets to the crux of a case quickly." **Recent work:** Acted for an employee of Royal Mail in a high-profile unfair dismissal case against his employers, concerning the claimant's dismissal for accidentally obscuring cages of mail with empty cages. The matter involved trade union involvement.

Julian Allsop (see p.535) Focuses his employment practice on representing respondents, and has substantial experience of representing public sector clients, including government departments and NHS trusts. He also has a national reputation for restrictive covenant expertise. **Strengths:** "He is quick to respond, even late at night or early in the morning. He understands what his clients want to achieve, and puts things in place to make sure they get a result as quickly as possible, although he can be incredibly patient when required." "He is forceful when needed, but never overly so. He is a safe pair of hands for all employment matters, offering pragmatic advice. He inspires confidence." **Recent work:** Represented a claimant against the Secretary of State for Health in an appeal at the EAT against a tribunal decision. The original judgment had declined to entertain the client's application for interim relief on the basis that the Secretary of State could not be her employer in the place of a dissolved NHS trust.

Douglas Leach Has broad experience across a range of tribunal and appellate cases, notably in cases involving TUPE issues. He is also frequently instructed on disability discrimination matters. **Strengths:** "He has an excellent analytical mind, and can floor people with academic points, which means he can't lose a case." "He is quick, efficient, focused, very knowledgeable and good with clients." **Recent work:** Instructed by the Department for Work and Pensions on a complex tribunal case regarding disability-related absences.

Allan Roberts (see p.708) A widely admired employment practitioner with considerable expertise in whistle-blowing and discrimination cases. He has built up a significant reputation for handling employment disputes for police forces. **Strengths:** "He is very good with witnesses, brilliant with clients, and very courteous to his opponent – he secures the sympathy of the tribunal." "Not only is he a trial advocate of absolutely amazing ability, but he's also really good with the clients." **Recent work:** Acted for Chief Constables of Derbyshire and Nottinghamshire as respondents in a whistle-blowing case against a counter-terrorist officer, concerning operational decisions associated with the Olympic Games.

Old Square Chambers

See profile on p.891

THE SET

Old Square is one of the Western Circuit's leading sets for high-end employment disputes, due to the vast experience and expertise available among its barristers on issues such as TUPE, equal pay, disciplinary action and trade union-related cases.

Client service: "The clerking, led by William Meade, is good here – they make sure you get matched with the right barrister for your case."

SILKS

Michael Ford QC An experienced silk whose vast expertise covers all aspects of employment law. He has been instructed in numerous precedent-setting employment matters, such as whole workforce claims, industrial action cases and judicial reviews. **Strengths:** "He is extremely sharp and able. He cuts through swathes of legislation to provide creative responses to tough legal questions. He's the guy you go to for solutions to difficult problems." "He is a truly outstanding advocate and a fantastic brain." **Recent work:** Instructed on Lock v British Gas, a high-profile case in the ECJ pertaining to the inclusion of commission in holiday pay for EU workers.

JUNIORS

Spencer Keen A recent addition to Old Square Chambers who has a commercially focused employment law practice. He offers clients considerable expertise in disability discrimination matters and EU employment law. **Strengths:** "He is excellent with clients – very committed." **Recent work:** Advised Trinity Hospice in a case against an employee who had developed a significant disability during the course of her employment, was dismissed for incapacity, and made claims of race and disability discrimination.

Toby Kempster An experienced employment and personal injury practitioner who often utilises both areas of expertise on stress at work and disability cases. He has had particular success in cases involving public sector clients. **Strengths:** "He is always very well prepared, and inspires full confidence in his work." **Recent work:** Acted for Leicestershire Primary Care Trust as one of two respondents on a TUPE claim brought by several prison officers whose work included assisting on the medical unit of a prison, claiming that they were taking responsibility for medical services and were transferred to the local NHS service.

Melanie Tether (see p.735) An experienced employment specialist noted for her expertise on discrimination claims. She also has considerable expertise in cases with high-profile union involvement, and is widely praised for her in-depth TUPE expertise. **Strengths:** "She is excellent on all things TUPE. Her technical knowledge is great." "Her knowledge is very impressive, and not just of the case law and academic side – she is also very practical." **Recent work:** Advised UNISON and UNITE union members as claimants on a case against North Lanarkshire Council, concerning the respondent's job evaluation scheme.

Hilary Winstone (see p.754) Experienced in advising both large private sector clients and public bodies such as police forces and NHS trusts. She handles a broad range of employment issues, and is particularly noted for her client-friendly approach. **Strengths:** "She is responsive and robust – a pleasure to work with." "She is very personable and easy to work with, and puts witnesses at ease." **Recent work:** Represented SITA Information Networking Computing in tribunal and appellate cases concerning the meaning of disability, including symptoms arising from obesity.

Andrew Midgley (see p.672) Focuses on discrimination cases, including whistle-blowing and disability claims. He is particularly active in representing public sector clients, such as NHS trusts, government departments and trade unions. **Strengths:** "He is very approachable and good with clients – an excellent advocate." "He is an astute advocate, and incredibly easy to get on with." **Recent work:** Represented Ealing Hospital NHS Trust in an appellate case against a consultant who was dismissed for conducting private work while certified as unfit for work for the Trust.

Mark Whitcombe Covers a wide range of employment law, including issues such as multi-claimant TUPE and equal pay disputes, and unfair and wrongful dismissal claims. He is regularly instructed on cases of all levels, right up to the EAT and Court of Appeal. **Recent work:** Instructed by Brighton and Sussex University Hospitals NHS Trust on its successful defence of a complex constructive dismissal claim against a consultant maxillo-facial prosthetist. The claim concerned allegations of bullying, excessive workload and inadequate support.

Helen Gower Advises claimants and defendants on numerous employment matters, notably involving discrimination, equal pay and trade union concerns. She has considerable experience of public sector cases involving local government and healthcare clients, and is able to draw upon the expertise gained by her work as a legal assessor for the Health and Care Professions Council. **Strengths:** "She is a very efficient adviser who has a good manner with the tribunal." **Recent work:** Represented Samba Financial Group in a tribunal case concerning harassment relating to the claimant's religious beliefs.

Band 2

3PB Barristers

See profile on p.846

THE SET

This set acts for claimants and respondents on all aspects of employment law, and has experienced advocates across all levels. 3PB boasts particular expertise in the enforcement of restrictive covenants, and maintains strong relationships with nationwide legal insurance companies.

Client service: "The clerking is good there. Russell Porter, the chambers director, is particularly helpful – whenever we phone up he will bend over backwards to assist us."

JUNIORS

Jack Mitchell Heads the employment team at 3PB, and has decades of experience across many high-profile employment matters. He is an expert on whistle-blowing issues, having co-authored numerous prominent publications on the topic. **Strengths:** "He is very good commercially and very robust. Whenever you have a complicated case he's the guy to go to, as he can bat off the other side quite well." "He's a fluent advocate – his submissions are very detailed, and he has an amazing ability to persuade the judge with his legal reasoning, and also convince the other side that they have something significant to consider in terms of legal argument."

James Dawson Offers in-depth employment law expertise to clients on complex cases concerning issues such as race discrimination and breaches of restrictive covenants. He is also a part-time employment judge. **Strengths:** "He is a clear, technically astute advocate who is very thorough and approachable." "His knowledge of law is almost nerdy, and he uses it to such a powerful extent that he is incredibly convincing." **Recent work:** Instructed by Larchcroft Education Trust on a claim against one of its schools concerning race discrimination and constructive unfair dismissal.

Harriet Fear-Davies A rising star on the Western Circuit who draws praise for her user-friendly approach. Her growing practice covers all aspects of employment law, on behalf of both public and private sector clients. **Strengths:** "She is highly commercial, always prepared and never lets you down – she always goes the extra mile." "Often in employment there can be industry-specific jargon – she can assimilate difficult concepts quickly, and performs well on her feet. She's also exceptionally bright." **Recent work:** Successfully represented Brimheath Developments & Ors in a case concerning a discrimination claim on the grounds of sex, sexual orientation and disability.

Andrew Macphail A junior who advises exclusively on employment law cases, often involving complex, multiple-day tribunal hearings. He has particular experience of cases relating to equal pay litigation. **Strengths:** "He is a thorough and systematic barrister. You always know when Andrew is instructed that he will devote his full care and attention to the case." "He's quite technical but very effective as an advocate, and always invested in his work." **Recent work:** Represented Community Options as respondent at tribunal and the EAT, against a claim of unfair dismissal and failure to make reasonable adjustments.

Stephen Wyeth Former solicitor and part-time employment judge, with strong experience of high-value discrimination claims. He also has noteworthy expertise in TUPE claims, particularly cases involving multiple respondents. **Strengths:** "He is very proactive and well prepared at all times. His skills and abilities as an advocate, and his client management skills, belie his relatively junior call." "He was a solicitor for a number of years so he knows the commercial reality for his clients, as well as being pragmatic and approachable. He's always been succinct and helpful, even with general queries. His presentational style is adaptable." **Recent work:** Represented outsourcing and distribution company Bunzl as the respondent in a tribunal claim of constructive unfair dismissal, concerning an alleged failure to provide a safe system of work and the instigation of a sham disciplinary process.

Gareth Graham Experienced in a range of employment cases on behalf of clients from a variety of sectors, including recent success with governmental, engineering and automotive clients. Alongside his traditional employment practice, he regularly acts on internal professional disciplinary matters for clients such as rugby clubs and universities. **Strengths:** "He is a reliable barrister who is willing to get stuck in." **Recent work:** Acted for Horfield Health Centre on an unfair dismissal case brought by a claimant who was dismissed on the grounds of capability.

Simon Tibbitts Frequently represents clients in tribunal courts nationwide, as well as at the EAT, in complex employment matters. He acts largely for respondents, with particular expertise in discrimination and whistle-blowing cases. **Strengths:** "He always has the confidence and respect of the tribunal." "He is practical, and good at explaining difficult concepts in simple terms." **Recent work:** Acted for an employer in a convoluted tribunal case involving two respondent companies, three claimants and two interpreters, concerning claims of race discrimination, victimisation, harassment and unfair dismissal.

Pump Court Chambers

See profile on p.851

THE SET

This team offers a commercially focused employment practice, with extensive High Court and County Court experience in business-related injunctions and restrictive covenant matters. Members also offer expertise in discrimination cases relating to housing and education.

Client service: "The clerks there, led by chief clerk David Barber, are always very helpful. The service is prompt and flexible."

JUNIORS

Timothy Dracass Respondent-focused barrister with considerable experience of representing major corporate clients in complex tribunal and appellate cases. He is renowned for his excellent client manner and strong advocacy skills. **Strengths:** "His knowledge and advocacy are good, and he's very straightforward, which makes him popular with clients." **Recent work:** Instructed by Smithie UK to defend the company against sex discrimination claims brought by a former employee.

Gary Self (see p.717) Joined Pump Court Chambers in 2013 from College Chambers, bringing a wide-ranging respondent-focused practice, notably focused on instructions from police force clients. He also sits as a part-time employment judge. **Strengths:** "He's very commercially focused, an excellent advocate and very responsive. Clients love him." **Recent work:** Represented Fitness First Clubs as respondent in a dismissal case relating to health and safety and whistle-blowing issues.

Heather Platt (see p.694) Covers both claimant and respondent work, and is best recognised for her work on behalf of public sector clients, such as schools, local authorities and housing associations. Her broad expertise encompasses disability, sex and racial discrimination claims. **Strengths:** "She is very good technically, but also approachable, with excellent client relationship skills." **Recent work:** Acted for multiple claimants on a collective redundancy case concerning redundancy payments against a fee-paying school. She was successful on behalf of the claimants at the EAT.

Band 3

Albion Chambers

See profile on p.889

THE SET

Albion Chambers' employment team provide its clients with the full range of advisory and advocacy assistance. Members of the set work with both employers and employees, and receive instructions from clients such as insurers, trade unions and local authorities.

Client service: "They have very accommodating clerks – they are responsive and customer-focused."

JUNIORS

Liz Cunningham One of only a small number of dedicated employment specialists on the Western Circuit. She offers both claimant and respondent clients expertise in areas such as unfair and constructive dismissal, and sex, race and disability discrimination. **Strengths:**" She is an approachable, practical advocate with an eye for detail." "She builds a very good rapport with clients, grasps facts and issues quickly, and is concise and robust in cross-examination."

Stephen Roberts Former employment and family law solicitor whose broad barristerial experience covers a range of employment law issues, including unfair dismissal, equal pay and pension claims. Interviewees appreciate the experience and gravitas he brings to complex, high-value employment disputes. **Strengths:** "He's good at dealing with clients because of his experience – he's very reassuring. He is also quite humble and toned down in his style of cross-examination, making him naturally persuasive and appealing to judges."

Other Ranked Lawyers

Graham Watson (Colleton Chambers) An Exeter-based employment specialist, with wide-ranging experience covering wrongful dismissal, discrimination, whistle-blowing and TUPE claims. He is praised by solicitors for his approach to client service. **Strengths:** "He is calm, focused and pragmatic, and has great client skills."

Matthew White (St John's Chambers) Acts primarily for respondents on employment disputes, and has particular expertise in representing government departments. He is highly experienced in discrimination cases. **Strengths:** "He is very able and prepared, and a thoroughly reasonable advocate." "His expert focus and questioning skills are excellent for concentrating the minds of witnesses." **Recent work:** Represented a high-profile retail client in a case concerning unfair dismissal on the grounds of age discrimination. The claim was successfully resisted at tribunal.

Fergus Currie (Unity Street Chambers) Has a strong presence in the Bristol employment market, alongside his personal injury and public law activity. He is particularly active in cases concerning TUPE regulations. **Strengths:** "He is a great barrister – a really safe pair of hands."

Energy & Natural Resources

Contents:

LONDON

Energy & Natural Resources London	
Leading Sets	
Band 1	Keating Chambers *
One Essex Court *	4 Pump Court *
Band 2	**Band 3**
Atkin Chambers *	Thirty Nine Essex Street *
Brick Court Chambers *	7 King's Bench Walk *
Essex Court Chambers *	
Leading Silks	
Star individuals	**Hancock** Christopher *20 Essex Street (ORL)* ◊
Rabinowitz Laurence *One Essex Court*	**Jowell** Daniel *Brick Court Chambers*
Band 1	**Parkin** Fiona *Atkin Chambers*
Davies Helen *Brick Court Chambers*	**Pollock** Gordon *Essex Court Chambers*
Foxton David *Essex Court Chambers*	**Schaff** Alistair *7 King's Bench Walk*
Glick Ian *One Essex Court*	**Sharpe** Thomas *One Essex Court*
Grabiner Anthony *One Essex Court*	**Taverner** Marcus *Keating Chambers* *
Howard Mark *Brick Court Chambers*	**ter Haar** Roger *Crown Office Chambers (ORL)* ◊
McCaughran John *One Essex Court*	**Tozzi** Nigel *4 Pump Court* *
Persey Lionel *Quadrant Chambers (ORL)* ◊	**Tromans** Stephen *Thirty Nine Essex Street*
Streatfeild-James David *Atkin Chambers*	**Walker** Steven *Atkin Chambers* *
Toledano Daniel *One Essex Court*	**Band 4**
White Andrew *Atkin Chambers* *	**Boswood** Anthony *Fountain Court Chambers (ORL)* ◊
Band 2	**Buehrlen** Veronique *Keating Chambers* *
Blanchard Claire *Essex Court Chambers*	**Gunning** Alexander *4 Pump Court* *
Brannigan Sean *4 Pump Court* *	**Hollander** Charles *Brick Court Chambers*
Bryan Simon *Essex Court Chambers*	**Hossain** Sa'ad *One Essex Court*
Catchpole Stuart *Thirty Nine Essex Street*	**Howe** Timothy *Fountain Court Chambers (ORL)* ◊ *
Choo Choy Alain *One Essex Court*	**Kendrick** Dominic *7 King's Bench Walk*
Constable Adam *Keating Chambers* *	**Malek** Hodge M *Thirty Nine Essex Street* *
Dennison Stephen *Atkin Chambers* *	**Masefield** Roger *Brick Court Chambers*
Doerries Chantal-Aimée *Atkin Chambers* *	**Matovu** Harry *Brick Court Chambers*
McMullan Manus *Atkin Chambers* *	**Moran** Vincent *Keating Chambers* *
Mildon David *Essex Court Chambers*	**Siberry** Richard *Essex Court Chambers*
O'Farrell Finola *Keating Chambers* *	**Vineall** Nicholas *4 Pump Court* *
Onions Jeffery *One Essex Court*	**Wilken** Sean *Thirty Nine Essex Street*
Rainey Simon *Quadrant Chambers (ORL)* ◊	**Wilmot-Smith** Richard *Thirty Nine Essex Street*
Tselentis Michael *20 Essex Street (ORL)* ◊	**Wolfson** David *One Essex Court*
Band 3	**New Silks**
Allen David *7 King's Bench Walk*	**Fealy** Michael *One Essex Court*
Bools Michael *Brick Court Chambers*	**Howells** James *Atkin Chambers* *
Brenton Timothy *7 King's Bench Walk*	**Mort** Justin *Keating Chambers* *
Dennys Nicholas *Atkin Chambers*	**O'Sullivan** Sean *4 Pump Court* *
Leading Juniors	
Band 1	**Parker** Matthew *3 Verulam Buildings (ORL)* ◊ *
Lewis Christopher *Atkin Chambers* *	**Pilbrow** Fionn *Brick Court Chambers*
Band 2	**Band 4**
Buckingham Paul *Keating Chambers* *	**Emmett** Laurence *One Essex Court*
Gledhill Orlando *One Essex Court* *	**Hanna** Ronan *Atkin Chambers* *
Hickey Alexander *4 Pump Court* *	**Harris** Christopher *3 Verulam Buildings (ORL)* ◊ *
Patton Conall *One Essex Court* *	**Healy** Sandra *7 King's Bench Walk* *
Shapiro Daniel *Crown Office Chambers (ORL)* ◊ *	**Jarvis** Malcolm *20 Essex Street (ORL)* ◊
Band 3	**Leabeater** James *4 Pump Court* *
Chambers Gaynor *Keating Chambers* *	**Lemon** Jane *Keating Chambers* *
Kramer Adam *3 Verulam Buildings (ORL)* ◊ *	**Sinclair** Duncan *Thirty Nine Essex Street* *
Lazur Thomas *Keating Chambers* *	**Up-and-coming individuals**
Midwinter Stephen *Brick Court Chambers*	**Watkins** Michael *One Essex Court*
Ng Jern-Fei *Essex Court Chambers* *	

** Indicates set / individual with profile.*
◊ (ORL) = Other Ranked Lawyer.
Alphabetical order within each band. Band 1 is highest.

Band 1

One Essex Court

See profile on p.790

THE SET

A leading commercial set that is home to a strong team of silks and juniors who are well at home in the energy field. The set's barristers act on a wide array of commercial disputes across the oil and gas and power sectors. Solicitors regard it as "an absolute go-to set" that is "at the top of the tree" for oil and gas work.

Client service: Senior clerk Darren Burrows' team is described by clients as "exceptional in terms of approachability and client service, and commendably direct when it comes to recommending the right person for the right job." Another source said: "The main clerk I deal with is David Amdor. He is always good to talk to about who is good for what, and I have always found his recommendations to be very good."

SILKS

Laurence Rabinowitz QC A commercial silk who is regarded by sources as "one of the leading barristers in London for oil and gas work." His practice includes representing clients in arbitrations and disputes with regard to issues such as gas price disputes, long-term energy supply agreements and joint operating agreements. **Strengths:** "Incredibly pragmatic and client-friendly, he is someone you can comfortably present to the clients. He will talk their language and he is very willing to engage with the clients properly, taking on board their points and concerns." **Recent work:** He acted for E.ON in a dispute concerning the termination of a natural gas sale and purchase agreement.

Ian Glick QC Renowned for his energy arbitration expertise, he regularly acts in power and upstream oil and gas disputes. **Strengths:** "He is an extraordinarily powerful opponent. He makes you focus on the real issues in the case and there can't be any flim-flam in your argument." **Recent work:** Represented Heritage Oil in a tax dispute concerning a sale and purchase agreement.

Anthony Grabiner QC A "heavyweight" commercial silk with an excellent reputation for oil and gas and power litigation. He also regularly handles arbitration. **Strengths:** "It was a joy to work with him. He was funny and persuasive, and the clients loved him – he was everything you'd want from a senior QC."

John McCaughran QC A contract lawyer with a practice focusing on contractual disputes related to issues such as long-term gas supply agreements and LNG gas price review disputes. **Strengths:** "He is exceptional, particularly in terms of contractual interpretation. He thinks of points and ways around issues that no one else can, and presents in a way that seems entirely logical and practical." **Recent work:** He represented BHP Billiton in a dispute concerning the termination of a gas supply agreement.

Daniel Toledano QC A commercial barrister who acts for clients in arbitrations and at court. His practice includes representing clients in disputes related to joint operating, long-term gas supply and gas transportation agreements. **Strengths:** "He is so easy to work with. He is just a great, great team player, who is really bright. He has incredible gravitas and can command the room." **Recent work:** Acted for Centrica in a long-term gas supply termination case.

Alain Choo Choy QC Represents clients in a wide range of commercial energy and natural resources disputes. **Strengths:** "He's very user-friendly, very articulate in submissions, and very keen and interested in the cases he handles." **Recent work:** Advised a group of sellers in relation to long-term gas supply agreements.

Jeffery Onions QC Represents clients in disputes related to the upstream and downstream oil and gas and power sectors. He acts in arbitrations and also advises clients in relation to contracts and statute. **Strengths:** "He is a real heavyweight, who really rolls his sleeves up and gets into it." **Recent work:** Represented British Gas in a dispute with Accenture that related to a customer billing system.

Thomas Sharpe QC A competition lawyer with an extensive practice in regulated sectors such as power and water. He acts for regulators and regulated companies in relation to investigations and disputes. **Strengths:** "An extremely pleasant and powerful advocate, who is very good on his feet. " **Recent work:** Instructed by Ofwat in a range of regulatory proceedings.

Sa'ad Hossain QC A new silk who acts for clients in disputes relating to the oil and gas sector. **Strengths:** "His preparation of a case is excellent, and his knowledge of this sector is invaluable." **Recent work:** Represented Endeavour Energy in a Commercial Court dispute relating to a contract for the provision of a wellhead drilling unit.

David Wolfson QC Acts for clients in arbitrations and Commercial Court disputes in the power and upstream oil and gas sectors. **Strengths:** "A counsel whom the tribunal finds very engaging, he is someone who puts forward attractive commercial points." **Recent work:** Acted for Tullow Uganda in a dispute concerning the ownership of two oilfields in Uganda.

Michael Fealy QC A commercial barrister who took silk in 2014. He acts in disputes in the oil and gas, renewable energy and carbon trading sectors. **Strengths:** "Very hard-working, very thorough and very clever." **Recent work:** Represented Sinclair in a multi-jurisdictional dispute concerning the ownership of an oilfield in Kazakhstan.

JUNIORS

Orlando Gledhill A senior junior who advises on a wide variety of energy disputes. Sources point to his expertise in emissions trading, describing him as a "leading expert on carbon trading disputes." **Strengths:** "He is fiercely independent, and really knows the meaning of 'without fear or favour'. He is prepared to stand up to judges, and is a great trial advocate, who is understated but effective." **Recent work:** Instructed on a dispute between CF Partners and Barclays Bank and Tricorona that related to a breach of confidence claim emanating from Barclays' acquisition of a carbon credit developer and trader.

Conall Patton (see p.690) Advises on upstream and downstream commercial oil and gas litigation and arbitration. **Strengths:** "He is a cerebral lawyer and an extremely hard grafter, who is well capable of contending with counsel well above his call." **Recent work:** Represented Rosneft in the Court of Appeal and the Eastern Caribbean Court of Appeal in a case concerning the ownership of companies in the former YUKOS oil group.

Laurence Emmett Acts in commercial litigation and arbitration, and is highly regarded by sources for his knowledge of the energy industry. **Strengths:** "He has excellent attention to detail and a forensic mind." **Recent work:** Junior to John McCaughran QC in a dispute concerning the supply of a semi-submersible drilling unit.

Michael Watkins A commercial barrister who has acted as a junior in major energy disputes both in court and at arbitration. **Strengths:** "Sensationally bright, hard-working and enthusiastic, he's a fantastic draftsman, who it is an absolute delight to instruct." "He is tipped for the top in the future." **Recent work:** Junior to Lord Grabiner QC in a dispute between Dow Chemical and Petrochemicals Industries.

Band 2

Atkin Chambers

See profile on p.762

THE SET

This excellent construction set is in great demand from solicitors, who are keen to use its services in the energy sector. Chambers' barristers regularly appear in cases in the TCC and in energy-related arbitrations around the world. Sources recognise the depth of expertise at the set and say that it is "right up there in terms of the energy and natural resources sector." **Client service:** "The clerking team is very good, in particular the head clerk, Justin Wilson, who I think is very responsive." "They have got things right in the clerking room: the clerks are very good, user-friendly and receptive. Also they don't double-book counsel."

SILKS

David Streatfeild-James QC A respected construction silk who impresses sources with his knowledge of the energy sector. His experience encompasses power plant design disputes and offshore and onshore energy engineering matters. **Strengths:** "He is a super-whizzo intelligent guy, and one of the brainboxes you bring in for the more way-out cases." **Recent work:** Appeared in the TCC for RWE npower renewables in a dispute with a contractor concerning a hydroelectric scheme in Scotland.

Andrew White QC A popular silk who acts for energy clients in construction and engineering disputes. Sources note his experience in disputes relating to oil pipelines, FPSOs, oil rigs, LNG facilities and power plants. **Strengths:** "Great in terms of the detail, he really rolls his sleeves up and he's excellent at getting on as part of the team." **Recent work:** He acted in a TCC case related to unpaid sums connected to the drilling of an offshore well in Guinea.

Stephen Dennison QC Has a great deal of experience of acting in energy arbitrations and litigation, and has a focus on engineering and construction matters. He has a good track record in disputes in the renewable energy and oil and gas sectors, and often acts in matters emanating from the Middle East. **Strengths:** "He is unruffled and he takes things calmly. Even if the wheels are coming off he manages to ride out the storm well." **Recent work:** Acted in a matter where a bond provider applied for an injunction to prevent the beneficiary from making demands on performance bonds worth USD40 million. The bonds were related to the supply, manufacture and installation of boilers for a power station in Brazil.

Chantal-Aimée Doerries QC A construction silk who has experience of acting in disputes connected with offshore oil and gas, renewable energy, power plants and mining projects. **Strengths:** "Helpful, business-savvy and pleasant to work with."

Manus McMullan QC Advises clients in relation to operational and construction-related upstream oil and gas disputes. Additionally, he has a strong reputation for his work advising on construction disputes in the power generation sector. **Strengths:** "One of the new generation of stars. He is user-friendly, good with clients, and clever. As a result, he has a great following."

Nicholas Dennys QC A construction lawyer who regularly appears in court and in arbitrations on behalf of his clients. He is recommended by sources for his energy work and particularly commended for his knowledge of offshore construction disputes. **Strengths:** "He is solid and safe but very clever, and also has a good way with tribunals and judges." **Recent work:** He appeared in the High Court in a dispute connected with the decommissioning of a North Sea oil platform.

Steven Walker QC (see p.745) Acts in engineering disputes in the power sector. He also regularly appears in cases related to wind farms, biomass plants, oil and gas infrastructure and conventional power generation plants. **Strengths:** "He is responsive, user-friendly, approachable and quite direct in ensuring he does what needs to be done." **Recent work:** Acted for a subcontractor in a dispute concerning performance bonds relating to the delivery of boilers for a power station in Brazil.

Fiona Parkin QC Acts as both litigator and arbitrator in energy disputes with a construction and engineering element. She advises in connection with biomass, hydropower, conventional power generation, and oil and gas matters. **Strengths:** "She gets to grips with the issues very quickly and is very good to work with as she is very collaborative and you feel you can just pick up the phone and chat to her. She is very eloquent and always has the right answer." **Recent work:** Represented a renewable energy developer in the TCC in a dispute connected with a hydroelectric scheme in Scotland.

James Howells QC A new silk with a practice that sees him acting in energy and power arbitration and litigation. He appears in engineering disputes connected with upstream oil and gas, electricity infrastructure and power generating plants. **Strengths:** "He's responsive and mucks in, which is what construction clients tend to want." **Recent work:** Advised in a dispute related to consultancy services used in the design of a high-pressure, high-temperature well in Georgia.

JUNIORS

Christopher Lewis A highly rated junior with an energy practice that predominantly focuses on engineering disputes in the oil and gas and renewable energy sectors. **Strengths:** "He is very bright and exceptionally diligent. He is always the best-prepared person in the room."

Ronan Hanna A junior who is singled out by sources for his ability to handle complex technical disputes. His energy practice involves him advising on oil and gas, power and renewable energy construction disputes. **Strengths:** "He has a very good brain on him." "He works every hour to deliver what he has promised to deliver, and is a real rising star at Atkin."

Brick Court Chambers

See profile on p.774

THE SET

An excellent commercial set with a strong line-up of silks and juniors practising in the energy field. Members of chambers act in a vast array of international and domestic disputes stemming from industries such as oil and gas, mining, carbon trading, and renewable and conventional power generation.

Client service: "The clerks, led by Julian Hawes and Ian Moyler, are very responsive, and keen to know what we need. They are not like the old style of barristers' clerks, but are instead proactive, modern team players."

SILKS

Helen Davies QC A commercial and competition silk who has a good reputation among instructing solicitors for her work in the energy sector. She advises major oil and gas companies in relation to matters such as joint operating agreements and gas purchase and sale agreements. She also acts in energy-related oligarch cases. **Strengths:** "She is outstanding, very forceful, very clear and very able." **Recent work:** She appeared in a case concerning the purchase and sale of gas from the North Sea.

Mark Howard QC A heavyweight commercial silk who regularly acts in energy matters, and is noted by sources as a good choice for "the grandest cases in this area." **Strengths:** "He is astonishing and an excellent cross-examiner." **Recent work:** Acted for Energy Venture Partners in a claim relating to the sale of a Nigerian oil concession.

Michael Bools QC Acts in litigation and arbitration in commercial matters connected to the energy industry. He has a great deal of experience related to offshore oil and gas disputes and power generation cases. **Strengths:** "He gets to grip with things very quickly, is very good with juniors, and is loved by clients. He delivers good advice and is good on his feet." **Recent work:** He appeared in a Commercial Court trial focusing on a USD30 million claim related to gas plants.

Daniel Jowell QC A commercial and competition silk who is noted for his work in oligarch cases. His experience includes acting in oil and gas and renewable energy disputes. **Recent work:** He represented National Oil Well in a claim stemming from a defective driller.

Charles Hollander QC Advises and appears in connection with commercial matters in the energy field. His practice includes acting on oil and gas and renewable energy matters. **Strengths:** "He has an intricate mind and can devise points that few others can think of." **Recent work:** Appeared in a Commercial Court trial centring on the termination of a natural gas sales agreement.

Roger Masefield QC A new commercial silk who has acted in a number of notable energy disputes. His practice includes acting in cases related to the oil and gas and power sectors. **Recent work:** Instructed on behalf of Standard Bank in a dispute connected to the sale of a company that had invested in an oilfield in Ghana.

Harry Matovu QC A well-respected silk with a broad commercial practice. **Strengths:** "A very smooth, personable lawyer who provides a very user-friendly service." **Recent work:** Involved in the long-running Excalibur and Keystone litigation, which focused on oilfields in Iraqi Kurdistan.

JUNIORS

Stephen Midwinter Appears in arbitration and litigation in a wide range of energy disputes. **Strengths:** "He is extremely impressive, and a bit like a thinking machine or a computer. He is an extremely logical and intellectually rigorous character who is destined to go far." **Recent work:** He appeared in a British Virgin Islands dispute related to an alleged equity interest in a Georgian oil terminal.

Fionn Pilbrow A respected junior with a broad commercial practice, who regularly acts in energy disputes. **Strengths:** "Very user-friendly and accessible, he's a delight to work with. He really rolls his sleeves up when necessary and produces brilliant work under pressure."

Essex Court Chambers

See profile on p.792

THE SET

A commercial set with a fine reputation among energy litigators. Noted for the ability of its counsel, it handles disputes drawn from around the world in the oil and gas, mining, renewable energy and power sectors. One source described the chambers as "a go-to set for complex, important commercial and arbitration matters. It is full of superstars."

Client service: "Senior clerk David Grief is honest and reliable. His opinion on the most appropriate counsel can always be relied upon." "The clerks are extremely responsive and reasonable when negotiating fees. They have an understanding of the client position and cost sensitivities."

SILKS

Claire Blanchard QC Has a broad commercial practice that encompasses shipping, insurance and commodities work. She regularly handles energy disputes, many of which often contain an element of the aforementioned disciplines. **Strengths:** "She is prepared to argue over every dollar if the client wants her to, but equally can charm the other side into a settlement."

Simon Bryan QC An experienced silk with an energy practice that draws upon his experience in the insurance, shipping and commodities sectors. **Strengths:** "Very user-friendly and easy to get on with." "Meticulous and prepared to comb through the detail." **Recent work:** Acted for ArcelorMittal in connection with a claim relating to a flooded coal mine in Australia.

David Mildon QC Acts in arbitration and litigation, and also appears as an expert determiner in energy cases. His wide field of experience includes advising on disputes stemming from areas such as oil and gas, carbon trading and mining. **Strengths:** "He knows the energy sector inside and out. He's fantastically clever and makes bold decisions."

Richard Siberry QC A commercial silk with a good pedigree in the energy sector. He has appeared in a large number of energy disputes over the years, and now often appears as an arbitrator.

David Foxton QC A commercial barrister who acts in litigation and international arbitration. He has a broad commercial practice that includes representing clients from the energy sector. **Strengths:** "He is a very clever and lateral-thinking lawyer." "He's a very knowledgeable and rigorous advocate, who brings an intellectual firepower to any case he is arguing."

Gordon Pollock QC A commercial silk who has acted in a number of energy disputes in the course of a glittering career. **Strengths:** "He just had a mastery of our case and seemed to be in complete control of the courtroom."

JUNIORS

Jern-Fei Ng A popular junior who acts in oil and gas, renewable energy, and metals and mining litigation and arbitration cases. He is often instructed on work emanating from, or connected with, Singapore. **Strengths:** "He comes up with extremely clever points." **Recent work:** Acted for the claimant in a multi-jurisdictional coal mining dispute related to two mines in Borneo.

Keating Chambers

See profile on p.824

THE SET

One of the top construction sets in London, it regularly handles major domestic and international energy disputes. Its members act in arbitrations and TCC cases in connection with oil and gas, renewable energy, power and offshore disputes. Sources are impressed by chambers' consistent quality: "Keating Chambers does not rest on its reputation but earns it anew every year."

Client service: Sources recognise the experience of Declan Redmond, brought into the set as director of clerking in 2014. As for the rest of the clerking team, one solicitor commented: "I'm very impressed, particularly with senior clerk Chris Sunderland, who is straightforward, efficient and commercial." For those that are interested in these things, the set also has "the best chocolate biscuit selection of any chambers."

SILKS

Finola O'Farrell QC (see p.684) Has a broad construction and engineering practice, and often appears in energy-related litigation and arbitration. She acts in renewable energy, power, and metals and mining matters, and often advises in relation to engineering, procurement and construction contract disputes. **Strengths:** "She is a safe pair of hands, who is loved by clients. She is very quick and very responsive, and she won't let you down."

Adam Constable QC A hotly tipped construction silk who has a great deal of experience of acting in engineering disputes in the energy sector. He has experience of disputes stemming from areas such as FPSOs, drilling, production sharing agreements and oil refineries. **Strengths:** "He has a very quick mind, and is able to digest huge volumes of very complex material." "His practice is going like a rocket. He is bright and very determined, and has very good common sense."

Marcus Taverner QC An experienced construction and engineering barrister with a thriving energy practice. He acts in arbitrations and courtroom disputes in connection with areas such as wind farms, energy from waste plants, biofuel plants and drilling matters. **Strengths:** "Once he gets his teeth into something he is not going to let go. He is all over the detail of the case. He gets his team working, both the barristers and the solicitors, and he has an ability to set both an overall strategy and get into the detail of what needs to be done." **Recent work:** Acted for Vivergo in a dispute related to the termination of a contract to carry out mechanical and piping work at a biofuel plant.

Justin Mort QC (see p.677) A new construction silk who often acts for clients in engineering litigation and arbitration matters in the energy sector. He regularly appears in power, mining and electricity infrastructure cases. **Strengths:** "He really thought about difficult issues and was prepared to tackle complex technical matters and challenge experts in order to get to the bottom of things. He's always prepared to get involved in every part of the dispute." **Recent work:** Headed a team representing Alstom in a dispute arising from the construction of Pembroke Power Station.

Veronique Buehrlen QC Acts for oil and gas clients in arbitrations and in the Commercial Court. She advises on disputes concerning issues such as drilling and oil and gas pipelines. **Strengths:** "She is excellent on the detail and very easy to get on with."

Vincent Moran QC Acts in construction and engineering disputes in the energy sector. Sources recognise his work in the upstream oil and gas sector, and in offshore wind farm disputes. **Strengths:** "Very charismatic, absolutely on the ball and able to think on his feet. He puts his position across forcefully and turns our weaknesses into strengths."

JUNIORS

Paul Buckingham Acts in energy disputes focused on engineering and construction issues. Clients appreciate his engineering background and the ease with which he is able to deal with technical issues and expert witnesses. He has appeared in arbitrations and in the courtroom in cases arising from the renewable energy, power and oil and gas sectors. **Strengths:** "A key linchpin in any case. He holds things together." **Recent work:** Acted for E.ON in two disputes related to the construction of the Robin Rigg offshore wind farm in the Solway Firth.

Thomas Lazur (see p.653) A construction and engineering junior who acts for clients in energy-related disputes. He has appeared in litigation in connection with solar farms and biomass plants, and in disputes between energy suppliers and customers. Clients appreciate his financial background and describe him as a "whizz with a spreadsheet." **Strengths:** "He gives straightforward, practical advice and, while he will argue his corner where he feels strongly about a point, he has the ability to see all sides of an argument." **Recent work:** Appeared in the Queen's Bench Division of the High Court in litigation stemming from the construction of five solar arrays.

Gaynor Chambers (see p.568) Has a domestic and international energy practice that focuses on representing clients in construction arbitrations and at court. **Strengths:** "Very good, very hard-working, easy to work with and down to earth."

Jane Lemon Focuses on acting for construction and engineering clients in both litigation and arbitration. Her practice includes appearing in energy cases, and she has handled a number of wind farm, power, and oil and gas disputes. **Strengths:** "Incredibly dedicated and very accessible. If you need something delivering she will deliver it and she is really good at getting on top of complex causation issues." **Recent work:** Appeared in a breach of contract dispute related to a flue gas desulphurisation project at Aberthaw Power Station.

4 Pump Court

See profile on p.849

THE SET

4 Pump Court is able to furnish clients with barristers who can act on both commercial and construction disputes in the energy sector. Counsel from the set act in the English courts and in the major arbitration centres across the world. Its barristers have expertise in a wide variety of industry sectors, including onshore and offshore oil and gas, renewable energy, conventional power generation and energy trading.

Client service: Sources say the clerking team, led by joint senior clerks Carl Wall and Stewart Gibbs, is "extremely good," and add: "They are good at not overcommitting the barristers, so you can feel comfortable that if they say someone will be available they actually are." Another solicitor said: "Carl runs a really good team. He is attentive, he takes an interest and he wants to know what the solicitors are concerned about and what appeals to them."

SILKS

Sean Brannigan QC A highly rated construction silk who regularly acts in arbitrations concerning energy projects. He has a good track record of dealing with disputes related to the power, oil and gas, water and hydroelectric sectors. **Strengths:** "He swings between a fireside chat style and the right level of impatience when people are putting stupid questions to him. He won't suffer fools and takes no prisoners; he is definitely robust, but is never over the top." **Recent work:** He appeared in an ICC arbitration that stemmed from an alleged breach of an agreement by a Middle Eastern government to award a contract to an energy construction company.

Nigel Tozzi QC Represents clients in commercial and construction disputes and arbitrations, and also sits as an arbitrator. He has a particular focus on the upstream oil and gas sector. **Strengths:** "A forthright and effective advocate who is very tough." **Recent work:** Instructed on behalf of Vitol in a breach of contract claim against the operator of an oilfield in Nigeria.

Sean O'Sullivan QC A new silk who is recommended by sources for his work in relation to energy trading, drilling contracts, offshore oil and gas construction disputes, and offshore oil and gas supply contract cases. He is noted for his ability to handle "big, document-heavy, technical cases." **Strengths:** "Combines huge intellectual horsepower with a very client-friendly approach." **Recent work:** Appeared in the Commercial Court in a dispute between a refinery and a fuel trader over the purchase of fuel oil.

Nicholas Vineall QC Noted for his skills in litigation and arbitration, and appreciated by solicitors for his expertise in offshore energy engineering disputes. **Strengths:** "Very good to work with and very much part of the team. He is personable and client-facing, and has none of the old-style stuffiness which you still get with some silks."

Alexander Gunning QC Acts in arbitrations and in courtrooms, handling offshore and onshore energy engineering disputes. **Strengths:** "He is pretty pragmatic and when dealing with a case with awkward points he can come up with solutions. He is very affable, good with clients and user-friendly from a solicitor's perspective."

JUNIORS

Alexander Hickey Handles construction and commercial disputes relating to onshore and offshore oil and gas, and conventional and renewable power generation. **Strengths:** "A very determined advocate." **Recent work:** Represented Nexen Petroleum in a dispute relating to the late delivery of components for the construction of oil and gas infrastructure in the North Sea.

James Leabeater Has a commercial and construction-focused practice that sees him acting for clients in domestic and international energy disputes. **Strengths:** "His attention to detail is incredible. He knew the documents inside out, and was brilliant. He has a very old head on his shoulders and gives nice, realistic legal advice."

Band 3

Thirty Nine Essex Street

See profile on p.797

THE SET

Home to a wide array of lawyers practising in the energy field. Its members act on commercial, construction, regulatory, environmental and competition matters on behalf of energy clients. Sources note the set's recent expansion and the addition of seasoned lawyers such as Peter Rees QC, the former Shell general counsel. One source said: "The set seems to be going great guns."

Client service: "Director of clerking David Barnes runs a very professional team." "The set has customer-friendly, helpful clerks, and the barristers give good customer value. Our clients ultimately pay and if they thought the rates were over-high for the quality of work they would be telling us."

SILKS

Stuart Catchpole QC Advises clients in connection with commercial and construction disputes relating to areas such as oil and gas, renewable energy and power projects. Much of his work involves acting in international arbitrations. **Strengths:** "Thorough and user-friendly, he is a very clever man. He has a great way with clients and he will have thought of 15,000 things you won't have."

Stephen Tromans QC An eminent environmental silk who is singled out by sources for his nuclear regulatory work and his advice on public law matters in the energy field. **Strengths:** "What he doesn't know about the nuclear industry isn't worth knowing." "When you get a paper from him, he doesn't waste a single word: everything is absolutely on point." **Recent work:** Advised the Nuclear Industry Association on its application to the Secretary of State for justification of a nuclear reactor type.

Sean Wilken QC Appears in international and domestic energy disputes. He acts in court and in arbitrations dealing with cases concerning the oil and gas and renewable energy sectors. His practice encompasses commercial, construction and public law cases. **Strengths:** "Immensely clever and a very able advocate."

Richard Wilmot-Smith QC A construction silk who acts in litigation, in arbitration and in an advisory capacity for energy clients. His practice sees him acting in power, renewable energy and oil and gas disputes. **Strengths:** "He has seen all the arguments, and he knows what will work and what won't work. He has very good judgement and is quick and efficient."

Hodge Malek QC Handles energy cases as part of his busy commercial practice, which is international in scope. He has acted for a number of large oil companies, advising them on exploration licences, solar energy projects and wind farms. He also represents the ICE in market abuse investigations and in connection with disciplinary matters. **Strengths:** "A robust advocate, who is insightful and excellent at getting to the core of the most complex cases." **Recent work:** He has recently been acting in a major case concerning alleged corruption in the Oman oil and gas sector.

JUNIORS

Duncan Sinclair (see p.721) A commercial, competition and EU lawyer with a great deal of experience in the UK power industry. His previous in-house role at Ofgem means that he is in demand for electricity and downstream natural gas regulatory work and public law challenges. **Strengths:** "He understands the law – not just the dry legal stuff, but the context around it." **Recent work:** Instructed by Ofgem to act as an intervener in a cartel claim made by National Grid against a number of parties. The case concerned the sale of gas-insulated switchgear.

7 King's Bench Walk

See profile on p.827

THE SET

Renowned for its insurance, shipping and commodities work, its barristers regularly bring their experience in these fields to bear in energy disputes. Counsel from the set advise on a wide variety of matters, including disputes relating to oil and gas trading, exploration and production, and oil shipment and carriage. Additionally, counsel advise on matters relating to the construction of energy infrastructure in the oil and gas and power sectors.

Client service: "The clerks, led by Bernie Hyatt and Greg Leyden, are very good, sensible and prepared to be reasonable on fees. The clients expect to see people being adaptable and they were very helpful in this regard." "The clerking was actually very good. Their clerk e-mailed me about the terms of engagement; he was very on top of it and knew how my firm had instructed them before."

SILKS

David Allen QC Has a good track record in commercial and construction cases with an energy element. He is particularly noted for his work connected with the offshore oil and gas sector.

Timothy Brenton QC An experienced silk with a varied practice in the energy field, who has acted in cases concerning commodities, offshore construction and commercial oil and gas. **Strengths:** "Has a real understanding of offshore operations. He is approachable and easy to work with."

Alistair Schaff QC Has a broad practice that takes in shipping, insurance, commodities and energy disputes. He regularly acts in international arbitration matters, and also sits as an arbitrator. **Strengths:** "A very easy-going and bright advocate."

Dominic Kendrick QC A well-regarded silk with a commercial practice that takes in shipping, insurance, commodities and energy work. In this field he handles cases that arise from energy trading, power and the offshore oil and gas industry. **Strengths:** "Bright, clear and a pleasure to work with," he is "exceptionally responsive and user-friendly." **Strengths:** Acted in an international arbitration that concerned a power supply contract in Pakistan.

JUNIORS

Sandra Healy A commercial junior with a practice that covers commodities, shipping, insurance and energy work. Much of her energy practice focuses on offshore oil and gas disputes. **Strengths:** "She is quick and has a good overview of a case. She checks everything and we never need to remind her of anything."

Other Ranked Lawyers

Roger ter Haar QC (Crown Office Chambers) An experienced QC with a wide commercial practice. Much of his energy work is focused on construction disputes in relation to areas such as renewable energy and conventional power generation projects. **Strengths:** "A hugely experienced guy." "One of the finest legal minds in the profession." **Recent work:** He acted in a case concerning the termination of a contract to do with the construction of a power plant construction.

Daniel Shapiro (Crown Office Chambers) Has a mixed commercial practice that involves insurance matters and construction disputes in the energy sector. He has appeared in a number of offshore oil and gas and wind construction disputes. **Strengths:** "He has great technical skills and is very intelligent. He's great on the detail and grasps things very quickly."

Michael Tselentis QC (20 Essex Street) Acts in litigation and arbitrations, and sits as an arbitrator in energy disputes. He has an internationally focused practice and appears in matters connected to areas such as oil and gas and mining. **Strengths:** "Very solid and very thorough, he leaves no stone unturned and has excellent analytical qualities."

Christopher Hancock QC (20 Essex Street) A commercial silk with a varied practice, who acts in insurance, shipping and energy disputes. **Strengths:** "He is absolutely excellent. He is very to the point and very good at the big picture. He has a lot of common sense and is a great pleasure to deal with." **Recent work:** Appeared in Petromec v Petrobras, a Commercial Court case relating to the sinking of an offshore production platform off the coast of Brazil in 2001.

Malcolm Jarvis (20 Essex Street) A commercial practitioner with a broad practice that includes acting in energy cases. He represents clients in offshore construction cases, upstream oil and gas operational disputes and matters relating to the sale and supply of energy. **Strengths:** "He is very helpful and gets to grips with a lot of complicated issues." **Recent work:** Appeared in a Commercial Court case focusing on the ownership of a consignment of oil in a storage facility in the UAE.

Anthony Boswood QC (Fountain Court Chambers) A well-respected barrister with a good pedigree in the energy sector. He now spends much of his time sitting as an arbitrator. **Strengths:** "An éminence grise of the Bar."

Timothy Howe QC (Fountain Court Chambers) Acts for energy clients in Commercial Court cases and arbitrations. He has experience of appearing in disputes focused on upstream joint venture agreements, mining projects and the ownership of oil concessions. **Strengths:** "One of the hardest-working silks at the Bar, and a real asset to any team." **Recent work:** Acted for a party in a joint venture in a dispute concerning the acquisition of Nigerian oil and gas interests.

Lionel Persey QC (Quadrant Chambers) A commercial silk with a practice that includes shipping, insurance and energy work. He often appears in international arbitrations that focus on offshore upstream energy infrastructure disputes. **Strengths:** "For the big, technical disputes he would be one of the first choice of counsel." "Very knowledgeable when it comes to the operations of offshore contracts. He is approachable and has a winning style with judges and arbitrators." **Recent work:** Appeared in a Commercial Court action, representing the owners of a drilling rig in a dispute about a drilling contract.

Simon Rainey QC (Quadrant Chambers) Acts in commercial disputes in the oil and gas sector. He represents oilfield services companies, exploration and production companies, and insurance companies in upstream oil and gas disputes. **Strengths:** "Very intellectually rigorous, he provides clear and accessible advice. He is also extremely knowledgeable in offshore matters." **Recent work:** Acted for Malta Oil in a Commercial Court case concerning its alleged failure to honour a partnership agreement to develop an oilfield off Malta.

Adam Kramer (3 Verulam Buildings) A junior with a varied commercial practice. He appears in a range of energy cases, including those related to long-term oil supply agreements, mining, power and upstream oil and gas. **Strengths:** "A very clever man, who is strong particularly on the academic side." **Recent work:** He appeared for Bankers Petroleum Albania in a dispute relating to the termination of a long-term oil supply contract.

Matthew Parker (3 Verulam Buildings) Acts in commercial cases to do with the upstream oil and gas, renewable energy and downstream electricity sectors. **Recent work:** Acted for an oil company in international arbitration relating to the cancellation of a production sharing agreement for an onshore oilfield development in Europe.

Christopher Harris (3 Verulam Buildings) Handles commercial litigation and international arbitration for clients in the energy sector. He has represented mining companies, oil trading groups, exploration and production companies and energy utilities. **Strengths:** "He is a rock in hard times. He is very steady, very considered and tenacious in fighting your corner." **Recent work:** Instructed in an international arbitration that was connected to uranium mining in Kazakhstan.

Contents:

LONDON

Environment London

Leading Sets	
Band 1	6 Pump Court *
Thirty Nine Essex Street *	**Band 3**
Francis Taylor Building *	Brick Court Chambers *
Landmark Chambers *	1 Crown Office Row *
Band 2	4-5 Gray's Inn Square
Blackstone Chambers *	Monckton Chambers *
Matrix Chambers *	Old Square Chambers *

Leading Silks	
Star individuals	Travers David *6 Pump Court* *
Tromans Stephen *Thirty Nine Essex Street*	Turner Jon *Monckton Chambers* *
Band 1	**Band 3**
Drabble Richard *Landmark Chambers*	Chamberlain Martin *Brick Court Chambers*
Elvin David *Landmark Chambers*	de la Mare Thomas *Blackstone Chambers*
Hart David *1 Crown Office Row*	Findlay James *Cornerstone Barristers (ORL)* ◊ *
Hockman Stephen *6 Pump Court* [A] *	Harwood Richard *Thirty Nine Essex Street* *
Howell John *Blackstone Chambers*	Maurici James *Landmark Chambers*
Lieven Nathalie *Landmark Chambers*	McCullough Angus *1 Crown Office Row*
McCracken Robert *Francis Taylor Building* [A]	Sands Philippe *Matrix Chambers*
Pleming Nigel *Thirty Nine Essex Street*	Smith Kassie *Monckton Chambers*
Band 2	Strachan James *Thirty Nine Essex Street*
Fordham Michael *Blackstone Chambers*	Straker Timothy *4-5 Gray's Inn Square* *
Gibson Charles *Henderson Chambers (ORL)* ◊ [A] *	Wolfe David *Matrix Chambers* *
Gordon Richard *Brick Court Chambers*	**New Silks**
Hermer Richard *Matrix Chambers*	Forsdick David *Landmark Chambers*
Jones Gregory *Francis Taylor Building*	Pereira James *Francis Taylor Building* [A]
Nardell Gordon *Thirty Nine Essex Street*	

Leading Juniors	
Band 1	Mehta Sailesh *Red Lion Chambers (ORL)* ◊ *
Bates John H *Old Square Chambers* *	Upton William *6 Pump Court*
Dixon Emma *Blackstone Chambers*	Watson Mark *6 Pump Court*
Harris Mark *6 Pump Court*	**Band 3**
Sheridan Maurice *Matrix Chambers*	Burton James *Thirty Nine Essex Street*
Thornton Justine *Thirty Nine Essex Street*	Busch Lisa *Landmark Chambers*
Wald Richard *Thirty Nine Essex Street*	Byrne Garrett *4-5 Gray's Inn Square* [A] *
Band 2	Collier Jane *Blackstone Chambers*
Badger Christopher *6 Pump Court* *	Galloway Malcolm *Old Square Chambers*
Banwell Richard *6 Pump Court*	Honey Richard *Francis Taylor Building* [A] *
Cook Kate *Matrix Chambers*	Riley-Smith Toby *Henderson Chambers (ORL)* ◊ [A] *
Facenna Gerry *Monckton Chambers* [A] *	Simons Zack *Landmark Chambers*
Hyam Jeremy *1 Crown Office Row*	**Up-and-coming individuals**
Macrory Richard *Brick Court Chambers*	Westaway Ned *Francis Taylor Building*

* Indicates set / individual with profile.

◊ (ORL) = Other Ranked Lawyer.

[A] direct access (see p.11).

Band 1

Thirty Nine Essex Street

See profile on p.797

THE SET

Contains some of the country's leading environmental barristers, who regularly act on complex cases in the highest courts in both the national and European spheres. Recent cases include R (RWE Npower Renewables Ltd) v Milton Keynes Council; a matter dealing with discrepancies between a development plan and a Supplementary Planning Document.

Client service: Numerous clients praise the calibre of the clerking. One source reports: "If I don't know who to use, I can absolutely rely on the clerk's recommendation." The environmental practice is led by Andrew Poyser.

SILKS

Stephen Tromans QC The leading environmental barrister of the day, who acts for regulators and commercial undertakings. He has particular strength in nuclear-related matters. **Strengths:** "He is very good when it comes to those tricky technical questions." "He has a straightforward style and presents arguments in a succinct, plain style." **Recent work:** Acted for the Canal and River Trust in its intervention in a Supreme Court case on the leakage of sewage into bodies of water.

Nigel Pleming QC Has a wide practice and represents clients acting against the state in judicial reviews and prosecutions. He regularly acts in high-profile cases in the Court of Appeal and the Supreme Court. **Strengths:** "He's spectacularly experienced and takes everything in his stride." **Recent work:** Appeared in Bancoult, R (on the application of) v Secretary of State for Foreign & Commonwealth Affairs, a case concerning a Chagossian Court of Appeal challenge to the marine protection area that was created around the Chagos Islands.

Gordon Nardell QC Acts in the planning and energy sides of the market, and regularly represents developers. **Strengths:** "He presses his points in court without annoying the bench." "He's extremely approachable and is willing to discuss matters with the client." **Recent work:** Appeared in R (Manchester Ship Canal Co) v Environment Agency; a Court of Appeal case concerning the formal treatment of sluice gates as flood defences.

Richard Harwood QC Works in the criminal, nuisance and impact assessment spaces, and has a complementary practice in planning law. **Strengths:** "He is good technically, and with clients and in cross-examination." "He is good at finding points to run and he is tenacious in his approach to cases." **Recent work:** Acted in Heard v Broadland District Council, in which planning policy for a large area was remitted as a result of an error in the SEA.

James Strachan QC Often appears in leading cases in the Supreme Court and Court of Appeal. He regularly acts for numerous large undertakings and public bodies. **Strengths:** "A measured, intelligent and thoughtful barrister with a good brain." **Recent work:** Appeared in RSPB v Secretary of State for Transport and Secretary of State for Local Government, in which he defended Lydd Airport. The case concerned a ministerial decision against requiring an assessment under the Habitat Regulations 2010.

JUNIORS

Justine Thornton Often works for government agencies and on large group actions. **Strengths:** "She gets very complex sets of facts over to the judge very effectively." "A safe pair of hands who gives very pragmatic advice." **Recent work:** Has been acting in Naaduebea v Shell Petroleum; a case concerning very large oil spills in the delta of the Niger. The case involves tens of thousands of claimants, and damages could run into hundreds of millions of pounds.

Richard Wald Operates a practice that spans environmental and planning law. **Strengths:** "He makes himself available and gives really practical advice." **Recent work:** Acted in Bancoult, R (on the application of) v Secretary of State for Foreign & Commonwealth Affairs; a case concerning the challenge of the Chagos islanders to the creation of a marine protected area around their historical home.

James Burton Deals with group actions, often with regard to common law and statutory nuisance. He acts in numerous courts and tribunals, and has a complementary planning law practice. **Strengths:** "Bright, clear and hard-working." **Recent work:** Acted in Various Claimants v TAG Farnborough Airport; a claim for compensation against the owner of the airport. The case concerned the noise, diminution in nearby house value and pollution allegedly caused by the expansion of said airport.

Francis Taylor Building

See profile on p.806

THE SET

Francis Taylor Building is a full-service set that covers the full spectrum of environmental work, from planning to criminal liability through common law and regulation. Its barristers are regularly involved in work in the appellate courts and, by way of example, recently appeared in the Supreme Court case of Coventry v Lawrence. They regularly represent companies involved in large infrastructure projects.

Client service: "The clerks are flexible and work very hard to ensure the people we want to use are available for us to use." The senior clerk is Paul Coveney.

SILKS

Robert McCracken QC An expert in environmental law, who regularly acts in all of the major forums. His client list is varied and it includes large companies, regulators and individuals. **Strengths:** "He will run difficult points and has an amazing success rate." "He is very experienced and fights hard for his clients. He's also pragmatic and realistic as to the likely outcomes." **Recent work:** Recently acted in the CJEU in Fish Legal & Shirely v Information Commissioner, a case in which the definition of public authorities for the purpose of the Environmental Information Directive was called into question.

Gregory Jones QC Combines his expertise across environmental and planning law with experience of the relevant criminal and European law. He regularly works for large companies. **Strengths:** "He is very much on the ball with regard to emerging EU case law and its application." "He gets to grips with complex intellectual issues very quickly." **Recent work:** Recently acted for Cornwall County Council in a legal challenge against planning permission for an incinerator located near two Special Areas of Conservation. He also advised the council about future potential litigation based on the Conservation of Habits and Species Regulations.

James Pereira QC Has a strong practice in planning and environmental law, and regularly handles cases with EU law aspects. **Strengths:** "He is first-class, particularly when it comes to Development Consent Orders and EU environmental impact legislation." "He really knows his law, and knows how to present arguments."

JUNIORS

Richard Honey (see p.630) Works in all areas of environmental law, and prosecutes and defends regulatory matters. **Strengths:** "He is excellent and is incredibly diligent." **Recent work:** Was the lead council for Natural England in R (Eaton) v Natural England; a successful Court of Appeal claim against refusal of permission.

Ned Westaway Works in numerous fields, including conservation, nuisance and contaminated land. He regularly acts for prosecutors and defendants in Magistrates' and Crown Courts. **Strengths:** "He is keen, very hard-working, responsive and bright." **Recent work:** Represented a local pressure group who attempted to have a skatepark registered as a village green, in R (Long Live Southbank) v Lambeth LBC.

Landmark Chambers

See profile on p.829

THE SET

Landmark Chambers' noted strength in planning and public law generally parlays well into its environmental work. Barristers from the set regularly appear at all levels, handling cases in local courts and in Europe. As an illustration of the set's reach, members acted in Morge v Hampshire County Council;a Supreme Court challenge to the grant of planning permission with regard to the Environmental Council Habitats Directive.

Client service: Senior clerk Jay Fullilove heads a team that is noted for its helpfulness and the speed of its responses to queries.

SILKS

Nathalie Lieven QC A silk with a broad, high-calibre practice, who handles environmental work as part of her mightily impressive public law workload. She regularly represents big institutions. **Strengths:** "She is a committed advocate, who offers robust, premier-league advice." "She presents very complex arguments in court, and is very knowledgeable on her feet when responding to questions." **Recent work:** Acted in R (Buckinghamshire CC) v Secretary of State for Transport, a case in which the relationship between EU directives and parliamentary sovereignty was at issue. This matter was heard in the Supreme Court.

Richard Drabble QC Has a wide environmental practice and regularly represents local authorities and developers. He has appeared at all levels in the UK, as well as in Luxembourg and Strasbourg. **Strengths:** "He has the ear of the judges and takes a strategic approach." "He is academically really good." **Recent work:** Acted in Eaton v Natural England; a case in which local objectors attempted to gain an injunction to stop the construction of a wind farm on the basis that it would harm bats. The matter involved interpretation of the Habitats Directive.

David Elvin QC An experienced barrister with a practice that ranges from planning to public law. He regularly appears in a wide variety of courts and tribunals, including the European courts and courts in Hong Kong. **Strengths:** "He is an absolute guru on compulsory purchase and the go-to man for town centre region schemes." "His advice has the commercial focus required and is delivered with authority."

David Forsdick QC Represents clients ranging from governments to private individuals. He advises on a wide range of issues, including permitting, environmental protection and assessment. **Strengths:** "He is through, detailed, bright and pleasant to deal with." **Recent work:** Acted in Ball v Secretary of State for Communities and Local Government; a judicial review in which he successfully defended a decision of the Secretary against a charge of personal bias.

James Maurici QC Has a wide-ranging practice and a particular specialism in climate change-related issues. He often works in the Luxembourg courts. **Strengths:** "He is extremely hard-working, highly skilled and knowledgeable." "He has a deep understanding of environmental law and has leapfrogged many long-established leaders." **Recent work:** He appeared in the Edwards cases in the Supreme Court and the CJEU. The matter involved discussion of the Aarhus Convention.

JUNIORS

Lisa Busch Acts for local authorities, individuals and central government. Her practice spans environmental and planning law. **Recent work:** Acted in Bayliss v SSCLG, Purbeck District Council and Purbeck Windfarms; a case concerning planning permission for a wind farm near an Area of Outstanding Natural Beauty. This involved the interaction between policy and legislation concerning sustainable energy.

Zack Simons Represents numerous interested parties in environmental and planning cases, and regularly handles inquiries and cases in the High Court and the Court of Appeal. **Strengths:** "Exceptionally talented and remarkably composed and authoritative given his experience." "He is professional and makes you understand difficult areas." **Recent work:** Appeared in the Javelin Park Incinerator Inquiry, an inquiry into the unanimous refusal of permission to build a £500 million incinerator in Gloucester.

Band 2

Blackstone Chambers

See profile on p.771

THE SET

Blackstone has a number of experienced practitioners who regularly act in domestic and EU environmental law cases. They regularly act in cases of great public interest. By way of example, they were involved in litigation surrounding the culling of badgers, and appeared in the Supreme Court on an important case concerning air pollution.

SILKS

John Howell QC Regularly advises non-government organizations (NGOs) and private concerns, among others. His environmental practice forms part of his wider successful public law practice. **Strengths:** "An exceptional advocate with an outstanding intellect." "He is academically brilliant." **Recent work:** Advised Natural England on a potential judicial review over the recent badger cull.

Michael Fordham QC Strong in EU environmental law, he routinely appears in judicial reviews and is a regular in the Court of Appeal. **Strengths:** "He is the go-to person for anything in relation to judicial review." "Commercial, down to earth and intellectually impressive." **Recent work:** Acted in the Court of Appeal in R (Infinis) v Ofgem; a case concerning promptness and impact assessment under EU law.

Thomas de la Mare QC His environmental work sits in the context of his wider EU and public law practice. **Strengths:** "He is smooth and unruffled when in court. A very impressive advocate." **Recent work:** Acted in EWRG v Philips & others; a competition dispute between an environmental collecting scheme and a processing company.

JUNIORS

Emma Dixon Acts in high-profile judicial reviews, both for and against public bodies. She has appeared many times in the Court of Appeal and the Supreme Court. **Strengths:** "She takes a creative approach and is good at coming up with new ideas." **Recent work:** Acted in R (Clientearth) v Secretary of State for EFRA; a Supreme Court challenge that argued successfully for the court to declare violation of EU clean air standards by the UK. The case led to numerous references to the CJEU.

Jane Collier Appears for a wide range of clients in judicial reviews. Has acted in numerous high-profile cases. **Strengths:** "She's very good at grasping the facts and the regulatory framework and distilling it down." **Recent work:** Acted in Ofcom v Information Commissioner & T Mobile; an appeal against a decision by the Commissioner. The case involved questions over the Environmental Information Regulations and its exemptions.

Matrix Chambers
See profile on p.832

THE SET

An accomplished public law set that brings its expertise to bear on environmental work. Its particular strength lies in the more complex cases, particularly those with an international flavour. Its lawyers regularly appear before numerous major courts and tribunals, including the ICJ. Examples of its work include the BP/Equion case, which concerned harm to the environment arising from an oil pipe build in Colombia.

SILKS

Richard Hermer QC Regularly handles cases arising out of large environmental disasters. He works mostly on the claimant side. **Strengths:** "He is very impressive at getting on top of the detail and presenting complex matters clearly." "He remains calm in very difficult circumstances." **Recent work:** Represented the claimants in Bodo v Shell; a case concerning the damage caused by a very large oil spill in the delta of the Niger. The claim was brought in the name of tens of thousands of individuals.

Philippe Sands QC An expert in public international law. He regularly represents states in the ICJ, and a number of his cases have an environmental angle to them. **Strengths:** "In an international tribunal he will know all of the judges – he is a world leader in his field." **Recent work:** Acted for the Australian government in an ICJ case against Japan with regards to its whaling programme.

David Wolfe QC (see p.755) Strong on claimant-side public law work, regularly appearing in the higher courts. Wolfe is an expert in EU, European human rights and international law. **Strengths:** "He is able to translate the most complex issues into clear and precise arguments." "He is a scientist and engineer who knows his stuff." **Recent work:** Currently acting for An Taisce (broadly equivalent to the National Trust) in Ireland in relation to the new nuclear power plants at Hinkley Point. The case raises issues of the need for cross-border consultation under international and European law.

JUNIORS

Maurice Sheridan Represents individuals, government agencies, companies and NGOs in a range of tribunals, including the CJEU. He works on the EU law side of the sector. **Strengths:** "He is a true environmental lawyer, who is robust and has a great understanding of EU law and institutions." "He has a measured approach – he's not confrontational and aggressive, but gets his point across clearly." **Recent work:** Acted in a test case judicial review on the Liability Directive.

Kate Cook Works on the public international side of environmental law. Her clients include NGOs and nation states. **Strengths:** "She has real in-depth knowledge." **Recent work:** Acted in Ecuador's successful action against Colombia over the deployment of toxic herbicides in the former's territory.

6 Pump Court
See profile on p.850

THE SET

6 Pump Court has experience of a wide range of environmental matters, with particular strength in regulatory law. Its barristers act in the Court of Appeal and Supreme Court for a variety of clients, from individuals to large undertakings.

Client service: The clerking team, led by Richard Constable, "get engaged quickly, are responsive and responsible, and will do pretty much everything they can, within reason, to provide an exemplary service."

SILKS

Stephen Hockman QC A long-established silk with experience and expertise across the gamut of environmental law. He acts in major cases in numerous tribunals, including the Supreme Court. **Strengths:** "He is a formidable advocate with great court presence." "He is enormously experienced, and really gets to the bottom of a case and works hard." **Recent work:** Acted in the Supreme Court in Coventry & Ors v Lawrence and Shields, a case concerning the interaction between nuisance (statutory and common law) and planning permission.

David Travers QC Regularly defends against regulatory decisions, but also represents government agencies. **Strengths:** "He prepares his cases very well and can consistently find the right word at the right time." "He is calm and effective in difficult circumstances." **Recent work:** Acted for the appellant in the ultimately settled Re: The Greenhouse Gas Emissions Trading Scheme. The case was an appeal against a £1 million fine levied on the basis of the Gas Trading Scheme Regulations, which involved an appeal to ministers and a judicial review.

JUNIORS

Mark Harris Acts on the regulatory side for various clients, and has additional strength in regulatory health and safety work. **Strengths:** "He is knowledgeable, explains matters clearly and is great with clients." "He is very well prepared and charming in court when he needs to be." **Recent work:** Appeared in R (Environment Agency) v Ideal Waste Paper Co Ltd; a Court of Appeal case concerning the definition of Green List Waste.

Mark Watson Both prosecutes and defends regulatory cases, and has an additional civil practice. He regularly works for local government and the Environment Agency. **Strengths:** "He is good at judging the court and getting the key message across." "He's extremely good at interpreting the case, advising the client and acting on the advice." **Recent work:** Acted in R (Environment Agency) v Thames Water Utilities Ltd, a decade-long action over a sewage leak that had previously involved reference to the CJEU.

Christopher Badger (see p.540) Both prosecutes and defends high-profile environmental matters. He regularly acts for the Environment Agency as well as private concerns. **Strengths:** "He has a tenacious ability to get to the root of a problem and he really knows his law too." "He has a nice court presence – he's very measured." **Recent work:** Acted in Environment Agency v Walker & Son (Hauliers), a Court of Appeal case over regulatory statutory construction.

Richard Banwell Handles complex regulatory cases on both the prosecution and defence sides. He regularly appears in the High Court and Court of Appeal. **Strengths:** "He is a very knowledgeable advocate and a good tactician." "His knowledge of environmental law is phenomenal." **Recent work:** In Peel Land & Property v TS Sheerness Steel, he advised the successful claimant on the environmental issues that arose in a dispute over the removal of waste from steel production.

William Upton Has additional experience on the civil side of the sector. **Strengths:** "He is a very capable practitioner, who is comfortable in all tribunals." "He is very easy to deal with." **Recent work:** Acted in the ultimately settled Ropers v Tussauds Theme Park Ltd & Ors; a case for damages and an injunction following a successful nuisance action against Alton Towers.

Band 3

Brick Court Chambers
See profile on p.774

THE SET

Although much better known for its environmental work, Brick Court has a small number of barristers who involve themselves in environmental law matters, some of which make it to Supreme Court level. Matters relating to climate change, aviation policy and emission targets and breaches are all handled.

SILKS

Richard Gordon QC A strong public lawyer with noted environmental expertise, who is an academic authority on the subject. He regularly appears in all the major courts in the UK and has regularly appeared in other common law jurisdictions. **Strengths:** "He has definitely got the ear of the court." "He is highly inventive, and can find an argument where others can't." **Recent work:** Acted in R (Hood) v Redcar & Cleveland BC, a case about the EU law implications of the development of an abattoir.

Martin Chamberlain QC Regularly appears in the highest appellate courts and acts for a wide variety of clients. He is one of the finest younger silks of his generation. **Strengths:** "He is incredibly dexterous in the way he deals with a court." "He has a fine brain and takes a sensible and pragmatic approach." **Recent work:** Appeared in Swiss International Airlines v Energy and Climate Change Secretary; a claim concerning Switzerland's omission from the suspension of the EU emissions trading scheme.

JUNIORS

Richard Macrory An experienced barrister who combines his practice with a role as a professor of environmental law at University College London. He has acted in cases in the Court of Appeal and House of Lords. **Strengths:** "He has a wealth of academic expertise that proves to be invaluable when you instruct him."

1 Crown Office Row
See profile on p.784

THE SET

Active and experienced in numerous areas of environmental law. Members advise on all issues of environmental regulation, and have given counsel on legislative proposals domestically and at EU level. The set is also strong on transactional work, particularly on issues concerning environmental warranties and indemnities. The barristers here often act in important, high-value cases with an international element. For example, members appeared in Guernsey v 3m; a £20 million case concerning water pollution.

SILKS

David Hart QC Experienced practitioner who regularly works in the appellate sphere. He has strength in regulatory and nuisance actions. **Strengths:** "He can make the most complicated areas of law simple." "He has an exceptionally vast knowledge of environmental matters." **Recent work:** Acted on appeal in a challenge against permit requirements placed on three water companies by the Environment Agency.

Angus McCullough QC Regularly appears at inquests and in court in important and high-profile cases. He has a complementary practice in public law. **Strengths:** "He is a clever, approachable and accessible barrister."

JUNIORS

Jeremy Hyam Particularly strong in his understanding of EU law. He appears on the Attorney General's A panel. **Strengths:** "He is thoughtful, studious and forceful on his feet."

4-5 Gray's Inn Square

THE SET

Barristers from the set regularly represent a variety of parties, from public bodies to NGOs and individuals. Its barristers act on a wide variety of environmental issues and in numerous courts and tribunals.

SILKS

Timothy Straker QC Regularly practises in the appellate courts and in other jurisdictions. His practice also takes in a good deal of planning and local government law. **Strengths:** "His advocacy skills are very good."

JUNIORS

Garrett Byrne (see p.562) Works in a wide variety of areas of environmental law, from waste to prosecutions and health and safety. He often represents public bodies and commercial undertakings. **Strengths:** "He is very approachable and a great advocate."

Monckton Chambers

See profile on p.833

THE SET

Barristers at Monckton act for a wide variety of clients, from NGOs to government departments and private clients. The set marries its environmental practice to a strong EU law offering, as illustrated by its involvement in Clientearth v Secretary of State for EFRA, a Supreme Court challenge to a failure to comply with EU pollution limits. Monckton's barristers regularly act in the domestic and European courts.

SILKS

Jon Turner QC Routinely present in major cases, he acts for a variety of clients including NGOs, regulators and commercial concerns. **Strengths:** "He has tenacity and an exceptional ability to get to the heart of the matter." **Recent work:** Led in the High Court in City Electrical Factors Ltd and Electrical Waste Recycling Group v Philips Electronics; GE Lighting & Ors. The case concerned a breach of EU environmental legislation.

Kassie Smith QC Regularly acts for large organisations, and appears in courts at all levels. **Strengths:** "She has an amazing knowledge of EU law and is an excellent member of the team." "Her paperwork is very good and done at exceptional speed." **Recent work:** Acted for Greenpeace and others in R (ex p UKAFPO) v Secretary of State; a case that raised complex issues of EU and human rights law. The matter concerned the reallocation of fishing quotas to smaller vessels.

JUNIORS

Gerry Facenna Regularly acts for government agencies and NGOs. He is strong in EU environmental and environmental information law. **Strengths:** "He is bright and pleasant." **Recent work:** Acted for Swansea Friends of the Earth in Roy Jones v Information Commissioner & Ors. The tribunal action concerned the decision of the Information Commissioner with regard to certain financial information.

Old Square Chambers

See profile on p.891

THE SET

Two strong senior juniors lead the way at a set that is proficient in a wide range of environmental cases. It represents a wide variety of clients, and is currently representing 150 claimants in the long-running Barr v Biffa litigation, which deals with the classification of odours as a nuisance, among other things.

JUNIORS

John Bates (see p.545) Strong in nuisance and water and drainage work, subjects upon which he has published several texts. He acts for individuals and local government organisations. **Strengths:** "He shows excellent attention to detail and is always prepared to think outside the box." "His judgement makes him a go-to man." **Recent work:** Represented North Lincolnshire Council in the Welham Estates case, a Court of Appeal matter concerning revocation of notice and denial of a permit variation.

Malcolm Galloway Regularly acts on both the prosecution and defence sides of major prosecutions. He represents regulators, companies and individuals. **Strengths:** "He is excellent on the criminal side of environmental and health and safety work." **Recent work:** Acted for the subjects of the Environment Agency's (EA) largest hazardous material investigation in advance of a possible prosecution. The case involved allegations under section 33 of the Environment Protection Act.

Other Ranked Lawyers

James Findlay QC (Cornerstone Barristers) Joint head of chambers, he regularly acts for councils and other organisations in environmental matters. **Strengths:** "He is a good advocate." "He is very thorough and user-friendly, and has a nice manner." **Recent work:** Acted for the appellant in the Supreme Court case Uprichard v Scottish Ministers, in which the duty to provide reasons was at issue.

Charles Gibson QC (Henderson Chambers) Regularly acts for defendants in large group-action cases. He often appears for large multinationals and other resource/energy companies. **Strengths:** "He is a fantastic advocate and a great people person." "He is supremely good when it comes to strategy and tactics." **Recent work:** Acted for an oil trader in Motto & Ors v Trafigura; a case concerning alleged injury from the dumping of waste near Abidjan in the Ivory Coast. This matter is one of the largest group actions seen in the environmental field.

Toby Riley-Smith of (Henderson Chambers) An expert in post-disaster litigation. He often acts in large prosecutions and tort claims, often with an international element. **Strengths:** "He is a clear thinker and a good advocate, who certainly gets the ear of the court." **Recent work:** Represented Shell in defending a group action brought against it by thousands of Nigerian citizens, arising out of damage allegedly caused by two oil spills in the Niger.

Sailesh Mehta (Red Lion Chambers) Often acts for the prosecution or defence in a number of complicated environmental matters, including issues of waste. He often represents the EA. **Strengths:** "He stands out as an individual because of his client service, and his knowledge and experience of criminal and environmental law."

MIDLANDS

Environment Midlands
Leading Sets
Band 1
No5 Chambers *
Leading Silks
Band 1
Cahill Jeremy *No5 Chambers* [A]
Leading Juniors
Band 1
Kimblin Richard *No5 Chambers* *
Band 2
Berlin Barry *St Philips Chambers (ORL)* ◊ *
Green Timothy *Outer Temple Chambers (ORL)* ◊ [A]
Wignall Gordon *No5 Chambers* [A]

Band 1

No5 Chambers

See profile on p.883

THE SET

No5 Chambers maintains its position as the leading set for environmental work on the Midland Circuit, and houses an impressive number of experienced environmental advocates. Its barristers utilise their considerable planning law expertise to offer comprehensive coverage of environmental matters such as pollution, energy and compulsory purchase orders. Individuals represent clients at public enquiries, in regulatory disputes and in judicial reviews.

Client service: "The service is brilliant. The clerks are very accessible, and it is a very easy set to deal with."

SILKS

Jeremy Cahill QC The Midlands' foremost environment silk. He has in-depth expertise in all aspects of planning and environmental work, including renewable energy, minerals and waste. **Strengths:** "He has an encyclopaedic brain – he adds a whole different dimension to discussions."

JUNIORS

Richard Kimblin Handles a range of environmental cases, with expertise in matters involving waste, water, energy and infrastructure. In addition to his strong litigation work, he also has a flourishing inquiry and advisory practice. **Strengths:** "He's a thoroughly respected barrister who is approachable and amiable. His style of advocacy is cool and calm." **Recent work:** Represented the defendant in LB Newham v John Knight (ABP); a case involving complex issues connected to odour abatement at a meat rendering plant.

Gordon Wignall An experienced junior who has an extensive planning and environmental practice. The majority of his environmental work involves regulatory disputes with local authorities, planning authorities and the Environment Agency (EA). **Strengths:** "He's a very experienced and knowledgeable barrister, and has a very pleasant manner." **Recent work:** Successfully represented Sydenham Scrap Metal in a case brought by the EA.

Other Ranked Lawyers

Timothy Green (Outer Temple Chambers) A junior whose environment practice sees him primarily operating on the enforcement side. He is particularly noted for his work on cases involving waste, and his handling of private prosecutions for water utility companies. **Strengths:** "Tim Green is fantastic, and a very good advocate." **Recent work:** Appeared in Environment Agency v Collins, prosecuting the defendant, who had been repeatedly convicted of running an unlawful waste operation, for multiple breaches of the environmental permitting regime.

Barry Berlin (see p.548) (St Philips Chambers) Has forged a reputation as a formidable environmental prosecutor. He is frequently instructed by the Environment Agency, and has considerable expertise in cases involving waste, pollution and water resources issues. **Strengths:** "He's a very thorough and tough environmental prosecutor, who knows his stuff and is very detailed."

NORTH EASTERN

Environment North Eastern
Leading Juniors
Band 1
Morgan Charles *Enterprise Chambers (ORL)* ◊

Ranked Lawyers

Charles Morgan (Enterprise Chambers) A well-regarded environment senior junior, widely recognised for his expertise in water law issues, although he also advises on sewage, water supply and flood management. He is also active in the waste and energy sectors, with experience in cases implementing WEEE directives. **Strengths:** "He certainly has a very sound knowledge of environment issues and is impressive on technical points of environmental law." "He is very pragmatic with the clients. He gives the advice and suggests what alternative solutions can be put forward by way of settlement. He doesn't just churn out a dogmatic answer, but points out how expensive litigation is as well. He certainly does have compendious knowledge of environmental law." **Recent work:** Acted on behalf of a statutory body in an appeal intervention before the Supreme Court relating to the water industry.

NORTHERN

Environment Northern
Leading Sets
Band 1
Kings Chambers *
Leading Silks
Band 1
Fraser Vincent *Kings Chambers* *
Manley David *Kings Chambers* *
Sauvain Stephen *Kings Chambers* *
Leading Juniors
Band 1
Barrett John *Kings Chambers* *
Hart Joseph *Deans Court Chambers (ORL)* ◊ *
Stockley Ruth *Kings Chambers* *
◊ (ORL) = Other Ranked Lawyer.
[A] direct access (see p.11).
** Indicates set / individual with profile.*
Alphabetical order within each band. Band 1 is highest.

Band 1

Kings Chambers

See profile on p.918

THE SET

Kings Chambers is the Northern Circuit's standout set for environmental law due to the substantial experience of its silks and juniors operating in this area. Its members are well placed to deal with all criminal and regulatory environment cases, and they draw instructions from a range of clients, including local authorities, private individuals and the Environment Agency. The barristers' environmental expertise is supplemented by knowledge of planning law and land developments, and they are experts in environmental issues affecting the energy, minerals and waste sectors.

Client service: "The clerking is very good – they're very responsive, always quick to get in touch with the barristers to pass messages on, and are good at dealing with the administrative side of things. They provide a good service."

SILKS

Vincent Fraser QC A silk with a strong environmental prosecution practice. He has been instructed on an array of matters across the energy, waste and water sectors, including issues relating to contaminated land, sewage and recycling. **Strengths:** "He gets to the bottom of every case. He's excellent at cross-examination because he has that detail – it's where he really excels. He's an extremely good advocate." **Recent work:** He was instructed by Lancashire County Council to oppose a challenge to development consent granted to the Council for construction of a new link road and motorway junction. Issues considered included the impact on protected species and interpretation of the Habitats Directive.

David Manley QC An experienced silk handling a wide range of planning and environment matters. He is highly sought after for renewable energy and waste advice, including inquiries relating to wind farms, landfills and turbines. He is also well versed on the enforcement and management of environmental issues surrounding rendering plants. **Strengths:** "He's thorough, and gets to the point, and doesn't always just tell you what you want to hear. He explains the law accurately and in an understandable way. He's very personable, so it is always a good experience working with him." "He is a very strong advocate. He's confident and excellent at cross-examination. He gets to the bottom of every case and knows the detail." **Recent work:** Instructed in relation to the proposal of a 12-year extension to a landfill site. The case involved consideration of odour, air quality and green-belt policy.

Stephen Sauvain QC A veteran silk with a strong background in planning and environmental law. He has considerable experience in inquiries relating to public footpaths, and handles a variety of environment issues relating to village greens. He has also developed expertise in issues surrounding the process of fracking. **Strengths:** "He's very much a gentleman – very clever but also a clear thinker. He has a convincing way of presenting things that always makes it sound like the most obvious thing at the time. He is very much an advocate's advocate." **Recent work:** Acted for a local authority in the court of appeal dealing with a lands tribunal decision where the principal issue was whether or not a derogation licence would have been issued for the translocation of newts from a quarry.

JUNIORS

John Barrett A senior junior praised for his work in environmental law. He has considerable expertise in permitting and European directives across a range of sectors, including waste and renewable energy. He has also advised on rendering plants and wind farms, with an emphasis on nuisance issues and pollution. **Strengths:** "He is an excellent advocate – very confident, assertive and good at cross-examination." "He is always very efficient and effective. He has a calm manner, and is particularly good at defending difficult positions." **Recent work:** Prosecuted United Utilities and a primary care trust in relation to pollution of the River Irk.

Ruth Stockley A junior whose practice encompasses a range of environmental and planning issues. She frequently acts on behalf of local authorities and developers on issues of mineral extraction, waste and noise pollution. She regularly defends prosecutions by the Environment Agency. **Strengths:** "She's tenacious in a quietly effective way." "She hugely impresses clients with her attention to detail." **Recent work:** Acted on behalf of the defendant in a prosecution by the Environment Agency, relating to the alleged pollution of a watercourse by kitchen waste that was coming from the defendant's sewage treatment plant.

Other Ranked Lawyers

Joseph Hart (see p.622) (Deans Court Chambers) An environmental specialist who acts for local authorities and health and safety organisations on general environment matters, including fire safety. His clients include large corporates and private individuals, in addition to law firms, which he advises on compliance. **Strengths:** "He has an excellent way of dealing with clients. He has a very patient, kind and genuine manner with people who are under a lot of pressure. He really puts his heart and soul into what he does." **Recent work:** Acted for the defendant in a case concerning a waste management company allegedly dumping waste into a public sewer.

WESTERN

Environment Western
Leading Silks
Band 1
Lawrie Ian *3PB Barristers (ORL)* ◊
Leading Juniors
Band 1
Moorhouse Brendon *Guildhall Chambers (ORL)* ◊
◊ (ORL) = Other Ranked Lawyer.

Ranked Lawyers

Brendon Moorhouse (Guildhall Chambers) Acclaimed for his expertise in prosecutions and defence work in the environmental field. He is frequently instructed to defend a range of clients in Environmental Agency prosecutions, and is well versed in regulatory matters. **Strengths:** "He's very easy to work with and he knows his stuff. It's a mix of knowledge of the criminal system with a good understanding of regulatory practices." **Recent work:** Successfully prosecuted R v Beavan, a high-profile Convention on International Trade in Endangered Species (CITES) case involving the illegal movement and theft of rare birds at the National Birds of Prey Centre.

Ian Lawrie QC (3PB Barristers) Well versed in a range of criminal and regulatory work, with impressive specialist expertise in the marine arena. He is highly sought after for his handling of complex maritime prosecutions and depth of experience in issues involving European Union regulations. **Strengths:** "He's a huge court presence, and a big personality."

Contents:

LONDON

European Law London	
Leading Sets	
Band 1	**Band 2**
Blackstone Chambers *	11KBW *
Brick Court Chambers *	
Monckton Chambers *	
Senior Statesmen	
Senior Statesmen	**Vaughan** David *Brick Court Chambers*
Beloff Michael *Blackstone Chambers*	
Leading Silks	
Star individuals	**de la Mare** Thomas *Blackstone Chambers*
Anderson David *Brick Court Chambers*	**Demetriou** Marie *Brick Court Chambers*
Band 1	**Fordham** Michael *Blackstone Chambers*
Dashwood Alan *Henderson Chambers (ORL)* ◊ [A] *	**Hoskins** Mark *Brick Court Chambers*
Lasok Paul *Monckton Chambers* [A] *	**Jowell** Daniel *Brick Court Chambers*
Mercer Hugh *Essex Court Chambers (ORL)* ◊	**Moser** Philip *Monckton Chambers* [A] *
Pannick David *Blackstone Chambers*	**Randolph** Fergus *Brick Court Chambers*
Rose Dinah *Blackstone Chambers*	**Robertson** Aidan *Brick Court Chambers*
Stratford Jemima *Brick Court Chambers*	**Smith** Kassie *Monckton Chambers*
Thompson Rhodri *Matrix Chambers (ORL)* ◊ *	**Swift** Jonathan *11KBW* *
Ward Tim *Monckton Chambers* [A] *	**Tridimas** Takis *Matrix Chambers (ORL)* ◊
Band 2	**Turner** Jon *Monckton Chambers* *
Beal Kieron *Blackstone Chambers*	**Wyatt** Derrick *Brick Court Chambers*
Beard Daniel *Monckton Chambers* *	**New Silks**
Chamberlain Martin *Brick Court Chambers*	**Bacon** Kelyn *Brick Court Chambers*
Coppel Jason *11KBW* *	**Rogers** Ian *Monckton Chambers*
Leading Juniors	
Band 1	**Blakeley** Richard *Brick Court Chambers*
Kennelly Brian *Blackstone Chambers*	**Facenna** Gerry *Monckton Chambers* [A] *
Lester Maya *Brick Court Chambers*	**Holmes** Josh *Monckton Chambers* *
Rhee Deok Joo *11KBW* *	**Scannell** David *Brick Court Chambers*
Band 2	**Segan** James *Blackstone Chambers*
Banner Charles *Landmark Chambers (ORL)* ◊ *	**Wakefield** Victoria *Brick Court Chambers*
* *Indicates set / individual with profile.*	
◊ *(ORL) = Other Ranked Lawyer.*	
[A] *direct access (see p.11).*	
Alphabetical order within each band. Band 1 is highest.	

Band 1

Blackstone Chambers

See profile on p.771

THE SET

A leading player in this market, with a strong offering of practitioners. Clients include the UK government, governments of other EU member states and private individuals. Members are particularly known for their top-quality advocacy skills.

Client service: The clerking team is led by senior clerk Gary Oliver. Clients say: "The clerks are very responsive. I can't think of anything they could improve on."

SILKS

David Pannick QC One of the true leading barristers of his generation, and a man with an incomparable reputation across a wide range of practice areas. His EU cases often involve civil liberties and human rights aspects. **Strengths:** "A fine litigator." "He is excellent – the kind of barrister who can really turn his hand to anything." "He provides beautiful advocacy." **Recent work:** Represented a former member of the Egyptian government, and another who complained that European regulations freezing their assets were a breach of EU law.

Dinah Rose QC Has a broad practice and is in high demand due to her excellent advocacy skills. Peers praise her ability to excel in any area she chooses to focus on. **Strengths:** "Amazing." "She's a passionate advocate in court, who is very compelling." **Recent work:** Represented the claimant in the case of R (ClientEarth) v Secretary of State. The case concerned the UK's breach of pollution limits.

Kieron Beal QC Has a practice that takes in commercial law, public law and human rights cases, alongside EU and competition cases. He has experience of acting before national courts and EU courts in cases concerning all areas of EU law. **Strengths:** "He is very approachable and will examine every angle of a case." **Recent work:** Appeared in United Kingdom v European Central Bank, regarding an application for annulment by the UK government in respect of the location policy issued by the European Central Bank.

Michael Fordham QC Recognised for his expertise in many practice areas, including public law, civil liberties and European law. Commentators admire him for the sheer depth of his knowledge. **Strengths:** "Intellectually, incredibly impressive." "He is both down to earth yet highly commercial in his approach." **Recent work:** Acted for a claimant generating company in a case against Ofgem in the Court of Appeal, regarding the accreditation of a power station for EU-based non-fossil fuel renewables certificates.

Michael Beloff QC Recognised for his depth of knowledge and experience. He has been particularly active of late in cases involving the energy and telecommunications sectors. **Strengths:** "Absolutely excellent." "His advocacy is always a masterclass in how things should be done." **Recent work:** Appeared in Daichi Sanyo v Department of Health, advising on the Pharmaceutical Price Regulation Scheme.

Thomas de la Mare QC Praised for the excellence of his advocacy and broad knowledge of European matters. He is sought after by major corporations to appear in cases involving novel points of law. **Strengths:** "He is a very entertaining and incisive advocate." "He is a very forceful advocate with a nice style to his submissions. He's absolutely great." **Recent work:** Advised British American Tobacco in relation to the freedom of movement, intellectual property and fundamental rights implications of the government's plain-packaged cigarette proposals.

JUNIORS

Brian Kennelly An excellent junior. There is a growing reputation for his skill in this area. He is in high demand and regularly acts unled in cases. **Strengths:** "Incredibly charming and incredibly good with clients." "He grasps a case immediately, and is able to project what the different scenarios are likely to be." **Recent work:** Acted unled on behalf of the British Medical Association in the case of AbbVie v European Medical Agency. The case concerns transparency and efforts to make information about clinical trials publicly available.

James Segan Has specific sector expertise in sport, telecommunications, media and entertainment, and financial services. Clients appreciate his high-quality drafting and responsiveness. **Strengths:** "Punches above his weight." "He's very helpful, sensible and easy to reach. He always delivers on time." **Recent work:** Acted for the claimants in a judicial review regarding fishing quotas assigned to the UK and the reallocation of such quotas by Defra.

Brick Court Chambers

See profile on p.774

THE SET

Brick Court's reputation in the market is undisputed. It boasts some of the top law firms as regular clients, many of which name the set as their first chambers of choice. It consistently receives praise for its barristers and its clerks, who offer a seamless service on a wide variety of EU matters.

Client service: The clerking team is led by joint senior clerks Ian Moyler and Julian Hawes. One client commented: "I have never had anything but good service from the clerks at Brick Court. They are always accommodating, helpful and responsive."

SILKS

David Anderson QC Praised time and time again for his matchless knowledge of this area. The mention of his name is instantly met with appreciation and approval of his status as a star individual. He has extensive experience of appearing before the European Court of Justice (ECJ) and the European

Court of Human Rights in a wide range of European (EU) law matters. **Strengths:** "David Anderson is amazing! He is one of the best barristers around." "The finest practitioner of European [EU] law in the market." **Recent work:** Represented AbbVie in a case against EMA concerning issues of transparency and privacy in relation to EU institutions and agencies.

Jemima Stratford QC Has a varied practice encompassing EU law, along with public law and human rights. She has particular experience of representing the government and various pharmaceutical companies. **Strengths:** "An extremely talented and dedicated lawyer, and a fount of all knowledge on EU law and regulations." **Recent work:** Intervening for Hospira in the case of Novartis v Commission. Hospira is seeking to defend its marketing authorisation for a medicinal product that is used to treat cancer and osteoporosis.

Marie Demetriou QC Earns praise from clients for her proactive approach to client service. She is particularly appreciated for her ability to explain complex issues in a concise yet effective manner. **Strengths:** "I found her EU legal expertise to be second to none." "She was extraordinarily impressive and responsive. She has a high degree of commitment and flexibility, meaning she is ready to comply with tight deadlines." **Recent work:** Acted as lead counsel for various pub landlords in FAPL v Berry; BSkyB v Polding. Her clients claim that the FA Premier League and Sky are continuing to unlawfully prevent them from televising premiership matches using Satellite decoder cards from other member states.

Mark Hoskins QC Rated highly for EU and competition law. He is held in high esteem by peers and clients alike, who praise not only his proficiency, but also his user-friendly attitude. **Strengths:** "When bringing him in on a case that was an intellectual bramble patch, he exhibited a very clear mind and provided razor-sharp advocacy." **Recent work:** Acted for AstraZeneca in AstraZeneca v Comptroller General of Patents. The case, concerning medicinal products, was referred to the ECJ by the High Court.

Daniel Jowell QC Has expertise in EU, competition and commercial law. He has been involved in numerous EU tax cases of late. **Strengths:** "Tenacious and articulate." "A very user-friendly guy, he is generous with his time, and his instructions are clear and easy to follow." **Recent work:** Advised HSBC regarding actions for restitution of tax paid contrary to EU legislation.

Fergus Randolph QC Has a practice that covers all areas of EU and competition law. He is currently active on a wide range of cases concerning different EU principles, including free movement of trade and public procurement. **Strengths:** "He is really forging ahead." "A great all-rounder who is very creative. He's good to have on your side when you are in a tight corner." **Recent work:** Acted for the claimant in Zanza v Kent Pharmaceuticals. The case related to EU law-governed marketing authorisations.

Derrick Wyatt QC An academic, as well as a practising barrister, who is recognised for his depth of knowledge. **Strengths:** "He's up there with the best." "He has been present on a huge number of notable cases."

Aidan Robertson QC Has experience in EU and competition law. He handles a number of EU law matters, and is particularly strong in tax and agriculture cases. **Strengths:** "He gets on top of large volumes of material quickly and gives definite and pragmatic advice. His turnaround time is impressive." **Recent work:** Involved in the case of WHA v HMRC; a successful defence of an appeal by a taxpayer against a VAT avoidance scheme that was deemed to be abusive.

Martin Chamberlain QC A young silk who gains strong praise from an impressive list of clients. Sources single him out for his superior intellectual ability. **Strengths:** "Phenomenally intelligent and sharply analytical. He cuts through the issues with speed and precision." **Recent work:** Represented Transport for London in the newsworthy case of Eventech v Parking Adjudicator. The case regarded Addison Lee's challenge to the rules on the use of bus lanes in London, which raises free movement and state aid issues.

David Vaughan QC A revered figure who is one of the founding fathers of this area of the law. His profound list of case highlights is testimony to his great experience. **Strengths:** "He is a leading figure in this field, and has really paved the way for European law." "Raising imaginative points is a real strength of his." **Recent work:** Acted in the case of Govt of Gibraltar v Commission, in which the government of Gibraltar challenged the Spanish listing of Gibraltar territorial waters under the European Habitats Directive.

Kelyn Bacon QC A new silk who is widely respected by peers and clients. She has worked on numerous highly publicised cases of late. **Strengths:** "Very quick, very thorough and very responsive." **Recent work:** Junior counsel for AstraZeneca in a reference to the ECJ concerning the interpretation of EU patent legislation; an area of much controversy and debate.

JUNIORS

Maya Lester Has a broad practice which, in addition to EU law, encompasses competition law, public law, human rights and public international law cases. She has created a strong reputation for herself as an excellent junior. **Strengths:** "Very impressive; her written work is concise and excellent." "She is fantastic – very bright and very hard-working. She has an excellent knowledge of EU law." **Recent work:** Acted for Chagossians in the case of R (Bancoult) v Foreign & Commonwealth Office. The case was a judicial review of the FCO's decision to impose a Marine Protection Zone around the Chagos Islands.

David Scannell Recognised for the quality of his EU practice and his competition law expertise. He rises in the rankings this year due to his activity in an impressive list of EU cases. **Strengths:** "Diligent, professional and responsive – nothing is too much trouble for him." **Recent work:** Acted for AbbVie in the high-profile case of AbbVie v EMA, regarding obligations of transparency on the part of EU agencies and institutions against the rights in property enjoyed by private undertakings.

Richard Blakeley Has a broad practice that encompasses EU law. Has been particularly active of late on sanctions cases. **Strengths:** "Very confident and very effective. He shows good judgement on the legal issues, and is very succinct in his advice." **Recent work:** Acted for the successful first defendant trade union (Sindicato Espanol de Pilotos de Linea Aereas) in a claim brought by BA and IAG alleging that strikes organised by the trade union had violated BA and IAG's freedom of establishment and freedom to provide services.

Victoria Wakefield Practises in European, competition, commercial and public law. Has been active in several high-profile cases of late. **Strengths:** "An excellent speaker." "She is able to pick up a case and familiarise herself with it very quickly." **Recent work:** Represented Eurostar International before the Channel Tunnel Intergovernmental Commission in a case concerning the transparency of Eurotunnel access charges.

Monckton Chambers

See profile on p.833

THE SET

A strong group of practitioners offering assistance in all areas of EU law. Members have deep experience of EU law and procedure due to their consistently high level of activity in this area. They receive strong praise from a long list of impressive clients.

Client service: The clerking team is led by senior clerk David Hockney. Sources say: "The clerks at Monckton are responsive and flexible."

SILKS

Paul Lasok QC A widely respected figure with great depth of expertise in this area. He advises a wide range of clients, from private individuals to government departments. **Strengths:** "He has an encyclopaedic knowledge of European [EU] case law." "He seemingly knows more about European [EU] law than anyone at the court itself." **Recent work:** Acted for HMRC in a VAT case being heard at the ECJ regarding the direct effect of directives.

Tim Ward QC Has a strong practice focusing on EU law, competition law and public law. He receives glowing praise from clients and is experienced in all areas of EU law. **Strengths:** "He is fantastic and definitely one of my top choices for EU law." "Approachable, accessible, sensible, hands-on and a persuasive advocate." **Recent work:** Acting in the case of McCarthy, a test case before the CJEU on whether the UK has the right to retain its own border checks under EU law.

Daniel Beard QC Excels in competition law and is also highly regarded for his work on wider European law matters. His cases are wide-ranging, covering everything from terrorism sanctions to disclosure of environmental information. **Strengths:** "He advises very well on the strategy and adds value to any case." **Recent work:** Acted for the UK in a leading case regarding international terrorist sanctions.

Philip Moser QC Singled out by clients as someone they can trust to get the job done. He practises in all areas of EU law, and is especially strong on fraud and tax cases. **Strengths:** "Very impressive." "He's very responsive and proved to be a calming presence at a very difficult time." **Recent work:** Represented a Libyan applicant in a case before the Grand Chamber of the CJEU. The matter concerned the question of continuing interest in applications for annulment by listed individuals in terrorist sanctions cases, where they have since been delisted by the UN Security Council.

Kassie Smith QC Specialises in EU, competition/regulatory and public law cases. She is well regarded by sources, who note her increasing presence in this field. **Strengths:** "Her paperwork is exceptional and she produces it at great speed." "Very calm and measured when dealing with the judiciary." **Recent work:** Acted for the Department for Transport in the Court of Appeal and the Supreme Court in a case that related to access to air travel for disabled persons.

Jon Turner QC Enters the rankings this year, having earned excellent praise from the market. He is best known for his competition expertise, but wider EU law also takes up a large part of his practice. **Strengths:** "He is always on top of issues and knows how to cut through the bluster of a case." **Recent work:** Active in a judicial review challenge to proposed changes to the EU carbon trading regime in relation to foreign airlines.

Ian Rogers QC Receives praise for his handling of a practice that spans European law, public law and human rights cases. **Strengths:** "Very thorough and very clear, he's always prepared to express an opinion rather than be non-committal." **Recent work:** Represented 750 Council of Immigration Judges in a Supreme Court appeal regarding discrimination in judicial pension rights against part-time workers.

JUNIORS

Gerry Facenna (see p.598) Regularly acts for the government and private parties across a range of EU matters. **Strengths:** "Hands-on and very straightforward. He doesn't over-complicate matters." **Recent work:** Defended the government in the High Court in a judicial review of UK immigration rules.

Josh Holmes A junior who is widely respected no matter what area he turns his hand to. He has experience of working for the European Court of Justice, and his EU practice covers a wide range of matters, taking in anything from food safety standards to emissions trading cases. **Strengths:** "A very able barrister whom it is a pleasure to work with."

Band 2

11KBW

See profile on p.823

THE SET

Fields high-level practitioners and has built a strong reputation within EU law. Members have extensive experience before UK and EU courts, and are appreciated by clients for the depth of their knowledge. Joint senior clerks Lucy Barbet and Mark Dann lead the clerking team.

SILKS

Jason Coppel QC (see p.578) Has a strong focus on EU law and human rights. He receives significant praise for his depth of knowledge. **Strengths:** "His level of intellect is quite outstanding." **Recent work:** Represented the Secretary of State in the Supreme Court and CJEU in a case that revolved around the rights of EU nationals to qualify for social security benefits due to pregnancy.

Jonathan Swift QC (see p.733) Regularly appears on behalf of the government. He has a wide practice that, apart from EU law, encompasses public law, human rights and civil liberties cases. **Strengths:** "A very compelling and bullish advocate." **Recent work:** Appeared for HMRC in the case of Littlewoods v HMRC, regarding the recovery of compound interest on VAT that was overpaid contrary to the requirements of EU law.

JUNIORS

Deok Joo Rhee (see p.706) A highly regarded junior who has a strong EU and public law practice. **Strengths:** "Clever, hard-working and very clued up." **Recent work:** Worked on the case of Refugee Action v SSHD, a challenge to the lawfulness of rates of support given under section 95 of the Immigration and Asylum Act.

Other Ranked Lawyers

Hugh Mercer QC (Essex Court Chambers) Recognised for his strong EU law knowledge, and held in high esteem due to the quality of his courtroom performances. **Strengths:** "He's so quick it's terrifying." "Excellent on his feet, he was really quite robust in a difficult case." **Recent work:** Acted in the case of Syngenta v European Commission, an application for judicial review of a European Commission ban on three pesticides.

Alan Dashwood QC (Henderson Chambers) A widely knowledgeable EU lawyer with more than 40 years of experience, who is good on the practical and academic side of the law. **Strengths:** "He is brilliant on the technical side of things." "He has an unrivalled and unique experience of the EU legislative system." **Recent work:** Counsel for the UK in three cases, which looked at the constitutional position of the UK specifically in relation to the opt-in nature of Title V of Part Three of the TFEU.

Charles Banner (Landmark Chambers) A junior with a broad practice area, who is also an EU academic. He has been active in a range of EU matters of late, including cases concerning fundamental rights and environment issues. **Strengths:** "He is capable of undertaking a tremendous amount of work with great enthusiasm." **Recent work:** Worked on the extremely high-profile challenge to the High Speed 2 rail link. The case involved an environmental aspect and the interpretation of a directive.

Rhodri Thompson QC (Matrix Chambers) Specialises in EU and competition law, and regularly acts for private and public clients. **Strengths:** "He's very organised, efficient, responsive and persuasive."

Takis Tridimas QC (Matrix Chambers) A leading writer on EU law, as well as a busy barrister practising in this area. He is active across all areas of EU law, and has particular expertise in human rights cases. **Recent work:** Appeared in (Iraq) v Secretary of State for the Home Department, a case concerning the issue of humanitarian assistance.

Extradition

Contents:

LONDON

Extradition London	
Senior Statesmen	
Senior Statesmen	
Nicholls Clive *3 Raymond Buildings Barristers (ORL)* ◊ Ⓐ	
Leading Silks	
Star individuals	**Band 2**
Fitzgerald Edward *Doughty Street Chambers (ORL)* ◊	**Garlick** Paul *Furnival Chambers (ORL)* ◊ Ⓐ *
Keith Hugo *3 Raymond Buildings Barristers (ORL)* ◊ *	**Hardy** John *3 Raymond Buildings Barristers (ORL)* ◊ *
Montgomery Clare *Matrix Chambers (ORL)* ◊	**Jones** John *Doughty Street Chambers (ORL)* ◊ Ⓐ
Perry David *6KBW College Hill (ORL)* ◊	**Knowles** Julian *Matrix Chambers (ORL)* ◊
Band 1	**Malcolm** Helen *3 Raymond Buildings Barristers (ORL)* ◊ Ⓐ
Jones Alun *Great James Street Chambers (ORL)* ◊	**New Silks**
Lewis James *3 Raymond Buildings Barristers (ORL)* ◊ Ⓐ	**Summers** Mark *Matrix Chambers (ORL)* ◊ *
Leading Juniors	
Band 1	**Watkins** Aaron *Matrix Chambers (ORL)* ◊
Brandon Ben *3 Raymond Buildings Barristers (ORL)* ◊	**Band 3**
Caldwell Peter *Dyers Chambers (ORL)* ◊ *	**Butt** Matthew *3 Raymond Buildings Barristers (ORL)* ◊ Ⓐ *
Cooper Ben *Doughty Street Chambers (ORL)* ◊ Ⓐ	**Davidson** Rosemary *6KBW College Hill (ORL)* ◊
Dobbin Clair *3 Raymond Buildings Barristers (ORL)* ◊ *	**Draycott** Natasha *5 St Andrew's Hill (ORL)* ◊ *
Lloyd Ben *6KBW College Hill (ORL)* ◊	**Grandison** Myles *Dyers Chambers (ORL)* ◊ *
Watson Ben *3 Raymond Buildings Barristers (ORL)* ◊ Ⓐ *	**Hobcraft** Gemma *Doughty Street Chambers (ORL)* ◊
Band 2	**Kapila** Rachel *3 Raymond Buildings Barristers (ORL)* ◊ Ⓐ *
Barnes Rachel *3 Raymond Buildings Barristers (ORL)* ◊ Ⓐ	**Sternberg** Daniel *9-12 Bell Yard (ORL)* ◊ *
Cumberland Melanie *6KBW College Hill (ORL)* ◊	**Weekes** Mark *6KBW College Hill (ORL)* ◊
Ezekiel Adina *6KBW College Hill (ORL)* ◊	**Westcott** Mary *Doughty Street Chambers (ORL)* ◊
Hill Rebecca *5 St Andrew's Hill (ORL)* ◊ *	**Up-and-coming individuals**
Hines James *3 Raymond Buildings Barristers (ORL)* ◊ Ⓐ *	**Hawkes** Malcolm *Doughty Street Chambers (ORL)* ◊
Keith Benjamin *5 St Andrew's Hill (ORL)* ◊ *	**Nice** Amelia *5 St Andrew's Hill (ORL)* ◊ *
Smith Joel *Furnival Chambers (ORL)* ◊ *	**Scott** Rachel *3 Raymond Buildings Barristers (ORL)* ◊ *

** Indicates set / individual with profile.*

◊ (ORL) = Other Ranked Lawyer.

Ⓐ direct access (see p.11).

Notable Practitioners

Daniel Sternberg (see p.728) (9-12 Bell Yard) Has a solid reputation in the extradition market, and a mainly prosecution-focused practice. **Strengths:** "He has an excellent eye for detail and is a barrister who truly sympathises with the emotional as well as the legal needs of his clients." "He is very bright, energetic and hard-working." **Recent work:** Acted in extradition proceedings concerning a Polish national who had been charged with four offences of robbery.

Edward Fitzgerald QC (Doughty Street Chambers) Highly acclaimed practitioner with expertise in administrative and public law. He regularly appears in leading extradition cases. **Strengths:** "He is very prominent and does some very interesting cases." **Recent work:** Handled the defence of a second extradition request made in relation to his client. The case concerned the Rwandan genocide and the defendant's right to a fair trial.

John Jones QC (Doughty Street Chambers) Has an established extradition-focused practice. Areas of specialism include international crime, war crimes and terrorism matters. **Strengths:** "He always prosecutes robustly but fairly and I always see if he is available if I have a leading brief in a case." "He is outstanding and a very charming silk." **Recent work:** Represented Croatia in its extradition request for an individual accused of war crimes in Croatia. The defendant had previously been convicted in Croatia for armed rebellion and was therefore discharged from the High Court on double jeopardy grounds.

Ben Cooper (Doughty Street Chambers) Has a predominantly defence-focused practice. He offers particular expertise in cases with a human rights angle. **Strengths:** "When he takes a case on you know nothing will be missed as he goes into such detail." **Recent work:** Acted on the extradition request for a Syrian national by the USA for importing chemical weapons to Syria. The case is controversial as it is public knowledge that the defendant is opposed to the Assad regime.

Gemma Hobcraft (Doughty Street Chambers) An up-and-coming practitioner with experience in extradition, professional discipline and public law cases. She has a particular interest in extradition cases where health concerns are an issue. **Strengths:** "She engages with people well and keeps their attention."

Mary Westcott (Doughty Street Chambers) Dedicated to the field of extradition, she is highly regarded for her ability to handle both the prosecution and defence of cases. **Strengths:** "She is conscientious, hard-working," and "very committed to her cases." "She excels in defending extradition cases, especially those involving human rights issues." **Recent work:** Represented the lead appellant in an appeal case that considered the effect of Lithuanian prison conditions on Article 3 rights.

Malcolm Hawkes (Doughty Street Chambers) Has a growing extradition practice. He is regularly instructed in significant cases concerning part 1 and part 2 countries. **Strengths:** "He is fearless and handles a lot of Russian-related cases." **Recent work:** Handled the US extradition request of a UK national alleged to have been linked to Al-Qaeda. The defence concerned the admissibility of evidence obtained by torture and the right to a fair trial.

Peter Caldwell (Dyers Chambers) Leading junior barrister active in many high-profile extradition cases. Many of the cases he deals with concern international crime, financial crime and human rights issues. **Strengths:** "He is a sensible and thoughtful advocate and a very fair prosecutor." "He is very good, and he handles very high-profile cases." **Recent work:** Acted for the Italian authorities in an extradition request for steelworks owner Fabio Riva. Riva is accused of breaches of health and safety law, manslaughter and environmental offences.

Myles Grandison (see p.613) (Dyers Chambers) Has a thriving extradition practice, and acts for both the defence and prosecution. **Strengths:** "When you are talking to him about a case he is always very reassuring." **Recent work:** Successfully appealed an extradition order against a single parent. It was found that extradition would be disproportionate to the offence committed by the appellant.

Paul Garlick QC (see p.606) (Furnival Chambers) A highly sought-after extradition practitioner, whose areas of specialism include international and corporate crime. **Strengths:** "He is very good and very experienced."

Joel Smith (see p.723) (Furnival Chambers) Recognised practitioner in the extradition arena. He regularly handles cases which are technically complex and high-profile in nature. **Strengths:** "He is a first-class counsel with superb analytical and advocacy skills."

Alun Jones QC (Great James Street Chambers) Has three decades of experience of handling extradition cases, and is well versed at acting at the appellate level. **Strengths:** "He is hugely experienced and was one of the first people to master extradition law."

David Perry QC (6KBW College Hill) Remains at the forefront of the extradition field, and has strong expertise and experience in handling appeals. **Strengths:** "He is one of the best silks at the Bar full stop." **Recent work:** Acted for the US government in an extradition request for a Pakistani individual resident in the UK. The case concerned a potential terrorist plot to be carried out in the USA and the UK.

Ben Lloyd (6KBW College Hill) Has a strong reputation in the defence and prosecution of extradition cases. His practice was bolstered following his secondment to the CPS Extradition Unit. **Strengths:** "He is absolutely unflappable in court and comes across as having authority." "He is a very good prosecutor, who is capable, well prepared and has an excellent knowledge of the law." **Recent work:** Acted for the Spanish authorities in their extradition request relating to a Spanish national alleged to have committed fraud. The case involved complex Article 8 issues.

Melanie Cumberland (6KBW College Hill) A highly rated junior barrister who offers expertise and experience in terrorism-related cases amongst others. **Strengths:** "Very experienced – she can be trusted to handle complex cases on her own." **Recent work:** Acted on behalf of the prosecution in an extradition request by the USA. The case concerned the alleged terrorist activities of the defendant.

Adina Ezekiel (6KBW College Hill) Recognised for her international capabilities, she maintains a reputable extradition practice. She is regularly instructed in cases concerning human rights issues. **Recent work:** Handled an extradition request on behalf of the Turkish government for an individual convicted of committing an honour killing. The case was made more complex by issues of alleged torture on the part of the Turkish authorities.

Rosemary Davidson (6KBW College Hill) Well versed in extradition and public law generally. She is experienced at all levels of the court system and has represented both states and requested persons. **Recent work:** Acted for the Polish authorities in an extradition request, which concerned Article 8 and Article 3 issues resultant from the requested person's suicide attempt after the first instance proceedings.

Mark Weekes (6KBW College Hill) Offers a wealth of experience in the field of extradition, and has a defence-focused practice. **Strengths:** "He is everything you would want in a junior; he's always available for you and puts his back into it." "He is extremely confident, bright and able." **Recent work:** Acted on behalf of the former president of Benfica FC in an extradition request made by Portugal. His client had been convicted of major fraud.

Clare Montgomery QC (Matrix Chambers) Considered a star in the field of extradition. She handles heavyweight cases in the area and also expertly covers criminal, regulatory and fraud law. **Strengths:** "She is undoubtedly at the very pinnacle of this area." "She is a formidable opponent and very bright." **Recent work:** Handled Shrien Dewani's appeal against extradition to the Republic of South Africa. The case related to Mr Dewani's medical condition.

Julian Knowles QC (Matrix Chambers) Handles high-profile extradition cases and has experience of acting for both individuals and states. **Strengths:** "A very clever man who is brought in for big cases." **Recent work:** Acted for government of Ukraine on its extradition request for Mr Kononko. The defendant was accused of involvement in the Ablyazov/BTA Bank matter.

Mark Summers QC (see p.732) (Matrix Chambers) Recognised for his skill and abilities in representing both states and individuals in extradition cases. He has particular expertise in terrorism-related cases. **Strengths:** "He is an excellent opponent and deserves his success." **Recent work:** Acted for Troitino Arranz, an ETA terrorist, in resisting an extradition request made by Spain. He was convicted of a fatal attack on a bus carrying Civil Guard officers.

Aaron Watkins (Matrix Chambers) He has experience in both the defence and prosecution of extradition cases. **Strengths:** "He is a highly experienced counsel, who has an in-depth knowledge of extradition law." "He is responsive and extremely knowledgeable, and his written advice is of a high quality." **Recent work:** Instructed by JUSTICE, acting as interveners, in a Supreme Court case concerning the human rights implications of extradition on the children of extraditees, and whether these should be taken into account.

Clive Nicholls QC (3 Raymond Buildings Barristers) Enjoys a commanding reputation in the field of extradition. He has expertise in terrorism offences, financial crime and drug trafficking matters. **Strengths:** "He is hugely respected." "He is very personable and charming." **Recent work:** Defended Viktor Kožený against a US extradition request. Mr Kožený was accused of money laundering and FCPA offences.

Hugo Keith QC (3 Raymond Buildings Barristers) Renowned for his skills in the criminal and extradition arenas. He is also experienced in handling mutual legal assistance requests. **Strengths:** "Phenomenal and very user-friendly." "He gives fantastic support on issues relating to Interpol and extradition." **Recent work:** Represented the Republic of South Africa in the extradition of Shrien Dewani to South Africa. This high-profile case concerns the murder of Mr Dewani's wife, in which he is alleged to be implicated.

James Lewis QC (3 Raymond Buildings Barristers) Offers clients a wealth of experience in the field of extradition. He has a good track record of handling appeals at the Supreme Court on behalf of governments and defendants. **Strengths:** "He is a very good problem solver, who is good at thinking outside the box and finding wider ways to deal with problems." "His experience of acting in multi-jurisdictional cases and representing governments is invaluable." **Recent work:** Acted for a former Portsmouth FC owner on an extradition request made by the Lithuanian authorities. His extradition was sought in relation to a banking fraud.

John Hardy QC (see p.619) (3 Raymond Buildings Barristers) An experienced practitioner in the criminal and extradition courts. He has been involved in some of the major cases over the course of his 25-year career at the Bar. **Recent work:** Lead silk in the extradition of Ravi Shankaran, a case which concerned the theft of India's national secrets. He acted on behalf of the Indian government.

Helen Malcolm QC (3 Raymond Buildings Barristers) Sought-after extradition practitioner with expertise in the area of European Arrest Warrants. She has handled some of the most significant extradition cases of recent times. **Strengths:** "She is stunningly good as an extradition lawyer." "She gives sound advice and doesn't mess around." **Recent work:** Represented the Republic of Kenya in its request for the extradition of former Triton Petroleum chairman Yagnesh Devani. Mr Devani is alleged to have defrauded financiers.

Ben Brandon (3 Raymond Buildings Barristers) Possesses wide-ranging experience and expertise in the area of extradition. His practice further sees him handling international crime, fraud, public law and financial crime cases. **Strengths:** "He is exceptionally bright, thinks of points others wouldn't, is tenacious in his approach and is excellent with clients." **Recent work:** Represented the only defendant in the USA to have been put on fraud charges arising out of the subprime mortgage market collapse. He acted for him in extradition proceedings in the UK and aided his US defence team.

Clair Dobbin (3 Raymond Buildings Barristers) Highly regarded junior barrister with extradition expertise. She is further skilled in human rights issues, international crime and civil recovery. **Strengths:** "She is exceptionally bright, highly organised, talented and hard-working." "She's highly knowledgeable when it comes to the service of foreign process rules." **Recent work:** Acted in an extradition request made by the USA. The case concerned a mother accused of kidnapping, having taken her children from the USA to the UK after the breakdown of her marriage.

Ben Watson (see p.747) (3 Raymond Buildings Barristers) Has experience of acting for all parties involved in extradition proceedings, and has been involved in some of the major cases of recent times. **Strengths:** "He is phenomenal, very good with the clients and user-friendly." "He is one of the first people who comes to mind, and is extremely good." **Recent work:** Acted for the Secretary of State for the Home Department in relation to the extradition of Gary McKinnon.

Rachel Barnes (3 Raymond Buildings Barristers) A revered criminal practitioner, who is dual-qualified in US and UK law. **Strengths:** "Everything she does is absolutely meticulous, and she really is someone you want to have on your side. She knows more about the case than anyone else and has all of the facts at her fingertips." "She has a super brain, is really smart and is also very strategic." **Recent work:** Acted as defence counsel in Ghanaian extradition proceedings concerning an alleged murder. This was a complex case as the penalty for such an offence in Ghana is the death penalty.

James Hines (3 Raymond Buildings Barristers) A crime specialist with expertise in the areas of international crime, financial crime, extradition and matters with civil aspects. **Strengths:** "He is vastly experienced," "and an absolute go-to person who instinctively knows where the issues lie in a case." **Recent work:** Instructed in an extradition appeal case involving a defendant accused of sexual offences in the USA. The case concerned how long the defendant would be held in custody upon the completion of his sentence.

Matthew Butt (3 Raymond Buildings Barristers) He is regularly instructed to represent requested persons and has experience at all levels of the court system, including in judicial review cases. **Strengths:** "He's impressive in his strategic thinking and provides considered advice." **Recent work:** Handled an extradition request for a defendant accused of murder in Bermuda. The defendant was successfully released on bail as it was argued that the law prohibits extradition to any British Overseas Territory.

Rachel Kapila (3 Raymond Buildings Barristers) Highly regarded junior barrister in the field of extradition. She brings invaluable prosecutorial experience, having completed a secondment with the CPS Extradition Unit. Her practice is now a mix of defence and prosecution work. **Strengths:** "She is extremely bright and charming but when you are at court you tend to have a tough time if you're against her because she is extremely sharp-witted." **Recent work:** Acted on behalf of one of the defendants accused of the Rwanda genocide in 1994. Extradition is being sought by the government of Rwanda after the first request was discharged on human rights grounds.

Rachel Scott (see p.716) (3 Raymond Buildings Barristers) Has a strong extradition practice, and also offers expertise in general crime, international crime and financial crime. **Strengths:** "She is very busy in big Russian banking cases." "She is extremely competent on her feet and very hard-working." **Recent work:** Led in an extradition case concerning a banking fraud allegedly committed by the former owner of Portsmouth FC.

Rebecca Hill (see p.627) (5 St Andrew's Hill) Has a wealth of experience and particular expertise in advising individuals at risk of extradition. **Recent work:** Acted as defence counsel to a British national resisting extradition to Argentina. She argued breach of Article 3 in relation to prison conditions and the appeal was allowed.

Benjamin Keith (see p.643) (5 St Andrew's Hill) An expert in political corruption matters, especially in countries such as Ukraine, Russia and Kazakhstan. He also offers expertise in human rights issues arising in extradition cases. **Strengths:** "He has an in-depth knowledge when it comes to ex-Soviet Union countries and he has defended numerous individuals in the most serious cases." "He is very diligent and he will pursue points without fear when he thinks they are right." **Recent work:** Instructed as defence counsel in an extradition request by Ukraine. The case concerned an alleged investment fraud and is the first case to be privately prosecuted under the Extradition Act.

Natasha Draycott (see p.590) (5 St Andrew's Hill) Highly regarded for her success rate in extradition cases involving Article 8 issues. **Strengths:** "Down to earth and industrious, she is an absolute pleasure to deal with and someone who adopts a proactive attitude to her work." "She is particularly good at handling clients and is very bright." **Recent work:** Acted for the USA in an extradition request for a Ukrainian national accused of wire and internet banking fraud. The case involved double jeopardy and abuse of process issues.

Amelia Nice (see p.682) (5 St Andrew's Hill) Has particular expertise in handling cases with a mental health suicide element to them. **Strengths:** "She's extremely straightforward in her approach and clients love her." **Recent work:** Acted for an appellant in a Lithuanian extradition case. This case turned on Lithuanian prison conditions.

FAMILY/MATRIMONIAL: An Introduction

Contributed by 1 Garden Court Family Law Chambers

2014/5 is a year of radical change in family law, with the creation of a unified Family Court and a major overhaul of public law proceedings. From 22 April 2014 all cases, other than those brought under the inherent jurisdiction of the High Court and Hague Convention/Brussels IIR abduction proceedings, are issued in the unified court, at which all levels of judge now sit. New gate keeping procedures are in place, designed to ensure that each case is allocated to the right level of judge and that there is continuity of tribunal. New court orders are in place across the spectrum of family law.

The passing of the Children & Families Act 2014 brought with it a number of changes designed to put children more at the heart of decision-making. A major change is the requirement to deal with cases from start to finish within 26 weeks. A new provision has been added to s.1 Children Act 1989, to the effect that, unless the contrary is shown, it will be in the interests of each child to have the involvement of both parents in his life.

In private law cases, the Child Arrangements Programme brings with it a greater emphasis on mediation, with a requirement, in most cases, that the applicant attends a mediation information and assessment meeting (MIAM) prior to issuing proceedings. New court orders have been drafted for public and private law children, as well as for financial remedy cases, and there is ongoing consultation on these drafts, which are likely to be revised further as the first year of the new family court progresses.

There are changes to divorce proceedings, with s.41 MCA 1973 repealed. If arrangements for children cannot be agreed, an application must be made for a child arrangements order under the Children Act 1989.

There are new truncated procedures for financial remedy proceedings. For straightforward proceedings with few issues, the shorter procedure – with exchange of a simplified financial statement within 14 days after issue and a first hearing between four and eight weeks after issue – will be effective. It will not suit all cases and there is provision for seeking a direction that the longer procedure should apply.

In January 2014, the President issued new Practice Guidance on transparency, effective from 3 February 2014, designed to produce 'an immediate and significant change in practice in relation to the publication of judgments in the Family Courts and the Court of Protection'. This guidance is the precursor to further measures expected to be rolled out in the next year, all of which are designed to bring about greater transparency in the way in which the family courts and Court of Protection operate, with a view to improving public understanding of the process and increasing confidence in the court system.

Jurisdiction issues

The EU has issued a consultation on the functioning of the Brussels IIA regulation (EC2201/2003) in the determination of cross-border disputes in children cases in light of the growing mobility of EU citizens and the increase in international families.

Financial remedy proceedings

The judgment of the President in S v S [2014] EWHC 7 (Fam) is of great interest. The President gave guidance as to how the court should approach the making of consent orders in family finance proceedings, based on awards made following arbitration by an IFLA arbitrator. He also made what he described as 'provisional comments' regarding what should happen if one party sought to resile from an arbitral award. The President said that, where parties had bound themselves to accept the award of a suitably qualified arbitrator operating within an appropriate scheme (such as that operated by he IFLA), this was likely to be a 'single magnetic factor of determinative importance' in the financial proceedings.

It will be interesting to see how this strong judicial encouragement of financial disputes being resolved through arbitration will develop over the next year.

Children: public law

Family practitioners are getting to grips with the changes introduced by the Children & Families Act 2014, mostly in force since April 2014. Early experience suggests that many care cases are capable of being dealt with within 26 weeks. However, there is a small cohort of complex cases where justice will require the court's oversight of the case to take longer. The President has been clear that the 26-week requirement is not to be seen as a straitjacket in those cases. Data being collated by the courts will show how the changes are working in practice

Since Re B-S (Children) [2013] EWCA Civ 1146 there is an enhanced focus on close analysis of the various welfare outcomes before determining what is in the best interests of the child.

Children: private law

Much focus currently is on how the CAP (Child Arrangements Programme) will work in practice and, in particular, on whether more disputes will be resolved by mediation.

The number of litigants in person in private law proceedings has grown exponentially, resulting in guidance for such litigants and the use of more 'user-friendly' terms in the CAP.

Early impressions are that hearings are slower where one or both parties is unrepresented and there has been an exponential growth of applications for pro bono assistance.

Contents:

LONDON

Family: Matrimonial Finance London Leading Sets
Band 1
29 Bedford Row Chambers *
1 Hare Court *
1 King's Bench Walk *
Queen Elizabeth Building *
Band 2
4 Paper Buildings *
Senior Statesmen
Senior Statesmen
Singleton Barry *1 King's Bench Walk*
Leading Silks
Star individuals
Marks Lewis *Queen Elizabeth Building* *
Band 1
Amos Tim *Queen Elizabeth Building* *
Chamberlayne Patrick *29 Bedford Row Chambers* *
Cusworth Nicholas *1 Hare Court*
Dyer Nigel *1 Hare Court*
Francis Nicholas *29 Bedford Row Chambers* [A] *
Howard Charles *1 King's Bench Walk*
Leech Stewart *Queen Elizabeth Building* *
Pointer Martin *1 Hare Court*
Scott Timothy *29 Bedford Row Chambers* [A] *
Stone Lucy *Queen Elizabeth Building* *
Todd Richard *1 Hare Court*
Turner James *1 King's Bench Walk*
Band 2
Bangay Deborah *1 Hare Court*
Bishop Timothy *1 Hare Court*
Blair Bruce *1 Hare Court*
Cayford Philip *29 Bedford Row Chambers* [A] *
Eaton Deborah *1 King's Bench Walk* *
Harrison Richard *1 King's Bench Walk* *
Hyde Charles *Albion Chambers (ORL)* ◊
Peel Robert *29 Bedford Row Chambers* [A] *
Pocock Christopher *1 King's Bench Walk* *
Wagstaffe Christopher *29 Bedford Row Chambers* *
Wilson John *1 Hare Court*
Band 3
Anelay Richard *1 King's Bench Walk* *
Balcombe David *1 Crown Office Row (ORL)* ◊
Cohen Jonathan *4 Paper Buildings*
Davidson Katharine *1 Hare Court*
Hale Charles *4 Paper Buildings*
Hussey Ann *1 Hare Court*
Le Grice Valentine *1 Hare Court*
Marshall Philip *1 King's Bench Walk* *
Southgate Jonathan *29 Bedford Row Chambers* *
Sternberg Michael *4 Paper Buildings*
◊ (ORL) = Other Ranked Lawyer.
[A] direct access (see p.11).
* Indicates set / individual with profile.

Family: Matrimonial Finance London Leading Juniors
Star individuals
Clarke Elizabeth *Queen Elizabeth Building* *
Molyneux Brent *29 Bedford Row Chambers* *
Oliver Harry *1 King's Bench Walk*
Band 1
Campbell Alexis *29 Bedford Row Chambers* *
Castle Richard *1 King's Bench Walk* *
Cook Ian *1 King's Bench Walk* *
Cowton Catherine *Queen Elizabeth Building* *
Ewins James *Queen Elizabeth Building* *
Glaser Michael *Fourteen* [A] *
Gray Nichola *1 Hare Court*
Kingscote Geoffrey *1 Hare Court*
Nagpal Deepak *1 King's Bench Walk* *
Roberts James *1 King's Bench Walk* *
Sear Richard *1 Hare Court*
Trowell Stephen *1 Hare Court*
Warshaw Justin *1 Hare Court*
Webster Simon *1 Hare Court*
Band 2
Allen Nicholas *29 Bedford Row Chambers* [A] *
Bailey-Harris Rebecca *1 Hare Court*
Bentham Daniel *Queen Elizabeth Building* *
Brazil Dominic *1 King's Bench Walk* *
Brooks Duncan *Queen Elizabeth Building* *
Burles David *1 Garden Court Family Law Chambers* *
Heaton Laura *29 Bedford Row Chambers* [A] *
Kelsey Katherine *1 King's Bench Walk* *
Lazarides Marcus *Queen Elizabeth Building* *
Murray Judith *4 Paper Buildings*
Phipps Sarah *Queen Elizabeth Building* *
Singer Samantha *Queen Elizabeth Building* *
Sumner Emma *1 Hare Court*
Tod Jonathan *29 Bedford Row Chambers* *
Yates Nicholas *1 Hare Court* *
Band 3
Allardice Miranda *5 Stone Buildings (ORL)* ◊ *
Anderson Nicholas *1 King's Bench Walk* *
Bates Richard *29 Bedford Row Chambers* *
Batt Charanjit *Queen Elizabeth Building* *
Bradley Michael *1 Hare Court*
Calhaem Simon *29 Bedford Row Chambers* *
Carew Pole Rebecca *1 Hare Court*
Chandler Alexander *1 King's Bench Walk* *
Emanuel Mark *29 Bedford Row Chambers* *
Faggionato Marina *Queen Elizabeth Building* *
Firth Matthew *Queen Elizabeth Building* *
Mitchell Peter *29 Bedford Row Chambers* *
Sirikanda Morgan *Queen Elizabeth Building* *
Thorpe Alexander *Queen Elizabeth Building* *
Band 4
Amaouche Sassa-Ann *29 Bedford Row Chambers* *
Boyd Kerstin *Tanfield Chambers (ORL)* ◊ *
Budden Rosemary *Queen Elizabeth Building* *
Cade Davies Lynsey *29 Bedford Row Chambers* [A] *
Cameron Gillon *Fourteen* *
Cassidy Sheena *3PB Barristers (ORL)* ◊
Chapman Nicholas *29 Bedford Row Chambers* *
Collins Ken *29 Bedford Row Chambers* [A] *
Domenge Victoria *29 Bedford Row Chambers* *
Duckworth Peter *29 Bedford Row Chambers* [A] *
Fox Nicola *1 King's Bench Walk* *
Kenny Christian *1 Hare Court*
Langridge Niki *Coram Chambers* *
Lister Caroline *1 King's Bench Walk*
Lyon Stephen *4 Paper Buildings*
Newman Peter *1 King's Bench Walk* *
Roberts Patricia *Fourteen*
Sheridan Amber *29 Bedford Row Chambers* *
Tambling Richard *29 Bedford Row Chambers* *
Teacher Petra *29 Bedford Row Chambers* [A] *
Wilkins Susan *1 King's Bench Walk*
Wilkinson Nicholas *1 Hare Court*
Woodham Samantha *4 Paper Buildings* *
Up-and-coming individuals
Kisser Amy *Queen Elizabeth Building* *
Tyzack William *Queen Elizabeth Building* *
Wiseman Naomi *Queen Elizabeth Building* *

The editorial is in alphabetical order by Set name.

42 Bedford Row

See profile on p.769

THE SET

42 Bedford Row has a national reputation and is a full-service chambers dealing with all aspects of family law. It has great strength in both public and private children law cases, and has developed very strong relationships with local authorities, particularly in the South of England. It also acts for guardians and parents.

Client service: "The clerk's team has got it just right and always delivers." Alan Brewer heads the team and is "a clerk of substance whose many years in the job give him an edge over many of his rivals."

SILKS

Frank Feehan QC A silk whose star is in the ascendancy. He handles high-value matrimonial finance cases, but is best known for his work in both public and private children law proceedings. Many of his cases relate to difficult care proceedings and non-accidental injury, and he has, of late, been appearing in the Supreme Court. **Strengths:** "Frank is a man who never gives up. He has dogged determination, and will never talk the client into settling something that they ought to contest." **Recent work:** Instructed in the Supreme Court in a complex case that pitted the right of a vulnerable witness to maintain anonymity against the right of the alleged perpetrator to a fair trial.

Tina Cook QC Specialist children barrister who principally handles public law care proceedings. Her cases generally concern allegations of serious physi-

Family: Children London Leading Sets
Band 1
4 Paper Buildings *
Band 2
1 Garden Court Family Law Chambers *
1 King's Bench Walk *
Band 3
42 Bedford Row *
29 Bedford Row Chambers *
Coram Chambers *
Fourteen *
New Court Chambers *

Leading Silks
Star individuals
Eaton Deborah *1 King's Bench Walk* *
Setright Henry *4 Paper Buildings*
Verdan Alex *4 Paper Buildings*
Band 1
Delahunty Jo *4 Paper Buildings* *
Feehan Frank *42 Bedford Row*
Geekie Charles *1 Garden Court Family Law Chambers* *
Gupta Teertha *4 Paper Buildings*
Storey Paul *29 Bedford Row Chambers* *
Wood Catherine *4 Paper Buildings*
Band 2
Bazley Janet *1 Garden Court Family Law Chambers* *
Connolly Barbara *7BR (ORL)* ◊ *
Cook Tina *42 Bedford Row*
Harrison Richard *1 King's Bench Walk* *
Howard Charles *1 King's Bench Walk*
Langdale Rachel *7BR (ORL)* ◊ *
Morgan Sarah *1 Garden Court Family Law Chambers* *
Pressdee Piers *29 Bedford Row Chambers* *
Scott-Manderson Marcus *4 Paper Buildings*
Turner James *1 King's Bench Walk*
Williams David *4 Paper Buildings*
Band 3
Ball Alison *1 Garden Court Family Law Chambers*
Crowley Jane *1 Garden Court Family Law Chambers* *
Hyde Charles *Albion Chambers (ORL)* ◊
Kirk Anthony *1 King's Bench Walk* *
Scriven Pamela *1 King's Bench Walk*
Sternberg Michael *4 Paper Buildings*
New Silks
Goodwin Nicholas *Harcourt Chambers (ORL)* ◊
Hale Charles *4 Paper Buildings*
Tyler William *36 Bedford Row (ORL)* ◊ *
◊ (ORL) = Other Ranked Lawyer.
[A] direct access (see p.11).
* Indicates set / individual with profile.

Family: Children London Leading Juniors	
Band 1	**Jones** Maggie *Garden Court Chambers (ORL)* ◊
Bagchi Andrew *1 Garden Court Family Law Chambers* *	**Kelsey** Katherine *1 King's Bench Walk* *
Cover Martha *Coram Chambers* *	**Markham** Hannah *36 Bedford Row (ORL)* ◊ *
Johnston Justine *4 Paper Buildings*	**McCormack** Philip *42 Bedford Row*
King Samantha *4 Paper Buildings*	**Murray** Judith *4 Paper Buildings*
McKenna Anna *42 Bedford Row*	**Pope** Sarah *Fourteen* [A] *
Mills Barbara *4 Paper Buildings*	**Segal** Sharon *1 Garden Court Family Law Chambers* *
Ramsahoye Indira *29 Bedford Row Chambers* *	**Selman** Elizabeth *1 King's Bench Walk* *
Band 2	**Tughan** John *4 Paper Buildings*
Bennett Jonathan *42 Bedford Row*	**Vavrecka** David *Coram Chambers* *
Cudby Markanza *1 King's Bench Walk*	**Woodward-Carlton** Damian *42 Bedford Row*
Devereux Edward *Harcourt Chambers (ORL)* ◊	**Band 4**
Forster Sarah *Fourteen* [A]	**Amiraftabi** Roshi *29 Bedford Row Chambers* *
Fottrell Deirdre *1 Garden Court Family Law Chambers* *	**Cameron** Gillon *Fourteen* *
Fox Nicola *1 King's Bench Walk* *	**Drew** Jane *Coram Chambers* *
Grief Alison *4 Paper Buildings*	**Geddes** Gillian *2-3 Hind Court (ORL)* ◊
Hames Christopher *4 Paper Buildings*	**Hoyal** Jane *1 Pump Court (ORL)* ◊
Jarmain Stephen *1 King's Bench Walk* *	**Jefferson** Helen *2-3 Hind Court (ORL)* ◊
Jerman Anthony *42 Bedford Row*	**Jones** Richard *1 Garden Court Family Law Chambers* *
Lister Caroline *1 King's Bench Walk*	**Jubb** Brian *4 Paper Buildings*
Poole Christopher *New Court Chambers* *	**Khan** Hassan *4 Paper Buildings*
Reardon Madeleine *1 King's Bench Walk* *	**Langridge** Niki *Coram Chambers* *
Renton Jacqueline *4 Paper Buildings*	**Lazarides** Marcus *Queen Elizabeth Building* *
Roberts James *1 King's Bench Walk* *	**Miller** Christopher *Fourteen* *
Tod Jonathan *29 Bedford Row Chambers* *	**Parker** Timothy *9 Gough Square (ORL)* ◊ *
Band 3	**Phillips** Katie *42 Bedford Row*
Arnot Lee *29 Bedford Row Chambers* *	**Stone** Sally *1 Garden Court Family Law Chambers* *
Bain Giles *New Court Chambers* *	**Vindis** Tara *9 Gough Square (ORL)* ◊ *
Brereton Joy *4 Paper Buildings*	**Wallace** Sam *New Court Chambers* *
Brooks Duncan *Queen Elizabeth Building* *	**Wan Daud** Malek *Garden Court Chambers (ORL)* ◊
Glaser Michael *Fourteen* [A] *	**Up-and-coming individuals**
Gration Michael *4 Paper Buildings*	**Sprinz** Lucy *1 Garden Court Family Law Chambers* *
Guha Anita *7BR (ORL)* ◊	**Stuart** Damian *Fourteen* *
Habboo Camille *Fourteen* *	**Tyzack** William *Queen Elizabeth Building* *
Jarman Mark *4 Paper Buildings*	**Wiseman** Naomi *Queen Elizabeth Building* *
Jenkins Catherine *1 Garden Court Family Law Chambers* *	

cal injury, sexual abuse and the examination of challenging medical evidence. **Strengths:** "Very affable and confident. She doesn't let the other side rile her and is very good with clients in terms of giving them robust advice in a friendly manner." "Tina is a good fighter for the client's cause."

JUNIORS

Anna McKenna A leading children public law junior who is particularly strong on care work. A number of her cases have involved infanticide and sexual abuse. **Strengths:** "She eloquently delivers sound, focused arguments and is a woman of great dynamism." **Recent work:** Appeared before the Supreme Court in a televised hearing of a case dealing with the legal definition of 'significant harm' and the possibilities of future harm to a newborn child.

Jonathan Bennett Specialises in public law children matters, and is effective at complex care proceedings. He has handled cases involving technical medical circumstances relating to serious injuries to, and the sexual abuse of, young children. **Strengths:** "We instruct Jonathan for complex cases. He has a calm authority and a great breadth of knowledge and skill."

Anthony Jerman Deals with both public and private law proceedings, and regularly represents parties in cases relating to serious and fatal injuries to children. He is also proficient at divorce and matrimonial finance matters. **Strengths:** "A strong, experienced advocate whose written documents are well formed and well reasoned."

Philip McCormack Works exclusively in the sphere of public law children proceedings, handling cases relating to serious injury, alleged sexual abuse and complex medical evidence. **Strengths:** "He's very personable and very well liked by judges."

Damian Woodward-Carlton Negotiates a well-respected practice across London and the South East of England. Public law children proceedings involving challenging circumstances of physical, sexual and psychological abuse are a particular forte. **Strengths:** "He's a strong advocate with a real presence, who's good for complex cases."

Katie Phillips Predominantly represents local authorities, parents and children in public law care proceedings concerning allegations of physical abuse and parties with complex health requirements. **Strengths:** "A silk in the making who is completely on top of her case and able to put clients at ease."

29 Bedford Row Chambers

See profile on p.767

THE SET

"Sound from the bottom upwards and a set with a very good spread of experience," 29 Bedford Row is a key player in the matrimonial finance market, and a chambers that also enjoys a good reputation in children law. Its members have handled many complex, multimillion-pound finance cases, and have established a strong reputation for themselves due to their provision of clear advice on issues relating to civil partnership, cohabitation and pre- and postnuptial agreements. Innovative in its approach, this chambers was the first to train in collaborative law, and has continued to involve itself in the latest trends in the market. By way of example, it has become one of the sets best known for providing private Financial Dispute Resolution Hearings (FDRs). Commentators say that the barristers here "pride themselves on being with it and very accessible. From very early on they have been very approachable and very switched on, and it's easy to use them. You get the feeling that the barristers are working with you to get a result. They are really easy to use."

Client service: "The clerks' room, headed by senior clerk James Shortall, is exceptionally well managed. They are an excellent, friendly bunch."

SILKS

Paul Storey QC (see p.730) A revered children law practitioner who receives great praise for his work in the field of public law proceedings, and often appears in the Supreme Court. His care cases involve complex medical considerations and frequently relate to serious circumstances of non-accidental injury. **Strengths:** "He is a powerhouse when it comes to non-accidental head injury cases, and he is a joy to work to work with." "He often destroys the arguments of local authorities when representing parents."

Piers Pressdee QC (see p.698) A dedicated children law specialist who places particular emphasis in his practice on private law cases. He frequently represents high-profile clients, and is instructed by the very best solicitors' firms in the country. **Strengths:** "He knows the law inside out, and wrote the book on Children Act law. He's accessible, and really gets invested in his cases." "Extremely thorough and very good in front of clients."

Jonathan Southgate QC (see p.725) A dedicated matrimonial finance silk who has particular expertise in cases pertaining to substantial assets, premarital holdings and complex nuptial agreements. **Strengths:** "He's a wizard who has great judgement and offers fine client-handling and advocacy skills." "Good with figures, he makes the complex appear simple."

Nicholas Francis QC (see p.603) Garners exceptional praise for his skill at handling complex matrimonial finance disputes. He is strong on handling cases pertaining to the distribution of substantial premarital and postmarital assets, and those with significant multi-jurisdictional considerations. **Strengths:** "He's got terrific attention to detail and is deadly in cross-examination. He doesn't miss anything." "He is approachable, highly knowledgeable and astonishingly good with even the most difficult of business clients." **Recent work:** Appeared in the Court of Appeal on a case dealing with the distribution of assets between a couple where the husband was a successful entrepreneur in the computer software industry.

Timothy Scott QC (see p.716) Frequently appears in the Supreme Court and Court of Appeal, representing clients in respect of complex international financial and private law children proceedings. **Strengths:** "In terms of the Europe scene and jurisdictonal arguments, there is no better." "He's very confident and he knows the law so well." **Recent work:** Represented a husband who challenged the jurisdictional basis of his wife's divorce petition. The case raised complex issues about the domicile of both parties and the circumstances in which a person acquires a domicile of choice.

Philip Cayford QC (see p.567) Very busy matrimonial silk who represents high net worth and high-profile clients in complex financial proceedings pertaining to maintenance orders, family trusts and significant postmarital assets. **Strengths:** "He's just superb in court, and very good at reasssuring the nervous and sometimes undermined wives of wealthy men." **Recent work:** Instructed in a case relating to two long-divorced parties, where the husband had created a very successful green energy business following their separation and the wife sought maintenance.

Patrick Chamberlayne QC (see p.568) Maintains a diverse and very well-respected practice dealing with complex and substantial ancillary relief matters, as well as civil partnership and Schedule 1 claims. Many of his cases involve cross-border considerations. **Strengths:** "Calm, cool and personable." "He's a very accomplished advocate who's very good on his feet. Clients feel confident with him because he obviously knows what he's talking about. He's a class act." **Recent work:** Instructed in a complex jurisdictional dispute concerning a couple of Indian descent resident in Singapore who were trying to establish legal domicile.

Christopher Wagstaffe QC (see p.744) Involved in numerous international financial disputes pertaining to complex trust and offshore asset holdings. **Strengths:** "Christopher is extremely approachable and good to work with. His client care skills are second to none and I have never had anything less than an excellent experience with him and glowing feedback from clients." "The go-to person for company and trust aspects." **Recent work:** Acted in Shield v Shield, a complex financial case complicated by the parties' own son intervening to claim that the family business was almost entirely owned by him.

Robert Peel QC (see p.691) Deals with complex financial disputes concerning substantial assets and property holdings. **Strengths:** "A hugely inspirational advocate who's abreast of all the changes in the law." "He's just excellent in every way. Extremely bright and user-friendly, he's measured and sensible in his approach."

JUNIORS

Indira Ramsahoye (see p.703) An extremely experienced private law children practitioner who receives praise for her skill in international abduction cases and proceedings relating to allegations of hostility. **Strengths:** "She has an amazing amount of enthusiasm for this work, and really does fight for every single case." "A very safe pair of hands in difficult and emotional children cases, who has very good client-handling skills." **Recent work:** Successfully represented a father in the Court of Appeal who countered the decision to terminate his direct contact on what were ultimately groundless fears of abduction.

Jonathan Tod (see p.738) Specialises in both matrimonial finance and private law children cases, and carries particular favour due to his knowledge of prenuptial agreements. His cases involve high-value financial disputes and complex Schedule 1 Children Act proceedings. **Strengths:** "He's absolutely charming and completely committed. He has a lovely manner with clients and they warm to him." "Excellent family practitioner with particular skill in the drafting and negotiating of prenuptial agreements." **Recent work:** Represented the father in a significant cross-border Schedule 1 Children Act case concerning complexities of jurisdiction and the correct law to apply.

Lee Arnot (see p.538) Manages a diverse practice relating to matrimonial finance as well as complex private and public law children proceedings. Some of his cases concern difficult circumstances of physical and emotional abuse and the examination of medical and police evidence. **Strengths:** "His breadth of knowledge is incredibly helpful, and he has an understanding of how conflict can affect clients."

Brent Molyneux (see p.675) Garners exceptional acclaim from the market for his skill in deeply complex financial remedy cases, especially those containing international issues and trust complexities. **Strengths:** "He's very good with his figures. He gets to the point very quickly, and clients feel confident in him."

Alexis Campbell (see p.564) A strong junior for complex cross-border financial disputes and international private law children matters. **Strengths:** "She is the complete deal. She is sensationally good at picking up papers and gets what the issues are. A brilliant advocate who has just got the lot."

Nicholas Allen (see p.534) A favourite among solicitors for high net worth financial remedy work involving substantial business holdings and the accrual of pre- and postmarital assets. **Strengths:** "His grasp of the law is phenomenal. His greatest talent is the depth in which he will go into a case. When I send him a brief I know he'll read it twice and be 100% prepared. I've never seen him flounder in court or not know a page number. He is a phenomenal comfort to those that instruct him." **Recent work:** Appeared in a substantial financial remedy case dealing with issues of special contribution, premarital assets and the sharing of risk.

Laura Heaton (see p.624) Focuses on matrimonial finance disputes, particularly cases concerning Schedule 1 relief applications. **Strengths:** "She gives very sensible advice, and is not afraid to pack a punch when she needs to."

Richard Bates (see p.545) Deals with high net worth ancillary relief proceedings, and is noted for having particular skill in handling cases with a farming background. He also has substantial recent experience of handling Children Act Schedule 1 matters. **Strengths:** "He pays a great deal of attention to the legal groundwork, and he's quite subtle and skilful in cross-examining witnesses." "He's measured, very thorough and also makes himself readily available. I was very impressed with his advocacy. He pitched it absolutely right."

Simon Calhaem (see p.563) Maintains a high profile in family and civil proceedings, and is particularly adept at cases relating to Inheritance Act claims and international divorces. **Strengths:** "He's great. A properly determined and punchy barrister who prides himself on doing a great job."

Peter Mitchell (see p.674) Handles the examination and preparation of nuptial agreements alongside complex ancillary relief proceedings, including those involving special contributions and non-marital assets. **Strengths:** "A real character. He's a man with a great brain who is a brilliant strategic planner. A first choice for top-end work." **Recent work:** Involved in a big-money case that involved consideration of special contribution, the care needs of disabled children, and contested and complex valuation evidence.

Mark Emanuel (see p.595) Manages a diverse family practice that takes in both high-value financial disputes and complex private law children proceedings. **Strengths:** "Very competent and extremely thorough. No one prepares as well as him." "Lovely to work with, he's very dependable, mature, and patient with clients."

Nicholas Chapman (see p.569) Has developed a strong matrimonial finance practice taking instructions in London and the South of England in high-value, complex ancillary relief proceedings concerning trust assets and inherited wealth. **Strengths:** "He's a very impressive individual. He's tough, he's helpful to lawyers and he's a lot of fun to work with. He has a good sense of humour and he's very attentive to clients' needs." **Recent work:** Acted for the intervener owners of an Edinburgh property portfolio who are the wider family of the husband and subject to freezing orders obtained by the wife. The case involved complex jurisdictional and property issues.

Amber Sheridan (see p.719) One of the best young juniors in the world of complex matrimonial finance. Her cases often concern issues of beneficial ownership of marital and overseas assets. **Strengths:** "She's a wonderfully talented young lady who's very poised and very nice to work with." **Recent work:** Instructed in a case concerning the beneficial ownership of company shares worth in the region of £25 million.

Lynsey Cade Davies (see p.562) Deals principally with complex matrimonial finance disputes, particularly those concerning multi-jurisdictional dimensions. **Strengths:** "Phenomenal, particularly in court appearances. He's forthright and extremely knowledgeable." "A very safe pair of hands and one of the brightest stars of her call at the Family Bar."

Ken Collins (see p.576) Does well receiving instructions on complex ancillary relief and private law children disputes. **Strengths:** "Very bright, quick to grasp the nettle, and able to provide pragmatic advice based upon both what the client wants and needs."

Victoria Domenge (see p.589) Specialises in both financial and private law children matters, and is strong on cases involving multi-jurisdictional disputes. **Strengths:** "She's very quick to pick up something. She grasps it, absorbs it and runs with it. She can step into the breach and get the result."

Peter Duckworth (see p.591) A gifted family law practitioner dealing with complex matrimonial finance proceedings. **Strengths:** "A very careful preparer of his papers, who also has a great deal of commercial acumen. He is very good at financial analysis."

Petra Teacher (see p.735) Regularly handles high-value disputes, many of which are international in nature. **Strengths:** "She's always done a very good job, and she offers very thorough, sensible and practical advice."

Richard Tambling (see p.733) Receives strong praise for his skill in handling complex matrimonial finance disputes and private law children cases. **Strengths:** "Has a proven track record in complex financial matters. Always calm and reassuring to his client," he is "highly approachable and very sympathetic."

Sassa-Ann Amaouche (see p.535) Manages a strong matrimonial finance practice, and deals principally in cases relating to complex forum disputes and multi-jurisdictional concerns. **Strengths:** "She's able to handle the most complex matters with confidence. She's a tenacious negotiator who always commits to her client's cause." "She has a good-quality brain, and adopts a lovely style with clients." **Recent work:** Acted in a complex contested forums case involving substantial assets. The case concerned jurisdictional, tax and trust issues.

Roshi Amiraftabi (see p.535) Specialises in public and private children law and is also an expert on abduction cases. **Strengths:** "A really good advocate who knows her way round international conventions."

Coram Chambers

See profile on p.779

THE SET

Coram Chambers maintains a stable of excellent senior juniors dealing with all facets of family law work including cases relating to finance, children, abduction and social care. Its barristers are especially known for their particularly powerful grasp of medically complex public law proceedings, and for their contribution to the law in terms of their provision of seminars, articles and legal training.

Client service: "Their clerks, led by Paul Sampson, are excellent. They keep you informed and they don't mess you about."

JUNIORS

Martha Cover (see p.579) Manages a strong practice representing local authorities, guardians and children in particularly complex care proceedings where there are circumstances of non-accidental injury. She also often represents older children in private proceedings, and takes cases involving complex human rights concerns. **Strengths:** "She has a wealth of experience and is incredibly approachable." "She has a very solid public law practice and is absolutely trusted by the judges." **Recent work:** Acted in complex High Court care proceedings concerning the father of a child who had been convicted of the attempted murder of its mother's partner.

David Vavrecka (see p.743) Handles complex private and public children law proceedings, and is strong on cases involving contentious adoptions, cross-border abductions and non-accidental injury to young children. **Strengths:** "He's quite softly spoken, but very persuasive, and judges like that. He's not histrionic and he doesn't over-egg the pudding." "He is extremely reliable, well known, and tenacious in his approach." **Recent work:** Acted in a case concerning an application for summary return of children to Australia after abduction by the father, who had submitted that it was unsafe for the family to return.

Jane Drew (see p.591) Adept at private and public law children proceedings, she represents local authorities, guardians, parents and children in cases relating to neglect, physical abuse and adoption. **Strengths:** "She is a practical, down-to-earth advocate with a great breadth of experience." **Recent work:** Acted in a case relating to a long history of child neglect that required the examination of complex medical evidence.

Niki Langridge (see p.651) Practises principally in the field of international matrimonial finance, but also has extensive experience in private law children proceedings. **Strengths:** "She'll go the extra mile and I can always count on her. Clients really feel that she's fighting for them."

Fourteen

See profile on p.805

THE SET

Fourteen is a set that has done more than most in the recent past to adapt itself to the challenges facing the Family Bar. Over the last couple of years it has hired a number of individuals from rival sets and taken on new pupils in order to revivify itself. In 2014 it also undertook a rebrand, changing its name and improving its website. Accordingly, it can look forward to the future with confidence. The set is best known for its handling of complex public and private law children cases, but it does also have a significant amount of members handling finance matters. It also has a successful Court of Protection team and a growing international children team.

Client service: "Head clerk Geoff Carr comes back with solutions and just sorts things out."

JUNIORS

Sarah Forster Undertakes matrimonial finance work, but receives the greatest plaudits for her private and public law children cases. She is frequently instructed in contentious residence cases and complex care proceedings. **Strengths:** "She is thoroughly professional and is very calm and in control in court."

Michael Glaser (see p.609) Receives great praise for his skill in handling very complex and high-value financial disputes as well as international private law children cases. **Strengths:** "He definitely punches above his weight. He is robust and tenacious when he needs to be and is quite dogged at pursuing points. I've been in cases where he's performed far better than silks ten years his senior. He's a very good lateral thinker too, and will find a way round a problem." "He brings great energy to a case."

Sarah Pope (see p.696) Specialist children practitioner dealing in both private and public law disputes, particularly those cases concerning allegations of violence and the fabrication of illnesses, as well as complex guardianship orders. **Strengths:** "She's very approachable, very good with the client, and she produces very good paperwork. Very gutsy, she always puts the clients' interests first." "She reads everything in detail and is very persuasive in front of a judge."

Gillon Cameron (see p.564) Represents clients in both children law and matrimonial finance proceedings, including complex trusts of land cases and cross-border contact disputes. **Strengths:** "He's very well prepared and isn't ruffled by judges or benches being fairly direct with him." "Very good at calming down an irrational opponent or an anxious client."

Camille Habboo (see p.616) Represents parents, guardians and local authorities in public and private law children proceedings pertaining principally to allegations of serious non-accidental injury and sexual abuse. She also handles contested adoption cases. **Strengths:** "She is extremely thorough and has an outwardly gentle approach to cross-examination that yields brilliant results." "She's really human and good with the clients."

Christopher Miller (see p.672) Undertakes very serious public law children matters involving allegations of physical and sexual abuse, as well as cases concerning the distribution of child pornography. Also tackles international relocation disputes. **Strengths:** "He's a dream to work with as he's highly conscientious."

Damian Stuart (see p.730) His family law practice deals with contested financial matters alongside children law proceedings. The children cases often relate to serious physical abuse or guardianship disputes. **Strengths:** "He's extremely hard-working, very fair and very good on his feet. He's always well prepared."

Patricia Roberts Handles complex financial remedy cases, including those with international dimensions or those concerning the examination of overseas assets. Also undertakes private children law proceedings. **Strengths:** "Has an excellent client manner, and comes over as being sensitive and understanding. At the same time, she can be tough in court, and she generally achieves very good results for clients."

1 Garden Court Family Law Chambers

See profile on p.810

THE SET

1 Garden Court's strength in the ancillary relief market may have waned recently but it remains a serious player on the children law front. It has a number of

talented barristers at all levels of call who undertake important care and adoption work, and handle challenging surrogacy cases and novel parental authority disputes. The members have also secured themselves an enviable reputation for handling international private children law work, and are the first choice of many for leave to remove applications and for arrangements for children that require negotiation across boundaries. Commentators say that all the barristers here are "very results-driven."

Client service: The clerks, led by Howard Rayner, are "very good at communicating with you. They are hands-on and make sure things are run across to court."

SILKS

Charles Geekie QC (see p.607) Practises at the highest level in significant children law cases, acting in both the public and private arenas on behalf of parents, children, guardians and local authorities. His cases often involve international aspects and circumstances of physical and emotional abuse. **Strengths:** "He picks things up and spots things early, gently guiding the case in the direction that he wants it to go." "Completely up on the law, he's very good with the clients, and has quiet authority." **Recent work:** Acted in a significant Court of Appeal case pertaining to the interplay between the courts and local authorities before, during and after care proceedings.

Sarah Morgan QC (see p.676) Instructed in relation to both private disputes between parents and very challenging public law proceedings, for which she receives particular praise. Her public law practice often involves cases concerning non-accidental injuries and complex medical circumstances. **Strengths:** "What she brings is the light touch. It's very tempting to become polarised in these cases, and the mixture of her light touch, high intelligence and humour often prevents this happening." "Clients love her, and she can get the best out of a witness."

Janet Bazley QC (see p.546) Tackles both cross-border ancillary relief proceedings and significant children law matters. Her children cases often involve complex international relocation considerations and circumstances of physical injury. **Strengths:** "Always calm and in control, yet at the same time strong and firm." "She combines empathy with the parents with deep knowledge of the difficult issues involved in the case." **Recent work:** Acted in Re H-L (A Child), a Court of Appeal case looking at Rule 25(1) FPR 2010 for the purpose of the court permitting the instruction of an expert in a children case.

Jane Crowley QC (see p.582) Instructed nationwide by clients seeking her expertise in the spheres of private and public children law. Her cases regularly concern care proceedings involving children with complex medical considerations, often in abusive circumstances, as well as challenging international relocation disputes. **Strengths:** "She is understated but very effective, hard-working, and careful in her approach." **Recent work:** Instructed by parents in a case relating to a young child with severe medical needs, which resulted in the local authority in question returning the child to its parents.

Alison Ball QC A long-serving and well-respected figure at the Family Bar. She serves clients in both complex children law proceedings and significant matrimonial finance cases. **Strengths:** "Her client care, her thoroughness, her preparation and her advocacy are all excellent." "Her depth of knowledge and ability to master the most complicated of details in a complex case are impressive."

JUNIORS

Andrew Bagchi (see p.540) Tackles complex areas of family law, including both international and domestic children law disputes, as well as cases pertaining to the wellbeing of incapacitated adults. **Strengths:** "Knowledgeable and constructive in his advice and guidance."

Deirdre Fottrell (see p.603) Has a strong children law practice that is often international in nature, and is also an expert on cases involving human rights. She is often instructed at the highest level in cases relating to complex medical evidence and allegations of abuse. **Strengths:** "She is very, very bright on the law, and presents it in a way that is completely understandable. She is totally in command of what she does." **Recent work:** Instructed in a novel case in which the age of a child was brought into question and medical evidence was required to be examined in relation to the welfare jurisdiction.

Catherine Jenkins (see p.638) Specialises in public law children proceedings concerning highly complex non-accidental injury and psychological as well as sexual abuse. **Strengths:** "She has common sense, and doesn't take stupid points for the sake of it. She knows when to push something and when to leave something."

Richard Jones (see p.641) A good choice for both private and public children law matters, and someone with a particular strength in international proceedings such as child abduction cases. He is regularly instructed by local authorities, guardians and parents in public law proceedings relating to non-accidental injury and the emotional abuse of children. **Strengths:** "He gets on well with the clients, takes a lot of trouble with his cases, and is now someone with a strong following."

Sharon Segal (see p.716) Strong in public law children cases, and a lawyer with a developing private law practice, she is instructed by local authorities, parents and guardians. **Strengths:** "Her passion, technical knowledge and preparation of cases inspire confidence in both solicitors and clients." **Recent work:** Acted as junior counsel on behalf of a local authority in a case relating to two orphaned children and the question of whether they should be put in the care of extended family.

Sally Stone (see p.729) Her practice embraces both private and public law cases, although there is a particular emphasis on the latter. She regularly represents individuals and local authorities in care proceedings relating to non-accidental injuries, as well as complex adoption matters. **Strengths:** "She is as thorough as it's possible to be – she doesn't miss a single point." "She's very sharp, hard-working, diligent and good on her feet."

Lucy Sprinz (see p.726) A rising presence in chambers who deals in both public law and private law matters, and predominantly acts on behalf of parents in cases concerning alleged neglect and physical violence. **Strengths:** "She's a very committed public law barrister who works very hard for her clients. She is a very good technical lawyer."

David Burles (see p.561) Recognised for his talent in the field of matrimonial finance, he handles international disputes including those involving jurisdictional complexities and the examination of offshore assets. **Strengths:** "Innovative, precise in his advice and a barrister who continually provides an excellent level of service. He understands high-value, complex cases, and has extensive knowledge of the interaction between company, trust and tax, and family law."

1 Hare Court

See profile on p.817

THE SET

Members at 1 Hare Court are "specialists in their field, who give great quality advice, produce sterling written work and are excellent in court." "Prompt and efficient in all their dealings," they tackle the most high-value and complex matrimonial finance cases, such as Prest v Prest, but also cater to a client base that ranges across all classes and income brackets. The set is active across the country and is noted not just for the top-quality work it undertakes but also for its provision of an annual seminar. Commentators also praise its specialist private dispute resolution practice – it has 18 mediators, eight arbitrators, two collaborative lawyers and ten senior barristers and previous members of the judiciary, all of whom are available for private FDRs.

Client service: "The clerks, headed by Steve McCrone, really do bend over backwards to help us, and they always turn up with something. They are always lovely to deal with."

SILKS

Nicholas Cusworth QC Specialises in very high-value financial remedy cases, but also has expertise in private law children matters. His cases generally relate to disputes concerning inherited assets and substantial wealth accrued during marriages. Many of them have cross-border aspects. **Strengths:** "He's an excellent all-round silk. He's good with clients, likeable, a great advocate and very bright." "Nick is a tough fighter. He's a very effective advocate, but he's not histrionic. He also has gravitas."

Nigel Dyer QC Handles very complex family cases and substantial financial remedy proceedings, particularly those with cross-border and trust considerations. **Strengths:** "He never misses a trick and is very good at cross-examination." **Recent work:** Acted on behalf of the husband in a High Court case relating to the ownership of very valuable shares. The matter also concerned issues relating to constructive trusts.

Martin Pointer QC Deals with the largest and most complex divorce proceedings both in the UK and abroad, in places such as Hong Kong. He regularly represents high net worth clients. **Strengths:** "Undoubtedly one of the finest silks at the Family Bar. You go to him and he makes the points that you don't think of yourself." "You can't beat Pointer if you have a real battle on your hands." **Recent work:** Represented the wife of a Russian oligarch in a case that the press has called the largest ever divorce payout.

Richard Todd QC Thrives when handling the most complex matrimonial finance disputes, particularly those with multi-jurisdictional aspects. He is an expert in Trusts of Land Act disputes and Inheritance Act claims, and has been called ad hoc to the Bars of the Cayman Islands and Hong Kong. **Strengths:** "He'd be my first choice in every big money case as he's a very clever, imaginative fellow. He's always doing the best work and he always looks after the clients in the best way. He knows the judges well, he knows other barristers well, and he's a good negotiator." **Recent work:** Appeared in the Supreme Court in a significant case dealing with piercing the corporate veil and matters pertaining to beneficial ownership of matrimonial homes.

Timothy Bishop QC Frequently instructed by the most prestigious firms in London for high-profile and very high-value cases, particularly those concerning sizeable international assets and other cross-border complexities. **Strengths:** "His sound practical advice and relaxed style make him a popular choice with clients."

John Wilson QC Specialises in complex, sizeable matrimonial cases, particularly those relating to trusts of land and cohabitation disputes. **Strengths:** "An unrivalled authority on cohabitation claims." "He has a formidable intellect. A robust and astute negotiator, he is particularly good with cases involving complex business issues and trust assets." **Recent work:** Acted for a husband's mother who claimed an interest in the matrimonial home through proprietary estoppel.

Deborah Bangay QC Deals in high-value matrimonial cases concerning sizeable assets. A number of her matters are international in nature, and she is a noted expert on prenuptial agreements. **Strengths:** "Simply brilliant. A tremendous proponent of her client's cause, she is very responsive to clients and an assertive advocate." "She is special. When you need someone to fight your corner, she is unparalleled." **Recent work:** Instructed in a complex financial remedy application concerning the distribution of assets held in Liechtenstein.

Bruce Blair QC Handles challenging financial remedy cases, often those containing complexities pertaining to the accrual of assets during a marriage and after separation. **Strengths:** "A man who is very good on the detail." "He shows very sound judgement, and has very many years of experience at the Family Bar."

Katharine Davidson QC An attractive choice for high-value ancillary relief cases, as she marries her past history in banking and accountancy with her strong legal experience. Her work often relates to complex cross-border matters and the examination of prenuptial agreements. **Recent work:** Acted in G-S v L, representing a wife in a Spanish postnuptial case that involved disputed expert evidence.

Ann Hussey QC Deals with complex matrimonial finance disputes, and has a particular interest in the complexities arising from trust structures. Commentators note that she is particularly good on agricultural cases. **Strengths:** "She's excellent in high-value cases, as she takes a detailed approach to examining business assets."

Valentine Le Grice QC Predominantly handles financial cases, but also provides counsel in private law children matters. The financial matters he deals with generally involve trust elements and jurisdictional complexities. **Strengths:** "He's just really clever. He's very good on his feet, and very good in court. He's got a deep knowledge of family trust issues." "Knowledgeable, confident, articulate and decisive."

JUNIORS

Richard Sear A highly respected junior with a growing financial practice. He deals with complex, cross-border ancillary relief proceedings and challenging maintenance orders on behalf of some of the most prestigious firms in London. **Strengths:** "He is a junior but has a courtroom style and a wisdom that would suggest much more experience. He has the gift of making anything seem reasonable and attractive." "District judges love him. Give him something and he just gets it immediately."

Nichola Gray Deals in high-value matrimonial finance disputes, often involving assets hidden in overseas jurisdictions. She is very good on cases concerning complex trusts. **Strengths:** "She's feisty, fantastic on her feet, thorough and very pragmatic. She has good all-round skill and is a delight to deal with." **Recent work:** Appeared before the Court of Appeal in the first civil partnership financial remedy case.

Geoffrey Kingscote Manages a very respected practice and works on substantial matrimonial disputes. His cases often contain complexities relating to premarital assets, overseas holdings and contested nuptial agreements. **Strengths:** "A persuasive advocate who is able to put forward all the salient points in a concise and articulate manner." "He's very good and calm. He gives advice clearly and is straight down the line."

Stephen Trowell Specialises in high-value financial disputes, particularly those involving international dimensions, overseas assets and complicated corporate structures. **Strengths:** "He has an authority that people respect and clients like." "He is the best junior we work with. Very diligent, a fantastic advocate, and someone whose preparation for hearings is second to none."

Justin Warshaw Receives extensive praise for his skill in handling substantial financial remedy proceedings. He is often sought out for his expertise in very complex and high-value multi-jurisdictional disputes. **Strengths:** "He is fantastic, a real force to be reckoned with, and excellent for high-value cases." "He is as tenacious as a terrier with a very large rat."

Simon Webster Garners much acclaim for his extensive matrimonial finance practice, and simultaneously displays an aptitude for private law children matters. His cases typically concern substantial assets and complex prenuptial agreements. **Strengths:** "He is worth his weight in gold." "You won't find a harder worker and he has a wonderful bedside manner."

Nicholas Yates (see p.757) Undertakes complex matrimonial disputes relating to high-value divorces and partnership dissolutions, as well as private law children matters. His cases often involve multi-jurisdictional disputes and the examination of challenging pre- and postnuptial agreements. **Strengths:** "An excellent tactician who gives incisive advice and is a real team player." "He is very charming and very calm, and he has a wonderful and appropriate sense of humour."

Emma Sumner Maintains an extensive matrimonial finance practice dealing with complex and high net worth cases that typically concern asset schedules and corporate structures. Many of her cases have international elements. **Strengths:** "She's fantastic to work with, and you can't fault her on the law. She's also incredibly personable and easy to approach." "Always so well prepared and her attention to detail is second to none."

Michael Bradley Singled out for his skill in complex financial remedy proceedings concerning difficult aspects of private equity and trust structures. He is also recognised for handling matters involving the tracing of overseas assets. **Strengths:** "He's incredibly urbane and charming. Very methodical and very polite, he is respected by judges." "Firm, scrupulously fair and compassionate."

Rebecca Carew Pole Appears in complex cases dealing with such matters as inherited wealth, and offshore corporate structures and assets. Also handles some contentious private law children disputes. **Strengths:** "She is very forceful in her presentation to the court, amazingly thorough, and has the patience of a saint."

Christian Kenny Undertakes both financial remedy and private law children proceedings on behalf of high net worth parties. Shows particular strength in the preparation of nuptial agreements and when handling multi-jurisdictional disputes. **Strengths:** "A solid performer with excellent court skills who has a keen eye for detail. He produces flawless paperwork for the court and for solicitors." "Very approachable, knowledgeable and helpful. He gives good, clear advice to clients."

Rebecca Bailey-Harris Handles European and multi-jurisdictional financial disputes, applying her extensive experience as a legal academic to her practice with great effect. **Strengths:** "She is an expert on jurisdictional matters and European work. Her knowledge of the law is second to none in terms of those areas, and she's a very good cross-examiner."

Nicholas Wilkinson An excellent junior barrister dealing with a broad family practice concerning financial remedy disputes and private law children proceedings. He also specialises in complex trusts of land matters. **Strengths:** "An extremely competent junior barrister with excellent client care skills, he's well able to deal with complex issues quickly and give good pragmatic advice."

1 King's Bench Walk

See profile on p.826

THE SET

1 King's Bench Walk remains unmatched among its rivals in being able to offer representation at all levels of call in all four areas of family law. Its members, many of whom are the authors of leading family law textbooks, can handle all manner of matrimonial finance, private and public law children work, and child abduction cases. "Highly competitive in terms of their skills and representing great value for money," they are all "very approachable and hands-on – working with them is a collaborative experience." Commentators feel that, under the stewardship of two new heads of chambers, the set is "poised to further reinforce its strong standing in the market."

Client service: "They're good from top to bottom, and the clerks, led by David Dear, are really helpful and really friendly."

SILKS

Deborah Eaton QC (see p.593) A deeply respected practitioner who handles a diverse practice, and deals with cases at the highest level in both the matrimonial finance and children law arenas. She is one of the few leading barristers who has the intellectual force to deal with both sides of the Family Bar. **Strengths:** "She probably has the best reputation at the Bar of anyone dealing with children issues. Clients love her, judges love her, and she speaks with immense authority and expertise." "She has a really good perception of clients' needs, feelings and wishes, and she displays a lot of empathy."

Richard Harrison QC (see p.621) Deals in both children law and finance matters, and receives praise from peers for his skill in both. His cases often concern complex international matters in both the private and public law children arenas, and he is an expert on relocations, abductions and high-value divorce proceedings. **Strengths:** "He's very agile in his thinking. When he is advocating in court, he doesn't give up on a point if the judge pushes him back. He's quite persistent and makes sure that the client's case is put across." **Recent work:** Acted in Mohan v Mohan, a case which is now the leading authority on the admissibility of documents and answers obtained by compulsion in judgment summons proceedings.

Charles Howard QC A very experienced advocate who is strong on complex children and matrimonial finance law matters. Many of his matters are high-value international cases. **Strengths:** "He's extremely clever and handles masses of reported cases."

James Turner QC Manages a sophisticated practice and is an expert in challenging multi-jurisdictional matrimonial finance matters and in cases pertaining to international abduction. He is a veteran of the Court of Appeal and the Supreme Court. **Strengths:** "Incredibly clever, very user-friendly and very happy to take original points." "He loves grappling with complex legal issues, and has the expertise to put cases to bed."

Anthony Kirk QC (see p.646) Specialises exclusively in the field of children law, and is particularly good on complex international cases and challenging care proceedings. He is a fine choice for cases concerning abduction, and the infliction of serious injury on children. **Strengths:** "He's amazing. He's so eloquent, he doesn't even have to look at his notes. I could sit and listen to him all day when he's on his feet." **Recent work:** Acted in a case where a young girl had suffered very serious physical trauma. There were issues surrounding allegations towards the parents and the misdiagnosis of some injuries.

Pamela Scriven QC Specialises in complex care proceedings where there have been serious injuries inflicted on young children. She is good on cases with difficult jurisdictional issues. **Strengths:** "She is quietly persuasive and a very safe pair of hands."

Christopher Pocock QC (see p.695) Has an extensive matrimonial finance practice, and handles a number of complex and high-value disputes concerning substantial trust assets, offshore structures, contested prenuptial agreements and diverse business holdings. **Strengths:** "He's really good with figures, really understands businesses and has a very persuasive way of writing and talking." "He has a razor-sharp intellect, and offers down-to-earth, practical advice."

Richard Anelay QC (see p.536) Has extensive experience of tackling both substantial matrimonial finance disputes, and complex public and private law children cases, including those relating to international abduction and adoption. **Strengths:** "An elder statesman of the Family Bar who still appears in big cases."

Philip Marshall QC (see p.663) Deals exclusively with very high-value divorce proceedings involving complex corporate and trust structures and contested pre-nuptial agreements. **Strengths:** "He provides sound, clear advice and is prepared to argue his corner. He's very accurate in assessing the quantum of financial settlements." "A thorough and determined counsel."

Barry Singleton QC Undertakes substantial ancillary relief proceedings as well as contentious private law children matters. He often appears in cases relating to multi-jurisdictional disputes and disguised asset holdings. **Strengths:** "I think he's phenomenal. If you have a complex case and you need someone to think outside the box, Barry's your man."

JUNIORS

Nicola Fox (see p.603) A respected senior junior dealing with both matrimonial finance and children law cases. She often handles substantial ancillary relief disputes and challenging private law matters relating to international complexities. **Strengths:** "Nicola is fast-thinking and robust in her advocacy, whilst also being extremely personable and popular with clients." "She is outstanding, and a pleasure to both work with and learn from."

Caroline Lister Specialises in substantial financial disputes and private law children proceedings. Some of her cases concern challenging questions of international relocation and parental responsibility in respect of young children. **Strengths:** "She takes a thorough, no-nonsense approach when handling both children and financial issues." "Caroline is immensely skilled in representing clients who are experiencing emotional difficulties as a result of the breakdown of their relationships. She leaves such clients in no doubt as to whose side she is on whilst always remaining realistic about possible outcomes."

Madeleine Reardon (see p.705) A rising talent, who deals with all facets of family law, and has a particular strength in private law children matters. Her cases often relate to complex issues of international relocation, surrogacy and allegations of abuse towards children. **Strengths:** "She is modest but you know that nothing will escape her. She is an effective but gentle cross-examiner who provides quiet assurance that comforts the clients."

Elizabeth Selman (see p.717) Specialises in both matrimonial finance and private law children cases, and is particularly respected for her skill in dealing with contentious matters. She handles challenging disputes where there have been allegations of neglect made against parents, as well as high-value financial proceedings. **Strengths:** "Her people skills make her so adept at children work. She is able to put forward and grasp what the client wants to say and is very persuasive." "She's very direct when she needs to be, and also very sensitve."

Markanza Cudby Manages a diverse children law practice dealing with both public and private law proceedings. She routinely represents local authorities, guardians and parents. **Strengths:** "A highly experienced counsel with a perfect skill set for complex children's proceedings. She is an effective advocate with a patient and creative negotiating style who remains calm and unflappable regardless of the toxicity of the case."

James Roberts (see p.709) Principally undertakes significant matrimonial finance cases, but also handles challenging private law children matters. His cases often contain complex cross-border and trust considerations, and regularly concern very substantial, disputed assets. **Strengths:** "He is pragmatic, sensible and a formidable advocate." "He definitely has a fine brain, is very hard-working and very thorough. He fights hard and serves his clients well."

Stephen Jarmain (see p.637) Manages both complex private law children matters as well as substantial financial disputes. He is good on cross-border cases pertaining to child abduction as well as matrimonial finance cases, and also has particular expertise in human rights law. **Strengths:** "Extremely well prepared, very approachable, and impressive to clients." "A clever chap who is meticulous and well prepared. He's one of the rising stars."

Katherine Kelsey (see p.644) Undertakes both matrimonial finance and private law children cases at a high level. She frequently represents parents in complex and acrimonious residence disputes and in matters where there are challenging mental health considerations. Also tackles sizeable financial remedy cases. **Strengths:** "She is extremely well prepared and great with the clients. She is second to none at preparing paperwork, and she's very good at grasping the nettle of a complicated point."

Harry Oliver Deals exclusively in high-value matrimonial finance cases, often those involving very complex business structures, family trust holdings, and jurisdictional issues. **Strengths:** "Exceptionally numerate. A man with a big personality, and someone with a bright future ahead of him." "Simultaneously charming and forthright, he makes complex situations and scenarios more simple to understand."

Richard Castle (see p.567) Specialises in complex financial disputes, and is often called upon as an expert on offshore jurisdictions such as Jersey and Gibraltar. His cases frequently concern interests in high-value property, as well as trust assets. **Strengths:** "Always on top form. He's efficient, he cuts through the issues and he's deadly in cross-examination."

Ian Cook (see p.577) Exclusively handles financial disputes between high net worth parties, and often appears in cases relating to extensive real property holdings and complex business structures. **Strengths:** "A great person to have on your side. He's effective in court and on paper, and is respected by judges and opponents." "He's a straight talker and is hugely practical."

Deepak Nagpal (see p.680) Has great knowledge of matrimonial finance, and is frequently instructed by prestigious firms in relation to complex cases concerning jurisdictional disputes, substantial corporate assets and elaborate prenuptial agreements. **Strengths:** "He has got a phemonenal brain" and is "very good on obscure bits of the law." **Recent work:** Acted for a wealthy businessman in a case arguing the legal validity of an Islamic marriage ceremony in London and a talaq in Saudi Arabia.

Dominic Brazil (see p.555) Marries expertise in matrimonial finance and cohabitation disputes with an extensive knowledge of private law children proceedings. **Strengths:** "Has a direct approach which finds favour with most clients and judges. In addition, his knowledge of obscure cases and law appears limitless, and he is particularly good on matters which have novel and complex features." "The judges are very respectful of his learning."

Nicholas Anderson (see p.536) Has expertise in both matrimonial finance disputes and private law children matters, and is frequently called upon for cases which involve elements of both fields. He is very strong on cases concerning international relocations and issues of residence in Hague jurisdictions. **Strengths:** "Very good with clients and very much a team player."

Alexander Chandler (see p.568) Handles financial remedy and cohabitation disputes, and is especially good on cases involving complex issues relating to trusts of land and company structures. **Strengths:** "Alex is a rising star whose intellect, advocacy and communication skills are excellent." "Meticulous in his preparation, he responds quickly to instructions and is pragmatic and sensible in his advice."

Susan Wilkins Manages a diverse family practice dealing with financial disputes beside private and public law children cases and challenging care proceedings. **Strengths:** "She's extremely thorough and never lets you down." "Susan in particular is highly competent in both children and finances."

Peter Newman (see p.682) A specialist family law junior whose practice has a particular emphasis on complex matrimonial finance proceedings and challenging international private law children matters. **Strengths:** "His mind can deal with any complexity of problem. He has an academic approach to his submissions which judges find appealing." "He has a fighting spirit." **Recent work:** Acted in the Supreme Court for the leading child abduction charity, Reunite, as an intervener in proceedings.

New Court Chambers

See profile on p.834

THE SET

New Court Chambers handles matrimonial finance work but is more celebrated for its efforts on the children side. It acts for over a dozen local authorities and regularly represents a growing number of children's guardians. Commentators believe the set has come along well in recent times, and praise it not just for the quality of its barristers but also for its provision of in-house training for social workers, team and senior managers and local authority lawyers. Those that instruct the set say: "The barristers here are very good at dealing with difficult clients" and "never lose sight of the fact that the child's welfare is paramount."

Client service: "The clerks are are willing to help outside of their remit. They're helpful, they try to sort out counsel straight away, and are friendly and reliable." Paul Bloomfield is the senior clerk.

JUNIORS

Christopher Poole (see p.696) Has a strong reputation in public law children proceedings, particularly in cases relating to medical negligence and serious physical and psychological abuse. **Strengths:** "He's solid on the law and very good on his feet. He's always able to put the client at ease and represent them well. He'll go a long, long way."

Giles Bain (see p.541) A specialist children lawyer who handles complex care cases involving non-accidental injuries and sexual abuse. He is particularly good at cases which involve the examination of challenging medical evidence. **Strengths:** "Giles is good in court, gives sensible advice to the client, and is good with judges. He has a sensible, matter-of-fact approach that gains respect."

Sam Wallace (see p.745) Specialises in children cases and routinely appears for parents, guardians and local authorities. He has handled a number of serious cases involving allegations of non-accidental injury and sexual abuse. **Strengths:** "A measured and thoughtful advocate who is calm under pressure, and presents things in a straight and fair way.

4 Paper Buildings

See profile on p.843

THE SET

4 Paper Buildings is a renowned set of chambers dealing with the most complex children law proceedings. Both private and public law children matters are accounted for, and members are expert in everything from paternity disputes to international abduction, parental authority, and serious injury to children cases. Members of the public, local authorities and solicitors all beat a path to its door in order to avail themselves of the superior representation on offer here. The set also has four experienced silks and a number of juniors who handle finance work. They have been involved in leading recent cases, including Young v Young.

Client service: Led by Michael Reeves, "the clerks are immensely helpful. They are realistic and honest and they always try to do what they can."

SILKS

Henry Setright QC Revered for his talents in the field of abduction law. He is frequently involved in the most significant and ground-breaking children law cases at an international level. **Strengths:** "Among the international children cases, he's God basically. He is utterly pre-eminent in what he does." "An absolute class above. His tactics are second to none." **Recent work:** Instructed in a landmark international case on the approach to the 1980 Hague Convention. The matter marked a major change in human rights law.

Alex Verdan QC Negotiates a highly touted children law practice, and receives great praise from his peers. He has more than two decades' experience in both private and public law proceedings, and has handled numerous cases involving complex international considerations, allegations of significant physical injury, and the death of children. **Strengths:** "He's a gifted advocate who can turn the impossible into the possible." **Recent work:** Represented appellant parents in the Supreme Court in a case relating to risks of future psychological and emotional harm.

Charles Hale QC Deals with both very high-value matrimonial finance proceedings and complex children law matters. He is regularly sought out for cases pertaining to cross-border children disputes and for his advice to alternative families. **Strengths:** "Charles is the ultimate negotiatior. If there is a good deal to get, he will get it." "When he speaks people are drawn to what he says; he's a very persuasive and powerful advocate. His bedside manner is great, and he captures the trust of a client instantly."

David Williams QC A specialist in international law relating to children, who is particularly strong on complex cross-border abductions and relocation cases involving both Hague and non-Hague jurisdictions. **Strengths:** "He is just superb. He's got a very good manner with clients and solicitors, and when it comes to overall tactical skills he's very good." **Recent work:** Was instructed in the first appeal to the Supreme Court in a Hague Convention case relating to the 'best interests' of children under Article 13.

Catherine Wood QC Has a deeply respected children practice focusing principally on complex and very contentious private law proceedings. Her cases often relate to the relocation and abduction of children. **Strengths:** "She is very sharp-witted and her advocacy is very skilful. She's a rising star and a lot of people here like her approach." "She has a fantastic bedside manner with clients, and an incredible eye for detail. Also, in the nicest possible way, she can destroy someone in cross-examination."

Jo Delahunty QC (see p.586) A dedicated children lawyer who focuses on difficult public law matters and care proceedings concerning allegations of sexual and emotional abuse. Also handles cases involving the death of children. **Strengths:** "A first port of call for care work," "she is extremely hard-working, knowledgeable and very committed to the client that she represents. Jo is a very tactical and effective advocate, who is good to observe and learn from."

Teertha Gupta QC A widely respected barrister who deals with the most complex and testing multi-jurisdictional matters. Child abduction cases are his strong suit. **Strengths:** "A very smooth operator with gallons of charm and a great mind to match." "We appreciate Teertha's considerable experience and his ability to understand the nuances of each specific case and advise accordingly. He is both approachable and pragmatic, and clients always warm to him."

Marcus Scott-Manderson QC Enjoys a position of authority as a respected private law practitioner dealing with cross-border children law work. **Strengths:** "I've done a lot with him on international work. He has a genuine passion for that type of work. He also has an incredible brain for it and is able to use that brain power to the best effect."

Michael Sternberg QC Highly recommended by peers for his work on both high-level matrimonial finance disputes and contentious children law matters. **Strengths:** "He's very proactive. If you've got a case on with Michael you know all the t's will be crossed and the i's will be dotted. He's very demanding of his solicitors and he's excellent in his preparation."

Jonathan Cohen QC Lauded for his skill in the field of very high-value financial disputes. He regularly handles cases with complex jurisdictional matters attached to them. **Strengths:** "Jonathan combines a fierce intellect with a depth of experience and a quiet authority. He commands the respect of his clients, peers and the judiciary."

JUNIORS

Justine Johnston Has a wide practice dealing principally with complex private law children proceedings and overlapping matrimonial finance disputes, including high-value ancillary relief cases and international relocation matters. **Strengths:** "She's relatively junior and up against people a lot more senior than her. A tenacious advocate, she's very strong in court, and can go up against anyone."

Samantha King Tackles a broad range of public and private law children work, including cases involving complex issues of surrogacy, non-accidental injury and the examination of complicated matters of medical evidence. **Strengths:** "She has a confident and reassuring manner." "She has a wonderful hands-on approach to cases, and is a joy to work with."

Barbara Mills Has great experience and a deservedly strong reputation for her work in private law children proceedings. She deals principally with international relocations and cases relating to same-sex families. **Strengths:** "She clearly knows the law well and has a good, sensible down-to-earth approach. She works very well with clients." "She's measured and sensible, and tells it how it is."

Alison Grief Has a broad practice that encompasses complex areas of public and private law children matters, including allegations of physical, emotional and sexual abuse, the death of children and international relocations. **Strengths:** "Has the ability to grasp complex medical evidence and get straight to the issues. Alison is very experienced in complex cases, particularly those involving deaths of children. She is extremely hard-working, thorough and very approachable."

Christopher Hames Maintains a strong private law children practice, and works in cases relating to residence, relocation and abduction in both Hague and non-Hague jurisdictions. **Strengths:** "Brilliant for complex, difficult cases. Great on the attention to detail, she's very thorough, good with clients and highly personable." **Recent work:** Instructed before the High Court in a case pertaining to the abduction of five children by their father.

Joy Brereton Undertakes both private and public law children proceedings, and has a particular affinity for cases with an international angle to them, particularly those concerning international abduction, relocation and serious injury to children. **Strengths:**

"Very sensible, very realistic and incredibly effective as an advocate."

Michael Gration A rising presence among juniors at the Family Bar who handles complex international children law cases, including those concerning abductions, relocations and forced marriages in Hague and non-Hague jurisdictions. **Strengths:** "He is a towering presence, both literally and figuratively, who is very strong on jurisdictional points and has a very good client manner."

Mark Jarman An experienced advocate in both private and public law proceedings, whose practice has a particular focus on cases relating to the international movement of children. He regularly handles leave to remove matters in both Hague and non-Hague jurisdictions. **Strengths:** "An unsung hero who is very self-effacing and just gets on with his work. Good in a crisis, he's very experienced and a safe pair of hands."

Judith Murray An accomplished junior who tackles both matrimonial finance and complex children law proceedings, and garners praise from peers and solicitors alike. **Strengths:** "She's a real client favourite who has got what it takes to be a silk one day."

Jacqueline Renton Has a specialised private law children practice dealing with cross-border disputes pertaining to international custody and abductions. **Strengths:** "A ball of energy who is going to go far. She's certainly doing work well above her call, and is one of the leading people on abduction outside of silk." "Jacqueline's appreciation and understanding of the complexities of child abduction cases ensure quick and client-focused outcomes." **Recent work:** Represented the mother in a wardship dispute concerning children who were wrongfully retained in Russia by their father.

John Tughan Deals with both public and private law proceedings, including cases of serious or fatal injury or sexual abuse, or those concerning challenging medical evidence. **Strengths:** "He believes in them and will fight for them however hopeless the case seems."

Brian Jubb An experienced advocate who focuses on all aspects of private and public children law, as well as community care law. She is particularly strong on cases where there are allegations of sexual abuse or questions of parental authority and competence.

Hassan Khan Manages a strong practice dealing principally with private law children matters, including surrogacy and parental authority cases. **Strengths:** "Immensely helpful and very approachable."

Samantha Woodham (see p.755) A rising junior dealing with high-value financial disputes and contentious private law children matters. **Strengths:** "A pleasure to work with and someone who is very on top of the facts. She's very good with clients."

Stephen Lyon Practises exclusively in the sphere of matrimonial finance, and is strong on cases concerning complex jurisdictional disputes. **Strengths:** "He's got a terrific ability to get to the heart of a problem, and has exceptional reserves of common sense." **Recent work:** Represented the husband in a much-publicised case in which the ex-wife commenced a high-profile relationship with international footballer Cesc Fabregas.

Queen Elizabeth Building

See profile on p.855

THE SET

QEB barristers handle challenging domestic and international matrimonial finance proceedings as routine, and are regularly instructed by all the major solicitors firms in the market. They are skilled at all aspects of family law, including civil partnerships, jurisdictional disputes, Inheritance Act claims and foreign divorces, and are also deeply involved in all forms of alternative dispute resolution. Recently, they have welcomed back former Court of Appeal judge Sir Alan Ward to boost their capacity in this regard. Although universally commended for its skill at handling money cases, the set is also beginning to become noticed in the children law field as it attempts to recapture some of the ground lost when its leading children practitioners left for the Bench some years ago.

Client service: "The clerks, led by Ivor Treherne, are courteous and careful in finding solutions for instructing solicitors."

SILKS

Lewis Marks QC (see p.663) A specialist matrimonial finance silk managing very high-value disputes, who often appears in cases concerning complex business holdings and private equity funds. **Strengths:** "He's the man for big money cases and those dealing with complicated areas of the law. He thinks very carefully about each issue, and is both thorough and pragmatic. He's very bright and very numerate, and he understands the nature of clients' businesses." "His command of maths is amazing."

Lucy Stone QC (see p.729) A revered matrimonial finance silk who represents very high net worth clients in substantial, often cross-border, disputes. She is renowned for her skill in examining complex prenuptial agreements. **Strengths:** One contented instructing solicitor comments: "When you want one of the best legal brains in the business, go to Lucy." Another comments: "With Lucy on board you'll know from day one that your client and your team are going to win." **Recent work:** Advised on a case in the Hong Kong Court of Appeal, appearing on behalf of the appellant wife. The parties owned a world-famous collection of Chinese furniture worth HKD750 million, and had both been directors of and major shareholders in a Hong Kong publicly listed company.

Stewart Leech QC (see p.654) Handles very high-value financial remedy disputes, many of which concern complex trust holdings and jurisdictional matters. He is particularly well versed in Anglo-French work. **Strengths:** "He's always immacuately prepared, and is an extremely polished advocate with a great reputation among the judges. When he speaks they attach great weight to what he says." "He has an excellent intellect, and an ability to grasp the guts of a case quickly."

Tim Amos QC (see p.535) A renowned international family law barrister who handles very substantial divorce proceedings, particularly those involving jurisdictional disputes. **Strengths:** "He is, in terms of European law, as good an adviser as one can have." "He's excellent, very detailed, thinks very carefully about everything, and is absolutely a go-to person for complex work." **Recent work:** Brought in to resist the appeal in a landmark case where the appellant wife sought to apply the decision of the ECJ in Owusu v Jackson, so as to prohibit the English court from staying its own divorce proceedings in favour of parallel similar proceedings in a non-European jurisdiction.

JUNIORS

James Ewins (see p.598) A matrimonial finance expert whose cases often relate to complex disputes over family trusts, nuptial agreements or forum challenges. **Strengths:** "He is very straightforward, no-nonsense and businesslike." "Absolutely charming – you couldn't fall out with him in a case if you tried."

Elizabeth Clarke (see p.572) Handles complex financial remedy disputes, often on behalf of international clients with significant overseas holdings and offshore trust assets. **Strengths:** "She is the best finance barrister at the junior Bar." "She is engaging, energetic, very accessible, hugely clever and an impeccable advocate."

Catherine Cowton (see p.579) Manages a diverse practice involving complex finance disputes, the examination of nuptial agreements, and private law children proceedings. **Strengths:** "She is robust and has great common sense. She displays amazing attention to detail, works very hard, and is fantastic with clients."

Samantha Singer (see p.721) Receives strong praise for her complex matrimonial finance and private law children practice, and frequently handles cases involving very sizeable international assets. **Strengths:** "She is a tigress. Incredibly hard-working, she never lets her levels drop."

Daniel Bentham (see p.548) Focuses principally on matrimonial finance disputes, particularly those cases concerning beneficial ownership in non-marital, premarital and overseas assets. **Strengths:** "He is utterly charming and a very able advocate." "His preparation is first-class and the documents he prepares are faultless."

Duncan Brooks (see p.557) Respected family law practitioner who deals with very complex matrimonial finance proceedings and children law matters. Many of his cases involve jurisdictional concerns and contact disputes. **Strengths:** "He is excellent on detail, and his paperwork is really good." **Recent work:** Represented the wife in a complex matrimonial finance matter where the husband had declared bankruptcy and it was contested that the son controlled a beneficial interest in the estate.

Marcus Lazarides (see p.653) Principally deals in complex, high-value financial disputes, but also undertakes private law children work, particularly residency and contact disputes where parents lack capacity. **Strengths:** "Marcus offers a nice, calm, measured approach which is particularly good for very highly strung clients. He has good client care and is always keen to find a way to settle a case if at all possible." "His calm persona and gentlemanly manner put clients at ease. He gives top-quality, direct advice that provides clients with what they need to make a well-informed decision about their case."

Sarah Phipps (see p.693) Comes recommended for her strengths across the Family Bar in finance disputes and private law children proceedings, particularly in Schedule 1 cases. **Strengths:** "Sarah is very stylish and an excellent advocate. She gives the clients the advice as she sees it, but is also prepared to push a point if that is what a client wants."

Morgan Sirikanda (see p.722) Focuses principally on financial disputes relating to complex multi-jurisdictional cases. **Strengths:** "He is committed, extremely clever and a delight to listen to." "He's very nice, very well organised, and takes a gentle, non-aggressive approach."

Alexander Thorpe (see p.737) Frequently called upon to handle substantial finance litigation, and particularly strong in cases relating to very complex trust considerations. **Strengths:** "Bright, quick on his feet, charming and liked by both judges and clients. He is very user-friendly and will not be a junior barrister for much longer." "He's tough, he's thoughtful and he gets to the point."

Marina Faggionato (see p.598) A successful junior barrister who tackles complex divorce proceedings, cohabitation disputes, the preparation of nuptial agreements, and private law children cases. **Strengths:** "She is a star of the future." "She is approachable and tenacious, and has a good manner with clients."

Matthew Firth (see p.600) A senior junior dealing principally in sizeable ancillary relief disputes. **Strengths:** "Matthew is absolutely fixed on what he does. He knows the papers, and he's straight with clients. He's absolutely rock solid on the work."

Charanjit Batt (see p.545) Handles substantial ancillary relief claims on behalf of very high net worth clients. A number of her cases involve complex multi-jurisdictional battles. **Strengths:** "She's a lovely advocate who is very organised, very calm, very confident, but never arrogant." "Provides detailed and technical advice in a clear manner, and quickly grasps the detail of a case. She definitely has the ear of the court."

Amy Kisser (see p.647) A growing presence among junior juniors dealing in both matrimonial finance and private law children disputes. She is good on cases with cross-border dimensions. **Strengths:** "She's very bright but down to earth and clients love her. She's very well prepared, and she manages to explain complex matters very easily to clients." "A prodigy. She is supremely clever and has the intellect of someone many years more experienced than her." **Recent work:** Acted in a complex international financial remedies case, representing the husband's companies, the key issue being whether the court could order the husband to transfer properties legally belonging to the companies to the wife as part of her award.

William Tyzack (see p.742) Manages a practice of equal parts matrimonial finance and private law children work, and has a particular specialism in Anglo-German work. **Strengths:** "He is certainly somebody to keep an eye on. He's very, very good and has a gravitas that is beyond his years."

Rosemary Budden (see p.560) Enjoys a strong reputation for dealing with international family cases. He is adept at both financial remedy and private law children cases. **Strengths:** "Very calm, very sensible, and someone with a good attitude to clients, she does not beat about the bush and gives clear and straightforward advice." "She is diligent and pragmatic."

Naomi Wiseman (see p.755) A rising star among juniors who deals with all facets of financial remedy as well as private and public law children proceedings. **Strengths:** "She's very hard-working and has a terrific future ahead of her." "She is highly intelligent, very personable, has very good common sense and is a meticulous lawyer."

Other Ranked Lawyers

Charles Hyde QC (Albion Chambers) Frequently instructed in sizeable financial remedy proceedings where there are complex overseas holdings and contested prenuptial agreements in issue. Also receives praise from peers for his expertise in the field of highly complex private law children proceedings. **Strengths:** "Combines exceptional advocacy with total approachability."

William Tyler QC (see p.742) (36 Bedford Row) Undertakes complex children law proceedings in both London and the East Midlands. His cases often involve child abuse, spousal abuse, international abductions and infanticide. **Strengths:** "He has a huge brain and also a very nice manner about him. He is easy to deal with, thoughtful and really thinks about things from the client's perspective."

Hannah Markham (see p.662) (36 Bedford Row) Specialises exclusively in private and public law children cases, and has particular expertise in matters concerning assessments of risk of future harm, serious physical abuse, contentious adoptions and international removals. **Strengths:** "She provides excellent attention to detail. We had a huge amount of medical evidence and her mastery of it was fantastic." "She is clever, very capable and a fighter."

Barbara Connolly QC (see p.576) (7BR) Tackles all facets of family law though specialises particularly in significant public and private law children matters. She is strong on cases relating to paternity disputes, non-accidental injuries and international child-trafficking. **Strengths:** "She has a really good presence, is very articulate, and is an appealing advocate. If you start listening to her, you want to listen more."

Rachel Langdale QC (see p.650) (7BR) A very experienced children law practitioner who deals with proceedings relating to allegations of non-accidental injury and infanticide. **Strengths:** "She was excellent throughout our case. There was a lot at stake for our clients, and at times there was a need to be really quite assertive with some senior people. She handled the clients very well indeed and proved to be a skilful advocate at the inquiry."

Anita Guha (7BR) A specialist in public and private children law matters who has extensive expertise in international abduction, care proceedings and wardship disputes, where she often represents parents. **Strengths:** "Thorough in her drafting skills," she "is very diligent and shows good attention to detail."

David Balcombe QC (1 Crown Office Row) Has a strong following among many of the best solicitors in the country, and handles matrimonial finance cases of weight and distinction. **Strengths:** "Calm under pressure, very responsive and down to earth in his approach." **Recent work:** Has been acting for Belgian hotelier Didier Thiry in connection with a multimillion-pound financial claim brought against him by Alisa Thiry.

Maggie Jones (Garden Court Chambers) Has a broad children law practice dealing with public and private law matters, and regularly handles matters concerning significant emotional harm, serious physical injury and neglect. She is also good on contact disputes. **Strengths:** "Her client care is outstanding."

Malek Wan Daud (Garden Court Chambers) Particularly noted for her handling of public law care cases that contain allegations of serious physical and sexual abuse, international abduction and child abandonment. **Strengths:** "He's very enthusiastic about his work and has a delightful personality."

Timothy Parker (see p.690) (9 Gough Square) Acts for local authorities in public law children proceedings relating to allegations of very serious physical negligence and abuse, cross-border abductions and issues of parental capacity. **Strengths:** "He's very popular with local authorities."

Tara Vindis (see p.743) (9 Gough Square) Deals principally in public law children matters, and is frequently instructed by local authorities. Her cases often relate to circumstances of domestic violence, serious physical abuse and the removal and adoption of young children.

Edward Devereux (Harcourt Chambers) A respected children law practitioner with a particular interest in international disputes, who has presented cases in the European Court of Human Rights, the USA and the Supreme Court. **Strengths:** "He has a razor-sharp mind and excellent advocacy skills."

Nicholas Goodwin QC (Harcourt Chambers) Involved in complex private and public law proceedings, many of which involve abuse and the exploration of challenging medical evidence. He is a fine choice for contentious parental authority and guardianship disputes. **Strengths:** "He is just very smart and his client care is very good. He is a one-stop shop, as he does complex children matters and also finance work."

Gillian Geddes (2-3 Hind Court) Specialist children law practitioner who often handles cases involving cross-border considerations, vulnerable parties, child trafficking and allegations of serious non-accidental injury. **Strengths:** "Having previously worked as an in-house lawyer for local authorities, she has a very sound knowledge and experience of public law children cases, immigration and child trafficking issues. She is able to consider the cases she is involved in from all angles."

Helen Jefferson (2-3 Hind Court) Manages a diverse family practice encompassing matrimonial finance and private law children matters. She is particularly good on contact disputes and complex remedy proceedings. **Strengths:** "She is an excellent advocate with strong analytical skills, who has a first-rate bedside manner." "Very good when you need someone to fight for your client. She gives straighforward advice and is very good on her feet."

Sheena Cassidy (3PB Barristers) Frequently undertakes complex matrimonial finance proceedings and cohabitation disputes on behalf of high net worth clients. **Strengths:** "Great at negotiation and not pompous in her approach."

Jane Hoyal (1 Pump Court) Handles both private and public law children proceedings. Cases concerning abduction, adoption and allegations of abuse all form part of her practice.

Miranda Allardice (see p.534) (5 Stone Buildings) Marries expertise in international matrimonial finance law with skill in complex chancery cases. As a result she is often brought in on cases where trusts are an issue. **Strengths:** "She is empathetic and able to give sensible and pragmatic advice. Her advocacy skills are great and she won't take any nonsense from opponents."

Kerstin Boyd (see p.554) (Tanfield Chambers) A barrister experienced at dealing with all facets of family law. Her practice has a particular emphasis on complex and sizeable financial remedy disputes, and challenging private law children proceedings. **Strengths:** "She's very, very good with clients and a highly committed barrister."

MIDLANDS

Family/Matrimonial Midlands Leading Sets
Band 1
No5 Chambers *
St Ives Chambers *
St Philips Chambers *
Leading Silks
Band 1
MacDonald Alistair *St Philips Chambers* *
Meyer Lorna *No5 Chambers*
Weston Jeremy *St Ives Chambers* *
Band 2
Isaacs Elizabeth *St Ives Chambers* *
New Silks
McGrath Elizabeth *St Philips Chambers* *
Leading Juniors
Band 1
Abberley Stephen *St Philips Chambers* *
Brown Stephanie *No5 Chambers* [A]
Friel Michele *No5 Chambers*
James Christopher *No5 Chambers* [A]
Lopez Paul *St Ives Chambers*
McCabe Louise *St Philips Chambers* [A] *
Mullen Jayne *St Ives Chambers* *
Nosworthy Jonathan *St Philips Chambers* [A] *
Rowland Robin *No5 Chambers* [A]
Starks Nicholas *St Ives Chambers* *
Walker Elizabeth *St Philips Chambers* *
Wynne Ashley *No5 Chambers* [A]
Band 2
Adams Christopher *St Philips Chambers* *
Bache Nina *St Ives Chambers* *
Baker Caroline *No5 Chambers*
Bond Leisha *St Philips Chambers* *
Cole Nicholas *St Ives Chambers* *
Day Andrew *St Ives Chambers* *
Gilead Beryl *St Mary's Chambers (ORL)* ◊
Hadley Richard *No5 Chambers*
Haynes Matthew *St Ives Chambers* *
Lakin Tracy *St Ives Chambers* *
Maynard Matthew *St Ives Chambers* *
Meachin Vanessa *St Philips Chambers* [A] *
Messling Lawrence *St Philips Chambers*
Nuvoloni Stefano *No5 Chambers* *
Page Nigel *St Mary's Chambers (ORL)* ◊
Smallwood Anne E *No5 Chambers*
Up-and-coming individuals
Gallacher Kirsty *No5 Chambers* *
* *Indicates set / individual with profile.*
◊ *(ORL) = Other Ranked Lawyer.*
[A] *direct access (see p.11).*
Alphabetical order within each band. Band 1 is highest.

Band 1

No5 Chambers
See profile on p.883

THE SET

No5 Chambers continues to enjoy a reputation as one of the leading sets in the Midlands, with capabilities across the full spectrum of family law issues. Its strong team of matrimonial finance specialists continue to be regarded as "pre-eminent in Birmingham and very well regarded nationally," particularly in complex and high-value matters. The set also boasts a growing reputation in both public and private law children work, including complicated care proceedings.

Client service: "The senior clerk, Tony McDaid, is well known for running a very efficient set of chambers and being in tune with current developments."

SILKS

Lorna Meyer QC Heads the set's family law team and regularly undertakes cases concerning international child disputes, child abduction and complex care proceedings. She acts for children, guardians and local authorities in often highly sensitive disputes. **Strengths:** "Lorna's attention to detail is spectacular – her notes are amazing." "She is totally unflappable." **Recent work:** Appeared in the recent Court of Appeal case of Re: W (A Child).

JUNIORS

Christopher James Enjoys a strong reputation as a finance specialist with the ability to handle cases of significant complexity, including those with overseas assets and corporate structures. He also undertakes private law children work and takes instructions on a direct access basis. **Strengths:** "A strong advocate who provides excellent client care and thorough case preparation." "Pragmatic and practical – clients are in safe hands."

Ashley Wynne Wins praise for his expertise in financial remedy proceedings, particularly matters with issues around inheritance, pensions or trusts. He is also noted for his knowledge of the law surrounding cohabitation disputes. **Strengths:** "An excellent advocate who is always calm, even under pressure." "Very safe pair of hands and brilliant with clients."

Caroline Baker Highly regarded in the public law arena, she frequently handles sensitive care proceedings and international child abduction matters. She also practises in the area of ancillary relief. **Strengths:** "Excellent for care work."

Stephanie Brown Continues to excel in complex financial remedy cases, including those with business and trust elements. She regularly appears in the High Court and Court of Appeal, acting for high net worth clients, including those from the agricultural sector. **Strengths:** "Stephanie is a very strong advocate who fights her client's corner with gusto." "She has a very empathetic, human approach to cases."

Michele Friel Wins praise for her handling of sensitive and complex public and private law children cases involving allegations of non-accidental injury, domestic violence and sexual abuse. She regularly acts for children, guardians and local authorities, and is experienced in the cross-examination of medical witnesses. **Strengths:** "First choice for children work." "She has that combination of an ability to be sensible and try to sort out the issues, but where that is not possible, she is a determined competitor."

Robin Rowland Receives plaudits for his ability to handle even the most complex of financial disputes. He regularly appears in the High Court and Court of Appeal, where peers have noted his composed demeanour and measured approach to cases. **Strengths:** "His presentation, orally and on paper, is immaculate. He is quick on his feet and seems to have the skills of an accountant as well as being a very persuasive advocate." "He is exceptionally knowledgeable and a true gentleman."

Stefano Nuvoloni (see p.683) Maintains a strong reputation as a specialist childcare practitioner who is regularly instructed in complex public law proceedings. He receives praise for his sensitive handling of cases involving non-accidental death, serious injury and abuse. **Strengths:** "He can pursue a case thoroughly and doggedly but retains a sense of humour throughout." "He is a very effective advocate."

Anne Smallwood Recognised for her expertise in ancillary relief matters, often handling cases with significant corporate or agricultural assets. **Strengths:** "A tenacious advocate who is always well prepared. She is very persuasive."

Richard Hadley Held in high regard for his work representing local authorities across the country in care proceedings involving non-accidental injury and fabricated illness. He also acts for parents and children, and is recognised for his expertise in cases involving immigration issues. **Strengths:** "He is really good with the client – they trust him, as he exudes confidence." "Very calm under pressure."

Kirsty Gallacher (see p.605) Quickly building a reputation in the public law children arena, regularly receiving instructions in cases involving allegations of injury, abuse or the death of a parent. She is singled out by peers for her empathetic manner with emotional clients. **Strengths:** "She has got flair and goes the extra mile." "She has been terrific in terms of client skills."

St Ives Chambers
See profile on p.885

THE SET

St Ives Chambers remains a firm favourite of many instructing solicitors in the Midlands, but is also "becoming a nationally recognised family chambers." Its members are particularly well regarded in children matters, boasting two specialist children silks, as well as a strong team of juniors. The set is also forging a reputation in the region for its "particularly strong finance team."

Client service: "The clerks are fantastic – they move heaven and earth for us. They have never let us down."

SILKS

Jeremy Weston QC (see p.749) A renowned child law specialist who is regularly instructed in the most complex of cases involving the death of children, serious non-accidental injury or sexual abuse. Acts for children, guardians and local authorities at all levels, including appellate work in the Court of Appeal. **Strengths:** "He is a skilled and intelligent advocate." **Recent work:** Appeared in the widely publicised case concerning the murder of schoolboy Daniel Pelka by his mother and her partner.

Elizabeth Isaacs QC (see p.636) Continues to be regarded as a go-to barrister for complex children matters involving death and serious injury. A former social worker, she is singled out for her depth of knowledge of child protection issues. **Strengths:** "She was a social worker and that comes out in her ability to make a client feel at ease." "She has a keen interest in the academic side of litigation and is a thorough and versatile advocate."

JUNIORS

Andrew Day (see p.585) Noted for his expertise in finance disputes between married or cohabiting partners, particularly those involving property or complicated onshore and offshore trust assets. He typically acts for high net worth individuals. **Strengths:** "He has a good, clear and concise manner with clients and a very tenacious manner in court." "We like him for technical cases – he is good at pulling out the detail from case law."

Jayne Mullen (see p.679) Acts for high net worth individuals including prominent business leaders and sports stars in financial remedy cases. She is well versed in cases involving pension provision and trust elements. **Strengths:** "Top of the tree in Birmingham, particularly with high-value financial remedy matters with complex accounting." "A real powerhouse in complex financial disputes."

Nicholas Starks (see p.727) Highly regarded in family financial provision matters, and particularly strong in ancillary relief claims. He wins praise for his technical skill and attention to detail. **Strengths:** "He has been up against a few silks and has wiped the floor with them." "He is absolutely superb and has a lot of gravitas."

Nicholas Cole (see p.575) Was elected head of chambers in May 2013, and is well respected in the area of matrimonial finance, particularly cases involving TOLATA. He also brings his science background to bear in his handling of cases with a medical element, including non-accidental injury.

Matthew Maynard (see p.665) Acts for children, parents and local authorities in complex care proceedings. He is recognised for his ability to communicate effectively with both High Court judges and lay clients. **Strengths:** "Matthew is destined for great things." "A breath of fresh air."

Paul Lopez Maintains a distinguished reputation in children matters, including cases involving non-accidental injury, sexual abuse and sudden death, including shaken baby syndrome. He garners praise for his experience in cases with medical evidence. **Strengths:** "He is silk in all but name. I've seen him with the most awkward clients and he just owns the room." "A calm and sensible pair of hands. He is always extremely thorough and able to present a case in a calm and reasoned fashion."

Tracy Lakin (see p.649) Represents children, parents and guardians in both public and private law Children Act proceedings. **Strengths:** "She has got a very quiet manner of advocacy but it is very effective." "Tracy deals with sensitive childcare cases in a very professional and client-focused manner."

Matthew Haynes (see p.622) Recognised for his strength in financial relief cases and matters involving trusts of land, which he handles as part of a broader practice that includes commercial dispute resolution, housing and property law. **Strengths:** "Matthew is an articulate and no-nonsense advocate who presents his case with the ear of the court and delivers in a cool, calm, collected and extremely measured way." **Recent work:** Acted for an offshore company group in a case involving the issue of the inclusion of companies in nuptial settlements.

Nina Bache (see p.540) Making waves in the public law arena, she is recognised for her representation of guardians and local authorities in care proceedings. She is noted for her ability to handle work beyond her level of call. **Strengths:** "She is really making her mark in heavier High Court work."

St Philips Chambers

See profile on p.886

THE SET

Housing 52 specialist family counsel, St Philips Chambers is recognised as "a big set with a broad range of work" and "very strong individuals." Its members are known for their ability to handle all aspects of family law, from complex care proceedings to high net worth ancillary relief. The set also offers a mediation service and accepts direct access instructions.

Client service: "The clerking team on the family side, led by Mark Mansell, is fabulous. Mark is the best clerk I've ever worked with – he's always willing to negotiate a fee and will move heaven and earth to make the right people available for you. He never over-promises but always delivers when he says he is going to."

SILKS

Alistair MacDonald QC (see p.659) Maintains a distinguished reputation in children matters, particularly complex private law cases. He remains the first choice of many childcare solicitors, who appreciate his technical skill and measured approach to sensitive facts. **Strengths:** "He is a High Court judge in the making – the pre-eminent silk in Birmingham." "The cream of the Children Law Bar."

Elizabeth McGrath QC (see p.668) Has dual expertise in ancillary relief and Children Act matters. Commentators single her out for her "devastating" skills of cross-examination. **Strengths:** "A great legal brain." "If there's a fight to be had she won't back away but if there's a deal to be done she'll get it done."

JUNIORS

Elizabeth Walker (see p.745) Acts for children, parents and local authorities in childcare proceedings. She is praised for her sensible approach to child protection issues. **Strengths:** "She is a passionate and articulate advocate who is well liked by the judiciary." "A tough fighter with very good client skills."

Jonathan Nosworthy (see p.683) A highly regarded finance specialist with particular skill in handling cases with hidden assets. He typically acts for professionals and those in the agricultural sector. **Strengths:** "Approachable and pragmatic, with an outstanding ability to understand and prepare a case which is used to great effect in cross-examination." "Easy to approach and excellent with clients."

Christopher Adams (see p.531) Recognised for his strength in public law child care matters. **Strengths:** "He is a really straightforward and measured opponent." "He has a consistently professional manner dealing with both lay and professional witnesses and an exceptionally courteous and helpful approach in the conduct of court matters."

Louise McCabe (see p.666) Has particular expertise in complex financial remedy proceedings with business assets, property portfolios and jurisdiction issues. She specialises in matrimonial finance and inquest law, and sits as both deputy coroner and deputy district judge. **Strengths:** "A tenacious advocate who gives sound financial advice." "Brilliant on her feet."

Leisha Bond (see p.552) Strong finance practice with the ability to handle cases involving businesses, pensions and farming assets. She also undertakes children work, primarily private law cases. **Strengths:** "Treads the path between being conciliatory and standing firm on a key issue." "She is fantastic."

Lawrence Messling Heads the family practice at St Philips Chambers and is known for his expertise in complicated public law children cases. He regularly advises local authorities on procedural issues, and is known for his adept handling of serious fact-finding hearings, including those involving the death of a child. **Strengths:** "A very articulate, persuasive advocate." "He carries a seniority that gives him authority."

Stephen Abberley (see p.531) Held in high regard for his expertise in care proceedings, including cases involving child death, serious abuse or factitious illness. He also wins praise for his handling of financial matters. **Strengths:** "He really gets to grips with the arguments." "I use him regularly and am always very impressed."

Vanessa Meachin (see p.669) Praised for her capabilities across all manner of financial matters and children work. Instructing solicitors are quick to point out her calmness under pressure. **Strengths:** "A well-prepared and robust advocate; very client-friendly and skilled at cross-examination." "She does everything in family law and handles it all brilliantly."

Other Ranked Lawyers

Beryl Gilead (St Mary's Chambers) Focuses her practice in public law children proceedings. She has particular expertise in cases with medical issues. **Strengths:** "She does a lot of local authority work and is well trusted."

Nigel Page (St Mary's Chambers) Continues to specialise in financial matters with unusual or complicated asset structures including businesses, property portfolios and agricultural assets. **Strengths:** "Exceptionally thorough with great attention to detail, a good manner with clients and a good negotiator as well." "Extremely sound, reliable and client-friendly."

NORTH EASTERN

Family/Matrimonial North Eastern Leading Sets
Band 1
Broadway House
Trinity Chambers *
Zenith Chambers
Leading Silks
Band 1
Lee Taryn *37 Park Square Chambers (ORL)* ◊
Band 2
Hayes John *Zenith Chambers*
Leading Juniors
Band 1
Cole Robert *Broadway House*
Hajimitsis Anthony *Zenith Chambers*
Isaacs Paul *Broadway House* *
Richardson James *Trinity Chambers* *
Saxton Nicola *St Pauls Chambers (ORL)* ◊
Wood Martin *Broadway House*
Band 2
Astbury Joanne *Parklane Plowden (ORL)* ◊
Bickerdike Roger *Zenith Chambers*
Knox Christopher *Trinity Chambers* *
Oliver Crispin *Dere Street Barristers (ORL)* ◊ *
Power Nick *Broadway House*
Shaw Nicola *Trinity Chambers* *
Spain Timothy *Trinity Chambers* *
Swiffen Guy *Parklane Plowden (ORL)* ◊
Band 3
Allman Marisa *Zenith Chambers*
Brown James *Dere Street Barristers (ORL)* ◊
Campbell Diane *Dere Street Barristers (ORL)* ◊
Glover Stephen J *37 Park Square Chambers (ORL)* ◊
Gray Justin *Trinity Chambers* *
Hargan James *Sovereign Chambers (ORL)* ◊
Marson Denise *Sovereign Chambers (ORL)* ◊
McCallum Louise *Zenith Chambers*
Murden Claire *Sovereign Chambers (ORL)* ◊
Myers John *Zenith Chambers*
Prest Charles *No 6 Park Square Chambers (ORL)* ◊
Shaw Elizabeth *37 Park Square Chambers (ORL)* ◊
Shelton Gordon *Broadway House*
Stanistreet Penelope *St Johns Buildings (ORL)* ◊
Stonor Nicholas *Trinity Chambers* *
Todd Martin *Dere Street Barristers (ORL)* ◊
Up-and-coming individuals
Checa-Dover Olivia *KBW (ORL)* ◊
Donnelly Lewis *Zenith Chambers*
Garnham Clare *Zenith Chambers*
◊ (ORL) = Other Ranked Lawyer.
** Indicates set / individual with profile.*

Band 1

Broadway House

THE SET

Broadway House remains at the forefront of family law in the North East. The set deals with all aspects of family law, but is particularly acclaimed for its expertise in delivering financial remedies. Its standing in the market is reflected by the high-value cases in which it is instructed.

JUNIORS

Paul Isaacs (see p.636) Widely known on the circuit for his work in matrimonial finance cases. His practise is focused on high-value ancillary relief matters. **Strengths:** "He will always fight a client's corner and his courtroom advocacy is legendary." "He is well prepared, thorough and hugely forensic."

Robert Cole Renowned for his proficiency in resolving high net worth matrimonial financial disputes. His previous work in accountancy appeals to solicitors, who regularly instruct him for high-profile clients in financial proceedings. **Strengths:** "He is a straight-talking barrister who has a background in accountancy so is excellent with figures. He cuts straight through to the detail."

Martin Wood Practises predominantly in ancillary relief matters for both spouses and civil partners. He is noted as a leader in the field of family law with a wealth of experience in dealing with high asset value cases. **Strengths:** "He is a key player in Leeds, and someone that you would expect to see on a high-quality case." "He is very experienced in financial relief and is regarded as a leader in the field."

Nick Power Demonstrates particular aptitude in financial proceedings but is also recognised for his practice in Children Act matters. His personal style is an asset to Broadway House; he is acclaimed as being both highly personable with clients and formidable in court. **Strengths:** "He is an approachable and engaging barrister who really fights his client's corner in court. He is a pleasure to work with. He is straight-talking and inspires confidence in his lay clients and instructing solicitors."

Gordon Shelton Well versed in all aspects of family law, ranging from complex matrimonial relief applications to complex children's proceedings. He is renowned for resolving the most challenging of cases and is praised by instructing solicitors for his creative approach. **Strengths:** "He is a strong practitioner in care work. You can throw anything at him and he'll remain calm and unflustered." "He is a very capable practitioner who demonstrates a sound intellect in his approach to cases."

Trinity Chambers

See profile on p.927

THE SET

Trinity Chambers is widely recognised on the North Eastern Circuit for its breadth of expertise in family law. Its high-calibre family team is accomplished in areas spanning challenging ancillary proceedings to sensitive children matters for a variety of lay, professional and high-profile clients.

Client service: "Its clerks, led by Alison Dickason, and reception staff are very efficient and helpful. They are a credit to the Chambers."

JUNIORS

James Richardson (see p.707) Specialises in financial disputes concerning matrimonial matters and cohabitation issues. He works with a wide variety of clients on high-value proceedings, and is particularly renowned for his meticulous and vigorous approach to his practice. **Strengths:** "He is silently lethal – well prepared and uber-confident, providing great financial counsel." "In his practice he is tenacious and forensically thorough."

Christopher Knox (see p.647) Handles a number of family finance matters on behalf of high net worth clients, and is noted for undertaking particularly challenging cases. He has a wealth of experience in dealing with ancillary relief proceedings and is highly praised for his innovative advocacy style. **Strengths:** "He fights his corner time and again. He is excellent at cross-examination." "He thinks outside of the box and his cross-examination is superb."

Nicola Shaw (see p.718) Regularly instructed on matrimonial disputes. She is particularly noted for her training in collaborative law, and her client-friendly approach and innovative thinking set her apart from other practitioners in the field. **Strengths:** "She sits as a Deputy District Judge and provides good, solid advice in financial cases. She is very accessible and takes a real interest in the case." "She is thoughtful, very client-friendly and a pleasure to work with."

Timothy Spain (see p.725) Focuses predominantly on ancillary relief issues. His reputation is centred on his expertise in matrimonial finance matters, and he is also well regarded for the plethora of work he has conducted involving vulnerable children and adults. **Strengths:** "He is excellent with his clients and gets impressive results." "He exhibits excellent attention to detail, as well as a commitment to great client care."

Justin Gray (see p.614) Focuses his practice on children law, although he is also highly respected for his handling of Court of Protection matters involving vulnerable adults. He has succeeded in establishing himself as a proficient child care practitioner and has considerable expertise in cases which feature cross-border aspects. **Strengths:** "He is an excellent advocate who gets immediately to the core of an issue."

Nicholas Stonor (see p.729) Demonstrates specialist expertise in cases that have particularly complex medical components to the evidence. He frequently acts on behalf of guardians and family members, and is praised for his ability to establish an easy rapport with his clients. **Strengths:** "He pays close attention to detail, and is always forensic and thorough in his preparation. He is a formidable adversary who is unfailingly courteous."

Zenith Chambers

THE SET

Zenith Chambers has cemented itself as a leading set for family law in the North East. It is most highly recognised for its work in challenging and sensitive care work for both children and adults, although the barristers here are proficient at dealing with all family law matters, including high-value family finance issues.

Client service: "Their administrative support is excellent. Rebecca Hartley, who acts as the senior family clerk, ensures that the client care is second to none."

SILKS

John Hayes QC Highly regarded for his practice at the heavy end of children's proceedings in public law. He is a vastly experienced practitioner who is frequently instructed on significant and sensitive cases concerning child abuse and child deaths. **Strengths:** "He is an extremely accomplished advocate. He has the ear of the court and deals exclusively with children work." **Recent work:** His advice on a potential revision to the phrasing of section 31 of the Children Act 1989 was sought and cited within a parliamentary debate in the House of Lords in December 2013.

JUNIORS

Anthony Hajimitsis Deals exclusively with matrimonial financial cases, particularly those involving international elements and those concerning high net worth individuals. He is praised for his courtroom manner as well as his negotiation skills, and his methodical approach to each case is greatly valued by instructing solicitors. **Strengths:** "He inspires full confidence from the clients. He is always very well prepared and doesn't raise the temperature. He just deals with things in a very straightforward manner." "He is exceptionally thorough and perfect for complex, high net worth cases where he grasps the issues quickly and with remarkable efficiency."

Roger Bickerdike Specialises in children's proceedings and ancillary relief cases. He demonstrates particular aptitude for more complex cases concerning the cross-border relocation of children. He is renowned for his professional yet personable manner with clients, and for delivering the results that they seek. **Strengths:** "He is very approachable and a pleasure to work with." "He is a superb advocate – very clear and very thorough." **Recent work:** Achieved the resolution of a complex, prolonged financial dispute issue in a lottery jackpot case.

John Myers Renowned for his work in both private and public children law. He demonstrates specific expertise in issues with international aspects, particularly child abduction and relocation cases. He has represented local authorities, relatives and guardians, and has a wealth of experience in dealing with expert witnesses. **Strengths:** "He is a tenacious advocate."

Marisa Allman Displays particular expertise in family finance cases. She is also noted for her considerable expertise in child abduction cases. **Strengths:** "She is quite tough and can certainly stand her ground. Her approach with the court is very successful, and her approach with clients is measured, balanced and well accepted." "She is not only very courteous, but very thorough." **Recent work:** Instructed in a complex cohabitation dispute involving assets of £2-3 million.

Louise McCallum Handles all family law matters, in both public and private law. She is regarded as an expert in forced marriage cases and has considerable experience in dealing with sensitive child abuse proceedings. **Strengths:** "She is a bright advocate who is an expert on forced marriages – she quite literally wrote the book it."

Lewis Donnelly Appears frequently on public law child care cases, many of which feature problematic medical evidence. The calibre of his caseload belies his relatively junior year of call, and he is regularly instructed on behalf of family members in child welfare proceedings. **Strengths:** "He is a passionate advocate. The skills and experience that he possesses at his age are phenomenal. He is well beyond his years."

Clare Garnham Specialises in multifaceted, highly sensitive child welfare proceedings. She regularly represents clients with disabilities and is highly sought after for her impressive courtroom manner. **Strengths:** "You cannot fault Clare. Her manner with her clients is brilliant and, coupled with that, her advocacy is excellent. Others are in awe of how she commands the courtroom."

Other Ranked Lawyers

Crispin Oliver (see p.685) (Dere Street Barristers) Specialises in financial relief and property disputes after separations. He also has considerable experience in representing children in public law matters. **Strengths:** "He is always incredibly well prepared, and he has a wonderful manner. He never gives up, and he's great on his feet."

James Brown (Dere Street Barristers) Focuses on Court of Protection matters and care proceedings for vulnerable clients. He acts on behalf of all parties within welfare cases, but principally represents local authorities. **Recent work:** Acted on behalf of a father who was accused of the drugging and attempted suffocation of his son. Medical elements of the case complicated the hearing.

Diane Campbell (Dere Street Barristers) Represents a wide variety of clients in both public and private children law matters. She displays particular expertise in cases that involve serious allegations of harm. **Strengths:** "She fights her corner very well, and in addition to that she is a good negotiator. She's very good on her feet." "She is a fierce advocate."

Martin Todd (Dere Street Barristers) Specialises in public child care matters. He focuses his practice on cases involving non-accidental injury, but is also known for his work within private law abduction and adoption proceedings. **Strengths:** "He is very competent, and indefatigable in the face of adversity." "He is very experienced and well regarded in family law."

Olivia Checa-Dover (KBW) Handles the full range of family law matters, with a particular specialism in sensitive public and private law children cases. She is instructed on behalf of a wide variety of parties, but has specialist experience in representing vulnerable victims of sexual abuse. **Strengths:** "She is excellent in the way she deals with clients." "She is very prompt with attendance notes and good with her clients as well, particularly in children matters."

Charles Prest (No 6 Park Square Chambers) Well versed in all areas of family law, but specialises in challenging children law matters. He has represented children in a number of high-profile cases, often involving medical complications and serious allegations of harm. **Strengths:** "He is phenomenally bright, very instinctive, and known for annihilating his opposition." "He is comfortable working on cases of the most serious nature. He is a safe pair of hands."

Taryn Lee QC (37 Park Square Chambers) Demonstrates considerable skill in handling sensitive family cases. She is particularly noted for her work in cases centred around highly contentious abuse evidence, and she has a wealth of experience in cross-examining child witnesses and representing a variety of vulnerable clients. **Strengths:** "She is a very capable advocate. She is approachable, works very hard, and sets out the information very clearly in court." **Recent work:** She successfully attained evidence that a parent had fabricated and induced illness in her child. This case was further complicated by pre-existing medical problems within the child that served to create further difficulty for healthcare expert witnesses.

Stephen Glover (37 Park Square Chambers) Regularly handles complex financial resolution cases concerning cohabitation disputes, trusts and inheritance issues.

Elizabeth Shaw (37 Park Square Chambers) Specialises in child care cases. She has particular expertise in dealing with proceedings concerning serious allegations of harm, and is widely known for working with clients with disabilities. **Strengths:** "She is very capable and very good with her clients. She has a good approach to her cases." "She is a very compassionate advocate."

Joanne Astbury (Parklane Plowden) Handles all aspects of family law but has noted expertise in care proceedings within public law. She regularly represents vulnerable clients, particularly children, in complex cases. **Strengths:** "She is a very fierce advocate, with very sound judgement. She sits as a recorder, so has the advantage of hearing cases, as well as being an advocate."

Guy Swiffen (Parklane Plowden) Renowned for his practice in sensitive, multifaceted child care proceedings. He represents a broad portfolio of clients and is well regarded on the North Eastern Circuit for his expertise in children law. **Strengths:** "He is highly rated by everyone as a very persuasive advocate."

James Hargan (Sovereign Chambers) Prominent in public law child care cases. He is particularly experienced with proceedings that involve challenging medical evidence, specifically non-accidental injury cases. **Strengths:** "He is a very experienced advocate. He is very good in both written and oral advocacy." "He is excellent in both the cross-examination of witnesses and his understanding of his cases."

Denise Marson (Sovereign Chambers) Practises principally in complex children's proceedings, usually involving elements of intentional harm and sexual abuse. She is particularly adept in cases that involve mental health complications. **Strengths:** "She is excellent; very thorough and to the point. She has very good advocacy and cross-examinations skills." "She is very personable and client-focused. She is a good advocate, and always remains focused on what the client needs."

Claire Murden (Sovereign Chambers) Focuses primarily on child care cases, and has a noted specialism in sensitive proceedings that involve serious harm and infant death. She is praised extensively for her outstanding advocacy style. **Strengths:** "She is certainly one of the brighter, younger members of the Bar. She is very hard-working, with a good courtroom manner." **Recent work:** Acted as junior counsel for the local authority on a case where two parents had allegedly introduced their child into a paedophile ring. Final care arrangements were commended by the judge for their ingenuity.

Penelope Stanistreet (St Johns Buildings) Focuses on all proceedings within children law, particularly cases that involve contentious medical evidence. She represents a very diverse client base, and receives instructions from local authorities, guardians and parents. **Strengths:** "She is a tough cookie in a very pleasant way. She is nice to be against in court." "She is a solid and consistent advocate."

Nicola Saxton (St Pauls Chambers) Practises predominantly on high-value matrimonial finance relief cases for high net worth individuals, and is widely praised for her excellent courtroom manner. **Strengths:** "She is a phenomenal advocate who battles hard for her clients and achieves excellent results." "She is one of the best counsels in the area. She is strident, well read, and a very good advocate."

NORTHERN

Family/Matrimonial Northern Leading Sets	
Band 1	
Deans Court Chambers *	
St Johns Buildings *	
Leading Silks	
Band 1	
Harrison Sally	*St Johns Buildings*
Band 2	
Cross Jane	*Deans Court Chambers*
Grocott Susan	*Deans Court Chambers*
Heaton Frances	*St Johns Buildings*
Irving Gillian	*15 Winckley Square (ORL)* ◊
Rowley Karl	*St Johns Buildings*
Leading Juniors	
Band 1	
Brody Karen	*Deans Court Chambers*
Eastwood Charles P	*St Johns Buildings*
Fordham Judith	*Exchange Chambers (ORL)* ◊
Murray Ashley	*Ashley Murray Chambers (ORL)* ◊
Band 2	
Bennett Martyn	*Oriel Chambers (ORL)* ◊
Bowcock Samantha	*15 Winckley Square (ORL)* ◊
Deas Susan	*Deans Court Chambers*
Fothergill Francesca	*Deans Court Chambers*
Guirguis Sheren	*Exchange Chambers (ORL)* ◊
Kloss Alexander W	*St Johns Buildings*
Reade Kevin	*7 Harrington St Chambers (ORL)* ◊
Band 3	
Birtles Samantha	*18 St John Street (ORL)* ◊ *
Cavanagh Lorraine	*St Johns Buildings*
Gee Caroline	*Exchange Chambers (ORL)* ◊
Gregory Karen	*Exchange Chambers (ORL)* ◊
Heppenstall Rachael	*9 St John Street (ORL)* ◊
Hillas Samantha	*St Johns Buildings*
Murray Stephen J	*18 St John Street (ORL)* ◊ *
Woodward Alison	*Deans Court Chambers*
Up-and-coming individuals	
Greenhalgh Emma	*9 St John Street (ORL)* ◊

◊ (ORL) = Other Ranked Lawyer.

** Indicates set / individual with profile.*

Band 1

Deans Court Chambers
See profile on p.915

THE SET

The family group at Deans Court Chambers is widely regarded as one of the top teams on the Northern Circuit, boasting "an array of top counsel who provide a seamless service to the lay client." Its members are highly regarded across all aspects of family law, demonstrating in-depth expertise in financial matters as well as issues related to children.

Client service: "The family clerking team is particularly good."

SILKS

Jane Cross QC Enjoys a strong reputation for childcare work. She has particular expertise in cases involving the death, serious abuse or chronic neglect of children. **Strengths:** "She is up there with the very best."

Susan Grocott QC A leading practitioner in financial matters and the law relating to children. Instructing solicitors particularly appreciate her straightforward approach to cases. **Strengths:** "She would be my first port of call. She is direct and has a down-to-earth approach to things which is not commonly found."

JUNIORS

Alison Woodward Continues to forge a strong reputation in care proceedings and private law children's cases involving cultural issues. Acts for local authorities, parents and children. **Strengths:** "She's sensitive and able to put even the most difficult and distressed clients at ease."

Francesca Fothergill Specialises in finance matters and has particular expertise in farming disputes. She has a special interest in cases with an international element. **Strengths:** "She has sound judgement and is very articulate on her feet." "She clearly takes an interest in clients and their cases."

Karen Brody Receives widespread praise for her ancillary relief practice. Sources single her out for her incisive grasp of the issues and pragmatic negotiation skills. **Strengths:** "She oozes experience and possesses really sound judgement." "A strident and formidable advocate with excellent client care skills."

Susan Deas Enjoys a strong reputation in financial remedy following divorce. She has particular expertise in cases with substantial assets, often involving corporate structures, pensions and trust elements. **Strengths:** "She is a brilliant advocate and goes the extra mile."

St Johns Buildings
See profile on p.921

THE SET

St Johns Buildings is acclaimed on the Northern Circuit for the depth of its family team, spread across the North West in offices including Manchester, Liverpool and Chester. The large team includes three specialist family law silks and a formidable group of juniors. The set's money specialists offer expertise in heavy-duty finance work, while "the Children Act set is particularly strong, with some outstanding barristers."

Client service: "They will go the extra mile to accommodate us. If we have a client and want a certain barrister they will try to move diaries for us. They won't leave us in a difficult place."

SILKS

Sally Harrison QC Continues to lead the field in complicated financial matters. She remains a first choice for many instructing solicitors, who praise her ability to bring a human touch to high-value cases. **Strengths:** "She has always been head and shoulders above everyone else." "She is an absolute superstar. If you have a big money or complex case in the North West it's a race to instruct her first."

Karl Rowley QC Remains a popular choice for complicated children's matters, both public and private law. He acts for local authorities, guardians and children, and has a particular focus on cases with complicated medical evidence. **Strengths:** "Calm and unflappable, he identifies even the smallest detail and has extremely intricate technical knowledge." "A polished advocate with a calming and reassuring demeanour for clients."

Frances Heaton QC Regularly instructed in child protection cases of the most complex and serious nature, including sexual abuse, chronic neglect and murder. She has noted expertise in child abduction. **Strengths:** "She is lethal in court. She has got me incredible results." "An incisive advocate. Excellent for getting clients on the right track."

JUNIORS

Charles Eastwood Specialises in complicated financial matters with substantial assets. He is well versed in ancillary relief cases involving pension or trust elements. **Strengths:** "He has an incredible eye for detail and is a stunning advocate." He has phenomenal attention to detail, which inspires huge confidence from clients."

Alexander Kloss Enjoys a strong reputation in ancillary relief matters. Respected among his peers as a strong fighter with exceptional client care skills. **Strengths:** "He has a disarming manner which works with even the most difficult client, but he is no pushover and when on his feet is a smooth, persuasive advocate." "A good all-rounder with strong analytical skills, a reassuring manner with clients and excellent advocacy."

Lorraine Cavanagh Respected childcare practitioner whose wider expertise includes human rights and public law. She specialises in non-accidental injuries and cases with complicated medical evidence. **Strengths:** "She works tirelessly to fight a client's corner."

Samantha Hillas Renowned for her down-to-earth manner with clients in financial remedy proceedings. She typically undertakes cases involving farming assets or business structures. **Strengths:** "A charismatic and client-friendly advocate who determinedly achieves results while retaining a sense of humour."

Other Ranked Lawyers

Ashley Murray (Ashley Murray Chambers) Continues to enjoy a reputation as one of the Northern Circuit's most experienced practitioners in financial remedy proceedings. He focuses his practice on high net worth cases. **Strengths:** "His knowledge of the law is first-class. He is probably the most experienced counsel on the circuit and his reputation precedes him." "An erudite and persuasive advocate who deals with complex financial cases conscientiously and sensitively. A real star of the Merseyside Family Bar."

Sheren Guirguis (Exchange Chambers) Has a broad practice which includes financial matters as well as both public and private law children work, in which she acts for local authorities, parents and children. **Strengths:** "She is thorough on financial matters, making sure the figures are correct with forensic detail, but then taking a broad-brush approach to achieving settlement. I have not yet had a client who didn't think she was amazing."

Caroline Gee (Exchange Chambers) Handles financial disputes and private law children work. She is well versed in all manner of high-value money claims involving business interests, pensions and properties. Her private law childcare practice focuses on residence and contact applications. **Strengths:** "She is first-class in court and will stand her ground even with difficult and highly charged opponents."

Karen Gregory (Exchange Chambers) Focuses her practice on matrimonial finance disputes, specialising in high-value ancillary relief matters. **Strengths:** "Karen is wonderful and absolutely first-class." "She has meticulous attention to detail and perseveres with amazing patience."

Judith Fordham (Exchange Chambers) Enjoys an excellent reputation in complex financial work. She undertakes ancillary relief, Inheritance Act claims and TOLATA issues, and also handles Children Act applications as well as being a qualified family arbitrator. **Strengths:** "She is dedicated and well prepared, and has an excellent rapport with clients." "Judith is totally first-class. Her client manner is excellent, as is her court work."

Kevin Reade (7 Harrington St Chambers) Has wide-ranging expertise in all aspects of family law, enjoying a strong reputation across money matters, care proceedings and private law child cases. **Strengths:** "Kevin is very bright, extremely witty and a talented advocate. He has an imposing manner about him and uses his experience to best advantage." "He has a very sensible and straightforward approach."

Martyn Bennett (Oriel Chambers) Specialises in matrimonial finance, including a particular interest in high-value cases with novel points of law. He also undertakes related private law childcare work. **Strengths:** "He is old-school, he is bright, he is hard-working and he immerses himself in the job." "His preparation is second to none, and his knowledge, realism and measured approach earn him the respect he deserves from the judiciary."

Rachael Heppenstall (9 St John Street) A care and adoption specialist, she focuses on cases involving non-accidental injury and abuse. She acts for local authorities, children and vulnerable adults, including those with significant learning difficulties. **Strengths:** "She is thoroughly reliable and very sympathetic in care proceedings. Very down to earth."

Emma Greenhalgh (9 St John Street) Continues to develop a strong reputation as a talented advocate in public law child proceedings. She wins praise for her work ethic and client care. **Strengths:** "She is exceptionally well prepared and insightful, with good client care skills and an ability to argue her points effectively." "She is a rising star in that set of chambers."

Samantha Birtles (see p.550) (18 St John Street) Recognised for her dedication to children's work, in both the public and private law spheres.

Stephen Murray (see p.680) (18 St John Street) Commended by sources as a robust advocate in high-value finance cases with complicated asset structures. **Strengths:** "He can deal with complex money cases and he likes a fight." "A good lawyer with attention to detail, thoroughness and a very powerful advocate."

Gillian Irving QC (15 Winckley Square) Continues to enjoy a strong reputation in child protection work, drawing particular praise for her handling of cases with complex medical issues. She regularly acts for local authorities, parents and children, and has been appointed in public inquiries.

Samantha Bowcock (15 Winckley Square) Has extensive experience of acting for local authorities, guardians and children in complicated care proceedings involving non-accidental injuries or the death of a child. Her practice also includes private law children's work. **Strengths:** "She is very good in children's work."

SOUTH EASTERN

Family/Matrimonial South Eastern Leading Sets
Band 1
Crown Office Row *
Harcourt Chambers *
Leading Silks
Band 1
Judd Frances *Harcourt Chambers*
Vater John *Harcourt Chambers*
New Silks
Goodwin Nicholas *Harcourt Chambers*
◊ (ORL) = Other Ranked Lawyer.
* Indicates set / individual with profile.
🄰 direct access (see p.11).

Family/Matrimonial South Eastern Leading Juniors	
Band 1	Bundell Katharine *Octagon House Chambers (ORL)* ◊
Carrodus Gail *Huntercombe Chambers (ORL)* ◊	Claridge Rachael *Crown Office Row* 🄰
Hay Fiona *Harcourt Chambers*	Espley Susan *Fenners Chambers (ORL)* ◊
Tattersall Simon *Fenners Chambers (ORL)* ◊	Farrington Gemma *Stour Chambers (ORL)* ◊ *
Band 2	Hall Jeremy *42 Bedford Row (ORL)* ◊
Elliot Margot *Regency Chambers (ORL)* ◊	Hancock Maria *Westgate Chambers (ORL)* ◊
Gibbons Sarah *Harcourt Chambers*	Haywood Janet *Guildford Chambers (ORL)* ◊
Kefford Anthony *Octagon House Chambers (ORL)* ◊	King-Smith James *Crown Office Row*
Sampson Jonathan *Harcourt Chambers*	Marsden Andrew *East Anglian Chambers (ORL)* ◊
Sharghy Pegah *Crown Office Row*	Mehta Anita *Crown Office Row*
Smith Adam *Crown Office Row* 🄰	Porter Joanne *Stour Chambers (ORL)* ◊ *
Tahir Perican *1 King's Bench Walk (ORL)* ◊ *	Spinks Roderick *Fenners Chambers (ORL)* ◊
Band 3	Topping Caroline *6 Pump Court (ORL)* ◊
Adamson Louisa *Becket Chambers (ORL)* ◊ *	Vine Aidan *Harcourt Chambers*
Battie Eleanor *Crown Office Row*	Watson Duncan *1 Garden Court Family Law Chambers (ORL)* ◊ *
Brooke-Smith John *Trinity Chambers (ORL)* ◊	

Band 1

Crown Office Row

See profile on p.888

THE SET

This group of "absolutely outstanding barristers" comprises the local presence of London's 1 Crown Office Row. While offering expertise across the board of family matters, including inheritance, divorce and financial provision, the set is particularly recognised for its expertise in handling children law matters. Areas of experience include issues such as care proceedings, emergency protection orders and child abduction.

Client service: "The clerks, led by David Bingham, are brilliant, approachable and always get back to you. They are friendly, upbeat and don't mess around."

JUNIORS

Eleanor Battie Respected for her broad expertise in children matters. She is particularly noted for her expertise in private law children matters, and for her handling of sensitive matters involving domestic violence, drug abuse and mental health. **Strengths:** "Eleanor prepares really well and is so eloquent; she's fluid and puts the arguments in a very compelling way." "She's fantastic for both the client and solicitor. She goes over and above what she needs to do and makes clients feel comfortable."

Rachael Claridge Focuses her practice on children act matters, care proceedings and emergency applications, and earns particular praise for her representation of parents. **Strengths:** "Rachael is excellent technically and communicates well with clients."

Pegah Sharghy Recognised for her skill in dealing with complex and high-value financial cases. She is experienced in all aspects of matrimonial finance, including ancillary relief, pensions and matters relating to complex property and business assets. **Strengths:** "Pegah is my go-to for family. She's very good on complex financial work; she's responsive, good with clients and prepares well." "I rate her very highly. She's extremely capable and knows procedure inside out. She's calm under fire and good in a tight corner – someone you really want on your side."

Adam Smith Highly experienced in public law children matters. He is recognised for representing all parties, including children, in complex care cases such as those concerning non-accidental injury. **Strengths:** "He's exceptionally experienced, articulate and determined, providing an excellent service to clients and solicitors." "Adam is experienced, thorough and steady. He's good with complex matters and he knows what he's doing."

James King-Smith Particularly noted for his strength in the realm of matrimonial finance, commonly handling matters involving substantial assets. He is also respected for his increasing role as a mediator, providing a rounded service in the realm of family law. **Strengths:** "He's very thorough and technically good, and he's very gifted and pleasant to deal with." "He is efficient and courteous. James knows his cases and presents them very well."

Anita Mehta Recognised for her work on both the children and financial aspects of family law. She is capable of dealing with complex financial cases involving trusts, business assets and pensions, and of handling private law children matters such as residence and leave to remove issues. **Strengths:** "She's extremely enthusiastic and works well with clients and solicitors. She's gutsy and will stand up for herself if necessary." "Anita is an incredibly strong and tenacious advocate." **Recent work:** Acted for a respondent in the successful appeal of a placement order.

Harcourt Chambers

See profile on p.815

THE SET

The strength and breadth of expertise present at Harcourt Chambers allows clients and solicitors alike to "feel confident that a case is in safe hands." The set is equipped to deal with financial cases involving significant assets and international elements, while also handling sensitive public law children matters involving complex issues of abuse. It is particularly noted for being "ahead of the curve when it comes to client care, providing an excellent service and great advocate skills."

Client service: "I find the clerks very efficient and helpful. They are led by Judith Partington, who is particularly good. Nothing is ever too much trouble and they go out of their way to be supportive."

SILKS

John Vater QC Respected for his wide-reaching practice in silk and for his ability to handle high-profile clients and sensitive cases, such as those involving allegations of abuse. He wins strong praise for his skills in cross-examination, particularly in private law cases involving complex medical issues. **Strengths:** "John is very good. He's highly regarded in children work and if I want a champion I'd have him in mind." "He's exceptionally strong; he has a real grasp of medical detail and is a tenacious advocate. He absorbs detail astonishingly well and has a lot of experience in the field."

Frances Judd QC Particularly renowned for representing children and local authorities in a variety of public and private law matters. She is praised for her ability to deal with vulnerable clients in relation to issues of violence and sexual abuse, as well as complex matters of surrogacy, relocation and abduction. **Strengths:** "She is patient and client-focused, while maintaining the confidence and respect of the judges she appears before." "Her cross-examination was fantastic and the client was thrilled. She's very down to earth when dealing with vulnerable clients. She handles sensitive matters well but is straight with her advice." **Recent work:** Acted in a complex case in which a parent was alleged to have exaggerated and induced medical symptoms in a child with serious disabilities.

Nicholas Goodwin QC Recognised for his work in the broad spectrum of family law matters, with notable expertise in financial disputes and complex public law care cases. His clients regularly include local authorities, children and parents. **Strengths:** "Nicholas is very well balanced; he thinks things through and is brilliant with the clients." "His attention to detail is second to none – nothing escapes him."

JUNIORS

Fiona Hay Highly regarded for her ancillary relief-focused practice, with market observers routinely praising her attention to detail and precise preparation in complex financial cases. She is also noted for her expertise in family law disputes with pensions or family business aspects. **Strengths:** "Fiona is excellent. She gives the client a lot of confidence and manages to translate the law so that clients can understand it." "She's pragmatic and consistent, and gets down to the issues very quickly."

Jonathan Sampson Represents local authorities, parents and guardians in a range of children and financial matters, and is praised for his representation of vulnerable clients and for dealing with complex issues. He is particularly noted for his expertise in Children Act matters, cohabitation disputes, and residence and contact order applications. **Strengths:** "He is so calm in the hotseat. His knowledge is second to none and he is very eloquent." "Jonathan has an excellent understanding of the law and is brilliant with the clients."

Aidan Vine Recognised for his capability in dealing with issues of complex human rights, as well as cases with international facets. He is particularly noted for his work on children matters, especially those regarding care, adoption and non-accidental injuries. **Strengths:** "His command of human rights law is second to none. He's incredibly well prepared and is not afraid to pursue difficult points." "Aidan is a skilled advocate and a hard worker, but is also very personable and good with clients. He gives the profession an excellent name."

Sarah Gibbons Handles a broad range of matrimonial issues, including cases involving children and financial matters. The emphasis of her practice is on financial cases, in relation to both matrimonial and cohabitation issues, while she also maintains a respected presence in child care and placement matters. **Strengths:** "She's calm, knowledgeable and pragmatic. She can see the bigger picture and takes the time to explain what's going on to clients."

Other Ranked Lawyers

Louisa Adamson (see p.531) (Becket Chambers) Garners particular praise for her work with vulnerable clients such as young mothers, in relation to children matters involving allegations of neglect and non-accidental injury. She also has expertise in children and financial issues stemming from divorce and separation. **Strengths:** "She has a very gentle nature but fights a case really well. She takes cases very seriously and is able to explain things clearly to clients." "Louisa is very experienced and comes across well with clients. She's fantastic, especially with public law and ancillary relief matters."

Jeremy Hall (42 Bedford Row) Skilled advocate across a broad range of matters, including ancillary relief and public law children cases. He has experience of complex financial cases involving business assets, trusts and pensions, and represents parents and children in cases involving allegations of abuse. **Strengths:** "He has an excellent client manner and is extremely thorough in his preparation and delivery." "He is a very solid advocate. He puts his case subtly but with the best impact."

Andrew Marsden (East Anglian Chambers) Respected for his work on the financial aspects of matrimonial law. He has particular expertise in family property disputes involving trusts, probate and inheritance matters. **Strengths:** "A force to be reckoned with."

Simon Tattersall (Fenners Chambers) Recognised for his expertise in areas such as ancillary relief, inheritance, cohabitation disputes and Children Act matters. He is well versed in handling cases with complex business and commercial aspects, as well as those involving pensions. **Strengths:** "He's very thorough and really cares about getting the right outcome."

Susan Espley (Fenners Chambers) Noted for her representation of vulnerable clients in matters involving complex issues of abuse and mental health. She represents a broad spectrum of clients, including parents, children's guardians and local authorities, in both private and public children law matters. **Strengths:** "The go-to barrister for children matters in the Cambridgeshire region. She has a reassuring manner with clients. She's very down to earth and approachable outside of court, but, when required, she's tenacious in the courtroom."

Roderick Spinks (Fenners Chambers) Receives praise for his work in a number of areas, including ancillary relief, private children matters and claims of unmarried couples. He is recognised for handling cases with both complex business assets and sensitive children and domestic violence issues. **Strengths:** "He's extremely capable and effective."

Duncan Watson (see p.747) (1 Garden Court Family Law Chambers) Areas of excellence include financial remedy, private law children matters and cohabitation disputes. He has an impressive track record in complex and high-value matters, as well as those involving trusts and inheritances. **Strengths:** "He does everything very thoroughly and is particularly good on complex cases with hidden assets." "The judges know him well and they respect him because they know he is a good advocate who pursues sensible arguments."

Janet Haywood (Guildford Chambers) Handles a wide range of family law cases, including those involving children matters, finance and domestic abuse issues. She often represents parents in proceedings against local authorities, and deals with financial cases involving issues of disclosure.

Gail Carrodus (Huntercombe Chambers) Particularly noted for her work on complex financial matters. She is capable of handling cases with high values and international aspects, and is considered a first choice by many instructing solicitors. **Strengths:** "She's powerful and fights her client's corner, and she's very nice to work with."

Perican Tahir (see p.733) (1 King's Bench Walk) Acts on the full range of family and matrimonial issues, such as financial and cohabitation disputes as well as matters concerning children. She is particularly noted for her work on high-value and complex ancillary relief matters. **Strengths:** "Perican is exceptionally client-friendly and very personable. She is a skilled negotiator in and out of court; she's an all-rounder and is exceptional across the board." "She's quick on the uptake and very thorough, and she has a polite way of refusing to be thrown off course. She works incredibly hard and has a good manner with clients."

Anthony Kefford (Octagon House Chambers) Widely respected for his practice spanning all aspects of family law. He is particularly noted for his work in financial matters, with particular expertise in ancillary relief. **Strengths:** "A robust and sound advocate."

Katharine Bundell (Octagon House Chambers) Handles a broad range of family law matters. She is particularly noted for her expertise in financial matters regarding trusts. **Strengths:** "She's extremely thorough and diligent. She's a good advocate and a good negotiator, and she's very good with clients."

Caroline Topping (6 Pump Court) Experienced in representing both parents and children in private and public law matters. She is increasingly involved in care work and contact matters, as well as cases involving non-accidental injury and complex medical issues. **Strengths:** "She works extremely hard and is particularly good with clients who are often extremely vulnerable." "Caroline has an absolutely fantastic manner with clients – she can communicate with them so that they are relaxed in stressful situations. She is one of the first names to spring to mind for complex cases."

Margot Elliot (Regency Chambers) Widely commended for her expertise in both public and private children law matters. She is particularly recognised for her work in care proceedings and residence and contact matters.

Gemma Farrington (see p.598) (Stour Chambers) Respected for her involvement in both public and private law children matters, earning particular praise for her expertise in care proceedings. She is also noted for her handling of complex multiparty matters, and non-accidental injury cases with conflicting expert evidence. **Strengths:** "Gemma has a wide range of abilities and expertise in handling clients across the board. She's particularly sensitive to the difficulties of representing young people." "She's very patient and decisive, establishing a good rapport very quickly with vulnerable clients."

Joanne Porter (see p.696) (Stour Chambers) Has impressive experience in cases concerning Eastern European families, and expertise in a range of matters including those involving non-accidental injury, sexual abuse and domestic violence. **Strengths:** "Joanne is a good advocate, particularly for people who are vulnerable. She really does fight on their behalf, but she does so with care." "She's gentle and doesn't tend to be unnecessarily aggressive. She chooses the right questions and picks her battles."

John Brooke-Smith (Trinity Chambers) Recognised for his expertise in areas such as financial remedy, cohabitation disputes and Children Act matters.

Maria Hancock (Westgate Chambers) Experienced in acting on behalf of both parents and children on public law children matters, with particular focus on care proceedings. She is further recognised for her understanding of mental health issues and Court of Protection proceedings. **Strengths:** "She gives very calm presentations but can also be persuasive in court; she's not frightened to stand up for her clients." "Maria is very good at cross-examinations. She can tease out information that sometimes even takes those in the case by surprise."

WALES & CHESTER

Family/Matrimonial Wales & Chester Leading Sets
Band 1
30 Park Place *
Leading Silks
Band 1
Furness Jonathan *30 Park Place*
Tillyard James *30 Park Place*
Band 2
Crowley Jane *30 Park Place*
Henke Ruth *30 Park Place*
Hopkins Paul *9 Park Place (ORL)* ◊
Leading Juniors
Band 1
Radcliffe Sheila *Cathedral Chambers (ORL)* ◊
Taylor Rhys *30 Park Place*
Thomas Owen *9 Park Place (ORL)* ◊
Band 2
Allen Mark *30 Park Place*
Barry Matthew *9 Park Place (ORL)* ◊
Douglas Colin *30 Park Place*
Edmondson Harriet *30 Park Place*
Felstead Christopher *9 Park Place (ORL)* ◊
Heyworth Catherine Louise *30 Park Place*
John Catrin *30 Park Place*
Leader Lucy *Angel Chambers (ORL)* ◊
Sandercock Natalie *30 Park Place*
Up-and-coming individuals
Seagrim William *9 Park Place (ORL)* ◊
Sutton Emma *30 Park Place*
Williams Claire *30 Park Place*
◊ (ORL) = Other Ranked Lawyer.
** Indicates set / individual with profile.*
Alphabetical order within each band. Band 1 is highest.

Band 1

30 Park Place

See profile on p.895

THE SET

30 Park Place maintains its status as the leading family law set on the Wales & Chester Circuit. Expertise in children law and financial family matters is present at both silk and junior level, and this depth of experience is unrivalled in the region. Instructing solicitors and clients are assured that the service they receive from the resident barristers will be of the highest quality.

SILKS

Jonathan Furness QC Praised for his work in sensitive children cases and complex, high-value ancillary matters. He receives instructions from a wide client base, including direct representation of children, and is commended by instructing solicitors for the rapport he builds with his clients. **Strengths:** "He is technically very good and extremely effective. He is also highly respected by the judiciary." "He is a well-prepared and conscientious practitioner."

James Tillyard QC Strong across the board when it comes to family matters, with a particular focus on children's welfare proceedings and financial disputes after a relationship breakdown. He is typically instructed on complex, high net worth cases involving international elements and hidden assets. He is also noted for his expertise in child care cases involving contentious medical evidence. **Strengths:** "He is extremely tenacious and robust." "He is very good at calculations and presenting cases. Most importantly, he establishes a good rapport with clients."

Jane Crowley QC Specialises in both public and private family law matters, and is particularly adept at cases with complicated medical aspects. She has a wealth of experience in representing vulnerable and disabled individuals. **Strengths:** "She is a very good advocate – understated but very effective."

Ruth Henke QC Widely well regarded for her work on cases concerning vulnerable adults and children, she is often instructed in the most serious of children's proceedings. She regularly appears on Court of Protection matters and acts for a wide client base.

JUNIORS

Rhys Taylor Focuses his practice on financial family matters, particularly medium to high-value ancillary relief cases. He specialises in TOLATA matters, and takes on a number of co-owner land and property disputes. **Strengths:** "He is extremely conscientious, and very good on financial-related matters."

Harriet Edmondson Known for her work in care cases involving inter-familial abuse, including instances of neglect, sexual abuse, non-accidental injuries and even death. She is praised for her pragmatic approach to sensitive proceedings and displays a particular aptitude for interacting with challenging and vulnerable clients.

Catrin John Highly regarded for her work in complex children's proceedings, particularly those concerning the physical and sexual abuse of children. She also undertakes work with a medical focus, including non-accidental injury matters, as well as ancillary relief cases. **Strengths:** "She is an extremely able and highly conscientious practitioner."

Mark Allen A family law practitioner with considerable expertise in complex care work and private children law. He has worked on numerous cases with challenging medical aspects, including shaken babies and factitious illnesses. **Strengths:** "He is a commanding advocate who is personable and engaging with clients."

Colin Douglas Demonstrates considerable expertise in children law, specifically within care cases. He is often instructed on sensitive children's proceedings, typically involving inter-familial abuse and neglect. He has a wealth of experience in interacting with vulnerable and challenging clients, and is lauded for his client care skills.

Catherine Heyworth Commended for her work in serious care cases, she is proficient within both children law and financial dispute resolution. She is adept in children's proceedings that involve the most serious allegations of neglect, physical and sexual abuse, and infanticide. She is frequently instructed by local authorities on such cases, but also represents parents, guardians and interveners.

Natalie Sandercock Practises across the full spectrum of family law, from children's proceedings to ancillary relief cases. She has a wealth of experience in financial relief matters of high value and considerable complexity. **Strengths:** "She is extremely thorough, practical and inventive."

Emma Sutton Specialises in public family law matters, including significant child care work and Court of Protection issues. She is instructed by local authorities, parents and guardians on cases concerning neglect, sexual abuse allegations and non-accidental injuries. Her popularity as a practitioner is evidenced by the large proportion of work she receives as a result of repeat instruction.

Claire Williams Lauded for her work in serious children's proceedings, she undertakes a variety of family law cases, including financial and cohabitee disputes. She is noted for her considerable strength in complex child care cases; she has represented local authorities, guardians and parents in sexual abuse, shaken baby and infanticide matters. **Strengths:** "The quality of her cross-examination and her command of extensive papers are impressive. She is always appropriate in her style." **Recent work:** Represented the local authority in a Court of Appeal case to determine whether a Gillick competent child had a right under Art 3 UNCRC to give evidence in relation to the issue of his future welfare. The child's appeal was ultimately dismissed.

Other Ranked Lawyers

Lucy Leader (Angel Chambers) Highly praised for her thorough approach and ability to establish good rapport with her clients. She often undertakes public and private children's proceedings and ancillary relief cases. **Strengths:** "She is vibrant, enthusiastic, and really good with clients."

Sheila Radcliffe (Cathedral Chambers) Focuses her practice on public law child protection proceedings. **Strengths:** "She produces good-quality work and is a fearsome opponent who is dogged in her determination." "She has many years of experience and the authority that comes with that."

Paul Hopkins QC (9 Park Place) Practises across the full spectrum of family law. On the financial side, he is commonly instructed on cases with farming interests, family trusts and third party claimants. With regards to children's proceedings, he deals with cases of the highest severity, involving serious injuries, sexual abuse and infanticide. **Strengths:** "He excels at complex matters involving cross jurisdictions and vulnerable clients. He can handle the most demanding of clients excellently."

Owen Thomas (9 Park Place) Regularly represents clients in extreme child care cases. He has been instructed on matters involving severe sexual and physical abuse, factitious illness, non-accidental injuries, neglect and emotional harm. He is particularly adept at handling contentious cases where children have given evidence either as victims or as perpetrators. **Strengths:** "He has an extraordinary ability to make the complex seem simple."

Matthew Barry (9 Park Place) Practises across the full range of family law, with notable involvement in private financial disputes and significant care proceedings. He is often instructed on behalf of local authorities in public children law matters that involve inter-familial sexual abuse, physical abuse and death. Furthermore, he has a considerable practice in representing high-profile and high net worth clients in matrimonial finance cases. **Strengths:** "He is absolutely excellent – a skilled advocate with an acute brain." "He is very easy-going and a delightful opponent, both pleasant and reasonable." **Recent work:** Represented local authorities in a Court of Appeal case concerning the causation of fractures in an infant's death, in relation to the welfare of the subsequent sibling. This case was complicated by contentious medical evidence and a large pool of potential perpetrators, and was ultimately resolved in favour of the local authorities.

Christopher Felstead (9 Park Place) Practises predominantly on substantial financial remedy cases. He also undertakes public care work, and demonstrates particular expertise in multifaceted, complex ancillary relief issues. He is applauded for his advocacy skills and for his adept handling of particularly challenging high-value financial matters, including family business, farming and land trusts-related disputes. **Strengths:** "He has sound judgement and a quick brain. He's very analytical and good at grasping the issues of a case."

William Seagrim (9 Park Place) Undertakes children's proceedings with international aspects and cases with allegations of familial abuse. He has represented a varied client base, including adult and child alleged perpetrators, victims and local authorities. **Strengths:** "He is deserving of wide recognition. He is an up-and-coming junior who is very confident and very able." **Recent work:** Appeared in the case of Bristol City Council and AA & HA, which dealt with complex jurisdictional matters in regards to whether a child was resident in this country or Lithuania and the implications of that decision.

WESTERN

Family/Matrimonial Western Leading Sets
Band 1
Pump Court Chambers *
St John's Chambers *
Band 2
Albion Chambers *
Leading Silks
Star individuals
Sharp Christopher *St John's Chambers* [A] *
Band 1
Jacklin Susan *1 Garden Court Family Law Chambers (ORL)* ◊ [A] *
Band 2
Ekaney Nkumbe *Albion Chambers*
Wills-Goldingham Claire *Albion Chambers* [A]
Band 3
Samuels Leslie *Pump Court Chambers* *
Tolson Robin *St John's Chambers* [A]
◊ (ORL) = Other Ranked Lawyer.
[A] direct access (see p.11).
* Indicates set / individual with profile.
Alphabetical order within each band. Band 1 is highest.

Family/Matrimonial Western Leading Juniors
Band 1
Boydell Edward *Pump Court Chambers* *
Dinan-Hayward Deborah *Albion Chambers* [A]
Leafe Daniel *Albion Chambers*
Miller Nicholas *St John's Chambers*
Sproull Nicholas *Albion Chambers* [A]
Band 2
Commins Andrew *St John's Chambers* [A]
Dixon Ralph *Clerksroom Barristers Chambers (ORL)* ◊
Duthie Catriona *St John's Chambers*
Goodall Rachael *3PB Barristers (ORL)* ◊
Hunter Susan *St John's Chambers* [A]
Naish Christopher *Magdalen Chambers (ORL)* ◊
O'Neill Louise *St John's Chambers* [A]
Whitehall Mark *Colleton Chambers (ORL)* ◊
Band 3
Atkinson Jody *St John's Chambers* [A] *
Chapman John *Pump Court Chambers* *
Elliott Colin *KBG Chambers (ORL)* ◊
Evans Judi *St John's Chambers*
Farquhar Fiona *Albion Chambers*
Godfrey Christopher *Colleton Chambers (ORL)* ◊
Kelly Geoffrey *Pump Court Chambers* *
Ker-Reid John *Pump Court Chambers*
Martin Nicola *3PB Barristers (ORL)* ◊
Mashembo Carol *St John's Chambers* [A]
Reed Lucy *St John's Chambers* *
Roberts Stephen *Albion Chambers*
Saunders Zoë *St John's Chambers* *
Small Gina *KBG Chambers (ORL)* ◊
Ward Annie *Pump Court Chambers*
Up-and-coming individuals
Darian Alice *Albion Chambers*
Elliott Mark *3PB Barristers (ORL)* ◊
Iten Corinne *Pump Court Chambers* *
Williamson Nicholas *Pump Court Chambers*

Band 1

Pump Court Chambers

See profile on p.851

THE SET

Pump Court Chambers has cemented its position as one of the leading family law sets on the Western Circuit. It boasts large specialist teams for family finance matters, public children law and private children law; consequently, the set receives frequent commendations for the depth and breadth of its expertise.

Client service: "The clerks, led by Tony Atkins, are absolutely fantastic; nothing is too much trouble. They're very proactive and efficient."

SILKS

Leslie Samuels QC (see p.714) Focuses on significant and high-value family cases, including financial remedy issues and children's proceedings. He often works on serious cases involving high levels of external complexities and is praised for his expertise across all family law matters. **Strengths:** "He is very insightful, and supportive of the client as he is sensitive to all the issues at hand."

JUNIORS

Edward Boydell (see p.554) Primarily handles financial proceedings within family law, often with large asset pools. He is heavily commended for both his advocacy skills and his interaction with his clients. **Strengths:** "He is a highly impressive advocate in complex financial cases and is exceptionally good with clients. A top senior junior choice for high-value money cases." "He is exceptional – the clients love him, judges love him, and he's great in court. He's just exceptional." **Recent work:** Acted on a case concerning up to 60 properties which involved complicating factors of a prenuptial agreement and pre-acquired wealth.

John Chapman (see p.569) Frequently acts on private law children's proceedings and the financial resolutions of separations. He is well regarded for his great manner with clients. **Strengths:** "He is extremely thorough in his preparation and good at dealing with all sorts of clients."

Annie Ward Specialises in family finance issues, particularly cases concerning inheritance disputes. In addition to her practice in financial proceedings, she is well regarded for her performance in private law children matters. **Strengths:** "She is a strong advocate and very good at setting the parameters of the work." "She has a sensible, no-nonsense approach which works particularly well on children's cases."

Geoffrey Kelly (see p.643) Focuses his practice on the resolution of ancillary relief issues. He has a tenacious approach to his advocacy that impresses clients and solicitors alike. **Strengths:** "He is really well prepared. You get to court and are absolutely confident that he will have a prepared brief. His clients are always impressed." "He is thorough, careful, and good with clients."

John Ker-Reid Well versed across the whole spectrum of family law. He has a wealth of experience in dealing with cases that feature sensitive religious, racial and cultural elements, and is praised for his innovative approach to resolving contact issues concerning vulnerable parties. **Strengths:** "He is absolutely amazing on complex cases."

Corinne Iten (see p.636) Particularly adept in public law children's proceedings, yet has a broad family law practice. She is regularly instructed on contentious matters on behalf of local authorities. **Strengths:** "Her expertise and strength as an advocate are very impressive, she is very up to date with current law and she has an ability to put witnesses at ease and make them feel comfortable before they give evidence."

Nicholas Williamson Handles all aspects of family law, drawing on his previous experience as a family solicitor. He represents a wide variety of clients in complex financial remedy cases, as well as care proceedings. **Strengths:** "He has great client care skills; his clients genuinely feel that he cares for them."

St John's Chambers

See profile on p.893

THE SET

St John's Chambers continues to show considerable expertise in its family practice. The high-calibre family barristers at the set represent all parties in family law matters and have particular strengths in resolving multifaceted financial disputes. Furthermore, client satisfaction is noteworthy at both silk and junior level.

Client service: "You always know that the clerks, led by Luke Hodgson, will deal with whatever you put to them. Barristers are booked well in advance, there are no last-minute changes or frantic phone calls, and you're left knowing that everything has been resolved."

SILKS

Christopher Sharp QC Highly respected for his expertise in multidisciplinary ancillary relief cases and serious care proceedings. He demonstrates particular expertise in the personal injury field, which he successfully utilises in family law cases involving serious injuries or infant death. **Strengths:** "He is incisive and clear, and always has every detail at his fingertips. He is a strong advocate with weight and authority." "He is hard-working and consistently excellent." **Recent work:** Instructed on a high-value financial matrimonial dispute case concerning a business developed during the marriage.

Robin Tolson QC Specialises in public children law and dealing with high-value financial remedy cases. He is particularly adept in sensitive and complex children's proceedings.

JUNIORS

Nick Miller Solely practises on matrimonial finance cases of substantial value and complexity. He is highly praised for his negotiation and advocacy skills, as well as his client interaction. **Strengths:** "He is quite exceptional. He stands out for his diligence – it is quite clear that whatever he is dealing with, he has an excellent understanding of it." "He is notably communicative and top of the range for counsel that is not silk."

Andrew Commins Focuses his practice on ancillary relief proceedings after relationship breakdowns. Despite his specialist knowledge of financial disputes, he has a wealth of experience in dealing with the heavy end of children law, including allegations of harm and abuse. **Strengths:** "He is a calm and diplomatic practitioner with a real eye for detail."

Catriona Duthie Well regarded for her practice in all areas of family law, particularly within complex care proceedings. She is commended for her strong client skills. **Strengths:** "She has a no-nonsense approach to cases. She will tell the client exactly how it is, which clients really appreciate."

Susan Hunter Continues to be highly rated for her family law practice, demonstrating particular expertise on financial remedy cases which are complicated by enforcement issues and multiple party claims. Her impressive rapport with clients is widely recognised. **Strengths:** "She is great, very tough and a strong advocate. She is always well prepared and she gets straight to the heart of a problem." "She has got a brilliant style with clients; she cuts straight to the point. She is a very personable barrister and particularly good on sensitive matters."

Louise O'Neill Regularly instructed on significant, contentious family law proceedings, particularly at High Court level. She demonstrates expertise in both financial disputes and private children law, especially cases with international complications.

Lucy Reed (see p.705) Specialises in children law and domestic violence cases. She regularly represents vulnerable parties on particularly challenging cases that involve international elements, serious allegations of harm and contentious medical considerations. **Strengths:** "She has excellent expertise and is highly experienced." "She is very accessible, with a sound understanding of all the latest developments within family law."

Judi Evans Practises across public and private family law, with particular expertise in cases of abduction and the international relocation of children. She is commended for her passionate style of advocacy and her commitment to her clients. **Strengths:** "She is a fantastic advocate and a fighter – she will fight for you. She manages to keep the best interests of her client at heart without losing her objectivity." "She is really tenacious and is involved more than you would usually expect."

Carol Mashembo Acknowledged for her expertise in financial resolutions and children's issues within family law. She draws praise from instructing solicitors for her user-friendly approach. **Strengths:** "She is a hands-on barrister who gives sensible and practical advice."

Susan Jacklin QC (see p.636)

Zoë Saunders (see p.715) Frequently instructed on complex ancillary issues. She has a wealth of experience in financial resolution proceedings associated with cohabitation disputes, especially those complicated by numerous properties, land trusts and pensions. **Strengths:** "She achieves great results and builds a lovely rapport with each client. She exhibits thorough preparation and possesses an ability to think on her feet." "She is brilliant – a real fighter for cases – and is very diligent and thorough." **Recent work:** Successfully represented a claimant who was involved in a TOLATA dispute after the death of a cohabitant.

Jody Atkinson (see p.539) Well versed in private law financial remedy cases. She has particular strengths in cases complicated by family trusts, inheritance disputes and child maintenance issues. **Strengths:** "She is very concise and straight-talking, with excellent written opinions."

Band 2

Albion Chambers

See profile on p.889

THE SET

Bristol's Albion Chambers maintains its strong family law presence on the Western Circuit. The set's particular strengths lie in matrimonial finance cases; however, its members provide experience across the board in family proceedings and deserve recognition for their extensive Court of Protection work.

SILKS

Nkumbe Ekaney QC Renowned for his work in sensitive and complex child welfare law, notably infanticide cases and those involving serious allegations of abuse and neglect. In addition to his expertise in children law, he is equally proficient in dealing with the legalities that arise after breakdowns in marriages and civil partnerships. **Strengths:** "He is a very polished performer in court."

Claire Wills-Goldingham QC Broadly practises within family law on financial disputes and public and private children's proceedings. She is widely respected for her experience of particularly tough child welfare issues, especially those including sexual abuse, non-accidental injury and infant death. **Strengths:** "She is a robust and tenacious advocate who fights hard for her clients." "She is smart, very capable, and very helpful with vulnerable and anxious clients."

JUNIORS

Deborah Dinan-Hayward Attracts a great deal of praise for her specialist practice in family law finance matters. Her client care skills and courtroom manner are widely acclaimed. **Strengths:** "She is very experienced and knows exactly what she is talking about." "She gives calm, thorough and effective advice to a range of clients and she is very easy to deal with."

Daniel Leafe Focuses his practice on cohabitation and ancillary relief matters. He is praised for his depth of knowledge in matrimonial cases and for his forthright style of advocacy. **Strengths:** "He is a tenacious advocate with thorough analytical skills, who thinks outside of the box." "He has an excellent intellect. He's quite hard-hitting but still very professional and extremely well prepared."

Nicholas Sproull Exclusively works on high net worth ancillary relief cases for privately funded clients. He is renowned for his financial insight and his sound judgement. **Strengths:** "He is charming and eloquent, and delivers excellent results." "He is impressive on his feet, very calm and he fills you with confidence."

Fiona Farquhar Specialises in children law, practising in both the public and private arenas for a broad client base. She is often instructed on cases with medical aspects, including sexual abuse, non-accidental injuries and fabricated illness.

Stephen Roberts Demonstrates aptitude in both public children law matters and high-value financial remedy cases. He draws on his previous experience as a family solicitor when dealing with particularly sensitive cases involving sexual abuse and allegations of harm.

Alice Darian Practises predominantly in sensitive care proceedings involving intentional harm and sexual abuse. She represents a broad client base, including parents, local authorities and children. **Strengths:** "She is clear and concise, and articulates her case in a very appropriate and sensible fashion."

Other Ranked Lawyers

Ralph Dixon (Clerksroom Barristers Chambers) Exclusively practises on family finance matters. He is widely recognised in the Western Circuit for his proficiency on high-value, complex ancillary issues. **Strengths:** "He is fastidious in his approach – an extremely safe pair of hands."

Mark Whitehall (Colleton Chambers) Specialises in children law, particularly complex cases involving child relocation and contact arrangements. He represents parents, local authorities and guardians in a wide variety of cases and is praised by all for keeping the best interests of the children at the forefront of his practice.

Christopher Godfrey (Colleton Chambers) Focuses his practice principally on public children law issues, representing children, relatives, local authorities and guardians.

Susan Jacklin QC (see p.636) (1 Garden Court Family Law Chambers) Practises across the full range of family law, with a focus on money matters and children's proceedings. She is commended for her outstanding client care skills. **Strengths:** "She is a heavyweight in financial remedy claims and can be relied upon to deliver practical, hands-on advice." "She has an ability to effectively manage client expectations which is fantastic."

Colin Elliott (KBG Chambers) Attracts praise for his expertise in ancillary relief, particularly on issues that involve land disputes. **Strengths:** "He is highly regarded for providing clear and pragmatic advice and being a robust advocate."

Gina Small (KBG Chambers) Frequently instructed on the heavy end of children's proceedings and complex financial family matters. She is noted for her work on cases involving serious allegations of sexual and physical abuse, child abduction and international adoption. **Strengths:** "She is not only very thorough, but also very experienced on children's matters."

Christopher Naish (Magdalen Chambers) Handles all aspects of family law but exhibits a particular flair for financial proceedings involving property and trust complications. **Strengths:** "He is very reliable and really knows his stuff – he is a good, solid performer." **Recent work:** Acted on a Court of Appeal case that sought to appeal against a placement order intending to separate two children.

Rachael Goodall (3PB Barristers) Handles a variety of cases within family law, with noted expertise in financial resolutions following the breakdown of a relationship. She has considerable experience in dealing with multifaceted cases involving concealed assets and third party claimants. She is also noted for her work in private children law issues involving domestic violence allegations and international relocations.

Nicola Martin (3PB Barristers) Covers the full range of family law, with particular strengths in challenging financial remedy matters, serious child welfare cases and private children's proceedings. **Strengths:** "She is an excellent advocate who is formidable in cross-examination."

Mark Elliott (3PB Barristers) Practises across the whole spectrum of family law. He is well regarded for his advocacy style, particularly when faced with challenging cases involving contentious medical evidence and vulnerable witnesses.

FINANCIAL CRIME: An Introduction

Contributed by Nicholas Purnell QC, of Cloth Fair Chambers

The exponential increase in 2013/2014 in cross-border investigations has shifted the focus from what used quaintly to be described as tackling 'white-collar crime', with its emphasis on the miscreant, dark-suited individual, to the more apt description of targeting 'business crime'. This altogether more resource-demanding process is directed at allegations of systemic abuse and misconduct in corporate behaviour: conduct which crosses continents and markets and which exposes the client, both corporate and individual, to very different jurisdictional cultures, within which these investigations are conducted. In particular there are striking differences of approach between UK prosecutors and regulators and those in the USA.

Corporations are waking up to the turmoil that such investigations wreak upon their business, upon share prices and upon long-term relationships with their regulators. There is, however, as yet insufficient appreciation by clients and even some lawyers of the tensions which may be created by the difference of approach required to respond to concurrent investigations by the SFO and the FCA in England and Wales on the one hand and by the DoJ and the SEC in the United States.

The American lawyer, schooled in the difficult skill of conducting plea and deferred plea negotiations with counterparts from the investigating authorities, who will often be former colleagues, will advocate an early approach to the prosecutor and the initiation of discussions on final outcomes. This strategy hopes to shape the scope, diminish the geographical reach and limit the period covered by any future indictment by offering co-operation to facilitate the investigation. The price for such 'co-operation' may be extracted by the prosecutor in the form of undertakings from the company to act as the self-investigating policeman, to provide transparency about that internal review process and to submit to full or partial waiver of privilege over employee interviews and forensic accountant's or business analysis reports.

This reflects the role of both the DoJ and the SEC as deal makers and generators of massive financial penal recoveries for the US Treasury. The US Deferred Prosecution Agreement has no statutory or legal foundation but has developed over time into an established, well-worn and familiar route to resolving criminal investigations. The DPA's strength is its flexibility and the openness to negotiation of its detailed components. The DoJ, in adopting this tough but more regulatory style, compels corporations to carry out the criminal investigation on its behalf, at the corporate entity's expense, and to settle the investigation against a background threat of criminal prosecution.

The same corporate client may receive different advice about responding to the concurrent demands of investigating authorities on this side of the Atlantic. The SFO is a prosecuting authority; it is neither a regulator nor a deal maker. It was created by statute to investigate and prosecute serious and complex crime. The 'global plea bargain' and the deferred plea quadrille are evolving and untested processes in England and Wales. The first UK DPA is yet to emerge at the time of going to press. While the applicable criteria have been set out and Guidance published, what they will mean in practice has yet to be determined. How gracious will the respective Directors of the SFO and Public Prosecutions become in extending their invitations to treat? Is the determination of 'co-operation with a prosecuting authority' to be defined only by the opinion of the prosecutor? The guidance indicates that an acceptance of guilt and the waiver of privilege are not conditions for a DPA but each will represent a significant factor in the prosecutorial evaluation of the extent of 'co-operation'.

The transatlantic concept of making disclosures to the DoJ or the SEC which do not waive legal professional privilege and the capacity to retain confidentiality over attorney-work product in documents a company may provide to the authorities find no equivalent place in England and Wales. Here, the prosecution has duties of disclosure to other parties where the relevant material may be considered harmful to the prosecution case or may assist in the defence of another. Material which is disclosed to the UK prosecutor has no axiomatic protection as privileged.

The object lessons are stark and their application produces a transforming effect upon the provision of external legal services to business. No longer is the corporate criminal investigation a distracting nuisance which City law firms wish to refer to lawyers with a specialism simply in criminal fraud. The exigencies of global investigations demand co-ordinated responses in all relevant jurisdictions of greater complexity than that. The company must have the benefit of the earliest advice from specialists in this type of business crime to enable it to balance properly the strategic consequences of their responses to authorities on either side of the Atlantic.

Across the world, prosecutors will want access to whatever documentary material, investigative reports and witness evidence may have been supplied to the authority who was first over the threshold. The company's response to problems in one jurisdiction will colour, or even create, problems confronting it in others. The key requirement is to have in place the right team. That team will have experience which has been forged in the heat of adversarial conflict. It will have access to litigators and advocates who will work together, collaboratively, with the individual professional advisers across multiple jurisdictions to assess, evaluate and advise upon the strategic options available to the company against a backdrop of commercial imperatives. The degree of knowledge and expertise required is not widely available. It is acquired from experience and results in this nascent specialism, making the pool from which genuine candidates can be drawn a tightly defined one.

Contents:

LONDON

Financial Crime London – Leading Sets
Band 1
2 Bedford Row *
Cloth Fair Chambers
2 Hare Court *
3 Raymond Buildings Barristers *
Band 2
25 Bedford Row *
Carmelite Chambers *
23 Essex Street *
6KBW College Hill
Matrix Chambers *
QEB Hollis Whiteman *
Band 3
9-12 Bell Yard
7BR *
The Chambers of Andrew Mitchell QC *
Outer Temple Chambers *
5 Paper Buildings *
Red Lion Chambers
◇ (ORL) = Other Ranked Lawyer.
[A] direct access (see p.11).
* Indicates set / individual with profile.

Financial Crime London – Leading Silks	
Star Individuals	**Salmon** Charles *25 Bedford Row*
Cameron Alexander *3 Raymond Buildings Barristers* [A]	**Trollope** Andrew *187 Fleet Street (ORL)* ◇ *
Gibbs Patrick *3 Raymond Buildings Barristers* [A] *	**Band 3**
Kelsey-Fry John *Cloth Fair Chambers* *	**Bogan** Paul *23 Essex Street*
Langdale Timothy *Cloth Fair Chambers* *	**Carlile of Berriew** Alex *9-12 Bell Yard* *
Montgomery Clare *Matrix Chambers*	**Doyle** Peter *25 Bedford Row*
Perry David *6KBW College Hill*	**Evans** David *The Chambers of Andrew Mitchell QC*
Purnell Nicholas *Cloth Fair Chambers* *	**Finnigan** Peter *QEB Hollis Whiteman*
Winter Ian *Cloth Fair Chambers* *	**Hicks** Martin *2 Hare Court* *
Band 1	**Jones** John Richard *Carmelite Chambers* *
Bott Charles *Carmelite Chambers* *	**Laidlaw** Jonathan *2 Hare Court* *
Caplan Jonathan *5 Paper Buildings* *	**Lewis** James *3 Raymond Buildings Barristers* [A]
Carter-Stephenson George *25 Bedford Row*	**Lodder** Peter *2 Bedford Row*
Chawla Mukul *9-12 Bell Yard* [A] *	**Macdonald** Ken *Matrix Chambers*
Ellison Mark *QEB Hollis Whiteman* *	**Malek** Hodge M *Thirty Nine Essex Street (ORL)* ◇ *
Fisher Jonathan *Devereux (ORL)* ◇ *	**Miskin** Charles *23 Essex Street*
Keith Hugo *3 Raymond Buildings Barristers* *	**Price** Tom *25 Bedford Row*
Mayo Simon *187 Fleet Street (ORL)* ◇ [A] *	**Russell Flint** Simon *23 Essex Street*
Milliken-Smith Mark *2 Bedford Row* *	**Sallon** Christopher *Doughty Street Chambers (ORL)* ◇ [A]
Mitchell Andrew *The Chambers of Andrew Mitchell QC* *	**Shears** Philip P *7BR*
Owen Tim *Matrix Chambers*	**Sherrard** Charles *Furnival Chambers (ORL)* ◇ [A] *
Radcliffe Andrew *2 Hare Court* *	**Smith** Leonard *Carmelite Chambers* *
Shaw Antony *Red Lion Chambers* *	**Wass** Sasha *6KBW College Hill*
Sturman Jim *2 Bedford Row* *	**Band 4**
Thompson Collingwood *7BR*	**Benson** Jeremy *Red Lion Chambers* *
Band 2	**Brodie** Graham *The Chambers of Andrew Mitchell QC*
Bailin Alex *Matrix Chambers* *	**Christopher** Julian *5 Paper Buildings* *
Bowes Michael *Outer Temple Chambers* *	**Enoch** Dafydd *23 Essex Street*
Boyce William *QEB Hollis Whiteman*	**Farrer** David *7BR* [A]
Burke Trevor *3 Raymond Buildings Barristers* [A] *	**Fortson** Rudi *25 Bedford Row*
Carter Peter *Red Lion Chambers* *	**Griffiths** Courtenay *25 Bedford Row*
Clegg William *2 Bedford Row* *	**Griffiths** Peter *2 Bedford Row* *
Darbishire Adrian *QEB Hollis Whiteman*	**Hales** Sally-Ann *Red Lion Chambers* *
Draycott Simon *5 St Andrew's Hill (ORL)* ◇ *	**Horwell** Richard *3 Raymond Buildings Barristers*
Etherington David *Red Lion Chambers* *	**Kark** Tom *QEB Hollis Whiteman*
Farrell Simon *3 Raymond Buildings Barristers* [A]	**Kinnear** Jonathan S *9-12 Bell Yard* [A] *
Hackett Philip *4-5 Gray's Inn Square (ORL)* ◇ *	**Malcolm** Helen *3 Raymond Buildings Barristers* [A]
Kelly Brendan *2 Hare Court* *	**Marshall-Andrews** Robert *Carmelite Chambers* *
Knowles Julian *Matrix Chambers*	**Pinto** Amanda *The Chambers of Andrew Mitchell QC*
Kovalevsky Richard *2 Bedford Row* *	**Sangster** Nigel *25 Bedford Row* *
Larkin Sean *QEB Hollis Whiteman* *	**Webster** Alistair *The Chambers of Andrew Mitchell QC*
Latham Richard *7BR*	**New Silks**
Lissack Richard *Outer Temple Chambers* *	**Armstrong** Dean *2 Bedford Row* *
McGuinness John *9-12 Bell Yard* *	**Coltart** Christopher *2 Hare Court* *
Nelson Cairns *23 Essex Street*	**Fenhalls** Mark *23 Essex Street*
Pickup James *2 Hare Court* *	**Henry** Annette *Furnival Chambers (ORL)* ◇ *
Pownall Orlando *2 Hare Court* *	**Penny** Duncan *6KBW College Hill*

Band 1

2 Bedford Row

See profile on p.763

THE SET

2 Bedford Row is a top-class set housing considerable financial crime strength, and is regularly instructed by some of the most active and highly rated firms in the area. Sources comment that its members "consistently perform excellently and offer a service which is unrivalled in regards to case preparation and relationships with clients." It often handles instructions on behalf of corporates and professional individuals, and is particularly adept at dealing with missing trader intra-community (MTIC) fraud. Barristers are frequently involved in some of the most serious and complex investigations in the market, particularly those with international elements. Of late they have acted in a case of alleged bribery in Indonesia and Iraq and an allegation of stamp duty fraud against a law firm partner based in the Turks and Caicos Islands.

Client service: The clerking team is led by John Grimmer.

SILKS

Mark Milliken-Smith QC A highly respected financial crime barrister who offers expertise in multi-jurisdictional fraud cases. **Strengths:** "He is utterly wonderful. He is client-friendly, hard-working and has a great track record. He is a clear favourite with us." **Recent work:** Instructed in a case involving allegations of bribery in Indonesia and Iraq.

Jim Sturman QC Handles corruption and fraud cases, and has expertise in representing both corporations and high-profile individuals. **Strengths:** "He offers an exceptional service, providing his clients with complete discretion by preventing the attraction of unwanted media attention. Nothing is ever too much bother for him." **Recent work:** Instructed in a case involving allegations of stamp duty fraud against a partner in a law firm based in the Turks and Caicos Islands.

William Clegg QC (see p.573) Experienced in acting for professional individuals and major companies. He handles heavyweight cases concerning insider dealing, fraud and corruption. **Strengths:** "He is excellent and his arguments are very robust." "He is simply a star and an absolute gentleman. He is persuasive and exceptionally bright."

Richard Kovalevsky QC (see p.648) Well versed in advising businesses and senior individuals faced with allegations of money laundering, fraud or bribery. **Strengths:** "He is first-class and a real game changer in a case. His involvement really can mean the difference between winning and losing."

Peter Lodder QC Held in high esteem for handling complex and high-profile fraud matters, including insider dealing and corruption cases. **Strengths:** "He is commanding in court."

Peter Griffiths QC (see p.615) Handles heavyweight fraud cases, often with cross-border elements. His recent caseload includes a number of significant money laundering instructions. **Recent work:** Acted for the lead defendant in a cyber-fraud cases concerning UK and European authorities, as well as the FBI.

Financial Crime London	
Leading Juniors	
Star individuals	**Baker** Simon *Goldsmith Chambers (ORL)* ◇
Pople Alison *Cloth Fair Chambers* *	**Carter-Manning** Jennifer *7BR* [A]
Saunders Neil *3 Raymond Buildings Barristers* [A] *	**Clarke** Sarah *Serjeants' Inn Chambers (ORL)* ◇ *
Sibson Clare *Cloth Fair Chambers* *	**Darlow** Annabel *6KBW College Hill*
Band 1	**Douglas-Jones** Ben *5 Paper Buildings* *
Ashley-Norman Jonathan *3 Raymond Buildings* [A] *	**Hawes** Neil *Charter Chambers (ORL)* ◇ *
Barclay Robin *Outer Temple Chambers* *	**Irwin** Gavin *Dyers Chambers (ORL)* ◇ *
Barnard Jonathan *Cloth Fair Chambers* *	**Lennon** John *23 Essex Street*
Bodnar Andrew *Matrix Chambers* *	**Marshall** Andrew *Red Lion Chambers* *
Clare Allison *Red Lion Chambers* *	**Payne** Tom *Red Lion Chambers* *
Forster Tom *Red Lion Chambers* *	**Phillips** Paul *Charter Chambers (ORL)* ◇ [A] *
Hill Miranda *6KBW College Hill*	**Raudnitz** Paul *QEB Hollis Whiteman* *
Hines James *3 Raymond Buildings Barristers* [A] *	**Tanchel** Vivienne *2 Hare Court* *
Kendal Timothy *2 Bedford Row*	**Wells** Colin *25 Bedford Row* *
Mansell Jason *7BR* [A] *	**Wheeler** Andrew *7BR*
Band 2	**Wormald** Richard *3 Raymond Buildings Barristers* [A]
Brandon Ben *3 Raymond Buildings Barristers*	**Yeo** Nicholas *3 Raymond Buildings Barristers* [A]
Ferguson Craig *2 Hare Court* *	**Band 4**
Ferguson Stephen Michael *2 Bedford Row*	**Allen** Tom *5 Paper Buildings* *
Furlong Richard *Carmelite Chambers* *	**Barnes** Rachel *3 Raymond Buildings Barristers* [A]
Grey Siobhan *Doughty Street Chambers (ORL)* ◇	**Bowers** Rupert *Doughty Street Chambers (ORL)* ◇
Guest Peter *187 Fleet Street (ORL)* ◇ *	**Caldwell** Peter *Dyers Chambers (ORL)* ◇ *
Harries Mark *Carmelite Chambers* [A] *	**Chalk** Alex *6KBW College Hill*
Howard Nicola *25 Bedford Row*	**George** Dean *2 Bedford Row*
Jones Gillian *Red Lion Chambers* *	**Hammond** Sean *2 Bedford Row* *
Kane Adam *Carmelite Chambers* *	**Hillman** Gerard *Carmelite Chambers* [A] *
Lennon Jonathan *The Chambers of Andrew Mitchell QC*	**Hopper** Stephen *5 Paper Buildings* *
Little Tom *9 Gough Square (ORL)* ◇ *	**Khan** Ashraf *2 Bedford Row* *
Mitchell Keith *The Chambers of Andrew Mitchell QC* *	**Mawrey** Eleanor *9 Gough Square (ORL)* ◇ *
Ramasamy Selva *QEB Hollis Whiteman* *	**Patterson** Gareth *6KBW College Hill*
Riggs Samantha *25 Bedford Row*	**Payne** Geoffrey *25 Bedford Row* *
Rudolf Nathaniel *25 Bedford Row* *	**Stern** David *5 St Andrew's Hill (ORL)* ◇ *
Summers Ben *3 Raymond Buildings Barristers* *	**Thacker** James *9 Gough Square (ORL)* ◇ *
Summers Gary *23 Essex Street*	**Weeks** Janet *5 Paper Buildings* *
Whittaker David *2 Hare Court* *	**Willcocks** Hannah *Red Lion Chambers*
Wong Natasha *187 Fleet Street (ORL)* ◇ [A] *	**Up-and-coming individuals**
Band 3	**Bentley** Harry *2 Hare Court* *
Aylott Colin *Carmelite Chambers* [A] *	**Gokani** Rachna *QEB Hollis Whiteman*

Financial Crime: Corporates London	
Leading Silks	
Band 1	**Band 2**
Cameron Alexander *3 Raymond Buildings Barristers* [A]	**Bailin** Alex *Matrix Chambers* *
Gibbs Patrick *3 Raymond Buildings Barristers* [A] *	**Bowes** Michael *Outer Temple Chambers* *
Kelsey-Fry John *Cloth Fair Chambers* *	**Clegg** William *2 Bedford Row* *
Langdale Timothy *Cloth Fair Chambers* *	**Keith** Hugo *3 Raymond Buildings Barristers* *
Montgomery Clare *Matrix Chambers*	**Kovalevsky** Richard *2 Bedford Row* *
Perry David *6KBW College Hill*	**Lissack** Richard *Outer Temple Chambers* *
Purnell Nicholas *Cloth Fair Chambers* *	**Malek** Hodge M *Thirty Nine Essex Street (ORL)* ◇ *
Winter Ian *Cloth Fair Chambers* *	**Sturman** Jim *2 Bedford Row* *
Leading Juniors	
Band 1	**Band 2**
Hill Miranda *6KBW College Hill*	**Barnard** Jonathan *Cloth Fair Chambers* *
Pople Alison *Cloth Fair Chambers* *	**Barnes** Rachel *3 Raymond Buildings Barristers* [A]
Saunders Neil *3 Raymond Buildings Barristers* [A] *	**Mansell** Jason *7BR* [A] *
Sibson Clare *Cloth Fair Chambers* *	**Medcroft** Nicholas *Wilberforce Chambers (ORL)* ◇ *
	Summers Ben *3 Raymond Buildings Barristers* *

◇ (ORL) = Other Ranked Lawyer.
[A] direct access (see p.11).
** Indicates individual with profile.*

Dean Armstrong QC (see p.537) An up-and-coming criminal silk with particular strength in high-profile fraud work. His experience encompasses tax fraud, boiler room fraud and money laundering cases. **Strengths:** "He's elegant in court and very persuasive." **Recent work:** Acted for one of 23 defendants in an HMRC fraud case concerning Construction Industry Scheme tax deductions.

JUNIORS

Tim Kendal A highly sought-after junior barrister with experience of handling corruption cases, money laundering and insider dealing matters. **Strengths:** "He is a very good senior junior with years of experience."

Stephen Ferguson Defends high-profile clients accused of a range of white-collar offences, including money laundering and fraud. **Strengths:** "He is very efficient and personable."

Dean George Regularly instructed as sole junior in complex fraud matters, he is also led in large-scale, high-profile financial crime cases. **Strengths:** "He's a brilliant advocate with a flair for jury trials. He has great judgement and is a brilliant tactician." **Recent work:** Acted as junior counsel for the defence in a complex, multi-jurisdictional cyber-fraud case.

Sean Hammond (see p.618) Represents professional clients in relation to financial crime matters including insider dealing, corruption, white-collar fraud and money laundering cases. **Strengths:** "He's got a great ability to analyse evidence. He's charming and turns out good skeleton arguments." "He's an incisive advocate, who can see the heart of a case and the way forward. In court he commands respect and has a good relationship with juries." **Recent work:** Represented an independent financial consultant facing allegations of conspiracy to defraud in a large boiler room case prosecuted by the SFO.

Ashraf Khan (see p.645) Has a nationwide financial crime practice and is regularly instructed to defend in complex fraud cases. **Strengths:** "Ashraf Khan has an A to Z knowledge of fraud work." **Recent work:** Acted for a mortgage broker charged with conspiracy to defraud and money laundering.

Cloth Fair Chambers

THE SET

Small in numbers but with consistently stellar performers at the QC and junior levels, Cloth Fair Chambers is a first-class boutique criminal fraud practice. Sources reserve particular praise for the quality of the barristers' advocacy, describing the set as "one of the best places to go if a case is going to trial." Recent highlights have included major victories in a number of high-profile SFO investigations, as well as OFT prosecutions and cases of alleged money laundering and market manipulation. Additionally, members have expertise representing corporates in this space, and are frequently instructed in international matters.

Client service: Instructing solicitors say they have "a great personal relationship with the clerks" at Cloth Fair Chambers, who are led by Nick Newman.

SILKS

John Kelsey-Fry QC (see p.644) Instructed in high-profile fraud cases as part of his celebrated criminal practice. He is also sought after to advise corporations on significant cross-border investigations. **Strengths:** "His advocacy style shines out; he commands the judge's respect and ear." "He brings an exceptional, logical, strategic analysis to the cases we do." **Recent work:** Represented Olympus at a hearing in which it was determined that the prosecutor could not bring charges against the company.

Timothy Langdale QC (see p.650) Operates at the highest level in relation to serious financial crime matters, including SFO and OFT investigations. **Recent work:** Instructed in a fraud and money laundering case arising out of the OFT and SFO investigation into a number of sports retailers.

Nicholas Purnell QC (see p.701) Has an excellent reputation for representing high-profile individuals and major corporations in financial crime matters. **Strengths:** "Despite his enviable reputation, he does not rest on his laurels." "His attention to detail and ability to see what matters in a case is really impressive." **Recent work:** Represented Victor Dahdaleh in relation to his prosecution by the SFO, which arose out of allegations of bribery and fraud totalling £700 million.

Ian Winter QC Highly sought after to act for corporations and individuals. He regularly receives instructions in a broad range of business crime matters, including complex fraud cases. **Strengths:** "He's exceptional, slick and commercially aware." "He is extremely intelligent and I trust his analysis and judgement." **Recent work:** Advised Serco in relation to allegations that it had overcharged the government for electronic tagging services.

JUNIORS

Alison Pople (see p.696) Handles some of the most significant fraud cases in the financial crime area. She is also called upon to advise corporations on investigations and self-reporting. **Strengths:** "She is extremely hard-working, excellent with the client and tactically very good." "She is a brilliant junior and immensely respected." **Recent work:** Represented the legal services director of Torex, who was charged with conspiracy to defraud.

Clare Sibson (see p.720) Has a stellar reputation for appearing in white-collar cases. She has experience of acting for corporations and high-profile individuals in financial crime matters. **Strengths:** "She is astonishingly bright, great on paper and has good client skills." **Recent work:** Advised Alstom in relation to a cross-jurisdictional SFO investigation.

Jonathan Barnard (see p.543) Acts for senior executives and high net worth individuals in large-scale financial crime investigations and trials. He is also noted for his corporate advisory work. **Strengths:** "He has extremely sound judgement." "He is a skilful, charismatic advocate who can communicate very difficult transactional processes." **Recent work:** Represented Victor Dahdaleh in relation to his prosecution by the SFO, which arose out of allegations of bribery and fraud totalling £700 million.

2 Hare Court

See profile on p.818

THE SET

2 Hare Court garners extensive praise in this space, with sources saying it is "top-tier for financial crime. The set has very strong juniors in the area and heavyweight silks." Members are experienced at prosecuting and defending the full range of serious fraud cases including those relating to carbon credit trading, tax evasion and boiler room fraud. Barristers at the set are well placed to advise on cases with an international dimension and are further recognised for their advice in relation to the Bribery Act. One interviewee notes: "Everyone from 2 Hare Court that I have encountered has had an impressive grasp of both facts and law."

Client service: "The standard of clerking there is fantastic. They place a significant emphasis on client care." Julian Campbell is the director of clerking at the set.

SILKS

Andrew Radcliffe QC (see p.702) A well-regarded financial crime practitioner, who regularly handles complex and sensitive cases. **Strengths:** "He is a real tactician; he is very intelligent, smooth and relaxed. He knows his stuff."

James Pickup QC (see p.693) A fraud defence specialist with particular expertise in tax cases. **Strengths:** "His principal skill lies in assimilating very significant documentation very quickly, efficiently and thoroughly. He is an accomplished advocate and his cross-examination of professional witnesses is very impressive. His mastery of a brief is as good as I have seen." "He is fearless and industrious with an intellect to match. He is a superb tactician and brilliant on paper." **Recent work:** Acted for the defence in a major MTIC case, which was brought against the directors of a mobile phone distribution company and linked organisations by the HMRC.

Orlando Pownall QC (see p.698) Highly sought after to defend clients accused of fraud offences, including insider dealing and tax evasion. **Recent work:** Acted for an individual accused of making a sham firm in order to fraudulently claim tax credits and VAT.

Martin Hicks QC (see p.626) Regularly instructed in serious fraud matters, including MTIC fraud, mortgage fraud and major boiler room fraud cases. **Strengths:** "We instructed him recently in a matter involving lots of complex technology and he straightaway found a way of advocating a case that we thought would be a nightmare to present." **Recent work:** Represented the defendant in a revenue fraud case concerning the importation of gold into the eurozone from Dubai and India.

Brendan Kelly QC (see p.643) Acts in a range of white-collar crime cases including tax fraud and corruption matters, in addition to related confiscation proceedings. Instructing solicitors admire his jury advocacy skills. **Strengths:** "He is very engaging, has a terrific sense of humour, and is both a quality advocate and a great personality." "He's an excellent and charming advocate. He is charismatic and persuasive, intelligent and quick to get to the issues."

Jonathan Laidlaw QC Highly respected for his expertise in criminal fraud and regulatory issues. Often instructed in novel and challenging cases. **Strengths:** "He is unbeatable in my opinion. He is amongst the top QCs in the area." "He is phenomenal. He was Treasury Counsel and historically he has done a lot of prosecution." **Recent work:** Acted for the defendant in a high-profile fraud case involving the manufacture and sale of fake bomb detectors.

Christopher Coltart QC (see p.576) Has impressive experience of advising on complex and sophisticated City fraud cases. **Strengths:** "He is incredibly organised and accessible. He is very engaged throughout the process, good with clients and trusted by everyone." "He is very good as an advocate and intellectually very bright." **Recent work:** Represented the defendant in a six-week trial concerning an alleged conspiracy to defraud Vodafone.

JUNIORS

Craig Ferguson Handles complex fraud work, including mortgage fraud, referral fee fraud and tax fraud cases. He is also instructed in insider trading and NHS fraud cases. **Strengths:** "He has developed into one of the finest advocates at the Bar. He is just a real natural talent."

David Whittaker (see p.751) Prosecutes and defends in serious fraud cases, including MTIC, advance fee and mortgage fraud cases. **Strengths:** "He has been consistently excellent over a number of years. He gives very good practical advice and often provides unique insights." **Recent work:** Acted for the former director of a significant mobile phone trading company in a multimillion-pound MTIC case, which arose out of Operation Chert.

Vivienne Tanchel (see p.734) A highly sought-after junior barrister for major FCA matters. She has a background as a trader, which appeals to many prospective clients. **Strengths:** "She is very straightforward, highly personable and has a real feel for the subject matter." "She is a very capable and industrious advocate. Her previous background in the financial industry is a great asset when it comes to her commercial perspective on financial cases."

Harry Bentley (see p.548) An up-and-coming junior with experience of handling an impressive array of serious fraud and money laundering cases. **Strengths:** "He really is exceptional for his years of call. His ability to get to the crux of the issue quickly is fantastic, especially when in fraud you have thousands of pages of disclosure." "He is thorough, always on top of all the papers in the case, receives very good client feedback and is very hard-working." **Recent work:** Acted for the defendant in a £20 million investment fraud.

3 Raymond Buildings Barristers

See profile on p.857

THE SET

Widely acknowledged as one of the leading sets in the financial crime arena. The set stands out for the fantastic quality of its team, evident all the way from its senior silks right down to its junior barristers. Sources confirm this, saying: "3 Raymond Buildings has some of the best barristers in the country with specialist knowledge of serious crime and fraud." The team's expertise is wide-ranging and includes a command of claims relating to fraud, insider dealing and corruption. It also offers expertise representing corporates and professionals in financial crime cases.

Client service: "The clerking is fantastic; the chief clerk Eddie Holland is nice to deal with, prompt and efficient, and nothing is too much trouble."

SILKS

Alexander Cameron QC An exceptional financial crime barrister with extensive experience of SFO and FCA cases. He is also sought after to advise corporate clients on sensitive liability issues. **Strengths:** "He really is first-class. He is an absolute pleasure to deal with, extraordinarily hard-working and really collaborative working with the solicitor team right from the start. Clients think he is absolutely fantastic." "He is fantastically good, respected by judges, really compelling, has a persuasive style of advocacy and is fluent in his written work. He is one of the top people at the Bar." **Recent work:** Defended an oil trader accused of defrauding his employers at Shell of £2.5 million.

Trevor Burke QC (see p.560) A criminal fraud specialist who has expertise in advance fee, mortgage, missing trader and tax frauds. **Strengths:** "He is well known, very able and has great experience." **Recent work:** Acted in a multimillion-dollar international bank fraud case involving the Cayman Islands.

Simon Farrell QC A leading practitioner in financial crime matters, with relevant expertise in Proceeds of Crime Act (POCA) proceedings. Areas of specialism include bribery and corruption, commercial fraud and money laundering. **Strengths:** "Judges give him credence because of his reputation in serious fraud. They ask his opinion and listen to what he says." **Recent work:** Acted for the prosecution in an immigration fraud case.

James Lewis QC Handles high-profile and complex financial crime matters. His practice is bolstered by his extradition expertise, which often comes into play in relation to international fraud allegations. **Strengths:** "He is a very elegant advocate." **Recent work:** Instructed to advise on a land fraud issue in Trinidad and Tobago.

Richard Horwell QC Well placed to advise on fraud cases involving cross-jurisdictional elements. He has recently handled a number of substantial money laundering cases. **Strengths:** "He has the ability to talk about something which is fairly complex in a way that everyone can understand." **Recent work:** Acted for the defence in a money laundering case in which the prosecution eventually offered no evidence after lengthy negotiations.

Helen Malcolm QC An impressive criminal fraud lawyer with particular expertise in international matters. She is instructed in major SFO cases. **Strengths:** "She is a fantastic barrister. When she stands up everyone listens." "She is very impressive and she communicates well with the judge." **Recent work:** Secured the acquittal of the wife of a tax consultant who was implicated in a £213 million tax fraud.

Hugo Keith QC A highly regarded criminal barrister, with a strong grasp of business crime issues including fraud, confiscation, restraint and economic sanctions. **Strengths:** "He is a very strong technical lawyer. He is great on the case law and good at looking at different angles." **Recent work:** Instructed for a defendant in an SFO case concerning alleged corruption in Nigeria.

Patrick Gibbs QC Regarded as one of the leading barristers at the Financial Crime Bar. He has been instructed in some of the most significant fraud investigations of recent times and is sought after to advise corporations in relation to liability. **Strengths:** "He is really good, really accessible, very clever, has a good court manner and is trusted by judges. He is also very persuasive with the jury. He is someone I would relish working with but wouldn't want to be against." "He is very bright, tactical, thoughtful, innovative and compassionate." **Recent work:** Defended a former bond trader against insider dealing charges brought by the FCA.

JUNIORS

Neil Saunders Held in high esteem by the criminal fraud market. He is instructed by major corporations, senior executives and prosecuting bodies in relation to SFO and FCA investigations. **Strengths:** "He is a very astute advocate, excellent with experts and tricky witnesses, who commands the confidence of the client." "He's at once very approachable and able to give difficult advice when needed." **Recent work:** Advised the FCA in relation to the Operation Tabernula insider dealing prosecutions.

Jonathan Ashley-Norman Instructed to prosecute and defend in complex cases, often those prosecuted by the SFO. He is increasingly called upon to advise corporates pre-charge. **Strengths:** "He is one of the most tactically astute barristers around." "He is hugely committed and open to ideas and different approaches. He has good leadership skills and takes a decisive approach to the case." **Recent work:** Represented the first defendant in a case involving an alleged multimillion-pound fraud on Vodafone.

James Hines (see p.628) Well versed in a range of financial crime matters, including market abuse, embezzlement and tax fraud cases. He is regularly instructed by the SFO, and also represents high-profile defendants. **Strengths:** "He is an absolute go-to person who instinctively knows, even in the midst of a huge case, where the issue lies." **Recent work:** Acted at trial and appeal for an individual convicted of conspiracy to defraud £20 million.

Ben Brandon Instructed to defend and prosecute in major fraud trials concerning multinational companies and high-profile individuals. **Strengths:** "He's a cerebral, intellectual lawyer and it's a great benefit that he was formerly a solicitor. He knows how to handle a client." **Recent work:** Defended the former director of Torex, who was prosecuted by the SFO for conspiracy to defraud.

Ben Summers (see p.732) Has extensive experience of SFO and FCA cases. His expertise encompasses fraud, bribery and cartel matters. **Strengths:** "He is a very clever advocate and a good tactician." "He is phenomenal in how he manages to analyse such a large amount of complex financial data in a short space of time and arrive at the key points for the defence." **Recent work:** Acted for a primary defendant in a case concerning an alleged fraud on the NHS.

Richard Wormald A highly sought-after criminal fraud junior, who has experience of defending major SFO and FCA cases and investigations. **Recent work:** Instructed in relation to Libor.

Nicholas Yeo Focuses his practice on fraud and money laundering. His recent experience includes Ponzi fraud, MTIC fraud and false accounting cases. **Strengths:** "He is incredible. He knows all the latest legal updates and developments in the field." **Recent work:** Defended an individual accused of orchestrating a £7 million Ponzi fraud.

Rachel Barnes Has a particular interest in sanctions and corruption matters, as well as large-scale, sophisticated fraud cases. She is a member of the New York Bar and therefore particularly well equipped to advise on transatlantic cases. **Strengths:** "She is very clever and very thorough." "She is bright, phenomenally hard-working and the ideal junior for fraud." **Recent work:** Instructed by the SFO to prosecute a high-value hedge fund fraud.

Band 2

25 Bedford Row

See profile on p.766

THE SET

A criminal defence set with a number of leading silks and high-quality juniors specialising in financial crime. Sources say 25 Bedford Row offers "excellent advocates who have the experience required to deal with heavy fraud cases." Instructing solicitors value the set's "wealth of knowledge and expertise in business crime, fraud and confiscation." Its members have broad expertise in MTIC, POCA and Bribery Act cases. Recent work highlights include high-profile instructions in Libor manipulation cases and a number of carbon credit fraud matters.

Client service: Instructing solicitors praise the team's "impeccable organisation" and comment on the "excellent communication skills" possessed by the clerks, who are led by Guy Williams.

SILKS

George Carter-Stephenson QC Highly sought after for financial crime matters, including market abuse, tax fraud and mortgage fraud cases. He is instructed in some of the most significant investigations in the area. **Strengths:** "He is one of the best fraud QCs in the country. He is a brilliant trial lawyer and incredibly hard-working." "He is second to none for case preparation, presentation and client care. You will not get a better QC in terms of attention to detail." **Recent work:** Acted for the first defendant in Operation Amazon, a case concerning a tax and carbon credit fraud.

Charles Salmon QC A heavyweight fraud practitioner, who has a wealth of experience in the area. He is regularly instructed in significant cases, and has tackled a number of substantial tax and mortgage fraud trials. **Strengths:** "He is incredibly shrewd and analytical. His experience means that he has a strong grasp of how the detail in a complex case will play out at trial. He instils complete confidence in the lay client." "He is a fantastic tactician and a very good advocate." **Recent work:** Acted for a key defendant in a VAT fraud case relating to manipulation of the EU Emissions Trading Scheme.

Peter Doyle QC A criminal fraud defence specialist, with expertise in money laundering, VAT fraud, insider dealing and related regulatory matters. **Recent work:** Instructed to defend a director of a company alleged to have obtained contracts by bribing public officials in Africa.

Courtenay Griffiths QC Has notable experience of advising on fraud and money laundering cases with international aspects. **Strengths:** "He is astonishing as an advocate: he commands everyone's attention." **Recent work:** Represented the former Chief Minister and first Premier of the Turks and Caicos Islands in relation to wide-ranging corruption allegations.

Nigel Sangster QC (see p.714) Well versed in handling complex fraud cases prosecuted by the SFO. His recent experience includes MTIC fraud, investor fraud and Ponzi fraud cases. **Recent work:** Acted in a complex MTIC fraud case involving multiple defendants and various cross-border elements.

Tom Price QC Has extensive experience in the criminal fraud arena. He has particular expertise in advance fee fraud, MTIC fraud and dishonest contra-trading cases. **Strengths:** "He is very incisive and identifies the issues very quickly. He is subtle and effective in his advocacy, and also has a good manner with his clients." **Recent work:** Represented the primary defendant in a fraudulent trading case, who was accused of being the architect behind the companies created to enable the fraud.

Rudi Fortson QC Has expertise in money laundering, fraud and confiscation proceedings. He has written extensively on fraud and confiscation. **Strengths:** "He cuts through the most difficult legal technicalities and puts clients at ease."

JUNIORS

Nicola Howard Has impressive expertise in fraud and corruption matters. Her recent experience includes identity, MTIC and mortgage fraud cases. **Strengths:** "Nicola Howard is a fantastic advocate with a technical mind." **Recent work:** She represented an extradited defendant, who was accused of involvement in a large-scale MTIC fraud.

Nathaniel Rudolf (see p.712) A highly respected criminal fraud junior with experience of a broad range of fraud and money laundering matters. He has particular expertise in obtaining evidence held in foreign jurisdictions. **Strengths:** "He is exceptionally bright and attentive, and well respected by the judiciary and peers alike." "He has a good grasp of this very complex area of law." **Recent work:** Instructed to defend an accountant charged as part of a 14-handed mortgage fraud trial.

Samantha Riggs Has experience of defending high-value money laundering, MTIC and benefit fraud cases. She is sought after to appear both as led junior and sole counsel. **Strengths:** "She is extremely dedicated and hard-working. She hates to lose an argument and puts clients at ease." **Recent work:** Acted in a multi-handed money laundering case arising from Operation Eclipse.

Colin Wells (see p.749) A well-regarded criminal fraud advocate, who is instructed in high-value cases. He has noted expertise in VAT tribunal proceedings. **Recent work:** Acted for the principal defendant in a major boiler room case prosecuted by the SFO.

Geoffrey Payne (see p.690) A criminal fraud specialist, who handles major MTIC fraud cases and high-value confiscation proceedings. **Strengths:** "He is nothing short of fantastic: a very meticulous operator, he is amazingly hard-working and very good in his written work." **Recent work:** Represented an HMRC officer accused of assisting his fellow defendants with the evasion of excise duty.

Carmelite Chambers

See profile on p.775

THE SET

Carmelite Chambers is an established criminal law set with particular expertise in financial crime. Its barristers have wide-ranging experience of serious fraud work including Ponzi schemes, MTIC operations and boiler room frauds. The team also handles matters relating to money laundering, market manipulation (including Libor) and insider trading. Members here act in cases both at home and abroad and have recently demonstrated their commitment to securing more civil fraud and asset recovery work by hosting a conference on the subject that attracted more than 100 attendees from around the globe.

Client service: The clerking team is headed by Marc King.

SILKS

Charles Bott QC (see p.553) An excellent criminal defence advocate, with experience across a range of business crime issues, including money laundering, fraud and tax evasion matters. **Strengths:** "His attention to detail marks him out, as does his measured style in court." **Recent work:** Represented a trader accused of market manipulation in the context of the Libor scandal.

John Jones QC (see p.640) An experienced criminal fraud practitioner whose practice extends to offshore jurisdictions. He is well versed in handling money laundering, insider dealing and corporate fraud matters. **Recent work:** Defended an individual accused of conspiracy to defraud and money laundering, in a case involving allegations that he abused the Hawala banking system.

Leonard Smith QC (see p.724) Handles high-profile and complex fraud matters, including insider trading, mortgage fraud and Ponzi fraud cases. **Strengths:** "He is in some of the best cases in the country, his strategy is second to none, he knows the law inside out and he works extremely hard." **Recent work:** Instructed to act for the principal defendant in a case concerning an alleged mortgage fraud valued at £200 million.

Robert Marshall-Andrews QC (see p.663) Distinguished white-collar practitioner, whose extensive experience includes carbon credit, MTIC and accounting fraud cases. **Recent work:** Acted for a former director of the software company iSOFT, in a case involving an alleged conspiracy to mislead the market.

JUNIORS

Colin Aylott (see p.540) Well versed in defending in complex fraud trials, including cases prosecuted by the SFO and BIS. His expertise encompasses market abuse, money laundering and tax matters. **Strengths:** "He is lovely and has a really nice style in court. He has done a lot of advocacy and is really switched-on." **Recent work:** Instructed to defended a currency broker accused of conspiring to manipulate the yen Libor rate.

Richard Furlong (see p.605) Has experience of defending mortgage fraud, pensions fraud and tax fraud cases. His previous career in financial services stands him in good stead when it comes to advising on sophisticated fraud cases. **Recent work:** Represented a former solicitor accused of a multimillion-pound mortgage fraud.

Mark Harries (see p.620) A highly sought-after white-collar junior barrister whose expertise includes fraud, asset recovery and confiscation proceedings. **Strengths:** "He is a very charming individual. He has got a phenomenal way of cutting through to the heart of a case and presenting his client's case in a very robust and effortless way." "He is an immaculate advocate and has a first-class client manner." **Recent work:** Acted as junior defence counsel in a multi-handed £200 million money laundering case.

Adam Kane (see p.642) Regularly instructed to act for company directors and other senior individuals in high-profile financial crime cases. He has experience of money laundering, tax and property fraud matters. **Strengths:** "He is very good in court." **Recent work:** Represented a defendant in a multi-handed MTIC fraud case.

Gerard Hillman (see p.628) Has experience in tax fraud, boiler room fraud and Ponzi fraud cases. He also has notable experience handling cases before the VAT tribunal. **Strengths:** "He's a brilliant junior counsel for fraud work." **Recent work:** Acted for a defendant facing serious charges in relation to an alleged immigration fraud.

23 Essex Street

See profile on p.795

THE SET

23 Essex Street is "able to offer a huge range of barristers at all levels," reports an interviewee. Members have significant expertise in a wide range of financial crime matters including money laundering, bribery and corruption and complex criminal fraud, and are regularly instructed by leading firms in the field. Both silks and juniors at the set are sought out for their ability to handle large multi-jurisdictional investigations.

Client service: "The clerking is very efficient. Whenever I make contact I get speedy responses – everything you would hope for and expect." Richard Fowler leads the clerking team.

SILKS

Paul Bogan QC Has extensive experience of defending SFO prosecutions. His expertise encompasses bank, mortgage and tax fraud. **Strengths:** "He is very bright, personable and hard-working. He has a fantastic court manner with a jury and is fearless when presented with obstacles by judges." **Recent work:** Acted for a defendant in an SFO case involving a bridging finance company that was alleged to have caused around £60 million loss to Barclays by borrowing to fund fictitious loans.

Cairns Nelson QC Has particular expertise in tax fraud cases. He is also instructed in significant bribery and corruption matters. **Strengths:** "He is extremely engaging and personable, great with clients and excellent in court." **Recent work:** Prosecuted a seven-handed election fraud on the Isle of Man.

Simon Russell Flint QC Well versed in handling major fraud and money laundering cases. He has notable experience in tax matters. **Strengths:** "He is very good with the clients, very good on paperwork and he has charisma." **Recent work:** Acted for a defendant accused of paying bribes to Nigerian state tax officials.

Dafydd Enoch QC Called upon to act for defendants and prosecuting authorities in a wide range of financial crime matters, including tax fraud, pension fraud and money laundering cases. **Strengths:** "He's a great trial advocate." **Recent work:** Represented the principal defendant in a complex and lengthy pension fraud case.

Mark Fenhalls QC Skilled at defending and prosecuting business crime cases. He has experience of acting in relation to SFO and FCA investigations, and a growing advisory practice. **Strengths:** "He is really good, very thorough and has a nice court manner. He is an all-round, adaptable opponent and is very good on the law." **Recent work:** Instructed to act as junior counsel for the CFO of Swift Oil, who was charged with bribery offences relating to Nigerian tax officials.

Charles Miskin QC Has extensive expertise and experience in criminal fraud investigations. His practice is supported by knowledge in related areas such as confiscation and human rights. **Recent work:** Prosecuted a large-scale tax fraud, which arose out of the Operation Amazon investigation.

JUNIORS

Gary Summers Has experience in fraud, money laundering and cybercrime cases. He is well placed to advise on matters with international elements.

John Lennon Has a wealth of expertise in the criminal fraud arena and is regularly instructed in complex matters, including tax fraud, mortgage fraud and money laundering cases. He is regularly instructed to prosecute and defend professionals. **Strengths:** "He is phenomenal and his work rate is astonishing." "He is a very serious fraud lawyer. He is very determined and exceptionally good at what he does." **Recent work:** Represented a leading conservation academic accused of being involved in a carbon credit fraud.

6KBW College Hill

THE SET

6KBW College Hill offers a broad range of skills across the gamut of financial crime, demonstrating expertise in areas such as fraud and investigations by the SFO, HMRC and the FCA. Its members have "a reputation for being fair, accurate and exemplary

prosecutors," according to one interviewee. It handles both the prosecution and defence of high-profile cases, regularly appearing on behalf of major corporate clients and taking on advisory work for the SFO.
Client service: The clerking team is led by the affable and very efficient Andrew Barnes.

SILKS

David Perry QC Has an outstanding reputation for advising significant corporate clients in relation to SFO, FCA and HMRC investigations. He is widely acknowledged for his masterful handling of cases involving difficult points of law. **Strengths:** "He is very clever, particularly when it comes to appellate work. The court just loves him as he is very reliable, accurate and very kind." "He is an intellectual giant." **Recent work:** Advised Barclays on SFO and FCA investigations into certain Qatari investments in the bank.

Duncan Penny QC Sought after to prosecute and defend in major SFO cases, involving serious fraud and bribery allegations. He was appointed Senior Treasury Counsel in 2014. **Strengths:** "He is clever, incredibly hard-working and a very formidable advocate." **Recent work:** Instructed for the SFO in relation to its investigation into an alleged accounting fraud committed by Olympus.

Sasha Wass QC Regularly called upon to prosecute large-scale SFO and CPS fraud trials. She has particular experience in fraud and money laundering cases arising in the City. **Strengths:** "She is really hard-working and delightful to work with." "She is very thorough, excellent with clients and a strong advocate. **Recent work:** Prosecuted the former governor of Delta State in Nigeria, who pleaded guilty to money laundering and defrauding the public purse.

JUNIORS

Miranda Hill A leading junior with extensive experience of handling financial crime matters including serious corruption and complex fraud cases. **Recent work:** Advised Barclays on SFO and FCA investigations into certain Qatari investments in the bank.

Gareth Patterson A strong criminal fraud practitioner with recent experience in market abuse, money laundering and 'cash for crash' cases. He is regularly a junior of choice for the SFO. **Strengths:** "He has a really methodical and thoughtful approach. He leaves no stone unturned." "He's really passionate about his work and incredibly bright. He has an awesome intellect and when he's on his feet he's really powerful." **Recent work:** Instructed to represent a broker accused of market manipulation in the context of the Libor scandal.

Annabel Darlow Frequently instructed by the SFO to act as junior counsel for the prosecution in high-value fraud cases. She has a growing advisory practice. **Recent work:** Instructed by the SFO to prosecute a £740 million mortgage fraud.

Alex Chalk Well versed in acting for the prosecution and defence in SFO and FCA cases. His recent experience includes a number of mortgage fraud and fraudulent trading cases. **Strengths:** "He's fantastically bright, extremely hard-working and wins the confidence of judges very quickly." "He's an excellent advocate and will fight his client's cause very strongly and effectively in court. He also provides excellent client care." **Recent work:** Acted for the SFO in a multi-handed fee fraud case.

Matrix Chambers

See profile on p.832

THE SET

Renowned for its depth at the top level, Matrix houses some of the leading financial crime silks in the country. Members of the set have a wide range of expertise and are able to advise on the full breadth of issues in the space. They are particularly skilled at handling criminal fraud and corporate crime investigations. The set is defendant-focused and often works on some of the largest and most high-profile cases both in the UK and abroad.
Client service: Paul Venables is the go-to clerk for cases of this nature.

SILKS

Clare Montgomery QC Has an outstanding reputation for appearing in the most legally complex and significant white-collar cases. She is also highly sought after to advise corporations in relation to large-scale investigations. **Strengths:** "She is an intellectual giant, who is often retained by massive corporations."

Alex Bailin QC (see p.541) An excellent choice to advise on cases involving financial crime and regulatory issues. He is regularly instructed to represent corporations and individuals who are exposed to criminal allegations. **Strengths:** "He understands the world of finance and is a good strategic and creative thinker. He's very charming, intelligent and energetic." **Recent work:** Advised an oil executive in relation to his fraud trial in Russia.

Julian Knowles QC Called upon to advise on sensitive pre-charge issues. His experience of public law and extradition matters makes him an ideal choice to handle cases involving human rights issues and cross-border elements.

Tim Owen QC Has an excellent reputation for representing senior individuals who are prosecuted in the course of investigations conducted by the SFO, FCA and foreign prosecuting authorities. **Recent work:** Defended a former director of iSOFT, who was charged with market abuse following an FCA investigation.

Ken Macdonald QC He is a highly regarded criminal fraud expert. He is sought after by major corporations and professional individuals for pre-charge advice. **Strengths:** "He is very good. He has a very light touch but he's incredibly effective."

JUNIORS

Andrew Bodnar Has a broad business crime practice, which encompasses bribery and corruption matters, fraud and confiscation proceedings. He is particularly well placed to advise on cases involving overlapping civil and criminal aspects. **Strengths:** "Impresses with his advocacy and thought process when handling confiscation proceedings in particular."

QEB Hollis Whiteman

See profile on p.853

THE SET

QEB Hollis Whiteman is "a top criminal set" and has a well-deserved reputation in the general crime and business crime spheres. It is hailed for its deep bench, has a "large number of very talented barristers," and possesses a standout track record for handling major fraud cases. Members prosecute and defend cases, and are frequently called upon by key investigating authorities such as the SFO and FCA to act in significant matters. Recent key instructions for the set have included cases involving bribery, insider trading and money laundering.
Client service: "They have an excellent clerking team led by Chris Emmings, who is very well supported by Faye Patis."

SILKS

Mark Ellison QC (see p.595) Has an excellent reputation for handling complex financial crime cases, as evidenced by the high-profile instructions he has recently received from the SFO and FCA. **Strengths:** "He is a first-class advocate and highly aware of what the other side is thinking. He takes a calm, intelligent approach to problems." **Recent work:** Instructed for the FCA in a large-scale insider dealing trial.

William Boyce QC Singled out as a leading financial crime practitioner, who has impressive experience of insider dealing, fraud and false accounting cases. **Strengths:** "His meticulous preparation, attention to detail and lethal intellect make him a very fine advocate." **Recent work:** Advised the SFO on allegations of bribery relating to an international organisation.

Adrian Darbishire QC Recognised for his excellent white-collar practice, which encompasses fraud, corruption and market abuse cases. **Strengths:** "He has a very nice relaxed manner with the clients and is forensic in his advice." "He is used on cases that are reserved for real stars. This shows the trust solicitors have in him." **Recent work:** Defended a managing director accused of money laundering.

Sean Larkin QC Known for prosecuting and defending fraud cases involving high-level professionals at major corporations. His recent experience includes money laundering, insider dealing and corruption matters. **Strengths:** "He's very, very client-focused, extremely hot on the details and has a very disarming manner." **Recent work:** Instructed by the FCA in the Operation Cotton land banking fraud case.

Peter Finnigan QC Regularly called upon by the SFO to advise on large-scale investigations. His expertise encompasses white-collar fraud, corruption, money laundering and revenue offences. **Strengths:** "A very safe pair of hands."

Tom Kark QC Well placed to advise on financial crime cases involving overlapping regulatory issues. **Strengths:** "He is very personable and great with clients."

JUNIORS

Selva Ramasamy Defends and prosecutes professionals in serious fraud cases. His recent experience includes a number of tax fraud matters. **Strengths:** "He is a very fluid advocate, who makes it all look so easy, and his cross-examinations are devastatingly incisive." **Recent work:** Defended an actress and a film producer implicated in a film fraud case prosecuted by HMRC.

Paul Raudnitz (see p.704) Sought after to defend and prosecute high-profile white-collar cases. He has key experience of corruption, benefit fraud and trading standards matters. **Strengths:** "He is very calm and prioritises well. He knows the cases so well and always has the details at his fingertips." **Recent work:** Instructed by the FCA in the Operation Cotton land banking fraud case.

Rachna Gokani Regularly instructed by blue-chip firms to advise on complex, business-sensitive matters. Her expertise includes money laundering, sanctions and corruption cases. **Strengths:** "She has a fantastic future ahead of her, and is an exceptionally hard worker."

Band 3

9-12 Bell Yard

THE SET

9-12 Bell Yard houses experts in criminal fraud matters and has experience in both the prosecution and defence of such cases. One commentator judges the set's members to be "ideally suited to fraud work," as they combine "keen analytical intellect" with "case-appropriate pragmatism and jury-friendly advocacy." Key areas of specialism include bribery and money laundering, and the barristers regularly provide advice and representation to companies and professional individuals.

Client service: The "helpful and effective" Angela May leads the set's clerking team.

SILKS

Lord Carlile of Berriew QC (see p.565) Has a great deal of expertise in serious and complex criminal matters. He has the skills and knowledge base to handle criminal fraud cases concerning tax evasion and carbon credits. **Strengths:** "He has got an amazing amount of experience."

Mukul Chawla QC (see p.570) Highly praised for his work in the white-collar crime arena. He has experience of both prosecuting and defending, and notable expertise in fraud matters. **Strengths:** "He is a great tactician. He can deal with the most complicated of cases and get to the bottom of them." "He has really good judgement. He very carefully thinks through his strategies and very rarely gets it wrong." **Recent work:** Instructed by the SFO to advise on various Libor manipulation investigations.

John McGuinness QC (see p.668) Has experience in serious crime cases, with particular expertise in fraud-related matters. **Strengths:** "He's a quality advocate with bundles of experience."

Jonathan Kinnear QC (see p.646) Has particular expertise in indirect tax cases, as well as enforcement matters and complex confiscation and restraint issues. **Strengths:** "He is enormously able and a really accomplished advocate." "He has an admirably robust approach – he is absolutely stunning as a prosecutor." **Recent work:** Acted for the CPS in confiscation proceedings involving asset tracing in multiple jurisdictions.

7BR

See profile on p.772

THE SET

The set houses an established financial crime team with specialist knowledge of complex criminal fraud. Barristers at 7BR advise on prosecution and defence matters, and regularly work on cases in the UK and abroad. The set has a growing workload involving advice to corporate clients on fraud and criminal investigations. Recent experience includes numerous high-profile prosecutions on behalf of the SFO and FCA, money laundering cases and market abuse matters.

Client service: Paul Eeles and Rod McGurk are the senior clerks at the set.

SILKS

Collingwood Thompson QC Offers particular expertise in high-profile money laundering, criminal fraud, corruption and asset recovery matters. **Strengths:** "He has substantial experience of dealing with privilege issues in the context of criminal investigations and prosecutions. He is well mannered, very diligent, proactive and responsive to any issues raised." "He is extremely good at listening to the client and responding to their concerns. He doesn't pull punches and gives clear advice." **Recent work:** Prosecuted a money laundering case on behalf of the CPS, successfully securing a conviction.

Richard Latham QC A highly sought-after criminal silk with experience of both the prosecution and defence of serious and complex fraud cases. **Recent work:** Prosecuted the former chairman and former directors of iSOFT in an FCA case concerning alleged conspiracy to mislead the market.

David Farrer QC Has significant experience in asset recovery, particularly with regard to the interaction between civil and criminal proceedings. He is also highly regarded for his capacity to handle fraud, corruption and money laundering cases involving multiple jurisdictions. **Strengths:** "He always offers first-class advice."

Philip Shears QC Has broad expertise in financial crime matters, with experience of cases involving allegations of corruption, money laundering and fraud. **Strengths:** "He's very impressive. He did an excellent job in cross-examination and his advocacy was excellent." **Recent work:** Instructed by the SFO in a high-profile case against Asil Nadir relating to an alleged theft from Polly Peck International.

JUNIORS

Jason Mansell Has a particular focus on the defence of individuals and corporates in financial crime matters. He has handled proceedings arising out of a number of FCA and SFO investigations. **Strengths:** "He has a great command over detail and he is unflappable." "He's a white-collar crime regulatory expert."

Andrew Wheeler Prosecutes and defends serious fraud cases and is regularly instructed by the SFO and FCA. He has particular expertise in tax fraud matters.

Jennifer Carter-Manning Has experience prosecuting and defending financial cases. She is regularly instructed in matters relating to fraud and money laundering.

The Chambers of Andrew Mitchell QC

See profile on p.776

THE SET

The Chambers of Andrew Mitchell QC is a boutique civil and criminal fraud set, with particular expertise in POCA work, asset recovery and market manipulation. Recent highlights have seen its barristers instructed on international criminal fraud investigations and prosecutions in a range of jurisdictions, including high-level political corruption and bribery cases. Members are also regularly called upon to advise corporate clients on regulatory compliance matters.

Client service: The clerking team is led by practice director Martin Adams.

SILKS

David Evans QC Has a criminal fraud specialism and is regularly instructed in major investigations. **Strengths:** "He is superb and to the point."

Graham Brodie QC Has expertise in confiscation proceedings and asset freezing. He is regularly instructed for the defence in financial crime cases. **Strengths:** "He does not put a foot wrong throughout the whole case and impresses everybody." "He's an impeccable barrister." **Recent work:** Acted for a defendant in the Innospec case, an SFO prosecution relating to alleged bribery and corruption in Indonesia.

Andrew Mitchell QC Prosecutes and defends serious fraud cases. He has notable expertise in asset forfeiture and money laundering. **Strengths:** "He is a giant in the bribery and corruption area and acts in some of the best and most significant international cases. He is a very good fraud lawyer." **Recent work:** Prosecuted a high-profile bribery and corruption case relating to a property development in the Turks and Caicos Islands.

Amanda Pinto QC Highly respected in the market for handling a broad range of financial crime matters. **Strengths:** "She is indefatigable, clever, has a great courtroom presence and is a real fighter."

Alistair Webster QC Has particular expertise in criminal fraud. Areas of specialism include VAT fraud, mortgage fraud, bribery and corruption, and money laundering. **Strengths:** "He is great on his feet and excellent at the paperwork."

JUNIORS

Keith Mitchell (see p.674) A highly reputed junior advocate with experience of prosecuting and defending significant fraud cases. **Recent work:** Lead junior defence counsel in an advance fee fraud case prosecuted by the SFO.

Jonathan Lennon Commands respect from the financial crime market. He has a specialism in criminal fraud matters and is well versed in handling POCA issues. **Strengths:** "He's knowledgeable and has been involved in leading cases in relation to proceeds of crime and money laundering. He has a very good client manner and is easy to work with."

Outer Temple Chambers

See profile on p.842

THE SET

Outer Temple Chambers continues to increase its presence in the financial crime arena and offers deep experience at the silk and junior level. Sources say its members are "always booked to handle large frauds," and that the set has "really established itself in this area." Barristers at the set are regularly called upon to prosecute and defend serious and complex fraud cases, including matters involving cross-border elements. The chambers boasts significant expertise in insider dealing, and has advised on major cases in the field including Operation Tabernula and Operation Saturn.

Client service: Steve Graham is the director of clerking at the set and leads a "very user-friendly and very professional" team.

SILKS

Michael Bowes QC Regularly instructed in relation to major corporate investigations. He offers expertise in financial services, regulatory issues and criminal fraud. **Strengths:** "He is doing very well at handling insider dealing work."

Richard Lissack QC Has a thriving financial crime practice and has been involved in a number of major SFO investigations, regularly representing corporates. **Strengths:** "An excellent lawyer – enthusiastic and client-friendly with a wealth of experience." **Recent work:** Instructed in an FCA investigation concerning international corruption.

JUNIORS

Robin Barclay (see p.543) A highly respected criminal fraud advocate with expertise in regulatory enforcement issues, corruption and market manipulation. **Strengths:** "He has a really good command of the law and he is realistic and sensible." "I was very impressed with him. He worked very hard and he was very effective – he knew the brief backwards." **Recent work:** Involved in a major insider dealing case arising out of the FCA's Operation Tabernula investigation.

5 Paper Buildings

See profile on p.844

THE SET

Noted for their work relating to criminal fraud, barristers at the set are frequently instructed for the prosecution and defence, and are often sought after by the SFO. Sources say "the calibre of members at the set is fantastic, and they provide robust and accurate advice." The team works on cases that are both publicly and privately funded and are often involved in high-profile cases, many of which involve multi-million pound frauds. Instructing solicitors appreciate that the team is "very organised and proactive." **Client service:** Sources say "the clerks will help if you are in a bind," and report that they are "extremely efficient and personable."

SILKS

Jonathan Caplan QC Has impressive experience of handling multi-jurisdictional fraud cases, particularly those involving Hong Kong. He is sought after by professional clients to provide pre-charge advice.

Julian Christopher QC (see p.572) Viewed as an up-and-coming fraud silk. He has particular experience of prosecuting and defending heavyweight tax fraud cases. **Strengths:** "He is without doubt a superstar fraud silk of the future. His grasp of the law and facts in a case is second to none." "He is very impressive and very intellectually gifted." **Recent work:** Represented the first defendant in a £10 million MTIC trial.

JUNIORS

Tom Allen (see p.535) Called upon to act as defence junior in high-end fraud cases. He is well versed in handling boiler room and mortgage fraud cases, and is praised for his strategy and tactical prowess. **Strengths:** "He's a thoughtful and pragmatic lawyer who identifies all the issues quickly." **Recent work:** Acted for the defence in a USD100 million boiler room case prosecuted by the SFO.

Ben Douglas-Jones (see p.590) Defends and prosecutes large-scale fraud cases. His recent experience includes mortgage fraud, trading fraud and investment fraud cases. **Strengths:** "He is very able and very meticulous, and he knows the law. He has his finger on the pulse." **Recent work:** Acted as junior prosecution counsel in a major mortgage fraud trial prosecuted by the London Central Fraud Group.

Janet Weeks (see p.748) A well-regarded junior with particular expertise in insider dealing, money laundering and tax fraud cases. **Strengths:** "She is very hard-working and has very good judgement." **Recent work:** Prosecuted a solicitor and costs draftsmen accused of submitting fraudulent bills to the LSC.

Stephen Hopper (see p.631) Has experience of prosecuting and defending financial crime cases, including major benefit frauds. **Strengths:** "He is really knowledgeable and has very strong communication skills. He is extremely thorough and very dedicated."

Red Lion Chambers

THE SET

Red Lion Chambers offers a strong bench of silks and juniors who have extensive expertise in a range of financial crime matters. Members prosecute and defend in this area, and demonstrate strength in handling major cases concerning international corruption, investment fraud and market manipulation. Barristers at the set often receive high-profile instructions from investigating authorities including the SFO, FCA and OFT.

Client service: Mark Bennett is practice director at the set.

SILKS

Antony Shaw QC A leader in the field of fraud. He undertakes a wide variety of cases and is regularly instructed in major SFO trials. **Strengths:** "He's an absolute star. He is extremely intelligent, he is a great lawyer and his real skill lies in being able to get to grips with complex issues and explain them in very simple terms. He has a clarity of thought which distinguishes him from other people." **Recent work:** Defended an individual in the Innospec investigation relating to allegations of bribery of officials in Indonesia.

Peter Carter QC (see p.566) A heavyweight criminal fraud practitioner who has experience of prosecuting and defending serious crime cases. **Strengths:** "He is very good and approaches the case and material in a sensible way." **Recent work:** Instructed in a VAT fraud concerning an offshore company trading in mobile phones.

David Etherington QC (see p.596) An experienced criminal practitioner. He has impressive expertise in criminal fraud and has prosecuted numerous cases for the SFO and HMRC. **Strengths:** "He is a delight to be in court with." **Recent work:** Represented one of the defendants in a significant immigration fraud case.

Jeremy Benson QC (see p.547) Recognised for his abilities in complex criminal matters and serious fraud cases. **Recent work:** Handled a tax evasion case on behalf of the HMRC.

Sally-Ann Hales QC (see p.617) Has significant experience handling criminal fraud cases for the SFO, and is an expert in corruption matters and multi-jurisdictional work. **Recent work:** Acted for the defendant in a case concerning alleged money laundering and conspiracy to defraud. The matter arose out of an international boiler room fraud.

JUNIORS

Tom Forster (see p.602) Handles the defence and prosecution of business crime matters. He is highly regarded by peers and has a particular specialism in confiscation proceedings. **Recent work:** Acted as defence counsel in a carbon trading tax fraud case which arose out of Operation Amazon.

Gillian Jones (see p.640) Has extensive experience in the criminal fraud arena. She has handled matters involving Libor manipulation, carbon credit fraud, money laundering and corruption. **Strengths:** "She has a stunning work rate. She knows the papers inside out and is a robust cross-examiner. For a junior, you couldn't wish for anyone better." **Recent work:** Acted for the SFO in a high-profile Libor manipulation matter.

Tom Payne (see p.691) A highly sought-after junior who has expertise in MTIC and tax fraud. **Recent work:** Prosecuted an HMRC fraud case which arose out of Operation Rust concerning the diversion of alcohol tax.

Andrew Marshall (see p.663) Has significant experience prosecuting serious and complex financial crime and regulatory cases. **Strengths:** "He is a junior of choice. He has good judgement and a good feel for cases." **Recent work:** Prosecuted an MTIC fraud case relating to the import and export of mobile phones.

Hannah Willcocks Broad criminal practice with expertise in asset forfeiture and complex financial crime. Frequently handles large-scale multi-jurisdictional matters. **Recent work:** Acted as junior counsel in a high-profile prosecution on behalf of the FCA concerning market abuse and insider dealing.

Allison Clare (see p.572) Expertise in criminal fraud and confiscation proceedings, including corruption and MTIC cases. **Strengths:** "She is incredibly thorough, really hard-working and an all-round excellent lawyer and advocate." **Recent work:** Acted on behalf of Lloyds Banking Group as third party and victim in a fraudulent trading and corruption case.

Other Ranked Lawyers

Neil Hawes QC (Charter Chambers) Well versed in commercial fraud cases. He is frequently instructed to defend significant SFO and FCA prosecutions. **Strengths:** "His eye for detail is fantastic and his preparation is right up there. He has great presentational skills in court." "He is a very hard-working silk, who is very reliable, good on the detail, thorough and well prepared."

Paul Phillips (see p.692) (Charter Chambers) Has a wealth of experience in financial crime matters and focuses his practice on criminal defence work.

Jonathan Fisher QC (Devereux) Defends and prosecutes serious fraud cases. He has a significant advisory practice. **Strengths:** "He is a very fine academic and a very good practitioner." "He's very knowledgeable and very responsive to queries, and provides good strategic advice based on a solid understanding of the law. He is an excellent advocate and an excellent public speaker." **Recent work:** Represented an RBS trader in a complex tax evasion investigation.

Christopher Sallon QC (Doughty Street Chambers) Has recognised international expertise in relation to financial crime matters, and specialist knowledge of bribery and corruption issues. **Strengths:** "He has a great manner with juries and clients. He is extremely accomplished, hard-working and thorough." **Recent work:** He acted as defence counsel in an international offshore money laundering case.

Siobhan Grey (Doughty Street Chambers) A criminal defence specialist with a focus on financial crime including boiler room frauds, insider dealing and corruption. **Recent work:** Involved in a long-running and significant pension fraud brought by the SFO.

Rupert Bowers (Doughty Street Chambers) Regularly instructed for the defence in criminal fraud investigations. His experience includes money laundering and carbon credit VAT fraud matters. **Strengths:** "He can advise on every aspect of a case, because he does a lot of civil and public law matters as well as criminal cases. He's very skilful and knowledgeable about a number of areas of the law and gives a complete service to the client." **Recent work:** Instructed in a large carbon credit fraud case.

Gavin Irwin (Dyers Chambers) Noted for his expertise in money laundering cases, and regularly handles corruption, sanctions breaches and fraud matters. **Strengths:** "He is very clued-up and switched-on." **Recent work:** Instructed on appellate and confiscation proceedings in relation to a benefit fraud case.

Peter Caldwell (see p.563) (Dyers Chambers) Has broad expertise in criminal fraud cases with experience of handling mortgage, boiler room and MTIC fraud. **Strengths:** "He's quite a cerebral character, who is thoughtful, tactically good and someone the clients are always happy with as they feel that he's making their points for them well." "He is unflappable in very difficult cases; he masters the evidence and papers." **Recent work:** Represented the defendant in a Serious Organised Crime Agency investigation relating to metal trading.

Hodge Malek QC (Thirty Nine Essex Street) Has an international presence in the financial crime arena. He has the ability to handle both civil and criminal aspects of commercial fraud cases. **Strengths:** "He's an astute tactician who gives clear strategic advice. He has a significant civil and criminal fraud track record, and is particularly strong when it comes to navigating complex international disputes. He's hard-working, incisive and good with clients." **Recent work:** Represented ICAP in a Libor manipulation case involving multiple jurisdictions.

Simon Mayo QC (see p.666) (187 Fleet Street) A criminal law specialist with experience in serious fraud and financial services regulatory issues. **Strengths:** "He is a very diligent practitioner who has won praise from prosecuting counsel in cases for his ability to cut to the core of the issue." "He is very good – very easy to get along with and very good in court."

Andrew Trollope QC (see p.740) (187 Fleet Street) A criminal fraud expert with notable experience of handling money laundering cases, restraint proceedings and tax fraud. **Strengths:** "He's very good at trial. He managed the difficulties of the case very well."

Peter Guest (see p.616) (187 Fleet Street) A highly respected criminal defence specialist who is frequently instructed in high-profile criminal fraud, confiscation and money laundering cases.

Natasha Wong (see p.755) (187 Fleet Street) Defends complex financial crime cases including serious fraud matters and regulatory proceedings. **Strengths:** "She has a very good rapport with her clients and a very easy courtroom advocacy style which is very endearing to the tribunal. She effortlessly masters her papers."

Charles Sherrard QC (see p.719) (Furnival Chambers) Has a broad criminal practice and particular experience in MTIC fraud matters. **Recent work:** Involved in a long-running carbon credit fraud case arising out of Operation Amazon.

Annette Henry QC (see p.625) (Furnival Chambers) Recently took silk and has significant expertise in serious crime, fraud and financial regulation matters. She has handled numerous money laundering and MTIC fraud cases.

Simon Baker (Goldsmith Chambers) Has experience in complex criminal fraud and regulatory matters and is often instructed in related confiscation proceedings. **Strengths:** "He is extremely efficient and wonderfully reliable." "He is able to turn around documents very quickly to a very high standard. He's incredibly easy to deal with and user-friendly." **Recent work:** Acted as junior defence counsel for the CEO of iSOFT in an FCA prosecution alleging market manipulation and revenue fraud.

Tom Little (see p.657) (9 Gough Square) Has experience in complex criminal fraud matters and often receives instructions in SFO investigations and prosecutions. **Strengths:** "He is hard-working, he has a deft touch, his drafting skills are very good and he understands both sides of the argument." **Recent work:** Prosecuted a high-profile international corruption case relating to oil and gas projects.

Eleanor Mawrey (see p.665) (9 Gough Square) Has particular expertise in insider dealing cases as well as experience of handling bribery and corruption matters. **Recent work:** Instructed by the FSA in a high-profile case involving a large insider dealing ring.

James Thacker (see p.735) (9 Gough Square) Has specific expertise prosecuting criminal fraud cases. **Strengths:** "He is very thorough, has good attention to detail and is very approachable." **Recent work:** Instructed as first junior for the prosecution in Operation Crystal, a complex money laundering and fraud case.

Philip Hackett QC (see p.616) (4-5 Gray's Inn Square) Has expertise in bribery and corruption matters, criminal commercial fraud and regulatory issues. He is often instructed on matters with an international element. **Strengths:** "He is brilliant at assessing the situation as it happens. He is very quick on his feet and very good at empathising with a jury or making them empathise with his client."

Sarah Clarke (Serjeants' Inn Chambers) Regularly instructed by the FCA on a range of matters, including market abuse, investment fraud and insider dealing cases. **Strengths:** "She's an advocate who works extremely hard for the clients and is not afraid to ask difficult questions." "She is very skilled in FCA and criminal fraud matters." **Recent work:** Instructed by the FCA on a major investment fraud case involving allegations of money laundering and FSMA offences.

Simon Draycott QC (see p.591) (5 St Andrew's Hill) Has experience of defending and prosecuting major fraud, money laundering and tax evasion cases. **Strengths:** "He very quickly gets his head around the detail of a case and deals with complex disclosure issues phenomenally." **Recent work:** Acted as defence counsel in relation to a mortgage and business loan fraud.

David Stern (see p.728) (5 St Andrew's Hill) Focuses his practice on the defence of financial crime and serious fraud, and handles complex regulatory matters. **Strengths:** "He is an absolutely first-rate junior and his intellectual and legal arguments are outstanding." "He is a talented and pragmatic defence counsel, who is tactically astute and very hard-working." **Recent work:** Acted for the lead defendant in a case alleging fraudulent conduct in relation to the provision of false information to the detriment of institutional investors.

Nicholas Medcroft (Wilberforce Chambers) Enjoys a strong reputation for his work in the financial services sector. He is frequently instructed by corporates and has experience of handling major fraud and regulatory matters. **Strengths:** "He's very collaborative and he works very hard. He's very good at listening and putting his own view across. He's very cautious and he'll look at things from various angles."

THE REGIONS

Financial Crime The Regions
Leading Silks
Band 1
Blair Peter *Guildhall Chambers (ORL)* ◊
Csoka Simon *Lincoln House Chambers (ORL)* ◊
Gozem Guy *Lincoln House Chambers (ORL)* ◊
Harrington Patrick *Farrar's Building (ORL)* ◊
Howker David *No5 Chambers (ORL)* ◊
Phillips Simon *New Park Court Chambers (ORL)* ◊ *
Pickup James *Lincoln House Chambers (ORL)* ◊
Sangster Nigel *St Pauls Chambers (ORL)* ◊
Webster Alistair *Lincoln House Chambers (ORL)* ◊
Leading Juniors
Band 1
Bridge Ian *No5 Chambers (ORL)* ◊ *
Grattage Stephen *Exchange Chambers (ORL)* ◊
Jebb Andrew *Exchange Chambers (ORL)* ◊
Johnson Nicholas *Exchange Chambers (ORL)* ◊
Kelly Mark *No5 Chambers (ORL)* ◊ [A] *
Lawton Paul A *Lincoln House Chambers (ORL)* ◊
MacAdam Jason *Exchange Chambers (ORL)* ◊
Whitehurst Ian *7 Harrington St Chambers (ORL)* ◊
◊ (ORL) = Other Ranked Lawyer.
[A] direct access (see p.11).
** Indicates individual with profile.*

Ranked Lawyers

Andrew Jebb (Exchange Chambers) Has extensive experience of both prosecuting and defending criminal fraud matters. **Recent work:** Instructed in Operation Valgus, defending a substantial mortgage fraud involving 800 properties and worth approximately £25 million.

Nick Johnson (Exchange Chambers) Has a strong criminal fraud practice. He principally acts as a defence counsel, but is also retained by specialist prosecution agencies. He is a veteran of a number of significant prosecutions brought by the SFO, FSA/FCA, HMRC and MHRA. **Strengths:** "He is bright and tactically aware, personable and also a very practically minded advocate."

Stephen Grattage (Exchange Chambers) Has an established criminal fraud practice. He both prosecutes and defends serious fraud cases, and has considerable experience of complex and paper-heavy cases. **Strengths:** "He is renowned for his care and attention to detail."

Jason MacAdam (Exchange Chambers) Well versed in a broad range of serious criminal matters. He has acted as defence counsel in a number of significant fraud and financial crime cases. **Strengths:** "He is a hard-hitting advocate, at ease in any trial."

Patrick Harrington QC (Farrar's Building) Has a wealth of experience in high-profile and serious criminal cases. He has handled a wide range of fraud cases, including those relating to mortgages, copyright, tax and Ponzi schemes. **Recent work:** Instructed in Operation Valgus, prosecuting a substantial mortgage fraud involving 800 properties and worth approximately £25 million.

Peter Blair QC (Guildhall Chambers) The head of Guildhall Chambers and a member of the SFO's list of prosecution counsel. He has extensive expertise in criminal fraud and corruption cases, and is noted for his work acting in cartel cases on behalf of the OFT. **Strengths:** "He is incredibly able – he is not just a very good lawyer but he's an agile advocate, he sees the wider picture, he's extremely good with clients, and he's just a wonderful person to have on your team, particularly when the going gets tough."

Ian Whitehurst (7 Harrington St Chambers) A noted criminal law practitioner with extensive expertise in fraud and financial crime matters. He has extensive expertise in missing trader intra-community (MTIC) fraud, tax fraud, false accounting and banking fraud. **Strengths:** "He has a very good client manner, and he has real strength in terms of his ability to tease out the issues of the case."

Simon Csoka QC (Lincoln House Chambers) Has a broad criminal law practice, and is noted for his particular expertise in serious fraud and MTIC cases. **Strengths:** "He is an incredibly good advocate."

Guy Gozem QC (Lincoln House Chambers) Has a broad criminal practice of which fraud cases form a significant part. He has been instructed on mortgage frauds, insurance frauds, and investment frauds and Ponzi schemes. **Strengths:** "He cuts through to the core issues incredibly quickly; there is very little padding in his advocacy and that helps in this type of work." "He is an exceptional advocate with a very calm client manner."

James Pickup QC (Lincoln House Chambers) A noted criminal fraud advocate with particular expertise in acting as the defence counsel in commercial fraud and financial crime cases. **Strengths:** "He is well known for his expertise in MTIC fraud work."

Alistair Webster QC (Lincoln House Chambers) Has extensive experience in the financial crime arena. He acts exclusively as a defence counsel, and receives instructions on cases relating to SFO fraudulent trading, counterfeiting, tax evasion and MTIC fraud. **Strengths:** "He has an outstanding intellect and is also very approachable. He also gets on well with judges, which is a real strength."

Paul Lawton (Lincoln House Chambers) Has considerable expertise in the financial crime arena. He has been instructed in a number of money laundering cases, and is predominantly recognised for his work as a defence counsel. **Strengths:** "He is an excellent advocate and particularly strong at pre-trial applications."

David Howker QC (No5 Chambers) A highly respected criminal fraud practitioner with particular expertise in tax fraud cases. He has considerable expertise in defending fraud cases concerning VAT, banking, insurance and mortgages.

Ian Bridge (see p.556) (No5 Chambers) Has an impressive criminal fraud practice covering financial, electoral, VAT and duty fraud cases. **Strengths:** "He's very down to earth and he relates very well to the lay clients." "He's a very good advocate; he engages well with the court. He judges the mood of the court. He presents and argues very well." **Recent work:** He acted in R v Nandan Pruthi, a large Ponzi fraud case. It was reported to be the largest in the UK and involved complex criminal and civil proceedings.

Mark Kelly (see p.644) (No5 Chambers) Handles heavyweight criminal fraud cases. His practice is defence-focused and covers a wide range of work, including MTIC, education, internet and banking fraud cases, amongst many others. **Strengths:** "He is an incisive cross-examiner in court, and is particularly good at looking at unusual legal angles for cases which challenge the other side." **Recent work:** Successfully defended in a complex mortgage fraud. He acted on behalf of the defendant, Surinderpal Bajwa, a professional client alleged to have obtained mortgages by defrauding banks and other financial institutions.

Simon Phillips QC (New Park Court Chambers) Has a strong financial crime practice focused on prosecuting criminal fraud matters and Proceeds of Crime Act cases. **Recent work:** Led the prosecution in R v Terry Stimpson, a test case challenge brought by fishermen in the 10 m and under fleet to the Marine Management Organisation's quota system.

Nigel Sangster QC (St Pauls Chambers) A highly regarded financial crime advocate, particularly noted for his expertise in MTIC cases. **Strengths:** "He is a great advocate with an impressive courtroom presence – when he walks into the room you know you're in the presence of a distinguished silk."

LONDON

Financial Services London
Leading Sets
Band 1
Blackstone Chambers *
Band 2
Fountain Court Chambers *
Outer Temple Chambers *
3 Verulam Buildings *
Band 3
South Square *
4 Stone Buildings *
Leading Silks
Star individuals
Blair Michael *3 Verulam Buildings*
Brindle Michael *Fountain Court Chambers*
Flint Charles *Blackstone Chambers*
Lissack Richard *Outer Temple Chambers* *
Band 1
Herberg Javan *Blackstone Chambers*
Malek Ali *3 Verulam Buildings*
Malek Hodge M *Thirty Nine Essex Street (ORL)* ◊ *
Vineall Nicholas *4 Pump Court (ORL)* ◊ *
Zacaroli Antony *South Square*
Band 2
Bompas George *4 Stone Buildings*
Crow Jonathan *4 Stone Buildings* *
Dohmann Barbara *Blackstone Chambers*
Eadie James *Blackstone Chambers*
Green Andrew *Blackstone Chambers*
Philipps Guy *Fountain Court Chambers* *
Russen Jonathan *Maitland Chambers (ORL)* ◊ *
Saini Pushpinder *Blackstone Chambers*
Thanki Bankim *Fountain Court Chambers* *
Band 3
Bowes Michael *Outer Temple Chambers* *
Brisby John *4 Stone Buildings*
Coleman Richard *Fountain Court Chambers* *
Davis Glen *South Square* *
Fisher Jonathan *Devereux (ORL)* ◊ *
Hunter Andrew *Blackstone Chambers*
Mitchell Andrew *Fountain Court Chambers* *
Odgers John *3 Verulam Buildings*
Peacock Nicholas *Maitland Chambers (ORL)* ◊
Powell John L *4 New Square (ORL)* ◊ *
Robertson Patricia *Fountain Court Chambers* *
New Silks
Allison David *South Square* *
Strong Benjamin *One Essex Court (ORL)* ◊ *
◊ (ORL) = Other Ranked Lawyer.
* Indicates set / individual with profile.
(A) direct access (see p.11).

Financial Services London
Leading Juniors
Band 1
Assersohn Oliver *Outer Temple Chambers*
George Andrew *Blackstone Chambers*
Hattan Simon *Serle Court (ORL)* ◊ *
Jaffey Ben *Blackstone Chambers*
Marquand Charles *4 Stone Buildings*
Mayhew David *Thirty Nine Essex Street (ORL)* ◊
Purchas James *4 Pump Court (ORL)* ◊ *
Purves Robert *3 Verulam Buildings*
Band 2
Brent Richard *3 Verulam Buildings*
Khan Farhaz *Outer Temple Chambers*
Lomnicka Eva *4 New Square (ORL)* ◊ *
Medcroft Nicholas *Wilberforce Chambers (ORL)* ◊ *
Pritchard Simon *Blackstone Chambers*
Band 3
Clarke Sarah *Serjeants' Inn Chambers (ORL)* ◊ *
Davison Eleanor *Outer Temple Chambers*
Eborall Charlotte *3 Verulam Buildings*
Hall Taylor Alex *4 New Square (ORL)* ◊ *
Hanif Saima *Thirty Nine Essex Street (ORL)* ◊ (A) *
King Henry *Fountain Court Chambers* *
Mallinckrodt Sophie *3 Verulam Buildings*
Mansell Jason *7BR (ORL)* ◊ (A) *
McClelland James *Fountain Court Chambers* *
Perkins Joanna *South Square* *
Shivji Sharif *4 Stone Buildings*
Smith Julia *Henderson Chambers (ORL)* ◊ *

Band 1

Blackstone Chambers

See profile on p.771

THE SET

Blackstone is unanimously regarded as being the preeminent chambers for all financial services matters due to its barristers' expertise in public and commercial law. It fields an enviable array of experts in this sector, who are often instructed on ground-breaking cases and the most complex disciplinary issues.

Client service: "When you need advice in a short timeframe, the clerks, led by Gary Oliver, will always pull something out of the bag."

SILKS

Charles Flint QC A favourite among the top global financial institutions, due to his quality performances in landmark cases. He is also frequently engaged by individuals who are under suspicion of having breached regulations. **Strengths:** "He's excellent, charming and has real gravitas. The tribunal hangs off every word he says, and there's no one better to present at board level." "He's extremely thoughtful and knowledgeable, and good at getting into the detail." **Recent work:** Defended the former chief executive of HBOS, Peter Cummings, in an Financial Services Authority (FSA) investigation alleging a breach of due care during the time period leading up to the financial crisis.

Javan Herberg QC Praised for his cerebral approach and his efficacy in testing boundaries and legal definitions. He is regarded as a go-to silk for cases that need a particularly intellectual approach, and he often acts for senior individuals and leading banks in front of the regulators. **Strengths:** "He is very user-friendly and knowledgeable. I don't think there is a barrister who has as good experience and knowledge of contentious Financial Services (FS) work as Javan." "He really knows FS enforcement inside out and backwards. He's a technical wizard." **Recent work:** Acted for the defendant, a senior individual at JPMorgan, in FCA (Financial Conduct Authority) v Achilles Macris, which concerned allegations arising out of trading losses built up by Bruno Iksil, the 'London Whale'. His application to the Upper Tribunal claiming third party rights was successful, and broke new ground as to how the regulator accords such rights.

Barbara Dohmann QC A doyenne of this sector, who continues to act in leading financial mis-selling cases, as well as judicial reviews and investigations. When she is not in London, she sits as a commercial judge in Qatar, dealing with related areas such as insolvency and civil fraud. **Strengths:** "She is hugely efficient, extremely quick and brilliant when you need a hard hitter. Her advocacy is tenacious and forthright." **Recent work:** Appeared in the Keydata SLS Proceedings, acting for a multitude of independent financial adviser defendants against claims of financial product mis-selling.

James Eadie QC The government's first choice to act on the Treasury's behalf in complex regulatory proceedings. He is also often instructed by the FCA as well as the Serious Fraud Office (SFO). **Strengths:** "He has an enormously broad practice and has to advise quickly on a broad range of very difficult issues. That requires a rare talent. He's also not at all stuffy or self-important, which makes him a real pleasure to work with." **Recent work:** Acted for the Treasury, the Financial Compliance Officer and the Home Office in connection with the planned implementation of the Single Tier and Public Service Pension.

Andrew Green QC Acts for an array of different clients, ranging from financial institutions and companies to individuals and the regulators themselves. Recently, he has found himself receiving instructions in cases relating to market abuse and insider trading. **Strengths:** "He's particularly good at representing very senior individuals, who find themselves under FCA investigation. He's good at getting them comfortable and inspiring confidence." "He is a high-level performer, who is massively intelligent, hugely quick and almost brutally efficient. He shows true leadership." **Recent work:** Acted for the defendant, a company and two directors, in FCA v African Land, which concerned the ongoing promotion of an investment scheme and the question of whether it counted as a collective investment scheme under section 235 of Financial Services and Markets Authority (FSMA).

Pushpinder Saini QC Represents individuals, hedge funds and institutions in disciplinary and enforcement cases. He is a particularly strong choice for matters involving complex structured products and sensitive information. **Strengths:** "He is extremely responsive, decisive, user-friendly and quick to respond. He can stand back and get a good, broad view of the issues and get right into the finer points as well." "He's discreet, very well informed, and very measured in his approach." **Recent work:** Acted on behalf of a trustee of Bernard Madoff in Eurofinance v Rubin as an intervener in Supreme Court proceedings regarding securities fraud insolvency.

Andrew Hunter QC Particularly well regarded due to his innovative solutions to problems. He is frequently called upon to represent the FCA, but also acts for financial institutions that have come under regulatory scrutiny, often in cases involving spread betting and price-fixing. **Strengths:** "He is phenomenally clever." "He knows his stuff and works really well. When the case demands cross-examination of witnesses with a hard edge, he's the man to do that."

Recent work: Appeared in the Upper Tribunal acting for the regulator in Arch Financial Products v FCA.

JUNIORS

Andrew George A leading financial services junior who is particularly well regarded for his ability to handle the entire spectrum of regulatory law, from admission issues and investigations, to advice on potential judicial reviews. He also has commercial law experience and is often engaged to act both for and against the FCA. **Strengths:** "He's extremely user-friendly and extremely sensible in his advice. On top of this area, he knows the letter of the law and what points work with the regulator and what points don't." "He's personable, intelligent and knowledgeable, and is clearly going to reach the top." **Recent work:** Acted for the defendant in FSA v Prudential, a case regarding allegations that Prudential had not given the regulator sufficient notice of a proposed transaction, which could possibly have been the largest in British corporate history.

Ben Jaffey An experienced junior who acts for foreign and domestic regulators, and represents financial institutions and individuals. He is also experienced in market abuse allegations and cases arising out of Libor manipulation. **Strengths:** "His particular specialism is his knowledge of public law. He's an incredibly impressive operator and has a charming manner with judges." "He takes a rigorous academic approach to cases, but, at the same time, is very commercial." **Recent work:** Acted on behalf of a former senior executive in FCA v Willford; a case concerning an alleged failure by FSA to give enough reason in a decision notice.

Simon Pritchard Demonstrates great skill in acting on behalf of the regulator. Having at one time been seconded to the FCA, he has a solid base of regulatory knowledge, and is regularly instructed in cases pertaining to collective investment schemes, enforcement proceedings, market abuse and insider dealing. **Strengths:** "He knows the regulatory framework and gives thoughtful advice." "An able and hungry junior, who is very keen, very enthusiastic, and quick to turn things around. **Recent work:** Acted on behalf of the regulator in FSA v Da Vinci Invest Limited and others, and successfully obtained a freezing injunction.

Band 2

Fountain Court Chambers

See profile on p.804

THE SET

Being a first-class set for banking litigation, Fountain Court has had little difficulty in forging a leading reputation in the financial services sector. Its practitioners have been heavily involved in the majority of the key issues of recent times, including the sagas relating to alleged mis-selling of interest rate swaps and PPI. They have also been heavily involved in matters arising out of the Libor scandal. Barristers here are often engaged by international financial institutions and high net worth individuals.

Client service: "The clerking team, which is led by senior clerk Alex Taylor, is extremely responsive. I've worked with them for many years, and they always make good recommendations. You can always rely on their advice."

SILKS

Michael Brindle QC A standout silk in the area, who has a truly stellar reputation for his work at home and abroad. He has vast experience of acting on behalf of the FCA, and is recognised for having an almost preternatural ability to see how a case will run. **Strengths:** "He has an amazing court manner. He is completely trusted by the Bench, and never takes a bad point." "A colossus in this area, he is incredibly bright and robust, doesn't pull any punches and has the ear of the court." **Recent work:** Acted on behalf of the FSA in a judicial review brought by the British Bankers' Association. The claim concerned the handling of complaints around the mis-selling of PPI.

Richard Coleman QC Gains instructions in a variety of the most important financial services cases. He has honed his expertise in acting on matters relating to Libor-rigging, interest rate swaps mis-selling and collective investment schemes. **Strengths:** "A go-to barrister for difficult pieces of work. He's brilliant, can distil concepts into simple ideas, and is incredibly flexible in the way he works. He gets things back to you in good time and he's incredibly willing to get into the detail. Nothing is too much trouble for him." **Recent work:** Acted for Rabobank with regard to the international regulatory investigations brought by the FCA, the Department of Justice and a host of other foreign regulators pertaining to the manipulation of Libor.

Bankim Thanki QC A silk with a leading reputation in banking and financial services, who is particularly well known for his specialism in legal privilege. He mainly focuses on representing banks under investigation by the FCA. **Strengths:** "He's quite adventurous. He's been taking on difficult cases with brave submissions and succeeding." "His manner in court is really terrific – it's soft and low key, but very much to the point. He's just a very impressive advocate and has a complete mastery of his brief." **Recent work:** Acted for Deloitte in an investigation carried out by the Financial Reporting Council (FRC) in relation to the client's role as a corporate finance adviser in the Phoenix Four/MG Rover case.

Guy Philipps QC Maintains an enviable practice at home and abroad in places like the Isle of Man, the Bahamas and the British Virgin Islands. He is a highly experienced advocate at appellate level. **Strengths:** "He's very helpful and puts in a lot of effort. He's very intelligent and very able, and adapts to different sorts of cases." **Recent work:** Successfully appealed to the Upper Tribunal in the case of John Pottage v FSA, completely exonerating Mr Pottage. Regarded as a test case, the matter concerned whether or not senior management should be held accountable for the alleged inadequate supervision of traders.

Andrew Mitchell QC An accomplished barrister whose practice straddles the divide between commercial cases and regulatory matters. He has experience in acting for the FSA in cases relating to collective redress compensation schemes, the mis-selling of financial products and market abuse. **Strengths:** "He is absolutely superb on his feet and makes you feel sorry for the barrister on the other side." "Clients, especially on the retail banking side, like him. He's always cheerful and there's never a dull moment with him." **Recent work:** Was involved in the litigation surrounding the collapse of the Arch Cru Investment Fund, which concerned allegations of mis-selling and breach of the FSMA.

Patricia Robertson QC Highly regarded by regulators, she has developed a strong focus on financial products mis-selling. Commentators note the quality of her advisory practice in particular. **Strengths:** "There are particular regulators who rate her very highly. Those regulators have a very tight list of barristers they regularly instruct and they like her because she's terribly quick and gets to the nub of the problem." **Recent work:** Represented AWD Chase De Vere – the main defendant in the Keydata litigation – against claims brought by the FSCS relating to the alleged mis-selling of investment products.

JUNIORS

Henry King (see p.646) Has a deep understanding of regulatory frameworks and the financial industry, as he is also a chartered accountant. His offshore expertise is notable, as is his strong capability in banking, making him a firm choice for complex cases in the Caymans, Trinidad and Tobago and the British Virgin Islands. **Strengths:** "He's very bright, very professional and committed to the client's best interests." "He's terrifically hard-working, diligent and easy-going." **Recent work:** Acted as junior counsel in the successful defence of Mr Pottage in John Pottage v FSA in the Upper Tribunal, and in front of the Regulatory Decisions Committee.

James McClelland A junior who is gaining a reputation for obtaining instructions in some of the standout cases in the sector, including cases relating to PPI mis-selling and collective investment schemes. **Strengths:** "His knowledge of details and his precision are second to none. He never misses a trick and always considers things from every angle." "He does exceptionally well – he's super-bright and very effective." **Recent work:** Successfully acted for Deutsche Bank in Deutsche Bank and Ors v Khan and Ors. This case raised questions over the management of credit facilities and the selling of investments.

Outer Temple Chambers

See profile on p.842

THE SET

Outer Temple Chambers has made great strides in the financial services sector due to its barristers' estimable strengths across civil, regulatory and criminal law. With so many strings to their bow, they have become well placed to gain instructions in a host of the major investigations at the forefront of the global regulatory market.

Client service: "The clerks are very good and very hospitable. They're always on top of things."

SILKS

Richard Lissack QC A standout silk with a great reputation for his courtroom prowess. He is an expert in a broad range of areas, and is particularly good on cases where criminal and regulatory law meet. He frequently finds himself instructed in cases of global significance. **Strengths:** "He really is a standout QC. He sees all the angles to complex problems and he's remarkable in his ability to address these complexities." "He has seen it all. As a rainmaker he's second to none, as he's heavily involved in the Financial Services Lawyers Association and has a very good client base." **Recent work:** Won a decisive victory for HSBC in Shah v HSBC, comprehensively striking out a USD400 million claim. The case raised significant principles in relation to compliance.

Michael Bowes QC (see p.553) A silk with expertise across a broad range of areas, who is especially good on criminal insider dealing cases. He acts for international financial institutions and regulatory bodies. **Strengths:** "He is impressive and has superb knowledge." **Recent work:** Acted on behalf of the FSA, successfully prosecuting an insider dealing ring in R v Mustafa and Others.

JUNIORS

Oliver Assersohn A barrister who has combined expertise in regulatory and civil law. He has deep knowledge of the RDC, having completed a secondment there, and is often instructed by that body. He demonstrates great ability in market-abuse proceedings. **Strengths:** "He's very bright, exceptionally hardworking, personable and very practical. He really understands the FCA's enforcement process." "He is calm, knowledgeable, diligent and keen to assist. A pleasure to work with." **Recent work:** Advised the Regulatory Decisions Committee in FSA v Mercurius, Visser and Fagbulu; an enforcement action alleging market abuse against a hedge fund, its CEO and its compliance manager.

Farhaz Khan Quickly became a leading junior in the field due to his evident skills. He has expertise not only in complex regulatory matters, but also in commercial, civil and criminal law, and is a firm favourite for instructing solicitors. Khan had a key role in setting up the Financial Services Lawyers Association. **Strengths:** "He is very impressive. He's got a tremendous eye for detail and he's a real hard worker. He's relatively junior, but brings great depth of experience to his cases." **Recent work:** Acted on the claimants' behalf in the Libor test case, Barclays Bank v Graiseley Properties, which arose out of the manipulation of the interbank offered rate.

Eleanor Davison Noted for having a practice that spans the criminal, regulatory and civil fields, she is a junior of choice for far-reaching investigations. She is also proficient in non-contentious compliance work for major banking institutions. **Strengths:** "Particularly good in cases relating to SFO investigations. She is great at hand-holding and adopts a very practical and focused approach." "She's a real powerhouse and packs a hell of a punch."

3 Verulam Buildings

See profile on p.875

THE SET

The members of 3 Verulam Buildings have significant expertise in banking litigation. Unsurprisingly, therefore, a good proportion of them, whether they be silks or juniors, have gravitated into financial services law. Many of its barristers were formerly at the FSA or have completed secondments with the regulators. As a result, they are able to demonstrate truly comprehensive knowledge of industry regulation. As well as aiding investors in collective investment schemes, the set is also known for its handling of the multitude of claims regarding the alleged mis-selling of interest rate hedging products.

Client service: "Definitely ten out of ten. Paul Cooklin's team really stands out in terms of the clerking they offer. They're good at recommending suitable people, they're commercial and they're realistic about pricing."

SILKS

Michael Blair QC A deeply experienced silk who garners tremendous respect from the market. His practice is mostly advisory, and he is sought out to guide his clients through the most turbulent regulatory waters. **Strengths:** "Absolutely first-rate, cerebral and great in litigation." "If you want someone who understands how one rule fits into the regulatory morass, then he's your man." **Recent work:** Acted for the Guernsey Financial Services Commission on a matter concerning enforcement actions against regulated firms.

Ali Malek QC A widely respected silk who successfully combines expertise in commercial law with strong regulatory knowledge. He is often called upon to advise on international regulatory frameworks and cross-border disputes. **Strengths:** "He is excellent at guiding a client through a difficult regulatory problem, especially where there is a twin-track civil claim." "Ali is a fierce cross-examiner, but he doesn't do that as a bar-room brawler. Instead, he's elegant in the way he deconstructs his opponents." "He's an intellectual trailblazer." **Recent work:** Acted for claimants bringing a case against Lloyds TSB alleging misrepresentation, breach of contract and breach of statutory and fiduciary duty surrounding the sale of highly complex multi-callable interest rate swaps.

John Odgers QC An authoritative voice on contentious and non-contentious regulatory matters. He is known for representing clients in front of both domestic and overseas regulators. **Strengths:** "He's incredibly responsive and highly intelligent." "Excellent on all fronts, he's a master of the detail, who brings a high level of analysis and a hands-on approach. He's a massive asset to any team." **Recent work:** Represented Dutch institutional pension fund Vervoer in a claim against Goldman Sachs, alleging negligent management of funds valued at more than EUR500 million.

JUNIORS

Robert Purves Former Chief Counsel at the FSA, who frequently acts both for and against the regulator. He has deep regulatory knowledge, and is a strong choice for cases that test regulatory boundaries and the deeper meaning behind regulation. **Strengths:** "He's got a very technical background, and is very good at putting complicated things very simply." "His legal work is of an extremely high quality. He has very high attention to detail and his advice is practical and thoughtful." **Recent work:** Acted for a major UK insurer, challenging the jurisdictional power of the Financial Ombudsman Service in relation to historic insurance product-related business acquired by the firm.

Richard Brent A junior with a leading reputation, who is known for his knowledge of European regulatory legislation. He is well known for handling cases involving complex derivative disputes. **Strengths:** "He has the ability to summarise complex concepts into simple language." "It is rare to find someone who combines broad commercial banking expertise with superb EU law regulatory knowledge." **Recent work:** Instructed as Barclays' junior counsel in the Libor test case, Graiseley Limited and others v Barclays Bank. The matter concerns allegations of swaps mis-selling and manipulation of the inter-bank offered rate.

Charlotte Eborall Continues to build on the tremendous regulatory experience she garnered from her two secondments at the FSA. Adept at acting on the regulator's behalf, she shows impressive strength in cases that have an insurance overlap, such as the PPI mis-selling litigation. **Strengths:** "She's very calm, measured, thoughtful and level-headed." "She really gets to know the client and gives good, practical, commercial advice. Her written work is really excellent as well." **Recent work:** Acted as sole counsel on behalf of the FCA in the final hearing of the sanction of a Part VII insurance business transfer as part of the reorganisation of Friends Life.

Sophie Mallinckrodt Adept at dealing with a broad range of topical issues, such as collective investment schemes and boiler-room scams. She has a particularly strong advisory practice and, having spent five years as a solicitor at Slaughter and May, has a strong grasp of her clients' needs. **Strengths:** "She's clever, reliable, hard-working, social and always willing to do the extra legwork." **Recent work:** Acted as Ali Malek QC's junior, appearing for a group of claimants against Lloyds TSB, in a case arising from the sale of complex interest rate swaps.

Band 3

South Square

See profile on p.861

THE SET

Insolvency set South Square's practitioners have been called upon to advise the administrators in some of the biggest cases arising out of the financial crisis. Examples include the recapitalisation of the Co-operative Bank and the client money claims against Lehman Brothers and MF Global. Members are noted for their high level of excellence in advisory work, and are consulted on multiple topics, such as client classification for regulatory purposes, the scope of the FCA to regulate insurance businesses, and the compliance of clearing houses with EU regulations.

Client service: "Ron Barclay-Smith's clerking team is very responsive and very helpful."

SILKS

Antony Zacaroli QC A heavy-hitting QC with an immense reputation, whose expertise spans a broad range of areas, including insolvency, banking and commercial disputes. He is often instructed by the FCA to advise on regulatory issues, with a particular focus on client money. **Strengths:** "He's incredibly user-friendly and able to articulate complicated stuff very clearly. He knows financial services law in incredible detail." "He's got a really well-honed bedside manner, which gives clients and instructing solicitors real confidence. He's also good at mucking in and working as part of a team." **Recent work:** Retained by the special administrators of MF Global to advise on regulatory issues relating to compliance and client classification stemming from the bank's special administration.

David Allison QC Demonstrates particular expertise in litigation relating to client money, and has additional strength in cases pertaining to collective investment schemes and mis-selling. He is a favourite of financial institutions and shareholders. **Strengths:** "David is incredibly calculating and very logical in the way he goes about things." **Recent work:** Acted on behalf of the clearing house LCH regarding a dispute with MF Global as to the title to T-bills lodged with such clearing houses.

Glen Davis QC Demonstrates expertise in tackling the insolvencies of insurer clients. He is also a noted expert on the special administration regime of investment banks. **Strengths:** "If you've got a tricky cross-border question, he's the guy to pick up the phone to. He's very businesslike and makes himself very available – he's very team-oriented." "He is quick to grasp, and is enthused by, technical regulatory issues, which he then explains to the court in detail." **Recent work:** Acted for the FCA in client asset and client money applications as part of the technical proceedings that arose out of the collapse of MF Global.

JUNIORS

Joanna Perkins (see p.691) Builds on a fantastic level of financial services knowledge garnered from her former career at the Bank of England. She is highly recommended for her ability to produce advice under pressure. **Strengths:** "She always has her finger on the pulse, from a regulatory and legal perspective. She's got a forensic, analytical mind, and has hugely impressive knowledge of the banking and financial markets." "She produces under pressure and makes things very clear." **Recent work:** Recently acted as counsel in a costs application.

4 Stone Buildings

See profile on p.865

THE SET

Barristers here often represent clients in all aspects of financial services law. As they possess related expertise in insolvency and company law, they are well placed to represent clients such as brokers, traders, funds and financial institutions in matters before regulatory tribunals. They also appear on behalf of the FCA.

SILKS

Jonathan Crow QC Respected by peers and well liked by the FCA. He is undoubtedly one of the leading barristers of his generation, and is noted for his peerless performances and for the variety of his caseload. **Strengths:** "A very doughty opponent who is right on top of the job." **Recent work:** Instructed by the FCA in the prosecution of Asset Land Investment, which had been found to be running an unauthorised collective investment scheme.

George Bompas QC Acts for a large base of foreign and domestic clients. He is noted as a strong choice for cases involving financial product mis-selling. **Strengths:** "He is outstanding in terms of the advice and the confidence he inspires in the client." "He is extraordinarily hard-working and spots points before they become points." **Recent work:** Acted on behalf of media tycoon Richard Desmond in his claim against Credit Suisse, alleging misrepresentation in the sale of a complex equity swap product.

John Brisby QC A highly experienced silk in the Chancery and commercial courts. He also has a formidable offshore practice, and has appeared in the courts of the Isle of Man, Gibraltar, Bermuda, the Bahamas and the Cayman Islands. **Strengths:** "He shows ingenuity and is a great advocate." **Recent work:** Has been involved in Libor-related litigation, defending a company against claims made by a major bank.

JUNIORS

Charles Marquand Has a flourishing financial services practice, and advises significant individuals in the UK and overseas. **Strengths:** "He is an expert on FSMA and the financial promotion regime." "He is very user-friendly; you can approach him with the odd question without formal arrangement." **Recent work:** Instructed by a financial services consultancy firm in a £20 million claim against a broker relating to the development of a mirror-based Forex trading system and its wrongful operation.

Sharif Shivji A former derivatives trader who has in-depth knowledge of the market and regularly acts for the FCA. He has been involved in a number of mis-selling claims in a host of areas, including PPI, interest rate swaps and Libor products. **Strengths:** "He's brilliant and lovely to work with. He is first-rate technically and a real gentleman." "He's very sharp and very good on his feet." **Recent work:** Acted for the claimants in Al Khorafi v Bank Sarasin-Alpen; a claim relating to the mis-selling of a USD150 million structured product.

Other Ranked Lawyers

Jason Mansell (see p.662) (7BR) Known for defending corporates and senior executives against FCA and SFO enforcement actions. He has related experience in accountancy regulation, having acted both for and against the FRC. **Strengths:** "He's an extremely calming influence and good on the detail." "He's always helpful, always available and always responsive. Added to this, he knows the approach the FCA will take." **Recent work:** Acted for former senior bank executives in relation to the FCA's investigation into Libor-rigging.

Jonathan Fisher QC (Devereux) Has a strong focus on the overlap of civil and criminal law. He is frequently instructed on market abuse, money laundering and market disclosure cases. **Strengths:** "He's cerebral, thorough, very industrious and very good on the black letter of the law. He really knows his stuff and he's completely immersed in the financial services world." **Recent work:** Acted for the defendant in FCA v Mineworld (AKA Da Vinci), resisting claims by the regulator that the defendant's high-frequency trading techniques should be seen as market abuse.

Benjamin Strong QC (see p.730) (One Essex Court) A recent silk who has joint strengths in the commercial and regulatory sectors, as well as international experience. He is a good choice for inter-jurisdictional complex derivatives disputes. **Strengths:** "He's always fired-up and on top of the brief. He's also very approachable and has great stamina." **Recent work:** Acted for the regulator in Hannam v FCA; an insider dealing case involving the former head of capital markets at JPMorgan.

Hodge Malek QC (Thirty Nine Essex Street) A commercial silk with an impressive reputation, who acts for the regulators as well as banks and individuals in disciplinary actions brought by the FCA. **Strengths:** "He's a very good operator and a master of the detail." "He is succinct, gives clear advice and always acts in the client's best interests." **Recent work:** Acted on behalf of ICAP in the investigations into the rigging of the Libor rate.

David Mayhew (Thirty Nine Essex Street) Formerly a partner at two leading law firms and the acting director of enforcement at the FSA. He frequently acts for financial institutions in high-profile regulatory investigations. **Strengths:** "He gives practical, sensible advice, is easy to get on with and has deep knowledge of the inside of the FCA." "He was previously a lead advocate at the FSA, so the Upper Tribunal places a lot of weight on what he says." **Recent work:** Advised UBS in an FCA enforcement investigation relating to Libor.

Saima Hanif (Thirty Nine Essex Street) Has built up broad experience, having had secondments to a significant solicitor firm, the Bank of England and the FCA. Noted for his commercial approach and great sector knowledge, he shows particular strength in representing individuals under investigation by the FCA. **Strengths:** "She's very user-friendly and very switched on to the issues at hand. She looks at instructions from the viewpoint of the client and gives a tailored work product." "Her advice is detailed, thorough, commercially focused and client-friendly. She has great knowledge of the FS industry and is very approachable and responsive." **Recent work:** Acted on behalf of mortgage broker Amir Khan, who was banned by the FCA due to an oversight in his personal mortgage application.

Julia Smith (see p.723) (Henderson Chambers) Focuses on advising banks on complex consumer credit matters. Recently, she has been advising on claims relating to the mis-selling of PPI. **Strengths:** "She's incredibly technical and knows the Consumer Credit Act inside out." "She's extremely calm under pressure and gets to the nub of the issue really quickly."

Jonathan Russen QC (see p.712) (Maitland Chambers) His financial services expertise is complimented by strengths in the related areas of company, partnership and insolvency. He also has a solid offshore practice, having been called to the Bar of the Eastern Caribbean Supreme Court, and having appeared in the past in the courts of Gibraltar and the Isle of Man. **Recent work:** Advised a high-street bank in relation to allegations of credit card insurance mis-selling.

Nicholas Peacock QC (Maitland Chambers) Maintains a broad commercial practice with a focus on financial regulation. He is regularly instructed by the FCA and has great experience in matters concerning the shutting down of unauthorised investment companies. **Strengths:** "He is very bright, very accessible to clients, a tough negotiator and a confident advocate. He is a favourite of the regulator and has a collective investment scheme speciality."

John Powell QC (4 New Square) Focuses on acting for claimants in investment, banking and corporate fraud cases. He also has a thriving advisory practice relating to regulation in the UK, US and Europe. **Strengths:** "He is first-rate and understands the balance between the law and the commercial realities of life." "A lawyer's lawyer, he is happy to discuss the reasoned views of his instructing solicitors." **Recent work:** Brought a high-profile claim against more than 50 defendants in Brown v Innovator and Others.

Eva Lomnicka (see p.658) (4 New Square) Unanimously regarded as an authority on the area, particularly on consumer credit issues. Also an expert in collective investment schemes, she regularly advises on the impact of new legislation in this area. **Strengths:** "She's a very well-respected academic in the FS area. When she writes an article, everyone reads it with interest." "Her quality of analysis cannot be matched."

Alex Hall Taylor (4 New Square) A conscientious junior with a growing reputation. He is particularly noted for his expertise in multimillion-pound claims on behalf of independent financial advisers against IFA networks. **Strengths:** "He has the ability to see the wood from the trees and drill down to what's important. He's extremely good on the paperwork, very sound and very commercially oriented." "Good at dealing with technical and regulatory issues affecting IFAs, he gives very clear advice and it feels like he knows what to do straight away." **Recent work:** Acted for Barclays in a claim against Knight Frank for its alleged £100 million over-valuation of the hotel portfolio of the Von Essen hotel group.

Nicholas Vineall QC (4 Pump Court) Successful in acting for the FCA and representing individuals under regulatory scrutiny. With a specialism in commercial fraud, he has acted on the FCA's behalf in matters concerning boiler-room scams, high-yield investment schemes, collective investment frauds and Ponzi schemes. **Strengths:** "He has a silken charm, and is a decent and honourable opponent." "He knows what the FCA wants and he gives it to them. He's very confident, very smart and very friendly." **Recent work:** Acted as lead counsel in a group action for the Arch Cru investors against Capita Financial Managers, the directors of a collapsed investment fund.

James Purchas (4 Pump Court) An immensely experienced junior whose regulatory knowledge was heightened after a secondment at the FSA's enforcement division. He is recognised for his charm and intellectual prowess. **Strengths:** "He's a go-to barrister for non-criminal contentious FS. He's brainy and reliable, gives brilliant notes and produces excellent written advice." "He's extremely thorough and hard-working." **Recent work:** Acted for the defendant in FSA v Swift Trade and Peter Beck. This case raised significant questions as to the FCA's power to pursue market abuse cases involving derivatives trading.

Sarah Clarke (see p.573) (Serjeants' Inn Chambers) A barrister with a great depth of regulatory knowledge, who spent five years at the FSA's enforcement division. She is regularly instructed by the FCA in cases relating to market misconduct, such as insider dealing and mis-selling. **Strengths:** "Experienced and sensible," "she is an expert on financial market fraud. She works very hard, is quick at seeing the point and writes very clearly and succinctly." **Recent work:** Instructed by the regulator in Westwood Independent Financial Planners v FCA.

Simon Hattan (Serle Court) Has good regulatory knowledge, having been seconded to the FSA's enforcement division. He is regularly instructed in cases relating to civil fraud and breach of fiduciary duty. **Strengths:** "He is very familiar with the FSA's approach and displays excellent judgement." **Recent work:** Acted for claimants and defendants in claims alleging mis-selling of interest rate hedging products.

Nicholas Medcroft (see p.670) (Wilberforce Chambers) Acts for financial institutions facing regulatory investigations relating to civil fraud and money laundering. His practice spans the commercial and regulatory spheres, and he has also represented the Financial Reporting Council. **Strengths:** "He's a great team player and clients love him. He really understands the sector and finds commercial solutions." "He's very thorough, well-prepared, hard-working and effective." **Recent work:** Successfully defended NatWest against a claim made by the FCA alleging money laundering, dishonest assistance and negligence stemming from the bank's involvement in a Ponzi scheme.

Contents:

LONDON Civil

Fraud: Civil London
Leading Sets
Band 1
Blackstone Chambers *
Brick Court Chambers *
One Essex Court *
Essex Court Chambers *
Fountain Court Chambers *
Maitland Chambers *
Serle Court *
4 Stone Buildings *
3 Verulam Buildings *
Band 2
XXIV Old Buildings *
11 Stone Buildings *
Wilberforce Chambers *
◊ (ORL) = Other Ranked Lawyer.
* Indicates set / individual with profile.
Alphabetical order within each band. Band 1 is highest.

Fraud: Civil London
Leading Silks
Band 1
Anderson Robert *Blackstone Chambers*
Brindle Michael *Fountain Court Chambers*
Girolami Paul *Maitland Chambers* *
Howard Mark *Brick Court Chambers*
Malek Ali *3 Verulam Buildings*
McGrath Paul *Essex Court Chambers*
McQuater Ewan *3 Verulam Buildings*
Miles Robert *4 Stone Buildings*
Montgomery Clare *Matrix Chambers (ORL)* ◊
Peto Anthony *Blackstone Chambers*
Rabinowitz Laurence *One Essex Court*
Smith Stephen *Erskine Chambers (ORL)* ◊ *
Smouha Joe *Essex Court Chambers*
Thanki Bankim *Fountain Court Chambers* *
Trace Anthony *Maitland Chambers* *
Band 2
Beltrami Adrian *3 Verulam Buildings*
Boyle Alan *Serle Court* *
Browne-Wilkinson Simon *Fountain Court Chambers* *
Choo Choy Alain *One Essex Court*
Cohen Lawrence *Wilberforce Chambers*
Collings Matthew *Maitland Chambers* *
Croxford Ian *Wilberforce Chambers*
de Garr Robinson Anthony *One Essex Court* *
Dohmann Barbara *Blackstone Chambers*
Freedman Clive *7 King's Bench Walk (ORL)* ◊
Grabiner Anthony *One Essex Court*
Jones Philip *Serle Court* *
Kitchener Neil *One Essex Court*
Marshall Philip *Serle Court* *
Mill Ian *Blackstone Chambers*
Onslow Andrew *3 Verulam Buildings*
Rubin Stephen *Fountain Court Chambers* *
Steinfeld Alan *XXIV Old Buildings*
Tolaney Sonia *3 Verulam Buildings*
Toledano Daniel *One Essex Court*
Wardell John *Wilberforce Chambers*
Band 3
Brisby John *4 Stone Buildings*
Chapman Jeffrey *Fountain Court Chambers* *
Dougherty Charles *2TG - 2 Temple Gardens (ORL)* ◊ *
Dowley Dominic *Serle Court* *
Dunning Graham *Essex Court Chambers*
Gee Steven *Stone Chambers (ORL)* ◊
Gillis Richard *One Essex Court* *
Gourgey Alan *11 Stone Buildings* *
Hill Richard G *4 Stone Buildings*
Hunter Andrew *Blackstone Chambers*
Malek Hodge M *Thirty Nine Essex Street (ORL)* ◊ *
Morgan Richard *Maitland Chambers* *
Moverley Smith Stephen *XXIV Old Buildings*
Norbury Hugh *Serle Court* *
Quest David *3 Verulam Buildings*
Ritchie Stuart *Littleton Chambers (ORL)* ◊
Saini Pushpinder *Blackstone Chambers*
Samek Charles *11 Stone Buildings* *
Stanley Paul *Essex Court Chambers*
Sutcliffe Andrew *3 Verulam Buildings*
Swainston Michael *Brick Court Chambers*
Band 4
Auld Stephen *One Essex Court*
Crow Jonathan *4 Stone Buildings* *
Fenwick Justin *4 New Square (ORL)* ◊ *
Howe Robert *Blackstone Chambers*
Howe Timothy *Fountain Court Chambers* *
Levy Robert *XXIV Old Buildings*
Mann Martin *XXIV Old Buildings*
Matovu Harry *Brick Court Chambers*
Matthews Duncan *20 Essex Street (ORL)* ◊
Newman Catherine *Maitland Chambers* *
Odgers John *3 Verulam Buildings*
Pollock Gordon *Essex Court Chambers*
Singh Kuldip *Serle Court* *
Talbot Rice Elspeth *XXIV Old Buildings*
Vineall Nicholas *4 Pump Court (ORL)* ◊ *
New Silks
Fraser Orlando *4 Stone Buildings*
Goodall Patrick *Fountain Court Chambers* *
Moeran Fenner *3 Stone Buildings (ORL)* ◊ *
Weisselberg Tom *Blackstone Chambers*

Band 1

Blackstone Chambers

See profile on p.771

THE SET

A set constituted of top silks and excellent juniors, who complement their civil fraud practice with highly regarded financial services and regulatory expertise. They have been involved in a number of the large-scale, high-profile disputes of recent times, including Weavering Capital v Peterson, and Otkritie Bank v Urumov and Others. Instructing solicitors value the members' client-handling skills: "All the barristers are good with clients. They are very commercial and don't just hide behind textbooks – instead they really get involved in case strategy."

Client service: "The clerks are responsive and take a commercial view on their fees. They get back to you very quickly and appreciate that you're the middle man between client and counsel." Gary Oliver leads the team here.

SILKS

Anthony Peto QC Joint head of chambers and a barrister whose practice is heavily freighted with international corporate fraud disputes. He has particular expertise in interim remedies. **Strengths:** "He knows anything and everything about freezing and search orders." "A brilliant analyst who will think outside the box and come up with fantastic ideas all the time. When speaking to him you can see his mind whirring away." **Recent work:** Acted for several defendants in Otkritie Bank v Urumov and Others, a USD170 million Russian banking fraud dispute.

Robert Anderson QC Handles a raft of international fraud disputes, many of which relate to hedge funds. Commentators praise him for his cross-examination skills. **Strengths:** "What distinguishes him is his level of preparation – he does not simply rely on juniors; he has read everything, knows everything, and has all the points in mind. He inspires total confidence." "A street fighter, but also a lawyer with a very balanced understanding of strategy." **Recent work:** Acted for the claimants in Dubai Islamic Bank v PSI Energy Holding Co & ors, a USD440 million claim involving a commercial credit fraud.

Barbara Dohmann QC Has extensive experience of handling a range of civil fraud disputes. Instructing solicitors particularly value her client-handling skills. **Strengths:** "She has incredible knowledgeable of civil procedure and international private law, and is a great team player. She remains at the top of her profession." "Barbara is very client-focused and commercially aware and, where necessary, very hands-on." **Recent work:** Acted for the successful claimants in Barclays Pharmaceutical Ltd v Waypharm LP & Ors, a letter of credit fraud case.

Ian Mill QC Joint head of chambers. He has handled a variety of commercial fraud disputes in a distinguished career. He acts for claimants and defendants. **Strengths:** "Tenacious and effective." "He has the ability to cut through to the core of the problem and is one of the toughest cross-examiners around." **Recent work:** Acted for the first defendant in Bankas Snoras v Antonov & Anor; a EUR500 million banking fraud dispute.

Pushpinder Saini QC Handles a mix of fraud disputes, many of which arise in an insolvency context. Sources particularly admire his written work. **Strengths:** "Particularly knowledgeable in the regulatory field." "He is terrific. I saw him on a case and he destroyed the witnesses one by one." **Recent work:** Acted for a major international metals broker in a dispute alleging breach of a trading contract and fraudulent misrepresentation.

Robert Howe QC Tackles civil fraud and asset recovery cases as part of his broad commercial practice. **Strengths:** "Intellectually impressive and a man with great client skills." "He's a smooth advocate and is always very well prepared." **Recent work:** Acted for the claimants in uSwitch Holdings v Marquess of Milford Haven et al, a USD200 million dispute arising out of the sale of a business.

Andrew Hunter QC Has extensive experience of handling disputes for claimants and defendants. He has appeared in a number of search order and freezing order applications, and impresses peers with his advocacy skills. **Strengths:** "Prodigiously bright and extremely hard-working." "He's extremely impressive in court and has a great ability to think on his feet."

Fraud: Civil London	
Leading Juniors	
Band 1	
Higgo Justin	*Serle Court* *
Hutton Louise	*Maitland Chambers* *
Mumford David	*Maitland Chambers* *
Penny Tim	*11 Stone Buildings*
Band 2	
Atrill Simon	*Fountain Court Chambers* *
Drake David	*Serle Court* *
Elliott Steven	*One Essex Court* *
Harrison Christopher	*4 Stone Buildings* *
Harrison Nicholas	*Serle Court* *
Haydon Alec	*Brick Court Chambers*
Hubbard Mark	*New Square Chambers (ORL)* ◊ *
Mallin Max	*11 Stone Buildings*
Parker Matthew	*3 Verulam Buildings* *
Pester Iain	*11 Stone Buildings* *
Pilbrow Fionn	*Brick Court Chambers*
Pillow Nathan	*Essex Court Chambers*
Polley Alexander	*One Essex Court* *
Powell Leona	*Blackstone Chambers*
Sinclair Paul	*Fountain Court Chambers*
Thompson Steven	*XXIV Old Buildings*
Valentin Ben	*Fountain Court Chambers* *
Winter Alexander	*Maitland Chambers* *
Band 3	
Denton-Cox Gregory	*4 Stone Buildings* *
Dilnot Anna	*Essex Court Chambers*
Gledhill Orlando	*One Essex Court* *
Hattan Simon	*Serle Court* *
Hayman George	*Maitland Chambers* *
Head David	*3 Verulam Buildings*
Holtham den Besten Ruth	*Serle Court* *
Hood Nigel	*New Square Chambers (ORL)* ◊ *
John Laura	*3 Verulam Buildings*
King Edmund	*Essex Court Chambers*
Kramer Adam	*3 Verulam Buildings* *
Lazarus Michael	*3 Verulam Buildings*
Midwinter Stephen	*Brick Court Chambers*
Nambisan Deepak	*Fountain Court Chambers* *
Ng Jern-Fei	*Essex Court Chambers* *
Pillai Rajesh	*3 Verulam Buildings* *
Smith Ian	*11 Stone Buildings* *
Weekes Robert	*Blackstone Chambers*
Willan James	*Essex Court Chambers*
Zellick Adam	*Fountain Court Chambers* *
Band 4	
Akkouh Tim	*Erskine Chambers (ORL)* ◊ *
Casey Aidan	*3 Hare Court (ORL)* ◊
Davies David	*Essex Court Chambers*
George Andrew	*Blackstone Chambers*
Gillett Emily	*Erskine Chambers (ORL)* ◊ *
Hall Taylor Alex	*4 New Square (ORL)* ◊ *
John Benjamin	*Maitland Chambers* *
Moran Andrew	*Serle Court* *
Morrison Matthew	*Serle Court* *
Peters David	*Essex Court Chambers*
Phelps Rosalind	*Fountain Court Chambers* *
* *Indicates individual with profile.*	
◊ *(ORL) = Other Ranked Lawyer.*	

Recent work: Acted for the claimant in Slocom v Sibir Energy and ors, a dispute against the Russian oil company centring on alleged fraud and forgery.

Tom Weisselberg QC A new silk who, as a junior, appeared in a variety of courts on a range of civil fraud disputes. He has particular experience of claims involving search orders, freezing orders, information orders and document preservation orders. **Strengths:** "Everyone loves Tom; he's just fantastic and so easy to work with. His legal knowledge is second to none and he's a great advocate." **Recent work:** Acted for a defendant in Otkritie v Urumov & Ors, a significant dispute involving allegations of fraud, breach of fiduciary duty, knowing receipt and dishonest assistance.

JUNIORS

Leona Powell Regularly instructed to act as sole counsel on large-scale, high-profile fraud disputes. Sources praise her intellect. **Strengths:** "Extremely bright, and a very able advocate, who is highly commercial and responsive. She is a leading junior in this area and tough to beat." "She's a true fraud specialist, who has wonderful tactical judgement." **Recent work:** Acted for the claimants in Times Newspapers Limited v Lance Armstrong, a dispute concerning the recovery of legal expenses and settlement of monies paid to the cyclist pursuant to an allegedly fraudulent libel action.

Robert Weekes Handles a range of commercial fraud matters, and acts as sole counsel and as junior to leading silks. He represents large organisations and high net worth individuals, and regularly appears for claimants and defendants. **Strengths:** "Approachable, likable and a pleasure to work with." "Shows fantastic attention to detail, is extremely hard-working and is a team player." **Recent work:** Acted as senior junior for the claimants in Madoff Securities v Raven & Ors, a claim to recover USD28 million arising out of a Ponzi scheme.

Andrew George A popular choice for instructing solicitors in the City, who has acted for a number of prominent individuals in large fraud disputes. **Strengths:** "He makes the client feel that they are being protected, and that their case is being vigorously pursued and defended." "A fantastic strategist, who has a brilliant mind and is good on any fraud involving financial services or regulated sectors." **Recent work:** Acted for the defendant in the Innovator Litigation, a £65 million dispute concerning a former partner of a City law firm who was accused of dishonestly assisting an alleged fraud.

Brick Court Chambers

See profile on p.774

THE SET

The set is home to a select team of talented silks and juniors who regularly handle significant fraud matters, many of which are international in nature. Members are frequently instructed on disputes concerning CIS clients. The "incredibly successful set" is backed up by a strong clerking team, with one source commenting: "They've got a superbly well-oiled machine behind them."

Client service: "Their clerking team really stands out. They are very commercial, they understand the relationship between barristers and solicitors very well, and are prepared to have a sensible discussion on fees."

SILKS

Mark Howard QC Receives glowing praise from instructing solicitors and peers for his appearances in major fraud disputes. He enjoys a reputation as a "leading super silk at the Bar." **Strengths:** "He is renowned across the land for being one of the most in-vogue QCs to have on your case." "Probably the most lethal cross-examiner at the Bar." **Recent work:** Acted for VTB Bank in its Supreme Court action against Nutritek concerning a USD200 million fraud on the bank.

Michael Swainston QC Singled out for his impressive advocacy skills. He has particular experience of litigation connected with Russia and the CIS. **Strengths:** "He is a fearless advocate, who is extremely knowledgeable, good on his feet and able to give practical and concise advice on key issues. His advocacy skills are first-rate."

Harry Matovu QC Has a broad commercial practice and experience of heavyweight civil fraud disputes. He frequently handles disputes involving offshore jurisdictions and international clients. **Strengths:** "A charming and unflappable advocate. He has developed real expertise in complex jurisdictional battles." "He has an incredibly good bedside manner, very intellectual and is very thoughtful about the work that he does." **Recent work:** Acted for two of the principal defendants in a USD1.1 billion fraud claim brought by Alliance Bank.

JUNIORS

Fionn Pilbrow Has a wide-ranging commercial practice that takes in notable fraud cases. He has been involved in multimillion-pound disputes, acting for claimants and defendants. **Strengths:** "A star of the future. He has a huge capacity to get things done and is brilliant on technical matters." "His advice is clear and logical." **Recent work:** Acted for a defendant in a multimillion-pound claim brought by Coca-Cola alleging bribery and corruption perpetrated by an employee of the company.

Alec Haydon Handles a range of civil fraud disputes and asset recovery actions. He has been involved in a number of high-profile, big-ticket disputes for clients from Russia and the CIS. **Strengths:** "Very good on fraud and careful to find the right strategy." "He has huge experience in heavyweight commercial fraud cases and is great at fighting his corner." **Recent work:** Acted in Kazakhstan Kagazy PLC v Zhunus & Arip; a claim against the former shareholders and directors of a company.

Stephen Midwinter Frequently appears in disputes involving offshore clients and jurisdictions. He has been called to the Bar of the BVI and has appeared in a number cases there. **Strengths:** "He's top-drawer, no doubt. He gives silk-quality advice even though he's a junior." "He has great turnaround times and is user-friendly." **Recent work:** Acted in a dispute in the BVI concerning an alleged equity interest in a Georgian oil terminal that was said to have been misappropriated by the defendant.

One Essex Court

See profile on p.790

THE SET

A top-tier set that is home to some of the most highly regarded silks and juniors in the field. Members of the set are sought out for their expertise on the gamut of fraud work, from search and seizure and other injunctive remedies to multi-jurisdictional investigations and proceedings. Recent work undertaken by chambers includes acting on the high-profile matters of Fortress v Blue Skye and Dar Al Arkan v Al-Refai. One Essex Court's ability to offer "talent at every single level," coupled with a clerking team that is "second to none," makes it a top choice for instructing solicitors.

Client service: "The clerks, led by Darren Burrows, are responsive and prepared to have a discussion on fees, and will only recommend barristers who are appropriate for the job."

SILKS

Anthony Grabiner QC Enjoys a strong reputation as a practitioner who "carries the greatest authority." He has impressive fraud-related experience and is an expert on asset tracing. **Strengths:** "One of the great names of the Bar. He's first-rate." "He's very impressive and good at the helicopter view – he provides an excellent strategic overview."

Laurence Rabinowitz QC In high demand for his civil fraud expertise, he frequently represents international clients in multimillion-pound disputes. **Strengths:** "He couples an incredibly incisive analytical mind with hugely reassuring client-handling skills." "The heir to Jonathan Sumption's intellectual crown. He's an extremely gifted lawyer, with a nuanced touch as an advocate." **Recent work:** Represented the defendant in a USD1 billion dispute relating to the alleged misappropriation of iron-ore assets.

Daniel Toledano QC Receives extensive praise from instruction solicitors, who value his drafting and advocacy skills. He has been involved in some of the biggest cases undertaken by the set. **Recent work:** "He's a gracious advocate: he's a self-effacing man of brilliance who just makes the complex look easy." "Being in court behind him is like receiving a tutorial from a wonderfully able teacher, and the judges love him." **Recent work:** Acted for the defendants in VTB Capital v Nutritek, a landmark ruling concerning the jurisdiction of the English courts to hear claims worth around USD350 million.

Alain Choo Choy QC Has a particular interest in disputes relating to banking and finance, and frequently handles matters with an international flavour. **Strengths:** "Brilliant on cases involving financial instruments." "He's doing big-ticket cases and still has that personal touch, which is impressive." **Recent work:** Acted for Stirling Mortimer in a EUR10 million dispute alleging fraudulent misappropriation of funds from an offshore property fund.

Anthony de Garr Robinson QC (see p.585) Handles large-scale fraud for large corporations. He has an impressive offshore practice, and has been admitted to the Bar in the British Virgin Islands and the Bahamas. **Strengths:** "As good as they come." "He's rapidly becoming one of the leading commercial silks of his generation; he always has the ear of the court and is extremely user-friendly." **Recent work:** Acted for the defendant in a £100 million shipping fraud claim in the Court of Appeal.

Neil Kitchener QC Receives a plethora of praise from instructing solicitors and peers in the market, who regard him as a "pugnacious opponent." His broad civil practice includes a lot of Russian-related work. **Strengths:** "A courtroom star and an absolute joy to work with. Combines intellectual prowess with a no-nonsense approach to advocacy." "He is one of the hardest-working silks around and is great fun to work with. He has a quick and sharp mind, and pays attention to detail." **Recent work:** Acted in commercial proceedings in the Isle of Man on a fraud dispute arising out of a scheme to purchase and develop land in India.

Richard Gillis QC Well equipped to handle fraud disputes arising in the insolvency context. He has experience of litigating under foreign laws, and has handled Russian and Kazakh cases. **Strengths:** "A very good lawyer and an extremely decent man." "A very wise man who sees the point quickly and argues it aggressively." **Recent work:** Acted for the late Boris Berezovsky in a EUR6 billion claim against Roman Abramovich.

Stephen Auld QC Handles a range of civil fraud, asset tracing and injunction proceedings. Instructing solicitors value his client-handling skills. **Strengths:** "He's got a nose for a good point and can latch on to it like a terrier." "A skilled advocate with a forceful and persuasive style. He's one of the most experienced fraud-related practitioners in the City." **Recent work:** Successfully represented a US hedge fund in opposing the grant of an anti-suit injunction to prevent proceedings against RBS in Texas.

JUNIORS

Steven Elliott (see p.595) Regularly handles disputes involving joint ventures. His experience includes acting on multimillion-pound disputes for international clients. **Strengths:** "One of the brightest juniors at the Commercial Bar." "He is very thorough, very calm to work with, and good at taking on complex issues and dealing with the detail." **Recent work:** Acted without a leader in a dispute in the British Virgin Islands on a claim for misappropriation of funds from a joint venture vehicle.

Orlando Gledhill (see p.609) Has experience on a range of fraud disputes, including rogue trading, Ponzi schemes and missing trader fraud. Instructing solicitors appreciate his drafting skills. **Strengths:** "He's incredibly hard-working and very smart. One of the best draftsman we've worked with at the Bar." "Very succinct, with exceptional clarity, and always focuses on the key issues." **Recent work:** Acted for numerous defendants in Fortress Recovery Value Fund v Blue Skye Special Opportunities Fund, a EUR108 million dispute alleging several claims, including conspiracy to injury and misrepresentation.

Alexander Polley (see p.695) Has handled a number of high-profile civil fraud disputes. Market commentators admire his ability to work quickly without sacrificing quality. **Strengths:** "He is frighteningly good. He's so fast at turning round quality material that I could not believe he was a junior." "He is incredibly intelligent and very dedicated, and spots arguments that even the best leaders don't." **Recent work:** Acted for HSBC in a dispute against a Middle Eastern Corporate Group alleging fraud and forgery of loan documents.

Essex Court Chambers

See profile on p.792

THE SET

A set of "superb barristers," who handle some of the largest cases in the field. Members here have broad-based commercial practices, so can advise and act on a range of disputes across industry sectors. The high calibre of practitioners with a wealth of experience is complemented by an "exceptional" clerking team, making the set a popular choice for instructing solicitors.

Client service: "The clerks, led by David Grief, are very good. Their customer-focused approach is outstanding and they conduct themselves in a way that supports me and my clients most effectively. Their style is collegiate and they appear happy to work closely with solicitors to ensure the smooth operation of the barrister-solicitor team."

SILKS

Joe Smouha QC Frequently acts for major international corporate clients across a range of industry sectors. He is a popular choice for instructing solicitors, who value his cross-examination skills. **Strengths:** "He is a skilled cross-examiner and an excellent all-round advocate." "A brilliant, clever and commercial advocate who is impressive with clients." **Recent work:** Acted for Robert Tchenguiz in a £100 million dispute against the SFO concerning an illegal dawn raid on the claimant's home and office.

Graham Dunning QC Has extensive experience of handling substantial fraud disputes, many of which have an international flavour. His experience includes appearing at all levels in courts in the UK and abroad. **Strengths:** "He is awe-inspiring as an advocate, and particularly good at cross-examination." "Graham is like a Panzer – he just moves forward relentlessly, crushing the opposition." **Recent work:** Acted for a defendant in the Fiona Trust Litigation. This was a large bribery case concerning allegations of fraud and breach of fiduciary duty relating to a Russian state-owned business.

Paul Stanley QC Has a broad commercial practice and acts for claimants and defendants in fraud disputes and asset recovery actions. **Strengths:** "His particular skill is his wealth of experience: we had several gaps in our knowledge that he was able to plug." "A very bright guy who's willing to consider all the arguments in difficult cases." **Recent work:** Defended Russian oligarch Oleg Deripaska in a USD1 billion dispute concerning ownership of shares in one of the world's largest aluminium companies.

Gordon Pollock QC An established commercial practitioner, who handles a number of fraud disputes across a wide range of industry sectors. **Strengths:** "He's obviously brilliant, and has been for years." **Recent work:** Acted in Crescent Petroleum and Crescent Gas v NIOC, an USD8 billion energy arbitration claim concerning allegations of fraud, price-fixing, bribery and corruption.

Paul McGrath QC Handles fraud as part of his extensive commercial practice and is a popular choice of counsel for City firms. **Strengths:** "He simply knows everything there is to know about commercial fraud. However difficult or tricky the problem, he has either come across it before or has a creative solution." "He's got common sense and is a good diplomat too." **Recent work:** Acted on Republic of Egypt v Mubarak, an asset recovery action to identify billions of dollars of assets allegedly misappropriated under the old Mubarak regime.

JUNIORS

Nathan Pillow Specialises in commercial dispute resolution, with a particular interest in civil fraud and asset recovery. He has been involved in a number of significant and high-profile disputes of late. **Strengths:** "He has a very nice manner with clients and is very good on his feet." "He's strong, clear and commercial." **Recent work:** Acted for the claimants in Otkritie Securities v Urumov & ors, a dispute concerning the alleged misappropriation of USD25 million golden hello bonus payments.

David Davies Has been involved in a number of major commercial fraud disputes, and is frequently instructed in disputes of an international nature. **Strengths:** "One of the first choices for a fraud case. He is technically very good and shows excellent judgement." "Very detail-oriented and able to analyse a large amount of information quickly and efficiently." **Recent work:** Acted in Dalemont v Senatorov, an action in the Jersey High Court alleging that the defendants set up a Foundation to fraudulently put the claimant's assets beyond the reach of creditors.

James Willan A popular choice of counsel for solicitors in the City. He has particular experience of freezing orders, and has been involved in a number of cases concerning the jurisdiction of English and offshore courts to grant such orders. **Strengths:** "It is uncanny how he stays abreast of all the case law. He can compare, contrast and distinguish cases to support the relevant facts." "He is a real team player and always brings out the best in everyone, whether it be co-counsel, instructing solicitors, witnesses, experts or the client." **Recent work:** Acted in Bitel v Kyrgyz Mobile, an USD800 million dispute concerning the misappropriation of a mobile telecoms company.

Anna Dilnot Has extensive litigation experience and was previously a solicitor. She has a broad commercial practice that encompasses acting for clients in large-scale fraud disputes. **Strengths:** "Her experience and approach belie her year of call." "Her preparation is extremely thorough and she has that rare ability to thoroughly consider the material, and identify and focus quickly on the key issues." **Recent work:** Acted for several parties connected with the Kingate Funds in a multimillion-dollar claim brought by the Trustee of Bernard L Madoff Securities.

Edmund King Frequently handles corporate disputes involving allegations of fraud. **Strengths:** "An extremely hard-working and bright junior." "He's approachable, intelligent and a quick thinker."

Jern-Fei Ng Has a broad commercial and tax practice that takes in significant fraud disputes. He regularly appears in London and Singapore, and has offices in both jurisdictions. **Strengths:** "He has the ability to sift through complex legal problems, and present practical legal solutions that not only win you the battles, but also the war." "He takes a very active role in helping clients manage their commercial needs and their budgets." **Recent work:** Acted for the ninth defendant in parallel proceedings in England and Singapore concerning a £40.5 million conspiracy to cheat.

David Peters Often handles cases with an international flavour, and has experience of acting as a sole advocate and adviser. **Strengths:** "A bright and commercial lawyer who is creative and effective in the use of his legal knowledge and skills." "Impressive when delivering oral submissions, he regularly outshines his opponents." **Recent work:** Acted for the claimants in a £100 million fraud dispute arising from the collapse of a Cayman Island investment fund.

Fountain Court Chambers

See profile on p.804

THE SET

Sources say this highly regarded set is "really going from strength to strength." It has been involved in a number of high-profile fraud disputes, which often run into millions of pounds, and has acted for a number of international business clients. Members have particular experience in Russian-related cases. **Client service:** "The clerking team, led by Alex Taylor, is responsive, efficient and attuned to the needs of clients."

SILKS

Michael Brindle QC Acts for a variety of domestic and international clients in large-scale disputes. Instructing solicitors admire his strong courtroom presence. **Strengths:** "He's one of the star silks and is truly excellent." "An assured advocate with a good bedside manner." **Recent work:** Acted for the claimant in Novoship v Mikhaylyuk, the last case in a series of actions alleging bribery in the Russian shipping business.

Bankim Thanki QC Deputy head of chambers and a popular choice for instructing solicitors. He regularly acts for international clients and appears in various offshore jurisdictions. **Strengths:** "He's really in a category of super silks, and his knowledge on privilege issues is market-leading." **Recent work:** Acted for several claimants in a dispute against the Serious Fraud Office (SFO), arising out of an illegal dawn raid and a criminal investigation by the SFO.

Simon Browne-Wilkinson QC (see p.558) Has a broad commercial practice with an emphasis on civil fraud. Commentators note his strong offshore practice and extensive experience of obtaining interim remedies. **Strengths:** "Meticulous and an excellent strategist, who is great with clients." "He has a very impressive intellect." **Recent work:** Successfully secured judgment in excess of £800 million for Access Bank in a claim against its former chief executive concerning the misappropriation of company assets and an unlawful share support operation.

Stephen Rubin QC Has been involved in a number of fraud disputes in the UK and overseas. Sources admire his courtroom manner and style of advocacy. **Strengths:** "He manages to combine a sense of humour with a serious side." "He copes well with being instructed on urgent matters, and has the ability to make difficult arguments appear reasonable and compelling." **Recent work:** Acted for the defendants in a dispute brought by the Attorney General of the Turks & Caicos Islands alleging bribery in relation to commercial contracts.

Jeffrey Chapman QC (see p.568) Has extensive experience of handling major fraud disputes, often of a cross-border nature. Sources value his approachability and strategic approach to litigation. **Strengths:** "A great commercial practitioner, who always has an eye on strategy and client objectives." "He gives you a 360-degree service and it's very much a team game with him." **Recent work:** Acted for Group Seven in a EUR100 million dispute brought against Allied Investment concerning an alleged bogus investment scheme.

Timothy Howe QC A talented all-rounder who counts major fraud cases as just one quiver to his bow. He frequently handles multimillion-pound disputes for prominent clients in the sector. **Strengths:** "He's very easy to work with, as he's efficient, practical and client-focused." "He's extraordinary. He's a deep thinker, who is highly collaborative and strategic in his approach." **Recent work:** Acted for HSBC, as corporate trustees of a Guernsey Trust, in an international dispute alleging multimillion-pound securities and tax fraud by the settler of the Trust.

Patrick Goodall QC Has experience in a range of civil fraud matters, and frequently acts for Russian clients in multimillion-pound disputes. **Strengths:** "He's efficient, practical, client-focused and always ready to answer questions." "A delightful advocate with a first-rate brain." **Recent work:** Acted for a Russian bank in a USD560 million dispute alleging unlawful means conspiracy arising out of the amendment of certain secured loan notes.

JUNIORS

Simon Atrill (see p.539) Has been involved in some of the largest civil fraud cases in recent years. His experience includes handling disputes involving offshore jurisdictions such as Russia and Trinidad and Tobago. **Strengths:** "He knows how to work with solicitors, support them and make sure that they run a happy ship." "One of the cleverest juniors I've come across. He's got a very unassuming manner." **Recent work:** Acted for the defendants, a Gibraltar solicitor's firm, in an £80 million claim alleging dishonest assistance with international money laundering.

Paul Sinclair Acts on disputes in a variety of industry sectors, and has handled numerous cases involving freezing orders and other injunctions. **Strengths:** "Judges trust what he's saying, respect him and find it easy to agree with his arguments – he presents things very attractively." "He quickly picks up the issues and gets straight to the key points. He's good at stripping away anything that's irrelevant." **Recent work:** Acted without a leader in a £25 million fraud dispute, representing the defendant.

Ben Valentin Has a broad commercial practice with particular emphasis on civil fraud. He frequently acts for clients offshore, and has experience of litigation in the Cayman Islands and British Virgin Islands. **Strengths:** "He's a solid operator, who is good on his feet." "Very smart and very practical, he writes beautifully and efficiently." **Recent work:** He acted without a leader at trial and in the Court of Appeal for the defendants in Weavering v Peterson and Ekstrom, a claim by liquidators of a collapsed hedge fund.

Adam Zellick (see p.758) Has been involved in a number of high-profile and international fraud disputes. He frequently handles multimillion-pound cases for large organisations. **Strengths:** "He is extraordinarily capable. He's always thinking laterally and continually comes up with solutions." "Adam is very clever, hard-working and always thorough in the work he produces." **Recent work:** Acted as sole counsel for a Latvian shipping company in a £140 million fraud claim.

Deepak Nambisan (see p.680) Has been in a number of leading civil fraud cases in his career, and has handled claims running into billions of pounds. He often undertakes cases with an offshore element. **Strengths:** "Very thoughtful, diligent, hard-working and someone who gives clear advice." **Recent work:** Acted in the Court of Appeal in a USD300 million dispute between a high net worth individual and Investcorp, a provider and manager of alternative investment products.

Rosalind Phelps Has experience in all aspects of fraud litigation, from handling interlocutory hearings to appearing in lengthy trials often without a leader. She has particular experience of fraud arising in the banking sector. **Strengths:** "She's very clever and has such a good manner. Clients love her." "She's extremely thorough, very co-operative, and she mucks in." **Recent work:** Acted for Vincent Tchenguiz in a £200 million claim against the SFO following a raid on his home and business premises that was declared unlawful in judicial review proceedings.

Maitland Chambers

See profile on p.831

THE SET

The set offers a good mix of silks and juniors who are highly regarded for their civil fraud expertise. Members of the set are particularly experienced in disputes involving interlocutory remedies and asset tracing, and are valued by instructing solicitors for the range of their expertise. One commentator stated: "Maitland offers a dynamic and effective combination of characters who are able to achieve results in the most difficult of circumstances."

Client service: "The clerks are polite, proactive and part of the overall excellent service that Maitland provides."

SILKS

Paul Girolami QC Represents claimants and defendants, and has particular experience in worldwide freezing and search and seizure orders. **Strengths:** "He's a very good cross-examiner and is someone you can bounce ideas off." "He's excellent. I have complete faith in all of the advice he provides." **Recent work:** Acted for the claimant in a multibillion-pound conspiracy claim relating to the expropriation of a state-owned cobalt and copper mining concession in the Democratic Republic of Congo.

Anthony Trace QC A popular choice of counsel for major fraud disputes, he is valued by instructing solicitors for his assertive advocacy style. **Strengths:** "He is a man who relishes a scrap, and somebody with a stellar fraud practice." "A street-fighting yet sophisticated silk who's astute and unflappable." **Recent work:** Acted in Aeroflot v Berezovsky, a dispute relating to an alleged fraud involving Aeroflot's foreign currency reserves.

Matthew Collings QC His fraud practice is complemented by his highly regarded company and insolvency expertise. He has been called to the Bar of the Eastern Caribbean Supreme Court. **Strengths:** "Masterfully on top of the law in this area and a clever and bold tactician." "Direct in his approach and a man with great creative ability." **Recent work:** Acted in the Supreme Court on a dispute concerning the issue of whether a secret commission is subject to a constructive trust.

Richard Morgan QC (see p.676) Frequently instructed on high-value commercial disputes and asset recovery matters. He is experienced in obtaining and resisting freezing orders, and is an expert on cross-border issues. **Strengths:** "First rate for jurisdictional issues and Russian and CIS work." "The guru on freezing orders – he's a real technical authority." **Recent work:** Represented the principal defendant in a USD1.1 billion claim brought by a Kazakh bank alleging fraud and embezzlement through a network of offshore companies.

Catherine Newman QC Has extensive experience of handling civil fraud claims, and frequently handles disputes in relation to property and company law. **Strengths:** "She's got a very good touch and is extraordinarily sensible and clever." "An excellent advocate who has the gritty determination to fight her client's cause." **Recent work:** Represented JD Wetherspoon in a dishonest assistance claim relating to various properties.

JUNIORS

Louise Hutton (see p.635) Undertakes a large amount of fraud work as part of her commercial chancery practice, and is noted for her banking and finance expertise. **Strengths:** "She is really on the ball and works very hard." **Recent work:** Acted in RBS v Highland Financial Partners.

David Mumford Has appeared in a number of leading fraud disputes on behalf of large corporates. He has experience of acting without a leader, and has been involved in a number of multimillion-pound disputes. **Strengths:** "First-rate advocate whose written work is turned around with amazing speed." "A very good draftsman and a very good all-round advocate." **Recent work:** Acted for several US property holding companies in a claim to recover USD45 million from a prominent property adviser who was alleged to have procured payment of funds through a series of false invoices.

Alexander Winter (see p.754) Specialises in large-scale commercial disputes with elements of fraud and dishonesty. He is a popular choice for instructing solicitors, with one source commenting: "There's an Alex Winter fan club here. He is seriously very good." **Strengths:** "He is the consummate junior. When called upon to do advocacy, he's smooth, calm, polished and artful, and he's got a great courtroom manner." "He's very able as an adviser and has an encyclopaedic knowledge of the relevant law." **Recent work:** Defended Berezovsky in a multimillion-pound embezzlement claim brought by Russian airline Aeroflot.

George Hayman (see p.622) Has been involved in a series of high-value disputes in recent years, as evidenced by his key role in the BTA Bank litigation. **Strengths:** "He's probably one of the best barristers I've ever worked with in terms of being so easy to deal with and being part of our team. It really sets him apart." "Always helpful in the face of adversity. Very good on his feet, courageous and willing to stand up and fight his client's corner." **Recent work:** Acted for the defendants in JSC BTA Bank v Solodchenko, a USD300 million fraud claim involving numerous interlocutory applications.

Benjamin John (see p.638) Has experience in a range of fraud disputes, from corporate fraud and insider dealing to government corruption claims. He has appeared both led and unled in a number of high-profile fraud cases. **Strengths:** "An excellent draftsman and tactician." "He has one of the finest legal minds I have come across, and he can unravel the most complex legal knots. His analytical skills are in a class of their own." **Recent work:** Acted for the defendant in a multimillion-dollar claim in deceit arising out of alleged fraudulent misrepresentations relating to the sale of substantial oil and gas assets in Kazakhstan.

Serle Court

See profile on p.860

THE SET

Hailed as "a powerhouse in the civil fraud space," the set is home to a range of silks and juniors offering a broad skillset. Recent work undertaken includes acting for Constantin Medien in its high-profile dispute against Bernie Ecclestone concerning the sale of Formula 1. Commentators say: "It is a fantastic chancery and commercial set with real strength in litigation and fraud work."

Client service: "The clerks handle matters efficiently and effectively. They try to understand the solicitors who refer work to them, and tailor their recommendations accordingly."

SILKS

Alan Boyle QC Head of chambers and a distinguished fraud practitioner, who is routinely praised for his legal acumen and strong client-handling skills. **Strengths:** "He devotes himself to the client's cause and always impresses with his ability to convert volumes of paper and vastly complex issues into clear and pragmatic advice." "Alan is a wonderful tactician – he is there well before others reach the same conclusion."

Philip Jones QC Has a broad chancery and commercial practice and extensive experience of handling fraud disputes. He has been in a number of reported cases, and has had two reported decisions in the past year in relation to civil fraud. **Strengths:** "A good advocate, who is very user-friendly and very bright." "Very competent, incredibly able and a sophisticated, charming barrister." **Recent work:** Acted in Sterling Mortimer Global Property v ELS International Lawyer, a dispute concerning the circumstances in which a subsequent fraud action can be struck out as an abuse of process where a related earlier fraud action has been compromised.

Philip Marshall QC Has been involved in a number of leading fraud disputes. Instructing solicitors value his "extraordinarily powerful advocacy skills," with one source commenting: "You feel slightly like someone's sent the army in." **Strengths:** "He provides direct and straightforward advice that gets to the heart of an issue, and it is all delivered in a reassuringly calm and measured manner." "A superb advocate who balances aggression with excellent judgement." **Recent work:** Acted in Constantin Medien v Ecclestone, a high-profile dispute alleging bribery and conspiracy to undervalue Formula 1.

Dominic Dowley QC (see p.590) Handles a broad range of civil fraud and asset tracing matters. Instructing solicitors and peers praise him for his attention to detail. **Strengths:** "He has a great ability to pull things together and find the connections because he has such a good grasp of the detail." "He's very good on the law and has an excellent bedside manner with clients." **Recent work:** Acted in Novoship UK Ltd v Mikhaylyuk, an international shipping fraud dispute involving asset tracing and freezing orders in various jurisdictions.

Hugh Norbury QC (see p.683) Undertakes a range of fraud disputes as part of his broad commercial and chancery practice. He has particular experience of obtaining and resisting interim relief, including disclosure orders and freezing injunctions. **Strengths:** "He's very good with clients and is able to adjust the way he delivers advice according to circumstance." **Recent work:** Acted for a defendant in BTA Bank v Ablyazov, a USD4 billion dispute involving banking frauds.

Kuldip Singh QC (see p.722) Has extensive experience of handling civil fraud disputes. He has been involved in international and domestic disputes on behalf of corporations, accountant firms, trust and individuals. **Strengths:** "He's very thorough and tenacious." "He gets the job done brilliantly." **Recent work:** Represented a wealthy Arab family and corporate entity in a multimillion-pound fraud claim against an employee.

JUNIORS

Justin Higgo (see p.627) Handles a wide range of fraud disputes in the UK and offshore. He has been involved in a number of international cases concerning issues of jurisdiction and foreign law. **Strengths:** "An excellent man to have on your side in a battle. He's extremely hard-working and very user-friendly." "He has noteworthy technical knowledge and a good grasp of the relevant areas of law." **Recent work:** Acted in Bank of St Petersburg v Arkhangelsky, a dispute concerning bank guarantees alleged to be forgeries.

David Drake Has acted for household names and for the government in a variety of civil fraud disputes. His experience includes handling parallel criminal proceedings and disputes over interim remedies. **Strengths:** "He's good if you have a really complicated case and you need someone who is going to think laterally and come up with a clever argument." **Recent work:** Acted for the NHS in a dispute against Servier Laboratories, alleging that the pharmaceutical company fraudulently obtained patents for one of its drugs.

Nicholas Harrison Has been involved in a number of actions in England and other jurisdictions, handling numerous disputes in the Isle of Man, Bermuda, the Bahamas and the BVI. **Strengths:** "If you have a very complex fraud case that will go on for years then you want Nicholas Harrison on your team." "He's remarkable for his ability to focus in-depth on one case and get to the bottom of the law and the facts." **Recent work:** Acted for a Bahamian politician in a dispute involving allegations of fraud.

Ruth Holtham den Besten (see p.630) Well equipped to handle fraud disputes as a result of her previous experience at a leading fraud firm in the City. She has been involved in multimillion-pound actions for domestic and international clients. **Strengths:** "Accessible, very good in court and good with clients. She's superwoman." "Very hard-working and a delight to work with." **Recent work:** Successfully represented BTA Bank in its action to recover USD1.5 billion improperly lent to companies connected with the bank's majority shareholder and chairman.

Simon Hattan (see p.622) Deals with many cases involving allegations of dishonesty and breach of fiduciary duty. He acts for claimants and defendants. **Strengths:** "A dogged, forthright and determined lawyer, and a strategic thinker who loves being on his feet." **Recent work:** Defended a claim for fraudulent misrepresentation concerning a property investment scheme.

Andrew Moran (see p.676) Handles civil fraud disputes as part of his commercial litigation practice. He has been involved in matters concerning the Channel Islands, the Isle of Man and various Caribbean jurisdictions. **Strengths:** "He has a wonderful legal brain and is hugely enjoyable to work with." "Very hands-on and user-friendly. He will go the extra mile." **Recent work:** Represented a number of defendants in a £75 million dispute involving allegations of conspiracy.

Matthew Morrison (see p.677) Acts for claimants and defendants in disputes concerning allegations of fraudulent misrepresentation, dishonest assistance, conspiracy and knowing receipt. He has experience of obtaining a number of freezing and disclosure orders, and often acts without a leader. **Strengths:** "Matthew combines a deep knowledge of the documentation and factual matrix, with a perceptive and commercial analysis of the prevailing legal issues." "He delivers his advice in a relaxed and accessible manner, often with an injection of humour." **Recent work:** Acted for an alleged shadow director facing disqualification proceedings following allegations of fraudulent tax evasion.

4 Stone Buildings

See profile on p.865

THE SET

The set complements its civil fraud practice with its highly regarded commercial chancery, company and insolvency expertise. Its select team of barristers acts for a range of clients, from corporate entities, including shareholders and liquidators, to public bodies such as the HMRC. The set also receives praise for its "commercial" clerking team.

Client service: "The clerks, led by David Goddard, are always very approachable, helpful and accommodating, and have been flexible in negotiating fees."

SILKS

Robert Miles QC Receives extensive praise from solicitors and peers alike for his experience in fraud disputes. He continues to be instructed on some of the biggest civil fraud claims and asset recovery actions. **Strengths:** "He has considerable gravitas and a compendious knowledge of the law, and is very quick to grasp complex factual issues." "Strategically very incisive, he's intellectually brilliant and courageous in terms of what he proposes." **Recent work:** Acted for the court-appointed receivers in a large-scale fraud dispute brought by JSC BTA Bank against Mukhtar Ablyazov and others.

John Brisby QC An established practitioner with a good reputation for cross-examination. He has been involved in a range of civil fraud disputes and asset recovery actions. **Strengths:** "Exceedingly tenacious and a fantastically accomplished cross-examiner." "He's brilliant. You can't beat him for quality." **Recent work:** Successfully represented the claimant in a fraudulent misrepresentation dispute concerning the purchase of a property on the Thames.

Richard Hill QC Has a strong track record for handling major fraud-related claims. He has particular experience in handling litigation for or against government departments. **Strengths:** "Very diligent and good to have on your side." **Recent work:** Defended Bernie Ecclestone in a claim brought by Constantin Medien alleging bribery surrounding the sale of Formula 1.

Orlando Fraser QC A new silk who handles major civil fraud disputes as part of his commercial chancery practice. He is frequently instructed on cases concerning various offshore jurisdictions. **Strengths:** "He's unbelievably thorough, extremely hard-working and tenacious, and he grasps even the most complex situations or scenarios very quickly." "He turns work around quickly and is a very reliable sounding board."

Jonathan Crow QC A popular choice of counsel for major corporates and financial services organisations. He handles fraud and asset tracing matters as part of his highly regarded commercial dispute resolution practice. **Strengths:** "He has a very commanding presence in court and he is someone you would go to when you want the judge to listen to what you've got to say." "He is pretty much an ideal barrister. He is clever, hard-working, accessible, a brilliant advocate and a delight to deal with." **Recent work:** Acted for the claimant in Abbar and another v Saudi Economic and Development, a dispute raising allegations of fraud in relation to a project to build the City's tallest skyscraper.

JUNIORS

Christopher Harrison (see p.621) Has experience in handling a range of civil fraud and asset recovery actions. He has been called to the Bars of the Cayman and Turks & Caicos Islands for specific cases. **Strengths:** "He is invariably charming and willing to put himself out, and finds creative solutions to difficult legal problems." "Unflappable, responsive, very good on his feet and totally committed to the cause." **Recent work:** Acted for fashion brand Michele Hope in a claim to recover funds stolen by its bookkeeper.

Gregory Denton-Cox (see p.587) Acts for claimants and defendants in fraud disputes and asset tracing cases. **Strengths:** "He is extremely diligent, always knows everything about the case and contributes good points. He is exactly what you would want from a junior." "He fights his client's corner without being overly aggressive." **Recent work:** Acted for several defendants in a post-acquisition claim alleging fraudulent completion of accounts.

3 Verulam Buildings

See profile on p.875

THE SET

A leading set with an impressive range of silks and juniors handling some of the biggest commercial fraud disputes. Its civil fraud expertise is strengthened by its highly regarded banking and finance and insolvency practice. Recent high-profile work for the set has included acting for Fortress Value Recovery Fund in a complex financial fraud dispute against Blue Skye Special Opportunities Fund. Members here act for a range of clients, including international companies, building societies and banks, high street stores and private individuals.

Client service: "The clerks are second to none and are very proactive."

SILKS

Ewan McQuater QC A gifted all-rounder who is fêted for his corporate and banking, and finance expertise. He is a regular presence in the most significant fraud disputes. **Strengths:** "A class act. He is the complete article: he's unbelievably intelligent, commercial and pragmatic in approach, and a good team player. He's also as tough as old boots." "A very, very effective operator: he's always on top of the case." **Recent work:** Acted for the Algosaibi family of Saudi Arabia in a USD10 billion fraud claim against multiple parties.

David Quest QC Handles a range of commercial fraud disputes, including corrupt commercial transactions, share ramping and rogue trading cases. He is frequently instructed to handle some of the most complex and high-value fraud work around. **Strengths:** "He is extremely intelligent, has a very good understanding of banking and financial transactions, and is quick to grasp and dissect complicated issues." **Recent work:** Acted for the claimants, Fortress Value Recovery Fund, in a EUR200 million fraud claim against the managers of the Blue Skye investment group.

Ali Malek QC Handles large-scale fraud disputes as part of his hugely impressive commercial litigation practice. **Strengths:** "First-class and a fine choice for the more substantial cases." **Recent work:** Acted for Russian oligarch Vasily Anisimov in a USD1.5 billion dispute brought by the estate of Arkady Patarkatsishvili.

Adrian Beltrami QC Tackles a broad range of civil fraud disputes and is particularly good when it comes to interim remedies, including search and freezing orders. **Strengths:** "He's well prepared and a very methodical, bright chap." "His understated approach can take the wind out of the sails of almost any opponent." **Recent work:** Acted for the claimant in a commercial dispute involving a freezing order and worldwide enforcement proceedings relating to a USD200 million arbitration award.

Andrew Onslow QC Acts for claimants and defendants on a variety of commercial fraud disputes. He frequently represents financial institutions. **Strengths:** "He's impressively clever and you know that if he says something you can absolutely rely on it." "He's someone who really does seem to be powering ahead in terms of giving good client care." **Recent work:** Acted for the claimants in a USD72 million deceit claim concerning the sale of CDO notes.

Sonia Tolaney QC Has extensive experience of handling commercial fraud disputes and worldwide asset tracing matters. She has been involved in a number of high-profile cases in recent years. **Strengths:** "A serious presence and a great strategist to have on your side." "She's clever and great to work with." **Recent work:** Defended Russian oligarch Vasily Anisimov in a USD1.5 billion dispute brought by Gudavadze relating to a 20% share in mining company Metalloinvest that was formerly held by Anisimov.

Andrew Sutcliffe QC Frequently instructed to advise and represent the National Crime Agency in relation to interim remedies and asset tracing. Those that instruct him appreciate his approachability. **Strengths:** "We take a very collaborative approach and he works incredibly well as part of the team." "Clear thinking, wise and approachable." **Recent work:** Advised the NCA under Part 5 of POCA on the consequences of the Supreme Court judgment in SOCA v Perry.

John Odgers QC Very strong on fraud relating to the banking and finance sector. He acts for claimants and defendants. **Strengths:** "His technical expertise is a given. What has impressed me most is his availability, his enthusiasm for the case and his practical commercial advice." "He's incredibly analytical in the way he goes about his business."

JUNIORS

Matthew Parker Acts for a range of corporate clients on major fraud disputes, appearing as lead junior or sole counsel. **Strengths:** "Very thorough, very good at lateral thinking, very hard-working and easy to work with." **Recent work:** Acted for the Central Bank of Ecuador on a USD150 million Privy Council appeal arising out of the collapse of an Ecuadorian bank.

David Head Frequently instructed on high-profile fraud and asset recovery claims. He has appeared as sole advocate on a number of matters. **Strengths:** "He's a very good advocate. If you want someone at a senior junior level to take on a silk then you'd strongly recommend him." "He has a very good manner with the non-lawyer client." **Recent work:** Acted on behalf of a defendant in a USD110 million fraud dispute brought by entities within a Kazakh recycling group. The case concerned alleged bogus construction contracts, false accounting and misappropriation of corporate funds.

Laura John Handles fraud claims as part of her wide-ranging commercial practice. Her experience includes obtaining interim remedies such as freezing and search orders. **Strengths:** "She is absolutely fantastic – one of the brightest, most diligent barristers in practice at the moment." "Excellent courtroom manner. She genuinely bosses the court in the manner that one would expect to see in a much more senior barrister." **Recent work:** Represented the defendants in a dispute against a professional services firm. The case concerned allegations of conspiracy, fraudulent misrepresentation and the tort of unlawful interference.

Adam Kramer Has acted as sole counsel and been lead junior in a number of fraud trials and appeals. **Strengths:** "Absolutely excellent. Very good on paper in terms of pleadings." "Very good, very bright and very personable." **Recent work:** Acted as sole counsel for the defendants in a £4 million dispute arising out of a French property transaction.

Michael Lazarus Impresses peers and instructing solicitors alike with his handling of fraud disputes. He is frequently instructed on matters in the banking and finance and IT/telecoms sectors. **Strengths:** "Very methodical, calm, easy to work with and great on his feet." "He should be a silk."

Rajesh Pillai Regularly works with lawyers from outside the UK on a variety of commercial fraud claims, and is frequently involved in multimillion-pound disputes. **Strengths:** "He is excellent. He demonstrates an ability to get a grip on a case and drive it forward." **Recent work:** Represented European derivatives investors in a EUR100 million fraud dispute against a leading UK spread bet and CFD provider.

Band 2

XXIV Old Buildings

See profile on p.838

THE SET

The set complements its staple of domestic cases with a significant amount of offshore and international work. Members are frequently instructed on matters in jurisdictions such as the BVI, Cayman Islands and Bermuda. Instructing solicitors regard the members here as being "always very approachable and very good on the technical aspects of the law."

Client service: "The clerking service is utterly excellent. What always impresses me is that they are spot on with giving and keeping to cost estimates, and could not be more helpful when it comes to setting up court hearings and liaising with the courts."

SILKS

Alan Steinfeld QC Enjoys a stellar reputation for work on offshore fraud matters. He is frequently involved in disputes relating to the BVI. **Strengths:** "Pre-eminent offshore fraud silk who commands enormous respect based on his track record and seniority." "He's a grandee in this area, who has had every experience in court that you could imagine." **Recent work:** Acted in a dispute concerning a £500 million shareholding in a failed Icelandic bank.

Stephen Moverley Smith QC Focuses his fraud practice on BVI and Caribbean cases, and frequently leads on big-ticket disputes for claimants and defendants. **Strengths:** "He's a proper team player, who is creative and innovative in his advice." "A heavyweight silk who brings a lot of energy to a case." **Recent work:** Acted for the defendant in a joint venture dispute alleging misappropriation of USD10 million.

Elspeth Talbot Rice QC Handles fraud and asset tracing claims as part of her commercial chancery practice. **Strengths:** "She's incredibly incisive and good at drilling down through all the facts: she can unpick a case in an instant." "She has quite a presence in court." **Recent work:** Acted in a dispute concerning a solicitor who defrauded the claimants of £5 million.

Robert Levy QC Regularly instructed on disputes concerning conflicts of laws and claims in numerous offshore jurisdictions. He is called to the Bar in BVI and Anguilla. **Strengths:** "A very effective fraud silk, who is brilliant, aggressive and user-friendly." "He brings a real heavyweight presence to a case, so you really feel like you've got somebody who knows what he's talking about." **Recent work:** Acted for the State Oil Company of Azerbaijan in its claim to seek enforcement of its security over shares following default.

Martin Mann QC Regularly appears in cross-border disputes. He has experience of handling disputes concerning issues of enforcement, anti-suit injunctions, stay proceedings and injunctive relief. **Strengths:** "His advisory work is absolutely first-rate." "He's very smooth and very smart, and sees things in a very helpful way." **Recent work:** Acted in an £18 million dispute concerning the purchase of The Waldorf premises.

JUNIORS

Steven Thompson Handles a variety of international fraud disputes. He is called to the Bar of the Supreme Court of the Eastern Caribbean and frequents the BVI High Court and Court of Appeal. **Strengths:** "He gave clear and unequivocal advice throughout, was consistently approachable and hard-working and generous with his time." "He's outstanding on fraud-related matters: very commercial, very sensible and has the right type of sleeves-up, crack-on attitude that clients love." **Recent work:** Successfully represented a defendant to a claim brought by the Attorney General of Turks & Caicos Islands for dishonest assistance, knowing receipt and unjust enrichment.

11 Stone Buildings

See profile on p.868

THE SET

A set with experts on all areas of fraud, including asset tracing. Members are frequently instructed to appear in cases involving foreign and private international law, and are highly skilled at obtaining and enforcing interim injunctions. Recent work undertaken by the set includes acting in the Supreme Court in VTB Capital v Nutritek International Corp; a landmark decision on piercing the corporate veil.

Client service: "The clerking services at 11 Stone Buildings are very good. We have a good, open and flexible working relationship and they understand our requirements with regard to recommendations, availability of counsel and fees."

SILKS

Alan Gourgey QC Has acted in a range of substantial fraud disputes relating to misappropriation of assets and deceit and bribery claims. Much of his workload has an international flavour. **Strengths:** "He's fast to spot the issues, and has great judgement as to how they will play out. He's authoritative in court and a clever cross-examiner." "He's really prepared to get involved in the detail of the case and provide creative solutions." **Recent work:** Acted for claimants in the petrochemical industry in an unlawful means conspiracy dispute concerning the alleged bribery of Iraqi officials.

Charles Samek QC (see p.713) Handles fraud as part of his wider commercial litigation practice. He has particular experience of obtaining and enforcing interim remedies in support of foreign proceedings. **Strengths:** "Shows absolute dedication to the task in hand and is a great lateral thinker." "Displays outstanding professionalism and first-class commercial acumen." **Recent work:** Successfully resisted an application to set aside a worldwide freezing order for the claimants in JSC VA Bank v Maksimov.

JUNIORS

Tim Penny In high demand as a "top senior junior, who can run heavy cases against top silks." He has been involved in a number of high-value commercial fraud disputes and has experience of acting without a leader. **Strengths:** "Great for cases involving complex detail – he's a very solid performer in court, who provides sensible commercial advice." "He keeps himself well abreast of developments in his specialist areas of the law and uses his knowledge creatively and effectively." **Recent work:** Acted for the Financial Conduct Authority in a dispute against Asset Land concerning a £20 million land-banking scheme. This was the FCA's first claim under s235 Financial Services and Markets Act to reach a full trial and be heard in the Court of Appeal.

Max Mallin Handles a range of commercial fraud and asset recovery claims. His background as an investment banker means he is a good choice for disputes relating to investment products. **Strengths:** "A superb cross-examiner who has the ear of the court." "He's very smooth and personable, and has a very quick mind. He gives clear directional guidance." **Recent work:** Acted as sole counsel for a number of defendants in a USD450 million fraud claim and breach of contract dispute.

Iain Pester Frequently acts in disputes involving clients from Russia and the CIS, and is particularly good at obtaining interim remedies. **Strengths:** "He's responsive and always makes time available to discuss matters." "He shows excellent judgement, produces first-class paperwork and is a deep thinker who anticipates issues before they arise." **Recent work:** Acted as junior counsel in VTB Capital plc v Nutritek International Corp, a USD200 million fraud dispute relating to the financing of a sale of a Russian dairy business.

Ian Smith His practice covers all aspects of civil fraud work, including international disputes and asset tracing. **Strengths:** "Very capable, especially where there are criminal issues in the case." "He's completely fearless and his tactical skills are first-rate." **Recent work:** Acted as sole counsel for a defendant in Otkritie v Urumov, a USD183 million dispute concerning alleged fraudulent trading.

Wilberforce Chambers

See profile on p.876

THE SET

Members are frequently instructed to handle multi-million-pound disputes on behalf of large corporations. Recent work undertaken by the set includes acting in Apex Global Management Limited v FiCall, a multimillion-pound shareholders' dispute. Individuals here are noted for being "straightforward" and "very personable to deal with."

Client service: "I have been impressed by the clerking service at Wilberforce Chambers: they are quick in responding to communications and excellent at making recommendations."

SILKS

Ian Croxford QC A leading silk who can be seen on the most complex and high-value fraud cases. **Strengths:** "A classic trial advocate who is superb on his feet." "He is very good at difficult cross-examinations." **Recent work:** Acted for the defendants in an £11 million multiparty claim concerning a shipping arbitration.

John Wardell QC Handles fraud work as part of his highly regarded chancery practice. Instructing solicitors particularly note his cross-examination skills. **Strengths:** "He has a great eye for detail, is incredibly numerate and user-friendly, and is a skilled cross-examiner." "Very few counsel will stick their neck out, but he's one of them: he's prepared to commit and say what he thinks." **Recent work:** Defended NatWest in a £20 million claim arising out of a Ponzi scheme, involving allegations of conspiracy and dishonest assistance.

Lawrence Cohen QC Has extensive experience of handling a wide range of fraud disputes. He frequently handles matters of an international flavour. **Strengths:** "Extremely innovative and thoughtful." "He is an effective cross-examiner and is willing to take on more difficult cases and fight hard."

Other Ranked Lawyers

Stephen Smith QC (Erskine Chambers) Has had a successful year. with a number of victories at appellate and first instance level. His practice is heavily international and he has been called to the Bar of the Bahamas, Cayman Islands and the Eastern Caribbean Supreme Court. **Strengths:** "At the top of the Premier League for major complex cross-border civil fraud." "He is robust and tenacious in relation to his approach to litigation and has an excellent courtroom style that commands the judge's attention." **Recent work:** Secured a USD1.5 billion judgment for JSC BTA Bank in its high-profile dispute against Mukhtar Ablyazov.

Tim Akkouh (see p.533) (Erskine Chambers) Has experience of handling major international fraud disputes. He is a key leading junior in several aspects of the JSC BTA Bank of Kazakhstan litigation. **Strengths:** "He is very responsive, turns work around quickly and is very affable." "A charming man to work with and someone who never loses his cool, whatever the pressure." **Recent work:** Acted for a defendant BVI company alleged to have received traceable proceeds of a fraud.

Emily Gillett (see p.608) (Erskine Chambers) Handles fraud disputes as part of her broad commercial chancery practice. She has extensive experience of Norwich Pharmacal applications and committal proceedings from her involvement in the Ablyazov litigation. **Strengths:** "Emily is robust and experienced in fraud work beyond her year of call." "Very good, very user-friendly and very diligent." **Recent work:** Handled the Kazakh law and Russian law issues governing JSC BTA Bank's high-profile claim against Mukhtar Ablyazov.

Duncan Matthews QC (20 Essex Street) Has a broad fraud practice that is heavily international. He handles large-scale fraud disputes for major organisations and high net worth individuals. **Strengths:** "He's a real class act and a truly hard hitting advocate." "He never panics, which is useful in fraud litigation." **Recent work:** Acted for Mukhtar Ablyazov in the high-profile dispute brought by BTA Bank, a USD6.5 billion claim involving disputes over freezing orders, receiverships, contempt and disclosure.

Hodge Malek QC (Thirty Nine Essex Street) Regularly handles fraud claims relating to the banking and financial services sector. He has particular experience of disputes involving the Middle East. **Strengths:** "When it comes to dealing with freezing injunctions in the Middle East, and compliance with international sanctions, you don't need to look any further." "A regulatory and disciplinary expert, he is supremely diligent and a top-class litigator." **Recent work:** Defended KPMG in a USD10 million claim in the Muscat Commercial Court, concerning an alleged failure to detect fraud by a former client's chief accountant.

Aidan Casey (3 Hare Court) Instructed by banks and other institutions in relation to fraud and asset recovery. He often handles cross-border disputes involving jurisdictions such as the Bahamas and the Isle of Man. **Strengths:** "He shows great attention to detail and is very conscientious while remaining user-friendly and good value." "He is totally trusted by lawyers in the City." **Recent work:** Acted for the claimants in Aeroflot v Berezovsky, a USD300 million dispute concerning an international management diversion fraud.

Clive Freedman QC (7 King's Bench Walk) Undertakes fraud as part of a wide-ranging commercial practice. He has appeared in the Court of Appeal on numerous occasions, and has been involved in a great number of reported cases. **Strengths:** "He is a forceful advocate who has great knowledge of the law and really devotes himself to cases." "He can really grasp foreign law concepts and explain them to the judge in a convincing manner. He has a good appreciation of Eastern European practice and continental systems." **Recent work:** Handled a dispute regarding a Ukrainian bank that concerned allegations of fraud, including forgery and unlawful transfer of secured property.

Stuart Ritchie QC (Littleton Chambers) Has particular experience in disputes concerning fiduciary duties. His practice is increasingly international, and he has experience of disputes involving the Cayman Islands, the BVI and Mauritius. **Strengths:** "He has the judgement of a seasoned silk, is superb on his feet and can read the mood of a court." "He has the potential to be a real star of the Bar." **Recent work:** Acted for the first defendant in Dar al Arkan v Al Refai; a significant dispute alleging conspiracy and breach of confidence.

Clare Montgomery QC (Matrix Chambers) Complements her civil fraud practice with her criminal and regulatory expertise. Sources admire her devastating cross-examination skills. **Strengths:** "One of the stars of the Bar." "If I got in trouble, I would want her. She's a very special advocate."

Justin Fenwick QC (4 New Square) Handles offshore and onshore commercial disputes, and frequently tackles disputes arising out of insolvency. **Strengths:** "He is a robust advocate and a fearless cross-examiner, and shows excellent all-round judgment." "He's never afraid to make a call, and is well able to lead a devastating forensic attack on his opponent's case." **Recent work:** Acted in a fraud dispute against three former employees of a Saudi Arabian construction company.

Alex Hall Taylor (4 New Square) Handles civil fraud cases as part of an illustrious chancery practice, and is frequently involved in significant disputes for prominent individuals and organisations. **Strengths:** "A tough and doughty opponent who diligently protects his client's interests." "Very softly spoken, but very articulate and very effective." **Recent work:** Represented four defendants in a multimillion-pound fraud dispute brought by Bank of Ireland, involving several claims including fraudulent misrepresentation, dishonest assistance and knowing receipt.

Mark Hubbard (New Square Chambers) Acts for individuals and organisations on a range of fraud disputes. He has particular experience in cases involving offshore trusts and shareholder disputes. **Strengths:** "Very practical and down to earth." "He thinks creatively and comes up with ideas no one else has thought of." **Recent work:** Successfully recovered a property in a claim based on dishonest assistance in a breach of trust by a trustee.

Nigel Hood (see p.630) (New Square Chambers) Handles many deceit, conspiracy and unjust enrichment cases, and has acted as sole counsel for claimants and defendants in multimillion-pound disputes. **Strengths:** "A very straightforward opponent in his dealings." "His advocacy is quite understated, and he doesn't start shouting, but in his own way he takes no prisoners and doesn't miss a point." **Recent work:** Acted as sole counsel for the defendants in a EUR100 million cross-border fraud claim.

Nicholas Vineall QC (4 Pump Court) Often handles cross-border disputes, many pertaining to the CIS. He has appeared for the FCA in a range of claims against unauthorised financial services schemes. **Strengths:** "Very confident, smart and friendly." "He is great fun to work with and gets on very well with clients." **Recent work:** Acted in a dispute involving a share sale fraud against Barclays Bank in the Supreme Court. This is now the leading case on the nature of a regulator's cross undertakings in damages when seeking injunctions.

Fenner Moeran QC (3 Stone Buildings) Receives extensive praise from peers, who comment that "his appointment to silk is richly deserved." He has particular expertise in pre-action and third-party ex parte disclosure, and is an expert in interim remedies, including freezing injunctions and restraint orders. **Strengths:** "If you want a barrister who you can rely on to impress the court and your client, he is your person." "Constantly energetic and enthusiastic, he's an extremely fast thinker, who throws himself into every argument and gives his best every time." **Recent work:** Instructed by Dalriada Trustees to recover mis-invested funds from more than 30 pension schemes.

Steven Gee QC (Stone Chambers) Head of chambers and renowned for his expertise on commercial injunctions, having written a book on the topic. **Strengths:** "The leading light on worldwide freezing orders and a hugely useful resource for complex litigation." "He seems capable of mastering a brief in a flash and can be extraordinarily persuasive with judges." **Recent work:** Acted in a dispute regarding the sale and purchase of a McLaren racing car.

Charles Dougherty QC (2TG – 2 Temple Gardens) Handles a number of offshore fraud disputes. He has particular experience of cross-border tracing and interim remedies to locate and freeze assets. **Strengths:** "He's really good on his feet. He will often win applications that we think are unachievable." **Recent work:** Acted for the Federal Republic of Brazil in a multimillion-dollar dispute against the former mayor of São Paulo, alleging the misappropriation of funds into offshore companies owned by the defendant.

HEALTH & SAFETY: An Introduction

Contributed by Crown Office Chambers

The past twelve months have done nothing to ease the pressure on businesses. The trend towards higher fines in health and safety cases has continued, there is a renewed focus on the individual and collective responsibilities of directors and senior managers, and the burdens imposed by the new defence costs regime and Fee for Intervention remain high. In short, it is set to be another demanding year for clients and practitioners alike.

Sellafield and Network Rail

In a striking decision, the Court of Appeal upheld fines of £700,000 imposed on Sellafield Limited and £500,000 imposed on Network Rail Infrastructure Limited. The appeals were heard together because they raised issues of principle in relation to the level of fines to be imposed on very large companies (those with a turnover of £1 billion or more). The Court of Appeal had already made clear, in cases such as R v Merlin Attractions Operations Ltd and R v Watkins Jones & Sons Limited, that fines for the largest defendants could be very high. The decision in Sellafield and Network Rail, however, places more emphasis than ever before on the means of corporate defendants.

The same theme is taken up in the new Sentencing Council Definitive Guideline: Environmental Offences. The Guideline requires sentencing courts to follow a prescriptive step-by-step sentencing process, with different starting points and ranges according to the defendant's means. It is understood that a similar Guideline may soon be introduced for health and safety offences.

Responsibilities of directors and senior managers

The spotlight has also fallen on the responsibilities of directors and managers. The Court of Appeal emphasised in Sellafield and the subsequent appeal in R v Southern Water Services Limited that the sentencing court will expect a corporate defendant's senior management to provide a detailed explanation of the company's offence and the steps taken to prevent further offences.

At the same time, the Health and Safety Executive has published a new edition of INDG 417 Leading Health and Safety at Work. The guidance applies to directors and other officers of organisations in both the public and private sectors. It sets out what is required under four broad headings – Plan, Do, Check, and Act. The guidance will be an important and helpful source of advice, but there is no doubt that in the event of prosecution it will be used to demonstrate the standards which should have been met.

Corporate manslaughter

It has been a year of mixed fortunes for defendants charged with corporate manslaughter.

R v PS and JE Ward Limited became the first company to be acquitted of the offence at trial. An employee was electrocuted when the trailer his tractor was towing came into contact with an overhead power line. The company was charged with corporate manslaughter and a health and safety offence. No individuals were prosecuted. After a 12-day trial at Norwich Crown Court the company was acquitted of corporate manslaughter, though convicted of the other charge.

The outcome was different in the prosecution of Prince's Sporting Club, which followed a tragic boating accident. In that case the company was charged with corporate manslaughter and a director was charged with neglect. The company pleaded guilty to corporate manslaughter and accordingly the prosecution did not pursue the criminal proceedings against the director.

The result in that case is not dissimilar to that of the previous corporate manslaughter case that went to trial: Lion Steel in 2012. In that case, after two of the three directors had made successful submissions of no case to answer to manslaughter charges, the prosecution agreed to withdraw the further manslaughter charge against the third director (and also the remaining health and safety offences) on the basis of a plea by the company to corporate manslaughter. It is likely that wherever possible prosecutors will bring charges against individuals so as to increase the pressure on the company.

Burdens on business

In October 2012 significant restrictions were placed on the recovery of defence costs. The harshness of the new regime is illustrated by the ruling that followed the acquittal of Mr Counsell, the fireworks operator charged with having caused the M5 motorway collision that left seven people dead.

The case is a rare example of a high-profile health and safety prosecution stopped at the close of the prosecution case. Originally the defendant was charged with seven offences of manslaughter. Following a review the prosecution discontinued all seven charges and proceeded instead with a single health and safety offence. That charge was withdrawn from the jury following a submission of no case to answer. The defendant applied for costs against the CPS. The trial judge declined to make the order in a ruling which emphasised that the bar for 'unnecessary or improper' conduct is high. The outcome was that Mr Counsell and his insurers were unable to recover any of the costs expended in having to defend an unmeritorious manslaughter prosecution and an unsuccessful health and safety trial.

Meanwhile, businesses will by now be familiar with the Fee for Intervention (FFI) scheme, which has been in operation since October 2012. The Health and Safety Executive undertook to review how FFI is working after the first twelve months of operation. The outcome of that review should therefore be published shortly.

Conclusion

Every year brings fresh challenges, and this year will be no exception. As ever, those in need of specialist advice and representation need look no further than the leading chambers and barristers listed in these pages.

Contents:

LONDON

Health & Safety London

Leading Sets	
Band 1	Outer Temple Chambers *
Crown Office Chambers *	Temple Garden Chambers *
Henderson Chambers *	**Band 3**
6 Pump Court *	2 Hare Court *
Band 2	3 Raymond Buildings Barristers *
2 Bedford Row *	

Leading Silks	
Star individuals	**Morton** Keith *Temple Garden Chambers* *
Lissack Richard *Outer Temple Chambers* *	**Sturman** Jim *2 Bedford Row* *
Matthews Richard *2 Bedford Row*	**Band 3**
Band 1	**Forlin** Gerard *Cornerstone Barristers (ORL)* ◊ *
Caplan Jonathan *5 Paper Buildings (ORL)* ◊ *	**Gibson** Charles *Henderson Chambers* [A] *
Darbishire Adrian *QEB Hollis Whiteman (ORL)* ◊	**Hockman** Stephen *6 Pump Court* [A] *
Killalea Stephen *Devereux (ORL)* ◊ *	**Lawrie** Ian *3PB Barristers (ORL)* ◊
Popat Prashant *Henderson Chambers* [A] *	**Walsh** Stephen *3 Raymond Buildings Barristers* [A] *
Travers David *6 Pump Court* *	**Watt-Pringle** Jonathan *Temple Garden Chambers* *
Band 2	**New Silks**
Compton Ben *Outer Temple Chambers*	**Campbell** Oliver *Henderson Chambers* [A] *
Laidlaw Jonathan *2 Hare Court* *	**Cooper** John *Crown Office Chambers* *

Leading Juniors	
Star individuals	**McLoughlin** Kevin *Temple Garden Chambers* *
Antrobus Simon *Crown Office Chambers* *	**Naqshbandi** Saba *3 Raymond Buildings Barristers* [A]
Band 1	**Riley-Smith** Toby *Henderson Chambers* [A] *
Ageros James *Crown Office Chambers*	**Ritchie** Shauna *2 Bedford Row* *
Harris Mark *6 Pump Court*	**Band 3**
Kay Dominic *Crown Office Chambers* *	**Atkins** Mike *Crown Office Chambers* *
Watson Mark *6 Pump Court*	**Buchanan** James *2 Hare Court* *
Band 2	**Daniels** Iain *Ely Place Chambers (ORL)* ◊ *
Adamson Dominic *Temple Garden Chambers* *	**Ferguson** Craig *2 Hare Court* *
Ashley-Norman Jonathan *3 Raymond Buildings* [A] *	**Galloway** Malcolm *Old Square Chambers (ORL)* ◊
Balysz Mark *Crown Office Chambers*	**Le Fevre** Sarah *3 Raymond Buildings Barristers* [A] *
Bates Pascal *6 Pump Court* [A] *	**Leonard** James *Outer Temple Chambers*
Bennett Lee *6 Pump Court* [A]	**McGee** Andrew *2 Bedford Row* *
Canby Fiona *Temple Garden Chambers* *	**Mehta** Sailesh *Red Lion Chambers (ORL)* ◊ *
Climie Stephen *Outer Temple Chambers*	**Purnell** James *Henderson Chambers* [A] *
Du Cann Christian *Thirty Nine Essex Street (ORL)* ◊	**Up-and-coming individuals**
Heer Deanna *5 Paper Buildings (ORL)* ◊ *	**Kendrick** Julia *Crown Office Chambers* *
Maxwell-Scott James *Crown Office Chambers*	**Sanderson** Eleanor *2 Bedford Row* *

◊ (ORL) = Other Ranked Lawyer.
[A] direct access (see p.11).
** Indicates firm / individual with profile.*

Band 1

Crown Office Chambers
See profile on p.782

THE SET

A large team, particularly strong on the junior side, that dedicates itself to health and safety regulatory work. A dominant player in the field, it advises on the gamut of cases, and has a number of high-profile matters to its name, such as the Lakanal House fire inquest. Solicitors say: "It has a number of excellent, technically gifted and client-focused advocates."

Client service: "The clerking is good and Steve Purse is always very helpful. What impresses me is that if you ring them up and get into the technical side of the industry, they'll understand it and know which sort of barrister you're after."

SILKS

John Cooper QC (see p.577) A well-regarded silk who has handled a number of the leading cases in the field. He is an obvious choice for fatality cases and is a regular feature in the appellate courts. **Strengths:** "Tenacious, combative and not scared to take the judge on." "A robust trial advocate and an aggressive litigator." **Recent work:** Acted for a national house builder in a case concerning the installation of a fireplace, which collapsed and killed a child.

JUNIORS

Simon Antrobus A leading practitioner in the field who is well known for his performance on heavyweight cases. By way of example, he was involved in the inquest into the death of a man in the process of being deported to Angola on a British Airways plane. **Strengths:** "Fiercely intelligent. He ticks all the boxes in terms of his knowledge of the law and his manner in court with the judge, jury and witnesses." "When he commits to a case there's no stopping him." **Recent work:** Acted on behalf of a fireworks operator during a criminal trial concerning a major road accident on the M5 that led to the death of seven motorists.

James Ageros Acts for both the defence and prosecution, and is noted for the volume of major inquest work he undertakes. **Strengths:** "It's spectacular to watch the legal arguments he puts together." "He is a very smooth, charming and effective advocate." **Recent work:** He is currently acting on the high-profile Hillsborough inquests.

Dominic Kay (see p.642) A heavyweight practitioner who acts predominantly on fatality and serious injury cases. He works across many industry sectors, and has had a high volume of instructions relating to leisure and construction companies, as well as care homes. **Strengths:** "He takes a dynamic approach and is always looking for an innovative solution." "A very client-focused, pragmatic and level-headed kind of guy." **Recent work:** Advised on a case arising from the death of a young girl at a council-owned swimming pool in Essex, where the number of lifeguards on duty did not meet the operating company's policy.

Mark Balysz Frequently leads on complex cases, including those concerning fatalities. He has recently advised on matters in the construction and gas engineering sectors. **Strengths:** "He's very diligent and fights vigorously." "He comes across very well and is very reassuring." **Recent work:** Advising recycling company Stercycle on a corporate manslaughter case arising out of an explosion at one of its waste plants.

James Maxwell-Scott Receives instructions on significant, high-profile inquests, and has recently been retained on Hillsborough. The majority of his caseload relates to death or serious injury. **Strengths:** "He is very good technically and on the detail." "He is very straightforward when explaining the issues." **Recent work:** Acted in the Lakanal House inquest regarding six deaths at a tower block in south London. He was the first to question most of the 100+ witnesses on behalf of the Coroner.

Mike Atkins (see p.539) Has a broad practice that takes in fire safety, fatality and serious injury cases, as well as appeals against enforcement notices. He increasingly appears on major cases in the media spotlight. **Strengths:** "He'll check every legal avenue to find the best possible outcome." "His capacity to work knows no ends." **Recent work:** Junior counsel to the Coroner in the Lakanal House fire inquests.

Julia Kendrick (see p.644) A rising star who is receiving an increasing number of instructions on significantly high-profile cases. She is experienced in a range of cases crossing several sectors, including fire safety, river pollution and residential care matters. **Strengths:** "Straightforward and easy to communicate with." **Recent work:** Acted for Hampshire Fire and Rescue Service in the Shirley Towers fire inquest, into the death of two firefighters.

Henderson Chambers

See profile on p.820

THE SET

Henderson Chambers has strength in depth and experienced practitioners at both silk and junior level who handle criminal, civil and regulatory work in this area. The set receives a significant number of rail-related instructions, such as crossing fatalities, and includes Network Rail amongst its clients. It has had involvement in a number of the most important cases of recent times, including the Casterbridge Nursery trial and the Bridgewater Place wind tunnel case.

Client service: "It is clerked extremely well. John White is very entrepreneurial. He gets his barristers out and about, works out who solicitors are at various firms and builds relationships with them. When you ring him up he does his best to get you the person you want and goes the extra mile. Others in his team are cut from the same cloth."

SILKS

Prashant Popat QC Conducts purely defence work, and undertakes a high volume of cases for the railway industry, in addition to some relating to the oil and coal sectors. He has appeared at a number of high-profile trials of late. **Strengths:** "He has huge gravitas and a very good manner. You can put him anywhere and his abilities are recognised by everyone." "He is the silkiest of silks; he's calmness personified." **Recent work:** Involved in a case brought against Network Rail following a death in the workplace.

Oliver Campbell QC Handles a large volume of cases relating to the construction, oil and gas industries. He generally deals with cases concerning very serious injuries, and is commended by market sources for his "razor-sharp" approach. **Strengths:** "He changes the difficult client's expectations and understanding of the outcome." "He has particularly good analytical skills, and his advocacy is very appealing." **Recent work:** Involved in a case brought against a nursery manager and class teacher following the death of a child whose neck became stuck in a wendy house.

Charles Gibson QC Exclusively defence-oriented practitioner, who has acted on a significant number of cases concerning the electricity generation industry. Interviewees regularly remarked on his commercial mindedness. **Strengths:** "He is the most commercially aware barrister I've ever dealt with. He's always thinking about the issues beyond the court process, such as reputation, future tenders and share impact." **Recent work:** Acted in a case where a man had died after being hit by a live electricity cable as he ran through a field.

JUNIORS

Toby Riley-Smith Has a mixed defendant criminal and civil practice, and handles a number of inquests. He often handles cases relating to the oil industry. **Strengths:** "He's a well road-tested advocate who is very affable." "He's very good at dealing with the client and empathising with them." **Recent work:** Acted for a construction company that built a canopy with defective welding at a school. The canopy collapsed, injuring five roofers who were working on it.

James Purnell Has recently handled fatality cases relating to the mining, transport and care home sectors. He is on the regulatory list for the HSE, Environment Agency and ORR. **Strengths:** "He's the sort of person who can deliver results through speaking in an informative and entertaining way." "He is great at giving tactical advice and advising on the procedural aspects of cases. He is aware of the need to present the right image to the public and ensure that the client's commercial reputation is preserved." **Recent work:** Advised a defendant facing a corporate manslaughter charge arising out of the Gleision mine flooding, which led to four deaths.

6 Pump Court

See profile on p.850

THE SET

6 Pump Court can devote a team of 25 barristers, including five silks, to health and safety work. It has two members who are Standing Counsel to the HSE and a further nine members on the Regulatory List, more than any other set. It also has strong links with the Office of Rail Regulation (ORR). Members here act for both the prosecution and defence, and have been involved in a number of significant disaster and fatality cases over the years, including Buncefield. They undertake work in a number of sectors, including the health, construction, rail, mining and oil industries, and were described as "the ultimate choice of the professional."

Client service: "The clerking, led by Richard Constable, is very good and very efficient. When we were faced with a potential inquest recently, there was certainly flexibility in terms of counsel availability and financial arrangements."

SILKS

David Travers QC (see p.740) A specialist in regulatory matters who acts for both the defence and prosecution. He has recently been involved in a number of fatality cases, including manslaughter by gross negligence. **Strengths:** "He is a fantastic regulatory lawyer who is able to reduce complex issues to a practical level." "He has the most charming advocacy style." **Recent work:** Represented the prosecution in a case against Network Rail and Carillion, arising out of the death of an individual due to a faulty piece of equipment used to maintain the railway infrastructure.

Stephen Hockman QC Recognised for his involvement in complicated and heavyweight cases. He is currently leading the set's health and safety team. **Strengths:** "His judgement is second to none. He is very calm and collected, and demonstrates fantastic client-handling skills." "A fantastic advocate with such authority and gravitas." **Recent work:** Advised TOTAL UK during the inquest into a death resulting from the Lindsay Oil Refinery explosion.

JUNIORS

Mark Harris Expert in a wide range of areas, but particularly well known for handling railway and construction cases. He was recently reappointed as Standing Counsel to the HSE and the ORR. **Strengths:** "A lawyer with a brilliant mind and brilliant judgement." "He's superbly organised and terrifically hard-working – you embark on almost a military operation when instructing him." **Recent work:** Advised on a case concerning a child who died when part of an improperly installed fireplace fell on him. This successfully led to the imposition of new construction standards for the industry.

Mark Watson Conducts both prosecution and defence work in equal measure. He has tackled a number of fatality cases, and has recently advised on matters relating to fire safety. **Strengths:** "He has all the winning qualities of an advocate, and exudes charm and intelligence by the truckload." "He is a delight with clients, being both incredibly responsive and extremely able." **Recent work:** He acted on behalf of the HSE in a case brought against the Environment Agency following a fatality during flood defence dredging work.

Pascal Bates (see p.545) Has acted on a significant number of cases relating to fatalities. He is currently Standing Counsel to the HSE and the Office of Rail Regulation. **Strengths:** "He is tenacious; every case he does is handled with meticulous precision." "He is an excellent lawyer, who is strong on the legal analysis." **Recent work:** Prosecuted a case regarding death of a dementia patient who fell from first floor windows that had been improperly fitted.

Lee Bennett Principally defends, and works on a wide range of cases in the field, many of which are highly complex. **Strengths:** "A very persuasive and competent advocate, who is also a team player." "Very capable on his feet and an all-round excellent performer." **Recent work:** Acting for the Football Association on the Hillsborough inquest, which is considering several issues, such as stadium and crowd safety.

Band 2

2 Bedford Row

See profile on p.763

THE SET

This heavyweight criminal set has the volume, expertise and numbers to make a strong impact in the health and safety sector. It handles an equal mix of prosecution and defence work, and is well known for its involvement in complex and high-profile cases. Examples of its cases include the proceedings arising out of the Lakanal House and Atherstone-on-Stour fires. The team has also been instructed by a number of FTSE companies.

Client service: "What you want is people available at the drop of a hat. You need billing done properly and on time. You need interaction. That's what the clerking team, led by John Grimmer, does. The clerks understand the commercial realities of these cases."

SILKS

Richard Matthews QC A pre-eminent practitioner in the field who is known for conducting inquest work arising out of major incidents, such as the Lakanal House fire. He has defended a number of significant FTSE companies. **Strengths:** "He's a lightning-sharp barrister who knows the law inside out." "Approachable, very easy to deal with and really good with clients." **Recent work:** Involved in the high-profile Lakanal House fire inquests, which resulted in a number of fatalities. He acted on behalf of the London Borough of Southwark.

Jim Sturman QC A renowned criminal silk who often handles health and safety cases at board level. He is experienced in cases of fatality and those concerning regulatory breach. **Strengths:** "He is clearly an excellent and seasoned jury advocate." "He is a master at jury trials."

JUNIORS

Shauna Ritchie (see p.708) Tackles a mixture of prosecution and defence work, and receives instructions from the HSE, CPS and ORR. She has specific experience in fatality cases and those relating to asbestos, the railways and the construction industry. **Strengths:** "She's a very appealing advocate who is good on her feet." "She's charming, tenacious and meticulous." **Recent work:** Prosecuted Balfour Beatty Railtrack Systems in a case concerning inadequate protection for staff working on a rail press that led to a number of injuries and amputations.

Andrew McGee (see p.668) Has experience on both the defence and prosecution sides in a range of matters, including corporate manslaughter matters. He is an 'A list' prosecutor to the Environment Agency, HSE and ORR. **Strengths:** "He knows his stuff and is very practical." "He gets on very well with clients." **Recent work:** Involved in a case relating to a go-karting accident that led to the death of a young woman. While a number of health and safety failings were found, no causal link was established between those offences and the fatality.

Eleanor Sanderson A criminal practitioner with an expanding health and safety practice. She takes on a significant number of fire safety cases for both the prosecution and defence. **Strengths:** "She is very thorough in her approach. She listens to her client and has very good knowledge." "I am really impressed with her advocacy and how she gets results." **Recent work:** Advised the London Borough of Southwark on the Lakanal House fire case.

Outer Temple Chambers

See profile on p.842

THE SET

Practitioners here focus on a broad range of health and safety areas, including major inquests and inquiries. They act exclusively for the defendant and approach cases from both the criminal and civil angles. Members have been involved in a number of big-hitting cases recently, including the Lakanal House fire inquest. Sources say the set is "well respected and at the top of its game."

Client service: "The clerks, led by Paul Barton, are very engaged and are an important part of the set's future strategy."

SILKS

Richard Lissack QC Handles major health and safety cases as part of a very broad practice. He has handled many significant matters, such as the case against Cotswold Geotech, the first prosecution under the Manslaughter Act. **Strengths:** "He's an absolute giant in terms of the quality of his advice and his presence in court." "He's very clever and has a lot of gravitas." **Recent work:** Advised in a case brought against a construction and management company following the collapse of the Gerrards Cross tunnel.

Ben Compton QC The vast majority of his practice is health and safety-related, and he handles cases for major clients, many of whom come from the construction industry. He has extensive experience of corporate manslaughter cases. **Strengths:** "Great with the lawyer, great with the judge, and great at cross-examination." "He's very good with clients, as he's keen to engage and be inclusive." **Recent work:** Advised Warwickshire Fire and Rescue Services on a case regarding a warehouse fire that resulted in the deaths of four firemen.

JUNIORS

Stephen Climie Expert in a range of health and safety areas, and strong on corporate manslaughter cases. He is particularly sought out for healthcare prosecutions. **Strengths:** "He quickly strikes up a relationship with the client and engenders their confidence and trust." "He's a good, solid performer." **Recent work:** Represented the Hospital Trust in a case brought by the HSE, following an incident whereby a mental health patient killed a worker at a residential home.

James Leonard Handles defence work and frequently appears on cases relating to fatal accidents. Significant companies he has acted for include Sainsbury's, Comet Group and Western Power. **Strengths:** "A very good negotiator who is extremely well prepared on the documents front." "He's very visible to those that instruct him and shares his knowledge about important cases." **Recent work:** Acted for the Princes Sporting Club and its director in a case arising from the death of a young girl who had been on a banana boat at a birthday party.

Temple Garden Chambers

See profile on p.872

THE SET

Temple Garden Chambers has a long track record in health and safety cases. It has a cluster of specialist practitioners of differing seniority, reflecting its strength in depth in the area. Barristers at the set overwhelmingly act for the defendant, and represent a whole range of clients, including large, multinational construction companies. Some practitioners also prosecute for local authorities and sit on the Treasury Solicitor's panel. Market sources say the team is a "seamless unit" that is "diligent, hardworking and inclusive."

Client service: "The clerks, led by Dean Norton, regard the set as specialist in this field and are keen to actively develop relationships with firms."

SILKS

Keith Morton QC The majority of his busy practice is dedicated to health and safety work, and he typically handles cases involving fatalities or those with difficult points of law attached to them. He almost exclusively represents the defendant. **Strengths:** "His attention to detail is phenomenal." "He's very fair, very straight and very balanced." **Recent work:** Represented the owners of Warwick Castle in a case relating to the death of a visitor who fell from a medieval bridge.

Jonathan Watt-Pringle QC (see p.747) Negotiates a mixed practice which, in addition to health and safety work, includes personal injury matters. He has a strong history of conducting cases involving Network Rail. **Strengths:** "A very astute and likeable barrister with a hidden cutting edge." "He is very professional and well prepared, and is aware of the sensitivities attached to these cases." **Recent work:** Advised Network Rail in a case arising from the death of a pedestrian at a level crossing.

JUNIORS

Dominic Adamson Predominantly acts for the defendant, and has appeared for a number of significant clients, such as Serco, Biffa and Empire Cinemas. He frequently advises on cases relating to the construction and transport industries. **Strengths:** "He is keen and good with clients." **Recent work:** Advised on a case brought by the HSE against Tata Steel UK arising out of a fatality that occurred during a vessel relining at the Lackenby site.

Fiona Canby (see p.564) Acts solely for the defendant and undertakes a mixture of criminal and civil work. She has expertise in a range of areas, including the transport, construction and manufacturing sectors. **Strengths:** "She works extremely hard and in any given case there isn't a piece of paper she wouldn't know." "Her legal submissions are great." **Recent work:** Acted on an inquest into the death of a Red Arrows pilot who died as a result of separate faults that led his seat to eject and the parachute to fail.

Kevin McLoughlin (see p.668) A former solicitor, who has built up a strong health and safety practice at the Bar. In addition to handling a busy workload he sits as an assistant coroner. **Strengths:** "An extremely bright man" who has "broad experience over the whole range of the health and safety field." **Recent work:** Acted for the prosecution in a case concerning the death of a dementia sufferer during respite care. While left unsupervised, the patient fell from a balcony.

Band 3

2 Hare Court

See profile on p.818

THE SET

A traditionally criminal set whose health and safety practice is going from strength to strength. It has expertise in cases emanating from a vast range of sectors, including construction, manufacturing, engineering, healthcare and energy. Practitioners have acted in a number of fatality cases and related inquests, and are experienced in dealing with corporate manslaughter investigations.

Client service: "The set is proactively promoting itself and its clerking team, headed by Julian Campbell, has proved very successful in reaching out to specialists in the field."

SILKS

Jonathan Laidlaw QC (see p.649) A barrister who is frequently involved in cases relating to the construction sector, and who receives a large number of instructions from US companies. Market sources speak about his practice in glowing terms, and note his involvement in the leading corporate manslaughter cases of the day. Laidlaw combines his health and safety practice with general criminal work. **Strengths:** "It's useful for a barrister to have a background that isn't just health and safety. It means he brings broad experience and can apply his superior courtroom skills to these cases." **Recent work:** Acting for Fluor in the HSE investigation into several deaths resulting from the construction of the Greater Gabbard wind farm.

JUNIORS

James Buchanan (see p.559) An experienced criminal barrister who also handles heavyweight health and safety work. He is increasingly dealing with cases relating to the construction sector. **Strengths:** "He's good at explaining the picture very clearly and in certain terms. He is very supportive of us, backing the advice we give the client. In that respect he's a real team player." **Recent work:** Acted on a case regarding the death of a young scaffolding labourer who fell from a great height.

Craig Ferguson Has a background in pure crime, but has successfully expanded into the health and safety field and gained instructions in some significant cases. He acts for both companies and directors, and also conducts inquest work. **Strengths:** "His advocacy is excellent. He's always been very strong and balanced, and he gets to the cut and thrust of the case." **Recent work:** Acted for the director of a scaffolding and construction company on a case arising from the death of an employee who fell from height.

3 Raymond Buildings Barristers

See profile on p.857

THE SET

A top-of-the-range criminal set that is also very strong on regulatory law. It handles both criminal and civil health and safety cases, appearing for both regulators and regulated companies and individuals. Everything from enforcement proceedings and inquests to corporate manslaughter cases is handled, and the set is known for its strong links with the entertainment, construction and transport sectors. A significant number of practitioners also have expertise in the niche area of fire safety.

Client service: "A very approachable set of clerks, led by Eddie Holland. They are willing to be transparent and open about the pricing."

SILKS

Stephen Walsh QC Acts on a range of cases, and has a particularly strong reputation in fire safety cases. His health and safety work sits alongside his busy licensing practice. **Strengths:** "A very good advocate who is good with clients." **Recent work:** Acted for the London Fire and Emergency Planning Authority during the three-month inquest into the Lakanal House fire, which led to multiple deaths.

JUNIORS

Jonathan Ashley-Norman Has recently handled a number of rail-related cases in the health and safety field. He has also been involved in a number of matters relating to fatalities. **Strengths:** "He displays great attention to detail. He pitches cases just right and doesn't overcomplicate them." "He was very on the ball throughout the process, and had a good turnaround time if I needed something." **Recent work:** Acted for the ORR in prosecuting First Capital Connect due to a failure to implement the appropriate rescue of passengers trapped on a train.

Sarah Le Fevre A large proportion of her caseload relates to fire safety and the rail industry. She acts for both the prosecution and the defence, and has a number of inquests to her name. **Strengths:** "Charming, eloquent and very persuasive." **Recent work:** Retained by the ORR to prosecute Network Rail for risk management and assessment failures after a young boy acquired serious brain injuries at a level crossing on private land.

Saba Naqshbandi Her specialist area is fire-related cases, and she also undertakes inquest work. She has frequently represented the London Fire Emergency Planning Authority. **Recent work:** "She's a very fearless advocate who is not cowed by a difficult case or difficult tribunal." "She really knows the area inside out." **Recent work:** Instructed by LEPFA in regard to the Lakanal House fire investigation and inquest.

Other Ranked Lawyers

Gerard Forlin QC (see p.601) (Cornerstone Barristers) Has a mixed practice that includes the related fields of environment, transport and product liability. His health and safety work is increasingly taking on an international profile. **Strengths:** "He communicates very well with a jury, and retains a sense of humour without losing any of his gravitas. He's a force to be reckoned with." "He is very focused on the client's hopes and ambitions." **Recent work:** Representing a US tour company in an inquest in the Falkland Islands arising from the death of a walker.

Stephen Killalea QC (Devereux) Has a background in criminal law and is an expert in risk assessment. He specialises in complex cases, including those relating to corporate manslaughter and serious injury. **Strengths:** "He is particularly good at sorting the wood from the trees." "He provides pragmatic advice, and is able to immediately engage with the client." **Recent work:** Advised a defendant in a case concerning a gas cylinder which exploded while being filled with nitrogen gas, causing the accidental death of an employee, major injury to a member of the public and extensive property damage.

Iain Daniels (Ely Place Chambers) Represents farmer organisations, including the NFU, alongside hospital trusts and police forces. He is also handling an increasing amount of work for private custody providers. **Strengths:** "He is a good jury advocate." **Recent work:** Represented the HSE against a hospital trust that was fined £175,000 in total for failures that led to an elderly patient falling from a window and a number of patients acquiring Legionnaires' disease.

Christian Du Cann (Thirty Nine Essex Street) Both prosecutes and defends health and safety cases in criminal courts. He has a mixed practice that includes personal injury. **Strengths:** "A superb advocate in Crown Court." "He's very good at taking difficult points and is really good at mitigation." **Recent work:** Involved in a week-long Crown Court trial regarding the catastrophic injury of a labourer who was fitting a swimming pool in the basement of a Kent property. It was particularly complex as several contractors and subcontractors sought to blame one another.

Malcolm Galloway (Old Square Chambers) On the A Panel of the Regulatory List for the HSE, ORR and EA. He works on the full spectrum of health and safety work, and has experience of NHS trust work and corporate manslaughter investigations. **Strengths:** "He is extremely pragmatic and builds very good relations with judges and coroners." "He is prepared to go the extra mile and is supportive to the client." **Recent work:** Acted for the defendant, a recycling company, in a case concerning significant injuries acquired by an employee.

Jonathan Caplan QC (5 Paper Buildings) Acts for companies, directors and individuals on health and safety matters, and does a large amount of work for the railway industry. He has a wide range of experience in the areas of transport, construction and shipbuilding. **Strengths:** "Clients absolutely love him. He has a beautiful manner in conference and in court." "A very senior and polished performer." **Recent work:** Represented BMI Healthcare in a case that arose after a post-operative patient fell from a hospital balcony.

Deanna Heer (see p.624) (5 Paper Buildings) Regularly both prosecutes and defends major companies in relation to fatality cases, including those concerning gross negligence manslaughter. Her work originates from a range of bodies, including the HSE, the CPS and the ORR. **Strengths:** "She's very fair and prosecutes in a clear way. She sticks to her guns." **Recent work:** Advised corporate defendants charged following the death of a tele-handler driver during the redevelopment of Newbury town centre.

Ian Lawrie QC (3PB Barristers) An expert in the niche area of marine-related cases. He advises both the defence and the prosecution. **Strengths:** "He's fantastic – the leading individual on shipping prosecution work." **Recent work:** Acted for the defendant, the captain of tug 'Chieftain', on a corporate manslaughter investigation after 'Chieftain' sank on the Thames.

Adrian Darbishire QC (QEB Hollis Whiteman) Has extensive experience in corporate manslaughter cases. He specialises largely in white-collar crime, and approaches his health and safety work from a criminal angle. **Strengths:** "Handles witnesses and juries superbly." "He's got very good judgement and is an attractive advocate – judges just like him." **Recent work:** Defended a firework operator charged with manslaughter following a crash on the M5 that killed seven people.

Sailesh Mehta (see p.670) (Red Lion Chambers) Handles a large volume of cases relating to accidental deaths or near fatalities. He acts for the HSE and also represents several fire brigades. **Strengths:** "He's a capable and thorough person who knows what he is doing." **Recent work:** Acted on a case arising from a fatal accident at a printing press.

MIDLANDS

Health & Safety Midlands
Leading Sets
Band 1
No5 Chambers *
St Philips Chambers *
Leading Silks
Band 1
Tedd Rex *No5 Chambers*
Leading Juniors
Band 1
Thorogood Bernard *No5 Chambers* *
Band 2
Berlin Barry *St Philips Chambers* *
Farrer Adam *No5 Chambers*
Gilchrist Naomi *St Philips Chambers* [A] *
Green Timothy *Outer Temple Chambers (ORL)* ◊ [A]
Puzey James *St Philips Chambers* *

Band 1

No5 Chambers
See profile on p.883

THE SET

No5 Chambers' strong regulatory group works with a wide range of clients, including local authorities, regulatory bodies and individual defendants. The set acts on some of the most notable health and safety matters in the country, including representing South Yorkshire Fire & Rescue Service on the inquest into the deaths of 96 Liverpool fans at Hillsborough Stadium.

SILKS

Rex Tedd QC A veteran criminal practitioner, he receives regular instructions from both the HSE and leading law firms on high-profile regulatory cases. He is praised by instructing solicitors as a highly user-friendly silk. **Strengths:** "He has so much experience, commitment and skill that he can turn any case and make it look easy." "He is obviously at the top of his game and does the whole breadth of criminal cases. This gives him a more balanced view in relation to the work." **Recent work:** Successfully prosecuted on a case concerning the death of a man who was hit by a loading vehicle.

JUNIORS

Bernard Thorogood (see p.737) Has focused his health and safety practice on cases of the utmost severity, on behalf of both defendants and prosecutors across the country. He acts for a range of clients, including major companies, individuals, emergency services and other public bodies. He is noted for his expertise in manslaughter cases with health and safety issues. **Strengths:** "He is very well established in this area. He is thorough, dotting every i and crossing every t." "He's a fountain of knowledge, and also very contactable and easy to speak to." **Recent work:** Acting for South Yorkshire Fire & Rescue Service on the high-profile Hillsborough inquest, which relates to a total of 96 deaths.

Adam Farrer A former solicitor who is on the HSE A List. He both prosecutes and defends health and safety cases, and he has considerable expertise of cases arising from construction, asbestos, farming and manufacturing. **Strengths:** "He is a safe pair of hands who will put the case fairly." **Recent work:** Prosecuted a case against a scaffolding company and the principal contractor after the accidental death of a labourer.

St Philips Chambers
See profile on p.886

THE SET

Barristers in this large regulatory team act on the full gamut of health and safety work, from prosecutions under the Health and Safety at Work etc. Act to corporate manslaughter cases. This 21-strong team is noted by commentators not just for its depth of expertise, but also for its commercial and user-friendly approach.

Client service: "They're much more competitive on the costs, and the clerks there are very good for regulatory work. You can have an open dialogue with them."

JUNIORS

Barry Berlin (see p.548) A veteran regulatory practitioner who is regularly instructed by the HSE, local authorities and the Environment Agency to prosecute heavyweight matters. **Strengths:** "He is very thorough and has a great command of the law in this area." **Recent work:** Instructed by Warwick District Council on a case arising from the fatal fall of a visitor to Warwick Castle.

Naomi Gilchrist (see p.608) A former solicitor who has focused her career at the Bar on criminal regulatory work. She is noted for her expertise on health and safety cases concerning injuries of the utmost severity. **Strengths:** "She is an extremely astute advocate who is a great planner and thinker on cases." **Recent work:** Advised and represented the defendant company in an HSE prosecution relating to an accident where an employee's fingers were cut off by a power press.

James Puzey (see p.701) A specialist regulatory practitioner noted for his expertise in prosecuting health and safety cases. **Strengths:** "He is calm, cool and unflappable. He is very good in front of the client, with his judgement being second to none."

Other Ranked Lawyers

Timothy Green (Outer Temple Chambers) A regulatory specialist who is regularly instructed in health and safety prosecutions by the HSE and local authorities. He is on the Attorney General's A Panel of approved regulatory advocates. **Strengths:** "He is pleasant, straightforward to deal with and a safe pair of hands." "He's really a jury advocate, but he's also very good with client and client handling." **Recent work:** Represented Barnsley Borough Council in its prosecution of ASDA for unsafe freezer systems that led to the injury of an employee.

NORTH EASTERN

Health & Safety North Eastern
Leading Silks
Band 1
Smith Robert *New Park Court Chambers (ORL)* ◊
New Silks
Pitter Jason *New Park Court Chambers (ORL)* ◊
Leading Juniors
Band 1
Cameron Neil *Wilberforce Chambers (ORL)* ◊
◊ (ORL) = Other Ranked Lawyer.
[A] direct access (see p.11).
** Indicates set / individual with profile.*
Alphabetical order within each band. Band 1 is highest.

Ranked Lawyers

Robert Smith QC (New Park Court Chambers) A revered criminal practitioner who is the North Eastern Circuit's go-to silk for complex health and safety litigation. He covers both defence and prosecution work. **Strengths:** "You can sit in ten-hour conferences with him and he'll be sharp while everyone else is knackered. He is courteous to a fault too – a true gentleman who is appropriate in his dealings with everyone."

Jason Pitter QC (New Park Court Chambers) Frequently prosecutes cases on behalf of the CPS and HSE. He is noted for his expertise in health and safety cases concerning fatalities and injuries of maximum severity. **Recent work:** Prosecuted a case arising from a fatal suffocation caused by the CO_2 fire extinguishing apparatus.

Neil Cameron (Wilberforce Chambers) A regulatory practitioner who specialises in environmental and health and safety cases. He acts predominantly for defendant companies.

NORTHERN

Health & Safety Northern	
Leading Silks	
Band 1	
Horlock Timothy	*Deans Court Chambers (ORL)* ◊
Band 2	
Denney Stuart	*Deans Court Chambers (ORL)* ◊ Ⓐ
Kennedy Christopher	*9 St John Street (ORL)* ◊
New Silks	
Lawrence Nigel	*7 Harrington St Chambers (ORL)* ◊
Leading Juniors	
Band 1	
Judge Lisa	*Deans Court Chambers (ORL)* ◊ Ⓐ
Band 2	
Donnelly Kevin	*Lincoln House Chambers (ORL)* ◊
McKeon James	*7 Harrington St Chambers (ORL)* ◊
Smith Peter	*Deans Court Chambers (ORL)* ◊
Snarr Matthew	*9 St John Street (ORL)* ◊

Ranked Lawyers

Timothy Horlock QC (Deans Court Chambers) Has a mixed practice that, in addition to health and safety, includes other areas of expertise such as personal injury. He acts for both the defence and the prosecution. **Strengths:** "He's very good and an authoritative advocate. He knows what he's doing." "He has the full package – he is clearly very bright and is also very hard-working."

Stuart Denney QC (Deans Court Chambers) Has a broad criminal practice that encompasses considerable regulatory and health and safety work. He is a member of the Attorney General's A-list of practitioners. **Strengths:** "He's a very succinct and to-the-point advocate."

Lisa Judge (Deans Court Chambers) One of the leading health and safety advocates on the Northern Circuit. She combines her regulatory work with a heavyweight criminal practice, and is noted by instructing solicitors for her highly skilled advocacy. **Strengths:** "She is one of the best jury advocates around." "She has a no-nonsense approach and gets down to the heart of the matter." **Recent work:** Represented National Grid during an inquest regarding the death of an elderly person due to carbon monoxide poisoning.

Peter Smith (Deans Court Chambers) Acts for both corporate and individual defendants on health and safety cases in a variety of sectors. **Strengths:** "He is very experienced and has a very understated but effective style of advocacy."

Nigel Lawrence QC (7 Harrington St Chambers) Frequently acts for the HSE as the prosecuting counsel. Has been retained to advise on the Hillsborough inquests. **Strengths:** "He distils down the complicated work into simple elements." **Recent work:** He acted in the prosecution of Greater Manchester Police and two of its firearms officers relating to the death of a police officer during a firearms training exercise.

James McKeon (7 Harrington St Chambers) Focuses on health and safety as part of his regulatory criminal caseload. He acts on behalf of the HSE, often in regard to fatalities, and for defendant NHS trusts.

Kevin Donnelly (Lincoln House Chambers) Has handled cases for the HSE, the Office of Rail Regulation and also the Environment Agency. He has a broad regulatory practice.

Christopher Kennedy QC (9 St John Street) Has focused his practice on health and safety and personal injury work. He is widely recognised for his work with defendant companies in HSE prosecutions. **Strengths:** "He is nicely commercial and pragmatic. He doesn't just give you a legal opinion – he also gives you a business opinion." **Recent work:** Instructed on behalf of Tata in an HSE prosecution relating to alleged health and safety breaches at a Cheshire chemical plant.

Matthew Snarr (9 St John Street) Splits his practice between personal injury and health and safety areas. He focuses on representing defendant companies in heavyweight health and safety prosecutions. **Recent work:** Acted on an inquest into the death of a gas maintenance engineer whose death was linked to the use of a diesel-fuelled portable generator.

WESTERN

Health & Safety Western	
Leading Silks	
Band 1	
Haggan Nicholas	*12 College Place (ORL)* ◊
Langdon Andrew	*Guildhall Chambers (ORL)* ◊
Leading Juniors	
Band 1	
Dixey Ian	*Guildhall Chambers (ORL)* ◊
Band 2	
Bennett James	*Guildhall Chambers (ORL)* ◊
Lowe Rupert	*Guildhall Chambers (ORL)* ◊
Morgan Simon	*St John's Chambers (ORL)* ◊
Vigars Anna	*Guildhall Chambers (ORL)* ◊
Up-and-coming individuals	
Jones Samuel	*Guildhall Chambers (ORL)* ◊
◊ (ORL) = Other Ranked Lawyer.	
** Indicates individual with profile.*	
Ⓐ direct access (see p.11).	

Ranked Lawyers

Nicholas Haggan QC (12 College Place) Retained by both prosecutors and defendants for health and safety work. His mixed practice is made up of criminal, regulatory and public access work. **Strengths:** "He never knowingly underprosecutes. He is tenacious and thorough."

Andrew Langdon QC (Guildhall Chambers) Handles complex cases such as major fatal accidents. He is a noted criminal silk with a mixed defence and prosecution practice. **Strengths:** "He has a huge command of the technical subject area; he is just the most persuasive trial advocate." "You will not find a more charming practitioner."

Ian Dixey (Guildhall Chambers) Acts for both the prosecution and defence, with his recent caseload including a number of fatal accidents relating to the construction industry. He is on the A-list of approved counsel to the HSE, ORR and EA. **Strengths:** "On significant cases he draws out, crystallises and succeeds on issues and arguments." "He's very calm and very measured. He doesn't get cross and go in all guns blazing. He gets his results by being right." **Recent work:** Instructed in a case brought against the primary contractor, employer and managing director regarding the death of a scaffolder who fell from a weak access platform.

James Bennett (Guildhall Chambers) His expertise covers the gamut of health and safety work. He is instructed on cases of fatality, including those leading to charges of corporate manslaughter and gross negligence manslaughter. **Strengths:** "He is very good on disclosure issues, and also at working in a team – be that with solicitors, clients or leading counsel." **Recent work:** Defended the director of a sports club in a corporate manslaughter case following a speedboat fatality at a boating lake near Heathrow.

Rupert Lowe (Guildhall Chambers) Has a strong health and safety practice focused on fatal accidents in the workplace. Market sources commend him for his stellar advocacy. **Strengths:** "He's very accurate and doesn't miss a thing in terms of evidential matters." "He is very determined and identifies key issues very early."

Anna Vigars (Guildhall Chambers) Has a mixed practice that, in addition to health and safety, includes criminal and environmental cases. She is particularly commended for her advocacy skills. **Strengths:** "She's a sensible advocate and highly effective." "She is highly rated in terms of her advice, approach and strategy."

Samuel Jones (Guildhall Chambers) Has a broad practice that includes a niche in health and safety and, in particular, in fire safety. He undertakes both prosecution and defence work. **Strengths:** "The quality of his advocacy, written work and advice belie his years. He performs and punches above his weight."

Simon Morgan (St John's Chambers) A heavyweight criminal practitioner who has forged a strong reputation in health and safety and other regulatory work. He advises both the prosecution and defence, and is recognised for his expertise in farm-related cases. **Strengths:** "He has the advantage of experience on both sides of the Bench." "He's a robust advocate, with good attention to detail." **Recent work:** Acted on the prosecution of Exeter City Council in connection with a fatal accident where an individual fell off the steps on the quayside while using a ferry.

Contents:

LONDON

Immigration London
Leading Sets
Band 1
Garden Court Chambers *
Band 2
Blackstone Chambers *
Doughty Street Chambers *
Matrix Chambers *
Band 3
Thirty Nine Essex Street *
Landmark Chambers *
1 Pump Court *
Senior Statesmen
Senior Statesmen
Macdonald Ian *Garden Court Chambers*
Leading Silks
Star individuals
Fordham Michael *Blackstone Chambers*
Fransman Laurie *Garden Court Chambers*
Husain Raza *Matrix Chambers*
Band 1
Carss-Frisk Monica *Blackstone Chambers*
Eicke Tim *Essex Court Chambers (ORL)* ◊
Giovannetti Lisa *Thirty Nine Essex Street*
Knafler Stephen *Garden Court Chambers*
Southey Hugh *Matrix Chambers* *
Tam Robin *Temple Garden Chambers (ORL)* ◊ *
Band 2
Farbey Judith *Doughty Street Chambers* [A]
Harrison Stephanie *Garden Court Chambers*
McCullough Angus *1 Crown Office Row (ORL)* ◊
Pannick David *Blackstone Chambers*
Band 3
Johnson Jeremy *5 Essex Court (ORL)* ◊ *
Kovats Steven *Thirty Nine Essex Street*
Rose Dinah *Blackstone Chambers*
New Silks
Bourne Charles *11KBW (ORL)* ◊ [A] *
◊ (ORL) = Other Ranked Lawyer.
[A] direct access (see p.18).
* Indicates set / individual with profile.

Immigration London
Leading Juniors
Star individuals
Dubinsky Laura *Doughty Street Chambers*
Band 1
Ahluwalia Navtej Singh *Garden Court Chambers*
Berry Adrian *Garden Court Chambers*
Buley Tim *Landmark Chambers*
Chapman Rebecca *Garden Court Chambers*
Chirico David *1 Pump Court*
Cronin Kathryn *Garden Court Chambers*
Henderson Mark *Doughty Street Chambers*
Khubber Ranjiv *1 Pump Court* [A]
Seddon Duran *Garden Court Chambers*
Toal Ronan *Garden Court Chambers*
Band 2
Armstrong Nicholas *Matrix Chambers*
Chandran Parosha *1 Pump Court* [A]
Chelvan S *No5 Chambers (ORL)* ◊ *
Denholm Graham *1 Pump Court*
Finch Nadine *Garden Court Chambers*
Fripp Eric *Lamb Building (ORL)* ◊
Goodman Alex *Landmark Chambers* [A]
Haywood Philip *Doughty Street Chambers* [A]
Jorro Peter *Garden Court Chambers*
Knights Samantha *Matrix Chambers*
Lewis Patrick *Garden Court Chambers*
MacKenzie Alasdair *Doughty Street Chambers*
Middleton Joseph *Doughty Street Chambers* [A]
Naik Sonali *Garden Court Chambers*
Payne Alan *5 Essex Court (ORL)* ◊ *
Pickup Alison *Doughty Street Chambers*
Sayeed Sadat *Garden Court Chambers*
Smith Abigail *Garden Court Chambers*
Symes Mark *Garden Court Chambers*
Walsh John *Doughty Street Chambers*
Weston Amanda *Garden Court Chambers*
Band 3
Bazini Daniel *No5 Chambers (ORL)* ◊ [A]
Blundell David *Landmark Chambers*
Brewer Michelle *Garden Court Chambers*
Dunlop Rory *Thirty Nine Essex Street* *
Hodgetts Glen *Glen Hodgetts (Barrister-at-Law) (ORL)* ◊
Jegarajah Shivani *Mansfield Chambers (ORL)* ◊
Jones David *Garden Court Chambers*
Kilroy Charlotte *Doughty Street Chambers*
Nicholson Edward *No5 Chambers (ORL)* ◊
O'Callaghan Declan *Landmark Chambers*
Waite John-Paul *5 Essex Court (ORL)* ◊
Yeo Colin *Garden Court Chambers* *
Band 4
Blum Doron *1 Pump Court*
Hirst Leonie *Garden Court Chambers*
Kiai Gilda *1 Pump Court*
Laughton Victoria *1 Pump Court*
Lemer David *Doughty Street Chambers* [A]
Palmer Robert *Monckton Chambers (ORL)* ◊ [A] *
Poynor Bryony *Garden Court Chambers*
Rothwell Joanne *No5 Chambers (ORL)* ◊ [A]
Ward Galina *Landmark Chambers*
Up-and-coming individuals
Knorr Michelle *Doughty Street Chambers*
Meredith Catherine *Doughty Street Chambers*
Moffatt Rowena *Lamb Building (ORL)* ◊
Robinson Catherine *1 Pump Court*

Band 1

Garden Court Chambers
See profile on p.808

THE SET

This impressively sized set leads the way at the London Immigration Bar, and offers an unrivalled range of capabilities across all types of work. Specialist areas of expertise include national security, family and child immigration and asylum matters. Sources say: "Their approachability and depth of knowledge are impressive, and they provide high-quality work often at short notice."

Client service: "The clerking has always been excellent – you can always get hold of the right person. They do a weekly immigration bulletin and Colin Yeo writes a blog called Free Movement which is wonderful. Their conference facilities are in a really nice location, and they are spacious and professional – you are treated really well."

SILKS

Laurie Fransman QC Draws effusive praise for his dedication to nationality and asylum work, and has produced major textbooks on these topics. In terms of asylum work, he focuses on complex protection and exclusion matters, often concerning several parties and different countries. **Strengths:** "One of the greatest minds in the immigration law field – he is particularly good on nationality matters and is the go-to person for this. He does lots of general ground refusals and his technical knowledge is second to none." **Recent work:** He is an appointed expert in UN High Commissioner for Refugees (UNHCR) meetings regarding international protection and the issue of statelessness.

Stephen Knafler QC Has a solid grounding in immigration, human rights, social welfare and community care law. He is regularly instructed to represent local authorities and claimants in ground-breaking cases, and regularly appears in the higher courts in the land. **Strengths:** "He is a very nice person to work with and is very hands-on from an early stage." "He is very clear-headed, determined and always very collaborative, whilst also knowing that it's up to him to run the case." **Recent work:** Fought an asylum case concerning three child migrants and their potential deportation to other EU member states.

Ian Macdonald QC An incredibly accomplished silk who has a long history of working at the forefront of immigration law, having practised since the 1960s. His workload sees him advising advising students, assisting those using the points-based system via the Tier 1 (Investor) route, and providing counsel to non-EEA nationals, among other matters.

Stephanie Harrison QC A pioneering human rights and public/administrative law silk who has more than 20 years' experience under her belt. She is known in the market for having helped develop key precedents in relation to unlawful detention and deportation appeals based on national security policies. **Strengths:** "Her background is very much immigration-based, and she is an expert in actions against the state. She is a really feisty operator and her advocacy skills are second to none – she brings a sharpness and determination to the case, and she has excellent client care skills." "The judges love her – she explains things really clearly." **Recent work:** Successfully obtained an appeal for an Ethiopian national threatened with deportation.

JUNIORS

Navtej Ahluwalia Devotes a significant portion of his practice to EU free movement law and deportation work. He is often asked to advise business immigration firms and is a familiar face in the Special Immigration Appeals Commission. **Strengths:** "He is able to provide sound advice with a fast turnaround." "Very approachable – he's always willing to take a call and talk through problems without turning the meter on." **Recent work:** Acted in R v Secretary of State for the Home Department, a case concerning administrative delays by the Home Secretary in responding to applications for judicial review.

Adrian Berry Has an excellent reputation for his work on British nationality, international protection and asylum matters. He is often called upon to advise the UNHCR on statelessness, and he provides businesses, schools and individuals with information on Tier 1 and Tier 4 applications. **Strengths:** "Incredibly knowledgeable across all areas of UK immigration law and always willing to take the time to have something run by him." "Very impressive on nationality issues and statelessness, and a very good advocate and communicator." **Recent work:** Acted in a Supreme Court case regarding a tortured migrant's right to local authority accommodation.

Rebecca Chapman A dynamic and professional immigration junior with significant experience of handling complex and sensitive immigration claims where vulnerable women or children are seeking assistance. She is frequently instructed to conduct ground-breaking judicial reviews. **Strengths:** "She brings a wealth of experience, and is excellent with clients, meticulous in her approach, and great at finding solutions. She is incredibly hard-working and prepares to a very high standard."

Kathryn Cronin An incredibly active dual-qualified (UK/Australian) barrister whose work centres on the movement of children and families. Her broad immigration practice includes handling complex asylum and employment issues, often involving detention, deportation and removal. **Strengths:** "She is amazing, and provides a unique service on the crossover between children's law/adoption and immigration. She is very busy but her work is of a really high standard." "She's tenacious; she never gives up and is a fearless advocate." **Recent work:** Instructed in a case concerning the detail required of a First-tier Tribunal decision and related issues surrounding Country Guidance.

Duran Seddon Represents and advises international sportspeople and senior public figures/individuals escaping persecution in their homelands. He is also sought after for his work on cutting-edge human rights, welfare and social security-related matters. **Strengths:** "He is really superb and has excellent experience." "A very good junior barrister with an intellectual edge. "

Ronan Toal An erudite immigration/asylum practitioner who specialises in human trafficking, and who continues to contribute to the most celebrated texts on the law. He routinely goes to the High Court and Court of Appeal to fight on behalf of his clients on crucial immigration points. **Strengths:** "He's extremely bright and writes beautifully." "He has done a mix of asylum work and detention work and is very knowledgeable." **Recent work:** Acted in Hounga v Adenike Allen, a human trafficking case brought to the Supreme Court on the basis of ECHR and the Convention Against Trafficking.

Peter Jorro Recognised for his ability to effectively manage an interesting mix of business and family immigration work, including matters that concern well-known people in the political and business worlds. Can be seen regularly at the Supreme Court and High Court, acting on sophisticated judicial reviews and appeals. **Strengths:** "His diligence and high standard of written and oral work are highly valued." "A real lover of the law, he will explain the issue to you and what the law says in a clear and comprehensive way. He's really good on technical stuff." **Recent work:** Represented his client in a case concerning the power of the Court of Appeal under the Civil Procedure Rules and judicial review proceedings.

Patrick Lewis Admired by the market for his astute immigration advice regarding individuals, entrepreneurs and businesses applying to reside in the UK under the points-based system. With over 22 years of expertise at the Immigration Bar, he is a confident advocate when it comes to representing his clients before UK or international courts. **Strengths:** "Very approachable and willing to take calls at all hours." "He gets good results at court and tribunal, and clients love him." **Recent work:** Advised in a judicial review of a migrant's application for leave to remain in the UK.

Sonali Naik Having previously worked at various refugee law centres, she brings invaluable immigration and asylum experience to the team. She regularly takes on difficult appeals and review cases before tribunals and higher courts. **Strengths:** "She is very good on unlawful detention cases, has lots of experience and gets good results." "Very knowledgeable – she is very good on her feet, and is not fazed by what is thrown at her." **Recent work:** Instructed in appeals where corrective relief was sought for the Home Secretary's failings as regards child refugees.

Sadat Sayeed A very successful junior with a wide-ranging practice that deals with various types of inter-country transfer from countries such as India, the Russian Federation, Kazakhstan and Ukraine. She advises a host of individuals, ranging from those who seek protection for political reasons to those in the top echelons of international sport. **Strengths:** "He will not rest until an appeal is prepared as best as it can be. He has an excellent legal mind, and is pragmatic, approachable and able to explain things in a very understandable way."

Abigail Smith Particularly active handling all aspects of public law, including prison law, asylum and immigration. She previously worked as a solicitor and in various NGOs, and has been involved in some incredibly high-profile immigration matters over the years. **Strengths:** "Tenacious and practical in her approach, she takes the difficult cases and achieves results that would elude many other representatives."

Mark Symes Specialises in human rights and asylum work, and also has extensive experience in international protection. **Strengths:** "He has encyclopaedic knowledge and takes an innovative approach to legal issues." "He is a real cut above – he pushes the areas we are trying to develop in the law and comes out with new arguments. He will introduce things you haven't thought of."

Amanda Weston Has a broad practice and is particularly proficient in handling human rights and children's rights-related immigration matters. She is often instructed to act for senior political or business figures and other very well-known individuals in the music industry. **Strengths:** "Thoughtful, tactical and really good at seeing the overall strategic picture. Excellent." "She has top creative skills – she never misses a point and is well loved by the judiciary." **Recent work:** Has advised well-known individuals from the music industry such as Snoop Dogg and Busta Rhymes in relation to immigration and national security law.

Michelle Brewer A true specialist in the illegal inter-country transfer of persons, who has been selected by the Council of Europe to provide evidence and training on these issues. She is also well versed in the global protection of vulnerable groups such as children and those targeted because of their gender. **Strengths:** "She is good on sensitive cases re women/trafficking and she does a lot of pro bono work." "She is very nice, open and easy-going."

Nadine Finch A pioneering family immigration practitioner who has an active practice in civil liberties, asylum and judicial review matters in relation to the rights of migrant children. She also sits as an immigration judge and provides recommendations on the development of government policy. **Strengths:** "She stands out because she is well versed in the crossover between family and immigration law. She is extremely nice with clients and sensitive when necessary." **Recent work:** Instructed in R v L & Others, combined appeals against the prosecution of trafficked children for drugs offences.

David Jones This effective immigration and public/administrative law advocate has built a formidable reputation for himself over his 16 years at the Bar. His areas of interest include the transfer of individuals with criminal convictions. **Strengths:** "He is really good at taking on board what you say and being collaborative with solicitors." **Recent work:** Acted in Amirfard v The Secretary of State for the Home Department, a case concerning denial of naturalisation on good character grounds as a result of the appellant's activity as a conscript in the Iranian penal system.

Colin Yeo (see p.757) A sought-after immigration junior who displays exceptional talent when representing refugees, high-profile individuals and businesses at court. He also edits the acclaimed Free Movement blog and 'Butterworths Immigration Law Service'. **Strengths:** "He has good knowledge of the broader palette of immigration and can always place the issue in the wider context." "He has a solid understanding of immigration law, including the very complex matters, and is able to deal with things promptly." **Recent work:** Acted in a pro bono public access case relating to complex asylum matters. The issues included scarring as proof of torture, the role of the medical expert and intentional scarring in order to obtain asylum.

Leonie Hirst Has a thriving appellant practice in which she confronts some of the most complex policy issues affecting immigration and public law. She is applauded for her excellent management of matters concerning the confinement and deportation of migrants, and for her assistance to individuals seeking refuge in the UK. **Strengths:** "She is very thorough, prepared, and always looking at cases in a realistic way." "A calming influence on clients, and very sensitive towards them." **Recent work:** Advised on a difficult High Court case regarding government policy towards migrant prisoners who refuse to eat and drink.

Bryony Poynor A leading immigration junior with an active caseload of refugee, free movement and human rights-related matters. She is routinely instructed to act in judicial review and ECHR cases due to her background in civil liberties work. **Strengths:** "Very hard-working and a safe pair of hands. Clients are comfortable and confident in her abilities," and "she is very good at fighting to win." **Recent work:** Advised in MA & Ors v Secretary of State for the Home Department, an ECJ case concerning the deportation of unaccompanied child migrants fleeing political persecution.

Band 2

Blackstone Chambers
See profile on p.771
THE SET
Blackstone Chambers remains synonymous with excellence in public law and human rights cases generally. The set is distinguished by its formidable concentration of silks who practise at the highest levels of the judicial system and who cover a variety of different immigration matters. They are backed up by juniors who are no strangers to the more complex cases of the day.
Client service: "The clerks are very responsive and friendly. Their conference facilities are also good and they offer great free seminars."

SILKS
Michael Fordham QC Identified by the market as a master of immigration and nationality work, he has significant expertise and experience in civil liberties, EU law and Country Guidance claims. **Strengths:** "His drafting style is amazing; he drafts in a very straightforward and simple way, covers everything and is straight to the point. Anyone can read it, and the judges really appreciate this." **Recent work:** Instructed in a Country Guidance case concerning the safety of asylum seekers returning to Iraq.

Monica Carss-Frisk QC An eminent immigration and nationality silk who appears in the most high-profile domestic and European courts. Routinely advises the government on seminal immigration cases involving unlawful imprisonment and the ECHR convention. **Strengths:** "She is very good. She is a calm but forceful influence, and has an air of authority without in any way being arrogant or pushy." "She certainly had the Court of Appeal eating out of her hand in one case we did with her." **Recent work:** Selected as counsel to the Treasury Solicitor regarding human rights and the best interests of migrants who are still minors.

David Pannick QC The best public lawyer of his generation and a barrister well versed in the intricacies of asylum and civil liberties appeals at the higher courts. **Strengths:** "He is very crisp and to the point in his approach." "A superstar, and so good at everything." **Recent work:** Represented the Director of Immigration in an appeal that discussed the rights of refugees to work in Hong Kong.

Dinah Rose QC Earns unanimous approval from peers and clients for her thorough and intelligent immigration work. Executes ECHR, asylum and deportation appeals with spirit and confidence. **Strengths:** "She's very good on her preparation, and is approachable, willing to listen and excellent on her feet." **Recent work:** Successfully challenged the transfer of migrants to Sri Lanka who were making complaints of torture.

Doughty Street Chambers
See profile on p.786
THE SET
This immigration powerhouse has a fine reputation within the sector. It handles business, commercial and employment migration cases, as well as asylum and unlawful detention cases. Its barristers also demonstrate particular strength in handling cases concerning the transfer of EU members and those planning to study in the UK. One source says: "The members are efficient, friendly and accommodating. They go the extra mile for their clients."
Client service: "The clerks are very accessible. They are always happy to discuss fees and suggest counsel, and they don't double-book barristers."

SILKS
Judith Farbey QC A strong and adaptable immigration silk at the top of her game. She provides counsel to a wide range of clients on EU and human rights law immigration cases, and offers general migration policy advice to businesses. **Strengths:** "The breadth and depth of her skill set and experience is fantastic. She is my absolute go-to barrister for complex matters. Her analytical approach and thought process in strategising complex situations are nothing short of breathtaking." "Her technical expertise is outstanding, and she's very accessible and great to run ideas by."

JUNIORS
Philip Haywood Has an all-encompassing immigration practice and regularly fights cases at all levels of the domestic and European court system, including at the ECJ and ECHR. Demonstrates sophisticated knowledge of difficult refugee and Country Guidance cases, as well as sponsor licences. **Strengths:** "Produces excellent written work and has a good eye for detail. He works on asylum, EEA and Article 8 matters, and has a wide range of knowledge and skills." "He is reliable, sensible and immediately responsive." **Recent work:** Advised in an appeal at the Upper Tribunal and Court of Appeal that determined the Country Guidance for Zimbabwe.

Alasdair MacKenzie A co-founder of and campaigner for the charity Asylum Aid, and one of the leading juniors at the London Immigration Bar. His civil liberties, family and EEA-related work has earned him significant recognition in the sector. **Strengths:** "His written work and advocacy are excellent; he pushes us as solicitors, which is really great." "He is thorough, provides an immediate response, and has an incredibly wide knowledge of almost every area of immigration law." **Recent work:** Acted for one of three claimants against the Home Office in a case concerning a backlog in asylum claims that allegedly prevented the claimant from obtaining residence.

Joseph Middleton Handles a variety of immigration matters, from legal aid and pro bono cases to larger-value work for business clients. He is a Russian speaker and has significant experience of working on complex extradition and human rights cases. **Strengths:** "He is very accessible and flexible, and this makes him easy to work with." "He's very knowledgeable and shows excellent attention to detail." **Recent work:** Engaged in the judicial review of the Quality Assurance Agency's refusal to grant quality assurance for a sponsor licence to a private college.

John Walsh Combines an active practice in corporate immigration with legal aid representation for detained migrants. He is regularly instructed to act on judicial review cases at the First-tier Tribunal as well as in cases brought to the ECJ. **Strengths:** "He is really calm, and he doesn't get flustered. He is very thorough and very reliable." "He is very good at very messy cases as he can cut to the quick on what is relevant, especially in cases where there is lots of immigration history. His written work is fantastic and he is responsive."

Laura Dubinsky Has appeared at the Court of Appeal and Supreme Court in relation to highly contentious areas of asylum and immigration detention law. She has a spectacular depth of knowledge when it comes to EU and ECHR law, and cases concerning the deportation or detention of convicted terrorists. **Strengths:** "She stands out as a result of her complete thoroughness and dedication to the job. She really pushes you as a solicitor to do things that help the case." "Meticulous and very driven, she is innovative in the way she approaches the law." **Recent work:** Acted as sole adviser and representative in an application to appeal to the Supreme Court in a case that concerned the imprisonment of EU migrants prior to their removal.

Alison Pickup Previously worked as a legal adviser to individuals wishing to escape their country because of political persecution. She has developed an all-encompassing immigration offering that not only focuses on obtaining asylum, but also helps with the wider needs of migrants such as the provision of community care and economic support. **Strengths:** "She is extremely reliable, well organised, calm, focused and able to think strategically." "Phenomenally bright and extremely thorough in terms of her paperwork, she is committed and extremely nice to work with." **Recent work:** Acted in Refugee Action's challenge to the government's decision not to raise the level of social security paid to refugees.

Catherine Meredith A dynamic and experienced junior who specialises in asylum and immigration cases before the higher courts. Her practice has a particular emphasis on EU, ECHR and family-related migrant cases. **Strengths:** "She has a lot of energy – she works incredibly hard and pushes for the best outcome." "She is an excellent, intellectual lawyer, who grasps cases very well." **Recent work:** Instructed in MA v Secretary of State for the Home Department, a case concerning the appropriate considerations when dealing with child migrants who are separated from their families.

Charlotte Kilroy Remains an integral player at the junior end of the London Immigration and Public Law Bar. She is noted for her aptitude in all aspects of the ECHR, and works extensively with vulnerable migrants such as the victims of trafficking and unlawful detention. **Strengths:** "She stands out due to her sheer effectiveness and brain power. She is a class act."

David Lemer A seasoned asylum, employment and civil liberties barrister, who is frequently instructed to act in matters before the High Court, Court of Appeal, ECJ and ECHR. He has a special interest in public authority litigation. **Strengths:** "Knowledgeable and responsive, with a solid grasp of the immigration rules." "He is incredibly thorough and really flexible with his time. You can phone and ask him questions and have an in-depth conversation about complex issues. He is also prepared to push parameters." **Recent work:** Currently involved in the judicial review of UKBA's withdrawal of a Tier 4 sponsor licence.

Michelle Knorr An "enthusiastic and imaginative" immigration and public law junior, whose practice continues to go from strength to strength. She principally fights for individuals seeking refugee status, and cases involving the interface between immigration, civil liberties and EU law. **Strengths:** "She really gets behind the client, and is very client-focused, communicative and collaborative." "An incredible fighter, she is passionate when arguing her points and she does really well in the tribunal and High Court. She is very good with vulnerable clients such as victims of trafficking and she thinks through absolutely everything." **Recent work:** Advised on a public law challenge to the Home Secretary's decision not to grant refugee status to a trafficked migrant.

Mark Henderson A long-standing executive member of the Immigration Law Practitioners' Association, who impresses with his top-notch courtroom skills and confidence in both national and international courts. His caseload focuses mainly on asylum, human rights and EU law. **Strengths:** "He is very enthusiastic and really pushes cases as far as he can. He has lots of experience and gets good results." "Very skilled on complex EEA appeal matters." **Recent work:** Appeared in CM (Zimbabwe) v Secretary of State for the Home Department, a case concerning the government's duties in Country Guidance cases.

Matrix Chambers

See profile on p.832

THE SET

This robust immigration team is renowned for its work in numerous areas, including international sports and commerce. It remains dedicated to publicly funded work and benefits from having barristers with additional expertise in mental health and community care.

Client service: "Their clerking team is the best of all I use – super-quick on things, and super-responsive."

SILKS

Raza Husain QC Combines a strong corporate practice, which sees him advise on the inter-country transfer of high-profile businesspeople and sportspeople, with a sturdy publicly funded practice. He has a growing international caseload and regularly represents clients in the European courts, the Cayman Islands and the British Virgin Islands. **Strengths:** "The smartest person doing immigration and asylum law. He knows all the cases and has been in a number of the significant ones." "Superb – he is great to work with, very concerned about his clients, and willing to hear input from solicitors. He has a uniquely brilliant legal mind." **Recent work:** Acted in EM Eritrea, a Supreme Court case dealing with the crossover between EU law, the ECHR and the removal of migrants to other EU states.

Hugh Southey QC Has expertise in several unusual areas of immigration and public law, including extradition, mental health and prisoner voting cases. He is regularly instructed to appear in the Supreme Court. **Strengths:** "He has a great ability to assimilate a large amount of material in a short space of time." "He is a fantastic public law barrister, who is really committed to the causes he is instructed to fight on. He drafts beautifully, is extremely thorough, and takes a very collaborative approach with solicitors – he is a general delight to work with." **Recent work:** Appeared in the case of Z, a decision relating to enforcement powers used when deporting immigrants.

JUNIORS

Nicholas Armstrong A senior practitioner and a talented advocate, who makes regular appearances in the higher courts. He has outstanding expertise in EU law, and is knowledgeable on the imprisonment of migrants and equality law. **Strengths:** "A very good, able barrister." **Recent work:** Acted in FV (Italy), an appeal regarding the deportation of EU migrants that will now proceed to the Supreme Court.

Samantha Knights Has a wide-ranging immigration, public law and international law caseload. Her keen interest in human rights, specifically the freedom of religion and religious discrimination, allows her to excel in European Court matters.

Band 3

Thirty Nine Essex Street

See profile on p.797

THE SET

This set maintains an exemplary reputation for its immigration work, and has a clear focus on judicial reviews relating to unlawful detention, removal and control orders. It is also regularly instructed to provide counsel to the Special Immigration Appeals Commission. "A really impressive set. It is well run and does a big proportion of high-end commercial work."

Client service: "The set offers training which is interactive and useful."

SILKS

Lisa Giovannetti QC An erudite immigration silk with a diverse immigration practice covering both government and publicly funded cases. She is widely recognised for her dexterity in handling asylum, human rights and sponsor licence matters. **Strengths:** "She is straight and exhibits integrity in representing her clients – she doesn't take unsustainable points and is a fair advocate." "She inspires trust and the court has faith in her judgement." **Recent work:** Acted for the government in several cases concerning the return of migrants to other EU states.

Steven Kovats QC Has a healthy public and immigration law practice centred on the representation of public authorities, as well as migrants, in matters relating to crime and civil liberties. He represents clients at various levels of the judicial system, including the highest UK and European courts. **Strengths:** "Steven has been very helpful and responsive in relation to our work. He does not hesitate to give very firm views in a short timeframe." "His written work is very clear, elegant and persuasive. The judges are already half-convinced by his paperwork before you get into court." **Recent work:** Advised in the review of the Home Secretary's decision not to release a migrant prisoner.

JUNIORS

Rory Dunlop (see p.592) Mostly instructed as appellate counsel for the Treasury Solicitor's Department in an array of immigration matters, from ECHR issues to illegal imprisonment and deportation cases. **Strengths:** "He is a very effective and bright opponent. One is always struck by the intellectual force he brings to bear on really quite difficult topics." "He has an intuitive knowledge and understanding of a case, and as an opponent you enjoy being with him. He has the law at his fingertips, and you feel you have to be on the top of your game." **Recent work:** Achieved a successful outcome for the government in a human rights/notice of right to appeal case.

Landmark Chambers

See profile on p.829

THE SET

This well-regarded public/administrative law set offers a high degree of expertise in a number of immigration matters. It is unusual in that its members represent both the claimant and government sides. Observers point out that "the clerking is absolutely brilliant – you couldn't ask for any more. Neil Perry, one of the clerks there, is wonderful."

Client service: "The clerks are extremely pleasant, responsive and helpful. They offer brilliant conference facilities and are approachable."

JUNIORS

Tim Buley Undertakes a mix of private and publicly funded immigration work, and acts for individuals in human rights, EU and social security-related cases, whilst also appearing for large corporations and government bodies. He is on the Attorney General's A Panel of Counsel to the Crown. **Strengths:** "On immigration detention work he is always good at focusing on the real issues." "His written work is second to none, and he has an immediate and incisive grasp of the key issues in complex cases." **Recent work:** Assisted in an appeal to the Court of Appeal regarding an injunction to preclude deportation.

Alex Goodman Acts mainly for claimants challenging immigration-related local authority decision-making. He has extensive experience of appearing in the highest UK courts as well as before the European Courts of Luxembourg and Strasbourg. **Strengths:** "He is just a superb advocate, who is incredibly impressive on his feet. He's one of those advocates who wins cases with his advocacy." **Recent work:** Acted in R (Hua He) v SSHD, R (Xue) v SSHD, and R (Jun Liu) v SSHD, three separate claims for judicial review relating to the removal of Chinese nationals.

David Blundell Previously worked as a judicial assistant to the Law Lords and was selected to be on the Attorney General's B Panel of Counsel to the Crown in 2010. His diverse courtroom experience has seen him act as sole counsel in the High Court, Court of Appeal, ECHR and ECJ. **Strengths:** "Straight and decent, he's very fair and a skilled barrister. Briefed by the government in a wide range of cases, he is always a pleasant person to work with." "A really fantastic junior, who is hard-working and gets the job done." **Recent work:** Represented the government in appeals at the Supreme Court concerning the system of appeal for immigration cases.

Declan O'Callaghan Has over 18 years of experience as an immigration practitioner and is a true expert in public law, international law, asylum and human rights. He lectures widely in the UK and abroad, and has delivered a speech about the subtleties of Article 14 ECHR in Strasbourg. **Strengths:** "His main strengths are his breadth of knowledge and his commitment to his clients." **Recent work:** Worked on a seminal case relating to the right of migrants to work under EU law.

Galina Ward Devotes a significant portion of her practice to assisting migrants and their families with asylum, social support and judicial review. Also works on the side of the government and with migrants who face deportation due to criminal offences. **Strengths:** "Her grounds are succinct and easy to follow, and her written work impresses the judges." "She is very sharp, gets right to the crux of the matter, can sum up something quite quickly, and doesn't miss out anything." **Recent work:** Advised on an immigration case where the legal definition of 'sole responsibility' in terms of child custody was decided.

1 Pump Court

See profile on p.848

THE SET

This thriving immigration set continues to grow in size and strength. It represents individuals before tribunals, the Administrative Court, the Court of Appeal and the ECHR, and houses experts in human rights, free movement in the EU and crossover areas where social welfare law, family law and immigration collide. According to commentators, "the barristers are brilliant; they take on urgent matters and turn them around speedily, producing work of a high quality. Together they form a pleasant and well-rounded team that works well with solicitors."

Client service: "The clerking, led by Ian Burrow, is really good and helpful. They are not too formal about things – you can ping e-mails and get a response. The set is good at keeping us updated on costs and they run training sessions that are helpful and open."

JUNIORS

David Chirico Handles a diverse range of immigration matters, including asylum for child migrants and other vulnerable groups and ECHR-related cases. His background in housing and criminal law enables him to excel in immigration work relating to social support and the provision of accommodation for migrants. **Strengths:** "He is extremely committed, passionate and a true advocate for the plights of migrants. He is also intellectually creative, which allows him to see cases differently and pursue arguments others might not have considered." "He is very skilled technically and super-brainy." **Recent work:** Acted in a landmark case regarding the removal of a migrant with a young son.

Ranjiv Khubber Recommended for his ability to effectively challenge the decisions of public authorities in immigration cases. He is also adept at the intricacies of human rights and social security law, and is praised for his holistic approach to matters. **Strengths:** "Very experienced in judicial review and unlawful detention matters, he gets very good results in tricky and complex cases." **Recent work:** Advised in an important case concerning housing support for migrants from the EU.

Graham Denholm Dovetails immigration imprisonment work with cases involving the removal of foreign criminals from the country. He is a regular before both the national and international courts. **Strengths:** "Incredibly knowledgeable, and someone who always has time to listen to a query." "His written work is impeccable – everything reads well, and is logical and thorough." **Recent work:** Counsel in Salimur Rahman v Secretary of State for the Home Department, a case concerning a migrant who sustained severe memory loss while awaiting deportation.

Parosha Chandran A leading junior at the London Immigration Bar who was selected to advise on the UK Human Trafficking and Modern Slavery Bills. She was also selected as an expert in human trafficking by the United Nations Office on Drugs and Crime. **Strengths:** "Extremely thorough, she is able to pick out the issues very quickly and ensure nothing is missed. She is also an amazing advocate, who is clear, authoritative and persuasive."

Victoria Laughton Provides a full suite of public and private immigration services, handling everything from advising high-end businesses to counselling refugees, victims of trafficking and imprisoned migrants. In a business immigration context, she specialises in overturning 7B bans. **Strengths:** "She combines real ability, determination and passion with great willingness to assist. She is really helpful to the solicitor." **Recent work:** Instructed by the Treasury Solicitor's Department in relation to a challenge to a decision to incarcerate a foreign prisoner due to be deported.

Catherine Robinson Works extensively with migrant prisoners as well as in judicial reviews at the Court of Appeal. Also volunteers with the UK Lesbian and Gay Immigration Group in relation to asylum matters. **Strengths:** "A very good advocate who gets really good results for clients." "She is meticulous and very responsive, and will think about every issue." **Recent work:** Acted in a case concerning the Home Secretary's refusal of indefinite leave to remain following large delays in responding to claims.

Doron Blum Acknowledged by the market for his deep understanding of refugee and deportation law, he frequently undertakes complex appeals and judicial reviews. He also sits as an immigration judge. **Strengths:** "Very responsive and good at updating you, he is thorough in what he does and realistic in terms of what can be obtained. He takes a practical, collaborative approach."

Gilda Kiai Handles a wide range of immigration and administrative law work, including civil liberties matters. She is commended for her ability to sensitively manage complex refugee claims involving child migrants and trafficked persons. **Strengths:** "She always delivers and is focused on winning; she's a very good and relentless barrister."

Other Notable Lawyers

Angus McCullough QC (1 Crown Office Row) Renowned for his government work, and has handled very high-profile work concerning terrorist suspects or migrants who have been involved in terrorist activities in the past. He has a particular interest in immigration matters relating to the ECHR, exclusions from the country and foreign criminal proceedings. **Strengths:** "He is thoroughly decent and thoughtful, and always does his absolute best for his clients, whether they be private individuals or larger bodies. He acts on both sides too, and this is rare." **Recent work:** Advised in a case concerning the withdrawal of British citizenship on national security grounds and the issue of statelessness.

Jeremy Johnson QC (5 Essex Court) A tenacious advocate who has featured in a plethora of groundbreaking immigration and public law cases. He specialises in national and international civil liberties, refugee and police/detention work.

Alan Payne (see p.690) (5 Essex Court) Frequently represents the Treasury Solicitor's Department and has fantastic experience of dealing with the interface between immigration, civil liberties, terrorism and prison law. He is regularly instructed to represent publicly funded individuals fleeing from their homelands as a result of fear of political persecution. **Strengths:** "He is reliable, hard-working, and straightforward in his dealings." **Recent work:** Represented the government in AB (Sudan), a case involving the judicial review of a decision to deport a refugee to Italy.

John-Paul Waite (5 Essex Court) Acts primarily for the Secretary of State, but has also acted for appellants. Has a broad range of knowledge, and is an expert in asylum, migrant imprisonment and sponsor licence cases. **Strengths:** "He is a personable and very able practitioner." **Recent work:** Advised in a case set to determine the relationship between EU law, asylum and third country nationals.

Tim Eicke QC (Essex Court Chambers) Highlighted for his incredible knowledge and skill in dealing sensitively with detained and traumatised migrants in cases involving the ECHR, refugee rights and family-related matters. **Strengths:** "He does deportation work, and is a very able chap, who has expertise in European and ECHR matters." **Recent work:** Counsel in ZZ, a leading case on the removal of EU migrants on the basis of national security and free movement.

Glen Hodgetts (Barrister-at-Law) A sole practitioner as of 2013, who fights tooth and nail for his legal aid clients in the upper immigration courts and tribunals. He has a wealth of experience, and has authored several celebrated publications on immigration and human rights law. **Strengths:** "He's very passionate and works intently to achieve the best outcomes. He thinks outside the box and has a meaningful and positive impact on clients."

Charles Bourne QC (see p.553) (11KBW) Combines an active practice in civil liberties, public law and employment law with a role as a Mediator and Crown Court Recorder. **Recent work:** As counsel to the Treasury Solicitor, he managed to defeat an appeal brought by a migrant claiming asylum where he had been involved in war crimes.

Eric Fripp (Lamb Building) Has developed a strong immigration practice that caters for both business clients and publicly funded individuals. She assists asylum seekers, and handles politically driven judicial review cases. **Strengths:** "He is very intellectual and thinks very deeply about things." "An excellent advocate for complex human rights-related cases." **Recent work:** Instructed in SE (Zimbabwe), Court of Appeal litigation in which Article 8 of the ECHR was determined in relation to government policy.

Rowena Moffatt (Lamb Building) A strong immigration practitioner with an excellent working knowledge of EU law, the ECHR and EEA law. She often represents imprisoned migrants, refugees and those seeking to use the points-based system.

Shivani Jegarajah (Mansfield Chambers) A powerful advocate who has been highly praised by the judiciary for her legal aid work. She is adept at dealing with cases relating to children and human rights, and has also assisted migrants from politically divided countries such as Sri Lanka and Pakistan. **Strengths:** "A clever, no-nonsense advocate who has a lovely touch with clients in stressful circumstances. Judges have a good deal of respect for her." **Recent work:** Advised in a ground-breaking Country Guidance case that concerned the safety of Tamils returning to Sri Lanka.

Robert Palmer (Monckton Chambers) Often instructed in seminal cases concerning the freedom of movement, civil liberties and national security, he regularly acts in Supreme Court and ECJ cases. He has been appointed to the Attorney General's A Panel. **Recent work:** Counsel in ECJ cases concerning the right of migrant criminals to remain in the UK under EU law.

S Chelvan (see p.570) (No5 Chambers) Has a thriving nationality and asylum practice that sees him appearing in all the major immigration tribunals and courts. He routinely advises migrants, corporations and educational entities, as well as the UNHCR and NGOs. **Strengths:** "Very intelligent, hard-working, and imaginative in his approach to cases." **Recent work:** Acted in a case that looked at the obligation to consider the welfare of the child in asylum claims for minors.

Daniel Bazini (No5 Chambers) An expert in refugee law, civil liberties and free movement. He is very strong on his feet when before domestic and international courts and tribunals, and has a burgeoning judicial review practice. **Strengths:** "He has lots of experience and you feel confident when you instruct him."

Edward Nicholson (No5 Chambers) Previously advised clients at a Law Centre before returning to chambers to help migrants and their families with complex immigration and ECHR cases. Also known for his excellent knowledge of the points-based system. **Strengths:** "He has the ability to think outside the box and find creative solutions." "He is very hard-working and very good with vulnerable clients. He gets good results." **Recent work:** Involved in a judicial review of the government's power to restrict educational institutions under immigration laws.

Joanne Rothwell (No5 Chambers) Has a broad nationality and immigration practice and regularly appears at the First-tier Tribunal and before the ECJ. She elicits much praise for her ability to put clients at ease, including those with mental health issues. **Strengths:** "She is responsive, thorough, and clear with her advice and her legal points. She's also authoritative when dealing with the courts, and she gets on well with clients."

Robin Tam QC (see p.733) (Temple Garden Chambers) Works extensively with refugees and migrants facing control orders or removal from the country in order to protect UK security. He held a post on the Attorney General's A Panel of Counsel before he took silk. **Recent work:** Acted in the highly publicised case to transfer Abu Qatada to Jordan in order to protect UK national security.

MIDLANDS

Immigration Midlands
Leading Sets
Band 1
No5 Chambers *
Number 8 Chambers
Leading Juniors
Band 1
De Mello Rambert *No5 Chambers*
Mahmood Abid *No5 Chambers* [A]
Pipe Adam *Number 8 Chambers* *
Band 2
Mandalia Vinesh *No5 Chambers* [A]
Muman Tony *43templerow Chambers (ORL)* ◊
Rutherford Emma *Number 8 Chambers* *
Vokes Stephen *Number 8 Chambers* *
◊ (ORL) = Other Ranked Lawyer.
[A] direct access (see p.11).
** Indicates set / individual with profile.*
Alphabetical order within each band. Band 1 is highest.

Band 1

No5 Chambers

See profile on p.883

THE SET

No5 Chambers is one of the Midland Circuit's leading sets for both publicly funded and corporate immigration work. Its members are experienced in advising refugees and other individuals on civil liberties and EU-related claims, as well as complex nationality and imprisonment cases.

JUNIORS

Abid Mahmood A seasoned immigration practitioner who combines an active practice with his roles as a part-time judge and recorder. He represents clients in complex cases at the Court of Appeal and Supreme Court, and has been instructed on many important national security matters. **Strengths:** "He is a very hard-working and able immigration barrister." **Recent work:** He acted for the appellant in a deportation case concerning a Nigerian national convicted of serious drug offences who has a British wife and child residing in the UK.

Ramby De Mello A true expert in the rights and freedoms conferred on individuals, especially migrants, through the ECHR. He has developed strong advocacy skills and has acted for his clients in the Supreme Court, the ECJ, and the Grand Chamber of the ECHR. **Strengths:** "He is a creative lawyer with a certain presence about him; a very experienced practitioner." **Recent work:** Acted on behalf of two claimants who sought amendments to the immigration rules governing the maintenance requirements for the admission of spouses to the UK.

Vinesh Mandalia Has a broad practice covering a range of public law and immigration work. He is a member of the Attorney General's panel of regional counsel and is regularly instructed to act on behalf of local authorities and government departments. **Recent work:** Acted for the defendant in Hassan v SSHD, a claim for judicial review which concerned how to interpret government immigration policy.

Number 8 Chambers

THE SET

Number 8 Chambers' immigration team is unrivalled in terms of its depth and breadth outside of London, and its members have significant experience in handling the full range of immigration and asylum claims.

Client service: "The clerking at Number 8 Chambers is brilliant and efficient – you can't fault them."

JUNIORS

Adam Pipe (see p.694) An immigration specialist with a particular focus on refugee law. He is an experienced advocate. **Strengths:** "He is a case law guru who is always very well prepared in front of the Tribunal."

Emma Rutherford (see p.712) Earns much praise for her vast knowledge and expertise in immigration and administrative law. She covers the full range of immigration and asylum cases, and is noted for her particular focus on nationality law. She acts for asylum seekers, other migrants and the government. **Strengths:** "She is an astute and tenacious barrister who is well liked by clients."

Stephen Vokes (see p.744) An experienced advocate who covers the full range of immigration and asylum law. **Strengths:** "He is very experienced and well respected, and strives for the best results for his clients in every case."

Other Ranked Lawyers

Tony Muman (43templerow Chambers) A veteran immigration barrister known for his comprehensive understanding of nationality and EU law.

NORTHERN

Immigration Northern
Leading Sets
Band 1
Doughty Street Chambers *
Garden Court North
Kenworthy's Chambers *
Leading Juniors
Band 1
O'Ryan Rory *Garden Court North*
Stanage Nick *Doughty Street Chambers* A
Band 2
Brown George *Kenworthy's Chambers*
Draycott Paul *Doughty Street Chambers*
Jagadesham Vijay *Garden Court North*
Khan Shazia *Kenworthy's Chambers* A
Nicholson John *Kenworthy's Chambers*
Patel Gita *Kenworthy's Chambers* A
Schwenk Mark *Kenworthy's Chambers*
A *direct access (see p.11).*
* *Indicates set / individual with profile.*
Alphabetical order within each band. Band 1 is highest.

Band 1

Doughty Street Chambers

See profile on p.786

THE SET

Doughty Street Chambers is a big name in immigration law not just on the Northern Circuit but nationally as well. Its barristers cover the full range of personal immigration work, and provide both advice and advocacy on issues relating to asylum, human rights and nationality.

JUNIORS

Nick Stanage An erudite immigration and public law barrister who is particularly quick on his feet in trial. He has a large judicial review practice and a solid grounding in civil liberties and police-related immigration litigation.

Paul Draycott A meticulous advocate who focuses on challenging legally aided work, particularly cases involving refugees and matters that concern the rights of migrants to housing and social support.

Garden Court North

THE SET

The set boasts an impressively high-calibre immigration team whose members are regularly instructed in cases that challenge the status quo. Particular areas of strength are cases involving migrant prisoners and extradition cases.

JUNIORS

Rory O'Ryan Devotes a significant portion of his practice to public law matters including personal immigration. He is noted for his expertise in obtaining emergency injunctive relief in deportation or removal cases, and is praised by instructing solicitors for his sensitive handling of refugees and vulnerable claimants.

Vijay Jagadesham An expert in cases involving detained migrants, children and the ECHR. He also has a burgeoning practice assisting organisations with obtaining sponsor licences. **Strengths:** "He is very thorough in his preparation, shows confidence in court, and is also very knowledgeable and easy to work with."

Kenworthy's Chambers

See profile on p.917

THE SET

An established immigration, nationality and asylum set, known in the market for its members' skilled advocacy at tribunals and courts across the country. The set is frequently instructed in complex deportation and nationality cases.

JUNIORS

George Brown An experienced immigration practitioner who covers the full range of immigration law, including asylum and nationality matters. **Strengths:** "A very experienced and dedicated tribunal advocate. He is also very approachable." "He gets good results in tribunals, and he gets good results at the highest levels too – he's a highly efficient and hugely effective immigration advocate."

Shazia Khan Focuses her practice on legally aided immigration and asylum work. She draws praise from peers not just for her considerable experience, but also for her dedication to the immigration law field. **Strengths:** "She is a really good advocate before the tribunal, with a good breadth of knowledge on all immigration matters."

John Nicholson A tenacious and dedicated legal aid practitioner who concentrates his immigration law practice on refugee and nationality issues. **Strengths:** "He is a great advocate – a real fighter."

Gita Patel A veteran immigration specialist noted for her particular expertise in asylum cases. Market commentators are quick to praise her skill in representing vulnerable clients, such as minors, and those with mental health issues.

Mark Schwenk A leading junior on the Northern Circuit practising in immigration, asylum and public law. Commentators also note his burgeoning judicial review practice.

Information Technology

Contents:
London p.304

LONDON

Information Technology London
Leading Sets
Band 1
4 Pump Court *
Band 2
Atkin Chambers *
Henderson Chambers *
8 New Square *
11 South Square *
Leading Silks
Band 1
Alexander Daniel *8 New Square* *
Carr Henry *11 South Square*
Charlton Alex *4 Pump Court*
Howe Martin *8 New Square* *
McCall Duncan *4 Pump Court*
Meade Richard *8 New Square* *
Storey Jeremy *4 Pump Court* *
Streatfeild-James David *Atkin Chambers*
Band 2
Akka Lawrence *20 Essex Street (ORL)* ◊
Blunt David *4 Pump Court* *
Dennys Nicholas *Atkin Chambers*
Douglas Michael *4 Pump Court* *
Silverleaf Michael *11 South Square*
Susman Peter *Henderson Chambers* 🄰 *
Tozzi Nigel *4 Pump Court* *
Vanhegan Mark *11 South Square*
Band 3
Baatz Nicholas *Atkin Chambers*
Croall Simon *Quadrant Chambers (ORL)* ◊
Gourgey Alan *11 Stone Buildings (ORL)* ◊ *
Mawrey Richard *Henderson Chambers* 🄰 *
Speck Adrian *8 New Square* *
New Silks
Howells James *Atkin Chambers* *
Leading Juniors
Star individuals
Bergin Terence *4 Pump Court* *
Lazarus Michael *3 Verulam Buildings (ORL)* ◊
Band 1
Henderson Simon *4 Pump Court* *
Lavy Matthew *4 Pump Court* *
Nicholson Brian *11 South Square*
Onslow Robert *8 New Square* 🄰 *
Band 2
Freedman Clive *3 Verulam Buildings (ORL)* ◊ *
Hicks Michael *Hogarth Chambers (ORL)* ◊
Saunders Nicholas *Brick Court Chambers (ORL)* ◊
Band 3
Campbell Douglas *Three New Square (ORL)* ◊ *
Kulkarni Yash *Quadrant Chambers (ORL)* ◊
Lewis Christopher *Atkin Chambers* *
McCafferty Lynne *4 Pump Court* *
Moody-Stuart Thomas *8 New Square* *
Osborne Richard *4 Pump Court* *
Pilling Benjamin *4 Pump Court* *
Robinson Thomas *11 Stone Buildings (ORL)* ◊
St Ville James *8 New Square* *
Taylor Michael *4 Pump Court* *
** Indicates set / individual with profile.*
◊ (ORL) = Other Ranked Lawyer.
🄰 direct access (see p.11).

Band 1

4 Pump Court
See profile on p.849

THE SET

4 Pump Court remains "the premier set in this sector" and is routinely sought out for the biggest and most significant technology cases. Its impressive array of leading barristers act for notable public and private sector clients on disputes involving an especially high level of complexity and technical detail. The set is at the forefront of emerging technology matters involving data analytics and cyber security.

Client service: "The clerking is truly outstanding, from top to bottom. Joint senior clerk Stewart Gibbs sets the tone and is excellent to deal with, as are the other clerks, who are very straight and will go out of their way to try and assist you."

SILKS

Duncan McCall QC Sought-after counsel who is known for his "impressive, measured" representation of IT users, particularly in the public sector, and who has an increasingly notable arbitration practice. He has long-standing expertise in software development and routinely advises on failed delivery matters. **Strengths:** "Seen very much as a go-to silk for complicated technology cases, he has very good strategic awareness and an eye for the big picture." "When you take clients to consultations they just sit there in awe of him because they're all IT experts and he seems to know as much about it as they do. That's the mark of someone who's an expert in the field." **Recent work:** Acted in BGL Group v Ciboodle, a dispute involving damages claims for inadequate software delivery of an online insurance system.

Alex Charlton QC Handles a wide range of IT disputes across an extensive client base, and has distinct expertise in matters involving complex contract interpretation. He has an increasing global presence and is instructed on large-scale project failures and safety software cases. **Strengths:** "A formidable opponent with a manner of delivery of advocacy which is very persuasive with the judges." "Very user-friendly, responsive and refreshingly unstuffy." **Recent work:** Appeared in Ceridian v Somerfield, a case concerning a terminated HR and payroll outsourcing contract and related issues with implementation.

Jeremy Storey QC (see p.730) Renowned for his ability to manage large teams on major, high-value cases, he advises on the supplier side and also regularly acts for public sector entities. **Strengths:** "An absolutely excellent leader and a joy to work with." "He has an ability to assimilate huge amounts of information very quickly but then, critically, sort out the wheat from the chaff." **Recent work:** Acted in litigation between In Practice Systems and EMC Computer Systems regarding storage hardware solutions for GPs throughout England.

David Blunt QC (see p.551) Has a distinguished history in IT law and is an accomplished advocate for both government entities and private companies. His highly respected practice covers software disputes and negligent consultancy, and is complemented by his judicial and arbitral experience. **Strengths:** "The best barristers are the ones that keep it short and succinct, and get straight to the point without messing about. He's razor-sharp, has a crystal-clear mind, picks the good points and deals with them well." "Very measured and calm, he gets on top of the points very quickly and always asks good questions." **Recent work:** Appeared in Fairstar Heavy Transport v Adkins, a dispute involving the existence of proprietary rights in relation to e-mail communications.

Michael Douglas QC Has significant public sector experience in defence-related contractual matters, and is further prized for his knowledge of hardware and software agreements and termination issues. **Strengths:** "He's got a very collaborative manner and is unstuffy, down-to-earth and likeable." "An impressive advocate, who is forceful and confident." **Recent work:** Instructed in a matter brought by Fujitsu against IBM for breach of contract in relation to systems supply for the DVLA.

Nigel Tozzi QC Has an impressive contractual disputes practice that takes in an array of cases, including many on behalf of software companies and insurers. He is also frequently instructed as an arbitrator on both the domestic and international stage. **Strengths:** "Apart from the fact that he's an excellent advocate, he's very quick to grasp and simplify difficult issues in an attractive way." "Personable and very bright, his written advice was good and his preparation was excellent."

JUNIORS

Terence Bergin (see p.548) A "standout junior" offering exceptional expertise in IT system provision and failure, and wider experience in contract interpretation. He also handles diverse matters relating to software, acting for users and suppliers. **Strengths:** "He always has his eye on the ball and his advocacy is certainly very good." "He is highly intelligent, has a lot of common sense and works very hard. He sees the point, is very tenacious and doesn't beat about the bush." **Recent work:** Advised on a complex case between Tarbs Europe and The Republic of Macedonia arising from the supply of satellite television infrastructure.

Simon Henderson A highly respected technology advocate who draws on his management consultant background when handling work on system development and implementation. He is also called upon by government authorities, both in the UK and globally, for counsel on contract termination. **Strengths:** "A class act, who is calm under pressure and always looking for another angle." "Very practical and down to earth, he is willing to roll his sleeves up and is very engaging." **Recent work:** Instructed by BT in its dispute against subcontractor Liberata concerning payment issues after contract termination.

Matthew Lavy Much admired for his in-depth understanding of the most difficult IT matters and aided by a professional background in software development. He frequently tackles highly technical project failure disputes in sectors ranging from financial services and telecommunications to equipment manufacture and the military. **Strengths:** "He has an incredibly good grasp of the legal and practical issues. He understands and can explain the technical software issues in a jargon-free and straightforward way." "His IT background was invaluable in helping us understand and distil the issues." **Recent work:** Recently engaged in complex litigation over failed ERP software provided to oil and gas contractor Lamprell by Epicor.

Lynne McCafferty Earns strong praise for her knowledge of hardware and bespoke software, and is also applauded for her superb drafting skills. She represents government bodies in major litigation and arbitration, and also counts private suppliers among her clients. **Strengths:** "A force to be reckoned with in terms of her attention to detail. Her contribution is really outstanding and her written advocacy is really impressive." "An intelligent, hard-working junior."

Benjamin Pilling Handles cases concerning everything from software code deficiencies to contractual issues involving specification fulfilment. He demonstrates notable strength in video games and ERP systems, and is further highlighted for his e-commerce and data protection work. **Strengths:** "He has a very good analytical brain, takes a commercial approach and is excellent with clients." "He rapidly got to grips with difficult technical issues and had all the detailed facts at his fingertips." **Recent work:** Appeared in a case between DNUK and Iomart in relation to the threatened termination of a data hosting contract.

Michael Taylor (see p.735) A much-in-demand junior described as "an ideal person to work with." He represents clients in a range of software disputes and is particularly adept at copyright-related technology matters. **Strengths:** "He's got a very good appreciation of the commercial drivers and pressures faced by our clients. He's not just looking at the legal side but also the wider impact on the client." "He's great at marshalling complex facts and is persuasive, prompt and good at turning around papers." **Recent work:** Acted in an IT data-hosting dispute involving Cable & Wireless and Capgemini.

Richard Osborne (see p.687) Acclaimed for his work in major cases, particularly in relation to failed transformational projects. He is especially good at disputes involving public sector entities and software defects. Instructing solicitors applaud him for his client skills and exemplary written work, and further praise him for his special insight into the use of expert determination to resolve cases. **Strengths:** "He's phenomenally easy to work with and a brilliant team player, who shows good attention to detail." "An excellent junior, who is really hard-working and user-friendly." **Recent work:** Appeared in Ericsson AB v EADS Defence and Security Systems, an IT infrastructure delay claim relating to the FiReControl project for the Fire Brigade.

Band 2

Atkin Chambers

See profile on p.762

THE SET

Atkin Chambers continues to impress within the IT sphere, drawing on a stable of talented and recognised specialists. Its members handle a range of outsourcing and IT project disputes and are often sought out for high-stakes matters involving big sums and heavyweight clients. Cases involving business-critical systems failure are a speciality.

Client service: "The clerking, led by Justin Wilson, was good. The clerks are very responsive and approachable. If they're having difficulty pinning people down, they come back to you."

SILKS

David Streatfeild-James QC A standout silk with an impressive track record of untangling complex, high-value disputes for public sector bodies and private companies, both domestically and internationally. He also has considerable experience of handling matters involving control and communication systems. **Strengths:** "Absolutely outstanding. He is strategically first class in terms of the advice that he gives and his advocacy is absolutely amazing." "He has incredible mental agility and is superb at putting concepts and principles to the arbitrators and judge. He presents his case in a very attractive way and the arbitrators resonate with what he's saying."

James Howells QC A talented telecommunications advocate who is called upon by both supplier and user-side clients, including manufacturers and contractors. He is also familiar with hardware and software systems, and is further recognised for his expertise relating to international disputes. He is experienced in litigation, arbitration and the full range of alternative dispute resolution. **Strengths:** "Has a very persuasive approach that is much backed up by the incredible detail he is able to retain, master and then explain." "Quietly authoritative, he is technically awesome." **Recent work:** Instructed by Autonomy Systems in its dispute with Cosin involving the termination of a contract for the provision of intelligent monitoring software to a North African government.

Nicholas Baatz QC Offers excellent legal analysis to customers and providers on a range of IT matters. He is an expert on software development and implementation, and is noted for his skill in telecommunications cases. **Strengths:** "He's superb and has an encyclopaedic knowledge of case law."

Nicholas Dennys QC Has established expertise in systems supply and implementation. His capacity for managing cases of significant financial value attracts an array of high-profile clients. **Strengths:** "He's very good at getting the confidence of clients and he gives good commercial advice."

JUNIORS

Christopher Lewis Has an international client list and handles software licensing, hardware systems and contractual IT matters. He is frequently sought out for alternative dispute resolution, and regularly appears in arbitrations and expert determination cases. **Strengths:** "Extremely diligent. His preparatory work was top notch and his cross-examination was superb and very incisive." "He does a very good job of taking very technical material and making it easy to understand for the judge."

Henderson Chambers

See profile on p.820

THE SET

Henderson Chambers is a versatile set that over the years has shown it has a taste for innovation. It has had a long-standing connection with IT cases, and its seasoned advocates are able to offer expert insight and analysis in relation to a number of issues concerning the area. Public and private sector clients instruct it in all manner of software disputes.

Client service: "Their chief clerk, John White, is outstanding; the most personable, organised and charming chief clerk I've come across. The clerks from top to bottom are polite and courteous, and go out of their way to be nice."

SILKS

Peter Susman QC (see p.732) Has attained a high standing in the technology market, particularly in relation to bespoke software implementation and failure cases. He regularly represents IT customers, especially on the public sector side, and has considerable knowledge of contractual matters. **Strengths:** "A very big name with a superb reputation right across the board in IT." "He's forceful in putting forward his client's interests, and also has the commercial judgement to find a sensible, agreed way forward in a case." **Recent work:** Acted for T.H. Baker in a claim against SDK Jewellers arising from a website crash caused by the use of electronic machinery to access price data.

Richard Mawrey QC (see p.665) Has an impressive pedigree in IT litigation, having appeared in precedent-setting cases, and is a natural choice as an advocate or arbitrator for high-profile, high-value disputes. He continues to offer counsel on hardware and software supply, as well as on matters relating to procurement and contract structure. **Strengths:** "It always astounds me how much of the detail he manages to retain, which is fabulous. He manages to put the client at ease and reassure them that he's looking after their interests." "He is certainly impressive on both the law and the IT factual stuff as well."

8 New Square

See profile on p.836

THE SET

8 New Square is a powerhouse for IP-heavy technology cases. A number of its members have scientific qualifications and previous programming experience, making them highly suitable for these type of cases. Clients seek them out for formidably technical matters, and they regularly act for high-profile litigants in big-value disputes across numerous territories.

SILKS

Daniel Alexander QC A go-to silk for design and patent-related IT disputes, who also advises on contractual matters. He has an excellent courtroom style and the ability to establish good rapport between parties. **Strengths:** "Extremely well regarded and an absolutely superb advocate." "He understands how judges' minds work, so knows how to manage the court really well."

Martin Howe QC A precise, detail-oriented authority on EU law, with a software programming background he uses to outstanding effect in tech-based IP cases. He exhibits further expertise in matters relating to decryption rights, databases and confidential information. **Strengths:** "He has terrific presence and a great ability to understand the commercial objectives of the client and the technical aspects of the business." "Very much a heavyweight silk in this area and well thought of."

Richard Meade QC When it comes to a technology case, his is "a name that would leap almost immediately to mind." He has the experience and technical expertise to manage all aspects of large-scale, IP-related cases and the complex web of information that they inevitably involve. **Strengths:** "Super-clever, he's always on top of everything and is very, very good as an advocate. He has a way of putting things across very effectively." "He shows incredible clarity of thought."

Adrian Speck QC Remains a popular choice for technology-based copyright and patent cases of major significance. He has a notable following of media, biotechnology and pharmaceutical industry clients. **Strengths:** "He always thinks of things from the judge's point of view, which is a real asset." "He has a good client manner, is very personable, is excellent on copyright and understands the commercial aims of the client."

JUNIORS

Robert Onslow A data and software specialist who provides counsel on domain name and other IP-based disputes. Highly knowledgeable and creative, he is able to pick apart the issues right down to source code level. **Strengths:** "A formidable opponent who is very incisive and well informed." "He has an excellent grasp of technical issues, and his programming background is very useful."

James St Ville Handles a broad scope of disputes work, and has special insight into cyber security-related cases involving hacker identification injunctions, disk imaging orders and source code delivery. He also offers advanced knowledge of overseas common law jurisdictions. **Strengths:** "Displays incredible attention to detail, is very responsive, gives sound commercial advice and has excellent IT industry knowledge."

Thomas Moody-Stuart Acts for clients across a number of industries, including media and industrial design. An expert in trade marks and trade names, he also handles copyright and complex patent cases. **Strengths:** "An effective, very thorough advocate who is able to grasp the main points in a case." "Very calm and considered, he is not prone to hyperbole or overstating his points and is popular with clients and judges."

11 South Square

See profile on p.862

THE SET

As one of the leading IP sets, 11 South Square is ideally placed to tackle highly technical IT disputes, and regularly handles patent and software licensing clashes between heavyweight telecommunications companies. Counsel at the set have a wealth of scientific knowledge, and have the standing to appear in the most complex litigation in the market. They are also often looked to for guidance on alternative dispute resolution.

Client service: "They are fantastic. I trust them and feel confident that the clerks will look after our clients' interests and make the barristers available. If they can't, they will do something to address that, and they are certainly a factor in my decision making when I'm instructing barristers. Head clerk Ashley Carr is second to none at getting you court dates."

SILKS

Henry Carr QC An esteemed practitioner with "incredibly good judgement," who routinely advises on issues at the intersection of IP and IT law. He takes on major, precedent-setting cases involving software and hardware patents and technology design. **Strengths:** "He is at the top of his game." "He's excellent. A very smooth, polished advocate with a really good grasp of the case." **Recent work:** Instructed by IPCom in multiple mobile phone patent disputes with HTC.

Michael Silverleaf QC Lauded silk who is a front-runner in matters involving the fast-developing area of internet trading law. He is renowned for his keen grasp of difficult details and his ability to work across technically complex areas such as mobile telephone technology and internet publishing. **Strengths:** "A longstanding heavyweight with a significant understanding of issues in the field of IT." "He's very positive about the client and the case, and very forthright and clear in what his opinion is. There's no sitting on the fence with him." **Recent work:** Engaged by Sportradar, a sports data collector and provider, on a database infringement claim brought by Football Dataco.

Mark Vanhegan QC Known for tackling cases concerning highly technical subject matter. He has specialist knowledge of software issues and knows how to untangle complex points. **Strengths:** "An engaging advocate," who is "commercial and very approachable." **Recent work:** Recently advised Data Transfer & Communications on a possible claim against multiple parties concerning data transfer technology between several mobile devices.

JUNIORS

Brian Nicholson Acclaimed for his handling of multi-jurisdictional telecommunication cases involving intricate technologies, he regularly handles cases involving major, household-name companies. He has a superb understanding of the IT market and often draws on prior industry experience when taking on directions. **Strengths:** "He's very able to get under the skin of the detail in a case." "He's very experienced, highly technical, intuitive and good fun to work with." **Recent work:** Acted in Nintendo v Philips, a case concerning Wii remote technology and console interaction.

Other Ranked Lawyers

Nicholas Saunders (Brick Court Chambers) Regularly instructed in mobile telephone technology, patent and design disputes. He also specialises in highly technical cases involving EU and competition law. **Strengths:** "He's got an extremely able technical grasp of the issues in complex cases." "He can see the wood for the trees, identify what the good points are and articulate them relatively simply."

Lawrence Akka QC (20 Essex Street) His technology practice spans a range of areas, including internet gambling and telephone tapping. He is regularly sought out for his expert handling of highly technical and high-value cases. **Strengths:** "Very impressive in terms of economy of expression and his ability to spot the right point and get there. He gets the ear of the court very effectively and is very straightforward to deal with." "A user-friendly silk with an eye for technical detail. He has produced written work which has gone to the client and it is always bang on point." **Recent work:** Instructed by Nokia on multiple high-profile disputes concerning mobile telephone patents.

Michael Hicks (Hogarth Chambers) Distinguished IP practitioner, who has an exceptional grasp of the complex detail in IT cases. He also undertakes significant advisory and written work, and routinely acts for an array of global corporate clients. **Strengths:** "He has outstanding technical ability and shrewd judgement, assets that have made him a popular choice in a succession of IT cases." "Amazingly user-friendly and practical, he has superb knowledge of the software industry." **Recent work:** Appeared in SAS Institute v World Programming, a precedent-setting copyright IT case concerning software source code infractions.

Douglas Campbell (Three New Square) Lauded for his software disputes work, and also offers expertise in technology-related patent infringement. He has a significant public sector client base and operates across a variety of fields, including the telecommunications and pharmaceutical sectors. **Strengths:** "He's got a very accessible style, is good with clients, clearly knows his area very well and is very engaging and capable." "He's very straightforward to deal with as an opponent and good on his feet." **Recent work:** Acted for Seiko Epson in litigation against DCI International relating to issues with ink jet printer and print cartridge patents.

Simon Croall QC (Quadrant Chambers) Demonstrates particular prowess in large-scale technology project litigation. He has acted of late in a number of international arbitrations and is adept at matters involving software and system defects. **Strengths:** "He's really sharp and massively bright – he's a joy to work with and very, very client-friendly. I never have worries about him being in front of a client in any shape or form because he explains things really well and makes them feel reassured. His written advice is also really clear." **Recent work:** Engaged by De Beers against Atos in a dispute arising from the failure of a major IT project.

Yash Kulkarni (Quadrant Chambers) "Very methodical and commercial" in his approach to technology disputes and arbitrations. He is highly rated for his handling of system implementation, coding defects and design issues. **Strengths:** "A confident advocate who is very powerful because he can really hit home hard with his arguments, and also has a good rapport with the judges. Anything that he delivers to us is always meticulous and he has a very calming manner which clients really like. On top of that, he's very decisive, will immediately see what's going on and can devise strategies and plans that work." **Recent work:** Appeared in NoemaLife SpA v Infinitt UK, a dispute over licence matters relating to copyright transfer.

Alan Gourgey QC (see p.612) (11 Stone Buildings) Acts on prominent, high-value litigation, often between contractors and public sector bodies. He has significant experience of handling arbitrations, both as advocate and arbiter, and also advises on contract termination and e-commerce issues. **Strengths:** "On these types of disputes you have to have a lot of softer skills because there might be a hundred guys on the project – we'll be talking to the design guys, the implementation guys, the testing guys, the system architect, and Alan's at home with all of them." **Recent work:** Engaged by Address Data International in a dispute over regulatory matters concerning a commercial agent.

Thomas Robinson (11 Stone Buildings) Has substantial knowledge of IT regulatory issues and notable expertise in relation to contractual disputes and data breaches. Of late he has acted in a number of significant arbitrations. **Strengths:** "A star in the making."

Michael Lazarus (3 Verulam Buildings) Exceptional junior who is a go-to for weighty outsourcing and licensing disputes, as well as cases involving innovative technology such as agile software. He is widely acclaimed for his standout cross-examination and calm, measured approach. **Strengths:** "He's absolutely outstanding. He's very effective, never flustered and has very good judgement." "Unsurpassed when it comes to complex, technology-heavy contractual disputes."

Clive Freedman (see p.604) (3 Verulam Buildings) A well-respected authority on matters such as e-banking and e-commerce, and a noted figure when it comes to arbitration and expert determination. He is "a big name in IT law," known for his thorough understanding of sophisticated technology. **Strengths:** "Probably the most technically gifted IT barrister at the Bar." "He has a very good technical grasp and a very effective advocacy style." **Recent work:** Provided counsel on matters concerning electronic money.

INQUESTS & PUBLIC INQUIRIES: An Introduction

Contributed by Temple Garden Chambers

Inquests

If evidence were needed of the impact and profile of modern inquests, it is writ large in the Hillsborough inquests, a coronial investigation of unprecedented scale. While atypical in complexity and duration, they illustrate the trend for inquests to assume increased legal and public significance. Families now benefit from coroners who are generally more willing to conduct inquests with a broader scope, and the greater use of narrative conclusions (formerly verdicts). For interested persons potentially responsible for a death, the reputational and commercial impacts, together with the potential influence on subsequent civil and criminal litigation, mean that inquests have never been more important.

Coroners and inquest practitioners alike are gradually settling into the reforms belatedly brought into force under the Coroners and Justice Act 2009, and the associated 2013 Rules and Investigations Regulations. In most respects these have been progressive rather than radical reforms, steered by the Chief Coroner.

The requirement to complete an inquest within six months of the death being reported, or as soon as is reasonably practicable after that date, has created the most noticeable change for inquest practitioners. Allied to the obligation to report to the Chief Coroner any investigation that is not completed within a year, coroners know they will be held to account if inquests are not conducted expeditiously. Practitioners, interested persons and investigating bodies are all feeling the effects of this change, at least when appearing in front of those coroners who have embraced the reforms. Numerous investigating bodies are involved in providing their own reports to coroners: the police, the Prison and Probation Ombudsman, the Independent Police Complaints Commission and the Health and Safety Executive to name but a few. Many coroners are now exerting considerable pressure on these and other bodies to produce their own reports more swiftly so as to inform the scope of the coroner's investigation at an earlier stage.

Inquest practitioners have long been accustomed to warning clients of the huge variation in practice and approach between different coroners. The Chief Coroner aims to bring greater consistency across coroner services, producing guidance in published legal notes as well as in judicial review judgments. Such assimilation of practice amongst historically independently minded coroners will doubtless take time. But the availability of clear and balanced guidance on important matters such as Preventing Further Deaths reports is both welcome and beginning to produce results. Gone are the days when a practitioner could all-but-guarantee that certain coroners would or would not issue a report regarding the risk of future deaths.

There remain, however, fundamental challenges for coroner services and those involved in inquests. Coroners remain funded by their local authorities, and their resourcing and accommodation varies enormously. In one coroner's area, interested persons will find themselves in a modern fit for purpose coroner's court, with consultation rooms and a coroner who readily provides paginated disclosure from their own office, and might instruct counsel to the inquest for a more complicated case. In the neighbouring coroner's area, inquests may be held in an ancient and ill-appointed converted magistrates' court with a coroner willing to exercise the statutory powers of disclosure, but unable to deal with the practicalities of doing so. Funding for the bereaved in complex cases remains an issue of contention. In the absence of centrally funded coroner services, it remains to be seen whether local funding can accommodate the Chief Coroner's calls for improved and more consistent coroner services.

Public Inquiries

Calls for a 'public' inquiry remain a frequent if not constant refrain in response to the weekly revelations of accidents, abuse and misconduct of every kind. If the Inquiries Act 2005 was intended to bring greater procedural consistency to the establishment and running of inquiries, it is arguably failing. The most striking feature of current inquiry practice is the prominence of ad hoc non-statutory inquiries in preference to inquiries established under the 2005 Act.

The reluctance to use the 2005 Act appears to derive from an assumption that inquiries under the 2005 Act tend to be longer and more expensive than non-statutory inquiries. It remains a matter of considerable debate amongst practitioners whether this assumed direct correlation is justified. Generally, although not without exception, inquiries under the 2005 Act (and the 1921 Act before it) have tended to be into the gravest matters of public concern. Often such inquiries will be those where the evidence is most voluminous, and the potential criticisms the most serious. Both factors increase the length of inquiries and hence the cost.

Moreover, non-statutory inquiries are not a panacea; they have not been immune from delay or increasing costs, as perhaps demonstrated by the Iraq inquiry. While some controversy remains over the powers retained by Ministers to restrict evidence on public interest grounds in 2005 Act inquiries, victims' groups remain concerned that non-statutory inquiries lack the powers of compulsion provided for by the 2005 Act.

The fact remains that those calling for an inquiry in today's climate undoubtedly need to overcome an increased scepticism about the effectiveness and proportionality of public inquiries in general, and statutory inquiries under the 2005 Act in particular. While there have been calls for the increased use of the 2005 Act, the likely trend will be towards the continued use of 'short, sharp' non-statutory inquiries. Equally, when inquiries are set up, practitioners will encounter conditions and terms of reference which more rigorously limit their duration and budget. Such an approach may yet yield an increase in satellite litigation, whether from victims concerned that inquiries are insufficiently effective or from witnesses concerned that procedural fairness is being curtailed in the rush to produce a speedy report.

Contents:

LONDON

Inquests & Public Inquiries London	
Leading Sets	
Band 1	**Band 3**
1 Crown Office Row *	5 Essex Court *
Band 2	Garden Court Chambers *
Doughty Street Chambers *	Matrix Chambers *
3 Raymond Buildings Barristers *	Temple Garden Chambers *
Leading Silks	
Star individuals	**Mansfield** Michael *Mansfield Chambers (ORL)* ◊
Garnham Neil *1 Crown Office Row* *	**Morton** Keith *Temple Garden Chambers* *
Band 1	**Phillips** Rory *3 Verulam Buildings (ORL)* ◊
Beer Jason *5 Essex Court* *	**Tam** Robin *Temple Garden Chambers* *
Beggs John *Serjeants' Inn Chambers (ORL)* ◊ *	**Whipple** Philippa *1 Crown Office Row*
Eadie James *Blackstone Chambers (ORL)* ◊	**Band 3**
Emmerson Ben *Matrix Chambers*	**Caplan** Jonathan *5 Paper Buildings (ORL)* ◊ *
Gibbs Patrick *3 Raymond Buildings Barristers* [A] *	**Davies** Hugh *3 Raymond Buildings Barristers* [A]
Grey Eleanor *Thirty Nine Essex Street (ORL)* ◊	**Dias** Dexter *Garden Court Chambers*
Lambert Christina *1 Crown Office Row*	**Francis** Robert *Serjeants' Inn Chambers (ORL)* ◊ *
O'Connor Patrick *Doughty Street Chambers* [A]	**Friedman** Danny *Matrix Chambers* *
Band 2	**Glasson** Jonathan *Matrix Chambers* *
Barton Fiona *5 Essex Court* *	**Kark** Tom *QEB Hollis Whiteman (ORL)* ◊
Giffin Nigel *11KBW (ORL)* ◊	**Leek** Samantha *5 Essex Court* *
Griffin Nicholas *5 Paper Buildings (ORL)* ◊ *	**Richards** Jenni *Thirty Nine Essex Street (ORL)* ◊
Horwell Richard *3 Raymond Buildings Barristers*	**Smith** Sally *1 Crown Office Row*
Johnson Jeremy *5 Essex Court* *	**Thwaites** Ronald *Ely Place Chambers (ORL)* ◊ *
Keith Hugo *3 Raymond Buildings Barristers* *	**New Silks**
Lissack Richard *Outer Temple Chambers (ORL)* ◊ *	**Hough** Jonathan *4 New Square (ORL)* ◊ *
Maclean Alan *Blackstone Chambers (ORL)* ◊	**Thomas** Leslie *Garden Court Chambers*
Leading Juniors	
Band 1	**Ballard** Briony *Serjeants' Inn Chambers (ORL)* ◊ *
Dobbin Clair *3 Raymond Buildings Barristers* *	**Butt** Matthew *3 Raymond Buildings Barristers* [A] *
Hill Henrietta *Doughty Street Chambers* [A]	**Gerry** Alison *Doughty Street Chambers*
Hill Matthew *1 Crown Office Row*	**Horstead** Sean *Garden Court Chambers*
O'Connor Andrew *Temple Garden Chambers*	**Mellor** Christopher *1 Crown Office Row*
Sheldon Neil *1 Crown Office Row*	**Naqshbandi** Saba *3 Raymond Buildings Barristers* [A]
Skelton Peter *1 Crown Office Row*	**Thomas** Owain *1 Crown Office Row*
Straw Adam *Doughty Street Chambers*	**Uberoi** Michael *Outer Temple Chambers (ORL)* ◊
Wakefield Victoria *Brick Court Chambers (ORL)* ◊	**Up-and-coming individuals**
Band 2	**Beattie** Kate *1 Crown Office Row*
Gallagher Caoilfhionn *Doughty Street Chambers* [A]	**Heaven** Kirsten *Garden Court Chambers*
Hewitt Alison *5 Essex Court* *	**Robottom** James *7BR (ORL)* ◊ *
Moss Nicholas *Temple Garden Chambers*	**Spurrier** Martha *Doughty Street Chambers*
Saunders Neil *3 Raymond Buildings Barristers* [A] *	**Stoate** Tom *Garden Court Chambers*
Band 3	**Tampakopoulos** Alex *2 Hare Court (ORL)* ◊ *
Antrobus Simon *Crown Office Chambers (ORL)* ◊ *	

** Indicates set / individual with profile.*

◊ (ORL) = Other Ranked Lawyer.

[A] direct access (see p.11).

Band 1

1 Crown Office Row
See profile on p.784

THE SET

1 Crown Office Row offers representation of the highest quality at inquests and public inquiries, and has an array of members who have appeared in a large number of the most significant proceedings of recent years. The expertise of the set is founded on its pre-eminence in the field of clinical negligence, which means its members are a first port of call for inquests and inquiries with pronounced medical elements. Additional areas of expertise include investigations into prisons, the media, the conduct of the military and rail disasters.

Client service: "The clerks are very good – they are easy to talk to and will always do their best to sort things out." The senior clerk is Matthew Phipps.

SILKS

Neil Garnham QC (see p.606) An advocate of the highest calibre, who handles inquests and public inquiries of great importance and sensitivity. He has represented clients from the military, the police, the NHS and the security services, and has represented the Secretary of State for the Home Office. **Strengths:** " He's excellent and has a very good pedigree in inquiries. His advocacy is fantastic and economical, and he is very good at gaining the confidence of the chairman." "He is an outstanding advocate, who is extremely intelligent and very thoughtful." **Recent work:** Acted for soldier witnesses in the high-profile Al-Sweady Inquiry, which investigated allegations of torture and unlawful killing carried out by British soldiers in Iraq.

Christina Lambert QC Focuses her inquests practice on cases concerning potential clinical negligence and mental health care provision. She has also provided counsel to a number of high-profile reviews into institutional misconduct. **Strengths:** "She is a very capable advocate and leader, a great team organiser and a team player." "A very, very good advocate, who's got the right approach for every situation." **Recent work:** Acted as lead counsel to the Hillsborough Inquests established following the recent quashing of the findings of the original inquests.

Philippa Whipple QC Has a broad practice encompassing tax, health and public law. Her experience in inquiries demonstrates an authoritative knowledge of the domestic and international rights of detainees. **Recent work:** Acted as lead counsel to the Detainee Inquiry, established to investigate allegations of collusion on the part of the British secret services in the detention of British citizens in Guantánamo Bay and elsewhere.

Sally Smith QC Focuses her inquiries practice on medical law, in relation to which she has appeared in a number of important proceedings in recent years. She is especially experienced at appearing for the NHS in investigations into institutional failings. **Strengths:** "She's very good – she has a thorough, in-depth understanding of the matter, and always knows the instruction inside out." "She's excellent with clients, and works well as part of the team – she's brilliant at pulling everyone together." **Recent work:** Appeared in the Mid Staffordshire NHS Foundation Trust Public Inquiry.

JUNIORS

Neil Sheldon Has particular expertise in medical inquests and clinical negligence, and has a growing reputation for his involvement in a number of high-profile cases over recent years. **Strengths:** "He's very good and very easy to get on with." "He's a counsel of choice if you're dealing with big witnesses, and he has a very economical style of advocacy." **Recent work:** Acted as first junior counsel to the military witnesses in the Al-Sweady Inquiry.

Matthew Hill Has appeared in a number of prominent inquiries and inquests, representing families, medical practitioners and soldiers. He was extensively involved, in the capacity of historian, in the Bloody Sunday Inquiry. **Strengths:** "He's a details man, who's very willing to roll up his sleeves and get into the facts and figures of a case." **Recent work:** Acted as second junior counsel to the Hillsborough Inquests.

Peter Skelton Represents both organisations and families in a broad variety of inquests and public inquiries. He has particular expertise in press freedoms and media expression, gained in part through his involvement in the Leveson Inquiry. **Strengths:** "He is right up there as an extremely bright and able junior. He's a great cross-examiner, and is a walking encyclopaedia of inquiry law." "He is very shrewd, has good tactical sense, writes well and, above all, is good company." **Recent work:** Acted in the Al-Sweady Inquiry for several Iraqi witnesses.

Christopher Mellor Incorporates his expertise in acting in clinical negligence proceedings into his inquests practice, and has a strong track record of representing interested persons in investigations into deaths involving the medical profession. **Strengths:** "His ability to assimilate a very large volume of information in a short time is extremely impressive." "He is clear and concise in his advice, and has an absolutely thorough understanding of the matters he deals with." **Recent work:** Acted as junior counsel to West Midlands Strategic Health Authority in the Mid Staffordshire NHS Foundation Trust Public Inquiry, established to investigate apparent severe failings in standards of care throughout the Trust.

Owain Thomas Regularly represents families, individuals, the Ministry of Defence (MoD) and health trusts in inquests. He has pronounced expertise in inquests touching on deaths as a result of surgical complications. **Strengths:** "He has a very sharp mind, is terrier-like on the detail and has always achieved a very good outcome for clients." "He is excellent as he is able to connect with people and is very robust in court." **Recent work:** Represented the bereaved family in an inquest examining the circumstances of the death of a baby killed by a falling lamp-post.

Kate Beattie Centres her inquests practice on professional negligence, disciplinary and human rights issues. She has particular experience in inquests investigating suicides of detainees in Young Offenders' Institutes. **Strengths:** "She is very thorough, very approachable, and very good with clients." "She has an infectious enthusiasm for what she does, and is completely committed." **Recent work:** Acted for the Brighton Marathon in an inquest into the death of a runner who suffered a cardiac arrest as a result of his suffering from ischaemic bowel disease.

Band 2

Doughty Street Chambers

See profile on p.786

THE SET

Doughty Street Chambers enjoys an excellent reputation for the quality of its representation of bereaved families at inquests and inquiries, typically those touching on deaths related, directly and indirectly, to the actions or failings of the state. Its members offer deep experience in such proceedings, including in investigations into deaths from police shootings, and are well versed in cases relating to mental health, prison law and immigration detention. They are also accomplished in handling judicial reviews arising from the findings of inquests.

SILKS

Patrick O'Connor QC A very well-regarded practitioner with a great deal of experience of appearing for bereaved families in both inquests and public inquiries. He is an expert in proceedings relating to the conduct of the military, deaths in custody and prison detention. **Strengths:** "An amazing advocate and adviser. He's incredibly diligent and thorough in his preparation." **Recent work:** Acted for the Iraqi citizens in the Al-Sweady Inquiry investigating possible violations of the Geneva Convention by British troops, including allegations of torture and unlawful killing.

JUNIORS

Henrietta Hill Focuses her inquests practice on representing families of the deceased in cases where it is alleged that state failings have been a contributing factor in their deaths. She enjoys a growing reputation for her appearances in some of the most high-profile inquests of recent years. **Strengths:** "She is very, very thorough and her legal knowledge is very impressive." **Recent work:** Represented 22 of the bereaved families of individuals who died in the Hillsborough disaster in the fresh inquests into their deaths.

Adam Straw Offers representation in highly significant inquests on behalf of bereaved families who seek to challenge perceived failings of state agencies. He has particular expertise in Article 2 right to life issues. **Strengths:** "He has a fantastic knowledge of the case law and the current legislative matters decided on by the court." "He is really accessible, and his knowledge of the law is unrivalled." **Recent work:** Represented the family of Mark Duggan in the high-profile inquest into his death at the hands of armed police, which sparked days of rioting in London.

Caoilfhionn Gallagher Centres her inquests and inquiries practice on addressing the deaths of people following potential failures of the police and various state agencies. She is also known for her expertise in fighting for open justice, and often acts for media organisations in challenges to reporting restrictions. **Strengths:** "She put her all into the inquest, in really difficult circumstances. She's a real fighter who presents detailed submissions." **Recent work:** Acted for the bereaved family of a 14-year-old boy who took his own life, in an inquest examining potential failings of multiple agencies in preventing his death.

Alison Gerry Has over ten years of experience of representing families in inquests into deaths in custody. She has particular expertise in deaths occurring during detention under the Mental Health Act. **Strengths:** "She knows her way around the prison system, and her drafting is very good as well." "Alison is really good in front of a jury and in understanding what the client wants, which is so important in inquests since you only have one shot at it." **Recent work:** Represented the family of James Herbert in the inquest into his death in custody, following his detention under the Mental Health Act.

Martha Spurrier Represents bereaved families in inquests, and has particular experience in proceedings that engage Article 2 of the ECHR. She is proficient in cases dealing with deaths of vulnerable adults and people in psychiatric care. **Strengths:** "She worked extremely hard, and gave a better performance than more experienced advocates working on the case." "She is very intelligent. In the inquest she was excellent, and the jury liked her and her approach."

3 Raymond Buildings Barristers

See profile on p.857

THE SET

The expertise of this set in inquests and public inquiries is closely related to its strength in a broad range of criminal issues. Its members are highly regarded for their prowess in handling matters in the context of complex fraud, serious violence, terrorism and institutional failings. They often appear for individual police officers and the fire services, as well as bereaved families.

Client service: "They've become our number one because they've got strength in depth. The clerks are up there with the best, too – they are super-efficient."

SILKS

Patrick Gibbs QC Enjoys an outstanding reputation for his work in high-profile inquests whose subjects range from terrorist attacks to deaths of prominent figures. He is proficient at examining the contentious actions or omissions of state agents. **Strengths:** "He has a fantastically easy style and a lovely manner in court that is very persuasive." "He is incredibly gentle, but has an incisive, surgical approach, and is very aware of the subtleties of the court." **Recent work:** Represented the Investigative Committee of the Russian Federation in the Litvinenko Inquest, established following his death by radiation poisoning in London.

Richard Horwell QC Acts for the police in coronial and judicial inquests. He has particular experience of handling proceedings arising from police shootings and suspicious deaths. **Strengths:** "An extremely wise and experienced advocate." **Recent work:** Acted for the Commissioner of the Metropolitan Police in the Litvinenko Inquest.

Hugo Keith QC (see p.643) Has extensive expertise in criminal trials and inquests into highly contentious deaths. He typically represents government bodies and prominent public figures, and has additional experience of acting as leading counsel to the inquest. **Strengths:** "He's a very charming and effective advocate." "He's ferociously hard-working and has a very good manner with witnesses." **Recent work:** Acted for the Metropolitan Police Service in the inquest into the death of Mark Duggan, whose shooting was a major catalyst for the London riots in 2011.

Hugh Davies QC Acts for the police in inquests examining deaths in custody and shootings. His adroit handling of such proceedings led to him being instructed as counsel to the inquest into the death of Alexander Litvinenko. **Strengths:** "He is responsive, accessible, and very good on the interrelationship of inquests and criminal law." **Recent work:** Represented Lincolnshire Police in the inquest into the death of a Red Arrows pilot following his ejection from a stationary aircraft on a runway.

JUNIORS

Clair Dobbin Very well regarded for her inquests and inquiry work, and has appeared in a substantial number of prominent proceedings. She specialises in cases concerning deaths in custody. **Strengths:** "She is super and very charming." "She was excellent in the Baha Mousa Inquiry." **Recent work:** Represented four officers of the Metropolitan Police Service in the Emmanuel Inquest, established following the death of Mr Emmanuel, better known as reggae artist Smiley Culture. The inquest investigated the circumstances of his suicide by stabbing during the execution of a search warrant of his house.

Neil Saunders A well-regarded criminal junior, who acts in a variety of inquests. He often represents housing associations in investigations into deaths in accommodation. **Strengths:** "He is a consummate professional and a highly able advocate." "He is conscientious, hard-working and realistic in the way in which he approaches cases." **Recent work:** Acted for ten families in the inquests into the deaths of 52 people in the London bombings on 7 July 2005.

Matthew Butt Specialises in inquisitorial proceedings examining contentious police shootings. He has particular experience of representing the tactical firearms commander involved in such instances. **Strengths:** "He is really good – very direct, very well prepared, and measured in his approach." "His oral advocacy is of a very high standard." **Recent work:** Represented the Trident Tactical Firearms Commander in the Duggan Inquest.

Saba Naqshbandi Acts for the full range of parties to inquests, including bereaved families, the police and witnesses. She is also a noted practitioner in the fields of crime and health and safety. **Strengths:** "An excellent junior, she is very intelligent and hardworking, and a pleasure to work with." "She's really thorough and well prepared, excellent on her feet and great on the detail in terms of her written work." **Recent work:** Acted for the London Fire & Emergency Authority in the inquest into the deaths of six people who were killed in a fire at Lakanal House in Southwark.

Band 3

5 Essex Court

See profile on p.791

THE SET

5 Essex Court is a leading set offering representation to individual police officers, police forces, private contractors and public bodies, on behalf of whom its members have appeared in a range of significant inquests in recent years. Members are particularly accomplished in matters relating to deaths in custody, fatalities following police shootings, acts of terrorism and major fires. The set is particularly strong on pre-inquest issues and the implementation of recommendations following proceedings.

Client service: "The barristers are all extremely user-friendly, and willing to muck in to meet deadlines. Clients find them sensitive, and tough when they need to be."

SILKS

Jason Beer QC Acts for a broad range of interested parties to inquests and inquiries of the highest significance. He is known for being particularly skilled in the representation of police officers. **Strengths:** "A very able and very intelligent advocate." **Recent work:** Acted for G4S in the inquest into the murder of Paul McGuigan, who was killed in Iraq by a fellow employee of the security firm he worked for.

Fiona Barton QC Primarily represents police forces in major inquisitorial proceedings, many of which carry a great deal of public and media interest. She is particularly experienced in matters concerning deaths in custody and those following contact with the police. **Strengths:** "She manages to effectively present the position for her clients, who are often the unpopular party in an inquest." "She is never fazed by difficult inquests and never lets her guard down." **Recent work:** Represented King Edward VII's Hospital in the inquest into the death of Jacintha Saldanha, a nurse who committed suicide after putting through a hoax call from a radio station regarding the Duchess of Cambridge, who was then an in-patient at the hospital.

Jeremy Johnson QC Typically acts for public authorities in a range of inquests and public inquiries. He has particular expertise in proceedings addressing the actions of police forces, the military and the security services. **Strengths:** "He has acted on a wide range of high-profile inquests, and is a very robust advocate." **Recent work:** Acted for West Midlands Police in the Hillsborough Inquest.

Samantha Leek QC Represents the interests of police forces, the MoD and the Home Office in high-profile inquests and inquiries. **Strengths:** "She is extremely approachable and has a great client manner." "In some problematic cases, her sensitive manner has allowed her to break down reluctant witnesses in the nicest possible way." **Recent work:** Acted for the Serious Organised Crime Agency in the inquest into the death of Mark Duggan.

JUNIORS

Alison Hewitt (see p.625) Acts for a wide range of clients in both inquests and public inquiries, and has particular expertise in inquests compliant with Article 2 of the ECHR and those touching on the deaths of people detained under the Mental Health Act. **Strengths:** "She is excellent in her attention to detail, and also has a great relationship with clients." "She's probably one of the best barristers I've ever seen in a coroner's court, as she's excellent on her feet, in her strategy and in her line of questioning." **Recent work:** Acted for G4S in the inquest into the death of Jimmy Mubenga, who died in the course of his deportation on an aircraft while being restrained by three security guards. At the centre of the inquest was the question of the existence of a causative link between the restraint and Mr Mubenga's death.

Garden Court Chambers

See profile on p.808

THE SET

The strong reputation of Garden Court Chambers for inquest work is rooted in the quality of its representation of bereaved families in investigations into deaths in custody, and instances where the State may have been responsible for the death. Members are noted experts in cases concerning deaths in the context of mental heath, immigration detention, following police contact and in hospital. They are also accomplished at pursuing civil claims for damages for their clients following inquisitorial proceedings.

Client service: "They have an exceptionally good nose for public interest inquests. The clerking there is extremely good, too. The clerks are very approachable both in terms of fees and in administering advocate appearances in court."

SILKS

Dexter Dias QC Enters the listings this year on the back of his highly regarded work in inquests. He has special expertise in proceedings arising from the deaths of young people in custody. **Strengths:** "He is fantastic, is a real team player and has a great advocacy style that's great to watch. He asks all the appropriate questions to the appropriate people." "He worked relentlessly for us, achieving a fantastic outcome." **Recent work:** Acted in the Jake Hardy Inquest, appearing for the deceased child's family. The proceedings were established to investigate the circumstances of Jake's death, after he hanged himself while in custody in HMP Hindley.

Leslie Thomas QC Has taken silk this year following over two decades of experience of handling inquests. He has particular expertise in acting for bereaved families in inquests arising from police shootings and restraint deaths. **Strengths:** "He is a fantastic advocate with a great jury style. When necessary, he takes witnesses apart forensically." "He is a fantastic jury advocate and tactician, whose cross-examination is brilliant. He is also superb at handling clients." **Recent work:** Acted for the family of Mark Duggan in the inquest into his death.

JUNIORS

Sean Horstead Represents the families of people who have died in custody, in prison or in circumstances involving police pursuits. He specialises in coronial proceedings. **Strengths:** "He is a fearless advocate, who is not shy of asking difficult questions to people in a position of authority. He demands answers and through his technical expertise will often achieve them in situations where others would fall away." **Recent work:** Represented the family of Habib Ullah, who had died from choking on a package concealed in his mouth during the course of forcible restraint by police officers.

Kirsten Heaven Has experience of representing bereaved families in a broad range of inquests. She has particular expertise in prison and police-related deaths, especially those that have occurred in custody or during detention under the Mental Health Act. **Strengths:** "She is relentless and completely comprehensive in her approach to matters. A fantastic and fearless advocate, she is appreciated by the bereaved families for whom she acts." "A brilliant inquest advocate who is exceptionally good with clients and at advancing the concerns of the family." **Recent work:** Acted for the family in the inquest into the death of anti-gun campaigner Pat Regan, who was stabbed to death by her schizophrenic grandson. The proceedings resulted in a narrative verdict highly critical of psychiatric care services.

Tom Stoate Enjoys a growing reputation for his inquests practice, and has acted as a junior in a number of high-profile proceedings. He specialises in representing bereaved families in investigations into deaths in custody. **Strengths:** "He is really personable, easy to work with, has some fantastic ideas and produces great written work." "He's very good with families and at engaging with the jury." **Recent work:** Represented the family of Sean Rigg, who died whilst being restrained on the floor of Brixton Police Station. The proceedings led to the first independent inquiry by the Independent Police Complaints Commission into one of its own investigations.

Matrix Chambers

See profile on p.832

THE SET

Matrix Chambers offers a full range of services in matters relating to inquests and public inquiries. It acts on behalf of clients including bereaved families, public bodies and media groups in proceedings investigating deaths from police contact, deaths in detention under the Mental Health Act, and cases concerning the conduct of the military and the media. A number of members are noted authorities in the area, being authors of leading textbooks on the subjects of coronial law, inquisitorial proceedings and the applicability of Article 2 ECHR. The set offers additional representation in a range of alternative proceedings challenging coronial decisions and the law informing the composition of inquests and inquiries.

Client service: "They are all very good, very commercial and solution-oriented. They are also equally happy acting on either side of a matter."

SILKS

Jonathan Glasson QC Has expertise in a wide range of inquests and inquiries, and particular experience of handling investigations into deaths related to military and police conduct. **Strengths:** "He's very thorough, and certainly a trusted pair of hands for matters concerning the Official Secrets Act." "He is a very fair counsel who is highly effective." **Recent work:** Represented the Independent Police Complaints Commission in the inquiry into the death of Azelle Rodney, in which it was found that the police shooter could not rationally have believed Mr Rodney had picked up a firearm immediately before he was shot.

Danny Friedman QC (see p.604) A noted authority in the field of inquests and public inquiries. His work in this area focuses particularly on highlighting duties incumbent on the state under international human rights law, and their implications for investigative obligations. **Strengths:** "He is absolutely top-notch – he has a brilliant brain and does excellent work." "He knows the area backwards." **Recent work:** Acted for the family of the deceased in an inquest into the death of a woman who committed suicide while detained under the Mental Health Act. The inquest examined issues of observation and resuscitation.

Ben Emmerson QC A renowned public law and human rights practitioner with a distinguished pedigree in representing bereaved families in inquests and inquiries of the highest significance. **Strengths:** "He is terrific in inquests and inquiries. He's very well known for everything he does and is absolutely excellent." **Recent work:** Acted on behalf of the widow of Alexander Litvinenko in the inquest into the circumstances of his death.

Temple Garden Chambers

See profile on p.872

THE SET

Temple Garden Chambers offers robust and experienced representation across a broad span of inquisitorial proceedings, its members often acting on behalf of government bodies or as counsel to the inquest. They demonstrate particular accomplishment in matters relating to the misconduct of the police and the press, and handle matters involving issues of national security.

SILKS

Keith Morton QC (see p.677) Brings his experience as a former member of the Treasury A Panel to his inquests practice, and recently acted in proceedings investigating the deaths of Royal Military Police in Iraq. He also has expertise of advising coroners in the capacity of counsel to the inquest. **Strengths:** "Always sound and sensible." **Recent work:** Acted for Transport for London in an inquest into the first death of a cyclist on the capital's new cycle super-highways. The proceedings did not find any causative relation between the cycle path and the accident.

Robin Tam QC (see p.733) Centres his inquests and inquiries practice on the representation of the police. He has acted in proceedings of the highest public significance, some of which concerned matters relating to national security. **Strengths:** "His submissions are calm, accurate and reliable." "Coroners want him as their counsel, since he can make their position invulnerable to judicial review." **Recent work:** Acted as counsel to the Litvinenko Inquest.

JUNIORS

Andrew O'Connor Acts in judicial and coronial inquests of high significance, and has a particular emphasis on matters involving national security and potential failings of state agencies. He also has expertise in proceedings arising from deaths in custody. **Strengths:** "He deals with very difficult topics in a straightforward way – he makes it seem very easy, when it's not." "Both on his feet and in negotiation, he is sensible, pragmatic and intelligent." **Recent work:** Represented the Independent Police Complaints Commission in the Hillsborough Inquests.

Nicholas Moss Has a strong track record appearing in prominent inquiries for the military, government and prisons. He has particular experience of acting in an advisory capacity to inquiry chairmen. **Strengths:** "He has an excellent reputation and shows great sensitivity when handling inquests." **Recent work:** Acted as junior counsel to the Detainee Inquiry.

Other Ranked Lawyers

James Eadie QC (Blackstone Chambers) Has acted on behalf of the government in his capacity as Treasury Devil in a number of the most high-profile inquiries of recent times. His exceptional expertise in public law and human rights informs his work in this area, and he is particularly good at cases concerning the conduct of the military and freedom of expression. **Strengths:** "He is absolutely superb and an advocate that the court loves." "He is conversational without being impertinent, and is also very clever and hard-working." **Recent work:** Acted for the government in the Leveson Inquiry.

Alan Maclean QC (Blackstone Chambers) An accomplished public law advocate with a great deal of experience of acting in sensitive and high-profile inquiries. He often appears on behalf of the government and individual politicians, and has additional expertise in acting in the capacity of counsel to the inquiry. **Strengths:** "A class act who always sees interesting new angles when handling matters."

James Robottom (see p.709) (7BR) An accomplished junior with a burgeoning practice in inquest work. He focuses on representing bereaved families in proceedings relating to mental health. **Strengths:** "He is really understanding, and has a really in-depth knowledge of the mental health system." "He was measured, took the points well and knew how to pick his battles, asking the questions that needed to be asked while ensuring the jury was engaged." **Recent work:** Acted for the identical twin brother of the deceased in the inquest into the death of Patrick Whiting, who had committed suicide following discharge from hospital. The jury recorded a narrative verdict, finding multiple failings on the part of the NHS trust.

Victoria Wakefield (Brick Court Chambers) Draws on her public law and civil liberties expertise when appearing in public inquiries. She is experienced in matters relating to the conduct of the military in the context of human rights. **Strengths:** "She is hugely bright and hugely hard-working." **Recent work:** Acted as junior counsel to the MoD in the Baha Mousa Inquiry.

Simon Antrobus (see p.536) (Crown Office Chambers) Brings his criminal regulatory and corporate manslaughter practice to bear in his inquests work. He specialises particularly in representing clients in inquest cases in which criminal proceedings are likely to follow. **Strengths:** "He puts his clients at ease supremely well, and never loses his air of confidence and professionalism." "He is a fantastic advocate, who is very dedicated." **Recent work:** Represented British Airways in the inquest into the death of Jimmy Mubenga.

Ronald Thwaites QC (see p.738) (Ely Place Chambers) A highly experienced and well-respected advocate in police and prison law. **Strengths:** "He is a very powerful presence in court."

Eleanor Grey QC (Thirty Nine Essex Street) A specialist in inquiries arising in the context of healthcare, in which area she has represented public bodies in a number of very high-profile proceedings in recent years. She is also expert in disciplinary and regulatory matters. **Strengths:** "She is extraordinarily good." **Recent work:** Acted for the former Healthcare Commission in the Mid Staffordshire NHS Foundation Trust Inquiry.

Jenni Richards QC (Thirty Nine Essex Street) Maintains a broad inquests practice, and has a particular interest in proceedings examining potential failings of the State. Her work in this regard typically addresses issues such as deaths in custody, and those arising from asbestos exposure. She is also an expert on inquests relating to the mental health system. **Strengths:** "A very compassionate person, who has fabulous advocacy skills and a vast knowledge of the law." **Recent work:** Acted for Yorkshire Ambulance Service in the Hillsborough Inquests.

Alex Tampakopoulos (see p.733) (2 Hare Court) Frequently instructed on behalf of a range of interested persons in inquests, including bereaved families, companies, healthcare professionals and schools. She has a particular interest in coronial law. **Strengths:** "She has a lovely manner that means the jury wants to trust her." **Recent work:** Represented the family of Lance Corporal Craig Roberts in the inquest touching on the deaths of three Territorial Army soldiers during an SAS selection exercise in the Brecon Beacons.

Nigel Giffin QC (11KBW) A well-regarded advocate in the fields of public law, and civil liberties and human rights. His expertise in these areas informs his work in inquiries, which typically concerns deaths in custody. **Recent work:** Acted as counsel to the inquiry into the death of Zahid Mubarek, who was killed while being detained at Feltham Young Offenders' Institution.

Michael Mansfield QC (Mansfield Chambers) Brings his vast experience in civil liberties and human rights issues to bear in his inquests practice. He has acted in a wide range of proceedings in this field, including in investigations into disasters and terrorist attacks. **Strengths:** "He's very pleasant to deal with, and as good an advocate as you'd expect someone of his stature to be." "He's a very effective advocate, and an absolute giant of the human rights world."

Jonathan Hough QC (4 New Square) Has a strong reputation for his consummate expertise in coronial law. He is often instructed as counsel to inquiries, and regularly acts for coroners whose decision are under challenge. **Strengths:** "He's very impressive, partly because he applies the law in a practical way. He doesn't just tell how it is – he thinks about how it will apply in the circumstances." "His strengths are his thorough presentation, attention to detail and ability to react quickly to changing circumstances." **Recent work:** Acted as counsel to the inquiry into the death of Dale Burns, who had died after taking designer drugs and being tasered in an encounter with the police.

Richard Lissack QC (see p.657) (Outer Temple Chambers) A versatile counsel with expertise in the law surrounding the financial services, health and safety and fraud. He draws on his experience in these areas when acting in and advising on major inquiries. **Strengths:** "He's an advocate who can turn his mind to anything." **Recent work:** Advised a publishing group regarding its participation in the Leveson Inquiry.

Michael Uberoi (Outer Temple Chambers) Has an established practice in public inquiries, with a particular emphasis on the culpability of healthcare institutions for suffering and loss of life. He is called to the Bar of Northern Ireland, and has participated in a number of inquiries there. **Recent work:** Acted for a consultant paediatric anaesthetist in the Inquiry into Hyponatraemia-related Deaths in Northern Ireland, established to investigate a series of deaths of young children in the Royal Belfast Hospital.

Nicholas Griffin QC (see p.615) (5 Paper Buildings) Offers expert representation to military personnel, government departments and police officers in major inquiries, including in the Bloody Sunday Inquiry, where he appeared on behalf of a large number of soldiers. **Strengths:** "He is a very good advocate, and is very fluent and persuasive." "He's making a really good reputation for himself." **Recent work:** Represented the police in the Rosemary Nelson Inquiry, established to examine the possibility that elements of the security services had colluded in her murder.

Jonathan Caplan QC (see p.565) (5 Paper Buildings) Known for his expertise in media law and crime, particularly in the context of fraud. He draws on this expertise when appearing in a number of significant inquiries. **Strengths:** "He is an excellent advocate, who enjoys the confidence of the media organisations that regularly brief him." **Recent work:** Represented Associated Newspapers in the Leveson Inquiry.

Tom Kark QC (QEB Hollis Whiteman) Has a broad range of expertise, particularly based in criminal law and medical professional discipline. He has, in recent years, appeared in a number of inquests in which Article 2 was engaged. **Strengths:** "He is fair-minded, and shows scrupulous attention to detail." **Recent work:** Represented the family of Red Arrows pilot Sean Cunningham in the inquest into his death, which established that accident did not occur as a consequence of his cognitive impairment, as had been suggested.

John Beggs QC (Serjeants' Inn Chambers) Extremely well regarded for his work in representing the police in inquests and inquiries, and for defending them in civil proceedings. He has appeared in a large number of the most significant cases of recent years. **Strengths:** "He is absolutely fearsome, but thoroughly nice and totally straight. He's able to be very robust with the judges when representing the police, without alienating the court." **Recent work:** Acted for the Chief Constable of Northumbria Police in the inquest into the death of Chris Brown, one of the victims of Raoul Moat. The inquest investigated whether the police acted appropriately given their knowledge about Moat at the time.

Sir Robert Francis QC (Serjeants' Inn Chambers) Commands a great deal of respect for his acuity in medical inquests and inquiries. He has decades of experience both as a counsel and in chairing significant proceedings. **Strengths:** "He is one of the best – he has a fantastic legal mind and can handle phenomenally complex issues." "He's one of the top people to instruct in a case dealing with complex medical issues." **Recent work:** Chaired the Mid Staffordshire NHS Foundation Trust Public Inquiry.

Briony Ballard (see p.542) (Serjeants' Inn Chambers) Acts for a diverse selection of interested persons in inquests, including bereaved families, the police, the Independent Police Complaints Commission and NHS trusts. She specialises in proceedings where Article 2 is engaged, particularly those concerning deaths in custody or of patients. **Strengths:** "She is always very well prepared, and doesn't miss anything at all." "She shows good judgement – she is forthright, but knows when to hang back." **Recent work:** Represented a cardiac anaesthetist in an inquest into the death of a man during a relatively new type of operation to replace his aortic valve.

Rory Phillips QC (3 Verulam Buildings) Focuses his work in this area on the conduct of the police, the press, the NHS and the banking industry. He has appeared in a number of high-profile proceedings in recent years. **Strengths:** "He is extremely bright, and is a heavyweight silk with great gravitas." **Recent work:** Provided advice in relation to a forthcoming Irish parliamentary inquiry into the banking crisis.

INSURANCE: An Introduction

Contributed by 7 King's Bench Walk

Asbestosis claims, typhoons, earthquakes, floods, fires, oil pollution, piracy, armed conflicts, riots, smuggling, pharmaceutical liability, negligence, economic sanctions and corporate failures are only some of the problems which confront companies and individuals both domestically and internationally. There are also the ever-attendant risks of carrying on business, such as damage to property, loss of income and third-party liability. These are the sorts of matters which have generated insurance claims and disputes in recent times. Marine, energy, financial institutions, professional indemnity, global liability, commercial property and consumer insurance policies are the protections designed to deal with these problems.

The past year has kept the Insurance Bar busy, with an even blend of disputes across most insurance products and all insurance markets. It is difficult to ascribe any economic or political reason to the current trends in such disputes. That said, the economy and politics are as often as much the stuff of insurance claims as are natural phenomena such as typhoons, earthquakes and floods. What remains of interest is the sheer range of claims arising not only in coverage disputes between insurers and assureds and, also in recent times, between reinsurers and reinsureds, but also in defence or subrogation proceedings managed by insurers. The skill and fairness of the profession in dealing with such claims reinforces the centrality of English law and London to the resolution of international insurance disputes.

There have been a number of sizeable marine insurance disputes over the past 12 months. Hull claims, including total loss claims, continue to dominate (Sea Glory v Al Sagr, Versloot Dredging v Gerling and Venetico v IGI). Indeed, two of the large trials to take place over the coming year are total loss claims, the 'B Atlantic' and the 'Brillante Virtuoso'. Commodities, cargo and energy claims remain steady. Other marine insurance claims also continue to attract considerable interest, including the 'Alexandros T' and the pollution claims in Gard v International Oil Pollution Compensation Fund and The Prestige.

As always, there is a wide spectrum of non-marine insurance cases which dominate the work of the Insurance Bar. There have been significant decisions of the Commercial Court and the Court of Appeal relating to liability insurance in Federal Mogul Asbestos Personal Injury Trust v Federal Mogul (asbestos liability claims), Rathbone v Novae (liability coverage for breach of trust claims and subrogation), and AstraZeneca v ACE (which settled a long-standing uncertainty concerning liability policies). There has also been more reinsurance litigation recently than in the last few years, especially coverage disputes (Amlin v Oriental, Tokio Marine v Novae, Federal Mogul Trust v Federal Mogul, AstraZeneca v ACE, Insurance Co of Pennsylvania v Equitas, and British-American v Matalec).

In addition, a large number of insurance and reinsurance disputes are resolved by means of arbitration. Very substantial claims under policies of liability and commercial property insurance, as well as treaty reinsurance claims and claims relating to the reinsurance of mass insurance products, continue to be dealt with by international arbitration under the aegis of most arbitral institutions (including LCIA, ICC and SIAC). Numerous claims are also dealt with by ad hoc arbitration. Arbitration, in particular international arbitration, has proved to be a popular choice of forum for insurance cases. This is an international practice in which English practitioners play a major part.

Many insurance disputes are commercial or international in character. There remain a large number of cases concerning consumer insurance claims, focusing mainly on motor insurance, personal injury claims and household policies. There have also been numerous small business claims under property, business interruption and professional indemnity policies. Indeed, professional indemnity claims against both insurers and insurance brokers continue to predominate (Equitas v Walsham, Rathbone v Novae, and European Risk v McManus). The coming year also includes the trial of professional indemnity insurance-related claims (Godiva v Travelers and AB Orlen v Aon).

Insurance fraud remains a blight continuously suffered by the insurance industry. Unsurprisingly, there have been a number of cases which are concerned with fraudulent insurance claims and the law's response to such fraud (Bate v Aviva, Liverpool Victoria v Thumber, Beacon v Maharaj, Savash v CIS General Insurance and Versloot Dredging v Gerling). Regrettably, there is no reason to suspect that fraud disputes will not continue.

Most insurance and reinsurance disputes continue to be litigated in the Commercial Court, with fewer insurance disputes apparently being determined in Chancery than in previous years. The Queen's Bench Division and the Technology and Construction Court continue to hand down decisions in insurance cases, with an emphasis on commercial property, liability, professional indemnity and consumer insurance policies. There were a considerable number of appeals heard in the Supreme Court and the Court of Appeal in insurance cases over the past year, with important legal developments being recorded in the process.

Perhaps the greatest development facing the work of the Insurance Bar in the near future will not emerge from the economic or political climate, but from the prospect of new legislation. In July 2014, the recently published Insurance Bill 2014 was introduced in the House of Lords. The Bill promises to make substantial changes to the law concerning fraudulent claims, the duty to present risks for insurance fairly (non-disclosure and misrepresentation) and insurance warranties. The proposed changes are a curious mixture and may well result in a substantial increase in insurance litigation in the future, at least while the meaning and intent of the new proposed changes to the law are evaluated and determined by the Courts.

Contents:

LONDON

Insurance London
Leading Sets
Band 1
7 King's Bench Walk *
Band 2
Brick Court Chambers *
Essex Court Chambers *
Fountain Court Chambers *
Band 3
Devereux *
20 Essex Street *
4 New Square *
3 Verulam Buildings *
Band 4
Crown Office Chambers *
4 Pump Court *
2TG - 2 Temple Gardens *
◊ (ORL) = Other Ranked Lawyer.
🄰 direct access (see p.11).
* Indicates set / individual with profile.
Alphabetical order within each band. Band 1 is highest.

Insurance London	
Leading Silks	
Star individuals	
Edelman Colin	*Devereux* *
Band 1	
Boswood Anthony	*Fountain Court Chambers*
Butcher Christopher	*7 King's Bench Walk*
Crane Michael	*Fountain Court Chambers*
Edwards David	*7 King's Bench Walk*
Foxton David	*Essex Court Chambers*
Gaisman Jonathan	*7 King's Bench Walk*
Hancock Christopher	*20 Essex Street*
Kealey Gavin	*7 King's Bench Walk*
Kendrick Dominic	*7 King's Bench Walk*
Lockey John	*Essex Court Chambers*
Railton David	*Fountain Court Chambers*
Schaff Alistair	*7 King's Bench Walk*
Band 2	
Adam Tom	*Brick Court Chambers*
Bartlett Andrew	*Crown Office Chambers* *
Berry Steven	*Essex Court Chambers*
Calver Neil	*Brick Court Chambers*
Christie Aidan	*4 Pump Court* *
Edey Philip	*20 Essex Street*
Eklund Graham	*4 New Square* *
Hirst Jonathan	*Brick Court Chambers*
Howard Mark	*Brick Court Chambers*
Jacobs Richard	*Essex Court Chambers*
MacDonald Eggers Peter	*7 King's Bench Walk*
Matovu Harry	*Brick Court Chambers*
Moriarty Stephen	*Fountain Court Chambers* *
Neish Andrew	*4 Pump Court* *
Stanley Paul	*Essex Court Chambers*
Symons Christopher	*3 Verulam Buildings*
Thanki Bankim	*Fountain Court Chambers* *
Weitzman Tom	*3 Verulam Buildings*
Wynter Colin	*Devereux*
Band 3	
Blanchard Claire	*Essex Court Chambers*
Bryan Simon	*Essex Court Chambers*
Cannon Mark	*4 New Square* *
Davies Helen	*Brick Court Chambers*
Elkington Ben	*4 New Square* *
Fenton Adam	*7 King's Bench Walk*
Fenwick Justin	*4 New Square* *
Green Andrew	*Blackstone Chambers (ORL)* ◊
Healy Siobán	*7 King's Bench Walk*
Hofmeyr Stephen	*7 King's Bench Walk*
Howe Timothy	*Fountain Court Chambers* *
Hunter Andrew	*Blackstone Chambers (ORL)* ◊
Lord David W	*3 Stone Buildings (ORL)* ◊ *
Lydiard Andrew	*Brick Court Chambers*
Milligan Iain	*20 Essex Street*
Moger Christopher	*4 Pump Court* *
Moody Neil	*2TG - 2 Temple Gardens*
Palmer Howard	*2TG - 2 Temple Gardens*
Phillips Rory	*3 Verulam Buildings*
Reed Paul	*Hardwicke (ORL)* ◊ 🄰 *
Salzedo Simon	*Brick Court Chambers*
Stewart Roger	*4 New Square* *
Swainston Michael	*Brick Court Chambers*
Waller Richard	*7 King's Bench Walk*
Band 4	
Bailey David	*7 King's Bench Walk*
Cogley Stephen	*Quadrant Chambers (ORL)* ◊
Cox Raymond	*Fountain Court Chambers* *
Day Anneliese	*4 New Square* *
Dougherty Charles	*2TG - 2 Temple Gardens* *
Harvey Michael	*Crown Office Chambers*
Houseman Stephen	*Essex Court Chambers*
Hubble Ben	*4 New Square* *
Jones Nigel	*Hardwicke (ORL)* ◊ 🄰 *
Masefield Roger	*Brick Court Chambers*
Mitchell Andrew	*Fountain Court Chambers* *
Moxon Browne Robert	*2TG - 2 Temple Gardens* *
Mulcahy Leigh-Ann	*4 New Square* *
Orr Craig	*One Essex Court (ORL)* ◊ *
Rigney Andrew	*Crown Office Chambers* *
Sabben-Clare Rebecca	*7 King's Bench Walk* *
Slade Richard	*Brick Court Chambers*
ter Haar Roger	*Crown Office Chambers*
Tozzi Nigel	*4 Pump Court* *
Webb Geraint	*Henderson Chambers (ORL)* ◊ 🄰 *
New Silks	
Blackwood Andrew Guy	*Quadrant Chambers (ORL)* ◊
Goodall Patrick	*Fountain Court Chambers* *
Hough Jonathan	*4 New Square* *
Miller Andrew	*2TG - 2 Temple Gardens* *
O'Sullivan Sean	*4 Pump Court* *
Quiney Ben	*Crown Office Chambers* *

Band 1

7 King's Bench Walk

See profile on p.827

THE SET

A go-to chambers for the largest and most complex insurance cases, which "operates at a much higher level than the majority of other sets in the market." "There's no better chambers when it comes to dealing with extremely high-value insurance coverage matters," according to commentators. Members here handle every type of insurance dispute, and act for insurers, reinsurers, brokers and insured companies worldwide. Of late they have handled a number of disputes arising out of the financial downturn, and have continued to tackle cases following on from events such as natural disasters and political crises.

Client service: "The clerks, led by Bernie Hyatt, are highly approachable, very responsible and good at getting things in the diary."

SILKS

Christopher Butcher QC A true heavyweight silk who is at home litigating the largest insurance issues right up to the Supreme Court. An instructing solicitor praised him as being "intellectually formidable and a go-to silk for high-value, complex insurance disputes." **Strengths:** "He seems to be a Terminator, to be quite honest. When he has a mission he is just going to do it." **Recent work:** Represented Equitas during its successful action against brokers Walsham Brothers. The case centred on contracts of insurance that had not been passed on, and raised important questions about duties of care.

Alistair Schaff QC Possesses huge expertise in international commercial, insurance and reinsurance law. His cases have brought him before the ECJ, Supreme Court and Privy Council. **Strengths:** "He is very smart and analytical. He breaks down problems issue by issue, and helps you see all the steps in the road while at the same time being far and away the most user-friendly barrister to work with." **Recent work:** Acted in Standard Life v Ace, a £100 million Commercial Court trial followed by an appeal to the Court of Appeal. Also acted in Imperial Marine v Allianz, a marine insurance claim involving microbially induced corrosion damage to a vessel.

David Edwards QC Has decades of experience in handling the most complex and high-value commercial, insurance and reinsurance cases. A fellow insurance silk described him as "extremely clear and diligent; he has a very calm and persuasive court manner and specialist knowledge of the Bermuda Form." **Strengths:** "He is a formidable advocate who is as good on his feet as he is on paper. He is always meticulously prepared and gets to the nub of the argument without fuss or waffle." **Recent work:** Represented XL and ACE in defending a claim by AstraZeneca's captive insurer for an indemnity of £135 million. The case had wide-ranging implications for Bermuda Form insurance.

Jonathan Gaisman QC A well-respected mediator and advocate within the insurance arena. One solicitor said: "It is amazing to me how quickly he grasps the issues and understands them." **Strengths:** "A super-bright barrister with a fearsome reputation. He can steamroller witnesses and opponents."

Gavin Kealey QC Head of chambers and much-admired international arbitrator and litigator on highly contentious insurance and reinsurance cases. **Strengths:** "He's fantastic to work with and very responsive. He explains matters clearly to clients and understands their needs."

Dominic Kendrick QC Specialises in handling complex, high-value commercial insurance cases. His practice is international in scope, as illustrated by the fact that his recent cases have involved Chinese, Pakistani and Indonesian concerns. **Strengths:** "Absolutely unflappable and really, really good." **Recent work:** Acted for Rathbones in the Commercial Court in a £100 million case concerning professional indemnity insurance and trust investments in Jersey.

Insurance London	
Leading Juniors	
Band 1	
Midwinter Stephen	*Brick Court Chambers*
Ratcliffe Peter	*3 Verulam Buildings*
Scorey David	*Essex Court Chambers*
Band 2	
Brocklebank James	*7 King's Bench Walk*
Craig Nicholas	*3 Verulam Buildings* *
Cutress James	*Fountain Court Chambers* *
Kerr Simon	*7 King's Bench Walk*
Khurshid Jawdat	*7 King's Bench Walk*
Lynch Ben	*Devereux* *
Padfield Alison	*Devereux* *
Band 3	
Burns Andrew	*Devereux* *
Harrison Richard	*Devereux* *
Kramer Adam	*3 Verulam Buildings* *
MacDonald Alexander	*7 King's Bench Walk*
Medd James	*Crown Office Chambers*
Nolten Sonia	*2TG - 2 Temple Gardens* *
Pliener David	*Hardwicke (ORL)* ◊ [A] *
Purchas James	*4 Pump Court* *
Shapiro Daniel	*Crown Office Chambers* *
Sutherland Jessica	*7 King's Bench Walk*
Band 4	
Chalmers Suzanne	*Crown Office Chambers* *
Green Alison	*2TG - 2 Temple Gardens* [A] *
Holmes Michael	*7 King's Bench Walk*
Pilbrow Fionn	*Brick Court Chambers*
Singla Tony	*Brick Court Chambers*
Tan Charlotte	*20 Essex Street*
* *Indicates individual with profile.*	
◊ *(ORL) = Other Ranked Lawyer.*	
[A] *direct access (see p.11).*	

David Bailey QC Has a very broad practice that encompasses aviation, banking, fraud and shipbuilding cases, as well as insurance work. **Strengths:** "He is hard-working and very thorough, and has a good style. He is a considered advocate who is not extrovert but gets his message across through being restrained and measured." **Recent work:** Successfully acted for the appellant solicitors Hill Dickinson in an appeal to the Supreme Court in a EUR150 million dispute concerning bribery and corruption.

Stephen Hofmeyr QC Possesses a varied commercial practice and provides assistance both in the courtroom and on an advisory basis. He is particularly strong in the marine sector. **Strengths:** "He has a mastery of the technical side of cases and he's also very approachable and easy to deal with."

Siobán Healy QC A multi-talented insurance barrister with a solid practice who focuses on marine, professional indemnity and D&O work for and against brokerages. She is equally adept on paper as she is on her feet in court. **Strengths:** "A very popular QC within the insurance market, who is hard-working, technically excellent, very responsive and easy to work with." **Recent work:** Acted for the claimant in a dispute concerning whether widespread theft and looting that occurred in Egypt during January 2011 fell within policy exclusions. The case is being heard in front of the Dubai International Financial Centre court.

Peter MacDonald Eggers QC Offers clients a vibrant insurance practice that focuses on high-end insurer and reinsurance work. He has particular expertise in marine, energy and natural disaster-related claims. **Strengths:** "A very user-friendly and commercial barrister who is outcome-focused." **Recent work:** Secured a victory for insurers in a case relating to subrogated rights and a £100 million claim for breach of trust.

Richard Waller QC Well known for his wide-ranging insurance and reinsurance practice. Instructing solicitors say he is "calm under pressure and able to come up with persuasive arguments." **Strengths:** "He is extremely good on his feet and outshines the opposition." **Recent work:** Instructed by the Lloyd's Market Association in regard to satellite litigation in the UK arising out of US-based antitrust class actions.

Rebecca Sabben-Clare QC Joins the rankings this year given her high-profile international insurance law practice. She has represented clients in front of the Supreme Court. **Strengths:** "She is exceptionally bright and extremely hard-working and thorough. She is very committed and always makes herself available, while also being an excellent advocate who establishes a good rapport with the judges." **Recent work:** Acted for Quadra in relation to an insurance claim for heat damage to soybeans that had been stored in Indonesia. The case was run under German, French and English law, and was eventually settled.

Adam Fenton QC An experienced litigator, arbitrator and mediator, who is experienced in complex international insurance, shipping and reinsurance work. **Strengths:** "Intelligent, utterly professional and hard-working." **Recent work:** Involved in a multimillion-dollar shipbuilding arbitration between North American and Chinese companies.

JUNIORS

James Brocklebank Possesses a diverse practice that covers the spectrum of commercial litigation. He has experience in dealing with cases involving energy, professional negligence and insurance, and is adept at all manner of contractual issues. **Strengths:** "He is very responsive, very commercial and very user-friendly." **Recent work:** Acted for defendant underwriters in a USD100 million claim under a marine cargo policy. The case subsequently settled after the first day of trial.

Jawdat Khurshid Noted for having a mature practice that encompasses all aspects of commercial law. He focuses on insurance and reinsurance cases along with shipping, energy and international trade matters. **Strengths:** "He is very bright, thorough and good at technical analysis. He's particularly good in the marine insurance sphere." **Recent work:** Represents reinsurers in a case concerning whether an asbestos personal injury trust may intervene in the contractual relations between an insured, an insurer and reinsurers in order to prescribe how claims are to be administered.

Jessica Sutherland A rising star junior within the Insurance Bar, who deals with high-profile disputes and arbitrations. She is also active in the shipping sphere and increasingly undertakes Bermuda Form arbitrations. **Strengths:** "She is capable and a pleasure to deal with." **Recent work:** Acted for Minister Insurance Services in relation to its recovery claim against its reinsurer, Simcoe. The matter concerned asbestos claims.

Michael Holmes Has a deep understanding of insurance and reinsurance policy construction. He is also often involved in insurance litigation dealing with the fallout from derivative transactions and the banking crisis. **Strengths:** "An excellent junior on complex arbitration claims who understands reinsurance, and takes time to really get to grips with the detail." **Recent work:** Represented Brit Insurance in a USD40 million claim following the splitting in two of a tanker off Suez Port.

Simon Kerr Active in high-profile insurance and commercial cases, and frequently instructed by very large insurers. **Strengths:** "He really gets stuck into the detail of a case." **Recent work:** Acted for Marsh in a £70 million insurance dispute with Rolls-Royce relating to marine propulsion for cruise liners.

Alexander MacDonald Possesses a broad-based commercial practice, and regularly handles insurance, reinsurance and shipping cases, alongside other areas. He has represented his clients at all levels of the English legal system. **Strengths:** "He's a very bright lawyer who you really get the sense is 100% committed to his cases." **Recent work:** Instructed in a £20 million claim made under a war risks marine insurance policy, which arose out of the alleged expropriation of a vessel by Venezuelan state authorities.

Band 2

Brick Court Chambers

See profile on p.774

THE SET

This hugely strong commercial set focuses its insurance practice on the very top-end work. Indicative of the level of work it undertakes, it has recently been handling multimillion-dollar reinsurance claims arising out of the 2010/2011 New Zealand earthquake. It has also been handling an insurance claim arising from the purchase of Kwikfit. Clients say it is "absolutely first-rate" and a "superb set."

Client service: "The clerks, led by Julian Hawes and Ian Moyler, were very efficient and as helpful as anything."

SILKS

Neil Calver QC A real authority within the Commercial Bar who is often involved in complex international insurance matters. He frequently appears in arbitrations, either sitting as arbitrator or representing clients. **Strengths:** "He is bright and hard-working, and can be relied upon to give advice on complex issues in a straightforward and uncomplicated manner."

Jonathan Hirst QC Co-head of chambers and a barrister who has seen every type of commercial case going, having spent the last quarter of a century in silk. He both sits on arbitration panels and litigates the most complex and contentious insurance cases. **Strengths:** "He is very confident and intelligent, and has both good relations with, and the respect of, judges." **Recent work:** Acted in a case that determined whether P&I insurance was frustrated as a result of sanctions against Iran.

Mark Howard QC Possesses a very broad practice and is a seasoned commercial barrister well known for his cross-examination skills. Along with insurance and reinsurance work, he is also frequently involved in cases relating to banking, competition, professional negligence, fraud and energy. **Strengths:** "He's a brilliant cross-examiner who has the respect of the court." **Recent work:** Instructed on a case concerning alleged fraud in a reinsurance scheme. The case was heard in front of the Privy Council.

Harry Matovu QC A robust litigator with an extensive insurance and reinsurance practice. He often leverages his expertise in energy, arbitrations and jurisdictional disputes to service large insurance clients. **Strengths:** "He is very bright, and is a real team player who produces very high-quality work." **Recent work:** Acted as leading counsel in a USD20 million property insurance case related to offshore gas and oil installations in the Gulf of Mexico.

Helen Davies QC A confident and effective commercial, EU and competition law advocate, who brings her expertise to bear on high-value international insurance and reinsurance cases. **Strengths:** "Fantastic. Her written work is sublime, she's proactive, and she really cuts to the meatier issues in a case." **Recent work:** Acted in a reinsurance claim that centred on damage to a road in Mexico caused by Hurricane Juliette.

Andrew Lydiard QC Approaches insurance and reinsurance work from a primarily aviation background. He is experienced in both arbitrations and litigation. **Strengths:** "He offered helpful opinions on time and in a very user-friendly manner."

Michael Swainston QC Possesses a very broad international commercial practice that is particularly focused on Russian work. **Strengths:** "He's dogged and gets his teeth into things." "He is a man with a lot of common sense."

Tom Adam QC Focuses on high-level broker D&O work as well as more traditional insurance and reinsurance cases. **Strengths:** "He is scarily bright." **Recent work:** Advised the insurers in a £30 million property damage claim related to repairs to the undersea Moyle Interconnector Cable that runs between Scotland and Northern Ireland.

Simon Salzedo QC Talented general commercial silk with a substantial insurance practice. As well as having a top legal practice he is also a qualified chartered accountant. **Strengths:** "His advocacy is second to none and you feel he really believes in every point." **Recent work:** Represented Standard Life in its successful £100 million claim against its professional indemnity insurers following a mis-selling issue.

Roger Masefield QC Joins the rankings this year as a result of the strength of his international insurance work. He earns plaudits from peers for his work ethic and smooth courtroom style. **Strengths:** "He gives very clear answers and doesn't sit on the fence. He's a very clever man indeed, and it's great to be able to tap into his intellect." **Recent work:** Acted for London Market reinsurers on a multimillion-dollar insurance claim arising out of the flooding of a Zambian copper mine.

Richard Slade QC Possesses a vibrant insurance, reinsurance and banking practice. He has recently been involved in a number of high-profile fire damage matters. **Strengths:** "He's very, very good. I've seen him on both sides and he is thorough and very capable." **Recent work:** He appeared in Sugar Hut v AJI, a case concerning fire insurance.

JUNIORS

Fionn Pilbrow Tackles a diverse practice that includes some very high-value insurance work, much of which is international in nature. He is widely held to be an outstanding all-round commercial junior. **Strengths:** "A first-rate junior with both a strong analytical mind and the ability to grasp the commercial realities of a case." **Recent work:** Acted for Equitas in its USD10 million dispute with The Insurance Company of the State of Pennsylvania.

Stephen Midwinter Experienced at handling insurance and reinsurance arbitrations in both London and Bermuda. He also frequently represents his clients in appellate and county courts across the country. **Strengths:** "Extremely good and very bright. He is efficient, gets to the point and takes a balanced view of how to apply the law in a commercial setting." **Recent work:** Appeared in a reinsurance dispute related to the Thai floods, which raised important questions about the interpretation of 'follow the settlements' clauses.

Tony Singla A gifted junior with a quality commercial practice. One solicitor who regularly instructs him says: "Not only is he an excellent barrister academically, but he is also a pleasure to work with on a practical and personal level." **Strengths:** "One of the brightest and most promising juniors around. He drafts documents excellently, and is also a calm, confident and eloquent advocate." **Recent work:** Instructed in a successful Supreme Court appeal concerning a marine insurance claim for £150 million damages brought by the owners of the 'Alexandros T' against London Market insurers.

Essex Court Chambers

See profile on p.792

THE SET

There is a sense in the market that if any set was to challenge 7KBW's pre-eminence in insurance law, it would be Essex Court. Commonly seen in the largest cases in the market, it has the ability to handle any insurance or reinsurance matter that comes its way. It is particularly noted for its strength in Bermuda Form arbitrations and is an obvious choice for big-ticket coverage disputes.

Client service: "The clerks, led by David Grief and Joe Ferrigno, are extremely responsive and understanding of the client's position."

SILKS

David Foxton QC A multi-talented advocate who is adept at a wide range of commercial work. In recent times he has increasingly focused his practice on big-ticket insurance arbitrations. **Strengths:** "He has a superb brain." "He's astute and client-friendly, and provides brilliant analysis of the case."

John Lockey QC Hugely prominent commercial barrister who specialises in insurance, reinsurance and arbitrations. He handles some of the largest insurance-related cases. **Strengths:** "He is outstanding. Sitting as an arbitrator he is fair and clever, while his style of advocacy is very much that of an iron fist in a velvet glove. Underestimate him at your peril." **Recent work:** Acted in the Commercial Court in Equitas v Walsham, a case concerning the duties owed by Lloyd's brokers to pass on monies to reinsurers and reinsureds.

Steven Berry QC Involved in the full spectrum of commercial cases. One solicitor who instructed him described him as being "pithy, informed and helpful." **Strengths:** "He's a fine advocate who commands the attention of the judges." **Recent work:** Acted in Bernina Maritime Inc v Royal and Sun Alliance Insurance, a case concerning chemical corrosion to a ship's tanks.

Richard Jacobs QC Exceptionally adept at coordinating large UK and US arbitrations and insurance claims. An authority on the Bermuda Form, he has co-authored one of the main texts on the subject. **Strengths:** "An extremely effective advocate, who sees the wood for the trees and is always a step ahead on a case." **Recent work:** Acted in Ace and others v Howden North America, an asbestos-related claim.

Paul Stanley QC "A towering intellect and someone who is destined for great things," who is known for the depth of his expertise. He is particularly good at Bermuda Form cases. **Strengths:** "He is a really deep thinker, and he is known for the marked quality of his analysis."

Claire Blanchard QC Has particular strength in offshore energy, shipping and marine claims, and is a seasoned operator when it comes to international arbitrations. **Strengths:** "She is extremely incisive and easy to deal with, has great command of the subject and is very hard-working. She has a mind like a steel trap."

Simon Bryan QC A long-standing commercial silk who has a far-reaching practice that features prominent shipping, marine and insurance cases. **Strengths:** "He is very effective and thorough, and prepares his cases very, very well." **Recent work:** Acted for the owners of 'Smyrni', a tanker hijacked by Somali pirates, in a case against underwriters. The matter related to a claim made under marine hull war risks policy.

Stephen Houseman QC A skilled advocate who is particularly experienced in dealing with complex arbitrations and reinsurance disputes in the mining and energy sectors. His cases often involve jurisdictional issues and are highly international in scope. **Strengths:** "He has good analytical skills, and he has a very nice, understated style in court that is very appealing. Judges trust him." **Recent work:** Instructed by Navigators to seek negative declaratory relief in the Commercial Court after a vessel caused damage to an underwater telecoms cable outside Abu Dhabi port.

JUNIORS

David Scorey Has a much-admired comprehensive commercial practice that has a focus on insurance and reinsurance matters. He is particularly adept at litigating Bermuda Form arbitrations and Lloyd's litigation. **Strengths:** "His knowledge of high-level casualty and Bermuda Form work is so deep, and his written work is first-class."

Fountain Court Chambers

See profile on p.804

THE SET

The barristers at Fountain Court are able to service any insurance issue that clients bring to their door, whether it be questions of insurance and reinsurance coverage or matters relating to policy construction. One solicitor who frequently instructs members of the chambers says: "The quality of advice is top-notch. These are excellent insurance lawyers with a wealth of experience and insight. They are far more down to earth, unstuffy and charismatic than many of their peers at other chambers."

Client service: "Alex Taylor and the rest of the clerks are extremely efficient and very responsive."

SILKS

Stephen Moriarty QC Heads chambers and specialises in advising on professional indemnity insurance for independent financial advisers as well as large coverage issues. **Strengths:** "He is exceptionally bright. He has a good reputation in the Commercial Court and with senior arbitrators, born out of the fact that he only ever makes credible arguments and good points. When he speaks, people pay attention."

Anthony Boswood QC A long-serving, leading light within the Insurance Bar. He now focuses on acting as an arbitrator on big-ticket insurance and reinsurance arbitrations. **Strengths:** "He's a reliable, heavyweight commercial barrister who is one of the best advocates and good fun to work with."

Michael Crane QC Handles headline insurance work that often focuses on the pharmaceutical or aviation industries. An instructing solicitor described him as "extremely user-friendly, down to earth, available and approachable." **Strengths:** "He appeals equally to solicitors and clients due to his knack of delivering extremely insightful advice on complex issues in a way that is easy to understand." **Recent work:** Acted for the reinsurer of aviation insurers of airline and security companies, dealing with arbitration claims and coverage issues arising from the 9/11 attacks on the World Trade Center.

David Railton QC Adept at litigating insurance and reinsurance cases across a wide spectrum of areas, ranging from professional indemnity to complex coverage matters. He is particularly skilled at resolving cases with multi-jurisdictional aspects. **Strengths:** "He has a beautifully poised, measured style and real strategic strength." **Recent work:** Acted for reinsurers following a claim from an insurance company related to shipbuilding reinsurance policies.

Bankim Thanki QC Although widely known for his work in the banking area, he also has a flourishing insurance practice, and has handled a number of major claims arising out of the financial crisis. **Strengths:** "He is very efficient and has a good manner with insurance clients. Extremely intelligent; he is a go-to barrister." **Recent work:** Advised insurers who subscribed to UBS's liability policy in reference to the collapse of Parmalat.

Timothy Howe QC Possesses a varied commercial practice that is particularly strong in the banking and financial services spheres. As such, he is regularly instructed by financial service clients to litigate large insurance claims. **Strengths:** "He stood out as someone who really thought about his case and was the most difficult for me to battle against as he really marshalled his arguments impressively." **Recent work:** Acted for Morgan Stanley in the Commercial Court against insurers Mitsui Sumitomo. The claim related to a commercial credit risk policy covering funding shortfalls following a failed US real estate development.

Raymond Cox QC (see p.580) An "extremely bright" lawyer who is admired for his solid insurance practice and all-round commercial law experience. **Strengths:** "Very knowledgeable on insurance coverage matters, he provides well-reasoned and thoughtful advice. He is delightful to work with."

Andrew Mitchell QC (see p.673) A strong commercial practitioner who, although quiet on the insurance front in the past year, has the experience to handle matters in this sector with aplomb. **Strengths:** "He brings great weight to the table, as he has gravitas, is respected before the tribunals, and is very good on his feet."

Patrick Goodall QC A barrister who took silk this year after a very fine career as a junior. He received universal praise for the strength of his insurance practice from those who had led him on cases. **Strengths:** "He knows what the instructing solicitor wants and is very succinct in his advice." **Recent work:** Acted in a USD150 million Commercial Court reinsurance claim relating to guarantees issued to Korean shipbuilders.

JUNIORS

James Cutress Has a mature and well-regarded insurance and reinsurance practice. One client praised him, saying: "He delivers work of a very high standard and is happy to get stuck into the nitty gritty." **Strengths:** "He's very approachable, hugely intelligent and very good at offering solutions and seeing around problems." **Recent work:** Instructed in a USD200 million claim relating to a fidelity insurance policy. The case arose out of a massive fraud in the Middle East.

Band 3

Devereux

See profile on p.785

THE SET

The set represents clients at the very highest levels in insurance work, and handles cases right up to the Supreme Court. A number of members of the set also edit key insurance law texts, displaying their position at the cutting edge of legal thought in the area. Commentators are impressed by the strength of the silks and by the quality of the work that they take on.

SILKS

Colin Edelman QC Universally seen as the leading silk for insurance and reinsurance matters, he has appeared in a whole host of leading cases, and has also handled a number of arbitrations and mediations. He takes on the very largest and most high-profile matters that come before the English courts. **Strengths:** "Incredibly sharp and someone with an excellent bedside manner." "At the top of his game; he is one of the very best." **Recent work:** Succeeded in the Supreme Court in Teal v W R Berkley.

Colin Wynter QC A proficient advocate with a track record of winning difficult insurance cases for both insurers and the insured. Sources praise his "knowledge and good judgement." **Strengths:** "He is very approachable and very bright, and has a work ethic that's second to none. He is always going the extra mile for clients." **Recent work:** Brought a test case to establish the extent of an insured's freedom of choice of lawyer under contracts of legal expenses insurance. The case was heard successfully in front of the Court of Appeal.

JUNIORS

Ben Lynch An impressive and versatile junior with a strong insurance and reinsurance focus. As well as maintaining his frontline practice, he is also editor of 'MacGillivray on Insurance Law'. **Strengths:** "He's a very bright guy, very nice and approachable, and has a huge following." **Recent work:** Instructed on a claim by the world's leading manufacturer of a chemical component found in all rubber tyres. The claim related to cover from a policy covering legal action.

Alison Padfield (see p.688) A truly outstanding junior who has deep insurance knowledge and is frequently led by some of the top silks at the Bar. She is equally at home in the courtroom or in arbitration. **Strengths:** "She writes the textbook, is in a lot of the cases and knows everything there is to know about insurance." **Recent work:** Acted for Adana in a multimillion-pound coverage dispute in the Commercial Court against Aspen Insurance following the collapse of a crane in Liverpool.

Andrew Burns (see p.561) Solid litigator who is building a strong practice following his high-profile appearance in the Supreme Court in the much-publicised Employers' Liability Policy Trigger litigation. He has recently been instructed on reinsurance aggregation, insurance fraud and brokers' D&O claims. **Strengths:** "He's down to earth and personable, gets on with people and is unfazed by difficult issues." **Recent work:** Acted for the insured against Aviva in handling a property insurance claim that led to a multimillion-pound dispute centred on whether the reinsurers were liable.

Richard Harrison (see p.621) Maintains a highly focused insurance and reinsurance practice, and is adept at handling the more technical cases. His work is increasingly international in scope, and he receives instructions directly from Hong Kong, Bermuda and the Cayman Islands, among a number of countries and territories. **Strengths:** "He's an exceptionally charming individual. He backs that up with also having a really impressive grasp of the issues and the ability to think laterally about the problems one encounters." **Recent work:** Represents an insured professional trustee who is facing a claim in excess of £100 million brought by a number of beneficiaries of the Jack Walker Trust who allege mismanagement of the trust's assets.

20 Essex Street

See profile on p.794

THE SET

Although well versed in a range of insurance matters, the set has a particularly strong reputation for marine work. Clients praise its members' user-friendly manner, intellectual capacity and focus on their cases. They are equally adept at serving insurer, reinsurer and claimant clients, and handle a raft of cases that are international in scope.

Client service: "Neil Palmer, Brian Lee and the clerking team have been responsive on administrative matters and often reach out unbidden to the instructing solicitor."

SILKS

Christopher Hancock QC A seasoned operator at the Insurance Bar who tackles the largest and most challenging international work. He is a top commercial litigator who is also noted for his vibrant arbitration practice. **Strengths:** "He's excellent for Bermuda Form work." **Recent work:** Successfully acted for The London Steam-Ship Owners' Mutual Insurance Association against the French and Spanish states in a multibillion-dollar oil pollution case.

Philip Edey QC Has a strong practice that centres on advising insurers and reinsurer clients in high-value arbitrations. He is an "extremely polished performer." **Strengths:** "He is a very good commercial advocate with very strong advocacy skills who is well liked by clients." **Recent work:** Acted for the insured following the hijacking of the 'Chemstar Venus' by Somali pirates and the resulting insurance claim for loss of hire.

Iain Milligan QC Venerable commercial silk who is often involved in key insurance and reinsurance matters. A solicitor who regularly instructs him says: "He is very senior and hugely talented. His advocacy is succinct and very precise." **Strengths:** "He is ferociously hard-working and a very good advocate with a great nose for an insurance dispute."

JUNIORS

Charlotte Tan Joins the rankings this year given the strength of her flourishing commercial practice. Within the insurance sphere she has been instructed on sizeable cases, many of which have an international flavour. **Strengths:** "She is phenomenally intelligent and hard-working, and has a maturity and knowledge beyond her call." **Recent work:** Acted for insurance brokers in the High Court on a case relating to claims for USD30 million of cargo damage and theft.

4 New Square

See profile on p.835

THE SET

Well known for its strength as a professional indemnity set, the team is leveraging its expertise in this area into high-profile insurance work. The set is known for handling all manner of insurance matters but proves particularly strong in the property damage, industrial disease and construction spheres. Clients praise its modern approach and the depth of its insurer client base.

Client service: "The clerks led by Lizzy Stewart are a lovely bunch, who do a good job and make sure their barristers are keenly priced."

SILKS

Graham Eklund QC A much-admired insurance and property damage silk who enjoys the full confidence of the market. One solicitor endorsed him as "a go-to counsel for policy wordings." **Strengths:** "He is very accessible and is really seen as someone who fights for the insurer and really looks after their interests." **Recent work:** Instructed on a claim relating to a fire at a hotel which caused £10 million of damage.

Mark Cannon QC A multi-talented silk who has a flourishing insurance and professional indemnity practice. He is "a very hard-working and serious lawyer." **Strengths:** "He is very learned and knowledgeable on insurance matters, and displays a very impressive intellect." **Recent work:** Acted on coverage issues related to a £90 million claim against Collyer Bristow. He advised two insurers who are on the second, third and fourth layers of coverage, representing them in mediations and advising them on partial settlements.

Ben Elkington QC Splits his practice equally between acting for insurers and the insured. He is very well regarded within the market and is viewed as a rising star within the Bar. **Strengths:** "He's very good with clients and has great strategic insight." **Recent work:** Advised a Lloyd's syndicate in relation to a claim under a product recall policy. The USD10 million claim concerned meat contamination at Canada's largest burger manufacturer, which resulted in a major product recall.

Justin Fenwick QC Handles complex international insurance claims and coverage matters, and ran the Bar Mutual Indemnity Fund between 1999 and 2013. **Strengths:** "A tremendous advocate," who is "brought in for the highest level disputes." **Recent work:** Engaged on a coverage issue against allegedly negligent solicitors.

Roger Stewart QC Well known for his broad practice covering professional negligence, construction and insurance work. He is acknowledged by peers for being "very user-friendly," and for having "a very good instinct for what judges want." **Strengths:** "He is ridiculously efficient, quick and bright." **Recent work:** Represented appellant insurers in a case involving coverage for employers' liability insurance for mesothelioma.

Jonathan Hough QC (see p.631) Has a highly focused insurance practice that one solicitor described as being "consistently outstanding." Interviewees highlighted the excellence of his advice, and his responsiveness in the face of a heavy caseload. **Strengths:** "He is bright and solution-oriented. He has an ability to present arguments in a clear and concise way, both on paper and on his feet, and is a very effective advocate." **Recent work:** Acting for RSA in test cases concerning subrogated motor claims that had far-reaching effects across the motor insurance market.

Ben Hubble QC Head of chambers and a rising star of the Insurance Bar. He has been particularly active on the policyholder side of disputes over the last year, often approaching matters from a professional indemnity point of view. **Strengths:** "It is easy for a QC to be intimidating or patronising but he is very approachable and you trust his advice on complex matters." **Recent work:** Acted for Homeserve, seeking an indemnity from RSA of £13 million in respect of a policy mis-selling claim initiated by an FSA-enforced remediation package.

Leigh-Ann Mulcahy QC Quality young silk with a practice that spans the divide between insurance, professional negligence and public law. She is experienced before all levels of the judicial system within England, and has appeared in the Supreme Court. **Strengths:** "She's very straightforward and tells the tale as it should be told." **Recent work:** Instructed by Zurich in a case concerning the scope of asbestos liabilities that has been sent to the Supreme Court.

Anneliese Day QC A skilled advocate and a comparatively recent silk, who has a practice with insurance at its heart. Instructing solicitors and insurer clients say she is "very bright and charming." **Strengths:** "She is brilliant, approachable and down to earth, and she really helps when you are around a table working towards a solution. Her written work is also very strong." **Recent work:** Acted on behalf of Zurich in relation to an arbitration claim brought under a jewellers' block policy.

3 Verulam Buildings

See profile on p.875

THE SET

The set enjoys a quality reputation for insurance work, and has a team that offers a nice balance of experienced QCs and highly talented juniors. It is especially adept at litigating insurance and reinsurance brokers' negligence claims, and in dealing with coverage issues.

Client service: "Paul Cooklin and the team are excellent, easy to deal with, always transparent about availability, and fair and reasonable on fees."

SILKS

Christopher Symons QC A hugely experienced insurance and reinsurance specialist who is very highly regarded within the market. He increasingly focuses on arbitration and mediation work, but also maintains an active courtroom practice. **Strengths:** "He is authoritative and brings a lot of gravitas to the leading counsel role." **Recent work:** Acted for a building society in a dispute with its insurers over the right to an indemnity in relation to mortgage fraud.

Tom Weitzman QC A very well-regarded insurance and reinsurance silk who has decades of experience. He is particularly adept at dealing with D&O and professional indemnity policy claims for both policyholders and insurers. **Strengths:** "Offers first-class advice on a number of complex issues of insurance law. He's very responsive and quickly gains the confidence of clients." **Recent work:** Advised insurers in respect of a claim under a D&O policy following claims made against directors of a major bank arising out of the sale of mortgage-backed securities by Fannie Mae and Freddie Mac.

Rory Phillips QC Has a very mixed practice that sees him handling high-profile insurance work alongside prominent public law cases. One peer described him as "a very smooth and competent operator." **Strengths:** "He is a first choice for insurance-related issues, whether they involve brokers or pure insurance. He is extremely good on the technical aspects of cases." **Recent work:** Worked on a coverage and brokers dispute arising out of a large fire at a well-known fish and chip restaurant in London.

JUNIORS

Peter Ratcliffe A leading junior at the Insurance Bar who receives universal acclaim from his peers. One solicitor described him as "diligent, bright and good to have on your side." **Strengths:** "A first-rate advocate who is very client-focused and knows reinsurance inside and out." **Recent work:** Defended a £120 million claim for Aon arising out of an oil refinery fire in Lithuania. The dispute centred on the placement and the operation of the refinery's property damage and business interruption insurance.

Nicholas Craig A high-flying junior who has particular expertise in assisting insurer and reinsurer clients facing challenging jurisdictional disputes. He is also noted for his experience in insurance arbitrations. **Strengths:** "Responsive and good to work with." "He is always proactively involved in matters at every stage of the case." **Recent work:** Instructed by reinsurers on a Section 69 appeal by retrocessionaires against a decision by arbitrators in which they found that losses sustained from the 9/11 attacks on the World Trade Center were caused by two separate occurrences rather than one.

Adam Kramer (see p.648) Balances academic rigour with courtroom nous. When focusing on insurance work he has been particularly active in the broker space. **Recent work:** Acted for claimants in a USD109 million power station dispute in the TCC. The matter related to a major warranty claim arising out of a share purchase agreement by which the Teesside-based power station was acquired.

Band 4

Crown Office Chambers

See profile on p.782

THE SET

Crown Office Chambers enjoys a fine reputation in non-marine insurance work and has a large number of both QCs and juniors who specialise in this work. The team is frequently instructed on substantial arbitrations and court proceedings concerning coverage disputes, fraud claims and policy construction. A client says: "They have some exceptionally big insurance coverage lawyers who really fight your corner in court."

Client service: "Crown Office Chambers' clerks are really helpful – they always find a way around a problem. Led by Andy Flanagan, they are sensible and knowledgeable, and really know their barristers' practices inside and out."

SILKS

Andrew Bartlett QC Has decades of expertise in highly technical insurance work and has built up a flourishing arbitration practice. **Strengths:** "An exceptionally bright and talented silk who is in very high demand. He is one of the best in the business for this sort of work."

Andrew Rigney QC A solid barrister with an eye for detail when handling very complicated cases. His background in construction and engineering disputes makes him particularly able to handle insurance matters that feature in these areas. **Strengths:** "Bright and personable, he strikes the right balance in his advice between the legal and commercial aspects of the case." **Recent work:** Instructed by Ted Baker's insurers on a £2 million claim concerning surreptitious thefts of stock by an employee.

Ben Quiney QC A rising star within the Insurance Bar who is accustomed to working on big-ticket international work. Those that engage him applaud the fact that "he works in an instructing solicitor's team in a highly effective manner." **Strengths:** "Good on his feet, he is incisive and always part of the team." **Recent work:** Acted in a multimillion-pound international arbitration. The case concerned business interruption and coverage issues arising from the collapse of a bridge in Russia that supplied one of the largest aluminium plants in the world.

Michael Harvey QC Veteran of the insurance world who takes on sophisticated and high-value work both domestically and overseas. Sources praise his methodical and meticulous working style. **Strengths:** "He is extremely user-friendly, reassuringly methodical and thorough. He gives very clear written and oral advice, and is extremely good on his feet." **Recent work:** Led on a multimillion-pound professional indemnity insurance claim relating to surveying works that were undertaken as part of the modernisation of the West Coast Mainline.

Roger ter Haar QC Frequently instructed on insurance matters with a professional negligence aspect, particularly those involving brokers and underwriters. His services as an arbitrator also remain in very high demand. **Strengths:** "Very intelligent." "He's a delight to be against and a very worthy opponent."

JUNIORS

James Medd Possesses a broad practice that encompasses significant insurance coverage work. **Strengths:** "You can have confidence in his advice and he is someone who looks at everything very thoroughly." **Recent work:** Acted in a dispute between Ascot and Embar Logistics. Ascot wrote fleet policies which Embar is alleged to have used to facilitate a business that uses self-employed couriers, something that was never disclosed to Ascot. Ascot sought recovery for any outlay from Embar.

Daniel Shapiro Much-admired senior junior whose practice sees him litigating for and advising leading insurers and brokerages. He frequently advises clients on foreign as well as English law. **Strengths:** "He's very bright and produces excellent opinions." **Recent work:** Acted for Aon in proceedings in the Mumbai High Court relating to a reinsurance policy for terrorism risk.

Suzanne Chalmers (see p.568) Has a strong insurance focus to her practice, and is especially adroit at cases involving aspects of professional negligence. **Strengths:** "She is no-nonsense and easy to deal with. She tells you what she thinks and gives good practical advice." **Recent work:** Instructed by insurers of a subcontractor in relation to multiparty proceedings in the TCC. The case has been brought against developers, subcontractors and designers of a luxury Knightsbridge apartment building that suffered flooding due to the failure of pressure control valves.

4 Pump Court

See profile on p.849

THE SET

A very strong set with a significant amount of insurance and reinsurance coverage work. Its members use their technical know-how across the construction, shipping, energy and other sectors to give themselves a crucial advantage in insurance cases. The team is actively promoting itself in the Middle East and Asia, and is increasingly assisting clients from those regions with London-based insurance issues.

SILKS

Christopher Moger QC A distinguished barrister who is often called upon by high-profile insurer clients to act in professional indemnity cover cases. Due to his decades of insurance law experience he is frequently asked to act as an arbitrator in international disputes. **Strengths:** "He is very smooth and great before a judge." **Recent work:** Advised the professional indemnity insurers of civil and structural engineers about coverage and aggregation issues arising from claims made in relation to commercial property developments in Guernsey.

Andrew Neish QC Has a highly international practice and operates at the very top end of the market. He also regularly handles high-value brokers' negligence cases. **Strengths:** "He is a terrier when he gets hold of a case. He never lets it go and works extremely hard." **Recent work:** Acted on a USD150 million claim by a Korean insurer of Advance Payment Guarantee liabilities in connection with shipbuilding contracts against a Kazakhstani reinsurer.

Aidan Christie QC Familiar with every aspect of insurance and reinsurance litigation, both within the UK and internationally. One client says of him: "He really gets to the issues very quickly and pulls out all the points, which he then makes very clearly." **Strengths:** "A very experienced insurance and reinsurance silk who is very client-friendly and who always takes a commercial approach." **Recent work:** Acted for the claimant in a non-declaration of liability case against Juridica concerning D&O and professional indemnity policies. The case involves a jurisdictional dispute between England and New York.

Nigel Tozzi QC Has a very broad commercial practice and receives a good number of insurance instructions. He is regularly involved in arbitrations and mediations within the field, but also regularly tackles more traditional contentious coverage issues. **Strengths:** "He is the most logical, organised and easy-to-deal-with barrister. He makes so much sense and really rolls his sleeves up." **Recent work:** Instructed in a case concerning material non-disclosure and coverage issues after sub-consultants had attempted to impose a cap on liability in respect of work they had carried out themselves.

Sean O'Sullivan QC Leverages his practice in energy and shipping into the insurance sector. He is highly active in broker's negligence and coverage cases. **Strengths:** "A first-rate advocate who's very client-focused and knows reinsurance backwards." **Recent work:** Acted on a USD10 million negligence claim against a London-based placing broker concerning reinsurance of shipbuilding refund guarantees.

JUNIORS

James Purchas (see p.700) Very well regarded within the junior Bar for his ability to handle highly sensitive and complex insurance and reinsurance matters. He is also active in assisting both financial institutions and their insurers in claims relating to professional indemnity work. **Strengths:** "A go-to senior junior for insurance and reinsurance disputes, who is straightforward, diligent and measured." **Recent work:** Assisted on a dispute between a PPI seller and its underlying insurers as to profit commission.

2TG – 2 Temple Gardens

See profile on p.873

THE SET

This 14-strong team, consisting of four silks and ten juniors, handles a wide range of insurance cases, marine insurance work aside. It undertakes matters relating to property damage, professional indemnity and employer's liability, amongst others, and has appeared in some interesting cases lately, including the Winterbourne Hospital Group litigation which followed on from an undercover investigation by the BBC. Sources praise 2TG as a modern, client-focused and approachable set. "The barristers know what they are talking about, are good on paper and on their feet. They are also nice individuals to work with, which is crucial as these cases can be very intense."

Client service: "The clerking is very efficient and the whole team, led by Lee Tyler, is great. The clerks are very approachable, and modern and commercial in their outlook, which is always a nice surprise."

SILKS

Neil Moody QC Frequently instructed in novel insurance and reinsurance matters, and strong on property-related insurance matters. He is "an excellent advocate who is great with clients and a leader in terms of knowledge in this practice area." **Strengths:** "He is tremendous as he is very clever and capable, and great on his feet." **Recent work:** Acted in Brumder v Aviva, an interesting case where the claimant was sole director and shareholder of the defendant company but nevertheless sought to claim on the defendant's insurance policy in respect of his own injury at work.

Howard Palmer QC Seasoned practitioner within the TCC who deals with substantial insurance matters alongside a flourishing professional negligence and construction practice. He is also noted for the property damage cases he takes on. **Strengths:** "He is highly approachable and a pleasure to deal with. He is very thorough and this is reflected in his advice." **Recent work:** Acted before the Supreme Court in a case examining the terms upon which the MIB is liable to pay compensation to victims of uninsured motor accidents abroad.

Charles Dougherty QC Only took silk in 2013 but is already establishing himself in the market and has led on several large cases for insurers. Sources laud him as being "clever and precise." **Strengths:** "He's intelligent, calm and measured, and thinks about the problem and the law before giving you sensible advice." **Recent work:** Acted for Hiscox in a claim brought by an alleged victim of extortion and kidnapping in Colombia under a kidnap and ransom policy.

Robert Moxon Browne QC A venerated advocate who takes on a large number of insurance cases. He is particularly expert in cases involving life insurance, and his judgement is described as being "spot on." **Strengths:** "He's a great advocate and a real courtroom presence. He is a leader in terms of cases where you need people to roll their sleeves up and get the work done." **Recent work:** Acted in a case that sought to define the scope of professional negligence insurance cover in relation to the embezzlement of trust funds.

Andrew Miller QC Possesses a broad commercial practice that places a heavy emphasis on insurance, construction and professional liability work. **Strengths:** "He's very user-friendly, effective and good to work with." **Recent work:** Represented the successful defendant in a subrogated claim brought by the insured in respect of flooding at a restaurant in Teddington.

JUNIORS

Alison Green (see p.615) Her highly focused insurance and reinsurance practice covers the full range of matters in the sector. She is frequently instructed in ADR cases and is an expert at dealing with matters that involve both property damage and insurance issues. **Strengths:** "She is good at analysis and gives clear advice." **Recent work:** Advised the General Osteopathic Council on the wording of insurance policies that comply with statutory rules requiring osteopaths to have professional indemnity insurance.

Sonia Nolten Enjoys a strong reputation within the insurance Bar and has experience in front of courts all the way up to the Supreme Court. She is adept at litigating high-profile contentious claims and property damage cases. **Strengths:** "She is very good technically, knows her subject very well and is an excellent advocate who pays attention to the details." **Recent work:** Instructed on three life and health cases which Friends Life is contesting in the courts. The cases centre on whether the people who took out the policies are unable to work because of illness and are therefore entitled to payment of benefit.

Other Ranked Lawyers

Andrew Green QC (Blackstone Chambers) Handles insurance and reinsurance work as part of a wider commercial practice. He has experience in dealing with large international arbitrations for blue-chip clients. **Strengths:** "An excellent and well-organised advocate who has a great capacity for work and a pleasant manner."

Andrew Hunter QC (Blackstone Chambers) Esteemed for the strength of his advocacy and for the quality of his insurance practice. One solicitor described him as being "outstanding and easy to deal with." **Strengths:** "He has a razor-sharp intellect, unflappable temperament and an excellent courtroom manner. He is great to work with and is clearly a rising star." **Recent work:** Leading counsel for the Tennessee Valley Authority in three multimillion-dollar arbitrations, seeking USD250 million following a major environmental disaster at a US power plant.

Craig Orr QC (see p.686) (One Essex Court) Regularly instructed on a broad range of insurance work. Over the last year he has been particularly active in claims involving solicitor negligence. **Recent work:** Acted for Hanover in a series of insurance claims arising out of mortgage frauds involving a number of firms of solicitors.

Paul Reed QC (Hardwicke) Especially strong within the construction insurance field, and has particular expertise in the Contractors' All Risk (CAR) arena. His knowledge of the technical side of the law enables him to get the very best out of expert witnesses in the courtroom. **Strengths:** "He's proactive, goes the extra mile, and is someone you would want with you in the trenches." "A tenacious advocate." **Recent work:** Successfully defended AXA against a claim brought by the Gleeson Group under a CAR policy following damage to a development in Watford.

Nigel Jones QC (Hardwicke) Has a broad commercial practice and represents some of the largest Lloyd's syndicates and insurers in the market. He is particularly strong at advising insurers facing product liability issues. **Strengths:** "Very experienced and very able," he is "a very good advocate." **Recent work:** Advised QBE in relation to multiple claims arising out of failed financial services investment products that minimised high net worth individuals' tax burdens but are now viewed as aggressive tax avoidance.

David Pliener (Hardwicke) Focuses his insurance practice on assisting clients with CAR, property damage and professional indemnity issues. He also acts on more conventional insurance cases, some of which have an international dimension. **Recent work:** Instructed on a dispute arising out of a solicitors' professional indemnity policy. He represented the solicitors seeking coverage under the policy.

Geraint Webb QC (Henderson Chambers) Frequently instructed by insurers and large claimants, particularly in relation to property or product liability-related claims. He is equally at home litigating or handling ADR. **Strengths:** "He is very good on the background, the detail of the case and the arguments. He's very good at trial." **Recent work:** Instructed by the reinsured claimant AstraZeneca in respect of a major reinsurance coverage dispute. The case concerned fundamental points of construction of Bermuda Form insurance policies, and arose from US-based pharmaceutical class action settlements.

Stephen Cogley QC (Quadrant Chambers) A well-rounded commercial silk. On the insurance side he frequently represents the insured in high-profile P&I and property damage work. **Strengths:** "An excellent advocate who is sharp on the facts, gets to the point and is very commercial." **Recent work:** Instructed on a £2 million claim by Paris Casino against its brokers arising out of failure to effect full cover for their business.

Andrew Guy Blackwood QC (Quadrant Chambers) Offers clients a real depth of knowledge in the insurance arena, and is praised for the practical nature of his advice. He commonly deals in large international coverage cases and complex reinsurance disputes. **Strengths:** "He has a good reputation and is known for his expertise on Lloyd's syndicates." **Recent work:** Acted on the first reinsurance dispute heard by the Court of the Dubai International Financial Centre. The case concerned the huge amount of property damage done to Egyptian cities prior to the resignation of President Hosni Mubarak.

David Lord QC (3 Stone Buildings) Enjoys a strong standing in the market as a solid commercial silk. His work is often international in scope, as illustrated by the fact that he is called to the New York State Bar. **Strengths:** "He's very persuasive in his manner and understands what judges want."

Intellectual Property

Contents:

LONDON

Intellectual Property London

Leading Sets

Band 1	Band 2
Three New Square *	One Essex Court *
8 New Square *	Hogarth Chambers *
11 South Square *	

Leading Silks

Star individuals	**Howe** Martin *8 New Square* *
Alexander Daniel *8 New Square* *	**Silverleaf** Michael *11 South Square*
Carr Henry *11 South Square*	**Speck** Adrian *8 New Square* *
Hobbs Geoffrey *One Essex Court* [A]	**Turner** Justin *Three New Square* *
Band 1	**Wilson** Alastair *Hogarth Chambers*
Bloch Michael *Blackstone Chambers (ORL)* ◊	**Band 3**
Burkill Guy *Three New Square* *	**Cullen** Edmund *Maitland Chambers (ORL)* ◊ *
Meade Richard *8 New Square* *	**Himsworth** Emma *One Essex Court*
Mellor James *8 New Square* *	**Mill** Ian *Blackstone Chambers (ORL)* ◊
Purvis Iain *11 South Square*	**Miller** Richard *Three New Square* *
Tappin Michael *8 New Square* *	**Platts-Mills** Mark *8 New Square* [A] *
Vanhegan Mark *11 South Square*	**New Silks**
Waugh Andrew *Three New Square* *	**Bacon** Kelyn *Brick Court Chambers (ORL)* ◊
Wyand Roger *Hogarth Chambers*	**Lykiardopoulos** Andrew *8 New Square* *
Band 2	**May** Charlotte *8 New Square* *
Acland Piers *11 South Square*	**Mitcheson** Thomas *Three New Square* *
Baldwin John *8 New Square* *	**Weisselberg** Tom *Blackstone Chambers (ORL)* ◊
Edenborough Michael *Serle Court (ORL)* ◊ *	

Leading Juniors

Star individuals	**Delaney** Joe *Three New Square*
Hinchliffe Thomas *Three New Square* *	**Harbottle** Gwilym *Hogarth Chambers* [A]
Band 1	**McFarland** Denise *Three New Square*
Abrahams James *8 New Square* [A] *	**Norris** Andrew *Hogarth Chambers*
Cuddigan Hugo *11 South Square*	**Pickard** Kathryn *11 South Square*
Hicks Michael *Hogarth Chambers*	**Pritchard** Geoffrey *Three New Square*
Hollingworth Guy *One Essex Court*	**Reed** Jeremy *Hogarth Chambers* [A]
Malynicz Simon *Three New Square* *	**St Quintin** Thomas *Hogarth Chambers*
Moody-Stuart Thomas *8 New Square* *	**St Ville** James *8 New Square* *
Nicholson Brian *11 South Square*	**Band 4**
Roberts Philip *One Essex Court* [A]	**Bowhill** Jessie *8 New Square* *
Band 2	**Chapple** Malcolm *New Square Chambers (ORL)* ◊ *
Brandreth Benet *11 South Square*	**Engelman** Mark *Hardwicke (ORL)* ◊ [A] *
Campbell Douglas *Three New Square* *	**Heal** Madeleine *New Square Chambers (ORL)* ◊ [A] *
Chacksfield Mark *8 New Square* *	**Hill** Jonathan *8 New Square* [A] *
Copeland Miles *Three New Square* *	**Jamal** Isabel *8 New Square* *
Edwards-Stuart Anna *11 South Square*	**Lawrence** Heather *11 South Square*
Lane Lindsay *8 New Square* [A] *	**Onslow** Robert *8 New Square* [A] *
Michaels Amanda *Hogarth Chambers*	**Reid** Jacqueline *11 South Square*
Saunders Nicholas *Brick Court Chambers (ORL)* ◊	**Up-and-coming individuals**
Tritton Guy *Hogarth Chambers* [A]	**Aikens** Chris *11 South Square*
Ward Henry *8 New Square* *	**Baran** Stuart *Three New Square* *
Whyte James *8 New Square* *	**Hall** Chris *11 South Square*
Band 3	**Heald** Jeremy *Three New Square*
Alkin Tom *11 South Square*	**Longstaff** Benjamin *Hogarth Chambers*
Berkeley Iona *8 New Square* *	**Moss** Jonathan *Hogarth Chambers*
Davis Richard *Hogarth Chambers*	

** Indicates set / individual with profile.*
◊ (ORL) = Other Ranked Lawyer.
[A] direct access (see p.11).

Band 1

Three New Square
See profile on p.834

THE SET

Three New Square continues to be regarded as one of the troika of great IP sets at the London Bar. It bristles with QCs and juniors at all levels of call who between them possess a staggering diversity and depth of scientific and jurisprudential knowledge and experience. With superb capabilities across all strands of IP law, the set is particularly well thought of for its members' records in complex patent litigation.

Client service: "The clerks take a user-friendly, modern approach" and offer support to "an approachable team of barristers who have great technical knowledge and experience."

SILKS

Guy Burkill QC (see p.561) One of the finest legal minds in the country with regard to the law on patents, who has played a prominent role in litigating the 'Smartphone Wars' of recent years. Many sources express admiration for his knowledge of computers and electrical engineering. **Strengths:** "Spectacular in front of the judge, he has absolute control over the courtroom." "He's very user-friendly and has a superb engineering brain that allows him to give practical advice." **Recent work:** Acted for Apple in an appeal of a case concerning four Apple patents alleged to have been infringed by smartphone manufacturer HTC.

Andrew Waugh QC (see p.747) Has a practice that spans the range of IP matters, although his chemistry background makes him an ideal choice for heavyweight chemical and life sciences patent litigation. He is also an expert in related areas of EU law. **Strengths:** "Very commercial and very tenacious, he's good on his feet and drills into the points." "An excellent QC for technically complex cases – he takes a very thorough approach." **Recent work:** Appeared in Generics/Mylan v Yeda Research and Development, an appeal which upheld the patent for Copaxone.

Justin Turner QC (see p.741) Has a superb academic background in life sciences, and is much sought after for his representations in pharmaceutical and biotech cases. He has also recently appeared in telecoms and confidential information disputes. **Strengths:** "A really tenacious advocate, who is effective in difficult cases." "A fantastic mix of strategic ability and a keen eye for detail."

Richard Miller QC (see p.672) Head of chambers, he is frequently instructed in complex and high-stakes matters by leading pharmaceutical and life sciences companies. He is also highly adept at telecoms patent infringement disputes. **Strengths:** "A good fighter, who is thorough and highly convincing." **Recent work:** Appeared in a patent infringement dispute between Nokia and IPcom.

Thomas Mitcheson QC (see p.674) One of the most admired and sought-after senior juniors, who was made silk in 2014. The majority of his work is related to life sciences and electronics patents but he also has a subs tantial trade marks practice. He has a specialism in Special Protection Certificate (SPC) cases in the life sciences sector. **Strengths:** "Razor-sharp and thoroughly charming." "He stands out for his dedicated and thorough approach and good advocacy skills." **Recent work:** Successfully represented Lilly in revoking Janssen's patent for use in treatments for Alzheimer's disease.

JUNIORS

Thomas Hinchliffe (see p.628) Seen as one of the top senior juniors for biotech, medical devices and pharmaceutical instructions, as well as telecommunications and semiconductor disputes. Sources consistently praise his diligence and collegiate approach. **Strengths:** "Excellent at both drafting and advocacy.

He's a first-choice senior junior for patent matters of any shade." **Recent work:** Acted for Hospira in a dispute with The Kennedy Institute of Rheumatology concerning a generic, or biosimilar, molecule used as a treatment for rheumatoid arthritis.

Simon Malynicz Without doubt one of the most accomplished barristers for trade mark disputes, and someone who has recently been instructed to act against silks. He is also one of the most experienced ECJ advocates with respect to trade mark and copyright cases. **Strengths:** "He's incredibly hard-working and has a vast knowledge of trade mark law." **Recent work:** Represented Nestlé in its successful appeal against Cadbury in a dispute over the registration of the colour purple as a trade mark.

Douglas Campbell (see p.564) Frequently appears as sole counsel in all manner of IP disputes. In the past year he has been instructed for patent, trade mark, breach of confidence and database right matters. **Strengths:** "Tenacious, extremely capable and excellent at fighting the client's position." **Recent work:** Represented Comic Enterprises against Twentieth Century Fox in a trade mark dispute regarding the latter's use of the name 'Glee' for the popular TV series.

Miles Copeland (see p.578) Fast establishing himself as one of the leading juniors for sophisticated patent trials. He is above all instructed for pharmaceutical, biotech and medical devices cases, and has a strong following for mandates concerning telecoms disputes. **Strengths:** "Hard-working, very bright, and very easy to work with. He really cares." **Recent work:** Acted for Novartis in its ongoing dispute with Hospira over a patented zoledronic acid product used to treat osteoporosis.

Joe Delaney He impresses peers and instructing solicitors with his easy-going manner and analytical powers. His practice is predominantly patent-focused, although he has also recently appeared in trade mark cases. **Strengths:** "Smart, efficient, capable and user-friendly." **Recent work:** Instructed by Apple in an appeal against HTC concerning Apple's 'slide to unlock' feature and elements of the Android operating system as found on HTC devices.

Denise McFarland A senior junior with great experience of handling IP instructions. She focuses mainly on trade mark, passing-off, design, data and confidential information matters. Also commended for her skills as a mediator. **Strengths:** "She's incredibly rigorous and efficient, as well as bright and personable." **Recent work:** Instructed in a series of disputes concerning designs for garments sold by fashion design house and retailer Superdry.

Geoffrey Pritchard Receives praise for his representations in matters across the spectrum of IP rights, from highly technical patent problems to business-critical trade mark disputes. He more often than not appears without a leader. **Strengths:** "Very capable in court and with clients." **Recent work:** Appeared for Apimed in a patent infringement and validity appeal against Comvita regarding the use of honey in wound dressings.

Stuart Baran (see p.542) An up-and-coming junior whose appearances as sole junior in deeply complex matters belie his recent call. His scientific research background predisposes him to patent cases, but he has also appeared in major trade mark disputes. **Strengths:** "He's very bright and doing a lot of big technical cases, ones which would often go to someone of more senior call." **Recent work:** Appeared as sole junior counsel in Resolution Chemicals v Lundbeck, a patent infringement case concerning antidepressant drug Cipralex.

Jeremy Heald A junior of recent call who has impressed numerous sources with his thorough preparation and well-developed arguments following high-profile instructions in patent and trade mark cases. **Strengths:** "Very young but calm, thoughtful and considered." **Recent work:** Instructed by Apple in a High Court patent dispute with Samsung.

8 New Square

See profile on p.836

THE SET

With almost 40 members, 8 New Square is by some measure the IP set with the most firepower, and houses an impressive contingent of ten silks. The level of scientific and legal expertise on hand here is staggering, and instructing solicitors find themselves presented with an all but unrivalled choice with respect to all areas of IP law and levels of call. A number of sources remark on the quality of service in chambers, with one praising its "highly efficient and accommodating clerks."

Client service: "We always feel confident in their hands."

SILKS

Adrian Speck QC A go-to barrister for heavyweight and deeply complex IP matters concerning patents, trade marks, copyright and designs. He is commended for his intellectual rigour, commercial sense and being easy to work with. **Strengths:** "A deep thinker, who is excellent with clients and a good team player." "An excellent advocate, who is very responsive and highly intelligent." **Recent work:** Acted for IPCom in a highly significant telecoms patent dispute with HTC.

Andrew Lykiardopoulos QC (see p.658) Took silk in 2014 and is expected to thrive in the role after a distinguished career as a leading senior junior. Before the Bar he was a solicitor, and sources say he combines the best elements of the two roles perfectly. **Strengths:** "One of the best for patent litigation – he's always a pleasure to work with, he always does a good job and is popular with clients." "A really thoughtful, hard-working team player." **Recent work:** Instructed by Virgin Media in a multi-patent series of trials against Starsight concerning set-top boxes.

Daniel Alexander QC Has enjoyed a career in IP few silks can match, and has appeared in many of the most significant patent, trade mark and copyright actions of the past 20 years. He is celebrated for his advocacy before UK courts and the European Patent Office (EPO). **Strengths:** "One of the best minds in a discipline that attracts first-class minds." "He is very much at the top of the tree, and is highly respected by judges." **Recent work:** Instructed by Motorola in its dispute with Microsoft regarding a patent for e-mail protocols used in smartphones and tablets.

Charlotte May QC Appointed silk in 2014, having been regarded as one of the leading senior juniors for pharmaceutical and life sciences matters, not least with regard to SPCs. She is also instructed for matters across the spectrum of IP rights. **Strengths:** "Exceptionally capable, she's always charming but never gives an inch." "A doughty opponent." **Recent work:** Acted for the UK government with respect to a reference to the ECJ (Eli Lilly v Human Genome Sciences) intended to clarify the meaning of Article 3(a) of the EU SPC regulation.

Richard Meade QC Focuses mainly on patent cases, although he is also a published authority on trade mark law (as a contributor to 'Kerly's Law of Trade Marks and Trade Names'). He has recently appeared in high-profile matters concerning SPCs and mobile phone patents. **Strengths:** "Has a low-key style but shows exceptional judgement and is a very effective cross-examiner." "Very determined, he never gives up and can make an argument from a difficult position." **Recent work:** Appeared in Schütz v Werit, an appeal to the Supreme Court concerning the difference between repairing a patented product and inventing it anew.

James Mellor QC Recommended for telecoms patent cases and, above all, trade mark actions. Sources frequently remark on his capacity to combine intellectual acuity with deft courtroom performance. **Strengths:** "He's someone you want on board for a trade mark case – especially since you want to deprive the other side of the opportunity of getting him first." "A formidable presence who is perfect if you want a heavyweight silk." **Recent work:** Acted for Media 10 in its dispute with IPC Media over the use of the Ideal Home trade mark.

Michael Tappin QC (see p.734) Particularly sought after for life sciences patent cases. He has a background in science and is noted for his marriage of technical insight and persuasive advocacy. **Strengths:** "He offers a strong mix of technical brilliance and practical advice, and is equally outstanding on his feet and on paper." "A very clear and effective advocate, who is calm and thoughtful." **Recent work:** Acted for Genentech in defence of an appeal lodged by Regeneron and Bayer Pharma concerning a patent claiming the use of human vascular endothelial growth factor (hVEGF) antagonists for the treatment of non-cancerous angiogenesis.

Martin Howe QC A popular choice for solicitors looking for advice and advocacy on complex copyright matters. His knowledge of EU law problems as they affect IP matters is highly prized. **Strengths:** "An accessible and pleasant team member, who is especially strong on written submissions but also good on his feet." "A fine, persuasive advocate who is strong on technical detail." **Recent work:** Instructed by Doncaster Pharmaceuticals Group in its defence of a trade mark case brought by Speciality European Pharma concerning parallel imports of urology treatments.

John Baldwin QC (see p.542) Handles cases focusing on all IP rights, but is held in especially high regard for his representations in copyright cases. He is also strong on pharmaceutical patent disputes. **Strengths:** "A superb cross-examiner. He's a real bulldog in court when the fight is on." "He has an excellent nose for a case." **Recent work:** Instructed by Alfa Laval in an alleged breach of confidence and copyright action against Separator Spares concerning drawings for marine separator parts.

Mark Platts-Mills QC (see p.695) Head of chambers, he brings an impressive amount of experience to cases. He has handled cases regarding all major IP rights, from electronics patent disputes to database right actions. **Strengths:** "Highly versatile and a good street fighter."

JUNIORS

James Abrahams (see p.531) Has a comprehensive IP practice, and is one of the most popular senior juniors for a range of matters. He has recently appeared in high-profile consumer electronics and telecoms patent cases. **Strengths:** "He's astute and tactically excellent, and has great drafting skills." **Recent work:** Acted for YouView in a trade mark infringement action concerning set-top boxes.

Thomas Moody-Stuart A senior junior with a magisterial command of trade mark and patent law, who has expertise on copyright and parallel trade issues. Sources say he is easy to work with and connects well with clients. **Strengths:** "He's very bright and has an excellent hands-on style." **Recent work:** Represented 32Red in a damages inquiry further to a trade mark infringement dispute with WHG over the latter's use of the mark 32Vegas.

Mark Chacksfield (see p.567) A seasoned junior who is expert in all fields of IP law, and has a particularly strong reputation for his handling of patent cases, be they pharmaceutical, electronic or mechanical in terms of technological focus. **Strengths:** "Enormously bright and diligent, with a keen focus on client demands." **Recent work:** Acted for Regeneron in a patent infringement dispute with Bayer and Genentech concerning the use of hVEGF inhibitors in the treatment of a number of conditions.

Lindsay Lane A highly versatile junior counsel with a strong track record in cases involving trade marks, patents and copyright. A number of sources attest to her impressive work ethic. **Strengths:** "Clients are very impressed by her personable manner and commercial outlook." **Recent work:** Represented Force of India in a Court of Appeal trial against Malaysia Racing concerning alleged breach of confidence with respect to Formula One car designs.

Henry Ward (see p.746) Has a CV bristling with significant matters concerning designs, copyright and trade marks, but is above all expert in complex patent litigation. He is noted for his robust advocacy and clear advice. **Strengths:** "An intelligent, confident and polished junior." **Recent work:** Appeared in Virgin Atlantic v Zodiac before the Supreme Court, a case concerning the application of res judicata principles to patent matters.

James Whyte (see p.751) Has distinguished himself in IP cases of all stripes but is perhaps most at home in patent actions, given his impressive academic career in genetics prior to being called to the Bar. **Strengths:** "Technically and scientifically impressive, he is hard-working and bright." **Recent work:** Represented Novartis before the Court of Appeal in a successful bid to secure an interim injunction against Hospira pending the hearing of a patent validity appeal.

Iona Berkeley (see p.548) Expert across the spectrum of IP rights, and someone whose practice extends to contract disputes in the media and entertainment industry. She is a co-author of key texts on trade marks and copyright. **Strengths:** "She has solid expertise and is very responsive." **Recent work:** Appeared in a complex dispute concerning the ownership of IP rights to software used by IKOS, an asset management company.

Isabel Jamal (see p.637) A confident and popular junior whose standing belies her year of call (2008). She mainly focuses on biotech and pharmaceutical patent disputes, and also software copyright matters. She has had a number of recent mandates concerning SPCs. **Strengths:** "A forceful advocate on her client's behalf and effective with it." **Recent work:** Represented Actavis in a dispute with Sanofi concerning SPCs and the circumstances in which patentees may have multiple SPCs for combinations of products based on the same patent.

Jessie Bowhill (see p.554) Best known for her representations in high-profile media and entertainment copyright cases. She also has an extensive practice in trade marks, designs and patents. **Strengths:** "Very thorough, responsive and good with clients." **Recent work:** Acted for Media 10 in its dispute with IPC Media over the use of the Ideal Home trade mark, with respect to concurrent rights.

Robert Onslow (see p.686) Much sought after for his expertise in technical aspects of software, its development and how it is protected by copyright law. He also has a successful designs, patent and trade mark practice. **Strengths:** "He gets to the nub of the case, however technically challenging, very, very quickly. A pleasure to work with." **Recent work:** Acted before the Court of Appeal in SAS Institute Inc. v World Programming analysing an ECJ judgment that copyright does not necessarily protect programming languages or computer program functions.

James St Ville (see p.727) Has a wide-ranging IP practice which mainly takes in trade mark, copyright, database right and engineering patent matters. He is also often instructed for IP-related IT contract disputes. **Strengths:** "He leaves no stone unturned – he offers superb detailed preparation on every case and first-class drafting." **Recent work:** Instructed by Balltec against First Subsea in a trial alleging constructive trust over an international patent. The case concerned deep-sea oil installation equipment.

Jonathan Hill (see p.627) An IP law all-rounder, who is spoken of in glowing terms by instructing solicitors. He is often favoured for matters involving particularly abstruse and challenging points of law. **Strengths:** "An incredibly bright and determined advocate who knows this area of law backwards and who takes a very welcome commercial approach; he's a breath of fresh air."

11 South Square

See profile on p.862

THE SET

11 South Square continues to be regarded by instructing solicitors as being at the summit of excellence for IP advice and advocacy. Patent and design cases of exacting technical complexity are a specialism, and members frequently appear in many of the landmark trade mark and copyright matters of the day. The set features silks and juniors of a wide range of experience and knowledge, and the quality of the clerking is praised to the rafters, with special mention going to head clerk Ashley Carr.

Client service: "They do their very best to provide a first-class service at all times. Every one of the clerks goes out of their way to help you and will do whatever is required to assist across the board – this makes a real difference."

SILKS

Henry Carr QC A versatile silk with an admirable record in patent, copyright and trade mark cases. His ability to assimilate vast amounts of information and find the key points, as well as his gifts as an advocate, are remarked upon by various sources. **Strengths:** "He has remarkable powers of cross-examination and his trial preparation is more thorough than that of anyone I've ever seen." **Recent work:** Instructed by Boehringer in a challenge brought by generic drug manufacturer Actavis regarding the validity of the client's SPC covering Telmisartan, an angiotensin receptor blocker used to treat hypertension.

Iain Purvis QC Has a broad IP practice, and has acted in some of the most significant patent, trade mark and design trials of the past year. Sources remark on his good client manner and collegiate approach to matters. **Strengths:** "He has a calm, balanced approach and is extremely bright." "An outstanding strategist with an unparalleled eye for detail who can spot the weaknesses in the other side's case. A great trial advocate." **Recent work:** Acted for ASSIA in a patent infringement case regarding digital subscriber line (DSL) broadband technology.

Michael Silverleaf QC A well-respected and highly experienced silk with an impressive range of IP cases under his belt concerning patents, trade marks and designs. His energy and confidence as an advocate in adversarial situations were highlighted by interviewees. **Strengths:** "He's really good at immersing himself in a case, and especially good on technical details." "He takes the direct approach and cuts through a forest of argument to focus on the key issues." **Recent work:** Recently obtained favourable judgment for client Interflora in a hard and long-fought trade mark infringement dispute with Marks & Spencer concerning Google adwords. Appeal pending.

Mark Vanhegan QC Much sought after for his combination of profound technological understanding, legal insight and persuasive advocacy. He is more often than not instructed on patent and design cases, and has featured prominently in the so-called 'Smartphone Wars'. **Strengths:** "A top-drawer technical analyst, who provides clear, concise advice." "Knowledgeable, charming and very client-friendly." **Recent work:** Acting for Samsung against Apple in a patent dispute concerning channel encoders in mobile phones.

Piers Acland QC In the four years since taking silk, he has established himself as one of the most popular choices for solicitors in need of a commanding QC who can take on the most challenging pharmaceuticals and life sciences patent cases. **Strengths:** "Very bright, easy to work with and hard-working – he's one of the team. He assimilates information quickly and has excellent cross-examination skills." "He has market-leading technical expertise and is a first-class team leader. His performance over the last few years has been awesome." **Recent work:** Acted for Glenmark and Mylan in a revocation action against GlaxoSmithKline concerning a drug combination patent sold as antimalarial treatment Malarone.

JUNIORS

Hugo Cuddigan A senior junior respected by peers at the Bar and instructing solicitors for his measured approach in court, his "user-friendly" manner in conference and his command of the facts. He has appeared in a number of landmark trade mark, database right and patent actions over the past year. **Strengths:** "He's brilliant – he really burrows down to the core issue of the case and then puts across his point very well. Good both as an analytical lawyer and as an advocate." **Recent work:** Instructed in proceedings concerned with Rihanna's claim that Topshop infringed her rights by selling a T-shirt with her image on it.

Brian Nicholson A favourite junior for computer software and electronics patent cases, who has recently distinguished himself in matters concerning mobile telephones. He has also appeared in landmark design right and trade mark cases over the past year. **Strengths:** "Superb – very experienced, highly technical, intuitive and good fun to work with." **Recent work:** He has acted, at times as sole counsel, for HTC in its long-running suite of disputes with Nokia concerning mobile device patents.

Benet Brandreth Representative of a younger breed of barristers noted for their collegiate approach to solicitors and clients. He has recently been instructed in trade mark, design and mechanical patent cases. **Strengths:** "A very bright and determined advocate, who is very good on his feet, and excellent at persuading judges of his argument." **Recent work:** Acted for Nestec in a patent infringement suit against Dualit, concerning the supply of coffee capsules compatible with Nespresso coffee machines.

Anna Edwards-Stuart Attracts significant instructions concerning patents and trade marks, and is consistently praised for her thoughtfulness and capacity to work as a valued team player. **Strengths:** "Impresses with her diligence, dogged determination and sound judgement." **Recent work:** Acted for Cadbury in its High Court dispute with Nestlé regarding the validity of three-dimensional trade marks embodied by the latter's Rolo chocolates.

Tom Alkin Commended by a number of sources for his advocacy, analysis and strategic thinking. He has recently received mandates for life sciences patent cases as well as some high-profile trade mark work. **Strengths:** "Enthusiastic, extremely approachable and practical in driving clients through to sensible results. A barrister who fully understands the need for responsive client service." **Recent work:** Instructed by Convatec in a dispute with Smith & Nephew regarding wound dressing patents.

Kathryn Pickard Impresses a number of sources with her prowess at patent matters, although she is also often instructed on trade mark cases. She is noted for her diligence and her calm demeanour. **Strengths:** "Outstanding – she's very thoughtful, writes really well and is very nice to deal with." **Recent work:** Instructed by Boehringer in its patent dispute with Actavis concerning Telmisartan, an angiotensin receptor blocker used to treat high blood pressure.

Heather Lawrence is a senior junior much sought after for complex technical patent matters, although she is skilled at all manner of rights issues. Sources remark on her capacity for hard work, her intelligence and her rapport with clients. **Strengths:** "Excellent at applying the intricacies of patent law in a practical way to achieve a tactical advantage; very thorough, and calmly effective in cross-examination." **Recent work:** Acting for chemicals giant BASF in a number of disputes concerning its agricultural herbicides.

Jacqueline Reid Has a broad IP practice which takes in trade mark, copyright and design, as well as data protection and confidential information cases. She has strong, long-running relationships with clients concerned with fashion and consumer brands, but counts companies across a very wide range of industries as part of her client base. **Strengths:** "She has encyclopaedic design right and trade mark knowledge, is very responsive, is impressive on her feet and is great with clients." **Recent work:** Acted for Bijou Brigitte in its defence of a claim brought by Monsoon concerning unregistered design rights for jewellery.

Chris Aikens Has a comprehensive IP practice which in the past year has seen him instructed in confidential information, electronics patent, design and copyright matters. **Strengths:** "He's very clever, easy to work with, and a good junior junior for all types of IP cases." **Recent work:** Instructed by Nintendo in a number of patent and design actions concerning its lead product, the Wii console.

Chris Hall Despite his relatively recent call (2010), he has established himself as a popular young junior for IP cases involving patents and trade marks. He also advises on commercial matters where IP and technology are significant factors. **Strengths:** "His advice is clear and commercially delivered." **Recent work:** Instructed by Amazon.com in a dispute with cosmetics company Lush concerning online adwords and user searches.

Band 2

One Essex Court

See profile on p.790

THE SET

Although this set has a much smaller contingent of IP experts than the other sets ranked in the table, the members rated here are roundly recognised as leading practitioners and consistently appear in the most significant matters of the day. The set is noted for the quality of members' work with regard to copyright, designs, trade marks and passing-off disputes. **Client service:** "They have a commercial and modern approach to clerking – it's very efficient."

SILKS

Geoffrey Hobbs QC Variously lauded for his "stellar" and "encyclopaedic" knowledge of trade mark law, and also its application to the internet. He is particularly sought after for representation before the higher courts. **Strengths:** "Provides strategically focused advice and has a very high technical understanding of the issues as well as outstanding advocacy skills." "Fluent, urbane and charming with clients." **Recent work:** Acted for Marks & Spencer in its long-running dispute with Interflora regarding Google adwords in online advertising.

Emma Himsworth QC An esteemed advocate and adviser on trade mark, comparative advertising, passing-off and media copyright matters. Numerous sources highlight her excellent communication skills with clients. **Strengths:** "She's technically excellent and has impressive knowledge of very recent case law. She's also extremely approachable and responsive." "Always thinking of different angles rather than just a straightforward analysis; she's a very good person to bounce ideas off." **Recent work:** Represented Cadbury in its landmark dispute with Nestlé over her client's application to register a shade of purple as a trade mark.

JUNIORS

Guy Hollingworth Has a wide-ranging IP practice, and concentrates mainly on copyright, trade marks, passing off, database rights and designs. He is also noted for his understanding of issues adjacent to IP, such as regulatory and competition law. **Strengths:** "He combines clear, focused and practical trade mark advice with a friendly and approachable attitude. He consistently delivers work well ahead of deadlines and is impressive on his feet." **Recent work:** Appeared in SAS Institute v World Programming, a case of alleged copyright infringement and breach of contract concerning WPS software.

Philip Roberts Noted for knowing trade mark law "inside out," he is also well regarded for his work on copyright matters, and for handling cases with a software or internet element. Sources appreciate his ability to relate highly technical issues lucidly. **Strengths:** "Very user-friendly, hard-working and someone with good instincts." **Recent work:** Acted for Zeebox in a trade mark infringement and passing-off action bought by Zee Entertainment Enterprises.

Hogarth Chambers

See profile on p.822

THE SET

Hogarth Chambers has a strong historic reputation for high-quality copyright law representation, but also has a deep well of expertise and experience in trade mark, patent and design matters. Sources consistently comment on the culture of accessibility and co-operation fostered by members and what is one of the best clerking teams in the Inns of Court.

Client service: "The clerks really go the extra mile, are proactive in communication and provide excellent back-office support; nothing is too much trouble for them. It's an excellent service."

SILKS

Alastair Wilson QC Few barristers have the sheer extent of experience in IP law to rival this august silk, who has recently led on a number of complex matters concerning patents, trade marks, copyright and confidential information. **Strengths:** "An absolute delight to work with – he has a great courtroom style and is excellent with clients." "Incredibly intelligent and brilliant, but also wonderfully approachable." **Recent work:** Appeared in TDY Industries & Kennametal v 1) Pramet Tools SRO & 2) Associated Production Tools Limited, in a case concerning alleged infringement of a mechanical patent.

Roger Wyand QC A veteran IP lawyer with 40 years of experience of litigating cases. He specialises mostly in patent disputes, be they electronic, mechanical or pharmaceutical, and has also featured in some of the leading trade mark disputes of the day. **Strengths:** "Hugely experienced, he's a pleasure to deal with and has a very calm and assured style in court." **Recent work:** Appeared in Actavis v Eli Lilly, an appeal concerning a generic oncology treatment.

JUNIORS

Michael Hicks One of the most experienced and respected juniors at the IP Bar. He is a mathematician by background, but is equally at home with trade mark mandates as he is with tough patent cases. He is commended for his magisterial understanding of chain of title issues with respect to IP ownership. **Strengths:** "Outstanding – a very thorough and creative thinker, who is highly committed and user-friendly." **Recent work:** Acted in SAS Institute v World Programming Limited, an ongoing test case regarding the protection afforded by copyright law to software programs.

Amanda Michaels Considered an oracle with regard to trade mark law, she is one of the most popular senior juniors for brands, media and passing-off cases. Sources speak highly of her clear, careful and practical advice. **Strengths:** "Authoritative, logical, personable and a perfectionist in her pleadings." **Recent work:** Acted for a beauty product manufacturer in Moroccan Oil Israel v Aldi Stores, a passing-off case before the Intellectual Property Enterprise Court (IPEC).

Guy Tritton An esteemed senior junior with a practice spanning all IP rights, he is particularly recommended for his work on trade mark and computer software matters. Sources remark on the practical nature of his advice and his abilities in the courtroom. **Strengths:** "Detailed, thorough and knowledgeable, he's fun to work with." **Recent work:** Appeared in Aircraft Medical Limited v Kingvision, a patent infringement case concerning medical endoscopes.

Gwilym Harbottle An authority on all areas of soft IP law who is particularly well thought of for his handling of copyright and related media disputes. Also noted for his strength in trade mark and designs cases. **Strengths:** "He knows his stuff – his advice is solid and well thought out." **Recent work:** Appeared in Copyright Licensing Agency v Capita, a case concerning copyright infringement in periodical articles.

Andrew Norris An experienced junior with a comprehensive IP practice, who is strong on copyright, trade marks and design cases. Numerous sources attest to his client-friendly and approachable demeanour. **Strengths:** "An excellent strategic barrister who goes straight to the issues." **Recent work:** Represented Sports Direct in a dispute with Boxing Brands concerning alleged trade mark infringement with regard to a new range of boxing apparel and equipment.

Jeremy Reed Has a wide-ranging IP practice although he has of late been associated principally with confidentiality and privacy matters, particularly the litigation concerning the News of the World and Mirror phone hacking claims. **Strengths:** "Incisive and approachable – he has a very good read on a given set of circumstances." **Recent work:** Acted in Alliance Boots v UDG Healthcare in a passing-off dispute regarding the name UDG Healthcare.

Jonathan Moss Has a broad practice which includes chancery and commercial contracts work in addition to IP. He is strongly recommended for his command of trade mark and design infringement matters. **Strengths:** "He's a brilliant junior. If you want a pleading done, you know he'll do a tip-top job out of proportion to his level of call." **Recent work:** Represented Microsoft in a breach of contract and copyright claim against LycaMobile.

Benjamin Longstaff With an impeccable background in the sciences – as a trained mathematician and contributor to New Scientist – this junior of recent call (2009) impresses sources with a maturity and easy-going, collegiate approach to mandates. **Strengths:** "Very bright and easy to get along with – solicitors really like working with him." **Recent work:** Instructed by HTC in a multi-patent action against Gemalto regarding smartphone technology.

Richard Davis A former patent attorney, he is a patent specialist for the most part, although he is also much sought after for design right mandates. Sources think particularly well of him for his practical, client-focused approach. **Strengths:** "An excellent junior, who is incredibly hard-working, responsive and conscientious." **Recent work:** Instructed by the Secretary of State for Defence in a patent revocation action concerning the treatment of ship hulls.

Thomas St Quintin Has established himself as a leading mid-call junior offering assured counsel and advocacy across the range of IP rights. He is also a published authority on copyright and trade mark law. **Strengths:** "A rising star who gives good, practical advice, is very responsive and has a good drafting style for pleadings and skeleton arguments." **Recent work:** Acted in the significant and long-running ITV v TVCatchup matter concerning internet streaming of free-to-air television channels.

Other Ranked Lawyers

Michael Bloch QC (Blackstone Chambers) Has moved from Wilberforce Chambers in a move which adds significant firepower to his new set's IP offering. He concentrates mainly on copyright and trade mark matters, as well as disputes over commercial IP rights licensing agreements. **Strengths:** "He puts all arguments through their paces, pays proper respect to the other side's cases and is a fantastic judge's advocate." **Recent work:** Appeared in Sky v Microsoft, a trade mark dispute concerning the use of skyDrive as the name of a Microsoft Windows platform.

Ian Mill QC (Blackstone Chambers) A luminary in the media and entertainment world with an impressive record in copyight-related cases, particularly in matters concerning music copyright infringement. **Strengths:** "A very forceful advocate, who is highly authoritative. Good in copyright tribunal and High Court litigation." **Recent work:** Appeared in The Football Association Premier League Limited v British Sky Broadcasting, a case concerning alleged illegal streaming of sporting events by the website First Row.

Tom Weisselberg QC (Blackstone Chambers) A much-admired senior junior with a wide-ranging commercial practice, who took silk in 2014. His IP work is mostly devoted to copyright and trade mark disputes. **Strengths:** "Excellent on paper, and very reasoned in his approach to advice. Also very good with clients." **Recent work:** Acted for BAT in a trade mark dispute with Imperial Tobacco concerning the brand name Golden Virginia.

Kelyn Bacon QC (Brick Court Chambers) Has recently taken silk, an appointment warmly welcomed by sources. She is particularly sought after for cases with a competition and European law dimension. **Strengths:** "Her knowledge of the pharma industry is valuable." "She impresses with the dexterity and speed with which she gets on top of things." **Recent work:** Represented AstraZeneca in a reference to ECJ from the patents court regarding a complicated question of the interpretation of EU patent legislation.

Nicholas Saunders (Brick Court Chambers) Has a broad IP practice which takes in trade mark, copyright and patent cases. He has extensive experience at appellate, international arbitration and ECJ level. **Strengths:** "He has a ready grasp of technical issues accompanied by a sound strategic view." **Recent work:** Acted for Nokia in a patent infringement case against HTC, in which it was established that his client is entitled to block UK sales of HTC's handsets.

Mark Engelman (see p.596) (Hardwicke) An esteemed trade mark law and passing-off expert with 25 years of experience of representing well-known brands as a solicitor and then barrister. Sources commend him for his refreshingly informal but highly commercial approach. **Strengths:** "He's incredibly approachable and has a fantastic knowledge base." "He has an inventive mind for challenging situations." **Recent work:** Acted for Apple in a trade mark dispute with Wapple.net, in which it was found that the latter's name was confusingly similar to that of his client.

Edmund Cullen QC (Maitland Chambers) A leading silk for disputes in the media and entertainment sector who appears in many of the most important copyright cases of the day, particularly where the internet is a factor. **Strengths:** "He's exceptionally bright and provides sound commercial advice." "He's brilliant at cross-examination" and "superb at drafting submissions." **Recent work:** Acted for the record industry in BPI v BSkyB and Others, a series of applications for blocking orders against internet service providers as a means to combat internet music piracy.

Malcolm Chapple (New Square Chambers) A junior with a great range of experience who has a wide-ranging chancery and commercial practice that includes IP matters, particularly allegations of breach of licence for IP rights and trade mark disputes. **Strengths:** "He has good business acumen but is approachable, lacking in pretension and very cost-effective." **Recent work:** Acted in Unicleaner Europa ApS v Miltek, a series of cases in which three UK distributors of Miltek products are alleged to have unlawfully used that trade mark after the termination of licence agreements.

Madeleine Heal (see p.623) (New Square Chambers) A senior junior with an admirably broad IP practice that takes in copyright, database, design, patent and trade mark cases. Has a strong record in cases relating to the media and entertainment industries. **Recent work:** Acting for Crocker in a patent and design infringement suit against Italian agro-industry company Giordano regarding a device which supplies clean water to poultry.

Michael Edenborough QC (see p.593) (Serle Court) Best known for trade mark matters, although he has an academic background in biophysics and so is highly adept at cases involving patent issues. **Recent work:** "He is a thoughtful advocate, able to get to the bottom of a point, place it in context, and present it simply and persuasively." "Very-user friendly, and clear – judges warm to him." **Recent work:** Acted in Merck v Merck Sharp & Dohme, an international trade mark dispute between two pharmaceutical companies with the same name.

THE REGIONS

Intellectual Property The Regions
Leading Juniors
Band 1
Craig Aubrey *St Philips Chambers (ORL)* ◊ *
Jones Victoria *3PB Barristers (ORL)* ◊
Lambert Jane *Northern Intellectual Property Chambers (ORL)* ◊
* *Indicates individual with profile.*
◊ *(ORL) = Other Ranked Lawyer.*

Ranked Lawyers

Jane Lambert (Northern Intellectual Property Chambers) Also a door tenant at 4-5 Gray's Inn Square in London, though the majority of her IP work derives from Northern-based clients. She specialises in advising start-up companies in the technology, media and telecommunications sectors on IP-related issues and is experienced in handling all matters heard by the Intellectual Property Enterprise Court. **Strengths:** "She is especially good at advising new businesses." "She is a strong trial counsel." **Recent work:** She successfully resisted an application by the Motion Picture Association of America for proprietary injunctions concerning certain assets held by a former director of the indexing website Newzbin. The rejected claim had alleged that the assets had been bought with monies acquired through copyright infringement.

Victoria Jones (3PB Barristers) Bristol-based and quickly establishing a strong following amongst the leading IP solicitors in the South West. She has recently been instructed on a number of significant trade mark and passing-off cases, and is a popular speaker on issues such as online IP. **Strengths:** "She is first-rate; she's personable, she gets stuck in, and her knowledge of the law is excellent." "She is very user-friendly and responsive, and clients really like her." **Recent work:** She defended Lidl in trade mark infringement and passing-off proceedings brought by Dairy Crest, concerning Lidl's Valley Spire and Dairy Crest's Cathedral City cheeses.

Aubrey Craig (see p.580) (St Philips Chambers) Birmingham-based advocate who handles matters for clients on both the Midland and Northern Circuits. He has a broad practice which embraces both advisory and contentious work. He represents small and medium-sized enterprises, assisting with cross-border licensing issues and the interrelationship between IP and competition law. **Strengths:** "He is experienced and very approachable, and gives very clear advice. I'm always ready to instruct him for an opinion."

International Arbitration

Contents:

LONDON General Commercial & Insurance

International Arbitration: General Commercial & Insurance London

Leading Sets

Band 1	7 King's Bench Walk *
Essex Court Chambers *	**Band 3**
Band 2	Brick Court Chambers *
One Essex Court *	Fountain Court Chambers *
20 Essex Street *	3 Verulam Buildings *

Leading Silks

Star individuals	**Persey** Lionel *Quadrant Chambers (ORL)* ◇
Landau Toby *Essex Court Chambers*	**Qureshi** Khawar *Serle Court (ORL)* ◇ *
Band 1	**Rainey** Simon *Quadrant Chambers (ORL)* ◇
Dunning Graham *Essex Court Chambers*	**Salzedo** Simon *Brick Court Chambers*
Foxton David *Essex Court Chambers*	**Siberry** Richard *Essex Court Chambers*
Joseph David *Essex Court Chambers*	**Stewart** Roger *4 New Square (ORL)* ◇ *
Kealey Gavin *7 King's Bench Walk*	**Toledano** Daniel *One Essex Court*
Malek Ali *3 Verulam Buildings*	**Wolfson** David *One Essex Court*
Milligan Iain *20 Essex Street*	**Band 4**
Rabinowitz Laurence *One Essex Court*	**Berry** Steven *Essex Court Chambers*
Smouha Joe *Essex Court Chambers*	**Black** Michael *XXIV Old Buildings (ORL)* ◇
Band 2	**Bloch** Michael *Blackstone Chambers (ORL)* ◇
Brindle Michael *Fountain Court Chambers*	**Butcher** Christopher *7 King's Bench Walk*
Crane Michael *Fountain Court Chambers*	**Calver** Neil *Brick Court Chambers*
Edelman Colin *Devereux (ORL)* ◇ *	**Choo Choy** Alain *One Essex Court*
Edey Philip *20 Essex Street*	**Collett** Michael *20 Essex Street*
Edwards David *7 King's Bench Walk*	**Gaisman** Jonathan *7 King's Bench Walk*
Flynn Vernon *Essex Court Chambers*	**Gee** Steven *Stone Chambers (ORL)* ◇
Howard Mark *Brick Court Chambers*	**Healy** Siobán *7 King's Bench Walk*
Kimmins Charles *20 Essex Street*	**Howe** Timothy *Fountain Court Chambers* *
Matthews Duncan *20 Essex Street*	**Hunter** Andrew *Blackstone Chambers (ORL)* ◇
Millett Richard *Essex Court Chambers*	**Jacobs** Richard *Essex Court Chambers*
Parsons Luke *Quadrant Chambers (ORL)* ◇	**Kendrick** Dominic *7 King's Bench Walk*
Schaff Alistair *7 King's Bench Walk*	**Key** Paul *Essex Court Chambers*
Thanki Bankim *Fountain Court Chambers* *	**Mildon** David *Essex Court Chambers*
Tozzi Nigel *4 Pump Court (ORL)* ◇ *	**Railton** David *Fountain Court Chambers*
Band 3	**Swainston** Michael *Brick Court Chambers*
Baker Andrew *20 Essex Street*	**Waller** Richard *7 King's Bench Walk*
Bright Robert *7 King's Bench Walk*	**Webb** Geraint *Henderson Chambers (ORL)* ◇ [A] *
Catchpole Stuart *Thirty Nine Essex Street (ORL)* ◇	**White** Andrew *Atkin Chambers (ORL)* ◇ *
Crawford James R *Matrix Chambers (ORL)* ◇	**Wordsworth** Samuel *Essex Court Chambers*
Green Andrew *Blackstone Chambers (ORL)* ◇	**New Silks**
Gruder Jeffrey *Essex Court Chambers*	**Lewis** David *20 Essex Street*
Gunning Alexander *4 Pump Court (ORL)* ◇ *	**O'Sullivan** Sean *4 Pump Court (ORL)* ◇ *
Hossain Sa'ad *One Essex Court*	

Leading Juniors

Band 1	**Riches** Philip *Stone Chambers (ORL)* ◇ *
Diwan Ricky *Essex Court Chambers*	**Scorey** David *Essex Court Chambers*
Douglas Zachary *Matrix Chambers (ORL)* ◇ *	**Valentin** Ben *Fountain Court Chambers* *
Harris Christopher *3 Verulam Buildings* *	**Willan** James *Essex Court Chambers*
Band 2	**Wood** Emily *Essex Court Chambers*
Byam-Cook Henry *20 Essex Street*	**Yeo** Nik *Fountain Court Chambers* *
Dhar Siddharth *Essex Court Chambers*	**Band 3**
Holmes Michael *7 King's Bench Walk*	**Meakin** Ian *XXIV Old Buildings (ORL)* ◇
Midwinter Stephen *Brick Court Chambers*	**Pearce** Luke *20 Essex Street*
Moollan Salim *Essex Court Chambers*	**Spalton** George *4 New Square (ORL)* ◇ *
Pilbrow Fionn *Brick Court Chambers*	**Walker** Damien *Essex Court Chambers*
Pillai Rajesh *3 Verulam Buildings* *	**Up-and-coming individuals**
Quirk Iain *Essex Court Chambers*	**Edwards** Patricia *20 Essex Street*

** Indicates set / individual with profile.*
◇ (ORL) = Other Ranked Lawyer.
[A] direct access (see p.11).
Alphabetical order within each band. Band 1 is highest.

Band 1

Essex Court Chambers

See profile on p.792

THE SET

Essex Court has a "wealth of expertise and knowledge within its four walls," making it the best in the business for international arbitration. Individuals from the set are instructed in disputes, including those in the shipping and energy sectors, that are governed by London, New York and UAE law. The set's members are particularly praised for their work in policyholder disputes and are known for their ability to dispense "sound and sensible advice on tricky issues."

Client service: "The clerks are very proactive and commercial. Their approach is very modern." "David Grief, their chief clerk, is honest and reliable. His opinion on the most appropriate counsel for a matter can always be relied upon."

SILKS

Toby Landau QC A standout arbitration practitioner who receives a broad range of instructions in jurisdictions across the world. His recent work has included disputes stemming from the break-up of high-value joint ventures and disputes between states in the energy sector. **Strengths:** "He is a phenomenal advocate, who is incredibly clear, concise and persuasive."

Graham Dunning QC Practises in London and in the world's major arbitration centres. He has recently acted in disputes relating to the mining and real estate sectors. He represents a variety of clients, including major commercial entities and high net worth individuals. **Strengths:** "He is thoughtful and very quick to turn around papers. Thoroughly impressive, he is also sensitive to client concerns." "He is able to step back and give a broad view. He shows the solicitor how to step through and over the problems in a case."

David Foxton QC Noted for his strong intellectual acumen and skill in a broad range of commercial matters. He receives instructions to act as counsel in international arbitrations, and also sits as an arbitrator. Areas of expertise include matters arising in the energy sector and professional negligence claims. **Strengths:** "He has a very pleasant demeanour. He is bright, but wears his intelligence lightly, and has the ability to get on top of papers and come up with clever and persuasive arguments."

Joe Smouha QC Handles international arbitration as part of his successful commercial practice. He has experience of matters relating to the CIS and the Middle East, and his clients include companies and high net worth individuals in the chemicals and metals industries, amongst others. **Strengths:** "He is very impressive. He has an easy style, he prepares thoroughly and he can always be relied on. He's a pleasure to work with and one of the very best in the business."

David Joseph QC Noted for his impressive practice in Singapore and Hong Kong, in addition to his work in London. Recent matters handled include fraud cases, major joint venture disputes in the energy field, and claims for intellectual property infringement. **Strengths:** "He is very enthusiastic and hard-working; he's strong on paper and he has got the ear of the judges." **Recent work:** Acted for Astro All Asia Networks in a Singapore arbitration against PT First Media relating to the break-up of a joint venture.

Vernon Flynn QC A commercial silk who gains praise for his effective performances before arbitration tribunals. Of late, he has handled some complex disputes, including an African mining arbitration and a big-ticket energy arbitration governed by Qatari law. **Strengths:** "A polished advocate, who regularly wins over the court or tribunal on difficult points."

Richard Millett QC He is highly regarded for his thorough understanding of arbitration procedures and is regularly instructed as counsel or arbitrator. He has handled disputes in London and in various offshore jurisdictions. **Strengths:** "He combines a first-class intellect with tenacious and effective advocacy."

Jeffrey Gruder QC A counsel and arbitrator with experience in various jurisdictions, who has handled a variety of contractual disputes, fraud cases and joint venture disputes. He has a number of clients in the oil and shipping industries.

Richard Siberry QC Represents clients in complex arbitration disputes, and also sits as an arbitrator. His recent matters have seen him handling a shipping arbitration and a coal dispute. **Strengths:** "He has an excellent analytical mind coupled with good judgement."

Paul Key QC Recognised as being good on strategy and someone with a fine knowledge of arbitration law and procedure. He represents clients from the energy and telecommunications sectors in worldwide disputes. **Strengths:** "He was tenacious, bold and confident in cross-examination. He had not only the legal team's confidence, but also that of the client." "He had complete command of the matter and was incredibly comfortable before the panel."

Samuel Wordsworth QC Focuses on international arbitration and public international law matters. His practice in the past year has included matters relating to the Law of the Sea and politically sensitive disputes between states in South America. **Strengths:** "He is effective, serious and responsive."

Steven Berry QC An experienced practitioner praised by sources for his advocacy skills. He has been instructed in a range of matters, and recently represented a client claiming damages in a coal sale and purchase dispute. **Strengths:** "He has been in the field a very long time and is very experienced."

David Mildon QC Known for his outstanding grasp of complex technical points of law and for his practice as both advocate and arbitrator. He represents clients in oil and gas and electricity disputes, and is an expert on matters arising from exploration contracts and coal price reviews. **Strengths:** "He is technically unrivalled and delivers potent advice in a succinct yet precise manner." "A strategic thinker who is able to grasp complicated technical concepts quickly and accurately, and distil them in a way that can be readily understood by the tribunal."

Richard Jacobs QC Acts as counsel and arbitrator in international arbitrations, and has a particular focus on insurance matters. Recent instructions have included joint venture disputes and professional liability claims in the pharmaceutical and shipbuilding sectors. **Strengths:** "An excellent advocate with a very relaxed manner, who is great academically."

JUNIORS

Ricky Diwan Qualified in both the UK and the USA, and known for having a strong commercial practice that is heavily weighted towards international arbitration. He has acted as co-counsel alongside leading practitioners in matters such as supply disputes. **Strengths:** "He has great knowledge of arbitration matters and knows the ICC rules inside-out. He identifies the strong points in a case and he brings them to the fore – he is just outstanding."

Salim Moollan Called to both the English and Mauritian Bars, and has acted on arbitrations governed by various national laws, including those of France and Iran. He has recently handled a number of sale and purchase disputes and matters involving parties in the petroleum industry. **Strengths:** "He absorbs volumes of detailed information very quickly and is highly responsive despite having a punishing schedule."

Iain Quirk Has a broad commercial international arbitration practice and has recently handled matters in Africa, the Middle East and Asia. Of late he has handled disputes relating to the coffee industry and the healthcare sector. **Strengths:** "He is incredibly thorough, very hard-working, clever and commercial."

David Scorey Recognised for having a commercial practice which includes a focus on international arbitration. He is renowned for his effective advocacy skills and counts an insurance dispute with complex points of US law amongst his recent cases. **Strengths:** "He is very user-friendly and responsive. He is good at handling clients and is a good team player."

Siddharth Dhar A dedicated junior who has developed an impressive international arbitration practice. Recent highlights include the representation of state-owned companies in the petroleum sector. **Strengths:** "Extremely user-friendly, bright and hard-working. He works well in a team." "A simply excellent junior, who is extremely hard-working and very personable."

James Willan Experienced practitioner who has handled a wide range of commercial arbitration matters, from film distribution to shipbuilding disputes. His recent instructions have involved freezing orders, anti-suit injunctions and disputes regarding the enforcement of foreign award decisions. **Strengths:** "Brilliant – he masters facts and legal issues with lightning speed."

Damien Walker A commercial barrister who regularly appears in international arbitrations. Recent instructions have come from the technology, mining and commodities sectors. **Strengths:** "He is a highly intelligent and energetic counsel who is always willing to look for constructive answers and move the client's case onto the front foot." "He is excellent on both the factual detail and the legal issues. He has very good drafting skills, and is happy to roll his sleeves up and get involved." **Recent work:** Acted for Central Asia Minerals and others in a USD2.7 billion dispute with Westchester Resources.

Emily Wood Has a broad commercial litigation and international arbitration practice. Recent instructions have included disputes in the steel industry. **Strengths:** "Her capacity to digest and assimilate information is really incredible, and her level of engagement has been really astonishing."

Band 2

One Essex Court

See profile on p.790

THE SET

The set has a strong reputation in the market for banking and finance disputes, in addition to more general contractual issues. The set's barristers appear in the world's major arbitration centres and a number of them are qualified in foreign jurisdictions.

SILKS

Laurence Rabinowitz QC A well-known silk with a wide commercial practice. He represents major clients in the energy, aviation and banking sectors, to name but a few. **Strengths:** "He is very approachable, gives sound and practical advice and commands a lot of respect amongst his peers."

David Wolfson QC Advises clients on commercial and banking arbitrations. He acts on a broad range of matters but is particularly commended by sources for his work representing corporations in disputes with financial institutions. **Strengths:** "He does not sit on the fence; he reaches considered views and sticks to his guns." "He is a real master of all trades. He is bright and hard-working, and is involved in a lot of major cases."

Sa'ad Hossain QC Represents clients in commercial arbitrations in the banking and energy sectors. **Strengths:** "We have found him to be thorough and robust." "He was very good technically, he knew the law and he knew the details of the case."

Daniel Toledano QC Praised by peers for his performance as an advocate. He is instructed by technology companies, clients in the banking sector and energy companies. **Strengths:** "He is a reassuring and unflappable presence, who is down to earth and has fine judgement." "He has a considered, intelligent style."

Alain Choo Choy QC Has advised on arbitrations arising in a range of countries, including Russia, the Caribbean and Egypt. His recent matters have included commodities, energy and telecoms disputes. **Strengths:** "He gets in to the detail so quickly and is on top of everything. He will respond to your e-mails efficiently, and provides great advice."

20 Essex Street

See profile on p.794

THE SET

20 Essex Street's barristers are noted for their expertise in shipping and insurance arbitrations, and in disputes arising from international trade and the energy sector. The set has expanded in recent years, adding an office in Singapore, and is a base for barristers working across the globe.

Client service: "I can rely on the clerks to recommend someone suitable who I may not otherwise know." Brian Lee and Neil Palmer head the clerks here.

SILKS

Iain Milligan QC Has a wide commercial practice with a particular emphasis on disputes arising from the financial sector. He has recently been involved in a major arbitration that related to an Indian oil and gas field. **Strengths:** "His ability to grasp technical detail is of the highest calibre."

Philip Edey QC Handles international arbitration for clients in the shipping and chemical industries, amongst others. He often advises on conflict of laws issues, and receives instructions from clients based in jurisdictions across the world, including China, Russia and India. **Strengths:** "He's very impressive. He's punchy, lively and a good advocate."

Charles Kimmins QC Has a strong commercial practice, and regularly acts in disputes in the international trade and shipping sectors. He has recently handled a number of insurance, banking and contract disputes.

Duncan Matthews QC Has a broad commercial practice and regularly advises clients in the shipping and commodities sectors. Recent mandates have included joint venture and insurance disputes in sectors including energy and construction. **Strengths:** "He is a very good arbitrator and an effective counsel."

Andrew Baker QC Represents clients such as charterers and tanker owners in matters related to insurance, international sale of goods and shipping. **Strengths:** "He is a very meticulous and aggressive advocate, who is also intellectual and measured in his approach."

Michael Collett QC A prominent name in the shipping, commodities and international trade sectors. He often appears in arbitrations seated in London and Hong Kong. **Strengths:** "He has a very good understanding of the commercial context of businesses and what the client's concerns are above and beyond pure legal issues."

David Lewis QC Handles international disputes in arbitration centres across the world. He was based in Singapore between 2009 and 2010 and is still regularly instructed on work in the city-state. Recent instructions have come from the power, commodities and engineering sectors. **Strengths:** "David has a great response time and unmatched clarity of thought. It is always a pleasure to work with him."

JUNIORS

Henry Byam-Cook Has a broad international arbitration practice encompassing shipping, commodities, insurance and information technology matters. He has recently represented clients in shipbuilding disputes and cargo contamination claims. **Strengths:** "He is going to do very well indeed. He is alert and he knows what he is about."

Patricia Edwards Has a wide commercial practice that focuses on international arbitration and litigation, and is increasingly engaged as sole counsel. She handles contract, international trade and financial disputes. **Strengths:** "She is incredibly bright and diligent, and her turnaround time for high-quality and complex submissions or opinions always impresses. A future star."

Luke Pearce Has a practice touching on a range of commercial areas, including banking, shipping and insurance. He counts oil and gas companies and banks among his clients. **Strengths:** "He strikes me as being very measured, careful and on top of what he is required to do."

7 King's Bench Walk

See profile on p.827

THE SET

The set's barristers are recognised for their excellence in all manner of insurance arbitrations. Its counsel also receive instructions on a wide spectrum of commercial matters, including energy and pharmaceutical disputes. The set has "heavy hitting individuals" at both junior and silk level, including individuals who regularly act on matters in jurisdictions such as Hong Kong, London, Singapore and Malaysia.

Client service: "The clerking service is very good. The chief clerks, Bernie Hyatt and Greg Leyden, were very user-friendly and we had a sophisticated discussion about fees."

SILKS

Gavin Kealey QC A leading practitioner who handles arbitrations focused on areas such as insurance and shipping. Recent instructions have come from energy and insurance companies on matters such as contract disputes and product liability claims. **Strengths:** "He expounded on the legal aspects of the case with great authority and terrific articulation." "He is incredibly quick and was able to really get into the details of our case very quickly. He grasped all the esoteric details of the case and was able to see the issues from multiple angles."

Alistair Schaff QC Acts as both counsel and arbitrator in general commercial arbitrations, particularly those focused on insurance, professional negligence and international trade matters. His clients include Middle Eastern and Asian entities such as pharmaceutical companies and hotel operators. **Strengths:** "I rate him very highly because of his deep analysis of detailed and complicated insurance coverage points." "His openness to my needs as a client is matched by his intellectual rigour and his disarming and incredibly insightful presentation."

David Edwards QC Has a strong reputation in the insurance sector and is particularly noted for his work on Bermuda Form matters. He has acted on insurance disputes related to the oil and gas, chemical and pharmaceutical sectors. **Strengths:** "He is a well-organised, clear advocate who is very good when on his feet and dealing with questions." "He is without exception always completely prepared. Whilst he is very determined once he has reached his position, he is also very easy to work with, and is very collaborative."

Richard Waller QC He is often instructed on shipping, commodities and energy arbitrations. Recent matters include arbitrations governed by Japanese law, and insurance matters arising from the financial crisis and the Arab spring. **Strengths:** "He is calm under pressure and can come up with persuasive arguments when it looks like we are in a pickle."

Robert Bright QC Acts on international arbitrations in the shipping, commodities and trading sectors. He has handled arbitrations seated in Europe, Singapore, Hong Kong and Malaysia. **Strengths:** "He is always accessible, unflappable and pragmatic. You feel like you are in safe hands with him. His advocacy is very measured and he responds well to changing circumstances."

Christopher Butcher QC Has an impressive range of clients, including major pharmaceutical and energy companies. His practice is insurance-based, and his recent work has included handling Bermuda Form disputes and matters subject to New York and Israeli law. **Strengths:** "He was so collaborative and very encouraging. He took our points and worked with us in formulating arguments. I found him to be extremely intelligent and efficient."

Jonathan Gaisman QC A leading commercial silk who acts as counsel and arbitrator on a broad range of international arbitration matters. Recent instructions include international energy arbitrations and Bermuda Form insurance disputes. **Strengths:** "An effective leader who is willing to roll his sleeves up and get involved in the detail."

Siobán Healy QC Advises clients on commercial arbitration matters, and also sits as an arbitrator. She receives a wide variety of instructions in areas such as insurance, shipping, commodities and conflict of laws issues. **Strengths:** "She is very user-friendly and approachable, and a very effective advocate."

Dominic Kendrick QC Instructed to handle significant arbitrations as both counsel and arbitrator. He advises on commodities, insurance and banking disputes, and he has handled recent arbitrations seated in South East Asia and Russia. **Strengths:** "An understated advocate who is forceful and bright."

JUNIORS

Michael Holmes Regularly advises on arbitrations in the shipping and insurance sectors. His clients include reinsurers, commodity trading houses and shipbuilders. **Strengths:** "He's very easy to work with, he shows good attention to detail and he thinks outside the box."

Band 3

Brick Court Chambers

See profile on p.774

THE SET

The set has been identified by peers as one to watch in the international arbitration world. It consists of "top-calibre people" who make regular appearances before the Commercial Court and in arbitration centres worldwide.

Client service: "Their clerks are user-friendly, and take a helpful approach. They are also very modern in their dealings with solicitors." "Their clerks are very responsive, prompt and approachable. The service there is excellent."

SILKS

Mark Howard QC A commercial silk with a "stellar reputation," who appears before arbitration tribunals in the UK and abroad. He is praised for his skills in cross-examination and for his experience of matters related to injunctions. His recent caseload has featured share disputes in the banking sector and matters related to sovereign immunity. **Strengths:** "He's a star performer."

Simon Salzedo QC A respected silk with a strong commercial practice who often acts for clients in arbitration matters. He is known for his strength in award challenges, and also handles enforcement, contract disputes and anti-suit injunctions. **Strengths:** "Intelligent and tenacious, he's a strong advocate." **Recent work:** Acted for Terna in successfully resisting a challenge by Al Shamsi to an AED84 million arbitration award.

Neil Calver QC Praised by peers for his impressive knowledge of the arbitration field and his track record in high-value disputes. Recent arbitrations he has handled include a metals dispute, a product liability case and a marine insurance matter. He is instructed as counsel and also sits as arbitrator. **Strengths:** "He is a very commercial and tactical practitioner who wins the confidence of clients very quickly. A very effective advocate."

Michael Swainston QC A well-regarded practitioner with a strong arbitration practice. He is recognised by peers for his knowledge of insurance matters, and for his work for Russian and CIS clients. **Strengths:** "The ideal advocate for a complex battle requiring powerful advocacy. He is also very likeable and user-friendly."

JUNIORS

Fionn Pilbrow Acts for clients in commercial arbitrations and is increasingly appointed as sole counsel. Recent instructions have included a joint venture dispute in the oil and gas industry and a contract matter related to an Indian company. **Strengths:** "He turns things around very quickly and is good at getting into the detail."

Stephen Midwinter Acts on arbitrations in the insurance, banking and shipping sectors. He has handled recent disputes in London, Bermuda and New York. **Strengths:** "He's very flexible, very willing and takes an enormous amount of time and trouble in his preparation. One of the stars of the future."

Fountain Court Chambers

See profile on p.804

THE SET

Fountain Court is a magic circle commercial set, whose barristers appear in arbitrations across a broad range of legal fields. They are particularly strong on disputes in the financial services and aviation sectors.

Client service: "The clerking is efficient, friendly and everything one would expect from an upper-tier set." "The clerks are very good and personable. They have the right balance between knowing what they are about, but also being flexible."

SILKS

Michael Brindle QC Has an established reputation in the sector and is often appointed as arbitrator or instructed as counsel. He is experienced in bringing matters before the Supreme Court, and he has an active practice in both the London and Singapore markets. **Strengths:** "He's an extremely experienced and eminent advocate. He is excellent and has a very assured touch in court." "He is a leader in his field and is highly respected. In terms of his ability to think around the problem and present solutions, he's very good."

Michael Crane QC An established practitioner in the commercial sphere, with experience of arbitration in various locations, including New York, Singapore and London. His areas of focus include Bermuda Form insurance disputes and arbitrations in the pharmaceutical and aviation fields. **Strengths:** "One of the most formidable silks at the Bar. He is an outstanding advocate." **Recent work:** Successfully represented a client in a Court of Appeal case concerning the enforceability of a London arbitration agreement.

Bankim Thanki QC Has a truly international practice, and has made recent appearances in Singapore, Hong Kong and BVI disputes. His instructions have featured matters related to enforcement and disputes arising from real estate and construction contracts. **Strengths:** "He was able to quickly get to the nub of the issues. His work was well structured and thought-out. It was particularly impressive." **Recent work:** Engaged by Indian contractors GMR for a USD3 billion dispute with the Maldives government related to the allegedly unlawful cancellation of an airport project.

Timothy Howe QC An experienced silk with an arbitration practice in the energy, finance and general commercial fields. His clients include multinational corporations and global financial institutions. **Strengths:** "He has great depth of knowledge and expertise in arbitration."

David Railton QC A well-regarded silk with a diverse commercial practice that sees him handling Bermuda Form arbitrations and business interruption claims. He acts as counsel and sits as an arbitrator in London and overseas.

JUNIORS

Nik Yeo A popular junior with a strong practice in the technology and financial sectors. He has represented major clients in recent matters relating to liability, award enforcement and licensing interpretation. **Strengths:** "He is very bright and an excellent practitioner. He has an easy manner about him and is formidably intelligent."

Ben Valentin (see p.742) A highly regarded junior with experience of acting on disputes governed by a range of arbitral rules. He has recently handled contractual, shareholder and insurance disputes in a variety of areas, including the oil and gas and pharmaceuticals sector. **Recent work:** Engaged by Sonera in BVI proceedings to enforce a USD1 billion arbitration award in a telecoms dispute with Cukurova.

3 Verulam Buildings

See profile on p.875

THE SET

3 Verulam Buildings has a strong reputation for fraud and general commercial matters and is regarded as "a go-to set for arbitrations in the banking sector." Its barristers have experience of the major arbitral institutions and often receive instructions from clients in jurisdictions such as Hong Kong and Singapore.

SILKS

Ali Malek QC Has a reputation in the international arbitration world as someone to go to for the "top cases." His clients include state authorities and governments, and his recent matters include disputes in Singapore and arbitration-related appearances in the Commercial Court. **Strengths:** "A strong punchy advocate with good instincts and good judgement."

JUNIORS

Christopher Harris (see p.620) Has an excellent reputation in the commercial arbitration field. His recent instructions have included an African telecoms dispute, a joint venture matter under Indian law, and an appearance as sole advocate for a major international investment bank. **Strengths:** "From the beginning, he showed an impressive knowledge of the process of international arbitration and the ICC rules. He has extra knowledge of how things work at the ICC, which was very useful to us." "He's an excellent junior. He is enthusiastic and is devoted to this area: a go-to junior for state/investor arbitration work."

Rajesh Pillai (see p.693) Has a well-established internationally focused practice. Recent disputes he has handled have been seated in the Middle East, India and Singapore. **Strengths:** "A solid, hard-working, reliable junior."

Other Ranked Lawyers

Andrew White QC (Atkin Chambers) Acts in arbitrations in the energy and maritime markets. His experience includes handling disputes arising from projects across the world, and representing clients in contract, professional negligence and product liability matters. He has had recent instructions in matters in Asia, Africa, the Middle East and Eastern Europe. **Strengths:** "He has an uncanny ability to get into the detail and come up with the perfect strategy." "One of the best advocates I've worked with. He's experienced, he gets to the issues quickly, and he's a powerful advocate." **Recent work:** Represented Flex LNG, purchaser of four LNG producer vessels worth USD1.8 billion from Samsung Heavy Industries. The dispute arose following the alleged termination of the contract, with the client claiming back USD300 million that had already been paid towards the vessels.

Andrew Green QC (Blackstone Chambers) Has received major instructions lately, reaffirming his already strong market reputation. He has handled an arbitration on behalf of one of India's major pharmaceutical companies and has brought a significant claim against the UK government. **Strengths:** "He's an excellent cross-examiner and I was very impressed by his contractual analysis in the case." **Recent work:** Acted for US defence contractor Raytheon in a dispute with the UK government following the termination of an IT contract.

Michael Bloch QC (Blackstone Chambers) Instructed in disputes under various arbitral rules in sectors such as IT and pharmaceuticals. He has recently handled a number of joint venture and acquisition disputes. **Strengths:** "He is respected and revered by clients, and he has an amazing ability to digest and present information." "He's a very technical practitioner, who is able to identify the main points of strength or weakness and focus on them effectively."

Andrew Hunter QC (Blackstone Chambers) Earns praise from peers and clients for his performance in a range of matters in the insurance sector. His recent instructions have included claims following major natural disasters and a real estate matter arising between high net worth individuals. **Strengths:** "His cross-examination skills are some of the best I've seen – he gets to the crux of the matter and he is a very good tactician." "He has a razor-sharp intellect, an unflappable temperament and an excellent courtroom manner."

Colin Edelman QC (Devereux) Handles international arbitration as both counsel and arbitrator. His expertise in insurance-related matters has earned him engagements on major disputes, including those concerning claims brought against reinsurers and issues arising from natural disasters. **Strengths:** "He really is a very, very well-established person in the field as both counsel and arbitrator." "He is absolutely fantastic. It is great to work with him."

Stuart Catchpole QC (Thirty Nine Essex Street) A respected QC who acts on commercial, construction-related and insurance arbitrations. His caseload over the past year has included representing a client in the banking sector in a joint venture dispute and multiple insurance matters, including claims relating to professional negligence and real estate. **Strengths:** "He concentrates on the points that really matter and he is very user-friendly."

Geraint Webb QC (Henderson Chambers) Has a broad commercial practice with a particular focus on insurance and property damage matters. Recent experience includes acting in multiparty commercial disputes, a construction dispute in West Africa and a matter in the Middle East subject to local law. **Strengths:** "His ability to see the relevant issues straight away is impressive. He is clearly very, very bright, and has an excellent legal mind."

James Crawford SC (Matrix Chambers) A leading practitioner who has received engagements for high-profile arbitration matters, including the internationally significant environmental dispute between Chevron and Ecuador. He has experience of a wide range of arbitral rules and also accepts instructions to sit as an arbitrator. **Strengths:** "An outstanding practitioner and a leading authority."

Zachary Douglas (Matrix Chambers) Well-regarded lawyer who is especially noted for his knowledge of investment treaty arbitrations. **Strengths:** "I was impressed that he could cross-examine on complex questions of Russian law and fact." **Recent work:** Engaged in a matter related to Chevron's liability for the pollution of an area of Ecuadorian rainforest.

Roger Stewart QC (4 New Square) An experienced commercial silk who acts as arbitrator and counsel on disputes in the insurance and construction sector. **Strengths:** "His advocacy really is top-notch. He is able to convey complex legal issues simply and clearly. He also understands the client's key drivers."

George Spalton (4 New Square) A junior with a developing profile in the sector, who has acted in arbitrations in a range of jurisdictions, including London, Dubai, Oman and Singapore. Recent instructions have included a banking matter in the Caribbean, a Middle Eastern real estate case and a joint venture dispute in Eastern Europe. **Strengths:** "His written advocacy is excellent and he produces good pleadings and good witness statements."

Michael Black QC (XXIV Old Buildings) Focuses his practice almost exclusively on international disputes across a range of areas, including healthcare, banking and real estate. He regularly appears before the Commercial Court in significant matters, such as the enforcement of high-value awards. **Strengths:** "He's an eminent silk. We had time-pressured situations, and he was good at keeping up team spirit. He is very proactive in wanting to know the details of a case."

Ian Meakin (XXIV Old Buildings) A well-regarded lawyer with a respected international arbitration practice. He has recently handled disputes in the shipping and oil and gas sectors for African and Middle Eastern clients, among other matters. **Strengths:** "He's very charming, very pleasant and good with the clients."

Nigel Tozzi QC (4 Pump Court) Practises in a range of fields, including energy, shipping and IT, representing clients in jurisdictions such as Russia, the CIS states, China and Israel. His recent cases have seen him acting in claims brought in the BVI. He is also experienced in obtaining emergency injunctions. **Strengths:** "He is outstanding as counsel, as he's as sharp as a razor and a fantastic cross-examiner." "He is a superb advocate, and he always knows how to respond to the tribunal. He seems to be able to get on top of a brief ridiculously quickly, getting straight to the important issues."

Alexander Gunning QC (4 Pump Court) Has built a commendable practice heavily weighted towards matters in the insurance, energy and shipping sectors. His recent achievements have included advising on the insurance implications of an aviation accident and the appeal of a major arbitral award. **Recent work:** Engaged to represent a shipping client in a matter regarding the termination of a charter party due to persistent failure to pay for hire.

Sean O'Sullivan QC (4 Pump Court) Has established a substantial practice focused on maritime, offshore and reinsurance cases. He has acted in arbitrations in London, Dubai, Hong Kong and Singapore. **Strengths:** "His advice is strategic and tailored to what will wash in the arbitration, and he is always considering the commercial realities." "Down to earth and a pleasure to work with, he fits smoothly into any team."

Luke Parsons QC (Quadrant Chambers) Acts as both counsel and arbitrator in disputes in jurisdictions such as Malaysia and Tokyo. He advises on insurance, energy, shipping and international trade matters. **Strengths:** "He is a very measured and smooth advocate who handles judges very well."

Lionel Persey QC (Quadrant Chambers) Has an excellent reputation for energy, mining and commodities sector disputes, acting as both counsel and arbitrator. His instructions have included high-value claims related to the sale and conversion of a vessel. He also advised on a major contract cancellation arising out of fraudulent misrepresentation. **Recent work:** Successfully represented Ferrostaal in a USD50 million dispute related to a contract to buy vessels that was terminated due to extensive delays. The company sought recovery of its deposit from the Indian shipyard, and further damages.

Simon Rainey QC (Quadrant Chambers) A respected commercial silk who acts for clients in shipping, energy, commodities and international trade matters. He is particularly noted for his work on arbitrations relating to the sugar industry. Recent instructions have come from a commodities company, and he has also represented an energy giant in an oil field production dispute. **Strengths:** "Hard-working, diligent and rapier-like in cross examination." "He is very user-friendly and a smooth practitioner." **Recent work:** Engaged by global trade house Sucden, in an arbitration against Rusagro-Sakhar, Russia's biggest importer of sugar and raw commodities. The matter raised questions relating to Russian law and trading practice.

Khawar Qureshi QC (Serle Court) Has a broad commercial and public international law arbitration practice. His expertise encompasses handling joint venture disputes, and obtaining and contesting anti-suit injunctions in the Commercial Court. **Strengths:** "He gets to grip with the issues, identifying the weaknesses and strengths accurately. He's also very easy to deal with."

Steven Gee QC (Stone Chambers) Has a broad commercial practice and acts as arbitrator and counsel in disputes arising from the insurance and shipping sectors. His recent engagements have included representing a shipping group in an investment fund dispute and appearing before tribunals to obtain injunctions for his clients. **Strengths:** "He always provides incisive and thoughtful advice."

Philip Riches (Stone Chambers) A respected practitioner in the energy and natural resources sector who also handles matters relating to jurisdictional disputes. His recent focus has been on the growing markets of China, Russia, Ukraine and Latin America. Areas of experience include enforcement of awards against sovereign states and matters concerning the construction of arbitration clauses. **Strengths:** "He obviously has a very astute legal brain." "He rolls up his sleeves and gets in to the less glamorous parts of the case. His written work is excellent, he turns things around quickly and he will come up with creative ideas."

LONDON Construction/Engineering

Band 1

Atkin Chambers

See profile on p.762

THE SET A leading chambers in the field of construction, whose barristers appear in infrastructure disputes across the world. The set is renowned for its broad selection of "high-calibre heavyweight construction silks," and is a clear first choice for many solicitors in the sector. The set's barristers are instructed in matters involving many jurisdictions, and are particularly known for their handling of disputes in the Middle East.

Client service: "The assistance and help received from the clerking team, and especially from the senior clerk Justin Wilson, have been always of a very high level."

SILKS

Andrew Goddard QC (see p.610) Has a great deal of experience of arbitration procedures in Hong Kong, where many of the construction and engineering disputes he advises on arise. He receives instructions from contractors, employers and governments involved in professional negligence claims and energy disputes. **Strengths:** "He is user-friendly, bright and good on his feet."

Stephen Dennison QC Has extensive experience of handling construction disputes governed by various arbitration rules. His work of late has included representing major European and Asian corporations and governments in claims related to energy and infrastructure projects. **Strengths:** "He is tactically astute in reading a tribunal and good at tailoring his submissions or cross-examinations accordingly." "He is very creative, which is important when you're in a difficult spot. He is very good at putting together forceful arguments when you need them." **Recent work:** He acted for a bond-provider on an application to prevent the beneficiary making demands on performance bonds worth USD40 million. The bonds related to the supply and installation of boilers for a power station in Brazil.

Manus McMullan QC Represents governments and international contractors in disputes across the world. Recent areas of focus include the transportation sphere and disputes related to contract terminations. **Strengths:** "Incredibly hard-working and really bright. I've seen him cross-examining witnesses, and he can be really devastating." **Recent work:** Instructed in a widely reported dispute between Grupos Unidos and Panama Canal Authority, regarding issues arising from a USD5 billion project to widen the Panama Canal. The matter involved complex Panamanian law and matters such as cost overruns and delays.

International Arbitration: Construction/Engineering London
Leading Sets
Band 1
Atkin Chambers *
Keating Chambers *
Band 2
Crown Office Chambers *
Thirty Nine Essex Street *
4 Pump Court *
Leading Silks
Band 1
Boulding Philip *Keating Chambers* *
Catchpole Stuart *Thirty Nine Essex Street*
Darling Paul *Keating Chambers* *
Dennison Stephen *Atkin Chambers* *
Harding Richard *Keating Chambers* *
McMullan Manus *Atkin Chambers* *
Streatfeild-James David *Atkin Chambers*
Taverner Marcus *Keating Chambers* *
ter Haar Roger *Crown Office Chambers*
White Andrew *Atkin Chambers* *
Band 2
Black Michael *XXIV Old Buildings (ORL)* ◊
Brannigan Sean *4 Pump Court* *
Buehrlen Veronique *Keating Chambers* *
Constable Adam *Keating Chambers* *
Dennys Nicholas *Atkin Chambers*
Doerries Chantal-Aimee *Atkin Chambers* *
Furst Stephen *Keating Chambers* *
Goddard Andrew *Atkin Chambers* *
Gunning Alexander *4 Pump Court* *
Hughes Adrian *Thirty Nine Essex Street*
Lofthouse Simon *Atkin Chambers* *
Manzoni Charles *Thirty Nine Essex Street* *
Moran Vincent *Keating Chambers* *
Parkin Fiona *Atkin Chambers*
Rigney Andrew *Crown Office Chambers* *
Thomas David *Keating Chambers* *
Wilken Sean *Thirty Nine Essex Street*
New Silks
Ansell Rachel *4 Pump Court* *
Howells James *Atkin Chambers* *
Leading Juniors
Band 1
Ghaly Karim *Thirty Nine Essex Street* *
Lewis Christopher *Atkin Chambers* *
Pimlott Charles *Crown Office Chambers* *
Band 2
Buckingham Paul *Keating Chambers* *
Chennells Mark *Atkin Chambers*
Chern Cyril *Crown Office Chambers* *
Garrett Lucy *Keating Chambers* *
Hickey Alexander *4 Pump Court* *
Hussain Riaz *Atkin Chambers* *
Kennedy Stuart *3PB Barristers (ORL)* ◊
Lamont Calum *Keating Chambers* *
Laney Anna *Crown Office Chambers*
Lemon Jane *Keating Chambers* *
Robb Adam *Thirty Nine Essex Street*
Walker Steven *Stone Chambers (ORL)* ◊ *
◊ (ORL) = Other Ranked Lawyer.
* Indicates set / individual with profile.
Alphabetical order within each band. Band 1 is highest.

David Streatfeild-James QC Regularly engaged by contractors and governments across Asia, Europe and the Middle East. His recent work has been heavily weighted towards construction and engineering disputes arising in the energy sector, many of which concern defective machinery and equipment. **Strengths:** "He is the most prepared barrister I have ever worked with and he makes it look so easy." "He is scarily intelligent and a real heavyweight."

Andrew White QC Well versed in large construction and project disputes arising in the energy sector. He handles cases in the UK and in jurisdictions across Asia, Africa and the Middle East. His recent work includes construction delay and defect claims, and cases concerning design project management. **Strengths:** "He is a go-to person for high-value, complex, business-critical disputes, in particular those with an international flavour to them."

Nicholas Dennys QC Handles international disputes in the construction field and in related areas such as insurance, professional negligence and insolvency. He is familiar with London, Singapore and Hong Kong arbitration rules and has had recent instructions relating to the retail and shipping sectors. **Strengths:** "He is brilliant in a deceptively laid-back way."

Chantal-Aimée Doerries QC Has a wealth of experience in construction disputes, particularly those in the energy and shipping sectors. Her practice spans Asia, the Middle East and South America, and she is experienced at handling Singapore-seated arbitrations. **Strengths:** "She is a very modern barrister, who is very commercial and obviously very smart, and knows how to deal with clients."

Simon Lofthouse QC Well known in the construction sphere, he represents governments, individuals and corporations, and is particularly strong on matters relating to the transport and infrastructure sectors. He is instructed by clients in Central America and the Middle East. **Strengths:** "He is diligent, robust and a very effective advocate." "He is one of the best at managing clients, and has a very loyal following."

Fiona Parkin QC Engaged by governments, state-owned entities and multinational companies in disputes related to projects and shipping construction contracts under a variety of arbitration rules. She is experienced in matters spanning multiple jurisdictions. **Strengths:** "She worked so hard, got in to the detail so quickly, and prepared so well. She is a dream to work with." **Recent work:** Engaged by the government of Gibraltar in a dispute with Spanish contractors related to a runway and tunnel project at Gibraltar airport.

James Howells QC (see p.632) Has a particularly strong practice in the energy sector, and acts in both an advisory and advocacy role. Recent instructions include design and construction contract arbitrations and disputes governed by Chinese, Thai and Singaporean law. **Strengths:** "Very bright and academic, he has a strong international practice."

JUNIORS

Christopher Lewis (see p.655) A construction and engineering specialist who receives instructions in matters in the renewable energy and oil and gas sectors. Recent arbitrations include a matter seated in Hong Kong and a construction dispute arising from a joint venture. **Strengths:** "He was excellent – it was quite a difficult case and he did a very good job of marshalling all the documents effectively. He took very technical material and made it very easy for the judge to understand."

Mark Chennells A construction specialist with a focus on the energy, defence and IT sectors. His recent work has seen him active in both Europe and the Far East, and he has handled contract disputes relating to a motorway construction, as well as a matter concerning design defects. **Strengths:** "He is a very good thinker who has great stamina, and is very easy to work with." "He gets stuck in to the detail and is always on top of it. He is very approachable and you will always have complete confidence in his handling of the case."

Riaz Hussain Gaining a strong reputation, he increasingly receives instructions as sole counsel in a wide variety of construction and engineering disputes. Recent matters have included a breach of agreement claim, a design negligence case and a high-value dispute relating to a construction defect. **Strengths:** "He has an exceptional knowledge of procedures and practices, and has demonstrated a very rare capability to quickly understand the technical aspects of a matter."

Keating Chambers

See profile on p.824

THE SET

An excellent construction and engineering set that has advocates who tackle numerous matters under the major arbitral rules. Chambers is home to "vastly experienced" members who earn instructions in a host of major infrastructure project disputes.

Client service: "Everyone at Keating Chambers is responsive, professional and accommodating. The experience of working with them is a positive and pleasant one."

SILKS

Philip Boulding QC (see p.553) Has a strong reputation in the UK and Asia. He represents government departments, local authorities and engineering companies in the construction and energy sectors. He is noted for his work in Hong Kong, where he has been instructed in such matters as professional negligence claims and joint venture disputes. **Strengths:** "He is hard-working, responsive and a good team player." "He is first rate, and an automatic choice for the heavy lifting – he gets results."

Richard Harding QC (see p.619) Regarded by sources as a go-to man for construction and engineering disputes in the Middle East. He has a knowledge of Arabic and a great deal of experience of handling disputes governed by Middle Eastern law. Recent matters he has handled include disputes between governments and contractors. **Strengths:** "He is very well known in the Gulf, and you don't get a reputation like his without being worthy of it. He is hard-working and knows his business." "He is very user-friendly and accessible, and he turns things around extremely quickly."

Marcus Taverner QC Advises on construction and design arbitration claims arising in the energy and renewables sectors. His recent instructions have included matters related to infrastructure projects and power stations. **Strengths:** "He is an extraordinary advocate. He is charming to the tribunal and brutal to the witnesses. A standout person in the market."

Veronique Buehrlen QC (see p.560) Known for her work representing clients on construction and engineering arbitrations in the energy sector. Sources appreciate her broad commercial experience and comment on the international nature of her practice, which involves appearances in jurisdictions ranging from the CIS to the Caribbean. Recent instructions have included disputes related to defective construction and oil rig operations. **Strengths:** "What is impressive is her ability to understand and assimilate the technical side of a case, whilst also understanding where the client is coming from." "She is incredibly impressive in cases with lots of detail. If you are looking for a needle in a haystack, she will find it."

Adam Constable QC Handles international arbitrations in the construction, infrastructure, shipbuilding and energy sectors. Recent highlights include disputes related to the negligent design and construction of projects in the Middle East and Europe. **Strengths:** "I value the clarity with which he delves into the arguments, as well as his ability to see the matter from all angles, and convey the points to the clients."

Stephen Furst QC (see p.605) Counts governments, contractors, developers and engineers among his impressive list of clients. He has been involved in high-value disputes in the chemical and oil and gas industries, including matters arising from pipeline construction and disputes related to costs. **Strengths:** "He is quick to respond and very helpful."

David Thomas QC (see p.736) Makes frequent appearances before the Dubai World Tribunal, and is also well versed in matters based in Asia-Pacific and African jurisdictions. He is regularly instructed in high-value disputes related to infrastructure projects, claims concerning construction delays and arbitrations brought against governments. **Strengths:** "He dealt with complex issues, was always approachable and handled the matter with excellent client care." "He is very good at reading the tribunal."

Paul Darling QC Has a global construction and engineering arbitration practice which has seen him tackle matters emanating from India, South East Asia and the Middle East. He has recently handled contract disputes in the oil and gas sector, as well as cases concerning public infrastructure projects. **Strengths:** "He has an ability to master complex technical engineering issues in a short time period and he has exceptional cross-examination skills." "An effective and passionate advocate."

Vincent Moran QC Instructed in construction arbitrations and related issues such as energy disputes and claims for professional negligence. His caseload of late has featured offshore energy arbitrations which have included construction defect claims and disputes with contractors. **Strengths:** "He was very impressive in his cross-examination, and is a real force to be reckoned with."

JUNIORS

Paul Buckingham (see p.560) A dual-qualified chartered engineer and barrister, who is renowned for handling highly complex technical points in disputes involving significant sums. He specialises in major cases arising from international projects, and both handles contractual claims against governments and represents European clients in oil and gas disputes. **Strengths:** "He is a real star. He has a fantastic practice and is skilled at tackling complicated technical issues."

Lucy Garrett Her recent matters include high-value arbitrations against governments and claims in the renewable energy sphere. Her practice is international, spanning jurisdictions as diverse as South America and the Middle East. **Strengths:** "Extremely bright, hard-working and a good cross-examiner." "She is very thorough, and her written work is absolutely excellent."

Calum Lamont Handles high-value international arbitration matters in the fields of infrastructure and offshore construction. He practises in jurisdictions such as Dubai, Qatar, China and Korea. **Strengths:** "He's very user-friendly and comes up with really good, strategic points." **Recent work:** Engaged by Nakheel, a Dubai state contractor, in a matter before the Dubai World Tribunal which related to facilities management services on the Palm development in Dubai.

Jane Lemon Concentrates her practice in the construction, energy and technology sectors. She receives instructions in matters in jurisdictions varying from Jamaica to the Far East. **Strengths:** "She is a good listener and she is very clever. Her drafting seems to be very good and she's very accessible."

Band 2

Crown Office Chambers

See profile on p.782

THE SET

The set is known for its talented construction lawyers, with one source claiming that "the secret of its success lies in the sheer strength and depth it has to offer." Members are adept at appearing in arbitrations in London, the Middle East and Asia. They have recently handed instructions in the energy and transportation sectors.

Client service: "They are terrifically nice and sensible, and pragmatic when it comes to fees."

SILKS

Roger ter Haar QC A renowned practitioner who handles construction and infrastructure disputes, and related insurance and professional negligence matters. His areas of focus in the past year have included construction costs cases, contract terminations and disputes following delays in construction work. **Strengths:** "He is an exceptionally clever and very persuasive advocate."

Andrew Rigney QC Leads large cross-sector teams in complex arbitrations relating to infrastructure projects and the oil and gas and renewable energy sectors. He has been involved in significant matters in East Africa and Asia, including product design claims, construction delay disputes and cases arising from power plant projects. **Strengths:** "He has an encyclopaedic knowledge of the law and has a good analytical mind." "He is incredibly academically gifted, has a charming manner, and is intellectually forceful."

JUNIORS

Cyril Chern (see p.570) Specialises in international construction disputes and has recently acted on matters in Eastern Europe and South America. He is dual qualified as both a barrister and a chartered architect. Some of his recent instructions have focused on disputes in the transportation sector.

Anna Laney Regularly instructed in construction international arbitrations. Her clients include employers and contractors, and those involved in contractual and professional negligence claims. **Strengths:** "She is a team player who is robust and decisive and who provides very clear advice."

Charles Pimlott (see p.694) Acts on significant construction matters arising in the Middle East, South East Asia and Europe. His recent experience includes project insurance cases, energy project disputes and arbitrations related to joint ventures. **Strengths:** "An intelligent individual who has a great manner towards both clients and tribunals."

Thirty Nine Essex Street

See profile on p.797

THE SET

This is a truly international set as evidenced by the fact that it has members practising across the globe, an outpost in Singapore and plans to launch a Malaysian base in 2014. Sources consider it a "fantastic set with a high calibre of arbitrators and counsel." Members receive instructions from governments, developers and contractors, and regularly tackle high-value infrastructure project disputes. The set is "forward-thinking and progressive, and has a good team of barristers who are capable of dealing with a wide range of arbitration matters."

SILKS

Stuart Catchpole QC A leading practitioner adept at handling disputes governed by a variety of arbitral laws, including those of Dubai, Hong Kong and Nigeria. He boasts an impressive range of experience in matters ranging from joint venture disputes to contract terminations. Recent instructions have taken him to Eastern Europe and South America. **Strengths:** "He is a force of nature. His ability to get on top of hugely complicated and technical material in no time at all is hugely impressive."

Adrian Hughes QC Has a notable construction arbitration practice and is especially well regarded for his work in Asia. He has a great deal of experience in acting on matters governed by Hong Kong arbitral rules. **Strengths:** "He has the ability to inspire confidence in his clients. His advice is delivered in a straightforward manner, and he realises the commercial requirements of the client."

Charles Manzoni QC (see p.662) An experienced construction silk who is especially noted for the strength of his Hong Kong-based arbitration practice. He has been called to the Bar in Hong Kong and England, and is also a qualified mechanical and electrical engineer. Manzoni is adept at handling claims arising from issues such as delayed completion, design defects and costs. **Strengths:** "A sensible, commercially minded and popular advocate."

Sean Wilken QC Focuses on construction matters in the projects and energy sectors and has experience of handling disputes governed by Hong Kong and Dubai law. His work of late has included matters involving international real estate developers and arbitrations concerned with construction funding. **Strengths:** "He is extremely good, unbelievably clever, efficient and attentive."

JUNIORS

Karim Ghaly (see p.607) Often receives instructions from clients in the Middle East, where he has established a strong reputation in the construction and natural resources fields. He has also handled arbitrations in South America and South East Asia. **Strengths:** "A great analytical thinker who any client would love." "He is very knowledgeable in this field and is an impressive advocate."

Adam Robb Has a practice that focuses on construction, infrastructure and engineering matters in the Middle East, Africa and Europe. He is a senior junior who is experienced in acting as sole counsel in disputes. **Strengths:** "He is very hands-on and a great team player."

4 Pump Court

See profile on p.849

THE SET

Home to a number of high-calibre individuals with practices focused on professional negligence, construction, energy and shipping disputes. Barristers at this set receive instructions in many of the world's most significant infrastructure disputes.

SILKS

Sean Brannigan QC Has experience in numerous jurisdictions around the world, including those in the Middle East, Europe, USA and Asia. He has recently been involved in significant disputes relating to oil and gas, infrastructure and power station construction. **Strengths:** "He's very astute and has huge brain power." "He's phenomenal on his feet."

Alexander Gunning QC Has a broad practice encompassing shipbuilding and energy-related construction arbitrations. He has handled a number of matters emerging from terminated projects and disputes over costs. **Strengths:** "He is extremely easy to work with and carefully thinks through what he does."

Rachel Ansell QC Has a great deal of experience of arbitrations in Middle Eastern and African jurisdictions, representing clients including oil and gas operators and major contractors. She has recently brought major counterclaims on behalf of clients and handled issues surrounding contract termination. **Strengths:** "She is very reliable and thorough and is a good, punchy advocate." "She is very good on the detail, and clients certainly warm to her."

JUNIORS

Alexander Hickey Has experience of handling arbitrations throughout the Middle East, Africa, Asia, Europe and Russia. His work is particularly weighted towards representing clients in disputes in the offshore energy and shipping industries. **Strengths:** "A complete tornado. He is incredibly dedicated and hard-working, and he gets results."

Other Ranked Lawyers

Michael Black QC (XXIV Old Buildings) Has an internationally focused construction disputes practice. He has been instructed in recent arbitrations in Africa, the Caribbean and the Middle East. Recent work has included matters emanating from the oil and gas and infrastructure spheres. **Strengths:** "His presentation and oral advocacy skills are excellent. His experience, legal knowledge and analysis of the law are very impressive, and his preparation for hearings is always thorough. In cross-examination, he is polite but highly effective."

Stuart Kennedy (3PB Barristers) A qualified quantity surveyor who both sits and acts as counsel in arbitrations. He has handled claims related to cost disputes, defective construction and value of work done. **Strengths:** "He is very perceptive and gets to the real issues in a case."

Steven Walker (see p.745) (Stone Chambers) Has a wide commercial practice with a focus on construction and engineering disputes in the offshore energy sector. **Strengths:** "His written work is excellent. He completely understands how to communicate with the client to make them feel at ease."

LONDON Arbitrators

International Arbitration: Arbitrators London
Star individuals
Hoffmann Lord *Brick Court Chambers (ORL)* ◊
Band 1
Black Michael *XXIV Old Buildings (ORL)* ◊
Blackburn John *Atkin Chambers (ORL)* ◊ *
Boswood Anthony *Fountain Court Chambers (ORL)* ◊
Brynmor Thomas David *Thirty Nine Essex Street (ORL)* ◊ *
Collins Michael *Essex Court Chambers (ORL)* ◊
Edelman Colin *Devereux (ORL)* ◊ *
Fernyhough Richard *Keating Chambers (ORL)* ◊ *
Furst Stephen *Keating Chambers (ORL)* ◊ *
Gaitskell Robert *Keating Chambers (ORL)* ◊ *
Glick Ian *One Essex Court (ORL)* ◊
Heilbron Hilary *Brick Court Chambers (ORL)* ◊
Hirst Jonathan *Brick Court Chambers (ORL)* ◊
Jacobs Richard *Essex Court Chambers (ORL)* ◊
Landau Toby *Essex Court Chambers (ORL)* ◊
Langley Sir Gordon *Fountain Court Chambers (ORL)* ◊
Leaver Peter *One Essex Court (ORL)* ◊
Lew Julian D. M. *20 Essex Street (ORL)* ◊
Marrin John *Keating Chambers (ORL)* ◊ *
Matthews Duncan *20 Essex Street (ORL)* ◊
Redfern Alan *One Essex Court (ORL)* ◊
Reichert Klaus *Brick Court Chambers (ORL)* ◊
Rokison Kenneth *Kenneth Rokison QC - (ORL)* ◊
Rowley William J *20 Essex Street (ORL)* ◊
Siberry Richard *Essex Court Chambers (ORL)* ◊
Smouha Joe *Essex Court Chambers (ORL)* ◊
Sutton David *20 Essex Street (ORL)* ◊
Symons Christopher *3 Verulam Buildings (ORL)* ◊
Tackaberry John *Thirty Nine Essex Street (ORL)* ◊
Tuckey Simon *20 Essex Street (ORL)* ◊
Uff John *Keating Chambers (ORL)* ◊ *
Veeder V V *Essex Court Chambers (ORL)* ◊
* *Indicates individual with profile.*
◊ *(ORL) = Other Ranked Lawyer.*

Ranked Lawyers

John Blackburn QC (see p.550) (Atkin Chambers) Has been appointed co-arbitrator and chair in disputes in jurisdictions such as Paris, London, Geneva and Hong Kong. His caseload has featured disputes related to energy, insurance and construction. **Strengths:** "He is incredibly well prepared and he is a great lawyer. You will get the right results with him."

Lord Hoffmann QC (Brick Court Chambers) Has a great deal of experience, having been an advocate in South Africa and England and a Judge in the High Court and Court of Appeal. His instructions as an arbitrator have included significant matters in the shipping sector and a major matter arising from the Russian market. **Strengths:** "He has a stellar reputation and is a great intellectual. He is the right person for arbitrations involving intricate pieces of law."

Hilary Heilbron QC (Brick Court Chambers) Sits as arbitrator for all the main arbitral bodies and handles many significant matters of high value. She has handled a variety of claims, including joint venture disputes and matters in the oil industry. **Strengths:** "Hilary's great skill at cutting to the essentials of a case keeps her in great demand."

Jonathan Hirst QC (Brick Court Chambers) Has a great deal of experience acting as both advocate and arbitrator. He sits on a wide range of disputes, including banking, insurance and shipping matters. **Strengths:** "He is very sensible, practical and intelligent."

Klaus Reichert (Brick Court Chambers) Often appointed to chair arbitrations on a broad range of commercial matters in Paris, New York, Dubai and Zurich. One particularly significant recent matter involved a corporate dispute connected to an African state's LNG sector. He is also noted for his involvement in sport arbitrations. **Strengths:** "He is a very well-regarded and sensible co-ordinator of a tribunal."

Colin Edelman QC (Devereux) Has a broad commercial practice and a particularly strong reputation for insurance-related matters. He has been appointed as arbitrator for matters concerning the pharmaceuticals industry, and has handled cases arising from natural disasters, as well as disputes relating to questions of professional liability. **Strengths:** "He is incredibly good. He has fantastic insurance credentials, and is very straightforward as an arbitrator." "He is the kingpin of the insurance and reinsurance arbitration world."

Ian Glick QC (One Essex Court) Receives regular appointments as sole arbitrator or tribunal chairman. He is well versed in insurance, oil and gas pricing, travel and shipbuilding arbitrations. **Strengths:** "He is very quick to master the technical issues and see what is coming next; he is very analytical in that respect. He combines that with a very experienced, pragmatic approach to disputes." "He has an absolutely first-class mind. He is extraordinarily clever and very calm. This enables him to smoothly manage any egos or tantrums. He is both extremely intelligent and totally calm."

Peter Leaver QC (One Essex Court) A seasoned professional with experience in a broad range of commercial disputes, including construction matters in Africa and Asia, gas pricing issues and sport disputes. He enjoys a busy practice as an arbitrator and has recently handled a joint venture matter in the gas industry and a negligence claim in the telecommunications sector. **Strengths:** "He is very diligent in his preparation and was miles ahead of the rest of us in understanding the issues." "He was extraordinarily well prepared and focused on reaching a commercial and fair result."

Alan Redfern (One Essex Court) Has a strong background as a litigation lawyer and now receives appointments to chair tribunals in disputes seated in a range of countries. Matters he has recently been involved in include a dispute in the oil and gas sector and a shareholder matter arising in the pharmaceutical industry. **Strengths:** "He is an extremely impressive construction specialist who offers concise instructions." "He is extremely experienced and highly commercial."

Michael Collins QC (Essex Court Chambers) Now exclusively works as an arbitrator. He has handled arbitrations in London, Bermuda and Hong Kong, and is strong on insurance and partnership-related matters. **Strengths:** "This is his bag; he is very experienced, and he runs the hearing in a pleasant and efficient way."

Richard Jacobs QC (Essex Court Chambers) A leading authority on Bermuda Form insurance disputes, who also handles matters relating to the oil, aviation and banking industries. His practice has seen him instructed in various Middle Eastern jurisdictions. **Strengths:** "Intelligent, collegiate, diligent and very willing to roll his sleeves up, he delivers awards to the parties on time." "He is very bright, fair and commercially minded."

Toby Landau QC (Essex Court Chambers) Has a stellar reputation for his work as both arbitrator and counsel in international disputes. He has been involved in numerous matters under the various institutional rules, and has been instructed for both investment treaty and commercial arbitrations. **Strengths:** "He is an expert on the law and procedure, and gives intelligent strategic direction. He is extremely good to work with."

Richard Siberry QC (Essex Court Chambers) Has a strong background in commercial matters as an advocate before the Commercial Court. As an arbitrator he continues to sit under a variety of institutional rules in sectors such as oil and gas, shipping and insurance. **Strengths:** "Very pleasant to appear in front of, he is thorough and well prepared."

Joe Smouha QC (Essex Court Chambers) Enjoys regular appointments as an arbitrator in commercial disputes, both in England and overseas. He has experience in sectors such as energy, insurance and advertising. **Strengths:** "He is really great and easy to work with. He gets to grips with the details of the case quickly and is able to identify the important points in an intelligent way."

V V Veeder QC (Essex Court Chambers) Has a great deal of experience in a range of commercial matters, including international trade, banking, insurance and oil and gas. As arbitrator, he sits in disputes in a huge range of jurisdictions, including Paris, Stockholm, Hong Kong and the USA. **Strengths:** "He is well informed and well read, and has a good presence."

Julian Lew QC (20 Essex Street) Has 30 years of experience of undertaking commercial disputes and now principally acts as arbitrator. His areas of focus and experience include cases arising from international transactions, corporate purchase and sales agreements and joint ventures. **Strengths:** "He is unparalleled and manages to remain unruffled when tackling difficult matters."

Duncan Matthews QC (20 Essex Street) Enjoys a broad commercial practice as both advocate and arbitrator, acting in England and abroad. He has a rich international trade background and also advises on banking and partnership disputes. Matthews is an established practitioner in the busy arbitration centre of Singapore. **Strengths:** "He has a very penetrating mind, and is a powerful character."

William Rowley QC (20 Essex Street) Practises in international commercial disputes relating to competition law, insurance and contracts in a variety of sectors, including energy. He has sat for matters subject to a broad range of national laws and has been engaged on matters in Europe, South America, Russia, Uganda and New York. **Strengths:** "He knows international arbitration procedures and rules back to front." "A bright light in the area."

Simon Tuckey QC (20 Essex Street) A retired Court of Appeal Judge who now has a wide practice in international disputes. He has been appointed to sit as arbitrator in disputes under a variety of institutional rules in sectors such as insurance, telecommunications and energy. **Strengths:** "A fantastic, no-nonsense practitioner who gets to the heart of the issue quickly."

David Sutton (20 Essex Street) Has a great deal of experience in the High Courts of England and Hong Kong and sits as an arbitrator in disputes across the world. He has significant experience of banking, pharmaceutical, oil and gas and project disputes. **Strengths:** "The quality of his analysis was very impressive. When the product came out, you could see it was a deeply impressive item. He shone out."

John Tackaberry QC (Thirty Nine Essex Street) A widely experienced lawyer, who is admitted to the Bar in multiple jurisdictions including California and Ireland. He has been appointed to matters subject to French, Spanish and Czech law in the recent past.

David Brynmor Thomas (see p.559) (Thirty Nine Essex Street) Highly experienced in disputes arising from the energy sector. Recent appointments have included construction and joint venture arbitrations in Pakistan, Ukraine and the UAE. **Strengths:** "David is an extremely experienced and highly regarded international arbitration lawyer. He is so thoughtful and knowledgeable."

Anthony Boswood QC (Fountain Court Chambers) Sits as an arbitrator under various institutional rules, in disputes relating to insurance, energy and the media, amongst other sectors.

Sir Gordon Langley QC (Fountain Court Chambers) Has a reputation as an arbitrator who produces work of the highest quality. A former High Court judge, he is known for his expertise in construction, commercial contract and insurance law. **Strengths:** "A very pleasant individual who is quick-witted and gets to the crux of the matter quickly." "He has great presence and command of the papers, and he is highly numerate."

Richard Fernyhough QC (see p.600) (Keating Chambers) Has a solid reputation in construction and engineering arbitrations. He is often appointed as sole arbitrator or chairman by the main arbitral institutions, and has sat recently in both Hong Kong and Cairo. **Strengths:** "He has a very clear grasp of the law and he goes about it properly and in a rigorous fashion."

Stephen Furst QC (see p.605) (Keating Chambers) Appointed by the main institutions as sole arbitrator in a variety of jurisdictions, including Middle Eastern states. Matters he has recently sat for include construction arbitrations relating to costs, energy matters in the Middle East and project disputes. **Strengths:** "As an arbitrator, he is completely on top of the relevant law and has a nice way about him. He is fair, but he gets to the point quickly." "There is no doubt that he is an excellent arbitrator."

Robert Gaitskell QC (see p.605) (Keating Chambers) Receives appointments to sit on complex and labour-intensive arbitrations. His recent instructions have featured oil and gas disputes in West Africa and Russia, in addition to a highly technical claim against a state government. **Strengths:** "He is an excellent international arbitrator, in terms of his ability to handle the tribunals which he chairs, his knowledge of the substantive law and the promptness with which he turns work around."

John Marrin QC (Keating Chambers) Has built a strong reputation among peers and has received some impressive instructions, including being appointed tribunal chair in a Dubai arbitration. Recent disputes he has sat for include energy, technology and construction matters. **Strengths:** "I was particularly impressed by his ability to deal with what was an awful amount of technical and legal submissions in a short period of time." "As an arbitrator he is balanced, impartial and very competent."

John Uff QC (see p.742) (Keating Chambers) Has a strong technical background which makes him a favourite for construction disputes. His international reputation has led to him securing numerous appointments as arbitrator under a range of arbitral rules. **Strengths:** "He is first rate. He is also greatly experienced and has a professional qualification in engineering."

Kenneth Rokison QC (International Commercial Arbitrator) Has 36 years of experience practising as a barrister in various fields of international commercial law. His work has spanned areas from shipping and insurance to oil and commodities, and he now sits in arbitrations in jurisdictions such as Singapore and Malaysia. **Strengths:** "He is meticulously prepared, keenly focused on the detail of the case and highly perceptive with regard to the key issues at play."

Michael Black QC (XXIV Old Buildings) Has a truly global arbitration practice with an emphasis on work in the Middle East. His recent instructions have featured construction, energy and financial services disputes. **Strengths:** "His experience, legal knowledge and analysis of law is very impressive."

Christopher Symons QC (3 Verulam Buildings) Has had recent appointments as an arbitrator on matters in the Far East and Australia. He has sat for contract interpretation disputes and various insurance matters, including business interruption claims. **Strengths:** "He offers great judgement and has a great presence."

Contents:

LONDON

Licensing London
Leading Sets
Band 1
Francis Taylor Building *
Band 2
3 Raymond Buildings Barristers *
Band 3
Cornerstone Barristers *
Leading Silks
Star individuals
Gouriet Gerald *Francis Taylor Building* Ⓐ *
Walsh Stephen *3 Raymond Buildings Barristers* Ⓐ *
Band 1
de Haan Kevin *Francis Taylor Building* Ⓐ
FitzGerald Susanna *One Essex Court (ORL)* ◊
Kolvin Philip *Cornerstone Barristers* *
Matthias David *Francis Taylor Building*
Band 2
Bromley-Martin Michael *3 Raymond Buildings Barristers* Ⓐ
Findlay James *Cornerstone Barristers* *
Heslop Martin S *2 Hare Court (ORL)* ◊ *
Moger Christopher *4 Pump Court (ORL)* ◊ *
Leading Juniors
Star individuals
Rankin James *Francis Taylor Building* Ⓐ *
Band 1
Grant Gary *Francis Taylor Building* Ⓐ *
Le Fevre Sarah *3 Raymond Buildings Barristers* Ⓐ *
Phillips Jeremy *Francis Taylor Building* Ⓐ *
Band 2
Butt Matthew *3 Raymond Buildings Barristers* Ⓐ *
Charalambides Leo *Francis Taylor Building*
Glenser Peter *9 Bedford Row (ORL)* ◊ *
Naqshbandi Saba *3 Raymond Buildings Barristers* Ⓐ
Ranatunga Asitha *Cornerstone Barristers* *
Band 3
Cannon Josef *Cornerstone Barristers* *
Kapila Rachel *3 Raymond Buildings Barristers* Ⓐ *
Lopez Juan *Francis Taylor Building* Ⓐ
Monkcom Stephen *Tanfield Chambers (ORL)* ◊
Whale Stephen *Landmark Chambers (ORL)* ◊ Ⓐ *
* *Indicates set / individual with profile.*
◊ *(ORL) = Other Ranked Lawyer.*
Ⓐ *direct access (see p.11).*

Band 1

Francis Taylor Building

See profile on p.806

THE SET

Francis Taylor Building maintains its standing as "the most dynamic set" for licensing law. Members of chambers represent both claimants and defendants in an array of issues, including betting and gaming, liquor, firearms, entertainment and sexual venue licensing. The set offers a full service, from handling applications in front of local authorities to debating the finer points of statutory law in the Supreme Court. Its members have both practical and academic knowledge of licensing law and are said to be steeped in the subject. By way of example, Simon Mehigan QC brings a wealth of academic knowledge to the set, as editor of 'Paterson's Licensing Acts' and contributor to 'Smith and Monkcom: The Law of Gambling'. As a consequence he is able to help clients with "particularly tricky definitional terms" of the Gambling Act 2005.

Client service: Senior clerk Paul Coveney heads a "hugely impressive" team that is "very communicative and efficient" and "highly responsive."

SILKS

Gerald Gouriet QC (see p.613) Handles a variety of licensing law matters both for and against local authorities. He is noted for his expertise in judicial reviews, large-scale venue licensing and betting and gaming. **Strengths:** "Everybody admires his honeyed tongue; he has a great turn of phrase." "We favour Gerald for the high-end complex cases; he is fantastic at simplifying very complex legal arguments." **Recent work:** He successfully acted for The Association of Licensed Multiple Retailers on opposing the Early Morning Restriction Order proposed by the local authority in Blackpool.

David Matthias QC Acts for a wide range of clients on licensing matters, and regularly advises some of the largest local authorities on the structure of their licensing policies. He is particularly recognised for his experience in front of Westminster committees. **Strengths:** "He was charming and had an extremely good relationship with the clients." "His advocacy is intellectual and persuasive." **Recent work:** Advised Newham Council on the most important case so far under the Gambling Act 2005, which concerned the spread of betting shops in the borough.

Kevin de Haan QC Celebrated for his work for online gambling operators, and also attracts praise for his general regulatory knowledge. **Strengths:** "His advice is forthright and robust." "He is extraordinary – so unstuffy. He knows gambling like the back of his hand and is hugely enthusiastic."

JUNIORS

James Rankin (see p.704) Acts for applicants and objectors on a raft of issues, including liquor, betting and gaming, and firearms licensing. He is noted for his expertise in judicial review hearings. **Strengths:** "Extremely clever and good on his feet, he will fight a client's corner tenaciously but always with good humour." "He has a good breadth of knowledge and amazing client skills, and adopts a superb approach." **Recent work:** Acted for Extreme Oyster on its successful claim that shadow licences can be granted to the freeholder of a nightclub premises under the Licensing Act 2003.

Gary Grant (see p.613) Negotiates a range of licensing work for some of London's leading leisure and hospitality operators. He is highly regarded for his work in large-scale venue licensing and for his skill in resisting police applications to revoke licences. **Strengths:** "He deploys excellent negotiating skills to achieve results in favour of the client." "He's a terrier; once he gets hold of the matter he's very quick at giving you advice and he's not afraid to get his hands dirty." **Recent work:** Secured a licence for TV chef Bill Granger's new restaurant in Islington's cumulative impact zone.

Jeremy Phillips (see p.692) Has a varied practice covering licensing law, regulatory law and judicial reviews. He has particular experience in acting for nightclubs and in securing sexual entertainment venue licences. **Strengths:** "Extremely able and very approachable. He manages to turn work around so quickly." "A very good advocate whose courteous and knowledgeable manner instils confidence in clients. He has gravitas before tribunals." **Recent work:** Raised novel questions of law in a case concerning whether a licence for a lap-dancing club should be granted when the future character of the area was under dispute.

Leo Charalambides Covers all aspects of licensing under the Licensing Act 2003 and Gambling Act 2005. His strengths lie in petrol forecourt licensing, sexual entertainment venue licensing and gambling premises licensing. In addition, he is the editor of the Journal of Licensing. **Strengths:** "Bright and tenacious." "He is very calm, meticulous and precise in all he does; he thinks outside of the box." **Recent work:** Has acted for several large petrol station forecourt operators with regard to licensing for the convenience stores located thereon.

Juan Lopez Represents clients in liquor and betting and gaming licensing matters. He is noted for his expertise in noise complaints, internet gaming products and vehicle operator licensing. **Strengths:** "A tenacious, fearless advocate." "He's extremely straightforward with the client and is very personable. He has very good legal knowledge and conveys it in a way that is understandable to the client." **Recent work:** Acted for Star of Kings in an appeal against a decision to reduce the venue's opening hours and capacity in Islington's saturation zone.

Band 2

3 Raymond Buildings Barristers

See profile on p.857

THE SET

3 Raymond Buildings remains "a first port of call" for licensing matters. The set offers a comprehensive service covering betting and gaming and liquor licensing. It also has a number of more niche offerings, including, for example, specialist knowledge in private security licensing and street trading. The set's expertise in criminal law complements its work with regard to compliance obligations and enforcement hearings.

Client service: "The clerks, led by Eddie Holland, are highly efficient and very helpful – they have a good idea of the marketplace."

SILKS

Stephen Walsh QC (see p.745) Handles all aspects of licensing for leading gambling, retail and leisure operators in the UK. He has successfully acted on a number of high-profile large-scale venue licences. **Strengths:** "Very cerebral and academically capable, he applies himself well to the legal arguments and has a fantastic relationship with the client." "A leading expert in his field, he takes a hard-working and commercial approach." **Recent work:** He acted in the Mayfield Depot case, concerning the redevelopment of an old railway station in Manchester to be used as an international events space.

Michael Bromley-Martin QC Advises on liquor, entertainment and gambling licensing for leisure and retail operators. He is particularly strong on applications for nightclubs and festivals. **Strengths:** "He knows his stuff very well indeed, and is an excellent operator." "He's a brilliant cross-examiner." **Recent work:** Acted for High Definition Festival in a review licensing hearing surrounding its East London event.

JUNIORS

Sarah Le Fevre (see p.653) Represents both applicants and objectors in the full remit of licensing issues in the High Court. Her capabilities extend to judicial reviews and complex cases concerning deaths on premises. **Strengths:** "She is a fair, honest, straight-bat practitioner." "She's an extremely competent advocate, who is particularly skilled at cross-examination, and has excellent client care skills." **Recent work:** Acted for 93 Feet East in its judicial review against a decision by Tower Hamlets to close its premises for a period of six months.

Matthew Butt Acts for nationally renowned clients in liquor, gambling and private security licensing cases. He regularly represents the Security Industry Authority (SIA) and is routinely instructed in licensing prosecutions and cases involving policy considerations. **Strengths:** "His core attribute is his tenacity; he really fights for his client." "An excellent advocate who provides considered written advice and impressive strategic thinking. He is also personable and pleasant to deal with." **Recent work:** Acted for the SIA in a three-day appeal against a decision to withdraw approved contractor status.

Saba Naqshbandi Known for her strong general licensing practice, she regularly represents both the police and leisure operators. Noted for her knowledge of gambling licensing, she represents clients in front of all levels of tribunals. **Strengths:** "She is a super advocate and is very, very clever." "Her detail is second to none and she is very popular with clients." **Recent work:** Acted for Minmar (929), which operates 70 arcades across the UK, in one of the first review hearings before the Gambling Commission.

Rachel Kapila (see p.642) Handles licensing and regulatory law for councils, objectors and applicants. She has expertise in stage licensing, taxi licensing and street trading. **Strengths:** "She shows meticulous attention to detail." "She leaves no stone unturned, and is a reliable pair of hands for difficult cases." "A determined advocate in court." **Recent work:** Acted for the Metropolitan Police in successfully restricting the opening hours of a club in Richmond.

Band 3

Cornerstone Barristers
See profile on p.781

THE SET

Cornerstone Barristers has "a formidable reputation as far as licensing expertise is concerned." Its members act for operators, the police, trade associations and licensing authorities on liquor, gambling, entertainment and taxi licensing. They have expertise in developing cumulative impact policies with local authorities, and have also worked with trade associations on their feedback to proposed legislative changes.

Client service: "The clerks are very helpful; they work like clockwork and are very co-operative and pragmatic."

SILKS

Philip Kolvin QC (see p.648) Heads the licensing team at Cornerstone, and is regularly involved in high-profile cases. He covers all areas of licensing but is particularly noted for his work in large-scale venue licensing and sexual entertainment venue licensing. **Strengths:** "An ambitious, deep statistics man who is clever and works hard." "He seems always to be found at the cutting edge of licensing decisions." **Recent work:** Acted for a number of Soho sex shops in a Court of Appeal case which saw them repaid more than £1 million in licensing fees by Westminster Council.

James Findlay QC Qualified to practise licensing across England, Wales and Scotland, and regularly acts for local councils. He has particular expertise in statutory appeals and judicial review, and has appeared in cases right up to the Supreme Court. **Strengths:** "A very canny operator, who is superb in the High Court. He was really cogent, knew the case inside out and presented the information in a clear and concise manner." **Recent work:** Acted successfully for Aylesbury Vale in an appeal where it was held that substantial compliance with the procedural requirements of the 1989 licensing scheme would suffice to bring the scheme into force and thereby entitle the council to prosecute an unlicensed taxi operator.

JUNIORS

Asitha Ranatunga Acts for both objectors and applicants in relation to the liquor licensing of pubs, nightclubs and academic institutions. He is highly regarded for his knowledge and capabilities in cases where there is a cumulative impact zone or stress area. **Strengths:** "Excellent, quiet and assured, he clearly knows his stuff and is not fazed by objectors who appear with off-piste arguments." "He is knowledgeable and approachable, and the clients like him because he's good at guiding them through the process." **Recent work:** Acted for Oxford Brookes University on securing a new premises licence after the redevelopment of the John Henry Brookes Building.

Josef Cannon (see p.565) Handles sexual entertainment venue licences and liquor licensing for objectors and applicants, including local authorities and the police. He has notable expertise in judicial review cases and has contributed to one of the leading textbooks, entitled 'Licensed Premises: Law and Practice'. **Strengths:** "He's very approachable and gets results." "Capable beyond his years, he's an impressive advocate. He knows which buttons to push." **Recent work:** Acted on a recent case that provides important guidance regarding the interface between licensing and planning and the breadth of discretion councils have when refusing sexual entertainment venue licences.

Other Ranked Lawyers

Peter Glenser (see p.609) (9 Bedford Row) Known for his expertise in firearms licensing, he regularly acts for appellants. **Strengths:** "Absolutely first-rate; he's a very good advocate." "His advocacy skills are fantastic and he's great with clients, as he's calm and really unflappable." **Recent work:** He successfully appealed against a decision to revoke the firearms licence of a champion international shot who had become obsessed with a work colleague.

Susanna FitzGerald QC (One Essex Court) Recommended for her expertise in all three licensing specialisms – liquor, gambling and entertainment. Heavily involved in licensing policy, she assisted in the development of the Gambling Bill. FitzGerald is highly regarded for her strength in front of regulators and appears for clients in cases up to the Supreme Court. **Strengths:** "She's got tremendous legal expertise combined with excellent adversarial skills. She's an accomplished advocate." "She takes a very commercial approach, gets on well with the clients and is impressive on her feet." **Recent work:** Acted for a table dancing club as an interested party in resisting an appeal for leave to allow a judicial review of the decision to grant the club a sexual entertainment venue licence.

Martin Heslop QC (see p.625) (2 Hare Court) Handles liquor licensing for objectors and applicants, and gambling licensing for some of the country's leading casino operators. His background in criminal and health and safety law enables him to handle complex licensing cases surrounding fatalities at venues. **Strengths:** "Extremely well prepared, he picks up information very quickly indeed. He has a remarkable memory and he's able to marshal a case very effectively." **Recent work:** Acted for Avalon nightclub on the review of its licence after a fatal shooting on the premises.

Stephen Whale (Landmark Chambers) Acts for applicants and objectors on liquor licensing, and regularly appears in the High Court. **Strengths:** "He is tremendous. He's a very sound pair of hands and is very likeable." "Bright and pleasant, he knows what he is doing." **Recent work:** Secured a late night premises licence for a venue in the Shoreditch special policy area in the face of a substantial police objection.

Christopher Moger QC (4 Pump Court) Known for his expertise in gambling licensing, he is particularly strong on gaming and lotteries cases and regularly acts for casino operators. He is primarily recognised for his work for the Gambling Commission. **Strengths:** "A formidable advocate." "I cannot praise his intellect or his analysis of the law highly enough."

Stephen Monkcom (Tanfield Chambers) Author of one of the leading textbooks, 'Smith & Monkcom: The Law of Gambling', he is regularly instructed by bookmakers and casinos. He has specific expertise in complex issues of licensing law. **Strengths:** "Highly intelligent, he has a width and depth of knowledge which is very special." "He's thoughtful and user-friendly, and with him there's no fuss and overdoing of the problem – he understands where you're trying to get to."

MIDLANDS

Licensing Midlands	
Leading Juniors	
Band 1	
Clover Sarah	*Kings Chambers (ORL)* ◊
Evans Andrew	*St Philips Chambers (ORL)* ◊ *
Williams Ben	*Kings Chambers (ORL)* ◊ *

Ranked Lawyers

Ben Williams (see p.752) (Kings Chambers) Acts for local authorities, the police and licensees on liquor, taxi and entertainment licensing matters. **Strengths:** "He has a calm manner but an authoritative presence. A lot of the arguments he wins on paper because he's very thorough." "He is practical and prepared." **Recent work:** He advised Blackpool Borough Council on its consultation into a proposed Early Morning Restriction Order in Blackpool.

Sarah Clover (Kings Chambers) Handles liquor and sexual entertainment venue licensing in both magistrates' courts and the High Court. She acts for a wide range of clients, including licensees, councils, residents, pub companies and the police. **Strengths:** "She is very helpful, approachable and always on hand to advise us." "She's really feisty, incredibly knowledgeable and well researched, and knows her case law really well." **Recent work:** She acted for Kirklees Council in an appeal of its decision to revoke the premises licence of the Alder House Hotel after a number of serious child exploitation crimes were committed there.

Andrew Evans (see p.596) (St Philips Chambers) Focuses on liquor and entertainment licensing in the Midlands. His practice extends to taxi and firearms licensing, and he represents clients from committee to court hearings. **Strengths:** "He is an excellent advocate, commercial, well prepared and good with clients." "He is measured in his approach and quietly persistent." **Recent work:** He acted in an appeal to secure a new premises licence for a venue previously closed due to Triad activity.

NORTH EASTERN

Licensing North Eastern	
Leading Juniors	
Band 1	
Holland Charles	*Trinity Chambers (ORL)* ◊ *
Band 2	
Smith Joan	*Trinity Chambers (ORL)* ◊ *

Ranked Lawyers

Charles Holland (see p.630) (Trinity Chambers) Handles the gamut of licensing work, including liquor, gambling and entertainment licensing. He is particularly noted for his expertise in large-scale venue licensing and taxi licensing. **Strengths:** "He is extremely personable and very thorough, and goes the extra mile for the client – he does an immense amount of research." "He stands out for his advocacy, his approach is not aggressive but firm and he doesn't talk down to anyone." **Recent work:** He successfully retained the licence of the Inside Out club in Darlington after it came under police review.

Joan Smith (see p.723) (Trinity Chambers) Acts for both applicants and objectors on taxi, firearms, liquor and gambling licensing before licensing committees and the magistrates' court. She is highly regarded for her taxi licensing practice, which includes advising statutory bodies on matters of policy. **Strengths:** "She is very approachable, thorough in her research and strong in her presentations in court."

WESTERN

Licensing Western	
Leading Juniors	
Band 1	
Light Roy	*St John's Chambers (ORL)* ◊ [A]
Band 2	
Barker Kerry	*Guildhall Chambers (ORL)* ◊
* *Indicates individual with profile.*	
◊ *(ORL) = Other Ranked Lawyer.*	
[A] *direct access (see p.11).*	

Ranked Lawyers

Kerry Barker (Guildhall Chambers) Acts for both applicants and objectors on all aspects of licensing. He is particularly noted for his expertise in liquor licensing and gambling matters. **Strengths:** "He has loads of experience and he has a genuine interest in horse racing so he knows the gambling cases; he's also very good at appeals."

Roy Light (St John's Chambers) Handles alcohol, entertainment, taxi and sexual entertainment venue licensing. He has particular expertise in the licensing issues governing large-scale venues and online alcohol delivery services. **Strengths:** "He is very pragmatic in his advice, and a personable and client-friendly advocate." **Recent work:** He successfully appealed a decision to impose licensing restrictions on a large-scale venue near Newquay after complaints from local residents.

Contents:

LONDON

Local Government London

Leading Sets	
Band 1	Thirty Nine Essex Street *
11KBW *	**Band 3**
Landmark Chambers *	Francis Taylor Building *
Band 2	
Cornerstone Barristers *	

Leading Silks	
Star individuals	**Lowe** Mark *Cornerstone Barristers*
Giffin Nigel *11KBW*	**Maurici** James *Landmark Chambers*
Howell John *Blackstone Chambers (ORL)* ◊	**Morris** Fenella *Thirty Nine Essex Street*
Band 1	**Mould** Timothy *Landmark Chambers*
Drabble Richard *Landmark Chambers*	**Sheldon** Clive *11KBW*
Elvin David *Landmark Chambers*	**Strachan** James *Thirty Nine Essex Street*
Goudie James *11KBW* *	**Warnock** Andrew *1 Chancery Lane (ORL)* ◊ [A] *
Lieven Nathalie *Landmark Chambers*	**Westgate** Martin *Doughty Street Chambers (ORL)* ◊
Straker Timothy *4-5 Gray's Inn Square (ORL)* ◊ *	**Band 4**
Band 2	**Béar** Charles *Fountain Court Chambers (ORL)* ◊ *
Arden Andrew *Arden Chambers (ORL)* ◊ *	**Brown** Paul *Landmark Chambers*
George Charles *Francis Taylor Building* [A]	**Clayton** Richard *4-5 Gray's Inn Square (ORL)* ◊ *
Glover Richard *Francis Taylor Building*	**Coppel** Jason *11KBW* *
McGuire Bryan *Cornerstone Barristers*	**Grodzinski** Sam *Blackstone Chambers (ORL)* ◊
Roots Guy *Francis Taylor Building* *	**Mountfield** Helen *Matrix Chambers (ORL)* ◊ *
Band 3	**Oldham** Peter *11KBW* *
Bhose Ranjit *Cornerstone Barristers* *	**Richards** Jenni *Thirty Nine Essex Street*
Coppel Philip *Landmark Chambers* [A]	**Webb** Geraint *Henderson Chambers (ORL)* ◊ [A] *
Faulks Edward *1 Chancery Lane (ORL)* ◊ *	**Williams** Rhodri *Henderson Chambers (ORL)* ◊ [A] *
Findlay James *Cornerstone Barristers* *	**Wise** Ian *Monckton Chambers (ORL)* ◊ [A]
Harwood Richard *Thirty Nine Essex Street* *	**New Silks**
Hockman Stephen *6 Pump Court (ORL)* ◊ [A] *	**Forsdick** David *Landmark Chambers*
Holgate David *Landmark Chambers*	**Steyn** Karen *11KBW* *
Knafler Stephen *Garden Court Chambers (ORL)* ◊	

Leading Juniors	
Band 1	**Harrop-Griffiths** Hilton *Field Court Chambers (ORL)* ◊
Kolinsky Daniel *Landmark Chambers* *	**Moffett** Jonathan *11KBW* [A] *
Sharland Andrew *11KBW* [A] *	**Band 4**
Band 2	**Beglan** Wayne *Cornerstone Barristers* *
Baker Christopher *Arden Chambers (ORL)* ◊ *	**Greatorex** Paul *11KBW* [A] *
Busch Lisa *Landmark Chambers*	**Green** Robin *Cornerstone Barristers* *
Hutchings Matthew *Cornerstone Barristers*	**Hannett** Sarah *Matrix Chambers (ORL)* ◊ [A]
Manning Jonathan *Arden Chambers (ORL)* ◊ *	**Honey** Richard *Francis Taylor Building* [A] *
Oldham Jane *11KBW* *	**Kinnier** Andrew *Henderson Chambers (ORL)* ◊ [A] *
Band 3	**Lawson** David *Hardwicke (ORL)* ◊ [A]
Auburn Jonathan *Thirty Nine Essex Street* [A] *	**Olley** Katherine *Landmark Chambers*
Clement Joanne *11KBW* *	

** Indicates set / individual with profile.*
◊ (ORL) = Other Ranked Lawyer.
[A] direct access (see p.11).

Band 1

11KBW
See profile on p.823

THE SET

11KBW continues to impress with its market-leading expertise in local government matters, proving particularly strong on education and public procurement cases. The set offers considerable strength in depth at both silk and junior level, and is a first choice for the most complex matters. The barristers often represent local authorities in defence of challenges to local government powers, and regularly handle high-profile judicial review proceedings.

Client service: Lucy Barbet and Mark Dann are the set's senior clerks. According to sources, "the clerking is flexible – they offer very good service and are prompt."

SILKS

Nigel Giffin QC Remains a highly sought-after silk for local authorities facing complex or high-stakes challenges. He has particularly strong expertise in public procurement matters. **Strengths:** "An exceptional talent who is known for his succinctness, and ability to explain complex issues in a straightforward way." "He shows great skill in presenting an argument in a low-key but convincing manner." **Recent work:** Acted as lead counsel for the defence in R (Buck) v Doncaster, a Court of Appeal dispute relating to the relative powers and responsibilities of elected mayors and the full council.

James Goudie QC (see p.612) A hugely experienced silk in local government matters, and a popular choice for borough councils. He is a first port of call for disputes involving local authority powers, and is an expert on judicial review proceedings. **Strengths:** "A very shrewd advocate." "He is very authoritative, makes it look simple, and is a very good lawyer. He presents cases in a way that courts find helpful." **Recent work:** Represented the London Borough of Barnet in an application for judicial review concerning the borough's decision to sell a piece of real estate to the first interested party.

Clive Sheldon QC A popular choice of silk for high-level matters with a public law element, including disputes concerning NHS and community care services. His key clients include a number of London boroughs, whom he represents on both the claimant and defendant sides. **Strengths:** "A very intelligent advocate who knows what points will interest the court." **Recent work:** Acted for the defence in Alsopp v London Borough of Camden, a judicial review challenging daycare provision for disabled residents of the borough.

Jason Coppel QC (see p.578) One of the more recent silks at 11KBW. He is frequently called upon to advise public bodies, including waste authorities and local councils. He is also sought out for matters such as tendering and state aid disputes. **Strengths:** "He gave us detailed advice on the local authority background." **Recent work:** Advised a number of local authorities, including Rotherham, on a challenge to the government's distribution of EU regional aid funds.

Peter Oldham QC (see p.685) Noted for his prowess in education law, and also regularly instructed on employment, governance and vires issues. He is frequently called upon to advise on challenges to local authorities' powers, including land disposals and withdrawal of grants. **Strengths:** "A very tenacious advocate." "Very smooth and impressive." **Recent work:** Advised West Lindsey District Council in defence of a complaint alleging unlawful land disposal to a third party.

Karen Steyn QC (see p.728) A new silk with a highly successful public law practice. She acts on high-level judicial review proceedings, and acts for a range of clients, from borough councils to the Treasury Solicitor. **Strengths:** "Produces top-notch pleadings." "She is very good and highly focused – she doesn't mess around, and says what she has to say." **Recent work:** Defended Oxfordshire County Council against a claim concerning the determination of whether a child requires a statement of special educational needs.

JUNIORS

Jane Oldham (see p.684) A high-profile senior junior who advises on substantial local government matters, including funding challenges and issues relating to the recent changes to council tax benefit arrangements. She remains a popular choice of counsel for local authorities across the country. **Recent work:** Defended North Somerset Council, in a challenge to the funding allocation for youth services. The case concerned allegations of breach of equality duty and consultation duties under the Education Act 1996.

Andrew Sharland (see p.718) Acts for both defendants and claimants, frequently representing coroners and local councils. He advises on a range of matters, including inquests, funding for social care services, and challenges to central government funding changes. **Strengths:** "He is fearless and his advocacy is punchy. He is not one for saying things diplomatically for the sake of it – he will go out there fighting." "He's very good tactically, and advises both on the law and as to what different approaches will work in court." **Recent work:** Advised Leicester City Council on a widely reported challenge surrounding the reburial of the remains of Richard III.

Jonathan Moffett (see p.675) Very strong on education matters, and also acts for a number of high-profile public defendants, including emergency services providers and local authorities. **Recent work:** Acted for the London Fire & Emergency Planning Authority on a challenge brought by Islington LBC relating to the closure of fire stations.

Joanne Clement (see p.574) Advises an array of clients, including local authorities both as claimants and defendants. She is particularly sought after for judicial reviews concerning changes to education policy and public service funding. **Strengths:** "Intellectually rigorous and focused." **Recent work:** Acted for Rotherham MBC as one of the claimants, in a judicial review looking at EU funding allocation.

Paul Greatorex (see p.614) Handles a range of matters for public bodies including school governing boards and local authorities. Key areas of influence including advising on vires and changes to the provision of public services. **Recent work:** Advised the governors of Uplands Junior School on a judicial review concerning Leicester City Council's powers of intervention.

Landmark Chambers

See profile on p.829

THE SET

Planning work forms the cornerstone of this set's local government practice, and it is also noted for its handling of matters involving immigration and human rights. Recent work highlights have seen barristers instructed on infrastructure, housing and public service funding changes. Its members undertake advisory work, and also act on major disputes and challenges all the way up to the Supreme Court and the ECHR.

Client service: Sources note that the clerks "work very hard to get you access to your counsel of choice." Jay Fullilove is the senior clerk at the set.

SILKS

Richard Drabble QC Instructed across a broad range of local government issues, including social housing. His clients include household-name transport bodies and notable local authorities, and he also represents individual claimants. **Strengths:** "Great at spotting and focusing on the good points of cases." "He as massive experience in public law from housing to benefits, and is an expert on human rights." **Recent work:** Instructed by the Mayor of London to defend judicial review proceedings challenging cuts to the number of fire stations in London.

David Elvin QC Brings considerable planning and environmental law expertise to his local government practice. In addition to helping defend local authorities on housing disputes, he has also advised claimant entities on compulsory purchase order (CPO) and parking matters. **Strengths:** "Effective, very knowledgeable and a clever opponent." **Recent work:** Advised Birmingham City Council in defending a case brought by Midlands Co-op concerning its sale of land in Stirchley to Tesco.

Nathalie Lieven QC Has an impressive local government practice and particular expertise in planning and civil liberties matters. Acts for a number of local authorities, both as defendant and claimant. **Strengths:** "A rising star and a naturally gifted advocate." "A committed performer, who offers robust, premier league advice." **Recent work:** Advised Westminster City Council in the Court of Appeal, on a matter concerning licensing charges for sex shops.

Philip Coppel QC A former solicitor who acts for local authorities as complainants and defendants, and also represents individuals. He frequently advises on public law and local government issues relating to data protection and freedom of information. **Strengths:** "He has always been clear and concise in providing advice. He is very thorough in his analysis of matters." **Recent work:** Acted on Djanogly v Westminster, a judicial review concerning the levying of motorcycle parking charges.

David Holgate QC Handles a range of work including vires, planning and rating, as well as election matters. He is a popular choice of counsel for claimants, and has acted for a number of political parties and private companies. **Strengths:** "He employs a detailed and thorough analytical approach to his work, and is convincing in his presentation." "A forthright barrister with encyclopaedic knowledge." **Recent work:** Advised Midlands Co-op in a challenge to a land sale by Birmingham City Council.

Timothy Mould QC Has a strong local government practice that is heavily dominated by planning work. In addition acting for borough and city councils, he also advises waste management companies and private landowners. **Strengths:** "He's very good at cutting through lots of conflicting evidence, and dealing with the law in a sensible way." "He has a reassuring manner with clients, and breaks down complex points into plain English. He's a joy to watch." **Recent work:** Defended Portsmouth City Council against a challenge to a retail site's change of use.

James Maurici QC One of the set's newer silks. He has a thriving public law practice, with particular expertise in the environmental and planning aspects of local government work. He acts for individual claimants as well as government departments. **Strengths:** "Always open to comment, he doesn't insist he is right – he genuinely listens." **Recent work:** Acted for the defence in Staple v Secretary of State for Communities & Local Government, a class action claim concerning local land charges and fees for searches.

Paul Brown QC Displays formidable skill across a variety of public law areas. He has recently acted for individuals challenging decisions, and has also acted in defence of a number of London boroughs. **Recent work:** Advised the claimant in Timmins v Gedling Borough Council, a case concerning planning permission for a crematorium.

David Forsdick QC Has a strong profile on planning cases, and also applies his skills successfully to the broader public law and local government arena. **Strengths:** "He does very high-quality cases, and he does them well." **Recent work:** Acted for the defence on Leeds Group v Leeds City Council, a dispute concerning retrospective application of town and village green laws.

JUNIORS

Lisa Busch A strong junior who is frequently instructed on some of the most high-profile local government matters. Her workload includes high-stakes planning and infrastructure matters. **Recent work:** Advising the Secretary of State in Select Committee proceedings regarding High Speed 2.

Daniel Kolinsky Handles a broad variety of local government matters. He is particularly known for acting for ratepayers challenging land ratings, and also advises on ratings matters as they affect charities. **Strengths:** "He's straightforward, very thorough and someone who takes a very sensible and logical approach." "He has an ability to think on his feet, combined with great judgement." **Recent work:** Successfully represented the claimants in Aviva Investors Property Developers Ltd v Whitby (VO), an Upper Tribunal (Lands Chamber) appeal on the rating status of warehouse properties.

Katherine Olley Regularly advises on contentious public law matters, including local government matters. She has recently acted on disputes surrounding local authority powers and healthcare service changes. **Recent work:** Advised an interested party in connection with the London Jewish Girls High School judicial review challenge brought against the London Borough of Barnet. This case concerned a local authority's right to sell property.

Band 2

Cornerstone Barristers

See profile on p.781

THE SET

Cornerstone Barristers maintains a strong reputation in local government matters, and is especially well known for handling social housing cases. Members are further active on matters involving waste disposal, planning, and healthcare, and also handle challenges to council tax benefit changes.

Client service: Jonathan Maskew is the director of client service at the set.

SILKS

Ranjit Bhose QC He has recently handled a number of judicial reviews concerning the closure of public facilities and the withdrawal of public funding. He also handles social housing matters. **Strengths:** "You have to work ridiculously hard to keep up with him, and you would probably never be able to ambush him." "He's very carefully considered in his approach, and very convincing." **Recent work:** Acted for the defence in R (Centerprise Trust) v London Borough of Hackney, a judicial review challenge examining the decision to withdraw grant funding to a charity.

James Findlay QC A popular choice of senior counsel for a number of local authorities. He has experience on both the claimant and defendant sides, and regularly handles planning disputes and challenges to reductions in public funding. **Strengths:** "His advice is so well structured and clear." **Recent work:** Acted for the defence in R (SAVE) v Sheffield City Council, a challenge concerning the decision to demolish a listed building.

Mark Lowe QC Boasts a formidable reputation for his handling of planning disputes. His workload includes cases connected with waste treatment and residential developments, and he is also strong on telecommunications disputes. **Strengths:** "His in-depth preparation of a counter-argument is great." **Recent work:** Led the team advising Hertfordshire County Council on a recycling and energy recovery facility in New Barnfield.

Bryan McGuire QC Has a substantial practice advising local councils facing challenges to funding decisions. He is experienced at appearing before a range of bodies, including the Administrative Court and the Court of Appeal. **Recent work:** Acted as lead counsel for the defence in Nfuni v Solihull Metropolitan Borough Council, which examined the local council's duty to continue to provide educational and support funding to an asylum seeker leaving care.

JUNIORS

Matthew Hutchings A solid choice for a number of local authorities facing challenges to their decisions. Key mandates include advising on disputes over benefits, residency and housing. **Strengths:** "He gets the local authority's point of view across clearly, and has a high degree of credibility when he talks about local government." **Recent work:** Defended Ealing Council in a claim brought by Purewal, concerning the local authority's duty to rehouse a disabled woman following an alleged sexual assault.

Wayne Beglan Handles high-profile social housing work as well as waste and planning matters. He represents a range of public bodies including local councils, and also acts for private entities such as property developers. **Strengths:** "He gave me good support and good advice, and performed well." **Recent work:** Advised Hertfordshire County Council on planning and public law issues associated with a recycling and energy recovery facility in New Barnfield.

Robin Green Frequently represents clients in planning and public procurement matters, and has a strong record advising local authorities as well as challenging local authority decisions. **Strengths:** "He gets to the point, gives clear advice and knows his stuff." **Recent work:** Advised on R (Stern) v Horsham, a dispute that arose following breaches of statutory enforcement procedures.

Thirty Nine Essex Street

See profile on p.797

THE SET

A popular choice for a number of county and city councils both individually and in joint representations. The set advises clients on key planning and environment matters, and is strong on community care cases.

Client service: Alastair Davidson and Michael Kaplan serve as the senior clerks. "The clerking staff are always helpful and prompt in dealing with any issues raised."

SILKS

Richard Harwood QC Has a strong profile acting for claimants against public bodies, including local councils as well as central government entities. He primarily focuses on planning and environmental cases, and also assists clients with other matters such as professional conduct disputes. **Recent work:** Advised the claimant in R (SAVE Britain's Heritage) v Secretary of State for Communities & Local Government, in a case concerning the legality of funding to demolish 5,000 houses, including Ringo Starr's birthplace.

James Strachan QC A first port of call for an array of local government matters, especially those related to planning and environment issues. He frequently acts for local authority clients in defending challenges brought against them. **Strengths:** "A tenacious guy, but not unnecessarily aggressive. He's measured and stays with things, but not to the extent that he loses the tribunal." "A smooth and polished advocate, who is very effective." **Recent work:** Acted for the co-defendant developer in R (Aston) v Secretary of State for Communities & Local Government and Taylor Wimpey, a challenge to planning permission granted for a real estate development.

Fenella Morris QC A popular choice of senior counsel for a number of local councils across England and Wales, who advises both claimants and defendants. Her capabilities in the local government arena include Court of Protection and community care work. **Strengths:** "She gets to grips with issues quickly, and provides really reliable advice." **Recent work:** Defended Shropshire Council against a multi-claimant challenge relating to the duty of a local authority to consult on cuts to public services.

Jenni Richards QC One of the set's newer silks, and someone with a practice that covers both defendant and claimant representation. Her practice includes advising on disputes concerning public budget cuts as well as public service disciplinary proceedings. **Recent work:** Acted for the claimants in R (LH and Others) v Shropshire Council, concerning the duty of a local authority to consult on cuts to public services.

JUNIORS

Jonathan Auburn (see p.539) A highly experienced junior barrister whose local government work sees him handling community care and education law cases amongst others. He is frequently instructed by claimants challenging local government decisions, and also acts for county councils on investigations into officer conduct. **Strengths:** "A model junior." "Very competent and on top of the material." **Recent work:** Acted for the respondent in Westminster City Council v SL, a Supreme Court appeal concerning a local authority's duties towards a vulnerable adult asylum seeker.

Band 3

Francis Taylor Building

See profile on p.806

THE SET

Francis Taylor Building's formidable public law expertise includes significant capabilities in the local government sphere. The barristers are frequently instructed on high-profile matters, including CPOs, planning and rating appeals work. Clients include household-name utility services providers as claimants, as well as local authorities and transport bodies as defendants.

Client service: Paul Coveney leads the clerking team, and is "good to deal with and very approachable." "The set as a whole is very commercially run, and they run very interesting seminar programmes."

SILKS

Charles George QC An experienced practitioner with a substantial reputation across a broad range of public law matters. He has many years of experience of matters concerning the Transport and Works Acts, planning inquiries and challenges to decisions taken by public bodies.

Richard Glover QC Instructed by a range of utilities providers involved in high-stakes disputes such as ratings challenges. He has also assisted a number of local authorities with regard to changes in funding for public services. **Strengths:** "He has vast experience of dealing with high-value and complex appeals. He has the knowledge and ability to apply what can appear somewhat opaque legal principles to very complex real-world situations." **Recent work:** Acted for the claimant in Margate Town Centre Regeneration Company v Secretary of State for Communities and Thanet, a hotly contested action concerning a CPO.

Guy Roots QC (see p.710) A popular choice of lead counsel for local authorities on high-stakes disputes, including appeals against rating decisions. His practice also includes representing private companies faced with public law issues. **Strengths:** "Eminent, deeply knowledge, experienced and a barrister with a graceful manner." "He offers great technical knowledge and always has a keen desire to give the best service." **Recent work:** Acted for the appellant local authority in Lancaster City Council v Thomas Newall Ltd, an appeal concerning the amount of compensation due from a CPO.

JUNIORS

Richard Honey (see p.630) Acts principally for local authorities on issues relating to compulsory purchase and compensation. **Strengths:** "He is very thorough, very meticulous, and instils confidence in clients." **Recent work:** Acted for the defendant in Ramac v Kent CC, a case concerning expert opinions and issues relating to the valuation of land and causation. The case was heard in the Upper Tribunal Lands Chambers over six days.

Other Ranked Lawyers

Andrew Arden QC (Arden Chambers) Acts for private companies, local councils and waste authorities. His skill set spans both advisory and contentious work, and he has handled a number of Supreme Court matters. **Strengths:** "He is very clever, bright and intelligent. He works on a solution for the client, and tries to be flexible within the law." "He has fantastic knowledge and unrivalled experience." **Recent work:** Acted for the defence on Islington v Unite Group, a dispute concerning regulations governing multi-occupancy buildings.

Christopher Baker (Arden Chambers) A frequent adviser on local government matters involving housing issues. Recent mandates include the defence of challenges to local authority housing decisions. **Strengths:** "Very clear in his advice. He's bright, accommodating, and understands things well." **Recent work:** Acted for the defence in R (Jakimaviciute) v Hammersmith & Fulham, judicial review proceedings examining the local authority's housing policies.

Jonathan Manning (Arden Chambers) Frequently instructed by a range of local authorities and charities, he advises both claimants and defendants. His workload encompasses social housing, as well as challenges to reductions in public services. **Strengths:** "Produces good-quality advocacy." **Re-**

cent work: Acted for the respondent on R (Buckley) v Sheffield City Council, a judicial review of the local authority's new council tax arrangements.

John Howell QC (Blackstone Chambers) A highly sought-after silk for the most complex disputes in the realm of local government. He acts for a range of local authorities, on both the claimant and defendant sides. **Strengths:** "He is probably one of the brightest at the Bar, and is very well respected by the courts." "He has vast legal knowledge, and is phenomenal, not just in his recall, but in the way he stitches everything he knows together in response to arguments." **Recent work:** Acted for the local authority appellant in Westminster City Council v SL, a Supreme Court case examining the definition of 'care and attention' as well as 'otherwise available'.

Sam Grodzinski QC (Blackstone Chambers) Sought out by a number of public bodies such as local authorities and police forces. Key work includes advising on the defence of challenges to changes in public policy and funding disputes. **Recent work:** Acted for the defence in the Commercial Court case of Mitsui Sumitomo v Mayor's Office for Policing & Crime. The dispute concerned the apportionment of liability for loss and damage caused during the August 2011 riots in London.

Edward Faulks QC (1 Chancery Lane) Advises a significant number of local councils. He is particularly noted for his strong expertise in allegations of negligence. **Strengths:** "He's very helpful, and always returns urgent calls." "I feel he really outgunned our opponents." **Recent work:** He was lead counsel for the defence in Suzanne Monk v Cann Hall Primary School and Essex County Council, a case concerning allegations of unfair dismissal and psychological harm.

Andrew Warnock QC (1 Chancery Lane) Has built a strong profile advising local authorities in defending actions. He is a first port of call for disputes involving alleged breach of duty of care to vulnerable individuals including children. **Strengths:** "An acknowledged expert in the field, who is very approachable and very client-friendly." "He is so insightful and incisive." **Recent work:** Advised the defendant local authority on Bright v Devon County Council, a dispute alleging negligence in assessing patient care needs.

Martin Westgate QC (Doughty Street Chambers) Noted for his handling of social care and housing cases, he represents both local authorities and claimants. **Strengths:** "He is a very measured and pragmatic advocate." "It was a tremendously complicated case, and I thought it was impressive the way he selected the right points, and ran with them." **Recent work:** He recently advised a number of families challenging changes to social security benefits, including the so-called 'bedroom tax'.

Hilton Harrop-Griffiths (Field Court Chambers) An experienced junior counsel with particular skills in community care matters. His practice includes advising defendant local councils on disputes over local authority duties. **Strengths:** "He does this very successfully, even when the local authority seems boxed into a corner." "A reliable and experienced practitioner." **Recent work:** Acted as junior counsel for the appellant in R (SL) v Westminster City Council. The case concerned the local authority's duties to an asylum seeker who had previously attempted to commit suicide.

Charles Béar QC (Fountain Court Chambers) Has extensive public procurement experience, and advises the NHS and a number of local authorities. **Strengths:** "A very punchy advocate."

Stephen Knafler QC (Garden Court Chambers) A much sought-after silk with a solid grounding in public and administrative law. Much of his work involves local authorities, and he regularly advises on immigration, social housing and community care issues. **Strengths:** "Very solid and experienced, he has been practising in the area for a long time." **Recent work:** Advised the defendants in Doncaster Care Homes Association v Doncaster Metropolitan Borough Council, a judicial review of changes to funding for community care.

Timothy Straker QC (4-5 Gray's Inn Square) A highly accomplished silk who has a strong reputation acting for public bodies and their employees, including returning officers. His areas of expertise include complex election law challenges, as well as community care funding disputes. **Strengths:** "Good at clarifying complex issues." "A barrister with a magisterial reputation." **Recent work:** Acted for the local authority on R (Southwest Care Homes) v Devon County Council, a dispute concerning costs of provision of care.

Richard Clayton QC (see p.573) (4-5 Gray's Inn Square) Has acted for a number of local authority clients defending challenges to decisions. He has also advised claimants including care home providers. **Recent work:** Advised the defendant borough council in R (Littlefair) v Darlington, an administrative court challenge to a reduction in public services for children.

David Lawson (Hardwicke) Acts on the claimant and defendant sides of public and administrative law disputes, and is strong on cases involving education or duty of care. His client base includes local authorities as well as individual claimants. **Strengths:** "Very approachable, and happy to give very detailed and useful advice via telephone. He picks things up and gets to grips with them in a short timeframe." **Recent work:** Acted for the claimants in X v LCC, a challenge to local authority reductions to library resources.

Geraint Webb QC (Henderson Chambers) A commercial silk who also has notable public law expertise and is an expert on public procurement. He advises public bodies such as local authorities on finance regulatory work and the exercise of local government powers. **Recent work:** Advised Cornwall Council on a range of local government issues, including the legality of the use of derivatives/interest rate swap contracts in relation to procurement projects.

Rhodri Williams QC (Henderson Chambers) His local government practice includes formidable knowledge of public procurement matters. He represents local authorities across the country. **Recent work:** Had a lead role on Montpellier Estates v Leeds City Council, defending allegations of breach of public procurement and regulatory statutes.

Andrew Kinnier (Henderson Chambers) A high-profile junior for the Welsh Government as well as for The Crown, who also acts for private entities as claimants. He frequently advises clients on vires and public procurement matters. **Strengths:** "He is very proactive and easy to work with." **Recent work:** Acted for the claimant in Tunstall Healthcare v Northern Housing Consortium, a challenge to the consortium's decisions relating to social services provision.

Helen Mountfield QC (see p.678) (Matrix Chambers) A highly accomplished public and administrative law silk, with strong local government expertise including a specialism in education law. She frequently advises on high-stakes public sector equality duty matters. **Strengths:** "She gives very sound, practical advice, and is good on her feet." **Recent work:** She advised The Office of Qualifications & Examinations Regulation (Ofqual) as a joint defendant, in an Administrative Court action brought by the London Borough of Lewisham. The dispute centred around the 2012 modification of examination grading thresholds for GCSE English.

Sarah Hannett (Matrix Chambers) Advises local authorities on challenges to decisions in education, planning and community care. Key clients also include public sector unions and public regulatory bodies. **Strengths:** "A very experienced local authority barrister." "She has good communication skills and an easy manner. She is a very competent advocate and demonstrates a sound understanding of the subject." **Recent work:** Acted as junior counsel for Ofqual, on the London Borough of Lewisham's judicial review challenge to the grades awarded in GCSE English in 2012.

Ian Wise QC (Monckton Chambers) Advises on a range of public law matters, including those involving duties to vulnerable individuals as well as council tax reduction disputes. **Strengths:** "He has a very adventurous approach." "An attractive advocate." **Recent work:** Advised the appellants in R (ET and Others) v Islington, a case surrounding the local authority's duties to children at risk from paedophiles.

Stephen Hockman QC (see p.629) (6 Pump Court) Has specific expertise in environmental and health and safety matters. In addition to advising defendant local councils in disputes, he is also a popular choice for advisory work covering issues such as vires and duty of care. **Strengths:** "Turns around paperwork very, very quickly, and represents excellent value for money." **Recent work:** Advised the defendant in R (on the application of Padden) v Maidstone Borough Council, which concerned scrutiny of a partly retrospective planning decision.

NORTHERN

Local Government Northern
Leading Sets
Band 1
Kings Chambers *
Leading Silks
Band 1
Sauvain Stephen *Kings Chambers* *
Band 2
Fraser Vincent *Kings Chambers* *
Leading Juniors
Band 1
Burns Paul *Exchange Chambers (ORL)* ◊ *
Band 2
Crawford Colin *Kings Chambers*
O'Brien Sarah *Exchange Chambers (ORL)* ◊

Band 1

Kings Chambers
See profile on p.918

THE SET

One of the giants of the Northern Circuit, the sheer depth and breadth of expertise available at Kings Chambers ensures that a number of local authorities and other public bodies turn to the set for assistance on local government law. Kings' local government team works with a real range of clients, including police and fire authorities, private sector companies, pressure groups and councillors.

Client service: "The clerking team, led by William Brown, is excellent and very efficient. The clerks always acknowledge instructions, and never promise what they can't deliver. It is a very professional team."

SILKS

Stephen Sauvain QC A go-to silk for local authorities faced with tricky issues. Commentators note his considerable expertise in infrastructure and redevelopment projects. **Strengths:** "He is extremely knowledgeable, and very approachable and easy to talk to." "He is very incisive, has very good tactical insights and is frankly extremely good value for money." **Recent work:** Advised East Sussex County Council on a high-profile appeal concerning the registration of a beach as a town or village green.

Vincent Fraser QC An experienced advocate who receives regular instructions from local authorities. His expertise covers the full range of local government law, including registration of commons land, finance and administration, and local government powers. **Strengths:** "His reports on village green inquiries are excellent." "He is detailed, thorough, excellent in cross-examination, and also extremely perceptive in terms of how to direct a case." **Recent work:** Advised Lancashire County Council, successfully resisting a challenge to development consent relating to the construction of new link roads.

JUNIORS

Colin Crawford Advises on public inquiries and matters connected with planning laws, compulsory purchase and wider local government rights and powers. He acts for both local authorities and private companies. **Strengths:** "He was excellent in an extremely long inquiry, which had many facets covering many different sites. He was always right on top of it." **Recent work:** Advised Harrogate Borough Council in connection with the Secretary of State's involvement in a land use dispute. The land in question formed an integral part of the borough's successful bid to host the Grand Départ of the Tour de France in 2014.

Other Ranked Lawyers

Paul Burns (Exchange Chambers) Leads Exchange Chambers' local government and social housing practice. He is instructed on a wide range of work by local authorities, including human rights and public law challenges, mental health issues and ASBOs.

Sarah O'Brien (Exchange Chambers) Acts for local authorities in all areas of housing law, including landlord and tenant claims, possession actions and antisocial behaviour orders.

SOUTH EASTERN

Local Government South Eastern
Leading Sets
Band 1
Becket Chambers
Leading Juniors
Band 1
Kee Peter *Becket Chambers* *
Tapsell Paul *Becket Chambers* *
Up-and-coming individuals
Coates Holly *Becket Chambers* *
** Indicates set / individual with profile.*
◊ (ORL) = Other Ranked Lawyer.
Alphabetical order within each band. Band 1 is highest.

Band 1

Becket Chambers

THE SET

Becket Chambers' members handle a variety of work, including planning and licensing matters, as well as food safety and employment law disputes. The set acts both for and against local authorities on a range of both civil and criminal law matters.

Client service: "The clerks, under the leadership of Paul Eaton, are always available, knowledgeable and friendly."

JUNIORS

Peter Kee (see p.643) Acts for local authority clients on issues relating to employment and social housing. **Strengths:** "He is very approachable and a skilled advocate – he's never aggressive, but he knows when to be firm." "His style of advocacy is calm, understated and gentlemanly, and he has a very good in-depth understanding of the law."

Paul Tapsell (see p.734) Works with local authorities on a range of matters, including environmental health, housing and planning. **Strengths:** "He's got a good bearing in court, and a very convincing manner." "He is very approachable, and he can pick up and run with any matter he is instructed on. He is a very persistent advocate." **Recent work:** Acted in a High Court challenge to the legality of a tree preservation order.

Holly Coates (see p.574) Acts both for and against local authorities on a range of issues, including social housing, personal injury and employment disputes. **Strengths:** "She is knowledgeable and pleasant, deals well with clients, and is able to explain complex legal issues to a client in non-legal terms. She never drops things, but always follows through." **Recent work:** Advised Thanet District Council on an application for possession of property, following allegations of antisocial conduct on the part of the council's tenant.

Contents:

LONDON

Media & Entertainment London
Leading Sets
Band 1
Blackstone Chambers *
8 New Square *
Band 2
Hogarth Chambers *
Band 3
5RB *
11 South Square *
3 Verulam Buildings *

Leading Silks
Star individuals
Mill Ian *Blackstone Chambers*
Band 1
Baldwin John *8 New Square* *
Cullen Edmund *Maitland Chambers (ORL)* ◊ *
Howe Robert *Blackstone Chambers*
Saini Pushpinder *Blackstone Chambers*
Spearman Richard *Thirty Nine Essex Street (ORL)* ◊ *
Band 2
Alexander Daniel *8 New Square* *
Englehart Robert *Blackstone Chambers*
Mellor James *8 New Square* *
Pannick David *Blackstone Chambers*
Sutcliffe Andrew *3 Verulam Buildings*
Band 3
Anderson Robert *Blackstone Chambers*
Barca Manuel *One Brick Court (ORL)* ◊ *
de la Mare Thomas *Blackstone Chambers*
Green Andrew *Blackstone Chambers*
Howe Martin *8 New Square* *
Hunter Andrew *Blackstone Chambers*
Jones Elizabeth *Serle Court (ORL)* ◊ *
Meade Richard *8 New Square* *
Silverleaf Michael *11 South Square*
Speck Adrian *8 New Square* *
New Silks
May Charlotte *8 New Square* *
Weisselberg Tom *Blackstone Chambers*

Leading Juniors
Bate Stephen *5RB*
Harbottle Gwilym *Hogarth Chambers* [A]
Hicks Michael *Hogarth Chambers*
Lane Lindsay *8 New Square* [A] *
Michaels Amanda *Hogarth Chambers*
Moody-Stuart Thomas *8 New Square* *
Norris Andrew *Hogarth Chambers*
Ratcliffe Peter *3 Verulam Buildings*
Vinall Mark *Blackstone Chambers*
Cuddigan Hugo *11 South Square*
Deacon Robert *11 Stone Buildings (ORL)* ◊
Edwards Richard *3 Verulam Buildings*
Hickman Tom *Blackstone Chambers*
Malynicz Simon *Three New Square (ORL)* ◊ *
Michalos Christina *5RB*
Richards Tom *Blackstone Chambers*
Segan James *Blackstone Chambers*
Singla Tony *Brick Court Chambers (ORL)* ◊
St Quintin Thomas *Hogarth Chambers*
Up-and-coming individuals
Takatsuki Yuli *5RB*
* *Indicates set / individual with profile.*
◊ *(ORL) = Other Ranked Lawyer.*
[A] *direct access (see p.11)*

Band 1

Blackstone Chambers

See profile on p.771

THE SET

Blackstone Chambers is considered synonymous with media and entertainment law. Its members are acclaimed not only for their strength and depth as a group, but also for the breadth of disputes they handle. Individuals here are particularly celebrated for their work in music industry disputes, and have enormous experience in performance rights cases and Copyright Tribunal work. The set also continues to develop a reputation for handling broadcasting regulation cases with significant EU components.

Client service: "Senior clerk Gary Oliver's friendly manner filters through to everyone in the clerksroom." "The clerks are very hospitable. At the tricky times when you need to discuss fees, they're fantastic and have a really nice touch."

SILKS

Ian Mill QC Unanimously hailed as the go-to practitioner for eminent artists, labels and publishers, Mill is one of the best music industry silks around. His authoritative presence and wealth of experience equip him to handle a range of high-profile contractual and intellectual property disputes in the field. **Strengths:** "The don of the entertainment and media world, who is rightly feared by his opponents as he is a formidable advocate and fine cross-examiner." "He's the very best, not just because of his intellect and his legal nous, but also because he understands the workings of the music business." **Recent work:** Acts for the UK record industry in its bid to get ISPs to block access to Bittorrent and Aggregator sites.

Robert Englehart QC Esteemed for his expertise in handling music publishing disputes, he is a veteran of high-profile media litigation. He is highly regarded for his immense depth of experience in the sector. **Strengths:** "He's charming, really knows his stuff, and what's great is that he has universal respect." **Recent work:** Acted for the widow of the author of 'Room at the Top' in a dispute with the BBC concerning film rights in the novel.

Robert Howe QC Acts for artists, record labels, collecting societies and media organisations on intellectual property and contractual matters. He is a heavyweight choice for cases with copyright issues and those with significant EU elements. **Strengths:** "Analytical, good on his feet" and "a brilliant fighter in court." **Recent work:** Acted for PRS in a dispute with B4U Network regarding rights in Bollywood songs.

Robert Anderson QC Acts for iconic artists in high-profile music industry disputes, including representing Rick Wakeman in a royalties case. He also represents record and publishing companies, and has an expanding film and television practice. **Strengths:** "He's an extremely engaging and fluent advocate." "A colourful character who knows the business very well." **Recent work:** Advised Princess Diana's former butler, Paul Burrell, in relation to phone hacking claims against News International.

Thomas de la Mare QC Handles a broad range of media and entertainment industry cases, including those concerning record companies, collecting societies, film finance and advertising regulation. He is highly regarded for his commercial expertise and is known for being a commanding presence in court. **Strengths:** "Feisty and a good advocate." "He can cut through all the chaff and get through to the real nub of the case very, very quickly." **Recent work:** Acted for Sodastream in relation to an ASA ruling that its advertisement denigrated competitor products.

Pushpinder Saini QC A highly respected player in the media field, who represents artists, record companies and film industry organisations. He has a depth of experience of acting on both sides of collection society disputes, and also has significant copyright and trade mark expertise. **Strengths:** "Forthright and straight talking, he has an excellent manner with judges, solicitors and clients." "He's very good in court and has a real intelligence that he wears lightly." **Recent work:** Represented the interested parties in R v Secretary of State for Culture, Media, Olympics & Sport, a case concerning the legality of copyright protection provisions of the Digital Economy Act 2010.

David Pannick QC "A superstar at the Bar," who handles media and entertainment industry disputes as part of a wider caseload. He has experience of advising publishers and broadcasters, and offers unparalleled regulatory expertise. **Strengths:** "He's very good at delivering arguments and making the court think that he's right." "Just very, very impressive on his feet." **Recent work:** Advised the BBC in a judicial review application concerning the lawfulness of the Lord Chancellor's refusal to allow a journalist to record and broadcast an interview with an individual detained in prison pending extradition.

Andrew Green QC An established media silk who regularly acts for artists, publishing concerns and record companies. He is highlighted as having "a wonderful way with clients." **Strengths:** "A clever guy with good judgement, who is super to work with." "A great cross-examiner, who is excellent at presenting cases." **Recent work:** Represented the founder of Island Records, Chris Blackwell, in a dispute with musician Steve Winwood, who had brought a claim for a share of the profits from the sale of the label.

Andrew Hunter QC Has firmly established himself as an impressive silk in the field after being appointed to the role in 2012. He acts for record and film companies, as well as artists, and has recently handled licensing and royalties disputes. **Strengths:** "He's very bright and gets on top of the issues quickly." "His trial advocacy and cross-examination is masterful, and he is loved by clients." **Recent work:** Acted for Blix Street Records in a dispute over profits from sales of Eve Cassidy's music, achieving success in a £2 million royalty claim and copyright counterclaim.

Tom Weisselberg QC Took silk this year after developing a reputation as one of the most accomplished practitioners in the field. He advises clients across the music, film, TV, radio and fashion industries, and offers expertise in copyright, partnership and performance rights disputes. **Strengths:** "Absolutely top notch and a delight to deal with." "He's a fantastic guy with an extremely good manner, who is very, very bright." "Smooth, relaxed and friendly, he's brilliant with clients and can really set them at ease." **Recent work:** Represented the producer of 'Monty Python and the Holy Grail' in a successful claim for rectification of an agreement concluded in 1974.

JUNIORS

Mark Vinall A strikingly knowledgeable and effective junior who "rolls up his sleeves." He demonstrates experience in a vast range of entertainment cases, and is particularly good on royalties and artist/manager disputes. **Strengths:** "Very good and very efficient, he turns stuff around quickly and knows his entertainment law." "Clever, keen, businesslike, methodical and thorough, he instils confidence." **Recent work:** Acted as sole counsel for the defendants in Staw v Jennings, a dispute concerning the distribution of profits from Eva Cassidy's work.

James Segan Handles commercial and regulatory work within the media and entertainment sector. He has experience of acting for collecting societies, and regularly handles management disputes. **Strengths:** "He's user-friendly, responsive and very smart." "A very firm but fair advocate." **Recent work:** Advised the FA Premier League in its dispute with BSkyB concerning unlawfully streamed sports coverage, a landmark case obtaining the first ever blocking order against UK ISPs.

Tom Hickman Handles an array of entertainment and media matters, and offers notable expertise in royalty and copyright disputes. He also acts in management and publishing cases. **Strengths:** "He brings authority to a case but is also a good listener and is very inquisitive." "He's very responsive, has good client management skills, and is a modern, commercial barrister." **Recent work:** Acted for the claimant in a royalties dispute between Rick Wakeman and BMG, led by Robert Anderson QC.

Tom Richards A skilled entertainment practitioner, who has experience of acting for record companies, film companies, agents and artists. **Strengths:** "His industry knowledge coupled with his excellent advocacy skills make him a formidable opponent." **Recent work:** Represented Playboy TV in the defence of regulatory proceedings brought by Ofcom.

8 New Square

See profile on p.836

THE SET

8 New Square is a celebrated IP set whose advocates continue to impress in media and entertainment industry disputes. Individuals here are frequently instructed on highly technical copyright and passing-off cases in the music, broadcast and publishing sectors. They also earn particular praise for their prominence in patent work.

Client service: "The chambers is very impressive, with quality from the top QC down to the junior barristers. The members are well clerked by a team led by John Call."

SILKS

John Baldwin QC (see p.542) An esteemed IP expert with a celebrated reputation for handling media cases with especially technical copyright components. He has a track record of acting in high-profile publishing disputes. **Strengths:** "A tough fighter, who is also very pragmatic and sensible." "A heavyweight QC, loved by clients, who is excellent technically."

Adrian Speck QC (see p.726) Acts for a range of media clients, from brand owners to authors, in IP-flavoured cases. He has particular experience with regard to television format disputes. **Strengths:** "He's very good on technical copyright cases." "He speaks his mind and is not afraid to tell a challenging client things they'd rather not hear."

Daniel Alexander QC (see p.533) A prominent IP silk, who is admired for his work in digital technology cases. He frequently acts in licensing, copyright and internet-related cases. **Strengths:** "Very smooth." "He's not precious in any way, and judges trust him because he only runs the best points."

Richard Meade QC (see p.670) Demonstrates substantial expertise when handling music industry disputes. He is particularly strong on complex trade mark and copyright cases. **Strengths:** "A brilliant barrister who can turn his hand to anything." "A lot of people are big admirers."

James Mellor QC (see p.670) Handles a range of media-related copyright work, and acts for clients from the literary, music and digital sectors. **Strengths:** "He has a very good manner and works well as part of the team. He's very informal and great with clients." "His cross-examination, his advocacy and his thought processes are all very impressive."

Martin Howe QC (see p.631) Acts in a range of broadcasting and internet-related disputes involving complex copyright concerns. He has experience of acting for media clients in cases with strong IP, IT and telecommunications components. **Strengths:** "A cerebral lawyer, who is also accessible and a pleasant person to have on the team." "He's especially strong on written submissions but also good on his feet."

Charlotte May QC (see p.665) A new silk and "a tenacious advocate," with a "very good courtroom presence." She has a depth of experience in copyright and broadcasting work. **Strengths:** "She's very careful and very methodical, and she has a fantastic way with clients. She has the ability to command the client's respect and at the same time help them understand what the best option is for them." "She'll drive down every point, and is very good at lateral thinking."

JUNIORS

Lindsay Lane (see p.650) Continues to impress as a senior junior handling media and entertainment-related IP cases. She is admired by peers for her strong advocacy and technical nous. **Strengths:** "Very smart and very tough. She is persistent in her advocacy, very commercial and great with clients." "She's sharp-witted and highly responsive."

Thomas Moody-Stuart (see p.675) Acts across a range of media and entertainment cases, and most notably appears in copyright disputes. He is admired as an efficient and "unflappable" junior. **Strengths:** "Offers commercial and pragmatic advice, and has a good rapport with clients." "He's very impressive and very enthusiastic in the way he goes about his work."

Band 2

Hogarth Chambers

See profile on p.822

THE SET

Hogarth Chambers continues to be a prominent force in the media and entertainment landscape, and offers a breadth of expertise pertaining to the sector. Its strong bench of junior members practising in the field have experience of appearing in music industry, publishing and film and television disputes. Its members are admired for their proficiency in handling IP work, and media industry-focused copyright and trade mark cases are meat and drink to them.

Client service: "The clerks, led by Clive Nicholls, are very supportive and user-friendly."

JUNIORS

Gwilym Harbottle Acts for collecting societies and industry bodies in copyright and performance disputes. He demonstrates particular expertise in cases involving criminal prosecutions. **Strengths:** "A safe pair of hands on media and entertainment matters," who is "very good on music copyright and the criminal aspect of copyright law." **Recent work:** Acted for All Around the World Recording in defending a claim brought by Jodie Henderson that release of the hit song 'Heartbroken' infringed her performer's rights.

Amanda Michaels Has a wide-ranging media and entertainment practice with a strong IP component. She has notable experience of handling complex issues as to title, and of advising in relation to rights to music, films and books. **Strengths:** "A very good practitioner who is straightforward in her approach." **Recent work:** Acted for Python (Monty) Pictures in the defence of a royalties claim brought by the producer of 'Monty Python and the Holy Grail'.

Andrew Norris Advises brand owners, film production companies and music industry clients in commercial and IP-oriented cases. He is particularly well regarded for his experience in sports broadcasting matters. **Strengths:** "Incredibly knowledgeable, user-friendly, quick-thinking and creative." "Gives sensible, commercial, down-to-earth advice, which is always clear and well thought out." **Recent work:** Represented pop star Rihanna in a dispute with Arcadia concerning the unauthorised use of a picture of the singer on a T-shirt sold by fashion retailer Topshop.

Michael Hicks Acts for corporate clients in disputes regarding copyright, trade mark, design rights and comparative advertising concerns. He is well regarded for his handling of cases with highly technical content, and advises on media and entertainment matters at the intersection with IP and IT law. **Strengths:** "Offers an excellent service, and is always thorough and reliable." "Great with clients – he always goes that extra mile." **Recent work:** Acted for Datel in a dispute with Nintendo concerning replacement handsets for Nintendo's 'Wii' gaming platform.

Thomas St Quintin Has experience in a wide range of media-related matters, from copyright issues to contractual disputes and privacy concerns. He is strong on IP, and admired for his proficiency in technical cases. **Strengths:** "Accessible and extremely commercial." "He's good at explaining complex concepts to creative people." **Recent work:** Acted for PPL in a successful claim against a nightclub owner for infringements of sound recording copyright made by playing music in public.

Band 3

5RB

See profile on p.858

THE SET

Illustrious defamation and privacy specialists 5RB display additional prowess in the interlinking area of media and entertainment law. Its members routinely turn their hands to copyright and passing-off cases, and are noted for their work on privacy, confidenti-

ality and libel claims. A number of the junior members are developing burgeoning practices handling contractual work within the industry.
Client service: "The service is always exceptional. Kim Janes, who leads the clerking team, is brilliant. As a team they are very easy to deal with and very straightforward."

JUNIORS
Stephen Bate Has experience of acting for media organisations, publishing companies, record labels and musicians in licensing disputes and copyright infringement cases. He is well regarded for his extensive arbitration work in the field. **Strengths:** "A well-known name in this area," and "a tenacious barrister."

Christina Michalos Has a keen interest in issues stemming from social networking and user-generated content sites, and regularly engages in innovative cases. Michalos is a leader in the field of image rights work and is lauded for her copyright expertise. **Strengths:** "Very businesslike and punchy." "She has an in-depth working knowledge of media law."

Yuli Takatsuki Handles a broad range of media and entertainment work, and regularly advises broadcasters, film producers and publishers. Peers and clients say she has tremendous ability and knowledge for one of such relatively recent call. **Strengths:** "A barrister with an intimidatingly large brain." "She has a gentle manner with clients, but can be incredibly tough when she needs to be." **Recent work:** Advised independent production company Altamar Entertainment in a dispute with Revelation Films concerning alleged breaches of a production agreement.

11 South Square
See profile on p.862
THE SET
An IP powerhouse that has built up impressive experience in media and entertainment industry disputes. Members here have had involvement in high-profile music industry cases, and have been instructed by iconic artists on a range of matters with IP components, such as infringement of song lyric matters and passing-off disputes. They are also noted for their brand protection work, and have acted for a number of fashion houses.
Client service: "Every one of the clerks goes out of their way to help you and will do whatever is required to assist across the board." Ashley Carr heads up the clerking team.

SILKS
Michael Silverleaf QC An eminent IP practitioner who demonstrates a high level of proficiency when advising high-profile clients on image and brand protection issues. Of late, he has been acclaimed for his involvement in the civil claims stemming from voicemail interception allegations, following his appearance as lead counsel for News Group Newspapers. **Strengths:** "A tenacious and skilled operator." "He's easy to deal with and makes everyone on the team feel valued." **Recent work:** Acted for Hong Kong media company Starbucks in a claim for trade mark infringement against BSkyB, relating to the mark 'Now TV' used for Sky's on-demand TV service.

JUNIORS
Hugo Cuddigan Adept at handling media and entertainment matters in an IP context, he is recognised as a lawyer with considerable commercial nous. He has experience of handling disputes relating to publishing rights, copyright and music contracts. **Strengths:** "He has very good instincts and offers insight both legally and strategically." **Recent work:** Acted for Arcadia Group in relation to a dispute concerning Rihanna's image rights after Topshop used a picture of the pop star on one of its T-shirts.

3 Verulam Buildings
See profile on p.875
THE SET
Although primarily considered a banking and finance-focused set, 3 Verulam Buildings has a flourishing media and entertainment offering. A number of its members advise publishing, film, television, radio, music and new media industry clients on issues relating to contract, copyright and licensing.

SILKS
Andrew Sutcliffe QC Advises publishing companies, record labels and collecting agencies on a range of copyright concerns. He has handled plagiarism cases, website and domain issues and finance disputes involving the entertainment industry. **Strengths:** "Solid, clever and resourceful." "He's extremely bright, highly commercial and good with clients." **Recent work:** Advised Bloomsbury in relation to a significant publishing dispute.

JUNIORS
Peter Ratcliffe Acts for broadcasting, film, music and advertising industry clients in contractual disputes. **Strengths:** "Gentle and very good with clients." "He's very bright, very able and good to work with."

Richard Edwards An emerging presence in the field of media and entertainment law, who acts for music, new media and film and television clients in copyright and contractual disputes. He is highlighted by peers as a particularly effective advocate, who has excellent client-handling skills, and is noted for his knowledge of the art world. **Strengths:** "He's unflappable, diligent and clever." "He's practical, sensible and commercial." **Recent work:** Acted for Sotheby's in a dispute concerning a painting alleged to be an original work by Caravaggio.

Other Ranked Lawyers

Manuel Barca QC (see p.542) (One Brick Court) Advises on media and information law matters, and is experienced in internet publishing matters and literary copyright disputes. **Strengths:** "He has an excellent brain and takes an analytical and pragmatic approach to his work." "A superb advocate who is very approachable and down to earth."

Tony Singla (Brick Court Chambers) Handles media cases at the intersection of commercial and competition work, and impresses in licensing and contract disputes. **Strengths:** "He has a voracious appetite for work, good judgement and terrific brainpower as well." "He is phenomenal value for money and very mature for his year of call." **Recent work:** Acted for ITV in a £30 million contractual licensing dispute with Scottish Television.

Richard Spearman QC (see p.726) (Thirty Nine Essex Street) A revered veteran of the media sector who acts in a range of high-profile disputes across the music, entertainment and sports industries. He continues to be a trailblazer in the privacy field. **Strengths:** "In terms of developing a brilliant rapport with the judge, there is no one better." "He's very tactically astute." **Recent work:** Successfully acted for Hollywood film studios in a major claim for infringement of copyright regarding the operation of the websites Newzbin and Newszbin2.

Edmund Cullen QC (Maitland Chambers) A relatively new silk, renowned for his work in contractual, licensing and copyright disputes. He is highly regarded for his experience in acting for major record labels, and has a burgeoning practice in the area of online exploitation of rights. **Strengths:** "Phenomenally good – he has great judgement and is so bright, easy to work with and good with clients." "He combines real fluency as an advocate with really good commercial nous." **Recent work:** Recently represented the Newspaper Licensing Agency in the Meltwater dispute, a case concerning the licensing of operators and users of online media monitoring services.

Simon Malynicz (see p.661) (Three New Square) Has broad expertise pertaining to the media industry, and is notably adept at handling cases with IP components. He has significant experience before tribunals and the CJEU. **Strengths:** "Demonstrates good understanding of matters and provides excellent practical advice." "A very good advocate who is very tenacious." **Recent work:** Acted for the UK government in a CJEU reference on injunctions against ISPs in relation to copyright in films on the internet.

Elizabeth Jones QC (Serle Court) Acts for record labels in contractual disputes, and has in-depth and well-honed industry knowledge. She has experience of acting in high-profile cases in the field. **Strengths:** "She's easy to deal with and fights her corner." "She has a very fluid advocacy style and a lovely manner, and is incredibly persuasive. You feel she's very much on top of everything."

Robert Deacon (11 Stone Buildings) Focuses on royalty disputes, and is highly regarded for his depth of experience in the area. He has particular expertise in how these issues relate to the increasingly digital market. **Strengths:** "Highly experienced and confidence inspiring, he is quick to respond and thorough in his approach." "He's really intelligent and gets right to the facts." **Recent work:** Acted for the defendant in a claim by The Ritz in respect of £2 million gambling debt.

Contents:

ALL CIRCUITS

Mediators All Circuits	
Leading Silks	
Band 1	
Kallipetis Michel	*Independent Mediators*
Lomas Mark	*Independent Mediators*
Ruttle Stephen	*Brick Court Chambers*
Wood William	*Brick Court Chambers*
Band 2	
Glasgow Edwin	*Thirty Nine Essex Street*
Jackson Rosemary	*Keating Chambers* *
Kershen Lawrence	*Doughty Street Chambers*
Sturrock John	*Core Solutions Group Ltd*
Band 3	
Jones Elizabeth	*Serle Court* *
Band 4	
Flint Charles	*Blackstone Chambers*
Owen David	*20 Essex Street*
Price OBE Richard	*Littleton Chambers* *
Reed Penelope	*5 Stone Buildings* *
Seitler Jonathan	*Wilberforce Chambers*
Leading Juniors	
Band 1	
Rogers Beverly-Ann	*Serle Court* *
Willis Tony	*Brick Court Chambers*
Band 2	
Johnson Paul	*Kings Chambers* *
Band 3	
Arkush Jonathan	*11 Stone Buildings* *
Manning Colin	*Littleton Chambers* *
Band 4	
Birch Elizabeth	*3 Verulam Buildings*
Evans Robert	*Keating Chambers* *
King Michael	*XXIV Old Buildings*
Shane Michael	*Atkin Chambers* *
* *Indicates individual with profile.*	
Alphabetical order within each band. Band 1 is highest.	

Band 1

Michel Kallipetis QC
Independent Mediators
Sources comment that Michel Kallipetis QC "knows when people are on weak ground, and he's astute in ascertaining if a settlement's coming on that day or not. For a technically forensic approach I'd go to him." He handles a wide range of disputes, covering fields including banking, IT, energy and construction, and he is frequently instructed in international work.

Mark Lomas QC
Independent Mediators
Mark Lomas QC receives widespread commendation for his formidable legal acumen and his expert handling of complex disputes. He is frequently instructed in areas such as professional negligence, employment and property, and sources say he is "really good. He gets stuck into the legal issues, he has his own opinion and he's friendly, but he can beat people up if they're going down the wrong line. He gets things into shape – he knows where he's going on the mediation."

Beverly-Ann Rogers
Serle Court
Beverly-Ann Rogers is praised for her handling of complex and volatile disputes, with sources commenting that "she's extremely good and very approachable. She gains the confidence of the clients, so they can trust that she's trying to find something that will suit everybody rather than feeling that she's there to bludgeon them into a settlement." She is regularly appointed to mediate on issues involving trust, probate and chancery.

Stephen Ruttle QC
Brick Court Chambers
Stephen Ruttle QC enjoys an excellent reputation for his ability in a broad range of disputes, handling "case after case" in areas including shipping, reinsurance and construction mediation. Sources point to his international expertise and praise his "amazing reputation and amazing job. I have no idea what he did but the outcome was extraordinary."

Tony Willis
Brick Court Chambers
Commentators praise Tony Willis's skill in high-level and international work, noting that "he goes beyond the call of duty." He brings his heavyweight litigation expertise to bear in a range of work across areas including professional negligence, shareholder and partnership disputes, trusts and probate, and the energy sector.

William Wood QC
Brick Court Chambers
Acclaimed for his "substantial intellect and good feel for clients," William Wood QC enjoys a sterling reputation for his work in complex and sensitive mediations. His expertise includes employment, professional negligence and IP disputes, with particular skill in insurance and finance, and sources describe him as "really good. He has a great, easy style with all the parties, he's pragmatic and he gets on top of stuff."

Band 2

Edwin Glasgow QC
Thirty Nine Essex Street
With expertise covering areas such as public and police law, construction, professional negligence and reinsurance, Edwin Glasgow QC is broadly recognised as an impressive force in commercial mediation. Sources praise his "unique talents" and say he is "incredibly charming, and able to get to the heart of the issues and resolve disputes where you think there might be no chance."

Rosemary Jackson QC
Keating Chambers
Well versed in construction and engineering disputes, Rosemary Jackson QC is described as "a highly effective mediator who provides clear, concise and commercial advice." She is also highly regarded for her expertise in areas such as professional negligence, and sources comment that "she's instinctively capable and like a lot of the better mediators, there's a touch of humility about her, which can make all the difference between being good and being great."

Paul Johnson
Kings Chambers
Sources praise Paul Johnson as being "really good – committed and friendly with a very approachable, easy manner. He gets you to a deal." Based in Manchester, he is held in high esteem for his practised handling of complex disputes in fields including professional negligence, probate and IP.

Lawrence Kershen QC
Doughty Street Chambers
Sources comment that Lawrence Kershen QC has "a very good rapport with people – he puts them at ease and helps them deal with their problems in a very sensitive way." Another source describes him as "exceptional. He enables all parties to feel heard and respected and to articulate their fundamental needs, and he has a unique approach and set of conceptual tools." His mediation experience covers charities, the public sector and the construction, IP and probate arenas.

John Sturrock QC
Core Solutions Group Ltd
Based in Edinburgh, John Sturrock QC is well regarded for his breadth of expertise and his poised, collected handling of complex negotiations. His experience covers a broad array of commercial issues, including sports law, construction, energy, IT and contract disputes.

Band 3

Jonathan Arkush
11 Stone Buildings
Jonathan Arkush is well known for his excellent depth of expertise in chancery and probate work, receiving frequent instruction in an array of complex mediations. He is also highly regarded for his skill in disputes relating to areas including property and professional negligence.

Elizabeth Jones QC
Serle Court
Sources describe Elizabeth Jones QC as "very good – she's quite forceful and very experienced, and she dealt with things very efficiently. For a heavy matter I'd recommend her." Her expertise includes handling mediations in areas such as banking and finance and shareholder disputes.

Colin Manning
Littleton Chambers
Colin Manning is highly sought after for his skill in mediating fractious disputes in areas including construction, insurance and commercial contracts. Commentators highlight his pragmatism, with one noting: "He excelled in cutting through what could have been a very fact-sensitive exercise, being commercial about it and putting personality to one side."

Band 4

Elizabeth Birch
3 Verulam Buildings
Elizabeth Birch enjoys a strong profile for her accomplished handling of disputes across a wide range of fields. Her experience includes energy, pharmaceuticals, professional negligence and partnership disputes, and she is regularly instructed on international disputes.

Robert Evans
Keating Chambers
Robert Evans is frequently instructed on an impressive range of disputes. His experience covers areas such as commercial contracts, landlord and tenant, construction and property, and he is acclaimed for his skill in steering convoluted matters to a conclusion.

Charles Flint QC
Blackstone Chambers
Charles Flint QC's mediation experience includes an impressive depth of specialist expertise in financial disputes. Noted for his "laid-back style," he is regularly instructed in complex and high-value mediations, and sources comment that "he takes gravitas into the mediation; he's a well-respected guy and he shows a lot of humility."

Michael King
XXIV Old Buildings
Well regarded for his specialist expertise in chancery and trust mediation, Michael King receives impressive acclaim for his direct handling of entangled disputes. Sources comment that "he's pretty no-nonsense and he gets things done. You can spend a lot of time arguing about peripheral nonsense but he cuts through that and pushes on."

David Owen QC
20 Essex Street
Active across an impressive array of mediations, David Owen QC is regularly instructed on international disputes in areas such as commodities and finance. He is also well regarded for his adept handling of work in fields including shipping, engineering and the public sector.

Richard Price OBE QC
Littleton Chambers
Richard Price OBE QC enjoys an impressive reputation for his adept handling of disputes in a range of fields. He is held in especially high regard for his depth of expertise in mediations across fields including professional negligence, construction, defamation and entertainment and media.

Penelope Reed QC
5 Stone Buildings
Sources praise Penelope Reed's strength in mediations, commenting that "she has a good manner and bags of experience." She specialises in trusts and probate, and brings an impressive degree of litigation expertise to the table in complex disputes.

Jonathan Seitler QC
Wilberforce Chambers
Commentators describe Jonathan Seitler QC as "very quick-witted, sharp and incisive – he's a standout. He has a very interesting and impressive style." His experience includes significant depth in property disputes, alongside expertise in professional negligence claims.

Michael Shane
Atkin Chambers
Michael Shane is described as "very good – he gets brought in for mega-cases. He cracks heads, tells people what's what and gets the deal done." He is held in especially high esteem for his expertise in construction disputes, and for his significant experience in handling mediations in areas such as IP, banking and insurance.

Motor Insurance Fraud

ALL CIRCUITS

Motor Insurance Fraud All Circuits
Leading Sets
Band 1
Temple Garden Chambers *
Leading Silks
Band 1
Kennedy Christopher *9 St John Street (ORL)* ◊
Band 2
Featherby William *12 King's Bench Walk (ORL)* ◊ *
Leading Juniors
Band 1
Crapper Sadie *Thirty Nine Essex Street (ORL)* ◊ *
Dawson Judy *Sovereign Chambers (ORL)* ◊
Grant Marcus *Temple Garden Chambers* *
Higgins Paul *Deans Court Chambers (ORL)* ◊
Laughland James *Temple Garden Chambers* *
McCann Simon *Deans Court Chambers (ORL)* ◊ A
McCluggage Brian *9 St John Street (ORL)* ◊ *
Wilson Peter J *Sovereign Chambers (ORL)* ◊
Band 2
Davies George *Temple Garden Chambers* *
Furness Corin *Parklane Plowden (ORL)* ◊
Glassbrook Alex *Temple Garden Chambers* *
Sharpe Tim *Temple Garden Chambers* *
Snarr Matthew *9 St John Street (ORL)* ◊
Symington Anna *St John's Chambers (ORL)* ◊ A
* *Indicates set / individual with profile.*
◊ *(ORL) = Other Ranked Lawyer.*
A *direct access (see p.11).*

Band 1

Temple Garden Chambers
See profile on p.872

THE SET

Home to a host of leading juniors, this set has members who handle a wide range of motor insurance fraud disputes. They act for both claimants and defendants in disputes concerning staged and induced accidents, bogus passenger claims, exaggerated claims, fraud rings and sham credit hire arrangements. They also work closely with insurers to develop methods for identifying and exposing fraud rings. Various barristers here have been at the forefront of developing the law in relation to committal proceedings and costs.

Client service: "The clerks, led by Dean Norton, are personable, approachable, and very good at solving issues. They provide an excellent service."

JUNIORS

Marcus Grant Has been at the forefront of tackling fraud in the motor insurance industry, and has had involvement in a number of reported cases concerning contempt of court. **Strengths:** "The go-to guy for the most complex of cases." "He works very hard for his clients and will give you no-nonsense advice." **Recent work:** Successfully represented several insurers in a group action alleging an attempt by an accident management company and its clients to defraud motor insurers through staged accidents.

James Laughland Handles motor insurance fraud claims for insurers as part of his personal injury practice. He has handled disputes involving phantom passengers, staged collisions and deliberately induced accidents. **Strengths:** "Robust, clear and organised, he takes a very thorough approach to cases." "He has a great ability to think on his feet." **Recent work:** Acted for a defendant in several consecutive claims held to be fraudulent based on deliberately induced accidents.

George Davies (see p.584) Handles a range of motor insurance fraud claims, including those relating to fraud rings, sham credit hire agreements and bogus passenger claims. He has prior experience of fraud litigation from working as a solicitor in a City law firm. **Strengths:** "Very helpful, he'll take time to go through things with the instructing solicitor, and is extremely helpful when it comes to complex matters." **Recent work:** Acted for two insurance companies subject to multiple claims arising from a number of related RTAs.

Alex Glassbrook (see p.609) Has experience in motor insurance fraud disputes and associated costs issues. He is frequently instructed to advise and act for insurance companies. **Strengths:** "A commercial, tactically aware barrister whose advocacy skills are first-class."

Tim Sharpe (see p.718) Has a busy common law practice that includes personal injury, fraud and insurance litigation. He acts for both claimants and defendants in road traffic claims alleged to be fraudulent. **Strengths:** "Tenacious, economical and full of ideas." "He inspires confidence." **Recent work:** Successfully defended contempt of court proceedings brought by an insurance company relating to statements given during the course of a personal injury claim arising out of an RTA.

Other Ranked Lawyers

Paul Higgins (Deans Court Chambers) Enjoys a national reputation for his work in the motor insurance fraud area. He has particular experience in committal proceedings where, sources say, "he has helped to stiffen up the law." **Strengths:** "He's excellent. What distinguishes him more than anything is his photographic memory." "He goes beyond what's expected. He's already got an amazing reputation but he's incredibly modest given how intelligent he is and how good he is at the job." **Recent work:** Acted in Israr Hussain Shah v Esure, the first successful committal proceedings against a claimant who conspired to incept fraudulent motor insurance policies online and organise false insurance claims.

Simon McCann (Deans Court Chambers) Acts and advises on all aspects of motor insurance fraud. He has a particular interest in fraud rings, staged accidents and contempt proceedings. **Strengths:** "He's the kind of person you'd want on your side in a courtroom fight: he's quick on his feet and not afraid to ask the difficult questions." "He is a details man who will pick out things that pass me by." **Recent work:** Acted in a dispute concerning a deliberately induced fraudulent RTA, where a finding of fraud was made against all three claimants.

Sadie Crapper (Thirty Nine Essex Street) Frequently acts for major insurers in substantial fraud and exaggerated claims. She enjoys a strong reputation, not least because of her efforts in Summers v Fairclough Homes, a leading judgment declaring the power of the courts to strike out a case for abuse of process. **Strengths:** "She delivers what is expected in a way that is client and solicitor-friendly." "She is very bright and her pleadings are excellent." **Recent work:** Successfully struck out a claim concerning an RTA involving a motorcycle and an allegedly defective road surface.

William Featherby QC (12 King's Bench Walk) Specialises in fraud and contempt of court cases. He has a reputation for his involvement in major contempt cases. **Recent work:** Appeared in Brighton Bus v Brooks, securing a contempt of court conviction.

Corin Furness (Parklane Plowden) Practises exclusively in personal injury law, and has a particular focus on fraudulent claims. He acts for both claimants and defendants. **Strengths:** "He's very good with the witnesses and insurers as he's very down to earth, has a good analytical style and is a good advocate." "He's very pragmatic and explains things very clearly." **Recent work:** Has recently settled a number of defences and Part 20 claims in low-velocity impact, staged accident and phantom passenger cases.

Judy Dawson (Sovereign Chambers) Practises exclusively in insurance fraud. She handles large-scale fraud rings and works with insurers to identify and expose fraudulent claims. **Strengths:** "Extremely good with clients, she produces quality work." "She is very thorough and has good cross-examination skills." **Recent work:** Involved in Operation G, an investigation concerning 120 RTAs which were deliberately induced. She successfully attained an order that several claims should be heard together.

Peter Wilson (Sovereign Chambers) Works exclusively for insurers defending RTA injury claims alleged to be fraudulent. He frequently handles low-velocity impact cases. **Strengths:** "I've never known anyone to prepare so much; he gives 110% of his attention to the case." "He keeps in contact, discusses matters with you and is happy to answer queries so you feel like you're in safe hands." **Recent work:** Defended a whiplash and psychological injury claim brought by several football fans involved in a low-velocity collision with a car whilst travelling home from an FA Cup match.

Anna Symington (St John's Chambers) Acts in a range of motor insurance fraud disputes, including phantom passenger claims, staged accidents and exaggerated claims. She appears almost exclusively for insurers. **Strengths:** "She is very sharp and is good at spotting issues." "She provides robust and straightforward advice and is an excellent advocate."

Christopher Kennedy QC (9 St John Street) Has a wide personal injury practice that includes RTA claims. He handles potentially fraudulent claims on behalf of major insurers relating to staged accidents and fraud rings. **Strengths:** "Very easy to deal with, he goes the extra mile and is extremely approachable." "Calm and considered, he's absolutely on the point when cross-examining witnesses." **Recent work:** Successfully represented two major insurers in a contested action to recover damages from those behind a fraud ring.

Brian McCluggage (9 St John Street) Specialises in high-value personal injury litigation. He is often instructed in cases involving allegations of fraud, including those relating to RTAs. **Strengths:** "He is technically very good and his strategic advice is always spot-on." "He is definitely leading the way, particularly in terms of complex fraud rings: he just gets it." **Recent work:** Successfully appealed on behalf of defendant insurers in a case relating to a point of principle arising out of the RTA Portal system.

Matthew Snarr of 9 St John Street)
Advises and acts in high-value fraud proceedings, particularly those relating to fraud rings. He focuses his practice on acting for defendants. **Strengths:** "He's a very determined litigator, who is very able, particularly when handling complex areas of law." "Very clever, very thorough and good on the detail."

OFFSHORE: An Introduction

Contributed by XXIV Old Buildings

It has been another busy year for the offshore world and one in which the English Commercial and Chancery Bar has played an ever-increasing role. Work from traditional offshore jurisdictions – the Channel Islands, the Isle of Man, Gibraltar, Bermuda and the Caribbean – is being increasingly augmented by cases from Dubai (with the development of the DIFC Court), Singapore and Hong Kong. As onshore litigation slows, so more and more of the Bar are embracing the possibilities the offshore world offers, marketing to the offshore world the undoubted pool of talent that the Bar represents.

The Caribbean Courts continue to attract significant litigation from China and the Middle East, with a steady stream of work, often routed through Hong Kong or Dubai, involving family or joint venture disputes engaging many from the Chancery and Commercial Bar. Thus, whilst the BVI was occupied with a fraternal dispute in Alhamrani v Alhamrani, the Cayman Islands has been dealing with a multibillion-dollar fight between in-laws in Algosaibi v Saad. Meanwhile, the Russian love affair with BVI corporate structures remains, with the resultant litigation when things go wrong occupying both the BVI High Court and Court of Appeal. 2014 sees the last full year of Judge Edward Bannister QC's tenure as the BVI's sole Commercial Court Judge. His rapid and decisive judgments have propelled the BVI into the forefront of international litigation. He will be a hard act to follow.

Elsewhere, the fallout from Bernie Madoff still dominates. The trustee for Bernard L. Madoff Investment Securities LLC, Irving Pickard, had a good year. He had previously been rebuffed in his attempts to obtain recognition in the BVI, but had more success in Cayman: not only did he obtain recognition, but he was permitted to bring a clawback claim under Cayman law. In contrast, the liquidators of Fairfield Security, a BVI hedge fund that invested in Madoff, saw their clawback claims based on mistake being thrown out by the Privy Council.

Problems generated by failed hedge funds with illiquid assets generally remain unresolved. The ability to wind such a fund up and the status and rights of unpaid redeeming shareholders are the subject of differing views across the Caribbean and may well be the subject of a number of further decisions in the coming months.

Perceived failings by hedge fund directors, brought into sharp focus by the well-publicised collapse of the Weavering Fund, have led to increased regulation in the Cayman Islands, with the Directors Registration and Licensing Bill 2014 being set to become law. The Cayman Islands legislature has also introduced revamped partnership and arbitration laws in an attempt to maintain a competitive edge over its offshore rivals. The BVI has followed suit with its own Arbitration Act, whilst belatedly signing up to the New York Convention to enable enforcement of foreign arbitration awards. Indeed, enforcement continues to play a dominant role in offshore litigation. The Eastern Caribbean Supreme Court Rules have recently been amended to facilitate the enforcement of foreign judgments; the trail blazed by the Cayman Privy Council decision of TMSF v Merrill Lynch, enabling creditors to attack offshore trusts, has been followed in the BVI High Court, and Bermuda has been revisiting submission to the jurisdiction as an enforcement pre-requisite.

Gibraltar, meanwhile, has been grappling with proprietary claims against banks in the wake of the UK Court of Appeal decision in Sinclair v Versailles, whilst Jersey offered its own solution to the problem in the context of bribes in Lloyds Bank Trust Co v Fargoso.

Outward Chinese investment has led to an increasing volume of international arbitration work, particularly in Hong Kong and Singapore, with the latter's Maxwell Chambers having for some time accommodated the satellite offices of several London Commercial sets. Other offshore centres in the region are also benefiting, with Mauritius and the Seychelles vying for Chinese, Indian and Indonesian business, whilst Dubai (with its DIFC Court) and (to a lesser extent) Qatar are becoming increasingly prominent. Africa, a market as yet little tapped, is seen by these jurisdictions as the next frontier to conquer.

Since 2008 tax and the moral obligation to pay it has become a recurring theme for politicians on both side of the Atlantic. David Cameron may have been prepared to concede that it was unfair to call overseas Territories or Crown dependencies tax havens, but others have no such qualms. Stigmatisation of those operating offshore is very much on the agenda, not least as a result of a massive leak of confidential information in April 2013, identifying those behind many offshore trusts and companies. It has led a significant number of private clients to relocate their wealth onshore, notwithstanding the adverse tax consequences. Tax Information Exchange Agreements have been commonplace for some time amongst most offshore jurisdictions, driven by fears of blacklisting by the OECD, or even by the French (which recently led Jersey to revise its transparency arrangements), but other developments are potentially more significant. The US Foreign Account Tax Compliance Act, which requires offshore financial institutions to report on US tax resident account holders or face a 30% withholding tax, is certain to have a big impact, whilst little publicised mutual assistance conventions, providing for the retrospective collection of foreign tax debts, seem likely to become increasingly commonplace. By contrast, the call for a register recording the beneficial ownership of shares is proving highly contentious: confidentiality is not something the offshore world will surrender willingly. The long-term implications of such a hardening of attitudes is difficult to gauge. What, however, can be said with confidence is that it seems unlikely it will have any immediate impact on what, for many at the Chancery and Commercial Bar, is a thriving litigation scene.

Contents:

LONDON

Offshore
London

Leading Sets

Band 1	Band 2
Maitland Chambers *	New Square Chambers *
XXIV Old Buildings *	South Square *
Serle Court *	3 Stone Buildings *
Wilberforce Chambers *	

Leading Silks

Band 1	**Band 3**
Boyle Alan *Serle Court* *	**Adkin** Jonathan *Serle Court* *
Crow Jonathan *4 Stone Buildings (ORL)* ◊ *	**Ayliffe** James *Wilberforce Chambers*
Dicker Robin *South Square* *	**Cohen** Lawrence *Wilberforce Chambers*
Girolami Paul *Maitland Chambers* *	**Collings** Matthew *Maitland Chambers* *
Green Brian *Wilberforce Chambers*	**Dohmann** Barbara *Blackstone Chambers (ORL)* ◊
Le Poidevin Nicholas *New Square Chambers* *	**Fenwick** Justin *4 New Square (ORL)* ◊ *
Moverley Smith Stephen *XXIV Old Buildings*	**Flynn** Vernon *Essex Court Chambers (ORL)* ◊
Parker Christopher R *Maitland Chambers* *	**Furness** Michael *Wilberforce Chambers*
Steinfeld Alan *XXIV Old Buildings*	**Hapgood** Mark *Brick Court Chambers (ORL)* ◊
Talbot Rice Elspeth *XXIV Old Buildings*	**Howard** Mark *Brick Court Chambers (ORL)* ◊
Taube Simon *Ten Old Square (ORL)* ◊ *	**Hubble** Ben *4 New Square (ORL)* ◊ *
Warnock-Smith Shân *5 Stone Buildings (ORL)* ◊ *	**Legge** Henry *5 Stone Buildings (ORL)* ◊ *
Band 2	**Levy** Robert *XXIV Old Buildings*
Atherton Stephen *20 Essex Street (ORL)* ◊	**Lowe** Thomas *Wilberforce Chambers*
Black Michael *XXIV Old Buildings*	**Marshall** Philip *Serle Court* *
Brownbill David *XXIV Old Buildings*	**McCall** Christopher *Maitland Chambers* *
Cooper Gilead *3 Stone Buildings* *	**McGrath** Paul *Essex Court Chambers (ORL)* ◊
Hacker Richard *South Square*	**Newman** Catherine *Maitland Chambers* *
Ham Robert *Wilberforce Chambers*	**Quest** David *3 Verulam Buildings (ORL)* ◊
Hinks Frank *Serle Court* *	**Rajah** Eason *Ten Old Square (ORL)* ◊ *
Hollington Robin *New Square Chambers* *	**Snowden** Richard *Erskine Chambers (ORL)* ◊
Jones Elizabeth *Serle Court* *	**Thom** James *New Square Chambers* *
Lord David W *3 Stone Buildings* *	**Todd** Michael *Erskine Chambers (ORL)* ◊ *
McQuater Ewan *3 Verulam Buildings (ORL)* ◊	**Trace** Anthony *Maitland Chambers* *
Millett Richard *Essex Court Chambers (ORL)* ◊	**Tregear** Francis *XXIV Old Buildings*
Mowschenson Terence *Wilberforce Chambers*	
Smith Stephen *Erskine Chambers (ORL)* ◊ *	
Thanki Bankim *Fountain Court Chambers (ORL)* ◊ *	

Leading Juniors

Band 1	**Langlois** Nicole *XXIV Old Buildings*
Brightwell James *New Square Chambers* *	**Mold** Andrew *Wilberforce Chambers* *
Hagen Dakis *Serle Court* *	**Mumford** David *Maitland Chambers* *
Harrison Nicholas *Serle Court* *	**Parker** Matthew *3 Verulam Buildings (ORL)* ◊ *
Richardson Giles *Serle Court* *	**Shah** Bajul *XXIV Old Buildings*
Singla Nikki *Wilberforce Chambers*	**Shivji** Sharif *4 Stone Buildings (ORL)* ◊
Tucker Lynton *New Square Chambers* *	**Band 3**
Wilson Richard *3 Stone Buildings* *	**Cumming** Edward *XXIV Old Buildings*
Band 2	**Holden** Andrew *XXIV Old Buildings*
Child Andrew J *3 Stone Buildings* *	**Hubbard** Mark *New Square Chambers* *
Cloherty Adam *XXIV Old Buildings*	**O'Mahony** David *7BR (ORL)* ◊ [A] *
Hilliard Jonathan *Wilberforce Chambers*	**Weaver** Elizabeth *XXIV Old Buildings*
Hochberg Daniel *Wilberforce Chambers*	

* *Indicates set / individual with profile.*
◊ *(ORL) = Other Ranked Lawyer.*
[A] *direct access (see p.11).*

Band 1

Maitland Chambers
See profile on p.831

THE SET

The barristers at Maitland Chambers regularly act for clients in the key Caribbean jurisdictions of Bermuda, the British Virgin Islands (BVI) and the Cayman Islands. Members are often instructed to act in high-profile, high-stakes cases involving banks, liquidators and notable individuals. In addition, the set can also deploy impressive advisory expertise in the Chwannel Islands jurisdictions, and members are also called upon to work with clients embroiled in disputes in Gibraltar, Hong Kong, the Isle of Man and the Bahamas.

Client service: "They are one of the best clerking teams. They are just very attentive and quick. If I phone up and can't get hold of someone another clerk will answer and will know what I have been dealing with. They are good at coming back to you promptly and politely." John Wiggs leads the team.

SILKS

Christopher Parker QC Maintains a significant commercial chancery practice and handles a range of issues in the offshore context. His cases regularly include company matters, such as shareholder disputes and breaches of fiduciary duty, as well as general insolvency and fraud matters. **Strengths:** "He's the recommended silk for offshore trust work. He really throws himself into a case." **Recent work:** Acted in an appeal in the BVI concerning the failure of a joint venture and resulting unfair prejudice cross-claims.

Paul Girolami QC A high-profile presence at the London Offshore Bar, handling notable cases relating to the Cayman Islands, as well as those involving the BVI, Dubai and Gibraltar. He regularly acts in cases concerning insolvency, civil fraud and company law, and is also a Deputy High Court Judge for the Queen's Bench and Chancery Divisions. **Strengths:** "He is an absolute delight to work with. He is absolutely phenomenal on his feet."

Christopher McCall QC He is especially well known for his extensive expertise in handling cases concerning trusts, and is also an authority on tax-related trust matters. He regularly works in the Cayman Islands and the Channel Islands. **Strengths:** "He has a huge amount of accumulated experience."

Catherine Newman QC (see p.681) A Deputy High Court Judge and a Lieutenant Bailiff of the Royal Court of Guernsey. She is a genuine commercial litigation and traditional chancery all-rounder, with a vast amount of international experience, both in the traditional offshore jurisdictions and elsewhere. **Strengths:** "In the courtroom she is extremely determined when she pleads a case. She will not give an inch in her advocacy. Extremely effective, she truly is the master of her brief." **Recent work:** She participated in an adverse possession claim in the BVI which is now to be heard by the Privy Council.

Anthony Trace QC His offshore experience includes sitting on a panel of silks that advises the government of Hong Kong, and he has also been called to the BVI Bar. He is a specialist in traditional chancery and commercial litigation, and is regularly involved in cases concerning professional negligence, insolvency and civil fraud. **Strengths:** "He is just an extremely good advocate, and first-rate when dealing with urgent matters." **Recent work:** He has advised Hong Kong philanthropist Sam Tak Lee on proceedings in the UK and in Hong Kong.

Matthew Collings QC Handles cases involving company, commercial and insolvency elements, both at trial and appellate level. His offshore work is spread among the Cayman Islands, the BVI, the Channel Islands and Hong Kong, as well as Jamaica and Iceland. **Strengths:** "He is incredibly creative, and is always coming up with new ideas and strategies. He is good fun to work with and is always cheerful. He keeps you going." **Recent work:** He acted in a significant case concerning share registers before the BVI Court of Appeal that is now moving to appeal in front of the Privy Council.

JUNIORS

David Mumford Regularly works on general commercial disputes, and is also active in cases brought against trustees and assorted fiduciaries involving professional negligence and other claims. His workload means he is active in Hong Kong, in addition to traditional offshore jurisdictions such as Channel Islands and the Cayman Islands. **Strengths:** "He is obviously very bright. He provides very clear advice, even on difficult technical legal issues." **Recent work:** He represented a trust in a Guernsey case concerning company and trust issues arising from the liquidation of an Icelandic bank.

XXIV Old Buildings

See profile on p.838

THE SET

The set has long played a leading role at the Offshore Bar, and is still the best-known chambers for this type of work. The strength and depth of the expertise deployed by XXIV Old Buildings in this area is consistently impressive across a variety of matters involving offshore elements. Members are well known for their visibility and activity in traditional offshore jurisdictions in the Caribbean and Channel Islands, as well as the Isle of Man. They are also acting with greater frequency elsewhere, in places such as Cyprus, Gibraltar and the Middle East.

SILKS

David Brownbill QC Has an extensive offshore practice which includes cases arising in all the key offshore jurisdictions in the Caribbean and the Channel Islands. He is also active in matters relating to Hong Kong, and his workload covers international and commercial trusts, investment funds and commercial and corporate structurings. **Strengths:** "He has a fantastic knowledge of trusts law and a fantastic knowledge of all the offshore jurisdictions." **Recent work:** He has been involved in a substantial Guernsey case considering the insolvency of trusts in the wake of the collapse of an Icelandic bank.

Stephen Moverley Smith QC Works in the offshore context on general commercial litigation cases. He is adept at advising and representing clients in a variety of areas, such as insolvency, banking, company and trust disputes in both traditional and fledgling offshore jurisdictions. **Strengths:** "He is a leading performer in the BVI Commercial Court." **Recent work:** He represented a group of companies subjected to public interest winding-up proceedings by the Financial Services Commission of the Isle of Man.

Elspeth Talbot Rice QC An experienced practitioner in a variety of offshore jurisdictions, who has a particularly strong reputation in Channel Islands and Isle of Man cases. She works on a wide range of matters and frequently handles issues regarding trusts, insolvency, civil fraud and professional negligence. She is also known for her banking and financial services expertise. **Strengths:** "She's someone who you really want to have on your side. She is fantastically responsive and has a great grasp of the detail." **Recent work:** She argued against Guernsey winding-up petitions made in the public interest against a hedge fund and a group of related entities.

Alan Steinfeld QC Has an exceptional reputation for his skill and experience in advising and representing clients in offshore matters. His workload is wide and varied, with regard to both matters handled and jurisdictions covered. He acts in cases including those relating to insolvency, fraud, professional negligence, international trusts and commercial litigation, and is active in the major Caribbean jurisdictions and the Channel Islands, as well as the Isle of Man and Gibraltar. **Strengths:** "He is the Godfather of offshore work and is excellent at handling most Caribbean bench judges. He shows both tenacity and enthusiasm."

Michael Black QC A seasoned international dispute lawyer, working on a range of commercial cases in established offshore jurisdictions. He frequently handles matters concerning professional negligence, insolvency and civil fraud, as well as general commercial litigation. He is also able to offer clients further expertise in construction matters and arbitrations, and is regularly involved in cases with Middle East aspects. **Recent work:** He acted in a case in front of the BVI Court of Appeal considering the court's own competence to interfere in liquidations.

Francis Tregear QC Called to the Bar of the Eastern Caribbean and also active in matters relating to Guernsey, the Isle of Man and Gibraltar. He advises and represents clients involved in cases concerning trusts, insolvency, funds and fraud, among other matters. **Strengths:** "He's a very quiet and gentle fellow with the most wonderful turn of phase. Judges love him." **Recent work:** He acted for the liquidator of a fund in a Cayman case regarding claims arising from the Madoff collapse.

Robert Levy QC Maintains a commercial and chancery practice that includes civil fraud and asset tracing, as well as insolvency and company matters and commercial litigation. He has been called to the Bar in Anguilla and the Eastern Caribbean, and is frequently involved in cases in the major Caribbean jurisdictions. **Strengths:** "He's smart and gets the issues across very quickly." **Recent work:** He acted on behalf of the State Oil Company of Azerbaijan in a USD500 million BVI case concentrating on its security over shares in the wake of a default.

JUNIORS

Adam Cloherty Called to the Bar in both the Eastern Caribbean and the Cayman Islands, but also an active participant in cases heard in the Channel Islands and the Isle of Man. His areas of expertise include commercial litigation, trusts and banking and financial services matters. **Strengths:** "He's extraordinarily intelligent, extremely responsive, and someone with a very wide range of knowledge." **Recent work:** He represented a prominent Russian businessman and politician in a Cayman case concerning beneficial interest in a London property.

Nicole Langlois Concentrates on fraud and asset tracing, trusts and the resolution of commercial disputes. She is active in a variety of established offshore jurisdictions, but is best known for her ability to appear before courts in Jersey. **Strengths:** "She is a Jersey advocate and is tough, but sensible." **Recent work:** She acted in a tracing claim made by a liquidator to set aside contributions made to a Guernsey employee benefit trust.

Edward Cumming Maintains a varied commercial chancery practice, including cases concerning insolvency, company, commercial and international trust disputes. His workload takes him to a range of jurisdictions in the Caribbean and the Channel Islands. **Strengths:** "He is extremely hard-working and diligent, and is a fine tactician." **Recent work:** He acted in the substantial Crociani v Crociani trust dispute in Jersey.

Andrew Holden Concentrates on commercial chancery matters including insolvency and commercial litigation, although he is best known for his expertise in trusts and probate disputes. He represents and advises clients in all the traditional offshore jurisdictions and is admitted to the Cayman Islands Bar. **Strengths:** "He's very industrious and tactically astute, and produces first-class written documents." "He deserves huge praise from the Bermuda trust industry for his work on legislative reform." **Recent work:** He acted for a subsidiary of HSBC in an Isle of Man case concerning claims of pension scheme maladministration.

Bajul Shah Works on a wide variety of commercial chancery matters, including insolvency, trusts, company and commercial litigation. He regularly acts on matters in the Channel Islands, and also appears in the Cayman Islands and the BVI. **Recent work:** He acted in a Guernsey trust case concerning a range of claims precipitated by the collapse of an Icelandic bank.

Elizabeth Weaver Called to the Bar of the Eastern Caribbean Supreme Court, and also active in other jurisdictions including the Channel Islands and the Isle of Man. Her workload comprises commercial chancery matters relating to insolvency, company and trust disputes, among others. **Strengths:** "She is robust and tenacious, and in both opinions and conference she is very strong." **Recent work:** She advised a Swiss trust company in respect of a Jersey beneficiary dispute.

Serle Court

See profile on p.860

THE SET

Serle Court has a well-established position among the leading sets at the London Offshore Bar. Members often represent clients involved in the most complex and significant commercial and chancery matters occurring in traditional offshore jurisdictions, including Bermuda, the BVI and the Cayman Islands. The Channel Islands remains the major source of work for the set, while barristers also see work in Gibraltar, Hong Kong and elsewhere.

Client service: "Expert, professional, flexible and cooperative, the clerking is exactly what is needed in this day and age."

SILKS

Alan Boyle QC One of the most recognisable names at the Commercial and Chancery Bar. His wide and varied offshore practice includes company and insolvency disputes and cases concerning trusts, probate and financial services issues. **Strengths:** "If you want an authority of trusts, he is your man."

Frank Hinks QC Well known for handling high-stakes, high-value international trust cases. He regularly acts in relation to Bermudian law, although he also has experience of cases involving Bahamian and Cayman law elements. **Strengths:** "His written and oral skills are exceptional."

Elizabeth Jones QC (see p.639) Called to the Bar in the BVI and regularly involved in cases in Jersey, as well as other key offshore jurisdictions. She specialises in contentious trust cases and fraud. **Strengths:** "She has a highly forensic mind and is very honest in her dealings." **Recent work:** She has recently acted in the significant Alhamrani litigation involving claims of ownership over shares in a BVI company.

Jonathan Adkin QC (see p.532) Maintains a practice comprising a full range of offshore issues, most notably trust cases. He also acts in general commercial disputes and is often called upon in Bermuda, the Cayman Islands, Jersey and Gibraltar. **Strengths:** "He really adds value and is of invaluable assistance in developing the strategy in a case." **Recent work:** He acted in a high-value trust and probate dispute concentrating on the estate of a high-profile Bahamian.

Philip Marshall QC He is especially active in cases concerning BVI law, although he also tackles matters in the contexts of Bermuda, Guernsey and the Isle of Man. He receives instructions relating to company law, insolvency and a variety of other commercial disputes. **Strengths:** "A forceful advocate who represents the heavy artillery in a case." **Recent work:** He advised Bermuda's Ministry of Finance on a significant winding-up petition relating to IPOC.

JUNIORS

Dakis Hagen Has an excellent reputation for his offshore work in the fields of asset tracing and fraud, as well as trusts. He is especially active in cases relating to Jersey and Bermuda, but is also involved in a number of other offshore jurisdictions. **Strengths:** "He very much likes to be part of the team. He takes a genuine and real interest and commits to the case." **Recent work:** Advised a trust company in a substantial Jersey case considering an alleged breach of trust claim resulting from investment losses.

Nicholas Harrison (see p.621) Regularly advises and represents clients involved in offshore commercial chancery disputes, including international trust and fraud cases. His workload takes him to a wide range of key offshore jurisdictions. **Strengths:** "He really cares and is a real fighter. He pushes it along and is very imaginative." **Recent work:** He was involved in the Bitel litigation, the most significant commercial case to be heard in the Isle of Man.

Giles Richardson (see p.707) A well-respected offshore practitioner with experience of substantial cases in a variety of jurisdictional settings. He is heavily involved in cases dealing with trust issues. **Strengths:** "He is very commercial and able to convert the esoteric into the everyday. You always feel like he has got it bang on right." **Recent work:** Acted in claims concerning breach of duty of care made before the Court of Appeal in Guernsey and the Privy Council.

Wilberforce Chambers

See profile on p.876

THE SET

The members at Wilberforce Chambers are among the most sought-after barristers operating in the offshore environment, and take instructions in a variety of contexts. Work routinely includes representing and advising clients involved in real estate, trusts and commercial cases in Bermuda, the BVI and the Cayman Islands. Members are also heavily involved in matters concerning the Channel Islands, as well as in those touching upon Singapore, Hong Kong, Russia and the Turks and Caicos Islands, among others.

Client service: "We have met a number of the clerks and feel we can pick up the phone and get a rapid response from them."

SILKS

Brian Green QC Enjoys a stellar reputation for his work at the Offshore Bar, particularly in respect of trust cases. He regularly takes instructions in Bermuda, BVI, Channel Islands and Hong Kong disputes. **Strengths:** "He is the doyen. His name sends shivers down the spines of the opposition. He portrays supreme confidence and can persuade just about anybody, whether a Supreme Court judge or the lady who brings the tea, that black is white. His skill is almost like witchcraft."

Terence Mowschenson QC Concentrates his offshore work on commercial chancery cases, including those concerning joint ventures, company disputes, partnerships and banking and financial services matters. Recent work has arisen from a range of jurisdictions, including the Cayman Islands, the Bahamas and Gibraltar. **Strengths:** "He is one of those who is extremely commercially savvy and practical and down to earth. He gets to the heart of a matter." **Recent work:** He acted in a case concerning the winding up of a fund that had made significant investments with Bernard Madoff.

James Ayliffe QC Known for his commercial practice, and his particular expertise in handling cases related to business and finance matters. He is also active in the area of asset tracing and recovery. Recent instructions have included those from the Channel Islands and the BVI. **Strengths:** "The advice is very commercial and he is unflappable in court." **Recent work:** He worked with the South African Revenue Service in its efforts to recover £220 million from a debtor who had hidden assets in the UK, the BVI, Guernsey and Mauritius, among other jurisdictions.

Lawrence Cohen QC Focuses his offshore practice on complicated, high-value matters, usually in the context of business disputes or transactions. Special areas of interest include investment funds and security transactions. He is active in the key traditional offshore jurisdictions, as well as other foreign jurisdictions. **Recent work:** He defended a notable international law firm against a claim alleging that a poorly executed restructuring cost its client significant sums in Mexican tax.

Robert Ham QC Concentrates his offshore practice on trusts, and advises and represents clients in related tax and pension matters. He is also active in professional negligence cases and is regularly called upon to act in Caribbean jurisdictions. **Strengths:** "He is a grandee and a very nice guy with it. He has so much knowledge and expertise."

Thomas Lowe QC Has extensive experience of representing clients in the Cayman Islands, the Bahamas and Bermuda, and has also worked on cases in Jersey. He regularly acts in multi-jurisdictional matters concerning trusts, insolvency, professional negligence and commercial fraud. **Strengths:** "He's very user-friendly and intelligent, and sees the big picture at all times."

Michael Furness QC A major figure in offshore trusts litigation who has appeared in cases in Bermuda, Hong Kong, the Cayman Islands and Jersey. **Strengths:** "An extremely authoritative barrister who is calm in court but quite capable of being very tough when necessary." **Recent work:** Appeared in a case against the trustee of a very large Bermuda trust, representing the present and former trustees. Also acted in the tax case of CoT v Nice Cheer Investments Ltd.

JUNIORS

Nikki Singla Often instructed in commercial litigation and trust matters. He has substantial experience of appearing before courts in the Cayman Islands and Bermuda, where he has twice been called to the Bar, and is also active in Dubai. **Strengths:** "A high-energy barrister who is very, very skilled." **Recent work:** He acted in a significant multiparty trust case in Jersey concerning claims of fraud, breach of fiduciary duty and conflict of interest.

Jonathan Hilliard Well known for his extensive work in highly complex and notable trust and company law cases. He acts in a broad range of offshore jurisdictions, including Gibraltar, the BVI and the Isle of Man. **Strengths:** "A very confident barrister who is good with clients, extremely well prepared and easy to work with." "He's quick both in terms of his intellect and his response times." **Recent work:** He represented an offshore law firm against accusations of dishonesty with regard to its administration of a trust.

Daniel Hochberg An established expert on offshore trust matters who has a broad commercial chancery practice. He is heavily involved in cases touching upon employee benefit trusts. His offshore work most usually sees him acting in Jersey and Guernsey. **Strengths:** "He is really my go-to barrister for particularly difficult points of trust law. He has a significant amount of experience in trust cases." **Recent work:** He acted for a group of Jersey trustees against a claim of breach of trust from a former hedge fund employee in respect of an employee benefit trust.

Andrew Mold (see p.675) Has continued to develop a significant practice advising and representing clients involved in offshore trust disputes. He often tackles matters in the Cayman Islands, where he has been called to the Bar, as well as in other key offshore jurisdictions. **Strengths:** "Polite and pleasant, he goes out of his way to make things easy for the instructing solicitor and to try and find a practical answer for the client." **Recent work:** He provided advice in a divorce concerning USD12 billion of assets placed in a variety of jurisdictions, including Cyprus, the BVI, England and Switzerland.

Band 2

New Square Chambers

See profile on p.837

THE SET

Members at the set have a fine reputation for advising and representing clients in a variety of offshore contexts, including contentious and non-contentious trusts, commercial contracts, company law and insolvency. The set also provides expertise with regard to jurisdictional questions. Much of the set's work derives from cases in the Channel Islands and the Caribbean, as well as Hong Kong.

SILKS

Nicholas Le Poidevin QC An experienced offshore practitioner who frequently acts for clients involved in contentious trust, estate and probate matters, as well as in cases concerning property. He is hugely active in disputes in the Channel Islands, and also appears in the Caribbean jurisdictions. **Strengths:** "Any superlative would not do him justice. He is amazing. His advice is superb, his drafting is elegant, and he is tremendous in conference. He has forgotten more about trust law than I'll ever know."

Robin Hollington QC Advises and represents clients in offshore company and insolvency matters. He is frequently involved in cases in the BVI, the Cayman Islands and Hong Kong. **Strengths:** "He is very steady and solid, and knows the law so comprehensively." **Recent work:** He acted in a Cayman

Islands case concerning the provisional liquidation of a company listed on the New York Stock Exchange after its listing had been suspended due to alleged mismanagement.

James Thom QC (see p.736) Admitted to the Bar of St Vincent and the Grenadines and of the BVI, and also active in the Cayman Islands, the Turks and Caicos Islands and the Channel Islands. He has a strong corporate practice and regularly acts in cases relating to hedge funds. **Strengths:** "He is very, very knowledgeable in relation to all aspects of offshore law." **Recent work:** He acted in a Cayman Islands case concerning a claim against the auditors of a hedge fund which had been defrauded by its investment manager.

JUNIORS

James Brightwell (see p.556) Continues to enjoy an excellent reputation as an authority and expert on trusts and related issues, both in the contentious and non-contentious contexts. His jurisdictional coverage notably includes the Channel Islands and the BVI. **Strengths:** "Some people just get it, and he has the right instincts, so even if there isn't a statute or case he can help you through." **Recent work:** He was active in a Guernsey case concerning a substantial claim following the liquidation of an Icelandic bank.

Lynton Tucker Devotes much of his offshore practice to advising and representing clients in contentious and non-contentious trust and estate matters. He is a seasoned practitioner, with experience of a wide range of traditional offshore jurisdictions. He is called to the Bar in the BVI and Anguilla. **Recent work:** He was involved in the Alhamrani litigation, which concentrated on the disputed ownership of an oil company.

Mark Hubbard (see p.632) Has a broad commercial chancery practice, although he most regularly handles matters relating to trusts and company issues, as well as insolvency and civil fraud matters. He works in a number of the key offshore jurisdictions, including the Bahamas, the Channel Islands and the Isle of Man. **Strengths:** "He is very strong in trust litigation, and is a go-to person. You can rely on him for good, sound advice." **Recent work:** He acted in a Guernsey trust case concerning a breach of trust claim made against a trustee following investment losses.

South Square

See profile on p.861

THE SET

South Square leads the way in insolvency matters, both onshore and offshore, and is becoming an increasingly notable force in other areas. Members are engaged in cases concerning commercial and company litigation, civil fraud and shareholder disputes, and regularly appear in Bermuda, the BVI and the Cayman Islands. They also appear in Channel Island jurisdictions.

SILKS

Robin Dicker QC Experienced in advising and representing clients involved in the full range of financial and business law cases, including insolvency. He is especially adept at matters concerning Bermuda, BVI and Cayman Islands law. **Strengths:** "He is absolutely top-drawer and is extremely clever. He has a wonderfully simple style of written and oral advocacy and is very convincing." **Recent work:** He acted in an appeal to the Privy Council from the Supreme Court of Bermuda concerning cross-border insolvency.

Richard Hacker QC A well-established presence in the key Caribbean jurisdictions, as well as in the Isle of Man. He handles a range of cases involving business, financial and commercial law, including banking and insolvency. **Strengths:** "Absolutely brilliant. He has a brain the size of a planet, and knows everything there is to know about offshore insolvency." **Recent work:** He acted in a protracted shareholder dispute involving Taiwanese shareholders of a Cayman company holding Vietnamese interests.

3 Stone Buildings

See profile on p.864

THE SET

3 Stone Buildings is well known for the international nature of its work and the comprehensive offshore expertise it can provide. Members are especially active in the Caribbean jurisdictions and also have established connections with Hong Kong, Singapore, Malaysia, Australia and a variety of other overseas jurisdictions.

Client service: "They are very commercially minded and realistic in suggesting counsel, and also savvy about appropriate rates. You feel you can form a working relationship. I can have very frank discussions about what I want from who I want." Andrew Palmer is the senior clerk.

SILKS

Gilead Cooper QC (see p.577) Frequently instructed by leading onshore and offshore law firms in cases arising in the BVI, the Cayman Islands and Bermuda. He regularly acts for clients involved in contentious trusts and property matters as well as general commercial chancery litigation. **Strengths:** "He is very measured and very impressive. Very good at looking at the overall strategy, he is insightful and very impressive on his feet." **Recent work:** He acted in BVI and Hong Kong proceedings concerning a significant Hong Kong estate along with a BVI trust.

David Lord QC (see p.658) Has been called to the BVI Bar and is a regular before the courts there, as well as in the Cayman Islands, the Bahamas and Bermuda. His wide and varied commercial chancery practice also encompasses cases in the Channel Islands and the Isle of Man. **Recent work:** He acted for banks in an appeal to the Privy Council in the litigation arising from the Fairfield Sentry liquidation.

JUNIORS

Richard Wilson A well-established presence before the Commercial Court of the BVI who also acts in cases arising in the Channel Islands, Gibraltar and the Cayman Islands. He often advises and represents clients in trust matters. **Strengths:** "He is a very approachable and clever chap. His technical expertise on more esoteric areas is absolutely exceptional."

Andrew Child Concentrates on offshore matters concerning contentious trusts and estates. He is active in a range of key traditional offshore jurisdictions. **Strengths:** "He's bright and he's built up a reputation as being good on the law and a good advocate." **Recent work:** He acted in the Al Sadi dispute, which considered the relationship between a Liechtenstein foundation and Shari'a inheritance provisions in relation to the estate of a Kuwaiti businessman.

Other Ranked Lawyers

Barbara Dohmann QC (Blackstone Chambers) Acts in cases in a number of significant offshore jurisdictions in the Channel Islands and the Caribbean. Her work ranges right across the spectrum of commercial litigation matters. **Strengths:** "She lives up to her reputation as one of the top silks – her name alone strikes fear in everyone." **Recent work:** She acted in the BVI in Inteco Beteiligungs AG v Sylmord Trade Inc., a case which focused on debt contracts.

David O'Mahony (see p.685) (7BR) Has been called to the Bar in Australia and the Turks and Caicos Islands. His practice has an emphasis on international criminal matters, particularly those concerning criminal fraud and money laundering, as well as commercial law. **Recent work:** He acted in civil and criminal proceedings in the Turks and Caicos Islands concerning a corruption investigation in the wake of the dissolution of the government.

Mark Hapgood QC (Brick Court Chambers) Handles a broad range of commercial cases. His offshore work takes him to the key traditional Caribbean jurisdictions of the BVI, Bermuda and the Cayman Islands. **Recent work:** He acted in the Fairfield Sentry litigation in the BVI concerning a Madoff feeder fund.

Mark Howard QC (Brick Court Chambers) Has a significant commercial litigation practice, and is adept at handling cases concerning professional negligence, banking and fraud. He is especially experienced in BVI matters. **Recent work:** He acted in a Bermuda case concerning an alleged fraud relating to a reinsurance treaty.

Stephen Smith QC (see p.724) (Erskine Chambers) Has been called to the Bar of the East Caribbean Supreme Court, as well as to the Bar of the Bahamas and of the Cayman Islands, and is also experienced in cases proceeding in a variety of other jurisdictions. His practice is focused on commercial litigation involving issues of fraud, insolvency and company law. **Strengths:** "He has a very good reputation for serious fraud cases. He has been doing that in England, and he has the profile in the BVI." **Recent work:** He acted in a set of BVI proceedings concerning the disputed ownership of a stake in a Turkish mobile telecommunications company.

Richard Snowden QC (Erskine Chambers) Well known for his expertise in cases concerning company law issues, and also experienced in corporate insolvency, commercial litigation and trusts matters. **Strengths:** "He is a technical lawyer with a very serious company law background. He is a meticulous lawyer who is great at company disputes." **Recent work:** He acted in a case concerning the disputed estate of a significant Hong Kong business tycoon.

Michael Todd QC (see p.738) (Erskine Chambers) Has extensive experience of advising and representing clients in a variety of offshore jurisdictions, having been active in Bermuda, the BVI, the Cayman Islands and the Turks and Caicos Islands, among others. He handles company law, corporate finance and insolvency and capital markets matters. **Strengths:** "You expect the right answer, that is a given, but, above that, his communication skills are such that the client feels they understand what is going on." **Recent work:** He acted in the first shareholder derivative action to occur in Guernsey.

Richard Millett QC (Essex Court Chambers) Has established expertise in a number of areas, including banking and finance, insolvency and insurance and reinsurance, as well as a specialism in insurer insolvency. He is a regular presence in courts throughout the Caribbean and Channel Islands. **Strengths:** "He is extremely responsive, down to earth and user-friendly, and his input consistently adds significant value. He is commercial and practical in his advice." **Recent work:** He was involved in a minority shareholder dispute in the BVI and Hong Kong concerning a clothing business operating in Hong Kong and China.

Vernon Flynn QC (Essex Court Chambers) He is regularly involved in high-stakes, high-value multi-jurisdictional commercial litigation. Major law firms instruct him in a variety of jurisdictions, including the Cayman Islands, Seychelles and Singapore. **Strengths:** "He has a very commercial mind."

Paul McGrath QC (Essex Court Chambers) Appears in the most substantial pieces of offshore litigation, many of which deal with sums amounting to hundreds of millions of dollars. He has been instructed to appear in the Cayman Islands since 1997 and the BVI since 2005. Of late he has been handling a number of large cross-border insolvency cases. **Strengths:** "He is a very easy man to work with indeed. He is extremely reliable in terms of making himself available and doing things on time. He is also extremely practical and supremely clever."

Stephen Atherton QC (20 Essex Street) Acts in civil fraud, insolvency and company law matters as part of a wide-ranging commercial law practice. His practice takes him to all of the traditional offshore jurisdictions, and he is also active in Hong Kong and Singapore, among others. **Strengths:** "He is perceptive and insightful." **Recent work:** He acted in Cha v Staray Capital Limited, an unfair prejudice dispute heard in the BVI.

Bankim Thanki QC (Fountain Court Chambers) Can often be found advising and representing clients involved in offshore cases, especially in the BVI, Trinidad and Tobago and the Isle of Man, where he is permitted to appear before the courts. His caseload includes professional negligence, banking and finance and civil fraud matters. **Strengths:** "He is strategically very astute. He has excellent client care skills, and is a good delegator and team leader." **Recent work:** He continued to act for the Central Bank of Trinidad and Tobago in the CLICO inquiry into the losses made by banks and insurers as a result of the 2008 crash.

Justin Fenwick QC (4 New Square) His offshore involvement includes cases in the BVI, the Cayman Islands and St Kitts and Nevis. He is adept at tackling a wide range of matters in the commercial litigation context. **Strengths:** "He has the facility to absorb vast quantities of information quickly and well." **Recent work:** He acted in a BVI case concerning the alleged fraudulent dissipation of proceeds deriving from the sale of a Ukrainian business.

Ben Hubble QC (4 New Square) Has a well-developed practice covering disciplinary and professional negligence matters. He notably participates in cases in the Caribbean and the Channel Islands. **Strengths:** "He listens well to instructions and is excellent at preparing for a hearing. He is very efficient with time." **Recent work:** He acted on the Spectacular Holdings litigation in the BVI, including the appeal to the Court of Appeal of the East Caribbean.

Simon Taube QC (Ten Old Square) An experienced offshore practitioner who remains active in a variety of jurisdictions, including Bermuda, the Cayman Islands, Guernsey and Hong Kong. His workload involves trust and estates, personal taxation and tax planning, while he also has expertise in charity and professional negligence matters, among others. **Strengths:** "He is very calm and pretty encyclopaedic on any sort of trust law matter." **Recent work:** He acted in a UDS10 billion Hong Kong case involving the will of Nina Wang.

Eason Rajah QC (Ten Old Square) Maintains a chancery litigation practice that touches upon issues arising from wills and trusts, as well as allied tax and professional negligence points. He is especially well known for his contributions to cases in Jersey. **Strengths:** "He really knows his stuff and is technically very good. He is great to work with and is a team player." **Recent work:** He acted in the Jersey proceedings of the Crociani v Crociani breach of trust case.

Jonathan Crow QC (4 Stone Buildings) Sits as a judge in the Courts of Appeal in Jersey and Guernsey, and regularly acts on cases heard before courts in the Caribbean. His practice is a combination of public law and commercial litigation, and takes in administrative, company and financial services disputes. **Strengths:** "If you need a good result in a really big case he is your man." **Recent work:** He acted in a Privy Council appeal concerning the liquidation of Fairfield Sentry following investments made in Bernard L Madoff Investment Securities.

Sharif Shivji (4 Stone Buildings) An expert in commercial litigation, especially in cases involving financial services and accounting issues. He has experience of advising and representing clients in a mix of offshore jurisdictions. **Strengths:** "He is calm, clever and intellectually curious and rigorous." **Recent work:** He continued to act in the Al Khorafi v Bank Sarasin-Alpen (ME) Limited litigation involving a claim made by a Kuwaiti family regarding structured investment products.

Shân Warnock-Smith QC (5 Stone Buildings) Enjoys an outstanding reputation for her offshore practice, especially with regard to private client work. She frequently advises and represents wealthy international families in matters concerning trusts and estates in a variety of key Caribbean jurisdictions. **Strengths:** "Absolutely one of the very top trusts lawyers." **Recent work:** She acted in a BVI case with allied Hong Kong proceedings which considered the meaning of a trust.

Henry Legge QC (5 Stone Buildings) Handles a varied workload of chancery cases, especially those concerning pension schemes, estates and trusts. He is regularly involved in cases in the Channel Islands, as well as those in England including offshore elements. **Strengths:** "He has an absolutely infallable understanding of trust law so you start from a very strong academic base. He is also very personable and very practical."

Ewan McQuater QC (3 Verulam Buildings) An established figure who handles a variety of matters, including fraud and insolvency cases. His practice covers all the key traditional offshore jurisdictions, as well as others, such as Hong Kong and Singapore. **Recent work:** He acted in a case concerning a USD10 billion fraud claim made by the Algosaibi family against the Saad Group.

David Quest QC (3 Verulam Buildings) Enjoys a wide commercial dispute practice, and regularly handles banking and finance, insurance, fraud and professional negligence cases. He is especially active in the Cayman Islands. **Strengths:** "He is very user-friendly, extraordinarily approachable and just a fabulous lawyer. He has incredible analytical skills." **Recent work:** He acted in a Cayman Islands case concerning a significant fraud claim made against the Saad Group.

Matthew Parker (3 Verulam Buildings) Tackles commercial litigation cases in a range of jurisdictions. He is called to the Bar in the BVI and the Cayman Islands, and also acts in Anguilla, the Bahamas and Jersey. **Strengths:** "He is a very down-to-earth and straight-talking barrister." **Recent work:** He acted for third party claimants in a Guernsey case concerning a £100 million damages claim following the collapse of a property development scheme.

PARTNERSHIP: An Introduction

Contributed by 48 Bedford Row (Partnership Counsel)

With the country finally emerging from the shadow of the financial downturn, it has nevertheless been a turbulent year for partnerships and LLPs. Under pressure from ever-increasing PI insurance costs, some have decided to call it a day voluntarily, with individual partners seeking safe havens at other firms (which will not be classed as successor practices) but themselves shouldering the heavy burden of run-off cover. At the same time, the tailwind of the spectacular Dewey and Halliwells collapses has seen a spate of other, well-established firms going to the wall and using the pre-pack administration route as a means of parcelling out their workforce and caseloads to white-knight or predator firms (depending on your point of view).

The rise of the ABS continues and is likely to accelerate as the large accountancy firms enter the fray, but it is increasingly noticeable that the new wave ABSs are tending to reject the LLP format in favour of a full corporate structure.

The above trend is only likely to be reinforced by HMRC's recent full-on assault on LLPs, justified by what is perceived as concerted tax avoidance by the use of salaried or fixed share members. Although self-employed status was deliberately conferred on all LLP members from the outset (in a move that many found surprising at the time, particularly in the case of employed members), mutterings began some years ago about abuses on the part of hedge fund LLPs. From these beginnings, the battleground has spilled over across the whole LLP market, with draft legislation and accompanying guidance seemingly being made up on the hoof against an increasingly unrealistic deadline of 6 April 2014. In the event, final but substantially revised guidance was only issued in February 2014, leaving firms to scramble towards compliance in the face of what proved to be an unalterable start date. It is ironic that, throughout the guidance, HMRC stresses the need for salaried/fixed share members to share the attributes of true partners if they are to continue to enjoy self-employed status, only to end up requiring such members to fail one or more of three arbitrary conditions which, on a true analysis, have nothing whatever to do with the true tests for partnership status. Faced with the need to fail the uncertain conditions A (the "disguised salary" test) and B (the "significant influence" test), it is perhaps not surprising that most firms decided that failing condition C was the best bet, even if a judgement call was necessary if it was to be ensured that the relevant member's capital contribution exceeds 25% of his disguised salary. This approach will, ultimately, result in a significant influx of unexpected additional funds for those firms, once the three-month period of grace allowed by the proposed legislation expires. Other firms have simply taken the changes on the chin and converted their fixed share members back to full employee status. Whether HMRC will resort to the anti-avoidance provisions under the new regime to attack the former arrangements remains to be seen but commentators are already talking of changes to its approach down the line if, as expected, the new measures do not raise the required level of revenue. All this before the relevant provisions have even hit the statute book!

Although the new measures do not apply to traditional partnerships, they still have to contend with HMRC's long standing de facto tests of partnership status, which are no more logical or justifiable but are at least more familiar to practitioners. However, this is unlikely to herald a surge in the popularity of partnerships; rather, the trend is likely to be towards full incorporation, where such tests can be escaped entirely and funds can be built up within the company at a favourable tax rate. The perceived advantages of incorporation are only likely to be reinforced by HMRC's other recent line of attack, aimed at the use of corporate partners to shelter profits in both LLPs and traditional partnerships. How long it will be before the inequity between the treatment of corporates and LLPs/partnerships is addressed remains to be seen.

What is clear is that abuse by a minority has had major ramifications across the whole marketplace and has stimulated extensive redrafting of partnership and LLP agreements and arrangements driven solely by tax considerations.

The rate of LLP conversions has slowed as most of the major players have already converted and new start-ups scarcely consider a traditional partnership. Yet it is a truism that LLP status does not bring any change of approach by law firms' management, who continue to risk litigation by ignoring the terms of the governing LLP agreement and seeking to go their own way in the perceived interests of the firm (even if some of the other members see things differently). Moreover, the uneasy compromise between partnership and company that is the LLP's hallmark has not only caused problems in the tax sphere. Following the Supreme Court's decision in Clyde & Co LLP v Winkelhof, all LLP members, both fixed share and equity, are now regarded as "workers" within the employment legislation. A welcome development in the case of whistle-blowing perhaps, but something that cannot be drafted around. LLPs will accordingly need to look to specific statutory opt outs where available but there may still be some unexpected surprises down the line, especially when removing members.

Partner mobility continues apace, with the big bucks offered by the US firms providing a significant stimulus, as the spate of international mergers reshapes the established order of things. On the home front, many of the mergers (at least on one side) have been driven more by desperation than anything else, a trend set to continue.

Interesting times.

Contents:

LONDON

Partnership London	
Leading Sets	
Band 1	
48 Bedford Row (Partnership Counsel) *	
Serle Court *	
Band 2	
XXIV Old Buildings *	
Ten Old Square *	
Band 3	
Maitland Chambers *	
Leading Silks	
Star individuals	
Machell John	*Serle Court* *
Band 1	
Jones Philip	*Serle Court* *
Band 2	
Steinfeld Alan	*XXIV Old Buildings*
Talbot Rice Elspeth	*XXIV Old Buildings*
Tipples Amanda	*Maitland Chambers* *
Band 3	
Blayney David	*Serle Court* *
Mill Ian	*Blackstone Chambers (ORL)* ◊
Ritchie Stuart	*Littleton Chambers (ORL)* ◊
Leading Juniors	
Star individuals	
Callman Jeremy	*Ten Old Square* *
I'Anson Banks Roderick	*48 Bedford Row* *
Band 1	
Gavaghan Jonathan	*Ten Old Square* *
Jelf Simon	*48 Bedford Row (Partnership Counsel)* *
Band 2	
Blackett-Ord Mark	*5 Stone Buildings (ORL)* ◊ *
Haywood Jennifer	*Serle Court* *
King Michael	*XXIV Old Buildings*
Band 3	
Braithwaite Thomas	*Serle Court* *
Mather James	*Serle Court* *
Mumford David	*Maitland Chambers* *
Up-and-coming individuals	
Winston Naomi	*Ten Old Square* *

◊ (ORL) = Other Ranked Lawyer.
** Indicates set / individual with profile.*
Alphabetical order within each band. Band 1 is highest.

Band 1

48 Bedford Row (Partnership Counsel)

See profile on p.770

THE SET

This niche set remains the first port of call for those faced with complex partnership matters. It has deep expertise in all areas of partnership law, but is particularly strong on cases involving either partner moves or the removal of partners. Mediation is the preferred process for resolving disputes, although counsel are more than prepared to engage in litigation should the need arise. The members here are renowned for their skill in handling disputes concerning professional firms and pride themselves on offering close involvement with clients. Sources remark: "The set is small – just Simon Jelf and Roderick Banks – but the standard could not be higher. They are the only true specialists in this area at the Bar, and have a 100% focus on partnership law."

Client service: The clerk, Tyroon Win, is "excellent, as he's both helpful and pragmatic."

JUNIORS

Roderick I'Anson Banks (see p.635) Acknowledged as the pre-eminent practitioner of partnership law, he has three decades of specialising solely in this practice area. He is expert in all partnership-related matters, including cases concerning compulsory retirement, expulsions and partner extractions. **Strengths:** "We only instruct Roderick I'Anson Banks in this field as he is the standout practitioner and editor of the leading text book on the subject." "He is clever, very experienced, good at working in a team, commercially astute, and non-pompous in his approach. He is also not afraid to deliver difficult messages to the client." **Recent work:** Has been advising on improvements and amendments to be made to the existing Jersey LLP Law 1997, which he himself had a hand in drafting when it first came into existence.

Simon Jelf (see p.638) Highly regarded junior who frequently represents solicitors, accountants and GPs on a wide variety of partnership matters. He is particularly strong at drafting partnership agreements, and cases concerning the enforceability of restrictive covenants and contested expulsions. **Strengths:** "A true expert in this area, who is capable, unpretentious and able to think several steps ahead of the opposition. He's an all-round oracle on partnership law, and there is nothing he's not seen."

Serle Court

See profile on p.860

THE SET

Serle Court boasts several talented partnership practitioners who are experienced in both contentious and non-contentious work. Its members act in high-profile, cutting-edge cases involving solicitors, medical professionals, hedge funds and family wealth management partnerships. Areas of expertise include LLP conversions, domestic and international mergers, restrictive covenants, expulsions and team moves. Sources state: "Serle Court is a go-to set for partnership disputes. The expertise of its silks is clearly being trickled down to the junior end, meaning there is great breadth and depth of experience on the partnership front."

Client service: "The clerks, led by Steve Whitaker, are extremely efficient and helpful."

SILKS

John Machell QC (see p.660) Highly regarded silk who is renowned as an authority on LLPs. The majority of his work involves disputes featuring financial services professionals, solicitors and accountants. He also carries out work concerning the use of partnerships and LLPs in hedge funds. **Strengths:** "Consistently superb, he is authoritative, excellent in conference and user-friendly." **Recent work:** Recently acted for a potential intervener in Bates van Winkelhof v Clyde & Co LLP, a Supreme Court appeal concerning whistle-blowing and the worker status of LLP members.

David Blayney QC (see p.551) Well-regarded commercial and chancery barrister, who conducts a large amount of partnership work. He is particularly skilled in disputes involving solicitors. **Strengths:** "User-friendly and extremely bright." "He's very clear in his thinking and has an extremely sound grasp of the law."

Philip Jones QC Widely admired silk who handles a wide variety of partnership work, and focuses in particular on LLPs. His partnership expertise is enhanced by his deep knowledge of company law. **Strengths:** "Extremely good; he appears in lots of very grand cases." **Recent work:** Appeared in Boghani v Nathoo, a high-profile case involving the dissolution of a partnership.

JUNIORS

Jennifer Haywood (see p.623) Extremely talented junior who is frequently instructed on high-profile partnership matters. She handles a wide range of contentious and non-contentious work, and has particular strength in LLPs, expulsions and team moves. **Strengths:** "Jennifer is a highly respected senior junior who is technically excellent and a great lateral thinker." "She's bright, hard-working and very good with clients."

James Mather (see p.664) Acts for medical practices, accountancy firms and law firms in partnership and LLP disputes. He is very strong when it comes to drafting documents, including partnership deeds and LLP members' agreements. **Strengths:** "Very responsive, incisive and user-friendly."

Thomas Braithwaite Appears in a wide range of partnership and LLP disputes. He regularly advises solicitors, doctors and other professionals. **Strengths:** "Knows partnership law inside and out. He's very quick, and very good on the detail." **Recent work:** Acted in Hanlon v Human Capital Investment Group, a dispute concerning the acquisition of a recruitment agency.

Band 2

XXIV Old Buildings

See profile on p.838

THE SET

XXIV Old Buildings is a distinguished chancery set with a great reputation for partnership and LLP work. Members of chambers handle a broad spectrum of contentious and non-contentious work, including cases with a cross-border dimension. The set boasts particular experience in disputes involving international joint ventures and insolvent partnerships. It is further noted for its skill in handling matters concerning restrictive covenants and the termination and dissolution of partnerships.

SILKS

Alan Steinfeld QC Eminent silk with an expansive practice, who is noted for his outstanding expertise in partnership matters. He appears regularly in complex and high-profile disputes, many of which have an offshore dimension. **Strengths:** "He is very clever and measured, and understands the legal principles in a way which surprisingly few people do." "He's a very lovely, soft-spoken, calming guy, who is just so clear in his advice and assertive in court." **Recent work:** Appeared in numerous hearings related to Shiraz Boghani v Bashir Nathoo, an ongoing high-profile case, concerning a substantial property business.

Elspeth Talbot Rice QC A high-profile chancery silk who is strong on both contentious and non-contentious partnership matters. She is skilled in handling cases concerning the dissolution of partnerships, issues relating to restrictive covenants and questions of partners' duties of good faith. **Recent work:** Appeared in Coward v Phaestos & IKOS, a partnership dispute regarding the ownership of software.

JUNIORS

Michael King Areas of strength include contentious matters involving solicitors, accountants and hedge funds. He also handles film partnership schemes and farming disputes. **Strengths:** "Has a wealth of experience and uses that to give sound, practical advice. He has a remarkable ability to gauge a chancery judge's reaction to a partnership dispute. This is invaluable as it gives you the upper hand on tactics and negotiations." "Incisive and capable, he leads clients through a maze of difficult legal concepts." **Recent work:** Appeared in the Court of Appeal case of Illiott v Bluecrest Capital & Others.

Ten Old Square

See profile on p.839

THE SET

This set has a fine pedigree in partnership matters, and contains a number practitioners skilled in the field. Contentious matters are a forte for the set, with counsel often being instructed on the highest-profile cases around. Sources state: "The members have an extremely good knowledge of this practice area, and of the associated areas of partnership solvency and employment/discrimination." They are particularly adept at solicitors' partnership/LLP breakdowns, but regularly appear for all manner of clients including farmers, doctors, accountants and hedge funds.

Client service: "The clerks are extremely accommodating to instructing solicitors. The team, led by Keith Plowman, has gone the extra mile for us on more than one occasion."

JUNIORS

Jeremy Callman (see p.563) Renowned for handling many significant contentious cases, including those concerning prominent law firm mergers and partner departures. He also handles highly acrimonious disputes concerning accountancy firms and hedge funds. **Strengths:** "Widely acknowledged as one of the leading partnership specialists, he is a great team player with a head for detail, who is loved by clients." "Extremely bright, hard-working and commercially aware, he's an individual who inspires confidence in clients." **Recent work:** Recently appeared in Eaton v Caulfield & Others, a landmark case involving unfair prejudice and just and equitable winding-up in the context of LLPs.

Jonathan Gavaghan (see p.606) A well-regarded junior with a broad partnership practice, who often acts in disputes involving medical practices, dentists and law firms. He has particular expertise in partner exits and team moves. **Strengths:** "He is able to produce work of the highest standard in a fast turnaround time. Extremely good at getting to the heart of a case, he provides guidance on the bigger picture, and keeps the client constantly aware of the costs implications of decisions. He's also excellent at drafting 'high-impact' letters." **Recent work:** Acted in McManus v Ghufoor, a partnership case which took place in the High Court and involved three former partners of a London doctors' surgery.

Naomi Winston (see p.754) Impressive junior who has gained deep experience from being led by Jeremy Callman and Jonathan Gavaghan. She now handles many of her own cases, and is skilled in both contentious and non-contentious partnership matters. **Strengths:** "Extremely hard-working, she provides clear advice and is good with clients." "She has impressive fingertip command of points of law and authorities."

Band 3

Maitland Chambers

See profile on p.831

THE SET

Maitland Chambers is well versed in a wide range of partnership and LLP matters, and frequently receives instructions from leading City firms. Counsel handle a broad array of contentious and advisory matters, offering assistance with international investment structures, restructurings and individual partner disputes. They regularly appear in high-profile and complex cases drawn from a variety of professions including the law and medicine.

Client service: "The clerks, led by John Wiggs, are responsive and commercial."

SILKS

Amanda Tipples QC Has significant experience of handling complex disputes involving both traditional partnerships and LLPs. She represents clients from a wide variety of backgrounds, appearing for doctors, solicitors and accountants. She is also expert in cases concerning farming and horse-racing partnerships. **Strengths:** "She has a first-class brain, and combines this with a sympathetic attitude towards clients. The way she approaches her advice, and her thoroughness in examining and analysing problems, are impressive." "Offers measured advice, and makes herself available at the crunch times." **Recent work:** Instructed by HMRC in a dispute involving Wrag Barn Golf & Country Club. The case concerned partnership and VAT issues.

JUNIORS

David Mumford (see p.679) A dynamic junior who has been involved in a number of high-profile partnership cases. He has particular expertise in dealing with partnership issues arising in the context of significant commercial disputes. **Strengths:** "Clear, simple and persuasive in his advice." **Recent work:** Appeared in Boghani v Nathoo, a significant partnership dissolution case.

Other Ranked Lawyers

Ian Mill QC (Blackstone Chambers) Superb silk who conducts a number of partnership disputes as part of his extensive commercial practice. He is known for handling partnership matters involving the legal and media sectors, and engages in a significant amount of overseas work.

Stuart Ritchie QC (Littleton Chambers) A barrister with a strong commercial and company law practice, who has a growing reputation for handling partnership matters. He is particularly skilled in cases involving LLPs, and often acts in disputes concerning team moves, unlawful competition and unfair prejudice. **Strengths:** "Stuart is intellectually top-drawer, thorough, meticulous and incisive. He has the unerring ability to identify what is important and to focus on the key issues." "His book on fiduciary duties is a key text in relation to that area of the law, and he is a formidable advocate."

Mark Blackett-Ord (see p.550) (5 Stone Buildings) Widely acclaimed practitioner with many years of experience in contentious partnership matters. He frequently acts in disputes involving professionals, farmers and venture capitalists. **Strengths:** "There aren't many arbitrators out there who know much about partnership law but he's one of them. He's very good, takes a practical approach, and moves proceedings on."

MIDLANDS

Partnership Midlands
Leading Silks
Band 1
Randall John *St Philips Chambers (ORL)* ◊ *
Leading Juniors
Band 1
Dean Paul J *St Philips Chambers (ORL)* ◊ *
Najib Shakil *St Philips Chambers (ORL)* ◊ *
Whitaker Stephen *No5 Chambers (ORL)* ◊

Ranked Lawyers

Stephen Whitaker (No5 Chambers) Highly experienced practitioner with a broad partnership disputes practice. **Strengths:** "He's great at forensic analysis and good with facts and figures." "He really grasps the nettle; he gets right to the core of the case and outshines the other side."

John Randall QC (St Philips Chambers) Impressive silk with a broad commercial practice that includes a significant amount of partnership work. He frequently advises firms of accountants and solicitors in relation to their internal partnership disputes. **Strengths:** "You would use John Randall QC if you needed a heavyweight name; he is one of the pre-eminent silks on the Midland Circuit." **Recent work:** He appeared in Rafiq v Faruq and Others and Qayyum v Faruq and Others, two cases tried together in the High Court, Chancery Division, which concerned both property and partnership issues.

Paul Dean (see p.586) (St Philips Chambers) Junior who conducts a considerable amount of contentious partnership work. **Strengths:** "The key to Paul Dean is that he gives you a very clear understanding of what he needs from you and in return you get access to his analytical and methodical mind." **Recent work:** He acted in Till v Morris, a dispute between partners regarding the final dissolution account for an insolvency practice.

Shakil Najib (see p.680) (St Philips Chambers) Talented junior who handles a significant number of partnership disputes as part of a wider commercial practice. **Strengths:** "He is incredibly knowledgeable on both law and process. His drafting skills are outstanding." "His advocacy skills are excellent, and he is very structured and clear in his presentation. He is commercial and thinks outside the box." **Recent work:** He was junior counsel to several of the defendants in Uzma Saleem v Asif Saleem and Eight Others, a case in which the claimant is alleged to be a partner in a multimillion-pound international baked goods business operated by the defendants.

NORTHERN

Partnership Northern
Leading Sets
Band 1
Kings Chambers *
Leading Silks
Band 1
Anderson Lesley *Kings Chambers* *
Band 2
Chaisty Paul *Kings Chambers* *
Leading Juniors
Band 1
Berragan Neil *Kings Chambers* *
Harper Mark *Kings Chambers* *
Band 2
Cadwallader Neil *Exchange Chambers (ORL)* ◊
** Indicates set / individual with profile.*
◊ (ORL) = Other Ranked Lawyer.
Alphabetical order within each band. Band 1 is highest.

Band 1

Kings Chambers
See profile on p.918

THE SET

The leading set in the North West for partnership matters, Kings Chambers contains a number of skilled practitioners who engage in a wide range of contentious and non-contentious work. Many counsel have well-established chancery and commercial practices and bring this experience to bear in their partnership work.

Client service: "Chief clerk Colin Griffin leads a friendly and efficient clerking team, who provide good feedback on work progress."

SILKS

Lesley Anderson QC Has a broad commercial and chancery practice, which encompasses a significant amount of partnership disputes. She often represents solicitors and medical professionals. **Strengths:** "A forthright advocate who doesn't miss any points."

Paul Chaisty QC Veteran advocate whose considerable expertise in the chancery and commercial fields informs his approach to partnership disputes. **Recent work:** Appeared in Muthana v Yafai, a contested claim as to the existence of partnership in a property development business.

JUNIORS

Neil Berragan An acclaimed junior with considerable expertise in partnership disputes, in which he often represents solicitors. He is widely praised by sources for his advocacy skills. **Strengths:** "He is a strong advocate with wide experience in partnership law. He is tactically good and able to forensically identify the relevant from the irrelevant."

Mark Harper (see p.620) Well-regarded junior who has forged a strong reputation for his skill in handling partnership matters. He is particularly experienced in partner exclusions, the protection of partnership assets and handling the breakdown in relationships between partners. **Strengths:** "He is very quick at spotting the issues and distilling them down into simple advice and action." **Recent work:** Appeared in Amin v Hossain & Others, an action which involved a dissolution in breach of the partnership agreement.

Other Ranked Lawyers

Neil Cadwallader (Exchange Chambers) Well-regarded junior noted for his expertise across a broad range of partnership work. He has a focus on professional partnerships, and frequently represents solicitors and medical practices in disputes. **Strengths:** "He's a very good and very measured counsel."

WESTERN

Partnership Western
Leading Sets
Band 1
Guildhall Chambers *
St John's Chambers *
Leading Silks
New Silks
Sims Hugh *Guildhall Chambers*
Leading Juniors
Band 1
Maher Martha *St John's Chambers* [A]
Band 2
Marsden Andrew *St John's Chambers* [A] *
Warner Malcolm *Guildhall Chambers*
* *Indicates set / individual with profile.*
[A] *direct access (see p.11).*
Alphabetical order within each band. Band 1 is highest.

Band 1

Guildhall Chambers

See profile on p.890

THE SET

Guildhall Chambers has a fine reputation in partnership matters, strengthened in part by the set's impressive commercial and chancery practice. Its counsel are experts in both contentious and advisory partnership matters. Sources state: "The set has a very well-deserved reputation. They are able to provide a barrister to fit the requirements of the case and are always happy to discuss matters in general terms prior to being instructed."

Client service: "The expertise of the barristers is matched by the quality of the clerks. In particular, Justin Emmett, who leads the team, is accommodating and friendly, which creates a good first impression."

SILKS

Hugh Sims QC New silk who is one of the leading practitioners of chancery and commercial work on the Western Circuit, with partnership matters making up a substantial part of his practice. His expertise includes dissolutions, breaches of duties of good faith and joint venture disputes. **Strengths:** "He has an impressive way of dealing with matters. He forms a good understanding of the case, develops a rapport with the client and instructing solicitors, formulates a strategy in conjunction with instructing solicitors, and works tirelessly on the matter." "He is super-bright, great with clients and impressively commercial. He is also a pleasure to deal with."

JUNIORS

Malcolm Warner A strong practitioner who engages in partnership work as part of a broader commercial and chancery practice. He has particular expertise in disputes involving medical partnerships.

St John's Chambers

See profile on p.893

THE SET

An impressive set offering counsel who are experienced in the full range of contentious and non-contentious partnership and LLP matters. Its members are often instructed to appear in high-profile cases, including those involving law firms and medical partnerships. Areas of strength include dissolutions, restrictive covenants and targeted discrimination. Sources state: "They are very approachable, have a refreshingly modern outlook and are highly efficient."

JUNIORS

Martha Maher Talented practitioner who frequently appears in high-profile partnership disputes. She is particularly skilled in partnership disputes that feature an insolvency element. **Strengths:** "She is very positive and a very good practitioner. She doesn't take things lying down." **Recent work:** Advised on the administration of Cobbetts LLP.

Andrew Marsden (see p.663) Undertakes a wide range of partnership disputes, with a particular focus on partner expulsions, restrictive covenants and managing the breakdown of relations between partners. **Strengths:** "He has great charisma and sets clients at ease, even in very tense circumstances. He is calm, always well prepared, very persuasive and extremely intelligent. He has a very useful knack of coming up with innovative solutions to seemingly intractable problems." **Recent work:** Advised on the break-up of a limited liability solicitors partnership.

Contents:

LONDON

Pensions London
Leading Sets
Band 1
Wilberforce Chambers *
Band 2
Outer Temple Chambers *
Band 3
3 Stone Buildings *
5 Stone Buildings *
Leading Silks
Star individuals
Green Brian *Wilberforce Chambers*
Simmonds Andrew *5 Stone Buildings* *
Band 1
Furness Michael *Wilberforce Chambers*
Newman Paul *Wilberforce Chambers*
Rowley Keith *Radcliffe Chambers (ORL)* ◊
Spink Andrew *Outer Temple Chambers*
Stallworthy Nicolas *Outer Temple Chambers*
Tennet Michael *Wilberforce Chambers*
Band 2
Agnello Raquel *Erskine Chambers (ORL)* ◊ *
Ham Robert *Wilberforce Chambers*
Short Andrew *Outer Temple Chambers*
Band 3
Bryant Keith *Outer Temple Chambers*
Legge Henry *5 Stone Buildings* *
Steinfeld Alan *XXIV Old Buildings (ORL)* ◊
Tidmarsh Christopher *5 Stone Buildings* *
New Silks
Evans Jonathan *Wilberforce Chambers*
Hitchcock Richard *Outer Temple Chambers*
Moeran Fenner *3 Stone Buildings* *
Leading Juniors
Band 1
Hilliard Jonathan *Wilberforce Chambers*
Sawyer Edward *Wilberforce Chambers*
Band 2
Campbell Emily *Wilberforce Chambers*
Clifford James *Maitland Chambers (ORL)* ◊ *
Goldsmith Joseph *5 Stone Buildings* *
Grant David E *Outer Temple Chambers*
Khan Farhaz *Outer Temple Chambers*
Mold Andrew *Wilberforce Chambers* *
Ovey Elizabeth *Radcliffe Chambers (ORL)* ◊ *
Walmsley James *Wilberforce Chambers*
Band 3
Burroughs Nigel *4 New Square (ORL)* ◊ *
Ling Naomi *Outer Temple Chambers*
McKechnie Emily *Wilberforce Chambers*
Rickards James *Outer Temple Chambers*
Robinson Thomas *11 Stone Buildings (ORL)* ◊
Band 4
Faulkner Benjamin *Wilberforce Chambers*
Margo Saul *Outer Temple Chambers*
Mathers Wendy *Radcliffe Chambers (ORL)* ◊
Seaman Jennifer *3 Stone Buildings* *
Stephens John *XXIV Old Buildings (ORL)* ◊
Up-and-coming individuals
Allen Sebastian *Wilberforce Chambers*
Friedman Bobby *Wilberforce Chambers*
Murphy Emer *Wilberforce Chambers*
** Indicates set / individual with profile.*
◊ (ORL) = Other Ranked Lawyer.
Alphabetical order within each band. Band 1 is highest.

Band 1

Wilberforce Chambers

See profile on p.876

THE SET

"The best-known and most highly regarded pensions set in the market," Wilberforce Chambers has many of the leading silks in the sector and is "the go-to set for pensions claims which are particularly difficult or technical." Several members of the set have been active in assisting the Pensions Regulator on matters including pension liberation schemes and financial support directions.

Client service: "You can rely on the clerking team led by Mark Rushton to deliver whatever they promise you. They will always be helpful and if they say something will get done, it will get done."

SILKS

Brian Green QC A market-leading practitioner with a deep knowledge of the law and impressive advocacy skills. He is particularly strong on issues relating to scheme construction and moral hazard. **Strengths:** "He provides pragmatic and often brilliant advice." "Personable and technically superior, he is excellent at applying the law to facts in challenging cases." **Recent work:** Advised Guinness Peat Group on the funding deficiencies of its occupational pension schemes.

Michael Furness QC A highly sought-after silk who is lauded by sources for the depth of his experience and for his analytical skills. He is noted for his expertise in liberation schemes and has advised the FCA in this regard. **Strengths:** "He's sensationally clever and makes pensions law readily digestible." "He has a sound intellectual grasp of the technical detail, and takes a practical approach to his cases. He impresses both clients and instructing solicitors." **Recent work:** Acted in Entrust v Capita, a case concerning the recollection of costs accumulated by correcting errors made by a former pension scheme trustee.

Paul Newman QC Acclaimed by sources for his commercial approach to pensions matters and noted for his skill in scheme constructions. He has regularly provided advice to the Department of Work and Pensions. **Strengths:** "He is a very impressive advocate, who is extremely good on his feet and very persuasive. He takes a very creative approach to problems, and is very helpful if you have something a bit tricky to deal with." "He is incisive, is prepared to make bold decisions and he sticks to them." **Recent work:** Instructed in ICM Computer Group v Stribley, a case dealing with the correction of a pension scheme amendment.

Michael Tennet QC A highly skilled advocate who garners accolades for his management of cases and his actuarial knowledge. Active in both litigious and advisory capacities, his areas of interest include discontinuance debt and good faith breaches. **Strengths:** "He is responsive and user-friendly, and has particular expertise in regulatory matters." "Very hands-on and good at leading a team of juniors, he's a strong advocate who puts points across forcefully." **Recent work:** Worked on behalf of the Nortel Networks UK pension scheme trustees in a dispute over fund deficiency.

Robert Ham QC An occupational pensions specialist who has great experience of cases concerning funding liabilities and moral hazard issues. He is noted by peers for his commercial focus and strong rapport with clients. **Strengths:** "He provides exemplary client service, and is always prepared to express a view in clearly understood language." **Recent work:** Represented Dresser-Rand in a dispute relating to its move to equalise the standard retirement ages.

Jonathan Evans QC A new silk with a strong pensions litigation practice, who is recommended by commentators for the quality of his presentations in court. He has experience in a variety of pension-related issues, including scheme construction and liberation. **Strengths:** "Technically excellent but also very approachable and willing to go the extra mile for the client." "He's conscientious and provides clear, constructive advice." **Recent work:** Acted in PPF v West of England Ship Owners, a case surrounding a claim that a failure score had been incorrectly calculated.

JUNIORS

Jonathan Hilliard A leading junior who has advised the Pensions Regulator on several disputes, including one regarding the misappropriation of fund assets. He has also acted on behalf of scheme trustees on a variety of matters, including the switch from the RPI to the CPI measure of inflation. **Strengths:** "He is intellectually extremely sharp, and brings a lot of commitment and drive to his cases." "Very intelligent, hard-working and a pleasure to deal with, he always provides sensible advice and is able to turn matters around speedily." **Recent work:** Acted in Nortel & Lehman v Pension Regulator, and also appeared unled for the trustee in Box Clever, which was the first Pensions Regulator case to consider the Upper Tribunal's powers to deal with financial support directions proceedings.

Edward Sawyer An increasingly prominent junior in complex pensions litigation. He has significant experience of acting for a variety of parties in occupational pension scheme disputes. **Strengths:** "The quality of his work is outstanding, and he has the ability to stay on top of really complex cases." **Recent work:** Acted in the litigation against IBM arising from the implementation of 'Project Waltz'.

Emily Campbell Highlighted by commentators for her strong technical knowledge of pensions matters and her highly cerebral approach to advocacy. Her areas of strength include Part 8 claims and scheme rectification. **Strengths:** "She is extremely bright and experienced." "She has an outstanding grasp of the most obscure technicalities of pensions law." **Recent work:** Instructed by trustees of BSS Group pension scheme in respect of a case concerning the equalisation of pension benefits.

Andrew Mold (see p.675) Highlighted by interviewees for his involvement in profes sional negligence disputes and for his knowledge of scheme construction. He also has significant experience in scheme rectification and equalisation proceedings. **Strengths:** "An excellent junior who copes well with the factual and legal complexities. He is extremely approachable and has an uncanny ability to explain technical issues in a clear and precise way." **Recent work:** Advised on claims against Honda that arose from rectification of pension scheme documentation.

James Walmsley A growing presence in the pensions field, he is a barrister who is particularly good on the regulatory side. **Strengths:** "He is highly intelligent and one of those who can turn his hand to a lot of different things. As well as being good on the technical aspects of the law, he is extremely hard-working, responsive and very easy to work with." **Recent work:** Assisted in the procurement of a rectification order for the MNOPF pension scheme.

Emily McKechnie A junior who applies a strong commercial focus to his pensions work. He has experience in pension construction, Part 8 claims and pension-related professional negligence. **Strengths:** "She has got a fantastically clear analytical mind, and is very commercial in her judgement." "A talented barrister who applies herself well to many complex areas of the law and has developed an impressive aptitude for pensions cases." **Recent work:** Instructed by Prospect Hospice against Entrust Pension in a dispute regarding pension scheme construction.

Benjamin Faulkner A strong and confident advocate who is well regarded by peers and clients. He has particular experience in disputes that involve financial support directions. **Strengths:** "He's very pleasant and really knows his stuff." "Bright, commercial, easy to work with and responsive," he is "strong on the procedural aspects." **Recent work:** Instructed in High Court proceedings regarding amendments to the IBM pension scheme.

Sebastian Allen Regularly instructed by the Pensions Regulator and the Pension Protection Fund on a variety of matters including regulatory work and the use of actuarial process. He also has experience with moral hazard matters. **Strengths:** "He is really good and very diligent." "Brilliant to work with, he gives clear advice and is prepared to go the extra mile." **Recent work:** Acted on behalf of British Airways in litigation pursued against trustees of its pension scheme.

Bobby Friedman An up-and-coming junior whom sources highlight for his tenacious advocacy style. He offers experience of pensions liberation schemes and regulatory matters. **Strengths:** "He takes a very thorough approach to matters and is a charming and friendly character." **Recent work:** Acted for Independent Trustee Services in order to recuperate assets lost as a result of fraud.

Emer Murphy Commercially minded junior with a growing pensions practice. She has notable experience in civil fraud litigation relating to pension fund asset recovery, and is also good on moral hazard matters. **Strengths:** "She is very persuasive and forthright in her views, and not afraid to take on a point that others perhaps wouldn't." "She has got very good drafting skills" and is "prepared to work all hours if necessary." **Recent work:** Instructed by Dresser-Rand on claims that benefit payments had been wrongly calculated.

Band 2

Outer Temple Chambers

See profile on p.842

THE SET

Interviewees commend Outer Temple Chambers for having produced a pensions team that is "looking increasingly strong and attractive." As one commentator put it: "The set offers a breadth of experience and a depth of knowledge which few can match. It truly specialises in pensions and employment law rather than simply dabbling in it."

Client service: "The clerks are really good with clients and just a really friendly bunch; they roll their sleeves up."

SILKS

Andrew Spink QC A prominent force in the pensions market who is particularly skilled at matters relating to liberation schemes. He is also strong on good faith breaches and Part 8 claims. **Strengths:** "An excellent barrister who comes up with well-considered, persuasive answers. A good man to use in practice and not just academically." "He has the ability to convey incredibly difficult matters clearly, and is terrifyingly good. He is tactically brilliant and is an exceptionally good all-rounder." **Recent work:** Instructed in a dispute relating to the Lehman Brothers' pension scheme.

Nicolas Stallworthy QC Pensions specialist who garners significant accolades from commentators for his incisive analysis and pragmatic opinions. Active on a broad range of pensions matters, he is particularly good at matters relating to rectification, good faith breaches and financial support directions **Strengths:** "He is incredibly helpful and his advice is incredibly digestible for the clients. He is also very commercial and very good on his feet." "Thorough and practical, he is the most deeply analytical thinker at the Pensions Bar." **Recent work:** Assisted in the 'Project Waltz' litigation relating to IBM pension schemes.

Andrew Short QC Sources speak highly of his commercial sensibilities and the clear and pragmatic advice he offers. He combines expertise in pensions and employment law, and is particularly adept at scheme rectification and Part 8 claims. **Strengths:** "He gives very clear advice, understands the commercial merits of the case and is able to put things across efficiently." "Always excellent, he is bright, perceptive and commercial." **Recent work:** Acted in the equalisation claim Vaitkus v Dresser-Rand UK.

Keith Bryant QC A standout advocate who earns excellent praise for his practical manner, impressive delivery and meticulous preparation. Sources highlight his expertise in Part 8 equalisation claims. **Strengths:** "He delivers when he says he will, and manages to condense very complex issues into client-friendly language." "He thinks outside the box and comes up with pragmatic solutions." **Recent work:** Advised NILGOSC on a dispute that arose out of the Local Government Pension Scheme.

Richard Hitchcock QC A new silk and an increasing presence in the pensions market. Known for his strong advocacy in court, his areas of strength include rectification and Section 75 debt matters. **Strengths:** "He has a very engaging courtroom presence." "He's very approachable, good with clients and very good on his feet." **Recent work:** Instructed on a fund deficit matter related to the pension scheme of now-defunct textiles company Desmonds.

JUNIORS

Farhaz Khan Maintains a broad practice that combines his extensive pensions knowledge with expertise in banking and finance matters. Areas of strength include professional negligence and Part 8 claims. **Strengths:** "He has an amazing ability to pick up anything and dissect it; he's a lovely guy to work with and a brilliant, brilliant lawyer." **Recent work:** Assisted the trustees of Philips' UK pension scheme in litigation against the advisers of a previous investment strategy that resulted in significant financial losses.

David Grant Maintains a good rapport with clients and is particularly adept at contentious pension matters. Specific areas of interest include rectification and professional negligence. **Strengths:** "Extremely user-friendly, bright and proactive, he gives good practical advice." "He has a very impressive grasp of detailed case law and applies it very well in complex cases." **Recent work:** Assisted in Thompson v Fresenius Kabi Ltd, a case concerning the prevention of new members joining a pension scheme.

Naomi Ling A well-regarded junior who boasts expertise in local government pension schemes. She has experience of matters involving Section 75 debt and Part 8 claims. **Strengths:** "Very knowledgeable and always prepared to put in unsocial hours and days to get the job done." **Recent work:** Instructed by the trustee of the Urenco pension scheme to assist in determining the statutory pension rights of its members.

Saul Margo A growing presence in the pensions market who combines his knowledge of employment and pensions law to great effect. He is particularly active in an advisory capacity, assisting several public bodies including the Redundancy Payments Service. **Strengths:** "He is very knowledgeable and has got a good grasp of pensions matters." "Incredibly hard-working, he has a really sharp, accurate brain and he works through issues quickly and impressively. He's also a really good team player." **Recent work:** Represented the interests of companies that were issued with financial support directions for the Lehman Brothers' pension scheme.

James Rickards Noted by sources for his involvement in cases that have a moral hazard aspect to them. He is particularly noted for his expertise in regulatory work following his time on secondment with the Pensions Regulator. **Strengths:** "An excellent commercial barrister with in-depth knowledge of pensions disputes." "He has great in-depth knowledge and produces clear advice." **Recent work:** Assisted the PPF in relation to claims of an error in an amendment to the Helix Group's pension scheme.

Band 3

3 Stone Buildings

See profile on p.864

THE SET

A set that has a proud history in pensions law, having been involved in some of the biggest cases in the sector over the years, including Courage, Equitable Life and the Pilots litigation. Its recent matters include the Flexiplan litigation and Dalriada Trustees Ltd v Pensions Regulator, a leading case on pension 'release' schemes. Members have expertise in all aspects of pensions litigation, drafting and advice.

SILKS

Fenner Moeran QC (see p.675) Particularly active on pension liberation schemes, he is commended by sources for the depth of his pensions law knowledge and his innovative case strategies. He also offers significant expertise when it comes to civil partner pension benefits. **Strengths:** "An articulate advocate who gives practical and workable advice." "Commercial, pragmatic and astute, he's someone you want on your side." **Recent work:** Instructed by Dalriada Trustees on the determination of whether a set of occupational pension schemes it administered were valid.

JUNIORS

Jennifer Seaman (see p.716) A junior rising in prominence who receives acclaim from peers for her capability in funding deficit and pension scheme benefit cases. **Strengths:** "She's a very good sounding board to bounce ideas off and develop them." **Recent work:** Acted in the case Futter v HRMC, which determined the extent of court intervention in the discretionary activities of pension scheme trustees.

5 Stone Buildings

See profile on p.866

THE SET

A leading chancery set that boasts several members with significant pensions expertise who act on a broad range of issues. Members of the set have been active in a number of complex and high-profile cases regarding the pensions schemes of Lehman Brothers, IBM and the Merchant Navy.

Client service: "The clerking quality stands out. Senior clerk Paul Jennings is really great, and will unfailingly help to sort things out."

SILKS

Andrew Simmonds QC (see p.721) Widely recognised in the market as one of the leading advocates for pension matters, he is frequently instructed on scheme disputes between trustees and employers. His areas of strength include financial support directions, Part 8 claims and fund deficits. **Strengths:** "Extremely thorough and tenacious, he leaves no stone unturned and is a measured and persuasive advocate." "A pleasure to instruct, he always finds a pragmatic solution to a complex set of facts." **Recent work:** Instructed by the Rigid Group, the principal employer of two pension schemes, in a dispute over whether the schemes' trustees could use the Eastearly v Headway precedent to decrease the fund deficit.

Henry Legge QC (see p.654) A well-regarded silk who earns excellent praise for his methodical advocacy style. His broad chancery practice sees him acting in a variety of pension matters, including Section 75 debt and actuarial valuation disputes. **Strengths:** "He is lovely to work with as he's supremely organised and calm." "He has a good reputation and a growing profile." **Recent work:** Advised BT on the pensions aspect of its case against the European Commission.

Christopher Tidmarsh QC (see p.738) A growing presence in the pensions market who is regularly instructed in an advisory capacity by public bodies of the DWP. He is also noted for his skill in handling highly complex technical matters. **Strengths:** "Careful and effective, he's excellent when you need rapid advice on difficult points." "Extremely good technically and very unpretentious in his manner, he is particularly good on advisory opinion work." **Recent work:** Advised the Pensions Regulator in relation to Visteon's pension scheme.

JUNIORS

Joseph Goldsmith (see p.611) Highly able junior who attracts praise from peers due to his robust advocacy and the quality of his paperwork. Areas of strength include scheme rectification, Section 75 debt and maladministration claims. **Strengths:** "Bright and thorough, he explains things very clearly, has a good courtroom manner and is a pleasure to work with." "A studious, hard-working chap who is very good on the paperwork." **Recent work:** Instructed by a local authority concerning the implementation of a salary sacrifice element into its pension scheme.

Other Ranked Lawyers

Raquel Agnello QC (Erskine Chambers) A well-respected silk who offers high levels of expertise in discontinuance debt and regulatory work. She is applauded for her pragmatic advocacy style. **Strengths:** "She is very good at engaging judges and making it absolutely clear what she is arguing for. Also good at managing teams of barristers, experts and solicitors." "She's a great advocate who is fun to work with and extremely energetic, reflecting the real passion she has for her work." **Recent work:** Advised the trustees of the KSF pension scheme with regard to a dispute over its funding deficit.

James Clifford (see p.574) (Maitland Chambers) Highlighted by peers for his analytical skills, clear opinions and commercial solutions. He has particular strength in matters related to pension scheme structures. **Strengths:** "A very good technical pensions lawyer who knows the intricacies of pensions law backwards." "Really approachable, he is willing to discuss advice and willing to provide commercial solutions." **Recent work:** Instructed by the trustees of the Honda pension scheme to advise in relation to the validity of an amendment.

Nigel Burroughs (see p.561) (4 New Square) He is praised for his succinct advice, commercial sensibilities and rapport with clients. Specific areas of strength include pensions-related professional negligence litigation and discontinuance debt. **Strengths:** "His opinions are clear-cut and straightforward." **Recent work:** Represented the interests of the sellers of a financial consultancy firm in a dispute with the new owners in relation to the construction of the pension scheme.

Alan Steinfeld QC (XXIV Old Buildings) Highlighted by sources for his excellent advocacy skills and significant experience in pensions matters. He is particularly strong on pensions-related professional negligence disputes, fund deficits and liberation schemes. **Strengths:** "He gives very incisive legal advice and is a superb advocate." "He's very confident and knows what he is doing." **Recent work:** Advised on a case that gave members the opportunity to access pension funds early through a liberation scheme.

John Stephens (XXIV Old Buildings) A commercially minded barrister who has experience of dealing with pension liberation schemes and funding deficits. **Strengths:** "Good at identifying an innovative approach to a case." **Recent work:** Instructed on the implementation of a pension liberation scheme.

Keith Rowley QC (Radcliffe Chambers) A much-admired silk who earns praise from sources for his commercial focus, clear advice and ability to home in on the key issues in cases. He is very good at pension age equalisation disputes, scheme construction and moral hazard matters. **Strengths:** "He cuts through the complexities to provide clear opinions and pragmatic ways forward." "Very clear and authoritative." **Recent work:** Assisted the Pensions Regulator in its case against a set of administrative bodies with regard to pension liberation schemes.

Elizabeth Ovey (see p.688) (Radcliffe Chambers) Proves particularly strong on scheme construction and pensions-related professional negligence matters. She was recently led by Keith Rowley QC in a case involving a pension liberation scheme. **Strengths:** "Excellent on complicated technical matters." **Recent work:** Instructed on a dispute relating to the Sears Retail Pension Scheme.

Wendy Mathers (Radcliffe Chambers) A junior known for her strong oratory skills and assertive advocacy style. She has experience in contesting the validity of pension scheme constructions and professional negligence claims. **Strengths:** "She impresses solicitors with her energy and commitment." **Recent work:** Acted for the trustees in relation to the validity of documentation used in the Gleeds pension scheme.

Thomas Robinson (11 Stone Buildings) A well-regarded junior who has particular expertise in regulatory matters. He is also strong on cases concerning moral hazard issues and contribution notices. **Strengths:** "He has acted on a number of matters for the pensions regulator and knows his way around pensions law like the back of his hand." "He's very, very bright and a good advocate." **Recent work:** Assisted Amcor in a matter related to the pension allowance of a former executive.

PERSONAL INJURY: An Introduction

Contributed by Andrew Hogarth QC, 12 King's Bench Walk

There are two questions causing concern to personal injury practitioners: "Where is the work going to come from?", and "How will we survive?"

At present the Court of Appeal's decision in Mitchell and the ever-increasing secondary litigation about costs has more than compensated for any decrease in the work involved in actually winning PI cases on the merits on behalf of clients. Soon, the flood of professional negligence claims will start and even the Court of Appeal will realise that their latest attempt at imposing discipline in the interests of judicial efficiency and time saving has had the opposite effect. Does no one who comes up with these ideas remember Order 17 Rule 11?

In the longer term the challenge is different. Smaller cases no longer present the opportunity to bill several times the actual value of the claim, and the abolition of the uplift on CFAs makes it difficult to accumulate fees on the scale we have seen in recent years. The only solution for smaller claims is to run them at a lower cost. Running large cases on a zero uplift CFA now entails a greater degree of financial risk, which fewer firms will be able to afford.

It is now apparent that these changes will accelerate the process of consolidation amongst solicitors and conveyor belt litigation that we have seen in the last few years.

Not many years ago my chambers received instructions each year from nearly 1,000 firms of solicitors. Today, despite the fact that we have grown considerably, the number of firms sending us instructions has fallen to under 200. Some of our largest clients have simply faded away, being unable or unwilling to change to meet the challenges of the modern legal services market. Others have grown from very modest beginnings to become national firms with many hundreds of employees. The Bar has also changed, with some chambers not keeping up with the changes in business practices and failing, whilst others which have been more aggressive in changing to meet modern market conditions have prospered.

The key to survival – if not to success – for claimant solicitors is money, not fee income as such but the ability to raise capital. Without capital it becomes difficult to maintain a large volume of substantial personal injury claims. Irwin Mitchell recently raised £60 million from a syndicate of three banks, allowing them to continue their expansion by opening new offices and buying smaller practices. The availability of funds has allowed small firms to take over larger firms. Gordon Dadds, then an eight-partner firm, took over Davenport Lyons, a 30-partner firm, earlier this year. Well-financed outsiders with access to the financial markets for capital have taken over law firms. This year the BGL Group, better known as the owners of comparethemarket.com, bought Minster Law, and the Fairport Group bought Simpson Millar for a reported £9 million in cash, £6million in shares and provided additional capital of £20 million. Slater and Gordon have the double advantage of access to capital as a result of being listed on the stock exchange and the experience they have gained from their expansion in Australia.

Access to capital does not appear to be as important for defendant-oriented firms, as their bills are likely to be paid more speedily. Their success depends on their ability to obtain the contracts from the large insurer clients, which in its turn depends upon their geographical spread and their willingness to accept lower hourly rates.

What has become more obvious is the way in which some firms have moved away from the older professional model to a purely commercial model. The ratios of partners to equity partners to non-equity partners has changed, with fewer equity partners being created. The ratios of partners to associates and associates to other staff has changed. Actual figures for equity partners are not easy to find, except when firms merge. In one recent merger, the number of associates and salaried partners per equity partner was 11.2:1. In some of the newer commercially run firms the number of non-lawyers has increased considerably. Whilst the norm for the top 200 UK firms by turnover is between two and three staff per qualified lawyer, at one major commercial PI firm it has reached 17 to 1. The number of staff undertaking legal work per equity partner at such firms will be enormous and the degree of supervision modest, but the scope for profit is substantial.

Contents:

LONDON

Personal Injury London
Leading Sets
Band 1
Crown Office Chambers *
Thirty Nine Essex Street *
9 Gough Square *
12 King's Bench Walk *
Outer Temple Chambers *
Band 2
1 Chancery Lane
Devereux *
Farrar's Building *
Temple Garden Chambers *
2TG - 2 Temple Gardens *
Band 3
7BR *
Cloisters *
1 Crown Office Row *
Doughty Street Chambers *
Old Square Chambers *
* *Indicates set / individual with profile.*
◊ *(ORL) = Other Ranked Lawyer.*
[A] *direct access (see p.11).*

Personal Injury London	
Leading Silks	
Star individuals	
Block Neil *Thirty Nine Essex Street* *	
Burton Frank *12 King's Bench Walk* *	
Gumbel Elizabeth-Anne *1 Crown Office Row*	
McDermott Gerard *Outer Temple Chambers*	
Weir Robert *Devereux* *	
Band 1	
Aldous Grahame *9 Gough Square* *	
Browne Benjamin *2TG - 2 Temple Gardens* *	
Cooksley Nigel *Old Square Chambers* *	
Cory-Wright Charles *Thirty Nine Essex Street*	
Faulks Edward *1 Chancery Lane* *	
Glancy Robert *Devereux* *	
Jeffreys Alan *Farrar's Building*	
Killalea Stephen *Devereux* *	
Lynagh Richard *Crown Office Chambers*	
Maskrey Simeon *7BR*	
Methuen Richard *12 King's Bench Walk* *	
Norris William *Thirty Nine Essex Street*	
Purchas Christopher *Crown Office Chambers* *	
Ritchie Andrew *9 Gough Square* *	
Rodway Susan *Thirty Nine Essex Street*	
Walker Ronald *12 King's Bench Walk* *	
Westcott David *Outer Temple Chambers*	
Worthington Stephen *12 King's Bench Walk* *	
Band 2	
Donovan Joel *Cloisters*	
Featherby William *12 King's Bench Walk* *	
Foy John *9 Gough Square* *	
Hermer Richard *Matrix Chambers (ORL)* ◊	
Hogarth Andrew *12 King's Bench Walk* *	
Kent Michael *Crown Office Chambers* *	
Leighton Williams John *Farrar's Building*	
McCaul Colin *Thirty Nine Essex Street*	
Oppenheim Robin *Doughty Street Chambers*	
Readhead Simon *1 Chancery Lane* *	
Rose Paul *Old Square Chambers* *	
Ross John *1 Chancery Lane* *	
Russell Paul *12 King's Bench Walk* *	
Warnock Andrew *1 Chancery Lane* [A] *	
Watt-Pringle Jonathan *Temple Garden Chambers* *	
Wilson-Smith Christopher *Outer Temple Chambers* *	
Band 3	
Bishop Edward *1 Chancery Lane* *	
Browne Simon P *Temple Garden Chambers*	
Ford Steven *7BR*	
Hitchcock Patricia *Cloisters* *	
Melville David *Thirty Nine Essex Street*	
Picton Julian *Hailsham Chambers (ORL)* ◊ *	
Platt David *Crown Office Chambers*	
Porter Martin *2TG - 2 Temple Gardens* [A] *	
Stevens Howard *3 Hare Court (ORL)* ◊	
Ullstein Augustus *Thirty Nine Essex Street*	
New Silks	
Antelme Alexander *Crown Office Chambers*	
Levy Jacob *9 Gough Square* *	

Band 1

Crown Office Chambers

See profile on p.782

THE SET

This large and impressive chambers deals with the full spectrum of personal injury matters, and handles everything from brain and spinal injuries claims to cases concerning fatalities or complex psychiatric pain. It acts for both claimants and defendants, and represents private individuals, companies, insurers, the NHSLA and other government bodies. One commentator said of the set: "Its counsel have a great depth and range of experience so you always know you're going to find someone who can cover the case however complex it is. They are also very good on industrial disease matters."

Client service: "The clerks are very helpful, accommodating and flexible." Senior clerk Paul Hurst was particularly singled out for praise.

SILKS

Richard Lynagh QC An undisputed leader at the Personal Injuries Bar who is only instructed on the most serious, high-value injury cases. He has a particularly strong workplace accident practice. **Strengths:** "He manages expectations well, gives it to the client straight and is charming in court and in conference. He is confidence-inspiring and intellectually rock hard." "Unflappable, easy to talk to and responsive." **Recent work:** Represented the defendant in a Court of Appeal traumatic brain injury claim where the claimant, who had allegedly been stealing a ladder, had fallen from a van that was being driven by his uncle. The maxim *ex turpi causa* was employed by the court and the case is now a key precedent in these kinds of matters.

Michael Kent QC (see p.644) A true titan of the Personal Injuries Bar, who regularly represents government departments and employers' liability insurers in a range of disease claims, including noise-induced hearing loss (NIHL), asbestos and dermatitis cases. He frequently appears before the appeal courts in complex cases. **Strengths:** "A highly intelligent advocate, who has particular experience in group actions." **Recent work:** Acted for the defendants in a contentious class action involving more than 17,000 claimants where serious health problems were allegedly caused by an industrial fire that burned for eight days in a Liverpool suburb.

Christopher Purchas QC (see p.700) A catastrophic injury silk who specialises in brain, spinal and fatal injuries. He regularly deals with claimants injured at work and on the roads, and is a familiar face at the Court of Appeal and Supreme Court. **Strengths:** "Deadly in court," "he has done some landmark cases and is very gifted and highly intelligent."

David Platt QC Although first and foremost an acclaimed industrial disease practitioner, he also demonstrates excellent skill in handling severe injury cases. He has handled a number of cases involving passive smoking, DVT and pilot acrotoxicity. **Strengths:** "The consummate tactician," he is "a persuasive advocate who is excellent at assimilating the detail of a case in a short space of time." **Recent work:** Led in the mesothelioma trigger litigation at the Supreme Court, a ground-breaking employers' liability claim involving various insurers and claimants.

Alexander Antelme QC A heavyweight silk who has made a name for himself handling cases with complex causation and quantum issues. He is renowned for his pragmatic approach. **Strengths:** "A very intellectual barrister who practises in a diverse range of areas. He is very competent and tenacious in his approach, and is unfazed when dealing with very high-value cases." "His impressive attention to detail and his ability to retain certain facts put him ahead of others." **Recent work:** Represented the defendant in a fatal accident claim involving a successful accountant.

JUNIORS

Patrick Blakesley (see p.551) An experienced senior junior who defends catastrophic injury claims where the claimant has been rendered tetraplegic, paraplegic or severely brain injured. Commentators say that he "punches well above his weight in terms of his performances in court." **Strengths:** "He's not frightened of having a conflict where it needs to be had, and his advocacy and negotiation skills are particularly strong." "He's measured and practical, and reduces things down to the key points." **Recent**

Personal Injury
London

Leading Juniors

Star individuals	
Latimer-Sayer William	*Cloisters*
O'Sullivan Derek	*Thirty Nine Essex Street*
Band 1	
Audland William	*12 King's Bench Walk* *
Bagot Charles	*Hardwicke (ORL)* ◇ *
Begley Laura	*9 Gough Square*
Blakesley Patrick	*Crown Office Chambers* *
Brown Geoffrey	*Thirty Nine Essex Street*
Charles Henry	*12 King's Bench Walk* *
Doherty Bernard	*Thirty Nine Essex Street*
Du Cann Christian	*Thirty Nine Essex Street*
Evans Lee	*Farrar's Building* *
Foster Catherine	*Crown Office Chambers* *
Freeman Peter	*Farrar's Building*
Grant Marcus	*Temple Garden Chambers* *
Hillier Nicolas	*9 Gough Square* *
Lawson Daniel	*Cloisters* *
Levinson Justin	*1 Crown Office Row*
Lewers Nigel	*12 King's Bench Walk* *
Matthews Julian D	*7BR*
McKechnie Stuart	*9 Gough Square* *
Sanderson David	*12 King's Bench Walk* *
Silvester Bruce	*Devereux* *
Snowden Steven	*Crown Office Chambers* *
Steinberg Harry	*12 King's Bench Walk* *
Todd James	*Thirty Nine Essex Street*
Witcomb Henry	*1 Crown Office Row*
Woolf Eliot	*Outer Temple Chambers* *
Band 2	
Ayling Judith	*Thirty Nine Essex Street*
Bate-Williams John	*Temple Garden Chambers* *
Bell James	*Temple Garden Chambers*
Brown Catherine	*12 King's Bench Walk* *
Davis Andrew	*Crown Office Chambers* *
Dignum Marcus	*12 King's Bench Walk* *
Ford Jeremy	*9 Gough Square* *
Glynn Stephen	*9 Gough Square* *
Goolamali Nina	*2TG - 2 Temple Gardens* *
Hamill Hugh	*12 King's Bench Walk* *
Harris Roger	*2TG - 2 Temple Gardens* [A]
Johnson Laura	*1 Chancery Lane* [A] *
King Simon	*7BR*
Laughland James	*Temple Garden Chambers* *
McCormick Alison	*Outer Temple Chambers*
McDonald John	*2TG - 2 Temple Gardens* [A]
Mendoza Colin	*Devereux* *
Phillips Matthew	*Outer Temple Chambers*
Roy Andrew	*12 King's Bench Walk* *
Russell Christopher	*2TG - 2 Temple Gardens*
Samuel Gerwyn	*Doughty Street Chambers*
Smith Alan	*Old Square Chambers* *
Tavares Nathan	*Outer Temple Chambers*
Trusted Harry	*Outer Temple Chambers*
Vincent Patrick	*12 King's Bench Walk* *
Weitzman Adam	*7BR*
Wilkinson Richard	*Temple Garden Chambers* *
Williams A John	*Crown Office Chambers* *
Woodhouse Charles	*Old Square Chambers* *
Band 3	
Adamson Dominic	*Temple Garden Chambers* *
Aldridge James	*Outer Temple Chambers*
Archer Stephen	*2TG - 2 Temple Gardens*
Baker Richard	*7BR* *
Baldock Nicholas	*6 Pump Court (ORL)* ◇
Bennett Daniel	*Doughty Street Chambers*
Boyle Matthew	*Crown Office Chambers* *
Cartwright Richard	*Devereux* *
Chapman Matthew	*1 Chancery Lane* *
Crapper Sadie	*Thirty Nine Essex Street* *
Davison Richard	*12 King's Bench Walk* *
Dawson Adam	*9 Gough Square* *
Dyer Simon	*Cloisters* *
Edwards Peter	*Devereux* *
Ferris Shaun	*Crown Office Chambers* *
Formby Emily	*Thirty Nine Essex Street* *
Furniss Richard	*42 Bedford Row (ORL)* ◇
Gregory Richard	*42 Bedford Row (ORL)* ◇
Haque Muhammed	*Crown Office Chambers* *
Hiorns Roger	*9 Gough Square*
Hunter Robert	*Devereux* *
Jones Rhiannon	*Farrar's Building*
Kellar Robert	*1 Crown Office Row*
Kemp Christopher	*Outer Temple Chambers*
Kilcoyne Paul	*Temple Garden Chambers* *
Levene Simon	*12 King's Bench Walk* *
Matthewson Scott	*42 Bedford Row (ORL)* ◇
Meakin Timothy	*7BR* [A]
Meredith-Hardy John	*Farrar's Building* *
Mooney Giles	*9 Gough Square* *
Nicholson Michael	*Old Square Chambers*
Peebles Andrew	*Farrar's Building*
Stagg Paul	*1 Chancery Lane* [A] *
Stephenson Christopher	*9 Gough Square* *
Walker Christopher	*Old Square Chambers*
Waters Julian	*1 Chancery Lane* *
Up-and-coming individuals	
Roche Maria	*Doughty Street Chambers*
Sullivan James	*12 King's Bench Walk* *

Personal Injury: Industrial Disease
All Circuits

Leading Silks	
Allan David	*Byrom Street Chambers (ORL)* ◇
Burton Frank	*12 King's Bench Walk* *
Cooksley Nigel	*Old Square Chambers* *
Huckle Theodore	*Civitas Law (ORL)* ◇ *
Kent Michael	*Crown Office Chambers* *
Limb Patrick	*Ropewalk Chambers (ORL)* ◇ *
Melton Christopher	*Byrom Street Chambers (ORL)* ◇ *
Platt David	*Crown Office Chambers*
Rawlinson Michael	*Kings Chambers (ORL)* ◇ *
Walker Ronald	*12 King's Bench Walk* *
Leading Juniors	
Bennett Daniel	*Doughty Street Chambers*
Bowley Ivan	*Lincoln House Chambers (ORL)* ◇
Brace Michael	*Civitas Law (ORL)* ◇ *
Cowan Peter	*Oriel Chambers (ORL)* ◇
Feeny Charles	*St Johns Buildings (ORL)* ◇
Foster Catherine	*Crown Office Chambers* *
Glynn Stephen	*9 Gough Square* *
Hiorns Roger	*9 Gough Square*
Levene Simon	*12 King's Bench Walk* *
McDonald John	*2TG - 2 Temple Gardens* [A]
McLaughlin Andrew	*St John's Chambers (ORL)* ◇ [A]
O'Leary Robert	*Civitas Law (ORL)* ◇ *
Phillips Matthew	*Outer Temple Chambers*
Reddiford Anthony	*Guildhall Chambers (ORL)* ◇
Snowden Steven	*Crown Office Chambers* *
Steinberg Harry	*12 King's Bench Walk* *
Todd James	*Thirty Nine Essex Street*
Woolf Eliot	*Outer Temple Chambers* *

◇ (ORL) = Other Ranked Lawyer.

[A] direct access (see p.11).

* Indicates set / individual with profile.

work: Defended a maximum severity spinal injury claim with a value of over £15 million.

Catherine Foster (see p.602) Has over 20 years' experience as an industrial disease and catastrophic injury junior. Her primary areas of interest include inquests and group actions relating to NIHL, hand-arm vibration syndrome (HAVS) and radiation exposure. **Strengths:** "A very direct and incisive operator, who is very strong at negotiating and good on her feet. When it needs to be a bit of a fight she's someone you welcome in your corner." "An excellent trial advocate with great expertise in disease cases." **Recent work:** Handled a pioneering vibration white foot claim involving complex causation and medical evidence. The case was dismissed after a five-day trial.

Steven Snowden (see p.724) An impressive junior who is often selected for serious leg and head injury matters and challenging RTA cases. He is as strong in court as he is in conference. **Strengths:** "A cut above the rest, he is a brilliant advocate, analyst and strategist." "He's very technically competent and accomplished at handling catastrophic injury claims. He's also a calm and diligent advocate whose opinions are respected by the judiciary." **Recent work:** Advised on several fatal and catastrophic RTA claims with hotly contested issues surrounding causation and quantum.

Andrew Davis (see p.584) Particularly active in maximum severity injury claims where the brain or spine has been damaged, as well as fatal accident and chronic pain cases. He also has a substantial disease practice. **Strengths:** "He has detailed knowledge of the application of the Brussels Regulation and Rome II." "He's very clever and hard-working, and impresses both in conference and on paper." **Recent work:** Acted in a multifaceted RTA claim where a whole family was injured, with the wife suffering severe neurological damage. The claim was further complicated by the issue of the family's immigration status.

John Williams (see p.752) Commended for the breadth of his expertise in both occupational disease and catastrophic injury work. He is highly experienced at cases concerning asbestos, occupational hearing loss and bullying in the workplace. **Recent work:** Acted in an industrial disease claim brought against Salford City Council by a living mesothelioma sufferer who alleged they had been exposed to asbestos as a child.

Matthew Boyle (see p.554) A strong junior whose broad practice sees him instructed in both catastrophic injury and disease work. He specialises in severe brain injury claims, and cases involving HAVS. **Strengths:** "He has a very good cross-examination style, which is calm, methodical and very effective." "He is very agile of mind and is able to appreciate all the points in a case." **Recent work:** Advised in a claim brought by a cyclist who was seriously brain-injured after an accident on the road involving another vehicle.

Shaun Ferris (see p.600) A junior barrister whose experience outstrips his years of call. He offers expert advice and advocacy in serious injury and disease matters including those involving severe brain damage, fibromyalgia and paraplegia. **Strengths:** "A robust advocate with a keen tactical appreciation of the complexities of catastrophic injury cases." "He's practical and down-to-earth, and has an excellent rapport with clients. He makes sensible commercial decisions and is collaborative in his approach." **Recent work:** Involved in a catastrophic brain damage claim where there were complex issues surrounding the mental capacity, care and accommodation needs of the claimant. The claim settled at £750,000 plus PPO.

Muhammed Haque (see p.619) A very experienced catastrophic injury junior who focuses his practice on head and other severe injuries, fraudulent RTAs and occupier's liability claims. **Strengths:** "He has excellent team leadership skills, displays sound tactical awareness and produces good-quality advocacy. He's very strong on the paperwork and shows great attention to detail." "He's exceptionally thorough, well prepared and highly knowledgeable." **Recent work:** Represented the fire service in group litigation arising from the injury of 13 claimants by a huge explosion at a fireworks factory.

Thirty Nine Essex Street

See profile on p.797

THE SET

This much-admired set is celebrated for its handling of complex, high-value personal injury litigation for both claimants and defendants. It covers the gamut of personal injury claims and has, of late, ramped up its involvement in related fraud claims. It is noted for having absorbed the impact of the Jackson reforms well, as evidenced by the fact it has enjoyed an increase in instructions from the previous year.

Client service: "The clerking is good and the conference facilities are very professional. The set also offers seminars with superb speakers."

SILKS

Neil Block QC Handles extremely high-value personal injury claims, appearing both for individuals and in group actions. His mastery of EL/PL, sporting and motor accident claims is well known throughout the Personal Injury Bar. **Strengths:** "A bold advocate and negotiator, who is tenacious to the end." "A heavyweight who carries a real gravitas about him and is respected by other counsel and the insurance industry." **Recent work:** Advised in a claim against a school concerning a young boy who had severely damaged his spine during a rugby match.

Charles Cory-Wright QC Acts for both claimants and defendants, and is renowned for his excellence in handling serious, high-value injury work. He is particularly adept at managing claims relating to sporting injuries, RTAs and EL/PL. **Strengths:** "His main attributes are his knowledge of large, complex and high-profile PI actions, and his approachability." "Impressive on his feet and in conference, he's not afraid to give clients a frank appraisal of their cases." **Recent work:** Represented the defendant in an unprecedented secondary victim case whereby the claimant witnessed the death of her mother due to an injury she had sustained at work three weeks earlier. The issues centred on whether there was sufficient proximity to the accident to incur the liability of the tortfeasor.

William Norris QC A standout personal injury silk with broad-ranging experience in fraud, catastrophic injury and EL/PL claims. He recently acted for a young tetraplegic and has handled a number of stress at work claims. **Strengths:** "An efficient, skilled advocate and a good team player." "He's not only a talented counsel but extremely entertaining with it." **Recent work:** Advised the fire service in a civil claim concerning the Lakanal House fire in South London, where six people died. There were alleged fire safety issues that may have eased the spread of fire in the tower block.

Susan Rodway QC A catastrophic injury silk working at the very top of the Personal Injury Bar. She specialises in head and back injuries as well as injuries where amputation is needed. **Strengths:** "Very forthright, great with clients and an excellent advocate." "Tenacious and committed, she doesn't shy away from the difficult cases." **Recent work:** Counsel to a local authority in a claim relating to the catastrophic brain injury of a child caused by attempted suicide.

Colin McCaul QC An extremely gifted silk who focuses his practice on maximum severity/large loss injury claims and disease work. He also has a talent for HSE matters due to his thorough understanding and knowledge of the statutory regulation. **Strengths:** "Tactically astute, approachable and delightful with clients. He is full of common sense and excellent on particularly complex RTAs." **Recent work:** Acted in an RTA claim, representing a motorcyclist who was rendered paraplegic following emergency surgery to treat a serious spleen injury.

David Melville QC Regularly represents clients in EL/PL and RTA claims where the injuries include paraplegia and limb amputation. **Strengths:** "Extremely approachable and always happy to help," he is "always willing to pursue and win difficult cases." **Recent work:** Represented a catastrophically injured claimant who had been involved in an RTA in London. There were difficult quantum issues due to the claimant being moved to Brazil.

Augustus Ullstein QC A renowned catastrophic injury and disease practitioner who focuses his energy on fighting neurological injury and asbestos-related claims. He is also a professional negligence and product liability silk, areas of expertise and experience that serve to further bolster his personal injury practice. **Recent work:** Counsel in Coles v Perfect, a marine case where a young girl travelling on a ring down the River Orwell was severely injured when the ring collided with a motorboat.

JUNIORS

Derek O'Sullivan A long-standing personal injury silk who handles matters with sophisticated medical, causation and quantum issues attached to them. He is also regularly instructed on complex cross-border and local authority matters. **Strengths:** "Great fun to work with, he shows excellent attention to detail and is a very bold negotiator and tactician." **Recent work:** Advised on a defective housing claim where the claimant sustained catastrophic injuries while visiting his mother in her local authority flat. The case has had a huge impact on housing in the borough.

Christian Du Cann Has a stellar reputation as one of the brightest juniors at the Personal Injury Bar. He regularly handles cases concerning spinal and amputation injuries, and is strong on complex quantum and liability issues. **Strengths:** "He's extremely intelligent, and very good at cutting through issues and seeing the nuances in a case. You can put him up against any silk you care to name." "He's a tremendous advocate, and somebody who really fights your corner in the courtroom." **Recent work:** Worked on a maximum severity motor claim concerning a serious back injury. The case was complicated by several issues surrounding causation, a pre-existing condition and 24-hour care needs.

Geoffrey Brown A leading junior and a fine choice for EL/PL, brain injury and stress claims. He also handles inquests and personal injury claims involving complex regional pain syndrome. **Strengths:** "He is very approachable and he delivers a good service. He's not pompous and speaks to you as an equal." "Extremely bright, he is able to deal with large amounts of paperwork and complex issues in a short period of time." **Recent work:** Acted in a public liability matter concerning a stress-related psychiatric injury sustained at a school.

Bernard Doherty A motor accident expert who works primarily on catastrophic injury matters in the UK and Europe. His particular areas of interest include claims relating to serious head and back injuries, and matters involving EU law. **Strengths:** "His key strengths are his incredible attention to detail, and his skill in explaining complex points in a clear and concise way. His advocacy is second to none." "He's very knowledgeable on conflicts of law in a personal injury context, and tactically astute in his application of foreign law arguments. Approachable." **Recent work:** Instructed in Majka v Pudlowski, a £22 million neurological injury claim by a Polish national.

James Todd A highly active maximum severity/large loss personal injury junior, who acts for defendants and claimants in RTA and fatal accident cases. **Strengths:** "Very pragmatic, forensic and precise, and someone with his eye on the bigger picture as to what is important to insured and insurer clients." "An excellent technical lawyer, who cross-examines to very good effect, and who has the ability to advise definitively on complex claims." **Recent work:** Acted for the defendant and managed to negotiate an appropriate settlement in a cycling accident claim where the claimant had suffered serious neurological injury.

Judith Ayling A remarkably polished junior who combines a thriving group litigation practice with a strong defendant practice acting for government departments. He has particular expertise in high-value catastrophic injury cases and those concerning interim and periodical payments. **Strengths:** "Has unrivalled costs experience, and provides clear, user-friendly advice." **Recent work:** Instructed one of the defendants in Beniston v Faun Zoeller, an accident at work matter where the claimant sustained a serious finger injury.

Emily Formby (see p.602) Has strong advocacy and negotiation skills, and is noted for her significant experience in inquests and human rights. Solicitors praise her client care. **Strengths:** "Good at giving clear practical advice, she is absolutely brilliant with clients and has a forensic mind." "She does a lot of cycling-related work and has extensive knowledge of liability issues."

Sadie Crapper (see p.580) An erudite junior who is well versed in high-value serious injury, fraud and abuse claims. She is an astute quantum expert and has worked on some key personal injury cases. **Strengths:** "She's very straight-talking, and will stick her neck out. She is a phenomenal barrister in terms of her technical arguments and her ability to tailor them to different people." "She is an expert in abuse and bullying cases, and strong on employers' liability matters." **Recent work:** Advised on a fraudulent knee injury claim that had been founded on deception as to the severity of the claimant's injury. This case represented the first ever strike-out under Summers v Fairclough.

9 Gough Square
See profile on p.812

THE SET

This top-tier personal injury set attracts predominantly claimant instructions and regularly tackles catastrophic injury claims, including brain, spinal and amputation cases. It also has members who are recognised for their ability to manage industrial disease claims effectively. Commentators say: "The barristers are accessible and modern in their approach. They don't scare the clients with 'other-worldly' behaviour and there is a professional but humane ethos to the set that is hugely appreciated by both clients and instructing solicitors."

Client service: "No call ever goes unanswered and requests for costs budgeting data are invariably dealt with in full within an hour."

SILKS

Grahame Aldous QC (see p.533) Experienced in handling amputation and severe leg and brain injury cases. His unique background in the Merchant Navy and his interest in competitive yachting have led to him building up a niche practice in claims arising from accidents at sea. **Strengths:** "He will fight your corner and is firm in his advice." "His cross-examination is masterly and he has an understanding of where judges will go in a case." **Recent work:** Handled a cross-border RTA claim and secured a total settlement of £24 million.

Andrew Ritchie QC (see p.708) An acclaimed expert in fatal accident, industrial disease (including mesothelioma) and PTSD claims. He is also regularly involved in cases at the intersection between personal injury and professional negligence. **Strengths:** "He is immensely intelligent and at the same time provides practical and realistic advice." "He has unrivalled knowledge of the Motor Insurers' Bureau (MIB) and is always prepared to argue difficult points." **Recent work:** Obtained a very substantial settlement for a neurologically injured claimant.

John Foy QC (see p.603) Very strong on maximum severity injury matters and costs cases. He usually represents those involved in accidents where the injuries are life-changing, and has handled a number of paraplegia and amputation claims. **Strengths:** "Extremely down-to-earth and approachable – he will always listen to and take on board the client's concerns. He is incredibly sharp and is fantastic in settlement negotiations." **Recent work:** Instructed in Stab v Bywaters, a claim regarding several serious injuries caused by an accident at work with a forklift truck.

Jacob Levy QC (see p.655) Has an incredible energy and passion for helping those involved in serious, often life-changing accidents. He has more than 27 years' experience in this field and is well known for his personable yet professional approach. **Strengths:** "He will never miss anything and nothing is too much trouble – he will explore every angle. He is very clever and his cross-examination skills are very good." "He has a lovely manner with clients, is very approachable and pays attention to detail."

JUNIORS

Stuart McKechnie (see p.668) Has developed an all-encompassing personal injury practice that focuses primarily on catastrophic brain, orthopaedic and spinal injuries. He is also experienced at handling abuse cases and has the skills to work with multiple experts on sensitive and complex issues. **Strengths:** "Very hard-working and tenacious." "His knowledge and expertise are vast, and he is fantastic with both clients and experts." **Recent work:** Acted in a high-profile case relating to sexual abuse by a Church of England priest in the 1980s. The claimant suffered a multitude of serious psychiatric injuries, including PTSD, personality disorder, alcohol dependency and depression.

Laura Begley A pre-eminent serious injury practitioner who regularly acts for trade unions in employment liability claims for assault and abuse. She is also well versed in difficult spinal and orthopaedic injury cases. **Strengths:** "She has a fantastic manner with clients, is incredibly approachable, is brilliant in court and displays good attention to detail." "She's extremely personable, great with clients and very thorough in her preparation."

Nicolas Hillier (see p.628) Has over 25 years' experience at the Personal Injuries Bar. He is praised by many for his in-depth knowledge of employers' liability and industrial disease cases, and for his ability to provide clear and detailed advice. **Strengths:** "An extremely experienced senior junior who shows fantastic attention to detail and can hold his own against any silk." "An excellent advocate and negotiator." **Recent work:** Advised in an RTA claim where the truth regarding the claimant's chronic pain syndrome was called into question by surveillance evidence.

Jeremy Ford (see p.601) Has appeared before a variety of courts in connection with fatal accidents, psychiatric and MIB-related claims. He is known for his strong yet empathetic manner, which allows him to effectively manage sensitive situations. **Strengths:** "Strong in every respect, particularly when it comes to handling catastrophically injured clients. He delivers sensible advice and has an extremely impressive knowledge of the law." **Recent work:** Represented the defendants in a claim concerning a road traffic accident that killed one passenger and brain-injured the other. The case settled for a lump sum of £430,000 plus an annual periodical payment order (PPO) of £115,000.

Stephen Glynn (see p.610) Has over two decades of personal injury experience and demonstrates key strengths in employers' liability, abuse and occupational disease claims. He is head of the personal injury team and is regarded as a great tactician. **Strengths:** "He has a huge amount of experience in asbestos claims and is very approachable and detailed in his advice. He is an effective advocate experienced at handling fast-track mesothelioma cases." **Recent work:** Achieved a £350,000 settlement for an unusually young claimant who developed mesothelioma after asbestos exposure at his secondary school.

Roger Hiorns Has a broad-ranging personal injury practice covering fatal accidents, mesothelioma and serious brain/back injuries, amongst others. **Strengths:** "RSI is definitely one of his strengths," and "he is very good on employers' liability cases."

Christopher Stephenson (see p.728) Highly sought after for his ability to handle catastrophic injury cases in the High Court. His caseload covers assaults at work, multiple-claimant RTAs and sexual abuse claims. **Strengths:** "He puts clients' minds at ease and gets so much more out of them because they are relaxed in his company." **Recent work:** Instructed in a complex employers' liability claim where causation was highly disputed; the claimant was suffering from fibromyalgia and settlement was achieved at a joint settlement meeting (JSM).

Adam Dawson (see p.585) A notable junior who works on the full suite of personal injury matters. He has handled RTA, EL/PL and industrial disease cases, including those relating to PTSD. **Strengths:** "He has a fantastic manner as he shows empathy with the clients and is good at managing their high expectations." "He's very intelligent and has very good drafting skills." **Recent work:** Advised a pedestrian who had been hit by a vehicle outside a pub, in a claim for £500,000 in damages.

Giles Mooney (see p.675) Represents claimants and defendants in workplace, RTA and sports-related claims, but is best known for his handling of Animals Act claims. He also has particular expertise in accidents at sea, and he mainly acts for defendant shipping companies in these cases.

12 King's Bench Walk
See profile on p.828

THE SET

A set noted for its depth, every one of whose barristers undertakes personal injury work. It appears in the most difficult and high-value cases in all the relevant courts up to and including the Supreme Court, and has been appointed to the panels of leading insurers and legal expenses providers. It further boasts strength in industrial disease claims, as evidenced by its recent appearances in Haxton v Philips Electronics UK Ltd and Zambarda v Shipbreaking Queenborough Ltd, two mesothelioma-related matters. Sources say the set "has a very good range of counsel from QC down and is an excellent one-stop shop that rivals the best chambers in terms of its coverage and expertise."

Client service: "They run a very tight ship – all the clerks are helpful and fee structures are well tuned to the current climate." John Cooper and Graham Johnson are the senior clerks.

SILKS

Stephen Worthington QC (see p.756) Handles a number of catastrophic claims, and also acts for claimants in cases involving stress at work or exposure to chemicals. He is also well respected by sources for his work on chronic fatigue, fibromyalgia, and complex care and accommodation claims. **Strengths:** "He's able to soak up the details of complex cases almost instantly and spots new angles that have not occurred to others." "He takes a pragmatic and client-focused approach, and has the ability to get to the heart of the matter, making him an effective negotiator." **Recent work:** Acted in an MIB RTA case involving issues concerning costs and untraced drivers.

Frank Burton QC (see p.562) A sought-after industrial disease and catastrophic injury expert with top-notch experience in asbestos and pleural plaque test cases. He also regularly deals with health and safety-related claims. **Strengths:** "A real high-powered silk in this area who is a thorough and brilliant advocate. He's a huge asset to the set." "He's calm, personable and hugely experienced, and provides well-judged advice." **Recent work:** Recently involved in a seminal Court of Appeal case concerning a clash between the Civil Procedure Rules and a consent order under the Rules of the Supreme Court Order 37 on the limitation for asbestos-related claims.

Ronald Walker QC (see p.745) A leading industrial disease silk specialising in cancer and respiratory diseases such as mesothelioma arising from sustained exposure to chemicals in the workplace.

He is also adept at handling catastrophic injury claims, including those involving severe brain injury. **Strengths:** "He has an exceptional intellect and years of experience that he brings to bear in high-value, complex cases." "A shrewd tactician with a very good legal mind."

Richard Methuen QC (see p.671) Combines an active practice in maximum severity injury work, including brain, spinal and sports injuries, with his duties as a mediator. He is widely regarded as being at the forefront of the Personal Injuries Bar. **Strengths:** "I rate him highly because his negotiation skills are spot-on. He doesn't try and overplay a hand and he is also good in settlements." "He has a fantastic overview of the issues and is a pleasure to work with. He handles complex cross-border litigation with ease." **Recent work:** Represented the client in a cross-border accident claim that involved in-depth analysis of European and German liability and quantum law.

Paul Russell QC (see p.712) A master of sophisticated, high-value catastrophic injury claims as well as MIB and RSI claims. He represents both claimants and defendants, and is renowned for his extensive medical knowledge. **Strengths:** "A rock-solid adviser and great tactician." "He's immensely thorough and interesting to work with." **Recent work:** Counsel in X v MS, a case concerning traumatic brain injury (TBI) where the causation and damages were in dispute.

William Featherby QC (see p.599) A seasoned trial silk who excels in accidents at work, RTA and occupational disease matters. **Recent work:** Acted in a contempt of court case where two family members of the injured claimant were convicted and given suspended sentences.

Andrew Hogarth QC (see p.629) Has extensive expertise in catastrophic injury and industrial disease, and is also a CEDR-accredited mediator. He is an employment lawyer as well, giving him the skills to effectively deal with cases involving injuries sustained at work. **Strengths:** "Very clever, impressive on his feet, and good at dealing with and communicating with clients." **Recent work:** Advised the defendant in a subtle brain injury claim.

JUNIORS

Henry Charles (see p.570) Routinely acts for claimants and defendants in high-value severe injury claims, including psychiatric and brain injury-related matters. He is also held in high regard by sources for his Criminal Injuries Compensation Authority (CICA) work. **Strengths:** "A very solid advocate" with a "great bedside manner." **Recent work:** Represented the defendant in a case concerning a serious head injury incurred in the workplace. The claim settled for £7 million.

William Audland Instructed on a wide range of personal injury work. He is particularly strong on cases involving local authorities, employers' liability, public liability and accidents abroad. **Strengths:** "He has a wealth of experience and takes a forensic approach to his cases." "When he is in court he is very well prepared and his cross-examinations are terrifying." **Recent work:** Counsel to a Premier League footballer who has an ongoing claim for loss of career earnings caused by injury in an RTA.

Nigel Lewers (see p.655) Adept at managing personal injury cases with difficult causation issues (for example, pleural plaque and asbestos matters) and accidents involving animals. He is also routinely sought after to work on highways, abuse and employers' liability claims. **Strengths:** "Provides clear and succinct advice, and has excellent strategic awareness." "Fantastic with clients; he's a delight to work with." **Recent work:** Obtained a settlement of more than £500,000 for a pedestrian who had suffered a severe head injury when hit by a car. The claim involved complex issues concerning quantum, contributory negligence and accommodation.

Catherine Brown (see p.557) Represents claimants who have sustained complex brain or spinal injuries. She also has deep knowledge of health and safety, local authority and stress at work matters. **Strengths:** "Not a showy advocate, she's very good in conference, and approachable and methodical in her advocacy." "She's able to explain complex issues in straightforward terms and has a good rapport with those she represents." **Recent work:** Acted in a claim by Travellers concerning alleged personal injury and human rights abuses perpetrated by the police, local authority and bailiffs during their eviction from land where they had been living.

Marcus Dignum (see p.588) Has a particular focus on serious head/spinal injury claims sustained on the public highway or while in employment. He is often instructed by large insurers, and also represents claimants. **Strengths:** "He had a calm, technical approach in negotiation, which helped us get the result we wanted." "He provides a polished service on higher-value and more complex claims." **Recent work:** Advised a claimant who had sustained a catastrophic head injury in an RTA while riding as a passenger without a helmet. The claim settled for £1.6 million.

Hugh Hamill (see p.618) A very strong personal injury practitioner who predominantly handles chronic pain, chronic fatigue and fibromyalgia claims. He is often instructed by major insurers and public authorities. **Strengths:** "He has good attention to detail, and is pragmatic and good at defending industrial disease claims." "He approaches claims with enthusiasm and is highly tenacious." **Recent work:** Secured judgment in favour of the MIB in a case concerning a passenger riding illegally on an uninsured, stolen trials bike.

Simon Levene (see p.655) Widely sought after for his aptitude in calculating losses and drafting complex schedules. He sits on the PNBA, PIBA, IIAC and Ogden Committees. **Strengths:** "Extremely thorough and unflappable." **Recent work:** Represented the claimant in an industrial disease claim concerning whether or not the limitation period started from the date of diagnosis or the date of knowledge of the significance of the diagnosis.

David Sanderson (see p.714) Acts for both claimants and defendants in a range of sophisticated personal injury cases. Sources are quick to praise his attention to detail and his effectiveness in settlement meetings. **Strengths:** "He will run a case and stick to his convictions." "A first-class advocate who is as excellent in writing as he is in conference."

Harry Steinberg (see p.727) A specialist in brain injury, industrial disease and product liability claims. He is highlighted for his prowess in producing complex schedules of loss and in resolving sophisticated legal issues. **Strengths:** "His working methods are efficient, organised and methodical." "He's bright and interested, and has the confidence to run interesting points." **Recent work:** Instructed on a seminal disease case brought by the disabled widow of a deceased mesothelioma sufferer. He successfully obtained damages of £242,000.

Andrew Roy (see p.712) A leading personal injury junior specialising in road traffic, employment liability and CICA claims. He has extensive experience in occupational disease claims and a strong knowledge of asbestos and RSI/HAVS claims. **Strengths:** "He is concise, pays enormous attention to detail and is excellent with clients." "A fighter who will take on cases others won't." **Recent work:** Acted in an employers' liability claim where the serious hand injury of the claimant police officer was held to have resulted from the lack of protective equipment provided. The claimant had inhaled cannabis fumes while taking down a cannabis factory.

Patrick Vincent (see p.743) Undertakes a great deal of defence work for the MIB and local authorities, and is well known for his dexterity in handling claims with difficult scientific or technical aspects. He is also very competent in harassment, industrial deafness and stress prosecutions. **Strengths:** "He's very approachable and makes himself available." **Recent work:** Advised the MIB in an RTA case where the claimant had suffered a double leg amputation.

James Sullivan (see p.731) A highly polished junior with a burgeoning multi-track practice covering sports injuries, head injuries and complex regional pain syndrome. **Strengths:** "An excellent barrister who picks up on all the key issues. He is very organised and will go the extra mile for you."

Richard Davison (see p.585) Has strength in serious brain and multiple injury cases, as well as CICA and sexual abuse claims. He acts for both claimants and defendants. **Strengths:** "Excellent at seeing the wood for the trees, and very to-the-point and approachable." **Recent work:** Advised on a claim against the Ministry of Defence (MoD) for psychiatric injuries caused by sexual abuse by senior soldiers.

Outer Temple Chambers

See profile on p.842

THE SET

A set that is at the forefront of defendant-side personal injury claims and which houses barristers who are experts in sexual abuse, asbestos and NIHL claims. The members also have great skill in handling sophisticated, high-value catastrophic injury and cross-border claims. Sources say: "Outer Temple has some very strong silks and continues to deliver great results and a great service." "Their facilities are more hi-tech than some other sets – they have video facilities and their conference rooms are better appointed."

SILKS

Gerard McDermott QC A veteran personal injury silk whose knowledge of employment and EU regulations informs his ability to negotiate and structure care regimes for catastrophic injury claimants. He has been instructed on several international claims involving the USA, EU and Middle East. **Strengths:** "A very high-calibre practitioner, who fights very hard for his clients. He is very dedicated, very approachable and a real grafter." "He is one of the best PI silks I have worked with – he lives and breathes the case, will immerse himself in it and has all the facts at his fingertips." **Recent work:** Handled a seminal fraud/insurance claim involving surveillance evidence and issues of disability.

David Westcott QC Handles some of the most valuable personal injury claims in the country, and has a very strong catastrophic RTA practice. He frequently works on sensitive cases involving life-changing conditions such as tetraplegia and severe brain injury. **Strengths:** "He's very able and a very effective advocate," who is "exceptionally bright and analytical."

Christopher Wilson-Smith QC (see p.753) An effective and experienced personal injury silk, active predominantly in the areas of HSE prosecutions and RTAs where serious injury to the head or spine has occurred. He also has particular expertise in defending police officers against personal injury claims. **Strengths:** "One of the best cross-examiners in the business, he is an outstanding advocate with finely tuned judgement." "A very good advocate and negotiator." **Recent work:** Lead silk in a claim concerning a complex RTA that left the claimant with severe brain damage and, as a consequence, multiple psychiatric disorders.

JUNIORS

Alison McCormick Has a particular interest in employers' liability and occupational disease claims, including asbestos litigation. She is highly praised by instructing solicitors and clients for her empathetic yet professional approach to dealing with claimants who lack mental capacity, are terminally ill or are recently bereaved. **Strengths:** "Very, very good with clients, very bright, incredibly thorough and good to work with. My go-to barrister for high-value cases." "A highly experienced and versatile counsel whose involvement in the landmark employers' liability policy litigation was invaluable." **Recent work:** Successfully obtained £728,000 at a JSM for a claimant whose arm was irreparably damaged in a motorcycle accident.

James Aldridge Highly regarded by instructing solicitors and peers alike for his handling of catastrophic brain and spinal injury claims, as well as those relating to psychiatric and lower limb injury. He is also regularly chosen to act on EL/PL claims. **Recent work:** Achieved a settlement of £125,000 in a fatal road accident claim involving a mother whose child was orphaned.

Christopher Kemp Handles a wide array of personal injury matters. His work includes severe brain and spinal injuries incurred by professional sportspeople and cases where local authorities may be liable. **Strengths:** "Thoughtful and thorough, his opinions are valued by claimants." **Recent work:** Represented a young claimant in an accident at work case where chronic pain and psychiatric harm had allegedly been caused.

Eliot Woolf An experienced advocate in road traffic, EL and travel personal injury claims. He has extensive experience of acting for both claimants and defendants. **Strengths:** "Very practical, good on the detail, sensible and straightforward." "Extremely knowledgeable, well prepared and highly analytical, he is an excellent advocate who inspires confidence." **Recent work:** Currently instructed in a siderosis and small airways disease claim brought under the Fatal Accidents Act.

Matthew Phillips A talented advocate who appears regularly before courts at all levels and in settlement meetings. He is an expert at advising on catastrophic head or back injuries, as well as multi-party asbestos and silicosis claims. **Strengths:** "Very experienced. He's a good communicator who is great with clients." **Recent work:** Handled a £4.5 million accident at work claim brought by a young man who had sustained horrific spinal damage.

Nathan Tavares Complements his duties as a leading personal injury junior with his role as a judge of the Mental Health Tribunal. He specialises in claimant and defendant work involving aviation accidents, road accidents and accidents abroad. **Strengths:** "His judgement is sound, he is hard-working, has a good brain and is a safe pair of hands." "He is a pleasure to work with as he is very good with clients and excellent at analysing medical reports and numbers." **Recent work:** Acted in a serious road accident claim involving an infant claimant, who had sustained unusual internal injuries making it difficult to produce a long-term assessment for damages.

Harry Trusted A leading junior who handles sophisticated quantum, care and accommodation issues with ease and precision. He regularly advises on and appears in catastrophic injury cases that often involve paralysis or amputation. **Strengths:** "He's extremely knowledgeable, sees the issues quickly, and is able to give clear and straightforward advice to clients." **Recent work:** Instructed in an employers' liability matter concerning a claimant who was paralysed in a workplace accident.

Band 2

1 Chancery Lane

THE SET

An outstanding set specialising in catastrophic injury (including brain injury claims), stress at work, highways and road accident claims. Practitioners have been involved in many high-profile claims based on sexual abuse matters, including the Jimmy Savile case and other sexual grooming matters. Sources report that the set is "open and friendly" and has "an impressive mix of people."

Client service: "The clerks are always accommodating, approachable and easy to work with. They are reliable and efficient, and they periodically send us a useful newsletter." Clark Chessis is the senior clerk.

SILKS

Edward Faulks QC (see p.599) A highly rated silk who is acknowledged for his experience in complex sexual abuse claims and group litigation. He is regularly involved in claims relating to highways and fatal accidents. **Strengths:** "He is simply the best public authority PI silk – no one can touch him. He has a good grasp of the law and his manner in court is commanding. Judges respect and listen to him." **Recent work:** Represented a local authority in a £10 million accident claim at the Court of Appeal. The argument turned on the council's failure to inspect the highway and the question of whether this had indeed caused the RTA and subsequent injury.

John Ross QC Has a broad personal injury practice with large loss catastrophic injuries and fatal accident cases at its core. He often handles multiple-claimant cases. **Strengths:** "His impressive intellect and attention to detail, seemingly endless capacity for hard work, brilliant advocacy and negotiation skills all serve him well. He also has an excellent rapport with clients." **Recent work:** Acted for the claimant in Michael Mullarney v Brenwell Limited, successfully arguing that quantum under Jersey law should be based on the Guernsey case of Helmot v Simon.

Edward Bishop QC A well-rounded personal injury practitioner who also benefits from knowledge of police law, clinical negligence and human rights. He is often instructed to act in NHS-related cases and frequently appears before the Court of Appeal. **Strengths:** "He stands out because he is very bright and a good cross-examiner; he also has excellent personal skills." **Recent work:** Acted for the local authority handling an assault claim where the victim had been attacked by a child in care, leaving him with severe neurological damage.

Simon Readhead QC (see p.705) An experienced severe injury practitioner who has substantial expertise in cases relating to head and back injuries. He handles claims for both claimants and defendants. **Strengths:** "He is an excellent advocate and tactician, and has the ability to put clients at ease. He achieves outstanding results in difficult and complex matters." "Very thorough, very responsive and easy to work with." **Recent work:** Advised the claimant in a personal injury claim against the police for a £3.8 million catastrophic head injury.

Andrew Warnock QC A celebrated personal injury silk who has a flourishing abuse and highways practice. He is also heavily involved in complex public liability litigation. **Strengths:** "He has fabulous ability and is a devastating advocate. I watched him reduce the claimant's barrister to absolutely nothing in two sentences." "Very easy and conversational in conference, he is approachable and very much part of the team. His legal knowledge in terms of public authority law is of the very highest level." **Recent work:** Represented the BBC in the highly publicised Jimmy Savile sexual abuse claim.

JUNIORS

Laura Johnson An experienced junior who is often chosen to act in severe injury and fraud claims. Observers note that she is excellent on her feet and in conference, and is also clear and concise in her advice. **Strengths:** "She is highly competent, knows her stuff and is a good trial advocate. She has a good manner with clients in conference and is a good judge of when to be impressive and when to be magnanimous." "She has a straightforward, pragmatic, logical and clear approach, and provides sound advice to clients." **Recent work:** Instructed on behalf of a claimant who sustained a catastrophic head injury in a motor accident.

Julian Waters (see p.747) Highly regarded by instructing solicitors and peers for his medical understanding and expertise when it comes to brain and psychiatric injury matters. He has worked on several large inquests, public liability cases and human rights-related claims.

Matthew Chapman (see p.569) Has cultivated a thriving practice in both national and international accident claims involving catastrophic and serious injuries. He also dedicates a lot of his time to defending public authority and employers' liability claims. **Strengths:** "He is incredibly tenacious and always goes the extra mile for you. He has got such a strong work ethic and is good at handling clients." "He always makes himself available and gives high-level advice." **Recent work:** Successfully defended a local authority in an unusual case where a social worker claimed psychiatric injury because of the negligent publishing of information concerning his conduct.

Paul Stagg Divides his practice between claimants and defendants, and acts on matters concerning all types of serious accidents, including those incurred at work and on the roads. He is further noted for his work on cases with social security and community care law aspects. **Strengths:** "He is good on the law and not fazed by difficult points." "He gives you personal attention and doesn't make you feel as if you are imposing. Bright and thorough, he will highlight the main concerns." **Recent work:** Instructed in a catastrophic injury claim concerning the duty of a hospital to prevent harm to a patient who had attempted to climb over a wall.

Devereux

See profile on p.785

THE SET

This prominent set is a good port of call for those with contentious brain and spinal injury-related claims, and it has barristers who are experienced at handling cases concerning injuries sustained by UK nationals abroad. Other niche areas of expertise include CICA, psychiatric injury and amputation cases. Commentators state: "The set has barristers who are prepared to fight really difficult cases and they have a number of specialists in brain injury. All the Devereux people we work with are committed to getting the best possible result for clients and they bring with them a wealth of experience."

Client service: "The clerks are brilliant. There is always someone available and they respond immediately." Vince Plant is the chambers director.

SILKS

Robert Weir QC A highly respected catastrophic injury and disease silk who is acknowledged as a true expert in cases involving severe head and back injuries and amputations. He also has unique experience in foreign PI cases, and has worked on matters where the injury occurred in France or Australia. **Strengths:** "He has had some absolutely fantastic results recently with novel cases. He is always trying to look at new angles to cases and come up with ingenious new arguments." "He is really razor-sharp in his analysis, cuts to the chase and doesn't pontificate." **Recent work:** Represented a mesothelioma sufferer who had contracted the disease because she had lived near an asbestos factory. The case was settled shortly before it was due to be heard at the High Court.

Robert Glancy QC (see p.609) Has formidable expertise and handles a range of accident claims relating to severe head, back and other near-fatal injuries. He also regularly acts on CICA claims and has been instrumental in the acquisition of damages for tunnel miners. **Strengths:** "His knowledge of the law is superb and he is particularly good at advocacy in the Court of Appeal." "He is modest and very cool under pressure." **Recent work:** Acted in a complex CICA claim that had arisen from a collision between a lorry and another vehicle that caused a fatality.

Stephen Killalea QC Identified by instructing solicitors and peers as an astute neurotrauma and spinal injury silk. He is particularly sought after for his careful and measured approach to cases involving children. **Strengths:** "He's got very good judgement, is well prepared, and has an easy and relaxed manner with clients and opponents alike. He gets the job done in the right way – by being combative but not aggressive." **Recent work:** Instructed in a seminal cross-border motor claim involving the TBI of a motorcyclist in Germany.

JUNIORS

Bruce Silvester Devotes much of his time to individual and group litigation concerning health and safety and catastrophic injury. He boasts a flourishing High Court practice and acts for both defendants and claimants. **Strengths:** "He is a phenomenally hard worker. Every point is taken, and he doesn't miss anything." "His advocacy is superb, and he is regularly up against silks, often coming out on top." **Recent work:** Acted as counsel in a high-value accident claim involving a child with serious neurological damage, where the damage could not be assessed properly until adulthood.

Colin Mendoza (see p.671) A personal injury junior whose sophisticated understanding of medicine enables him to deal with cases involving severe, often life-changing back and head injuries, as well as injuries involving the loss of major organs. He is also a specialist in amputation and chronic pain syndrome matters. **Strengths:** "He's very, very hard-working and doesn't shirk the difficulties in a case." **Recent work:** Advised a claimant who, following an accident at work, had developed a chronic pain condition that meant he was severely dehabilitated.

Peter Edwards (see p.594) Has a practice strong in catastrophic injury, industrial disease and psychiatric injury cases. He regularly handles cases involving severe injuries to the spine, brain damage and fatalities. **Strengths:** "He is energetic, hard-working and adept at marshalling huge amounts of information very quickly. He is also a very engaging guy who can make quite boring things lift off the page, so that a lay person, judge or client can see how they work." **Recent work:** Worked on behalf of a claimant who was paralysed and severely brain damaged following an RTA in the Vatican.

Richard Cartwright (see p.566) An eminent junior with a considerable personal injury practice that covers mostly high-end head and back injuries incurred on the roads and highways. His background in finance means he is good at structuring schedules of loss and other damages work. **Strengths:** "He is very good on detail and up to date on all developments in the law." "He engages well with clients and tends to be more innovative than other barristers." **Recent work:** Managed to obtain a £2.1 million settlement for a neurologically injured claimant who suffers from speech deficit and dysarthria following an RTA.

Robert Hunter (see p.634) A well-regarded large loss/severe injury practitioner who excels in accidents that involve spinal trauma, complex regional pain or amputations. He also undertakes CICA claims and is mainly instructed by the leading personal injury firms. **Strengths:** "His opinions are really thorough and detailed, and he thinks about all the issues, not just the ones you have identified for him to consider." "He is also very good with clients, works really hard, and is very thorough and well prepared." **Recent work:** Acted for the claimant in a high-value motor claim where catastrophic spinal damage was sustained.

Farrar's Building

See profile on p.800

THE SET

This heavyweight personal injury set continues to build its reputation in a range of areas, from mesothelioma to catastrophic brain and spinal injury claims. Practitioners are experienced at tackling cases with complex liability and causation issues, and represent both claimants and defendants. This is "a friendly but professional set that always produces work of the highest standard."

Client service: "The clerks are helpful and hard-working, and they are always able to accommodate instructions, however late they might be sent." Alan Kilbey is the senior clerk.

SILKS

Alan Jeffreys QC An established personal injury silk who is particularly adept at handling cases concerning maximum severity head and back injuries and difficult issues of causation. Other areas of practice include matters relating to highway authorities, tramways and the Mental Capacity Act. **Strengths:** "He's meticulous and a very good advocate. At trial he is exceptionally good, and he easily outperforms his opponents." "He is very experienced, accurately assesses cases, and is charming and persuasive in court." **Recent work:** Handled a motorcycle RTA claim involving three defendants where severe injury was caused to one of the riding passengers.

John Leighton Williams QC An excellent choice for catastrophic PI claims such as those involving serious orthopaedic or head injuries and amputations. He is also distinguished by his experience on international and ground-breaking personal injury matters. **Strengths:** "He has a great breadth of experience and is able to use his judicial experience to good effect. He also has a good aura about him in terms of leading JSMs, and is very personable and good with clients." **Recent work:** Instructed in a maximum severity RTA claim where TBI and orthopaedic injuries were sustained by the claimant.

JUNIORS

Lee Evans (see p.597) Highly praised for his confident tackling of serious accident claims such as those relating to large loss head/spinal trauma, severe pain disorders and amputations. He is regularly selected to act on behalf of large insurers. **Strengths:** "He is a very able senior junior who always does a good note for conferences. He is extremely through and very, very competent." "He's very efficient and gets on with the clients."

Peter Freeman An outstanding catastrophic injury junior who represents both claimants and defendants, and regularly goes head to head with QCs. He is noted for his skill in handling difficult liability and causation matters, and is further celebrated for his knowledge of sporting injuries. **Strengths:** "Always thoroughly prepared, he puts clients and witnesses at ease, and is a fantastic courtroom lawyer who combines legal knowledge and ability with presence and gravitas." "He's extremely commercial and knows which buttons to press with defendant insurers." **Recent work:** Obtained a strike-out of a fraudulent injury claim relating to a brain injury.

John Meredith-Hardy (see p.671) Has considerable experience across the breadth of the personal injury sector. He shows a particular aptitude for industrial disease cases, including those relating to asbestos and psychiatric injuries such as nervous shock. **Strengths:** "He has very good attention to detail, and is thorough and responsive. He can deal with points as they arise, takes a pragmatic view of matters and is good at managing clients' expectations." **Recent work:** Acted for one of the defendants in a multiparty employers' liability action where two employees were seriously injured during an excavation in Northern Ireland.

Andrew Peebles A superb junior who works on a wide range of personal injury matters, from fatalities to sports and highways litigation. He also specialises in defending local councils faced with defective housing claims. **Strengths:** "Good on paperwork, and knowledgeable and forthright in negotiations.

He gets his point across forcefully, but never in an aggressive or rude way, and he is always to the point."

Rhiannon Jones Has established herself as one of the leading catastrophic injury juniors, and frequently advises on RTA, occupational liability and sporting claims. She also has a substantial disease practice. **Strengths:** "She has the ability to get to the heart of the matter and give pragmatic advice." "She is tactically very, very good, gets on well with clients, and puts time and effort into her preparation of cases." **Recent work:** Advised the defendant in an accident claim at the High Court involving a severely brain-damaged claimant.

Temple Garden Chambers

See profile on p.872

THE SET

This set continues to perform to a consistently high standard when handling all manner of personal injury work. It has a strong team of catastrophic injury, industrial disease stress and sexual abuse specialists, and features in high-profile work for the MIB and the Treasury Solicitor's Department. Commentators remark that Temple Garden Chambers is "a large and well-organised set with sophisticated facilities."

SILKS

Jonathan Watt-Pringle QC (see p.747) Has a fine track record of handling health and safety, inquest and insurance work. He also chairs the Appeal Committee of the Human Fertilisation and Embryology Authority. **Strengths:** "He is very sensible, has a good bedside manner and is extremely capable." "He gets on really well with clients, is tactically very good and is always very thorough." **Recent work:** Represented a motorcyclist in an RTA claim concerning the loss of a leg.

Simon Browne QC Practises primarily in catastrophic spine and brain injury claims and has niche experience in aviation accident cases. He is regularly instructed on both the claimant and defendant sides. **Strengths:** "A very bright guy, who is very good on costs issues." **Recent work:** Acted for the defendant in Sale v Sale, an extremely high-value catastrophic injury case where the claimant, a teenage girl, had been left paralysed.

JUNIORS

Marcus Grant (see p.614) Has a broad personal injury practice that encompasses chronic pain, employers' liability and insurance fraud cases. He has also been involved in some seminal TBI matters. **Strengths:** "Extremely able and passionate, he is very communicative and always responsive. His submissions are very impressive, as is his legal argument." **Recent work:** Worked on a controversial motor accident case where there was much debate between experts over whether the claimant had suffered a brain injury.

James Bell An expert in large loss national and international severe injury claims. He regularly deals with cases concerning multiple, often life-threatening head and back injuries arising from road or work accidents. **Strengths:** "A very well-liked senior junior who is tenacious, able, organised and innovative. He has a national practice of real standing."

John Bate-Williams (see p.545) Continues to go from strength to strength, and has built a formidable serious accident practice that covers head, back and psychiatric injury claims. Although he works for both sides, he takes on significantly more defendant claims. **Strengths:** "A superb negotiator who displays great attention to detail and has excellent client skills." **Recent work:** Advised the defendant in Stockman v Sharpe, a claim involving severe neurological injury.

James Laughland (see p.651) A seasoned junior instructed by the most prominent personal injury firms, who is renowned for his strong cross-examinations. Particular areas of expertise for him include cases concerning employers' liability and RTAs causing serious injury. **Strengths:** "He is excellent – he takes a lot of time when preparing, is knowledgeable and gets on well with clients. He is very reliable." **Recent work:** Acted for the claimant in an employers' liability matter that arose as a result of pre-existing medical condition and poor working conditions.

Richard Wilkinson (see p.752) Has over 20 years' experience in personal injury, and concentrates his practice on large loss serious accident claims arising from injuries sustained on the roads or while at work. Orthopaedic, neurological and abdominal injury claims are handled, as are those relating to amputations. **Strengths:** "His attention to detail is second to none, and he is approachable and totally realistic about cases." **Recent work:** Instructed to represent the family of the deceased in the inquest into his murder by one of his colleagues in the Royal Navy.

Dominic Adamson (see p.531) Has a busy, mostly defendant personal injury practice that focuses on sports injury, and injuries caused in the workplace or on the roads. He deals regularly with matters where the client has suffered seriously debilitating injuries such as severe spinal injury or brain damage. **Strengths:** "Very astute, methodical and organised in his approach, he's a heavyweight junior who is very capable of taking the lead in cases." "A really approachable, nice chap who is very clear in his advice." **Recent work:** Counsel in Bhatti v Smith, a cyclist accident case where surveillance evidence was used to assess the appropriate level of compensation.

Paul Kilcoyne (see p.645) Has a niche in military and government defence-type personal injury claims and is frequently sought after by the Royal British Legion Panel and the Special Forces. He advises on serious accidents that occur during military training, and also handles inquests and post-traumatic stress claims. **Strengths:** "He is unflappable, approachable as far as the clients are concerned and analytical. He gets good results in workplace stress claims, which aren't the easiest cases to handle." **Recent work:** Advised on three military claims brought against the MoD concerning two deaths and the severe injury of a serviceman in a bomb blast in Afghanistan in 2009.

2TG – 2 Temple Gardens

See profile on p.873

THE SET

This set frequently works on behalf of claimants and defendants involved in complex insurance-backed personal injury claims. Workplace stress and bullying, cyclist and vicarious liability cases feature prominently in its caseload.

Client service: "The clerks are very easy to deal with and I receive dates to avoid by e-mail within minutes. The conference facilities are excellent and they organise lots of high-quality seminars." Lee Tyler is the senior clerk.

SILKS

Benjamin Browne QC Frequently represents defendants and claimants before the Court of Appeal and has a particular interest in sporting injuries, especially equestrian-related ones. He also demonstrates strength in EU-related personal injury cases. **Strengths:** "He has an outstanding reputation as a representative for both claimants and defendants. He is an excellent advocate and negotiator, which, combined with his down-to-earth and caring manner, makes clients feel they are in very safe hands." "Commands authority in negotiations, and is unerring in his analysis of cases."

Martin Porter QC (see p.697) Dubbed "the cyclist silk" by his peers, Porter shows extraordinary skill when handling maximum severity injury claims, especially brain injury claims arising from cycling or other RTAs. He is also known for his excellent knowledge of industrial disease, and for his ability to consume and process information at a phenomenal rate. **Strengths:** "Very impressive." "He gives very direct, uncomplicated advice, and there's no sitting on the fence with him."

JUNIORS

Stephen Archer Has a strong accident practice centred on handling claims involving severe spinal cord and brain damage. He is also renowned for his expertise in sporting litigation, including cyclist claims. **Strengths:** "He does a lot of great work, has a really nice manner about him and can smooth-talk and charm his way to solutions." "He's detailed and commercial in his approach."

Nina Goolamali (see p.611) Specialises in defending bullying and harassment at work claims, HSE and catastrophic injury work. He often appears against high-level silks and is able to manage particularly difficult and sensitive issues in a professional way. **Strengths:** "An exceptional senior junior, who just keeps getting better. She is incredibly good on paper, and very detailed and forensic in her approach."

Roger Harris Has impressive employers' liability experience, especially in relation to workplace assault and stress claims. He is also highlighted for his profound knowledge of Animal Act cases. **Strengths:** "He is technically brilliant and understands the law and its intricacies to a very high level." "He is hard in negotiations and he's got a very nice manner with insurers and other barristers. Personable and unassuming, he makes people feel at ease."

John McDonald Employment liability work is at the cornerstone of McDonald's practice, and he demonstrates particular wisdom in asbestos, stress and harassment claims. He routinely appears against silks and is known for his effective, well-judged advocacy. **Strengths:** "He is very thorough, has a great eye for detail and has particular expertise in the area of MIB agreements. He's very easy to deal with and a very nice man."

Christopher Russell A leading junior with a broad personal injury practice covering all manner of accident and disease work. He has been instructed in landmark health and safety claims as well as catastrophic injury claims involving paralysis and severe head injuries. **Strengths:** "An excellent technical lawyer and a formidable trial advocate."

Band 3

7BR
See profile on p.772

THE SET

7BR offers an excellent concentration of expertise in the full range of personal injury work, including maximum severity brain/spinal injury and RTA claims. The barristers here are regularly instructed to defend large institutions such as the Medical Defence Union, Medical Protection Society and Met Police. One observer remarked that "the barristers have great breadth and depth in terms of their experience and knowledge, and the set as a whole has a good mix of commercially minded silks and juniors."

Client service: "It's a very good service. They have great conference facilities and the clerks are accommodating."

SILKS

Simeon Maskrey QC A go-to barrister for catastrophic injury work due to his unrivalled medical knowledge. He has appeared in all of the major courts, including the Supreme Court and the European Court of Justice, and is also a strong mediator. **Strengths:** "His cross-examination and advocacy are both superb." **Recent work:** Counsel in Da Costa v Uloho, a catastrophic injury claim brought by a paralysed and blind Portuguese national. The claim revolved around issues of contributory negligence, causation and damages.

Steven Ford QC A leader in the field of institutional abuse and neglect claims, who has worked on matters involving local authorities, charities and religious/educational establishments. He is adept at handling accident claims involving serious injury and stress at work cases. **Strengths:** "A thorough and calm advocate who is effective and persuasive. The judges listen to him, and he speaks with authority." "He's an expert in the field of claims relating to abuse." **Recent work:** Defended a group sexual and physical abuse claim relating to care homes in Nottinghamshire.

JUNIORS

Julian Matthews Has earned himself a tremendous reputation among instructing solicitors for his maximum severity accident work. He has significant experience in brain injury and amputation cases, and also routinely undertakes complex stress at work claims. **Strengths:** "An expert in catastrophic brain injury work, who has incisive views on quantum. He is very responsive and provides thoughtful assistance at every turn." "He instils great confidence in his clients. They feel well supported by him through what is an extremely frightening process."

Simon King Possesses a wealth of experience in cases concerning severe brain and spinal injuries caused by major RTAs. He also has an active practice in matters regarding injuries sustained at work, including those relating to chronic pain syndrome. **Strengths:** "He knows his stuff. I use him when I need someone with an air of gravitas about him." "He's professional, displays good attention to detail and is very good with clients." **Recent work:** Represented the claimant in a public liability claim involving serious neurological damage.

Adam Weitzman A widely respected high-value injury junior who frequently works on serious injury claims involving amputations or severe brain/spinal damage. He is also heavily involved in abuse work relating to the Church, local authorities and other voluntary organisations. **Strengths:** "He's very dogged and always up for a scrap." "A dependable advocate, particularly in document-heavy and complex serious injury litigation." **Recent work:** Successfully defended an orphanage in a matter concerning complex allegations of vicarious liability for sexual abuse made by a former resident.

Richard Baker (see p.541) Acts for claimants and defendants in complex accident cases involving serious injuries to the head and limbs. He also demonstrates strength in handling defective property claims and fatality cases.

Timothy Meakin A specialist in military accidents and group litigation relating to abuse by public authorities. He further has in-depth knowledge of brain and spinal injuries. **Strengths:** "He masters a case superbly and inspires confidence in his ability." **Recent work:** Acted for the claimant in a complex military claim concerning serious injury to an employee of the Parachute Regiment sustained during mortar shelling in Afghanistan. Liability was admitted and the case settled at a roundtable meeting.

Cloisters
See profile on p.778

THE SET

Cloisters has a core of highly regarded personal injury experts who represent mainly claimants in complex brain injury, high-value quantum and psychiatric injury cases. The barristers here also demonstrate a particular aptitude in RTA, amputation and stress at work claims.

Client service: "The clerks, led by Glenn Hudson, are always responsive, friendly and good at negotiating fees. The set's seminars are very good as they are clear, concise and accessible."

SILKS

Joel Donovan QC An erudite claimant-focused silk specialising in large loss accident claims. He is highlighted for his experience in cases dealing with head and back injuries, and is also strong on psychiatric claims. **Strengths:** "He's very helpful and good to work with."

Patricia Hitchcock QC (see p.628) A medical and criminal law expert, who has a flourishing personal injury practice. She is particularly adept at handling serious orthopaedic and neurological injuries, and also deals with sophisticated liability and quantum issues. **Strengths:** "She has wide-ranging knowledge, and gives very level-headed advice."

JUNIORS

William Latimer-Sayer A leading expert in calculating schedules of loss, he is a dynamic junior with an excellent reputation. He frequently works on serious accident cases, many of which involve tetraplegic, paraplegic or severely head-injured claimants. **Strengths:** "Absolutely excellent, he knows his quantum forwards, backwards and upside-down. He's a very careful barrister and has good client skills." "He is exceptional at special damages work." **Recent work:** Acted as sole counsel in a catastrophic accident case that left a 67-year-old man completely paralysed. The claim settled just two weeks before trial for £2.8 million.

Daniel Lawson (see p.652) Wins strong praise for his skills in the courtroom, particularly when handling matters that involve difficult issues of liability. He works mainly on behalf of claimants. **Strengths:** "Has outstanding advocacy skills, and is extremely bright and approachable." **Recent work:** Advised the claimant in Cooper v Bright Horizons Family Solutions Ltd in a unique employers' liability claim that was decided in the claimant's favour.

Simon Dyer (see p.592) Has over two decades of experience in personal injury and is normally instructed as sole counsel for hearings, conferences and roundtable meetings. He mainly represents claimants in large loss accident claims, and has proven himself very adept at calculating large schedules. **Strengths:** "Practical and objective in his advice. He has a very good style when dealing with clients and opponents." **Recent work:** Acted in Caracciolo v Kingman Services, a catastrophic back injury claim.

1 Crown Office Row
See profile on p.784

THE SET

Has a strong reputation for handling a range of personal injury claims, including those relating to RTAs and institutional child abuse. Several of the members here have exceptional medical and health law knowledge, which bolsters their capabilities even further. The members act for both claimants and defendants, and their clients include private individuals, health authorities, government departments and NHS trusts. They are also well versed in handling group litigation.

Client service: "The clerks are very helpful, and this is a well-run, extremely professional set. Sometimes barristers get busy but the clerks are always helpful in finding alternatives."

SILKS

Elizabeth-Anne Gumbel QC Has expertise in sophisticated maximum severity injury claims, including the more unusual road traffic cases and those relating to farming accidents involving multiple claimants. She has also been involved in high-profilew sexual and physical abuse cases. **Strengths:** "She's an intellectual powerhouse, who is incredibly hard-working. She is very tenacious and knowledgeable, and has an incredible level of experience." "Possessed of boundless energy, she knows the case inside-out and no detail is missed. She is at the forefront of writing the law in this area." **Recent work:** Engaged to represent the claimant in an unusual RTA claim where the defendant claimed the accident was caused by the claimant standing in the middle of the road with his trousers down.

JUNIORS

Justin Levinson An expert on the technicalities and process of institutional sexual abuse claims. He has acted in seminal sexual abuse cases against the Catholic Church, schools and social services. **Strengths:** "Extremely approachable and hands-on, she is one of the country's leading sexual abuse counsel." "A lateral thinker, who is experienced in a wide range of personal injury claims arising from sexual abuse and/or neglect." **Recent work:** Instructed in an unprecedented Court of Appeal decision whereby a Catholic bishop was held vicariously liable for the sexual abuse perpetrated by one of his priests.

Henry Witcomb Works tirelessly on behalf of catastrophically injured claimants in ensuring they receive the appropriate compensation for their future care and accommodation. He is praised for his detailed knowledge of complex liability and quantum issues. **Strengths:** "Hugely capable and incredibly good with the clients. He's very sensible, very down-to-earth and a very skilled advocate." "He's extremely organised, efficient and personable." **Recent work:** Involved in group litigation relating to allegations that Simon Wood, a British Airways pilot, sexually abused children in Kenya.

Robert Kellar Singled out by instructing solicitors as a junior with excellent courtroom skills who acts for both sides. He is a member of the Treasury Solicitor's panel and has been heavily involved in defending claims made against the MoD for serious injuries caused by assault and cold weather training. **Strengths:** "Very competent and diligent, he always helps me if I want to run something past him. His advice is excellent and thorough, and his way of handling clients is very good." **Recent work:** Defended the MoD in a five-day trial concerning an assault that ensued from a fight between a senior officer and another soldier at a work barbecue.

Doughty Street Chambers

See profile on p.786

THE SET

Provides a high-calibre offering across the board and is regularly involved in some major national and international personal injury cases. Key areas of specialism include catastrophic injury, quantum and torture/unlawful detention matters. One source says: "The barristers are helpful, very down-to-earth, always very responsive and thoroughly prepared. They are particularly good on very complicated issues."

Client service: "They are absolutely fine when it comes to negotiating fees, as they are very reasonable in their approach. The conference facilities at the set are good too."

SILKS

Robin Oppenheim QC Centres his practice on serious accident claims, including severe brain and spinal injuries arising from RTAs. He is sought after for his knowledge of quantum and periodical payment, and is good on the technical law surrounding mental capacity. **Strengths:** "He prepares cases wonderfully and manages to master even the most difficult legal cases." "A supremely intelligent clinical negligence/product liability silk with a great eye for detail."

JUNIORS

Gerwyn Samuel Recognised for his skilful handling of complex personal injury claims, Samuel is a true force to be reckoned with at the junior Bar. He is often instructed to handle inquests, RTAs and accident at work matters. **Strengths:** "A hard-working, well-prepared and tenacious advocate, who regularly competes against silks." "Thorough and analytical, he's not afraid to push the boundaries to get the best for the client." **Recent work:** Instructed in a catastrophic neurological injury claim where the claimant had fallen from a roof. The claim settled for a lump sum and PPO of £3 million.

Daniel Bennett Previously worked as a solicitor at a leading claimant-side personal injury firm. He demonstrates great ability in both industrial disease and workplace injury cases, and handles niche areas such as claims arising out of occupational cancer and workplace assault. **Strengths:** "Extremely knowledgeable when it comes to disease-type work and at the forefront of hospital-acquired disease issues." "He's immensely hard-working and immensely proactive." **Recent work:** Instructed in Cain v Blackmoor Estate, an employers' liability claim regarding the death of a worker from exposure to a nitrogen cooling system.

Maria Roche Specialises in psychiatric injury and extraordinary rendition and torture claims. **Strengths:** "Deals with cases in a way that would suggest she is more senior. She has a fantastic grip on all the detail." "She's very bright, assiduous, thorough and intellectually capable." **Recent work:** Counsel in a high-profile rendition/torture claim brought against members of the UK government and secret services. The case concerned a Libyan politician and his wife, who had allegedly suffered serious physical and psychiatric injuries.

Old Square Chambers

See profile on p.891

THE SET

An impressive set for both claimant and defendant-based work, although one that has more recently focused on defendant-side claims. Old Square barristers have extensive experience of handling multi-million-pound personal injury claims, particularly in relation to injuries sustained while on the road or at work. Interviewees note: "They have an abundance of experienced counsel so you can generally find someone to suit your needs."

Client service: "Such a user-friendly chambers. The clerks, led by William Meade, are brilliant and nothing is too much trouble for them."

SILKS

Nigel Cooksley QC (see p.577) Joint head of chambers and a barrister with more than 25 years' experience at the Personal Injury Bar. He has proven skills in maximum severity accident claims involving acute brain and spinal injury, and is also an expert in occupational disease. **Strengths:** "He's down-to-earth and identifies the contentious issues at an early stage." "He has immense experience, he regards solicitors as part of the team and he fine-tunes a case very well." **Recent work:** Led in Kerr v Kerr and BMW, a claim relating to the injury of a minor caused by an airbag.

Paul Rose QC (see p.710) A deeply skilled advocate who advises soldiers and other employed individuals on catastrophic injury claims, particularly those involving TBI, amputations or other severe limb injuries. He also has extensive experience in handling aviation accident claims. **Strengths:** "He is very tough and principled. You're in very good hands with him, since he has a lot of experience." **Recent work:** Achieved a favourable outcome on liability when he advised on a high-value motor claim concerning a TBI.

JUNIORS

Charles Woodhouse (see p.755) An expert in multi-track accident claims, including those that involve neurological and orthopaedic damage and sophisticated mental capacity issues. **Strengths:** "He gives incredibly pragmatic advice, backed up by detailed legal analysis of the court rules." "He is good on higher-value cases, including claims against the MoD, as he has a military background." **Recent work:** Defended and settled an accident claim relating to an injury that occurred in a car wash and resulted in the loss of the claimant's leg.

Michael Nicholson An experienced industrial disease and multi-track claims junior who regularly appears opposite senior counsel. He has an aptitude for highway, tramway and rail accident claims as well as HAVS and NIHL work. **Strengths:** "He's warm and kind with the clients; they really appreciate his ability to explain things accurately but simply. He's also ever so good with experts and brilliantly works out the best strategy to get results."

Christopher Walker A well-respected personal injury junior, who has a burgeoning practice in health and safety, inquests and human rights-related work. He is also a renowned catastrophic injury practitioner and has fantastic knowledge of cases concerning orthopaedic and neurological injuries. **Strengths:** "He gets down to the issues and absorbs vast amounts of information very quickly." "An experienced and high-calibre barrister, who is technically excellent and has superb client skills." **Recent work:** Acted in a case regarding a teenager who was catastrophically injured in a motorcycle accident.

Alan Smith (see p.723) A seasoned large loss catastrophic injury junior with a particular interest in motorcycle claims. He has a wealth of experience in matters relating to serious and life-changing head and back injuries caused by accidents on the roads or at work. **Strengths:** "He has the ability to turn cases around, and is also a superb negotiator." "He explains things in an easy fashion and puts clients at ease, and in the process makes difficult cases seem relatively straightforward."

Other Ranked Lawyers

Richard Furniss (42 Bedford Row) Highly experienced at handling a variety of claims regarding serious injuries caused by RTAs and assaults, including matters concerning traumatic brain psychiatric injuries. He is recognised for his confident courtroom demeanour and his excellence when it comes to strategy. **Strengths:** "A consummate PI lawyer, who has seen everything and worked out how to deal with it. Light on his feet, flexible in his approach and able to think ahead when faced with a problem, he's very handy to have on your side."

Recent work: Advised on a motor claim where the claimant, a professional footballer, suffered severe head injuries after falling off the roof of a car.

Richard Gregory (42 Bedford Row) A very proficient high-value accident practitioner who shows great dexterity when handling difficult spinal damage and fatality claims. He is also a familiar face in the world of occupational disease, and acts for claimants suffering from mesothelioma and lung cancer. **Strengths:** "He's an almost perfect junior, who is very good on paper, extremely thorough and highly conscientious. He is carving out a niche in MIB and difficult RTA liability cases." **Recent work:** Acted in an employers' liability claim where an employer admitted liability for the claimant's fall in slippery weather conditions. The issue of causation was complicated by the presence of prior medical conditions, and the claim ended up settling for £575,000 at a JSM.

Scott Matthewson (42 Bedford Row) Noted for the depth of his knowledge of medical law, he has a thriving personal injury practice. He is particularly well known for his performances in psychiatric and neurological injury cases. **Strengths:** "He's just so technically amazing and a real fighter – if he says he'll do a case for you, he'll see it through to the end. He's won some really, really difficult cases for me." **Recent work:** Represented the claimant in Campbell v MOJ, a maximum severity TBI claim following the assault of a prison officer by prisoners.

Julian Picton QC (Hailsham Chambers) A renowned maximum severity injury silk with a practice encompassing claims regarding neurological and orthopaedic injuries as well as fatalities. He is an expert in assessing damages in all types of personal injury claims, including those arising from RTAs and EL/PL.

Charles Bagot (see p.541) (Hardwicke) An extremely popular choice for insurers and solicitors faced with serious accident claims. He does a lot of international personal injury work, regularly appearing opposite silks, and is great on quantum. **Strengths:** "He is extremely thorough and great on the paperwork." "He is the consummate professional: he is always prepared and he manages your expectations. In joint settlement meetings he is clear and sets out the position so reasonably and sensibly that it is difficult for the other side to come back and oppose him." **Recent work:** Instructed in a £10 million RTA case where the claimant had sustained serious neurological damage that left her completely paralysed.

Howard Stevens QC (3 Hare Court) Combines an active practice in multi-track personal injury claims, especially those relating to serious head and back injury, with his work as a mediator. He also has extensive experience of cross-border personal injury claims involving conflicts of laws and jurisdictional problems. **Strengths:** "A fantastic advocate whose attention to detail is legendary." "He has a superb brain and exudes a quiet confidence."

Richard Hermer QC (Matrix Chambers) Leads the way in human rights-related group litigation and has handled torture, killing and rendition claims from around the world relating to acts perpetrated by the British armed forces and British colonial administrations. He advises on seminal cases that will change the prevailing precedent in this area of personal injury law, especially with regard to limitation periods. **Strengths:** "He's got great strategic insight and has developed a real niche in the area of domestic and international private law. He is a sharp-witted advocate who is very good on his feet and can read the court." **Recent work:** Successfully provided counsel to thousands of Kenyans in group litigation concerning their torture by British colonial officers in the 1950s. A multimillion-pound settlement was achieved and the Foreign Secretary formally apologised to those who had suffered.

Nicholas Baldock (6 Pump Court) A renowned personal injury junior who acts for claimants and defendants in health and safety and inquest matters. He regularly appears in the Court of Appeal. **Strengths:** "Extremely thorough and methodical, he takes a common-sense approach and is able to speak to clients almost irrespective of who they are. He's a very good advocate who is not easily riled." **Recent work:** Successfully settled a catastrophic injury case concerning a claimant who had suffered a severe head injury.

MIDLANDS

Personal Injury Midlands
Leading Sets
Band 1
No5 Chambers *
Band 2
Ropewalk Chambers *
Leading Silks
Band 1
Bleasdale Paul *No5 Chambers* [A]
Hunjan Satinder *No5 Chambers*
Limb Patrick *Ropewalk Chambers* *
Nolan Dominic *Ropewalk Chambers* *
Band 2
Bright Christopher *No5 Chambers* *
Jones Jonathan *No5 Chambers* *
Leading Juniors
Band 1
Duthie Malcolm *No5 Chambers*
Moat Richard *No5 Chambers*
Band 2
Adams Jayne *Ropewalk Chambers* *
Brunning Matthew *No5 Chambers* [A] *
Campbell Stephen *No5 Chambers* [A] *
Coughlan John *No5 Chambers* *
Cox Jason *Ropewalk Chambers* *
Dean Peter *36 Bedford Row (ORL)* ◊
Evans Paul *No5 Chambers*
Gregory Richard *Ropewalk Chambers*
Herbert Douglas *Ropewalk Chambers* *
Hirst Karl *No5 Chambers*
Michael Simon *No5 Chambers* *
Pitchers Henry *No5 Chambers* *
Rochford Thomas *St Philips Chambers (ORL)* ◊ *
Stewart Toby *Ropewalk Chambers*
Turton Philip *Ropewalk Chambers* *
* *Indicates set / individual with profile.*
◊ *(ORL) = Other Ranked Lawyer.*
[A] *direct access (see p.11).*
Alphabetical order within each band. Band 1 is highest.

Band 1

No5 Chambers

See profile on p.883

THE SET

No5 Chambers garners a great deal of praise for the breadth and depth of its expertise in high-value personal injury matters. It is particularly well regarded for its claimant practice, and draws praise for the user-friendly approach of its barristers. Instructing solicitors appreciate the reliable quality of the chambers, noting you "always know with No5 that you're going to get a great advocate."

Client service: "Their clerks are one of the best teams in the country, ready to discuss anything and everything and assist in any way they can." "Everything goes smoothly; everyone knows what they're supposed to be doing, and they're an efficient team."

SILKS

Paul Bleasdale QC A personal injury specialist with extensive experience acting for claimants and defendants in catastrophic claims. He is noted for his aptitude in claims involving brain injury and industrial disease. **Strengths:** "He is a go-to silk for tricky cases in liability; he's incredibly tenacious, willing to stand up and fight, and not afraid of difficult cases at all." "He's got very good tactical awareness and negotiating skills, so he's very accomplished not only in trials but also in settlement meetings." **Recent work:** He recently led a matter in the Court of Appeal concerning complex liability issues relating to driving speed in an RTA.

Satinder Hunjan QC Acts on behalf of claimants and defendants in high-value claims involving brain and spinal injuries. He is lauded by instructing solicitors as an experienced silk with first-rate negotiating skills. **Strengths:** "He is very sharp intellectually and gets a very good result for the client – he's very good tactically." "He is a really tough negotiator."

Christopher Bright QC (see p.556) Highly regarded for his experience in complex personal injury claims, often involving catastrophic brain and spinal injuries in RTAs. He acts for both claimants and defendants. **Strengths:** "He doesn't get flustered at thorny, difficult issues: he can look at things, break them down, approach things logically and come up with thoughtful options." "He's got a very good bedside manner and a good way of explaining things to clients in easy, comprehensible terms." **Recent work:** He represented the defendant in a head injury claim involving complicated issues concerning loss of earnings. A six-figure settlement was reached.

Jonathan Jones QC (see p.640) Noted for working on complex RTA cases, in particular those involving serious head injuries. He handles matters for both defendants and claimants. **Strengths:** "He is thorough and forensic. He's great on his feet, with first-class technical skills." **Recent work:** Represented the claimant in a complex RTA where the claimant had climbed onto the bonnet of a car which had subsequently driven off. The case concerned complicated contributory negligence issues.

JUNIORS

Malcolm Duthie A senior junior with extensive experience in complex personal injury claims. Interviewees praise his tenacious approach and his ability to work well with clients. **Strengths:** "His attention to detail is second to none." "He is one of the best senior juniors on the Midland Circuit, and is always thoroughly prepared." **Recent work:** Acted on behalf of a local authority in an inquest into the death of a teenager in foster care.

Simon Michael (see p.671) Focuses his practice on catastrophic injury litigation, and receives instructions from both claimants and defendants. He regularly deals with cases involving fatal accidents, brain and spinal injury, and mesothelioma. **Strengths:** "He is a very experienced senior junior, thorough and with a good eye for detail. He's also excellent on medical issues." **Recent work:** Instructed in Hicks & Hicks v Wingrove, a case involving brain and other injuries caused to a couple involved in an RTA.

Matthew Brunning (see p.559) Divides his practice between claimant and defendant work, and is frequently instructed in cases concerning brain injuries. He is praised by instructing solicitors for his provision of balanced and insightful advice. **Strengths:** "He is a very good advocate in court. He's very calm but at the same time can be quite bullish when it comes to certain points." "He has a superb legal brain and a good client manner. He gets to the crux of the matter quickly."

Stephen Campbell (see p.564) Focuses on cases involving brain injury and amputation. He is highly regarded for his work on behalf of insurer clients, although he is also frequently instructed on behalf of claimants. **Strengths:** "He demonstrates excellent technical skills and provides sound and common-sense advice to clients." "He has a very measured approached in trial; he's calm and manages to get the key points across in an effective way." **Recent work:** Worked on liability in a case for a defendant involving a motorcycle accident which led to brain injury. Arguments put forward by Campbell regarding contributory negligence led to a 50% reduction in damages.

Paul Evans Divides his catastrophic injury claims practice between defendant and claimant work. He has a particular expertise in cases involving fraudulent claims. **Recent work:** Represented the claimant in Pikina v Krzyjawiak and UK Insurance, a case concerning numerous catastrophic injuries including loss of kidney and brain injury.

Karl Hirst Covers a wide range of personal injury work and acts on behalf of both claimants and defendants. He has considerable expertise in cases concerning employers' liability, criminal injury and RTAs. **Strengths:** "He has a good tactical approach with defendants." "He is very good with clients, and is a very capable advocate."

Richard Moat Focuses his personal injury practice on matters involving brain and spinal injuries, industrial disease and fatal accidents. Interviewees appreciate his commercial and pragmatic counsel. **Strengths:** "He's an all-rounder: if you need advice on paper, advice in conference, need representation in a JSM or trial advocacy – then he'd be a go-to." "He provides realistic, balanced advice which gets to the heart of the matter." **Recent work:** Acted for a claimant with partial tetraplegia, in a complex case involving both an RTA and clinical negligence. The claim settled for £1.25 million.

Henry Pitchers (see p.694) An experienced personal injury practitioner who acts on RTA cases, employers' liability, and brain and psychiatric injury. He acts for both claimants and defendants. **Strengths:** "He has a personable, client-friendly manner and provides a robust approach to challenging cases." "He is excellent technically and tactically." **Recent work:** Represented a claimant before the Criminal Injuries Compensation Authority who had sustained brain injuries as a baby following assault. The claimant was awarded approximately £4.3 million.

John Coughlan (see p.579) Advises claimants and defendants on catastrophic injury cases, covering brain injury and occupational disease work. **Strengths:** "He is methodical and presents points in a strong way." **Recent work:** Acted for the claimant in a motorcycle accident which led to liver failure. The case was further complicated as while the accident created a need for care, it added to the claimant's life expectancy.

Band 2

Ropewalk Chambers

See profile on p.928

THE SET

Based in Nottingham, Ropewalk Chambers is home to the leading personal injury group in the East Midlands. The set undertakes the full range of personal injury claims, from minor accidents right through to catastrophic injuries, and acts on behalf of both claimants and defendants. Its members are praised as highly efficient, approachable and "always willing to put themselves out to try to help." This attitude is shared by the clerks, with interviewees commenting: "Nothing is too much of a problem to them."

Client service: "It is a seamless service; the clerks are extremely approachable and helpful."

SILKS

Patrick Limb QC (see p.656) An expert in high-value catastrophic injury claims, with a particular reputation for handling industrial disease matters on behalf of defendants. He impresses instructing solicitors with his skill at negotiations. **Strengths:** "He's very bright, very sharp and a safe pair of hands." "He has an amazing memory for detail, and he's very kind to the clients – he puts them at ease while still being straight with them." **Recent work:** Acted for the defendants on Harrison v Jagged Globe, a much-publicised case concerning a mountaineering accident staged for television which led to injury.

Dominic Nolan QC (see p.683) A highly respected advocate who acts in catastrophic personal injury cases. He receives instructions from a range of clients, including major insurers, public authorities and individual claimants. **Strengths:** "He is formidably clever, very easy to work with and a good team player." **Recent work:** Successfully defended a major financial institution against an occupational stress claim brought by a high net worth claimant.

JUNIORS

Jayne Adams (see p.531) Acts for both claimants and defendants across the full range of personal injury work. She is particularly noted for her expertise on claims relating to spinal injuries. **Strengths:** "She is good with clients and speaks to them naturally and without jargon. She's got a very good brain, and takes a sensitive approach to cases."

Jason Cox (see p.579) Acts on personal injury claims for both defendants and claimants, and focuses his practice on cases concerning catastrophic injuries or fatalities. **Strengths:** "He is a very thorough, very responsive and very able advocate."

Douglas Herbert (see p.625) Handles high-value cases, particularly those involving RTAs, for both defendants and claimants. He draws praise for his strident advocacy and his good manner with clients. **Strengths:** "He is just a delight: an old-school charmer who knows his stuff inside-out." "He's good on cases with difficult clients as he's good at being firm, but in a nice way."

Philip Turton (see p.741) A veteran personal injury practitioner. He acts for both claimants and defendants, and is noted for his expertise in cases concerning child abuse, spinal injuries and limitation. **Strengths:** "He is very user-friendly, and has a good rapport with clients." "Arguing technical procedural points is a key strength of his."

Richard Gregory An experienced personal injury specialist who acts on behalf of both claimants and defendants. **Strengths:** "He has an excellent legal mind, and is a good choice for fighting difficult cases." "He has a refreshingly commercial approach."

Toby Stewart A veteran practitioner with a broad personal injury practice which encompasses RTAs, factory accidents, construction site accidents, and claims for psychiatric injury by secondary victims. **Strengths:** "He is a sharp, incisive, and user-friendly advocate." "He's great with clients – he has a brilliant bedside manner."

Other Ranked Lawyers

Peter Dean (36 Bedford Row) A veteran practitioner whose broad personal injury practice covers a wide range of claims including those relating to the Fatal Accidents Act and RTAs. **Strengths:** "He's good at anticipating defendants' arguments and understanding complex expert medical evidence. He's a shrewd negotiator."

Thomas Rochford (see p.709) (St Philips Chambers) Focuses on handling catastrophic injury claims on behalf of claimants. He has considerable expertise in cases concerning employers' liability, RTAs and fatal accidents. **Strengths:** "He can foresee the arguments the defence will present – his good preparation follows him through negotiations." "He makes himself available for advice and the advice he gives is sound, robust and impartial." **Recent work:** Acted for a claimant who incurred a psychiatric injury following an armed robbery of her workplace.

NORTH EASTERN

Personal Injury North Eastern
Leading Sets
Band 1
Parklane Plowden *
Leading Silks
Senior Statesmen
Brown Stuart *Parklane Plowden*
Band 1
Lewis Andrew *Sovereign Chambers (ORL)* ◊
Leading Juniors
Band 1
Axon Andrew *Parklane Plowden*
Copnall Richard *Parklane Plowden*
Exall Gordon *Zenith Chambers (ORL)* ◊
Friday Stephen *Parklane Plowden*
Murphy James *Parklane Plowden*
Band 2
Ditchfield Michael *Kings Chambers (ORL)* ◊
Edwards Daniel *Dere Street Barristers (ORL)* ◊ *
Elgot Howard *Parklane Plowden*
Furness Corin *Parklane Plowden*
Souter Catherine *Parklane Plowden*
Turner Steven *Parklane Plowden*
Williams Christopher *Parklane Plowden*
◊ (ORL) = Other Ranked Lawyer.
** Indicates set / individual with profile.*

Band 1

Parklane Plowden

See profile on p.907

THE SET

A dominant practice in the North Eastern Circuit, Parklane Plowden is capable of tackling the most complex and high-value personal injury claims. The set has seen an uptake in instructions regarding catastrophic injuries, inquests and fraud on behalf of a variety of clients. Its stellar roster includes a group of silks and talented juniors, many of whom are leaders in their respective fields. Sources affirm that "they are specialised in personal injury and clinical negligence, and the barristers are doing a good job."

Client service: "Andy Gray is very approachable and the clerking is generally very good. I would certainly recommend them to anybody."

SILKS

Stuart Brown QC A seasoned personal injury counsel acting on behalf of both individuals and insurers. With over 20 years in silk, he has rich experience in handling serious RTA injuries, occupational disease and various kinds of liability mandates.

JUNIORS

Richard Copnall Specialises in high-figure clinical negligence and personal injury cases. He is also heavily engaged in inquests with regard to human rights issues in custody. **Recent work:** He acted in Iris Alison Pearson v South Tees Hospitals, a fatal claim arising from a post-operative overdose of anti-coagulant that caused brain haemorrhage.

Andrew Axon Has extensive experience in relation to personal injury and clinical negligence work across the region and beyond. As the head of chambers, he is widely noted for his advocacy in courts and outstanding client service. **Strengths:** "He is the sort of guy you want in the court. He exudes confidence, has detailed knowledge of the case and understands the law inside-out." "He has very good client skills and I won't hesitate to instruct him."

Stephen Friday Adept at complex personal injury matters, with particular expertise in chronic pain cases and RTAs causing severe injuries. **Strengths:** "He works very hard and will always try his best for the clients. He is widely respected by the judiciaries." "He did an excellent job in negotiating the compensation figure and explaining that to the client." **Recent work:** He acted on behalf of the claimant in Janine Casey v Hull and East Yorkshire Hospitals, regarding a slipping accident resulting in disability.

James Murphy Advises predominantly on personal injury and disease work on behalf of trade unions and insurers nationwide. He is an expert on asbestos injuries, with particular knowledge of mesothelioma. **Strengths:** "He is very persuasive and can extract exactly what we want the witness to say in cross-examinations." "His client care skills are exceptional." **Recent work:** He acted in Russell Moulton v Midlands Co-Op & Others in relation to mesothelioma and issues of breach of duty.

Howard Elgot Well versed in catastrophic injury and clinical negligence litigation. Commentators praise him highly for his strong technical skills and knowledge in industrial disease cases, including asbestos and respiratory. **Strengths:** "He is very capable and a tenacious advocate." "He has a sharp mind and is one of the best counsels in the region, even a match for a QC." **Recent work:** He acted in the fatal incident claim Chapman and Gibbs v Bradley, which involved dependency claims as well.

Corin Furness Earns recognition for his breadth of expertise in multi-track matters, including severe injuries and employers' liability work. His practice also covers fraud claims and injuries arising from criminal acts **Strengths:** "He is regarded as a thorough lawyer."

Steven Turner Continues to provide high-calibre advice on an array of matters, incorporating fatal accidents, industrial diseases and fraud. He is lauded for his speciality in legal compliance in this sector. **Strengths:** "He is a careful and meticulous practitioner." "He is excellent in handling high-profile litigation and Court of Protection work."

Catherine Souter Singled out for her experience in employers' and occupiers' liability issues. Clients are drawn from a wide range of sectors and include insurers, trade unions and local authorities.

Christopher Williams Offers solid expertise in a range of matters, including workplace accidents, fatal incidents and industrial disease, and is renowned for his strength in industrial deafness and upper limb disorders. **Recent work:** He acted in Cleveland Potash Deafness and HAVS, a class action of deafness claims and HAVS claims against the same employer.

Other Ranked Lawyers

Daniel Edwards (see p.594) (Dere Street Barristers) Makes his debut in the ranking table this year. He handles a wide range of matters, from injuries of maximum severity to industrial diseases, and splits his time between claimants and defendants. **Strengths:** "He is a very competent practitioner and has a national practice."

Michael Ditchfield (Kings Chambers) Hailed for his exclusive practice in the personal injury sector. Market sources are quick to praise his strength in occupational disease issues covering noise damage and vibration work. **Recent work:** He acted in Swinburne v ConocoPhillips with regard to a noise-induced asymmetrical hearing loss.

Andrew Lewis QC (Sovereign Chambers) Heads the set and has a depth of knowledge in relation to brain and spinal cord injuries. Also notable is his experience in a broad range of claims, including fraud and disease work. **Strengths:** "He is a charming person and is capable of simplifying challenging law and medical issues." "An absolutely superb barrister, he is tremendous with clients and never lets us down."

Gordon Exall (Zenith Chambers) Has considerable experience in personal injuries and clinical negligence. As the head of the personal injury group, he is particularly sought out for his expertise in worksite injuries, fatalities, limitation and civil procedures. **Strengths:** "He is very good at dealing with clients. I will not hesitate to instruct him."

NORTHERN

Personal Injury Northern
Leading Sets
Band 1
Byrom Street Chambers *
Band 2
Deans Court Chambers *
Exchange Chambers *
Band 3
Kings Chambers *
St Johns Buildings *
9 St John Street *
Leading Silks
Star individuals
Allan David *Byrom Street Chambers*
Hunter Winston *Byrom Street Chambers* *
Band 1
Braithwaite Bill *Exchange Chambers*
Grime Stephen *Deans Court Chambers*
Hartley Richard *Cobden House Chambers (ORL)* ◊
Heaton David *Byrom Street Chambers*
Horlock Timothy *Deans Court Chambers*
Kennedy Christopher *9 St John Street*
Machell Raymond *Byrom Street Chambers*
Melton Christopher *Byrom Street Chambers* *
Rawlinson Michael *Kings Chambers* *
Rowley James *Byrom Street Chambers* *
Waldron William *Exchange Chambers*
Yip Amanda *Exchange Chambers*
Band 2
Braslavsky Nicholas *Kings Chambers* *
Hinchliffe Nicholas *9 St John Street*
Martin Gerard *Exchange Chambers*
Poole Nigel *Kings Chambers* *
Redfern Michael *St Johns Buildings*
New Silks
Allen Darryl *Byrom Street Chambers* *
◊ (ORL) = Other Ranked Lawyer.
* Indicates set / individual with profile.
[A] direct access (see p.11).

Personal Injury Northern
Leading Juniors
Star individuals
Feeny Charles *St Johns Buildings*
Band 1
Bowley Ivan *Lincoln House Chambers (ORL)* ◊
Burns Peter *Byrom Street Chambers*
Cooper Douglas *St Johns Buildings*
Cowan Peter *Oriel Chambers (ORL)* ◊
Grace Jonathan *Deans Court Chambers*
Grundy Philip *St Johns Buildings*
Kilvington Simon *Byrom Street Chambers* *
Whitehall Richard *Deans Court Chambers*
Willems Marc *Cobden House Chambers (ORL)* ◊
Band 2
Ashworth Fiona *Kings Chambers* *
Gregory Peter *7 Harrington St Chambers (ORL)* ◊
Harrison Peter *St Johns Buildings*
Howells Catherine *Exchange Chambers*
Jones Michael *Cobden House Chambers (ORL)* ◊
Knifton David *Exchange Chambers*
Laprell Mark *18 St John Street (ORL)* ◊ *
Lemmy Michael *9 St John Street*
Little Ian *9 St John Street*
Maguire Stephen *Kings Chambers*
McCann Simon *Deans Court Chambers* [A]
McCluggage Brian *9 St John Street* *
Paul Daniel *Deans Court Chambers*
Pearce Richard *Byrom Street Chambers*
Snarr Matthew *9 St John Street*
Stockwell Matthew *St Johns Buildings*

Band 1

Byrom Street Chambers
See profile on p.914

THE SET

Byrom Street Chambers is the leading set for catastrophic personal injury on the Northern Circuit. The set is lauded for its excellent depth of expertise, with one interviewee noting: "Whoever a case ends up with there, you know you're in a safe pair of hands." The clerking team is also highly praised, with senior clerk Terry Creathorn described as "just fantastic."

Client service: "Great clerking; you get a personal service there which you don't get elsewhere." "The clerking team will bend over backwards to help you."

SILKS

David Allan QC A leading figure in high-value, catastrophic personal injury, with particular expertise in industrial disease. His skilled advocacy ensures his peers view him as a very tough opponent in court. **Strengths:** "He is very sharp, prepares forensically and is feared by opponents."

Winston Hunter QC (see p.634) Garners a great deal of acclaim for his work on high-profile and complex personal injury cases for both claimants and defendants. Sources recommend him for his depth of knowledge, and his calm and polished manner in negotiations. **Strengths:** "He is exceptionally bright and very gifted. He's very calm under pressure, and very good with clients." "He is just hypnotic before the judge."

David Heaton QC Well known for his skilled handling of catastrophic injury claims for defendants, although he does also act for claimants on occasion. He has a good deal of experience in cases involving brain and spinal injuries. **Strengths:** "His preparation for trial was second to none." "He is hugely empathetic, with real insight into the difficulties his clients and their families encounter."

Christopher Melton QC (see p.670) Noted for leading on numerous complex claims on behalf of claimants. He has considerable experience of cases relating to brain injury, fatal accidents and industrial disease. **Strengths:** "He genuinely has a personal desire on behalf of the claimant to get the best outcome possible, and will be tireless in his efforts to take a point as far as it needs to go to get the right outcome." "He is thorough and innovative – he is willing to fight, and he achieves outstanding results."

Raymond Machell QC Recognised for his proficiency in catastrophic personal injury cases, particularly those involving brain injury. He is instructed by both defendants and claimants. **Strengths:** "You know you're in safe hands because he will leave no stone unturned and will spot the tiniest detail in papers – he can add value just from being so thorough." "He dispenses wise and shrewd advice."

James Rowley QC (see p.711) Works with both claimants and defendants on serious personal injury claims. He is noted by interviewees for his ability to quickly get to grips with complex cases. **Strengths:** "He displays an unerring ability to get quickly to the root of the case and achieve the best outcome for the client." "He is incredibly bright, very precise and very tactically adept."

Darryl Allen QC (see p.534) Known for his concentration on claimant work in catastrophic injury matters, particularly brain and spinal injury. His attention to detail is widely praised by instructing solicitors, who believe this makes him ideal for complex cases. **Strengths:** "His preparation is absolutely meticulous, and clients find him very approachable." "He is a strong advocate, both in writing and on his feet."

JUNIORS

Peter Burns Much-admired junior with extensive experience in industrial disease and catastrophic injury claims. He is frequently instructed to act on behalf of defendants. **Strengths:** "A senior junior who is far ahead of all his peers and most of his seniors. His analytical ability in complex causation cases is phenomenal."

Simon Kilvington (see p.646) Receives acclaim from solicitors for his advocacy skills in severe personal injury cases. He handles a range of claims, and is recognised for his experience in asbestos-related disease work. **Strengths:** "He is an impressive advocate who is very thorough, with an admirable intellect and a good deal of pragmatism." "He's utterly dependable, and really wants what is best for the client."

Richard Pearce Focuses primarily on claimant work, with a track record of working on brain and spinal injury cases. Sources are impressed by his impressive command of the law relating to complex personal injury cases. **Strengths:** "He's got a very good, incisive mind, which is made for dealing with complicated issues. He is very composed, and gives you a sense of confidence." "His knowledge of the law is unbelievable."

Band 2

Deans Court Chambers
See profile on p.915

THE SET

Deans Court Chambers is highly regarded for its work with both defendants and claimants in severe personal injury claims, although it is also home to a number of specialist defence advocates. Sources praise the depth of the set's expertise in personal injury law, as well as its commercially savvy outlook. Solicitors also appreciate the user-friendly nature of its barristers.

Client service: "The clerking team are very personable and very capable." "Senior clerk Matthew Gibbons and his team are very efficient and very responsive."

SILKS

Stephen Grime QC Highly experienced silk with a strong specialisation in catastrophic personal injury work, often acting on behalf of defendants. He is cited as a "fearless" advocate for his clients. **Strengths:** "He does both claimant and defendant work, is very measured in his advice, and his judgement is very good." "He is tactically very able, with good client skills, and is a very approachable barrister."

Timothy Horlock QC Widely recognised as an expert in severe injury claims. He divides his practice between claimant and defendant work, although he is particularly known for his expertise in dealing with insurer clients. **Strengths:** "He has sympathy and compassion, and is able to make hard decisions sometimes and take a tough line when necessary and appropriate." "He is an outstanding QC. In addition to having an excellent grasp of the details he is excellent with people."

JUNIORS

Richard Whitehall Deals with a variety of complex personal injury cases, primarily on behalf of defendants. He has considerable expertise in cases concerning severe brain and spinal injuries. **Strengths:** "He is very bright and very thorough." "He is very good for hearings, applications, and on papers."

Jonathan Grace Praised for his calm but forceful style of advocacy, acting for both claimants and defendants. He is well known for handling cases concerning amputation, brain and spinal injuries. **Strengths:** "He is very good in negotiations. He's a calm but forthright individual who gets his points across well." "He is always a reassuring pair of hands; very calm and very well prepared, with a very easy manner."

Simon McCann Well regarded for his expertise in road traffic accidents. He handles matters for claimants and defendants. **Strengths:** "He's the kind of person you would want on your side in a courtroom fight – quick on his feet and not afraid to ask the difficult questions." "He is straightforward and candid in his views. That is appreciated by clients, who want to be told how it is." **Recent work:** Acted on behalf of the defendant in Morris v Greater Manchester Fire & Rescue Service, a matter concerning occupational stress.

Daniel Paul Acts for defendants and claimants on a range of personal injury matters, including those concerning road traffic accidents, fatal accidents and employers' liability. **Strengths:** "He is an incredibly effective advocate but very measured in his approach." "He is always available for advice, and goes the extra mile."

Exchange Chambers

See profile on p.910

THE SET

This Liverpool-based set is particularly highly regarded for its ability to skilfully handle high-value, complex catastrophic injury work on behalf of claimants. Interviewees praise the availability and efficiency of both the clerks and the barristers, and regard them as "approachable and supportive."

Client service: "The clerking is excellent, responsive and helpful." "Tom Handley, the chambers director, is very approachable, very reliable and very organised."

SILKS

Bill Braithwaite QC One of the most experienced silks on the Circuit, acting exclusively for claimants. Sources praise his immense expertise in brain and spinal injury cases. **Strengths:** "He is really passionate about pursuing justice for the claimant. He's a brilliant advocate – incredibly sharp on his feet." "He is an immensely experienced barrister who has the ability to put clients at ease while simultaneously being a fierce advocate for them."

William Waldron QC Adept at handling catastrophic injury claims, especially those concerning amputation, spinal and brain injuries. He is considered a pleasure to work with by both opposing counsel and solicitors. **Strengths:** "He is a first-rate negotiator. His calm and measured approach is a huge advantage in high-value litigation." "He is completely unflappable, and terrific with clients."

Amanda Yip QC Concentrates on claimant work, and is recognised for her expertise in cases covering military claims, spinal and brain injury. She is noted in particular for her work in cases involving children, and is known for her sensitive manner with vulnerable clients. **Strengths:** "She has an empathetic way with clients, grasps the key issues at an early stage and is able to present them simply to client and court." "She is an academic powerhouse."

Gerard Martin QC Well regarded for his primarily claimant-focused practice. He has a deep knowledge of brain injury claims, and is also skilled at handling matters involving spinal injuries and amputations. **Strengths:** "He's a new breed of QC. He takes a team approach and brings out the best in all the experts." "He is direct, and takes a no-nonsense approach."

JUNIORS

Catherine Howells Experienced at dealing with complex, high-value injury claims. Her practice is divided between claimant and defendant work, and covers brain, spinal and orthopaedic injuries. **Strengths:** "She's intelligent, tenacious in her approach, and never gives up." "She has a great empathy with the clients and is extremely thorough."

David Knifton Focuses in particular on claimant work, with notable skills in dealing with matters involving brain, spinal injury and military claims. Interviewees particularly praise his excellent client skills. **Strengths:** "He is fiercely intelligent whilst also being tactically brilliant." "He is very practical, and has a very nice manner with clients and opponents."

Band 3

Kings Chambers

See profile on p.918

THE SET

Kings Chambers is well respected for its broad coverage of personal injury work, with barristers conducting matters on behalf of both defendants and claimants. Counsel frequently deal with complex brain and spinal injury cases, and are also able to offer expertise in military claims. Sources particularly praise the quality of the silks at the set.

Client service: "They are excellent, very accommodating and prepared to take a commercial view on how best to deal with cases."

SILKS

Michael Rawlinson QC (see p.704) An expert across a broad range of personal injury litigation, with in-depth knowledge of military claims, industrial disease, and brain and spinal injuries. He is adjudged to be a strong advocate by instructing solicitors. **Strengths:** "No one has a better knowledge of asbestos disease litigation over the last 30 years." "He is uncompromising, and thrives on difficult cases." **Recent work:** Acted in the Aviva v Cape Asbestos test cases regarding the defendant's potential product liability in mesothelioma claims.

Nicholas Braslavsky QC (see p.555) Highly respected for his representation of both claimants and defendants in severe personal injury matters, often involving spinal and brain injuries. He also handles professional negligence and product liability claims relating to personal injury. **Strengths:** "He is an imaginative, innovative silk." "He has a brilliant and incisive mind. His advice is always extremely well thought-out and he is very impressive at trial, with a talent for cutting straight to the point." **Recent work:** Instructed in Farghar v Quinn Neal, a professional negligence claim concerning under-settling in a road traffic accident case.

Nigel Poole QC (see p.696) Well known for his skilfull handling of a range of catastrophic personal injury claims for both claimants and defendants. He is noted for his ability to conduct complex psychiatric injury claims. **Strengths:** "Intellectually, he's one of the strongest. He's got a very wide range of experience because he advises claimants and defendants." "He works well with clients." **Recent work:** Successfully handled a matter involving severe neck injury in a go-karting incident for defendants.

JUNIORS

Fiona Ashworth (see p.538) Has a strong specialisation in cases involving chronic pain syndromes such as fibromyalgia. She acts of behalf of both claimants and defendants. **Strengths:** "It's not just that she's very good technically; it's also her delivery and her relationship with the clients that sets her apart." "She has a good eye for detail."

Stephen Maguire Particularly noted for his claimant practice, which is focused on brain and spinal injuries. He is recommended by instructing solicitors for his efficiency and tough manner in negotiation. **Strengths:** "He is robust in negotiation." "He is very good technically, and always has the answers." **Recent work:** Instructed in Robert Fox v Nicola Patching, a successful secondary victim action brought by a father.

St Johns Buildings

See profile on p.921

THE SET

St Johns Buildings is considered a preferred destination for defendant clients on a wide range of personal injury claims. Solicitors comment on the superb technical ability of counsel, as well as their range of expertise. The clerking team is also praised for its organisational abilities.

SILKS

Michael Redfern QC Highly experienced advocate with wide-ranging knowledge of a variety of catastrophic injury claims, including brain injury, employers' liability and group actions. He concentrates especially on the claimant side. **Strengths:** "He has an exceptional legal mind; his advice is always thoroughly thought-out." "He is dogged, but imaginative in terms of spotting an angle on a case and pursuing it successfully."

JUNIORS

Charles Feeny Personal injury specialist with considerable expertise in handling industrial disease and other occupiers' liability work. He works with both claimants and defendants. **Strengths:** "He has a very good feel for the case – a kind of sixth sense." **Recent work:** Represented the defendants in a case brought by a nurse claiming chronic pain disorder following an incident at work.

Philip Grundy Noted for his depth of knowledge in matters involving brain injury, amputation, paraplegia and tetraplegia. He divides his work between defendants and claimants, with a particular emphasis on the latter. **Strengths:** "He instils confidence through his detailed preparation and sound advocacy skills." "He's brilliant in court, very persuasive."

Douglas Cooper Recommended for industrial disease work, with a focus on representing defendants. His expertise covers noise-induced hearing loss and asbestos-related disease. **Strengths:** "He takes a robust approach in terms of how he prepares his cases, and when you get to trial, he's a good advocate." "He is an excellent negotiator."

Peter Harrison Adept at handling a multitude of personal injury matters for both claimants and defendants, including fatal accidents. **Strengths:** "He is very good in conference, and has a good client manner; he knows how defendant clients think." "He is very thorough, knows his stuff and is extremely personable." **Recent work:** Instructed in West v Lancashire County Council, an industrial disease case concerning the development of asthma.

Matthew Stockwell Well known for handling complex personal injury cases, particularly those involving brain injury and issues relating to mental capacity. Interviewees praise his high level of technical skill. **Strengths:** "Out of all the barristers I deal with he has a unique ability to spot appeal points and persuade the court to accept his point of view." "He is very good on paper and on his feet."

9 St John Street

See profile on p.923

THE SET

The personal injury group at 9 St John Street is well regarded for providing a broad range of expertise, encompassing both claimant and defendant work in complex cases. Practitioners have considerable experience in brain and spinal injuries and amputations. The set also receives high praise for the organisation and knowledge of its clerks.

Client service: "This is a very good clerking team; very accessible and very pleasant to deal with." "They are always prompt."

SILKS

Christopher Kennedy QC Has significant expertise in conducting catastrophic injury claims on behalf of defendant clients. He has substantial experience of brain injury cases, including psychiatric injury. Sources admire his tough demeanour in the courtroom. **Strengths:** "He is very good on his feet: calm and considered, and absolutely on the point when cross-examining the witness." "He is excellent in conference and always meticulously well prepared." **Recent work:** Acted on Wright v O'Hara & MIB, a high-value brain injury case rendered more complex by issues concerning future employment and psychological injury.

Nicholas Hinchliffe QC Highly regarded for working with both claimants and defendants on serious personal injury and industrial disease claims. He is recommended for his excellent advocacy in court. **Strengths:** "He is a terrific courtroom performer – he cuts to the chase." "He is an outstanding and robust silk."

JUNIORS

Michael Lemmy Divides his practice between claimant and defendant work, covering a range of complex personal injury claims. He is adept at handling matters involving brain and spinal injury and chronic pain. **Strengths:** "He is very good on his feet, good on paperwork and good with clients." **Recent work:** Instructed on behalf of the defendants in Armstrong v Haslam Homes, a case concerning a brain injury resulting from a road traffic accident. The claim was dismissed.

Ian Little Praised for his thorough knowledge of catastrophic injury claims, including industrial disease. He focuses primarily on claimant work, and is known for his impressive manner with clients. **Strengths:** "He comes across as being really laid-back, but he is as sharp as a tack." "He has a detailed knowledge of high-value accident and industrial disease claims."

Brian McCluggage (see p.667) Held in high esteem for handling higher-value personal injury claims for defendants, including fatal accidents. He is well versed in dealing with fraudulent claims. **Strengths:** "He is very analytical, very robust in dealing with negotiations and very good on his feet." "He is very good technically and incredibly experienced in fraud issues." **Recent work:** Represented the defendant in Dunleavy v Walsh Construction, a case concerning a spinal injury.

Matthew Snarr Handles severe personal injury cases on behalf of both defendants and claimants. He has considerable experience in matters involving brain injuries and fatal accidents. **Strengths:** "He's very clever, thorough, good on the detail, a good negotiator and very good on his feet." "He is exceptionally well prepared." **Recent work:** Acted for the defendants in a road traffic accident case involving severe leg injury. Following an initial claim of £2.3 million, the matter settled for £825,000.

Other Ranked Lawyers

Richard Hartley QC (Cobden House Chambers) Highly regarded for his catastrophic injury work, including occupiers' liability and road traffic accidents. He receives instruction from both claimants and defendants. **Strengths:** "He thinks on his feet, and clients like him because of his down-to-earth style." "He can negotiate his way through numerous difficulties on cases, and has a very relaxed style of advocacy that is impressive."

Marc Willems (Cobden House Chambers) Focuses on brain and spinal injury cases on behalf of both claimants and defendants. He is frequently singled out for praise by both solicitors and fellow counsel for his excellent advocacy skills. **Strengths:** "He has a very eloquent style of advocacy, provides sound tactical advice, and has a fantastic manner with clients and a genuine commitment to doing the best for them."

Michael Jones (Cobden House Chambers) Recognised for his breadth of knowledge in catastrophic injury claims. He conducts cases on behalf of both claimants and defendants. **Strengths:** "He is an outstanding junior doing high-quality work."

Peter Gregory (7 Harrington St Chambers) Commended for his representation of defendants in complex personal injury claims, including industrial disease and other forms of employers' liability. **Strengths:** "He is a robust and delightful advocate: a proper opponent."

Ivan Bowley (Lincoln House Chambers) Widely regarded as a top industrial disease specialist, with expertise in cases involving asbestos-related disease and noise-induced hearing loss. **Strengths:** "He is very well prepared, and a pleasure to deal with – very approachable." "He is a QC-level disease specialist."

Peter Cowan (Oriel Chambers) Noted for his expertise in occupational disease claims, particularly those related to asbestos. **Strengths:** "He has a detailed knowledge of asbestos-related disease claims and other complex industrial disease litigation."

Mark Laprell (see p.651) (18 St John Street) Lauded for his tough demeanour in court and negotiation. He handles a range of catastrophic personal injury cases, including brain injury cases and fatal accidents. **Strengths:** "He is a terrifying advocate – you always want him on your side." "He is very experienced, and you can always be confident that he will be good with clients."

WALES & CHESTER

Personal Injury Wales & Chester
Leading Sets
Band 1
Civitas Law *
Band 2
30 Park Place *
Leading Silks
Band 1
Huckle Theodore *Civitas Law* *
Williams Lloyd *30 Park Place*
Leading Juniors
Band 1
Brace Michael *Civitas Law* *
Davies Ben *30 Park Place*
Jones Nicholas David *Civitas Law* *
O'Leary Robert *Civitas Law* *
Thomas Bryan *Civitas Law* *
Band 2
Arentsen Andrew *Civitas Law* *
Brooks Peter *9 Park Place (ORL)* ◊ *
Callow David *12 King's Bench Walk (ORL)* ◊ *
Harrison Robert *30 Park Place*
Puar Mikhael *30 Park Place*
Williams Joanne *Civitas Law* *
◊ *(ORL) = Other Ranked Lawyer.*
* *Indicates set / individual with profile.*

Band 1

Civitas Law

See profile on p.894

THE SET

Civitas Law maintains its reputation as the pre-eminent personal injury set in Wales. It covers the full spectrum of claims, including catastrophic injuries and industrial diseases. Its members win acclaim from clients for their user-friendly and commercial approach.

SILKS

Theodore Huckle QC (see p.632) Has expertise spanning complex catastrophic injury claims as well as clinical and medical negligence matters. He is particularly noted for his advocacy skills.

JUNIORS

Michael Brace (see p.555) Has a well-established personal injury practice, and is highly regarded for his representation of trade unions and individuals in industrial diseases claims. **Strengths:** "His work is always of an extremely high standard. He is very reliable; he will never miss a deadline."

Nicholas David Jones (see p.640) Impresses sources with the depth of his knowledge in the personal injury arena. He focuses on catastrophic injury claims, covering traumatic brain injuries, spinal cord injuries and amputations. **Strengths:** "He has a very calm authority and is excellent in his interactions with clients."

Robert O'Leary (see p.685) Undertakes the full spectrum of disease work, and is particularly noted for his encyclopaedic knowledge of the issues surrounding noise-induced hearing loss cases. He receives instructions from a range of clients, including individuals, trade unions and the government. **Strengths:** "He is very approachable and easy to work with."

Bryan Thomas (see p.736) A veteran practitioner who focuses on handling complex and high-value personal injury cases. **Strengths:** "He is very good with clients. He can relay complex legal issues in a language that a non-legally minded person could understand."

Andrew Arentsen (see p.537) Has considerable expertise in complex cases featuring conflicting medical evidence. He is instructed on behalf of both claimants and defendants in an array of matters, including cases relating to head and spinal injuries, RTAs and occupiers' liabilities. **Strengths:** "He is a great tactician and is very practical. He will really roll up his sleeves to look at the legal issues."

Joanne Williams (see p.752) Has built up considerable expertise in work-related injuries and liability claims. She is also well regarded for her prowess in handing disease work, such as hearing loss and stress matters.

Band 2

30 Park Place

See profile on p.895

THE SET

Offering a multifaceted service, 30 Park Place has considerable expertise in both claimant and defendant work. Its specialists are regularly instructed on head and spinal injuries, high-end RTAs and occupational disease, especially asbestos and vibration claims. Market sources are effusive in praising the set's quality of service, noting that "it's a strong set and has the complete breadth and depth of experience."

Client service: "The clerking structure is very good. If you need anything, you give them a call and it will be done quite swiftly."

SILKS

Lloyd Williams QC Widely recognised in the personal injury space for his expertise in cases concerning catastrophic head injuries and fatalities. **Strengths:** "He is very bright and creative, and thinks outside the box."

JUNIORS

Robert Harrison Focuses his personal injury practice on cases concerning injuries of the utmost severity. **Strengths:** "He understands the medical terminology well and is extraordinarily thorough. He makes sure nothing is missed in the case."

Ben Davies Highlighted by sources for his outstanding cross-examination and advocacy skills. His personal injury practice focuses on high-value RTA claims. **Strengths:** "He provides detailed advice and has a very good style of advocacy in court."

Mikhael Puar An accomplished personal injury litigator acting on behalf of both claimants and defendants in Wales and the South West of England. He frequently advises on workplace injuries, RTA claims and inquests.

Other Ranked Lawyers

David Callow (see p.563) (12 King's Bench Walk) Has extensive knowledge of a variety of personal injury claims, with a particular focus on those relating to industrial and occupational disease. He receives instructions from a wide range of clients, including NHS trusts, local authorities, blue-chip companies and individuals.

Peter Brooks (see p.557) (9 Park Place) Has a well-established personal injury practice focusing on high-value catastrophic injury claims. He appears in all major courts and is noted for his work on behalf of the Criminal Injuries Compensation Authority.

WESTERN

Personal Injury Western	
Leading Sets	
Band 1	
Guildhall Chambers *	
Old Square Chambers *	
St John's Chambers *	
Leading Silks	
Band 1	
Palmer Adrian	*Guildhall Chambers*
Sharp Christopher	*St John's Chambers* Ⓐ *
Leading Juniors	
Star individuals	
Edwards Glyn	*St John's Chambers*
Band 1	
Benson Julian	*Guildhall Chambers*
Grice Timothy	*St John's Chambers*
McLaughlin Andrew	*St John's Chambers* Ⓐ
Reddiford Anthony	*Guildhall Chambers*
Snell John	*Guildhall Chambers*
Stead Richard	*St John's Chambers* Ⓐ
Walker Christopher	*Old Square Chambers*
Band 2	
Farmer Gabriel	*Guildhall Chambers*
Isherwood John	*Unity Street Chambers (ORL)* ◊
Kempster Toby	*Old Square Chambers*
Lomas Mark	*3PB Barristers (ORL)* ◊
Symington Anna	*St John's Chambers* Ⓐ
Taylor Christopher	*Queen Square Chambers (ORL)* ◊
White Matthew	*St John's Chambers* Ⓐ
Woodhouse Charles	*Old Square Chambers*
Band 3	
Bennett Daniel	*Doughty Street Chambers (ORL)* ◊
Chippindall Adam	*Guildhall Chambers*
Dennis Rebecca	*Queen Square Chambers (ORL)* ◊
Haines David	*Doughty Street Chambers (ORL)* ◊
Posta Adrian	*Albion Chambers (ORL)* ◊ Ⓐ
Risoli Andreá	*Old Square Chambers*
Rivers David	*Old Square Chambers*
Zeb Emma	*St John's Chambers* Ⓐ
◊ (ORL) = Other Ranked Lawyer.	
Ⓐ direct access (see p.11).	
** Indicates firm / individual with profile.*	
Alphabetical order within each band. Band 1 is highest.	

Band 1

Guildhall Chambers
See profile on p.890

THE SET

Guildhall Chambers maintains its position at the forefront of the market, representing both claimants and defendants. Its members have considerable expertise in dealing with the full spectrum of personal injury claims nationwide, including injuries of utmost severity. The barristers are praised by clients as being "very approachable."

Client service: "The clerks led by Justin Emmett provide excellent back support to barristers." "The clerking system there is superb."

SILKS

Adrian Palmer QC One of the leading personal injury silks on the Western Circuit. His practice is focused on catastrophic injury claims, including brain and spinal injuries. He remains a popular choice for both defendants and claimants.

JUNIORS

Julian Benson Noted for his experience in high-value personal injury work, ranging from brain and limb injuries to fatal accidents. He is praised by market sources for his representation of claimants. **Strengths:** "He is a very dynamic and very skilled litigator. He works 25 hours a day, seven days a week." **Recent work:** Acted for the claimant in Curtis v NIG, a four-day liability trial concerning an amputation following an RTA.

Anthony Reddiford Has a broad personal injury practice with a focus on industrial disease work, and especially on mesothelioma and asbestos-related claims. He receives instructions from both claimants and defendants. **Recent work:** Successfully acted for the defendant in Williams v John's Travel, a case concerning an RTA and a feud between rival coach companies.

John Snell Receives instructions from both regional and national clients on personal injury claims, and has a particular niche in those relating to the Animal Act 1971. **Strengths:** "He has an excellent understanding of Animal Act claims." **Recent work:** Instructed in Bell v Professor Congdon, a claim brought under the Animal Act 1971.

Gabriel Farmer Leads the set's personal injury team and is noted for his expertise across a wide span of injury claims. He is particularly adept at handling liability and quantum disputes. **Strengths:** "He understands this area of the law extremely well, and he turns things around very quickly."

Adam Chippindall Has a broad practice covering a range of personal injury work, including claims in relation to RTAs, industrial disease, employers' liability, psychiatric injury and inquests.

Old Square Chambers
See profile on p.891

THE SET

Old Square Chambers has a strong team of personal injury practitioners. The set receives instructions in a wide array of claims, including serious and catastrophic injuries, and is also able to draw upon the resources of its London office. Solicitors described their services as "beyond expectations."

Client service: "William Meade's clerk team are friendly and helpful. They always offer suitable alternatives when booking barristers." "The clerks know their stuff and understand the business precisely."

JUNIORS

Christopher Walker Acts on personal injury claims on behalf of both claimants and defendants. He receives regular instructions on cases concerning fatal accidents and injuries of utmost severity. **Recent work:** He acted in Watson Woodhouse v The Chief Constable of Cleveland Police in relation to the false imprisonment of a leading criminal defence solicitor.

Toby Kempster Has focused his personal injury practice on employers' liability and industrial diseases. He is also recognised for his expertise in claims relating to RTAs. **Strengths:** "He adds a lot of value to the case." **Recent work:** He acted in Preux v Hot Liquid, a claim concerning a serious head and neck injury resulting from an offshore sailing accident.

Charles Woodhouse (see p.755) Has a strong track record in high-value personal injury matters, such as claims relating to workplace injuries, RTAs and fatal accidents. **Strengths:** "We instruct him not only for his excellent advocacy but for his unique client skills and for his commercial approach as well." **Recent work:** He acted for the claimant in Kerr v Kerr & BMW, a case concerning a nine-year-old child who suffered catastrophic eye damage due to a car airbag.

Andreá Risoli (see p.708) Practises exclusively in the personal injury and clinical negligence domain. Commentators note his expertise in high-value claims, especially those regarding workplace accidents. **Strengths:** "He prepares fantastically well, has a good knowledge of cases, is good with figures and has a good manner with clients – he really gets them on board." **Recent work:** He acted in Ahmed Saleh Al Abd v Owen R Williams on behalf of the claimant, who suffered a severe spinal injury in an RTA.

David Rivers Represents claimants in a wide range of personal injury issues. He is noted for his expertise in employers' liability matters and high-value quantum cases. **Strengths:** "He offers really sound advice." "He has dealt with a lot of tricky cases."

St John's Chambers
See profile on p.893

THE SET

St John's Chambers has a deep bench of strong advocates with considerable expertise in handling complex and high-value personal injury cases. Instructing solicitors are quick to praise the set's commercial ethos, with the user-friendly nature of the clerking team being reflected by similarly approachable and helpful advocates.

Client service: "Annette Bushell's clerking team is very efficient. They do things in the right way and at the right time." "The clerks there are fantastic."

SILKS

Christopher Sharp QC (see p.718) Handles high-value personal injury claims on behalf of both claimants and defendants. He is instructed on a wide range of cases, including catastrophic brain injuries and fatalities. **Strengths:** "He is incredibly clever, works extremely hard, and gets all the minute detail of the case exactly right. He's also pretty good with clients and a good advocate."

JUNIORS

Glyn Edwards A go-to senior junior whose practice covers the full range of personal injury claims. He has a wealth of knowledge in serious injury claims and employers' liability litigation. **Strengths:** "He deals extremely well with clients. It's good to have him on your side." "His ability to achieve excellent settlement results is impressive. He is also a superb advocate."

Timothy Grice Well-regarded specialist in high-value catastrophic injury claims and fatal incidents. He has focused his practice predominantly on claimant work. **Strengths:** "He is extremely reliable, very knowledgeable and a good person to have on your side."

Andrew McLaughlin Sought out by some of the leading national firms for his talent and experience in cases with regard to severe and catastrophic injuries, serious psychiatric injuries and asbestos-triggered disease. Instructing solicitors are unanimous in praising his strong client care skills. **Strengths:** "He never misses deadlines and always delivers advice of high quality."

Richard Stead Acts for both claimants and defendants on catastrophic injury claims. He is also recognised for his expertise in cases relating to the Animals Act. **Strengths:** "He is fabulous to deal with." "He is very thorough and has good cross-examination skills."

Anna Symington Has a broad practice covering a range of personal injury work, including catastrophic injuries, fatalities and fraudulent claims. **Strengths:** "She is very sharp and can anticipate and spot problems early."

Matthew White Receives frequent instructions from local authorities and statutory undertakers regarding RTAs. He also has considerable expertise in industrial disease claims, including those concerning asbestos. **Strengths:** "He is a thorough and intelligent advocate, and good with witnesses."

Emma Zeb Handles a wide range of personal injury disputes encompassing fatal accidents and severe injuries. She is also known for her skills in handling RTA fraud claims on behalf of major insures. **Strengths:** "She is very accurate in writing and performs well in conferences."

Other Ranked Lawyers

Adrian Posta (Albion Chambers) Highly respected for his broad personal injury practice, which covers claims relating to RTAs, employers' liability and fatalities. He is in much demand by insurer clients for his high-quality advice.

Daniel Bennett (Doughty Street Chambers) Handles workplace injury claims and industrial disease litigation. He also acts for claimants on public liability and product liability cases.

David Haines (Doughty Street Chambers) Advises claimants and defendants on a wide range of work, with a particular focus on workplace injury and occupational diseases. **Strengths:** "He is very good at engaging clients." "He is very approachable and won't mind doing the extra work. "

Mark Lomas (3PB Barristers) Focuses on high-value injury claims arising from RTAs. He is widely praised for his ability to handle highly technical details in complex cases. **Strengths:** "He is extremely good and his attention to detail is second to none."

Christopher Taylor (see p.734) (Queen Square Chambers) Focuses on personal injury claims concerning severe brain and spinal injuries, industrial disease and fatalities. He principally represents claimants. **Strengths:** "He is excellent with clients."

Rebecca Dennis (Queen Square Chambers) Lauded for her specialist knowledge of employers' liability issues. She is praised by instructing solicitors for her fantastic client care skills. **Strengths:** "She always gives 100% for the cause, and does not step back from any tricky case."

John Isherwood (Unity Street Chambers) Focuses on complex injury personal injury cases, including catastrophic injuries and industrial disease claims.

Planning

Contents:

LONDON

Planning London	
Leading Sets	
Band 1	**Band 3**
Landmark Chambers *	Cornerstone Barristers *
Band 2	**Band 4**
Thirty Nine Essex Street *	6 Pump Court *
Francis Taylor Building *	

Leading Silks	
Senior Statesmen	**Band 3**
George Charles *Francis Taylor Building* [A]	**Cameron** Neil *Landmark Chambers*
Star individuals	**Drabble** Richard *Landmark Chambers*
Corner Timothy *Landmark Chambers*	**Edwards** Douglas *Francis Taylor Building* *
Elvin David *Landmark Chambers*	**Glover** Richard *Francis Taylor Building*
Humphries Michael *Francis Taylor Building* [A] *	**Hobson** John *Landmark Chambers* [A]
Katkowski Christopher *Landmark Chambers*	**Howell Williams** Craig *Francis Taylor Building* [A] *
Purchas Robin *Francis Taylor Building* [A] *	**Jones** Gregory *Francis Taylor Building*
Band 1	**Maurici** James *Landmark Chambers*
Clarkson Patrick *Landmark Chambers*	**McCracken** Robert *Francis Taylor Building* [A]
Ellis Morag *Francis Taylor Building*	**Price Lewis** Rhodri *Landmark Chambers*
Harris Russell *Landmark Chambers*	**Strachan** James *Thirty Nine Essex Street*
Holgate David *Landmark Chambers*	**Straker** Timothy *4-5 Gray's Inn Square (ORL)* ◊ *
King Neil *Landmark Chambers*	**Tait** Andrew *Francis Taylor Building*
Kingston Martin *No5 Chambers (ORL)* ◊	**Tromans** Stephen *Thirty Nine Essex Street*
Lieven Nathalie *Landmark Chambers*	**Warren** Rupert *Landmark Chambers*
Lockhart-Mummery Christopher *Landmark Chambers*	**Band 4**
Lowe Mark *Cornerstone Barristers*	**Boyle** Christopher *Landmark Chambers*
Mould Timothy *Landmark Chambers*	**Dinkin** Anthony *Cornerstone Barristers*
Phillips Richard *Francis Taylor Building*	**Findlay** James *Cornerstone Barristers* *
Village Peter *Thirty Nine Essex Street*	**Harwood** Richard *Thirty Nine Essex Street* *
Band 2	**Horton** Matthew *Thirty Nine Essex Street*
Ash Brian *Thirty Nine Essex Street*	**Humphreys** Richard *No5 Chambers (ORL)* ◊ [A]
Bird Simon *Francis Taylor Building* *	**Karas** Jonathan *Falcon Chambers (ORL)* ◊ *
Brown Paul *Landmark Chambers*	**Litton** John *Landmark Chambers*
Dove Ian *No5 Chambers (ORL)* ◊	**Nardell** Gordon *Thirty Nine Essex Street*
Hicks William *Landmark Chambers*	**Ornsby** Suzanne *Francis Taylor Building* [A] *
Hill Thomas *Thirty Nine Essex Street* *	**White** Sasha *Landmark Chambers*
Roots Guy *Francis Taylor Building* *	**New Silks**
Steel John *Thirty Nine Essex Street* [A] *	**Forsdick** David *Landmark Chambers*
Stinchcombe Paul *Thirty Nine Essex Street* [A]	**Pereira** James *Francis Taylor Building* [A]
	Sheikh Saira Kabir *Francis Taylor Building* [A]
	Taylor Reuben *Landmark Chambers*
	Willers Marc *Garden Court Chambers (ORL)*

Leading Juniors
Star individuals
Cook Mary *Cornerstone Barristers*
Philpot Hereward *Francis Taylor Building*
Band 1
Bedford Michael *Cornerstone Barristers* *
Lyness Scott *Landmark Chambers*
Band 2
Banner Charles *Landmark Chambers* *
Beard Mark *6 Pump Court* [A]
Cosgrove Thomas *Cornerstone Barristers* *
Ground Richard *Cornerstone Barristers* *
Reed Matthew *Landmark Chambers*
Band 3
Booth Alexander *Francis Taylor Building* [A] *
Burton James *Thirty Nine Essex Street*
Honey Richard *Francis Taylor Building* [A] *
Kolinsky Daniel *Landmark Chambers* *
Lewis Meyric *Francis Taylor Building* [A] *
Morgan Stephen *Landmark Chambers*
Murphy Melissa *Francis Taylor Building* *
Wald Richard *Thirty Nine Essex Street*
Walton Robert *Landmark Chambers*
Whale Stephen *Landmark Chambers* [A] *
Williams Guy *Landmark Chambers*
Band 4
Busch Lisa *Landmark Chambers*
Clay Jonathan *Cornerstone Barristers*
Colquhoun Celina *No5 Chambers (ORL)* ◊
Fraser-Urquhart Andrew *Francis Taylor Building* [A] *
Green Robin *Cornerstone Barristers* *
Keen Graeme *Landmark Chambers*
Ranatunga Asitha *Cornerstone Barristers* *
Shadarevian Paul *Cornerstone Barristers*
Tabachnik Andrew *Thirty Nine Essex Street*
Upton William *6 Pump Court*
Band 5
Banwell Richard *6 Pump Court*
Druce Michael *Cornerstone Barristers* *
Goodman Alex *Landmark Chambers* [A]
Grant Edward *6 Pump Court*
Hannett Sarah *Matrix Chambers (ORL)* ◊ [A]
Kohli Ryan *Cornerstone Barristers* *
Moules Richard *Landmark Chambers*
Moys Clive *Radcliffe Chambers (ORL)* ◊
Parry Clare *Cornerstone Barristers* *
Pike Jeremy *Francis Taylor Building* [A]
Simons Zack *Landmark Chambers*
Thomas Megan *6 Pump Court*
Townsend Harriet *Cornerstone Barristers* *
Trevelyan Thomas Adrian *Cornerstone Barristers*
Westmoreland Smith Mark *Francis Taylor Building*
Williams Anne *6 Pump Court*
Zwart Christiaan *Thirty Nine Essex Street* *
Up-and-coming individuals
Flanagan Hugh *Cornerstone Barristers* *
Graham Paul Annabel *Francis Taylor Building* *
Helme Ned *Thirty Nine Essex Street*
Turney Richard *Landmark Chambers*
Westaway Ned *Francis Taylor Building*
Wills Jonathan *Landmark Chambers*

** Indicates set / individual with profile.*
◊ (ORL) = Other Ranked Lawyer.
[A] direct access (see p.11).

Band 1

Landmark Chambers

See profile on p.829

THE SET

Landmark continues to rank as the leading London planning set. With star performers among its silks, highly regarded senior juniors, and a strong contingent of younger planning barristers, it is able to provide counsel for any planning inquiry or High Court challenge. Members of chambers have appeared in a number of the most significant planning cases of the past year, and demonstrate particular expertise in the fields of commercial development, infrastructure projects, heritage matters and tree preservation orders. "If there's something complex that we want advice on, we go to Landmark," states a client; "in our view they're the best set of planners."

Client service: "The clerking team at Landmark is always extremely helpful and very prompt at responding to queries, on potential new instructions as well as ongoing matters." "Landmark's clerks, led by Jay Fullilove, are much the same as their barristers – approachable, friendly and down to earth. The team is always available and queries are responded to promptly."

SILKS

Timothy Corner QC One of the standout silks at the Planning Bar, he is regularly instructed on the largest public inquiries and High Court challenges, and is frequently commended by instructing solicitors for his strong work ethic and dedication to client care. **Strengths:** "His attention to detail is quite something. He is very thorough and he won't stop until he is happy with a particular answer." "He is an outstanding barrister and a delightful man to work with. He puts clients and the team at ease." **Recent work:** Appeared for the developers in a public inquiry concerning the £1.2 billion redevelopment of the Shell Centre on London's South Bank.

David Elvin QC Recommended by instructing solicitors as a first-rate barrister for complex, intellectually demanding problems. He is particularly noted for his expertise in planning matters involving environmental law. **Strengths:** "David is a giant of the Planning Bar and is often the go-to silk if your client wants to terrify the other side. He has an enormous brain, coupled with a worldly and approachable manner." "He's one of the country's leading advocates."

Christopher Katkowski QC Handles many of the most high-profile development matters. He is a highly experienced inquiry advocate, and advises and represents clients in statutory challenges and judicial reviews. **Strengths:** "He is very competent and a delight to appear against." "Extremely experienced and knowledgeable, he inspires confidence in clients and is very highly regarded by the judiciary." **Recent work:** Represented the developers in a judicial review concerning the major redevelopment of land in the Earl's Court Opportunity Area.

Timothy Mould QC Renowned for handling large infrastructure developments for promoters and challengers. He demonstrates particular expertise in matters concerning compulsory purchase and development consent orders. **Strengths:** "His advocacy is first-rate and he has a lightning-fast mind. He provides the confidence that clients require when presenting high-profile cases to public inquiries." **Recent work:** Successfully defended a judicial review challenge to the decision of the Secretary of State to promote the High Speed 2 rail project. The challenge was brought by a number of campaigning groups.

Patrick Clarkson QC Demonstrates particular expertise in the field of residential and retail development planning. He regularly handles matters involving food store applications and large housing developments, and has appeared in numerous appeals and inquiries. **Strengths:** "He is first-rate on all fronts, and offers an exceptional strategic understanding of the retail sector and the key operators in the market. His authoritative yet commercial opinions can make or break transactions." "He is very good, and is clear and robust in his advice." **Recent work:** Represented Taylor Wimpey in a test case concerning the new National Planning Policy Framework. The case related to the house builder's application to develop 700 homes near Swindon.

Russell Harris QC Well known for handling major regeneration and development matters. Of late he has been instructed on several cases concerning skyscrapers. **Strengths:** "He is excellent at distilling large volumes of information into coherent and succinct advice for clients, and he is often a first choice for high-profile and complex London planning matters." **Recent work:** Successfully secured consent for the promoters of the Vauxhall Island twin towers at a public inquiry.

David Holgate QC Widely regarded as a leading advocate for statutory challenges and judicial reviews in the High Court. He has a particular interest in compulsory purchase order (CPO) cases, and is often instructed by landowners and developers to advise on objections to the core planning strategy of local authorities. **Strengths:** "He is very sharp and very incisive, and focuses in on the key points immediately." "He has an outstanding intellect."

Neil King QC Advises and represents developers and local authorities on infrastructure, residential and commercial development matters. He often handles work concerning high-value tall-building developments in the capital. **Strengths:** "He is extremely user-friendly and a very good team player, and he delivers easy-to-understand advice on often very complex matters." "A great choice for CPO matters."

Nathalie Lieven QC Widely regarded as a top-flight advocate in planning inquiries and judicial review proceedings. Her areas of particular exper tise include major infrastructure matters and retail development. **Strengths:** "She is a superb advocate – absolutely fantastic. She is very quick-thinking and can lead witnesses on a merry path then snag them at the end." "She is very adept at presenting a case, is in full command of all the evidence and is very sharp in cross-examination." **Recent work:** Successfully defended EDF Energy in a judicial review concerning the development of a new nuclear reactor at Hinkley Point C. The proceedings were brought by the Irish National Trust and involved complex cross-border environmental impact issues.

Christopher Lockhart-Mummery QC Handles retail and residential matters for a wide range of clients. He is admired for his proficiency when handling inquiries, High Court challenges and strategic advisory work. **Strengths:** "His intellectual ability and hard work are second to none, and he is an extremely nice man to deal with." "He is a planning heavyweight and a force to be reckoned with." **Recent work:** Acted for the objectors on a CPO inquiry concerning the redevelopment of White Hart Lane football stadium.

Paul Brown QC Frequently appears in significant appeals and inquiries. He is renowned for his expertise in statutory challenges and judicial review proceedings. **Strengths:** "He is great at written advice and excellent as an advocate. He gives clear, concise and logical advice that is always practical." "He is intellectual, hard-working and a superb advocate." **Recent work:** Represented the London Borough of Tower Hamlets at a CPO inquiry relating to the Blackwall Reach regeneration project.

James Maurici QC Renowned for his handling of high-profile appeals and inquiries. He is able to advise on the full range of planning matters, and is particularly well regarded for his work in judicial review proceedings. **Strengths:** "He has been a find: he is a refreshing change. He is forthright and to the point, and you feel he is 100% in your corner. I was bowled over by his responsiveness and the clients were too." "One of the up-and-coming stars of the Planning Bar. He is very impressive and very solution-focused, and the clients really like him." **Recent work:** Appeared before the Supreme Court for the Secretary of State in a judicial review challenge to the proposed development of the High Speed 2 railway project.

Neil Cameron QC Handles complex planning applications and public inquiries for promoters and local authorities. He appears regularly in major statutory challenges and judicial reviews at the High Court and the Court of Appeal. **Strengths:** "He is counsel of choice for the City planners, which is an accolade in itself." "He is bright, well prepared and good on detail."

Richard Drabble QC Offers advice and representation on a broad range of planning, environmental and social housing issues. He acts for developers and local authorities, and often appears before planning inquiries. **Strengths:** "He brings great depth of knowledge and experience, and is a formidable public lawyer." "He's the person I would aspire to be in terms of his advocacy skills, attention to detail, and ability to cut down a complicated matter to a point which is really worthy of argument." **Recent work:** Represented Associated British Ports in a judicial review challenge relating to the refusal of the Marine Management Organisation to make a harbour revision order regarding a jetty serving a refinery.

John Hobson QC Regularly instructed by local authorities on a broad spectrum of planning matters. He has considerable experience of handling public inquiries and High Court challenges. **Strengths:** "He has a lovely manner with clients. In conference he is relaxed, personable, engaged and good at listening." "He offers excellent advocacy skills, is good at research and has the ability to respond to a wide range of issues." **Recent work:** Represented Birmingham City Council in a CPO hearing concerning the redevelopment of the Paradise Circus city centre site.

Rhodri Price Lewis QC Demonstrates particular expertise in planning cases involving environmental matters. He is often sought out for complex energy, infrastructure and mining cases. **Strengths:** "He puts people at their ease, can speak their language, and has the ability to establish a rapport and get the answers clients want." "He is always willing to listen and is effective at engaging a team." **Recent work:** Advised on a proposal to develop a large open-cast mine in Caerphilly.

Rupert Warren QC Specialises in compulsory purchase cases and major redevelopment projects. He is admired for his commercial and pragmatic approach to complex planning matters. **Strengths:** "He phrases things very well, puts the case across very clearly in a manner that is appreciated by the judge, and makes some key points." "His advice is rock-solid. He's got a good way with the court, is personable and respectable, and just really knows his subject." **Recent work:** Acted for the developer Orion in a challenge brought by local traders to its redevelopment of Shepherd's Bush Market.

Christopher Boyle QC Well known for promoting large residential developments and infrastructure projects, and frequently appears before public inquiries. **Strengths:** "Brilliant – absolutely fantastic. I've always found his advice to be very good; he cuts to the quick and is always very clear." "He is always on top of his brief and very easy to work with." **Recent work:** Advised on the promotion of an urban extension to Ashford in Kent, comprising 5,500 homes at Chilmington Green.

Sasha White QC Handles a range of planning inquiries and statutory challenges before the High Court. He is often instructed by high-profile developers, and also acts for local authorities on issues including compulsory purchase, village green applications and listed buildings. **Strengths:** "An absolutely brilliant advocate." "He provides practical and commercial solutions to difficult situations. He is not afraid of putting his neck on the line and provides very robust advice." **Recent work:** Appeared in judicial review proceedings concerning a challenge to the granting of planning permission for an agricultural development.

John Litton QC Focuses on handling matters involving highways and compulsory purchase compensation. He is adept at handling environmental and public law issues arising in the field of planning, and frequently acts for developers. **Strengths:** "He is fantastic on his feet and clients are always impressed." "He's an incisive and approachable QC who is on the rise." **Recent work:** Acted for a developer on a challenge to the Secretary of State's decision to recover a planning appeal and determine it himself.

William Hicks QC Acts on large-scale development matters. He demonstrates particular expertise in retail and residential development and infrastructure projects. **Strengths:** "He anticipates the commercial angle to the case."

Reuben Taylor QC Acts for local authorities and developers on inquiries and planning appeals. He demonstrates a particular interest in matters concerning noise nuisance. **Strengths:** "He's very good on the technical side, forensic with numbers and good at getting to the key issues."

David Forsdick QC Handles matters involving infrastructure projects, CPOs and environmental planning issues. He is often instructed by challengers, including environmental charities, and also acts for the Secretary of State, local authorities and developers. **Strengths:** "He cuts to the chase and gives advice that is pragmatic and commercial." "He has a very keen eye for detail and is thorough in his preparation." **Recent work:** Acted for the RSPB on its objection to the granting of a development consent order for Able Marine's Humber Port project.

JUNIORS

Scott Lyness Regularly appears on inquiries into city centre regeneration schemes. Also advises on energy infrastructure projects. **Strengths:** "He is very thorough and has a really good grasp of the issues, so he is able to offer a view quite quickly." "Clients appreciate his approachable manner and depth of knowledge." **Recent work:** Advised the promoters of the Battersea Power Station redevelopment on planning issues, including those concerning the delivery of the site masterplan.

Charles Banner (see p.542) Renowned for handling planning matters arising in the energy sector. He is particularly adept at advising on cases involving questions of European law and public law. **Strengths:** "He is personable and ready to listen, and gives clear and decisive answers to questions." "He is a highly effective advocate with an approachable manner." **Recent work:** Acted for Heathrow Hub on a judicial review of the High Speed 2 railway project.

Matthew Reed Instructed by local authorities on a range of matters, including High Court challenges. He is particularly well regarded for his advice on developments in the education, infrastructure and housing sectors. **Strengths:** "He is a strong advocate who has the ability to present a case clearly and effectively, and forcefully when required." "He's very client-friendly and helpful in conference." **Recent work:** Represented Tower Hamlets Council in a planning appeal and CPO concerning an industrial wharf.

Stephen Morgan Handles a broad range of housing and infrastructure cases. He demonstrates particular expertise in matters concerning the harnessing of energy from waste, and has experience of sitting as a planning inspector. **Strengths:** "He is a master of detail and understands the bigger commercial picture without losing sight of where the strengths and weaknesses of the case are." "A good organiser, he is strong on the detail of a case and very competent."

Daniel Kolinsky (see p.648) Represents developers, objectors and local authorities before planning inquiries and in the High Court. He has a strong reputation for advising on matters concerning redevelopment. **Strengths:** "He is always totally prepared, gives commercially astute and succinct advice, and can always be relied on. Clients love him." "His pleadings, advocacy and opinions are of exceptional quality. He is a real team player, and a firm favourite of clients and instructing solicitors who favour pragmatic solutions." **Recent work:** Acted for the London Borough of Islington on a public inquiry into a proposed ten-storey tower development on Pentonville Road, North London.

Robert Walton Noted for his work on planning matters in the energy sector. He is an authority on compulsory purchase issues, and is adept at handling matters relating to the environment and local government. **Strengths:** "He is commercial, down to earth and highly regarded." "Very clear, concise and quick to respond." **Recent work:** Advised Cambridge University Hospitals NHS Foundation Trust on the drawing up of plans for the expansion of Addenbrooke's Hospital. The plans included designs for a new energy-generating incinerator.

Stephen Whale (see p.749) Handles a range of matters relating to planning, the environment and local government. He regularly appears in large public inquiries and High Court challenges. **Strengths:** "He is excellent as he's very persuasive and comes across very well." "He is very good in conference because he sets out issues clearly and concisely." **Recent work:** Represented the Leith Hill Action Group in its challenge to exploratory drilling for oil and natural gas in an area of outstanding natural beauty in Surrey.

Guy Williams Advises on a wide range of planning matters, including those concerning residential development and infrastructure. He has a particular interest in CPOs and waste-to-energy projects, and acts for both local authorities and objectors. **Strengths:** "He provides very helpful advice – he is fantastic." "He provides clear planning advice on development projects and he is extremely approachable." **Recent work:** Represented Tower Hamlets Council in the examination process of the Thames Tideway Tunnel project. The council's objections questioned the scope of the examining authority's powers.

Lisa Busch Handles a broad range of planning and environment cases for central government agencies and local authorities. **Strengths:** "She is direct and encouraging when working on difficult material." "She's very friendly and co-operative, and is able to secure satisfactory outcomes for her client while remaining fair." **Recent work:** Acted for the team representing the Department for Transport in the High Speed 2 Select Committee proceedings in Parliament.

Graeme Keen Renowned for his handling of large public inquiries. He is also well known for the expertise he brings to matters involving CPOs. **Strengths:** "He is always a safe pair of hands, and is extremely knowledgeable and practical." "He offers clear, concise advice, is sound in his tactics and takes a no-nonsense approach." **Recent work:** Represented Cherwell District Council in a public inquiry into a 145-home development at Salt Way, Banbury, which raised challenging heritage issues concerning a medieval bridle path.

Richard Moules Handles a broad range of matters relating to planning and the environment. He often acts for local government, developers and action groups. **Strengths:** "He has great cross-examination skills and a personable manner." "He is well prepared, unfazed, clear on his legal arguments, and methodical. He carries the tribunal with him." **Recent work:** Acted for the London Borough of Islington and other London councils in a challenge to the central government policy of allowing permitted development rights for those seeking to make residential use of office properties.

Alex Goodman Well known for his handling of complex judicial review and statutory appeal cases. He often acts for challengers to infrastructure projects and residential developments. **Strengths:** "He is very good at investigating and building the legal case." **Recent work:** Represented the objectors in a judicial review concerning large housing developments in Carmarthenshire.

Richard Turney Represents local authorities, developers and objectors in a wide range of planning and environment matters. He has a particular interest in development consent order work for infrastructure projects. **Strengths:** "He offers fantastic advocacy, and has a fantastic working knowledge of the papers." "A rising star, he delivers excellent advocacy, and is very user-friendly." **Recent work:** Acted for the London Boroughs of Hammersmith & Fulham and Kensington & Chelsea in their successful defence of a challenge to the redevelopment of the Earl's Court Opportunity Area.

Zack Simons Demonstrates particular expertise in energy infrastructure planning. He is admired for the experience he brings to public inquiries. **Strengths:** "He is really good. He manages his client effectively and presents a thoroughly good case." **Recent work:** Instructed by Stroud District Council on an inquiry into a proposed waste-to-energy facility at Javelin Park, in Gloucestershire.

Jonathan Wills Handles a broad range of matters relating to planning and the environment. He has appeared in a number of public inquiries and High Court proceedings. **Strengths:** "He is courteous and effective, and helps to focus discussion on the essential issues. His manner with clients is very good." "He is excellent in conference. He seems to have a knack for making the complicated seem simple and straightforward." **Recent work:** Represented Ashford Borough Council in a public inquiry in which he successfully defended an enforcement notice concerning a caravan site.

Band 2

Thirty Nine Essex Street

See profile on p.797

THE SET

Thirty Nine Essex Street continues to benefit from the recent integration into its planning team of a number of former members of 4-5 Gray's Inn Square. These additions have allowed the set to expand its client base of local authorities and central government agencies to include high-profile developers. In addition to the work it handles in the fields of planning and the environment, the set is attracting a growing number of instructions relating to residential and commercial development. Many members here are able to draw on their expertise in public law to handle planning-related judicial reviews and statutory challenges.

Client service: "They are user-friendly and the clerks are quite entrepreneurial. They work hard to make sure you're happy with the service and suggest the names of others you might want to try. They're very proactive." "Planning and environment manager Andrew Poyser has never given me a bad recommendation for a barrister, which is one of the main reasons we keep going back. In terms of client service

Thirty Nine Essex Street has absolutely nailed it."

SILKS

Peter Village QC Renowned for his handling of CPO matters on behalf of objectors. He is also well known for handling judicial reviews and statutory challenges on behalf of developers and landowners. **Strengths:** "A passionate and effective advocate, who is enthusiastic and committed to his clients' cause." "He is very robust. He doesn't take any nonsense, is user-friendly, is very direct and to the point, and quickly gets to the nub of the issue." **Recent work:** Represented the University of Sheffield in its application to redevelop the Jessops Hospital site. Mr Village successfully defended the £81 million proposal from applications for injunctions that would prohibit the demolition of the existing buildings.

Paul Stinchcombe QC Noted for the experience he brings to judicial review proceedings and large inquiries. His recent cases have involved issues relating to the Localism Act, transport infrastructure and the national planning policy framework. **Strengths:** "Very impressive and good to work with." "He's an excellent campaigning barrister who is highly regarded." **Recent work:** Acted on a judicial review challenge to the granting of conservation area consent for the redevelopment of a site at Ward's Corner, Tottenham. The case raised issues concerning environmental impact assessment for areas of historical or cultural significance.

Brian Ash QC Offers specialist advice on planning matters concerning CPOs. He also appears before planning inquiries and at core strategy hearings. **Strengths:** "He spots the issues and delivers cases calmly and strongly." "He is a very steady soul and an extremely able, very calm influence." **Recent work:** Advised the London Borough of Enfield on the regeneration of the High Street at Ponders End.

Thomas Hill QC (see p.627) Demonstrates particular strength in planning matters involving residential development and urban extension. He is renowned for his handling of public inquiries, and frequently advises on infrastructure developments in the transport and energy sectors. **Strengths:** "A smooth and precise advocate." "Clients are very at ease with him." **Recent work:** Acted for a consortium of developers on a four-week public inquiry into a proposed urban extension at Stratford-upon-Avon.

John Steel QC (see p.727) Regularly appears in public inquiries. His areas of expertise include noise and pollution issues, and aviation-related matters. **Strengths:** "He is courteous and has an incredible sense of purpose. He'll move heaven and earth to secure the outcome that's best for his client, and is friendly and amenable." "His advice is first-class and he is also very personable. He's a perfect gentleman." **Recent work:** Represented the developers in a three-week public inquiry into the continued use of Dunsfold Aerodrome. The proceedings raised noise and pollution issues relating to the use of the airport for business aviation.

James Strachan QC Renowned for the strength of his technical understanding of planning law, he represents developers, local authorities and central government in a wide range of matters. **Strengths:** "An outstanding lawyer, who is a pleasure to work with. If you've got a seemingly unwinnable case he's the only one that's going to win it – and if you've got a marginal case he will ensure that it will become a shoo-in." "An incredibly talented barrister with a modest but highly effective style." **Recent work:** Appeared for Taylor Wimpey in the High Court, successfully defending a challenge to its residential development proposals for an area of outstanding natural beauty.

Stephen Tromans QC Draws on his expertise in environmental law to handle an array of sophisticated planning matters. **Strengths:** "He gives extremely helpful advice, and is very pleasant to work with and very helpful." "He's the master of environmental law. If you want a view on a point that is as definitive as you can get, you go to him." **Recent work:** Advised the Met Office in connection with proposed wind farm developments. The developments had the potential to affect its weather-monitoring radar stations.

Richard Harwood QC (see p.622) Specialises in handling planning matters that raise questions of environmental law. **Strengths:** "He is technically very good and can grasp technical evidence quickly. At inquiry his cross-examination is absolutely forensic – the best I've ever seen." "He knows planning and environmental law inside out and has a really nice manner that appeals to clients." **Recent work:** Appeared in a judicial review brought by RWE challenging Milton Keynes Council's policy on required distances between residential properties and wind turbines.

Matthew Horton QC Handles a wide range of planning cases and public law matters. He acts for both developers and objector groups on residential development initiatives, and appears in planning inquiries. **Strengths:** "I rate his advocacy highly. He is very thorough." "A very experienced advocate who comes across with gravitas."

Gordon Nardell QC Noted for his high-quality representation in judicial reviews. He also appears in High Court challenges. **Strengths:** "His written opinions are very good, easy to read, and explained very well. He's very much prepared to talk to you and deal with any queries." "Incredibly cerebral and very good in court; he does an excellent job."

JUNIORS

James Burton Frequently cited as a rising star at the Planning Bar, Burton has had a good year acting on CPO matters and renewable energy projects. He wins the acclaim of instructing solicitors and fellow counsel for his performances in inquiries. **Strengths:** "He's incredibly hard-working and turns things around quickly. Very good at taking on board a significant amount of information, he distils a case down to the key points." **Recent work:** Represented the landowner in a five-week CPO inquiry concerning the Orchard Wharf cement manufacturing development in Poplar, in East London.

Richard Wald Often instructed by local authorities and developers on High Court statutory challenges and judicial review matters. Interviewees are quick to highlight his commercial awareness and his dynamic and incisive advocacy style. **Strengths:** "Offers QC quality at junior rates. A complete all-rounder, he's everything you'd want as an instructing solicitor." "Very good with lay clients, he explains things carefully but not in a condescending way. Clients come away impressed and reassured." **Recent work:** He is advising HS2 on planning issues for the High Speed 2 rail project, including the hybrid bill enabling the project to go ahead.

Andrew Tabachnik His broad practice takes in a significant amount of planning work, and he has tackled a number of planning inquiries and statutory challenges of late. He is particularly active in the residential development sector, acting for major house builders. **Strengths:** "He's very responsive and good at communicating matters. He is also very quick, and gets to the point very quickly." **Recent work:** He acted for developers Grainger on a judicial review of Haringey Council's decision to grant planning permission to redevelop Seven Sisters Underground station.

Christiaan Zwart (see p.758) A new entry in the rankings, he has acted on a number of high-profile infrastructure projects in the energy and water sectors over the past year. He is highlighted by sources for his intellectual capability and his ability to quickly identify the most pertinent issues in complex cases. **Strengths:** "There's an academic excellence to Christiaan Zwart – he'll come forward with a solution and it'll have a well-founded academic base. He's also a masterful negotiator, a sound adviser and a good draftsman, and is very affable and easy to work with." "He demonstrates an exceptionally high level of attention to detail." **Recent work:** He acted for the Environment Agency on the development consent order process for the Thames Tideway Tunnel.

Ned Helme An up-and-coming junior with experience in a range of planning and environment matters. His recent cases have included a number of residential developments, and he has also acted on transport and energy infrastructure schemes. **Strengths:** "He is excellent and as bright as a button." "He has demonstrated an eye for detail and the ability to get stuck in and work with the team under pressure." **Recent work:** He represented Cherwell District Council in a public inquiry into its refusal to grant permission for an 85-dwelling development at Deddington, Oxfordshire.

Francis Taylor Building

See profile on p.806

THE SET

Francis Taylor Building offers a comprehensive service for those seeking senior planning and environment counsel. The set is particularly well known for handling complex, long-running and often legally intensive planning applications for infrastructure developments. Its members are also regularly instructed on more traditional residential, commercial and retail planning matters, both in the High Court and at inquiry, with compulsory purchase forming an area of particular strength. Many tenants here are able to complement their planning practices by drawing on their proficiency in the law relating to local government and the environment.

Client service: "They are very hard-working, responsive, user-friendly, discreet, constructive and helpful." "They are always very helpful, courteous, polite and businesslike in their approach. The administration is smooth and the clerks are very good."

SILKS

Michael Humphries QC (see p.633) Renowned for his expertise in infrastructure planning law. He is also a recognised authority on compulsory purchase, development consent orders and nationally significant infrastructure projects. **Strengths:** "An extremely intelligent operator, with a laser-like focus on the issues." "Excellent on CPO compensation, he is very practical and user-friendly." **Recent work:** Represented Thames Water before the examining authority of the Planning Inspectorate. The proceedings involved assessing a development consent order application for the Thames Tideway Tunnel project.

Robin Purchas QC (see p.700) Advises on complex development and environment matters. **Strengths:** "He is brilliant on all planning and environmental advice, as he's forthright and easy to comprehend." "He has an incredible technical grasp and attention to detail. He is a go-to man for any problems and issues, and his advice is always clear, concise and accessible."

Morag Ellis QC Admired for the strength of her advocacy in public inquiries and her personable manner with clients. She is renowned for her handling of High Court statutory challenges and judicial reviews. **Strengths:** "Her reputation precedes her. She is a very effective advocate in court as she's very focused, crisp and a tenacious cross-examiner." "She creates a professional but friendly relationship with clients." **Recent work:** Represented Taylor Wimpey in a judicial review of the local planning authority's decision to designate a Neighbourhood Forum under the Localism Act 2011.

Richard Phillips QC Well known for his expertise in handling matters involving waste-to-energy projects. He also advises developers on the promotion of large housing schemes. **Strengths:** "What is most impressive is the thoroughness of his preparation and reading. He is a highly authoritative but also very penetrative advocate." "A technical expert, an assiduous advocate on waste planning cases, and very much a team player on public inquiries." **Recent work:** Acted on a called-in application for a waste-to-energy plant in Kings Lynn in Norfolk. The proceedings raised issues concerning flood risk and sustainability.

Simon Bird QC (see p.550) Admired for his handling of large planning inquiries. He acts for developers and objectors, and is often instructed by local authorities. **Strengths:** "A very smooth and efficient advocate with an unbelievable command of an immense volume of information, who is ideally suited to inquiry proceedings." "He provides practical, no-nonsense advice that is delivered in a friendly manner." **Recent work:** Appeared for Powys County Council in a conjoined inquiry concerning five separate applications for wind farm developments in the area.

Guy Roots QC (see p.710) Offers considerable expertise in the field of compulsory purchase. He is often instructed on CPO compensation cases. **Strengths:** "He delivers very good advocacy. He comes across as an elder statesman and his experience clearly carries a lot of weight before the tribunal and judges." "He's very thorough and works well with instructing solicitors. A Rolls-Royce advocate." **Recent work:** Appeared for Lancaster City Council before the Court of Appeal on a CPO compensation issue.

Richard Glover QC Specialises in planning matters involving CPO and land valuation. **Strengths:** "He's got a certain style in his advocacy – he very much commands the room." "He's extremely good with lay clients, very personable and well prepared." **Recent work:** Represented the Canal & River Trust before the examining authority of the Planning Inspectorate on the Thames Tideway Tunnel project.

Robert McCracken QC Represents landowners and objector groups in a broad range of planning and environment matters. Renowned for his expertise in environmental impact assessment, and for his command of EU environment law. **Strengths:** "Even as part of an intellectual profession, his intellect and wit are beyond compare. His ability to analyse and solve problems is a pleasure to observe." "He's very polished, able to put the arguments succinctly and very successfully, and he instils a great deal of confidence in the client." **Recent work:** He appeared before the Supreme Court in Coventry v Lawrence. The case raised the issue of whether a specific use of land can be considered an actionable private nuisance where the local planning authority has granted permission for that use.

Douglas Edwards QC (see p.594) Acts on major development and redevelopment matters on behalf of local government, developers and objectors' groups. He is particularly well known for his expertise in town and village green applications. **Strengths:** "Efficient and commercial in his approach." "Very capable, approachable and able to assimilate complex technical issues quickly." **Recent work:** Acted for the Mayor of London and the London Borough of Lambeth on a called-in public inquiry into the redevelopment of the Shell Centre in London.

Craig Howell Williams QC (see p.632) Instructed on large residential development matters and infrastructure projects by developers and local authorities. **Strengths:** "Very polite, easy-going, and good to work with. He is very good at outlining the strategy – that's very important for clients." "He's very able and extraordinarily solid in his approach." **Recent work:** Represented retailer Abercrombie & Fitch in an inquiry into its proposal to carry out structural works on a Grade II*-listed building in the Savile Row special policy area.

Gregory Jones QC An authority on environmental impact assessment, habitats directives and wider planning and environment issues. He is also renowned for his expertise in matters involving CPOs. **Strengths:** "A likeable, quick-thinking advocate who is always fun to work with and who shows a deep understanding of the implications of EU environmental law on the UK planning system." "He has a very calm and reassuring approach, and his expertise in environmental impact assessment matters is invaluable."

Andrew Tait QC Specialises in handling complex infrastructure planning matters. He is an authority on compulsory purchase compensation cases and the environment. **Strengths:** "He is an expert at infrastructure." "A very able and effective advocate, especially when handling inquiries, he is someone who is very easy to deal with."

Suzanne Ornsby QC (see p.686) Handles high-value residential development applications for promoters of and objectors to a range of housing schemes. She is also renowned for her utilities infrastructure planning practice. **Strengths:** "An excellent advocate. She is able to marshal complex legal arguments in a palatable and convincing style, and achieves successful results."

Charles George QC Advises on a broad range of planning matters. He also appears in public inquiries and High Court challenges. **Strengths:** "An exceptionally good lawyer on CPO work." "He has enormous gravitas and ability."

James Pereira QC Handles a broad range of planning matters, often relating to the environment and local government. He demonstrates particular expertise in infrastructure projects and when handling CPOs. **Strengths:** "He's just got it all – he's approachable, easy to work with, very bright, knows his stuff and clients like him." "He is brilliant at drafting written submissions and developing attractive lines of legal argument. A very able advocate who is a pleasure to work with." **Recent work:** Represented the Greater London Authority before the Lands Tribunal in a compulsory purchase compensation case relating to the acquisition of the Queen Elizabeth Olympic Park.

Saira Kabir Sheikh QC An authority on infrastructure planning work. She demonstrates particular expertise in handling matters involving development consent orders and compulsory purchase. **Strengths:** "She is a versatile all-rounder, perceived by clients as being highly approachable and user-friendly. A strong advocate with a great approach to client care, she also produces acutely incisive yet pragmatic opinions on deadline." **Recent work:** Represented a number of local authorities in special Parliamentary proceedings concerning the Rookery South waste-to-energy facility development consent order application.

JUNIORS

Hereward Phillpot Renowned for his handling of complex infrastructure projects in the transport and energy sectors. **Strengths:** "He is our go-to barrister. He is very efficient, really gets to the problem quickly, is very good at thinking around the issues, gives clear advice and guidance, and is just a really nice guy to work with. He's definitely our number-one choice. " **Recent work:** Acted for Thames Water on the promotion of the Thames Tideway Tunnel project.

Richard Honey (see p.630) Particularly adept at handling cases that raise both planning and environment issues. He often advises campaign groups opposed to wind energy developments, and is also instructed by developers. **Strengths:** "He is exceptionally good: bright, persuasive and easy to understand. Clients understand what he's saying even when he's discussing something very tricky." "He is superb. He is always well prepared, works very hard, goes the extra mile and has a very good legal brain." **Recent work:** Acted at a public inquiry for a group objecting to the granting of permission to build a wind farm in Northamptonshire. The application was recovered for determination by the Secretary of State.

Meyric Lewis (see p.655) Well known for representing local authorities in inquiry proceedings and High Court challenges. He also acts for developers on a range of residential and commercial schemes, and is a recognised authority on CPO matters. **Strengths:** "His drafting of pleadings is excellent." "He's helpful and approachable, and gives clear advice." **Recent work:** Appeared at a two-week public inquiry into the development of a 'mega-dairy' in Powys. Mr Lewis represented the World Society for the Protection of Animals, who objected to the proposal on the grounds of animal cruelty.

Alexander Booth (see p.552) Specialises in handling compensation claims arising from compulsory acquisitions. He also acts for promoters on infrastructure development matters. **Strengths:** "Very much a rising star, he has particular expertise in CPO compensation. He is experienced and clear in his advice." "He is bright and has good attention to detail. He is very good at public inquiries for town and village green applications." **Recent work:** Represented the Greater London Authority in a CPO compensation claim concerning land acquired for the construction of the Queen Elizabeth Olympic Park.

Melissa Murphy (see p.679) Focuses on handling town and country planning and compulsory purchase matters. She is also an expert in listed buildings prosecutions. **Strengths:** "She is technically excellent, has a quick grasp of the issues and is very user-friendly." "She is clear, methodical and gives good reliable advice." **Recent work:** Acted for Basildon Council in the High Court and the Court of Appeal on a Section 289 challenge to the council's enforcement decision over a Gypsy/Traveller site.

Andrew Fraser-Urquhart (see p.604) Well regarded for his handling of compulsory purchase cases and development consent orders. **Strengths:** "He is a very robust advocate, who is very thorough and offers a terrific service." "A highly effective junior who is increasingly leading cases himself. He is well liked by clients." **Recent work:** Acted for C.Ro on its opposition to an order for the compulsory acquisition of the railway serving its port.

Mark Westmoreland Smith Handles a broad range of planning matters relating to infrastructure projects. He demonstrates particular expertise in proceedings involving waste-to-energy facilities. **Strengths:** "He is a very tenacious advocate, who has a good manner with clients." "He is practical, experienced and down to earth, and always gives clear advice." **Recent work:** Represented electricity utility SP Manweb in the Powys conjoined wind farms inquiry. The proceedings concerned five separate applications for wind turbine developments in Wales.

Jeremy Pike Offers advice and representation on planning matters relating to renewable energy development and town and village green applications. He is an authority on environmental impact assessment. **Strengths:** "He is very good on his feet and can hold his own against silks." "An effective advocate, who is responsive and personable, and very good to work with."

Ned Westaway Well regarded for his expertise in energy and transport infrastructure projects. He also handles matters relating to the environment, and has a particular interest in cases involving European law. **Strengths:** "I think he's excellent. He is very calm and articulate, very quick on his feet, and thinks strategically." "He will be one of the greats of the future." **Recent work:** Represented Natural England in development consent order examination hearings for the Humber's Able Marine Energy Park, a new port that will house facilities for the construction of offshore wind turbines.

Annabel Graham Paul (see p.613) Handles a broad range of planning matters. Her areas of expertise include residential development, compulsory purchase and the environment. She also has experience of sitting as an inspector on town and village green applications. **Strengths:** "Her advice is well reasoned and clear, and comes with a solid plan of action. She is very useful and also very quick – she will turn things around quickly and appreciates when urgency is needed." **Recent work:** Acted for the claimant before the Court of Appeal in a case concerning the applicable principles of public law for substituting grounds of challenge in planning appeals.

Band 3

Cornerstone Barristers

See profile on p.781

THE SET

The set remains an attractive option for local authority clients looking for advice and representation in planning inquiries and High Court challenges. Chambers has both well-regarded silks and senior juniors, and a strong contingent of up-and-comers under ten years' call. Residential development matters are the core of the planning practice, and this year Cornerstone has seen a great deal of renewables work, regularly representing councils, landowners and developers on wind farm schemes. Planning issues relating to waste-to-energy facilities is another area of growing strength for the chambers. Clients further note the set's expertise on CPOs and related compensation claims.

Client service: "I've got a very good relationship with Paul Cray, who is absolutely fantastic. He knows when we're up against it and we need advice very quickly. He's good on budgets as well – they're very competitive in the market. "

SILKS

Mark Lowe QC A strong generalist planning silk with a busy housing and retail practice and specific expertise in heritage issues. Instructing solicitors reserve particular praise for Lowe's ability to organise and lead a professional team in a complex matter. **Strengths:** "He excels in client conferences; he's just very good and I can tell clients respond well to the way he approaches the matter. He immediately makes people feel at ease." "He delivers concise advice in an authoritative manner." **Recent work:** He appeared for Hertfordshire County Council in a public inquiry into the proposed New Banfield waste to energy development, which was opposed on the grounds of its proximity to listed heritage sites.

James Findlay QC (see p.600) A new entry to the table this year, his expertise spans the complementary disciplines of planning, local government, licensing and environment law. He is recognised by sources for his work representing local authorities in public inquiries and statutory challenges. **Strengths:** "He's got a certain style and delivery, and is absolutely fantastic when it comes to his knowledge of planning." "He is very thorough and user-friendly, and he has a very nice manner." **Recent work:** He represented Mole Valley District Council in a challenge to its decision to allow the development of a golf course in an area of outstanding natural beauty.

Anthony Dinkin QC A highly experienced silk who maintains a noteworthy planning, environment and local government practice. He has particular expertise in compulsory purchase and related compensation issues. **Strengths:** "A safe pair of hands, who is a pleasure to work with." "He's an all-rounder and has enormous experience."

JUNIORS

Mary Cook Widely regarded as one of the top-performing senior juniors at the Planning Bar. She has been particularly busy of late on residential developments on restricted land, advising both promoters and local authorities. **Strengths:** "She's fantastic on her feet, excellent. She doesn't waste her time arguing points that are lost and always puts across hard-hitting stuff when she speaks to the court." **Recent work:** She appeared at a public inquiry for developers promoting a scheme for 250 houses in an area of outstanding natural beauty at Tetbury in Gloucestershire.

Michael Bedford (see p.546) Receives praise for his clear and comprehensive written advice, his manner with clients and expert witnesses, and his eloquent advocacy. He primarily acts for local authorities in public inquiries. **Strengths:** "He was great; he's an excellent advocate, unflappable and really adaptable in his style." "He always provides strong and decisive opinions." **Recent work:** He represented Basingstoke & Deane Borough Council in a public inquiry into a proposal for 450 homes at Popley, in Hampshire.

Thomas Cosgrove A recognised expert in planning and regulatory law, who frequently represents local government bodies in public inquiries. He also appears in High Court challenges and judicial reviews. **Strengths:** "He is a phenomenally hard worker; the effort he puts into mastering the papers and turning work around is amazing." "Extremely able and a good advocate, he's very straight-up and down to earth." **Recent work:** He acted for Powys County Council on a conjoined inquiry into five wind farm applications and related overhead grid connection proposals.

Richard Ground (see p.616) Combines infrastructure expertise with an active housing inquiry practice, representing local authorities. He is praised for his clear thinking in complex cases, and for his ability to offer robust, practical advice. **Strengths:** "He provides no-nonsense, efficient advocacy." "He wins the client's confidence absolutely." **Recent work:** He represented Sheffield City Council in a judicial review into its decision to allow Sheffield University to demolish and redevelop Jessops Hospital.

Robin Green (see p.615) A well-regarded planning and local government junior, noted for his understated, persuasive style of advocacy. He is most frequently instructed by local planning authorities, but also acts for promoters. **Strengths:** "His written advice is always very thorough and considered." "He has an excellent reputation in this field and a down-to-earth manner." **Recent work:** He appeared for Babergh District Council in an inquiry into a brownfield housing development application concerning a site in Mendlesham, in Suffolk.

Asitha Ranatunga (see p.703) Acts for local government and developers on housing, commercial developments and planning enforcement cases. He has particular expertise in wind farm development matters. **Strengths:** "He's excellent, very intelligent and gives robust advice." "He has a methodical approach, is relaxed in his delivery and provides those that instruct him with a lot of confidence." **Recent work:** He appeared at a public inquiry for South Northamptonshire Council into its refusal of permission for three commercial-scale wind turbines.

Jonathan Clay A noted public inquiry advocate, who regularly acts for councils on housing and renewables matters. He also undertakes judicial review and enforcement work for a range of clients. **Strengths:** "He has a good manner with clients, and handles them very well." "He can always come up with some inventive argument which usually gets your client where they need to be." **Recent work:** He represented Cornwall Council in an inquiry into the refusal of permission for the development of a wind farm.

Paul Shadarevian Advises developers and local authorities on major housing and infrastructure developments. Also receives praise for his busy CPO compensation practice. **Strengths:** "A very smooth operator, who is very cultured and measured in his approach, and has good skills as an advocate." "He's good to work with, very thorough and a hard worker." **Recent work:** He advised Thurrock Borough Council on planning and environment issues relating to the London Gateway port project.

Clare Parry (see p.690) An up-and-coming junior with a growing reputation in planning. Instructing solicitors and clients praise her advocacy when handling inquiries and when before the High Court. **Strengths:** "Very good at getting an early and strong grip on a complex case." "She's very diligent and very good value for the client." **Recent work:** She represented Powys County Council in the conjoined mid-Wales wind farm inquiry.

Michael Druce (see p.591) Advises planners, developers and councils on a range of planning matters and has expertise in a number of specialised issues, including flood risk. He has previously acted on large-scale infrastructure and retail developments. **Strengths:** "Michael has a no-nonsense style and is determined to make the strongest possible case. He puts up a fight where necessary and is keen not to leave opposing points unchallenged." **Recent work:** He advised the planning consultants on John Busch House, Isleworth, assisting with heritage issues and viability.

Adrian Trevelyan Thomas A highly experienced senior junior with a track record of representing local planning authorities and developers in inquiries and High Court challenges. He is particularly active on residential schemes. **Strengths:** "His written opinions have always been very clear and concise, and have come to a firm conclusion." "He's forceful, tough and well organised." **Recent work:** He represented Test Valley Borough Council in an inquiry concerning a proposed 150-home development at Andover in Hampshire.

Ryan Kohli Quickly making a name for himself in planning matters, he regularly appears for councils and objector groups on planning appeals and inquiries. He also acts for central government bodies. **Strengths:** "He did a thorough assessment of the case and was very helpful. Very understanding of our needs, he was able to discuss issues with clients in a manner they understand." "He's quite upfront and strong, and doesn't take prisoners in cross-examination." **Recent work:** He acted for a group of residential leaseholders in a judicial review of the decision of Westminster City Council not to allow a site to be used for food retail purposes.

Harriet Townsend (see p.739) Acts on a range of planning cases as part of her wider local government and public law practice. She is praised for the clarity and efficiency of her approach to matters, and for her robust advocacy. **Strengths:** "She's very good at chairing a meeting and making sure that it's very productive. She has a businesslike approach but is also good with the people involved." "She's able to look at a huge range of documents and get to the heart of matters." **Recent work:** She appeared for the appellant in a Section 289 appeal against an enforcement notice relating to an agricultural barn, which raised issues concerning demolition where parts of the pre-existing building had been retained within the new development.

Hugh Flanagan (see p.601) An up-and-coming junior who has quickly won the admiration of more senior counsel for his work on planning appeals and inquiries. He wins particular praise for his advocacy in these matters. **Strengths:** "I find his written work to be focused, lucid and persuasive." "His advocacy is very thorough, and he's confident and shows a bit of steel." **Recent work:** He represented Wokingham Borough Council as sole counsel before the Court of Appeal. The appeal concerned a tree preservation order.

Band 4

6 Pump Court

See profile on p.850

THE SET

A new entry for this year, 6 Pump Court has been steadily growing its planning offering and is increasingly recognised as a player in the highly competitive London planning market. The set's core specialism in regulatory work feeds into its planning offering, and chambers is able to provide well-regarded planning juniors for inquiries and High Court challenges, particularly where matters require expertise in both planning and environment law. The set wins plaudits for the modern, commercial approach of its barristers and its clerks. "I think 6 Pump Court is an exceptionally good chambers to work with," explained one client, adding: "They manage to balance professionalism with approachability; they take the stuffiness out of what has been over the years a very forbidding environment for some."

Client service: "They are friendly and efficient, and come back promptly with fee queries. They are knowledgeable about the strengths of their barristers and who is at the right level." "The clerks, led by Richard Constable, value each and every one of us as instructing solicitors, and if there's something they can do to make it better for us they will go out of their way to do it."

JUNIORS

Mark Beard An adept planning junior with complementary expertise in environment and local government issues. He is most frequently instructed by local authorities, and also acts for developers and challengers. **Strengths:** "I rate him very highly – he's quick to grasp points, builds a good rapport with the person conducting the investigation and more importantly the clients love him." "His written opinions are insightful and concise, and they always address clearly the matters at issue." **Recent work:** He represented the Royal Borough of Kensington & Chelsea in a listed building prosecution over the stripping out of the internal fabric of a Grade II-listed building.

William Upton A well-regarded junior proficient in planning and environment matters, who is recommended for his intelligent, creative advice. He is frequently instructed by the Environment Agency on planning cases, and also acts for local authorities. **Strengths:** "He does very well at reading the examiner and intervening at the correct points." "He provided detailed and considered written advice, raising relevant issues and possible solutions." **Recent work:** Represented Tunbridge Wells District Council in a contested planning application for 120 houses on greenfield land at Fowlers Park, Hawkhurst.

Anne Williams A qualified planner, she brings pragmatic and commercial expertise to a range of planning matters. She earns extensive praise from lay clients and instructing solicitors for her client care skills and strong advocacy when handling public inquiries and High Court challenges. **Strengths:** "She's really approachable, and was on the ball from the word go. She put everyone at ease and developed a really good rapport." "Anne has great attention to detail and also thinks on a strategic level." **Recent work:** She acted on the application for the development of a very large mosque complex on brownfield land in East London.

Richard Banwell A highly skilled public inquiry advocate with a strong grounding in planning and environment law. He acts for landowners, developers and local authorities on all types of planning cases. **Strengths:** "He's excellent, and well known for his planning work with an environmental aspect to it." "In his advice he gives detailed and realistic options for consideration." **Recent work:** Advised a local authority client on an application to extend a landfill site, and on the development of a landfill gas utilisation plant.

Edward Grant Acts for developers and local authorities on a range of matters, and has particular expertise in housing schemes. He is a highly skilled advocate, praised for his structured approach to conferences. **Strengths:** "His advocacy is thorough and well prepared. At times he can do the unexpected in his line of inquiry, which can pose problems for the opposition. He's a very intense and close cross-examiner of the facts." **Recent work:** He acted for Arun District Council in a public inquiry into a proposal to develop 45 homes in a controversial location near Yapton in West Sussex.

Megan Thomas Specialises in planning, environment and local government law for local authorities and design professionals, amongst other clients. She is widely praised by clients and instructing solicitors for her thorough preparation and clear, considered advice. **Strengths:** "She works well with experts and is informed, friendly and accessible throughout." "She brings a good degree of realism and incisive thinking to the case." **Recent work:** She represented Maidstone Borough Council in a judicial review challenge to the granting of retrospective planning permission for five fishing lakes.

Other Ranked Lawyers

Jonathan Karas QC (Falcon Chambers) Receives praise for his breadth of knowledge of land law, including planning matters. He is highly regarded by instructing solicitors for his compulsory purchase compensation work. **Strengths:** "Extremely good at advising on the cusp between planning and property litigation." "He's excellent – he has the ability to span lots of areas and can really see through a case."

Marc Willers QC (Garden Court Chambers) A new silk in 2014, who has long been recognised as an expert on planning issues for the Gypsy, Traveller and Roma communities. He regularly appears on High Court challenges to local planning authority decisions. **Strengths:** "He's the first point of call for any Gypsy or Traveller planning matters – he's extremely knowledgeable and an exceptional advocate." "Marc Willers is superb at dealing with Traveller families; he has a breadth of knowledge and understands minutely the cultural issues that face this client group." **Recent work:** He acted on a High Court challenge to the refusal of temporary planning permission for a Gypsy site. The case raised issues under Article 8 of the ECHR.

Timothy Straker QC (see p.730) (4-5 Gray's Inn Square) Has an active practice handling complex infrastructure projects, with particular focus on the rail and shipping sectors. He also advises on residential and retail development matters. **Strengths:** "His knowledge of planning is second to none, and his advocacy skills are very good." **Recent work:** He represented Cheshire East Borough Council in an inquiry into controversial residential development proposals.

Sarah Hannett (Matrix Chambers) Making a name for herself in planning as part of her wider public law practice. She is often instructed by the Secretary of State for Communities & Local Government. **Strengths:** "A rising star, she'll go far quickly." "Excellent, very client-friendly and good value; her written advice is very clear and her advocacy and client handling are both very good." **Recent work:** She represented a parish council in a dispute with the local planning authority over planning guidance which was issued without complying with the formalities set out under the Planning and Compulsory Purchase Act 2004.

Martin Kingston QC (No5 Chambers) One of the top planning silks, who is lauded for his advocacy and for his strategic thinking on development proposals. He primarily represents developers in public inquiries and High Court planning appeals. **Strengths:** "Always consistently fantastic, he offers strategic thinking from somebody who has seen all the angles before." "A very skilful and sought-after advocate; simply the best."

Ian Dove QC (No5 Chambers) Praised for his advocacy and his commercial awareness, he acts for local authorities and developers on a range of planning and environment matters, including protected species cases, Core Strategy issues and conservation area management. **Strengths:** "What impresses me is that he's got a very practical commercial attitude. He's a very comforting presence, who has great client care skills – it's hard not to like Ian Dove." "He's very practical, calm and approachable." **Recent work:** He appeared in a judicial review action brought by Chalfont St Peter Parish Council against a decision of Chiltern District Council concerning the Holy Cross Convent School site.

Richard Humphreys QC (No5 Chambers) Recently moved to No5 from Francis Taylor Building. His busy practice encompasses planning and local government work, and he is praised for his attention to detail. **Strengths:** "He's good at amassing a lot of detail and using it to move the case forward."

Celina Colquhoun (No5 Chambers) Noted for her involvement with nationally significant infrastructure projects matters. She also represents local authorities and developers in High Court planning appeals and enforcement actions. **Strengths:** "She provides dynamic and swift advice, and is very good with clients." "Very strong, she is doing lot of national infrastructure work." **Recent work:** She is sitting as part of the examining panel for the Thames Tideway Tunnel development consent order process.

Clive Moys (Radcliffe Chambers) Advises clients on a range of planning issues, including compulsory purchase and rating law. He receives praise for his client-handling skills and his ability to quickly get up to speed on complex matters. **Strengths:** "He is very helpful and very approachable, has a good grasp of the issues and is very good as an advocate." "Clive is a master of explaining complex, technical issues and their immediate implications for the client's situation in a very clear and practical way. He also has great commercial understanding."

MIDLANDS

Planning Midlands
Leading Sets
Band 1
No5 Chambers *
Leading Silks
Star individuals
Kingston Martin *No5 Chambers*
Band 1
Cahill Jeremy *No5 Chambers* [A]
Crean Anthony *Kings Chambers (ORL)* ◊ *
Dove Ian *No5 Chambers*
Leading Juniors
Band 1
Goatley Peter *No5 Chambers* [A]
Kimblin Richard *No5 Chambers* *
Young Christopher *No5 Chambers*
Band 2
Choongh Satnam *No5 Chambers* [A] *
Jones Timothy *No5 Chambers* [A] *
Machin Graham *Ropewalk Chambers (ORL)* ◊
Richards Hugh *No5 Chambers*
* *Indicates set / individual with profile.*
◊ *(ORL) = Other Ranked Lawyer.*
[A] *direct access (see p.11).*

Band 1

No5 Chambers

See profile on p.883

THE SET

No5 occupies an undisputed position at the head of the Midlands planning circuit, and enjoys a well-established reputation as a leading set outside London. Its members, whose expertise spans the full range of planning work, comprise a heavyweight roster of leading silks backed by an excellent group of juniors, and the set is well recognised for its ability to offer top-tier advice in sophisticated and challenging matters.

Client service: "The clerking's very good. They're always very quick to respond, very good on phone and e-mail, and very clear in their responses and advice." "Their response levels are absolutely excellent."

SILKS

Martin Kingston QC Enjoys an enviable standing as a leading planning silk in the Midlands and nationwide, with unquestioned expertise across the full spectrum of planning work. He is held in particular esteem for his clear, precise analysis of complex issues, and for his handling of major infrastructure work. **Strengths:** "He's at the top of the tree. He's fantastic – absolutely phenomenal in terms of intellectual firepower." "He keeps things so simple and makes arguments extremely forcefully. He has a wonderful advocacy style."

Jeremy Cahill QC Broadly regarded as a standout in the field. He maintains an impressive reputation for providing clear, commercial advice in complex areas, with particular strength in the residential sector. **Strengths:** "He's a very capable advocate in judicial review proceedings." "He's pretty much closed the market on speculative five-year land supply cases. There's nobody in the country better on that."

Ian Dove QC Garners significant plaudits for his wide-ranging experience in the area and for his precise, effective advocacy. He is especially highly regarded for his expertise in high-profile residential work and his skill in inquiries and appeals. **Strengths:** "He's an excellent barrister, and particularly strong on large-scale development work. He's vastly experienced and excellent with clients." "He's tenacious and very commercial." **Recent work:** He appeared in an application for a mixed-use development, successfully appealing South Staffordshire Council's decision to refuse planning permission.

JUNIORS

Peter Goatley Receives praise for his impressive range of experience and his track record in large-scale renewable and infrastructure work. Sources highlight his advocacy and his detail-oriented approach. **Strengths:** "He's accessible, user-friendly, quick-thinking and generous with his time." "I've been impressed with him in inquiries. He conducts himself very well and has a very good manner."

Christopher Young Widely acclaimed as a leading planning junior, with an impressive reputation for precision and strategic thinking in both advice and advocacy. He is especially well known for his residential-side expertise and his experience in compulsory purchase order (CPO) work. **Strengths:** "His advice and input were invaluable, and he was clearly well researched. He knew every document and he was firm when he needed to be." "Chris impressed me. That young man has a bright future." **Recent work:** Acted in an appeal to secure planning permission for a major mixed-use development at Lichfield Road.

Hugh Richards Receives praise for his extensive experience in planning and his clarity of advice. He is especially highly regarded for his handling of work relating to Traveller sites and in Local Development Framework matters. **Strengths:** "He's a good strategist who provides solid, practical advice to lay clients."

Satnam Choongh (see p.571) Frequently instructed on complex residential and retail mandates, with impressive experience in waste developments. Sources point to his persuasive advocacy and thoughtful approach. **Strengths:** "He's a superb cross-examiner – he really punches above his weight." "He's excellent. He's very solid and he really knows his stuff. I'm always confident in his advice, and he's robust when he needs to be – a very sound advocate." **Recent work:** Successfully defended against Tewkesbury Borough Council's High Court challenge against planning permission for a major greenfield residential development.

Richard Kimblin (see p.646) Enjoys an enviable reputation for his experience in major energy, commercial and residential sector developments. He is praised by sources for his advocacy and his written work, with an impressive reputation for practical and clear-sighted advice. **Strengths:** "Great fun to work with. He doesn't get bogged down in the peripheral detail. He sees the issue and he's on it, and he's very good with the clients." "He's razor-sharp. On the ball, to the point and very good in court – he tells you how it is." **Recent work:** Acted in Bloor v HCA, an Upper Tribunal case relating to a valuation exercise arising from a CPO of land for the King's Way business park.

Timothy Jones (see p.641) Well versed in a wide range of planning issues and maintains an excellent profile in the circuit. Sources commend his expertise in and deft handling of complex public inquiries. **Strengths:** "He's well prepared and well briefed in everything he does on our behalf."

Other Ranked Lawyers

Anthony Crean QC (see p.581) (Kings Chambers) Heads the set's offering in the Midland Circuit, and is acclaimed for his depth of experience. His practice covers sophisticated residential and energy sector mandates, and sources highlight his precision and clarity in advocacy for major developments. **Strengths:** "He's very charming. He speaks softly and carries a big legal stick. He tends to be very succinct in what he does, whether it's written or rhetorical presentation skills – there's nothing wasted in what he says." **Recent work:** Acted in Victoria Gregory v Welsh Ministers, successfully applying to quash the planning permission for a wind farm development in Bodneithior.

Graham Machin (Ropewalk Chambers) An experienced junior with a broad planning practice. He has considerable expertise in relation to significant planning public inquiries, and is noted for his niche expertise in the intersection of nature conservation and land-use planning. **Strengths:** "He is a real authority on the application of the Habitats and Wild Birds Directives."

NORTHERN

Planning Northern
Leading Sets
Band 1
Kings Chambers *
Leading Silks
Band 1
Crean Anthony *Kings Chambers* *
Fraser Vincent *Kings Chambers* *
Manley David *Kings Chambers* *
Sauvain Stephen *Kings Chambers* *
Tucker Paul *Kings Chambers* *
Leading Juniors
Band 1
Barrett John *Kings Chambers* *
Lancaster Roger *Kings Chambers* *
Ponter Ian *Kings Chambers* *
Band 2
Cannock Giles *Kings Chambers* *
Carter Martin *Kings Chambers* *
Easton Jonathan *Kings Chambers* *
Hunter John *Kings Chambers* *
Stockley Ruth *Kings Chambers* *
* *Indicates set / individual with profile.*

Band 1

Kings Chambers
See profile on p.918

THE SET

Kings is recognised across the board as a leader in the planning sphere. The set boasts an enviable breadth of experience, and is home to a formidable group of silks and an impressive team of juniors. Its offering spans the full spectrum of planning work, with notable expertise acting in appeals and judicial reviews relating to heavyweight instructions in the energy and infrastructure sectors.

Client service: "They're very straightforward to deal with, and they're certainly the only recognised planning chambers in the North. They're easy to deal with, always prompt, the clerks are excellent and they always deliver on time." "They're brilliant – they really put themselves out for you and try to make things work. The service is second to none."

SILKS

Anthony Crean QC (see p.581) Is widely acclaimed as a heavyweight in the field. His expertise covers major developments in the residential, infrastructure, energy and retail sectors and he is praised for his clarity and precision in written work and advocacy. **Strengths:** "He's robust and a great tactician." "He's bright and a showman – an ideal choice in tricky situations, or where spoiling tactics are required. Ingenious." **Recent work:** Acted in an appeal regarding the refusal of permission for a waste management proposal with associated landfill and recycling facilities, representing the developer.

Vincent Fraser QC (see p.604) Operates a broad practice covering retail and residential work, with particular expertise in renewable energy matters. He is especially highly renowned for his surgical cross-examinations. **Strengths:** "His advice is very sage – he makes you stretch your thoughts on the matters you're dealing with. For a dogfight, I'd instruct Vincent." "Clients really rate his advice on CPOs." **Recent work:** He represented RES in an inquiry into several wind farm applications, with issues raised in the inquiry covering areas such as highway access and ecological, ornithological and landscape impact.

David Manley QC (see p.661) Is well recognised as a heavyweight in the Northern Planning Bar, heading the chambers' planning team and handling a wide range of complex appeals. His experience encompasses work for a range of clients, including developers and local authorities, and he is well versed in matters in the energy and residential sectors. **Strengths:** "He's incredibly intellectual but very approachable as well – he gives very commercial advice, he's quick to respond and he's a brilliant advocate. Very client-friendly." "He's the king of inquiries." **Recent work:** He brought a successful challenge against the Inspector's decision to dismiss an appeal against enforcement notices requiring the removal of 88 mobile homes occupied by retired individuals.

Stephen Sauvain QC (see p.715) Enjoys an enviable reputation for his formidable depth of experience across a broad array of work, including highways and village greens. He is also highly regarded for his experience in work relating to the minerals industry. **Strengths:** "He's fantastically knowledgeable and intelligent and he has a fantastic, quite dispassionate approach – he can see the wood for the trees, and his experience is second to none." "He's a brilliant planning QC who provides an extremely thorough service, and he's an excellent orator." **Recent work:** Successfully represented East Sussex County Council in an appeal against the registration authority's decision to register the West Beach at Newhaven as a village green.

Paul Tucker QC (see p.741) Receives widespread acclaim for his deft handling of an impressive range of complex planning work, including major infrastructure and residential inquiries. Sources highlight his pragmatic approach and his clear, effective advocacy. **Strengths:** "He's bright, approachable and pragmatic – a team player." "He's very client-friendly. He gets into the skin of the client's business, and he's very effective." **Recent work:** Acted in an inquiry into Trafford MBC's refusal to give permission for the redevelopment of an Edwardian house.

JUNIORS

John Barrett (see p.543) Widely considered a leading planning junior in the Northern Bar, with an impressive depth of experience across the area. Known in particular for his expertise in residential matters and his practical, committed advocacy. **Strengths:** "He's an excellent advocate and a team player – easy to deal with and efficient." "He's very experienced in all areas of planning law and he fights hard for his clients, offering a highly skilled service." **Recent work:** He successfully dismissed an appeal against a proposal for the demolition of a care home and replacement building in a conservation area.

Ian Ponter (see p.695) Recognised for his expertise in compulsory purchase order (CPO) matters and his experience in handling renewables work. He is also well versed in residential sector matters, with a clear track record in complex inquiries and appeals. **Strengths:** "He's a clear and pragmatic adviser, and a hands-on all-rounder." "He's extremely good at driving a case on a CPO, marshalling a team of advisers and working with the solicitor." **Recent work:** He represented the owner of a boutique hotel close to York Minster in an appeal against an enforcement notice.

John Hunter (see p.634) Is well recognised for his formidable breadth of knowledge throughout the planning field. His expertise covers high-profile infrastructure and energy projects alongside complex residential and retail matters, and he is highly regarded for his handling of appeals. **Strengths:** "He's extremely bright, and when dealing with clients and solicitors he's always able to listen and then formulate the best possible case." "He provides clear and concise advice to clients, and he's very approachable." **Recent work:** He represented Anglesey County Council in a public inquiry into the development of a biomass energy plant and combined heat and power plant.

Roger Lancaster (see p.650) Receives praise for his extensive specialist expertise in residential matters, with significant experience handling complex and high-profile developments throughout the area.

He is also well known for his experience in CPO work. **Strengths:** "He's good on land supply issues, and thorough – you know he covers everything." **Recent work:** He represented the appellants in a public inquiry regarding Cheshire West & Chester Council's refusal of planning permission for a mixed-use development.

Ruth Stockley (see p.729) Noted for her wide-ranging practice, covering areas such as CPOs, village greens and highways work. Sources point to her impressive track record and practical approach. **Strengths:** "She's very measured and pragmatic, and she's receptive to what the solicitor says on behalf of the client – she's a good listener and good to work with." "She gives clear, cool and concise advice on a range of matters." **Recent work:** She represented Solihull Council in a public inquiry regarding a CPO relating to a new carriageway bridge on the A45.

Giles Cannock (see p.565) Recognised for his handling of high-profile matters in areas such as waste, infrastructure and energy, alongside significant expertise in retail and mixed-use developments. He is commended both for his meticulous written work and for his persuasive advocacy. **Strengths:** "His preparation's second to none in my view. His attention to detail is brilliant." "He's excellent. He gets to grips with things very quickly, he's a good team player and he punches above his weight for his years." **Recent work:** Acted in the combined Mid-Wales inquiry promoting the 30-turbine Llanbrynmair wind farm.

Martin Carter (see p.566) Impresses with his clear breadth of expertise and skill in appeals. He is known for his strength in town and village green work, and he also handles complex energy mandates. **Strengths:** "He's well respected and rightly so – he has a really good balanced and analytical approach to things." "He's very personable and he's got an easy style – he's not an aggressive, in-your-face barrister. He's very user-friendly." **Recent work:** He represented Ryedale District Council in a proposed wind turbine development in the Yorkshire Wolds.

Jonathan Easton (see p.593) Enjoys an excellent profile in the sector, with sources pointing to his clear grasp of the technical detail of complex cases and his effective advocacy. His practice spans a wide range of instructions, and he is well known for his skill in CPO work and cases relating to Traveller sites. **Strengths:** "He's highly intellectual, approachable, pragmatic and user-friendly – a canny and impressive individual." "He is excellent as an inquiry advocate." **Recent work:** He successfully defended Preston City Council in an appeal against the Secretary of State's decision to uphold the council's refusal of permission.

POCA WORK & ASSET FORFEITURE: An Introduction

Contributed by The Chambers of Andrew Mitchell QC

Since the enactment of the Proceeds of Crime Act 2002, no area of law has developed so rapidly, or caused the courts such difficulty. The Supreme Court (and before that the House of Lords) has already considered various aspects of the Act several times. POCA issues are argued in a disproportionately high amount of appellate court hearings.

Recent developments in confiscation following conviction are of great interest to practitioners within this field. The cases of R v Waya [2012] UKSC 51 and R v Ahmad [2014] UKSC 36 have placed a greater emphasis on proportionality, a defendant's Article 1 Protocol 1 ('A1P1') ECHR rights and the discretion of the sentencing judge in balancing the competing interests of criminal benefit and available funds. These are not new concepts within the confiscation regime. However, to date, the language of the statute and the so-called 'draconian' nature of POCA have resulted in a variety of interpretations on the same facts. What has now emerged is a more purposive application: in construing the 2002 Act, guidance from the Supreme Court is that sentencing courts must take account of the overall aim of the confiscation legislation, as well as the need for practicality, to ensure that the law is clear and predictable in relation to an inherently difficult procedure. Whether or not the breadth of discretion afforded results in greater predictability or greater variance remains to be seen. The decision in Paulet v UK ECHR 134 (2014) reinforces Waya, the cumulative effect of the decisions introducing an aspect of uncertainty for prosecuting agencies which was hitherto absent from the confiscation regime.

A1P1 has been further considered in the course of remuneration for a Management Receiver appointed under s.41 of the 2002 Act. The case of Barnes (as former Court Appointed Receiver) v The Eastenders Group and another [2014] UKSC 26 considered proportionality in relation to POCA restraint. The SC concluded that to permit the receiver to recover his expenses and remuneration from assets which should never have been within the receivership would infringe the A1P1 rights of the third party. However, to take away the receiver's ability to recover his proper remuneration and expenses without compensating him would violate his rights under A1P1. In seeking a proportionate resolution, the court drew on the doctrine of unjust enrichment. Whilst this was a fact-specific case in relation to who should pay the costs and expenses of a management receiver, appointed by the Court under an order which ought not to have been made, the Supreme Court provided guidance on receivership in general terms. The crucial lesson for courts and prosecutors is the need for careful preparation, and anxious scrutiny, of future applications for s.41 POCA orders.

The decision in R v Zinga [2014] EWCA Crim 52 confirmed that a private prosecutor can bring confiscation proceedings. A consequence is that local authorities, who are technically private prosecutors, have increased their efforts in the lower courts to prosecute financial wrongdoing in order to recover their losses incurred as a consequence of criminal conduct.

Moving away from the conventional sphere of criminal law, the Money Laundering Regulations 2007 have consequences on those employed within the regulated sector, and touch on all financial institutions. The European Commission has made substantial progress on the Fourth Money Laundering Directive, seeking to enhance safeguards for the single-market financial system to prevent it being abused for money laundering purposes. At the date of writing, the proposals had passed the first vote stage. Statements issued by the Commission suggest that greater transparency in relation to the beneficial ownership of property is a focus for the Fourth Directive. Once implemented in Europe, and changes in the UK follow, the regulated sector will have to adapt to the higher standards of scrutiny expected in the field.

Under Part 5 of POCA, the National Crime Agency (formerly the Serious Organised Crime Agency) may bring civil proceedings to recover the proceeds of unlawful activity even if there has been no criminal conviction. The High Court may make such an order, under s.241 POCA, if it is satisfied that the alleged unlawful conduct occurred to the civil standard – "the balance of probabilities". In Gale v Serious Organised Crime Agency [2011] UKSC 49, the Appellant unsuccessfully contended that the application of the civil standard in determining that his assets were the proceeds of crime, particularly in the context of his acquittal in Portugal, was a breach of Article 6 ECHR. However, the jurisdiction to impose property freezing orders for the purposes of Part 5 recovery only extends to property within the jurisdiction of the UK (Serious Organised Crime Agency v Perry [2012] UKSC 35, [2012] 3 WLR 379). Given the inevitable international aspects to many such cases, POCA civil recovery proceedings are complex, dealing with ECHR issues and Strasbourg authorities alongside assessments of the merits of alleged criminality. Given the emphasis on A1P1 in recent POCA decisions concerning restraint and confiscation, it is inevitable that proportionality arguments will arise within the civil avenue open to the National Crime Agency.

Proceeds of crime is an area which continues to grow and develop. It is a specialist area, not restricted to pure crime; issues relating to POCA draw criminal, commercial, insolvency, receivership, international and equitable principles together.

ALL CIRCUITS

POCA Work & Asset Forfeiture All Circuits
Leading Sets
Band 1
The Chambers of Andrew Mitchell QC *
Band 2
6KBW College Hill
Matrix Chambers *
3PB Barristers *
3 Raymond Buildings Barristers *
5 St Andrew's Hill *
Leading Silks
Star individuals
Mitchell Andrew *The Chambers of Andrew Mitchell QC* *
Perry David *6KBW College Hill*
Band 1
Farrell Simon *3 Raymond Buildings Barristers* Ⓐ
Owen Tim *Matrix Chambers*
Shaw Antony *Red Lion Chambers (ORL)* ◊ *
Band 2
Brodie Graham *The Chambers of Andrew Mitchell QC*
Campbell-Tiech Andrew *Dyers Chambers (ORL)* ◊ *
Fisher Jonathan *Devereux (ORL)* ◊ *
Montgomery Clare *Matrix Chambers*
Peto Anthony *Blackstone Chambers (ORL)* ◊
Rainsford Mark *The Chambers of Andrew Mitchell QC* *
New Silks
Hall Jonathan *6KBW College Hill*
Leading Juniors
Star individuals
Bird Andrew *5 St Andrew's Hill* *
Talbot Kennedy *The Chambers of Andrew Mitchell QC*
Band 1
Bodnar Andrew *Matrix Chambers* *
Cassidy Sheena *3PB Barristers*
Evans Martin *The Chambers of Andrew Mitchell QC* *
Fletcher James *5 St Andrew's Hill* *
Jones Rupert *3PB Barristers*
Smith Ian *11 Stone Buildings (ORL)* ◊ *
Band 2
Ashley-Norman Jonathan *3 Raymond Buildings* Ⓐ *
Convey Christopher *The Chambers of Andrew Mitchell QC*
Fisher Richard *Doughty Street Chambers (ORL)* ◊ Ⓐ
Jackson Fiona *The Chambers of Andrew Mitchell QC*
Jarvis Paul *6KBW College Hill*
Lennon Jonathan *The Chambers of Andrew Mitchell QC*
Stancombe Barry *The Chambers of Andrew Mitchell QC*
Band 3
Freeman Lisa *Furnival Chambers (ORL)* ◊
Green Timothy *Outer Temple Chambers (ORL)* ◊ Ⓐ
Hannam Timothy *Citadel Chambers (ORL)* ◊
Irwin Gavin *Dyers Chambers (ORL)* ◊ *
Krolick Ivan *Lamb Building (ORL)* ◊
Liddiard Martin *No5 Chambers (ORL)* ◊ Ⓐ
Newcomb Quinton *Fulcrum Chambers LLP (ORL)* ◊
Yeo Nicholas *3 Raymond Buildings Barristers* Ⓐ
Up-and-coming individuals
Hays William *6KBW College Hill* *
Powell Oliver *3PB Barristers*
* *Indicates set / individual with profile.*
◊ *(ORL) = Other Ranked Lawyer.*
Ⓐ *direct access (see p.11).*

Band 1

The Chambers of Andrew Mitchell QC
See profile on p.776

THE SET
Widely hailed as the go-to set for proceeds of crime, it is home to a host of leading silks and juniors with impressive experience on the gamut of POCA work. Members have been involved in a number of defining cases on the application of POCA, including R v Ahmad and Ahmed, a Supreme Court decision concerning the compatibility of multiple confiscation orders with Article 1 Protocol 1 of ECHR. The set's enviable reputation and ability to offer a range of barristers to meet all clients' demands make it *"the* specialist chambers in this area of work."
Client service: "They are very helpful, and are responsive about helping us to get in touch with counsel. We get the commitment that we need to make sure we meet deadlines." Martin Adams is the practice director at the set.

SILKS
Andrew Mitchell QC (see p.674) A major name for POCA work, who specialises in civil and criminal asset forfeiture and has been involved in a number of the leading cases right from the inception of this area of the law. **Strengths:** "Absolutely and unequivocally the obvious choice for POCA." "A great star in the confiscation arena." **Recent work:** Acted in Namli v NCA, appearing on behalf of the former chairman of an offshore bank in a civil recovery action concerning funds laundered through the bank.

Graham Brodie QC Acts for both claimants and defendants in civil fraud claims and POCA proceedings. He has particular expertise in restraint, freezing and confiscation orders. **Strengths:** "He's an impeccable barrister. I feel like getting into trouble just to use him again!" "He's impressive and inspires confidence." **Recent work:** Continued to act for former Goldman Sachs banker Elias Preko in confiscation proceedings following his conviction for laundering proceeds of political corruption in Nigeria.

Mark Rainsford QC (see p.702) Focuses his practice on corporate criminal wrongdoing and associated fraud disputes. He represents companies and individual directors facing restraint or confiscation orders. **Strengths:** "Clients really admire him as he makes things straightforward for them." **Recent work:** Acted for the receivers in R v Alex Windsor (also known as the Eastenders case) in successfully resisting applications for restraint and management receivership orders.

JUNIORS
Martin Evans (see p.597) Represents prosecuting agencies, defendants, receivers and third parties in the gamut of POCA proceedings. He has been involved in a number of reported cases in the Court of Appeal. **Strengths:** "Very good on exceptional matters of restraint and confiscation, particularly in relation to High Court proceedings that have to be dealt with under EU legislation and POCA." "He's very industrious, has a very quick mind and is very personable and conscientious." **Recent work:** Involved in Operation Xclusive, an SFO prosecution which led to subsequent confiscation orders against individuals convicted of fraud concerning the non-supply of tickets sold online for a range of events, including the Beijing Olympics.

Christopher Convey Frequently instructed to represent third parties' interests in restraint, confiscation and receivership proceedings. His experience includes appearances in courts of all levels, including the Supreme Court. **Strengths:** "An extraordinarily talented junior who works tirelessly for his clients." "He is just superb, and is able to make intricate and complex points easily understandable to the client." **Recent work:** Advised and represented the US Department of Justice in relation to POCA restraint and international receivership following the collapse of a multibillion-dollar Ponzi fraud operated through Stanford International Bank by Allen Stanford.

Fiona Jackson Has acted on behalf of a range of prominent defence and prosecution clients, individuals and companies. She also has experience of representing foreign governments and receivers through her international fraud practice. **Strengths:** "She's practical and when you're in a case against her you can often reach an agreement." "Very clever, user-friendly, accessible and modest to boot, given her ability." **Recent work:** Acted on behalf of an Iranian businessman in an appeal against conviction and in related confiscation and condemnation proceedings concerning the breach of export restrictions to Iran.

Jonathan Lennon Has been involved in some of the leading cases in the POCA field. He is often instructed to take over confiscation proceedings in matters where he has not previously been involved at trial. **Strengths:** "He knows the law inside out and is a damned good negotiator." "He's great at managing clients and fantastic at leading conferences." **Recent work:** Acted in Gale v United Kingdom, a dispute in the European court concerning the relevance of Article 6 ECHR in state-initiated civil recovery proceedings where the defendant has been acquitted in criminal proceedings.

Barry Stancombe Acts for a range of parties involved in restraint, receivership and confiscation proceedings, including prosecuting authorities, defendants and interested third parties. He is frequently instructed on multimillion-pound disputes. **Strengths:** "His advocacy is very good but it's his application, practicality and commerciality that really stand out." "A fierce cross-examiner who won't give an inch but does so with great courtesy and dignity." **Recent work:** Acted in SFO v Afzal & McGarry, confiscation and appeal proceedings concerning a £51 million mortgage fraud.

Kennedy Talbot Receives extensive praise from solicitors and peers for his impressive POCA expertise. His practice encompasses all aspects of restraint, confiscation and receivership, and he has been involved in a number of reported cases in recent years. **Strengths:** "He's got an encyclopaedic knowledge of the area." "He's one step ahead of everyone." **Recent work:** Acted for the claimant in Namli v SOCA, a civil recovery action concerning USD7 million of funds laundered through an offshore bank.

Band 2

6KBW College Hill

THE SET

The set offers barristers at all levels to advise and act on a range of POCA matters. Members of the set cover all aspects of proceeds of crime, from cash forfeiture and restraint to contested confiscation hearings and enforcement proceedings. The set has been involved in a number of leading Supreme Court cases and is frequently instructed in judicial review proceedings relating to POCA.

SILKS

David Perry QC Receives glowing praise from peers and solicitors, who regard him as a "star silk." He frequently handles confiscation, restraint and receivership proceedings, and is a regular attendee at the Supreme Court. **Strengths:** "When he does a case he is head and shoulders above the rest." "It goes without saying that he is one of the best in this field." **Recent work:** Acted for the claimant in BDO Stoy Hayward & CPS (Eastenders), a Supreme Court case concerning raids and seizures by HMRC and associated receivership.

Jonathan Hall QC A new silk who handles a range of POCA work, including restraint and receivership and civil recovery under Part 5. He acts for the CPS on confiscation matters at the appellate level. **Strengths:** "He thinks critically about cases: he considers matters well and dispenses very clear advice and instructions." "Clever, courteous and modest." **Recent work:** Acted in Serious Organised Crime Agency v Azam, a leading Court of Appeal authority concerning the ability to vary property freezing orders under Part 5 of POCA.

JUNIORS

William Hays (see p.623) Advises prosecuting authorities, companies and overseas governments on restraint, confiscation and enforcement matters. He has appeared in a number of significant cases on confiscation, including a number in the Supreme Court. **Strengths:** "He is a very impressive young man, who has plainly focused himself on POCA work." "He is superb." **Recent work:** Acted in R v Jawad, a case concerning whether it was permissible to impose both a confiscation order and a compensation order following the decision in R v Waya.

Paul Jarvis Handles the full range of POCA work, from cash forfeiture to contested confiscation hearings. He both defends and prosecutes, and has experience in acting as a leader. **Strengths:** "He's very perceptive about the issues that are involved in POCA cases, and takes a no-nonsense approach which I really rate." "He has encyclopaedic knowledge of POCA and is very quick on his feet." **Recent work:** Acted for the defendant in proceedings to appoint a receiver following failure to pay a £272,000 confiscation order.

Matrix Chambers

See profile on p.832

THE SET

Home to a number of highly regarded barristers, this set displays particular strength in confiscation proceedings. Its select membership is made up of barristers who are frequently instructed to act and advise on proceeds of crime matters arising from large-scale frauds, many of which involve overseas assets.

SILKS

Tim Owen QC Acts for defendants in confiscation and asset recovery proceedings. He has appeared in a number of the leading confiscation and civil recovery cases in recent years. **Strengths:** "A fantastic advocate, who is not just a good lawyer but also a fantastic communicator." "He is very thorough." **Recent work:** Appeared in the Supreme Court in R v Fields and Others, a case concerning proportionality in jointly obtained benefit in confiscation proceedings.

Clare Montgomery QC A highly regarded criminal, regulatory and fraud practitioner, who frequently advises companies in connection with money laundering issues. **Strengths:** "She's formidable and massively in demand." "She continues to be really at the top of her game and is involved in all cutting-edge cases."

JUNIORS

Andrew Bodnar (see p.552) Admired by peers and instructing solicitors, who value his "encyclopaedic knowledge of the subject." He handles restraint and confiscation proceedings arising out of large-scale frauds. **Strengths:** "He's head and shoulders above everyone else and a go-to counsel for this kind of work." "He's one of the leading juniors and his advocacy is very smooth." **Recent work:** Acted in £16 million confiscation proceedings concerning an investment fraud.

3PB Barristers

See profile on p.846

THE SET

A highly regarded team of juniors handling the full range of POCA work. Members of the set are particularly strong on confiscation proceedings concerning third party rights, and many of the individual barristers have carved out a niche for themselves in more esoteric areas of POCA work and asset forfeiture. Recent work undertaken by the set includes acting for a third party in a claim relating to a £14 million confiscation order.

Client service: "They're trustworthy and they'll go out of their way to make something work. If we get an unusual matter in, I can phone and they will know who to deal with it or who to recommend. They've got the instructing solicitor's best interests at heart."

JUNIORS

Sheena Cassidy Highly regarded for her expertise in asset forfeiture matters that overlap with family law. She also has extensive experience of handling confiscation proceedings involving third party rights. **Strengths:** "You feel comfortable when you know she's in charge of a case. You know you're going to get sensible arguments, properly made and well prepared." "She is a good advocate who can think very quickly on her feet, and who gets on very well with clients." **Recent work:** Acted in a claim by a wife for a financial remedy concerning a £14 million confiscation order made against her husband following conviction for money laundering offences.

Rupert Jones Handles all aspects of the law of restraint, receivership, confiscation and civil recovery. He has experience of acting for a range of clients, including third parties, companies, liquidators and administrators. **Strengths:** "He's in a league of his own. He's very good at receivership and restraint, and he's never out of court." "His advocacy and written submissions are extremely good." **Recent work:** Acted for the defendant in confiscation proceedings relating to a fraudulent evasion of VAT worth £600,000.

Oliver Powell Acts for the prosecution, defence, third parties and receivers in the full range of POCA proceedings. He is regularly instructed by HMRC in relation to missing trader intra-community and carousel frauds. **Strengths:** "He's extremely ambitious and also the real deal: he's got what it takes to really succeed." "Very intelligent, approachable, commercial and phenomenal on his feet." **Recent work:** Instructed by the SFO to oppose an application by self-styled 'Lord' Edward Davenport to vary a multimillion-pound restraint order following his conviction for an advance-fee fraud.

3 Raymond Buildings Barristers

See profile on p.857

THE SET

The set is home to a number of highly regarded fraud practitioners, making it well equipped to deal with POCA matters. Members of the set advise and act for prosecuting agencies as well as defendants and affected third parties on the full range of restraint, confiscation and civil recovery proceedings. One source comments: "They are my go-to chambers for anything to do with serious crime. There are absolutely no weak links at all: you can get anybody and be sure to get quality out of them."

SILKS

Simon Farrell QC Highly sought after by both prosecution and defence clients to handle a range of criminal and civil issues under POCA. He has appeared in a number of leading confiscation cases in the Court of Appeal and Supreme Court. **Strengths:** "He really knows his courts and is really tenacious in achieving his aims." **Recent work:** Acted in R v Ahmad, a Supreme Court case concerning joint benefit and proportionate confiscation orders in a high-value tax fraud.

JUNIORS

Jonathan Ashley-Norman (see p.538) Undertakes confiscation work as part of his fraud and regulatory practice. He frequently represents defendants in such proceedings. **Strengths:** "Excellent on his feet, hard-working and quick to respond. A silk in the making." "He's very polite and very eloquent, and gets his point across very well." **Recent work:** Advised UK Real Estate on confiscation aspects following the property company's prosecution for offences contrary to advertising control regulations.

Nicholas Yeo Has experience in fraud, money laundering, confiscation and cash recovery proceedings. He has been involved in a number of appeals against interim remedies and confiscation orders. **Strengths:** "He's got a lot of expertise." "He's very clever and very user-friendly, and has a unique way of looking at problems, which has got us good results." **Recent work:** Acted in an appeal against a million-pound civil recovery order and property freezing order against an alleged drug dealer now resident in Spain.

5 St Andrew's Hill

See profile on p.863

THE SET

A select team of highly regarded juniors at this set specialises in confiscation and asset forfeiture and recovery. Members of the chambers frequently appear in the Administrative Court, High Court and

Court of Appeal, on behalf of defendants, third parties, prosecuting authorities and victims of fraud. Sources report: "The calibre of all the practitioners is impressive."

Client service: "It's a really well-run team. They are very aware of their clients and what we need out of their clerking." Wayne King is the senior clerk.

JUNIORS

James Fletcher (see p.601) Handles all aspects of asset forfeiture, confiscation and enforcement. He acts for government agencies, defendants and third parties, and is increasingly instructed in relation to civil recovery proceedings. **Strengths:** "He has a first-class analytical mind, and is able to assimilate and consider huge volumes of detailed material." "He's a great advocate who shows diligence throughout and is great in terms of preparing skeleton arguments." **Recent work:** Acted for the City of London Police in a successful application for the cash forfeiture of £3.2 million seized on the basis that the cash was the proceeds of money laundering and fraud.

Andrew Bird (see p.550) A highly regarded specialist in civil and criminal asset forfeiture. He has particular experience in civil recovery and cash forfeiture. **Strengths:** "He understands and has experience of asset recovery from both the proceeds of crime angle and the commercial fraud angle." "He is very bright and has a really good tactical sense of how to get where we need to go." **Recent work:** Appeared in R v Taylor & Wood, a Court of Appeal case looking at liability to excise duty of freight forwarders involved in smuggling cigarettes.

Other Ranked Lawyers

Anthony Peto QC (Blackstone Chambers) Best known for handling civil recovery proceedings as part of his international fraud practice. He frequently represents the Serious Organised Crime Agency (SOCA) in cases with jurisdictional issues. **Strengths:** "A real thinker and master strategist." "A calm head in a crisis and a barrister who is a team player." **Recent work:** Acted for the claimants in SOCA v Gale, a civil recovery action in the Supreme Court concerning the application of Article 6 of the ECHR and the costs of receiverships.

Timothy Hannam (Citadel Chambers) Receives instructions from HMRC and the Department for Work & Pensions in relation to fraud and money laundering. He is based in Birmingham and handles disputes and claims in the locality. **Strengths:** "He is excellent and a very nice chap."

Jonathan Fisher QC (Devereux) Handles confiscation and civil recovery proceedings in the commercial, finance and tax context. He is frequently instructed in relation to multimillion-pound frauds. **Strengths:** "He's academically very highly regarded and respected by all jurisdictions, including appellate courts." "Clear and consistent in his advice, he's able to see the bigger picture."

Richard Fisher (Doughty Street Chambers) Undertakes the gamut of POCA work, including cash forfeiture and civil recovery applications. He frequently appears in court in relation to confiscation proceedings. **Strengths:** "He is absolutely excellent." "He always got back to me really quickly and didn't mind me calling him in my hour of need. He gave good suggestions of how to progress with the case which I hadn't thought about." **Recent work:** Acted in the Court of Appeal in confiscation proceedings with a benefit figure of £196 million initially sought by the prosecution.

Andrew Campbell-Tiech QC (see p.564) (Dyers Chambers) Best known for handling restraint and confiscation matters. He has a substantial advisory practice, which involves both civil and criminal law. **Strengths:** "He genuinely cares about clients. He understands that POCA is terribly unfair towards the defence and he's someone who really takes that on board and fights against it." "A fantastic lawyer with a fantastic intellect and fantastic judgement." **Recent work:** Successfully reduced a £5 million confiscation order to £50,000 under Section 23 of POCA.

Gavin Irwin (see p.635) (Dyers Chambers) Handles asset freezing and confiscation matters as part of his criminal fraud practice. He frequently advises on proceeds of crime issues in the context of criminal investigations and civil proceedings. **Strengths:** "A brilliant lawyer who has a tremendously good manner with prosecutors, judges and clients." "Very good indeed, he gets stuck in and does the work."

Quinton Newcomb (Fulcrum Chambers LLP) Frequently instructed to advise on proceeds of crime and money laundering issues. He is a regular contributor of updates and articles on confiscation and POCA.

Lisa Freeman (Furnival Chambers) Acts for claimants and defendants in civil recovery, restraint and receivership proceedings. Her practice includes advising solicitors, financial institutions and banks in relation to proceeds of crime and money laundering. **Strengths:** "She knows absolutely everything there is to know about POCA, and she is totally fearless in putting her case forward." "She is very easy to work with as an opponent. She's very affable, which really makes a difference when you're getting a deal done."

Ivan Krolick (Lamb Building) Often brought in as leading counsel to conduct confiscation proceedings. He has handled a number of successful appeals in the Court of Appeal and Supreme Court, and acted for the successful applicant in R v Waya, a leading case concerning the issue of proportionality in confiscation proceedings. **Strengths:** "He is a very determined lawyer." "Juries find him very likeable and he's very good with clients."

Martin Liddiard (No5 Chambers) Undertakes POCA work as part of his wider fraud practice. He is best known for confiscation proceedings and inadequacy certificates, and tends to act for defendants. **Strengths:** "He's very well known in the fraud arena."

Timothy Green (Outer Temple Chambers) A regulatory barrister best known for POCA work in the context of regulatory proceedings. He acts exclusively for regulators or private clients. **Strengths:** "He's probably one of the best out there in terms of confiscation work." "He's very switched-on, approachable and easy to deal with." **Recent work:** Successfully represented a defendant in reducing a £2.3 million confiscation order to £240,000.

Antony Shaw QC (see p.718) (Red Lion Chambers) Handles proceeds of crime work as part of his serious fraud practice. He receives glowing praise from peers and solicitors, who value his sharp intellect. **Strengths:** "He's top-drawer and a consummate professional." "He takes time to familiarise himself with the nitty gritty matters in a case." **Recent work:** Acted in confiscation proceedings concerning a £28 million money laundering.

Ian Smith (see p.723) (11 Stone Buildings) Undertakes a large amount of advisory work in relation to proceeds of crime law. He is a founding committee member of the Proceeds of Crime Lawyers' Association. **Strengths:** "He's one of the very few at the Bar who can do criminal and civil confiscation work." "A very good lawyer who's very astute." **Recent work:** Acted in a claim brought by SOCA seeking to raise and enforce tax assessments against a foreign national with whom SOCA had previously settled civil recovery claims under POCA.

Contents:

ALL CIRCUITS Mainly Claimant

Police Law: Mainly Claimant All Circuits
Leading Sets
Band 1
Doughty Street Chambers *
Band 2
Garden Court Chambers *
Matrix Chambers *
Leading Silks
Star individuals
Kaufmann Phillippa *Matrix Chambers*
Band 1
Ryder Matthew *Matrix Chambers*
Southey Hugh *Matrix Chambers* *
Williams Heather *Doughty Street Chambers*
Band 2
Bowen Nicholas *Doughty Street Chambers* A
Bowen Paul *Brick Court Chambers*
Cragg Stephen *Doughty Street Chambers*
Hermer Richard *Matrix Chambers*
Laddie James *Matrix Chambers*
Metzer Anthony *Goldsmith Chambers (ORL)* ◊
Owen Tim *Matrix Chambers*
Tomlinson Hugh *Matrix Chambers*
New Silks
Thomas Leslie *Garden Court Chambers*
Leading Juniors
Band 1
Brander Ruth *Doughty Street Chambers* A
Hill Henrietta *Doughty Street Chambers* A
Macdonald Alison *Matrix Chambers* *
Simblet Stephen *Garden Court Chambers*
Band 2
Brown Nick *Doughty Street Chambers*
Bunting Jude *Doughty Street Chambers*
Gallagher Caoilfhionn *Doughty Street Chambers* A
Gask Alex *Doughty Street Chambers*
Gerry Alison *Doughty Street Chambers*
Hemingway Sarah *Garden Court Chambers*
Hutchinson Colin *Garden Court Chambers*
Law Helen *Matrix Chambers*
Morris Anna *Garden Court Chambers*
Roche Patrick *Garden Court Chambers*
Sikand Maya *Garden Court Chambers*
Stanage Nick *Doughty Street Chambers* A
Straw Adam *Doughty Street Chambers*
Thacker Rajeev *Garden Court Chambers*
Up-and-coming individuals
Heaven Kirsten *Garden Court Chambers*
* *Indicates set / individual with profile.*
A *direct access (see p.11).*
Alphabetical order within each band. Band 1 is highest.

Band 1

Doughty Street Chambers

See profile on p.786

THE SET

A consistently excellent police law set, undertaking the full range of actions against the police, including public law challenges, private law claims and inquests. Interviewees commented that "Doughty Street Chambers stands out as a leader in actions against the police and human rights work." "Its barristers are all very approachable and give extremely detailed advice. They show dedication, commitment and professionalism." With 41 barristers in the team, it is no surprise that market commentators refer to Doughty Street as "one of the strongest claimant sets." **Client service:** "They are still at the forefront in terms of their ethos and the level of service they give to solicitors and clients." The civil clerking team is led by Richard Bayliss.

SILKS

Heather Williams QC Regarded as "a forerunner in actions against the police," she undertakes the most contentious and high-profile cases in the field. **Strengths:** "She is a masterful advocate, who has fantastic judgement." "She is completely measured, thorough and amazing in cross-examination." **Recent work:** Acted in ZH v Commissioner of Police for the Metropolis, a matter concerning a severely autistic claimant who had been handcuffed, arrested and detained in a police van after becoming transfixed by the water of a swimming pool. The case has groundbreaking implications for disability discrimination in police interaction with the public. She is also engaged in the Hillsborough inquiry.

Stephen Cragg QC A human rights specialist with significant experience in judicial reviews and inquest work. **Strengths:** "He is great at the very technical cases." "He continues to be extremely innovative, and has a niche in data retention work." **Recent work:** Acted in R (Ali) v Justice Secretary in a case seeking compensation for three claimants who had suffered miscarriages of justice.

Nicholas Bowen QC A vastly experienced public law practitioner who is particularly adept at cases challenging the police over failures to protect those to whom they may owe a duty. **Strengths:** "He has a fantastic breadth of knowledge of the liability of the police and public authorities, and one is always confident that he leaves no stone unturned." **Recent work:** Acted in Williams v Chief Constable of Gwent Police, a Human Rights Act and negligence claim arising out of police failures to arrest a known perpetrator of domestic violence who went on to kill his estranged wife.

JUNIORS

Ruth Brander Receives regular instructions in cases where miscarriages of justice have occurred, and where police officers have acted ultra vires. She has linked prison law, criminal law and public law knowledge. **Strengths:** "She is absolutely brilliant. She develops novel legal arguments and is incredibly bright and hard-working." "You have absolute confidence that she won't miss anything and will do everything in the best possible way." **Recent work:** Acted on behalf of protesters arrested in the G20 protests of 2009 in the case of Walpole v Commissioner of Police of the Metropolis.

Henrietta Hill Undertakes a wide range of actions against the police, and has extensive discrimination and general public law experience. She has also acted in inquests and public inquiries. **Strengths:** "Very bright, very quick and really hard-working, she has a phenomenal grasp of the facts." "She is very persuasive and manages to win over everyone's confidence." **Recent work:** Acting on behalf of 22 families of victims at the new Hillsborough inquest, and has recently handled numerous cases concerning deaths in custody.

Nick Brown Regularly handles allegations of miscarriages of justice, where claimants have often spent long periods in prison, and other cases concerning police misconduct. **Strengths:** "He is relentless in his cross-examination and questioning." **Recent work:** Acted in AKJ v Commissioner of the Police of the Metropolis in a case where police officers are alleged to have deceived women into sexual relationships.

Jude Bunting Particularly skilled in the areas of civil liberties and discrimination law, and handles claims against the police when rights are violated. **Strengths:** "He is extremely erudite, and strong on the less mainstream aspects of human rights law and their application to unusual situations." "He has great strategic knowledge, is very personable and methodical, and will strive to get the right result for the client." **Recent work:** Handled the case of Michael v Chief Constables of South Wales and Gwent Police, which featured a clarification of the duty of care owed to those who call the emergency services.

Caoilfhionn Gallagher A human rights specialist, who regularly challenges the actions of police authorities via judicial review. She further acts in cases where child rights and prison law matters are engaged. **Strengths:** "She is very industrious and very thorough in going through documents." **Recent work:** Acts for families involved in a new inquest into the Hillsborough disaster.

Alison Gerry Acts in significant civil claims against the police where allegations are made of malicious prosecution, misfeasance in public office and unlawful detention. She often handles inquests relating to death in custody. **Strengths:** "She is very good at explaining what are often complex legal matters in a way that puts the clients at ease." **Recent work:** Acted in R (Miller and Others) v Justice Secretary, a judicial review into the decision not to launch a public inquiry following the collapse of a large-scale police corruption trial.

Nick Stanage An assistant coroner, who in private practice is particularly effective in inquests following deaths in custody. He is also regularly instructed in cases of misfeasance and false imprisonment, and undertakes judicial reviews challenging the decisions of the Independent Police Complaints Commission and police authorities.

Adam Straw He is particularly proficient at utilising the judicial review mechanism to challenge police and public authorities in cases where they are found to have acted unlawfully or used practices that violate human rights. He is further experienced in areas including miscarriages of justice and inquest work. **Strengths:** "He is a good technical lawyer." "He is able to advise on the real make-or-break questions to ask the experts." **Recent work:** Acted in the inquiry into the death of Azelle Rodney and the inquest into the death of Mark Duggan.

Alex Gask Conducts cases across the full range of civil actions against police and other public bodies. Areas of expertise include the law relating to protesters and data protection breaches. **Strengths:** "He is incredibly bright and hard-working." **Recent work:** Instructed in Taylor Myers v Commissioner of Police for the Metropolis, in a case where officers were alleged to have intentionally knocked the claimant from his bicycle.

Band 2

Garden Court Chambers

See profile on p.808

THE SET

Garden Court has an accomplished actions against the police team that provides comprehensive coverage of the full range of civil proceedings against the police, including actions for the torts of negligence, misfeasance in public office, assault and false imprisonment. The practitioners are also experts in human rights law, and have significant experience of judicial review proceedings. This set is "easy to deal with, committed to upholding civil liberties and preserving fundamental rights."

Client service: "Phil Bampfylde is one of the best clerks around. He's just fantastic and everyone likes him for his professionalism, efficiency and helpfulness." He leads clerks who are "flexible on fees and happy to talk, whatever the problem is."

SILKS

Leslie Thomas QC A celebrated police law expert, highly valued for his human rights law expertise and his experience of handling inquests. His police practice sees him receiving high-profile instructions in civil claims launched in response to police negligence and misuse of power. Market commentators praise his cross-examination skills. **Strengths:** "He is very much a leading figure in this area." "I don't think anyone can doubt he has been in the most significant inquests for the last 25 years." **Recent work:** Instructed as lead counsel in inquests following the shooting of Mark Duggan and the death of musician David Emmanuel.

JUNIORS

Stephen Simblet Displays excellent ability in cases of wrongful detention, particularly where the claimant suffers from mental health issues. His wider work includes challenges on human rights grounds and inquests resulting from police-related deaths. **Strengths:** "He is a superb trial advocate, who has inside-out knowledge of the process. He is one of the first names that comes to mind for difficult and hard-fought police trials." "He is very bright and very good at building relationships with clients." **Recent work:** Acted in Creamer v Chief Constable of North Wales, where the female claimant was subjected to an unlawful strip search.

Maya Sikand Has a broad practice encompassing areas including malicious prosecution, trespass to person and property, and false imprisonment claims. She also has strong judicial review experience. **Strengths:** "She is a good advocate, and is able to stand her ground and respond effectively to unexpected questions." "She is obviously passionate about the client's best interests and that shines through in her advocacy." **Recent work:** Acted in Abdullah v Greater Manchester Police, an Article 8 challenge to a raid conducted upon a residential home under terrorism legislation.

Sarah Hemingway Highly regarded for her handling of civil claims brought against the police and public organisations, many of which relate to negligence and assault. She has appeared in the Court of Appeal. **Strengths:** "I am really impressed by the level of detail and care that goes into her advice." "She does not seem fazed when a hearing is not going the right way, and she has the ability to turn things around." **Recent work:** Acted on behalf of Abdulla, Arif and Faratol v Commissioner of the Metropolitan Police, a case where four youths suffered psychiatric and physical damage following a 'hard stop' being carried out on their car.

Colin Hutchinson Exhibits strong expertise in the area of inquests, particularly where the police have used unlawful or excessive force. He also has prison law expertise. **Strengths:** "He is someone who knows his stuff, particularly on inquests."

Anna Morris Has considerable understanding of police law and human rights-related claims. She is particularly good at handling cases resulting from the police treatment of protesters or those concerning mass arrests. **Strengths:** "She is brilliant. She is on the ball and positive but realistic in managing client expectations." "She is forensically analytical in her approach." **Recent work:** Acted for Lindis Percy in her unlawful arrest case against the Chief Constable of West Yorkshire Police.

Patrick Roche Enjoys a strong reputation in the field, and receives high-profile instructions in judicial reviews, inquests and wrongful arrest cases. He has previously undertaken work including failures to protect. **Strengths:** "He is totally calm at all times, and patient and courteous where others would lose their temper." "He is very knowledgeable and his advocacy is very good." **Recent work:** Instructed in both the judicial review quashing previous inquests and the new inquest into the Hillsborough Stadium disaster of 1989.

Rajeev Thacker Impresses market commentators with his strong civil liberties practice and discrimination law background. He is regularly engaged in challenges to police and public authority actions through the use of the Human Rights Act. **Strengths:** "He's immensely likeable, really easy to work with and constructive in his approach." "He is determined to utilise his knowledge to ensure that his clients get the right result." **Recent work:** Acted in Yousif v Commissioner of Police for the Metropolis, a challenge to police detention based on Articles 3 and 8 of the ECHR.

Kirsten Heaven Handles all aspects of public and private law proceedings that may arise from police mistreatment and malfeasance. She is well known for her ability in inquests and has taken on cases where police officers are accused of using excessive force in the execution of their duties. **Strengths:** "She is relentless and completely comprehensive in her approach to matters that need to be examined." "She is a fantastic advocate for bereaved families, who absolutely love her."

Matrix Chambers

See profile on p.832

THE SET

A robust team that provides high-quality representation for those wishing to make civil claims against the police. Areas of expertise include a vast array of torts, including malicious prosecution, trespass to the person and property, and also claims arising from miscarriages of justice and the application of terrorism legislation. With linked criminal law, discrimination law and civil liberties teams, the set is well placed to advise clients on the human rights implications of their cases. Matrix Chambers is particularly strong in the silk department.

SILKS

Phillippa Kaufmann QC Pre-eminent in the field, and holds public authorities and police bodies to account in all of the major courts, including the Supreme Court. She is consistently involved in the biggest civil claims made against the police for acts of negligence and the deliberate commission of wrongs against members of the public. **Strengths:** "She is a great trial advocate who knows her law and tactics inside out, and is extremely dedicated." "She is superb at thinking on her feet, and is as good at presenting innovative and detailed submissions as she is at responding off the cuff." **Recent work:** Instructed in DSD and NBV v Commissioner of Police for the Metropolis, a civil case stemming from the failure of police to arrest John Worboys after a complaint. Twenty-nine women were sexually assaulted subsequent to the complaint being brought.

Tim Owen QC Enjoys a sizeable profile, and represents clients in actions that give rise to important clarifications of significant points of law. He has handled a vast amount of judicial reviews in his distinguished career. **Recent work:** Acted in the case of R (Catt) v Commissioner of the Metropolitan Police Force, where a protester launched a judicial review against police data collection practices.

Matthew Ryder QC Advises clients seeking to make private law claims against the police for acts of malpractice. He also has major experience of criminal and civil liberties cases. **Strengths:** "His legal mind is incredibly sharp." "He has an amazing ability to connect with the client and to understand their needs. They always feel he's speaking directly on their behalf."

Hugh Southey QC (see p.725) Well regarded for his work challenging the actions of police and other detaining authorities, including private contractors fulfilling public functions. He has a strong record of appearing in Supreme Court cases. **Strengths:** "He's fantastic on his feet. If there is a novel point of law, he'll find it." **Recent work:** Acted in a case where the law was clarified in terms of the amount of force permissible for agents to use in immigration removals. Further acted in Sarjantson v Chief Constable, where the police duty to protect was said to extend to unnamed individuals.

Hugh Tomlinson QC A vastly experienced practitioner with significant human rights and public law variants to his practice. **Strengths:** "He is an outstanding all-round silk."

Richard Hermer QC Undertakes civil litigation as part of a wider practice strongly featuring public international law work. He has a strong reputation in cases where there are multiple parties to the case. **Strengths:** "He's creative, thorough and very agile in his thinking."

James Laddie QC Conducts a wide range of claims against the police arising from causes of action including false imprisonment, malicious prosecution and battery. He excels in civil actions where there is a discrimination element. **Strengths:** "His advice is excellent. He strategically thinks about the end results and gets to grips with detailed and complex evidence very well." "Where others might get a little excited, he's calm and assured." **Recent work:** Acted in Cary v Commissioner of Police for the Metropolis, a case alleging sexual orientation discrimination in the way the claimant's police reports were handled.

JUNIORS

Alison Macdonald Regularly acts in civil actions against the police concerning various torts, including negligence. She has handled major judicial reviews into significant areas of public policy. **Strengths:** "She makes things very clear for clients in terms of her written advice and produces lovely pleadings." "She's very good at getting to grips with complicated medical evidence." **Recent work:** Acted in a judicial review on behalf of David Miranda, challenging police powers to detain.

Helen Law Practises across criminal, public and human rights law, giving her particularly strong insight into actions against the police. **Strengths:** "She's extremely approachable, knowledgeable and thoroughly reliable." **Recent work:** Acted in AKJ v Metropolitan Police, a case concerning the sexual conduct of undercover police officers.

Other Ranked Lawyers

Paul Bowen QC (Brick Court Chambers) Specialises in bringing civil law claims against police and other public bodies for negligence and acts of misfeasance. He further acts in inquests. **Recent work:** Represented the claimants in S v Chief Constable of Gwent Police, a matter concerning the death of a family member in custody.

Anthony Metzer QC (Goldsmith Chambers) Well respected for his actions against the police in areas ranging from false imprisonment and negligence to assault and judicial review of police actions. **Strengths:** "Approachable, knowledgeable and excellent at cross-examination." "He is incredibly good in the way he deals with vulnerable clients, especially those who have post-traumatic stress disorder." **Recent work:** Acted in Seaford, Pugh and Others v South Wales Police, a case where police officers arrested for the murder of a prostitute brought misfeasance proceedings when their trial collapsed.

ALL CIRCUITS Mainly Defendant

Police Law: Mainly Defendant All Circuits
Leading Sets
Band 1
5 Essex Court *
Serjeants' Inn Chambers
Band 2
1 Chancery Lane
Band 3
9 Gough Square *
Leading Silks
Star individuals
Beggs John *Serjeants' Inn Chambers* *
Band 1
Barton Fiona *5 Essex Court* *
Beer Jason *5 Essex Court* *
Johnson Jeremy *5 Essex Court* *
Band 2
Leek Samantha *5 Essex Court* *
Studd Anne *5 Essex Court* *
Waldron William *Exchange Chambers (ORL)* ◊
Warnock Andrew *1 Chancery Lane* [A] *
Band 3
Bishop Edward *1 Chancery Lane* *
Keeling Adrian *No5 Chambers (ORL)* ◊ [A] *
Watson James *Serjeants' Inn Chambers* *
Whyte Anne *Atlantic Chambers (ORL)* ◊
New Silks
de Bono John *Serjeants' Inn Chambers* *
◊ (ORL) = Other Ranked Lawyer.
[A] direct access (see p.11).
* Indicates firm / individual with profile.
Alphabetical order within each band. Band 1 is highest.

Police Law: Mainly Defendant All Circuits
Leading Juniors
Band 1
Boyle Gerard *Serjeants' Inn Chambers* *
Ley-Morgan Mark *Serjeants' Inn Chambers* *
Waters Andrew *5 Essex Court*
Band 2
Basu Dijen *5 Essex Court* *
Berry James *Serjeants' Inn Chambers* *
Branston Barnabas *5 Essex Court* *
Buckett Edwin *9 Gough Square* *
Daniels Iain *Ely Place Chambers (ORL)* ◊ *
Holdcroft Matthew *5 Essex Court* *
Johnson Laura *1 Chancery Lane* [A] *
Morley Stephen *Serjeants' Inn Chambers* *
Simcock Sarah *Serjeants' Inn Chambers* *
Stagg Paul *1 Chancery Lane* [A] *
Thomas George *Serjeants' Inn Chambers* *
Weddell Geoffrey *1 Chancery Lane* *
Wells Graham *Oriel Chambers (ORL)* ◊
Williams Vincent *9 Gough Square*
Wynn Toby *KBW (ORL)* ◊
Band 3
Boon Lucinda *5 Essex Court*
Clemens Adam *7BR (ORL)* ◊
Cornell Kate *5 Essex Court* *
Fortt Russell *5 Essex Court*
Hare Ivan *Blackstone Chambers (ORL)* ◊
Mortimer Sophie *1 Chancery Lane* *
Sandhu Harpreet Singh *No5 Chambers (ORL)* ◊ [A]
Ventham Charlotte *5 Essex Court* *
Wolfe Georgina *5 Essex Court* *
Up-and-coming individuals
Collier Beatrice *5 Essex Court* *
Dixey Jonathan *5 Essex Court* *
Dobie Lisa *1 Chancery Lane* *
Williamson Oliver *Serjeants' Inn Chambers* *

Band 1

5 Essex Court

See profile on p.791

THE SET

Maintains a strong reputation for providing high-quality advocacy in the major police law cases, and devotes 35 barristers to this area of the law. Its silk line-up is particularly strong, and the set has the strength and depth to cover all instructions in matters ranging from public law challenges and inquests to civil claims for police misfeasance and negligence. Matters handled by the set include Morgan v South Wales Police, a case arising from the Lynette White murder, and Alam v Cleveland Police, a £1 million claim for abuse of powers and malicious prosecution. Speaking about the set's members, clients say: "You can be sure that they will know the issues that are important to the police force."

Client service: "The clerking team there is excellent. They are flexible and never let us down, so much so that I see them as an extension of our team. Mark Waller is an excellent chief clerk."

SILKS

Jeremy Johnson QC (see p.639) Acts for claimants and defendant police authorities in the full range of civil proceedings. He represents police authorities in matters concerning public law, employment law and internal disciplinary hearings, and is particularly good at dealing with claims that police officers have acted outside the law. **Strengths:** "He is a very effective opponent, who is focused and prepares his cases very well." "He is logical and calm." **Recent work:** Acted in R (Roberts) v Commissioner of Police for the Metropolis, in a judicial review of the use of stop and search powers in the Court of Appeal.

Fiona Barton QC A popular advocate tackling public and private law actions on behalf of police bodies, in cases ranging from the retention of information to deaths in custody. She also conducts internal hearings relating to police misconduct. **Strengths:** "One of the finest police law barristers in the country, she is very approachable and good at advising on complex legal issues." "Her advice is always very useful and her pleadings are second to none." **Recent work:** Acting in the Hillsborough inquest, and instructed in Nunn v Chief Constable of Suffolk Constabulary, a case concerning a challenge to CPS disclosure practices.

Jason Beer QC A public law specialist with a strong focus on public inquiries. He regularly defends police discrimination and misconduct claims. **Strengths:** "He is incredibly astute and very client-friendly." "He is extremely well respected by judges for his intellect and for his understated and reliable advocacy." **Recent work:** Acted for the Metropolitan Police in judicial review hearings brought by David Miranda following his detention at Heathrow airport.

Samantha Leek QC (see p.654) Expertly acts in civil and public law proceedings, defending police and other public authorities. Practice areas include the torts of malicious prosecution, negligence and unlawful detention. **Strengths:** "She is highly personable, approachable and accommodating." "She is very knowledgeable in what is a difficult area to understand." **Recent work:** Instructed to appear in the inquest following the death of Ian Tomlinson. Also acted in the inquest following the death of Mark Duggan.

Anne Studd QC (see p.731) Highly regarded for her efforts in high-profile and emotive police law cases. Her recent work has included claims of discrimination by the police. **Strengths:** "She is very decisive and intellectually very bright." **Recent work:** Acted in ZH v Commissioner of the Metropolitan Police, where the police faced allegations of disability discrimination in their handling of an autistic child. Also appeared in the inquiry following the death of Azelle Rodney.

JUNIORS

Andrew Waters A vastly experienced police law advocate with significant experience of handling allegations of misfeasance in public office and false imprisonment, among others. He has also regularly acted in public inquiries and internal disciplinary proceedings. **Strengths:** "He identifies the strengths and weaknesses of a case and presents it in a streamlined way that is palatable for the panel." **Recent work:** Acted in Evans v Chief Constable of South Wales Police, a case concerning a claimant who was tasered in his home. Also appeared in Phillips v Chief Constable of Staffordshire, where it was alleged that police officers conducting a lawful search stole £700,000 worth of property.

Dijen Basu (see p.545) Has a varied practice that is strong on human rights and protest law cases. He is also a specialist in public law challenges and advises regularly on the impact of equality legislation on police practices. **Strengths:** "He has good communication skills and is well liked by clients." "He is very thorough and approachable at any time of day." **Recent work:** Instructed in R (R) v Chief Constable of West Midlands Constabulary, a case regarding the collection of DNA of offenders not on the current database.

Barnabas Branston (see p.555) Well known for his inquest work at the Coroners' Courts. His wider practice includes internal disciplinary proceedings and actions against the police brought by members of the public. **Strengths:** "He is great; the clients absolutely love him." **Recent work:** Acted in an inquest on behalf of the Metropolitan Police into the shooting of Dorothy Groce in her home in 1985.

Matthew Holdcroft Defends in cases where police officers are accused of tortious acts including assault, wrongful arrest and misfeasance in public office. He is further experienced in judicial review and police misconduct hearings. **Strengths:** "He is very confident and businesslike, and he manages the client's expectations appropriately." **Recent work:** Acting in the inquest over the deaths of 96 people at Hillsborough stadium in the 1989 FA Cup Semi-Final.

Georgina Wolfe (see p.755) Has a wide-ranging practice that covers claims resting on civil liberties arguments and cases of failure to protect. She also undertakes employment and inquest work on behalf of police clients. **Strengths:** "She is extremely friendly, very bright and good to work with." **Recent work:** Acted in R (AXT) v Chief Constable of Kent Constabulary, which concerned a decision to close a rape investigation without informing the CPS.

Lucinda Boon Provides high-quality advice to police clients on matters varying from malicious prosecution to trespass to the person. She also advises on policy issues with regard to the Human Rights Act. **Strengths:** "She is very thorough and presents everything in a very calm way."

Russell Fortt Regularly acts in cases regarding false imprisonment, malicious prosecution and police omissions, among other matters. He also provides advice in disciplinary and misconduct hearings, and is experienced in judicial review. **Strengths:** "He has superior cross-examination skills and is impressive in terms of his oral submissions." **Recent work:** Represented the Metropolitan Police in a judicial review regarding a human rights challenge to the retention of identifying data for non-convicted individuals.

Charlotte Ventham (see p.743) Held in high regard due to her significant defendant practice that covers the full range of civil and public claims relating to acts of police negligence, misfeasance and malice. She is capable of handling inquests. **Strengths:** "She is very, very good at going through complex medical records and picking out the best points to use." "She has a very analytical, scientific way of going through the evidence." **Recent work:** Acted in Vian v Commissioner of Police for the Metropolis, defending against a claimant suing for malicious prosecution and misfeasance following acquittal in a murder trial.

Beatrice Collier (see p.575) Displays skill in both employment law and cases of police malpractice, but is also known for her ability in cases with a human rights dimension. **Strengths:** "She has an excellent grasp of employment law and is an effective advocate." **Recent work:** Acted in the important case of T v Chief Constable of Nottinghamshire Police, a matter that had significant data protection implications for Enhanced Criminal Record Certificates.

Kate Cornell (see p.578) Enjoys a strong reputation in this area and defends in a vast array of civil causes of action, including those concerning negligence, police omissions and unlawful detention. **Strengths:** "She has a very strong grasp of the details of police regulations and is authoritative as a legal adviser." "She has a good blend of practicality, pragmatism, academic ability and commercial awareness." **Recent work:** Acted in CLG, AJD and JAD v Merseyside Police, a case featuring human rights claims for breaches of Articles 2 and 8 of the ECHR.

Jonathan Dixey (see p.588) An excellent trial advocate with comprehensive knowledge of police law and experience of handling inquiries, inquests and employment law matters. His personal injury expertise is particularly useful in negligence and assault claims against the police. **Recent work:** Engaged on behalf of the Metropolitan Police to provide disclosure advice on the high-profile phone hacking case involving Mirror Group Newspapers.

Serjeants' Inn Chambers

THE SET

From its London base, the exceptional Serjeants' Inn Chambers is instructed in some of the most prominent cases in the country. This powerful police defence set has a multitude of barristers handling everything from private tort law claims to judicial reviews, civil liberties and employment matters. Inquests and public inquiries are also particular areas of expertise, and members have been involved in investigations into the Hillsborough disaster of 1989 and the death of Mark Duggan.

Client service: Lee Johnson leads a clerking team that is "always able to find someone who can help. They are amenable and able to accommodate tight deadlines."

SILKS

John Beggs QC At the very forefront in this area of law, he undertakes the most significant cases with the biggest implications for policing practice, including those that clarify the scope of the duty of care owed by officers. He has considerable expertise in cases spanning public, criminal and civil law. **Strengths:** "He is deservedly the most desired barrister in this area. Without a doubt, he is our first choice for jury trials." "He is a force to be reckoned with." **Recent work:** Acted on behalf of West Yorkshire Police on a claim made by Leeds United FC, which wanted £1.3 million in security fees repaid.

James Watson QC (see p.747) A specialist in actions against the police, who defends claims ranging from unlawful arrest to assault. **Recent work:** Involved in Hegazy and Others v Commissioner of Police of the Metropolis and Others.

John de Bono QC (see p.585) Acts in police misconduct hearings and has a strong reputation for defending cases where there is corruption. **Recent work:** Acted in Merseyside Police v Heath and Turner, where it was alleged that officers traded contraband for a confession.

JUNIORS

Gerard Boyle Has a leading police law practice but is especially known for his work in the area of police misconduct. He further acts on high-profile judicial reviews and provides policy advice. **Strengths:** "He is an effective advocate with an excellent knowledge of police disciplinary procedures." **Recent work:** Acted in disciplinary proceedings brought against PC Rice, a police officer assigned to then Home Secretary Alan Johnson, who was accused of bringing the Met into disrepute after having an affair with Mr Johnson's wife.

Mark Ley-Morgan A general specialist in all areas of police law practice. He regularly undertakes cases concerning negligent police actions, and has a significant profile in police misconduct hearings where officers are charged with deaths in custody and sexual misdemeanours. **Strengths:** "He is an excellent jury advocate who provides sensible and pragmatic advice." **Recent work:** Acted in Walker v Commissioner of Police of the Metropolis, an unlawful detention claim.

James Berry (see p.549) Impresses market commentators with high-profile and high-quality work in judicial reviews, inquests and other civil actions. **Strengths:** "The attention to detail he displays when he's on his feet is amazing." "He is well prepared and very thorough in his openings and cross-examinations." **Recent work:** Engaged in the new Hillsborough inquest, and has been providing advice to the Chief Constable of West Mercia on the 'Plebgate' scandal.

Stephen Morley (see p.677) Routinely acts in internal disciplinary hearings and public law proceedings on behalf of police authorities. He has particular experience of handling cases concerning deaths in custody. **Strengths:** "He understands the tactics we employ and is comfortable following those instructions." **Recent work:** Acted in S, F, L v Chief Constable of British Transport Police in a judicial review regarding the legality of searches conducted in solicitors' offices.

Sarah Simcock (see p.721) A civil law expert acting in tort law claims concerning negligent or malicious acts of police officers. She regularly handles cases where discrimination is alleged and where excessive force is used. **Strengths:** "She is a charismatic presence in court, but also displays that seriousness and modesty which encourages judges and juries to trust her." **Recent work:** Acted in the disciplinary case of DS Blackbrow, who did not investigate or record a rape allegation due to the effect unsuccessful prosecution would have on crime rates.

George Thomas (see p.736) Advises authorities planning policing operations and acts across the range of private and public law proceedings. He is proficient in handling protest law cases. **Strengths:** "He is a real expert in public order claims, and is meticulous in his preparation." **Recent work:** Instructed in Wright v Commissioner of the Police of the Metropolis, where a protester was detained before a planned protest against the Israeli President.

Oliver Williamson (see p.753) Admired for having a broad practice that incorporates public law and professional discipline matters. His police law work centres around civil actions for false imprisonment and malicious prosecution, among other matters. **Recent work:** Instructed in the Hillsborough inquest, and engaged in corruption investigations.

Band 2

1 Chancery Lane

THE SET

1 Chancery Lane provides consistently strong advice and representation for its police authority clients. It advises police authorities on matters of policy and practice, and also represents them in cases where officers have fatally wounded members of the public, displayed excessive force or failed to fulfil the duty to protect. Members have acted for the police forces of Essex, Sussex and the Thames Valley, among many others across the country.

Client service: "It is a very friendly, approachable and helpful chambers, with an excellent clerking team." The clerks are led by Clark Chessis.

SILKS

Andrew Warnock QC Excels in cases where claimants have suffered significant injury. His wider practice features public law challenges arising out of civil liberties violations and private law negligence claims. **Strengths:** "His quiet manner belies a steely determination and intellectual rigour." **Recent work:** Acted in Newbold v Sussex Police, a claim alleging excessive force, arising from a brain injury suffered by a man in police restraint.

Edward Bishop QC (see p.550) Receives praise from market commentators for his ability to handle large and complex cases. His particular areas of experience include negligence claims and failures to fulfil the duty to protect. **Recent work:** Instructed in Boyle v Commissioner of Police for the Metropolis, a case concerning a claimant who had been hit by a police car.

JUNIORS

Laura Johnson (see p.639) An assistant coroner in east London, who specialises in a variety of public law and private law cases. Areas of practice include police malpractice and unlawful detention. **Strengths:** "She thinks on her feet and is received very well by judges." **Recent work:** Acted in Boyle v Commissioner of the Police for the Metropolis, a case brought by a claimant who had been left paraplegic after being hit by a police car.

Paul Stagg (see p.727) A strong inquests advocate, who has extensive experience of handling police malfeasance claims. He further acts in cases with a human rights dimension. **Strengths:** "He's very good at inquests. He works very hard and always knows the case inside out." "He is forthright and unafraid of asking difficult questions." **Recent work:** Appeared in Mahieldin v Chief Constable of Sussex, a claim arising from the alleged discriminatory application of stop and search powers.

Geoffrey Weddell (see p.748) Undertakes defence work on behalf of police authorities in cases where there is alleged false imprisonment or personal injury caused by police action. He is very experienced in cases of excessive force, especially where such force involves the use of police dogs. **Strengths:** "He's very quick, very good on his feet and clients love him." **Recent work:** Instructed in Gardner v Chief Constable of Wiltshire Constabulary, a case involving an assault claim made against an officer.

Sophie Mortimer (see p.677) Defends police authorities in the full range of civil litigation, and appears in significant cases including inquests and tort law claims for injuries inflicted. **Strengths:** "She is sensible and easy to work with. Witnesses and clients like her." **Recent work:** Acted on a wrongful arrest claim made in Nicholson v Commissioner of Police for the Metropolis.

Lisa Dobie (see p.589) Represents numerous public and police bodies in personal injury claims, including those arising from road traffic incidents. Also regularly appears in inquests. **Strengths:** "She is a very able junior, who is bright and passionate." "She gives very clear advice." **Recent work:** Instructions include a case where there was an allegation of unlawful arrest.

Band 3

9 Gough Square

See profile on p.812

THE SET

9 Gough Square fields a solid police law team known for covering the full range of police law matters. It handles challenges to police protocols and practices, inquests and public inquiries, amongst other matters. Other areas of interest include false imprisonment, malicious prosecution and trespass, both to the person and to property. Regular clients include the Metropolitan Police Force and the Constabularies of Hertfordshire, Bedfordshire and Norfolk.

JUNIORS

Edwin Buckett (see p.559) Acts in cases where negligence and other tortious claims have been brought against the police authorities. He is also regularly seen handling inquests and cases of officer misconduct. **Recent work:** Appeared in re Wayne Broad, a jury inquest where the investigation centred upon the healthcare provision for a man who died in custody after suffering alcohol withdrawal symptoms.

Vincent Williams Defends police authorities and has a broad practice that includes judicial review proceedings, as well as cases where officers act without lawful authority. He also regularly advises on disclosure obligations. **Strengths:** "He is very able, very cool under pressure and very effective." **Recent work:** Acted in the inquest following the death of Gareth Williams.

Other Ranked Lawyers

Anne Whyte QC (Atlantic Chambers) Undertakes instructions on behalf of police authorities in everything from Coroners' Courts proceedings to judicial reviews of current policy and practice. She further acts in civil claims brought against the police. **Strengths:** "She consistently provides exceptional advice and demonstrates fantastic ability throughout complex cases."

Ivan Hare (Blackstone Chambers) Instructed in public law challenges to police authorities, and regularly engaged in cases for the Independent Police Complaints Commission. **Recent work:** Acted for the IPCC in a judicial review of its powers relating to the oversight of police forces.

Adam Clemens (7BR) Advises public authorities and police bodies on policy matters, data retention issues and Human Rights Act obligations. He is regularly instructed to act in inquest hearings and internal employment matters. **Strengths:** "He is very easy to deal with and has a good rapport with the witnesses. He is an excellent advocate, who shows good judgement." **Recent work:** Acted in Lerwill v Commissioner of Police of the Metropolis, a case concerning the arrest of animal rights protesters.

Iain Daniels (see p.582) (Ely Place Chambers) Acts for both claimants and defendants in cases where officers are accused of negligence, misfeasance and malicious activity. He is known to specialise in cases where injuries are caused by police animals, and also has good experience of handling inquests.

William Waldron QC (Exchange Chambers) Has a broad personal injury expertise and is highly valued in cases where it is alleged that negligence has caused a catastrophic injury. He represents a number of police forces across the North West, including the Merseyside and Cheshire police forces. **Strengths:** "He is a likeable opponent and a good jury advocate."

Toby Wynn (KBW) Represents a number of police authorities in matters ranging from the torts of wrongful arrest and assault to matters of data protection and disclosure. He is regularly briefed in cases where prima facie liability stems from the negligence of an officer, and has handled a number of matters relating to deaths in custody. **Strengths:** "He is an excellent all-rounder with good analytical skills, who gives pragmatic advice."

Adrian Keeling QC (No5 Chambers) Has a practice that comprises a variety of civil actions against the police. He regularly handles cases of false imprisonment and misconduct in public office. **Strengths:** "He is very well prepared and is an expert cross-examiner. He also has a wonderful rapport with clients." **Recent work:** Recently defended in a case where a police officer was charged with dangerous driving during a police chase.

Harpreet Singh Sandhu (No5 Chambers) Brings his specialist knowledge of criminal law and procedure to bear in a police practice where he represents the Federation of England and Wales. He acts across the spectrum of police law litigation. **Strengths:** "He is very well prepared and gets the best result for the client." **Recent work:** Acted on behalf of Daniel Watts in a case where it is alleged that he conspired to pass information to people suspected of being drug dealers.

Graham Wells (Oriel Chambers) Has a wealth of experience in personal injury and wider civil litigation. He regularly tackles cases involving injuries sustained in the course of police interaction. **Strengths:** "He is an excellent technician in terms of his attention to detail." "He is precise, thorough and robust."

PRODUCT LIABILITY: An Introduction

Contributed by Serjeants' Inn Chambers

Over the past year there have been two landmark cases in the field of European product liability: one substantive, the PIP-TUV case, and one procedural, Allen v DePuy International Limited. These highlight the importance of both regulatory controls and jurisdiction. There continues, however, to be a lack of hard jurisprudence delimiting the key concepts of the Consumer Protection Act (CPA) and its associated Directive including the vital concept of "defect". One often has to look further afield for substantive decisions which may, given the limited case law here, be applied by the UK courts in the future.

The PIP-TUV case arose out of the PIP breast implant scandal, the facts of which will be familiar as a result of widespread media coverage. In short, silicone breast implants manufactured by PIP in France were found to have been filled with an unapproved silicone gel and redesigned to dispense with an integral protective barrier. In the UK a group litigation order has allowed claims to be brought by hundreds of UK women against private clinics and such claims are ongoing. In the French courts a regulator has been in the frame: TUV Rheinland, a German company responsible for awarding EU safety certificates for the breast implants, was ordered to pay compensation to affected women. Whilst not strictly speaking part of the Directive, defendants often rely on regulatory approval in seeking to establish that a product is not defective. This decision against a regulatory body creates a new area of exposure and avenue for claimants to explore.

The PIP breast implant scandal and the alarming extent of concern regarding metal-on-metal hip prostheses have exposed the need for a new regulatory framework in respect of in vitro medical devices. The EU has proposed reforms for regulating product safety and market surveillance, which are currently expected to take effect in 2015. Further, in April 2013 the Keogh report reviewed the regulation of cosmetic interventions. The importance of the pharmaceuticals and medical devices in this legal field has been underscored by the recent release of the excellent "Medicinal Product Liability and Regulation" by Richard Goldberg, which "attempts to address the major problems which typify claims for drug induced injury as well as highlighting the complex interrelationship between liability exposure and drug regulation."

Procedurally, although England remains the forum of choice in many multi-jurisdictional claims, the lines have now been drawn in Allen v DePuy, with the High Court rejecting claims that the euro-centric CPA applied to damage caused outside the EU or EEA irrespective of the geographical location of the manufacturer. In Allen, South African and New Zealand claimants brought an action against a UK-based manufacturer of hip prostheses as a result of failed metal-on-metal hip implants. A trial on the preliminary issue of applicable law determined that – in respect of claims where the Rome II Regulations did not apply – the CPA had no extraterritorial scope. The case further indicated that the date of the event giving rise to damage should be the date of supply of, in this case, hip prostheses, rather than the date of manufacture or distribution. One can foresee that there will be further arguments in relation to this in the future given its importance to limitation.

Love v Halfords highlighted well-known issues around proof of defect, what evidence is allowable and the boundaries of acceptable inference. The case, involving a fractured bicycle steering tube, provides a stark example of the inherent evidential complexity which abounds in this area, despite the declared aim of the directive to simplify matters of proof for claimants. The court ruled that the claimant bore the burden of proving that he had suffered an accident and head injuries as a consequence of a steering tube failure, but that the defendant bore the burden of proving the CPA section 4 defence that the defect in the steering tube did not exist in the bicycle at the relevant time of supply to the claimant. Both sides relied on expert engineering evidence but a joint fractography expert's microscopic examination revealed stresses which he said could only be due to an earlier accident, which was held by the Court to support the defendant expert's theory. This case illustrates the enormous difficulties faced in accessing key evidence, despite the essential need to gain as much detail as possible of the mechanism of failure of a product, and understanding of the original design/specification, testing and manufacturing/quality control processes involved in advance of trial.

A warning for manufacturers is provided in the Court of Appeal decision in Manton Hire and Sales Ltd v Ash Manor Cheese Company Ltd, where it was held that there was no failure to mitigate where a proposal by a manufacturer to modify a defective product was insufficiently detailed and a fully informed decision could not be made.

The PIP Breast Implant Litigation has further highlighted the implications of manufacturer insolvency and the need for claimant lawyers to consider pursuing concurrent claims under the Consumer Credit Act 1974 where a claimant has used a credit card or has been provided with any other form of credit, to finance or part-finance their operation.

The recent news that eight victims of the Thalidomide disaster have launched legal action against the drug's manufacturer and distributor and that hundreds of Scottish women are considering launching legal action in relation to distressing injuries caused by vaginal mesh implants means that product liability claims will no doubt remain in the news and in the public consciousness for many years to come. However, where the usual defendant has gone bust claimants may find it necessary to look further afield for pockets deep enough to meet any liability, something of which both insurers and regulatory bodies need to be aware.

Contents:

LONDON

Product Liability London
Leading Sets
Band 1
Henderson Chambers *
Band 2
7BR *
Crown Office Chambers *
Doughty Street Chambers *
4 New Square *
Band 3
Thirty Nine Essex Street *
Fountain Court Chambers *
Serjeants' Inn Chambers

Leading Silks
Star individuals
Gibson Charles *Henderson Chambers* [A] *
Oppenheim Robin *Doughty Street Chambers*
Band 1
Maskrey Simeon *7BR*
Popat Prashant *Henderson Chambers* [A] *
Preston Hugh *7BR* [A] *
Prynne Andrew *Temple Garden Chambers (ORL)* ◊
Waite Jonathan *Crown Office Chambers*
Band 2
Block Neil *Thirty Nine Essex Street* *
Brook Smith Philip *Fountain Court Chambers* *
Dougherty Charles *2TG - 2 Temple Gardens (ORL)* ◊ *
Eklund Graham *4 New Square* *
Johnston Christopher *Serjeants' Inn Chambers* *
Mulcahy Leigh-Ann *4 New Square* *
Spencer Michael *Crown Office Chambers*
Webb Geraint *Henderson Chambers* [A] *
Band 3
Dashwood Alan *Henderson Chambers* [A] *
Fenwick Justin *4 New Square* *
Glasson Jonathan *Matrix Chambers (ORL)* ◊ *
Lawson Robert *Quadrant Chambers (ORL)* ◊ *
Moody Neil *2TG - 2 Temple Gardens (ORL)* ◊
Shah Akhil *Fountain Court Chambers* *
Turner David *4 New Square*
New Silks
Antelme Alexander *Crown Office Chambers*
Campbell Oliver *Henderson Chambers* [A] *
* Indicates set / individual with profile.
◊ (ORL) = Other Ranked Lawyer.
[A] direct access (see p.11).

Leading Juniors
Band 1
Medd James *Crown Office Chambers*
Riley-Smith Toby *Henderson Chambers* [A] *
Sheehan Malcolm *Henderson Chambers* [A] *
Band 2
Dilworth Noel *Henderson Chambers* *
Feldschreiber Peter *4 New Square* *
Kinnier Andrew *Henderson Chambers* [A] *
Korn Adam *7BR*
Pilgerstorfer Marcus *11KBW (ORL)* ◊ *
Powell Katie *4 New Square* *
Band 3
Bennett Daniel *Doughty Street Chambers*
Bradley Matthew *Henderson Chambers* [A] *
Gee Toby *Crown Office Chambers*
Knight Heidi *Serjeants' Inn Chambers* *
Matthews Julian D *7BR*
Power Eloise *Doughty Street Chambers* *
Power Erica *Crown Office Chambers*
Purnell James *Henderson Chambers* [A] *

Band 1

Henderson Chambers
See profile on p.820

THE SET

A true market leader in terms of specialisation and bench strength, Henderson Chambers sits at the very top of the tree and is noted for its superior product liability work, particularly on the defence side. Members of the team appear in all major group litigations currently going through the courts and prove especially strong in the pharmaceutical and medical device sectors. Commentators say: "This is a go-to set and the strongest team for product liability work." **Client service:** "We have a fantastic relationship with senior clerk John White. I often ask who he suggests and we talk about which barrister is most suitable and pick counsel based on the client's characteristics. I don't find that most other chambers are as switched on to that as them."

SILKS

Charles Gibson QC (see p.607) The leading light of the Product Liability Bar, who is completely at home defending the largest and most complex group action litigations. There are very few cases at the top level that he is not involved with on the defence side. **Strengths:** "He is absolutely first-class and easy to work with." "He is the leading product liability silk and possesses very good strategic sense and very good advocacy skills, and is also highly commercial. Clients love him." **Recent work:** Instructed by Acomplia manufacturer Sanofi in a potential pharmaceutical group action concerning alleged adverse reactions to the drug.

Prashant Popat QC (see p.696) Trailblazing young silk who has really taken the market by storm. He is tackling some of the biggest work in the product liability arena and is very strong in the medical device field. Solicitors admire him for his highly effective style and the way he inspires confidence in clients. **Strengths:** "He is very effective, has excellent technical knowledge and is balanced and practical in his approach." "He is very strong when it comes to the cross-examination of expert and factual witnesses." **Recent work:** Acts for a major supplier of PIP breast implants, defending it against claims that numerous individuals suffered alleged injuries from ruptured implants.

Geraint Webb QC Incredibly well-regarded silk with a broad commercial practice that spans property damage, insurance and product liability matters. His product liability work has seen him tackling the very highest-value and most complex drug liability cases. **Strengths:** "Absolutely first-rate. He is very bright, writes very well and is extremely nice to work with." "He is intellectually brilliant and has a really great way about him when on his feet. In addition, he's very hard-working and meticulous." **Recent work:** Instructed by GlaxoSmithKline to defend claims brought against it concerning alleged side effects caused by diabetes medication Avandia.

Alan Dashwood QC (see p.583) One of the UK's foremost experts in EU law and how that impacts on product liability issues. He defends pharmaceutical clients, amongst others. **Strengths:** "He is able to get to grips with the most complex issues without delay. He then provides clear, practical solutions to seemingly the most insurmountable of problems. His manner in conference inspires absolute confidence, but at the same time he is careful to ensure that the views of others are properly considered and addressed." **Recent work:** Instructed on a group action brought by over 400 claimants against the manufacturer of antidepressant medication Seroxat.

Oliver Campbell QC (see p.564) Has a practice that is especially strong on group actions and commercial liability claims. Pharmaceutical, rail and energy companies all form part of his client base. **Strengths:** "He stepped into hearings at short notice in someone's stead and the transition was seamless." "Quietly confident and easy-going with judges, he doesn't get flustered at all." **Recent work:** Instructed in the OCENSA Pipeline group litigation by the defendant, a former BP subsidiary. One hundred Colombian farmers allege that their farms have been damaged as a result of the pipeline, which crosses the country.

JUNIORS

Toby Riley-Smith (see p.708) One of the strongest juniors at the Bar, he is often top silks' first choice for large group actions, but is also well capable of handling matters in a solo capacity. He is regularly instructed on pharmaceutical, medical device and commercial claims. **Strengths:** "He is an excellent product liability specialist, who has in-depth knowledge and displays impeccable attention to detail." "He is good on his feet and commands the respect of solicitors, barristers and clients alike." **Recent work:** Acted for hospital group Aspen Healthcare, which supplied and implanted PIP breast implants.

Malcolm Sheehan Another hugely talented junior within the Product Liability Bar, who focuses his practice on medical device, pharmaceutical and automotive claims. Clients praise his ability to proactively pursue a case and assist solicitors in a strategic manner. **Strengths:** "He's extremely thorough and very user-friendly, and gets on very well with the clients." "He is very easy to work with and very responsive." **Recent work:** Sole counsel for LTI following a product recall of taxis. Five hundred taxi drivers are seeking damages, claiming that defects in the vehicles caused engine fires that resulted in a collective seven-figure loss.

Noel Dilworth (see p.588) Actively represents both claimants and defendants in a wide range of product liability issues, and has handled cases relating to animal feed, motor vehicles and pharmaceuticals. His intellect and coolness under pressure really make him stand out. A client described him as an "outstanding junior who is my first choice for non-insurance product liability disputes." **Strengths:** "Combines great intellect with a practical approach." "Very knowledgeable, he provides good, prompt and concise written advice." **Recent work:** Acted on behalf of a claimant company for commercial butchers in a claim against the manufacturer of PVC curtains used on its premises.

Andrew Kinnier Focuses his practice on cases concerning medical and defective pharmaceutical products. Solicitors applaud him for his client-friendliness and his approachability. **Strengths:** "He is so easy to work with and he really tailors his service to the client." "We rate him very highly for his technical expertise and commercial approach." **Recent work:** Acted for 12 plastic surgeons in defending a claim brought by 53 patients who alleged that the nature of the Isolagen cosmetic treatment they had received was misrepresented to them.

Matthew Bradley (see p.555) Has a broad commercial and civil practice that spans product liability, contractual disputes and employment law. His High Court practice is especially strong. **Strengths:** "His preparation is meticulous and he has a really smart way of approaching things in terms of his legal arguments." **Recent work:** Instructed by the defendant in a £1 million claim for loss and damage due to the supply of allegedly defective organic growing media to a commercial producer of herbs.

James Purnell (see p.701) Specialist in medical device and pharmaceutical product litigation. He offers particular insight into the law surrounding products containing nicotine, such as e-cigarettes. **Strengths:** "He's a good junior who is very easy to work with and who produces strong written work." **Recent work:** Instructed by the defendant pharmaceutical client in the fetal anticonvulsant group litigation. The action was brought by 166 children alleging congenital defects as a result of exposure in utero to the anti-epilepsy drug.

Band 2

7BR
See profile on p.772

THE SET

A very strong set that focuses on representing claimants in product liability cases. Its members are highly active in the medical device sector, and have taken leading roles in both the PIP and metal-on-metal hip group litigation orders. Beyond that they have also represented claimants in the automotive and agricultural machinery areas.

SILKS

Hugh Preston QC (see p.698) One of the best claimant barristers for product liability issues currently practising, he has an enviable track record of leading very large group litigation cases. He focuses his practice on matters relating to medical devices and clinical negligence. **Strengths:** "He is a really bright guy who is very approachable for a QC. He is also very easy to work with and is able to deal with very complex litigation in a straightforward way." "A smooth, understated performer." **Recent work:** Co-head of the claimant side of the PIP breast implant group litigation. This case involves several thousand claimants and several hundred defendants.

Simeon Maskrey QC Veteran within the field who focuses on servicing claimants. He is hugely respected by the market for the strength of his advocacy and for his deep understanding of the sector. An interviewee described him as "fearsomely bright, but approachable and easy to work with." **Strengths:** "Be very afraid if you are against him. He is very confident, competent and compelling." "Cerebral, thoughtful and pragmatic, he's one of a small group of silks whose contribution on behalf of claimants has been fundamental."

JUNIORS

Adam Korn Highly respected for his medical product liability work. His practice covers cases relating to vaccines, implants and prosthetics, as well as pharmaceutical claims. **Strengths:** "He is approachable, flexible and dependable, and also fantastic with clients." "He's a senior junior who is like a silk without the title. He has criminal experience which really helps his advocacy." **Recent work:** Instructed in the Medtronic defibrillator group litigation.

Julian Matthews Acts for defendants as well as claimants, most often in cases relating to medical or pharmaceutical products. He is also experienced in automotive product work. **Strengths:** "He is very good and a pro at this work." **Recent work:** Instructed by the claimants in the Seroxat group litigation.

Crown Office Chambers
See profile on p.782

THE SET

Possesses expertise in defending large group litigation actions, especially in both the pharmaceutical and medical device arenas. The team is also adept at litigating non-medical work, and proves proficient in industrial, consumer and automotive cases. Interviewees praise its "strength in depth" and overall capability in the area.

Client service: "Their clerks, led by Andy Flanagan, are brilliant. If I e-mail them they get back to me straight away. They are the best chambers in terms of responsiveness from the clerks."

SILKS

Alexander Antelme QC Offers clients a broad practice that focuses on commercial liability. In the product liability field he is renowned for both his high-profile medical and non-medical work, and covers anything from food contamination to industrial failures. **Strengths:** "A first-class advocate who pays great attention to the detail." **Recent work:** Instructed by metal-on-metal hip defendant DePuy in its group litigation. The case involved thousands of individual claims relating to several different prostheses.

Jonathan Waite QC An astute and seasoned leader, who defends clients involved in large group litigation work. He has an especially weighty medical device practice, and is praised for his "fantastic attention to detail." **Strengths:** "Very detail-oriented and practical, he gets to grips with the facts very readily." "He has excellent legal and procedural knowledge, and is able to grasp complex facts quickly." **Recent work:** Represented Transform Medical Group, the second largest supplier of PIP breast implants, in the PIP group action.

Michael Spencer QC A veteran of the product liability field who has a keen eye for tactics and procedure regarding group action litigation. **Strengths:** "He is high-profile and an obvious choice for defence work on the bigger cases." "A leader in the field who has vast experience. His tactical and procedural knowledge is excellent." **Recent work:** Defended DePuy in the metal-on-metal hip group litigation case.

JUNIORS

James Medd A talented common law barrister who specialises in product liability claims relating to property damage caused by fires and floods. **Strengths:** "It's staggering that he is not in silk as he is phenomenally capable." "His paperwork is good and very thorough." **Recent work:** Acts for Halfords in defending a claim brought by a customer who was injured following a bike failure. The case centres on technical issues relating to the bicycle steerer stem.

Erica Power Having recently spent time abroad, she has now returned to full-time practice. She is commonly instructed by the very top QCs in the area on large group litigation. A peer described her as "the defence's linchpin" when seeing her in action in a recent large group litigation order. **Strengths:** "She is a brilliant junior who provides strong support on the technical side." "Very approachable, intelligent and thorough, she has a good courtroom presence." **Recent work:** Instructed on the defence team for Schering and Wyeth in the Oral Contraceptive Group Litigation. Claimants alleged injury relating to deep-vein thrombosis and pulmonary emboli following their use of the contraceptive.

Toby Gee Practises both medical and non-medical product liability to a very high standard, and regularly handles cases concerning medical devices and fires resulting from defective products. He impresses with his technical and detail-oriented approach. **Strengths:** "He is very detailed and doesn't leave anything to chance." "He's very approachable and responds very quickly with detailed advice." **Recent work:** An allegedly defective grid heater relay installed in an Iveco vehicle caused significant fire damage to a claimant's premises. Gee represented Walton Summit, the authorised Iveco dealer, against both Iveco and the claimant.

Doughty Street Chambers
See profile on p.786

THE SET

The strongest claimant set currently in the market. The team has extensive experience of handling cases in the medical device and pharmaceutical sectors, and its members have been involved in the majority of the largest group litigations over the last decade.

Client service: "Richard Bayliss and the team are very approachable. They always pick up the phone and make it very easy to organise conferences and court hearings."

SILKS

Robin Oppenheim QC Quite simply the best claimant silk at the Product Liability Bar. When large group litigations come along it is more often than not he who takes the overall lead in these sprawling and hugely complex matters. **Strengths:** "His expertise is a given and his name is on most big cases." "He is supremely intelligent and highly experienced, and has a great eye for detail." **Recent work:** Led the six-counsel team on the claimant side of the DePuy Pinnacle Cup metal-on-metal hip replacement group litigation.

JUNIORS

Daniel Bennett Undertakes a very strong product liability practice that focuses on medical device and drug cases. He also has a significant personal injury practice. **Strengths:** "He is very user-friendly and very helpful, and he presents well to the clients." "Absolutely fantastic. He is good on the limitation issues relating to products from outside the EU." **Recent work:** Acts in both individual cases and group litigations for claimants who face metal-on-metal hip injuries. These cases have involved blood metal contamination and early hip revisions.

Eloise Power (see p.697) Acts both alone and led on major pieces of litigation. She has particular experience of co-ordinating group litigations for large numbers of claimant clients in both product liability and clinical negligence cases. **Strengths:** "She is a very hard worker who fights the client's corner and maximises the damages. She is prepared to take on the toughest cases." "She gets to grips with matters very quickly and is very approachable and easy to work with." **Recent work:** Acted as first junior on the Pinnacle metal-on-metal hip group litigation case.

4 New Square

See profile on p.835

THE SET

Product liability is a core focus for this highly respected commercial set. Its barristers commonly act for the defendant on a wide range of product liability matters, and handle anything from cases emanating out of defective machinery to pharmaceutical and medical device work. They are also frequently instructed by the government on big-ticket cases.

Client service: "The clerking team led by Lizzy Stewart offers very good advice."

SILKS

Leigh-Ann Mulcahy QC Frequently represents government bodies including the Ministry of Defence and was recently appointed First Counsel to the Welsh Government. She is a confident and able advocate who has litigated cases at the Supreme Court level. **Strengths:** "She has the ability to put difficult legislation and points of law into plain English." "Her deep grasp of the subject means that she can identify the key issues and concentrate on them." **Recent work:** Acted on behalf of a private clinic defendant in the PIP breast implant group litigation.

Justin Fenwick QC Has a broad commercial litigation practice and proves particularly strong on professional and product liability cases, as well as those relating to the life sciences sector. When not attending to his busy practice he sits as a deputy High Court judge. **Strengths:** "He is very, very good indeed and is often retained by government bodies."

Graham Eklund QC A hugely impressive barrister who has a broad practice. He has had good recent success handling product liability cases relating to fires caused by defective products. **Strengths:** "A formidable opponent." "A very strong barrister who is good at coverage work." **Recent work:** Acted in a £2 million claim following damage caused to newspaper printing machinery when a jaw blade fractured.

David Turner QC Possesses a substantial and broad-ranging product liability practice, and has a particular specialism in cases relating to fires. **Strengths:** "A very good advocate who gives succinct advice." **Recent work:** Instructed in a case in which Pilkington sought indemnity from its insurers to settle proceedings brought in Kentucky concerning damage to a glass factory.

JUNIORS

Peter Feldschreiber (see p.599) A qualified medical practitioner as well as a barrister, he offers clients an unrivalled level of medical and pharmaceutical understanding. His practice sits at the intersection of health and product liability law. **Strengths:** "Offers clients an unparalleled understanding of every aspect of the pharmaceutical sector." **Recent work:** Provided advice on the duties of the regulator to protect commercially sensitive clinical development data and confidentiality.

Katie Powell A highly skilled junior who focuses her practice on product liability, and in particular cases relating to the construction and insurance sectors. She wins praise for her client-centric outlook and strong work ethic. **Strengths:** "She is really excellent and very hard-working." **Recent work:** Acted in a case arising from the manufacture of allegedly defective pressure equipment used in a shell and heat condenser.

Band 3

Thirty Nine Essex Street

See profile on p.797

THE SET

A hugely able personal injury and clinical negligence set whose product liability barristers are perfectly positioned to take on complex medical product liability work. The team has been involved in both the Seroxat and toxic sofa group litigation cases.

Client service: "A very efficient clerking team led by David Barnes. They are well organised and when they commit to dates on papers they always stick to them. They also make an effort to get to know instructing solicitors."

SILKS

Neil Block QC Focuses his product liability practice on defending medical professionals and pharmaceutical companies against group litigation claims. He is also experienced in assisting individual claimants in product liability cases that result in injury. **Strengths:** "He is extremely able and an excellent negotiator." "He is very easy to engage with and as good with insurers as with lay clients who are not used to the litigation process." **Recent work:** Represented the NHS surgeons who fitted patients with metal-on-metal artificial hips.

Fountain Court Chambers

See profile on p.804

THE SET

The product liability work taken on by the set tends to be high-value in nature and typically emanates from either the pharmaceutical or aviation sectors. Clients appreciate the technical nous that the set is able to bring to bear on these complex matters.

Client service: "What I particularly like about the clerking team, led by Alex Taylor, is the way they get alongside my colleagues here so the client gets the benefit of an integrated team."

SILKS

Philip Brook Smith QC (see p.557) A highly respected silk who has recently focused his practice on the PIP litigation. Clients praise him for his analytical and statistical prowess and the edge that it gives him when dealing with expert witnesses, who are often involved in product liability cases. **Strengths:** "He is thoroughly excellent. His knowledge of product liability issues is second to none and he has great commercial acumen." "He is very sensible and gives good strategic advice." **Recent work:** Represented a defendant client in the PIP group litigation.

Akhil Shah QC Offers clients a unique practice that focuses on aerospace and industrial product failures and liability. The work he is instructed on is high-value, involves serious injury and often has widespread implications for markets. **Strengths:** "He is utterly professional and provides detailed advice on very technical matters." "His written work is very good."

Serjeants' Inn Chambers

THE SET

An impressive claimant set that has made a name for itself on high-profile group litigations. Clients praise the team for being "commercially aware."

Client service: "The efficient clerks, led by Lee Johnson, are well organised and respond to you very quickly."

SILKS

Christopher Johnston QC (see p.639) A talented claimant advocate who is currently focusing his practice on metal-on-metal hip litigation. Clients say he is "a really very strong advocate who is good on the strategic side and brings his clinical negligence knowledge to bear on product liability work." **Strengths:** "A confident and forthright barrister who is able to assimilate scientific information very quickly." "He is superb and has a deeply analytical mind."

JUNIORS

Heidi Knight (see p.647) A personal injury specialist who has broadened her practice to include product liability and clinical negligence work. She has impressed her peers with her efforts as first junior in metal-on-metal cases. **Strengths:** "Highly committed, phenomenally hard-working, highly cerebral and an excellent advocate." "Before the conferences she produced these amazing and detailed notes, which were really impressive."

Other Ranked Lawyers

Marcus Pilgerstorfer (see p.693) (11KBW) Offers a highly respected claimant product liability practice, as displayed by his deep involvement in the PIP group litigation. He impresses clients with his eye for detail and strong work ethic. **Strengths:** "A detail person who is very thorough and misses nothing. A crucial part of the team." "Very bright and hard-working, he's a man with a commercial brain." **Recent work:** Advised claimants in an action against surgeons, private cosmetic clinics and credit card companies resulting from defective PIP breast implants.

Jonathan Glasson QC (see p.609) (Matrix Chambers) Has a broad international practice that includes elements of product liability, insurance and clinical negligence work. **Strengths:** "He is a very level-headed individual who doesn't get flustered by the big challenges that arise in these cases." "He has excelled over the last 20 years in the battle for redress for victims of iatrogenic CJD." **Recent work:** Represented claimants in the DePuy metal-on-metal hip group litigation.

Robert Lawson QC (Quadrant Chambers) An aviation specialist who is frequently instructed by defendants on air incidents that involve some aspect of product failure. **Strengths:** "He's very quick at mastering very difficult cases." **Recent work:** Acted in the Court of Appeal for the appellant in a case concerning the admissibility in civil proceedings of the findings of an air crash investigation report.

Andrew Prynne QC (Temple Garden Chambers) Frequently instructed for the defence in large group litigations. His practice sees him involved in cases ranging from food contamination to clinical error and medical device failures. **Strengths:** "Experienced and regularly involved in key cases." "He has a proper product liability practice that deals in high-end cases." **Recent work:** Involved in a case where a product liability claim was made following a mountain biking accident. The claimant alleged that the accident was caused by a design defect in the front forks.

Charles Dougherty QC (2TG – 2 Temple Gardens) A very well-regarded commercial silk who takes on significant product liability work. His expertise in jurisdictional and insurance matters is what sets him apart. **Strengths:** "He is extraordinarily impressive and is sensible and incredibly persuasive in court." "He's polite and charming to be against and an intellectual heavyweight." **Recent work:** Instructed by the defendant in the DePuy metal-on-metal hips litigation.

Neil Moody QC (2TG – 2 Temple Gardens) A well-respected property damage lawyer who handles a number of cases revolving around loss caused by product defects. He also acts for clients in the medical device sector and is instructed in the PIP breast implant case. **Strengths:** "Excellent on his feet." "Softly spoken but a formidable advocate who is clear, concise and has a great court presence." **Recent work:** Acted in a multimillion-pound fire claim at an aircraft manufacturing plant caused by allegedly defective components in a grain etch line. He acted for the designers of the machinery.

Professional Discipline

Contents:

LONDON

Professional Discipline London
Leading Sets
Band 1
Blackstone Chambers *
1 Crown Office Row *
Thirty Nine Essex Street *
Serjeants' Inn Chambers
Band 2
Fountain Court Chambers *
2 Hare Court *
Outer Temple Chambers *
QEB Hollis Whiteman *
Band 3
2 Bedford Row *
23 Essex Street *
Hailsham Chambers *
4 New Square *
Band 4
5 Essex Court *
Old Square Chambers *
3 Raymond Buildings Barristers *
* *Indicates set / individual with profile.*
◊ *(ORL) = Other Ranked Lawyer.*
[A] *direct access (see p.11).*

Professional Discipline London	
Leading Silks	
Star individuals	**Sutton** Mark *Old Square Chambers*
Dutton Timothy *Fountain Court Chambers*	**Williams** Geoffrey *Farrar's Building (ORL)* ◊ *
O'Rourke Mary *Old Square Chambers*	**Band 3**
Band 1	**Aaronberg** David *15 New Bridge Street (ORL)* ◊
Beggs John *Serjeants' Inn Chambers* *	**Barton** Fiona *5 Essex Court* *
Coonan Kieran *1 Crown Office Row*	**Davies** Hugh *3 Raymond Buildings Barristers* [A]
Edis William *1 Crown Office Row*	**Havers** Philip *1 Crown Office Row*
Englehart Robert *Blackstone Chambers*	**Herberg** Javan *Blackstone Chambers*
Forde Martin *1 Crown Office Row*	**Hutton** Alexander *Hailsham Chambers* *
Foster Alison *Thirty Nine Essex Street*	**Lawrence** Patrick *4 New Square* *
Glynn Joanna *1 Crown Office Row*	**McLaren** Michael *Fountain Court Chambers* *
Hopkins Adrian *Serjeants' Inn Chambers* *	**McPherson** Graeme *4 New Square* *
Kark Tom *QEB Hollis Whiteman*	**Band 4**
Lambert Christina *1 Crown Office Row*	**Bebb** Gordon *Outer Temple Chambers*
Malek Hodge M *Thirty Nine Essex Street* *	**Beer** Jason *5 Essex Court* *
Miller Stephen *1 Crown Office Row*	**Beloff** Michael *Blackstone Chambers*
Moon Angus *Serjeants' Inn Chambers* *	**Booth** Richard *1 Crown Office Row*
Shaw Mark *Blackstone Chambers*	**Coleman** Richard *Fountain Court Chambers* *
Stern Ian *2 Bedford Row*	**Enoch** Dafydd *23 Essex Street*
Treverton-Jones Gregory *Thirty Nine Essex Street*	**Finucane** Brendan *Outer Temple Chambers*
Band 2	**Grey** Eleanor *Thirty Nine Essex Street*
Flint Charles *Blackstone Chambers*	**Hendy** John *Old Square Chambers* *
Francis Robert *Serjeants' Inn Chambers* *	**Milliken-Smith** Mark *2 Bedford Row* *
Gibbs Patrick *3 Raymond Buildings Barristers* [A] *	**Monty** Simon *4 New Square* *
Hubble Ben *4 New Square* *	**Morris** Fenella *Thirty Nine Essex Street*
Hugh-Jones George *Serjeants' Inn Chambers* *	**Mylonas** Michael *Serjeants' Inn Chambers* *
Johnson Zoe *QEB Hollis Whiteman* *	**Pleming** Nigel *Thirty Nine Essex Street*
Larkin Sean *QEB Hollis Whiteman* *	**Price OBE** Richard *Littleton Chambers (ORL)* ◊ *
Pannick David *Blackstone Chambers*	**Richards** Jenni *Thirty Nine Essex Street*
Pittaway David *Hailsham Chambers* *	**Seabrook** Robert *1 Crown Office Row*
Plaschkes Sarah *QEB Hollis Whiteman*	**Winter** Ian *Cloth Fair Chambers (ORL)* ◊ *
Robertson Patricia *Fountain Court Chambers* *	**New Silks**
Rose Dinah *Blackstone Chambers*	**Gallafent** Kate *Blackstone Chambers*

Band 1

Blackstone Chambers

See profile on p.771

THE SET

Blackstone Chambers "have no equal when it comes to breadth of experience and accessibility." The set offers regulatory expertise in all manner of areas, including the financial services, medical and sport sectors. It is regularly instructed on judicial review matters and cases on appeal.

Client service: Gary Oliver leads a clerking team that is "prompt and helpful."

SILKS

Robert Englehart QC Especially well regarded for his general public law expertise and his work on behalf of a range of regulatory bodies, including the General Medical Council (GMC) and Nursing & Midwifery Council (NMC). **Strengths:** "He provides clear and comprehensive advice." "He is a gentle, but forceful advocate." **Recent work:** Acted on behalf of the NMC in a Court of Appeal case relating to allegations of improper and sexualised misconduct.

Mark Shaw QC Regularly acts on behalf of a range of healthcare regulators, including the GMC and General Dental Council (GDC) in high-profile and complex proceedings often in statutory tribunals and administrative courts. **Strengths:** "His knowledge is encyclopaedic and he is always willing to look at practical solutions." "He is just a super brain." **Recent work:** Represented the NMC in a case concerning its ability to replace lesser sanctions with striking-off orders.

Charles Flint QC Highly regarded for his disciplinary and regulatory expertise in the financial sector. **Recent work:** Represented a former HBOS executive in FSA disciplinary proceedings concerning his alleged failure to act with due care and skill while managing HBOS's corporate lending division.

David Pannick QC A highly regarded practitioner with a particularly broad practice. He often advises on high-profile and complex matters. **Strengths:** "He is a superb advocate, and a man with a superb brain." **Recent work:** Acted for the Horserace Betting Levy Board in a judicial review case brought by William Hill concerning the meaning of the word bookmaker.

Dinah Rose QC Advises a range of industry giants in highly significant regulatory cases. **Strengths:** "She is very hands-on and will get to grips with absolutely every detail of the case." "She is practical, outcome-focused and a brilliant advocate." **Recent work:** Acted on behalf of Ernst & Young in a tribunal before the Financial Reporting Council.

Javan Herberg QC Hailed for his regulatory expertise within the financial services sector. **Strengths:** "One of the leading lights on the financial defence side." "He knows the area very thoroughly and is a very sensible person to deal with." **Recent work:** Acted on behalf of Prudential in a disciplinary case before the Financial Services Authority (FSA) that related to the failed AIA takeover.

Michael Beloff QC Handles a range of disciplinary work in the legal, sports and education sectors. **Recent work:** Advised Paul Hastings in relation to proceedings before the Law Society. This matter related to the hiring of a solicitor who had false qualifications.

Kate Gallafent QC A recent silk, she has a particularly broad regulatory practice, and represents clients from the healthcare, sport and accountancy sectors, to name but a few. **Recent work:** Acted on behalf of the Lawn Tennis Association on a number of claims concerning race discrimination.

JUNIORS

Ivan Hare Has handled a number of high-profile disciplinary proceedings on behalf of the GMC and the Independent Police Complaints Commission. **Recent work:** Acted on behalf of the GMC in Uddin v General Medical Council. This was an appeal concerning a decision taken by a Fitness to Practise Panel to remove the appellant from the medical register.

Professional Discipline London	
Leading Juniors	
Band 1	**Parker** Paul *4 New Square* *
Barnfather Lydia *QEB Hollis Whiteman* *	**Powell** Giles *Old Square Chambers* *
Boyle Gerard *Serjeants' Inn Chambers* *	**Sachdeva** Vikram *Thirty Nine Essex Street* *
Bradly David *Thirty Nine Essex Street*	**Sheldon** Neil *1 Crown Office Row*
Brassington Stephen *2 Hare Court* *	**Singh** Sandesh *2 Bedford Row*
Ferguson Craig *2 Hare Court* *	**Thomas** Owain *1 Crown Office Row*
Foster Charles *Serjeants' Inn Chambers* *	**Band 4**
Haycroft Anthony *Serjeants' Inn Chambers*	**Allen** Rupert *Fountain Court Chambers* *
Hockton Andrew *Serjeants' Inn Chambers* *	**Baumber** Kevin *3 Raymond Buildings Barristers*
Holl-Allen Jonathan *Serjeants' Inn Chambers* *	**Bex** Kate *2 Hare Court* *
Jenkins Alan *Serjeants' Inn Chambers* *	**Butt** Matthew *3 Raymond Buildings Barristers* [A] *
Kennedy Andrew *1 Crown Office Row*	**Callaghan** Catherine *Blackstone Chambers*
Lambis Marios *2 Hare Court*	**Climie** Stephen *Outer Temple Chambers*
Leonard James *Outer Temple Chambers*	**Fortune** Malcolm *Serjeants' Inn Chambers*
Morris David *Serjeants' Inn Chambers*	**Greaney** Nicola *Thirty Nine Essex Street* *
Ozin Paul *23 Essex Street*	**Harris** Rebecca *QEB Hollis Whiteman* *
Partridge Richard *Serjeants' Inn Chambers* *	**Heppinstall** Adam *Henderson Chambers (ORL)* ◊ [A] *
Peacock Nicholas *Hailsham Chambers* *	**Hobcraft** Gemma *Doughty Street Chambers (ORL)* ◊
Ramasamy Selva *QEB Hollis Whiteman* *	**Hodivala** Jamas *2 Bedford Row* *
Band 2	**Hyam** Jeremy *1 Crown Office Row*
Bradley Clodagh *1 Crown Office Row*	**Price** Clare *Hailsham Chambers* *
Colman Andrew *2 Hare Court* *	**Spencer** Paul *Serjeants' Inn Chambers* *
Counsell James *Outer Temple Chambers*	**Band 5**
Griffin Lynn *23 Essex Street*	**Atchley** Richard *3 Raymond Buildings Barristers*
Hare Ivan *Blackstone Chambers*	**Colin** Giles *1 Crown Office Row*
Horlick Fiona *Outer Temple Chambers*	**Cosgrove** Thomas *Cornerstone Barristers (ORL)* ◊ *
Hurst Andrew *2 Hare Court* *	**Dobbin** Clair *3 Raymond Buildings Barristers* *
McCartney Kevin *5 Paper Buildings (ORL)* ◊ *	**Emlyn Jones** William *3 Raymond Buildings Barristers*
McDonagh Matthew *Outer Temple Chambers*	**Hanif** Salma *Thirty Nine Essex Street* [A] *
Neale Fiona *Hailsham Chambers* *	**Hearnden** Alexis *Thirty Nine Essex Street*
Pardoe Rupert *23 Essex Street*	**Holdcroft** Matthew *5 Essex Court* *
Rahman Shaheen *1 Crown Office Row*	**Jones** Tristan *Blackstone Chambers*
Tabachnik Andrew *Thirty Nine Essex Street*	**Ladenburg** Guy *3 Raymond Buildings Barristers* *
Watson Claire *Serjeants' Inn Chambers* *	**Przybylska** Sarah *2 Hare Court* *
Band 3	**Saunders** Neil *3 Raymond Buildings Barristers* [A] *
Campbell Sarah *23 Essex Street*	**Sleeman** Susan *Doughty Street Chambers (ORL)* ◊
Carpenter Chloe *Fountain Court Chambers* *	**Spalton** George *4 New Square* *
Cridland Simon *Serjeants' Inn Chambers* *	**Uberoi** Michael *Outer Temple Chambers*
Gollop Katharine *Serjeants' Inn Chambers* *	**Whitelaw** Francesca *5 Essex Court* *
Hamer Kenneth *Henderson Chambers (ORL)* ◊ [A] *	**Up-and-coming individuals**
Ley-Morgan Mark *Serjeants' Inn Chambers* *	**Lazarus** Robert *Thirty Nine Essex Street*
McClelland James *Fountain Court Chambers* *	**Price** Louise *Doughty Street Chambers (ORL)* ◊
Newman Philip *42 Bedford Row (ORL)* ◊	**Sanderson** Eleanor *2 Bedford Row* *
* *Indicates individual with profile.*	
◊ *(ORL) = Other Ranked Lawyer.*	
[A] *direct access (see p.11).*	
Alphabetical order within each band. Band 1 is highest.	

SILKS

William Edis QC Highly regarded for his professional discipline work in the healthcare sector. He also regularly appears before the Royal College of Veterinary Surgeons. **Strengths:** "He is a brilliant advocate, who is very eloquent and very good at looking after the client."

Kieran Coonan QC Regularly defends doctors and dentists in Fitness to Practise tribunals before the GMC and GDC. **Strengths:** "He is fantastic – a clever, subtle and fearless advocate."

Martin Forde QC Regularly represents a host of medical practitioners including doctors and optometrists in regulatory and disciplinary proceedings. He also has experience in acting on behalf of healthcare regulators. **Strengths:** "He is particularly passionate about defending his clients." "He is robust and has a certain charisma and presence in court."

Joanna Glynn QC Frequently undertakes advisory work for regulators and regulated professionals in the financial, legal and healthcare industries. As a published author in the healthcare regulatory sector, she is frequently cited for her expertise in this area. **Strengths:** "She has an encyclopaedic knowledge of the law."

Christina Lambert QC Hailed for her expertise in professional discipline matters in the healthcare and legal services sector. **Strengths:** "She manages the appropriate balance of rigour and elegance." "She has good analytical and tactical skills, and gets on well with clients."

Stephen Miller QC Veteran advocate who acts on behalf of medical professionals before the GMC.

Philip Havers QC Has a broad practice in areas ranging from sports law to healthcare law and boasts a well-respected professional discipline practice. **Strengths:** "He is extremely competent, very astute, relaxed on his feet and a very experienced advocate."

Richard Booth QC Acts for regulators and regulated individuals on healthcare professional discipline matters. He also has a well-respected sports practice. **Strengths:** "He is incisive in his analysis, good with clients, and adept at handling tense situations." **Recent work:** Acted on behalf of a breast surgeon in a tribunal before the GMC. The case concerned allegations of giving substandard surgical treatment to 12 patients.

Robert Seabrook QC Has a depth of experience in healthcare professional discipline matters and regularly appears before the GMC. He also has expertise in associated criminal matters.

Catherine Callaghan Consistently represents a range of regulators in the healthcare, media and accountancy sectors, and routinely handles complex judicial review cases and appeals. **Strengths:** "She is incredibly bright, positive and direct." **Recent work:** Represented the Human Fertilisation & Embryology Authority in various challenges made by the Assisted Reproduction & Gynaecology Centre. The case concerned its decision to apply a new condition to the claimant's fertility centres' licences.

Tristan Jones Acts in disciplinary proceedings on behalf of both individuals and regulatory bodies in the teaching, healthcare and sport sectors. **Recent work:** Represented a teacher in a High Court appeal against a decision made by the General Teaching Council.

1 Crown Office Row

See profile on p.784

THE SET

1 Crown Office Row offers an enviable breadth of expertise at all levels of seniority, with professional discipline being considered among the set's "bread-and-butter work." This chambers provides representation for regulators and regulated individuals in a plethora of areas, including the healthcare, legal and financial services sectors. The volume of its involvement in medical disciplinary matters is exemplified by the set's having use of a Manchester annexe, which is in the same building as the hearing room of the GMC.

Client service: The clerks, led by Matthew Phipps, are "efficient and very commercially attuned."

JUNIORS

Andrew Kennedy Receives praise for his disciplinary work on behalf a range of healthcare professionals including doctors and dentists. He has also recently been involved in a number of significant inquiries in this sector. **Strengths:** "He sets clients at ease and is very knowledgeable about the process." "He is a thorough and attractive advocate." **Recent work:** Appeared before the GDC representing a dentist who was alleged to have acted dishonestly.

Clodagh Bradley Particularly regarded for her work in healthcare regulatory matters. She regularly acts for practitioners in proceedings brought by a range of regulators including the GMC and GDC. **Strengths:** "She gets stuck in and gets some great results against some far more senior people." "She is ferocious and doesn't take any prisoners." **Recent work:** Appeared in GMC v Scholten, acting on behalf of a renowned cosmetic surgeon, specialising in female genital cosmetic surgery, who took a photograph of an anaesthetised patient's genitalia without consent when performing a breast augmentation.

Shaheen Rahman Regularly represents medical practitioners before regulators following instruction by indemnity organisations. She is also active in a range of other related proceedings, including High Court appeals and judicial reviews. **Strengths:** "She is articulate, makes her points precisely and clearly and covers all the ground." "She is down to earth and user-friendly." **Recent work:** Acted in Dr C v GMC; a case concerning allegations of multiple inappropriate sexually motivated examinations of patients.

Neil Sheldon Defends a wide range of medical practitioners before the GMC and GDC. **Strengths:** "He is fabulous, a really great person to have on the team: endlessly enthusiastic, hard-working, works extraordinarily well under pressure, produces very high-quality work to tight deadlines, and is not fazed by things blowing up at the last moment."

Owain Thomas Frequently acts for a range of healthcare practitioners, including doctors and dentists in regulatory proceedings. **Strengths:** "He is intelligent and applies his mind to the facts and law in equal measure." "He has an eye for legal principle and how it works with the facts."

Jeremy Hyam Public and administrative law specialist with expertise on doctors' disciplinary cases. **Strengths:** "He can see the legal and procedural points that others don't." "He is a first-class advocate with an intellectual approach." **Recent work:** Appeared in Alexandridis v GMC; a misconduct case concerning a renowned plastic surgeon.

Giles Colin Has a wealth of experience in healthcare matters and frequently appears in GMC proceedings. **Strengths:** "He has a good manner with clients and keeps them cheerful." "He is an engaging advocate."

Thirty Nine Essex Street

See profile on p.797

THE SET

Thirty Nine Essex Street receives praise for the breadth of its professional discipline practice, whereby it offers expertise in a range of sectors including healthcare, legal services and sport. Its members consistently act both for and against regulators, and are frequently involved in the most high-profile and complex cases. The set continues to benefit from a considerable influx of new members from 4-5 Gray's Inn Square, who have been absorbed into the fold with considerable success.

Client service: The clerking team receives praise for its "willingness to go the extra mile."

SILKS

Alison Foster QC Has a breadth of experience in regulatory issues, and has recently been involved in cases within the legal services, healthcare and veterinary sectors. **Strengths:** "She is a competent advocate who inspires confidence." "She commands the attention of senior judges when she appears before them." **Recent work:** Appeared in SRA v Fuglers, a High Court challenge to a substantial fine issued by the Solicitors Disciplinary Tribunal.

Hodge Malek QC (see p.661) A highly experienced silk who acts in complex heavyweight regulatory and disciplinary matters. He has experience of acting on behalf of regulators and regulated individuals, and is especially regarded for his work in the legal services and financial sector. **Strengths:** "He has unbelievable confidence, and is very straightforward when dealing with cases." "You get a fully hands-on approach with him." **Recent work:** Represented the Law Society in an administrative court appeal against Dean & Dean.

Gregory Treverton-Jones QC Well regarded for his regulatory expertise in the legal services sector. He regularly represents solicitors facing prosecution at tribunals and in subsequent High Court appeals and judicial reviews. **Strengths:** "He is a low-key but incredibly effective advocate." "He can bring out a respondent's personal attributes in a realistic and acceptable way." **Recent work:** Defended the partners at solicitors' firm Andersons in a case against the Solicitors Regulation Authority (SRA) that concerned the terms and conditions of their business.

Nigel Pleming QC A respected practitioner in the regulatory field who regularly appears in public inquiries and before administrative courts. **Strengths:** "He has been doing this work a long time and is very effective."

Eleanor Grey QC Highly regarded for her regulatory expertise within the healthcare sector, and is regularly involved in high-profile public inquiries and hearings. **Strengths:** "She is extremely thorough and has good judgement." **Recent work:** Represented the former Healthcare Commission and its chair in the Mid Staffordshire Public Inquiry.

Fenella Morris QC Has broad professional discipline expertise, and appears in cases relating to the accountancy, veterinary and healthcare sectors. **Strengths:** "She has the right sort of instinct and judgement when dealing with cases of this nature." **Recent work:** Represented the Royal College of Veterinary Surgeons in a disciplinary hearing against a vet accused of a number of misdemeanours, including animal cruelty and clinical incompetence.

Jenni Richards QC Acts in disciplinary proceedings in a range of sectors including teaching, accountancy and healthcare. She represents regulators and individuals. **Recent work:** Acted on behalf of the Teaching Agency in a High Court appeal relating to a head teacher who had been barred due to irregularities in his school's exam proceedings.

JUNIORS

David Bradly Receives a great deal of praise for his work on behalf of regulators in the healthcare sector. He also defends solicitors and accountants in disciplinary proceedings. **Strengths:** "He is very bright and is able to see the bigger picture." "He is great to work with and works incredibly hard." **Recent work:** Acted on behalf of the GDC in a Fitness to Practise hearing against a Professor of Oral Medicine in Belfast who faced allegations of misconduct while treating 33 patients with oral lesions.

Andrew Tabachnik Respected for his work on behalf of regulators and regulated individuals. He has recently been involved in high-profile professional discipline cases in the legal and financial sectors. **Strengths:** "He is a very good technical lawyer who is top-drawer." **Recent work:** Acted on behalf of a solicitor facing prosecution by the Solicitors Regulation Authority (SRA) due to allegations of dishonesty relating to evidence he had previously given at a civil trial.

Nicola Greaney (see p.614) Regularly acts for regulatory bodies and regulated individuals on a range of matters, including disciplinary proceedings in the health and social care sectors.

Vikram Sachdeva (see p.713) Has recently been involved in numerous cases before the SRA, but also frequently appears before other regulators such as the GDC and NMC. **Strengths:** "He is a high-energy advocate, who is keen to do well for his clients." **Recent work:** Appeared in R (Bass) v Solicitors Regulation Authority, an appeal that considered the extent of a partner's obligation to supervise another partner.

Alexis Hearnden Acts for and against a range of healthcare regulators, including the Royal College of Veterinary Surgeons and the General Osteopathic Council. She also has experience in advising on solicitors' disciplinary matters. **Strengths:** "She has a very good technical brain." "She has got good judgement." **Recent work:** Acted on behalf of the Royal College of Veterinary Surgeons in a case against a vet who was accused of a number of indiscretions, including dangerously poor animal care.

Saima Hanif (see p.618) Advises professionals in the financial services and healthcare sectors in disciplinary proceedings. **Recent work:** Appeared in Tim Roberts v FCA; an Upper Tribunal appeal concerning the barring of the former CEO of Catalyst from working in the financial services sector.

Robert Lazarus Regularly appears before the Health and Care Professions Council on behalf of psychologists. He also advises other professionals on disciplinary matters, including architects and solicitors. **Recent work:** Represented a clinical psychologist, before the Health and Care Professions Council, who was facing numerous allegations of misconduct including a fraudulent claim for fees.

Serjeants' Inn Chambers

THE SET

Serjeants' Inn Chambers has a pre-eminent and growing professional discipline team. Its expertise in healthcare discipline matters is particularly respected, but it also offers strength in a range of other areas such as the police and legal services sectors. Sources are complimentary about the quality of the individuals at the set, noting that there are "plenty of options to choose from."

SILKS

Adrian Hopkins QC (see p.631) Regularly advises doctors on complex and high-profile professional discipline cases before the GMC. He also provides ad-hoc advisory services relating to regulatory developments in the healthcare sector. **Strengths:** "He is very thorough and concise, and has a very attractive court manner." **Recent work:** Acted on behalf of a former forensic pathologist in cases before the GMC concerning alleged misconduct during post-mortem examinations.

John Beggs QC (see p.547) Hailed for being a supremo in police discipline cases, especially on the prosecution side. He also appears in healthcare and solicitors' disciplinary tribunals. **Strengths:** "He has an awesome, fearsome reputation." "He is known for having a Rottweiler approach to defending." **Recent work:** Represented the Chief Constable of West Mercia on matters relating to the Plebgate scandal.

Angus Moon QC (see p.675) Particularly regarded for his work in acting on behalf of doctors before the GMC, he handles complex and challenging cases. **Strengths:** "He is a very clever and intelligent advocate." **Recent work:** Acted on behalf of a doctor in a complicated case before the GMC, which concerned the misdiagnosis of a patient with lead toxicity.

Sir Robert Francis QC (see p.603) Has extensive experience of professional discipline matters in the healthcare sector and is frequently instructed in GMC proceedings. **Strengths:** "He has a brain the size of a planet; his advice is always absolutely bang-on."

George Hugh-Jones QC (see p.633) Highly experienced in representing healthcare practitioners before the GMC and GDC. **Strengths:** "He is a very knowledgeable and persuasive advocate." "He takes a sensitive and pragmatic approach." **Recent work:** Acted on behalf of a doctor in a case before the GMC concerning allegations relating to mistreatment of a fatal asthma attack.

Michael Mylonas QC (see p.680) Highly regarded for his healthcare regulation expertise. He regularly represents doctors in disciplinary proceedings before the GMC. **Strengths:** "He is very sharp and very well placed to deal with complex issues in a very understated and effective manner."

JUNIORS

Gerard Boyle (see p.554) Highly respected for his police disciplinary work. He also has expertise in defending healthcare practitioners and acts on behalf of the Bar Standards Board. **Strengths:** "He is very good at establishing a rapport with clients and getting down to the nitty-gritty of cases." "He is intelligent, perceptive, has good judgement and is an attractive advocate." **Recent work:** Presented a case on behalf of the Police Appeals Tribunal against an officer accused of engaging in an affair with the Home Secretary's wife, while he was protecting him.

Charles Foster (see p.603) Focuses his practice on disciplinary matters in the healthcare sector. **Recent work:** Appeared in GDC v Patel, a disciplinary case concerning numerous allegations of misconduct such as failing to ensure that a patient had been safely sedated.

Anthony Haycroft Particularly experienced at representing doctors and dentists in disciplinary tribunals. His significant expertise in the Criminal Bar also enables him to advise on disciplinary cases with criminal regulatory elements. **Strengths:** "He leaves no stone unturned." "He is very good at seeing what the issues are and where one needs to go with the case." **Recent work:** Acted on behalf of a doctor before the GMC in a case concerning allegations of sexual assault during clinical examinations.

Jonathan Holl-Allen (see p.629) Highly respected junior for professional discipline matters in the healthcare sector. He is regularly instructed by indemnity organisations to act on behalf of practitioners before the GDC and GMC. **Strengths:** "He is very good at being robust when he needs to be, but also at pouring oil on troubled waters."

Alan Jenkins (see p.638) Regularly represents healthcare practitioners in complex Fitness to Practise hearings and tribunals. **Strengths:** "He is very keen and highly experienced. He fights for his clients." **Recent work:** Represented a GP in a case before the GMC relating to allegations of sexual assault on 11 female patients.

David Morris A new addition to Serjeants' Inn, he regularly represents healthcare professionals in cases before disciplinary bodies and on appeal. **Strengths:** "He is a reliable, experienced and dedicated practitioner." **Recent work:** Appeared in Kakade v GMC. This was an administrative court appeal relating to an interim suspension order imposed by a disciplinary tribunal.

Richard Partridge (see p.690) A trained doctor, who is particularly knowledgeable on healthcare professional disciplinary matters. He regularly represents doctors and dentists in tribunals. **Strengths:** "His medical knowledge is very impressive." **Recent work:** Acted on behalf of a dentist before the GDC, following allegations of misconduct while providing clinical care.

Claire Watson (see p.747) Well regarded for her work on behalf of medical and dental practitioners in regulatory proceedings. She advises police on an array of disciplinary matters, including misconduct tribunals. **Strengths:** "She is fiercely protective of her client." **Recent work:** Successfully appeared on behalf of a doctor in a Fitness to Practise proceeding. The practitioner had been charged with misconduct arising out of transcribing errors that resulted in the death of a patient.

Simon Cridland (see p.581) Frequently represents healthcare practitioners before a range of healthcare regulators including the GDC, NMC and GMC. **Strengths:** "He is a very good advocate, who grasps the issues quickly." **Recent work:** Acted on behalf of an obstetrician facing prosecution by the GMC for six cases of alleged misconduct that resulted in the death of two children.

Katharine Gollop (see p.611) Hailed for her work in the professional discipline sector, she regularly acts for healthcare professionals before the GMC. **Strengths:** "Her submissions are always very forceful and persuasive." "She is very good with clients and is able to look at the matters in terms of how it will impact them." **Recent work:** Assisted a senior doctor in resisting an interim suspension sought by the GMC due to alleged misperformance.

Mark Ley-Morgan (see p.656) Highly knowledgeable on police misconduct matters, and noted for his prosecution practice and developing defence practice. He is also applauded for his defence work on behalf of doctors. **Strengths:** "He is incredibly experienced and generally formidable." "He is someone to use if you want to get a really difficult point of law across."

Malcolm Fortune Noted for his experience in the healthcare sector and his frequent instructions on GDC and GMC Fitness to Practise cases. **Recent work:** Represented a dentist at the GDC in relation to allegations of dishonesty concerning additional fees he was charging to NHS patients.

Paul Spencer (see p.726) Has extensive experience in regulatory matters in the health and social care sectors. **Strengths:** "He is an excellent advocate, with a beautiful courtroom manner – he is totally unflappable."

Andrew Hockton (see p.629) Acts on behalf of prominent medical practitioners in a range of medical disciplinary matters. **Strengths:** "He is an experienced advocate who brings a reassuring gravitas."

Band 2

Fountain Court Chambers

See profile on p.804

THE SET

Leading commercial set Fountain Court draws upon its substantial expertise to offer regulatory advice in the financial services, accountancy and legal sectors. Members are frequently sought out by the SRA in solicitors' disciplinary cases, and maintain strong relationships with other regulatory bodies including the Financial Reporting Council.

Client service: Alex Taylor heads a strong clerking team which is considered "responsive and problem-solving."

SILKS

Timothy Dutton QC A particularly respected advocate in the field of professional discipline, who is consistently instructed on the most complex and high-profile cases in the legal and financial services sector. **Strengths:** "What makes him so strong is his exacting approach to cases, combined with his incredible presence in court." "He fully appreciates the needs and expectations of regulators." **Recent work:** Acted on behalf of the SRA in Solicitors Disciplinary Tribunal proceedings. This case considered allegations against a solicitor who was accused of acting without integrity and misleading the court in relation to the outing of NightJack.

Michael McLaren QC (see p.668) Well-respected commercial silk, who regularly conducts disciplinary cases in the legal services sector. He frequently acts on behalf of the SRA in Solicitors Disciplinary Tribunals and related appeals. **Strengths:** "He is a very bright and able advocate who is very good at getting to grips with tricky issues." **Recent work:** Represented the SRA in the first contested Solicitors Disciplinary Tribunal case arising from stamp duty avoidance schemes.

Patricia Robertson QC Highly knowledgeable on legal services regulation, she acts in tribunals and regularly provides ad hoc compliance advice. She offers expertise in the accountancy sector. **Strengths:** "She is enormously bright and incisive, and very clear in the advice she gives." "The thing I appreciate most about her is that she is sure of her views and doesn't waver around." **Recent work:** Advised Harbottle & Lewis on an SRA investigation emanating from the Leveson Inquiry. This concerned advice that the firm provided to News International.

Richard Coleman QC (see p.575) Regularly acts on behalf of the SRA in professional discipline cases. **Strengths:** "He has superb analytical skills, is very clear in his drafting and can break things down." **Recent work:** Prosecuted a solicitor in the Solicitors Disciplinary Tribunal who was accused of receiving unlawful commissions.

JUNIORS

James McClelland (see p.667) Has a strong reputation for his involvement in high-profile solicitors' regulatory matters. **Strengths:** "He is highly intelligent, responsive and alert to regulators' needs." "He is extraordinarily bright, and combines this with a great deal of user-friendliness and a calm manner." **Recent work:** Advised the SRA on the prosecution of two solicitors for the alleged improper instruction of an expert witness.

Chloe Carpenter (see p.565) A respected junior in the field of solicitors' regulation, who regularly acts on behalf of the SRA on regulatory matters. **Strengths:** "She is a very thorough and persuasive pleader." "She is very responsive, clear and practical." **Recent work:** Acted on behalf of the SRA in the QASA judicial review.

Rupert Allen (see p.534) Offers a breadth of expertise in solicitors' regulatory matters and is regularly involved in complex tribunals and judicial reviews. **Strengths:** "He is confident, quick to grab the issues and always approachable and client-friendly." "He has an analytical mind and an eye for detail." **Recent work:** Represented the SRA in disciplinary proceedings against solicitors involved in Stamp Duty Land Tax avoidance schemes.

2 Hare Court

See profile on p.818

THE SET

2 Hare Court has "quickly established a reputation for high-quality advocacy in this field" and is frequently complimented for its ability to draw upon its expertise as a pre-eminent criminal set. It has recently won a tender to prosecute on behalf of the National College of Teaching & Leadership in a joint venture with solicitors' firm Nabarro. It is also active in representing healthcare professionals in disciplinary cases.

Client service: Julian Campbell runs a clerking team that is considered to be "efficient, user-friendly and professional."

JUNIORS

Andrew Colman (see p.576) A highly regarded junior with previous experience of the Criminal Bar, who regularly defends a plethora of medical practitioners in Fitness to Practise tribunals. **Strengths:** "He has a reputation for having a very finely tuned sense of procedure." "If you need a person to deal with a vast amount of information, and advise in a client-friendly way, he is the man." **Recent work:** Successfully represented a doctor in Fitness to Practise proceedings who had been accused of misdiagnosing cardiac chest pain as gastroenteritis.

Craig Ferguson (see p.599) Exclusively defends in professional discipline cases. He is highly regarded for his work on behalf of an array of healthcare professionals including doctors and dentists. **Strengths:** "He is a beautiful, silky smooth and persuasive advocate." "He has skill and judgement, and an attractive way of conducting a case."

Marios Lambis Works entirely on behalf of professionals in disciplinary cases and regularly appears before a range of regulatory bodies, including the GMC and the NMC. **Strengths:** "He is a classy advocate who has a very smooth style in front of any tribunal." "He has a good sense of the tribunal he's appearing in front of, and is firm and robust where appropriate." **Recent work:** Defended a GP before the GMC who faced allegations that she had deficiently treated a patient who subsequently died.

Stephen Brassington (see p.555) Hailed for his representation of healthcare professionals on a range of matters including disciplinary tribunals. He is also highly knowledgeable on sports and teaching disciplinary matters. **Strengths:** "He has a charisma and style about him that is underpinned by hard work." "He can take on the most difficult cases."

Andrew Hurst (see p.634) Frequently instructed by medical defence organisations to represent medical practitioners before the GMC. He also advises on GDC proceedings. **Strengths:** "He is calm, reliable and, when things go wrong, he resolves it." **Recent work:** Represented a doctor before the GMC, who was facing allegations relating to sexual misconduct and probity.

Kate Bex (see p.549) Regularly appears before a range of healthcare regulators, including the GMC and the NMC, on professional discipline matters. **Strengths:** "She can deal with very difficult cases and witnesses in a manner that is exemplary."

Sarah Przybylska (see p.700) Acts on behalf of healthcare regulators and regularly defends practitioners before the GMC. She also prosecutes teachers in disciplinary cases. **Recent work:** Appeared in a disciplinary case before the NMC. The tribunal was looking into allegations of dishonesty and misconduct that could have caused death.

Outer Temple Chambers

See profile on p.842

THE SET

Outer Temple Chambers has a prominent team who regularly represent healthcare practitioners in disciplinary cases. It has a Manchester annexe that enables it to service GMC cases in the North West, and it also offers strength in the legal and financial services sector. Sources appreciate the "unstuffy" nature of its members.

Client service: Sources note that "the clerks are very approachable and flexible."

SILKS

Gordon Bebb QC Receives regular instructions to act on behalf of a breadth of healthcare practitioners in Fitness to Practise hearings. He is regularly instructed to act on behalf of doctors, chiropodists and dentists. **Recent work:** Acted on behalf of a GP at a Fitness to Practise hearing who was accused of having entered into a sexual relationship with a patient.

Brendan Finucane QC Frequently represents doctors and dentists before Fitness to Practise hearings, inquests, and criminal court trials. **Recent work:** Represented an orthopaedic surgeon in Crown Court and GMC proceedings concerning allegations that he examined a patient's genitalia in a car park.

JUNIORS

James Leonard Regularly acts for practitioners before a range of regulators, including the GMC and General Pharmaceutical Council. Many of his misconduct cases involve alleged criminal activity. **Strengths:** "He has an ability to assimilate vast amounts of information at short notice and distil it in coherent form." "He is very good at reading the panel when he is doing his advocacy." **Recent work:** Represented a doctor at GMC proceedings who faced allegations of deliberately ending a patient's life.

James Counsell Noted for his breadth of regulatory expertise, he represents and prosecutes practitioners in the healthcare and legal services sectors. **Recent work:** Appeared in a GMC Fitness to Practise case concerning a doctor who faced numerous allegations, including sexual assault against a patient.

Fiona Horlick Has a strong practice defending healthcare practitioners in an array of professional discipline hearings and associated criminal trials. She also represents solicitors before the Solicitors Disciplinary Tribunal. **Strengths:** "She exudes an air of confidence." "She's an excellent advocate who is very good at cross-examination." **Recent work:** Defended a dentist against the GDC, who faced allegations of dishonesty and of removing an incorrect tooth.

Stephen Climie Has a vibrant healthcare regulatory practice that is supported by his strength in criminal and clinical negligence law. **Recent work:** Acted on behalf of a psychiatrist at a GMC Fitness to Practise hearing who was facing allegations of sexual impropriety with four patients.

Michael Uberoi Regularly represents healthcare professionals and sportspeople on disciplinary matters. He also represents doctors on associated inquiries and employment issues. **Strengths:** "He did an extremely good job in difficult circumstances." **Recent work:** Represented a GP convicted of drink driving, and of injecting his wife with heroin, in a GMC Fitness to Practise hearing.

Matthew McDonagh Both prosecutes and defends in disciplinary proceedings in the healthcare sector. **Strengths:** "His client care is great and he sticks to very tight deadlines."

QEB Hollis Whiteman

See profile on p.853

THE SET

QEB Hollis Whiteman is frequently instructed by a breadth of regulators, including the SRA, Gambling Commission and Bar Standards Board, but has also developed a focus in regulatory defence work. The set receives praise for the quality of its individuals, and is noted for the rigour of its recruitment process.

Client service: Chris Emmings receives praise for running a clerking team that is "proactive in managing client relationships."

SILKS

Tom Kark QC Particularly praised for his prosecution work on behalf of a range of healthcare prosecutors including the GMC and GDC. **Strengths:** "He provides the reassurance that a case will be handled with incredible experience and care." "He is incredibly approachable and easy to talk through things with." **Recent work:** Acted for the GMC in its prosecution of three doctors who were involved in the Stafford Hospital scandal.

Sean Larkin QC (see p.651) Experienced in acting for and against regulators on disciplinary matters in a range of sectors. His professional discipline practice is enriched by his substantial expertise in criminal law. **Strengths:** "He always provides high-quality, level-headed advice, and a clear strategy." **Recent work:** Appeared in GDC v Mr Almasi, acting on behalf of the GDC. The accused faced allegations of dishonesty and clinical failings.

Sarah Plaschkes QC Frequently prosecutes on behalf of a breadth of healthcare regulators in professional discipline matters. She also has expertise in the police and legal services sector. **Strengths:** "She is instructed in awkward cases that are high-profile." "She is scrupulously fair and straight down the line." **Recent work:** Acted on behalf of the NMC in its prosecution of numerous nurses who were accused of providing substandard care to a patient who died from diabetic ketoacidosis.

Zoe Johnson QC (see p.639) Has a strong regulatory practice and frequently represents doctors at GMC proceedings. She also appears before other regulators including the GDC. **Strengths:** "She is a first-class advocate and tactician." "She controlled the proceedings and the tempo, and got the panel focused on the medical issues." **Recent work:** Appeared in GMC v Dr Carl Clinton. This case concerned an expert in sports medicine who faced allegations of conducting sexually inappropriate examinations on two female patients.

JUNIORS

Lydia Barnfather (see p.543) Highly regarded for prosecuting complex and high-profile disciplinary cases on behalf of a range of regulators in the health and social care sectors. **Strengths:** "There are very few questions that she hasn't seen or that she doesn't have an informed viewpoint on." "She sees the wood from the trees on the most technical of cases and presents superbly." **Recent work:** Prosecuted a dentist before the GDC who had been accused of witness interference and three counts of NHS fraud.

Selva Ramasamy (see p.703) Has had recent instructions to prosecute on behalf of healthcare and legal services regulators. **Strengths:** "An exceptionally thorough counsel who gets to the bottom of the facts in every case." **Recent work:** Represented the SRA in a case against an individual who had conducted numerous cases as a solicitor despite being unqualified.

Rebecca Harris (see p.621) Has previous experience at the criminal bar, and is particularly adept in handling high-profile professional discipline cases. She has particularly broad expertise in healthcare regulatory matters and she regularly appears in cases before the GMC, GDC and General Optical Council (GOC). **Strengths:** "She is very sensible, experienced and has good judgement." "She is extremely able and gives highly effective, practical solutions to complex legal problems." **Recent work:** Instructed by the GDC to represent a case against a dentist who had been convicted of committing £1.4 million worth of fraud against the NHS.

Band 3

2 Bedford Row

See profile on p.763

THE SET

2 Bedford Row is respected for providing depth of expertise in the healthcare sector. Its members regularly act for healthcare regulators such as the GDC, but the set is also renowned for its defence work, especially on behalf of optometrists. One client notes: "We have complete confidence in all of them and they are also very likeable."

Client service: John Grimmer leads a particularly strong set of clerks who "are very helpful and certainly not shy of putting in the leg work."

SILKS

Ian Stern QC A highly regarded silk who is consistently involved in the highest-profile and most complex regulatory cases. His expertise covers a breadth of areas, and he is particularly regarded for his knowledge on police and healthcare disciplinary matters. **Strengths:** "His cross-examination of witnesses is excellent, and he is very organised and good at focusing on the key issues." "He is clear and concise in how he presents cases." **Recent work:** Represented at inquest the firearms officer who shot Mark Duggan.

Mark Milliken-Smith QC Regularly appears before a range of regulators including the GMC, GDC and the Institute of Chartered Accountants in England & Wales (ICAEW). He is particularly regarded for his knowledge on sports matters. **Strengths:** "He has outstanding client care skills." **Recent work:** Represented an accountant against the ICAEW who faced accusations of dishonest conduct in relation to certain investments and FSA activities.

JUNIORS

Jamas Hodivala (see p.629) Offers a breadth of regulatory expertise encompassing sectors such as healthcare, legal services and sport. **Strengths:** "He is an intellectual giant who is extremely thorough in terms of preparation and the way he conducts hearings." "He is a calm and measured advocate, he leaves no stone unturned and possesses excellent forensic skills." **Recent work:** Represented a cricketer charged with spot-fixing in disciplinary proceedings before the England & Wales Cricket Board and in an associated criminal prosecution.

Sandesh Singh Frequently appears in complex professional discipline cases on behalf of a breadth of healthcare regulators including the GDC, GMC and GOC. He also frequently acts on behalf of individuals facing prosecution. **Strengths:** "He is very meticulous in his attention to detail and will leave no stone unturned." "He presents the case very clearly and sets out all the relevant facts."

Eleanor Sanderson (see p.714) Has a respected healthcare professional discipline practice that is enriched by her expertise in criminal proceedings. **Strengths:** "She will go the extra mile to put her clients at ease, her preparation is good and her submissions are clear and very well thought out." "She grasps the facts very quickly."

23 Essex Street

See profile on p.795

THE SET

23 Essex Street is a criminal set that has successfully branched out into regulatory work. The set receives regular instructions from numerous healthcare and financial regulators, and also offers expertise in police work. Boasting an annexe in Manchester, the set also has a recognised presence in the North West. **Client service:** Sarah Reynolds is the set's regulatory clerk. Sources note: "The clerks are very responsive, listen to our needs and try to facilitate what we need."

SILKS

Dafydd Enoch QC Has expertise in representing practitioners and regulators in professional discipline cases. He is particularly regarded for his knowledge of healthcare regulation.

JUNIORS

Paul Ozin Leads the chambers' professional discipline team, and advises on a truly broad array of matters in sectors ranging from healthcare to accountancy. He is highly respected for his work on high-profile and complex cases. **Strengths:** "We instruct him on highly complex matters and seek his advice on high-level, complex cases. He is of the highest calibre and has a forensic brain that can deal with any level of detail." **Recent work:** Represented the GMC in its prosecution of a doctor who had run an out-of-hours healthcare service, and faced numerous allegations of misconduct including the dishonest taking of unauthorised money.

Lynn Griffin Recognised for her strength in healthcare disciplinary cases. She acts at all levels, including the tribunal and judicial review stages.

Rupert Pardoe A recognised practitioner in the field of police law, who regularly acts for officers in disciplinary proceedings. **Strengths:** "He is extremely friendly and approachable, and also very meticulous." **Recent work:** Represented a police officer in a disciplinary hearing who was alleged to have abused his power and arrested someone unnecessarily.

Sarah Campbell Represents a breadth of healthcare regulators in complex disciplinary cases. She is also involved in associated criminal prosecutions of medical professionals. **Strengths:** "Sarah is very user-friendly and great to work with." **Recent work:** Appeared in GMC v Gauci. This disciplinary case concerned an anaesthetist who had been accused of misappropriation and the use of Class C drugs.

Hailsham Chambers

See profile on p.814

THE SET

Hailsham Chambers draws upon its strong expertise in professional negligence to provide a healthy contingent of professional discipline practitioners. Its members advise regulators and regulated individuals, and are regularly active in healthcare matters. The set is also developing a regular involvement in other areas such as the legal and accountancy sectors. **Client service:** Stephen Smith leads a clerking team that wins praise for being very "businesslike."

SILKS

David Pittaway QC (see p.694) Defends healthcare professionals in disciplinary tribunals, and also prosecutes on behalf of the SRA. He has also recently provided advice to numerous regulators on reforms to their disciplinary procedures. **Strengths:** "He is forensic, comprehensive in his preparation, and masterful in his advocacy. He is especially devastating in cross-examination." "His ability to take a pretty complex point and make it into a simple submission is laudable." **Recent work:** Represented the SRA in its prosecution of a former partner at McKeowns for his dishonest misconduct in accepting commission from an ATE insurance broker.

Alexander Hutton QC (see p.635) Has a respected practice in healthcare disciplinary matters. **Strengths:** "His advocacy is unflowery and very clear."

JUNIORS

Nicholas Peacock (see p.691) Regularly represents medical practitioners in a range of professional disciplinary matters, appearing before regulators such as the GOC and GMC. **Strengths:** "He knows the law backwards and is very thorough." **Recent work:** Represented a dentist before the GDC in relation to allegations of misconduct regarding gum remodelling.

Fiona Neale (see p.681) Regularly represents healthcare practitioners in disciplinary hearings before the GDC and GMC. **Strengths:** "She is liked by clients for her sound and pragmatic approach." **Recent work:** Represented a dentist at the GDC in a disciplinary hearing relating to his late diagnosis of oral cancers.

Clare Price (see p.699) Has a strong professional discipline practice, and is noted for her expertise in proceedings in the healthcare sector.

4 New Square

See profile on p.835

THE SET

4 New Square's strong professional liability practice complements its highly regarded work in financial services and accountancy disciplinary matters. Members continue to be involved in high-profile and complex matters in these sectors, and have received much work as a result of the repercussions of the financial crisis. The set also provides additional expertise in the sports and legal services sectors.

Client service: Lizzy Stewart leads a clerking team, which is considered to be "commercial, approachable and solution-oriented."

SILKS

Ben Hubble QC Head of chambers who is particularly regarded for his professional discipline work in the financial and legal services sector. He regularly acts on behalf of regulators and regulated individuals. **Strengths:** "He is the first name I think of for professional discipline accountancy cases." "He is very experienced and can adapt his advocacy style to the particular tribunal he is addressing." **Recent work:** Acted on behalf of a partner at Haines Watts who was prosecuted by the Financial Reporting Council (FRC) due to allegations of incompetence in his auditing that misled the public about a business flotation.

Patrick Lawrence QC Hailed for his involvement in professional discipline cases against auditors. He is also noted for his expertise in disciplinary matters in the legal sector. **Recent work:** Represented the FRC Conduct Committee in its prosecution of an accountant at Ernst & Young on matters relating to the collapse of Farepak.

Graeme McPherson QC Highly regarded for his work on sports disciplinary matters, particularly equine-related cases. He also offers expertise in cases involving the legal and veterinary professions. **Strengths:** "He is a very thorough advocate who prepares his cases brilliantly." "He is extremely good at handling clients in consultation and is very good to deal with." **Recent work:** Successfully represented the British Horseracing Authority in its prosecution of a Godolphin trainer for his misuse of anabolic steroids while training approximately 200 horses.

Simon Monty QC (see p.675) Well respected for his significant presence in solicitors' disciplinary matters. He also has expertise on cases relating to accountancy and surveying. **Strengths:** "His performance is measured and well considered, and he commands respect." **Recent work:** Appeared in SRA v Giambrone and others. This case considered numerous allegations against three European lawyers, including breaches of accounts rules.

JUNIORS

Paul Parker (see p.689) Offers expertise on a breadth of disciplinary matters. He has a particular involvement in solicitor disciplinary cases, and is also respected for his knowledge on accountancy matters. **Strengths:** "He is very diligent, very thorough and offers detailed forensic analysis. He is very good at intricate legal arguments." **Recent work:** Appeared in Solicitors Disciplinary Tribunal proceedings that considered numerous allegations including a dishonest involvement in money laundering.

George Spalton Regularly instructed in disciplinary proceedings relating to accountancy, legal and tax professionals. **Recent work:** Represented the Chartered Institute of Taxation in its prosecution of two members on the grounds of breach of confidentiality.

Band 4

5 Essex Court

See profile on p.791

THE SET

5 Essex Court is a pre-eminent name in the field of police law. As such, it receives praise for its extensive involvement in police disciplinary cases, and regularly acts on behalf of the Independent Police Complaints Commission, chief constables and police authorities. The set also receives instructions from the NMC and GDC.

SILKS

Fiona Barton QC (see p.544) A well-respected advocate in the field of police law. She regularly acts for constabularies and panels in misconduct hearings, and is also active in judicial review proceedings. **Strengths:** "She is a thorough advocate in terms of her preparation."

Jason Beer QC (see p.547) Often appears in high-profile police misconduct cases. **Strengths:** "He is bright, very good on the law, tactically very astute and a top-drawer advocate."

JUNIORS

Matthew Holdcroft (see p.629) Regularly appears as a presenting officer and legal adviser in police misconduct hearings and in matters before the Police Appeals Tribunal. **Strengths:** "He is a very thorough and robust advocate." "He is very intelligent and grasps the issues of the case very quickly." **Recent work:** Represented the claimant in R (Commissioner of Police for the Metropolis) v Police Appeals Tribunal. This matter related to disciplinary proceedings concerning a police inspector who was caught travelling in first class without a ticket.

Francesca Whitelaw (see p.751) Has a plethora of experience of handling police disciplinary matters and regularly advises on misconduct hearings. **Strengths:** "She is very effective and doesn't overstate her case." **Recent work:** Represented the Chief Constable of Norfolk Constabulary in an expedited misconduct case against a police officer who was accused of child sexual offences.

Old Square Chambers

See profile on p.891

THE SET

This thriving employment law set provides a strong service in professional discipline cases. It has particular expertise in healthcare cases, but individual members are also highlighted for their strength in the sports, education and financial services sectors. **Client service:** William Meade leads a team of "responsive clerks."

SILKS

Mary O'Rourke QC Exclusively defends, and frequently handles the most complex and high-profile healthcare professional discipline cases before the GMC. **Strengths:** "Clients love her, as she is fearless and will do anything that is in the interests of her client's case." **Recent work:** Represented a GP in a successful High Court appeal, and in its subsequent remittal to a GMC tribunal. The doctor had been erased from the register for dishonestly running a care home.

Mark Sutton QC Regularly advises on healthcare disciplinary matters and associated internal discipline and employment issues. **Strengths:** "He is very assured, has a lot of gravitas with the courts and gets his points across very clearly." "He inspires confidence in his clients." **Recent work:** Appeared in West London Mental Health Trust v Chhabra, a Supreme Court hearing that considered the power of the High Court to grant injunctions to regulate internal disciplinary proceedings.

John Hendy QC (see p.624) An employment practitioner who is recognised for his considerable expertise in doctors' disciplinary proceedings.

JUNIORS

Giles Powell (see p.697) Frequently involved in disciplinary cases involving individuals in a breadth of professions ranging from healthcare to legal services. **Strengths:** "He is very user-friendly and grasps the difficult issues." "He has a robust advocacy style." **Recent work:** Assisted a solicitor in resisting an appeal sought by the SRA against a decision made by the Solicitors Disciplinary Tribunal.

3 Raymond Buildings Barristers

See profile on p.857

THE SET

3 Raymond Buildings is a well-respected set in police discipline cases. Its members receive praise for their work in defending officers facing misconduct tribunals. Its members also appear in other forums, and regularly handle cases before the GMC and Health & Care Professions Council. One client notes: "3 Raymond Buildings clearly selects people who are very, very bright, and the set offers a whole range of people we can instruct."

Client service: Eddie Holland runs a clerking team that is "very easy to deal with, efficient and can be relied upon."

SILKS

Patrick Gibbs QC (see p.607) Extensively experienced in high-profile police regulatory matters and often involved in disciplinary matters involving criminal elements. **Strengths:** "A principled, deeply professional and proper barrister. When he takes points they carry great authority." **Recent work:** Represented an officer in disciplinary and criminal proceedings in relation to the death of a news vendor during the G20 disturbances.

Hugh Davies QC Has experience of handling complex police disciplinary matters and is regularly present in judicial reviews and inquests. **Strengths:** "He is a very astute tactician and a very effective cross-examiner." "He literally wrote the book on professional misconduct when it comes to police officers." **Recent work:** Defended a police officer in a misconduct hearing who faced allegations of dishonestly selling ex-covert police cars to fellow police officers.-

JUNIORS

Kevin Baumber Highly regarded for his work in representing police officers in misconduct cases and associated judicial reviews. **Strengths:** "He is devastating in cross-examination and has a rapier-sharp mind." "He is very measured and is excellent at dealing with very complex matters." **Recent work:** Represented a police officer in a high-profile gross misconduct case that concerned allegations of corruption in the Lancashire Constabulary.

Clair Dobbin (see p.589) Hailed for her representation of police officers in disciplinary matters. **Strengths:** "She is academically very ferocious, very easy to deal with, and someone who communicates well with the lay client." **Recent work:** Represented a police officer at first instance and on appeal in relation to a sanction that had been issued for the use of a racist word.

William Emlyn Jones Regularly acts for police offices in disciplinary hearings and associated criminal proceedings. **Strengths:** "A man with a high level of intellect, he cross-examines with devastating effect." "He is charming and goes an extra mile to defend police officers." **Recent work:** Acted in a misconduct hearing, appearing on behalf of a police officer who had attempted to kill herself.

Guy Ladenburg (see p.649) Represents police officers on a range of misconduct matters. His disciplinary practice is informed by his expertise in criminal law. **Strengths:** "He has a very charming and approachable outlook, and is sensible in approaching cases." "He is a very able advocate, who knows his technical law very well in a highly regulated area." **Recent work:** Represented a police officer in a misconduct hearing who faced accusations of sexual misconduct and harassment.

Richard Atchley Has an extensive criminal practice and is heavily involved in police discipline matters. **Strengths:** "He is conscientious, hard-working and realistic in the way he approaches cases." **Recent work:** Defended three police officers who faced disciplinary action in relation to accusations of corruption within the borough of Enfield.

Matthew Butt (see p.562) Offers extensive expertise on police disciplinary matters, and regularly appears before misconduct panels, administrative courts and the Police Appeals Tribunal. **Strengths:** "He is a very thorough and good advocate." **Recent work:** Successfully represented a police officer in an appeal against dismissal before the Police Appeals Tribunal.

Neil Saunders (see p.715) Regularly appears in police discipline hearings on behalf of officers, and is also a talented criminal practitioner. **Strengths:** "He is someone who is immensely reassuring because of his presence in court and his command of the case."

Other Ranked Lawyers

Philip Newman (42 Bedford Row) Has experience in acting on the prosecution and defence sides of professional discipline cases. His expertise covers a range of sectors and he regularly handles healthcare, accountancy and engineering cases. **Strengths:** "He is very knowledgeable and straightforward, and has a breadth of experience." **Recent work:** Defended a doctor in a GMC Fitness to Practise case who faced numerous allegations of misconduct, including withholding information from a hospital.

Ian Winter QC (see p.754) (Cloth Fair Chambers) A highly regarded criminal barrister whose skills also branch into regulatory law. He advises on a range of discipline matters, including GDC and GMC cases. **Strengths:** "He is a fantastic barrister."

Thomas Cosgrove (see p.579) (Cornerstone Barristers) Regularly acts on behalf of healthcare regulators in Fitness to Practise hearings and associated judicial reviews and appeals. **Strengths:** "Tom is a pleasure to work with. He provides direct and practical advice ahead of hearings and is a strong advocate." **Recent work:** Acted on behalf of the GDC in a case against a dentist who had been accused of providing a deficient standard of care to 34 patients.

Gemma Hobcraft (Doughty Street Chambers) Regularly appears on behalf of medical practitioners before a breadth of healthcare regulators. She is particularly knowledgeable in the area and is a published author on health law. **Strengths:** "She is a clear-headed and compassionate person when it comes to dealing with regulated persons." "She is incredibly thorough and leaves no stone unturned." **Recent work:** Acted in a disciplinary hearing before the NMC on behalf of a nurse who was alleged to have put a newborn baby in a stationery cupboard.

Susan Sleeman (Doughty Street Chambers) Frequently acts for a breadth of professionals, including medical practitioners and lawyers. **Strengths:** "She is very confident, clear and concise." "She is slightly understated, which makes her a rather effective advocate." **Recent work:** Represented a mental health nurse who faced numerous accusations of misconduct, including the provision of inadequate care to vulnerable patients in a case before the NMC.

Louise Price (Doughty Street Chambers) Regularly represents a broad range of healthcare professionals in regulatory cases. **Strengths:** "She is very clear and concise and very engaging." "She always has time for you, and nothing is too much trouble."

Geoffrey Williams (see p.752) (Farrar's Building) Former solicitor who was called to the Bar in January 2014. He has practised in the professional disciplinary field for more than 25 years, and is particularly noted for his expertise in SRA proceedings. **Strengths:** "He is incredibly thorough, incredibly practical and incredibly knowledgeable – he has had so much experience over the years."

Kenneth Hamer (see p.618) (Henderson Chambers) Experienced in representing cases on behalf of a breadth of regulatory bodies, including the General Pharmaceutical Council, the Bar Standards Board and the GOC. **Strengths:** "He is very knowledgeable and has a very good grasp of the law." **Recent work:** Appeared in R (Hill) v ICAEW, which considered whether a tribunal hearing was conducted in accordance with the rules of natural justice.

Adam Heppinstall (see p.625) (Henderson Chambers) Acts in disciplinary proceedings on behalf of healthcare professionals, solicitors and accountants. **Recent work:** Appeared in John Smalley v UK Council for Psychotherapy. This was a disciplinary case against a Jungian psychotherapist.

Richard Price OBE QC (see p.699) (Littleton Chambers) Has a breadth of experience on regulatory matters concerning a range of professions, and has recently handled numerous judicial reviews for the GOC. **Strengths:** "He speaks with a lot of authority." "He is a senior and knowledgeable practitioner in the disciplinary field."

David Aaronberg QC (15 New Bridge Street) An established practitioner in the Criminal Bar who also has a significant presence in disciplinary matters, especially in the pharmaceutical sector. **Strengths:** "He is a hard-working and successful advocate in healthcare Fitness to Practise work."

Kevin McCartney (see p.667) (5 Paper Buildings) Regularly instructed by practitioners in Fitness to Practise cases before the GMC and General Pharmaceutical Council. **Strengths:** "His advocacy is always to the point, effective and measured." "He has a comprehensive knowledge of the law."

THE REGIONS

Professional Discipline The Regions
Leading Sets
Band 1
Deans Court Chambers *
Band 2
New Park Court Chambers
Leading Silks
Band 1
Keeling Adrian *No5 Chambers (ORL)* ◊ 🄰 *
O'Rourke Mary *Deans Court Chambers*
Phillips Simon *New Park Court Chambers* *
Sephton Craig *Deans Court Chambers*
New Silks
Pitter Jason *New Park Court Chambers*
◊ (ORL) = Other Ranked Lawyer.
🄰 direct access (see p.11).
* Indicates set / individual with profile.
Alphabetical order within each band. Band 1 is highest.

Professional Discipline The Regions
Leading Juniors
Band 1
Baxter Bernadette *Lincoln House Chambers (ORL)* ◊
Beattie Sharon *New Park Court Chambers*
Kitching Robin *Deans Court Chambers* 🄰
Band 2
Atherton Peter *Deans Court Chambers* *
Cartwright Sophie *Deans Court Chambers* *
Grundy Nigel *9 St John Street (ORL)* ◊
Tyson Richard *3PB Barristers (ORL)* ◊

Band 1

Deans Court Chambers

See profile on p.915

THE SET

Deans Court Chambers offers extensive experience on GMC disciplinary cases, with members that prosecute and defend. As well as providing representation before disciplinary panels, its members also act in an advisory capacity on regulatory matters.

Client service: "Matthew Gibbons leads a clerking team that is very user-friendly and willing to go the extra mile for you."

SILKS

Mary O'Rourke QC Exclusively defends and frequently handles the most complex and high-profile healthcare professional discipline cases before the GMC. **Strengths:** "She has an absolutely 100% recollection of details." **Recent work:** Represented a GP who was erased from the register for dishonestly running a care home in a successful High Court appeal, and in its subsequent remittal to a GMC tribunal.

Craig Sephton QC Regularly prosecutes on behalf of the GMC in fitness to practise proceedings. **Strengths:** "He is very experienced in doing regulatory work and is a thorough cross-examiner."

JUNIORS

Robin Kitching Has a great deal of experience in prosecuting fitness to practise cases on behalf of the GMC. **Strengths:** "My most feared opponent is Robin Kitching. I call him 'Rapier Robin'. He has done me in a couple of times and there is not a thing you can do to stop him. He is serious business."

Peter Atherton (see p.539) Has a breadth of expertise in professional discipline matters in the healthcare industry, particularly in fitness to practise inquiries. **Strengths:** "He is a very experienced practitioner, particularly in the healthcare sector."

Sophie Cartwright (see p.566) Regularly represents the GMC in professional discipline cases. She also has experience in inquests and public law work, and is frequently instructed by NHS trusts and local authorities. **Recent work:** Acted on behalf of the GMC in a case concerning a doctor who applied to become a member of the Royal College of General Practitioners using incorrect information.

Band 2

New Park Court Chambers

THE SET

New Park Court Chambers is particularly well regarded for its involvement in regulatory and disciplinary cases in the medical profession. Its members frequently prosecute in fitness to practise tribunals on behalf of the GMC.

SILKS

Simon Phillips QC (see p.692) Handles complex and sensitive professional discipline cases. He receives regular instructions to prosecute cases on behalf of the GMC and is also on the Bar Standards Board's panel of prosecution counsel.

Jason Pitter QC Prosecutes and defends healthcare practitioners before the GDC and GMC. He is also active in police misconduct tribunals, and has significant involvement in associated criminal cases.

JUNIORS

Sharon Beattie Regularly acts on behalf of the GMC in regulatory cases involving complex and technical medical evidence.

Other Ranked Lawyers

Bernadette Baxter (Lincoln House Chambers) Praised for her work in representing police officers in disciplinary proceedings. She is also regularly instructed by the GMC. **Strengths:** "She is diligent and a good performer in hearings." "She was first-rate in terms of her cross-examination, and she also presents very well to the panel."

Adrian Keeling QC (see p.643) (No5 Chambers) Noted for his work in representing police officers in misconduct tribunals and subsequent appeals. **Strengths:** "He is incredibly tactically astute, has a very reassuring manner with clients and panels, and has an innate sense of the right way to play a case." **Recent work:** Appeared in R v Corsford & Falloon. This case concerned a prison officer who was charged with misconduct in public office for having sex with an inmate and providing him with prohibited items.

Richard Tyson (3PB Barristers) Regularly prosecutes fitness to practise cases on behalf of the GMC. **Strengths:** "He deals with a difficult case with aplomb." **Recent work:** Represented the GMC at the Court of Appeal in relation to disciplinary proceedings against a doctor who faced a number of allegations, including accusing a mother of murdering her child.

Nigel Grundy (9 St John Street) Respected for his work on behalf of the GMC in disciplinary proceedings against medical practitioners. His practice also covers employment and personal injury cases.

PROFESSIONAL NEGLIGENCE: An Introduction

Contributed by 4 New Square

2014 was supposed to be the year when the post-credit crunch claims came to an end and the professional negligence market started to cool. In fact, the contrary was the case and, throughout 2014, the post-credit crunch claims continued to come through thick and fast. The expiry of six years from the events of 2008 brought a rash of professional liability actions either because claimants were forced to issue proceedings because of limitation, or because limitation standstill agreements were terminated by one or other parties. The result is that the Professional Liability Bar continues to be busy with washing the consequences of the boom and bust period of the 'Noughties' through the legal system. Lenders' claims against solicitors and valuers continue. Disappointed counterparties to Sale and Purchase Agreements, whose Earn Outs were not what they hoped, turned their attention to their former professional advisers. Tax avoiders felt the force of the HMRC's assault on tax advantaged investment schemes, and so looked to their former accountants and tax advisers for compensation.

In relation to the final surge of lender claims, they tend now to be high value and complex. Claimant lenders have concluded that the remaining high-value claims are simply too large to ignore. Such claims are complex, because the easier claims have now been processed through the dispute resolution systems devised by the lenders and the professional indemnity insurers. What remains, when the lenders looked at the back of their filing cabinets, were claims that engaged more difficult legal issues, such as whether a lender can be said to have suffered a loss in non default mortgage cases. Lenders continue to seek to frame their claims in imaginative ways, often falling back on equity and trust principles to try to overcome defences of causation and imprudent lending; hence, the Supreme Court was asked to reconsider the appropriate remedies for breach of a bare trust in AIB v Redler & Co. Meanwhile, the Professional Negligence Bar could not fail to notice the irony of poring over the worst excesses of pre-credit crunch lending by banks, whilst the seeds of the next boom and bust in the UK housing market are being played out around them now. So the cycle continues.

But it is not all boom for the Professional Negligence Bar domestically. The downward pressure on fees continues. Claimants chasing credit crunch and other losses are usually sophisticated users of legal services and rightly press for value for money from their representatives. On the defence side, the pressure from professional indemnity insurers on costs ever increases. Defendant panel solicitor firms are feeling the full force of repeated panel reviews and a downward spiral on and indeed away from hourly rates. The challenge for the Professional Negligence Bar is to continue to offer flexibility and value for money to clients in such a changing world. So far this is a challenge that the Professional Negligence Bar has risen to, capitalising on their lower cost base to offer high-value service at relatively low rates. The pressure on costs has also seen a further blurring of the line between the solicitors' and the barristers' professions. Claimant corporate and financial institutions and defendant insurers now require both the right team and the right price, and whether the individuals within that team are solicitors or barristers is of less importance than the overall skill set and cost of the team.

Those domestic costs pressures are part of the explanation for the increasing internationalisation of the Professional Negligence Bar. Another factor behind such expansion is the growth of high-value litigation in the Caribbean jurisdictions and in the Far East. Again, many of these claims have their origin in the credit crunch. The market corrections of 2008 as well as various high-profile frauds and oligarch battles have brought enormous losses to funds based offshore. Those losses have in turn resulted in huge claims, often against auditors, brought by liquidators or funds in distress. The final factor behind such expansion is the particular skill set of the Professional Negligence Bar, which is positioned at the crossover between commercial and chancery litigation, and so ideally placed to deal with such claims.

The final growth area goes perhaps to a misnomer. For some time, the Professional Negligence Bar has really been the Professional Liability Bar. However, increasingly in recent years, professional defendants are faced not just with compensatory claims, but with a two or even three-pronged assault: compensatory, regulatory and disciplinary. Consequently, the professional negligence market is evolving into what might be called the professional problem resolution market. Many clients face not just the threat of compensatory claims by disappointed former clients or customers, but also the threat of large regulatory fines (now typically assessed by reference to a percentage of relevant revenue), remediation and redress packages and associated disciplinary proceedings. Accordingly, the most sought-after practitioners in the field are now those who can advise on and identify a strategy that addresses all of a client's (whether claimant, defendant or insurer) aims and objectives across these three inter-related areas.

So, whilst this calendar year must surely see the back of much of the post-credit crunch litigation, there is every reason to believe that the Professional Negligence Bar will continue both to thrive and to evolve in the year to come.

Professional Negligence London

Contents:

LONDON

Professional Negligence London — Leading Sets
Band 1
4 New Square *
Band 2
Brick Court Chambers *
Fountain Court Chambers *
Hailsham Chambers *
4 Pump Court *
3 Verulam Buildings *
Wilberforce Chambers *
Band 3
1 Chancery Lane
Crown Office Chambers *
Maitland Chambers *
Band 4
7 King's Bench Walk *
XXIV Old Buildings *
Serle Court *
2TG - 2 Temple Gardens *
◇ (ORL) = Other Ranked Lawyer.
[A] direct access (see p.11).
* Indicates set / individual with profile.
Alphabetical order within each band. Band 1 is highest.

Professional Negligence London — Leading Silks
Star individuals
Fenwick Justin *4 New Square* *
Pooles Michael *Hailsham Chambers* *
Stewart Roger *4 New Square* *
Band 1
Brindle Michael *Fountain Court Chambers*
Davidson Nicholas *4 New Square* *
Edelman Colin *Devereux (ORL)* ◇ *
Gaisman Jonathan *7 King's Bench Walk*
Howard Mark *Brick Court Chambers*
Hubble Ben *4 New Square* *
Lawrence Patrick *4 New Square* *
McPherson Graeme *4 New Square* *
Moger Christopher *4 Pump Court* *
Onslow Andrew *3 Verulam Buildings*
Powell John L *4 New Square* *
Rowley Keith *Radcliffe Chambers (ORL)* ◇
Simpson Mark *Fountain Court Chambers*
Tozzi Nigel *4 Pump Court* *
Weitzman Tom *3 Verulam Buildings*
Band 2
Adam Tom *Brick Court Chambers*
Bartlett Andrew *Crown Office Chambers* *
Butcher Christopher *7 King's Bench Walk*
Croxford Ian *Wilberforce Chambers*
Douglas Michael *4 Pump Court* *
Elkington Ben *4 New Square* *
Flenley William *Hailsham Chambers* *
Halpern David *4 New Square* *
Harvey Michael *Crown Office Chambers*
Hollander Charles *Brick Court Chambers*
Jones Philip *Serle Court* *
Patten Ben *4 New Square* *
Salzedo Simon *Brick Court Chambers*
Smith Joanna *Wilberforce Chambers*
Steinfeld Alan *XXIV Old Buildings*
Symons Christopher *3 Verulam Buildings*
Thanki Bankim *Fountain Court Chambers* *
Wardell John *Wilberforce Chambers*
Band 3
Ayliffe James *Wilberforce Chambers*
Brannigan Sean *4 Pump Court* *
Cannon Mark *4 New Square* *
Christie Aidan *4 Pump Court* *
Cousins Jeremy *11 Stone Buildings (ORL)* ◇ *
Dale Derrick *Fountain Court Chambers*
Day Anneliese *4 New Square* *
Dougherty Charles *2TG - 2 Temple Gardens* *
Dutton Timothy *Fountain Court Chambers*
Eklund Graham *4 New Square* *
Howe Timothy *Fountain Court Chambers* *
Jones Nigel *Hardwicke (ORL)* ◇ [A] *
Lord Tim *Brick Court Chambers*
Marshall Philip *Serle Court* *
Moriarty Stephen *Fountain Court Chambers* *
Neish Andrew *4 Pump Court* *
Newman Paul *Wilberforce Chambers*
Ross John *1 Chancery Lane* *
Seitler Jonathan *Wilberforce Chambers*
Trace Anthony *Maitland Chambers* *
Turner David *4 New Square*
Band 4
Cross James *4 Pump Court* *
Cullen Edmund *Maitland Chambers* *
de Waal John *Hardwicke (ORL)* ◇ [A] *
Grant Thomas *Maitland Chambers*
Kinsky Cyril *3 Verulam Buildings*
Livesey Bernard *Hailsham Chambers* *
Moxon Browne Robert *2TG - 2 Temple Gardens* *
Mulcahy Leigh-Ann *4 New Square* *
Philipps Guy *Fountain Court Chambers* *
Picton Julian *Hailsham Chambers* *
Railton David *Fountain Court Chambers*
Robertson Patricia *Fountain Court Chambers* *
Sabben-Clare Rebecca *7 King's Bench Walk* *
Sinclair Fiona *4 New Square* *
Tregear Francis *XXIV Old Buildings*
Wales Andrew *7 King's Bench Walk*
Warnock Andrew *1 Chancery Lane* [A] *
New Silks
Chapman Graham *4 New Square* *
Goodall Patrick *Fountain Court Chambers* *
Reed Rupert *Wilberforce Chambers*

Band 1

4 New Square

See profile on p.835

THE SET

4 New Square has long led the way in professional negligence work, and has the finest pedigree of any set working in this market. Members represent claimants and defendants on the full remit of matters relating to professional negligence, and have expertise from baby junior to senior silk level. They frequently act on the most high-profile and complex cases before the English courts, and also act in matters in a number of foreign jurisdictions.

Client service: "The clerks, led by Lizzy Stewart, take a very user-friendly 21st century approach to clerking. They're not frightened to have conversations about fees and they are very good at having frank discussions when things aren't going right."

SILKS

Justin Fenwick QC (see p.599) A highly regarded silk who is noted for his expertise in insurance and financial negligence cases, particularly those with an element of fraudulent activity. **Strengths:** "A top-class advocate who reads a court very well." "He is a very good advocate who is calm and unflustered when on his feet." **Recent work:** Acted for PwC in defence of a £1.5 billion claim for audit negligence by Cattles plc.

Roger Stewart QC (see p.728) A pre-eminent silk who advises clients across the full scope of professional negligence matters. He is especially recommended for financial services-related claims. **Strengths:** "Tough, practical, commercial and clever." "He knows it all backwards and he's very confident in his delivery." **Recent work:** Successfully represented a firm of solicitors in Gabriel v Little in the Court of Appeal. The case set out an important distinction between the information and advice given by solicitors. The judge dismissed the claim for damages against the solicitors on the basis that it went beyond the scope of their duty.

Nicholas Davidson QC (see p.583) Acts for claimants in financial and legal professional negligence disputes. He is highly regarded for cases involving high-value or complex litigation. **Strengths:** "A robust advocate." **Recent work:** Acted for the claimant company in Newcastle International Airport Ltd v Eversheds. The case concerned issues of solicitors' negligence in relation to contracts that contained bonuses and benefits not intended by the employer.

Ben Hubble QC (see p.632) Advises clients on a variety of professional negligence matters. His capabilities extend to multiparty litigation, including those which are particularly complex or document-heavy. **Strengths:** "He's very personable and has a good way of putting clients at ease." "Absolutely at the top of his game and excellent to work with." **Recent work:** Acted for law firm Collyer Bristow in the Innovator and Keydata litigation. The case concerned 550 investors who sought £60 million on the basis that their 19 investment schemes were fraudulent.

Patrick Lawrence QC (see p.652) Handles a variety of professional negligence matters for claimants and defendants. He is known for his expertise in high-profile, large-scale solicitors' claims. **Strengths:** "Very charismatic and good with clients; he is able and approachable in equal measure." "He knows the area very well and he's tactically very astute." **Recent work:** Advised in a solicitors' negligence claim brought by Petrocapital Resources PLC against Morrison & Foerster.

Graeme McPherson QC Known for his powerful advocacy skills. He is highly regarded for his expertise in solicitors' negligence claims. **Strengths:** "He

Professional Negligence London	
Leading Juniors	
Star individuals	**Oppenheimer** Tamara *Fountain Court Chambers*
Charlwood Spike *Hailsham Chambers* *	**Plewman SC** Thomas *Brick Court Chambers*
Livesey Kate *4 Pump Court* *	**Troman** Carl *4 New Square* *
Smith Jamie *4 New Square* *	**Weaver** Elizabeth *XXIV Old Buildings*
Band 1	**Band 4**
Holwill Derek *Hailsham Chambers* *	**Cutress** James *Fountain Court Chambers* *
Mitchell Paul *Hailsham Chambers* *	**Dixon** Clare *4 New Square* *
Phipps Charles *4 New Square* *	**Evans** Helen *4 New Square* *
Pilling Benjamin *4 Pump Court* *	**Ferguson** Eva *Hailsham Chambers* *
Savage Amanda *4 New Square* *	**Harris** Miles *4 New Square* *
Band 2	**Head** David *3 Verulam Buildings*
Allen Scott *4 New Square* *	**Jackson** Matthew *Hailsham Chambers* *
Bacon Francis *Hailsham Chambers* *	**Lynch** Ben *Devereux (ORL)* ◊ *
Brocklebank James *7 King's Bench Walk*	**McCann** Sarah *Hardwicke (ORL)* ◊ [A] *
Dumont Thomas *Radcliffe Chambers (ORL)* ◊	**Norman** John *1 Chancery Lane* *
Evans Hugh *4 New Square* *	**Powell** Katie *4 New Square* *
Evans-Tovey Jason *Crown Office Chambers*	**Sawyer** Edward *Wilberforce Chambers*
Hall Taylor Alex *4 New Square* *	**Shuman** Karen *1 Chancery Lane* [A] *
Mirchandani Siân *4 New Square* *	**Spalton** George *4 New Square* *
Parker Matthew *3 Verulam Buildings* *	**Spencer** Andrew *1 Chancery Lane* *
Shapiro Daniel *Crown Office Chambers* *	**Stanley** Clare *Wilberforce Chambers*
Wilton Simon *Hailsham Chambers* [A] *	**Trigger** Simon *1 Chancery Lane* *
Yeo Nik *Fountain Court Chambers* *	**Wygas** Luke *4 Pump Court* *
Band 3	**Yates** David *Pump Court Tax Chambers (ORL)* ◊ *
Carpenter Jamie *Hailsham Chambers* *	**Up-and-coming individuals**
Collett Ivor *1 Chancery Lane* *	**Barter** Isabel *2TG – 2 Temple Gardens* *
Howarth Simon *Hailsham Chambers* *	**Colter** Lucy *4 New Square* *
Jackson Hugh *Selborne Chambers (ORL)* ◊ *	**Wood** Benjamin *4 New Square* *
Liddell Richard *4 New Square* *	

** Indicates individual with profile.*
◊ (ORL) = Other Ranked Lawyer.
[A] direct access (see p.11).

has a great capacity for analysing a huge quantity of documents and information." "He's very thorough, a very good advocate, and he has an excellent way with clients." **Recent work:** Acted for the defendant solicitors in Allied Irish Bank v Mark Redler & Co. The claim was for failure to discharge a pre-existing mortgage on a remortgage, and is the leading case on breach of trust and equitable compensation in professional negligence.

John Powell QC (see p.697) Represents clients in complex financial professional negligence claims. He is recognised for his strength in very high-value claims. **Strengths:** "He's very measured. He knows the subject inside out and back to front, and is also very user-friendly and easy to deal with." "He has a good strategic brain on him in terms of mapping out the strategy around the legal arguments." **Recent work:** Acted for the claimants in the £60 million Innovator litigation concerning financial negligence and fraud.

Ben Patten QC (see p.690) Advises clients in a wide range of professional negligence disputes. He is recommended for property-related solicitors' negligence claims and construction-related disputes. **Strengths:** "You can throw anything his way and he will deal with it." "He has a mild and gentle manner with clients, but is determined and clear in his advice. He is also very effective as an advocate, as he's calm but good at focusing on the right issues and directing judges' attention to them." **Recent work:** Acted for a property developer in a claim against a firm of solicitors for negligent advice.

David Halpern QC Specialises in cases relating to professional negligence. His particular strength lies in professional negligence claims arising from property disputes. **Strengths:** "He does well in cases where you want someone to approach a situation with novel ideas." "He has a very wide breadth of knowledge." **Recent work:** Acted for the defendants in Ridgewood Properties Ltd v Finers Stephens Innocent. The claimants were suing their solicitors after they secured the options on 11 petrol station sites, but Texaco sold the sites in spite of the options.

Mark Cannon QC (see p.565) Known for his wide-ranging professional negligence practice spanning financial and solicitors' negligence and construction-related disputes. He demonstrates a strength in defending claims against solicitors, where they are alleged to have failed to identify potential clinical negligence cases. **Strengths:** "He is exceptionally clever and gives superb written advice and submissions." "He is a very clear-thinking lawyer and his manner of expression as an advocate is very impressive." **Recent work:** Acted for the defendant solicitors in a claim brought by the parents of a severely disabled girl alleging that the NHS had failed to identify a case of wrongful birth.

Anneliese Day QC (see p.585) Focuses on acting for claimants and defendants in complex and high-profile professional negligence cases. She is noted for the strength of her client-handling skills. **Strengths:** "She is fiercely intelligent, but also perfectly human. She has excellent client care skills, is exceptional on her feet, and her advice is succinct and to the point." "She has a tremendous brain, but what differentiates her is her unflappability – she is calm, methodical and logical, and always a pleasure to work with." **Recent work:** Defended BDO in a complex tax negligence case.

Graham Eklund QC His cases range from general insurance brokers' issues to a claim for the negligent design of a racecourse. **Strengths:** "Clients value his direct, no-nonsense approach and his judgement." "He is very good at getting to the heart of the issues and not being distracted by a large volume of information." **Recent work:** Acted on a claim for £2 million against an insurance broker relating to significant under-insurance of gross profit.

Ben Elkington QC Advises on the full remit of professional negligence disputes. He demonstrates a particular expertise in insurance brokers' negligence cases. **Strengths:** "He is professional, incredibly bright and offers commercial, practical and strategic advice." "Fantastic to work with; he's very reliable and down to earth." **Recent work:** Represented the claimant in a £2 million claim against insurance brokers concerning a factory that had been destroyed in a fire.

David Turner QC Represents clients in a host of professional liability cases, but is best known for the strength of his financial professional negligence practice. **Strengths:** "He is commercially very astute and exceptionally good at grasping audit complexities extremely quickly." "He offers robust advice, and is a strategist extraordinaire." **Recent work:** Acted on a £4 million claim against a fund manager for negligent calculations of the value of funds.

Graham Chapman QC (see p.568) Focuses on some of the biggest and most high-profile financial professional negligence disputes. He is noted for his expertise in claims with a multi-jurisdictional element. **Strengths:** "He gets through voluminous and complex instructions at impressive speed, and consistently provides robust and commercial advice, as well as advocacy of the highest quality." "He is quietly spoken, but his words are powerful and his advice is terrific." **Recent work:** Acted as junior counsel for PwC in the £1.6 billion Cattles litigation.

Fiona Sinclair QC (see p.721) Handles all professional negligence matters for claimants and defendants. She demonstrates notable expertise in financial and construction disputes. **Strengths:** "Very bright and very good at making complex issues understandable." "She is controlled, thorough and resilient." **Recent work:** Defended the largest group of solicitor defendants in the £24 million Concord Street litigation.

Leigh-Ann Mulcahy QC (see p.678) Advises clients in multiparty and complex professional liability matters. She regularly appears before the Court of Appeal and the Supreme Court. **Strengths:** "She is very efficient, very good on her feet and has a good manner with clients." "She is an iron fist in a velvet glove, who is happy to tell judges what she thinks if they go off at a tangent." **Recent work:** Advised a defendant firm of solicitors on a claim of negligence arising from a product liability case that had been lost.

JUNIORS

Scott Allen (see p.534) Acts for claimants and defendants, and is known for the strength of his solicitors' and surveyors' negligence practice. **Strengths:** "He is a talented advocate who has a nice, concise way of expressing himself in clear and understandable language." "Very approachable and absolutely sound on all aspects." **Recent work:** Represented the defendant in an £8 million surveyors' negligence case.

Hugh Evans (see p.597) Represents clients in all manner of professional indemnity matters, and demonstrates notable expertise in financial and legal negligence cases. **Strengths:** "He is extremely bright and very good tactically." "He is excellent and very persuasive on his feet." **Recent work:** Acted for claimants suing their firm of solicitors for negligent advice that resulted in the failure to secure a mortgage on a foreign property.

Alex Hall Taylor (see p.617) Specialises in complex, document-heavy professional negligence cases for claimants and defendants. He is recommended in disputes with a tax or fraud element. **Strengths:** "He's very nice to work with, as he's user-friendly and supportive. He's also very quick to see the dynamics of a case, and he'll come to a conclusion early on." "He has an ability to see the wood from the trees and drill down into what's important. He's also extremely good on paperwork and very commercially orientated." **Recent work:** Acted for Barclays Bank in a £40 million claim against Knight Frank concerning a negligent valuation.

Miles Harris (see p.620) Handles defendant and claimant professional negligence cases, and is celebrated for his knowledge of insurance-related negligence claims. **Strengths:** "He is well organised and has good client-handling skills. He's also very efficient and it is cost-effective having him on board." "He is an outstanding barrister whose personal skills are superb. He has a great ability to make you feel comfortable, and he is able to soak up a wide range of facts." **Recent work:** Represented the defendant in a £1.6 million brokers' negligence claim.

Clare Dixon (see p.588) Advises on the full range of professional negligence matters for claimants and defendants. She regularly acts on cases involving lenders and allegations of fraud. **Strengths:** "Her speed of turnaround and the quality of her work are impressive." "She is extremely charming and nice to work with, but also packs an intellectual punch." **Recent work:** Advised a defendant firm of solicitors in an £11 million claim for negligent drafting of a sale agreement.

Helen Evans (see p.597) Has a broad professional negligence practice and acts for defendants and claimants. She is noted for her capabilities in multiparty litigation and complex cases. **Strengths:** "Very efficient, very bright and gives very good advice." "The reason that you go to a barrister is to get advice from somebody cleverer than you. She never disappoints in this regard and brings an angle that you're not clever enough to have thought about." **Recent work:** Defended a firm of conveyancing solicitors against 12 claimants in a £1.8 million claim for negligence.

Lucy Colter (see p.576) Acts on the full remit of professional negligence cases, including technology and construction issues. She is notably strong in claims involving valuers and surveyors. **Strengths:** "She is good at the detail, very positive and has good knowledge of the law." "She works hard under difficult circumstances and is very approachable and normal." **Recent work:** Acted for the defendant valuers in a negligence case concerning allegations of overvaluation on 91 properties.

Jamie Smith (see p.723) Outstanding junior who acts for claimants and defendants on the full remit of professional negligence matters. He is noted for his expertise in complex financial and property-related claims. **Strengths:** "He is a good team player with a fine legal brain. He is highly analytical and is able to see through complicated legal issues and distil them down to the essential points." "He is extremely intelligent, very approachable and a strong advocate. He adds value throughout the process and he's always engaged." **Recent work:** Acted on landmark valuers' negligence case MASNOL v Edward Symmons.

Amanda Savage (see p.715) Handles professional negligence disputes for claimants and defendants, and demonstrates particular expertise in solicitors' and barristers' negligence claims. **Strengths:** "She's fierce, very responsive and very forensic." "Clients think she is fantastic as she is straightforward to work with and will go much further than others would." **Recent work:** Represented a junior barrister in a claim for negligent action arising out of a trial and criminal conviction.

Charles Phipps (see p.693) Represents claimants and defendants, and attracts particular praise for his knowledge of financial disputes. **Strengths:** "He is very bright academically, analytical, intelligent and a safe pair of hands." "He is very clever and thorough, and has a particular expertise in financial disputes." **Recent work:** Advised a firm of solicitors in a negligence case stemming from an unsuccessful ATE litigation funding scheme.

Carl Troman (see p.740) Focuses on professional negligence claims for architects, accountants, solicitors and surveyors. He is particularly recommended for multiparty actions. **Strengths:** "He just makes any situation easier. He is also thorough and prompt." "He is my first choice for property-related professional negligence, as he always provides commonsense advice. He also looks at things from a different angle and puts forward a refreshing view." **Recent work:** Acted on the multimillion-pound solicitors' negligence case Northern Rock plc v DLA Piper UK.

Siân Mirchandani (see p.673) Regularly acts in complex professional negligence disputes. She demonstrates notable expertise in financial claims and cases with an international element. **Strengths:** "The great thing about her is that on every occasion her advice is strong, firm and consistent, which allows us to get an excellent settlement." "She's very strong on complex matters." **Recent work:** Acted for the defendant solicitors in the Court of Appeal case AIB v Redler & Co concerning a mortgage conveyancing transaction. The case was recently heard in the Supreme Court.

Katie Powell (see p.697) Handles a full range of professional negligence claims, and is recommended for valuers' negligence and financial services disputes. **Strengths:** "She is incredibly dedicated and has a very sharp mind." "She is a very clear advocate who gets to the issues very quickly." **Recent work:** Acted for the claimant, Nationwide, in a £2 million claim against a valuer for negligence.

Richard Liddell He regularly acts in high-profile and complex cases for lawyers and construction professionals among others. **Strengths:** "He is very well liked by clients, works hard and has a very amicable manner." **Recent work:** Defended AMEC in a case for negligence against a planning consultant.

George Spalton (see p.725) Frequently acts unled in high-value professional negligence cases. He is noted for the strength of his solicitors' negligence work. **Strengths:** "He is very, very client-friendly, has a relaxed, easy manner and knows his stuff." "He is very quick and very commercial – a rising star." **Recent work:** Represented the claimant in the Court of Appeal in a solicitors' negligence case.

Benjamin Wood (see p.755) Covers the full scope of professional negligence issues for claimants and defendants. He demonstrates particular expertise in complex financial negligence claims. **Strengths:** "He is brilliant in cross-examination." "He has a real depth of knowledge in the area, which adds real value." **Recent work:** Led by Nicholas Davidson QC, he acted for the claimant in Newcastle International Airport v Eversheds.

Band 2

Brick Court Chambers

See profile on p.774

THE SET

An excellent set that is seen in some of the most complex and high-value professional negligence cases. Members are noted for their expertise in commercial cases, particularly financial negligence claims. They frequently act both for and against banks and accountants.

Client service: Julian Hawes and Ian Moyler head a team of clerks who are "excellent because they don't just act as a postbox; they are proactive at making sure any issues are dealt with. Their fees are at the top end, but the clerks are flexible in negotiation when they need to be."

SILKS

Mark Howard QC Attracts praise for his knowledge of financial negligence issues and is noted for his deadly cross-examinations. **Strengths:** "He is really strong in court and a very strong analyst and examiner. One of the first you would go to if you wanted a heavy hitter." "He is a superb barrister." **Recent work:** Defended Goldman Sachs in a claim for negligence arising from advice and investment given to a Dutch pension body.

Tom Adam QC Frequently acts in high-profile professional negligence claims. He is noted for his particular strength in insurance and solicitors' cases. **Strengths:** "A superb analyst and excellent to work with." "He is bright, hard-working, lateral thinking, and he has a good sense of what argument will work with a particular judge." **Recent work:** Acted for the defence in Metro Baltic Horizon v Ernst & Young. The case involved six separate jurisdictions.

Simon Salzedo QC Acts for claimants and defendants across a range of issues, and is highly commended for his high-profile accountants' negligence work. **Strengths:** "He has good tactical awareness, is calm and unflappable, and is good at balancing the legal issues with human and commercial considerations." **Recent work:** Defended Grant Thornton in a complex £20 million claim relating to audit negligence and conflicts of interest.

Charles Hollander QC Acts on a number of different professional negligence matters. He is noted for his expertise in cases arising from conflict of interest. **Strengths:** "Gets on top of the papers in a really impressive way." **Recent work:** Acted in Muirgold v SJ Berwin, a solicitors' negligence action concerning the Paddington Hilton.

Tim Lord QC Focuses on complex commercial litigation for financial institutions, and a number of his cases involve professional negligence. He is recommended for his handling of high-value and commercially sensitive claims. **Strengths:** "He's in the vanguard when it comes to claims against banks and finance houses." **Recent work:** Acted in J.P. Morgan v BVG v Clifford Chance, a negligence case pertaining to a USD250 million synthetic collateralised debt obligation.

JUNIORS

Thomas Plewman SC Handles a heavy commercial litigation caseload. His strength lies in acting for financial services companies in high-value negligence claims. **Strengths:** "His knowledge is excellent, as is his advocacy. He shows good judgement as to how to engage with judges and he is good tactically." "He is fantastically good value because he's really experienced and happy to get involved with the clients." **Recent work:** Acted for PwC in defending a £1.6 billion negligence claim brought against it by Cattles plc.

Fountain Court Chambers

See profile on p.804

THE SET

Fountain Court Chambers is a leading commercial litigation set. Members bring their wealth of knowledge to professional negligence cases. They act for claimants and defendants in financial, legal and insurance-related claims. Individuals here have been particularly active in claims that have arisen out of the credit crunch, and have routinely advised investment managers, financial advisers, brokers and solicitors in this regard.

Client service: Alex Taylor heads a team that provides "a good professional service." The clerks are "very helpful, always responsive and are willing to go the extra mile."

SILKS

Michael Brindle QC Acts for claimants and defendants and is noted for his expertise in financial negligence cases. **Strengths:** "He's extremely bright and client-friendly, and he provides good leadership."

Mark Simpson QC Handles a wide range of professional negligence matters. He is especially recommended for claims against valuers and accountants. **Strengths:** "He is an outstandingly good advocate and a very good person to deal with." "He is one of those silks that has great gravitas, but is also a very good team player." **Recent work:** Represented the defendant valuers in the Court of Appeal case of Mortgage Agency Services Number One Ltd v Edward Symmons.

Bankim Thanki QC Frequently acts on some of the most high-profile financial professional negligence cases. He demonstrates particular expertise when defending well-known financial institutions. **Strengths:** "He has a pleasant, understated advocacy style, and is a very good orator." **Recent work:** Advised Rathbone Brothers in relation to a financial negligence claim brought by two beneficiaries of the Jack Walker Trust.

Timothy Dutton QC Advises clients in legal and financial professional negligence disputes. His strength lies in handling very high-value, sensitive solicitors' negligence cases. **Strengths:** "A terrific advocate with a very good court presence." "He's intellectual and erudite, but also a man without arrogance." **Recent work:** Defended Herbert Smith in the £148 million case of London Underground Ltd v Freshfields Bruckhaus Deringer and Herbert Smith.

Timothy Howe QC Represents clients in complex financial and legal negligence claims. He is often seen in the Supreme Court and is recommended in cases with an international element. **Strengths:** "He is intelligent, thoughtful and he crafts his cases well." "He has experience of complex, high-value investment banking disputes, and gets on top of the detail very well. He understands financial products and provides excellent analysis." **Recent work:** Acted for KfW in its multimillion-dollar claim against Euroclear for financial negligence.

Derrick Dale QC Focuses on legal and financial professional negligence disputes. He is regarded for his work in high-profile, sensitive matters. **Strengths:** "He is excellent and very knowledgeable when it comes to investment advice." **Recent work:** Defended Freeth Cartwright in a claim by two former clients who sued the firm, claiming that it had negligently handed litigation for them against SJ Berwin.

Stephen Moriarty QC (see p.676) Handles high-profile legal and financial professional negligence matters. He is frequently seen at the forefront of landmark cases and demonstrates expertise in cases with an international flavour. **Strengths:** "He is exceptionally bright and really committed. He gets involved in all the detail and doesn't rely too heavily on juniors." "He has a good reputation in the Commercial Court and with senior arbitrators, as he only ever makes credible arguments. When he speaks, judges and arbitrators pay attention." **Recent work:** Defended Pioneer Alternative Investments in a high-value claim by the hedge fund Primeo Fund.

Patrick Goodall QC (see p.611) Advises clients in financial and legal negligence matters. He is particularly recommended for complex, high-profile disputes, including mis-selling and mismanagement cases. **Strengths:** "He is very thoughtful, very diligent and has very good judgement." "He is superb – he has a first-rate brain and is a delightful advocate." **Recent work:** Represented Coutts & Co in a number of mis-selling claims relating to AIG investment products.

David Railton QC Specialises in professional negligence claims in the banking and finance sphere, and demonstrates particular expertise in misstatement claims. **Strengths:** "He is extremely impressive, as he is thoughtful, articulate and all over the detail in a case." **Recent work:** Acted for Sebastian Holdings in its USD8 billion dispute with Deutsche Bank.

Guy Philipps QC (see p.692) Handles insurance and finance-related negligence disputes, many of which are high-value, sensitive matters. **Strengths:** "Top-rate and active in many of the big cases." **Recent work:** Acted for the claimant in the £20 million case of Basma Al Sulaiman v Credit Suisse.

Patricia Robertson QC (see p.709) Acts in banking and financial services negligence matters. She is recommended for high-value cases, particularly those arising from mis-selling. **Strengths:** "An energetic advocate with masses of intellect, who applies herself very well." **Recent work:** Defended AWD Chase De Vere in the Keydata litigation.

JUNIORS

Nik Yeo (see p.757) Advises clients on a wide range of financial and legal negligence matters. He demonstrates notable expertise in negligent valuation cases. **Strengths:** "He's very impressive. He has immense intellectual ability, is extremely good at the paperwork, is user-friendly and is easy to get along with." "He is hands-on and very pleasant to deal with." **Recent work:** Acted for the issuer in Gemini v CBRE and King Sturge. The case concerned the negligent valuation of commercial property and is worth £1.2 billion.

Tamara Oppenheimer Frequently handles high-profile financial negligence claims. Her expertise lies in representing financial professionals in swap mis-selling litigation. **Strengths:** "She is superb. She has fantastic attention to detail, and is very commercial and very sensible." "She's very hard-working, very good company and very clever." **Recent work:** Represented RBS/NatWest in a number of swap mis-selling claims.

James Cutress (see p.582) Handles negligence claims arising from financial disputes. He is noted for his work in relation to negligent valuations, mismanagement of investments and interest rate swaps. **Strengths:** "Makes clients feel reassured and confident, and has the ability to understand and digest large amounts of evidence in a short timescale." **Recent work:** Represented a fund manager in a USD500 million claim by Primeo Fund.

Hailsham Chambers

See profile on p.814

THE SET

Hailsham Chambers' members act on the full range of professional negligence work, and regularly handle cases relating to lawyers, accountants, brokers and surveyors among others. The 40-strong team is seen to be at the forefront of legal development in the field, and is noted for the consistently high quality of advice it offers.

Client service: Stephen Smith leads a team of clerks who are seen as being "efficient and approachable," "very helpful" and "always keen to accommodate."

SILKS

Michael Pooles QC (see p.696) Attracts widespread praise for his client skills and the strength of his professional negligence practice. He is recommended for insurance policy coverage matters and, in particular, contract interpretation issues. **Strengths:** "Confident, inspiring and reassuring, he's a superb lawyer with a refined and smooth style." "He is extremely clever, has very good instincts and stands by them." **Recent work:** Acted on the multimillion-pound solicitors' negligence case Wellesley LLP v Withers.

William Flenley QC (see p.601) Handles negligence claims against professionals connected with the insurance, legal and financial sectors. **Strengths:** "He is very tenacious and, unlike a lot of QCs, he handles much of the legwork himself. He has an eye for detail and is very good at thinking outside the box." "He is very clever, meticulous in his approach and an excellent cross-examiner." **Recent work:** Acted on a £1.5 million solicitors' negligence matter.

Bernard Livesey QC (see p.657) Acts on legal, insurance and finance-related professional negligence disputes. He is known for handling high-value and complex matters, and is regularly seen in the higher courts. **Strengths:** "Has gravitas and commands respect." **Recent work:** Acted on a solicitors' negligence case in the Court of Appeal.

Julian Picton QC (see p.693) Advises clients on a wide range of professional negligence issues. He is noted for his expertise in claims arising from solicitors' negligence. **Strengths:** "He is razor sharp." "A safe pair of hands and someone you can throw anything at." **Recent work:** Acted for the claimant in Haskew v Pannone LLP, Wacks Caller, Michael Booth QC and David Casement QC.

JUNIORS

Spike Charlwood (see p.570) Regularly acts in complex legal and financial negligence cases. He demonstrates notable expertise in cases arising from the negligent valuation or surveying of properties. **Strengths:** "He's extremely intelligent and very, very perceptive in terms of getting to the nub of the case."

"Absolutely top class." **Recent work:** Acted in breach of trust case, Ikbal v Sterling Law.

Derek Holwill (see p.630) Handles the full scope of professional negligence matters. He frequently acts for claimants and defendants in solicitors' negligence cases. **Strengths:** "A silk in all but name, he is incredibly user-friendly and not afraid of pointing out the errors of your ways." "If you give him something that is a hot potato, he is very good at turning it around." **Recent work:** Defended European Risk Insurance in a claim by the law firm McManus Seddon Runhams concerning the issue of indemnity cover.

Paul Mitchell (see p.674) He is noted for his expertise in legal and financial negligence cases. **Strengths:** "He offers clear, user-friendly advice and has strong advocacy skills." "He often pulls things out of the hat – you can ring him up and he will give you really good advice on very difficult points. He is fantastic and really commercial." **Recent work:** Acted for the claimant in Owners of M/V Avenir v Holman Fenwick Willan.

Francis Bacon (see p.540) Represents clients in a wide range of professional negligence cases. He is noted for the strength of his insurance practice and, in particular, his capabilities in coverage disputes. **Strengths:** "He is very sound and unflappable, and has a wealth of experience in his core areas." "He is outstanding, as he is extremely commercial and personable, and his advocacy style is fantastic – he always comes across in court as if he is just having a chat." **Recent work:** Successfully defended a chartered surveyor in a £3 million negligence claim.

Simon Wilton (see p.754) Handles the full scope of professional negligence cases for claimants and defendants. He is recommended for surveyors' and solicitors' negligence matters. **Strengths:** "He is concise, clear, practical and commercial." "He's intellectually very able and a very good, confident speaker who doesn't talk nonsense." **Recent work:** Acted for the defendant solicitors in a multiparty claim concerning fraudulent purchase arrangements.

Jamie Carpenter (see p.565) He demonstrates notable expertise in legal and financial matters, and frequently acts in high-value cases. **Strengths:** "He is very positive, very easy to talk to, and very approachable." "He's very easy to work with, incredibly thorough, and his advice has a very good structure to it." **Recent work:** Acted for the lead claimant in Haskew v Pannone LLP, Wacks Caller, Michael Booth QC and David Casement QC, a £2.5 million legal negligence case.

Simon Howarth (see p.631) Focuses on legal, insurance and financially related professional negligence claims. He is noted for the depth of his knowledge of coverage disputes. **Strengths:** "He has a wonderful turn of phrase, is pragmatic, fun and quirky to work with." "He is the standout junior for claims against financial professionals. He is a very bright chap who is good on his feet and a team player." **Recent work:** Acted for the insurers of the defendant in Farmer v Deferred Finance and others. The case concerned a coverage dispute and unique queries on the impact of the construction of an exclusion clause.

Matthew Jackson (see p.637) Acts in solicitors' and financial negligence disputes. He is noted for his strength in multiparty claims. **Strengths:** "An excellent cross-examiner who is very intellectually able and gives robust advice." "He has a good handle on the realities of litigation and gives commercially aware advice." **Recent work:** Advised three firms of solicitor defendants in the vibration white finger litigation.

Eva Ferguson (see p.599) Represents claimants and defendants in solicitors' negligence claims. She is also very strong on clinical negligence matters. **Strengths:** "She's approachable, user-friendly, very bright and technical." "She has a no-nonsense approach and regularly delivers." **Recent work:** Acted for the claimant in Duglan v Borneo Hughes Martell Solicitors.

4 Pump Court

See profile on p.849

THE SET

4 Pump Court is highly regarded for general professional negligence disputes and technology and construction-related claims. Members advise claimants and defendants on a wide range of cases, many of which are complex in nature. The barristers are frequently to be seen acting in the higher courts.

Client service: "The clerks are really efficient, proactive, quick and friendly." Stewart Gibbs and Carl Wall are the joint senior clerks.

SILKS

Christopher Moger QC (see p.675) Acts for and against professionals in negligence cases. He has notable expertise in claims with an international element. **Strengths:** "He is very impressive and he does his homework. Despite being brought into our case at a late stage, he covered the ground very thoroughly." "He is a jolly, confident advocate of the old school and a formidable opponent." **Recent work:** Acted in a £120 million claim arising out of an allegation that defendants had been negligent in their provision of administration services to an offshore group of companies engaged in a property development project in London.

Nigel Tozzi QC Handles a broad range of professional negligence matters for claimants and defendants. His strength lies in insurance coverage disputes, in particular, cases with an element of fraud. **Strengths:** "He is excellent, as he is a terrific advocate and a very nice man who has a charming and easy style with judges." "He is very sensible and commercial." **Recent work:** Acted for the defendant, Knight Frank, in a £40 million claim by Barclays for a negligent valuation.

Michael Douglas QC (see p.589) Advises on technology and construction disputes, as well as general professional negligence matters. He demonstrates notable expertise in high-value cases, many of which have an international element. **Strengths:** "He is very, very good with judges; they really like him. He is also very bright, and a fantastic advocate who is very tenacious." "He is a formidable opponent. He gets to the heart of things and gives the right answer." **Recent work:** Acted in a very complex multi-jurisdictional solicitors' negligence case.

Sean Brannigan QC (see p.555) Handles a diverse range of work from construction-related matters to solicitors' negligence cases. He is recommended for complex multiparty litigation. **Strengths:** "He is very intelligent, but not lofty. He's grounded and clients like him as he has no ego." "If you want a fighter he's the one to go to." **Recent work:** Defended an £8 million claim for financial negligence arising from failure to spot a very substantial and high-profile fraud.

Aidan Christie QC (see p.571) Focuses on acting for claimants and defendants in all manner of professional negligence matters. He demonstrates particular expertise in complex financial claims and disputes over coverage. **Strengths:** "Offers perfectly balanced advice and has a quick turnaround of papers." "Takes a careful, thorough and analytical approach to difficult and novel insurance coverage disputes." **Recent work:** Acted for The Funding Corporation in its negligence claim against Barclays Bank.

Andrew Neish QC (see p.681) Represents clients across the full spectrum of professional negligence disputes. His strength lies in insurance brokers' negligence claims. **Strengths:** "His work is excellent and he always delivers when he says he's going to." **Recent work:** Advised professional indemnity insurers on professional negligence claims brought against a firm of insolvent valuers.

James Cross QC Acts for both parties in general professional negligence and technology and construction-related matters. He is particularly strong in complex and high-profile claims. **Strengths:** "He is a very safe pair of hands" who is "very good on his feet and tactically astute."

JUNIORS

Kate Livesey (see p.657) Acts for and against a wide range of professionals in liability claims. She is particularly capable when it comes to high-value, multiparty matters. **Strengths:** "She is highly intelligent, tactically astute, always commercial and has a keen eye for detail." "She is a superstar, she is very open and receptive." **Recent work:** Led by Christopher Moger, acted in a financial negligence claim worth £120 million.

Benjamin Pilling (see p.694) Handles general professional and technology and construction-related negligence matters. He demonstrates notable expertise in cases with complex financial elements. **Strengths:** "He is very good on paper, and has a clear and crisp writing style." "He does a great job of sifting through papers and his work is technical and practical." **Recent work:** Acted in a complex auditors' negligence cases concerning the forced sale of shares belonging to a start-up company.

Luke Wygas (see p.756) Acts both for and against a wide range of professionals in negligence cases. He is recommended for complex, multi-jurisdictional matters. **Strengths:** "He is very impressive. He rolls up his sleeves and gets on with stuff." **Recent work:** Advised on a claim of negligence against a valuer and a solicitor relating to the sale of a country house.

3 Verulam Buildings

See profile on p.875

THE SET 3 Verulam Buildings is one of the pre-eminent London sets for professional negligence work. Members act for claimants and defendants on all professional liability matters, including large-scale commercial disputes and smaller private claims. They are regularly seen in the higher courts acting on complex and high-value cases.

Client service: Paul Cooklin's clerking team attracts widespread praise. Clients say: "The clerks are excellent. They are easy to deal with, always transparent about availability and fair and reasonable on fees."

SILKS

Andrew Onslow QC Represents clients across the full range of professional liability issues, but is particularly recommended for cases involving negligent mis-selling of financial products. **Strengths:** "He is very experienced and easy to work with. He is clear-thinking and will give a view rather than talking about it and not doing anything." "A good lawyer and litigator who deals with judges very well and has good personal skills." **Recent work:** Represented the defendant stockbrokers in a £20-30 million case concerning the negligent creation and management of an investment scheme.

Tom Weitzman QC Regularly acts on complex insurance and brokers' negligence cases. He is noted for his expertise in large, multiparty claims. **Strengths:** "He gives very precise advice and is very good with clients. He has a clear, logical and structured approach which clients love." "He is exceptionally bright, but what makes him stand out is that he is easy to work with and collaborative." **Recent work:** Defended a large independent financial adviser network against claims of mis-selling by several hundred investors.

Christopher Symons QC Acts for clients on the full remit of professional negligence disputes. He demonstrates particular expertise in valuers' and surveyors' negligence. **Recent work:** Advised case against a firm of valuers concerning negligent valuation of a property in Germany.

Cyril Kinsky QC Represents defendants in a wide range of professional negligence claims, and is particularly recommended for his work on financial and legal negligence cases. **Strengths:** "He is very pragmatic and provides a very good service." **Recent work:** Acted for Collyer Bristow in a £25 million claim brought against it by Rangers FC.

JUNIORS

Matthew Parker (see p.689) Acts for claimants and defendants in an array of negligence matters, and is especially strong on claims relating to solicitors. **Strengths:** "He is very thorough, very good at lateral thinking, very hard-working and easy to work with." "He is a tough, forthright and plain-speaking advocate." **Recent work:** Advised the claimants in a £5 million action against their solicitors relating to diminished value of a loan stock.

David Head Focuses on advising claimants in a wide range of professional negligence matters. He is particularly strong on financial matters and claims arising from negligent valuations. **Strengths:** "He is sensible to work with, responsive and quite pragmatic." "He's much more results-focused than some barristers can be. Barristers can get bogged down in the legal arguments, but he's good at keeping things at the right level." **Recent work:** Acted in a complex accountants' negligence matter.

Wilberforce Chambers

See profile on p.876

THE SET

Wilberforce Chambers is a leading chancery set that handles a host of professional negligence cases, many of which are high-value and complex in nature. Members demonstrate notable expertise in negligence cases arising from property transactions, but also routinely handle matters relating to lawyers, auditors, accountants, actuaries and individuals from the financial sector.

Client service: Mark Rushton "runs a slick outfit." The clerks are "very helpful and responsive, and are contactable outside of office hours."

SILKS

James Ayliffe QC He is an established commercial silk who demonstrates notable expertise in financial and banking negligence matters. **Strengths:** "He is highly cerebral, but also pragmatic in his approach." "A go-to chancery barrister with a charming manner." **Recent work:** Advised the claimant bank in a multimillion-pound negligence case concerning a firm of project monitors.

John Wardell QC Focuses on financial and legal professional negligence matters. He is well known for acting for barristers faced with negligence suits. **Strengths:** "He gives bold advice and sticks to it. He is very calm, good on his feet, clever and has a nice touch with clients." "He is very experienced, and has an unnerving instinct for what is important in a case and the way it will go. An outstanding advocate and a consummate team player." **Recent work:** Acted in Wilson v Grant Thornton, an £18 million auditors' negligence case.

Ian Croxford QC His professional negligence practice primarily involves legal and financially related matters. **Strengths:** "Ian's attention to detail and ability to identify alternative and sustainable arguments prove invaluable." "He is exceptional especially when cross-examining vulnerable witnesses, and he has a real presence in court."

Joanna Smith QC Represents clients across a range of professional negligence cases, and is noted for her capabilities in high-value, complex and document-heavy work. **Strengths:** "Her advocacy really marks her out, and she is a good person to have on side in court. She comes across as very reasonable but firm." **Recent work:** Acted in a high-value claim against valuers for negligent overvaluation of a holiday park in Cornwall.

Paul Newman QC Handles financial negligence matters for claimants and defendants. He is particularly recommended in pensions-related disputes. **Strengths:** "He's very impressive in court and has great presence." "He is very imaginative and dynamic." **Recent work:** Defended Scottish Widows against a claim by the trustees of a pensions scheme alleging negligence in regard to documentation and administration services.

Jonathan Seitler QC Demonstrates expertise in negligence cases relating to property matters. He acts for claimants and defendants, and is frequently seen in high-value cases. **Strengths:** "A forceful advocate." **Recent work:** Advised in the property-related negligence case of Trustees of the Portman Family Estates v Radcliffe Le Brasseur. The case concerned a large West End building.

Rupert Reed QC Specialises in legal and financial professional negligence disputes. He regularly acts for lawyers accused of negligence when handling property transactions. **Strengths:** "Extremely good at fighting his client's corner." **Recent work:** Acted for the claimant in the £18 million auditors' negligence case of Wilson v Grant Thornton.

JUNIORS

Edward Sawyer Handles financial and legal negligence cases for clients. He is recommended in cases with an international element. **Strengths:** "He is very bright, has a fantastic grasp of the detail, possesses exceptionally good drafting skills and is very user-friendly." "He's good with the client and extremely hard-working."

Clare Stanley Has a commercial-trust background and regularly acts in high-profile legal and financial negligence claims. She is noted for her forensic and detailed approach to cases. **Strengths:** "An effective cross-examiner" who "gives full and carefully considered advice. She grapples with the minutiae of a case, and puts everything into a commercial context." **Recent work:** Acted for the defendant in Rentokil v Goodman Derrick, a solicitors' negligence case.

Band 3

1 Chancery Lane

THE SET

1 Chancery Lane handles a wide range of professional negligence disputes. Members offer services in cases ranging from solicitors' negligence to insurance coverage disputes and also handle claims against teachers and social workers. They frequently appear in the higher courts and are popular with instructing solicitors due to their approachability.

Client service: Clark Chessis leads a team that is "very efficient and straightforward." He is "helpful and turns things around quickly."

SILKS

John Ross QC Acts for claimants and defendants in a wide range of professional negligence matters. He has a particular strength in cases involving coverage disputes. **Strengths:** "He is brilliant in court, and has a mind like a razor." "He's a very punchy character who has a no-nonsense style. He consistently gets it right."

Andrew Warnock QC (see p.746) Defends solicitors and barristers in negligence claims. He also regularly acts for teachers and social workers. **Strengths:** "Sharp-witted, pragmatic and charismatic." **Recent work:** Defended a firm of solicitors in a claim for negligence arising from their work in a claim against a school.

JUNIORS

Ivor Collett (see p.575) He is recommended for the strength of his insurance-related work, including coverage disputes and brokers' claims. **Strengths:** "In court he is such a gentleman, but he is also ruthless in a gentle way." "He's very client-friendly and easy to work with. He is good on his feet, confident and would never annoy judges." **Recent work:** Defended a firm of solicitors in a professional negligence counter-claim.

Andrew Spencer (see p.726) Handles solicitors' and surveyors' negligence cases for claimants and defendants. He demonstrates notable expertise in claims arising from property disputes. **Strengths:** "He is methodical and considered," and "has a brilliant mind." **Recent work:** Represented a claimant suing solicitors for negligent advice provided in relation to an action against the police.

John Norman (see p.683) Acts for clients on a range of professional liability matters, and has special expertise in education claims. **Strengths:** "Intellectually brilliant and very commercial." "He is excellent with clients."

Karen Shuman Handles solicitors', surveyors' and valuers' negligence cases for claimants and defendants. She is especially recommended in cases arising from property-related disputes. **Strengths:** "She works so hard it's frightening." "She's very good, down to earth, prepared to say what needs to be said and also approachable."

Simon Trigger (see p.740) Acts for claimants and defendants in legal and financial negligence claims. He has handled a number of professional negligence claims against solicitors for failure to pursue personal injury cases. **Strengths:** "He's very good, as he's approachable and sensible." **Recent work:** Defended a firm of solicitors against a claim for negligence in failing to pursue a personal injury claim worth £1 million.

Crown Office Chambers

See profile on p.782

THE SET

Crown Office Chambers is recommended for general professional negligence matters as well as technology and construction claims. Its members have a wealth of experience of acting for a range of professionals, but they are particularly capable in solicitors' negligence cases.

Client service: Steve Purse leads the clerking team and "provides a good service."

SILKS

Andrew Bartlett QC Particularly noted for his capabilities in insurance claims, and those of a very technical nature. **Strengths:** "He will grind out all the detail in a case." "A formidable opponent and an experienced operator."

Michael Harvey QC Has an established professional negligence practice, and is praised for his knowledge of solicitors' negligence matters. **Strengths:** "Meticulous and user-friendly." "He is old-school and precise in all he says and does." **Recent work:** Led the defence in Woolfe, Collyer Bristow LLP v Lockton International, a £30 million coverage dispute.

JUNIORS

Jason Evans-Tovey He primarily acts for insurers in complex solicitors' negligence matters. **Strengths:** "Understands the commercial angle of the case straight away." "A great strategist who puts the fear of God into the other side – he's great to have in your camp." **Recent work:** Acted in McCallister v Shulmans, a complex £1.5 million solicitors' negligence case.

Daniel Shapiro Acts for claimants and defendants. Brokers' and solicitors' negligence cases are his forte and he is often to be seen in the appellate courts. **Strengths:** "He is a very well-rounded senior junior who really gets the bit between his teeth when instructed on a case." "Highly intelligent, responsive and tactically astute." **Recent work:** Acted for the defendant insurance broker in Woolfe, Collyer Bristow LLP v Lockton International.

Maitland Chambers

See profile on p.831

THE SET

Maitland Chambers offers a wide range of professional negligence expertise. Members act for claimants and defendants in financial, insurance and legal negligence cases. They frequently act in multiparty disputes and regularly receive instructions from abroad.

Client service: John Wiggs heads a team regarded as "approachable, honest about workloads and receptive to negotiating on fees."

SILKS

Thomas Grant QC Handles legal and financial professional negligence matters. He is recommended for his ability to provide novel arguments in cases. **Strengths:** "He is very bright, thorough and effective." "He's very creative and is a fine advocate and a good man to have on your side if you have got a bad case." "His technical and analytical skills are first-rate and he is a powerful advocate." **Recent work:** Acted in the Court of Appeal case of Santander v RA Legal. This is the leading decision on claims for breach of trust against solicitors.

Anthony Trace QC Acts for clients in a range of professional negligence cases, and is noted for the strength of his cross-examination skills. **Strengths:** "A real fighter who is 100% behind everyone in the team."

Edmund Cullen QC (see p.582) Has an established commercial litigation practice, as part of which he handles financial and media-related professional negligence claims. **Strengths:** "He's good at unpicking difficult cases."

Band 4

7 King's Bench Walk

See profile on p.827

THE SET

7 King's Bench Walk handles a number of professional negligence-related disputes for claimants and defendants. Members are often seen in insurance brokers and coverage disputes, and high-profile financial negligence cases.

Client service: Bernie Hyatt and Greg Leyden lead a "very good" clerking team.

SILKS

Jonathan Gaisman QC Has a strong reputation in professional negligence litigation, and is particularly noted for his capabilities in high-profile financial claims. **Strengths:** "One of the superstars of the Bar, he's a very serious trial lawyer who is intellectually outstanding." "An extremely effective advocate who is very impressive in court." **Recent work:** Acting for Cattles in its £1.6 billion claim against PwC.

Christopher Butcher QC Handles brokers', accountants' and solicitors' negligence cases. He has unique expertise in advising Lloyd's agents. **Strengths:** "He is very good, clearly very clever and a good advocate." **Recent work:** Successfully represented the claimant in Equitas v Walsham Brothers, a brokers' negligence case.

Andrew Wales QC Acts for insurers and professionals in negligence claims. He is regarded for his handling of high-value financial cases and complex insurance matters. **Strengths:** "A details person who has an excellent intellect."

Rebecca Sabben-Clare QC (see p.713) Advises in insurance and financial negligence disputes. She is also recommended for tackling very high-value auditors' negligence cases. **Strengths:** "A modern practitioner who is very clever, user-friendly and a pleasure to deal with." "Very clever and a barrister with a great commercial mind, she picks up the complexities really quickly and has sound judgement." **Recent work:** Represented Cattles in the £1.6 billion auditors' negligence case of Cattles v PwC.

JUNIORS

James Brocklebank Frequently acts on complex insurance-related negligence disputes. He is noted for his capabilities in cases with an international element. **Strengths:** "He is very sound technically on insurance law; he will not make mistakes." "A very clever guy and a pleasure to work with." **Recent work:** Acted for the defendant in Financial Services Compensation Scheme v PKF, a case concerning the mis-selling of financial products.

XXIV Old Buildings

See profile on p.838

THE SET

Members frequently act for and against negligent trustees, solicitors and financial advisers. They are recommended for their handling of sensitive and high-value cases. Recent important matters handled include Stephen and Leslie Plant v Orientfield Holdings, a property-related professional negligence claim, and Montpelier v Lighthousewealth, a £1 million claim brought by an investor against an independent investment adviser.

SILKS

Alan Steinfeld QC Has a substantial commercial litigation practice and often acts on complex cases. He is noted for his strength in financial negligence disputes. **Strengths:** "Brilliant in court." "For high-value claims he is the one to go to. He's a masterful advocate and when he forms a view about something he sticks to it." **Recent work:** Acted in Stephen and Leslie Plant v Orientfield Holdings, a professional negligence claim in relation to a property dispute.

Francis Tregear QC Handles financial negligence cases primarily for claimants. He is recommended in cases arising from breach of trust or breach of contract. **Strengths:** "A calming influence and a respected figure in the room. When he speaks he has gravitas." "He's really client-friendly and creative – an impressive barrister." **Recent work:** Advised on a substantial financial negligence claim against tax advisers.

JUNIORS

Elizabeth Weaver Acts for claimants and defendants in financial negligence cases. She demonstrates particular expertise in negligence disputes arising from breach of trust. **Strengths:** "She is straightforward and commercial in all her dealings." **Recent work:** Represented trustees in a case against former trustees concerning allegations of gross negligence.

Serle Court

See profile on p.860

THE SET

Serle Court is a strong commercial chancery law set with an excellent reputation in professional negligence. Members are often used in very high-value, complex financial cases.

Client service: "Steve Whitaker and the rest of the best clerks keep on top of things, send you reminders without prompting and organise listings." "They are very modern clerks who are down to earth and happy to talk about fees."

SILKS

Philip Jones QC Handles legal and financial negligence claims primarily for claimants. He is particularly recommended for his work in high-value accountants' liability cases. **Strengths:** "He is calm and measured when handling high-pressure, high-profile cases. His name strikes fear into opponents' hearts." "He's more user-friendly than most silks, has a good brain and is proactive and responsive."

Philip Mar shall QC Acts on a range of professional liability matters, and is noted for his unique knowledge of negligence disputes relating to valuations of fine art. **Strengths:** "He is an awesome advocate who is fabulously bright, and can come up with a strategy extremely quickly even after being dumped with bundles overnight." "A very aggressive litigator and a fearsome cross-examiner." **Recent work:** Acted in Thwaytes v Sothebys, a case concerning misattribution of a possible Caravaggio painting.

2TG – 2 Temple Gardens

See profile on p.873

THE SET

2 Temple Gardens has talented juniors and silks well capable of offering advice and representation in professional negligence. Members cover multifarious professional liability disputes from insurance coverage issues to high-value solicitors' negligence claims. They are recognised for their skill in handling complex, document-heavy cases.

Client service: "The clerks are good. Lee Tyler runs a tight ship and he is always available to have a chat. He's really responsive and willing to negotiate on fees."

SILKS

Charles Dougherty QC Has an extensive professional negligence practice, and is recommended for complex, financial and legal negligence claims. **Strengths:** "He is terrific, very reliable, very clever and very focused." "He is a superb lawyer who is clever, erudite and also incredibly user-friendly. He wears his learning lightly, and you can ask him anything." **Recent work:** Acted for the defence in the £14 million solicitors' negligence case of Wellesley v Withers.

Robert Moxon Browne QC Handles the full range of professional liability work. He frequently acts on complex cases and is noted for the strength of his advocacy. **Strengths:** "Always clear and definite in his views, he gives you a proper steer in the direction you need to go." **Recent work:** Acted in an insurance coverage dispute concerning allegations that negligent healthcare caused a fatal accident at a care home.

JUNIORS

Isabel Barter (see p.544) Advises clients in legal and financial negligence disputes, and is comfortable with the largest and most complicated cases. **Strengths:** "Driven and intelligent, she is excellent." "She is really user-friendly, conscientious and gets to grips with documents like no other junior." **Recent work:** Led by Mark Simpson QC, she successfully acted for the claimant in the accountants' negligence case of Mehjoo v Harben Barker.

Other Ranked Lawyers

Colin Edelman QC (see p.593) (Devereux) Has a significant professional negligence practice, and demonstrates expertise in sensitive solicitors' negligence cases and insurance coverage disputes. **Strengths:** "He is the first person we go to with tricky points because of the depth of his expertise. He's very good at distilling information and getting to the crux of the matter." "He is very down to earth and straightforward and firm in his advice."

Ben Lynch (Devereux) Handles a range of legal and financial professional negligence disputes, and is recommended for handling high-value, very sensitive cases. **Strengths:** "He is user-friendly, supportive and nice to have as part of a team because he is prepared to get stuck in."

Nigel Jones QC (see p.641) (Hardwicke) Frequently represents solicitors, valuers and banking institutions in professional negligence matters. He is noted for his expertise in cases with an international element. **Strengths:** "There are very few advocates who really do stand out in terms of advocacy, but he's one of them. He also has a very impressive manner and is collaborative in his approach." "He is clearly very bright and looks at finding ways around things." **Recent work:** Acted for the defence in Bancroft v Weil Gotshal, a solicitors' negligence case.

John de Waal QC (Hardwicke) Regularly acts for the insurers of solicitors in negligence claims. He is noted for his expertise in cases arising from property disputes. **Strengths:** "He is extremely thorough, legally sound and he has good commercial understanding." "His advocacy is persuasive, and he is quick on his feet and adaptable to what is thrown at him." **Recent work:** Represented the defendant solicitors in a claim for the loss of £2 million due to the negligent drafting of an option for sale.

Sarah McCann (see p.666) (Hardwicke) Handles professional negligence cases for clients in the legal, financial, property and insurance markets. She is notably strong in valuers' and solicitors' negligence disputes. **Strengths:** "A very tenacious advocate with a very analytical mind." **Recent work:** Acted for the defendant in the £1.6 million surveyors' negligence case of Lloyds TSB v McBains Cooper.

David Yates (see p.757) (Pump Court Tax Chambers) An expert in tax-related cases, he regularly defends solicitors accused of giving negligent advice. **Strengths:** "He has an encyclopaedic knowledge of tax rules." "He is commercial and effective."

Keith Rowley QC (Radcliffe Chambers) Acts for and against professionals in the legal, insurance and financial worlds. He is extremely highly rated for his pensions-related negligence work. **Strengths:** "He is fearless, meticulous in his preparation and very able."

Thomas Dumont (Radcliffe Chambers) A very good private client lawyer who shows particular skill when handling property-related professional negligence claims. He frequently acts in cases involving solicitors and accountants. **Strengths:** "He is extremely pragmatic, clear in his advice and client-friendly." "On his feet, he shows a good sense of humour, is straight down the line and commands the attention of the room." **Recent work:** Acted for the defence in a million-pound negligent tax planning case.

Hugh Jackson (see p.636) (Selborne Chambers) Regularly acts for institutional lenders in professional negligence claims. He is particularly well regarded for his handling of claims against solicitors and surveyors. **Strengths:** "He gets into the detail and under the skin of a case. He's very user-friendly and clients like and respect him." **Recent work:** Acted for the claimant mortgage lender in a negligence case against a firm of solicitors.

Jeremy Cousins QC (see p.579) (11 Stone Buildings) Acts for claimants and defendants in a number of professional negligence matters. He is noted for his knowledge of solicitors' and surveyors' negligence matters, and cases arising from breach of trust. **Strengths:** "He is an extremely intelligent and user-friendly QC who gives concise advice and always comes back to you when he says he will." "An expert on breach-of-trust cases, he is fantastic and turns instructions around very quickly." **Recent work:** Acted in AIB v Redler, a case concerning the correct remedy for a bank when there has been breach of trust by solicitors.

LONDON Technology & Construction

Professional Negligence: Technology & Construction London
Leading Sets
Band 1
Atkin Chambers *
Keating Chambers *
4 Pump Court *
Band 2
Crown Office Chambers *
4 New Square *
Band 3
Thirty Nine Essex Street *
* *Indicates set with profile.*
Alphabetical order within each band. Band 1 is highest.

Band 1

Atkin Chambers

See profile on p.762

THE SET

Atkin Chambers "is as good as it gets" when it comes to technology and construction-related professional negligence disputes. Members are held in high regard for the strength of their advocacy skills, and often appear in very high-value and complex cases. Many of the cases undertaken are international in nature.

Client service: "The clerks, led by Justin Wilson, are really responsive, deal with issues immediately and are very nice people."

SILKS

Manus McMullan QC (see p.668) Acts for and against technology and construction professionals in negligence cases. He is capable of handling claims nationally and internationally. **Strengths:** "We use him to provide the strategic steer in a contentious situation, and like him because he's responsive and accessible." "He's an attractive advocate who is extremely thorough on paper and a good negotiator. He has a manner of putting things across to you that makes you feel drawn to reach a compromise." **Recent work:** Acted for the claimant contractor in a £3 million case for negligence on the part of an engineer.

David Streatfeild-James QC Advises in high-value negligence claims against construction profes-

Professional Negligence: Technology & Construction London
Leading Silks
Band 1
Bartlett Andrew *Crown Office Chambers* *
Brannigan Sean *4 Pump Court* *
Catchpole Stuart *Thirty Nine Essex Street*
Douglas Michael *4 Pump Court* *
Rigney Andrew *Crown Office Chambers* *
Stewart Roger *4 New Square* *
Streatfeild-James David *Atkin Chambers*
Taverner Marcus *Keating Chambers* *
ter Haar Roger *Crown Office Chambers*
White Andrew *Atkin Chambers* *
Williamson Adrian *Keating Chambers* *
Wilmot-Smith Richard *Thirty Nine Essex Street*
Band 2
Baatz Nicholas *Atkin Chambers*
Bowdery Martin *Atkin Chambers*
Cross James *4 Pump Court* *
Darling Paul *Keating Chambers* *
Day Anneliese *4 New Square* *
Dennison Stephen *Atkin Chambers* *
Dennys Nicholas *Atkin Chambers*
Doerries Chantal-Aimée *Atkin Chambers* *
Fraser Peter D *Atkin Chambers* *
Friedman David *4 Pump Court* *
Lofthouse Simon *Atkin Chambers* *
Marrin John *Keating Chambers* *
McMullan Manus *Atkin Chambers* *
Moody Neil *2TG - 2 Temple Gardens (ORL)* ◊
Nicholson Jeremy *4 Pump Court* *
Rawley Dominique *Atkin Chambers* *
Sears David *Crown Office Chambers*
Band 3
Cannon Mark *4 New Square* *
Constable Adam *Keating Chambers* *
Hargreaves Simon *Keating Chambers* *
Moran Vincent *Keating Chambers* *
Nissen Alexander *Keating Chambers* *
Parkin Fiona *Atkin Chambers*
Sinclair Fiona *4 New Square* *
Soole Michael *4 New Square* *
New Silks
Ansell Rachel *4 Pump Court* *
Quiney Ben *Crown Office Chambers* *
◊ (ORL) = Other Ranked Lawyer.
** Indicates individual with profile.*
Alphabetical order within each band. Band 1 is highest.

sionals. He frequently acts for contractors, government departments and private employers. **Strengths:** "He is a standout barrister who has great technical knowledge."

Andrew White QC (see p.750) Represents a variety of clients in professional negligence matters arising from construction disputes. He is recommended for very high-value cases arising from defective design. **Strengths:** "His advocacy is excellent, he is very well prepared and he has an understated but assured manner. He also has seniority that clients appreciate." "He's part of the team, he understands the sensitivities and the issues, and he communicates very well."

Dominique Rawley QC (see p.704) Handles high-value cases arising from commercial disputes in a construction setting. She is frequently seen in fire cases, infrastructure disputes and matters relating to waste and energy projects. **Strengths:** "She is an extremely impressive advocate at cross-exam-

Professional Negligence: Technology & Construction London
Leading Juniors
Band 1
Pilling Benjamin *4 Pump Court* *
Band 2
Henderson Simon *4 Pump Court* *
Hickey Alexander *4 Pump Court* *
McCafferty Lynne *4 Pump Court* *
Band 3
Collings Nicholas *Atkin Chambers* *
Coplin Richard *Keating Chambers* *
Garrett Lucy *Keating Chambers* *
Hanna Ronan *Atkin Chambers* *
Hussain Riaz *Atkin Chambers* *
Leabeater James *4 Pump Court* *
Lemon Jane *Keating Chambers* *
Robb Adam *Thirty Nine Essex Street*
Slow Camille *Atkin Chambers* *
Up-and-coming individuals
Colter Lucy *4 New Square* *

ining witnesses and when dealing with legal arguments. She is also very courteous and effective, and always on top of her brief." "She's very hard-working, has exceptional attention and the ability to understand the bigger picture." **Recent work:** Successfully defended fire safety engineers in a £120 million negligence claim arising from the destruction by fire of the Cadbury factory in Pontefract.

Nicholas Baatz QC Specialises in construction and technology-related professional negligence cases. He is recommended for high-value construction disputes both nationally and internationally. **Strengths:** "His manner with clients is excellent, and he has an ability to cut through the issues. I would want him on my team every time." **Recent work:** Acted for the piling subcontractor in the £120 million case of Accolade Wines Limited v Volker Fitzpatrick.

Stephen Dennison QC (see p.587) Has an established construction practice and often represents clients in negligence disputes. He is noted for his expertise in high-value litigation and cases with a foreign element. **Strengths:** "He's got gravitas. He's calm and collected and open to suggestions regarding alternative approaches to cases."

Nicholas Dennys QC His strengths lie in engineering, oil and gas and major construction matters, many of which involve governmental or quasi-governmental bodies. **Strengths:** "He has a great strategic view of the issues, and always offers practical advice." **Recent work:** Acted for the defendant in the £120 million Cadbury v ADT case.

Chantal-Aimée Doerries QC (see p.589) Represents clients in construction-related professional negligence disputes. She has notable expertise in complex design and construction disputes. **Strengths:** "She is proactive, pugnacious and her language skills prove extremely helpful when she's dealing with international clients." "She is very bright, but not overly academic in presentation, which means that the client always feels comfortable that they understand what she's saying."

Peter Fraser QC (see p.603) Acts for claimants and defendants in professional negligence cases arising from construction defects. He regularly acts for private employers, contractors, governments and manufacturers. **Strengths:** "He is very thorough, and has that attention to detail you need in the construction field." **Recent work:** Acted in a claim for losses after seismic exploratory services were supplied to BP in Jordan.

Simon Lofthouse QC (see p.658) Handles the full range of construction-related professional negligence cases. He is regularly instructed by local authorities, and also acts for contractors and corporate entities. **Strengths:** "He is exceptionally knowledgeable and easy to work with." "He's very good technically, very good on the law and excellent at dealing with clients. He's also industrious and really puts in the hours." **Recent work:** Advised Portsmouth CC in a dispute over quayside anchor works at Camber.

Martin Bowdery QC Regularly appears before the domestic High Court and Court of Appeal, and also handles international arbitrations. He has acted in a number of professional negligence disputes arising from capital projects. **Strengths:** "He's very easy with clients, extremely intelligent, great at cross-examinations and very quick on his feet." **Recent work:** Acted in a professional negligence claim against the project managers of works in Ampleforth school in Yorkshire.

Fiona Parkin QC Handles domestic and international professional negligence disputes in relation to construction matters. She regularly acts in cases arising from energy infrastructure projects. **Strengths:** "She is extremely good on her feet, very eloquent and highly persuasive when arguing a position. She is also hard-working and tactically astute." **Recent work:** Acted in a £16 million claim brought against engineers by a developer of a business park.

JUNIORS

Nicholas Collings (see p.575) Acts in commercial, construction and technology-related professional negligence disputes. He is recommended in multiparty cases and disputes arising out of design and contract matters. **Strengths:** "His knowledge of construction law is just incredible." "He is just spot-on in terms of getting things together." **Recent work:** Acted for the piling subcontractor in the £120 million case of Accolade Wines Limited v Volker Fitzpatrick.

Camille Slow (see p.722) Handles broad-ranging disputes and acts in claims nationally and internationally. She regularly advises on matters arising out of urban construction projects. **Strengths:** "She is really good on her feet, and very unassuming and gentle in conference." **Recent work:** Represented the claimant in a multiparty professional negligence action concerning the construction of the Hub sports facility in Warrington.

Ronan Hanna (see p.618) Acts in construction and engineering professional negligence disputes representing contractors, engineers, architects and contractors. **Strengths:** "Very steady, mature beyond his years and someone who works very hard." **Recent work:** Acted in a professional negligence claim brought by the Isle of Man government against an engineer. The case related to design defects in a harbour bridge.

Riaz Hussain (see p.634) Noted for his expertise in international arbitration and his handling of high-value claims in the High Court. He often acts for insurers as well as construction professionals. **Strengths:** "He has an ability to absorb and distil detailed evidence extraordinarily quickly. A ferocious cross-examiner, he is highly intelligent." "He stands out as a very strong lawyer, who is hard-working and very good at getting to the point." **Recent work:** Advised a defendant structural engineer in a claim brought by a homeowner relating to the duty to warn of dangerous works.

Keating Chambers

See profile on p.824

THE SET

Keating Chambers houses professional negligence barristers who "are all clever, articulate and easy to work with." The set offers expertise at all levels from junior juniors to senior silks. Members act domestically and overseas for a range of clients, including government departments, contractors and surveyors, and are recommended for their handling of high-value and sensitive commercial disputes.

Client service: "The clerks, led by Chris Sunderland, are very helpful and proactive."

SILKS

Paul Darling QC (see p.583) Regularly handles professional negligence matters in the construction and energy spheres. He often appears in cases arising out of the highest-profile infrastructure projects. **Strengths:** "He has a disarming approach. He pretends he isn't as bright as he is, and then before you know it he has slit your throat." **Recent work:** Acted for the claimant in National Grid Gas v Veolia Water Central; a case concerning faulty joints in water pipes that caused damage to gas mains and service apparatus.

Marcus Taverner QC (see p.734) Represents clients in professional negligence cases arising from infrastructure projects and power stations. He is recommended in high-value cases domestically and overseas. **Strengths:** "Very good, very clever and very easy to deal with." "She's diligent, bright and quite formidable." **Recent work:** Acted in Accolade Wines v GJ3, a high-value multiparty claim.

Adrian Williamson QC (see p.753) Specialises in all forms of construction litigation, including professional negligence claims. He regularly acts on matters both for and against contractors. **Strengths:** "He doesn't sit on the fence when giving his advice. He sticks his neck out, which sets him apart from other barristers." "His turnaround times are excellent, and he has a relaxed, easy-going manner with the client." **Recent work:** Handled a professional negligence claim brought by a bank against managing surveyors.

John Marrin QC (see p.663) Acts in professional negligence cases arising from private finance initiative projects and rail sector matters. He represents clients in the higher courts and international tribunals. **Strengths:** "He is very accomplished and knowledgeable." **Recent work:** Advised E.ON in a £25 million negligence claim against its subcontractor over the construction of a wind farm.

Adam Constable QC (see p.577) Focuses on professional negligence disputes in construction and engineering matters. He is noted for his expertise in cases involving shipbuilding, large infrastructure projects and offshore construction. **Strengths:** "He is very quick, excellent with clients, commercially minded and someone who always provides practical and user-friendly advice." "He is extremely hard-working and very popular with clients because they feel they can trust him."

Simon Hargreaves QC (see p.620) Acts in a wide range of professional negligence cases, notably those arising from energy projects and infrastructure matters. He represents clients in all forums, including the higher courts in England and Wales. He also regularly handles international arbitrations. **Strengths:** "His pleadings are amazingly comprehensive, he's very thorough, and he leaves no stone unturned." **Recent work:** Represented one of the defendants in a £5 million dispute in the Court of Appeal concerning floods caused by mechanical defects in a block of residential flats.

Vincent Moran QC (see p.676) Handles professional negligence cases in the construction sector. He is recommended in high-value, sensitive cases and regularly acts for architects and engineers. **Strengths:** "He is extremely hard-working, imaginative, safe and commercial." "He has an extraordinary ability to distil a large amount of information into a fantastic defence."

Alexander Nissen QC (see p.683) Handles professional negligence disputes arising from the construction, energy and engineering sectors. He acts for and against engineers, architects, valuers and surveyors. **Strengths:** "He will turn stuff around at very short notice, and is very easy to work with." **Recent work:** Acted in the £150 million construction negligence case of Accolade v Volker Fitzpatrick.

JUNIORS

Richard Coplin (see p.578) A qualified engineer who is recommended in cases that require technical and forensic expertise. He regularly acts in claims for and against architects, engineers, surveyors and valuers. **Strengths:** "He's excellent, extremely accommodating, and cuts to the chase. Very commercial and someone who sees the bigger picture; he's the man you want in your corner." "He's very good on highly technical cases." **Recent work:** Acted for the defendant designer in a water damage claim at a luxury high-rise development.

Lucy Garrett (see p.606) Specialises in professional negligence claims arising from construction, shipbuilding and energy matters. She frequently acts for architects and engineers. **Strengths:** "She is fantastic with clients, works phenomenally hard and is really incisive." "Everything she writes is always absolutely to the point, she does everything with a light touch and she has a great sense of humour." **Recent work:** Represented the structural and civil engineers in Capita v Jubilee, a multimillion-pound professional negligence case.

Jane Lemon (see p.654) Handles a range of construction work, including professional negligence matters. She acts for and against architects, engineers and developers domesti cally and overseas. **Strengths:** "You can depend on her to get stuck in to the documents in a very thorough and detailed way." "She is bright, hard-working and amenable." **Recent work:** Defended Menard in a £1 million claim arising from defective specialist ground treatment design.

4 Pump Court

See profile on p.849

THE SET

4 Pump Court is highly regarded for general professional negligence disputes and technology and construction-related claims. Members advise claimants and defendants on wide-ranging and complex matters. Barristers are frequently seen in the higher courts in England.

Client service: "The clerks, led by Carolyn McCombe, are really efficient, proactive, quick and friendly."

SILKS

Sean Brannigan QC (see p.555) Handles a diverse range of work from construction matters to solicitors' negligence cases. He is recommended for complex multiparty cases. **Strengths:** "He is very intelligent, but not lofty. He is grounded and ordinary, and has no ego." "If you want a fighter, he's the one to go to as he's tenacious, bright and client-friendly." **Recent work:** Acted in a EUR400 million arbitration over the construction of a power station in Bulgaria.

Michael Douglas QC (see p.589) Demonstrates notable expertise in high-value cases and matters with an international element, and has particular experience of government technology contracts. **Strengths:** "He is very, very good with judges. He is also very bright, a fantastic advocate and very tenacious." "He is a formidable opponent who gets to the heart of things and gets the right answer." **Recent work:** Handled a substantial case brought by a bank against a firm of surveyors for the overvaluation of 67 properties.

James Cross QC Acts for claimants and defendants on complex and high-profile claims, notably those that arise out of catastrophes and natural disasters. **Strengths:** "He is a very safe pair of hands." "He is very good on his feet and is tactically astute." **Recent work:** Acted for risk management consultants defending a multimillion-pound claim for damages arising from a fire at a chemical plant in Yorkshire.

David Friedman QC (see p.604) Offers notable expertise in cases with an international element, and has specific experience of disputes arising out of the construction of power stations. He is regularly instructed by government departments. **Strengths:** "He is particularly charming and friendly." **Recent work:** Acted for the developer in a claim by tenants relating to defects in a flat.

Jeremy Nicholson QC (see p.682) Known for his expertise in multiparty construction-related professional negligence cases. He regularly acts for insurers of construction professionals. **Recent work:** Advised on a multiparty £11 million case relating to defects in a large retaining wall at a retail park.

Rachel Ansell QC New silk with extensive experience of representing construction professionals in negligence disputes. She is recommended in high-value cases domestically and internationally, and has a particular focus on the Middle East. **Strengths:** "She has a real grasp of the detail and, unlike many barristers, she thinks strategically about cases and works hard on building team rapport." "She's really detailed and thorough on paper, and is an attractive advocate in court."

JUNIORS

Benjamin Pilling (see p.694) Regularly works with construction professionals on technology and construction-related matters. He demonstrates notable expertise in cases with complex financial elements. **Strengths:** "He is very good on paper, and has a crisp writing style. He has a clear way of viewing things and is good at expressing himself." "He does a great job of sifting through papers, and his work is technical and practical." **Recent work:** Acted for the consultant engineer in a £12 million case arising from the negligent construction of a warehouse.

Simon Henderson (see p.624) Has a diverse practice acting for and against professionals, and is noted for his experience in the energy sector. He is particularly capable when it comes to sensitive and complex cases, and matters with an international element.

Recent work: Defended EMC Computer Systems in a claim relating to the negligent design of a storage solution for software.

Alexander Hickey (see p.626) Acts for and against construction professionals in negligence cases. He is noted for his experience in international disputes concerning pipelines, bulk containers and power stations. **Strengths:** "Gives accessible, proactive and commercial advice." "He gets to grips with things quickly, really gets his hands dirty and gets involved." **Recent work:** Advised a cladding contractor in its claim against Galliford Try for loss and delays to the completion of the Athletes' Village prior to the Olympic Games 2012.

James Leabeater Advises on a range of construction-related negligence disputes. He frequently acts in claims against surveyors, architects, engineers and project managers. **Recent work:** Acted for the building contractor in Millharbour Management v Weston Homes relating to a block of flats in the London Docklands area.

Lynne McCafferty (see p.666) Specialises in technology and construction negligence cases for claimants and defendants. She acts for a wide range of clients, from IT professionals to government departments. **Recent work:** Successfully defended property developers against a claim by an architect for unpaid fees.

Band 2

Crown Office Chambers

See profile on p.782

THE SET

Crown Office Chambers is recommended in general professional negligence as well as technology and construction claims. Its members offer a wealth of knowledge across the entire spectrum of professional negligence litigation. On the construction and technology side, members are notably active in claims arising out of catastrophes and natural disasters. They also handle defective design cases.

SILKS

Andrew Bartlett QC Represents clients in all professional negligence disputes. He is noted for his capabilities in insurance claims. **Strengths:** "He will grind out all the detail in a case." "A formidable opponent and an experienced operator."

Andrew Rigney QC Specialises in professional negligence disputes arising from major construction projects. He acts for and against architects, engineers and surveyors. **Strengths:** "A very good barrister who knows the law, is fun and hard-working, and has a very practical approach." **Recent work:** Acted in a large claim against a contractor concerning the negligent design of a residential extension.

Roger ter Haar QC Handles a full range of construction and technology-related professional negligence cases. He is notably strong in engineering matters. **Strengths:** "He is excellent, charismatic and a good appellate advocate." "A delight to deal with and a very good opponent."

David Sears QC Handles professional negligence cases arising from construction and engineering disputes. He acts for and against architects, engineers, surveyors and project managers. **Strengths:** "He is very good with clients and very charming." "A total knockout and a class act." **Recent work:** Acted in 199 Knightsbridge Ltd v WSP UK; a case concerning the alleged negligent design of a cold water system.

Ben Quiney QC A new silk who handles professional negligence cases against construction professionals. He is recommended for high-value and high-profile matters. **Strengths:** "He has very good client care, is open to new ideas, and is easy to discuss matters with." **Recent work:** Acted for the defendant engineer in a multimillion-pound construction dispute relating to a leisure centre in Warrington.

4 New Square

See profile on p.835

THE SET

Members represent claimants and defendants on the full remit of professional negligence-related matters and have an outstanding reputation for advocacy. Barristers frequently act in the highest-profile and most complex cases. They appear before all of the higher courts in England and have acted in a number of foreign jurisdictions.

Client service: "The clerks, led by Lizzy Stewart, take a very user-friendly, 21st century approach to clerking – they're not frightened to discuss fees, and they are very good at having frank discussions when things aren't right."

SILKS

Roger Stewart QC (see p.728) A pre-eminent silk who advises clients on a full range of professional negligence matters. He is recommended for financial services-related claims. **Strengths:** "Tough, practical, commercial and clever." "He knows it all backwards and he's very confident in his delivery." **Recent work:** Advised on a case against contractors and builders concerning the alleged negligent construction of a large private house.

Anneliese Day QC (see p.585) Acts for claimants and defendants in complex and high-profile professional negligence cases. She is noted for the strength of her client-handling skills. **Strengths:** "She is fiercely intelligent, but also perfectly human. She has excellent client care skills, is exceptional on her feet and her advice is succinct and to the point." "She has a tremendous brain, but what differentiates her is her unflappability – she is calm, methodical, logical and always a pleasure to work with." **Recent work:** Acted for the defendant engineers in Igloo v Powell Williams.

Fiona Sinclair QC (see p.721) Handles all professional negligence matters for claimants and defendant. She demonstrates notable expertise in financial and construction disputes. **Strengths:** "Very bright and very good at making complex issues understandable." "She is controlled, thorough and resilient." **Recent work:** Defended the design and build contractor in a £13 million case over the alleged negligent design of a warehouse and distribution centre in Rugby.

Mark Cannon QC (see p.565) Known for his wide-ranging professional negligence practice that spans financial and solicitors' negligence as well as construction-related disputes. **Strengths:** "He is exceptionally clever and gives superb written advice." "He is a very clear-thinking lawyer and his manner of expression as an advocate is very impressive." **Recent work:** Acted for a third party in Co-operative Group Ltd v Birse Developments, a case concerning the negligent design of a distribution centre.

Michael Soole QC (see p.725) Specialises in construction-related professional negligence disputes. He frequently acts for consultants and engineers, and is noted for his expertise in multiparty litigation. **Strengths:** "A big beast who is well known in the market. He is very clever and urbane."

JUNIORS

Lucy Colter (see p.576) Acts on the full remit of professional negligence cases, including technology and construction issues. She is notably strong in claims involving valuers and surveyors. **Strengths:** "She is excellent, good at the detail, very positive and has a good knowledge of the law." "She is first-rate – someone who works hard under difficult circumstances and is very approachable and normal." **Recent work:** Acted in Clegg Construction Ltd v Frank Shaw Associates Limited, a case concerning the responsibility for the design and construction of a roof in an office building.

Band 3

Thirty Nine Essex Street

See profile on p.797

THE SET

Thirty Nine Essex Street handles a range of technology and construction-related professional negligence cases. Its members act for and against professionals in domestic and international disputes, and are highly regarded for their knowledge of insurance issues that arise in this context.

Client service: Alastair Davidson and Michael Kaplan lead a team, which is described as "superb" and "very responsive. They are really good at re-listing hearings and speaking to the other side. They are also very flexible on fees."

SILKS

Stuart Catchpole QC Focuses on very high-value professional negligence cases domestically and overseas. He is frequently instructed in design and build disputes. **Strengths:** "A very impressive performer." "He's very client-friendly and really understands the commercial needs of the client."

Richard Wilmot-Smith QC Specialises in construction and engineering-related professional negligence matters. He is recommended for complex disputes and cases with an international element. **Strengths:** "He has sound judgement, gives clear, easily understood and pragmatic advice, and can be quite frightening in cross-examination when he needs to be." "He gives strategic advice and has a real interest in what the client wants to get out of the litigation." **Recent work:** Acted for the owner of a shop who sued the contractor and surveyor for negligence after his sign fell down and injured a family.

JUNIORS

Adam Robb Handles professional negligence matters arising from construction, engineering and infrastructure disputes. He is noted for his expertise in high-value, complex, multiparty cases. **Strengths:** "He is very thorough and gets into the real legal detail." "His strength lies in handling technical, knotty legal problems." **Recent work:** Successfully acted in the £11 million professional negligence case Oakapple v DTR.

Other Ranked Lawyers

Neil Moody QC (2TG – 2 Temple Gardens) Acts for and against construction professionals in negligence disputes. He frequently advises architects and engineers in claims arising from major construction works, fires and floods. **Strengths:** "He is sensible, effective, articulate and highly intelligent." **Recent work:** Successfully recovered £23 million for clients in a claim concerning the negligent design and installation of a roof.

MIDLANDS

Professional Negligence Midlands
Leading Silks
Band 1
Anderson Mark *No5 Chambers (ORL)* ◊ 🄰 *
Pepperall Edward *St Philips Chambers (ORL)* ◊
Randall John *St Philips Chambers (ORL)* ◊ *

Ranked Lawyers

Mark Anderson QC (see p.536) (No5 Chambers) Exclusively receives instructions from claimants. He predominantly acts on cases regarding solicitors' negligence, although he has also been instructed on claims against accountants and architects. **Strengths:** "He is very good at preparation. When you have a conference, he has a detailed agenda and picks up the issues." "He has the edge and is technically superb. He is a bit of a brain on legs." **Recent work:** Advised on a multimillion-pound case involving 200 clients against a Cypriot bank arising from its alleged negligent financial planning advice.

Edward Pepperall QC (St Philips Chambers) Has a mixed practice covering a range of commercial and professional negligence claims. He is frequently instructed in cases brought against accountants, surveyors and solicitors, and is noted for his expertise in cases concerning social workers. **Strengths:** "He is a very measured and persuasive advocate." **Recent work:** Represented the claimant in the case against a local authority that concerned allegations of social workers' negligence in failing to identify significant abuse and failing to take the claimant into care.

John Randall QC (St Philips Chambers) A noted commercial practitioner who is regularly instructed on complex professional negligence claims. He is noted for his expertise on cases involving solicitors and accountants. **Strengths:** "He's a very clever chap. He's a good opponent who does well for his clients." **Recent work:** Acted on a complex solicitors' negligence claim concerning a decade-long history of issues that included tax avoidance and offshore trusts.

WESTERN

Professional Negligence Western
Leading Silks
New Silks
Sims Hugh *Guildhall Chambers (ORL)* ◊

Leading Juniors
Band 1
Pearce-Smith James *St John's Chambers (ORL)* ◊
Virgo John *Guildhall Chambers (ORL)* ◊
Band 2
Briggs Nicholas *Guildhall Chambers (ORL)* ◊
Dickinson John FH *St John's Chambers (ORL)* ◊ 🄰 *
◊ (ORL) = Other Ranked Lawyer.
🄰 direct access (see p.11).
** Indicates individual with profile.*
Alphabetical order within each band. Band 1 is highest.

Ranked Lawyers

Hugh Sims QC (Guildhall Chambers) Has a broad and celebrated commercial practice, spanning a number of legal disciplines. He is frequently instructed on substantial negligence claims against a range of professionals, including solicitors, accountants, surveyors and those in the construction industry. **Strengths:** "He makes fairly complex cases seem very easy and very effortless. He's good on paper and good on his feet." "He goes above and beyond the call of duty, and that is recognised by clients." **Recent work:** He successfully acted for the claimant in a negligence claim brought against a construction engineer in relation to a residential development.

John Virgo (Guildhall Chambers) A commercial law specialist with considerable experience in handling professional negligence claims. Sources recognise his significant expertise in relation to high-value claims involving financial product mis-selling. **Strengths:** "He has first-class advocacy skills." "Having him in the toolbox sends such a strong message to the other side – he's got a big reputation. They know you're serious about this if you've got him." **Recent work:** Instructed in Rubenstein v HSBC Bank, a case concerning the mis-selling of AIG bonds.

Nicholas Briggs (Guildhall Chambers) An experienced junior whose background as a solicitor adds depth to his practice. He is frequently instructed by lenders to pursue claims against solicitors, valuers and insurance brokers. He also has strong expertise in defending claims against legal professionals and insolvency practitioners. **Recent work:** Advised on Platform Homes Limited v Zena Solicitors, a claim concerning an alleged dishonest breach of fiduciary duty.

James Pearce-Smith (St John's Chambers) Focuses his practice on commercial litigation and property disputes. He has considerable expertise in professional negligence claims, having practised as a solicitor in this area for several years, and is often engaged by lenders to pursue claims against solicitors and surveyors. **Strengths:** "He is well prepared, knowledgeable and good on his feet." "He has a very logical mind; he's very bright. If you were going for a very tricky point of law you should probably go to James." **Recent work:** Advised Lloyds in Lloyds v Cooke & Arkwright and Cluttons, an £8 million valuer's negligence claim arising from the valuation of a residential development site.

John Dickinson (see p.588) (St John's Chambers) Has a broad practice covering a range of disciplines, including professional negligence. He is particularly sought after by lenders to advise on claims involving accountants and independent financial advisers due to his background as a chartered accountant. **Strengths:** "He is a nice mix of being very approachable, but is also first-class on the technical details."

PROPERTY DAMAGE: An Introduction

Contributed by Michael Curtis QC and Michele De Gregorio of Crown Office Chambers

Recent years have seen record costs to the insurance industry from fires, floods and one of the largest explosions in peacetime Europe, at the Buncefield Oil Terminal in Hertfordshire.

The Buncefield explosion resulted in total claims of approximately £1 billion, a series of High Court actions between 2008 and 2010 and an important decision by the Court of Appeal on the duty of care owed to beneficial owners of property in the law of tort.

In 2007 the UK suffered flooding on an unprecedented scale at an estimated cost to the insurance industry of £3 billion. Further extreme rainfall in 2012 prompted the government to intervene by committing to additional spending on flood defences and to propose legislation to implement the Flood Re scheme to protect households at greatest risk of flooding. The winter of 2014 was the wettest on record and the increase in flood damage claims is expected to continue.

The general trend away from strict liability in the law of tort has continued over recent years, with the Court of Appeal limiting the application of Rylands v Fletcher in cases involving the spread of fire (Gore v Stannard), following the restatement of the general rule by the House of Lords in Cambridge Water and Transco. Similarly, the Court of Appeal has confined vicarious liability for independent contractors engaged in extra-hazardous activities to exceptionally dangerous acts (Biffa Waste).

Practitioners in this field are often specialists in related areas of construction, insurance, product liability and professional negligence, with expertise in handling disputes requiring technically complex expert scientific and forensic evidence.

A recurring difficulty in this area is the evidence required to prove causation, particularly in fire and explosion cases where the evidence is often largely, if not totally, destroyed. In Milton Keynes v Nulty the Court of Appeal reviewed the approach in such cases (upholding the first-instance decision of Edwards-Stuart J), providing valuable guidance on the balance of probabilities test, the role of circumstantial evidence in fire cases and how judges should approach the issue of competing possible causes in fire claims.

Aside from fires, floods and explosions, much litigation in this field is generated by damage caused by trees, including tree root subsidence. In two recent decisions (Robbins v Bexley, Berent v Family Mosaic Housing) the Court of Appeal has clarified the liability of local authorities for tree root damage. The liability of private owners in negligence for damage caused by trees has been subject to a detailed review by Coulson J (Stagecoach v Hind).

At the end of 2013 the Court of Appeal handed down judgment in Coles v Hetherton, a case concerning the proper measure of damages in subrogated claims by motor vehicle insurers, with ramifications for subrogated actions by buildings and contents insurers. The parties are waiting to hear whether the case will go to the Supreme Court in 2014/15.

Contents:

LONDON

Property Damage London	
Leading Sets	
Band 1	
Crown Office Chambers *	
2TG – 2 Temple Gardens *	
Leading Silks	
Band 1	
Bartlett Andrew	*Crown Office Chambers* *
Eklund Graham	*4 New Square (ORL)* ◊ *
Elkington Ben	*4 New Square (ORL)* ◊ *
Moody Neil	*2TG - 2 Temple Gardens*
Moxon Browne Robert	*2TG - 2 Temple Gardens* *
Palmer Howard	*2TG - 2 Temple Gardens*
Rigney Andrew	*Crown Office Chambers* *
Band 2	
Cross James	*4 Pump Court (ORL)* ◊ *
Reed Paul	*Hardwicke (ORL)* ◊ 🄰 *
ter Haar Roger	*Crown Office Chambers*
Waite Jonathan	*Crown Office Chambers*
Band 3	
Allen David	*7 King's Bench Walk (ORL)* ◊
Webb Geraint	*Henderson Chambers (ORL)* ◊ 🄰 *
New Silks	
Ansell Rachel	*4 Pump Court (ORL)* ◊ *
Antelme Alexander	*Crown Office Chambers*
Miller Andrew	*2TG - 2 Temple Gardens* *
Quiney Ben	*Crown Office Chambers* *
Leading Juniors	
Band 1	
Brown Geoffrey	*Thirty Nine Essex Street (ORL)* ◊
Crowley Daniel	*2TG - 2 Temple Gardens*
Shapiro Daniel	*Crown Office Chambers* *
Band 2	
Field Julian	*Crown Office Chambers*
Green Doré	*2TG - 2 Temple Gardens* *
Nolten Sonia	*2TG - 2 Temple Gardens* *
Pliener David	*Hardwicke (ORL)* ◊ 🄰 *
Up-and-coming individuals	
Boon Elizabeth	*Crown Office Chambers* *
* *Indicates set / individual with profile.*	
◊ *(ORL) = Other Ranked Lawyer.*	
🄰 *direct access (see p.11).*	

Band 1

Crown Office Chambers

See profile on p.782

THE SET

A serious player in the property damage world due to the depth of its barristers' experience in construction, professional negligence and insurance law. A large number of the group were involved in the highly publicised Buncefield litigation of a few years ago, and members here continue to advise on some of the largest property damage cases currently coming before the courts.

Client service: "The clerks, led by Andy Flanagan, are very efficient and professional without being pushy."

SILKS

Jonathan Waite QC Possesses one of the strongest product liability practices at the Bar, and brings this considerable expertise to bear when dealing with property damage cases. He is particularly proficient at flood and fire damage cases. **Strengths:** "He is a true heavyweight who you'd be happy to use against anyone." **Recent work:** Instructed by insurers on behalf of the defendant in Carver (Wolverhampton) Ltd v Talbotts Biomass Energy Ltd. The claim related to a fire in a large DIY store in Wolverhampton, which was said to be caused by a wood burner installed by Talbotts, the defendant.

Andrew Bartlett QC (see p.544) Has a strong grasp of the technical elements of construction and insurance cases, making him a perfect fit for property damage work. Sources say he is "super-intelligent and calm and collected." **Strengths:** "He has very good judgement and a wealth of experience, meaning that you feel that you are in very good hands. He is not a barrister who is going to take points unless there is a real prospect of being able to get home on them." **Recent work:** Acted for the defendants and their insurers in a number of test cases concerning the liabilities of drivers for financial losses suffered by Network Rail as a result of road-on-rail incidents.

Andrew Rigney QC (see p.707) Has extensive knowledge of construction and insurance law, and the intersection between the two. As a result, he is frequently involved in large property damage claims, particularly those relating to fires. **Strengths:** "He is an incredibly clever individual, a joy to work with, and a very gifted cross-examiner." **Recent work:** Acted for the owner of a recycling factory on a £5 million claim brought in the TCC arising out of a catastrophic fire.

Roger ter Haar QC A seasoned veteran with an incredibly broad practice who handles some very large property damage cases. **Strengths:** A great courtroom performer who is "highly intelligent and bags of fun to work with." **Recent work:** Acted in a £5 million claim relating to the catastrophic flooding of a residential development owned by Greenwich Millennium Village, caused by the failure of a boosted cold water system.

Ben Quiney QC (see p.701) Strong on the professional negligence and insurance fronts. His skill in this regard stands him in good stead when he deals with complex property damage work. **Strengths:** "He is clever and really has the respect of his peers." **Recent work:** Acted alongside Roger ter Haar QC for the claimants in a £100 million recovery action brought against defendant engineers. The case concerned the destruction of a large popcorn factory arising from the installation of a CO_2 fire suppression system.

Alexander Antelme QC Awarded silk this year, and a lawyer with a very strong and very diverse practice. He is adept at dealing with cases that focus on property damage, but is also an expert at product liability, clinical negligence and personal injury matters. **Strengths:** "A very cool, calm and efficient operator, who is phenomenally hard-working." **Recent work:** Acted for a subcontractor working at Hatfield Colliery, who made a claim following a large landslide at the site that led to disruption of the rail network.

JUNIORS

Daniel Shapiro (see p.718) Established a reputation in the property damage sphere for his work on cases arising from the Buncefield Oil Terminal fire. He continues to practise in the property damage area, and deals with large flood and fire claims. **Strengths:** "He is extremely hands-on and very good at thinking around problems." **Recent work:** Represented the successful defendant in a claim concerning damage caused to the Shepherds Rest public house due to extensive flooding.

Julian Field Has a broad commercial practice that covers insurance, construction and professional negligence cases. He is adept at dealing with technical issues, and is also a specialist in fraudulent claim work. **Strengths:** "When instructing him you get someone as good as most silks for the cost of a junior. He is very easy to work with, very grounded and a go-to for difficult work." **Recent work:** Represented AXA in a series of test cases brought against three insurers by the leading credit hire scheme, Accident Exchange.

Elizabeth Boon (see p.552) Called to the Bar in 2006, and now making a real name for herself in the property damage area. Her cases often involve aspects of professional negligence and subsequent property damage. **Strengths:** "She's a very good, younger barrister who is professional, focused and driven." **Recent work:** Worked as the junior on a £7 million claim concerning alleged professional negligence by contractors that led to a large fire in a local authority timber-framed building.

2TG – 2 Temple Gardens

See profile on p.873

THE SET

Offers real strength in depth throughout its property damage team and is noted for representing good value for money. The members have experience of handling damages claims, ranging from tree root subsidence to the fallout from major, multinational construction projects.

Client service: "The clerking team, which is led by Lee Tyler, is very good. The clerks are approachable and if you need a quick turnaround they will deal with issues very quickly."

SILKS

Neil Moody QC Heads the property damage group within chambers, and is a real heavyweight in the field. **Strengths:** "He is tremendous as he's very clever, capable and great on his feet. He's very hands-on and good at working out a route to success." One commentator described his style as "more thousand-bomber raid than silent assassin." **Recent work:** Successfully recovered £23 million for Mueller in the Technology and Construction Court. The claim arose out of negligent roofing work that led to a fire at the client's copper factory.

Robert Moxon Browne QC (see p.678) Veteran of the field with a particular specialism in causation questions arising from failures of fire and flood prevention systems. **Strengths:** "It is always a pleasure to work with him, and he is very experienced on property damage issues. When you see him both in court and in conference, it takes your breath away how good he is." **Recent work:** Involved in a case that examined the relative responsibilities of contractors and architects following a fire in a shopping mall.

Howard Palmer QC Has a broad property damage practice, with particular expertise in flooding claims and matters involving highly technical engineering points. **Strengths:** "He has great presence in court and offers a wealth of knowledge and experience. He's adept at highlighting the strengths and weaknesses of a claim, and really helps the client." **Recent work:** Instructed on a flood damage claim caused by the overtopping of the River Taff at Aberfan.

JUNIORS

Daniel Crowley Strong on a wide range of property damage cases. He is especially active in tree root and subsidence cases, and is adept at dealing with issues concerning the Defective Premises Act. **Strengths:** "He is a very astute individual, who has a keen eye for detail, and is very thorough in what he does. He is always methodical, clear and concise, and you can see his passion for the law." **Recent work:** Acted successfully for the claimant in a tree roots damage case.

Doré Green (see p.615) Handles highly technical cases relating to all types of property damage, including fire, flood and landslip issues. Commentators praise his eye for detail and strong work ethic. **Strengths:** "He gets good results, is highly intelligent and really understands the law." **Recent work:** Instructed by insurers and reinsurers in a £10 million fire claim involving a large Georgian property in Mayfair that had recently been refurbished. The case focused on the question of fire-stopping design within the building.

Sonia Nolten (see p.683) Recognised for her ability in general insurance and property damage cases, she is often pitted against more senior barristers, and more than holds her own. **Strengths:** "She is intelligent and takes great pride in getting the answer to any question you pose her." **Recent work:** Acted for paint booth manufacturer AGM Services in a claim concerning a car re-spraying plant that suffered £700,000 of damage in a fire.

Andrew Miller QC (see p.672) Plays a central role in representing clients in challenging international insurance claims. **Strengths:** "He was very commercially aware, understood our position, and was forceful in fighting for us." **Recent work:** Represented the successful defendant and third party in a subrogated claim brought by a claimant's insurers concerning flood damage to a restaurant.

Other Ranked Lawyers

Geoffrey Brown (Thirty Nine Essex Street) One of the most experienced and adept juniors in the field, he has been at the coalface of property damage law for 20 years and is practised at dealing with complex fire, flood subsidence and landslip claims. **Strengths:** "He is commanding. What comes over is that he is smooth and unflappable. If you put him before an insurer client they calm down very quickly." **Recent work:** Instructed on a claim relating to damage of a public house caused by water penetration via an adjacent mound of earth.

Paul Reed QC (see p.705) (Hardwicke) The architect of a healthy construction and insurance practice, he often acts on high-profile cases such as the dispute relating to fire damage at the Royal Marsden Hospital. **Strengths:** "I think that he is phenomenal. He has an inexhaustible appetite for work and an unbelievable eye for detail." **Recent work:** He acted for the defendant in a £175 million claim concerning damage to Europe's largest warehouse.

David Pliener (see p.695) (Hardwicke) Frequently instructed by insurers in relation to fire claims. He has a keen understanding of both construction and insurance law. **Strengths:** "He is a superb advocate who is extremely likeable and very able." **Recent work:** Instructed on a £500,000 claim involving water damage to Ovaltine Court caused by alleged negligent plumbing that led to leaks across the development.

Geraint Webb QC (see p.748) (Henderson Chambers) Has a particularly broad practice and is experienced in dealing with product liability, insurance and general commercial dispute resolution cases. **Strengths:** "He put in an outstanding performance in court that was pivotal in the case. On his feet he is one of the best." **Recent work:** Acted in a multimillion-pound TCC claim concerning an electrical fire in a London hospital allegedly caused by a malfunctioning commercial voltage reducer.

David Allen QC (7 King's Bench Walk) Experienced commercial litigator with an insurance background who is a formidable property damage practitioner. **Strengths:** "Very able," and "very good on the technical detail of a case." **Recent work:** Acted for Barloward Handling in defending a major claim arising out of a Serviceair cargo warehouse fire at Stansted Airport that resulted in millions of pounds of lost cargo.

Graham Eklund QC (see p.594) (4 New Square) Hugely experienced and knowledgeable barrister, who has a vibrant property damage practice. He has handled a number of catastrophic fire cases of late, but he also tackles matters resulting from flood damage. **Strengths:** "He has very good judgement, gives very clear advice, and takes a robust approach. He's a great character to deal with." **Recent work:** Instructed on a claim centring on whether defective lighting, which caused a large paper warehouse fire, should have been detected by electrical contractors.

Ben Elkington QC (see p.594) (4 New Square) Recognised in the insurance, professional negligence and general commercial dispute resolution fields. Over the past year he has focused his practice on large fire and subsidence claims. **Strengths:** "Ben is professional and incredibly bright, and offers commercial, practical and strategic advice. He is also very responsive and an excellent team player." **Recent work:** Represented the owners of Camden Market in a dispute with Network Rail arising out of a substantial fire at the market in 2008, which damaged a train line.

James Cross QC (see p.581) (4 Pump Court) His proficiency in professional negligence, construction and insurance law ensures that he is regularly instructed on a large number of property damage claims. **Strengths:** "We were facing a complex coverage matter and he provided some very well thought-out and comprehensive advice. If you've got something very tricky that needs detailed analysis he is the man." **Recent work:** Acted for the insurers of Middlesex University in a multimillion-pound claim brought against contractors on a neighbouring site. The allegation was that the contractors were liable for a fire that destroyed a timber-framed university building.

Rachel Ansell QC (see p.536) (4 Pump Court) Expert in fire and fraudulent insurance claim cases, she is known for her diligence and skill on her feet in court. **Strengths:** "She is exceptionally good. Advocacy is her real strength, and her cross-examination is especially devastating." **Recent work:** Represented the defendants in a high-value claim arising out of a fire at a timber-flamed building which was allegedly caused by carelessly discarded cigarette butts.

Contents:

LONDON

Public International Law London	
Leading Sets	
Band 1	
Essex Court Chambers *	
Band 2	
Blackstone Chambers *	
20 Essex Street *	
Matrix Chambers *	
Leading Silks	
Senior Statesmen	
Berman Franklin	*Essex Court Chambers*
Lauterpacht Elihu	*20 Essex Street*
Star individuals	
Crawford James R	*Matrix Chambers*
Lowe Vaughan	*Essex Court Chambers*
Band 1	
Bethlehem Daniel	*20 Essex Street*
Sands Philippe	*Matrix Chambers*
Shaw Malcolm	*Essex Court Chambers*
Band 2	
Landau Toby	*Essex Court Chambers*
Mendelson Maurice	*Blackstone Chambers*
Otty Timothy	*Blackstone Chambers*
Wordsworth Samuel	*Essex Court Chambers*
Band 3	
Eicke Tim	*Essex Court Chambers*
Hermer Richard	*Matrix Chambers*
Qureshi Khawar	*Serle Court (ORL)* ◊ *
New Silks	
Dixon Rodney	*Temple Garden Chambers (ORL)* ◊
Leading Juniors	
Band 1	
Douglas Zachary	*Matrix Chambers* *
Fatima Shaheed	*Blackstone Chambers*
Wood Michael	*20 Essex Street*
Band 2	
Boyle Alan	*Essex Court Chambers*
Goodwin-Gill Guy	*Blackstone Chambers*
Macdonald Alison	*Matrix Chambers* *
Sander Amy	*Essex Court Chambers*
Sarooshi Dan	*Essex Court Chambers*
Verdirame Guglielmo	*20 Essex Street*
Band 3	
Lester Maya	*Brick Court Chambers (ORL)* ◊
Olleson Simon	*13 Old Square Chambers (ORL)* ◊
Patel Naina	*Blackstone Chambers*
* *Indicates set / individual with profile.*	
◊ *(ORL) = Other Ranked Lawyer.*	
Alphabetical order within each band. Band 1 is highest.	

Band 1

Essex Court Chambers

See profile on p.792

THE SET

Essex Court Chambers boasts a superb stable of barristers and remains the benchmark set others aspire to in the PIL field. It attracts accolades for its efforts across the full spectrum of international law, and handles maritime and law of the sea disputes, as well as sovereign state immunity matters and human rights-related cases. Commentators praise it for having the largest spread of interesting and prestigious cases in the market.

SILKS

Vaughan Lowe QC One of the most sought-after authorities in PIL, he has outstanding capability in all aspects of the field. He is highly regarded for his land and maritime limitations expertise, as well as his investment treaty work, and both serves as counsel and sits as arbitrator in major cases. **Strengths:** "Exceptionally good." "He's in hot demand and is very good as an arbitrator. A delight to work with as he is good humoured and analytically excellent." **Recent work:** Successfully assisted the government of Nicaragua in gaining maritime zones in a boundary dispute against Columbia.

Malcolm Shaw QC A widely acknowledged leader in international law, with a broad-ranging practice that encompasses territorial and boundary disputes and state immunity cases. He has an impressive track record in the human rights sphere, and has appeared before the highest courts on cases of notable import. He is also a distinguished force in academic circles. **Strengths:** "He has a well-established position as one of the leading practitioners in international law in the world and is among the very first tier of experts." "Powerful and persuasive, he has sound judgement." **Recent work:** Appeared in Noor Khan v Secretary of State for Foreign and Commonwealth Affairs, a case concerning drone attacks in Pakistan.

Samuel Wordsworth QC Acclaimed boundary disputes expert, who is particularly good on maritime and law of the sea matters, including environmental harm issues. He is routinely engaged on high-profile, politically sensitive cases, and also focuses on investment treaty arbitration. **Strengths:** "His academic prowess in addition to his practical experience makes him a prototype PIL lawyer. He is the crown prince in this area." "He's fantastic – one of those PIL practitioners who is completely absorbed in the topic." **Recent work:** Instructed in a dispute between the UK and Mauritius before a specially convened tribunal over an alleged violation of the UN's Law of the Sea. The case arose out of the UK's institution of marine protections around the Chagos Islands.

Toby Landau QC Has an excellent reputation in the international law market and significant experience in BIT arbitrations, as well as NAFTA and international trade matters. He has a long-standing history of acting in precedent-setting cases. **Strengths:** "He's at the very top of the international arbitration game, which is in turn a large part of PIL." "Phenomenally good. His work is of such high quality."

Tim Eicke QC Has an accomplished practice and is particularly involved in the interaction between PIL and international human rights. Immigration and rendition cases are a particular forte, and he is frequently instructed by governmental bodies on investment treaty matters. He also has additional expertise in sanctions and issues surrounding conflicting laws and conventions. **Strengths:** "He comes at problems from different angles and knits things together well." "He's highly able and very user-friendly." **Recent work:** Engaged by the UK in a case addressing ECHR law and its intersection with the UN Convention against Torture in relation to the deportation of an Islamist preacher to Jordan. Major issues included the notion of 'flagrant denial' and the extra-territorial effect of the right to a fair trial.

Franklin Berman QC Eminent and much-admired PIL practitioner who has an outstandingly wide scope of expertise, encompassing matters from state responsibility to the laws of war and neutrality. He is sought out for a vast range of advisory work and sits as both an ICSID arbitrator and an ad hoc judge, notably on disputes involving maritime boundaries. **Strengths:** "Tremendously well thought of and definitely a go-to person in the area."

JUNIORS

Alan Boyle Offers in-depth environmental and law of the sea expertise, which is prized by governments and global entities. He receives plaudits for his authoritative advice in relation to damage and liability issues, and is also noted for his handling of marine pollution cases. **Strengths:** "He's really impressive, has done a great range of cases, and is really turning into a great PIL advocate." "Very, very able indeed and one of the stars of the constitutional Bar. He's masterful, convincing, and shows great learning."

Amy Sander Has extensive PIL focus coupled with standout academic expertise. She undertakes complex and diplomatically sensitive work for states and governmental bodies, and has substantial knowledge of ECHR law. **Strengths:** "She's really efficient and impressive, and is building up a great practice." **Recent work:** Appeared in an ICJ dispute brought by Australia in relation to alleged violations of international whaling regulations by Japan.

Dan Sarooshi Brings his thorough academic knowledge of PIL to bear on a caseload rich in environmental law and immunity cases. He has considerable experience in the oil and gas sector and is recognised as an expert on WTO disputes. **Strengths:** "He's extremely knowledgeable and has a very good understanding not just of the law but also of the frameworks and what happens at the governmental level." **Recent work:** Acted in Taurus Petroleum v Iraq's State Oil Marketing Company, Shell and Credit Agricole in a dispute concerning garnishee orders and bank immunity.

Band 2

Blackstone Chambers

See profile on p.771

THE SET

Blackstone Chambers is an international human rights powerhouse, rated for its history of handling complex, challenging cases and admired for the often innovative approach to cases taken by its barristers. Its members are particularly experienced in all aspects of refugee law, the crossover between international conventions and domestic law, and the effect of war on human rights during conflicts. Other areas of interest include BIT arbitration and economic sanctions cases.

SILKS

Timothy Otty QC Brings his human rights and civil liberties expertise to his international law practice, and specialises in matters concerning armed conflict, especially within states. He is also strong on conflict of laws cases, and further commands respect for his work in secession claims. **Strengths:** "He does a lot of impressive and interesting cases," and "produces very good written work." **Recent work:** Advised on Caleb Orozco's challenge to the Attorney General of Belize concerning the criminalisation of homosexual conduct.

Maurice Mendelson QC A high-quality, much-in-demand arbitrator on investment treaty disputes. He has a laudable academic profile, multilingual ability and comprehensive experience of a vast swathe of PIL areas. **Strengths:** "A very intellectual man who provides thorough analysis of cases." **Recent work:** Acted in NML v Argentina, a dispute concerning state immunity following the detention of an Argentine warship in port.

JUNIORS

Shaheed Fatima A highly rated human rights specialist who regularly handles innovative work at the interface of PIL and domestic law. She is hailed both for her written work and her oral advocacy, and she has considerable capability in sanctions, wrongful detention and immigration cases. **Strengths:** "A fantastic, real-deal PIL lawyer, and a hard-hitting advocate." "She really impresses with her thinking-outside-the-box solutions to difficult problems and her ability to speak authoritatively about the area." **Recent work:** Instructed by Mukhtar Djakishev in a case pending before the UNHRC, brought against Kazakhstan for human rights abuses including wrongful detention and violation of the right to a fair trial.

Guy Goodwin-Gill An authority on international refugee law, from statelessness and refugee protection for ICJ testifiers to forcible transfers and resettlement. His broader PIL practice takes in matters concerning issues as diverse as fisheries delimitation, the accountability of international organisations and treaty interpretation. **Strengths:** "He has this blend of great intellectual power, not just in refugee law but in other areas of PIL, and a very down-to-earth manner, and that's something that is very, very effective." "He is knowledgeable and has written a lot, so has a lot of advice worth taking." **Recent work:** Engaged by the Secretary of State for the Home Department against Al-Jedda in a case concerning the state's ability to revoke British citizenship in the interests of the public good and the capacity of an occupying power to amend a country's nationality law.

Naina Patel Has an expanding human rights PIL focus to her practice, and is strong on matters concerning the interrelation and conflict of domestic and international laws. She also provides quality counsel on matters concerning international development, such as aid distribution. **Strengths:** "She has strong analytical skills and understands the broader policy context. She has a great deal of knowledge of international development issues." "She's able to apply the law to facts in a complex case in a logical and helpful manner." **Recent work:** Appeared for the UNHRC in a matter concerning the application of HJ (Iran) v Secretary of State for the Home Department [2010] to cases involving the persecution of politically indifferent individuals as opponents of Zimbabwe's government.

20 Essex Street

See profile on p.794

THE SET

A natural choice for complex investment treaty cases, 20 Essex Street is a major player in this field. Its prominent, highly experienced barristers tackle a breadth of PIL work and are at the forefront of government advisory matters involving political considerations and state security. Members have noted and are particularly good on cases at the intersection of commercial arbitration and international law. Commentators say they are drawn to the set as it has an exciting mix of both new and established talent.

SILKS

Daniel Bethlehem QC Renowned for his government representation and advisory work, and also recommended for his extensive WTO expertise. He regularly receives instructions on sophisticated investor-state arbitrations, both as serving counsel and as sitting arbitrator, and is involved in crucial, security-sensitive cases for a diverse client list. **Strengths:** "He is a huge name and he has a huge effect when he walks into a room and presents his submissions." "Calm, sophisticated and undoubtedly impressive."

Elihu Lauterpacht QC An esteemed figure in the field of international law with a highly distinguished track record in major ICJ disputes and arbitrations before numerous tribunals. He couples this with an exceptional advisory practice, and is often called on by states and governmental bodies, who value him for his outstanding track record and superior academic knowledge of the sector. **Strengths:** "A legendary name in the field who has seen and done it all."

JUNIORS

Michael Wood A former FCO counsel, who offers high-calibre advice to the government. He combines his UN law expertise with deep knowledge of the law relating to boundary disputes, overseas territories and international human rights. **Strengths:** "In this area, it's not possible to be effective at the highest level without a hands-on understanding of how international institutions operate, and he brings an abundance of that." "He's a junior but in terms of practice, he probably rivals most silks." **Recent work:** Acted for Peru in its ICJ dispute against Chile, a case concerning extensive maritime boundary issues.

Guglielmo Verdirame Has strengths in investment treaty arbitration, international trade law and issues surrounding wars. He has a particularly robust advisory practice, and is further noted for his academic excellence in the field. **Strengths:** "Extremely strong, he's very much sought after by certain very senior silks and that's a testament to how good he is. He is a true future star individual." **Recent work:** Advised the claimant in a case against Peru heard before the Inter-American Court of Human Rights, involving assertions of torture, including sexual assault and wrongful arrest.

Matrix Chambers

See profile on p.832

THE SET

Sovereign states, international organisations and individuals look to Matrix Chambers for assistance in the PIL area due to the presence of its committed and highly respected barristers. Home to outstanding individuals, it acts on important cases at the forefront of the overlap between PIL and international criminal law and is a central player in human rights matters. It is also strong on BITs and territorial and maritime delimitation cases.

SILKS

James Crawford SC A leading light whose exceptional knowledge and experience of PIL matters mark him out as a go-to for high-profile cases. His pedigree in ICJ cases is widely acknowledged, as is his expertise in ICSID and UNCITRAL investment treaty arbitration cases. He acts both as counsel and as arbitrator, and enjoys a phenomenal academic standing in the PIL sector. **Strengths:** "A legend in the PIL world." "Unquestionably one of the top PIL practitioners globally, and probably the person who's had the most influence in terms of the development of PIL in the past two to three decades. A brilliant mind." **Recent work:** Engaged in Croatia's genocide cases brought against Serbia before the ICJ, which raised key questions about the capacity and applicability of the Convention on the Prevention and Punishment of the Crime of Genocide.

Philippe Sands QC An esteemed silk well known for his extensive international law practice, which covers an array of matters including environment, trade and international criminal law. He acts in major, diplomatically critical state-to-state disputes and is also much sought after as an ICSID arbitrator. **Strengths:** "An important and talented figure with a diverse practice." "He's very dynamic, with a diverse range of experience in different contexts and fields of international law. Very prominent, influential, extremely good and one of the big names of his age." **Recent work:** Appeared for Libya in its challenge against the ICC's prosecution of Saif Al-Islam Gaddafi and Abdullah Al-Senussi for war crimes on the grounds that they should be charged and tried in Libya as opposed to the Hague.

Richard Hermer QC Well respected for his international human rights and humanitarian law expertise, especially in relation to reparations for victims of large-scale ethnic and racial violence. He has impressive knowledge of arbitrary detention and rendition, and further strength in environmental matters, particularly in the oil and gas sector. **Strengths:** "He demolishes cases and is really very impressive." **Recent work:** Appeared in Ahmed v HM Treasury and Foreign & Commonwealth Office, a case before the UK Supreme Court concerning the legality of terrorist asset freezing measures as directed by the UN.

JUNIORS

Zachary Douglas (see p.590) Excels in investment treaty cases before the major arbitral courts, and has also sat as arbitrator in numerous cases. He maintains a notable practice in boundary disputes and also demonstrates expertise in state immunity and human rights. Commentators note that he has a strong governmental advisory practice. **Strengths:** "His capacity to understand and explain is exceptional." "He's a very good advocate and has a sense of priorities in terms of presenting persuasive arguments on the issues." **Recent work:** Appeared in Chevron v Ecuador, a major environmental case concerning Chevron's liability for contamination of a large swathe of Ecuadorian rainforest.

Alison Macdonald (see p.659) Has a great reputation for PIL contentious and advisory work, drawing on her international criminal and human rights law experience to provide counsel on issues including war crimes, sovereign immunity and corruption. She is well regarded for her grasp of ICSID annulments and international trade law, and advises an array of clients in diverse sectors. **Strengths:** "Extremely good and one of the very few barristers who works at the confluence between criminal, public and commercial law." **Recent work:** Instructed by Bangladesh in ICSID claims of corruption against Niko Resources in connection with a gas extraction project.

Other Ranked Lawyers

Maya Lester (Brick Court Chambers) Seamlessly brings together practices in EU, public and human rights law. Her PIL work sees her representing individuals and companies against governmental and EU bodies. She has a distinct specialism in targeted sanctions, with significant expertise in the listing of terrorist sanctions, and experience in pursuing infraction proceedings against states for violations of the EU Charter on Fundamental Rights. **Strengths:** "A very impressive operator." **Recent work:** Acted for the Central Bank of Iran in its challenge against its placing on the EU sanctions list by the European Council.

Simon Olleson (13 Old Square Chambers) Has a core focus on PIL work and a practice that spans the full spectrum of the field. He tackles inter-state disputes, the law of the sea and investment treaty arbitration, and is an experienced performer in international human rights and environmental law. Also has an in-depth understanding of matters concerning state responsibility. **Strengths:** "He's fantastic. He's done a lot in this area with Professor James Crawford, which speaks for itself."' **Recent work:** Appeared for Kazakhstan in an ICSID arbitration brought by AES and Tau Power.

Khawar Qureshi QC (see p.702) (Serle Court) Has a broad-ranging practice that sees him handling instructions on BIT cases from both states and private investors. He is also active in UN and EU sanctions and ECT matters, and underpins his PIL expertise with excellent human rights and commercial litigation work. **Strengths:** "Very able and a powerful advocate." **Recent work:** Acted for a major oil company in a case before the ICC brought against an East African state for improper levying of taxes.

Rodney Dixon QC (Temple Garden Chambers) An acclaimed new silk who regularly represents governments, political figures and military leaders. He has gained considerable experience of matters relating to the Arab Spring and further specialises in corruption, detention rights and asset freezing. **Strengths:** "He has an outstanding intellect, works very, very hard and is rated very highly as an advocate. He's seen as being a real force to be reckoned with." "Amazing. He's really on top of all the case law and procedure, and knows exactly what he's doing." **Recent work:** Instructed by Libya's ex-security chief Abdullah Al-Senussi in an action before the ICC seeking a transfer to the Hague in compliance with the UN Security Council as an alternative to facing trial in Libya.

PUBLIC PROCUREMENT: An Introduction

Contributed by Joanne Clement and Joseph Barrett of 11KBW

2014 is, on any view, a significant year for EU procurement lawyers.

As all procurement lawyers will know, the EU has now adopted a new trio of procurement directives governing public service, utilities and concession contracts. The new public service directive alone runs to over 250 pages, excluding appendices. The stated aims of the new instruments are enhanced clarity, simplicity and flexibility. Whether these objectives will be achieved remains to be seen. In the short term at least, the substantive and procedural changes introduced by the new directives will increase, rather than diminish, the need for expert legal advice in what remains a specialist field.

A particular word is merited on the entirely new concession contract directive. Litigation on concession contracts in the UK has to date been limited. This is likely to be attributable to a number of causes, not least that historically UK contracting authorities have made less frequent use of the concession model than some other EU member states. The new directive, for the first time, provides businesses and public bodies with a single, accessible and (relatively) clear statement of their respective rights and obligations. Importantly, it also incorporates the provisions of the Remedies Directive. The position of aggrieved tenderers for concession contracts is thus significantly strengthened. We may well see legal challenges in this area becoming more commonplace.

We understand that the Government intends to consult shortly, and before the end of the year, on implementing the new directives.

A critical issue remains whether domestic law, and the Courts, provide effective remedies for aggrieved bidders. The clear trend in English procurement litigation over the last ten years has been to refuse to grant an injunction preventing the award of a public contract when a legal challenge is made. The claimant is then no longer able to achieve at trial what is invariably its primary (and usually only) objective: the opportunity to be awarded the relevant contract.

In Covanta Energy Ltd v Merseyside Waste Disposal Authority [2013] EWHC 2922 the High Court broke with trend and granted an injunction prohibiting the award of a very substantial £1.2 billion energy from waste facility contract. The decision of Coulson J was a welcome fillip for those who act for challengers, and perhaps a timely reminder for contracting authorities that breaches of the EU procurement regime can have potentially grave consequences for the implementation of significant public projects.

This approach has been endorsed by the very recent decision of the Court of Appeal in DWF v Insolvency Service [2014] EWCA Civ 900. DWF is the first case in which the Court of Appeal has had the opportunity to consider the correct approach to applications to lift the automatic suspension in EU procurement litigation. The reasoning of the Court will make welcome reading for those advising procurement challengers. The Covanta principles are applied and the Court held that the application to lift the automatic suspension should be rejected.

There have also been a number of other cases in recent months where contracting authorities have issued an application to lift the suspension but then abandoned the application shortly before a hearing.

EU procurement remains a growth area – for both advisory and litigious work. There remains a sustained focus on public bodies seeking to share services, use an increasingly innovative range of public/private joint venture and partnering structures and, in some cases, conduct significant restructurings of existing (major) public contracts. These endeavours have continued to demand high levels of creativity on the part of the lawyers responsible for ensuring EU law compliance.

Where are we seeing most challenges? The construction industry continues to provide a strong stream of EU procurement litigation. Bidders in this field appear to have long since dispensed with any serious concern about challenging adverse decisions. Similarly, the waste sector continues to generate a significant number of challenges – perhaps unsurprisingly given the value of some of the contracts awarded in this field.

Growth areas include ICT and defence-related disputes. Historically, bidders active in these fields have been reluctant to litigate. However, we see signs that this is now changing and there are several challenges currently before the Courts. By far the biggest growth area in procurement litigation is the health sector. Recent NHS reforms made broad swathes of NHS commissioning subject to the rigours of procurement law. These changes have now been in force for a little over a year. It is no exaggeration to say that the changes in the sector have been seismic. Long-term and substantial contracts are being tendered, often via complex procurements. The upswell in procurement disputes in this sector is unsurprising and, so far, we see no signs of it abating.

Both the Chancery and QBD divisions of the High Court continue to see a number of EU procurement cases. The TCC continues to be the forum of the greatest number of claims. However, it is noticeable that an increasing number of cases appear to be being issued in Chancery. Each division obviously has its advantages and disadvantages (some real and some perceived). However, the depth of experience in EU law of a number of the Judges sitting in Chancery make it a particularly attractive destination for EU procurement claims raising novel or complex issues.

We can confidently predict that the next year will be a busy, and interesting, one for EU procurement specialists.

Contents:

LONDON

Public Procurement London	
Leading Sets	
Band 1	
Monckton Chambers *	
Band 2	
11KBW *	
Band 3	
Blackstone Chambers *	
Keating Chambers *	
Band 4	
Henderson Chambers *	
Leading Silks	
Star individuals	
Bowsher Michael	*Monckton Chambers* 🄰 *
Giffin Nigel	*11KBW*
Hannaford Sarah	*Keating Chambers* *
Band 1	
Goudie James	*11KBW* *
Howell John	*Blackstone Chambers*
Lasok Paul	*Monckton Chambers* 🄰 *
Band 2	
Béar Charles	*Fountain Court Chambers (ORL)* ◊ *
Coppel Jason	*11KBW* *
Lewis Adam	*Blackstone Chambers*
Moser Philip	*Monckton Chambers* 🄰 *
Williams Rhodri	*Henderson Chambers* 🄰 *
Band 3	
Herberg Javan	*Blackstone Chambers*
Kerr Tim	*11KBW* *
McCredie Fionnuala	*Keating Chambers* *
Quigley Conor	*Serle Court (ORL)* ◊
Leading Juniors	
Band 1	
Sloane Valentina	*Monckton Chambers* 🄰
Williams Rob	*Monckton Chambers*
Band 2	
Gollancz David	*Keating Chambers* *
Lamont Calum	*Keating Chambers* *
Rhee Deok Joo	*11KBW* *
Segan James	*Blackstone Chambers*
West Ewan	*Monckton Chambers* 🄰
Band 3	
Barrett Joseph	*11KBW* *
Gray Margaret	*Brick Court Chambers (ORL)* ◊
Holmes Elisa	*Monckton Chambers*
Kinnier Andrew	*Henderson Chambers* 🄰 *
Taylor Simon	*Keating Chambers* *
Up-and-coming individuals	
Osepciu Ligia	*Monckton Chambers* *

** Indicates set / individual with profile.*

◊ (ORL) = Other Ranked Lawyer.

🄰 direct access (see p.11).

Band 1

Monckton Chambers

See profile on p.833

THE SET

Monckton Chambers devotes more than 20 barristers to this area and has been at the forefront of the sector from its inception. Its strong team of silks and juniors has the pedigree and skill to tackle the larger matters of the day, as evidenced by its members' key role in the dispute concerning the Department for Transport's decision to award the West Coast Main Line contract to First Group rather than Virgin Trains. The group acts for public sector bodies and private companies in both an advisory and litigious role. The set is active in the energy, construction, transport, pharmaceutical and aviation sectors, amongst many others, and remains, without doubt, a pre-eminent name in the field.

Client service: David Hockney is the senior member of a clerking team that is praised as being "flexible, accommodating and very easy to deal with."

SILKS

Michael Bowsher QC (see p.554) Credited as being one of the first barristers to develop a practice in this niche, he has enjoyed considerable success over the years. He remains a popular choice of silk for the UK government and for a number of public bodies, such as the NHS. **Strengths:** "Michael is very intelligent and highly creative in his thinking, and is not afraid to get stuck into a case in order to find the right arguments." "He is the indisputable leading heavyweight in public procurement, and has encyclopaedic knowledge of the law in this area. He identifies key issues and answers difficult questions with unmatched authority." **Recent work:** Advised on the high-profile Alstom v Eurostar dispute, concerning the award of a contract for train replacement.

Paul Lasok QC Has broad EU and competition law capabilities, which dovetail effectively with his public procurement work. His client base includes a number of public bodies, and he has recently undertaken a good deal of work for transport infrastructure operators. **Strengths:** "He's very clear in his answers and can turn complicated issues into yes/no answers." **Recent work:** He provided advice to the Laidlaw Inquiry on processes associated with the West Coast Main Line franchise tender.

Philip Moser QC One of the newer silks at the set, widely praised for his strong European law knowledge. Multinational companies and local authorities alike seek out his counsel. **Strengths:** "He is user-friendly and has achieved great results for our clients."

JUNIORS

Valentina Sloane Rapidly becoming a go-to junior for this practice area, her skill set ensures she is selected to advise on an array of procurement matters. She is especially known for advising companies as potential challengers to alleged procedural impropriety. **Strengths:** "She's very approachable, straight-talking and commercial." "She was on top of not just the law but also the procedural stuff in preparation for trial." **Recent work:** Acted for the complainant in Pearson v Cabinet Office, a case concerning alleged regulatory breaches made when awarding a driving theory testing contract.

Rob Williams Acts for a number of public bodies, including government departments, as well as private companies. His key areas of interest include advising on policy reviews, challenges and compliance. **Strengths:** "He's very knowledgeable on his subject and a good team player, who is very easy to work with." "Very sensible and pragmatic in his advice, he gives a credible and clear view on the merits of a case." **Recent work:** Advised Learn Direct on Pearson's challenge to the award of a driving theory testing contract in the case of Pearson v Cabinet Office.

Ewan West A senior civil servant before being called to the Bar, he has a client list that includes losing bidders as well as notable government departments. **Strengths:** "Ewan is clever, articulate and committed to finding answers to difficult questions." "He's responsive, practical and firm in his dealings." **Recent work:** Advised on the procurement dispute of Apollo Property v Circle Housing.

Elisa Holmes A proven EU and regulatory law professional who is also admitted to practice in Australia. She has advised a number of private parties of late, including unsuccessful bidders on various procurement questions. **Strengths:** "She is a fiery, punchy advocate. Sometimes you need to tip that balance in your favour." "She's a great junior for challenging cases, as she is enthusiastic and tenacious." **Recent work:** She acted for Photo-Me in a procurement challenge against the Secretary of State for Transport. The matter concerned a contract to provide photo booths at UK railway stations.

Ligia Osepciu A younger yet highly capable barrister who punches above her weight. She acts both led and unled, and has recently advised a number of claimants on challenges to procurement awards. **Strengths:** "Excellent, with a capability well beyond her years of experience. She is also very pleasant to work with." "She was very helpful and responsive, and able to put the clients at ease."

Band 2

11KBW

See profile on p.823

THE SET

11KBW excels in procurement work as it does in so many other areas of public law. It is best known for acting for public bodies, but also increasingly acts for private parties, handling everything from initial advice and regulatory compliance counselling to the hardest-fought courtroom battles. As an indication of its strength in this area, it was involved in Covanta Energy v Merseyside Waste Disposal Authority, representing the claimant in successfully obtaining an injunction under the Public Contracts Regulations 2006 prohibiting the award of a £1.2 billion contract for the construction, financing and operation of a major waste-to-energy facility. The case was one of the most important of the year in the procurement field. Members of the set at all levels of call tackle the work, and the future seems bright, as commentators are swift to note that there are "plenty of good juniors rising up the ranks here."

Client service: Lucy Barbet and Mark Dann are the set's joint senior clerks. Sources describe the client service they provide as being "very good and very efficient; we have never had a problem."

SILKS

Nigel Giffin QC A hugely respected counsel for public procurement matters and local government work generally. He is equally adept in representing local authorities and in advising losing bidders on potential challenges. **Strengths:** "Nigel is outstanding because he's knowledgeable, pragmatic, articulate and responsive." "Top-notch intellectually, he's extremely tactically astute and very flexible. He's also helpful when dealing with clients." **Recent work:** Had a lead role for the claimant in the high-profile procurement dispute of Covanta Energy v Merseyside Waste Disposal Authority.

James Goudie QC (see p.612) A first port of call for local authorities facing procurement-related issues, he advises on disputes as well as pre-dispute regulatory compliance. **Strengths:** "A man with a great intellect who has a real gift for providing straightforward, user-friendly advice on complicated problems." "He doesn't sit on the fence, but gives his opinion, is very easy to deal with and is down to earth." **Recent work:** Advised on R (RB) v Devon County Council, a case concerning a contract to provide integrated children's services for the local authority.

Jason Coppel QC (see p.578) One of the newer silks at the set. He is a proven counsel who acts for both private parties and local authorities on procurement challenges. **Strengths:** "Extremely good technically and very knowledgeable in this area." "He provides astoundingly clear and thoughtful written advice, and is very sensible." **Recent work:** Acted for the complainant in Phoenix Commercial Collections v Leicestershire County Council, a matter concerning the tender for provision of bailiff services.

Tim Kerr QC Known for education work, but has built a respectable practice in the highly regulated public procurement space. His recent work includes handling a number of high-level procurement defence matters on behalf of local authorities. **Recent work:** Acted for the London Borough of Hammersmith & Fulham in connection with challenges to the award of new home construction contracts pertaining to a site near Earl's Court.

JUNIORS

Deok Joo Rhee (see p.706) Acts for private companies as challengers to procurement awards, including private party health service companies. European law is the mainstay of her practice. **Strengths:** "She did a very good job of reacting to unusual points brought up by the judge in the case she handled for us." "She is very bright." **Recent work:** Advised successful tenderer Addaction on defending a losing bidder's charge of procedural impropriety.

Joseph Barrett (see p.543) One of the younger crop who enjoys a rising profile in public and administrative law matters, and is noted for his education and public procurement prowess. **Strengths:** "He is very user-friendly and good with clients. His written advice is clear and concise." "He has superb drafting skills, and is always ready to roll up his sleeves and go the extra mile." **Recent work:** Acted as junior counsel to the claimant in the high-profile waste-to-energy procurement challenge, Covanta Energy v Merseyside Waste Disposal Authority.

Band 3

Blackstone Chambers

See profile on p.771

THE SET

Blackstone Chambers has all the public law muscle you could hope for, so it is unsurprising that it has more than an interest in procurement work. Its members act for procuring authorities such as county councils, as well as private parties, and are sought out to advise on high-stakes regulatory compliance matters, potential procurement challenges and judicial review proceedings.

Client service: Gary Oliver is the senior clerk. Commercial pragmatism characterises both his approach and that of the set, and both are noted for their "sensitivity to the needs of those that instruct them."

SILKS

John Howell QC Undertakes public procurement cases as part of his sparkling administrative and public law practice. His clients include a host of key government and regulatory bodies. **Strengths:** "He has a low-key but commanding court manner, so judges really sit up and listen to him." "He often thinks of a point nobody else has, and applies it brilliantly." **Recent work:** Advised North Yorkshire County Council on the judicial review of a decision to withdraw waste infrastructure PFI credits.

Adam Lewis QC A major player in the sporting law world, Lewis handles regulatory challenges to decisions affecting sports clubs. He acts for a number of sporting organisations as well as local authorities. **Strengths:** "He is very responsive, very can-do and very hard-working." **Recent work:** Advised Leyton Orient FC on a judicial review of the decision not to consider it for co-tenancy of a sports stadium.

Javan Herberg QC He is both a talented financial services and public procurement lawyer, and his client base includes insurance brokers and healthcare entities. **Strengths:** "He's both very charming and very clever." **Recent work:** Acted for insurance broker Risk Management Partners in a Supreme Court challenge to the award of insurance contracts by the London Borough of Brent.

JUNIORS

James Segan Medical equipment manufacturers and facility management companies have utilised his strength in procurement law in recent times. **Strengths:** "He provided just what we needed in a 'no fuss, no bother' way, offering excellent turnaround of papers and faultless attention to detail." **Recent work:** Advised on the High Court challenge to the Ministry of Defence's contract for facilities management in the Falkland Islands. He acted for Sodexo as claimant.

Keating Chambers

See profile on p.824

THE SET

Keating Chambers is a market-leading construction set that displays undisputed acumen when handling procurement cases. Its gifted team of talented silks and juniors offers early-stage strategic advice to both authorities and bidders when tenders are up for grabs, but also offers all the advocacy skills required should matters proceed to the courtroom. Members at the set are expert in tackling cases involving the health, construction and professional services, the three biggest areas of public procurement by spend. Recent cases have seen them acting for local authorities, transport companies and technology providers, amongst others.

Client service: Declan Redmond is the CEO and clerking director. Sources note that the clerks are "very open to discussion; we have never had an issue with them." One commentator stated: "The back office support is excellent. The clerks are responsive and pragmatic when it comes to fees."

SILKS

Sarah Hannaford QC (see p.618) A highly sought-after lead counsel who frequently advises private parties on potential challenges to contract awards in sectors such as waste management and transport. She also acts for public bodies. **Strengths:** "User-friendly, efficient and good with clients." "A very committed procurement specialist. She really gets into the detail of a case and is one of the best in her field." **Recent work:** Had a lead role on the high-profile Covanta Energy v Mersey Waste Disposal Authority dispute, advising the complainant on alleged irregularities surrounding a tender for a waste-to-energy plant.

Fionnuala McCredie QC (see p.667) One of the newer silks at the set, she has a very strong name for both construction and procurement matters. She acts for potential challengers and contracting authorities alike. **Strengths:** "A very good procurement specialist who gets into the detail, understands the commercial drivers of a case, and always makes herself available." "She has a great strategic eye, and is good at anticipating the other side's moves." **Recent work:** Advised Pearson Driving Assessments as the challenger to the contract award for evaluation of drivers.

JUNIORS

David Gollancz (see p.611) A solicitor of 20 years who later retrained as a barrister. He has recently acted for a number of losing bidders in cases relating to transport infrastructure and IT systems. **Strengths:** "Very knowledgeable about the area, he really understands not only the letter of the law, but also the policy and reasoning behind it." "He presents both his written advice and advocacy in a calm style, which is appreciated by clients." **Recent work:** Had an advisory role for the claimant in the high-profile Pearson Driving Assessments litigation.

Calum Lamont (see p.650) An increasingly popular choice for private parties seeking to challenge the award of contracts. His work roster includes disputes surrounding the provision of administrative and building maintenance services. **Strengths:** "A very able junior with a 'can-do' attitude." "He's strong with clients and exudes calmness and confidence." **Recent work:** He advised the claimant in Gurney v HCPC, a case concerning a contract for typing and stenographical services for the healthcare sector.

Simon Taylor (see p.735) Won considerable acclaim as an EU law solicitor, before returning to the Bar in 2012. He already appears as sole counsel in disputes, and has previously advised hospital trusts on procurement challenges. **Strengths:** "He understand the client's perspective and matches this with a forensic approach to detail which is highly valued by clients in difficult situations." "Very user-friendly and good with clients, particularly more demanding ones." **Recent work:** He appeared as led junior counsel for the defence in the high-profile Covanta Energy v Merseyside Waste Disposal Authority case.

Band 4

Henderson Chambers

See profile on p.820

THE SET

This set houses a smaller but nevertheless good-quality public procurement team. Its members act for an interesting spread of clients, including the UK and Welsh governments, a number of local authorities and a raft of NHS trusts. They also assist private bodies such as pharmaceutical and construction companies. Most contentious and non-contentious work is undertaken.

Client service: "The Henderson Chambers experience from initial contact to final advice is without equal. At all times it is entirely professional, thoroughly transparent in terms of fee structure and, given the quality of the end product, superb value for money." John White is highlighted as one of the most popular chief clerks around.

SILKS

Rhodri Williams QC (see p.752) An eminent silk with great experience, who regularly acts for public bodies, including large local authorities, on high-value procurement challenges. **Strengths:** "Balanced and measured in his approach." "He is amenable and knows how to look after his instructing solicitors. He also has a good brain and can think well on the hoof." **Recent work:** Acted for the defendant in the procurement dispute of Montpellier Estates v Leeds City Council.

JUNIORS

Andrew Kinnier (see p.646) A junior counsel to The Crown, who is recognised for his growing prominence in both public procurement and general local government work. His practice sees him advising on procurement challenges and broader issues of regulatory compliance. **Recent work:** Advised the Welsh government on the exclusion from public tender of a number of construction firms, related to alleged 'blacklisting' of employees that was undertaken by those construction firms.

Other Ranked Lawyers

Margaret Gray (Brick Court Chambers) Has developed a broad EU, competition public law practice. She has appeared in the ECJ in Luxembourg, and has been called to the Bars of Ireland and Northern Ireland as well as England and Wales. **Strengths:** "Very good, succinct advice delivered within a short timeframe." **Recent work:** She acted as a led junior on the procurement contract award dispute of Communicaid v EU Commission.

Charles Béar QC (see p.546) (Fountain Court Chambers) Has a strong administrative and public law practice that includes public procurement work. He is equally comfortable acting in court or on mediations, and his key clients include government departments as well as commercial enterprises who are losing bidders. **Strengths:** "He's acutely intelligent and fiercely supportive." **Recent work:** He had a lead role advising on a number of IT procurement disputes.

Conor Quigley QC (Serle Court) Noted for his state aid and procurement expertise. A number of city councils and local authorities rely on his advice. **Strengths:** "He is very commercial – he won't just give you a legal answer, but also a practical one."

Real Estate Litigation

Contents:

LONDON

Real Estate Litigation London
Leading Sets
Band 1
Falcon Chambers *
Band 2
Landmark Chambers *
Maitland Chambers *
Wilberforce Chambers *
Band 3
Enterprise Chambers *
Selborne Chambers *
Serle Court *
Tanfield Chambers *
Band 4
Hardwicke *
New Square Chambers *
Radcliffe Chambers *
◊ (ORL) = Other Ranked Lawyer.
[A] direct access (see p.11).
* Indicates set / individual with profile.

Real Estate Litigation London	
Leading Silks	
Star individuals	**Band 3**
Dowding Nicholas *Falcon Chambers* *	**Bhose** Ranjit *Cornerstone Barristers (ORL)* ◊ *
Band 1	**Elvin** David *Landmark Chambers*
Driscoll Michael *Maitland Chambers* *	**Furber** John *Wilberforce Chambers*
Fancourt Timothy *Falcon Chambers* *	**Hutchings** Martin *Wilberforce Chambers* *
Fetherstonhaugh Guy *Falcon Chambers* *	**Laurence** George *New Square Chambers* *
Gaunt Jonathan *Falcon Chambers* *	**Stoner** Christopher *Serle Court* *
Johnson Edwin *Maitland Chambers* *	**Tager** Romie *Selborne Chambers* *
Jourdan Stephen *Falcon Chambers* *	**Wonnacott** Mark *Maitland Chambers*
Karas Jonathan *Falcon Chambers* *	**Band 4**
Male John *Landmark Chambers*	**Ayliffe** James *Wilberforce Chambers*
McGhee John *Maitland Chambers* *	**Crampin** Peter *3 Stone Buildings (ORL)* ◊ *
Reynolds Kirk *Falcon Chambers* *	**de Waal** John *Hardwicke* [A] *
Seitler Jonathan *Wilberforce Chambers*	**Dutton** Timothy C *Maitland Chambers* *
Small Jonathan *Falcon Chambers* *	**Grant** Thomas *Maitland Chambers*
Wicks Joanne *Wilberforce Chambers*	**Halpern** David *4 New Square (ORL)* ◊ *
Band 2	**Jackson** Judith *Maitland Chambers* *
Barnes Michael *Wilberforce Chambers*	**Pearce** Robert *Radcliffe Chambers*
Bhaloo Zia *Enterprise Chambers*	**Rowley** Keith *Radcliffe Chambers*
Holland David *Landmark Chambers*	**Stevens-Hoare** Brie *Hardwicke* [A]
Holland Katharine *Landmark Chambers*	**Tipples** Amanda *Maitland Chambers* *
Morshead Timothy *Landmark Chambers*	**Trace** Anthony *Maitland Chambers* *
Pymont Christopher *Maitland Chambers* *	**Warwick** Mark *Selborne Chambers* *
Rainey Philip *Tanfield Chambers* [A] *	**New Silks**
Walker Andrew *Maitland Chambers* *	**Reed** Rupert *Wilberforce Chambers*

Band 1

Falcon Chambers

See profile on p.799

THE SET

Falcon Chambers is a set that is "at the top of the game for property law." As a completely dedicated real estate set, it is noted for the exceptional depth and breadth of its expertise, and is further applauded for the technical acumen and superior advocacy skills of its members. Its litigation and advisory work spans the gamut of real estate issues, and a number of the individuals here have active practices in specialist facets of the sector, including enfranchisement, compulsory purchase, agriculture and rights of light. This year, the set has inaugurated a new arbitration service that provides a pool of talented arbitrators from the set's deep bench of silks.

SILKS

Nicholas Dowding QC (see p.590) A magisterial presence at the Real Estate Bar, and a man trusted to handle major real property disputes in any forum. He is active in all areas of property law. **Strengths:** "He is the fount of all knowledge when it comes to property disputes." "He is engaging, innovative and hugely bright, and has a good feel for what a judge wants." **Recent work:** Acted for a large corporate landlord in the Court of Appeal and before the Supreme Court. The landlord, Daejan Investments, was seeking to recover costs incurred in a major refurbishment of the common parts of a block of flats.

Stephen Jourdan QC (see p.641) A strong advocate, as well as an inventive and erudite thinker. His expertise in property litigation is wide-ranging, although his aptitude for dealing with adverse possession claims is particularly well noted. **Strengths:** "Absolutely superb, he is meticulous in his approach and very smooth." "Technically brilliant, he has sound commercial judgement, and is one of the leading enfranchisement specialists." **Recent work:** Successfully represented Hutchison Whampoa in a High Court trial dealing with title, mooring rights, slander of title, adverse possession, conspiracy and harassment.

Timothy Fancourt QC (see p.598) His practice spans a wide range of cases, including residential and commercial property disputes, freehold disputes, restrictive covenants and other matters. He is highly rated for his ability to handle complicated, technical arguments, and to think creatively around a case. **Strengths:** "He is very refined; he knows what he is talking about, and there is no messing around." "A quick-thinking and highly effective advocate." **Recent work:** Acted for a vendor in a dispute regarding a price under contract to sell a plot of development land.

Jonathan Gaunt QC (see p.606) Recognised for his skill in handling leasehold enfranchisement disputes, as well as a wide range of other landlord and tenant matters. His knowledge and guidance are much sought after by a wide spectrum of clients. **Strengths:** "He makes complex cases look effortlessly simple, and he really jumps off the fence." "He is extremely impressive on his feet, being both authoritative and calm." **Recent work:** Acted in a major Supreme Court case concerning the definition of a 'house' under the Leasehold Reform Act 1967.

Jonathan Karas QC (see p.642) Represents clients in all aspects of land law and real property, including disputes surrounding waterways and common land. Many of his clients are major property developers. **Strengths:** "A technically skilled and highly approachable practitioner, who turns things around very quickly. He's a joy to work with." "An engaging character, who is very good at giving proactive advice." **Recent work:** Led in a substantial case concerning the statutory rights of utility companies to discharge into waterways and canals.

Guy Fetherstonhaugh QC (see p.600) A formidable real property practitioner, with his own niche expertise in rent review issues. His exceptional technical knowledge and forceful advocacy are highly valued by his clients. **Strengths:** "He writes very clearly and persuasively, and when he makes oral submissions they are direct and persuasive." "He is bright, innovative and charming, and inspires confidence in clients." **Recent work:** Acting for Marks & Spencer, he demonstrated that in a situation where a tenant successfully exercises a break clause, they are entitled to a repayment of rent paid in advance.

Kirk Reynolds QC (see p.706) Has a broad practice covering all aspects of property law. His advocacy, advice and client service are all highly rated. **Strengths:** "Very good with clients, he's always on top of the job, and is a very good advocate." "He thinks creatively and innovatively, and is willing to go into areas that have not been tested." **Recent work:** Handled an important case on behalf of Marks & Spencer regarding potential repayment of rent paid in advance after the successful operation of a break clause.

Jonathan Small QC (see p.722) Primarily handles development-led disputes regarding commercial property, but also has an active telecoms practice, and is skilled in handling professional negligence

Real Estate Litigation London — Leading Juniors	
Band 1	
Bignell Janet	*Falcon Chambers* *
Clark Wayne	*Falcon Chambers*
Johns Alan	*Maitland Chambers* *
Radevsky Anthony	*Falcon Chambers* *
Rosenthal Adam	*Falcon Chambers* *
Sefton Mark	*Falcon Chambers*
Shea Caroline	*Falcon Chambers*
Stacey Myriam	*Landmark Chambers*
Taggart Nicholas	*Landmark Chambers*
Tozer Stephanie	*Falcon Chambers* *
Band 2	
Bruce Andrew	*Serle Court* *
Buckpitt Michael	*Tanfield Chambers* *
Cole Edward	*Falcon Chambers* *
Cowen Gary	*Falcon Chambers*
Denehan Edward	*9 Stone Buildings (ORL)* ◊
Dray Martin	*Falcon Chambers* *
Duckworth Nathaniel	*Falcon Chambers*
Fieldsend James	*Tanfield Chambers* [A] *
Francis Andrew	*Serle Court* *
Greenhill Julian	*Wilberforce Chambers*
Harpum Charles	*Falcon Chambers* *
Harry Timothy	*Maitland Chambers* *
Healey Greville	*Falcon Chambers*
Heather Christopher	*Tanfield Chambers* *
Hornett Stuart	*Selborne Chambers* [A] *
Lamont Camilla	*Landmark Chambers*
Peters Edward	*Falcon Chambers* *
Pryor Michael	*Maitland Chambers* *
Scott Tiffany	*Wilberforce Chambers*
Tanney Anthony	*Falcon Chambers* *
Weekes Tom	*Landmark Chambers*
Windsor Emily	*Falcon Chambers*
Band 3	
Bleasdale Marie-Claire	*Radcliffe Chambers*
Calland Timothy	*Enterprise Chambers*
Fitzgerald Elizabeth	*Falcon Chambers*
Higgins Gabrielle	*Maitland Chambers*
Hutton Caroline	*Enterprise Chambers*
Jefferies Thomas	*Landmark Chambers*
Kalfon Olivier	*Enterprise Chambers*
Kitson Justin	*Selborne Chambers* *
Letman Paul	*3 Hare Court (ORL)* ◊
Margolin Daniel	*Maitland Chambers* *
Muir Nicola	*Tanfield Chambers* [A] *
Polli Timothy	*Tanfield Chambers* [A] *
Radley-Gardner Oliver	*Falcon Chambers*
Rolfe Patrick	*5 Stone Buildings (ORL)* ◊ *
Steinert Jonathan	*Henderson Chambers (ORL)* ◊ [A] *
Taskis Catherine	*Falcon Chambers* *
West Mark	*Radcliffe Chambers* *
Band 4	
Bickford-Smith Stephen	*Landmark Chambers*
Blaker Gary	*Selborne Chambers* [A] *
Braithwaite Thomas	*Serle Court* *
Bredemear Zachary	*1 Chancery Lane (ORL)* ◊ [A] *
Butler Andrew	*Tanfield Chambers* [A] *
Chorfi Camilla	*Selborne Chambers* *
Clarke Ian	*Selborne Chambers* *
Clegg Richard	*Selborne Chambers* [A] *
Crail Ross	*New Square Chambers* *
Demachkie Jamal	*3PB Barristers (ORL)* ◊
Denyer-Green Barry	*Falcon Chambers* *
Dovar Daniel	*Tanfield Chambers* *
Gatty Daniel	*Hardwicke* [A] *
Gibbons Ellodie	*Tanfield Chambers* [A] *
Gunaratna Kavan	*Enterprise Chambers*
Harrison Philomena	*Maitland Chambers* *
Isaac Nicholas	*Tanfield Chambers* [A] *
Ollech Joseph	*Falcon Chambers*
Robinson Daniel	*Falcon Chambers*
Selway Kate	*Radcliffe Chambers* *
Sheehan Malcolm	*Henderson Chambers (ORL)* ◊ [A] *
Shuman Karen	*1 Chancery Lane (ORL)* ◊ [A] *
Smith Adam	*Maitland Chambers*
Trompeter Nicholas	*Selborne Chambers* [A] *
Ward Galina	*Landmark Chambers*
Watkin Toby	*Landmark Chambers*
Williams Simon	*Radcliffe Chambers* *
Band 5	
Barker James	*Enterprise Chambers*
Barton Zoe	*Selborne Chambers* *
Bastin Alexander	*Hardwicke* [A] *
Caun Lawrence	*Lamb Chambers (ORL)* ◊
Cox Tamsin	*Falcon Chambers*
Davey Jonathan	*Wilberforce Chambers*
Davies Andrew	*Henderson Chambers (ORL)* ◊ [A] *
Fain Carl	*Tanfield Chambers* [A] *
Falkowski Damian	*Thirty Nine Essex Street (ORL)* ◊ [A]
Francis Edward	*Enterprise Chambers*
Hicks Edward	*Radcliffe Chambers* *
Ilyas Shaiba	*Enterprise Chambers*
Keller Ciaran	*Maitland Chambers* *
Kokelaar Sebastian	*13 Old Square Chambers (ORL)* ◊
Kremen Philip	*Selborne Chambers* *
Lidington Gary	*11 Stone Buildings (ORL)* ◊ *
Loveday Mark	*Tanfield Chambers* *
Mendoza Neil	*Selborne Chambers* *
Moffett William	*Radcliffe Chambers*
Palfrey Monty	*Hardwicke*
Rowntree Edward	*Hardwicke* [A] *
Sissons Philip	*Falcon Chambers*
Walder Aaron	*Landmark Chambers*
Yates Katrina	*Landmark Chambers*
Up-and-coming individuals	
Helmore Katie	*Landmark Chambers*

◊ (ORL) = Other Ranked Lawyer.

[A] direct access (see p.11).

* Indicates individual with profile.

issues. His courtroom advocacy and incisive mind make him a popular choice. **Strengths:** "He is bright, brave, willing to think outside the box, and someone who understands the client's commercial as well as legal needs." "Jonathan's cut and thrust in the courtroom is a joy to behold." **Recent work:** Acted successfully for the Port of London Authority in a complex suit dealing with a number of issues. The case most notably established the impossibility of claiming adverse possession of the River Thames.

JUNIORS

Joseph Ollech Handles disputes regarding commercial, residential and agricultural property. He also has a specialist niche in riverine property disputes, and professional negligence-related issues. **Strengths:** "He is able and affable, and knows his stuff. He doesn't give any quarter in court." **Recent work:** Represented the Port of London Authority in a dispute regarding mooring rights and adverse possession.

Mark Sefton An experienced and talented practitioner, who practises in all areas of residential and commercial property law. He also acts for clients in leasehold enfranchisement, insolvency and professional negligence disputes. **Strengths:** "His advice is always down to earth, sensible, reasonable and practical." "He is very good, and very easy to get on with." **Recent work:** Acted for Humber Oil Trustees on a number of significant interim rent applications.

Anthony Radevsky (see p.702) Recognised at the Bar and beyond as being the leading authority on leasehold enfranchisement. He co-authors a text on the subject. **Strengths:** "He is a walking encyclopaedia of leasehold enfranchisement law." "His advice is always rock-solid, and if he thinks you will win, you probably will." **Recent work:** Acted for the lessee in an important dispute on whether houses in commercial use fall within the Leasehold Reform Act 1967.

Stephanie Tozer (see p.739) Has a broad property practice, and represents a range of clients on a spread of issues. She has particular niche expertise in mortgage-related work. **Strengths:** "Excellent technically, as well as being very commercial and responsive." "She is very bright and pleasant to deal with." **Recent work:** Acted in the Hackney v Parshall appeal.

Caroline Shea Mainly acts in agricultural, commercial landlord and tenant and real property disputes. She is recognised as being an effective and committed advocate. **Strengths:** "She is a realistic advocate, who is efficient in the way she puts her points. She's well prepared and knows her stuff." "Highly intelligent, she is easy to deal with, very forthright and very clear in her advice." **Recent work:** Represented a defendant through to a successful mediation in a terminal dilapidations claim arising from an assigned interest in a commercial property.

Janet Bignell (see p.550) Represents and advises clients in real property and landlord and tenant disputes. She frequently undertakes disputes for major developer clients. **Strengths:** "She is a walking textbook." "She is very meticulous, and a very impressive advocate on her feet; everything that she says she has clearly thought about." **Recent work:** Represented Landprop in a major damages claim relating to a proposed mixed-use development in the Olympic Park.

Wayne Clark Advises and litigates in all areas of real property law, but is particularly adept at handling commercial property disputes. His advice on business tenancies is particularly sought after. **Strengths:** "His advice is clear and comprehensive, and he is very good with clients." "A very clever man and a very good fighter in court."

Edward Cole (see p.575) Acts in all areas of property law, including residential, commercial and agricultural property disputes. He is well experienced at handling rent reviews, easements and restrictive covenants. **Strengths:** "His written advice is succinct and punchy, and he gets straight to the point." "He speaks with absolute authority; he's a fabulous, silver-tongued advocate." **Recent work:** Acted in a dispute over a commercial lease in which the guarantor was deemed to be released from liability.

Gary Cowen Continues to represent clients in major disputes arising from valuations, leasehold enfranchisement, mortgages and rights of way. He also has particular skill in adverse possession disputes. **Strengths:** "He provides practical, clear advice, and is also very personable." **Recent work:** Acted in a high-value lease renewal dispute concerning an address in Berkeley Square.

Charles Harpum (see p.620) A recognised authority when it comes to cases dealing with land registration and conveyancing. He's a go-to practitioner for clients with detail-heavy issues to resolve. **Strengths:** "If you want a barrister with an exceptional technical mind, he is the man you want." "He is the leading authority on all aspects of land registration and obscure or archaic aspects of the law." **Recent work:** He acted for the landowner in a dispute concerning the ownership of the bed of the Swale Estuary.

Greville Healey A rising star at the Property Bar, who acts in disputes relating to any aspect of land law. He is active in disputes surrounding highway and waterway law, telecoms issues, and all aspects of landlord and tenant law. **Strengths:** "He is outstanding on obscure and technical areas of the law, and is always willing to go the extra mile to get the best outcome." "He is approachable, has a nice style of communication, and is easy to work with." **Recent work:** Acted in a major landlord and tenant dispute surrounding fixtures in a commercial property.

Edward Peters (see p.691) Recognised for his skill and expertise in handling all manner of property disputes, including agricultural, commercial and residential landlord and tenant law cases. **Strengths:** "He gives clear advice, and is a good performer in courts and tribunals." "He is very easy to deal with, and extremely bright." **Recent work:** Handled an appeal from an arbitration concerning rent payable on an agricultural holding.

Martin Dray (see p.590) Best recognised for his comprehensive knowledge of the law of adverse possession. He represents clients in cases concerning all aspects of property law. **Strengths:** "He quickly appreciates the key issues from a client's perspective, and provides thorough and practical advice." "He is incredibly persuasive." **Recent work:** Appeared in a case concerning No.1 Deansgate, a prestigious block in Manchester which is home to several celebrities. The issue at hand was whether the building is 'structurally detached' within the meaning of S72 of the Commonhold and Leasehold Reform Act 2002.

Nathaniel Duckworth A leading junior, acting in disputes in all areas of property law, including public sector and agricultural cases. He has growing experience of representing clients in other Commonwealth jurisdictions. **Strengths:** "He is seriously clever, articulate, and impressively well organised." "He is very focused on the issues, very approachable and someone who gives sound advice." **Recent work:** Acted for the landlord in an appeal concerning whether costs incurred in proceedings were recoverable under a lease.

Elizabeth Fitzgerald A well-rounded and skilful practitioner, who handles disputes in all areas of property law. She has an active practice dealing with compulsory purchases, insolvencies and professional negligence issues. **Strengths:** "She is very thorough and very user-friendly." "Very knowledgeable and good to deal with in conference."

Oliver Radley-Gardner A rising figure of the Property Bar, who represents clients in all areas of real property law, including issues concerning professional negligence and insolvency. **Strengths:** "He is a very able junior, who is both incredibly intelligent and one of the friendliest barristers you could meet." **Recent work:** He has been active in a number of claims concerning trusts of land and dilapidations.

Adam Rosenthal (see p.710) Acts in a broad spectrum of real property disputes, including landlord and tenant cases. He is widely recognised for his expertise in mortgage-related work. **Strengths:** "He really is a very good advocate; he can take a difficult case and fight it well." "He is very good indeed on his feet; he is completely unflappable, and impressive on the academic side." **Recent work:** Acted in a damages claim relating to an alleged breach of option agreements to develop airspace above Texaco petrol stations.

Barry Denyer-Green (see p.587) Has carved a space for himself in the representation of local government and authorities in real property disputes. He is a widely recognised expert on compulsory purchase and compensation. **Strengths:** "He is very good on commons and rights of way matters." **Recent work:** Successfully represented a local authority in a dispute regarding compensation payable following the development of land it had purchased.

Tamsin Cox A well-regarded and knowledgeable junior, who is praised for her advocacy skills. She focuses on residential and commercial landlord and tenant disputes. **Strengths:** "She has an understated but tenacious style." "A very pleasant, amenable and able junior, who knows the law through and through." **Recent work:** Acted successfully before the Land Registry Adjudicator in a family mortgage fraud case.

Daniel Robinson An effective and intelligent counsel, who is recognised for punching above his weight. He is active in all areas of commercial, residential and agricultural landlord and tenant law. **Strengths:** "He is very good, clever, well organised, and effective as an advocate." "He is energetic and good in court, and wise beyond his years."

Anthony Tanney (see p.734) A knowledgeable and proficient adviser and advocate. He advises on all areas of real property law, and has particular expertise in rights of way, restrictive covenants and mortgage redemption. **Strengths:** "He is very sharp on the law, and provides good, erudite opinions." "A very technically sound practitioner, he has excellent court skills and an engaging personality which puts even difficult clients at ease." **Recent work:** Acted successfully for the trustees of a property who were seeking to have Family Law Act rights registered against the property removed from the register.

Catherine Taskis (see p.734) Acts in all areas of commercial and residential landlord and tenant law, and has a well-recognised specialism in agricultural cases. **Strengths:** "She is very knowledgeable and gives extremely clear opinions." "She is bright and creative, and extremely easy to work with." **Recent work:** Acted successfully in a dispute concerning the validity of a notice to quit an agricultural holding served by only one of three joint landlords.

Philip Sissons Has substantial experience of all areas of property law, and is particularly adept at handling mortgage-related matters. He is also active in rent review disputes and insolvency matters. **Strengths:** "He is thoughtful, patient and a good lateral thinker." "He provides very fast but very thorough responses, and really gets to grips with the technical, practical and commercial issues." **Recent work:** Acted as a junior in a High Court claim relating to the boundaries of a private fishery over an area of foreshore.

Emily Windsor Active in all areas of property law, but particularly talented at handling agricultural and commercial property disputes. She is also experienced at undertaking corporate and personal insolvency-related work. **Strengths:** "She is a formidable advocate, who is client-friendly and commercially astute." "She is lovely to work with and very able." **Recent work:** Acted for the Guildford Diocese of the Church of England in successfully enforcing a consent order.

Band 2

Landmark Chambers

See profile on p.829

THE SET

Landmark Chambers is a leading presence in the real estate market, due to its deep pool of experienced and innovative practitioners at both silk and junior level. Its undoubted real estate expertise is augmented by its recognised abilities in environmental and planning law. All manner of property law cases are handled and the set leads the way in advising companies and institutions wishing to injunct or remove protestors from their premises. Members handle matters of great import and have handled cases right up to the Supreme Court, the recent case of Cusack v London Borough of Harrow being one example.

Client service: "Their clerks are incredible, and give great client service. In particular, their head clerk Jay Fullilove is fantastic."

SILKS

Katharine Holland QC Has appeared before a range of courts and tribunals at various levels, and is recognised as a formidable presence on her feet. Her practice covers a broad swathe of property-related litigation. **Strengths:** "Her ability to get to the heart of a dispute never ceases to impress." "She is amazingly helpful, particularly on urgent matters." **Recent work:** Represented the administrators of Portsmouth FC in a dispute concerning restrictions around the sale of their football stadium.

David Holland QC A hugely experienced and well-regarded property practitioner, whose work encompasses all kinds of property litigation. He is also skilful in handling professional negligence disputes. **Strengths:** "He inspires confidence, as he's decisive, robust and knows the detail." "He is concise, erudite and good value for money. " **Recent work:** Acted in the Court of Appeal in a dispute concerning ancient mooring rights on the River Thames.

David Elvin QC Specialises in environment, planning and public law, alongside his vibrant property-related practice. He is particularly good on cases with a human rights aspect. **Strengths:** "He gives sound commercial advice and is an excellent advocate." "He is very clear in conference and puts the client at ease." **Recent work:** Advised the Ministry of Sound on potential noise and nuisance issues arising from an adjacent residential development.

John Male QC A significant figure at the Property Bar, who regularly advises on rent review issues. He is well recognised as a formidable advocate, as well as an experienced hand in arbitration cases. **Strengths:** "He is very clear-thinking and very knowledgeable." "He is a delight in conference with clients; he's hands-on and practical, and has a good bedside manner."

Timothy Morshead QC Has a broad-based practice, encompassing all aspects of property law. He's also experienced in public law, planning, valuation and compulsory purchase cases, and has experience of advocacy at all levels. **Strengths:** "His ability to digest complex situations and quickly get to the heart of a case is very impressive." "He is just viciously intelligent and extremely reliable." **Recent work:** Acted in a case dealing with indemnities payable by innocent victims of forged land registrations.

JUNIORS

Katrina Yates Specialises in landlord and tenant issues, real property and land registration disputes. She frequently acts for the Chief Land Registrar, as well as a range of other clients. **Strengths:** "She's great on her feet and also commercial and responsive." **Recent work:** Defended a decision of the Land Registrar barring squatters committing the criminal offence of trespassing in a residential building from claiming adverse possession.

Myriam Stacey Her practice covers all areas of commercial and residential property law. She acts for a wide range of clients, from private individuals to property developers and local government bodies. **Strengths:** "She is meticulous in her advice and pragmatic in her conclusions." "You could go to her with any real estate issue, and she will be all over it in a flash." **Recent work:** Represented the claimant in a professional negligence claim against the conveyancing solicitor involved in the purchase of a number of off-plan homes in the Cotswolds.

Nicholas Taggart Specialises in commercial real estate dispute resolution. He is particularly recognised for his skill in handling major dilapidations claims and rent reviews. **Strengths:** "His combination of technical expertise, commercial astuteness and comprehension of the importance of the client relationship is unique." "He is very personable, and gives timely, clear and pragmatic advice on complex issues." **Recent work:** Acted for the landlord in a rights of way dispute surrounding a number of parking spaces, which may have ramifications for a major development.

Camilla Lamont Primarily acts in disputes relating to commercial property, appearing on behalf of developers, major retailers and landlords. She also has recognised skill in dealing with property disputes with an environmental angle. **Strengths:** "She is technically excellent, good on her feet, but is also down to earth and has a relaxed but authoritative manner with clients." "She cuts to the chase, and provides quality advice and sensible solutions." **Recent work:** Successfully obtained the rectification of a transfer of a landed estate in Wiltshire. The original transfer had mistakenly only included the land, and excluded the buildings.

Thomas Jefferies A lawyer building a reputation as an expert in the field of collective enfranchisement. He acts for a variety of private clients, as well as for public bodies. **Strengths:** "He provides sound, specialist advice, turns papers around very quickly and is very user-friendly." **Recent work:** Acted in a collective enfranchisement action concerning a block of flats near the Tower of London.

Stephen Bickford-Smith A leading authority on the law surrounding rights of light, and the co-author of a leading textbook on the subject. His practice is driven by dispute resolution, real property and construction. **Recent work:** Acted in a boundary dispute relating to a development site in Twickenham. The case dealt with issues relating to the interpretation of deeds and plans.

Aaron Walder Has developed a substantial and broad real property practice, and regularly acts for commercial and residential landlords and tenants. He has a particular aptitude for boundary and easement issues, as well as cases concerning restrictive covenants. **Strengths:** "He is very knowledgeable, very able, and fights tooth and nail for his clients." **Recent work:** Acted on behalf of the City of Westminster College to obtain an urgent possession order to remove protestors from vacant buildings.

Katie Helmore Has a broad commercial and residential property practice that sees her acting for both landlords and tenants. She is frequently instructed on enfranchisement and service charge disputes. **Strengths:** "She works very hard and uncovers every point." **Recent work:** Acted for Southampton City Council, dealing with a restrictive covenant on a broadcast centre.

Tom Weekes An experienced trial advocate at all levels. He has written a leading text on notices, and also has expertise in rights of light cases. **Strengths:** "His advice covers all the pertinent issues and is both concise and commercial." **Recent work:** Represented Hampstead Garden Suburb Trust in a dispute regarding a major basement development in a freehold property.

Galina Ward Has a particular specialism in dealing with issues for both landlords and telecommunications operators under the Electronic Communications Code. Her practice is wide-ranging, and she deals with issues for landlords and tenants relating to commercial and residential property. **Strengths:** "She is great to deal with. She gives positive advice, and sticks to it to good effect."

Toby Watkin Experienced at handling business lease renewals, and has also carved out a growing practice in telecoms disputes. He has recently advised on property issues surrounding major development projects. **Strengths:** "He is excellent on his feet and very good on complicated cases." **Recent work:** Acted for the tenant in a valuable commercial property in New Bond Street in a contested Landlord and Tenant Act 1954 lease renewal.

Maitland Chambers

See profile on p.831

THE SET

Maitland Chambers provides its clients with a deep and experienced team of advocates who have broad expertise in both minor and top-level, high-value real estate disputes. Barristers at the set are regularly involved in important cases, some of which make it to the Supreme Court. Recent matters handled include Favor Easy Management Ltd (Seychelles) v Favor Easy Management (BVI) and Wu, Lloyds Bank v Crowborough, and Parshall v Hackney. One client said of the set: "Whichever barrister is instructed, whether very junior or not, the level of service is always excellent, and the advice is thorough and accurate."

Client service: "The clerks are very professional and efficient, and always go out of their way to help. Senior clerk John Wiggs personifies this and is extremely good."

SILKS

Michael Driscoll QC (see p.591) An experienced and talented practitioner, who has a broad chancery practice heavy on property law. He has handled a number of high-profile cases concerning trusts, professional negligence, telecoms issues and rent reviews. **Strengths:** "An advocate of the highest quality, and a man with a huge intellect." "He has a lovely, understated style, and is very knowledgeable."

Edwin Johnson QC (see p.638) Has a strong real estate practice heavily freighted with property-related professional negligence cases. He is a highly experienced and successful courtroom advocate. **Strengths:** "The right man for a hard fight, he is a fantastic courtroom advocate." "He is extremely thorough, very good with clients, and a really good team player." **Recent work:** He successfully appeared in the Court of Appeal, handling a substantial collective enfranchisement claim. The matter raised important points regarding the construction of the relevant legislation in the case.

John McGhee QC (see p.668) Combines a pedigree in property law with extensive experience of broader chancery disputes. He is regarded as a perfect practitioner for any large, complicated dispute with a property angle to it. **Strengths:** "He has a formidable grasp of the most complex cases, and is an advocate par excellence." "He is very, very user-friendly, and very pragmatic in his advice." **Recent work:** Acted in a dispute where an adjoining property owner sought an injunction to prevent the redevelopment of Tottenham Court Road station as part of the Crossrail project.

Timothy Dutton QC (see p.592) An experienced specialist handling all aspects of property litigation. He has recently tackled major cases relating to rent reviews, enfranchisement, lease renewals and insolvency. **Strengths:** "He is excellent on paper, in conference and in court." "He is easy to work with and very good at explaining difficult legal points to the lay client." **Recent work:** Acted in an enfranchisement claim in the Court of Appeal regarding whether the enfranchisement price should include redevelopment costs.

Judith Jackson QC (see p.636) Acts for a variety of commercial and residential property clients, particularly in leasehold enfranchisement, rent review and dilapidation claims. She is also an experienced and respected mediator. **Strengths:** "She is extremely user-friendly, and very quick to turn things around." "She is very calm under pressure and great with clients." **Recent work:** Acted in an important action concerning damages awarded in a terminal dilapidations claim, which were only slightly higher than the defendant's original settlement offer.

Thomas Grant QC Well recognised as a courtroom advocate of significant skill and great presence. He is active in a broad swathe of property disputes. **Strengths:** "He is very impressive on his feet." "Very intelligent and articulate, he gives detailed advice." **Recent work:** Obtained a summary judgment in proceedings brought to recover a substantial sum allegedly payable under a contract to purchase a large country house in Yorkshire.

Christopher Pymont QC (see p.701) Brings his experience to bear in landlord and tenant, property and insolvency-related disputes, whilst also maintaining a broader chancery practice. **Strengths:** "His court craft is excellent; he is a master tactician." "He is a no-nonsense practitioner, who is very measured in his approach." **Recent work:** Acted in a claim for damages for alleged breach of development agreements conditional on planning permission.

Andrew Walker QC (see p.744) Specialises in development-led disputes, land disputes and professional negligence-related property issues. Clients seek him out for his broad chancery expertise and for his well thought-out advice. **Strengths:** "His paperwork and advice are highly detailed and display a high degree of commercial awareness." "He provides first-rate advice on extremely complex matters in a very user-friendly way."

Mark Wonnacott QC A property law specialist, who acts for clients across the full spectrum of disputes. He is highly regarded for his advocacy, his grasp of detail and his excellent legal mind. **Strengths:** "He provides concise, understandable and commercial advice when dealing with complex matters." "His sheer intellect and gravitas instil complete confidence in clients."

Amanda Tipples QC (see p.738) An experienced advocate, who acts in a variety of chancery and property cases. Her extensive courtroom experience and manner impress both peers and clients. **Strengths:** "She's especially good on incredibly complex cases as she's amazing at getting into the detail very quickly." **Recent work:** Acted for HMRC in an appeal brought by a charity regarding the stamp duty land tax payable on a property bought in combination with other buyers.

Anthony Trace QC Treasured by his clients for the quality of his advocacy, which has been honed over many years. His cross-examination skills in particular are highly praised. **Strengths:** "He appreciates the sensitivities of the matters he is handling for clients and is very good at building relationships with them." "He is incredibly hard-working and a fantastic team player." **Recent work:** Acted for Lloyds Bank in a case seeking to rectify a mistake in an earlier Tomlin order.

JUNIORS

Timothy Harry (see p.621) Maintains a broad real estate practice, and acts in a variety of conveyancing, leasehold enfranchisement and commercial lease disputes. He is also strong on the professional negligence side. **Strengths:** "He is phenomenally hard-working and doesn't leave any stone unturned." "He is a delight to work with, and homes in on the real issues of a case." **Recent work:** Acted in a dispute concerning whether a cricket club in Charlton King's, in Gloucestershire, had acquired title to its ground through adverse possession.

Philomena Harrison (see p.621) Acts in property, professional negligence and broader chancery disputes. Her property practice is strongly based in the representation of corporate clients and high net worth individuals. **Strengths:** "She is thorough and tenacious, gets on well with the clients and is easy to work with." **Recent work:** Acted in a case concerning the beneficial ownership of a valuable London apartment.

Alan Johns (see p.638) A well-established property litigator, who is rated for his rights of light work, and for his talented advocacy. He has a broad practice and represents a variety of clients. **Strengths:** "He has a straightforward, down-to-earth way of dealing with clients, and is very analytical and direct." "He is very client-friendly, bright and articulate." **Recent work:** Acted in a rights of light dispute in the High Court which dealt with the availability of declaratory relief.

Michael Pryor (see p.700) Active in a broad range of real estate disputes for both commercial and residential clients. He has further established a practice in professional negligence-led disputes, and cases with leasehold enfranchisement issues. **Strengths:** "Most barristers are bright, but he is really over and above the norm, particularly when handling cases that turn on numbers." "He is very good at producing written work, is immensely hard-working and is pleasant to be around." **Recent work:** Acted on an appeal regarding a premium on a leasehold extension.

Gabrielle Higgins Her practice covers all areas of property law, particularly landlord and tenant disputes. She also works extensively on property issues involving telecoms equipment. **Strengths:** "She is extremely professional with clients in conference and is good on her feet." "She gets to the point and provides a comprehensive view of a case." **Recent work:** Acted in Twinmar Holdings v Klarius UK, a major terminal dilapidations claim concerning a newbuild warehouse.

Daniel Margolin (see p.662) A highly articulate advocate, who acts in a wide range of residential and commercial property disputes. He has wide expertise, particularly in dealing with issues under the Electronic Communications Code. **Strengths:** "He is approachable and commercial in his advice." "A bright and level-headed advocate, he is very user-friendly." **Recent work:** Acted in Freemont Ltd v Beldor Management Ltd, a case concerning liability for disrepair.

Ciaran Keller (see p.643) An increasingly celebrated presence at the Property Bar, who is active in a wide spread of real estate litigation. **Strengths:** "He is diligent and impressive." **Recent work:** Acted for the claimant, a billionaire private client, in a major dispute relating to two hotel properties in London.

Adam Smith An effective junior who is active in both property and trusts disputes. He is particularly sought out for his innovative and technical advice, and for his excellent client service. **Strengths:** "He is very capable and is very detailed in his advice." **Recent work:** Acted in a party wall dispute arising from the refurbishment of a number of high-value properties in Chelsea.

Wilberforce Chambers
See profile on p.876

THE SET

Wilberforce Chambers is a chancery titan and a serious force in the real estate market. Within its ranks it has a number of key people in the market, not least Jonathan Seitler QC, one of the big beasts in the field. Its members regularly handle substantial, complex property-related litigation and are involved in the most important matters of the day. By way of illustration, Seitler himself was involved in Clutterbuck v Al Amoudi, the 'vamp in the veil' property fraud case which attracted significant press attention. The team here is thoroughly committed to this area of the law and has recently released a new publication dealing with current issues in development-led real estate disputes.

Client service: "The clerks are brilliant; they're proactive, and will let you know when you can expect something. Their head clerk, Mark Rushton, is really interested in client service."

SILKS

James Ayliffe QC A hugely experienced silk, who brings his substantial chancery experience to bear when handling property cases. He edits a major volume dealing with landlord and tenant issues. **Strengths:** "A lawyer with a first-class brain" who "gets on very well with the clients and is very communicative." **Recent work:** Acted in defence of Texaco in a major claim from a property developer relating to alleged breach of options to grant airspace leases.

Michael Barnes QC An experienced, effective and talented advocate, who has appeared in landlord and tenant disputes, and has handled a host of other real property issues in courts to the highest level. **Strengths:** "A strong advocate, who is very determined and single-minded." "He is utterly dedicated and extremely thorough."

John Furber QC Practises in all areas of property law, but is particularly adept at handling issues surrounding commercial leases and property development. **Strengths:** "He is accessible and responsive, and provides a clear steer on cases." "He is quietly spoken, thoroughly professional, and razor-sharp in his analysis." **Recent work:** Dealt with restrictive covenant issues and rights of pre-emption surrounding the BBC studios in Southampton.

Martin Hutchings QC (see p.634) An experienced real property practitioner, who has a particular talent for handling major dilapidations claims. Hutchings is a veteran when it comes to commercial landlord and tenant disputes. **Strengths:** "Straight-talking, no-nonsense and great with clients." "He is responsive, and fantastically clever." **Recent work:** Acted for Dorchester in a major breach of contract and confidence claim concerning a development near the Olympic Park.

Rupert Reed QC Particularly skilled at handling disputes arising from commercial agreements concerning property developments. **Strengths:** "He is really good; he thinks outside the box, and outside the remit of his instructions." "He is very user-friendly and gives sensible, practical advice." **Recent work:** Acted for the defendants in a dispute with a Saudi investor in the 'Pinnacle' skyscraper.

Jonathan Seitler QC A property professional negligence specialist, who acts as both an advocate and a mediator. He regularly represents blue-chip individuals. **Strengths:** "He is a highly commercial and highly effective advocate, with a refreshingly unstuffy style." "He is down to earth, client-friendly and flexible. He's happy to drop everything to handle something urgent." **Recent work:** Acted for the defendant in Clutterbuck v Al Amoudi, dealing with allegations of fraud relating to property ventures.

Joanne Wicks QC A highly regarded specialist in property and professional negligence disputes. **Strengths:** "A fierce advocate who is intelligent and entirely lacking in pretension." "She is adept at giving practical, as well as technical, advice." **Recent work:** Acted for the tenant in two opposed lease renewals arising from redevelopment schemes at Waterloo and Euston stations.

JUNIORS

Tiffany Scott Active both advising and representing clients in a wide range of property-related disputes. She handles matters ranging from landlord and tenant issues to rights of light and professional negligence cases. **Strengths:** "She is brilliant under pressure," "very, very approachable and good to work with." **Recent work:** Represented Peel Land & Property in an appeal against a decision allowing a tenant to remove millions of pounds of equipment from a steel recycling plant.

Julian Greenhill Focuses his efforts on dealing with landlord and tenant disputes, and also handles a range of development and commercial transaction-related disputes. **Strengths:** "He is a highly effective draftsman," who is "bright, measured and personable." **Recent work:** Represented the owner of a race horse stud in Warwickshire in a boundary dispute with a neighbouring caravan park.

Jonathan Davey Primarily handles complex and high-value real estate issues, particularly landlord and tenant disputes. He regularly represents The Crown. **Strengths:** "He is practical and commercial, and not shy of giving a view." **Recent work:** Acted on behalf of the Ministry of Defence (MoD) in a trial concerning whether the Crown exemption in landlord and tenant legislation is compatible with the ECHR.

Band 3

Enterprise Chambers

See profile on p.788

THE SET

Enterprise Chambers has a well-regarded team capable of handling property disputes of every nature. Its members are noted for their versatility but have particular expertise in landlord and tenant and insolvency-led matters. Of late they have handled a number of instructions relating to development projects and the enforceability of leases. The set has a strong client base of mid-tier City and regional solicitors firms, and is noted for the "commercial and streamlined" approach it takes to litigation.

Client service: "The clerks, led by Antony Armstrong, are very responsive and open."

SILKS

Zia Bhaloo QC A leading silk who is particularly good at handling landlord and tenant issues, as well as telecoms-related disputes. Her advocacy and client service are highly praised. **Strengths:** "Really, really excellent; she knows property law inside out and is fantastic at cross-examination." "She's approachable, charming, bright and efficient." **Recent work:** Acted in a major dilapidations dispute regarding a hotel in Bournemouth, as well as an action to strike out permission to demolish and redevelop the premises.

JUNIORS

Caroline Hutton Handles a broad diet of real estate disputes. She acts for public bodies and private and corporate clients, and is further noted for her work in agricultural cases. **Strengths:** "She has an extremely acute mind, and gets straight to the heart of the problem." "She is very down to earth and clearly very experienced." **Recent work:** Acted in a major dispute between the MoD and its agricultural tenants, dealing with important issues surrounding agricultural rent reviews.

Kavan Gunaratna Focuses his efforts on handling commercial property cases for landowners, developers, local authorities and church bodies. He is also active in handling insolvency-led property disputes. **Strengths:** "His intellectual ability is unquestionably high, and his pleadings are exceptionally well drafted." **Recent work:** Acted successfully for Network Rail in a dispute arising from the forfeiture of premises occupied by a tenant following a Class A drugs raid by the Metropolitan Police.

Olivier Kalfon An adept property litigator, who also maintains an active practice in insolvency-led disputes. He handles a range of landlord and tenant issues both in the UK and overseas. **Strengths:** "He was superb, both with his written work and during trial." "He is a very good advocate with a really effective cross-examination style."

Edward Francis An experienced property litigator, who primarily handles commercial and residential landlord and tenant disputes, and matters relating to easements, covenants and mortgages. **Strengths:** "He has an in-depth knowledge of property law, and is exceptionally good with clients." **Recent work:** Acted for the claimant in a trial dealing with claims for damages resulting from alleged misrepresentations made on the sale of land for development.

Shaiba Ilyas A highly experienced practitioner, who tackles all manner of real property disputes and handles numerous landlord and tenant cases. He acts for a broad spectrum of clients, from private individuals to major corporations. **Strengths:** "An effective advocate, who offers practical advice and is good with difficult clients." **Recent work:** Advised a landlord seeking to forfeit a long lease held by the defendant of a property adjoining a hotel on Kilburn High Road.

Timothy Calland Has developed an impressive practice in real property and landlord and tenant disputes. He is highly rated by both his clients and his peers for his skills as an advocate. **Strengths:** "He is clever and approachable, and has an excellent knowledge of property law."

James Barker Frequently advises on issues regarding the legal and beneficial ownership of land, and is an expert on mortgage issues, easements and covenants. **Strengths:** "He is very strong and highly capable." **Recent work:** Successfully obtained relief and declarations relating to a property registered in the name of an offshore company which refused to acknowledge the claimant's rights.

Selborne Chambers

See profile on p.859

THE SET

Selborne Chambers is recognised as a growing presence in the real estate market and has members who are known for their tenacious advocacy and the commitment they display. The individuals here cover a broad range of real estate and chancery issues, and have recently published a new book dealing with the issue of break clauses.

Client service: "What makes them stand out from other property sets is the quality of their clerking. Led by Greg Piner, the team will do what they say they will do, and they are always very clear about commitments."

SILKS

Romie Tager QC (see p.733) A highly regarded commercial and property law specialist, who is a veteran of many a hard courtroom battle. He is instructed by a wide variety of clients who seek to draw on his deep experience. **Strengths:** "He is very feisty, and gets stuck into the last detail of everything." "He cross-examines excellently, and is exceptionally good at thinking on his feet." **Recent work:** Acted in the Supreme Court in a case dealing with the equitable doctrine of marshalling.

Mark Warwick QC (see p.747) Works in all areas of real estate litigation, and also tackles many professional negligence disputes. He is viewed in the market as a practitioner with the skill and dedication to handle a dispute on any scale. **Strengths:** "He is astonishing in terms of his speed of response, attention to detail and range of knowledge and experience." "He is pleasant, sharp, and works like a Trojan. " **Recent work:** Advised the government of Brunei in a dispute concerning lease options and damages for breach of covenant concerning a property in Mayfair.

JUNIORS

Stuart Hornett (see p.631) An experienced practitioner, who primarily handles landlord and tenant and property-related professional negligence cases. He is well regarded as both a courtroom advocate and adviser. **Strengths:** "A great advocate who gives no-nonsense advice." **Recent work:** Counsel to De Montfort University in relation to a road scheme and access ways for a major development site.

Justin Kitson (see p.647) Regularly appears in both commercial and residential property disputes, and also has an active property-related professional negligence practice. His work ethic and client service are particularly highly praised. **Strengths:** "He works very, very hard and is very accessible. He's an extremely bright junior." **Recent work:** Acted for the claimant in a dispute over the ownership of a moat surrounding an Elizabethan hall in Essex.

Gary Blaker (see p.551) Has a broad real property practice, and extensive experience of representing clients in property-related professional negligence disputes. He is highly rated by his clients for his approachability. **Strengths:** "A very good junior, able to provide accurate, relevant and commercial advice." "He is very user-friendly, and always willing to talk through issues." **Recent work:** Acted in a complex dilapidations dispute on behalf of the landlord of a property used by the UK Border Office to house asylum seekers.

Camilla Chorfi (see p.571) A strong property law generalist who has recognised expertise in professional negligence issues, particularly those relating to mortgages. **Strengths:** "She is extremely conscientious and very strong tactically." "She is helpful, grasps issues very quickly and gives solid advice." **Recent work:** Acted on behalf of a tenant in a dispute regarding a compulsory purchase order, which was successfully settled before trial.

Ian Clarke (see p.572) A recognised leader for real estate matters including property-related professional negligence disputes. He is particularly expert in cases involving mortgages or the registration of land. **Strengths:** "An ideal person to work with in a technically difficult case." "He has first-class drafting skills, and tells it how it is." **Recent work:** Acted successfully for a private client in dispute with their mortgage provider, RBS.

Richard Clegg (see p.573) Has vast experience of real property law, and has acted in landlord and tenant disputes for both commercial and residential clients for many years. He is highly rated in the market for the skill and determination he shows in bringing a case to conclusion. **Strengths:** "He is very bright and absolutely dogged, but at the same time personable and user-friendly." **Recent work:** Handled a case for a private client regarding the recovery of a high-value property in Islington which was fraudulently sold while the owner was wrongly imprisoned in Dubai.

Nicholas Trompeter (see p.740) Acts in both commercial and residential landlord and tenant disputes, and regularly appears on behalf of banks and institutional lenders in property-related professional negligence disputes. **Strengths:** "He is insightful, responsive, and great to work with." "He is a strong up-and-coming junior, who will always go the extra mile for clients and solicitors." **Recent work:** Acted for Standard Life in a dilapidations claim brought against the Co-operative Group relating to premises on an industrial site.

Philip Kremen (see p.648) An experienced practitioner who routinely represents clients in landlord and tenant, conveyancing, restrictive covenant and related professional negligence claims. **Strengths:** "His attention to detail and cross-examination skills are second to none." **Recent work:** Acted in a case dealing with an attempt to set aside the sale of a property portfolio. He appeared for one of the purchasers.

Neil Mendoza (see p.671) An experienced advocate, who is particularly skilled at dealing with commercial landlord and tenant issues, but who provides highly expert advice on a broad range of real property disputes. **Strengths:** "He is robust, thoughtful, hard-working and very easy to deal with." **Recent work:** Acted for the claimant in a long-running dispute over his entitlement to a new long lease in a central London block of flats.

Zoe Barton (see p.544) Has a broad property and chancery practice, and primarily handles disputes relating to trusts, estates and related professional negligence issues. She undertakes a variety of landlord and tenant cases, and is also regularly instructed by major landowners. **Strengths:** "She has a confident manner, is very direct with judges and is very persuasive."

Serle Court

See profile on p.860

THE SET

Serle Court is a respected chancery set with wide property expertise. It houses a number of capable and dedicated practitioners, whose breadth of knowledge is much appreciated by clients. A number of the members here handle disputes in niche areas of property law, such as the law regarding inland waterways.

Client service: "The clerking team, headed by Steve Whitaker, is really very good at identifying the right barrister who is suited for the job."

SILKS

Christopher Stoner QC A specialist in property litigation, who has developed a niche in the law surrounding canals and waterways. He acts extensively for both public bodies and private individuals. **Strengths:** "He displays meticulous attention to detail in his written opinions, and is a powerful and persuasive presence in court." "His work is clear, concise and considered." **Recent work:** Represented the Port of London Authority in a case concerning its ability to establish paper title.

JUNIORS

Andrew Bruce (see p.558) Regularly represents commercial and residential landlords and tenants. He has a varied practice handling land law cases and property-related negligence actions. **Strengths:** "A charming opponent, who is very clever, and very good at drilling down into the details." "He is very easy to deal with; he thinks about things hard and gives the right advice." **Recent work:** Represented the claimant landlord in a dilapidations claim relating to the White Cube gallery in Bermondsey.

Andrew Francis (see p.603) A major figure when it comes to rights of light, party wall, rights of way and restrictive covenant cases. He co-authors an important work dealing with the law surrounding rights of light. **Strengths:** "He is erudite, detailed and logical."

Thomas Braithwaite (see p.555) Has a broad property and chancery practice, and acts for clients ranging from private individuals to public bodies. **Strengths:** "He is very good at analysis and research, and knows how to explain the results to the client." "He has a very nimble mind and is a very approachable character, who is extremely good with clients." **Recent work:** Acted for a solicitor defending a professional negligence claim relating to the premature service of forfeiture notice.

Tanfield Chambers

See profile on p.870

THE SET

Tanfield Chambers is a set with a strong junior offering that provides broad chancery expertise with a strong property law bent. Particularly strong on residential property disputes, it has cultivated a reputation as a go-to group for handling right to manage, leasehold enfranchisement and service charge disputes. It also has an active insolvency-led property practice.

Client service: "It has a fabulous clerking team under Kevin Moore and Joanne Meah, that is always willing to find ways of working within clients' budgets."

SILKS

Philip Rainey QC (see p.702) A seasoned practitioner and a well-recognised expert in leasehold enfranchisement and service charge cases. He works in all areas of real property law, acting for a wide spectrum of clients. **Strengths:** "His expertise and knowledge of long leasehold and enfranchisement work are hard to beat." "A very good advocate with a commercial, client-friendly approach." **Recent work:** Successfully represented the respondent in an appeal concerning whether a purpose-built mansion block of flats could be considered a 'house' under the Leasehold Reform Act 1967.

JUNIORS

Michael Buckpitt (see p.560) A seasoned senior junior, who is a real specialist in handling property disputes, particularly those relating to residential property issues. He is also particularly highly regarded for his expertise in leasehold enfranchisement. **Strengths:** "He is an excellent all-round property litigator." **Recent work:** Acted for the respondents in an appeal concerning a notice to complete relating to a mixed-use property.

James Fieldsend (see p.600) Strong on commercial and residential landlord and tenant work, he is an experienced and capable advocate at all levels. **Strengths:** "He is particularly experienced with regard to service charge disputes." "He's practical, sensible, and a good trial advocate." **Recent work:** Acted in a major service charge dispute concerning a residential development in Paddington Basin.

Ellodie Gibbons (see p.607) Specialises in residential leasehold and freehold law, enfranchisement disputes, service charge cases and variations of leases. She also acts in commercial landlord and tenant disputes. **Strengths:** "Hard-working, focused and likeable." **Recent work:** Successfully acted for the respondent in a collective enfranchisement claim revolving around the value of the freeholder's interest.

Andrew Butler (see p.562) A property practitioner who specialises in dealing with professional negligence and insurance-led disputes. He is a trained mediator, and is rated by his clients and peers as a practical and efficient practitioner. **Strengths:** "A personable man, who has a keen intellect and a very commercial attitude." "A tough, able and sensible practitioner." **Recent work:** Acted in a partnership dispute dealing with differences arising from the dissolution of the partnership. The case involved property-related issues.

Daniel Dovar (see p.590) Has a well-developed residential property practice, acting for both owners and occupiers, and has also developed a respectable commercial property practice. His clients particularly praise his high level of engagement with them. **Strengths:** "He is an incredible advocate." "He offers a comprehensive and friendly service." **Recent work:** Acted in a disputed rent renewal case regarding a Grade 1 listed church in Shoreditch which is currently in use as a reclamation yard.

Carl Fain (see p.598) Brings his commercial experience and excellent client service to bear when handling commercial and residential property disputes. He is an experienced and effective courtroom advocate. **Strengths:** "He is very responsive and easy to work with." "An enthusiastic advocate who gets good results." **Recent work:** Acted in a dispute regarding whether mixed-use premises can be defined as a house for the purposes of the Leasehold Reform Act 1967.

Christopher Heather (see p.623) Advises and represents clients primarily in landlord and tenant and leasehold reform disputes. He is instructed by a number of major estate clients, and also represents tenants. **Strengths:** "A very professional advocate, who has a good style of delivery in court, and is above all easy to deal with." "He is responsive and excellent with clients." **Recent work:** Acted in Hauser v Howard De Walden Estates Limited, an appeal to the Upper Tribunal.

Nicola Muir (see p.678) Handles both residential and commercial property disputes, and is highly experienced in tackling landlord and tenant issues. She is particularly experienced at representing clients in the Property Chamber. **Strengths:** "A very down-to-earth and practical barrister." "Her knowledge of leasehold enfranchisement and general leasehold matters is very strong." **Recent work:** Acted for a receiver appointed under the Proceeds of Crime Act in a dispute over a life tenancy granted over a property.

Timothy Polli (see p.695) Focuses on landlord and tenant property disputes, and related professional negligence cases. He is particularly expert at handling matters relating to easements, boundaries and restrictive covenants. He is also adept at service charges cases and management disputes. **Strengths:** "A calm and effective advocate."

Nicholas Isaac (see p.635) His practice covers all areas of property law, but he particularly specialises in boundary issues, easements and party wall issues. **Strengths:** "He has a very smooth style of advocacy." "He is extremely knowledgeable and very incisive in his analysis." **Recent work:** Successfully challenged a consent order in the Court of Appeal on the grounds of judicial misconduct.

Mark Loveday (see p.658) Acts for both residential and commercial clients in landlord and tenant disputes. He has handled a number of rent reviews, leasehold enfranchisements and service charge disputes. **Strengths:** "He displays an impressive depth of knowledge of landlord and tenant issues, as well as leasehold enfranchisement." "He's very thorough and very good with clients." **Recent work:** Handled high-value leasehold acquisitions relating to a group of valuable properties in St John's Wood.

Band 4

Hardwicke
See profile on p.816
THE SET
Hardwicke is a set which is highly praised by clients for the "refreshing level of attention and customer care" both its barristers and clerks provide. Its 20-strong team has members who are active in all areas of real property law, and are known for the "practical, reasonable and sensible" advice they give. One solicitor said of them: "They have a very commercial approach both in terms of their advice and the fees they charge. Clients can actually understand their opinions, which saves me the need of having to translate things into layman's terms."
Client service: "The clerks are very good at client care, and get the job done very effectively." "The clerks and practice managers make a real effort to build relationships with instructing solicitors." "Practice manager Annabelle Lock is particularly impressive."

SILKS
John de Waal QC (see p.586) Works primarily on property disputes and property-related professional negligence issues. He mainly represents large commercial landlords, professional indemnity insurers and developers. **Strengths:** "An exceptionally responsive barrister, who knows how to give the lay client confidence and understanding." "He's very thoughtful about the client's position, and very supportive and encouraging." **Recent work:** Appeared in Walton Homes Ltd v Staffordshire County Council, an application to set aside a payment determined by experts under an overage agreement on the basis that the expert involved had made a manifest error.

Brie Stevens-Hoare QC A recognised authority on commercial and development-led property disputes, who also maintains an active professional negligence practice. In addition, she is an experienced mediator. **Strengths:** "She understands property law, and sensibly puts the client's best interests to the fore." "Straightforward and clear in her delivery, she is liked by judges." **Recent work:** Acted in a major professional negligence action relating to a substantial Kensington estate.

JUNIORS
Daniel Gatty (see p.606) Has a broad landlord and tenant and real property law practice, with a specialisation in mortgage and land registration issues. He also acts regularly as a mediator. **Strengths:** "His advice is well set out and competent." "He is pleasant, efficient and willing to help wherever possible." **Recent work:** Successfully acted in a dispute concerning the interpretation of a lease covering a bridge over a railway line.

Alexander Bastin (see p.544) Majors in property litigation and acts for a wide variety of clients across a range of issues. He is particularly valued for his clear, strategic advice. **Strengths:** "In a case where you can't see the wood for the trees, he will provide clarity." **Recent work:** Acted successfully for a management company in a service charge dispute. The court ruled that a landlord's legal costs could be recovered as both a service charge and an administration charge.

Monty Palfrey Admired by clients and peers for his clear, persuasive advocacy and proactive approach to dispute management. He is an experienced courtroom advocate, and has acted extensively in landlord and tenant cases and boundary disputes. **Strengths:** "Clients love his no-nonsense approach and practical advice." "He's a charming opponent, who is very sharp." **Recent work:** Acted in Northumberland & Durham v Ouahib, acting for a landlord in a claim for possession of a very valuable property following the death of a Rent Act protected tenant.

Edward Rowntree (see p.711) Handles property disputes as part of his wider chancery practice. He tackles all aspects of real property law, including easements, boundaries and trusts of land, and has contributed to a textbook on the law of mortgages. **Strengths:** "A compelling advocate, who is detailed and commercial in his approach." "He's accessible and turns work around quickly." **Recent work:** Acted for an executor in successfully defeating a claim of beneficial entitlement to a Docklands apartment brought by the wife of the deceased.

New Square Chambers
See profile on p.837
THE SET
An active presence in the real property market, New Square Chambers is a set with a number of highly proficient and experienced practitioners. Its barristers act for a wide range of corporate and individual clients and can handle all manner of property cases. Landlord and tenant, easement and boundary, and leasehold enfranchisement matters are all tackled by a team that is known for its technical excellence. This is also the best set to go to if you have a matter concerning public rights of way or common land.
Client service: "The clerking team is helpful and efficient."

SILKS
George Laurence QC (see p.652) A recognised expert in disputes surrounding rights of way, access to land and village greens. He is a regular in the Supreme Court. **Strengths:** "For anyone with a village green, common or right of way dispute, he is the number-one man." **Recent work:** Represented Newhaven Town Council in an appeal concerning the registration of a beach as a village green.

JUNIORS
Ross Crail (see p.580) Has developed a practice focused on rights of way, highways and common land. She counts a number of local authorities amongst her clients. **Strengths:** "She's academically excellent and definitely someone you want on your side." **Recent work:** Resisted the confirmation of an order at a public inquiry upgrading a footpath across private land to bridleway status.

Radcliffe Chambers
See profile on p.856
THE SET
Property cases form a large part of Radcliffe Chambers' broad diet of chancery work. The set excels at handling work for private clients, but also acts for local and other public authorities, chartered surveyors, architects and structural engineers. It handles cases in all courts domestically and also regularly tackles work overseas.
Client service: "I have nothing but praise for the clerks, who are always helpful and pleasant." Both Keith Nagle and John Clark "have the human touch." "They can be completely trusted and are men of great integrity."

SILKS
Robert Pearce QC Handles a broad range of contentious and non-contentious real property issues. He is an accredited mediator, and represents a wide range of institutional and private clients. **Strengths:** "He has an incisive and forensic mind, and finds solutions where others only find problems." **Recent work:** Retained by an Oxford college to provide advice regarding complex chancel repair liabilities.

Keith Rowley QC An experienced and highly dedicated advocate, who takes a robust approach to the most complex property disputes. **Strengths:** "He is fearless and prepares meticulously." "He's an extremely knowledgeable and user-friendly counsel."

JUNIORS
Marie-Claire Bleasdale A very proficient courtroom advocate, who handles a broad range of property disputes, including both commercial and residential landlord and tenant cases. **Strengths:** "Able, efficient and someone who speaks honestly." "She gives exceptionally clear and user-friendly advice."

Mark West (see p.749) An experienced property practitioner, who is also active in related professional negligence claims. **Strengths:** "Extremely able and very thorough. He's a lawyer who treats everyone on the team with respect."

Kate Selway (see p.717) Handles a wide range of property disputes, and is also an expert on trust and probate issues. She has handled a number of high-profile cases relating to easements, and has regularly acted for public bodies. **Strengths:** "She is accessible, good at problem solving and excellent on the detail."

Simon Williams (see p.752) Sought out by solicitors as both a mediator and an advocate for a range of chancery and real property issues. He frequently appears in property-related professional negligence claims. **Strengths:** "He is a very impressive barrister, both in terms of his written advice and his performances when on his feet."

Edward Hicks (see p.626) An experienced courtroom advocate, with a broad range of experience and skills. He is capable of handling trusts of land, conveyancing, boundary and easement disputes, to name but a few. **Strengths:** "His meticulous attention to detail, thorough preparation and rigorous analysis mean that you get the right answer from the outset."

William Moffett Represents clients in property and professional negligence cases. He is particularly adept at handling commercial property disputes. **Strengths:** "Always pragmatic and very personable, he is a lawyer with a real eye for detail."

Other Ranked Lawyers

Zachary Bredemear (see p.556) (1 Chancery Lane) Has an active practice in property-related professional negligence claims, particularly those concerning development land. He also represents clients in commercial and residential landlord and tenant disputes. **Strengths:** "He has a deep understanding of property-related professional negligence." "Friendly and robust, he provides good practical advice." **Recent work:** Acted in a professional negligence claim on behalf of a developer who mistakenly bought a plot of land from an insolvent entity.

Karen Shuman (see p.720) (1 Chancery Lane) Impresses in property-related professional negligence, but also handles mainstream property law cases. She is particularly skilled at handling commercial landlord and tenant disputes, as well as matters relating to easements and conveyancing. **Strengths:** "She is very strong in mediation." "A very impressive and very approachable practitioner." **Recent work:** Acted successfully on behalf of the landlord in a dispute with the anchor tenant of a newly completed development.

Damian Falkowski (Thirty Nine Essex Street) Acts in, and advises on, a broad spectrum of property, planning and local authority law disputes. He is sought out particularly for his practical, no-nonsense approach. **Strengths:** "He is user-friendly, approachable, and always happy to roll up his sleeves and get stuck in." **Recent work:** Acted for the claimants in a fraud case concerning a defective newbuild property.

Paul Letman (3 Hare Court) A highly regarded senior junior, who represents clients in landlord and tenant disputes, and is particularly strong on enfranchisement cases. He also handles property-related professional negligence disputes. **Strengths:** "He is very bright, has a very nice style in court and doesn't take bad points." "He is very good at developing points in a way that is persuasive." **Recent work:** Acted successfully for the traders of Smithfield Meat Market in seeking the renewal of 51 business tenancies.

Jonathan Steinert (see p.727) (Henderson Chambers) A highly experienced property practitioner, who specialises in freehold and leasehold commercial property issues, development disputes and environmental law issues. He acts on both contentious and non-contentious matters. **Strengths:** "A resolute character who is a robust and strong advocate." "He is just very fun to work with."

Malcolm Sheehan (see p.719) (Henderson Chambers) Has extensive experience of representing social landlords, estates, developers and local authorities in commercial and residential property disputes. He is highly regarded in the market as a proficient, all-round practitioner. **Strengths:** "He combines thoroughness and intellectual rigour with superb advocacy skills." **Recent work:** Acted in a dispute concerning the operation and control of the UK's largest cemetery.

Andrew Davies (see p.583) (Henderson Chamber) Represents a range of clients in commercial, residential and real property disputes, and also handles property-related professional negligence actions. He has particular experience in cases relating to party wall, easement and beneficial interest issues. **Strengths:** "He is extremely thorough in his written opinions." "He is a real gentleman, who is very straightforward and easy to deal with." **Recent work:** Acted in a service charge claim on behalf of the residents of a large block of flats.

Lawrence Caun (Lamb Chambers) Handles a broad diet of property and commercial chancery work, and is capable of representing a broad spectrum of clients in a wide range of issues. He is recognised for his approachable manner with clients.

David Halpern QC (see p.617) (4 New Square) Has long experience of both litigation and mediation. He has a wide property and professional negligence practice, and specialises particularly in negligent valuation claims. **Strengths:** "A very bright guy, who gets all the angles of a case. He's diligent and conscientious." "He is very thorough, as well as good-humoured and approachable." **Recent work:** Acted for Rentokil in a professional negligence action relating to the drafting of a contract involved in the sale of a major property.

Sebastian Kokelaar (13 Old Square Chambers) A figure on the rise at the Property Bar, whose practice encompasses all areas of contentious and non-contentious property law. **Strengths:** "He has flair and enthusiasm, and displays real focus." "He will always make himself available; no job is too small for him." **Recent work:** Acted successfully for the landlord in a claim for possession of the car park of a pub in Cambridge.

Jamal Demachkie (3PB Barristers) Represents clients in landlord and tenant cases (commercial and residential), and boundary, easement and covenant disputes, amongst others. **Strengths:** "He is very technically able, and very quick to give practical and sensible advice." "Efficient and personable, he has a calming influence on parties." **Recent work:** Acted in Codling v Harlow, an appeal to the High Court concerning the interrelationship between Sections 28 and 29 of the Landlord and Tenant Act 1954.

Ranjit Bhose QC (Cornerstone Barristers) Specialises in real property and housing law, and is also active in local government cases. He is a dedicated and highly commercial barrister, who works doggedly to achieve the best results for his clients. **Strengths:** "He is very smooth in negotiation, and keeps his eye on the ball." **Recent work:** Defended easements granted by the Conservators of Wimbledon and Putney Common to provide rights of way to a development site within the common.

Peter Crampin QC (see p.580) (3 Stone Buildings) A senior silk with great experience of advocacy at all levels. He handles a variety of property, trust and charity disputes. **Strengths:** "A class act and a man to go to if you have difficult points to contend with."

Patrick Rolfe (see p.710) (5 Stone Buildings) A real property specialist, dealing primarily with landlord and tenant, mortgages, easements and restrictive covenants. He also acts in property-related professional negligence claims. **Strengths:** "A very bright and consistent performer." "He gives the client a great deal of confidence." **Recent work:** Acted for a developer in a service charge dispute relating to a mixed-use development in Docklands.

Edward Denehan (9 Stone Buildings) A specialist property practitioner and an experienced advocate who represents clients in landlord and tenant, easement, boundary and professional negligence disputes. **Strengths:** "He is a very robust advocate, who has a good way of speaking in layman's terms and is able to get his message across." "He is pretty impressive when he is on his feet." **Recent work:** Represented the tenants in a noise nuisance claim in the Court of Appeal.

Gary Lidington (see p.656) (11 Stone Buildings) An experienced and well-rounded property lawyer, who is renowned for his commercial approach. He is particularly sought after for his skill in handling property disputes with fraud or insolvency aspects. **Recent work:** Acted successfully for the mortgagee in a claim for possession of a high-value development property.

MIDLANDS

Real Estate Litigation Midlands
Leading Sets
Band 1
St Philips Chambers *
Band 2
No5 Chambers *
◊ (ORL) = Other Ranked Lawyer.
[A] direct access (see p.11).
* Indicates set / individual with profile.
Alphabetical order within each band. Band 1 is highest.

Real Estate Litigation Midlands
Leading Silks
Band 1
Randall John *St Philips Chambers* *
Leading Juniors
Band 1
Verduyn Anthony *St Philips Chambers* [A] *
Band 2
Mitchell David *No5 Chambers* [A]
Taylor David *No5 Chambers* [A]
Band 3
Caney Michelle *St Ives Chambers (ORL)* ◊ *
Eyre Stephen *St Philips Chambers* *
Kelly Emma *St Philips Chambers* *
Warner David *New Square Chambers (ORL)* ◊ *

Band 1

St Philips Chambers

See profile on p.886

THE SET

Unanimously regarded as the standout set in the region, with a large and experienced team of specialist barristers. Areas of focus include landlord and tenant disputes, rights of way and boundary disputes. Planning issues are becoming an increasingly prominent area of activity.

Client service: "The clerks are excellent. You can drop them an e-mail on Sunday and get a response on the same day. They will bend over backwards to accommodate and always make sensible recommendations."

SILKS

John Randall QC (see p.704) Maintains a tremendous reputation in the field and wins a wealth of exceptional feedback from market commentators. He predominantly works for high-profile developers. **Strengths:** "He has a mind-blowing brain capacity." "He has an uncanny ability to make the complex seem simple without distorting the complexities.

He has a clear and useful way of expressing himself." **Recent work:** He acted on an application to appeal the results of an arbitration that found Morris Homes to be in breach of Clause 3.1 following its suspension of the construction of a medical centre because of the financial crisis.

JUNIORS

Anthony Verduyn (see p.743) An esteemed practitioner who attracts enviable praise for his impressive technical know-how as well as his top-class communication skills. He covers a substantial amount of real property work, including boundaries, rights of way and restrictive covenants. **Strengths:** "He is a superb communicator who gets on top of the most complicated briefs very quickly." **Recent work:** He represented the claimant in a High Court case concerning the frontage of a nightclub on Broad Street in Birmingham. The case involved issues of adverse possession, breach of fiduciary duty, and duties of loyalty.

Stephen Eyre Manages a wide-ranging commercial litigation practice of which property constitutes a significant part. Work highlights include enforcements of restrictive covenants and development disputes. **Strengths:** "He has the ear of the court and attracts the judge's attention." "He is no-nonsense and doesn't get bogged down. He cuts straight to the key issues." **Recent work:** He acted on a multiparty dispute regarding the rights of various occupiers on an industrial estate.

Emma Kelly (see p.643) A property litigation specialist capable of covering easements, covenants, boundary disputes and adverse possession claims. She is noted for her drafting skills and her prompt responses. **Strengths:** "She is thorough and just seems to get under the skin of the case. She really explores all the options." "She is able to give very clear advice on technical issues and matters that needed urgent attention."

Band 2

No5 Chambers

See profile on p.883

THE SET

No5 Chambers' strong concentration of junior talent ensures clients receive a fine service in real property and landlord and tenant law. Typical areas of activity include contracts for the sale and purchase of land, conveyancing disputes, easements and restrictive covenants. The set's client base ranges from high-profile developers to local authorities.

Client service: "The clerks, led by Tony McDaid, are very efficient and helpful. They are always available and have excellent drafting skills."

JUNIORS

David Mitchell Has a particular focus on real property disputes. He receives regular instructions on planning issues and development disputes. **Strengths:** "He leaves no stone unturned." "He is a very good team player, as well as being practical and pragmatic." **Recent work:** He acted on an adverse possession claim regarding part of a cricket ground.

David Taylor Covers all issues related to real property and commercial landlord and tenant law. He also sits as a judge in the Property Chamber of the First-tier Tribunal. **Strengths:** "He has a very calming effect on his clients and never puts them at risk." "He is very good for factually complicated cases; he sees the wood through the trees." **Recent work:** He acted on an injunction application concerning access disputes.

Other Ranked Lawyers

David Warner (see p.746) (New Square Chambers) Offers notable expertise in commercial litigation with a particular focus on property law and landlord and tenant matters. He is also an accredited mediator. **Strengths:** "He is incredibly good with clients and very user-friendly." "He remains solid and composed in a courtroom setting."

Michelle Caney (St Ives Chambers) A specialist property practitioner with a significant emphasis on landlord and tenant law. She also has a strong commercial property practice. **Strengths:** "She is incredibly efficient and extremely organised." "She is exceptionally thorough and knows her stuff inside out." **Recent work:** She acted for a number of claimants on a complex claim for rescission and/or damages following a fraudulent sale and leaseback agreement, where the claimants sold their home on the understanding that they would have a lifetime tenancy of the property on a rent-free basis.

NORTH EASTERN

Real Estate Litigation North Eastern
Leading Sets
Band 1
Enterprise Chambers *
Leading Juniors
Band 1
Howd Stephen *Zenith Chambers (ORL)* ◊
Klein Jonathan *Enterprise Chambers*
Band 2
Fletcher Stephen *Dere Street Barristers (ORL)* ◊ *
Griffin Margaret *Enterprise Chambers*
Jarron Stephanie *Enterprise Chambers*
◊ (ORL) = Other Ranked Lawyer.
** Indicates set / individual with profile.*
Alphabetical order within each band. Band 1 is highest.

Band 1

Enterprise Chambers

See profile on p.788

THE SET

Enterprise Chambers retains its position as the North Eastern Circuit's leading set for property litigation. Its specialist members handle an array of property disputes with notable expertise in both commercial and residential landlord and tenant litigation. Its members receive instructions from a diverse client base including property developers, individual tenants and statutory bodies.

JUNIORS

Jonathan Klein An expert in landlord and tenant litigation, he is also particularly adept at handling matters relating to boundary disputes. **Strengths:** "He has an incredible mastery of detail and is a very effective advocate." **Recent work:** He represented multiple claimants in successfully combating two stay applications relating to a dispute for possession of commercial and residential property.

Margaret Griffin Regularly called upon by solicitors to advise clients in relation to landlord and tenant disputes. She also handles contentious issues regarding restrictive covenants, easements and adverse possessions. **Recent work:** She represented a client in a professional negligence claim brought against solicitors who provided negligent advice on a commercial property transaction.

Stephanie Jarron Well regarded for her skill in handling dilapidations claims, boundary disputes and lease renewals. She is praised for her commerciality and her ability to explain complex legal terms in a straightforward manner. **Strengths:** "She is well prepared, commercial and a punchy advocate." **Recent work:** She successfully represented a landlord in recovering outstanding rent from a company that had recently gone into liquidation.

Other Ranked Lawyers

Stephen Fletcher (see p.601) (Dere Street Barristers) Receives considerable praise from solicitors due to his excellence in commercial property disputes. He regularly handles contentious landlord and tenant issues, professional negligence claims and matters relating to adverse possession. **Strengths:** "He is always available and very approachable, and is a good fighter in court."

Stephen Howd (Zenith Chambers) Handles a range of real estate litigation matters, including contentious easements and rights of way matters, issues relating to trusts of land, and boundary disputes. **Strengths:** "He is a first-rate advocate." **Recent work:** He represented a developer in the Court of Appeal with regards to the termination of a contract for a sale of land.

NORTHERN

Real Estate Litigation Northern
Leading Sets
Band 1
Kings Chambers *
Leading Silks
Band 1
Anderson Lesley *Kings Chambers* *
Chaisty Paul *Kings Chambers* *
Leading Juniors
Band 1
Horne Wilson *Kings Chambers* *
Lander Richard *Kings Chambers* *
Band 2
Green David *Atlantic Chambers (ORL)* ◊ *
Hall Matthew *Kings Chambers* *
Band 3
Foster Ian *Exchange Chambers (ORL)* ◊
Halliwell Mark *Kings Chambers* *
Walker Bruce *Exchange Chambers (ORL)* ◊
Wheatley Geraint *Kings Chambers* *

Band 1

Kings Chambers
See profile on p.918
THE SET
Kings Chambers maintains its position as the preeminent set for property litigation on the Northern Circuit. It possesses notable strength in handling disputes regarding titles to land, landlord and tenant litigation, and issues relating to easements and restrictive covenants. It is also well regarded for its ancillary insolvency and mediation offering. Members act for a wide range of clients, including public bodies, development companies and charities.
Client service: "The clerking team are very good; they will go that extra mile for us when we need something urgently."

SILKS
Lesley Anderson QC Highly regarded for her commercial real estate litigation practice. She is frequently instructed in property-related negligence disputes and also advises on commercial landlord and tenant issues. **Strengths:** "She is very hands-on and the quality of her advice is excellent." **Recent work:** She recently represented Lloyds TSB in an alleged breach of contract claim and a claim of alleged selling at undervalue of commercial properties.

Paul Chaisty QC Lauded for his deep expertise in commercial property litigation. He receives instructions on property-related professional negligence issues, dilapidations claims, insolvency issues and sale of land contracts. **Strengths:** "He has every legal argument a lawyer could possibly require and the ability to translate those in conference with clients." **Recent work:** He represented a client in a high-value dilapidations claim with regards to a commercial property.

JUNIORS
Wilson Horne (see p.631) Handles a variety of property litigation work on behalf of estate agents, public bodies and developers. He concentrates primarily on commercial real estate disputes, including contentious landlord and tenant issues. **Strengths:** "He is very well prepared and very robust, and explains the risks clearly to the client." "He is recommended for his specialist knowledge of property law and business tenancy law." **Recent work:** He handled a contested lease renewal of a floating dock on Lake Windermere. The dispute concerned whether a rent review provision should be included in the business tenancy of the property.

Richard Lander (see p.650) Held in high regard for his representation of clients before the Property Tribunal and the Court of Appeal. He is frequently instructed on disputes arising between cohabitants, and on issues concerning covenants. He is also experienced in professional negligence and insolvency-related property matters. **Strengths:** "He is excellent; he is always prepared and is easily able to take part in discussions of complex points of law with judges." **Recent work:** He was instructed on a number of hearings before the Mercantile Court concerning a freezing order application and a summary judgment application for commercial real estate in Birmingham.

Matthew Hall (see p.617) Advises in cases relating to property acquisitions, landlord and tenant disputes, and issues regarding titles to land. **Strengths:** "He is very accessible, excellent at thinking on his feet and persuasive in his approach." "He is very well prepared and gets to the heart of the issue." **Recent work:** He successfully defeated a possession claim on a property meant for use as a nursery. He also won on the counterclaim regarding the rectification of the property's lease.

Geraint Wheatley (see p.750) Focuses his practice on easements, trusts of land and boundary disputes. He acts of behalf of banks, Law of Property Act receivers and landlords. **Recent work:** He represented HSBC in a complex possession dispute.

Mark Halliwell (see p.617) Commended for his expertise in handling property litigation cases with a trusts law crossover. He is also adept at advising on landlord and tenant disputes, dilapidations claims, easements and covenants, and break clauses. **Recent work:** He was instructed in a series of claims regarding the rights of way to an access road leading to a number of residential and commercial properties in Shropshire.

Other Ranked Lawyers

David Green (see p.615) (Atlantic Chambers) Enjoys a strong reputation for handling both commercial and residential real estate matters. He regularly advises on boundary disputes, easements and rights of way issues, matters relating to titles to land, and contentious landlord and tenant issues. **Strengths:** "He makes it easy for clients to understand difficult concepts about their case and provides practical and sensible advice."

Ian Foster (Exchange Chambers) Well known for his strength in handling litigation regarding property rights and ownership. He possesses extensive experience in representing clients before the Land Registry and County Court. **Strengths:** "He is very enthusiastic and a canny advocate who really knows his stuff."

Bruce Walker (Exchange Chambers) Assists in disputes relating to rights of way, boundaries and titles to land. He is also experienced in handling complex commercial landlord and tenant disputes, and is commended for his ability to provide clear and prompt advice.

SOUTH EASTERN

Real Estate Litigation South Eastern
Leading Juniors
Band 1
Sinnatt Simon *Crown Office Row (ORL)* ◊ *
Band 2
Redmayne Simon *East Anglian Chambers (ORL)* ◊
◊ (ORL) = Other Ranked Lawyer.
** Indicates set / individual with profile.*

Ranked Lawyers

Simon Sinnatt (see p.722) (Crown Office Row) Has a varied practice encompassing landlord and tenant disputes, propriety estoppels, funding and local government work. He has a niche specialism in cases involving the travelling community. **Strengths:** "He is technically very good on all aspects of property litigation. He has great drafting skills and a great client manner." "He is creative and incisive."

Simon Redmayne (East Anglian Chambers) Has a broad contentious practice of which property litigation forms a substantial part. He is particularly noted for his expertise in easements and rights of way disputes. **Strengths:** "He is persuasive and practical, with a sharp eye for detail." "He has great energy and enthusiasm, and really puts clients at ease."

WESTERN

Real Estate Litigation Western
Leading Sets
Band 1
St John's Chambers *
Band 2
Guildhall Chambers *
Leading Silks
Band 1
Blohm Leslie *St John's Chambers*
Leading Juniors
Band 1
Sharples John *St John's Chambers* [A]
Band 2
Auld Charles *St John's Chambers*
Jones Christopher *St John's Chambers*
Paton Ewan *Guildhall Chambers*
Sahonte Rajinder *Guildhall Chambers* *
Wales Matthew *Guildhall Chambers*
Walsh Timothy *Guildhall Chambers* *
[A] *direct access (see p.11).*
* *Indicates set / individual with profile.*
Alphabetical order within each band. Band 1 is highest.

Band 1

St John's Chambers

See profile on p.893

THE SET

St John's Chambers has a long-standing reputation and "the best range of experience" in real estate on the Western Circuit. Its members provide across-the-board services on the full range of commercial and private property issues. The set is particularly renowned for its conveyancing work.

SILKS

Leslie Blohm QC Heads the set's chancery and commercial department and has extensive experience in farming and development projects. He enjoys a stellar reputation on the Western Circuit for his property practice. **Strengths:** "He certainly brings a wealth of experience of how judges approach cases. His style of advocacy is very measured and solid; he's a man of substance." "He is excellent and extremely intelligent, and always gives clear advice in good time." **Recent work:** Acted for a landowner on claims of non-disclosure and misrepresentation against a house builder concerning the sale of a large plot of farming land.

JUNIORS

Christopher Jones A chancery specialist with considerable real estate expertise. He frequently advises on wills, trusts and landlord and tenant matters. **Strengths:** "He is a regular recommendation for clients looking for commercial and practical advice on property dispute matters." "He is very thorough in the examination of paperwork and comes up with realistic solutions." **Recent work:** Represented the respondent to an application before the Land Registry concerning a boundary dispute.

Charles Auld Handles a variety of agricultural and domestic property disputes on behalf of both private and commercial clients. He focuses his extensive chancery practice on land-related matters. **Strengths:** "He is very good with clients, particularly when it comes to putting them at ease and explaining his legal arguments in lay terms." "He gets the job done very quickly and efficiently." **Recent work:** Acted for a farm owner on a boundary dispute against a neighbour.

John Sharples Focuses his practice on property matters. He is a popular choice among instructing solicitors due to his considerable real estate expertise. **Strengths:** "He is particularly user-friendly and wise as can be." **Recent work:** Advised Mayo Property Developments on a dispute relating to a conditional contract for sale against the trustees of the Rest Bay Convalescent Home.

Band 2

Guildhall Chambers

See profile on p.890

THE SET

Guildhall Chambers is frequently instructed in commercial property disputes and real estate issues arising from insolvency. Instructing solicitors in the region note that "its pool of expertise rivals that of London sets, and it has the advantage of being geographically so much closer."

JUNIORS

Ewan Paton Specialises in property and enjoys a good reputation in the market. He handles the full spectrum of real estate and frequently advises on professional negligence issues. **Strengths:** "He has a fierce intellect and is pretty quick on his feet; he is the one you go to when you have a difficult problem and need a sharp answer." "He is very credible on paper, quite accessible and clear, and has a calm and studious approach." **Recent work:** Acted for the trustees of Bath Football Club on land and assets disputes and claims.

Matthew Wales Handles the gamut of real estate issues, including covenants, boundary disputes and professional negligence. He is an experienced junior with a solid presence on the Western Circuit. **Strengths:** "What he puts on paper is always very good, and in court he will pick up the point and put up a good case." "He is very good at dealing with people but also quite direct – he manages to be firm without being aggressive."

Rajinder Sahonte (see p.713) Covers commercial and residential real estate matters. He is particularly renowned for his expertise in issues relating to village greens and contentious probate. **Strengths:** "He is extremely knowledgeable, good with clients and firm with judges."

Timothy Walsh (see p.745) Specialises in property and probate disputes. He has extensive experience in trusts, wills and estates. **Strengths:** "He is very diligent, thorough, quick to pick up things and a safe pair of hands. He makes you feel very reassured."

RESTRUCTURING/INSOLVENCY: An Introduction

Contributed by South Square

The UK economy has now emerged from its slump, growing by 0.8% in the second quarter of 2014, equivalent to an annualised rate of around 3%. Unemployment is also down, although wage growth remains sluggish. While the USA is also experiencing similar levels of growth, the most recent GDP figures for the Eurozone are dire, suggesting the situation on the Continent could yet have an adverse effect on the UK economy. The impact of the withdrawal of easy money by the Federal Reserve and the Bank of England is not yet, however, mapped out with any certainty and a softening is anticipated in the housing market.

As might be expected from an economy in recovery, formal insolvencies are lower than the comparable period in 2013, with fewer liquidations, administrations and bankruptcies. The recovery has not, however, impacted on the restructuring market, which remains vibrant, in particular, from European companies seeking to take advantage of the tools available under English law and experience built in the City over many years.

The recovery has also yet to slow litigation in this area, with a number of important decisions having been handed down over the past year.

Demonstrating the longevity of large insolvency cases, litigation arising from the demise of Lehman Brothers in 2008 continues in the High Court. In Re Lehman Brothers International (Europe) (LBIE) (No 4) [2014] 3 WLR 466 (the Waterfall Application), David Richards J determined a number of questions relating to the priority of claims in the administration of LBIE, holding, inter alia:

- LBHI2, a subordinated creditor of LBIE, ranked behind the claims of ordinary unsecured creditors for statutory interest.
- Creditors with contractual foreign currency claims could claim for any shortfall caused out of the statutory scheme of currency conversion, such currency conversion claims being non-provable debts ranking behind statutory interest but ahead of the subordinated claims of LBHI2.
- The liability of members under s74(1) of the Insolvency Act 1986 extended to funds requir ed for the payment of statutory interest and non-provable liabilities.
- Where a liquidation was immediately preceded by an administration, statutory interest was not payable for the period of the administration.
- The contributory rule, whereby a creditor-contributory cannot receive any dividend until he has paid any calls made upon him, did not apply to a company in administration.
- The contingent liability of a member under s74(1) was a provable debt in the insolvency of that member.

Overall, the judgment vindicated the position taken by the administrators; it is now under appeal. Also in the offing is the Waterfall II Application, which concerns the division of the very substantial surplus in the administration of LBIE, which is estimated between £3.5billion and £6.99billion.

Another key aspect of insolvency law came before the Court of Appeal in Re Game Station Ltd [2014] BCC 165, which concerned the application of the Lundy Granite principle. In a number of first instance decisions, it had been held that, since rent payable in advance could not be apportioned, the liability of an administrator to pay such rent would depend upon the date of administration. This led to the undesirable consequence that the date of administration would be chosen by reference to quarter days to the detriment of landlords. The Court of Appeal overruled these judgments, holding that the Lundy Granite principle did not depend on apportionment but simply treated rent over the period when the property was used for the benefit of the administration as if it were an expense of the administration. Rent should therefore be paid for the period when the property was used for the benefit of the administration, whether it was payable in advance or in arrears. Permission has been sought to appeal this decision to the Supreme Court, but has not yet been granted.

It has also been a significant year for cross-border insolvency cases. In Re Olympic Airlines SA [2014] 1 WLR 1401, the Court of Appeal considered the meaning of 'establishment' within Council Regulation (EU) No 1346/2000 (the Insolvency Regulation). The Court of Appeal held that for an entity to have an establishment in a member state, and thus be eligible for secondary insolvency proceedings, it had to be engaged in activity exercised on a market, that is external activity, at the relevant time. Such activity must involve both human and physical resources. In so holding, the Court of Appeal reversed Sir Andrew Morritt C, who had afforded the requirement of 'economic activity' a broader definition. Permission to appeal has been granted by the Supreme Court and the appeal is listed for February 2015.

In Fibria Celulose S/A v Pan Ocean Co Ltd [2014] EWHC 2124 (Ch), a Korean administrator applied for relief under the Cross-Border Insolvency Regulations 2006 (CBIR) in relation to a contract governed by English law. The contract contained an ipso facto clause, which was valid under English law but not under Korean insolvency law. The Korean administrator applied for an order restraining the counterparty from relying on the clause by means of a stay of proceedings. Morgan J declined to provide this relief, holding that the relief available under the CBIR was restricted to that available when dealing with a domestic insolvency. In so holding, he appeared to deviate from the approach taken by the US courts under Chapter 15 of the US Bankruptcy Code. Permission to appeal was granted to the Korean administrator and an expedited appeal is due to be heard in October 2014.

Finally, the attractiveness of the English jurisdiction for restructuring has received a boost following the sanction of nine schemes of arrangement in In Re Apcoa Parking Holdings GmbH [2014] EWHC 1867 (Ch). In order for a court to have jurisdiction to sanction a scheme of arrangement, there must be a "sufficient connection" to the jurisdiction. Often this is demonstrated if English law governs the debt instruments. In the Apcoa case, the facilities agreements had not originally been governed by English law but had been so amended by the vote of a majority of creditors. This was novel, but sufficient for the court to exercise jurisdiction.

Contents:

LONDON

Restructuring/Insolvency London

Leading Sets

Band 1	South Square *
Band 2	Enterprise Chambers *
	Erskine Chambers *
	Maitland Chambers *
	4 Stone Buildings *
	11 Stone Buildings *
Band 3	New Square Chambers *
	XXIV Old Buildings *
	Serle Court *

Leading Silks

Star individuals	Dicker Robin	South Square *
	Moss Gabriel	South Square
	Snowden Richard	Erskine Chambers
	Trower William	South Square
	Zacaroli Antony	South Square
Band 1	Arden Peter	Erskine Chambers *
	Miles Robert	4 Stone Buildings
	Phillips Mark	South Square *
	Sheldon Richard	South Square
Band 2	Atherton Stephen	20 Essex Street (ORL) ◊
	Chivers David	Erskine Chambers *
	Crow Jonathan	4 Stone Buildings *
	Davis-White Malcolm	XXIV Old Buildings
	Girolami Paul	Maitland Chambers *
	Hilliard Lexa	11 Stone Buildings
	Jones Philip	Serle Court *
	McQuater Ewan	3 Verulam Buildings (ORL) ◊
	Toube Felicity	South Square *
Band 3	Agnello Raquel	Erskine Chambers *
	Alexander David	South Square *
	Bompas George	4 Stone Buildings
	Brisby John	4 Stone Buildings
	Collings Matthew	Maitland Chambers *
	Crystal Michael	South Square
	Hill Richard G	4 Stone Buildings
	Hollington Robin	New Square Chambers *
	Isaacs Barry	South Square *
	Marshall Philip	Serle Court *
	Mortimore Simon	South Square *
	Pascoe Martin	South Square
	Tolaney Sonia	3 Verulam Buildings (ORL) ◊
Band 4	Beltrami Adrian	3 Verulam Buildings (ORL) ◊
	Davis Glen	South Square *
	Gibbon Michael	Maitland Chambers *
	Moverley Smith Stephen	XXIV Old Buildings
	Steinfeld Alan	XXIV Old Buildings
	Stubbs Rebecca	Maitland Chambers *
	Trace Anthony	Maitland Chambers *
Band 5	Arnold Mark	South Square *
	Frazer Lucy	South Square
	Gillis Richard	One Essex Court (ORL) ◊ *
	Goldring Jeremy	South Square
	Parker Christopher R	Maitland Chambers *
	Potts James	Erskine Chambers *
New Silks	Allison David	South Square *
	Hardwick Matthew	3 Verulam Buildings (ORL) ◊
	Smith Tom	South Square *

Leading Juniors

Star individuals	Bayfield Daniel	South Square *
Band 1	Fisher Richard	South Square *
	Robins Stephen	South Square *
	Shekerdemian Marcia	11 Stone Buildings
	Tamlyn Lloyd	South Square
Band 2	Addy Catherine	Maitland Chambers *
	Al-Attar Adam	South Square *
	Boardman Christopher	11 Stone Buildings
	Briggs John	South Square *
	Gledhill Andreas	Blackstone Chambers (ORL) ◊
	Kalfon Olivier	Enterprise Chambers
	Lightman Daniel	Serle Court *
	Ritchie Richard	XXIV Old Buildings
	Shaw Peter	9 Stone Buildings (ORL) ◊
	Stonefrost Hilary	South Square
Band 3	Eaton Turner David	New Square Chambers *
	Goodicon Adam	South Square *
	Griffiths Ben	Erskine Chambers
	Haywood Marcus	South Square
	Ife Linden	Enterprise Chambers
	Kyriakides Tina	11 Stone Buildings
	Leahy Blair	20 Essex Street (ORL) ◊
	Page Rebecca	Enterprise Chambers
	Robinson Thomas	11 Stone Buildings
	Zelin Geoffrey	Enterprise Chambers
Band 4	Adair Stuart	XXIV Old Buildings
	Bailey James	New Square Chambers *
	Barker James	Enterprise Chambers
	Curl Joseph	9 Stone Buildings (ORL) ◊
	Deacock Adam	11 Stone Buildings
	Groves Hugo	Enterprise Chambers
	McCulloch Niall	Enterprise Chambers
	Meyer Birgitta	11 Stone Buildings *
	Pester Iain	11 Stone Buildings *
	Prentis Sebastian	New Square Chambers *
Band 5	Beswetherick Anthony	20 Essex Street (ORL) ◊
	Burton Paul	3 Stone Buildings (ORL) ◊ *
	de Mestre Andrew	4 Stone Buildings *
	Jordan Ruth	Serle Court *
	Markham Anna	4 Stone Buildings
	Nersessian Tiran	4 Stone Buildings
	Pickering James	Enterprise Chambers
	Riley Jamie	11 Stone Buildings *
	Shepherd Tom	11 Stone Buildings
	Start Angharad	3 Verulam Buildings (ORL) ◊
	Thompson Steven	XXIV Old Buildings
	Thornley Hannah	South Square *
Up-and-coming individuals	Hinks Philip	11 Stone Buildings
	Markandya Susannah	Enterprise Chambers
	McCambley Dawn	11 Stone Buildings
	Willson William	South Square *

* Indicates set / individual with profile.

◊ (ORL) = Other Ranked Lawyer.

Band 1

South Square

See profile on p.861

THE SET

South Square remains recognised as the leading set in the restructuring and insolvency market. Members of the set at both silk and junior level routinely appear in the highest-profile disputes, and are lauded both for their technical knowledge of insolvency law, and for their polished advocacy. The set is a firm favourite with instructing solicitors, and is rightly regarded as an unbeatable repository of specialist insolvency advisers and advocates.

SILKS

Robin Dicker QC (see p.588) Highly praised for his commercial approach and intimidating intellect. Sources applaud him for his exceptional knowledge of insolvency law and his undoubted skill in presenting a case. **Strengths:** "He has a powerful intellect, and is confident in his own judgement." "An erudite and clever silk." **Recent work:** Acted for Barclays Bank in a case relating to derivative contracts.

Gabriel Moss QC A towering figure at the Insolvency Bar, dubbed "the godfather of insolvency law," he is praised for his comprehensive knowledge of insolvency case law. He is also lauded for his exceptional advocacy and his clarity of presentation. **Strengths:** "He is a fount of knowledge, and so clear in his exposition of complex legal issues." "He is very calm and deliberate, and a walking encyclopaedia of insolvency law."

William Trower QC Has a first-class reputation, which has only been further enhanced by his recent work on the Lehman Brothers insolvency. He is praised for his advocacy, quality advice, and client-driven approach to his instructions. **Strengths:** "An outstanding advocate." "He is very urbane and relaxed, and always has the ear of the court." **Recent work:** Acted for Nortel in a case relating to the treatment of liabilities under the Pensions Act 2004 in an administration.

David Alexander QC (see p.533) Widely praised for his judgement and strategic skills. His advocacy is highly valued by his clients, and he is active in major insolvency disputes in both the UK and overseas. **Strengths:** "A very, very powerful advocate, with the confidence to cut through a case and identify the winning points." "He always gives sensible and commercial advice." **Recent work:** Acted in a significant breach of trust claim relating to the insolvency of MF Global.

Tom Smith QC (see p.724) A force at the Insolvency Bar, who is noted for his incisive mind and the quality of his client service. He has handled a number of major insolvency disputes. **Strengths:** "He is approachable, easy to work with and fiercely intelligent." "He is very bright, very quick, and very easy to work with." **Recent work:** Acted in the restructuring of Vietnam Shipbuilding Industry Group, handling proceedings to ensure a stay of claims against the company whilst a scheme of arrangement was implemented.

Antony Zacaroli QC A significant figure at the Insolvency Bar, well recognised for his technical legal knowledge, good client service and strong courtroom presence. He is widely regarded as a first port of call for clients dealing with heavy-duty insolvency disputes. **Strengths:** "An incredibly intelligent and able advocate, whom clients like working with." "Commanding, well prepared, and on top of his material." **Recent work:** Led in Hunt v Hosking in the Court of Appeal.

Felicity Toube QC (see p.739) Has an active practice in both the UK and offshore jurisdictions, and specialises in heavy insolvency litigation, as well as civil fraud and company issues. She is well regarded as both a gifted advocate and an intelligent adviser. **Strengths:** "Very user-friendly, she's a strong advocate, who is very knowledgeable about insolvency law." "Very clear-thinking and practical." **Recent work:** Acted in both the Cayman Islands and the UK in relation to civil fraud issues in English insolvency cases involving Saad.

Mark Phillips QC Has acted in and advised on many of the most high-profile insolvencies of recent years, and is clearly seen in the market as one of the heavyweight practitioners at the Insolvency Bar. Sources say he is both a user-friendly adviser and a robust advocate. **Strengths:** "He is fearsomely bright, and doesn't pull his punches." "A good barrister to have on your side in very confrontational situations." **Recent work:** Acted for Lehman Brothers in a successful appeal to the Supreme Court regarding whether shortfalls in Lehman-connected pension funds should be paid as administration expenses.

Richard Sheldon QC Practises in insolvency and restructuring law, both onshore and offshore, and is experienced in company law, and banking and financial services issues. He has been instructed on a number of major administrations, including those relating to Nortel and Portsmouth City FC.

Michael Crystal QC Widely sought after for his experience and skill in handling major cross-border insolvency litigation. He is rated highly for his strategic vision, and maintains an active practice both in the UK and offshore. **Strengths:** "An experienced, established and respected silk."

Barry Isaacs QC (see p.635) A rising star, who is highly rated for his tremendous work rate, his exhaustive knowledge of insolvency law and his excellent client-facing skills. **Strengths:** "He is incredibly knowledgeable, practical and accessible." "His knowledge of the area is absolutely encyclopaedic." **Recent work:** Acted in Rubin v Eurofinance; Re New Cap Reinsurance in the High Court, Court of Appeal and Supreme Court.

Simon Mortimore QC (see p.677) A highly experienced and effective adviser and advocate, who specialises in domestic and cross-border insolvency issues. He maintains an active offshore practice, and is highly rated for his intellect and excellent courtroom skills. **Strengths:** "He is intellectually incredibly strong." "A good silk to use if you want the ear of the judge." **Recent work:** Instructed to act by the secured creditor of the Arcapita group, particularly in relation to the ongoing restructuring of the group in the Cayman Islands.

Martin Pascoe QC Well regarded in the market as an excellent adviser and advocate. He has handled a number of major cross-border restructurings, and is seen as being an experienced and subtle advocate. **Strengths:** "A consummate professional, who is a calming, steady presence in a crisis." **Recent work:** Acted as lead counsel for the administrators of MF Global UK in two major pieces of litigation.

Glen Davis QC (see p.584) Highly regarded for his work with special administration regimes for troubled banks, and also noted for his skill at dealing with partnerships in insolvency. He is very good on cross-border insolvency matters. **Strengths:** "He is very quick on the uptake, and very good on the law." "His advice is consistently technically excellent." **Recent work:** Acted extensively for the FSA in issues arising from the collapse of MF Global.

Jeremy Goldring QC Has broad experience and excellent knowledge of both banking and finance and restructuring and insolvency law. He has been active in many of the major restructurings of recent years, including Eurosail and Landsbanki. **Strengths:** "He is very commercial and excellent on technical insolvency points." "A good all-rounder, who is a pleasure to work with."

David Allison QC (see p.535) Specialises in cross-border and domestic corporate restructurings, and is well recognised in the market as a practical and driven adviser. He maintains an active practice offshore. **Strengths:** "He is very thorough and happy to roll his sleeves up and get stuck in." "He is flexible, nice to deal with and a very strong technical lawyer." **Recent work:** Acted for the trustees of the Lehman Brothers Pension Scheme in a case concerning administration liabilities in the Supreme Court.

Mark Arnold QC (see p.538) Advises on and acts in major cross-border restructurings and insolvencies, particularly in relation to financial institutions. He is highly rated in the market for his strong intellect and exhaustive approach to his cases. **Strengths:** "His technical ability and close attention to detail are his real strong points." "He is a very intelligent, very careful and very thorough lawyer." **Recent work:** Instructed to act in a significant trial on behalf of Lehman Brothers Holdings, known as the Waterfall Application.

Lucy Frazer QC Specialises in insolvency and restructuring, both in the domestic market and further afield. She is characterised as a staunch advocate and a sophisticated adviser. **Recent work:** Acted for HMRC in a labyrinthine multiparty litigation relating to issues arising from the administration of Rangers FC.

JUNIORS

Stephen Robins (see p.709) Known for his expert advice and skilful advocacy when handling a wide range of insolvency and restructuring cases, both at home and abroad. He is particularly strong on financial services insolvencies. **Strengths:** "He is very quick, very intelligent, and gets to the heart of the matter." "He is very good at judging the client's needs, and is a pleasure to work with." **Recent work:** Acted in the Court of Appeal in a matter related to the court's jurisdiction to make an administration order over a Jersey company.

William Willson (see p.753) Acts on all aspects of domestic and cross-border insolvency and restructuring, and has a particular focus on issues emanating from the Commonwealth of Independent States. He also handles personal insolvency disputes. **Strengths:** "He has good client skills, and is a tenacious, gifted and hard-working lawyer." "He's strategically excellent, pragmatic and commercial." **Recent work:** Defended in an appeal against an order for possession and sale of the home of two bankrupts.

Daniel Bayfield One of the finest juniors in the restructuring and insolvency market. He acts on major national and cross-border insolvencies and restructurings, and has developed a niche expertise in advising sports teams in financial difficulties. **Strengths:** "He is very inventive and imaginative, and great to have as a member of the team." "He is a thorough, sensible and solid senior junior." **Recent work:** Acted in the high-profile Lehman Brothers 'Waterfall Application', regarding the proper payment of creditors of the collapsed bank.

Lloyd Tamlyn His advocacy is highly praised by sources in the market, as is his pragmatic and commercial advice. He acts in all aspects of domestic and cross-border insolvency, and maintains an active offshore practice. **Strengths:** "Nothing fazes him; he doggedly argues points until he wins." "He is economical with what he says and writes, and will use very few words to get the job done." **Recent work:** Acted in a claim for damages brought against the purchaser of a steel mill by the administrator of Alphasteel.

Richard Fisher (see p.600) Advises and represents clients in domestic and international restructurings and insolvencies. He is recognised by his peers as an experienced and talented practitioner. **Strengths:** "A brilliant, technical lawyer." "He is brilliant, very responsive, and turns things around quickly and confidently." **Recent work:** Advised on a major restructuring of ATP Oil & Gas UK, via a company voluntary arrangement.

Marcus Haywood A specialist in cross-border and domestic restructurings and insolvencies, who also has broad experience of banking litigation. He has represented clients in offshore disputes, including in the Cayman Islands. **Strengths:** "He is pragmatic, exceptionally user-friendly and a compelling advocate." "A strikingly pleasant person to deal with, but no less effective for being so." **Recent work:** Acted on behalf of trustees of the Olympic Airlines pension scheme in an action to ensure the scheme's eligibility to enter into the Pension Protection Fund.

Adam Al-Attar (see p.533) Has enviable experience of acting in major banking and fund insolvencies. He is highly praised both for his advocacy and for the robustness of his advice. **Strengths:** "He is intelligent, very easy to work with and incredibly helpful." **Recent work:** Acted in a dispute in relation to the administration of MF Global, which determined the use of hindsight in calculating claims linked to open derivative contracts.

John Briggs (see p.556) Particularly highly regarded for his experience and skill in handling personal insolvency disputes in courts of all levels. He is highly praised by sources for his courtroom skills. **Strengths:** "He is second to none when it comes to guiding you through large and complex matters." **Recent work:** Acted for the respondent in the Court of Appeal in McGuire v Rose, a case concerning claims brought by a bankrupt against his trustee.

Adam Goodison (see p.611) A practical, pragmatic senior junior, who acts on a range of domestic and cross-border insolvency and restructuring issues. He has experience of representing clients in the Cayman Islands. **Strengths:** "He is very proactive, accessible and hard-working." "He is phenomenally helpful; he couldn't be more supportive." **Recent work:** Acted in a dispute over the administration of Coventry FC, as well as related disputes over the Ricoh Stadium.

Hannah Thornley (see p.737) Specialises in advising and representing banks, companies and private individuals in insolvency disputes. She is also experienced in advising on directors' disqualification actions. **Strengths:** "A very robust advocate."

Hilary Stonefrost Acts in domestic and cross-border restructurings and insolvencies, and is highly praised by market sources for her advocacy and written advice. She has been involved in a number of high-profile insolvencies of domestic football clubs. **Strengths:** "Easy to deal with, very bright and practical, and very good at finding a commercial way through a technical problem." "A standout barrister."

Band 2

Enterprise Chambers

See profile on p.788

THE SET

Enterprise Chambers is widely recognised for the excellence and range of talent it has to offer, particularly when it comes to its juniors. Members are noted for their flexible and client-centric approach to instructions, and are supported by clerks who always endeavour to match the right counsel to the right case. **Client service:** "The service provided by the clerking team really is superb." Antony Armstrong is the senior clerk.

JUNIORS

Hugo Groves Brings a wealth of experience and commercial good sense to the table, and handles both major domestic and cross-border insolvency cases. He is very highly rated by sources for his straightforward and sensible approach to advice and advocacy. **Strengths:** "He is unpretentious, quick to respond, knows his stuff and is very calm at all times." "He is an expert insolvency lawyer who is acutely aware of the commercial realities."

Susannah Markandya Has a broad practice covering commercial, chancery and insolvency issues. She is known for her excellent client service and persuasive advocacy. **Strengths:** "She is incredibly well organised and thorough." "She is very approachable, quick on her feet, and knows insolvency like the back of her hand."

Olivier Kalfon Highly regarded for his technical aptitude and comprehensive approach to his instructions. He acts on domestic and international insolvency cases, and maintains an active offshore practice. **Strengths:** "He is a safe pair of hands, and he gets to grips with the background of a case very quickly." "His research is very thorough and he covers all the angles."

Linden Ife A specialist insolvency and business litigator, who acts for lenders and other stakeholders in disputes. She regularly acts in disputes regarding the duties of directors and office holders. **Strengths:** "A formidable advocate with great judgement." **Recent work:** Acted for the administrators of Spithead Business Centre in successfully resisting an application for an injunction by the company director to prevent them from carrying out their role.

James Barker Primarily represents office holders in disputes arising out of corporate insolvencies. He also acts in personal insolvency disputes, and is an experienced adviser on directors' disqualification claims. **Strengths:** "He is tenacious, very thorough and very commercial." **Recent work:** Successfully acted for a trustee in bankruptcy in an appeal against an order by the Registrar suspending the automatic discharge of a bankruptcy.

James Pickering Highly rated by sources due to his calming and focused approach to advocacy. A lawyer who has undoubted expertise in handling major corporate insolvency disputes, he is noted for the quality of both his client service and his cross-examination. **Strengths:** "Very approachable, thoughtful and thorough." **Recent work:** Instructed to act in a number of disputes relating to the liquidation of A1 Grand Prix Operations, including a number of complex retention of title matters.

Geoffrey Zelin An able and experienced adviser, who is recognised for his skill in handling major insolvency disputes. He acts in both personal and corporate insolvency disputes. **Strengths:** "A very pleasing advocate, who does a very effective job." **Recent work:** Instructed by ATAG in a claim against an English company alleging the sale of an asset at an undervalue of EUR1 billion.

Niall McCulloch An experienced and tested courtroom litigator, who advises on and handles cases in all areas of insolvency law. He maintains an active practice in offshore jurisdictions and frequently acts in the British Virgin Islands (BVI). **Strengths:** "Very astute, he is a good choice for a case that needs a real fighter." "He is exceptionally user-friendly and good on his feet." **Recent work:** Acted for the administrators of Harlequin Management Services in an application regarding the validity of their appointment.

Rebecca Page Works in company and insolvency disputes, and advises and acts on both corporate and personal insolvency issues. She is highly valued for her intellectual agility and vigour. **Strengths:** "She is meticulous, helpful, good on her feet and excellent on the law." "She is very quick to grasp issues and turn around written advice." **Recent work:** Advised with regard to the liquidation of Alexander Samuel LLP in connection with potential legal action against the former administrators.

Erskine Chambers

See profile on p.789

THE SET

This company law powerhouse draws praise for its undeniable expertise in handling insolvency issues. Its members are noted for their academic rigour and keen understanding of insolvency law. As one observer commented: "The people here are stronger intellectually than most, and are good at dealing with the intricacies of the law."

SILKS

Richard Snowden QC A real star of the Insolvency Bar, who is known for his intellectual depth and mastery of the law. He acts in insolvency and company disputes, and is seen as a pragmatic and dogged advocate. **Strengths:** "A premier division silk, who is very intellectually incisive." **Recent work:** Acted on behalf of the security agent in the restructuring of ATU.

Peter Arden QC (see p.537) Focuses on advising and acting in corporate insolvency and company issues, and is noted for his extensive experience of handling restructuring cases. He is very well regarded for his intellectual vigour and incisive advice. **Strengths:** "He is incredibly perspicacious, and very good at untangling complicated issues." "He is one of the most user-friendly advocates at the Bar." **Recent work:** Advised on the administration of the accountancy firm RSM Tenon, and its eventual sale to Baker Tilly.

David Chivers QC (see p.571) A hugely talented adviser and advocate with a first-class mind, who is excellent in the fields of company and insolvency law. He works on both domestic and offshore instructions, and is highly praised for his strategic brilliance. **Strengths:** "His paperwork is superb." "His ability to understand his clients' needs is really first-rate." **Recent work:** Instructed to act in both the High Court of Appeal for Bermuda and the Privy Council in PwC v Saad Investments Company.

Raquel Agnello QC (see p.532) Acts in both corporate and personal insolvency disputes, and also advises on directors' duties and voluntary arrangements. She is widely acknowledged as a leader at the Bar, and is known for her commercial thinking. **Strengths:** "She can break down complex matters and provide commercial, strategic advice." "She grasps issues really quickly, particularly when there's no obvious answer to them." **Recent work:** Instructed in Hathaurani v Jassat, a major bankruptcy case involving complex issues regarding the possession of a property.

James Potts QC (see p.697) Primarily acts in relation to corporate insolvencies, and also maintains an active practice advising on directors' liabilities, administrations and company voluntary arrangements. **Recent work:** Acted for a former partner of insolvent firm Halliwells LLP in successfully opposing the attempt of the administrators to pursue the former partners for cash.

JUNIORS

Ben Griffiths Recognised by sources as a "standout junior" who is regularly involved in major insolvency litigation. He acts for and advises clients in corporate insolvency disputes, and is highly regarded for his skill in the field. **Recent work:** Acted for the provisional liquidators of Beppler & Jacobsen in successfully opposing an application for the return of monies paid by a minority shareholder.

Maitland Chambers

See profile on p.831

THE SET

Maitland Chambers boasts an impressive bench of highly experienced silks, who specialise in representing and advising clients in major cross-border and domestic insolvencies. Sources praise the commercial good sense and "uniformly high" standard of advice and representation provided by all members of the team. As a group, the individuals here are recognised as a first port of call for heavy insolvency litigation.

Client service: "The clerks are friendly and responsive, and develop an understanding of which members of chambers will work best with a particular client." John Wiggs is the senior clerk.

SILKS

Paul Girolami QC (see p.608) Acts in both corporate and personal insolvency matters, as well as restructurings and voluntary arrangements for both domestic and international clients. He has significant expertise in company and commercial law, and is highly sought after as an advocate and adviser. **Strengths:** "Extremely bright and tremendously experienced."

Matthew Collings QC (see p.575) Handles insolvency cases as part of a broad chancery commercial practice. He primarily acts in significant corporate insolvencies, both at home and abroad. **Strengths:** "He is very good, and very polished." **Recent work:** Acted in the administration of Equity Trading Systems, a company involved in a significant fraud.

Michael Gibbon QC Praised for his enviable skills both in the courtroom and in conference. He is regarded as being particularly well suited to an insolvency or restructuring matter involving heavy litigation. **Strengths:** "He is thorough, calm, user-friendly and commercially astute." "An outstanding advocate, who is extremely user-friendly." **Recent work:** Retained by a third party in Goldtrail v Aydin, a case involving claims of dishonest assistance relating to a misfeasance claim.

Rebecca Stubbs QC (see p.730) A well-recognised specialist in insolvency law, who also has an active company and banking law practice. She is highly praised by her clients for being a user-friendly and enjoyable adviser to work with, and is recognised in the market as being an intelligent and articulate advocate. **Strengths:** "She is very focused, clever and to the point."

Anthony Trace QC (see p.739) A formidable advocate, whose services and skills are sought after for a range of commercial chancery cases. He has been active in a number of major matters arising out of the financial distress of major banks and corporate entities. **Strengths:** "Immensely bright and formidable in court." **Recent work:** Instructed by the Bank of Ireland in relation to a number of cases arising from the failure of the McFeely property empire.

Christopher Parker QC (see p.689) A company and insolvency law specialist who frequently acts in domestic insolvency disputes, and also has an active practice in offshore jurisdictions. He is well regarded as a likeable, sensible and effective adviser and advocate. **Strengths:** "He's one of the best insolvency silks, as he's clever, easy to use and very commercial." "He doesn't mince his words, and is a good team player." **Recent work:** Acted for Ebbvale in successfully opposing a winding-up petition in the Bahamian Court of Appeal and the Privy Court.

JUNIORS

Catherine Addy (see p.532) Acts in both personal and corporate insolvency disputes, and advises government departments amongst other clients. She is highly regarded for her courtroom skills and for her tireless analysis of the most thorny cases. **Strengths:** "Thorough, precise and highly practical when on her feet." "She has superb analytical skills, and a user-friendly manner." **Recent work:** Acted in the Court of Appeal on behalf of the administrators of the Game group in a case concerning whether rents should be paid as an expense of administration.

4 Stone Buildings

See profile on p.865

THE SET

4 Stone Buildings is more associated with company law work, but nevertheless enjoys a good reputation in the closely aligned insolvency and restructuring market. It has a long history of handling insolvency cases, and over the years has been involved in such matters as Maxwell and BCCI. Matters of more recent vintage include Lehman Brothers, MF Global and cases arising out of the liquidation of the Icelandic banks. The set is noted for representing the government in insolvency issues, and has a number of members on the Attorney General's panels.

Client service: "The clerking team, led by David Goddard, is efficient, friendly, and willing to go the extra mile."

SILKS

Robert Miles QC Highly regarded as a proactive and exceptionally able adviser and advocate, who has acted in many of the most significant insolvencies, both domestically and further afield. His area of special interest is in cases involving capital markets. **Strengths:** "He is brilliant to work with, brilliant on his feet and his technical knowledge of the law is brilliant as well." "If there is a task that needs to be done, he will roll up his sleeves and do it." **Recent work:** Instructed to act for the defendants in a number of claims brought following the collapse of Madoff Investment Securities LLC.

Jonathan Crow QC Handles a broad range of commercial and chancery issues, and is well recognised for his superior advocacy and strategic good sense. He has an active insolvency practice both onshore and offshore, and is recognised as a barrister who gets results for his clients. **Strengths:** "An incredibly able silk, who handles an enormously broad spectrum of work." **Recent work:** Instructed in an appeal to the Privy Council from the BVI Commercial Court, regarding repayment of investors into Fairfield Sentry.

George Bompas QC A highly experienced counsel who acts with distinction in insolvency and professional negligence disputes. He is singled out in the market as an affable and approachable adviser, noted for his technical skill. **Strengths:** "He is meticulous and highly responsive." **Recent work:** Acted in an important professional negligence claim related to the insolvency of Aqua Design & Play International.

John Brisby QC Highly regarded in the market for his determined and effective advocacy style, which he brings to bear in a variety of insolvency, chancery and commercial issues. He acts in major domestic and international insolvencies. **Recent work:** Retained to advise on the administration of the Gemini property structure, which involved the realisation of a major property portfolio.

Richard Hill QC Widely recognised as a rising star at the Bar, he is a formidable advocate and adviser. His forte is insolvency advice in the financial services industry, and he also has an active commercial and company practice. **Recent work:** Acted in the Court of Appeal for the former owners of Liverpool FC, who were in dispute with RBS.

JUNIORS

Tiran Nersessian Represents parties involved in both corporate and personal insolvency situations. He regularly acts for HMRC, and is highly rated by sources for his courtroom skills. **Recent work:** Defended four directors in a misfeasance claim brought by the liquidators of Houghton Bhatti Segurola. The case settled successfully.

Andrew de Mestre (see p.585) Rated in the market for his intelligent approach to his instructions, and his well-balanced advocacy. He acts in all aspects of insolvency law, and has expertise in company and commercial disputes. **Recent work:** Acted for the receivers of over 700 companies owned by Mukhtar Ablyazov in a number of jurisdictions globally.

Anna Markham Primarily acts in, and advises on, issues arising from corporate insolvencies, and is well regarded for the quality of her advice and expertise in the field of directors' duties. She is particularly rated by sources for her meticulous organisation and for her personable approach. **Strengths:** "She is able to process voluminous evidence and to cut through to the nub of the issue." "Very intelligent and sharp, she provides excellent written advice." **Recent work:** Acted at trial for the defendants in directors' disqualification proceedings resulting from the insolvency of a property services company based in the City of London.

11 Stone Buildings

See profile on p.868

THE SET

11 Stone Buildings has a well-deserved reputation as a one-stop shop for handling the full spectrum of insolvency issues. It advises and represents bankrupts, insolvency practitioners, companies and office holders in contentious scenarios, and also handles significant non-contentious restructurings and insolvencies. Sources praise it for being a modern set that has a strong commitment to client service.

Client service: "The clerks are very informative, happy to help, and almost always find a barrister that fits a particular case, even at short notice." Chambers director Michael Couling has over 20 years of experience of working in top commercial chambers.

SILKS

Lexa Hilliard QC An experienced adviser and advocate, who is particularly highly praised by sources for the high quality of her written advice. She acts in both corporate and personal insolvency cases, and is recognised as being particularly adept at advising on cross-border issues. **Strengths:** "Displays real class and is good with multi-jurisdictional issues." **Recent work:** Represented and advised an Israeli trustee in bankruptcy, who is looking to set aside an anti-suit injunction.

JUNIORS

Christopher Boardman Specialises in both personal and corporate insolvencies, and also has an active practice advising on directors' liabilities and disqualification actions. He is particularly praised by sources for his clear understanding and articulation of legal issues. **Strengths:** "He has an excellent ability to synthesise complex information into a clear line of argument." "Incisive, and he understands the core issues of complex legal problems effortlessly." **Recent work:** Acted in a contested administration application on behalf of a petitioning creditor in the High Court.

Philip Hinks Has a strong corporate and personal insolvency practice, and is also effective in banking cases. He is regarded as a sophisticated and erudite adviser. **Strengths:** "He exudes authority, and has the ability to grasp complex issues quickly." **Recent**

work: Acted for the liquidators in a major wrongful trading claim against the directors of an insolvent construction company.

Tom Shepherd Has a broad commercial chancery practice, and frequently acts in insolvency and fraud-related disputes. He is highly praised in the market for his commercial good sense and solid advice. **Strengths:** "He is extremely clever and his drafting skills are very good." "He has a great deal of commercial acumen and a sharp legal mind." **Recent work:** Acted in an application seeking a winding-up order for a sports and social club.

Marcia Shekerdemian An excellent senior junior, capable of taking on large-scale corporate and personal insolvency cases. She is highly rated for her intelligent and committed approach. **Strengths:** "Has a very incisive mind and a comprehensive knowledge of insolvency law." "She always delivers good, practical advice and tackles problems with vigour." **Recent work:** Represented Bank of Moscow in its challenge to the UK bankruptcy of the Russian 'banana king' Vladimir Kekhman.

Tina Kyriakides Recognised by sources for her excellent client care skills, and her ability to produce high-quality advice at very short notice. She acts in both corporate and personal insolvency disputes. **Strengths:** "She is very good at handling a difficult appointment, and has a very user-friendly approach." **Recent work:** Advised and represented 21st Century Lifts in a dispute with HMRC over a winding-up petition regarding a substantial alleged sum of outstanding PAYE and NIC.

Thomas Robinson A commercially savvy and technically adroit counsel, who primarily works in insolvency and pension-related disputes. He also has experience of acting in offshore jurisdictions. **Strengths:** "He combines a surefooted academic approach with a practical slant." **Recent work:** Advised and acted for the provisional liquidators of a UK company which possesses major Montenegro hotels.

Birgitta Meyer (see p.671) Works extensively in the insolvency sphere, and advises on corporate and personal insolvency issues, as well as directors' disqualifications, and fraud. **Strengths:** "She is very approachable, very bright and a very easy person to deal with." **Recent work:** Advised Universal Pictures regarding the use of goods supplied prior to an administration which were retained or used without the supplier's permission.

Iain Pester (see p.691) An experienced and impressive junior, who is a particularly able courtroom advocate. He specialises in corporate and personal insolvency work, and also advises on directors' disqualification proceedings. **Strengths:** "He is a very confident advocate." **Recent work:** Acted for Ernst & Young (Canada) in an action brought regarding its conduct as interim receivers of a Canadian company.

Adam Deacock Specialises in acting in corporate insolvency situations, and is valued by his clients for his sound judgement and perspicacity. **Strengths:** "He gives firm, robust advice, and picks up issues very quickly." "His attention to detail is second to none, and he has an impressive ability to grasp issues immediately."

Jamie Riley (see p.708) Has an established reputation as an adviser in commercial and company law, and regularly handles insolvency and fraud cases. He advises on both domestic and cross-border issues. **Strengths:** "He is poised and thorough. He's very together, very reassuring and very calm." **Recent work:** Instructed by the liquidators of D&D Wines International on various claims arising from the liquidation.

Dawn McCambley Has an active company, commercial and insolvency practice. She acts in both personal and corporate insolvency disputes, and also deals with directors' duties issues. **Strengths:** "Impressively practical and commercial." "She is approachable, and her drafting and advice are both very good." **Recent work:** Acted for the creditor in an application by a debtor to set aside a statutory demand on the basis that the debtor lacked the capacity to enter into a guaranteed share option agreement.

Band 3

New Square Chambers
See profile on p.837

THE SET

New Square Chambers is regarded as a set that provides a thorough and comprehensive service in all areas of corporate and personal insolvency law. It acts for a host of insolvency practitioners, and also represents individuals and companies in financial distress. Members here are very highly rated for their strong client service and their flexible approach to disputes.

Client service: "The clerks provide a good all-round service and are pleasant and approachable."

SILKS

Robin Hollington QC (see p.630) A well-respected and experienced advocate, who specialises in corporate and personal insolvency cases. He is a leading figure in the law of shareholder disputes and directors' duties. **Strengths:** "He is brilliant and he lends a great deal of gravitas to a case." "He turns around instructions very quickly, and provides very thorough advice." **Recent work:** Acted for a number of companies controlled by the Tchenguiz brothers in resisting attempts by RBS to gain administration orders against them.

JUNIORS

David Eaton Turner (see p.593) A highly experienced advocate, known for his skill in handling corporate and personal insolvencies. He acts in both domestic disputes and those with international elements. **Strengths:** "A very wise head, who provides good, considered, careful advice." **Recent work:** Acted for the trustee in bankruptcy in a matter regarding the right of the trustee to claim part of the bankrupt's pension entitlement for the estate.

James Bailey (see p.541) Rated in the market for his tact and skill in handling clients, and for the focus he shows when handling complex cases. He has a broad commercial chancery practice, part of which sees him acting on corporate and personal insolvencies. **Strengths:** "He is incredibly good in difficult conferences, and has an impressive ability to retain the details of a case." **Recent work:** Retained as an expert witness for Hanjin, in a dispute arising from the rehabilitation in South Korea of Samsun Logix.

Sebastian Prentis (see p.698) Widely praised for his excellent presentation in court, and for his client-facing skills. He has a broad insolvency practice, and is recognised for his imaginative approach to cases. **Strengths:** "He is incredibly clever, sensible, approachable and a team player." **Recent work:** Acted on behalf of Olympic Airlines in a case dealing with the meaning of the term 'establishment' in the EC Insolvency Regulation.

XXIV Old Buildings
See profile on p.838

THE SET

XXIV Old Buildings has established itself as a go-to set for handling restructuring and insolvency disputes in offshore jurisdictions, and a number of its members are particularly active in the Cayman Islands. The set is also recognised as being a capable player when it comes to handling domestic insolvency disputes. Individuals at the set are used to handling complex litigation, and, by way of example, have been handling matters arising out of the collapse of Carlyle Capital.

Client service: "Their clerks are polite, friendly, and will always find the time to help."

SILKS

Malcolm Davis-White QC Recognised as a leading practitioner in the field of directors' duties, and known for his expertise in handling both personal and corporate insolvency cases. He is highly rated for his team-driven approach and dazzling advocacy. **Strengths:** "A brilliant advocate, whose written work is also excellent. He really rolls up his sleeves and gets involved in a case." **Recent work:** Acted for the defence in disqualification proceedings arising out of the collapse of a number of companies.

Stephen Moverley Smith QC Has an active practice in offshore jurisdictions, particularly the BVI and Cayman Islands. He is relied on by his clients for his exhaustive knowledge of insolvency law. **Strengths:** "His work is always top-notch, his advocacy is really effective and clients like his mix of gravitas and approachability." "He has vast experience and understanding of the intricacies of insolvency law." **Recent work:** Acted in proceedings in the BVI to terminate the liquidation of a company on the grounds that the applicant was party to a fraud.

Alan Steinfeld QC A legendary figure at the Chancery Bar, who handles a range of major corporate and personal insolvency disputes. **Recent work:** Acted in Carlyle v Conway, a major dispute in Guernsey concerning a failed investment fund.

JUNIORS

Richard Ritchie A solid and experience advocate, who has advised on a number of major insolvency cases. **Strengths:** "He has a very firm grasp of the law, as well as of the facts in any particular case." **Recent work:** Acted on behalf of the defendant in a disqualification case against the Official Receiver.

Steven Thompson An experienced and sought-after adviser for cross-border insolvency matters, particularly those relating to the aviation industry. He acts for directors, office holders and companies, and also regularly acts in personal bankruptcy disputes. **Recent work:** Acted for the creditors of the insolvent MK Airlines on a variety of issues.

Stuart Adair Known in the market as a go-to practitioner for clients in need of powerful advocacy. He provides clear and well thought-out advice, and is particularly skilled at handling corporate insolvency disputes. **Strengths:** "A strong advocate who is very technically astute." "He is very thoughtful, and has a very good courtroom presence." **Recent work:** Instructed by the liquidator of Icon Eyewear Distribution in a claim for fraud against a former director.

Serle Court

See profile on p.860

THE SET

Serle Court has a well-deserved reputation as a strong resource for both personal and corporate insolvency work. It provides capable advice on major cross-border issues and acts in disputes in a number of offshore jurisdictions.

Client service: "Their clerks, led by Steve Whitaker, provide an excellent, well-rounded service."

SILKS

Philip Jones QC A tremendously experienced and highly regarded insolvency silk, who has an active practice in corporate and personal insolvency matters both in the UK and abroad. He is highly praised for being both an effective advocate and a good team player. **Recent work:** Instructed in a huge claim against directors in the Isle of Man, originating out of the collapse of the Heather hedge fund.

Philip Marshall QC (see p.663) A highly experienced practitioner in the fields of banking, insolvency and fraud, who is noted as being a fearsome cross-examiner and a highly industrious lawyer. He has an active practice offshore, and has advised on matters relating to a number of major administrations. **Strengths:** "He is fabulously bright and can come up with a strategy extremely quickly." **Recent work:** Instructed by the directors in a significant claim in Guernsey arising from the collapse of an ABS trading company.

JUNIORS

Ruth Jordan (see p.641) Acts in insolvency, charity, tax and trust disputes, and maintains an active practice offshore. Sources single her out as being an astonishingly thorough and user-friendly advocate. **Strengths:** "Her grasp of factual information is incredible." **Recent work:** Instructed by the Charity Commission to act in proceedings against trustees, employees and directors of a now insolvent charity.

Daniel Lightman (see p.656) Widely recognised as a lawyer with a brilliant intellect, who is highly inventive. He is particularly sought out for the quality of his opinions and is further fêted for his excellent advocacy skills. **Strengths:** "He is extremely bright and the sort of the counsel you would use on a particularly technical matter, or for an unusual point of law." **Recent work:** Acted for telecoms company Fi Call, the respondents to a winding-up petition bought by the corporate vehicle of a Saudi prince.

Other Ranked Lawyers

Andreas Gledhill (Blackstone Chambers) An excellent team player and a very thorough practitioner. His written advice on corporate insolvency issues is well spoken of, and he is recognised for his handling of cases when acting both led and unled. **Strengths:** "Exceptionally good for cases that are highly legalistic and detailed." "Very clear in his thinking, and very flexible with his time." **Recent work:** Instructed in two separate disputes arising out of the insolvency of MF Global.

Richard Gillis QC (see p.608) (One Essex Court) Has an active and varied insolvency practice, primarily representing clients in corporate insolvency disputes. **Strengths:** "A very polished and forceful advocate." **Recent work:** Instructed for the defendant in Dorchester Project Management v FREP 2 (Heyford Park).

Stephen Atherton QC (20 Essex Street) Acts in domestic and international corporate insolvencies and restructurings, and has an active company and fraud practice. He is highly rated for his skills as a courtroom advocate and is praised for his meticulous advice. **Strengths:** "Has a rumbustious approach, and he will certainly fight your corner." "Thorough in his efforts and a pleasure to work with." **Recent work:** Instructed to act on behalf of the joint receivers of the estate of Boris Berezovsky.

Blair Leahy (20 Essex Street) A practical and intelligent adviser, who handles a range of corporate insolvency and fraud cases. She is seen as being a solid performer in court. **Strengths:** "She is just great in court." **Recent work:** Acted for the landlords in proceedings against the administrators of the Dream group of companies.

Anthony Beswetherick (20 Essex Street) Regularly acts in contentious insolvencies and restructurings, many of which have an international aspect to them. He is well regarded as a responsive and effective adviser and advocate. **Strengths:** "His attention to detail and speed of delivery make him invaluable." "He is very approachable and thorough, and brilliant both on the paperwork and in court." **Recent work:** Acted for the trustee in bankruptcy in Hunt v Salliss, a case concerning the rights of insolvency practitioners to remuneration.

Paul Burton (see p.562) (3 Stone Building) A robust and steady presence in the courtroom, who is valued for his pragmatic advice. He handles insolvency disputes as part of a broad commercial chancery practice. **Recent work:** Instructed by an action group of investors in a dispute with the insolvent Instant Access Properties group, alleging a significant fraud.

Peter Shaw (9 Stone Buildings) A hugely experienced senior junior, who acts in corporate and personal insolvency cases representing trustees, liquidators, administrators, and supervisors of voluntary arrangements. He is recognised for his courtroom presence and his strong technical skills. **Strengths:** "A valued member of the team, and someone who is good on technical pieces of litigation." **Recent work:** Acted in the Court of Appeal on behalf of a liquidator in a dispute over a substantial sum paid by the director of a company to a colleague in Singapore.

Joseph Curl (9 Stone Buildings) Has developed a strong reputation as a technically adept and client-friendly junior to instruct in personal and corporate insolvency cases. He is clearly viewed by sources as a good all-rounder, who provides excellent advice and presents well on his feet. **Strengths:** "He provides advice in an extremely unstuffy manner, and has extremely good insolvency expertise." "He is clever, commercial and reliable."

Ewan McQuater QC (3 Verulam Buildings) An eminent practitioner who maintains an active corporate insolvency practice. Sources particularly note his forceful advocacy style. **Strengths:** "He has a lot of panache." "He is absolutely brilliant." **Recent work:** Instructed by Glitnir, an insolvent Icelandic bank, in a dispute with TD Bank.

Sonia Tolaney QC (3 Verulam Buildings) Well recognised as a banking law specialist, who also brings her skills to bear in corporate insolvency cases. Her legal acumen is there for all to see. **Recent work:** Instructed by Deutsche Bank to oppose an application for a major recovery by Kaupthing Bank.

Adrian Beltrami QC (3 Verulam Buildings) Active both domestically and offshore, he is particularly noted for his work in corporate insolvency disputes and for his expertise in civil fraud. **Strengths:** "He is a measured and effective advocate." **Recent work:** Instructed in a case in Bermuda concerning a claim by the liquidators of feeder funds of Madoff Securities, seeking to recover monies lost through fraud.

Matthew Hardwick QC (3 Verulam Buildings) A rising star at the Insolvency Bar, who maintains an active corporate insolvency practice. His advocacy is highly praised by sources and he is known for his approachable and affable manner. **Strengths:** "Extremely clever, charming and a good, tough advocate." **Recent work:** Acted in a major conspiracy claim arising from the administration and liquidation of Rangers FC.

Angharad Start (3 Verulam Buildings) An expert in large-scale personal and corporate insolvency disputes. Sources praise her for her creativity and idiosyncratic approach to issues. **Strengths:** "Her great strength is that she is a person who can think outside the box." **Recent work:** Acted for the liquidators of Gizmondo UK in an undervalue transaction claim against a former director.

MIDLANDS

Restructuring/Insolvency Midlands
Leading Sets
Band 1
St Philips Chambers *
Leading Silks
Band 1
Khangure Avtar *St Philips Chambers*
Leading Juniors
Band 1
Morgan James *St Philips Chambers* *
Band 2
Bristoll Sandra *St Philips Chambers*
Brown Marc *St Philips Chambers* *
Ensaff Omar *No5 Chambers (ORL)* ◊
Eyre Stephen *St Philips Chambers* *
Weaver Matthew *St Philips Chambers* *

Band 1

St Philips Chambers
See profile on p.886
THE SET
St Philips Chambers is the dominant insolvency team in the Midlands, with a talented group of counsel at all levels of seniority providing considered and effective advice and advocacy across the full range of insolvency-related issues. The set itself is recognised for its highly commercial approach, with solicitors keen to praise its refreshingly relationship-driven service.
Client service: "The clerking is very good; overall the set is just a very slick, very commercial outfit."

SILKS
Avtar Khangure QC A standout insolvency practitioner with a vast amount of experience and an intimidating intellect. He acts for a broad spectrum of clients in insolvency disputes, as well as maintaining a wider commercial and company practice. **Strengths:** "He is the leading insolvency silk in the Midlands." "He is intellectually outstanding."

JUNIORS
James Morgan (see p.676) Highly rated by solicitors for the high standard of his advocacy, and for his considerable experience of handling insolvency disputes. He also represents clients in commercial and company disputes. **Strengths:** "He is technically excellent and incisive." "He is very experienced in all areas of insolvency law, and is an excellent advocate." **Recent work:** He acted successfully for the liquidator of Brian Livesey in securing a major recovery on grounds of misfeasance from three respondents.

Matthew Weaver (see p.748) Strongly recommended by sources as an excellent all-round advocate who provides a high level of technical expertise, quality advocacy and a user-friendly attitude. He acts on all aspects of corporate and personal insolvency. **Strengths:** "He has an excellent technical knowledge of insolvency, and an outstanding commercial approach." "He is knowledgeable, commercial, user-friendly and good on his feet." **Recent work:** He acted for a creditor that put a British Virgin Islands-registered company into administration, opposing applications to terminate the appointment of administrators.

Stephen Eyre (see p.598) A hugely experienced counsel, frequently sought out for his exceptional knowledge of insolvency law. He acts in a variety of commercial and chancery disputes, as well as insolvency issues, and is an accredited mediator. **Strengths:** "He has excellent technical knowledge, and is very user-friendly." "He is reliably excellent, and always well prepared." **Recent work:** He acted in a number of cases covering misfeasance, the validity of a debenture and directors' liabilities arising from litigation against Norton Aluminium.

Marc Brown (see p.558) Highly regarded in the market for his commercial nous and pragmatic approach. He represents clients in a broad range of commercial cases, as well as acting in both corporate and personal insolvency disputes. **Strengths:** "He is reliable, commercial and good value." **Recent work:** He successfully acted for Sparkasse Ludensheid in an action concerning alleged bankruptcy tourism.

Sandra Bristoll A seasoned insolvency practitioner, who primarily acts and advises in corporate insolvency disputes, and also handles directors' duties disputes. She is singled out by sources for her mental agility and stellar client service. **Recent work:** She advised the voluntary liquidators of RC Breweries, and appeared at a hearing regarding a compulsory winding-up petition issued by HMRC.

Other Ranked Lawyers

Omar Ensaff (No5 Chambers) Highly rated in the market for his responsiveness and his considered advice. Sources also praise him as a flexible and effective advocate. He maintains a broad commercial practice, and represents a variety of clients in insolvency and banking litigation. **Strengths:** "He is practical, thinks on his feet, and aims to get his clients what they want." "He is very quick and responsive." **Recent work:** He acted successfully in a challenge to the appointment of an administrator of Care People Limited.

NORTH EASTERN

Restructuring/Insolvency North Eastern
Leading Sets
Band 1
Enterprise Chambers *
Band 2
Kings Chambers *
Leading Silks
New Silks
Jory Hugh *Enterprise Chambers*
Leading Juniors
Band 1
Groves Hugo *Enterprise Chambers*
Jackson Claire *Kings Chambers* *
Temple Eleanor *Kings Chambers* *
Band 2
d'Arcy Eleanor *Kings Chambers* *
Rodger Jonathan *Enterprise Chambers*
Up-and-coming individuals
Bond Kelly *Enterprise Chambers*
◊ (ORL) = Other Ranked Lawyer.
** Indicates set / individual with profile.*
Alphabetical order within each band. Band 1 is highest.

Band 1

Enterprise Chambers
See profile on p.788
THE SET
Enterprise Chambers is a popular choice for insolvency and restructuring matters in the North Eastern Circuit. It offers a strong bench of barristers whose experience covers a wide array of matters, from complex personal insolvency cases to high-value corporate insolvencies.
Client service: "The clerking is excellent – different from the traditional clerking arrangements and far more user-friendly."

SILKS
Hugh Jory QC Has been make silk this year, a move which peers and clients agree was well deserved. He is a first choice for both local and national law firms when contentious insolvency work or shareholder disputes arise. **Strengths:** "He's excellent. He's the shining star of Enterprise Chambers because clients adore him. He's always pragmatic and he rolls up his sleeves." "He's intelligent and extremely relaxed in conference."

JUNIORS
Hugo Groves Qualified as a solicitor, a US attorney and a barrister, and brings this collection of skills to the work he is instructed on. Groves has recently been involved in a range of matters including claims against directors, claims based on failed tax avoidance schemes and breaches of duty cases. **Strengths:** "If you want somebody to fight your corner on his feet there are none better than Hugo." "He is one of the leading cross-border insolvency barristers in the UK."

Jonathan Rodger Handles commercial and chancery matters including a high volume of insolvency cases. He frequently appears in courts across the North of England, most recently focusing on pursuing claims for misfeasance and asset recoveries. **Strengths:** "Jonathan is always willing to give firm advice and back that up in court." **Recent work:** He acted for the administrators of Leaseway Vehicle Services in a series of actions pursuing asset recoveries.

Kelly Bond An up-and-coming chancery practitioner with recognised expertise in insolvency work and a burgeoning client base comprising insolvency practitioners and distressed companies. **Strengths:** "She's very good at anticipating what the opposition's next move will be." "I would have no hesitation putting her up against someone 30-years qualified. I'm confident in her ability." **Recent work:** Acted for the lender in a case against a bankrupt borrower who had failed to execute a mortgage deed over a leasehold property after receiving a mortgage advance.

Band 2

Kings Chambers

See profile on p.918

THE SET

This set has a strong offering in the restructuring and insolvency market, often acting on high-profile cases throughout the North East. Members of chambers act for debtors, companies and office holders in relation to a wide range of issues, including liquidations, receiverships and personal bankruptcies.

Client service: "They have a wide skill set in terms of the nature of the work they can assist on."

JUNIORS

Claire Jackson (see p.636) Centres her work on corporate and personal insolvency law and disputes. She has recently been involved in several high-profile insolvency cases dealing with high-street chains, athletes and sports clubs. **Strengths:** "She always impresses me with her advice and willingness to tackle the matter at hand wholeheartedly and efficiently." "She's technically very strong, solution-focused and commercial." **Recent work:** Acted on behalf of Manchester City Council in relation to the bankruptcy of an individual, successfully opposing numerous appeals to annul the bankruptcy.

Eleanor d'Arcy (see p.583) Remains a popular choice for advocacy concerning insolvency and restructuring issues. **Strengths:** "She's very well respected by colleagues and the judiciary, and her addressing skills are very good." **Recent work:** Represented a claimant in the Court of Appeal, where she succeeded in proving unlawful eviction of the claimant. She also proceeded to successfully appeal the quantum of damages to the claimant.

Eleanor Temple (see p.735) An established restructuring and insolvency barrister with noted expertise in corporate governance and shareholders' rights. **Strengths:** "She has a sound grasp of everything arising in the context of insolvency cases and she's also very user-friendly." "She has proven ability both before judges and on paper. She can persuade a judge and is a forceful and robust advocate." **Recent work:** Acted on a wrongful trading action against four directors of circuit board manufacturer Circatex, in relation to a claim of £12.5 million. Successfully achieved a recovery on behalf of the liquidators.

NORTHERN

Restructuring/Insolvency Northern	
Leading Sets	
Band 1	
Exchange Chambers *	
Kings Chambers *	
Leading Silks	
Band 1	
Anderson Lesley	*Kings Chambers* *
Cawson Mark	*Exchange Chambers*
Chaisty Paul	*Kings Chambers* *
Band 2	
Casement David	*Kings Chambers* *
Leading Juniors	
Band 1	
Berragan Neil	*Kings Chambers* *
Doyle Louis	*Kings Chambers* *
Maynard-Connor Giles	*Exchange Chambers* *
Mohyuddin David	*Exchange Chambers* *
Walmisley Lisa	*Kings Chambers* *
Band 2	
Sandbach Carly	*Exchange Chambers* *
Band 3	
Linklater Lisa	*Exchange Chambers*
Tindall Paul	*St. James's Chambers (ORL)* ◊
* *Indicates set / individual with profile.*	
◊ *(ORL) = Other Ranked Lawyer.*	

Band 1

Exchange Chambers

See profile on p.910

THE SET

Exchange Chambers offers a wealth of experience in all matters pertaining to restructuring and insolvency issues. The set is a popular choice for both individuals and office holders in relation to misfeasance claims, asset tracing and recovery and injunctive relief, among other work.

Client service: "They're first class. They don't just give legalistic advice, they're commercial too."

SILKS

Mark Cawson QC Continues to be recognised as a market-leading restructuring and insolvency barrister. Areas of expertise include defence against deceit claims and claims against directors. **Strengths:** "Ten out of ten. His legal knowledge is superb and it's a great advantage that he sits as a judge as you get extra perspective on problems you might face." **Recent work:** Successfully represented a bank in a multimillion-pound guarantee claim against the director of a property development company.

JUNIORS

Giles Maynard-Connor (see p.665) Highly regarded for his work on complex insolvency cases in the Northern Circuit and elsewhere. **Strengths:** "He's first rate. He's a bright guy and thinks well on his feet." "He's very easy to get along with, and clients like him. He is someone whose advice I have faith in and trust." "He is commercial, robust and supportive of the client in difficult circumstances."

David Mohyuddin (see p.675) Handles all aspects of insolvency work and regularly represents the Secretary of State for Business, Innovation & Skills in directors' disqualification and public interest winding-up cases. **Strengths:** "He's a rising star in the region. He's good technically and also extremely commercial as he understands what the client wants." "He gets you from A to B as cost-effectively as possible and delivers a good outcome." **Recent work:** Has continued to represent Sonae Group in an ongoing instruction regarding a freezing injunction.

Lisa Linklater Has a growing reputation in the region for her insolvency practice. She covers a broad spectrum of insolvency matters from corporate to personal insolvency. **Recent work:** Represented a creditor of MF Global in the process of appealing the administrators' refusal of proof of debt.

Carly Sandbach (see p.714) Considered to be a rising star in restructuring and insolvency matters. She has experience in a wide range of insolvency regimes, including administrations, receiverships and corporate voluntary arrangements. **Strengths:** "A good, confident advocate and mediator."

Kings Chambers

See profile on p.918

THE SET

Kings Chambers operates throughout the Northern and North Eastern Circuit. Members of this set have considerable experience in a range of matters including corporate voluntary arrangements, personal bankruptcy and cross-border insolvency.

Client service: "They've always had a number of exceptional people there. They are true specialists."

SILKS

Lesley Anderson QC (see p.536) Hugely well respected in dispute resolution pertaining to corporate and personal insolvencies. She regularly acts for the UK government in directors' disqualification and public interest winding-up cases. **Strengths:** "She is as impressive as ever and works on high-profile cases." "A truly exceptional silk." "If there's anything difficult or complex you need your number-one team on, she's your first port of call." **Recent work:** Successfully acted for Lloyds TSB and the receivers in a case concerning claims of breach of contract and duty relating to the alleged undervalued sales of commercial properties.

Paul Chaisty QC (see p.568) Considered a market leader in insolvency litigation and is renowned in the region for his work for banks, major public companies and multinationals. **Strengths:** "A first-class barrister." "An unbelievably effective advocate who is best on his feet. His cross-examination can be devastating." **Recent work:** Instructed on a director disqualification case relating to Magnus Properties, a group of companies that were placed into administration and the subject of allegations of breach of fiduciary duty.

David Casement QC A recognised commercial chancery silk with an emphasis on heavyweight insolvency cases. He regularly appears in the High Court and has recently been appointed chairman of the Northern Circuit Commercial Bar Association. **Strengths:** "He is very bright, very articulate and a real team player." "When you have him on your side you really do feel special." **Recent work:** Acted on the bankruptcy of Al Midani, where he represented a trustee in tracing assets across the Middle East and Europe.

JUNIORS

Neil Berragan (see p.548) Handles a range of company and insolvency disputes. Berragan regularly advises and acts on shareholder disputes, among his other insolvency work. **Strengths:** "He is a strong and measured advocate." "He has a real gravitas about him." **Recent work:** Acted in connection with a claim against a former director by an insurance company regarding the fraudulent misappropriation of funds.

Louis Doyle (see p.590) Regularly acts on novel and urgent insolvency matters, predominantly focusing on breach of duty and transaction avoidance. Doyle often handles cases with a cross-border component. **Strengths:** "A leader in his field – the go-to guy in insolvency in Leeds." "He's well informed, down to earth, very good with clients and performs well on his feet." **Recent work:** Acted for the administrators of high-street retailer Burdens, which involved issues over security, title and credit claims.

Lisa Walmisley (see p.745) Recognised expertise in transaction avoidance litigation, bolstered by wide experience in the full spectrum of restructuring and insolvency issues. Often represents the office holder and insolvent entity. **Strengths:** "She's always well prepared and goes that extra mile for the client." "A strong performer in court." "She's good at interacting with clients in conferences, and she's very user-friendly." **Recent work:** Advised in connection with a claim against former directors of Dunweedin for misfeasance, transactions at an undervalue and preferential payments.

Other Ranked Lawyers

Paul Tindall (St. James's Chambers) Focuses on insolvency law alongside his commercial and property practices. Tindall's strength in the insolvency sphere has led him to work on some complex administrations in the region. **Strengths:** "Sensible, pragmatic advice." "He thinks outside the box." **Recent work:** Advised in relation to the administration of Arthur Holgate, with particular reference to an application to revoke alleged partisan proposals by the administrator.

WESTERN

Restructuring/Insolvency Western
Leading Sets
Band 1
Guildhall Chambers *
Leading Silks
Star individuals
Davies Stephen *Guildhall Chambers*
New Silks
Sims Hugh *Guildhall Chambers*
Leading Juniors
Band 1
Ascroft Richard *Guildhall Chambers* *
Bamford Jeremy *Guildhall Chambers*
Brockman Christopher *Guildhall Chambers*
French Paul *Guildhall Chambers*
Ramel Stefan *Guildhall Chambers*
Band 2
Briggs Nicholas *Guildhall Chambers*
Brown Daisy *Guildhall Chambers*
Doyle Holly *Guildhall Chambers*
Gibb Katherine *Guildhall Chambers*
Levy Neil *Guildhall Chambers* *
Maher Martha *St John's Chambers (ORL)* ◇ Ⓐ
Passfield Simon *Guildhall Chambers*
* *Indicates set / individual with profile.*
◇ *(ORL) = Other Ranked Lawyer.*
Ⓐ *direct access (see p.11).*

Band 1

Guildhall Chambers
See profile on p.890

THE SET

Guildhall Chambers is recognised across the country as the leading specialist restructuring and insolvency team on the Western Circuit, in terms of both the undoubted expertise of the set's members and the unparalleled level of client care provided by staff and members alike.

Client service: "The clerks, led by Justin Emmett, are reliable, commercial and willing to invest in building a strong relationship with clients."

SILKS

Stephen Davies QC Widely recognised as the circuit's leading insolvency silk, he is especially highlighted for his expertise in handling directors' disqualification proceedings. His courtroom presence and team approach to cases are frequently highlighted. **Strengths:** "He is a phenomenal counsel – an aggressive advocate, yet extremely affable." "He is a tenacious advocate, and a robust cross-examiner."

Hugh Sims QC Acts in both corporate and personal insolvency situations, and is particularly adept at managing directors' disqualification proceedings. He is highly regarded as a go-to practitioner for heavy insolvency disputes. **Strengths:** "He has a very keen mind, and is a simply excellent trial advocate." "He is exceptional both with clients and at trial."

JUNIORS

Stefan Ramel Well recognised for his impressive contributions to both corporate and personal insolvency cases. He is highly praised in the market for his articulate strategic thinking and courtroom flair. **Strengths:** "He is very thorough and effective, in court and out." "He has a good tactical mind, and provides useful insights." **Recent work:** He acted for the Secretary of State in a successful disqualification action in Truro County Court.

Richard Ascroft (see p.538) Highly regarded as an expert adviser in the field of corporate and personal insolvency, as well as for his technical knowledge of directors' duties. Aside from his undoubted intellectual strength, sources also highlight him as an affable and approachable client-friendly counsel. **Strengths:** "He is very user-friendly, and particularly strong on technical matters." "He is very good on claims against directors." **Recent work:** He acted for the trustee in bankruptcy in a claim for declaratory relief in respect of a property in the name of the bankrupt, occupied by his parents.

Paul French Hailed by market sources as a true expert in insolvency law, whether it be corporate or personal. He is rated most highly for his technical excellence and seemingly inexhaustible knowledge of the law. **Strengths:** "He a walking, talking, charming encyclopaedia of insolvency law." "He has a fantastic knowledge of case law, and is very responsive." **Recent work:** He was instructed by the defendants in disqualification proceedings relating to alleged misfeasant loans to connected companies.

Simon Passfield Praised extensively for his intellectual strength, his work ethic and his knowledge of insolvency law. He advises and represents clients in corporate and personal insolvency situations. **Strengths:** "He is unbelievably sharp; he knows the answers to the most complex questions almost immediately." **Recent work:** He acted for a trustee in bankruptcy in an action alleging that several major transfers of property between a bankrupt and his wife were shams.

Christopher Brockman Highly regarded as an experienced and effective counsellor, capable of handling disputes in all areas of corporate and personal insolvency. He is particularly praised by sources for his willingness to "roll up his sleeves" and take charge of a dispute. **Strengths:** "He is a good lateral thinker, and a good all-round insolvency counsel." **Recent work:** He acted on behalf of HMRC in appointing a provisional liquidator, and obtaining an urgent freezing order against a recipient of company funds.

Nicholas Briggs Has a broad commercial and insolvency practice, and is highly rated for his intellectual agility and pragmatic advice. Sources appreciate his experience, client care skills and commercial sense. **Strengths:** "He has an ability to pick up issues quickly, and provide concise, clear advice." "He is good with clients, calm, practical and knowledgeable." **Recent work:** He acted for the liquidators in a high-value claim against company directors for transactions at an undervalue, preferences and unlawful dividends.

Holly Doyle Acts in a wide range of commercial and insolvency disputes, and is highly regarded for her work in both corporate and personal insolvencies. She is recognised as a commercial and effective adviser and advocate. **Strengths:** "She is a pragmatic and very proactive advocate." **Recent work:** She acted successfully for the trustee in bankruptcy in seeking a possession and sale order of a property seemingly owned by the bankrupt and his wife and son as joint tenants.

Jeremy Bamford Specialises in insolvencies, directors' duties claims and insolvency-related professional negligence claims. His experience, attitude and creative strategy are all singled out for high praise by sources. **Strengths:** "He is always innovative in his approach, and operates with an invaluable commercial realism." "He is experienced, user-friendly and a safe pair of hands." **Recent work:** He was instructed by RBS to seek retrospective permission to pursue professional negligence actions against bankrupt former solicitors.

Daisy Brown Has a broad chancery and commercial practice, as well as being an experienced property and insolvency adviser and litigator. Her insolvency work covers both corporate and personal issues, and she is highly recommended by sources in both areas. **Recent work:** She was instructed to act in a contested winding-up petition in First Choice Build Group v Seasons Solutions Ltd.

Katherine Gibb Acts in all areas of commercial and personal insolvency, representing a wide range of clients. She is particularly skilled at handling employment-related insolvency issues. **Recent work:** She successfully acted for the claimants in a number of bankruptcy petitions arising out of a partnership dispute.

Neil Levy (see p.655) A highly regarded specialist in banking and financial services law, he leverages that significantly in his insolvency work. He is particularly adept at handling Law of Property Act receiverships, and is highly praised for his thorough and commercial advice. **Strengths:** "He provides comprehensive and clear-cut advice." **Recent work:** He acted in a successful appeal against a judge's refusal to act on a bill of sale after a debtor's bankruptcy.

Other Ranked Lawyers

Martha Maher (St John's Chambers) Highly rated as an adviser and advocate for handling corporate, personal and partnership insolvencies. She is particularly highly praised for her team-driven and engaging approach to her instructions, and for her exhaustive attention to detail.

SHIPPING & COMMODITIES: An Introduction

Contributed by Simon Rainey QC Quadrant Chambers

Shipping and commodities practitioners have remained busy in 2014, with the economic downturn continuing to fuel litigation, and geopolitical upsets have started to translate into legal disputes. There is no apparent sign of these trends changing in 2015.

The rush of work arising directly from the 2008 crash in the shipping market is starting to slow as cases relating to the immediate aftermath of the economic collapse in mid-2008 are resolved. Nevertheless, recent decisions such as Fulton Shipping v Globalia on the effect of the 2008 crash on the measure of damages in a charter party dispute are a timely reminder that crash-related litigation is still working its way through arbitrations and the courts.

More generally, the economic downturn continues to make for difficult trading conditions and to exert a significant influence on shipping and commodities practice. The oversupply of tonnage, built in the relatively prosperous times preceding the crash, remains the major problem. The increasing cost of fuel has exacerbated the harsh trading environment and resulted in a sharp rise in the number of charter party bunker disputes.

Happily, Gulf of Aden piracy continued its steady decline during 2013 following the introduction of armed guards in the Gulf of Aden. This, combined with increasing use of detailed piracy clauses in shipping contracts, had been thought to herald a falling-off in piracy-related litigation. However, as the problem is abated on the East coast of Africa, different but equally difficult problems have arisen from the increasing number of West African vessel seizures and cargo thefts, especially of oil and petroleum products in increasingly sophisticated piratical ship-to-ship enforced transfers of cargoes. Subsequent detentions of vessels post-piracy by local states have added to the complexities. Piracy, now in its changed West African guise, looks set to remain an important area of practice for some time to come.

Economic sanctions have continued to be a considerable source of work, especially at the advisory level. Over the past few years, Iranian sanctions have been the most prevalent and have caused the greatest disruption to international trade. With the Geneva talks in November 2013 and the subsequent relaxing of Iranian sanctions, some predict a decline in Iranian sanctions work in the medium term, although given the Protean nature of the complex scope of sanctions to imagine that the fallout from Iranian sanctions will not continue to raise interesting and difficult questions for practitioners is perhaps premature. Outside Iran, sanctions in Syria and Sudan remain important for shipping and commodities practitioners. However, the most immediate pressing concern in 2014 is the impact of sanctions imposed by the EU and the USA against Ukrainian and Russian individuals and companies as a result of the turmoil in Ukraine. This is likely to have a considerable impact on commodities trading. The scope of these sanctions remains unclear, and significant disputes as to the effect of these sanctions (and to whom they apply) look inevitable. Going forward, contracts with a Ukrainian element are likely to adopt more bespoke sanctions clauses following in the steps of Iranian sanctions clauses which have become common in the past few years.

Another important geopolitical issue which has reverberated around these practice areas is natural resource protectionism. Governments faced with economic fragility and political instability are increasingly focusing on commodities control, as recently seen in Indonesia's ban on the export of unprocessed mineral ores and Bolivia's recently increased expropriation powers. The impact on shipping and commodities practice is likely to be appreciable in the year to come, mirroring the similar impact which the Russian ban on various agricultural commodities in August 2010 had. In the Courts, a number of cases on appeal from trade arbitration panels dealing with the consequences of that ban have been a feature of 2014, e.g. Bunge v Nidera (now on its way to the Supreme Court).

Certain trade associations have sought in the light of the experience of the Russian ban to revise their standard form provisions where sellers are prevented in this way from performing. GAFTA introduced a new standard "Prevention of Shipment" (CIF) and "Prevention of Delivery" (FOB) clause, replacing the much litigated Prohibition, Force Majeure and Strikes Clauses in various forms, with effect of all new contracts from 1st June 2014. Time will tell if these new clauses reduce disputes.

As with last year, 2014 has seen a great many shipbuilding arbitrations being brought in London. The volatility of pricing for tonnage in the present market has left both builders and buyers exposed to potentially heavy losses. Naturally, cancellations and litigation have ensued. The lack of available credit has aggravated these problems for parties to shipbuilding contracts, which show no sign of abating in 2014. Sales of existing vessels have also proven again to be a fertile source of litigation. The most prominent recent example is The Griffon, deciding an important point of principle under the Norwegian Saleform.

From a procedural perspective, the Supreme Court in The Alexandros T has given further guidance on the important question of when parallel European proceedings will be permissible. This is a helpful reminder that conflict of laws continues to provide a steady stream of work for shipping and commodities practitioners despite European harmonisation measures.

Domestically, the important procedural matters to note in the past year are the introduction of costs budgeting for smaller Commercial Court cases and the new rigorous approach to procedural deadlines following Mitchell v News Group. These changes are not, as yet, relevant to arbitration proceedings and the Commercial Court has thus far taken a pragmatic approach to both these new developments. Practitioners will no doubt get a better feel for the limits of the costs control and Mitchell jurisdictions through more interim applications over the next year.

Contents:

LONDON

Shipping & Commodities London
Leading Sets
Band 1
20 Essex Street *
Quadrant Chambers *
Band 2
7 King's Bench Walk *
Band 3
Essex Court Chambers *
Stone Chambers *
Band 4
4 Pump Court *
Alphabetical order within each band. Band 1 is highest.
** Indicates set / individual with profile.*
◊ (ORL) = Other Ranked Lawyer.

Shipping & Commodities London
Leading Silks
Band 1
Ashcroft Michael *20 Essex Street*
Brenton Timothy *7 King's Bench Walk*
Goldstone David *Quadrant Chambers*
Matthews Duncan *20 Essex Street*
Parsons Luke *Quadrant Chambers*
Persey Lionel *Quadrant Chambers*
Rainey Simon *Quadrant Chambers*
Young Timothy *20 Essex Street*
Band 2
Baker Andrew *20 Essex Street*
Berry Steven *Essex Court Chambers*
Blackburn Elizabeth *Stone Chambers* *
Bright Robert *7 King's Bench Walk*
Croall Simon *Quadrant Chambers*
Dunning Graham *Essex Court Chambers*
Edey Philip *20 Essex Street*
Hancock Christopher *20 Essex Street*
Healy Siobán *7 King's Bench Walk*
Hill Timothy *Stone Chambers* *
Jacobs Nigel *Quadrant Chambers*
Kendrick Dominic *7 King's Bench Walk*
Kimmins Charles *20 Essex Street*
Milligan Iain *20 Essex Street*
Russell Jeremy *Quadrant Chambers*
Schaff Alistair *7 King's Bench Walk*
Southern Richard *7 King's Bench Walk*
Waller Richard *7 King's Bench Walk*
Band 3
Allen David *7 King's Bench Walk*
Bailey David *7 King's Bench Walk*
Blanchard Claire *Essex Court Chambers*
Bryan Simon *Essex Court Chambers*
Butcher Christopher *7 King's Bench Walk*
Coburn Michael *20 Essex Street*
Cooper Nigel *Quadrant Chambers*
Flynn Vernon *Essex Court Chambers*
Kverndal Simon *Quadrant Chambers*
Lord Richard *Brick Court Chambers (ORL)* ◊
MacDonald Eggers Peter *7 King's Bench Walk*
Melwani Poonam *Quadrant Chambers*
Smith Christopher *Essex Court Chambers*
Thomas Robert *Quadrant Chambers*
Band 4
Collett Michael *20 Essex Street*
Eaton Nigel *Essex Court Chambers*
Gee Steven *Stone Chambers*
Gunning Alexander *4 Pump Court* *
Hofmeyr Stephen *7 King's Bench Walk*
Karia Chirag *Quadrant Chambers* *
Kenny Stephen *7 King's Bench Walk*
Masters Sara *20 Essex Street*
Saloman Timothy *7 King's Bench Walk*
Selvaratnam Vasanti *Stone Chambers* *
Tozzi Nigel *4 Pump Court* *
Turner James M *Quadrant Chambers* *
Vineall Nicholas *4 Pump Court* *
New Silks
Davey Michael *Quadrant Chambers*
Lewis David *20 Essex Street*
O'Sullivan Sean *4 Pump Court* *
Russell John *Quadrant Chambers*
Leading Juniors
Band 1
Kenny Julian *20 Essex Street*
Priday Charles *7 King's Bench Walk*
Band 2
Aswani Ravi *Stone Chambers* *
Buckingham Stewart *Quadrant Chambers*
Nolan Michael *Quadrant Chambers*
Phillips Nevil *Quadrant Chambers*
Smith Christopher M *Quadrant Chambers*
Band 3
Byam-Cook Henry *20 Essex Street*
Craig Nicholas *3 Verulam Buildings (ORL)* ◊ *
Holmes Michael *7 King's Bench Walk*
Hopkins Philippa *Essex Court Chambers*
Jones Mark *Stone Chambers* *
Jones Susannah *20 Essex Street*
Kimbell John *Quadrant Chambers*
King Edmund *Essex Court Chambers*
Leabeater James *4 Pump Court* *
Macey-Dare Thomas *Quadrant Chambers*
Parker Benjamin *7 King's Bench Walk*
Passmore John *Quadrant Chambers*
Pillow Nathan *Essex Court Chambers*
Pounds Caroline *Quadrant Chambers*
Whitehead Thomas *Stone Chambers* *
Wright Alexander *4 Pump Court* *
Band 4
Casey N G *7 King's Bench Walk*
Debattista Charles *Stone Chambers* *
Healy Sandra *7 King's Bench Walk* *
Hosking Ruth *Quadrant Chambers*
Lightfoot Jeremy *Stone Chambers* *
Morgan Gemma *Quadrant Chambers*
Pearce Luke *20 Essex Street*
Riches Philip *Stone Chambers* *
Sutherland Jessica *7 King's Bench Walk*
Toms Paul *Quadrant Chambers*
Toney Rachel *Stone Chambers* *
Watthey James *4 Pump Court* [A] *
Up-and-coming individuals
Davies Josephine *20 Essex Street*
Henderson Neil *4 Pump Court* [A] *
Sarll Richard *7 King's Bench Walk*
Stevens Andrew *4 Pump Court* *
Turner Adam *7 King's Bench Walk*
Walsh David *Quadrant Chambers*

Band 1

20 Essex Street

See profile on p.794

THE SET

This highly regarded commercial set is considered by many to be "the market leader on both the commodities side and the shipping side." It is noted for its depth and quality of expertise, especially amongst its silks, who are consistently involved in the most complex and high-profile dry shipping and commodities disputes in the industry.

Client service: Neil Palmer and Brian Lee head up a highly regarded and "very service-oriented" clerking team.

SILKS

Timothy Young QC Has a broad practice encompassing a range of issues, including insurance, shipping and commodities disputes. He appears before all manner of fora, including the Court of Appeal and international arbitration tribunals. **Strengths:** "His advocacy is smooth, effortless and effective." "He is good at identifying issues and solutions."

Michael Ashcroft QC Advises on a range of matters, including shipping, commodities and insurance disputes. His clients include both shipowners and insurance brokers. **Strengths:** "He is a brain on legs who has a very succinct way of putting things." "He gets into the detail and masters the papers impeccably." **Recent work:** Represented the shipowners of the 'Alexandros T' in a Supreme Court appeal concerning questions of jurisdiction arising out of an insurance dispute.

Andrew Baker QC Represents clients in a variety of cases, including both dry and wet shipping disputes. He is experienced at assisting clients with arbitrations, and is strong on commodities and international sale of goods disputes. **Strengths:** "He has a very straightforward analytical approach, which he puts forward in an attractive manner without histrionics." "He needs an incredibly bright judge to follow his incredibly clever arguments." **Recent work:** Acted in a USD5 million loss of earnings claim arising out of a collision between the 'Astipalaia' and the 'Hanjin Shenzhen'.

Philip Edey QC Appears for clients in both arbitration and judicial proceedings. He advises on international cases concerning a range of matters, including charter party, shipbuilding and cargo disputes. **Strengths:** "He is off the Richter scale in terms of cleverness." "He is very good at putting across a difficult point and making clear." **Recent work:** Acted in Maple Maritime Inc v Wengfu Intertrade, successfully obtaining an anti-suit injunction.

Christopher Hancock QC Highly regarded by the Shipping Bar for his work in both dry and wet disputes, he regularly handles shipbuilding contract and collision cases. He is also noted for his cargo and insurance-related expertise. **Strengths:** "He is extremely knowledgeable about all forms of insurance and shipping law." "He is one of the best performers at the Shipping Bar." **Recent work:** Acted for the London Steam-Ship Owners' Mutual Insurance Association in a EUR4.5 billion oil pollution case against the Kingdom of Spain and the French Republic.

Charles Kimmins QC Particularly highly regarded for his expertise in dry shipping matters, including charter party and bill of lading disputes. He is also noted for his work in trading disputes concerning petroleum products. **Strengths:** "He has a very smooth, attractive way about him and he puts things across very well." "He is very thorough and looks at all the angles in a case." **Recent work:** Represented Vitol in a Court of Appeal hearing concerning the alleged unlawful detention of a vessel in Nigeria.

Iain Milligan QC Head of chambers, who advises on a wide range of commercial matters. Although his practice is broad, he is particularly well regarded for his work in a range of shipping, commodities and insurance disputes. **Strengths:** "His advocacy style is very economical. He speaks clearly and only makes the points he wants to make once." **Recent work:** Represented the shipowners of the 'Alexandros T' in a Supreme Court appeal concerning questions of jurisdiction arising out of an insurance dispute.

Michael Collett QC A recent silk, particularly noted for his work in commodities and international trade disputes. He also regularly acts on a range of dry shipping disputes, including charter party and bill of lading claims. **Strengths:** "He is very good at thinking on his feet." "He is terribly meticulous and polite." **Recent work:** Advised on cargo claims and a limitation action arising out of the total loss of the 'Atlantik Confidence'.

Sara Masters QC Has a particularly broad practice with expertise in both dry and wet shipping cases, as well as sale of goods and commodities disputes. Also regularly acts as both an arbitrator and a mediator. **Strengths:** "She is very responsive and commercial." "She is very client-friendly and works well in a team." **Recent work:** Acted for United Arab Shipping on an application to vary an anti-suit injunction against an insurance company located in Kuwait.

David Lewis QC Represents a range of clients, including charterers and international energy companies, in international trade and dry shipping matters. He is noted in particular for his international arbitration work. **Strengths:** "He is responsive, effective and clear in his analysis of problems." "He is an amazingly easy person to work with and a good strategist." **Recent work:** Advised on a USD4 million claim concerning the non-performance of a sale contract to supply crude oil to Ghana.

Michael Coburn QC Advises on a range of international sale of goods, shipping and commodities disputes. He acts in both judicial and arbitration proceedings. **Recent work:** Acted in Griffon Shipping LLC v Firodi Shipping Ltd, an appeal concerning the remedies available to a seller when a buyer fails to make a deposit under a Norwegian Saleform.

Duncan Matthews QC Acts for a range of clients in an array of shipping and carriage of goods disputes. He is particularly noted for his role in advising shipyards on shipbuilding contractual disputes. **Strengths:** "He knows how to take all the good points and really makes it work for him."

JUNIORS

Julian Kenny A particularly highly regarded junior, who advises on a range of dry shipping cases, including shipbuilding, ship sale and charter party disputes. **Strengths:** "He distils issues into succinct points." "He is able to go through a set of documents, work out the important issues and provide clear analysis."

Henry Byam-Cook Regularly appears in high-profile shipping disputes. He is particularly noted for his expertise in charter party disputes, and is praised for his efforts in a range of other matters, including shipbuilding arbitrations and cargo claims. **Strengths:** "He is very thoughtful and hard-working." "He is succinct and to the point." **Recent work:** Acted for the claimants in Caresse Navigation v Office Nationale de l'Electricité, an appeal concerning whether a jurisdiction clause had been incorporated into a bill of lading.

Susannah Jones Handles a range of dry shipping and insurance disputes, and acts on behalf of charterers and commodities houses, amongst other clients. **Strengths:** "She is very diligent and has an impressive command of detail when handling complex cases." **Recent work:** Acted for the director general of a major state-owned Russian shipping company in relation to allegations of fraud.

Luke Pearce Considered by many to be a rising star, he advises on a range of dry shipping disputes, including matters concerning charter parties and bills of lading. He is also noted for his commodities and insurance expertise. **Strengths:** "He drafts very well." "He was unflappable, very polite and quick as a flash with all the detail." **Recent work:** Represented Ecom in a Commercial Court claim for an anti-suit injunction arising out of a contract concerning the sale of cotton.

Josephine Davies An up-and-coming advocate, noted in particular for her involvement in a range of shipping disputes, from piracy to charter party-related matters. She is also active in a number of commodities disputes. **Strengths:** "She is able to interpret the technical aspects of a case and put it in a language that the client understands." **Recent work:** Advised on Kuwait Rocks Co v AMN Bulkcarriers, an arbitration appeal concerning the meaning of the payment obligation in a NYPE charter party.

Quadrant Chambers

See profile on p.854

THE SET

Quadrant Chambers has an enviable pedigree in shipping law and offers an array of talent across all levels of seniority. Sources highlight the "sheer approachability" of the members here and applaud them for their efforts in tackling the most complex dry and wet shipping disputes. Individuals here are regularly involved in the most important cases of the day. For example, they acted in the 'Saga Explorer' case, the leading authority on the construction of so-called Retla clauses, and were involved in 'Ocean Victory' and 'Nordstar', the biggest safe port cases of the year.

Client service: Gary Ventura leads a team of clerks who are considered "very efficient and easy to deal with." The barristers at the set are noted for their commerciality and represent "great value," according to instructing solicitors.

SILKS

David Goldstone QC A highly respected silk, who has expertise in wet and dry shipping disputes, and leads on a range of high-profile, complex matters. **Strengths:** "He is extremely bright and capable of getting on top of a lot of material very quickly." "He has one of these excellent brains that surprises you." **Recent work:** Acted for the sub-charterers in the 'Ocean Victory' case, USD150 million safe port litigation concerning the total loss of the vessel.

Luke Parsons QC Head of chambers and hugely respected by both peers and clients. He is particularly well regarded for his breadth of expertise in shipping, and is noted for his involvement in complex and high-value wet and dry litigation and arbitrations. **Strengths:** "He is a very measured and smooth advocate." **Recent work:** Acted in a case concerning a sugar party charter. The claim arose after a ship was stuck in port for over a month waiting to load a cargo.

Lionel Persey QC A respected advocate, noted in particular for his work on complex dry and wet shipping cases. His broad practice sees him handle various shipbuilding disputes, safe port and salvage claims. **Strengths:** "He has a very good sense of judgement." "He is a focused and tenacious advocate." **Recent work:** Acted for Ferrostaal in a shipbuilding arbitration arising out of the cancellation of contracts for two vessels.

Simon Rainey QC A widely admired advocate, who is highlighted for his expertise in high-value dry and wet shipping disputes. His affectionate nickname 'Brainy Rainey' serves as a testament to his reputation among his peers. **Strengths:** "He is one of those super silk guys who has judges eating out of his hands." "He has the gift of going straight to the problem." **Recent work:** Acted for Front Ace in a high-value collision case where damages exceeded USD50 million.

Simon Croall QC Has a broad practice encompassing international trade, shipping and commodities disputes. His clients include commodities companies, charterers and shipowners. **Recent work:** Represented Glencore in a USD10 million dispute relating to the misappropriation of a cargo of oil in Kenya.

Nigel Jacobs QC Has a broad marine practice and advises on a range of high-profile cases. He represents clients in a breadth of marine insurance and wet shipping matters, and is also particularly well regarded for his expertise in admiralty disputes. **Strengths:** "He is very responsive and his advice is strategically very good." **Recent work:** Represented the cargo interests in the 'Atlantik Confidence' case, which concerned the total loss of a ship in the Arabian Sea.

Jeremy Russell QC Particularly highly regarded for his work in complex wet shipping disputes, including unsafe port and salvage cases. He also acts as an accredited mediator and salvage arbitrator. **Strengths:** "He is very commercial and knowledgeable, and understands the industry." "He is a confident advocate who is at the top of his game." **Recent work:** Acted for hull insurers Gard on a dispute against China National Chartering concerning recovery of a wrecked vessel.

Nigel Cooper QC Particularly well regarded for his work in dry shipping and insurance disputes. He is also noted for his niche superyacht practice and offshore-related work. **Strengths:** "He is very approachable and conveys his points with clarity." **Recent work:** Acted in the case of BHP Billiton AG v TMT Asia, successfully representing the claimant in obtaining a claim of USD114 million.

Simon Kverndal QC Praised for his work in dry and wet shipping disputes, including shipbuilding and ship sale disputes. He is particularly renowned for his international arbitration practice. **Strengths:**

"He effortlessly fuses remarkable legal proficiency with commercial mindedness and pragmatism." "He is exceptionally able and knows how to present the case best according to the court in which he has to operate."

Poonam Melwani QC Has a broad commercial practice, and expertise in dry and wet shipping and marine insurance disputes. She regularly advises clients in both judicial and arbitration hearings. **Strengths:** "She has a good ability to think outside the box." "She is very tenacious and hard-working." **Recent work:** Advised in Latin American Investments Ltd v Maroil Trading, a USD100 million dispute concerning the operation and management of 15 ships.

Robert Thomas QC Particularly highly regarded for his dry shipping and commodities expertise, and also noted for his wet shipping background. His practice covers a range of matters, including claims relating to charter parties, bills of lading and shipbuilding contracts. **Strengths:** "He is very accessible and user-friendly." "He is willing to roll his sleeves up and get into the detail." **Recent work:** Acted for the claimants in the 'Saga Explorer' case, a misrepresentation matter brought against issuers of bills of lading.

James Turner QC (see p.741) A barrister with considerable experience in wet and dry shipping matters. He is also noted for his expertise in trade finance matters. **Strengths:** "He is incredibly hard-working and manages to get to grips with enormous quantities of facts." "He is exceptionally responsive." **Recent work:** Acted on behalf of the owners in the 'Ocean Victory' case, a major salvage claim worth more than USD130 million.

Chirag Karia QC (see p.642) Noted for his broad practice encompassing dry shipping, international trade and insurance disputes. He also has previous experience as an attorney in California. **Strengths:** "He is good at explaining to clients how the law works." **Recent work:** Represented the shipowners in the 'Crudesky' case, which considered whether a detention and fine imposed by the Nigerian government constituted a force majeure.

Michael Davey QC Advises on salvage disputes and other wet shipping-related matters, as well as a number of dry shipping and insurance disputes. **Strengths:** "He has superb judgement and is intelligent and hard-working." "The advice that we have had has been very clear and to the point." **Recent work:** Acted on behalf of Fish & Fish, a claimant in a collision dispute against Sea Shepherd UK.

John Russell QC Particularly highly regarded for his dry shipping work, acting on cargo claims, charter party and bill of lading disputes. He is also noted for his expertise in yacht claims. **Strengths:** "What really stood out was his attention to detail, and the way he cut through difficult issues to come up with an answer that appealed to the tribunal." "He is very approachable and clear in the advice he gives." **Recent work:** Represented BP in a charter party dispute against Target Shipping.

JUNIORS

Stewart Buckingham A well-regarded junior in the shipping industry. He advises on a plethora of maritime disputes, including those relating to shipbuilding and commodities. **Strengths:** "He makes his point calmly and precisely." "I have never seen him get worked up under pressure." **Recent work:** Acted on Minerva Navigation v Oceana Shipping, a charter party dispute concerning the correct interpretation of an off-hire clause.

Michael Nolan Acts on a range of dry shipping disputes, including bill of lading, charter party and shipbuilding claims. He is also noted for his knowledge of the sea fishing industry and harbour law. **Strengths:** "He is tenacious in arguing our cases." "He is considerably experienced, very knowledgeable and a good team player." **Recent work:** Acted for the sellers in the Seagrain v Glencore grain case, which concerned attempts to cancel a contract following actions taken by the Russian government prohibiting the export of grain.

Nevil Phillips Noted for his encyclopaedic knowledge and is a contributor to leading maritime law texts. His expertise covers a range of wet and dry shipping disputes, as well as international trade matters. **Strengths:** "He strikes the right balance between being easy to work with and being thorough technically." "He gives very clear and cogent advice." **Recent work:** Represented the shipowners in the 'Spar Vessels' case, a claim arising out of three letters of guarantee against the insolvent charterer's parent company.

Christopher Smith Has a broad practice encompassing an array of dry shipping and shipbuilding disputes. He is also noted for his role in energy disputes. He appears in both judicial proceedings and arbitral tribunals. **Strengths:** "He is thoroughly commercial and has sound judgement as to what points to fight." "He is very responsive and has a quick turnaround." **Recent work:** Instructed in SC DG Petrol SRL v Vitol Broking Ltd, a dispute concerning a petroleum trade. This matter concerned alleged false accusations made to the Romanian authorities that caused subsequent losses to the claimant.

Thomas Macey-Dare Represents a range of clients, including shipowners, P&I clubs and commodities traders, in shipping, insurance and trading disputes. He is particularly noted for his wet shipping expertise and his specialism in freezing injunctions. **Strengths:** "He is a dogged and persistent advocate who leaves no stone unturned for his client." "He is very thorough and very detailed." **Recent work:** Acted for the owners of the 'Perla' in relation to disputes that arose following a serious fire en route to Iran.

John Kimbell Particularly highly regarded for his broad shipping practice, which encompasses dry, wet and piracy disputes. He is noted for his knowledge of the German market, having also qualified as a lawyer in Germany. **Strengths:** "He is very tactical and deals with the points that need dealing with." "His advocacy style is very clear and he establishes a good rapport with judges." **Recent work:** Represented the German owners of the 'Cape Bird', which was hijacked by pirates off the Nigerian coast, in a dispute with cargo owners.

John Passmore Advises on a range of shipping disputes, including charter party, groundings and shipbuilding cases. He is regularly instructed by shipowners, insurers and purchasers of ships in high-value matters. **Strengths:** "He always shows great clarity in his advice." "He is excellent in front of clients and is user-friendly." **Recent work:** Advised the carriers and insurers on a cargo dispute against BAT relating to a consignment of cigarettes stolen in transit. The case considered matters of jurisdiction relating to shipping law.

Paul Toms Advises on a range of shipping and commodities disputes and is particularly noted for his dry shipping expertise, proving particularly strong on charter party and bill of lading matters. **Strengths:** "We call him 'the brain' here." "He is completely on top of his game in terms of knowing the law and being able to give commercial user-friendly advice." **Recent work:** Represented BP in a dispute with Target Shipping concerning the amount of freight that was due under a voyage charter for the carriage of fuel.

Ruth Hosking Represents clients in both arbitral and judicial proceedings in a range of cases, including charter party, commodities and bill of lading disputes. She also represents clients in anti-suit injunctions. **Recent work:** Acted on a USD1 million case concerning a superyacht that had allegedly been defectively repaired.

Caroline Pounds Noted as a specialist in dry shipping matters, she regularly acts in a range of charter party and shipbuilding disputes. **Strengths:** "She is tough as nails, very bright and very succinct." **Recent work:** Advised on an urgent inspection in Singapore and subsequent arrest in Hong Kong of the vessel the 'Ruby Star'.

David Walsh "One to watch," he acts on a range of shipping disputes including unsafe port and charter party claims. He also advises on a range of international trade disputes in the commodities sector. **Strengths:** "He is very confident and composed, and does not take any nonsense." "He is incredibly bright and very easy to get on with." **Recent work:** Acted on CHS Europe v Far East Marine, representing cargo interests in relation to a dispute concerning the delayed delivery of a large consignment of corn.

Gemma Morgan A well-regarded junior, who regularly advises on a range of commodities and dry shipping cases in both judicial and arbitral fora. **Recent work:** Acted for the owners in the 'Pacific Challenger' case on a claim issued by the cargo interests for deviation and unseaworthiness.

Band 2

7 King's Bench Walk

See profile on p.827

THE SET

This highly regarded commercial set is noted for its broad shipping expertise, supported by a market-leading insurance practice. It is consistently present in high-value international wet and dry disputes, ranging from shipbuilding to unsafe port claims. Sources note that "by and large, whoever you get there is right at the top."

Client service: The clerking team led by Bernie Hyatt receives praise for its "very responsive and transparent" service.

SILKS

Timothy Brenton QC An experienced QC with a broad commercial practice, who often works on large cases involving losses of ships. **Recent work:** Acted for MSC in a dispute over liability arising out of its charter of the 'Rena', after the ship ran aground.

Dominic Kendrick QC A well-regarded commercial silk, who is noted for his involvement in complex charter party and shipbuilding disputes. **Strengths:** "He is very authoritative and what he says is treated as having weight." "He has raw intellect and is extremely bright." **Recent work:** Represented Bunge in a dispute with Kyla Shipping relating to the frustration of a charter party agreement.

Richard Waller QC Noted for his strength in arbitration and judicial proceedings, he is highly regarded for his broad expertise in shipping law on matters ranging from charter party disputes to piracy. **Strengths:** "He's excellent on his feet," and "he's not afraid to point out the difficulties in a case to his instructing solicitor."

Robert Bright QC Advises on a range of international trade and shipping disputes. He has particular expertise in complex shipbuilding and charter party disputes. **Strengths:** "His advocacy is very measured and he responds well to changing circumstances." "He has a good way of making unattractive points sound more persuasive." **Recent work:** Acted for the shipowners on the Navig8 v South Vigour case, a USD10 million claim concerning four charter parties which the shipowners deny entering into.

Siobán Healy QC Handles an array of shipping cases involving issues ranging from unsafe ports to bills of lading and charter parties. She also represents both sellers and buyers in trading disputes. **Recent work:** Represented Louis Dreyfus in a dispute with Carboex concerning the application of a voyage charter party strikes exception clause.

Alistair Schaff QC Advises on a range of marine-related disputes, and acts on wet and dry shipping matters as well as insurance disputes. **Strengths:** "He engenders confidence and you feel he totally gets to grips with the arguments." "He has an understated and measured style, and is also incredibly bright."

Richard Southern QC Particularly well regarded for his work in charter party disputes, and also frequently instructed on other matters, including contract of affreightment and grounding cases. **Strengths:** "He is extremely skilled and quick at slicing through some difficult issues." "My perception is that his instincts are almost invariably right." **Recent work:** Defended Glencore in a USD100 million claim over crude oil sold in Romania in the mid-2000s.

Peter MacDonald Eggers QC Has a broad practice and expertise relating to the marine industry in a number of areas, including sanctions, trading disputes and charter party claims. **Strengths:** "He is extremely diligent and will leave no stone unturned." "He is enormously bright, has an excellent personality and works well with correspondent counsel." **Recent work:** Acted on behalf of the London reinsurers, Amlin Corporate, defending a claim arising from the loss of the 'Princess of Stars'.

David Allen QC Has a broad shipping practice and acts for international clients ranging from Russian oligarchs to US shipping companies. His expertise covers a range of matters, including those relating to the engineering of vessels and the purchase of ships. **Recent work:** Acted for Arcadia Energy in a dispute with Falkonera Shipping concerning the refusal to grant permission to transfer cargo.

Christopher Butcher QC Highly regarded for his marine insurance expertise and his advice across a range of other matters, including charter party disputes. **Strengths:** "He bent over backwards to ensure that we got the advice when we needed it." "He is a very intelligent guy."

David Bailey QC Advises on a range of matters, including shipbuilding, international trade and insurance disputes. **Strengths:** "He is brilliant on his feet and an absolute gentleman to work with." "He is a seriously heavyweight appellate advocate." **Recent work:** Acted on behalf of the appellants in the Supreme Court case regarding the 'Alexandros T'. The matter concerned allegations of bribery and corruption relating to previous insurance litigation.

Stephen Hofmeyr QC Represents clients in shipbuilding, charter party and carriage disputes, amongst others. **Strengths:** "He is intelligent, professional and hard-working." **Recent work:** Represented Monaco Yachting & Technologies in a dispute concerning the termination of a contract to build a superyacht.

Stephen Kenny QC Advises clients on a range of dry shipping and trade matters, including commodities and charter party disputes. **Strengths:** "He is always a very good legal analyst and very thoughtful as to the preparation of a case." "He is always excellent for a case where someone needs to put their back into it and get dug into detail."

Timothy Saloman QC Handles judicial and arbitral proceedings concerning matters such as shipbuilding, charter party and bill of lading disputes. **Strengths:** "He is a very straight-talking, no-nonsense barrister who can be aggressive when needed." "He has a brilliant mind, is client-friendly and is excellent on his feet." **Recent work:** Acted for Sinochart in the 'Ocean Victory' case, an unsafe port claim relating to the total loss of a bulk carrier.

JUNIORS

Charles Priday A particularly highly regarded senior junior advising on a range of marine matters. He is noted for his involvement in a breadth of shipping, shipbuilding and international trade matters, and is also noted for his work as an arbitrator. **Strengths:** "He is a silk in all but name." "I think he is an extremely good lawyer, who is direct and easy to deal with." **Recent work:** Represented the appellant in BAT v Exel Europe, a case concerning the convention for the international carriage of goods by road.

Michael Holmes Advises a range of clients, including insurers and shipowners, on a host of marine disputes. He is particularly highlighted for his expertise in charter party disputes involving issues ranging from cargoworthiness to unsafe ports. **Strengths:** "What particularly strikes me about him is that he is not overawed by the fact that he is up against a silk." "He is very careful and clear in his submissions." **Recent work:** Represented Brit Insurance in a USD40 million insurance dispute concerning the 'Elli', a vessel which split in two in the Gulf of Suez.

Benjamin Parker Has a broad practice and advises on both wet and dry shipping matters, including salvage and shipbuilding disputes. **Strengths:** "He is very knowledgeable and able." **Recent work:** Represented MSC in relation to matters arising from the containership ship 'Rena' that ran aground off the coast of New Zealand.

N G Casey Regularly advises on charter party disputes. In addition, he has recently worked on numerous matters relating to the construction of superyachts. **Strengths:** "He is good to work with, bright and responsive." "He was very confident in what was quite a difficult job." **Recent work:** Representing Lakatamia Shipping in a USD46 million dispute with Nobu Su relating to a number of freight forwarding agreements.

Sandra Healy (see p.623) Represents clients in a range of shipping and commodities issues, and has recently acted on matters such as cargo and superyacht finance disputes, as well as applications to discharge freezing injunctions. **Strengths:** "She is very user-friendly and punches above her weight." "She has that commercial touch and solicitors absolutely love her." **Recent work:** Acted for the claimant in Glencore Energy UK v Cirrus Oil services, a commodities dispute concerning USD3 million worth of West African crude oil.

Jessica Sutherland Has a broad commercial practice, and is noted for her insurance expertise and work in shipping matters, including charter party and shipbuilding litigation and arbitrations. **Strengths:** "She has excellent attention to detail for both the law and the practical side of matters." "She is unflappable and very sound in her advice." **Recent work:** Represented Trafigura in the Court of Appeal on the 'Crudesky' case. This appeal related to liability for demurrage.

Richard Sarll Particularly well regarded for his admiralty law expertise, and acts on matters such as salvage and collisions. He is also noted for his expertise in issues relating to insurance and the carriage of goods by sea. **Strengths:** "He has made a real effort to understand the commercial realities of the business." **Recent work:** Successfully acted for the owners of the 'Theresa Libra' in a dispute arising from the ship's collision with the 'MSC Pamela'.

Adam Turner Regarded as an up-and-coming junior who acts on a range of international shipping and trade disputes. **Recent work:** "He is extremely capable and has a very good grasp of all the documents." "He is user-friendly and easy to work with." **Strengths:** Represented the intermediate charterers in Dannebrog Rederi v Galana Petroleum, a USD1.6 million claim arising from the collision of two vessels.

Band 3

Essex Court Chambers

See profile on p.792

THE SET

Essex Court Chambers is highly regarded for its particularly broad commercial practice. It receives praise for its dry shipping and commodities work, and has had involvement in numerous shipbuilding and charter party disputes. Sources are appreciative of the members at the set, noting that the "barristers speak to you in a respectful way and never as though it was beneath their dignity."

Client service: Senior clerk David Grief is "very helpful and quick with recommendations on which counsel to use depending on your budget."

SILKS

Steven Berry QC A highly regarded silk who advises on a range of shipping, insurance and commodities disputes. **Strengths:** "He is very enjoyable to watch and puts on a good show." "He has a great ability to pick out and present the one or two points that are at the heart of a case."

Graham Dunning QC He regularly represents clients in a range of fora, and handles international shipping and trade disputes concerning matters such as charter parties and shipbuilding contracts. **Strengths:** "He is very bright and good on his feet." **Recent work:** Acted for the former general director of Sovcomflot, who was facing an accusation of fraud in the 'Fiona Trust' trial.

Claire Blanchard QC Acts for a range of clients, including shipowners and charterers, in a breadth of international shipping and trade disputes. **Strengths:** "She is formidable and incredibly thorough, and her ability to focus and drill down to the issues is amazing." "She is good at mastering a lot of detail and is tenacious."

Simon Bryan QC Represents a breadth of clients, including commodities companies, shipping interests and insurance concerns, in an array of shipping and commodities matters. **Strengths:** "He has a good understanding of the technical issues." "He is very smooth and also a very aggressive cross-examiner when he needs to be." **Recent work:** Represented the charterers of the 'MSC Flaminia' in cargo claims worth USD100 million. The case concerned damage arising from a containership fire.

Vernon Flynn QC Represents clients in a range of multi-jurisdictional shipping and trade disputes, and is noted for his expanding offshore practice. He is also experienced in LNG pricing matters. **Strengths:** "He had a difficult case and he made the most of it in a charming way."

Christopher Smith QC Advises clients ranging from insurers to shipowners in wet and dry shipping cases. He has noted expertise in charter party and bill of lading disputes. **Recent work:** Represented yacht insurers in Zelikov v Merlin, a case concerning issues related to the EU Judgments Regulation.

Nigel Eaton QC Represents clients in a range of dry shipping matters, including shipbuilding, charter party and bill of lading disputes. **Strengths:** "He prepares thoroughly and makes sure all the points are covered."

JUNIORS

Philippa Hopkins Has a broad commercial practice that encompasses international trade, shipping and insurance disputes. **Strengths:** "A true shipping specialist."

Edmund King A rising star at the Commercial Bar, whose practice includes a broad range of commodities, insurance and shipping instructions. **Strengths:** "He is phenomenally bright in a problem-solving kind of way." "He is a really clever and striking advocate."

Nathan Pillow Represents clients in a range of matters relating to international trade and shipping. **Strengths:** "He is very robust and unflappable." "He's very easy to work with and personable." **Recent work:** Acted on behalf of the defendant, Yuri Nikitin, in the 'Fiona Trust' litigation.

Stone Chambers

See profile on p.869

THE SET

Stone Chambers is highly regarded for its involvement in a broad range of international shipping and commodities disputes. It has cemented its international credentials with the opening of an office in Singapore, and is noted for its expertise in matters ranging from dry shipping cases to superyacht and marine insurance disputes. Sources appreciate the "collegiate feel" of the set.

Client service: J-P Schulz leads a team of clerks who are described as "very responsive, efficient and easy to deal with."

SILKS

Elizabeth Blackburn QC (see p.550) Represents a broad array of clients in a breadth of shipping matters. She is particularly noted for her admiralty expertise, advising on high-value casualty work. **Strengths:** "She is a first-rate commercial barrister, who is approachable and very practical in the advice she gives." "She is very detailed and very knowledgeable." **Recent work:** Acted for the owners of the 'Renate Schulte' in an action arising out of its collision with the 'Marti Princess'.

Timothy Hill QC (see p.627) Advises clients on a range of shipping matters, including charter party, shipbuilding and sale and purchase disputes. He is also noted for his international trade and insurance work. **Strengths:** "He is a very tenacious and ferocious advocate." "He gets to grips with technical detail very quickly and homes in on issues very well." **Recent work:** Instructed in Dalmare SpA v Union Maritime, a contractual dispute over the incorporation of the implied terms of the Sale of Goods Act into a Norwegian Saleform 1993.

Steven Gee QC Represents clients in a range of court and arbitral proceedings in marine matters ranging from sale of goods to insurance and shipbuilding. **Recent work:** Acted for the Lloyd's market insurers in the disputes that arose following the grounding of the 'Alexandros T'.

Vasanti Selvaratnam QC (see p.717) Advises on all manner of wet and dry shipping disputes, and is noted in particular for her involvement in highly technical cases. She regularly advises on jurisdiction points and urgent interim relief issues. **Strengths:** "She is one of those QCs who does not show arrogance." "She is very calm and steady." **Recent work:** Advised on Algoma Shipping v Assicurazione Generali, a general average and salvage dispute that looked at a number of issues, including due diligence and unseaworthiness.

JUNIORS

Ravi Aswani (see p.538) Has a breadth of experience in dry shipping matters, including bill of lading and charter party disputes. He also advises on an array of wet shipping matters, including salvage and wreck removal cases. **Strengths:** "He is very good at understanding the clients' needs and putting their minds at rest when they have specific concerns or worries." "He is a very experienced and articulate advocate who has a good manner with the judge." **Recent work:** Represented the cargo claimants in disputes arising from the grounding of the 'Pacific Challenger'.

Mark Jones (see p.640) Advises on a range of dry and wet shipping matters. He has additional experience in international trade matters, including those relating to the carriage and sale of goods. He is particularly noted for his expertise in shipbuilding and marine insurance disputes. **Strengths:** "He has been a solicitor before so he appreciates the client's perspective more easily than barristers who don't have the same experience." "He is very energetic and not in the least bit fazed by coming up against top QCs." **Recent work:** Represented London underwriters in an insurance claim exceeding USD5.6 million brought by the owners of the 'HANDY V'.

Thomas Whitehead (see p.751) Represents clients in the full range of marine matters relating to shipping, international trade and the carriage of goods. **Strengths:** "He is very personable and gets straight to the point." "He is not an aggressive cross-examiner but gets all the answers he needs." **Recent work:** Acted for the owners of the 'Joy of Ladram' in a claim for damages arising out of the poor performance of a repair contract.

Jeremy Lightfoot (see p.656) Acts for a range of clients, including insurers and major oil companies, in an array of shipping and commodities disputes. **Strengths:** "He is able to zoom in on the most important issues that affect the case." "He is very hard-working and committed." **Recent work:** Acted for BP in its dispute with Sanders Trading Canada concerning substantial losses resulting from a failure to provide the correct documentation relating to a cargo of fuel.

Philip Riches (see p.707) Experienced in representing clients in international arbitration and litigation proceedings. He is noted for his role in advising shipping clients on matters relating to interim injunctions and jurisdiction disputes. **Recent work:** Advised on a commercial dispute relating to the termination of an agency relationship between a Japanese shipping line and a Romanian agent.

Rachel Toney (see p.738) Has a particularly broad shipping practice that encompasses both wet and dry matters, ranging from shipbuilding disputes to admiralty claims. She has additional expertise in international trade cases. **Strengths:** "She is very proactive and does not rely on instructing solicitors." **Recent work:** Represented both the owners and insurers of the 'White Cloud' in a dispute relating to alleged damage caused to coral reefs in the Turks & Caicos Islands by anchor dragging.

Charles Debattista (see p.586) Noted for his academic background, he uses his extensive knowledge to advise on matters relating to dry shipping and international trade. **Strengths:** "He was elegantly aggressive in putting forward his case." "He was very quick in amending his strategy to get aligned with the evolving situation."

Band 4

4 Pump Court

See profile on p.849

THE SET

4 Pump Court has a growing profile in this area, and has expertise that spans the breadth of the shipping and commodities sector. It works on both dry and admiralty cases, and fields barristers possessed of both drive and enthusiasm. Commentators note that its hunger for work in this sector has resulted in it being quite flexible on fees.

Client service: Stewart Gibbs and Carl Wall lead a clerking team that receives positive reviews. One solicitor noted: "I like the clerking team. I quite often call them for informal discussions and they look after me well."

SILKS

Alexander Gunning QC (see p.616) A relatively new silk, particularly noted for his expertise in shipbuilding disputes and his work on behalf of P&I clubs. **Strengths:** "He fights for the client and does it in a way that wins the respect of the tribunal and the judge." "When dealing with a case with awkward points he can come up with solutions and ways to handle them."

Sean O'Sullivan QC (see p.688) A recent silk who receives universal praise for the breadth of his shipping work. He is noted for his dry shipping expertise, especially charter party and bill of lading disputes. **Strengths:** "He is incredibly bright and has an incredibly good touch with tribunals." "He is always extremely clear, short and concise in what he wants to say." **Recent work:** Advised in the 'Seacrown' case, a dispute between a refinery and oil trader that raised issues relating to hedging.

Nigel Tozzi QC (see p.739) Has a broad shipping practice covering a range of matters, including ship repair and offshore construction disputes. **Strengths:** "He is very commercial, quick and accurate." "He is not the sort of guy who loses the interest of the judge." "He is one of those people who has the ear of the court." **Recent work:** Acted in a USD4–6 million professional negligence claim brought by a New York property developer who alleged that his solicitors had failed to properly protect his interests when acting for him in the acquisition of a yacht.

Nicholas Vineall QC (see p.743) Particularly highly regarded for his involvement in both offshore engineering and shipbuilding disputes. He regularly appears in LMAA arbitrations. **Strengths:** "He has a very persuasive, eloquent style." "He can be very innovative and come up with new points."

JUNIORS

Alexander Wright (see p.756) Particularly well regarded for his work in dry shipping and commodities matters, and has recently been involved in a number of high-value charter party and shipbuilding disputes. **Strengths:** "He is incredibly bright," and is "unbelievably good for the level of call he is." **Recent work:** Advised on the 'Fortune Plum' case, a charter party dispute relating to the law of affirmation.

Andrew Stevens (see p.728) Advises on a range of shipping and commodities matters, including shipbuilding and piracy cases. He is a fluent Mandarin speaker, and is particularly noted for his developing practice in the Far East. **Strengths:** "He punches above his weight," and is "responsive, approachable and smart."

James Leabeater (see p.653) Advises on dry shipping disputes and is particularly noted for his involvement in shipbuilding and offshore shipping construction work. **Strengths:** "He has a very good ability to put things well and get straight to the point." "He is very good at thinking of good and creative solutions to a problem." **Recent work:** Advised on the Dalmare SpA v Union Maritime arbitration, a dispute arising out of the sale of the 'Union Power'.

James Watthey (see p.747) A new addition to 4 Pump Court, who is particularly highly regarded for his involvement in complex charter party disputes. **Strengths:** "He is very reliable, provides a very good analysis of the issues, can identify and articulate forceful arguments and is generally very helpful in providing timely and cost-effective advice." "He is very approachable and fantastic with clients." **Recent work:** Advised on a claim for a declaration of non-liability relating to damage caused to the 'Conti Cartagena' while it was performing tug and tow services.

Neil Henderson (see p.624) Noted for his commodities expertise as well as his shipping work, particularly on the dry side. Sources say that his previous experience working for investment banks gives him a good commercial edge. **Strengths:** "He has a very good eye for detail, is user-friendly and very bright." "He is persistent in his advocacy and won't be bullied or pushed around." **Recent work:** Acted for the defendant shipowners in the 'Eems Solar' case, a dispute concerning damage to a cargo of rolled steel coils.

Other Ranked Lawyers

Richard Lord QC (Brick Court Chambers) Well regarded for work on both dry shipping and admiralty matters. He is particularly noted for his work on charter party, bill of lading and commodities disputes. **Strengths:** "He is a very shrewd strategist and a very effective and persuasive advocate." **Recent work:** Advised on the 'Athena' case relating to an off-hire clause in a NYPE timecharter.

Nicholas Craig (see p.580) (3 Verulam Buildings) Noted for his work on charter party matters and cargo claims. He also advises on a number of sale of goods disputes. **Strengths:** "He is quick and practical, and doesn't mess about. He spots the points." "He is quite hands-on and very commercial."

Contents:

LONDON

Social Housing London
Leading Sets
Band 1
Arden Chambers *
Cornerstone Barristers *
Garden Court Chambers *
Band 2
Doughty Street Chambers *
Five Paper *
Band 3
Hardwicke *
1 Pump Court *
Leading Silks
Star individuals
Arden Andrew *Arden Chambers* *
Luba Jan *Garden Court Chambers*
Band 1
Drabble Richard *Landmark Chambers (ORL)* ◊
Knafler Stephen *Garden Court Chambers*
McGuire Bryan *Cornerstone Barristers*
Band 2
Bhose Ranjit *Cornerstone Barristers* *
Lieven Nathalie *Landmark Chambers (ORL)* ◊
Westgate Martin *Doughty Street Chambers*
Band 3
Bhaloo Zia *Enterprise Chambers (ORL)* ◊
Rutledge Kelvin *Cornerstone Barristers*
◊ (ORL) = Other Ranked Lawyer.
[A] direct access (see p.11).
* Indicates set / individual with profile.

Social Housing London	
Leading Juniors	
Star individuals	**Rowlands** Catherine *Cornerstone Barristers*
Davies Liz *Garden Court Chambers*	**Vanhegan** Toby B *Arden Chambers*
Band 1	**Band 3**
Baker Christopher *Arden Chambers* *	**Baldwin** Timothy *Garden Court Chambers*
Bates Justin *Arden Chambers* *	**Bhogal** Kuljit *Cornerstone Barristers* *
Bretherton Kerry *Tanfield Chambers (ORL)* ◊ [A]	**Blackmore** Sally *Ely Place Chambers (ORL)* ◊ *
Burton Jamie *Doughty Street Chambers*	**Bowen** James *Garden Court Chambers*
Carter David *Doughty Street Chambers*	**Brownhill** Joanna *Five Paper* *
Dymond Andrew *Arden Chambers* *	**Chataway** Ben *Doughty Street Chambers*
Holbrook Jon *Cornerstone Barristers* *	**Colville** Iain *Arden Chambers* *
Hutchings Matthew *Cornerstone Barristers*	**Cottle** Stephen *Garden Court Chambers*
Lane Andrew *Cornerstone Barristers* [A] *	**Davies** Sian *Cornerstone Barristers* *
Manning Jonathan *Arden Chambers* *	**Etiebet** Peggy *Cornerstone Barristers* *
Nabi Zia *1 Pump Court*	**Gannon** Kevin *1 Pump Court*
Osler Victoria *Five Paper* *	**Hodgson** Jane *Five Paper* *
Preston Dominic *Doughty Street Chambers*	**Hodgson** Martin *1 Pump Court*
Underwood Dean *Cornerstone Barristers* [A] *	**Lintott** David *Cornerstone Barristers* *
Band 2	**Madge-Wyld** Sam *Arden Chambers* *
Beckley John *Garden Court Chambers*	**Maltz** Ben *Five Paper* [A] *
Beecham Sara *Five Paper* *	**Meacher** Alison *Hardwicke*
Beglan Wayne *Cornerstone Barristers* *	**Naidoo** Maya *Garden Court Chambers*
Berry Adrian *Garden Court Chambers*	**Orme** Emily *Arden Chambers* *
Cattermole Rebecca *Tanfield Chambers (ORL)* ◊ *	**Oscroft** Jennifer *Cornerstone Barristers*
Evans Stephen *Five Paper* *	**Roberts** Clare *Arden Chambers*
Fitzpatrick Edward *Garden Court Chambers*	**Sergides** Marina *Garden Court Chambers*
Gallivan Terence *Five Paper* [A] *	**Shepherd** Jim *Doughty Street Chambers*
Grundy Nicholas *Five Paper* *	**Tueje** Patricia *1 Pump Court*
Harris Bethan *Garden Court Chambers*	**Tweedy** Laura *Hardwicke* [A] *
Johnson Lindsay *Doughty Street Chambers* [A]	**Up-and-coming individuals**
Kohli Ryan *Cornerstone Barristers* *	**Brown** Robert *Arden Chambers* *
Nicol Nicholas *1 Pump Court* [A]	**Johnston** Connor *Garden Court Chambers*
Paget Michael *Cornerstone Barristers* *	**Salmon** Sarah *Arden Chambers* *
Prevatt Beatrice *Garden Court Chambers*	**Smith** Stephanie *Arden Chambers* *
Reeder Stephen *Doughty Street Chambers*	

Band 1

Arden Chambers

See profile on p.761

THE SET

Arden Chambers offers dedicated advice and representation to a diverse client base that includes local authorities, central government and social tenants. Its range of work includes high-profile possessions, homelessness and allocation cases, as well as welfare benefits, family law and general public law matters. Around half of its work is funded by legal aid, the other half being handled on behalf of landlords. Commentators note that its barristers are particularly adept at advising on long leasehold property management issues.

Client service: "The clerking team is extremely helpful, is able to react quickly and has an excellent working knowledge of our sector." It is led by Mike Alexander and includes experienced clerks Neil Goodwright and Sam Windle.

SILKS

Andrew Arden QC (see p.537) Specialises in pure housing matters and has a superb reputation. His distinguished career at the Housing Bar has seen him handle countless major cases, many of which have made it to the House of Lords and the Supreme Court. **Strengths:** "He has an excellent handle on housing law, and the pressures on the public purse." "He has deep expertise in the sector and a common-sense approach that means he can provide swift and solid advice." **Recent work:** Appeared in two Supreme Court cases, LB Camden v Sharif and LB Lambeth v Loveridge, representing the local authorities. He also appeared in R (CN) v Lewisham LBC, and in Sims v Dacorum BC.

JUNIORS

Christopher Baker (see p.541) Has an outstanding reputation for social housing work and is known for the quality of his local government work generally. His practice encompasses high-profile judicial reviews and appeals up to the Supreme Court. **Strengths:** "A smooth and polished courtroom presence." "A go-to barrister for appeals and higher court housing work." **Recent work:** He recently represented the landlord in Blyth and others v Notting Hill Home Ownership, a claim by multiple leaseholders alleging defects in the build. In another case, he advised the authority in Birmingham City Council v Balog.

Andrew Dymond (see p.592) Praised for his excellent understanding of social housing and his ability to work on complex matters. His practice covers private housing, licensing and service charge disputes. **Strengths:** "Highly intelligent and extremely knowledgeable." "He's simply excellent as he's cool, calm and measured." **Recent work:** Advised the accommodation provider as junior counsel in Islington LBC v Unite Plc, a case regarding the licensing of student accommodation as HMOs. He has also represented leaseholders and landlords in service charge disputes, appearing in such cases as Hackney LBC v Leaseholders of Hackney.

Justin Bates (see p.545) A barrister with a "genuine interest in the development of the law," he is highly regarded for his expertise in housing matters. He acts for both social landlords and their tenants, and is noted for his expertise in human rights issues. **Strengths:** "Clear when advancing complicated arguments, he delivers well in court." "He is widely recognised as one of the best of his generation." **Recent work:** Acted for a defendant in possession proceedings initiated by Circle 33 Housing Trust. He also assisted the tenant in Wandsworth LBC v Maggot, a case establishing that tenancy agreements can regulate the use of land, not moral behaviour.

Jonathan Manning (see p.662) Attracts high praise for his social housing, public law and human rights expertise. His recent work has included high-profile cases on welfare reform and the 'bedroom tax', and he has often appeared for Shelter acting as an intervener. He is further expert in matters involving possession claims and antisocial behaviour injunctions. **Strengths:** "Judges think highly of him because he is thorough and has an excellent command of the papers." "He's an expert on proportionality, having appeared in all leading cases." **Recent work:** Appeared for Birmingham City Council and Shelter as interveners in R (MA) v Secretary of State for Work and Pensions, a case challenging the 'bedroom tax'. He also appeared for Shelter in R (JS) v Secretary of State for Work and Pensions, a judicial review on welfare reforms.

Toby Vanhegan Leads on a series of high-profile housing matters, and is noted for his human rights, public law and EU law expertise. He is especially highlighted for his advice on allocation, eligibility and homelessness, and typically, though not exclusively, acts for tenants. **Strengths:** "A greatly respected, serious opponent." "He turns cases around with clear and effective arguments." **Recent work:** Acted for the tenant in two high-profile Supreme Court appeals, R(CN) v Lewisham LBC and R(ZH) v Newham LBC. He also advised on Sims v Dacorum BC.

Iain Colville (see p.576) Offers a wide-ranging housing practice covering all aspects of the area, including property and social housing cases. **Strengths:** "He picks up matters well, and becomes familiar with the issues in a case quickly." "He's very persuasive." **Recent work:** Acted for the local authority in Sharif v Camden LBC, a Supreme Court case concerning separate units of accommodation.

Sam Madge-Wyld (see p.660) Considered by sources to be a "bright spark in the sector." He advises on antisocial behaviour proceedings, allocation policies and disrepair, among other matters. **Strengths:** Offers "smooth negotiation of the cases." "He's balanced and ensures we follow our positions." **Recent work:** Appeared in Asghar v Barnet LBC, a case involving an Article 8 defence against retaliatory eviction.

Emily Orme (see p.686) Handles a range of work, including possession claims and homelessness appeals. Often acts for local authorities. **Strengths:** "Keeps her composure and works well with the judge." "An excellent advocate, who is professional, knowledgeable and thorough." **Recent work:** Represented the local council in Brent LBC v Chakdouf, seeking possession of two properties let on secure tenancies. She also assisted the authority in Mohamoud v Birmingham CC, a homelessness appeal concerning discharge of duty and review procedures.

Clare Roberts Advises on social housing, private property, public law and local government issues. **Strengths:** "She always takes a professional approach," and "knows what points to take."

Stephanie Smith (see p.724) Has a good court presence and offers excellent client care, according to solicitors. She is an expert in homelessness, possession and tenancy fraud cases. **Strengths:** "She will find a way, as she knows the weaknesses in an opponent's case and works on them." "She thinks quickly on her feet."

Robert Brown (see p.558) Handles a broad range of housing, property, public law, and landlord and tenant matters, including matters before the Leasehold Valuation Tribunal. Sources describe him as a junior who "punches above his call year." **Strengths:** "He is quick on his feet and passionate about his public work." "He's commercially astute and considers the final objective." **Recent work:** Assisted the local authority in RB Greenwich v Hammett, a possession claim against an introductory tenancy.

Sarah Salmon (see p.713) Attracts wide praise from sources for her client care skills and her comprehension of complex points of law. Her practice extends to homelessness and antisocial behaviour cases. **Strengths:** "A first-class litigator." "She's personable, proactive and a real favourite with clients." **Recent work:** Successfully represented the housing provider in Melin Homes v Leanne Price, a case concerning possession proceedings against a non-secure tenant.

Cornerstone Barristers
See profile on p.781

THE SET

Cornerstone Barristers maintains an impressive reputation for social housing work and typically assists local authorities and housing associations on a cross-section of matters, such as homelessness, asylum, possession claims, contested succession, antisocial behaviour and disrepair cases. It has a strong offering of barristers at all levels of call.

Client service: "It is a very professional and efficient set, whose barristers are thorough and well prepared."

SILKS

Bryan McGuire QC Has a broad practice that encompasses homelessness, asylum, social services and community care cases. He is an experienced litigator, who acts for both social landlords and for tenants. **Strengths:** "A standout individual," who has "excellent knowledge of the interplay between community care and housing." **Recent work:** He recently led in Hammersmith & Fulham LBC v George.

Ranjit Bhose QC (see p.549) Described as "the smoothest advocate in court imaginable," he has a long-standing reputation in social housing and typically represents local authorities and registered providers. His advice extends to advising on regeneration schemes, tenancy agreements and policies. **Strengths:** "Provides excellent, concise advice and is impressive on his feet." "You know he will run the case hard." **Recent work:** Recently advised on Tachie v Welwyn Hatfield DC, a case concerning a series of homelessness appeals. He also assisted the housing provider in Francis v Brent Housing Partnership, a Court of Appeal case regarding a new secured tenancy.

Kelvin Rutledge QC An established name for social housing work, who is especially noted for his work on public inquiries and children services cases. **Recent work:** Represented the local authority in Hotak v LB Southwark, a homelessness case seeking to define the term 'vulnerability'.

JUNIORS

Jon Holbrook (see p.629) Has an outstanding reputation and is highly praised for his style, popularity with instructing solicitors and passion for the sector. His practice almost exclusively comprises representing and advising local authorities and housing associations. **Strengths:** "A major strength is his approachability." "He knows his client and fully appreciates the difficulties that social housing providers face. As a result clients have confidence in his abilities." **Recent work:** Handled a number of possession claims, disrepair matters, leaseholder disputes and flexible tenancy cases.

Matthew Hutchings Commands great respect from all corners of the sector, with opponents describing him as "someone you can engage with in a meaningful way." He has recently represented local authorities in major housing disputes at Supreme Court level. He also receives excellent praise for his work on behalf of tenants. **Strengths:** "He has great confidence, presence and authority." "He is razor sharp and excellent at seeing what the hot point in a case is." **Recent work:** Advised on two of the most high-profile cases currently running, R(CN) v LB Lewisham LBC and R(ZH) v Newham LBC. He acted for the local authority in both these matters.

Dean Underwood (see p.742) Receives praise for the expertise and client care he brings to a variety of social housing matters, most notably when acting for local authorities. He is particularly adept at handling human rights and public law arguments, as well as questions relating to welfare reform. **Strengths:** "He is outstanding." "He produces clear paperwork, writes well and has an excellent grip on all the legal issues." "Clients have a lot of faith in him." **Recent work:** Appeared for the local authority in the Court of Appeal in Michael Sims v Dacorum Borough Council.

Andrew Lane (see p.650) Widely respected for his housing practice, he "wins difficult cases" and "works out the important points in language everyone understands." He is especially highlighted for his Court of Appeal practice, where he typically acts for housing providers. **Strengths:** "Efficient, polite and very effective," he is "a collaborative team player" whose "advocacy is second to none." **Recent work:** Advised the housing provider in Swan Housing Association v Gill.

Catherine Rowlands Handles housing and community care matters, and has an excellent reputation for assisting local authorities. Her practice extends to representing clients in age assessment and Court of Protection cases that have a social housing angle to them. **Strengths:** "Extremely popular with clients." "She is thorough with her paperwork and has an enviable array of skills." **Recent work:** Represented the local authority in Johnson v Solihull MBC, a homelessness appeal concerning how to determine if a homeless person is vulnerable. She has also advised on Muema v Muema and Croydon LBC, a case regarding Article 8 and joint tenancy.

Wayne Beglan (see p.547) Handles social housing cases as part of a wide local government practice. Has extensive experience in the appellate courts. **Strengths:** "Clear, determined and hard-working." **Recent work:** Recently advised Croydon LBC on a County Court case regarding possession against former service tenants. He also appeared for the local authority in Poorsalehy v Wandsworth LBC, a case regarding an out of time homelessness appeal.

Ryan Kohli (see p.647) Enjoys an excellent reputation, with senior practitioners in the field describing him as "exceptional" and "highly accomplished." He typically acts for local authorities. **Strengths:** He has "a crystal-clear mind" and "real confidence in what he does." **Recent work:** Assisted the local authority in Hyde Housing v Lorraine Newman, a case to suspend the warrant for possession. His work has also included unlawful subletting and contested succession matters.

Michael Paget (see p.688) "A persuasive advocate" who advises on the full range of high-profile housing matters. His practice includes private property work, and he is very good on leasehold disputes. **Strengths:** "He cannot do enough for you from the moment you pick up the phone." "He has a quick understanding of the key legal principles." **Recent work:** Advised, alongside Jan Luba QC, on Loveridge v Lambeth LBC, a statutory damages case concerning the unlawful eviction of a secure tenant that advanced to the Supreme Court.

David Lintott (see p.656) A favourite of instructing solicitors, he has developed a strong practice in homelessness challenges against public authorities. He has appeared in significant cases before the Court of Appeal. **Strengths:** "He has a wonderfully approachable nature." "Clients have confidence in him." **Recent work:** Has assisted local authorities on cases involving allocation policies, review procedures and intentional homelessness. He represented the local authority in Wandsworth LBC v NJ, a successful case involving refuge accommodation.

Jennifer Oscroft Acts for both housing providers and their tenants. She is an expert in judicial review and increasingly appears in the Court of Appeal. **Strengths:** "A real star." "She is accomplished in what she does, and offers sensible and practical advice." **Recent work:** Appeared in R(CN) v LB Lewisham LBC and R(ZH) v Newham LBC.

Kuljit Bhogal (see p.549) Handles social housing matters for local authorities, including antisocial behaviour possession cases. She has particular expertise in cases involving public law defences and the public sector Equality Duty. **Recent work:** Advised as junior counsel on Tachie v Welwyn Hatfield LBC, a series of appeals regarding procurement and contracting-out by the council.

Sian Davies (see p.584) Has a strong understanding of EU law and welfare benefits, and is particularly strong on immigration-related housing cases. **Strengths:** "Incredibly clever." "She knows everything there is to know about eligibility." **Recent work:** Advised the tenant in Viackiene v Tower Hamlets LBC, a case involving rent liability between co-tenants.

Peggy Etiebet (see p.596) Handles community care and local government cases, and is particularly highlighted for her knowledge of EU law in the context of social housing. **Strengths:** "A clear and forceful advocate, who is very much up and at 'em."

Garden Court Chambers

See profile on p.808

THE SET

Garden Court Chambers has a long-standing reputation for social housing work and its members have regularly appeared in major housing cases over the years, many of which have made it to the House of Lords/Supreme Court. It acts for tenants, other occupiers and the homeless, with most of its work being legal aid-funded. An approachable set, it is home to a deep bench of committed practitioners who remain the first port of call for a host of instructing solicitors throughout the UK.

Client service: "The clerks are excellent. You always get through to someone and they are extremely reliable." "The set has friendly clerks who are on the ball, and barristers who are ready to step in and deal with urgent work." Phil Bampfylde leads the clerking team.

SILKS

Jan Luba QC One of the biggest names in the field and someone who receives effusive praise. One interviewee summed up the situation by saying: "Not only is Garden Court Chambers lucky to have him, but so is the sector as a whole." Luba has handled countless cases against government authorities and public bodies. **Strengths:** "Jan Luba is without doubt the foremost silk working within social housing." "An advocate in the true sense of the word." **Recent work:** Represented the tenants in the Court of Appeal cases of Francis v Brent Council, Loveridge v Lambeth Council and Malik v Persons Unknown.

Stephen Knafler QC Maintains an impressive reputation for handling housing cases involving community care, immigration and welfare benefit issues. He notably advises housing authorities on their allocation schemes and policies. **Strengths:** "Judges listen to him as he is a real authority with a background in social housing." "He's a serious player on cases at the interface between community care and housing." **Recent work:** Acted for the respondent, a failed asylum seeker, in R (SL) v Westminster CC, a Court of Appeal case determining if the local authority had a duty to accommodate.

JUNIORS

Liz Davies A former solicitor, who is praised by clients for her impressive knowledge of the sector and her tactically astute approach. She is especially noted for her advice on homelessness and allocation cases, and is regularly cited by instructing solicitors as a leading authority for complex matters in this area. **Strengths:** "She goes that little bit further in her advice, reminding you what you need to do. She does not miss a thing and keeps you informed." **Recent work:** Appeared in R (Alansi) v Newham LBC, a case regarding legitimate expectation and the local authority allocation scheme.

John Beckley Widely endorsed by instructing solicitors for his effective representation of vulnerable and distressed clients. His practice takes in homelessness, antisocial behaviour possession claims and disrepair cases. **Strengths:** "Excellent in court." "From the moment he was on board I felt like he was really working for us," said one solicitor. **Recent work:** Represented a series of tenants or intentionally homeless individuals in successful appeals against London-based local authorities.

Adrian Berry An acknowledged expert on EU law in the context of social housing, who is involved in many of the leading cases in the area. He is considered to be the best source of advice on migrant rights issues. **Strengths:** "There would be a large number of homeless children if it was not for his persistence." "What he does not know is not worth knowing." **Recent work:** Advised as lead counsel on the test case of HB v Secretary of State for Work and Pensions, a case concerning the social entitlement of asylum seekers.

Edward Fitzpatrick Maintains a wide social housing practice that encompasses homelessness, antisocial behaviour and possession proceedings. "He will fight the client's corner until we are blown out of the water," note impressed sources. **Strengths:** "He is a robust advocate for vulnerable clients." "Meticulous with his case preparation, he offers excellent advocacy and great client care skills." **Recent work:** Acted as junior council on Chishimba v Royal Borough of Kensington & Chelsea, a case regarding a tenant's misconduct.

Bethan Harris Excellent with clients and thoroughly prepares her cases. Her practice is wide and she is particularly adept at handling vulnerability and mental health issues. **Recent work:** Acted on a number of appeals for vulnerable clients with mental health issues.

Beatrice Prevatt She proves particularly strong on disrepair cases, but is also praised for handling antisocial behaviour possession matters and homeless ness appeals. **Strengths:** "Authoritative and knowledgeable, with huge command of her cases." "You can have the utmost confidence in her advice on quantum and in her assessment of the merits of the case." **Recent work:** She recently represented tenants in a range of homelessness and possession claims.

Timothy Baldwin Described as a "real asset" by instructing solicitors, he is known primarily for his expertise on welfare benefit and community care cases. He also advises on possession claims and disrepair. **Strengths:** "Extremely well attuned to the law." "He is clever, knowledgeable and up-to-date on the latest changes." **Recent work:** Acted in Lee Verrall (1 & 2) v Chichester Council, a homelessness appeal.

James Bowen A highly experienced barrister with an excellent reputation for social housing cases, especially those dealing with possession and homelessness. **Strengths:** "Down-to-earth, very approachable and good on complex legal issues." "He is excellent on his feet; judges like him and he comes across effectively." **Recent work:** Has recently handled a number of statutory appeals and antisocial behaviour possession cases.

Stephen Cottle Tackles a range of social housing matters but is particularly highlighted for his work challenging the eviction of Travellers. **Strengths:** "His advocacy is excellent, and he does not falter." "Has impressive all-round knowledge of many areas." **Recent work:** Appeared in Eastwood v Royal Borough of Windsor and Maidenhead, which looked at whether a council's decision to evict Travellers was wrong in law.

Maya Naidoo Specialises in advising vulnerable clients and families, including those with mental health and capacity issues. Her practice takes in antisocial behaviour, homelessness and disrepair cases. **Strengths:** "Excellent with vulnerable clients." "She gets results in very difficult situations."

Marina Sergides Well versed in possession proceedings, homelessness appeals, disrepair claims and unlawful eviction cases, she is often instructed by the Official Solicitor to represent vulnerable tenants with mental health problems, where capacity is in issue. **Strengths:** "Excellent with clients and very sympathetic." "She is impressive on her feet and gets to grips with arguments quickly." **Recent work:** Assisted a tenant in an action against Lambeth LBC concerning vacant possession.

Connor Johnston Instructing solicitors highlight this relative newcomer as an "excellent example of the standard of the barristers at Garden Court." He can typically be found in the County Court advising on housing and community care cases. **Strengths:** "He worked well under pressure, got to the issues and inspired real trust." "He represented the interests of the client well in court."

Band 2

Doughty Street Chambers

See profile on p.786

THE SET

A popular choice for social housing cases and a set that commands real respect for its approach to public law and human rights cases generally. It is praised for its strong commitment to the area and its protection and enforcement of the housing rights of vulnerable individuals. Cases concerning eligibility, community care and mental health issues are a particular speciality.

Client service: "When you instruct someone from there, you are getting a team effort and collective discussion as a bonus." Paul Friend is the senior civil clerk.

SILKS

Martin Westgate QC Handles complex social housing matters, dealing with matters such as welfare benefits and disputes against matters of public policy, such as the benefit reforms. His wider understanding of public law issues enables him to "think out of the box on more challenging cases," note impressed sources. **Strengths:** "He is a clever man who translates his thoughtfulness into creative and effective legal arguments." "He's bright and destined to be a judge." **Recent work:** Represented the claimants in R (MA and others) v Secretary of State for Work and Pensions, a high-profile challenge to the 'bedroom tax'. He is highlighted for his work on NJ v Wandsworth LBC, a homelessness appeal concerning refuge accommodation.

JUNIORS

Jamie Burton "A rising star within the set," he has handled cases concerning challenges to council tax payment thresholds, refuge accommodation and housing benefit reductions. He also tackled a successful High Court human rights case relating to social welfare, called Almeida. **Strengths:** "A persuasive advocate." "His reputation is phenomenal." **Recent work:** Advised on R (M) v Haringey Council, a challenge to the government's changes to council tax benefit. Also represented the claimant in NJ v Wandsworth LBC.

David Carter Has established a strong social housing practice and is particularly good on judicial review cases relating to allocation and refusal to supply accommodation. He has also handled appeals against breaches of statutory public sector duties. **Recent work:** Acted for the claimant, a child, in TS v Croydon LBC, a judicial review seeking interim relief against the authority's refusal to supply accommodation pending a community care assessment.

Dominic Preston Handles difficult disrepair matters and homelessness proceedings. He is praised for his robust style, strategic handling of cases and excellent manner with vulnerable and challenging clients, and for his wider understanding of property and leasehold matters. **Strengths:** "He is a fearless fighter, not afraid of tackling a contentious case." "He is a straight opponent, capable of being robust in the interest of the vulnerable client." **Recent work:** He has an excellent appeals practice representing potentially homeless individuals in issues such as rent affordability and the application of the Pereira test to determine vulnerability.

Lindsay Johnson A popular barrister who specialises in tenants' housing issues. He regularly handles cases involving allocation schemes, possession proceedings and unlawful eviction, and is particularly adept at Article 8 arguments. **Strengths:** "Produces first-class drafting." **Recent work:** He was recently led by Jan Luba QC in Malik v Fassenfelt, a case stating evicted private tenants are entitled to a determination of proportionality.

Stephen Reeder A broad-based practitioner whose mandates include homelessness appeals, possession claims and community care cases, including mental health and Court of Protection matters. **Strengths:** "He has an excellent reputation, and is utterly charming." **Recent work:** Defended the tenant successfully in Douglas Haig Memorial Homes v Donlevy, a possession claim against a secure tenant.

Jim Shepherd Has an excellent reputation for his dedication to the client. He advises on a range of housing matters, and receives particular praise for his representation of vulnerable tenants in possession claims and discrimination cases. **Strengths:** "He's incredibly easy to work with, helpful and supportive." **Recent work:** Represented the tenants in House Owners v Berry, a case which seeks to clarify the position in Malik v Fassenfelt on the application of human rights law to private landlord possession claims.

Ben Chataway Handles a broad range of housing matters and is noted for his background working as a solicitor in this field prior to joining Doughty Street. Those that instruct him say this gives him "an understanding of the grittier issues in a case." **Strengths:** "Clear, thoughtful and considered." **Recent work:** Appeared for the claimants in R (MA) v Secretary of State for Work and Pensions.

Five Paper

See profile on p.845

THE SET

Five Paper has a strong team for social housing matters that acts for local authorities, private registered providers of social housing, landlords and private individuals. It has barristers who are specialist at all levels, and who are particularly praised for their work in antisocial behaviour, homelessness and disrepair cases.

Client service: "The team assists us on urgent matters at short notice, and there is always someone to pick the case up." The senior clerk is Alan Stammers.

JUNIORS

Victoria Osler (see p.687) Widely admired for her expertise across a diverse range of social housing matters, she acts for both tenants and public authorities. Her practice takes in service charge and lease cases, and commentators describe her as "a bright and extremely tenacious" barrister. **Strengths:** "She has a very technical mind and is able to pick through the issues." "She offers faultless advocacy." **Recent work:** Recently represented the claimant in R (on the application of IA) v Westminster CC, a case concerning the council's refusal to supply housing.

Sara Beecham (see p.546) Has a broad practice and acts for housing associations and public authorities, amongst others. **Strengths:** "Universally excellent." She has a "pleasant and efficient manner," and provides "great perspective on cases."

Stephen Evans (see p.597) Focuses on work for social housing providers and public authorities. He is especially praised for his technical understanding of complex areas of housing law, such as disability discrimination. **Strengths:** "My clients ask for Stephen because he gets excellent results, and he is an expert on particularly ground-breaking areas." **Recent work:** He recently appeared for the authority at the High Court in Lane v Royal Borough of Kensington & Chelsea, a case involving questions on disability.

Terence Gallivan (see p.605) Advises and acts on a range of matters for social landlords and individuals. His practice comprises property, landlord and tenant, local authority and judicial review cases. **Strengths:** A good advocate who "offers good, clear, concise advice in a charismatic way." **Recent work:** He recently appeared for the landlord in Smart v LB Lambeth, an adverse possession case. In other matters, he represented a homeless person without capacity in R (Selvarajah) v LB Croydon.

Nicholas Grundy (see p.616) Praised for his work on "complex cases of high importance," he has great depth of experience in acting for housing providers. His practice includes serious antisocial behaviour cases, as well as high-profile homelessness matters. **Strengths:** "A safe pair of hands and a fierce advocate." "He gets to grips with the papers very quickly and sees the bigger picture." **Recent work:** He appeared for the public authority on appeals in two important cases, Chishimba v RB of Kensington & Chelsea and Southend-on-Sea BC v Armour.

Joanna Brownhill (see p.558) A well-regarded practitioner who acts for housing providers and local authorities on matters such as possession proceedings and long leases. **Recent work:** Obtained an outright possession order in the case of Woking Borough Council v Wiseman.

Jane Hodgson (see p.629) Handles a range of social housing matters for both landlords and tenants, and is "a solid performer," according to sources. Her practice encompasses homelessness, security of tenure, succession rights and unlawful eviction cases. **Strengths:** "She really knows her homelessness cases, and her skeletons are excellent." "Clients are very happy with her." **Recent work:** Acted for the council in ZN, BB, JHS v LB Redbridge, a case concerning overpayment of welfare benefits. She also represented a vulnerable tenant in LB Brent v Ashok Savjani.

Ben Maltz (see p.661) Advises social landlords, including public authorities and housing trusts, on possession claims and antisocial behaviour proceedings. His practice also includes work on service charge disputes and matters relating to general landlord and tenant law. **Strengths:** "He is an incredibly safe pair of hands," and provides "clear and fast advice." **Recent work:** Acted for the landlord on appeal in Southern Land Securities Ltd v Hodge & Carpenter, a recent service charge dispute.

Band 3

Hardwicke

See profile on p.816

THE SET

This set's barristers are praised for their "rounded advice," and typically act for housing providers and local authorities. Those that instruct them do so as they offer "real passion and the personal touch." The individuals here specialise in all manner of housing-related work, such as allocation reviews, possession actions, anti-social behaviour cases and disrepair claims, to name but a few.

Client service: The barristers provide "excellent handling of urgent work, and pull out all the stops." They benefit from a "smooth clerking team" that is "responsive and friendly." Paul Horsfield is the senior practice manager for the property and private client division.

JUNIORS

Alison Meacher Has significant expertise in cases involving mental health and Court of Protection issues, and is good on cases relating to welfare benefit. She generally acts for local authorities. **Strengths:** "Confident in court, she certainly had the judge.s ear," said one instructing solicitor. "She was able to see our position and work from that standpoint." **Recent work:** She recently appeared for the local authority in Babergh DC v Grimsey, a case involving possession proceedings against a vulnerable tenant.

Laura Tweedy (see p.741) Has a broad social housing practice, and regularly handles complex antisocial behaviour injunctions. **Strengths:** "She is robust, and you can see the passion in her to get things done." "Energetic and thorough." "Her advice is always concise and tailored to our clients' needs." **Recent work:** She recently acted for the tenant in Leicester Housing Association v Armstrong, which involved defending a claim for possession.

1 Pump Court
See profile on p.848

THE SET

A set that is committed to social housing and receives excellent praise for its work on behalf of vulnerable tenants and applicants in judicial review. The team routinely receives instructions on homelessness and antisocial behaviour cases, and includes a number of key practitioners with supplementary expertise in community care, disability law and mental health cases.

Client service: "The team assists on urgent, out-of-hours work and is fantastic. There is always a rota of barristers, and always a call back from the clerks." Senior clerk Ian Burrow was highlighted by interviewees.

JUNIORS

Zia Nabi Represents clients in complex homelessness and possession appeals in the higher courts. Also regularly handles judicial review proceedings and matters relating to community care and social welfare. He is praised for his tactically astute handing of cases. **Strengths:** "He is perceptive, creative, approachable, and full of humanity and charm." "Zia has a talent for picking up interesting appeal points in cases." **Recent work:** Acted in Ali & Others v Birmingham City Council & Secretary of State for Communities & Local Government. Also appeared in Birmingham City Council v Balog, a homelessness appeal relating to the affordability of rent.

Nicholas Nicol Highlighted for his broad expertise in housing, and particularly well regarded for his work on behalf of tenants in disrepair, leasehold and Leasehold Valuation Tribunal cases. He has a reputation for fearless advocacy, and is also known for his understanding of priority needs and social welfare. **Strengths:** "Provides excellent written work, and is a skilful and effective advocate." "He's a great authority." **Recent work:** Appeared in Solihull MBC v Hickin.

Kevin Gannon Praised for his thoroughness and efficiency, especially when handling urgent homelessness matters and judicial review proceedings. **Strengths:** "Very knowledgeable on all aspects of social welfare law." **Recent work:** He was junior counsel in the Supreme Court case of Hounslow LBC v Powell.

Martin Hodgson Praised by sources as an excellent advocate for vulnerable clients. He advises on a range of housing matters, including appeals against the Housing Act, and is described as having "a brilliant legal mind." **Strengths:** "He has such a great way with clients." "He's experienced, persistent and appropriately cautious." **Recent work:** He is respected for his work for the tenants in Sharif v Camden LBC.

Patricia Tueje Advises on landlord and tenant issues such as possession, antisocial behaviour, disrepair and unlawful eviction. She is particularly praised for her judicial review work, and is a first choice for a number of instructing solicitors. **Strengths:** "Calm, polite and firm, she has an excellent manner when dealing with challenging clients. She is prompt and responsive in all her dealings."

Other Ranked Lawyers

Sally Blackmore (see p.550) (Ely Place Chambers) Acts regularly for tenants, landlords and authorities on both public and private housing matters. **Strengths:** "She gets very good results and is very thorough." **Recent work:** Acted on a series of possession claims for tenants and social landlords.

Zia Bhaloo QC (Enterprise Chambers) A highly respected barrister with excellent knowledge of property law. She frequently acts for registered providers on issues relating to redevelopment and regeneration schemes. She is also often instructed by leading housing firms. **Strengths:** "An excellent advocate, one of whose many strengths is that she knows how important it is to be part of the team. She will go the extra mile to help and she is brilliant with clients." **Recent work:** Represented the registered provider in Gavin v Community Housing Association, a case concerning a landlord's implied duties to repair.

Richard Drabble QC (Landmark Chambers) A much-celebrated lawyer who handles social housing cases with the same aplomb as he does all manner of public law cases. He is especially respected for his work on cases involving social security and welfare benefits. **Strengths:** "One of the best advocates of his generation." "He is fantastic on welfare benefits cases and one of the few who understands this work." **Recent work:** Appeared for one of the claimant tenants in R(MA) v Secretary of State for Work and Pensions, a high-profile judicial review challenge to the size criteria for the calculation of housing benefit. He is also noted for his work on R (JS) v Secretary of State for Work and Pensions.

Nathalie Lieven QC (Landmark Chambers) Handles a wide range of social housing and public law matters. Her clients include central government and social security claimants, and she is especially noted for her work on high-profile cases in the sector. **Strengths:** "Top drawer." "She is always able to find a novel point of law." **Recent work:** Represented the tenant in Sharif v Camden LBC, a Supreme Court case concerning the council's decision to split families between two separate units of accommodation.

Kerry Bretherton (Tanfield Chambers) Particularly good on complex social housing cases, and routinely acts on possession claims and homelessness cases. She has a strong Court of Appeal practice. **Strengths:** "A very strong and forceful advocate, who will always explore all possible avenues and provide clear, well set-out advice." **Recent work:** Acted for the tenant in a significant case on homelessness, Haile v London Borough of Waltham Forest.

Rebecca Cattermole (see p.567) (Tanfield Chambers) Highly praised for her advocacy skills and broad understanding of social housing and property law. She has particular experience of high-value dilapidation cases. **Strengths:** "Loved by clients, she is very efficient, and has an excellent presence in court." "She always seems to get results." **Recent work:** Recently advised parties in the private sector on housing transfers from the public sector. Issues touched upon included secure tenancies, recovery of possession and the sale of land.

MIDLANDS

Social Housing Midlands	
Leading Sets	
Band 1	
St Ives Chambers *	
Leading Juniors	
Band 1	
Singleton Michael	St Ives Chambers *
Band 2	
Caney Michelle	St Ives Chambers *
McNamara Andrew	Ropewalk Chambers (ORL) ◊ *
Up-and-coming individuals	
Newman Anya	St Ives Chambers *

◊ (ORL) = Other Ranked Lawyer.

[A] direct access (see p.11).

** Indicates set / individual with profile.*

Band 1

St Ives Chambers
See profile on p.885

THE SET

St Ives Chambers is widely known for its strength in the social housing arena, with its barristers handling a range of matters including antisocial behaviour and possession proceedings. Members routinely acting for tenants, local authorities and housing associations in courts across England and Wales.

Client service: "The clerking team will bend over backwards to accommodate us when we need something. We get on with them very well."

JUNIORS

Michael Singleton (see p.722) Particular expertise handling possession claims based on antisocial behaviour-related issues. Singleton acts for housing associations and tenants. **Strengths:** "He is a good analytical lawyer and very careful. He does his research thoroughly." "He is robust but always fair and appropriate. Nothing gets past him. He has a great eye for detail." **Recent work:** Acted in South Staffordshire HA v Abraham Suffolk, a successful possession claim following the antisocial behaviour of a tenant's mentally disabled daughter.

Michelle Caney (see p.564) Acts predominantly for social landlords and housing associations, advising on a range of issues including injunctions and service charge disputes. Caney is also experienced in mental capacity and disability discrimination matters. **Strengths:** "She listens to her clients carefully and does what they want her to do. She will fight tooth and nail if she feels it is a good case to argue." "Technically she is excellent, but she is also down to earth, which is crucial with social housing." **Recent work:** Successfully represented a council in a trial to obtain a possession order and injunction against a vulnerable tenant following a display of antisocial behaviour.

Anya Newman (see p.681) Advises clients on complex matters of antisocial behaviour, usually raising issues of human rights or breaches of the Equality Act. She often advises local councils and also offers specialised training on social housing litigation. **Strengths:** "She is fresh and determined. She is always enthusiastic, practical and very approachable." "She has an excellent rapport with clients and is always willing to argue hard for the outcome desired by those instructing her." **Recent work:** Assisted Leasowe Community Homes with possession proceedings following a tenant's attempted retraction of a notice to quit.

Other Ranked Lawyers

Andrew McNamara (see p.669) (Ropewalk Chambers) Advises both landlords and tenants on a range of social housing issues, from possession claims to property litigation. He is well regarded for his work with local councils. **Strengths:** "He exudes confidence in what he is saying. He is not easily put off his stride and he is very sure of how he delivers his arguments." **Recent work:** Successfully represented the City of Lincoln in possession proceedings against an introductory tenant.

NORTHERN

Social Housing Northern
Leading Silks
Band 1
Bartley Jones Edward *Exchange Chambers (ORL)* ◊
Leading Juniors
Band 1
Burns Paul *Exchange Chambers (ORL)* ◊ *
Fullwood Adam *Kings Chambers (ORL)* ◊ *
McCormack Ben *Garden Court North (ORL)* ◊
Stark James *Garden Court North (ORL)* ◊
Band 2
Byles Andrew *Garden Court North (ORL)* ◊
Cawsey Laura *Garden Court North (ORL)* ◊
Hobson John S *Doughty Street Chambers (ORL)* ◊
O'Brien Sarah *Exchange Chambers (ORL)* ◊
Up-and-coming individuals
Willock Gary *Garden Court North (ORL)* ◊
◊ (ORL) = Other Ranked Lawyer.
* Indicates set / individual with profile.

Ranked Lawyers

John Hobson (Doughty Street Chambers) Offers a broad social housing practice for tenants and homeless individuals. His practice includes possession claims, antisocial behaviour and disrepair, alongside issues such as mental health and public law defence. **Strengths:** "He is very down to earth and approachable for the client." "An excellent advocate who takes a sensible, pragmatic approach and looks at the problem as a whole." **Recent work:** Acted in a case concerning a claim for possession and injunctive relief against a social housing tenant.

Edward Bartley Jones QC (Exchange Chambers) Widely recognised as a leading silk for social housing matters outside London. He advises on complex matters in the sector typically for social landlords, praised for his practical advice and technically astute reasoning. He frequently acts before the Court of Appeal and Supreme Court. **Strengths:** "To my mind he is probably the best lawyer in the North of England. His ability to analyse issues and to get a grip on them is phenomenal. His ability as an advocate is massively impressive."

Paul Burns (see p.561) (Exchange Chambers) Impressive reputation for social housing work on the Northern circuit on matters involving public law and human rights challenges, as well as social security and mental health issues. Acts for housing providers and local authorities. **Strengths:** "Doesn't exclude anyone from the legal process and explains every step." "He is absolutely excellent on all areas, he takes it further, asks the questions." **Recent work:** Assisted Wigan MBC with a range of disputes and advices including tenancy agreements and possession proceedings against vulnerable tenants. Burns also represented Rochdale Boroughwide Housing in a case concerning gas safety and capped supplies which engaged the HSE.

Sarah O'Brien of Exchange Chambers Represents local authorities, social landlords and local government in social housing disputes. Her practice includes possession actions, disrepair, homelessness and antisocial behaviour, and extends to private housing matters. **Strengths:** "She is really good. She's very thorough and she knows her stuff."

Ben McCormack (Garden Court North) Formerly a solicitor and continues to receive effusive praise from sources. He represents tenants and vulnerable clients in a range of social housing mandates which include social welfare and community care. **Strengths:** "He is very well prepared and an excellent advocate in court." "A reasonable opponent who does not give concessions where he should not, but will focus on key points for the client."

James Stark (Garden Court North) Highly reputed junior for social housing matters. His expertise includes a full range of matters including complex possession proceedings, homelessness appeals and disputes involving multiple parties and agencies. **Strengths:** "He is pretty much excellent at everything. He's so intelligent."

Andrew Byles (Garden Court North) Acts exclusively for social housing tenants and occupiers on matters including those involving antisocial behaviour, nuisance and homelessness. **Strengths:** "He is the walking, talking dictionary of housing law who never stops working." "Excellent knowledge and then did everything he could above and beyond from the court work."

Laura Cawsey (Garden Court North) Maintains an excellent reputation for social housing work including matters involving antisocial behaviour cases, homelessness, possession proceedings and disrepair claims.

Gary Willock (Garden Court North) Handles a range of social housing matters including the representation of vulnerable clients in cases such as antisocial behaviour and claims for possession. **Strengths:** "He advises clients tactically, and really understands the vulnerable clients we see."

Adam Fullwood (see p.604) (Kings Chambers) Handles social housing work as part of a broader public and administrative law practice. His practice includes advising local housing authorities, social landlords, charities and private organisations. **Recent work:** Recently represented a claimant against the Secretary of State for the Home Department in a challenge against the Worker Registration Scheme.

SPORT: An Introduction

Contributed by Jim Sturman QC and Mark Milliken-Smith QC 2 Bedford Row

Football has perhaps again provided UK sports lawyers with its greatest breadth of work in 2013-2014. Disciplinary issues ranged from players (the Anelka "quenelle" gesture and the Townsend, Jerome and Gosling betting rule breaches) to the managers (the Pardew headbutt and McDermott "sacking" affairs). Each brought with them significant issues of reputation management. The consequences for Anelka of a finding of guilt after his denials, and the benefits to Pardew of his immediately expressed contrition, are worth noting, as perhaps is the public reaction to the initial refutations of an affair by Olivier Giroud (who was supported by his Club) before he was forced to admit his indiscretion. The lie then becomes the story and not necessarily the conduct.

Corruption in a multiplicity of sports, nationally and internationally, has dominated the sports law headlines in the past year. Recent allegations of match fixing and spot fixing in football support the observations of Jacques Rogge that fixing poses an even greater threat to the integrity of sport than doping. Sallie Barker, Chief Executive of the Sport and Recreation Alliance, has said that "match fixing, specifically spot fixing, has become one of the biggest threats facing the integrity of sport… sport can't afford to be complacent about the risks posed by corrupt and illegal betting." The UK is not alone: as this is written there has been a warning that Australian sport is facing a "tsunami of corruption" emanating from Asia – this comes after the break-up of an illegal match fixing syndicate targeting a local soccer club.

In late 2013 some 13 players were arrested and questioned over allegations of bribery and money laundering. They include former Premier League player DJ Campbell and Portsmouth player Sam Sodje, the latter having allegedly told an undercover reporter that he could arrange yellow and red cards for cash. The first trial arising out of yet another case "unearthed" after an undercover "sting" by journalists is fixed for May 2014 at Birmingham Crown Court.

In February 2014, six of nine individuals charged with corruption charges brought by the ICC pertaining to the Bangladesh Premier League, including England's Darren Stevens, were cleared. Two players and one franchise owner were convicted. In separate proceedings last year an umpire was convicted of similar charges. Three Rajasthan Royals cricketers in the 2013 Indian Premier League were arrested and convicted of spot fixing, including the Indian international Sreesanth. Fresh reports name six capped Indian players as falling under suspicion in recent revelations, and the fallout of Lou Vincent's apparent "plea bargain" with the ICC one suspects will be worldwide.

Governing bodies have awoken to the need to implement educational programmes for players, perhaps following the lead taken by the Professional Cricketers' Association in its mandatory anti-corruption instruction. Such solutions, supplemented by action in the criminal courts and strong internal sanctions on behalf of governing body and club alike, are the obvious answer.

Another growing trend has been high-profile dismissals in sport providing no little mystery for the public and work for sports lawyers. The ECB faced significant criticism and consequent speculation about its reticence in explaining the decision to axe Kevin Pietersen, both parties having apparently been bound by confidentiality. Owner Vincent Tan's public sacking of Cardiff City's Malky Mackay has perhaps made it wise in future to include a liquidated damages clause for "bosses". And then there was the bizarre – but short-lived – removal of Brian MacDermott from his job as manager of Leeds United. He had apparently received a call from a lawyer acting for a company which was in talks to take over the club informing him his contract was terminated. However, since that company was yet to complete the purchase the termination was legally ineffective. The following day he was told by a director of the club that he had not been sacked and returned to manage the club.

As we predicted in last year's overview, Financial Fair Play is now a hot topic, with proposed sanctions by UEFA against nine clubs. The threat by Manchester City to refuse to accept a "plea bargain" that has been offered may lead to contested proceedings before UEFA and ultimately CAS. It remains to be seen whether any Club that has transgressed against the Football League's rules will be fined.

With the organisers of the World Cup in Brazil facing difficulties, speculation as to the readiness of the Rio Olympics in 2016, and constant rumours about Qatar 2022, the work does not seem to be in any danger of abating.

The sports law sector in the UK continues to expand. Those who practise in it are increasingly required to possess multidisciplinary skills and to work nationally and internationally.

Contents:

LONDON

Sport London	
Leading Sets	
Band 1	
Blackstone Chambers *	
Band 2	
2 Bedford Row *	
4 New Square *	
Leading Silks	
Star individuals	
Lewis Adam	*Blackstone Chambers*
Band 1	
Harris Paul	*Monckton Chambers (ORL)* ◊
McPherson Graeme	*4 New Square* *
Mill Ian	*Blackstone Chambers*
Sturman Jim	*2 Bedford Row* *
Band 2	
Pannick David	*Blackstone Chambers*
Phillips Mark	*South Square (ORL)* ◊ *
Band 3	
Beloff Michael	*Blackstone Chambers*
Hunter Andrew	*Blackstone Chambers*
Kerr Tim	*11KBW (ORL)* ◊ *
Randall Nicholas	*Devereux (ORL)* ◊ *
Band 4	
Green Andrew	*Blackstone Chambers*
Hollander Charles	*Brick Court Chambers (ORL)* ◊
Howe Robert	*Blackstone Chambers*
Milliken-Smith Mark	*2 Bedford Row* *
Saini Pushpinder	*Blackstone Chambers*
Band 5	
Brown Damian	*Littleton Chambers (ORL)* ◊
Glyn Caspar	*Cloisters (ORL)* ◊ *
Goulding Paul	*Blackstone Chambers*
Jeans Christopher	*11KBW (ORL)* ◊ *
Jones Seán	*11KBW (ORL)* ◊ *
Stoner Christopher	*Serle Court (ORL)* ◊ *
New Silks	
Gallafent Kate	*Blackstone Chambers*
Mulcahy Jane	*Blackstone Chambers*
* *Indicates set / individual with profile.*	
◊ *(ORL) = Other Ranked Lawyer.*	
Ⓐ *direct access (see p.11).*	

Sport London	
Leading Juniors	
Band 1	
De Marco Nick	*Blackstone Chambers*
Band 2	
Crystal Jonathan	*Goldsmith Chambers (ORL)* ◊
Weston Louis	*3PB Barristers (ORL)* ◊
Band 3	
Bayfield Daniel	*South Square (ORL)* ◊ *
Kennelly Brian	*Blackstone Chambers*
Liddell Richard	*4 New Square* *
Meakin Ian	*XXIV Old Buildings (ORL)* ◊
Segan James	*Blackstone Chambers*
Band 4	
Banks Fiona	*Monckton Chambers (ORL)* ◊ Ⓐ
Dean Jacob	*5RB (ORL)* ◊
Richards Tom	*Blackstone Chambers*
Saoul Daniel	*4 New Square* *
Band 5	
Afeeva Mark	*Matrix Chambers (ORL)* ◊
Butler Rupert	*3 Hare Court (ORL)* ◊ Ⓐ
Draper Owain	*One Essex Court (ORL)* ◊
Hickman Tom	*Blackstone Chambers*
Mehrzad John	*Littleton Chambers (ORL)* ◊ *
Up-and-coming individuals	
Mountford Tom	*Blackstone Chambers*

Band 1

Blackstone Chambers

See profile on p.771

THE SET

Blackstone Chambers is acknowledged as the leading sports set at the Bar. The breadth of its barristers' sports law expertise enables it to represent clients from across all sporting arenas and in all areas of sports law. Its members are frequently instructed directly by governing bodies and sporting organisations to act on employment, disciplinary and doping disputes, as well as a wide range of commercial disputes. The set stands apart from its peers for sports work: no other set can match either the breadth of its expertise or the sheer number of its sports experts.

Client service: "The clerks at Blackstone know who to bring on to sports matters and know which barristers will play well with which clients." "They have a man or a woman for every job. You know if you go to the clerk and your first choice is taken, their second choice will still have the experience to meet your needs."

SILKS

Adam Lewis QC Enjoys a stellar reputation amongst both peers and clients for his expertise in sports matters. He has acted with distinction on anti-doping, match fixing and disciplinary proceedings, as well as on player transfer and agents disputes. He is frequently instructed directly by sports governing bodies on regulatory issues in football, rugby and athletics. **Strengths:** "He is a true sports law specialist." "He's the standout – accessible, extremely nice to deal with and an all-round brilliant advocate." "When you have a case that requires you to pull out all the stops you simply have to select Adam Lewis QC." **Recent work:** He successfully defended UEFA against three appeals brought by football clubs relating to match fixing.

Ian Mill QC Has significant experience in acting on employment, anti-corruption, anti-doping and IP disputes as they relate to various sports, particularly tennis, cricket and football. **Strengths:** "He has a robust manner that conveys an absolute confidence in what he's saying." "He has a good reputation in sports regulatory matters and is an outstanding character; he swiftly grasps issues, is very personable and has a detailed legal mind." **Recent work:** He defended the FA Premier League against a claim brought by Leyton Orient in connection with the decision to allow West Ham to move into the Olympic Stadium.

David Pannick QC Has a wide-ranging practice and a strong profile across a number of areas of law, including public law, EU law and employment. Sport is not the focal point of his practice, but his reputation is such that he is frequently on the teamsheet for any high-stakes sports disputes. **Strengths:** "He is an extraordinary and impressive advocate." **Recent work:** Represented the Horserace Betting Levy Board in a judicial review application brought by William Hill.

Michael Beloff QC Has a wealth of experience in the sports sector, having acted on a wide range of regulatory matters in athletics, football and rugby. He is a member of the International Association of Athletic Federation's (IAAF) ethics commission and a member of the Court of Arbitration for Sport (CAS). **Strengths:** "He is one of those advocates who can charm the birds from the trees. He's very bright, charming and elegant." **Recent work:** He acted for a London Irish rugby player in a successful disciplinary appeal after the player had originally been found guilty of a tip tackle offence.

Andrew Hunter QC Acts on a wide range of commercial matters as well as acting on player and agent disputes. He has recently acted on cases in football, cricket and taekwondo. **Strengths:** "He's aggressive and persuasive in the way he puts his case forward." **Recent work:** He acted for a Premier League football club in a dispute with an agent relating to fee and commission arrangements.

Andrew Green QC Has significant experience in acting for sports governing bodies, in relation to both disciplinary matters and commercial disputes. He is particularly noted for his rugby union expertise. **Strengths:** "He's very effective because he's a tough operator." **Recent work:** He successfully acted for the RFU in its move to get ticketing website Viagogo to reveal the identity of ticket sellers for England rugby matches.

Robert Howe QC Advises on commercial issues in sport, including sponsorship and media rights for both event organisers and clubs, as well as handling kit manufacturing disputes for clubs and manufacturers. **Strengths:** "He's tremendous – clear, sensible and smart in his advice. He listens to you and is a credit to the profession." **Recent work:** He acted for a Premier League club on a dispute following the termination of merchandising agreements.

Pushpinder Saini QC Has worked with clients from the worlds of football, rugby and cricket on a wide range of matters, including media disputes, disciplinary matters, transfer disputes and integrity issues. **Strengths:** "He's a class act; a very smooth and accomplished advocate."

Paul Goulding QC Frequently instructed to act on football disputes involving managers, agents, clubs and players, and also sits on sports disciplinary panels. **Strengths:** "He's a pleasure to work with – very hands-on and very accessible. On his feet he has a very gentle manner, which always wins favour from judges." **Recent work:** He was the chair of the Independent Regulatory Commission, hearing the case brought by the FA against Luis Suarez.

Jane Mulcahy QC A highly regarded new silk with significant experience in acting on employment and disciplinary-related disputes for both football and rugby clubs, governing bodies and individuals. **Strengths:** "She's very client-friendly, quick and successful in her approach to litigation, and very effective in front of a tribunal." "She knows the sporting world inside-out." **Recent work:** She was appointed by the RFU to act on behalf of Slough RFC in a successful appeal against a decision that one of Slough's players was not racially abused.

Kate Gallafent QC A well-respected new silk who has a wide range of experience in handling anti-doping and wider disciplinary matters in tennis, rugby and athletics. She is noted for her expertise in advising on child protection matters in a sports context. **Strengths:** "It's no surprise she's taken silk. She's done a lot of tricky stuff and is quietly effective. She has a lovely way of presenting things." **Recent work:** She defended the Lawn Tennis Association against three race discrimination claims.

JUNIORS

Nick De Marco Praised by peers for his knowledge of employment and regulatory matters, especially in connection to football. He has significant experience in handling disciplinary matters, contract disputes and discrimination cases. **Strengths:** "As a junior, he stands out. He knows sport and is technically a good lawyer, very good in court and very enthusiastic." **Recent work:** He represented the England and Wales Cricket Board (ECB) in disciplinary proceedings against Essex Country Cricket Club players, which led ultimately to a lifetime ban for Danish Kaneria.

Brian Kennelly Well regarded for his expertise in handling sports cases with European law and competition angles. He is particularly noted for his expertise in football-related disputes, and has acted on transfer disputes and match-fixing allegations for both clubs and governing bodies. **Strengths:** "He was thorough on the European law aspects, and pleasant to work with – calm, methodical and effective." **Recent work:** He acted for FC Metalist on the club's appeal to UEFA following its expulsion from the Champions League following an investigation into match fixing.

James Segan Has advised on a number of football, rugby and athletics cases. He brings expertise in commercial, public and European law to bear on both sports broadcasting cases and disciplinary issues within sport. **Strengths:** "He is a lovely advocate and has a winning way with submissions." **Recent work:** He acted for the Premier League on obtaining a blocking order against UK ISPs in connection with illegal streaming of sports matches via the site FirstRow.

Tom Richards Has represented both sports clubs and individuals in boxing, football and rugby cases relating to public law and disciplinary matters. **Recent work:** He acted for Leyton Orient Football Club in a judicial review challenge in connection with the future of the Olympic Stadium.

Tom Hickman Represents clients from the football industry in connection with commercial and contractual disputes. He is also well regarded for his expertise relating to sports disciplinary issues, and in particular to anti-doping cases. **Strengths:** "He takes an intellectual approach. He comes at sport from a black letter lawyer's perspective and his cerebral approach is evident." **Recent work:** He acted for Leyton Orient in a challenge relating to the lease on the Olympic Stadium.

Tom Mountford Has experience in handling rugby, football and boxing matters concerning anti-doping and contract disputes. He has a commercial law background and brings it to bear in the sports sector. **Strengths:** "He is absolutely brilliant; he can make really complex areas of the law sound actually quite straightforward – on his feet he is really impressive." **Recent work:** He defended the British Boxing Board of Control against claims of breach of statutory duty, breach of competition law and unlawful interference with economic interests.

Band 2

2 Bedford Row

See profile on p.763

THE SET

2 Bedford Row's members continue to play a prominent role in the sports sector, most notably in football, but also in rugby, cricket and athletics, amongst many others. Commentators are quick to highlight the set's criminal expertise as core to its sports offering, and while a significant amount of its sports cases do concern representing sports organisations or individuals facing allegations of criminal wrongdoing, it does also provide considerable advice on sports governance issues.

SILKS

Jim Sturman QC (see p.731) Has significant experience of acting on behalf of players, clubs and agents on integrity issues, disciplinary matters, and player and agent disputes. He is principally noted for his expertise in football and rugby, although he has also acted on doping and corruption cases in boxing, motor sport and tennis. **Strengths:** "His knowledge of the sports sector – especially football – is completely comprehensive. He is an extremely thorough and tenacious advocate." **Recent work:** He was instructed by Tottenham Hotspur Football Club on England international Andros Townsend's charge of breaching the FA's betting regulations.

Mark Milliken-Smith QC (see p.672) Principally acts for individual sports clients against governing bodies in both cricket and rugby on regulatory and disciplinary matters. He has also acted on anti-doping matters in rugby, corruption issues in cricket, and a range of issues in boxing and football. **Strengths:** "He's very persuasive – being a criminal lawyer really helps him in disciplinary cases because he's used to the cut and thrust of witness handling." **Recent work:** He defended Mervyn Westfield against the ECB in connection to spot-fixing in a professional cricket match.

4 New Square

See profile on p.835

THE SET

4 New Square's sports practice is anchored in its horse racing expertise, although the set is increasingly instructed to act for governing bodies, sports clubs and individuals in rugby, Formula 1 and boxing disputes. The set also acts for clients on regulatory matters, including anti-doping, corruption and disciplinary matters in tennis, rugby, football and horse racing.

SILKS

Graeme McPherson QC (see p.669) One of the leading experts on horse racing disputes, frequently instructed by governing bodies on regulatory issues. He also has significant experience in handling both contractual disputes and disciplinary matters for clients within Formula 1, football and boxing. **Strengths:** "He's top-notch; his knowledge of the racing industry is fantastic." **Recent work:** He acted for the British Horseracing Authority (BHA) on prosecuting the Godolphin stable's trainer for the misuse of anabolic steroids in the training of racehorses.

JUNIORS

Richard Liddell (see p.656) Frequently represents horse racing and rugby governing bodies in disciplinary and regulatory cases. He also has experience in handling commercial and doping cases in relation to football. **Strengths:** "He's a talented performer in the courtroom." **Recent work:** He successfully acted for the BHA in a disciplinary inquiry in connection to a trainer, Ian McInnes, who was banned for disregarding horse welfare.

Daniel Saoul (see p.714) Has a wide-ranging sports regulatory practice, and acts for both governing bodies and individual sportsmen and women. He has acted on selection disputes, doping cases, contract disputes and governance matters in sports such as Formula 1, rugby and ice skating. **Strengths:** "He used to be a solicitor, so he understands how that side of things works. He's also got a keen interest in sport and is enthusiastic about getting involved in sports matters." "He's very businesslike, very commercial, very thorough and also very creative." **Recent work:** He defended rugby league player David Cookson against breaches of anti-doping rules regarding the use of stimulants.

Other Ranked Lawyers

Charles Hollander QC (Brick Court Chambers) Has been instructed on disputes across a wide range of sports, including motor racing, football, boxing and athletics. **Strengths:** "He is very incisive and has a good feel for the reality of a situation. He gives very clear advice with a clear aim and outcome." **Recent work:** He was instructed on a Formula 1 management dispute between Lewis Hamilton's father Anthony and British driver Paul di Resta.

Caspar Glyn QC (see p.610) (Cloisters) Well regarded by peers for his employment expertise, especially in relation to football. He specialises in acting on regulatory and contractual disputes for managers, players and senior executives. **Strengths:** "He is a lively and knowledgeable advocate, and brings a practical real-world view, which is important in sport." **Recent work:** He acted for Cardiff City in connection with the dismissal of its manager, Malky Mackay.

Nicholas Randall QC (see p.704) (Devereux) Handles a wide range of sports disciplinary cases, contractual disputes, and player and agent disputes. He has a strong reputation for his work in football, but is increasingly active across sports such as boxing, athletics and golf. **Strengths:** "He has a tremendous calm about him. He is wholly unflappable and has a gentle charm about him. He has a down-to-earth, realistic approach that works well in the sports world." **Recent work:** He acted for Senegalese international and Newcastle United forward Papiss Cissé in connection with his refusal to wear the team sponsor's logo on his shirt.

Owain Draper (One Essex Court) Acts for clients primarily on competition and commercial law matters, most notably in football. **Strengths:** "He's sharp, personable and hard-working, and gets the right answers."

Jonathan Crystal (Goldsmith Chambers) Has a long history of acting on contract disputes and injury claims in football, and has also worked with notable clients within tennis, boxing and athletics.

Strengths: "His knowledge of the sports industry is invaluable." **Recent work:** He successfully defended Barry Town United FC against the Football Association of Wales' decision to deny the team full membership to the league.

Rupert Butler (3 Hare Court) Acts for individuals and governing bodies on regulatory and disciplinary matters as well as contractual disputes. **Recent work:** He acted for former England manager Sven Goran Eriksson on a bid to reclaim £10 million which had been misappropriated by his former independent financial adviser.

Tim Kerr QC (see p.645) (11KBW) Frequently appointed as an arbitrator on anti-corruption and anti-doping hearings in sports such as tennis, cricket and football. He has also sat as an arbitrator on disciplinary, player and agent disputes and public law matters relating to sport. **Strengths:** "He's a very clever guy, gets to the point really quickly, is calm with clients and knows this area of the law very well." **Recent work:** He chaired the International Tennis Federation's anti-doping tribunal, which handed Marin Cilic a nine-month ban for doping offences.

Christopher Jeans QC (see p.637) (11KBW) Has advised sports clubs, players, managers and agents on a wide range of employment contract matters. **Strengths:** "He is one of the most senior and respected silks around, and brings that gravitas into the sports sector." **Recent work:** He represented the former agent of a prominent international football player in relation to claims concerning both remuneration and restraint of trade.

Seán Jones QC (see p.641) (11KBW) Acts predominantly for football players and managers on employment disputes. **Strengths:** "He is a clever and ruthless advocate – you must never underestimate him." **Recent work:** He acted on the high-profile Papiss Cissé v Newcastle United case, where the Senegalese international declined to wear the club's shirt due to the sponsors' logo.

Damian Brown QC (Littleton Chambers) Acts on behalf of clubs and individual players within football and rugby, handling employment disputes and wider regulatory and disciplinary matters. **Recent work:** He acted in the David Jones v Cardiff City case concerning bonuses owed by the club to its former manager.

John Mehrzad (see p.670) (Littleton Chambers) Has been involved with employment disputes, contractual disputes and disciplinary proceedings in football and rugby, acting on behalf of players, managers and agents. **Strengths:** "His diligence, advice, responsiveness and willingness to see the bigger picture are impressive." **Recent work:** He acted for a football agent in an appeal concerning the non-payment of a commission following a transfer of a player from Sparta Prague to Genoa.

Mark Afeeva (Matrix Chambers) Brings his expertise in employment, discrimination and media law to bear on sports matters. He acts for clubs, sportsmen and women and agents from a wide variety of sports.

Paul Harris QC (Monckton Chambers) A competition specialist who has worked with clients from a wide array of sports and is noted for his expertise on Formula 1, rugby and football cases. **Strengths:** "He's an extremely good sports lawyer who provides pithy, commercial advice." **Recent work:** He acted for the Mercedes-Benz GP team in connection with the Formula 1 'tyregate' affair concerning the illegal testing of tyres.

Fiona Banks (Monckton Chambers) Acts for governing bodies and federations on contractual and doping disputes. She also acts for players, agents and clubs on a wide range of contractual and disciplinary matters. She has worked in a range of sports, including rugby league, Formula 1, football and swimming. **Strengths:** "She picked up doping issues very quickly and really understood the issues and background of a case." "She is really something – she's very bright and able to absorb huge quantities of information very quickly and pick out the salient points." **Recent work:** She acted for a number of governing bodies in an appeal against Ofcom's decision to make Sky provide a regulated wholesale supply of Sky Sports 1 & 2 to other pay TV retailers.

Ian Meakin (XXIV Old Buildings) Acts on contentious and non-contentious contractual issues on behalf of motor racing clients. **Recent work:** He acted on the contract dispute between racing driver Nick Heidfeld and the Lotus F1 team.

Louis Weston (3PB Barristers) Has represented governing bodies from horse racing and greyhound racing in connection with corruption and disciplinary matters. He has also acted on corruption and doping matters in athletics, snooker, football and rugby. **Strengths:** "He's a natural advocate; very skilful and unflappable." "Advice from Louis Weston is like receiving advice from Zeus – you know it's right and if it's not then a fork of lightning will come down and make it right." **Recent work:** He prosecuted a corruption case for the BHA against jockey Eddie Ahern and four other individuals.

Jacob Dean (5RB) Acts on regulatory and disciplinary matters in relation to horse racing, as well as acting for governing bodies. He has also acted for sportsmen and women and clubs on commercial, libel and privacy matters. **Recent work:** He acted on the appeal of a harassment claim brought by a former director of Leeds United against a former chairman of the club.

Christopher Stoner QC (see p.729) (Serle Court) Advises individuals and sporting organisations on regulatory and disciplinary matters in football, swimming and athletics.

Mark Phillips QC (see p.692) (South Square) Represents sporting organisations, clubs and individuals in regulatory disputes. He is highly regarded by sources for his expertise in anti-doping cases. **Strengths:** "He is a very good advocate in court; he's robust and bullish when you need him to be." **Recent work:** He successfully acted for the Football League against HMRC in defending the introduction of insolvency policies and procedures to avoid excessive financial risk-taking by clubs.

Daniel Bayfield (see p.545) (South Square) Acts for governing bodies, individuals and clubs on disciplinary and contractual disputes in football, boxing and cricket. He also has experience of acting in relation to insolvency proceedings in football. **Strengths:** "He's thoroughly reliable, highly intelligent, easy to get on with and a pleasure to work with." **Recent work:** He defended Scottish boxer Ricky Burns against claims brought by leading boxing promoter Frank Warren in connection with alleged breaches of management and promotional agreements.

THE REGIONS

Sport The Regions
Leading Silks
Band 1
Casement David *Kings Chambers (ORL)* ◊ *
Quinlan Christopher *Guildhall Chambers (ORL)* ◊
Smith Richard *Guildhall Chambers (ORL)* ◊
Band 2
Gilroy Paul *9 St John Street (ORL)* ◊ *
Greaney Paul *New Park Court Chambers (ORL)* ◊ *
Unsworth Ian *7 Harrington St Chambers (ORL)* ◊
Leading Juniors
Band 1
Budworth Martin *Kings Chambers (ORL)* ◊
Leach Robin *3PB Barristers (ORL)* ◊
Turner Steven *Parklane Plowden (ORL)* ◊
Band 2
Moore Craig *Parklane Plowden (ORL)* ◊
Sadiq Tariq *St Philips Chambers (ORL)* ◊ 🄰 *
* *Indicates individual with profile.*
◊ *(ORL) = Other Ranked Lawyer.*
🄰 *direct access (see p.11).*
Alphabetical order within each band. Band 1 is highest.

Ranked Lawyers

Christopher Quinlan QC (Guildhall Chambers) Handles a number of sporting disciplinary matters concerning anti-doping misconduct cases. He is retained as an arbitrator on a number of sporting panels across various sports, including football and rugby. **Recent work:** Has chaired disciplinary proceedings for the ERC and RFU.

Richard Smith QC (Guildhall Chambers) Has considerable expertise in handling regulatory, disciplinary and doping disputes in rugby, horse racing and football. He acts for a range of sports clients, including players, clubs and governing bodies. He is frequently instructed by the latter to adjudicate on disciplinary matters. **Strengths:** "He is a leading advocate in rugby disciplinary matters. He puts his case across fantastically well, he can read a panel extremely well, and his ability to make it aware of his best point is unsurpassed." **Recent work:** He acted for two professional footballers accused of conspiring with a prominent jockey to fix horse races.

Ian Unsworth QC (7 Harrington St Chambers) Experienced in acting for sportsmen and women and their agents on regulatory issues. He is particularly noted by peers for his expertise in rugby matters. **Strengths:** "He's a great cross-examiner – a great advocate who really knows rugby."

David Casement QC (see p.566) (Kings Chambers) A commercial and insolvency specialist who acts for sports clubs, governing bodies, agents and players on a wide range of issues, including sponsorship and contractual disputes. **Strengths:** "He's an intellectual heavyweight, a very good advocate." **Recent work:** Represented the Super League and RFL in a sponsorship dispute with Elonex in connection with pitch-side LCD advertising.

Martin Budworth (Kings Chambers) Has developed a strong sports disciplinary practice, and is regularly instructed by notable clients from within football, rugby and boxing. **Strengths:** "He's very hard-working and really understands the sports sector." **Recent work:** He represented a rugby league player in a wrongful dismissal claim against Huddersfield Giants. The dismissal was directly linked to use of social media.

Paul Greaney QC (see p.614) (New Park Court Chambers) Acts for governing bodies in disciplinary cases, most notably in football, where he acted for the FA in the high-profile Luis Suarez v Patrice Evra case. **Strengths:** "I was impressed with how he set out his case from the start. He know where he was going and got there."

Steven Turner (Parklane Plowden) Has a general commercial practice and brings this expertise to bear on sports contract disputes within football and cricket. **Strengths:** "An advocate you can turn to for really thorny problems."

Craig Moore (Parklane Plowden) Acts for sports governing bodies and individuals on commercial matters, including sponsorship and insurance. He works with clients from a broad range of sports, including cycling, football, rugby and extreme sports.

Robin Leach (3PB Barristers) Noted for his expertise in horse racing, frequently defending jockeys and trainers against a wide range of disciplinary matters, including safety and riding offences, as well as against allegations of corruption. **Recent work:** He represented a trainer who was alleged to have committed acts of cruelty against a race horse by depriving it of water.

Tariq Sadiq (see p.713) (St Philips Chambers) Represents governing bodies, sports organisations, and sportsmen and women in both disciplinary employment matters. He receives instructions from clients in football, cricket and pigeon racing. **Recent work:** He represented Bangladeshi cricketer Mohammad Ashraful at his spot-fixing trial at the ICC in Doha, Qatar.

Paul Gilroy QC (see p.608) (9 St John Street) Handles a number of employment-related cases for clients within football. He has successfully acted for a number of football managers in wrongful dismissal claims against clubs.

Contents:

LONDON

Tax London	
Leading Sets	
Band 1	
Gray's Inn Tax Chambers *	
Pump Court Tax Chambers *	
Band 2	
Devereux *	
Field Court Tax Chambers *	
11 New Square	
Tax Chambers 15 Old Square *	
Temple Tax Chambers *	
Leading Silks	
Star individuals	
Gardiner John	*11 New Square*
Goldberg David	*Gray's Inn Tax Chambers*
Milne David	*Pump Court Tax Chambers* *
Peacock Jonathan	*11 New Square* *
Prosser Kevin	*Pump Court Tax Chambers* *
Band 1	
Baker Philip	*Field Court Tax Chambers* *
Ewart David	*Pump Court Tax Chambers* *
Flesch Michael	*Gray's Inn Tax Chambers*
Gammie Malcolm	*One Essex Court (ORL)* ◊
Ghosh Julian	*Pump Court Tax Chambers* *
Goy David	*Gray's Inn Tax Chambers*
Thornhill Andrew	*Pump Court Tax Chambers* *
Band 2	
Baldry Rupert	*Pump Court Tax Chambers* 🄰 *
Brandon Stephen	*Tax Chambers 15 Old Square* *
Brennan Timothy	*Devereux* *
Furness Michael	*Wilberforce Chambers (ORL)* ◊
Goodfellow Giles W J	*Pump Court Tax Chambers* 🄰 *
Jones Philip	*Serle Court (ORL)* ◊ *
Shaw Nicola	*Gray's Inn Tax Chambers* *
Band 3	
Cullen Felicity	*Devereux*
Fisher Jonathan	*Devereux* *
Gibbon Michael	*Maitland Chambers (ORL)* ◊ *
Green Michael	*Fountain Court Chambers (ORL)* ◊ *
Jowell Daniel	*Brick Court Chambers (ORL)* ◊
Venables Robert	*Tax Chambers 15 Old Square*
Way Patrick	*Field Court Tax Chambers* *
Whiteman Peter	*QEB Hollis Whiteman (ORL)* ◊
New Silks	
Thomas Roger	*Pump Court Tax Chambers* *
◊ (ORL) = Other Ranked Lawyer.	
🄰 direct access (see p.11).	
* Indicates set / individual with profile.	

Tax London	
Leading Juniors	
Band 1	
Fitzpatrick Francis	*11 New Square*
Maugham Jolyon	*Devereux* *
McDonnell Conrad	*Gray's Inn Tax Chambers*
Nathan Aparna	*Devereux* *
Ridgway Philip	*Temple Tax Chambers* *
Rivett James	*Pump Court Tax Chambers* *
Schwarz Jonathan S	*Temple Tax Chambers* *
Sherry Michael	*Temple Tax Chambers* *
Sykes Laurent	*Gray's Inn Tax Chambers*
Thomas Michael	*Gray's Inn Tax Chambers*
Vallat Richard	*Pump Court Tax Chambers* 🄰 *
Band 2	
Bremner Jonathan	*Pump Court Tax Chambers* *
Henderson James	*Pump Court Tax Chambers* 🄰 *
James Alun	*Temple Tax Chambers* *
Jones Michael	*Gray's Inn Tax Chambers*
Lemos Marika	*Devereux* *
McCarthy Hui Ling	*Gray's Inn Tax Chambers* *
Mehta Nikhil	*Gray's Inn Tax Chambers* *
Nawbatt Akash	*Devereux* *
Soares Patrick	*Field Court Tax Chambers* *
Walford Philip	*11 New Square* *
Woolf Jeremy	*Pump Court Tax Chambers* 🄰 *
Yates David	*Pump Court Tax Chambers* *
Band 3	
Chacko Thomas	*Pump Court Tax Chambers* *
Murray Rebecca	*Temple Tax Chambers* *
Yang Zizhen	*Pump Court Tax Chambers* *
Up-and-coming individuals	
Ripley Michael	*11 New Square*
Stone Christopher	*Devereux* *

Band 1

Gray's Inn Tax Chambers

See profile on p.813

THE SET

Gray's Inn Tax Chambers is firmly in the vanguard of tax law and is replete with "fantastic names" and "deadly advocates." The set is well known among clients and peers alike for its broad expertise across the tax spectrum, and has members who act for clients in all forms of tax disputes. Its barristers regularly appear in the most significant tax cases, representing both HMRC and taxpayers.

Client service: "I like the clerks' availability, flexibility and friendliness – I feel I get treated like royalty at times. They really go out of their way to help and it's an absolutely outstanding service." Chris Broom is the senior clerk.

SILKS

David Goldberg QC Enjoys an excellent reputation and represents clients in the most sophisticated and challenging of tax cases. He is known for his work in tax planning and also has a raft of courtroom victories under his belt. **Strengths:** "He is brilliant. A very clever and engaging man who thinks a lot about tax."

Michael Flesch QC A seasoned performer who handles a broad range of advisory and litigation work. He handles large corporate transactions for the most part, but also acts for non-domiciled clients. **Strengths:** "His bedside manner is excellent. He knows his tax inside out and takes a measured and prudent approach to his work."

David Goy QC Takes on substantial contested matters, but also has a highly regarded advisory practice, and is brought in to counsel on the most complex issues. **Strengths:** "Very much the gentleman lawyer, he is softly spoken but very effective. He is supremely good at getting on top of the detail, both legal and economic, in a case."

Nicola Shaw QC (see p.719) Works on all aspects of tax litigation, both in the direct and indirect contexts. She regularly appears before tax tribunals and higher courts, and is involved in judicial review proceedings. **Strengths:** "You wouldn't want to be against her if you could help it. She is a thoroughly gracious and worthy opponent, and a very powerful advocate." **Recent work:** Represented Marks & Spencer in a cross-border group relief claim relating to EU subsidiaries.

JUNIORS

Michael Thomas Earns plaudits from clients and peers alike for his expertise in property tax issues. He handles tax matters in relation to significant property transactions and regularly handles contentious cases. **Strengths:** "Very practical, very knowledgeable and very proactive in his advice. He's also very collaborative in his approach, and you can always talk through issues with him."

Conrad McDonnell Regularly represents notable corporate organisations in sophisticated, high-stakes disputes. He also provides advice to businesses and private clients on a range of tax issues, including corporation, partnership and pension tax matters. **Strengths:** "He is controlled and calculated and understands the issues beyond the immediate question at hand." **Recent work:** He acted for BT Pension Scheme before the Court of Appeal in a group litigation order (GLO) concerning foreign dividends and tax credits.

Laurent Sykes Has recently been involved in a number of notable tax deed and employment tax cases. His advisory practice also takes in business and corporation tax issues. **Strengths:** "Exceptionally able and very willing to challenge the instructing solicitors. He's both definitive in his advice and commercially very sound."

Michael Jones A familiar figure at the Tax Bar who handles both contentious and advisory tax work. He specialises in corporate and commercial tax issues, representing the Revenue and taxpayers in a variety of court settings. **Strengths:** "He is extremely bright in a world of extremely bright people. He has clarity of thinking and his experience in tax is complemented by a commercial mindset."

Nikhil Mehta (see p.670) Works on a wide range of tax issues, but is particularly appreciated by clients for her perspective on cross-border matters involving Indian tax elements, in both the corporate and private client contexts. **Strengths:** "He has a number of strong qualities, in particular his reliability, his technical ability and his awareness of the commercial implications of his advice."

Hui Ling McCarthy (see p.667) Has a growing reputation, with regard to both her litigious and advisory work. Her workload covers both direct and indirect taxation. **Strengths:** "She takes her litigation very seriously. A good, straightforward but fierce opponent in court." **Recent work:** She acted for the taxpayer in the significant Icebreaker litigation, where she appeared in the lead-case appeals before the First-tier Tribunal concerning income tax relief based on trading losses.

Pump Court Tax Chambers

See profile on p.852

THE SET

This chambers, very much in the first rank of tax sets, is noted for the "collegiate environment" it fosters and for the creativity of its barristers – "they are always trying to think of new approaches and are very receptive to ideas." It enjoys an excellent reputation for the strength and depth of the tax expertise it offers, and is a regular in all the leading matters of the day. Cases with a European dimension remain an important part of members' workload, including those considering the tax status of dividends paid by, and money lent to, foreign subsidiaries. Peers and clients alike acknowledge that the reputation of the set is something for others at the Tax Bar to aspire to. **Client service:** "Everything always runs very smoothly and the clerks are very prompt in getting back to you." Nigel Jones is the senior clerk.

SILKS

David Milne QC (see p.673) One of the best-known and most highly regarded silks at the Tax Bar. He acts in high-stakes matters in front of the highest courts and has recently been involved in notable cases representing both taxpayers and the Revenue. **Strengths:** "He is very well respected by the court and is not one of those who is histrionic. He is very measured. The courts and judges like him and believe him." **Recent work:** He represented Marks & Spencer in its case concerning cross-border loss relief relating to subsidiaries in Belgium and Germany.

Kevin Prosser QC (see p.700) Enjoys an outstanding reputation for his expertise across a wide range of direct and indirect tax cases in the UK and Europe. He represents HMRC and the Revenue, and also has a strong advisory practice which sees him offering counsel on Islamic finance matters, among other things. **Strengths:** "He digs deep to understand the issues and discover what the client wants. He is commercially sound, quick-thinking, flexible and very easy to work with. His technical and commercial abilities are excellent." **Recent work:** He acted for the Revenue against Vaccine Research in a case concerning alleged tax avoidance schemes.

David Ewart QC (see p.597) Highly regarded by the Revenue and often instructed in its most challenging and significant cases. He also has a healthy taxpayer practice. **Strengths:** "He has particularly good insight into how HMRC think." **Recent work:** He represented HMRC in its case involving Marks & Spencer concerning cross-border loss relief relating to European subsidiaries.

Julian Ghosh QC (see p.607) A hugely respected figure at the London Tax Bar, with superior experience, knowledge and advocacy skills. In corporate tax matters he is an expert on EU issues and loan relationships. **Strengths:** "He is very robust and you have to admire the way he stands up to the tribunal." **Recent work:** He acted for HMRC against Versteegh in a case concerned with a loan relationship scheme.

Andrew Thornhill QC (see p.737) Adept at advising and representing clients in corporate tax matters relating to employee benefit trusts. He is also an authority on corporate reorganisations and UK property issues involving offshore elements. **Strengths:** "He is authoritative on his feet and very clear, composed and unruffled. He is easy to follow and understand." **Recent work:** Acted on behalf of the Murray Group, which owns Glasgow Rangers Football Club, in a case concerning National Insurance contributions.

Rupert Baldry QC (see p.542) Has a fine reputation for his work representing HMRC, and is also continuing to grow his taxpayer practice. His cases include those considering foreign dividend and pension tax, and he is also active in indirect tax matters. **Strengths:** "He has the ability to get to the heart of the legislation and deliver his analysis in a clear and concise manner." **Recent work:** Acted for the Revenue in a GLO concerning the tax status of dividends paid by foreign subsidiaries into the UK.

Giles Goodfellow QC (see p.611) Handles employee benefit and income tax cases, and has also developed notable expertise in relation to tax-related professional negligence and tonnage tax. He represents both the Revenue and taxpayers. **Strengths:** "His all-round tax knowledge, advocacy skills and ability to communicate complex technical issues to the client are impressive." **Recent work:** Acted successfully on behalf of Euroceanica in a tonnage tax case considering whether interest on a loan to buy a ship is subject to tonnage or corporate tax.

Roger Thomas QC (see p.736) Possesses great experience of representing clients in significant corporate tax cases before the highest courts, both in the UK and in Europe. He is an authority on stamp duty land tax (SDLT) and stamp duty reserve tax. **Strengths:** "My impression is that he is very responsive. His advice is crisp and pragmatic, and based on a very deep knowledge of tax law." **Recent work:** He acted for the taxpayer in a Court of Appeal case considering sub-sale relief relating to SDLT.

JUNIORS

Jonathan Bremner (see p.556) Has been involved in a variety of impressive cases recently, and concentrates his practice on the corporate side of tax. Remuneration cases are a particular area of expertise. **Strengths:** "A very bright young man. He provides sound, clear advice." **Recent work:** He was involved for the taxpayer in the Murray Group Glasgow Rangers tax case concerning National Insurance contributions.

James Henderson (see p.624) Has consolidated his reputation as a tax barrister through his involvement in some of the most notable recent tax cases. His is a broad practice, which takes in a host of contentious and non-contentious matters. **Strengths:** "He gets to the bottom of what is going on. Tax is a logical discipline, and he is a very logical man. He understands the philosophy of tax, is measured and speaks well." **Recent work:** Acted on behalf of HMRC in a case involving Bristol & West concerning a group mismatch in derivative contracts.

James Rivett (see p.708) Regularly involved in significant cases, either in support of silks or acting alone. He is an all-round tax expert who is as comfortable working on private client matters as corporate tax cases. **Strengths:** "He seems to hit the nail on the head and thinks very quickly on his feet." **Recent work:** He represented HMRC in a case against BT Pension Fund considering tax credits relating to dividends deriving from investments made in foreign companies.

Richard Vallat (see p.743) Regularly represents taxpayers and HMRC in significant and complex corporate tax cases. His work includes disputes concerning capital allowances and tax planning schemes, and he has also been involved in matters concerning tax-related professional negligence and contractual disputes. **Strengths:** "A very talented junior who is clear, confident, intelligent and pragmatic." **Recent work:** He represented Reed in a case concerning the taxation of travel expenses.

Jeremy Woolf (see p.756) Maintains a balanced practice of advisory work and litigation engagements. His non-contentious work often involves advising clients on tax-efficient corporate structures and professional negligence issues involving tax elements. He is also an authority on employee benefit trusts and income tax. **Strengths:** "He is painstaking, engaged and intelligent."

David Yates (see p.757) A leading junior who often represents HMRC against silks, often without a leader. He provides advice in the context of tax-related negligence, as well as in relation to double tax treaties and cross-border dividends. **Strengths:** "He is clearly a very bright person who comprehends technical issues very quickly and is very rational in his view of the world." **Recent work:** He acted for HMRC in a novel case concerning the treatment of interest on a loan used to purchase a ship, looking at whether it was subject to tonnage or corporation tax.

Thomas Chacko (see p.567) Regularly led by notable silks in significant and complex corporate tax cases. He has also appeared before the First-tier Tribunal without a leader. **Strengths:** "A very well-organised young barrister. He is very good in a supporting role, and offers input into the arguments." **Recent work:** Led by Andrew Thornhill QC in representing the Murray Group in the Glasgow Rangers case concerning National Insurance contributions.

Zizhen Yang (see p.757) Singled out by clients for her dedication to the task and her grasp of the finer points of cases. Her corporate tax expertise covers double tax treaties, company reconstructions and cross-border group relief. **Strengths:** "A tenacious advocate with an in-depth understanding of the matter at hand and the legal background." **Recent work:** She appeared alongside Giles Goodfellow QC for Euroceanica in a case considering the applicability of tonnage tax to the interest on a loan for the purpose of purchasing a ship.

Band 2

Devereux

See profile on p.785

THE SET

Devereux Chambers is a set that "is making a big play for tax work." It has had a good footing in the market for some time, but has, of late, made a real effort to woo the major accountancy firms and build up a strong tax team through lateral hires. It is now seen as being a real force in the market, and is noted for having members who provide "fantastic technical and strategic tax advice." The individuals here are especially good at representing HMRC, some of them having been former Standing Counsel to the Revenue.

Client service: Chambers director Vince Plant leads "a forward-thinking, modern set."

SILKS

Timothy Brennan QC (see p.556) Regularly represents the interests of taxpayers and the Revenue in a broad selection of tax disputes. He acts in cases concerning all taxes, but he is especially active in corporation tax, capital gains tax, National Insurance and income tax matters. **Strengths:** "He is great at public law and great for judicial review. He understands the Revenue very well and is a marvellous cross-examiner." **Recent work:** He represented Next Distribution in a capital allowances case centring on the tax status of import and distribution warehouses.

Felicity Cullen QC Regularly provides advice on sophisticated City transactions, especially those involving private companies and businesses. In addition, she has an active contentious practice acting for taxpayers and HMRC in notable cases. **Strengths:** "She is very bright and diligent, but also very practical. She is also very good at taking clients with her – they have great confidence in her and she will help them navigate the issues." **Recent work:** She provided advice to Hong Kong clients wishing to invest in the Greenwich Peninsula property development scheme.

Jonathan Fisher QC (see p.600) An established expert in tax investigations concerning avoidance and fraud, who represents clients before the tax tribunals and criminal courts. He acts for the taxpayer and the Revenue. **Strengths:** "His years as standing counsel to the Revenue at the Old Bailey have given him unparalleled insight into the mind of CPS case workers." **Recent work:** He advised a group of RBS bankers in relation to an accusation by HMRC that they evaded tax by investing in film schemes.

JUNIORS

Jolyon Maugham (see p.665) His practice is focused on litigation relating to direct and indirect tax. He often acts for clients involved in cases concerning schemes, intangible property, film financing and employment tax. **Strengths:** "He has a first-class brain and an impressive ability to explain complex tax law in simple terms." **Recent work:** He represented the taxpayer in the Icebreaker litigation concerning £300 million of unpaid income tax owed by 500 investors, including members of Take That.

Akash Nawbatt (see p.681) Acts for taxpayers and the Revenue at all levels of the court system. His tax work is focused on cases relating to employment, and typically involves questions of remuneration and the taxation of employees. **Strengths:** "He has a very sharp, agile intellect and is very good strategically. He is also very user-friendly and affable." **Recent work:** He acted for the Revenue in a significant case before the First-tier Tax Tribunal concerning group loss taxation.

Marika Lemos (see p.654) Has a wide-ranging practice, but is particularly noted for her advice on offshore tax planning issues, particularly those involving trusts, and tax issues relating to pensions. Also a noted expert on tax avoidance schemes and tax as it interacts with human rights law. **Strengths:** "Very, very good and thorough." **Recent work:** She acted in a case involving EU elements considering whether exit charges on a migration of a settlement impede EC treaty freedoms.

Christopher Stone (see p.729) Regularly represents the Revenue and is increasingly acting for taxpayers in a variety of tax cases. Areas of expertise include employment-related tax issues, particularly those concerning employment status. **Strengths:** "He is very diligent and highly committed. He will stay up all night if you need him to. He has very good judgement and you can rely on any research he does." **Recent work:** He represented HMRC before the Upper Tribunal in a case considering the tax deductibility of travel expenses for doctors working in private practice.

Aparna Nathan (see p.680) Routinely assists the Revenue in tax disputes. Her practice also includes advisory work, especially in relation to tax planning for non-domiciliaries and high net worth individuals. **Strengths:** "She is technically good and very practical in her approach. She is very good to work with." **Recent work:** Acted for HMRC in a challenge made against a structured avoidance scheme involving loans on depreciating currencies.

Field Court Tax Chambers

See profile on p.801

THE SET

A new set that came into being on 1st August 2014. The chambers comprises four well-respected former members of Gray's Inn Tax Chambers – two silks and two juniors. All are well experienced in handling major tax cases and, accordingly, the market confidently expects their new enterprise to be a great success.

SILKS

Philip Baker QC (see p.541) An international tax expert who is particularly strong on treaties. His practice covers both corporate and private client issues. **Strengths:** "He gives advice quickly and has a wonderfully commercial approach, which is appreciated by clients and instructing solicitors alike."

Patrick Way QC (see p.748) Has recently handled a variety of tax cases, including those concerning group transactions, property transactions, film schemes and intermediaries. His practice comprises advisory work and litigation, and he represents both the Revenue and taxpayers. **Strengths:** "He is a big-picture person. One of the things that is refreshing is that because of his solicitor background he is very good at reassuring clients. He creates an aura of trust."

JUNIORS

Patrick Soares (see p.724) Well known for his advice on tax issues arising in an offshore context. He is also an expert on the tax implications of property transactions. **Strengths:** "He's just incredibly good at looking at a problem, thinking laterally and coming up with solutions."

11 New Square

THE SET

11 New Square is a well-established presence in the marketplace and home to "excellent individuals." The barristers here offer genuine expertise in all areas of tax law, and regularly take on cases for taxpayers and the government before domestic and European tribunals and courts at all levels. The set's international reputation is such that individuals regularly advise on matters relating to foreign jurisdictions, including Hong Kong, India, Singapore, Malaysia and the Channel Islands.

Client service: "An organised set that understands what is needed. Particular mention must go to the clerks, who have a commercial outlook and provide detailed fee estimates." John Moore is the senior clerk.

SILKS

John Gardiner QC Works in a wide range of tax contexts, and has been involved in a number of major and influential cases. While he predominantly works with clients in a UK context, he also has an enviable track record in Hong Kong, where he represents clients in cases with UK tax elements. **Strengths:** "A doyen of the tax world. He is such an experienced advocate that you know your case is in good hands."

Jonathan Peacock QC (see p.691) Has a broad corporate tax practice which includes advising and representing major clients in relation to capital market, employee remuneration and corporate finance matters. He is also well known for his work in tax avoidance cases, where he works for taxpayers and HMRC. **Strengths:** "A technically excellent and impressive advocate who is thorough in all aspects of case preparation. He works efficiently and has a calm and measured approach." **Recent work:** He acted for ITV before the Court of Appeal in a case considering the National Insurance contributions of television actors with reference to industry standard contracts.

JUNIORS

Francis Fitzpatrick A regular presence before UK and European courts and tribunals, who represents both HMRC and the taxpayer. He is experienced in a range of tax areas, and handles issues relating to corporate and structured finance, venture capital and employee remuneration. **Strengths:** "He is technically strong, covers a broad range of work, and always gives practical and well-considered advice." **Recent work:** He acted for the taxpayer against HMRC in a case concerning the recovery of UK tax paid in contravention of EU law.

Philip Walford (see p.744) An expert in both direct and indirect tax who is especially adept at advising clients with regard to corporation tax. Other areas of special expertise include statutory construction tax issues relating to the oil and gas industry. **Strengths:** "His written work is concise, punchy and very readable."

Michael Ripley Has a growing reputation and appears regularly before UK tribunals and courts, with and without a leader, in significant corporate tax cases. He is highlighted by observers for his intellect and for his excellent client-handling skills. **Strengths:** "A future star of the Tax Bar. He has a first-class intellect and excellent client skills. He is particularly strong in cases concerned with complex accountancy principles." **Recent work:** He represented Greene King in a case considering tax relating to intra-group financing transactions under loan relationship provisions.

Tax Chambers 15 Old Square

See profile on p.871

THE SET

Clients admire the "high quality of service and advice" provided by the barristers at Tax Chambers 15 Old Square. The set continues to enjoy a fine reputation for its work as a specialist tax offering, and provides clients with strong expertise in a wide variety of tax contexts, not least on cross-border issues. Cases concerning the interplay between EU and UK law and employee remuneration matters are also areas of strength.

Client service: "The clerks, led by Tony Hall, are attentive, responsive, solutions-based and constructive."

SILKS

Stephen Brandon QC (see p.555) Maintains a wide and varied tax practice, advising corporate and private clients. His corporate caseload presents as a healthy mix of complex international and domestic matters. **Strengths:** "He has an unsurpassed grasp of very difficult tax issues and can very well convey his views to clients not involved in tax. His advocacy before the tax tribunals is excellent." **Recent work:** He acted for Tullow Oil in a significant income tax case before the Ugandan Tax Tribunal.

Robert Venables QC Brings a vast amount of experience and handles tax cases involving employee remuneration, offshore issues and inheritance tax.

He is frequently engaged in cases before the highest courts in Europe and the UK, including the ECJ and House of Lords. **Strengths:** "He is stunningly brilliant, and I would go to him if I was at the bottom of a very deep pit."

Temple Tax Chambers

See profile on p.874

THE SET

The set is a respected presence at the London Tax Bar and its members are known for the ease with which they provide clients with advice on domestic and international tax issues. The set has been taking on an increasing caseload of complex and significant matters in recent times for clients, which include both taxpayers and the Revenue.

Client service: "The clerks are very efficient and polite. Very efficient and very devoted, they are clearly concerned about the client."

JUNIORS

Philip Ridgway (see p.707) Has a broad corporate tax practice and is a noted expert on tax issues as they relate to insolvency cases. **Strengths:** "He is calm and decisive. He plans his strategy in advance, and always has a plan B. He has the ability to dissect an argument put forward by the opposition – he goes through it atom by atom and dismantles it piece by piece." **Recent work:** He acted for the taxpayer in a case investigating the potential for an employee to make a loss and the question of whether this can be deducted from earnings.

Jonathan Schwarz (see p.715) Concentrates his practice on the resolution of cross-border international tax disputes and problems. He is an authority on transfer pricing, tax treaties and domicile questions. **Strengths:** "A recognised expert on treaty disputes. He gives very practical and sensible advice, and clients can relate to that." **Recent work:** He represented the taxpayer in a case concerning use of the retirement scheme of the World Bank by former employees residing in the UK.

Michael Sherry (see p.720) Head of chambers, and a barrister known for his commercial approach to direct tax problems, income tax issues and questions relating to capital gains tax. **Strengths:** "Very commercially minded. He's inventive, a very good technician, and good at coming up with solutions to problems – we go to him when we hit a brick wall." **Recent work:** He acted for the taxpayer in a capital gains tax case concerning enterprise investment scheme and taper relief.

Alun James (see p.637) Regularly engaged by accountants in corporate tax matters, in both the litigation and advisory contexts. He maintains a strong practice in a number of areas, and is an expert on corporate reorganisations, share buy-backs, buyouts and securities. **Strengths:** "He is very down-to-earth and quick-witted. He listens carefully to his clients, thinks widely, and encourages you to challenge him. In addition, he articulates clearly, and has the emotional intelligence to adapt and act appropriately when faced with changing scenarios." **Recent work:** Acted on behalf of McLaren Racing in an Upper Tribunal appeal relating to the tax deductibility of a fine imposed by the FIA.

Rebecca Murray (see p.679) Continues to enhance an already fine reputation with high-profile instructions in notable cases. Her workload covers both direct and indirect tax issues, and she represents both the Revenue and the taxpayer. **Strengths:** "She's smart, presentable, determined and dogged. She's steely in her approach."

Other Ranked Lawyers

Daniel Jowell QC (Brick Court Chambers) Concentrates his practice on competition and EU law, and on the tax implications of such cases. He is also heavily involved in significant commercial matters. **Strengths:** "His opinions are clear and direct, and he is articulate and impressive in front of clients."

Malcolm Gammie QC (One Essex Court) A go-to individual for noteworthy City law firms, who also acts on behalf of HMRC on some of its most significant cases. His practice covers all aspects of UK and European tax. **Strengths:** "He is absolutely excellent. He has got all the skills. He was a solicitor and that means he has a natural understanding of the documents." **Recent work:** He represented the Revenue before the Upper Tribunal in a case concerning the Eclipse film scheme.

Michael Green QC (see p.615) (Fountain Court Chambers) Regularly represents the Revenue in cases concerning tax avoidance and transfer pricing issues. He is an experienced presence in court and has also taken on cases with insolvency and financial services elements. **Strengths:** "He is articulate, hard-working and measured, and has an engaging courtroom manner. He also displays a can-do attitude."

Michael Gibbon QC (see p.607) (Maitland Chambers) Especially well known for acting on behalf of HMRC, although he does represent taxpayers. He is often involved in high-stakes cases with significant commercial considerations. **Strengths:** "He is really fantastic. He has an amazing handle on the technicalities." **Recent work:** He acted for the Revenue in a case concerning a hedge fund manager's involvement in a film finance scheme.

Peter Whiteman QC (QEB Hollis Whiteman) Has a broad practice which covers a variety of areas within corporate and commercial tax. Areas of special interest include, but are not limited to, M&A, structured finance and a range of matters relating to international tax. **Strengths:** "He has great practical flair and immense experience."

Philip Jones QC (see p.641) (Serle Court) Focuses his practice on Revenue work, and appears in substantial and noteworthy tax cases before the Supreme Court. He has been at the forefront of the Revenue's recent moves against alleged tax avoidance schemes. **Strengths:** "He has a good tactical awareness about what points to take and how to react to tricky issues that arise." **Recent work:** He successfully represented HMRC in a case concerning an avoidance scheme created by a tax silk for his own personal use.

Michael Furness QC (Wilberforce Chambers) Well known for his expertise in UK and offshore trusts and the tax issues surrounding them. His practice also sees him acting on behalf of revenue authorities in Hong Kong. **Strengths:** "A great advocate who is measured and careful in his approach." "He's very supportive and easy to bounce ideas off."

LONDON Indirect Tax

Tax: Indirect Tax London
Leading Sets
Band 1
Monckton Chambers *
Pump Court Tax Chambers *
Band 2
Essex Court Chambers *
Gray's Inn Tax Chambers *
Band 3
1 Crown Office Row *
Thirty Nine Essex Street *
Temple Tax Chambers *
* *Indicates set with profile.*
Alphabetical order within each band. Band 1 is highest.

Band 1

Monckton Chambers

See profile on p.833

THE SET

"The leading European chambers covering VAT and other European issues," Monckton has a strong group of silks and juniors regularly engaged in notable cases, acting for both taxpayers and HMRC. The members' significant expertise in EU matters means that they act for clients at European level, as well as in the UK before Tax Tribunals, the Court of Appeal and the Supreme Court.

Client service: "The set provides a high standard of service. Correspondence, calls and e-mails are always dealt with promptly and staff are helpful and accommodating." David Hockney leads the clerking team.

SILKS

Melanie Hall QC (see p.617) A VAT expert of great repute who is well known for handling complex and significant cases both for the Revenue and taxpayers. **Strengths:** "She is a real VAT specialist who has a lot of experience on both sides of disputes (HMRC and taxpayer). A creative and independent thinker who, at the same time, is receptive and sympathetic to the views of those instructing her." **Recent work:** Represented HMRC in a case concerning the lawfulness of the UK VAT status of hot takeaway food.

Paul Lasok QC (see p.651) A well-established presence at the Tax Bar with respect to VAT and customs duty matters. He works with HMRC and private clients in cases of great substance and significance. **Strengths:** "If you had a really big VAT case you would be thinking about going to him." **Recent work:** Acted for HMRC in a case involving BT relating to UK rules concerning VAT bad debt relief.

Philip Moser QC (see p.677) Represents a variety of clients, including NGOs, companies, private indi-

Tax: Indirect Tax London	
Leading Silks	
Star Individuals	
Cordara Roderick	*Essex Court Chambers*
Milne David	*Pump Court Tax Chambers* *
Band 1	
Hall Melanie	*Monckton Chambers* *
Lasok Paul	*Monckton Chambers* [A] *
Peacock Jonathan	*11 New Square (ORL)* ◇ *
Pleming Nigel	*Thirty Nine Essex Street*
Prosser Kevin	*Pump Court Tax Chambers* *
Whipple Philippa	*1 Crown Office Row*
Band 2	
Baldry Rupert	*Pump Court Tax Chambers* [A] *
Eadie James	*Blackstone Chambers (ORL)* ◇
Foster Alison	*Thirty Nine Essex Street*
Ghosh Julian	*Pump Court Tax Chambers* *
Grodzinski Sam	*Blackstone Chambers (ORL)* ◇
Hitchmough Andrew	*Pump Court Tax Chambers*
Lyons Timothy	*Thirty Nine Essex Street* [A] *
Shaw Nicola	*Gray's Inn Tax Chambers* *
Band 3	
Beal Kieron	*Blackstone Chambers (ORL)* ◇
Goy David	*Gray's Inn Tax Chambers*
Key Paul	*Essex Court Chambers*
Moser Philip	*Monckton Chambers* [A] *
New Silks	
Southern David	*Temple Tax Chambers* *
Thomas Roger	*Pump Court Tax Chambers* *
Leading Juniors	
Band 1	
Hamilton Penny	*Pump Court Tax Chambers* [A] *
Mantle Peter	*Monckton Chambers* [A]
Scorey David	*Essex Court Chambers*
Sloane Valentina	*Monckton Chambers* [A]
Thomas Owain	*1 Crown Office Row*
Band 2	
Hill Raymond	*Monckton Chambers*
McDonnell Conrad	*Gray's Inn Tax Chambers*
Mitrophanous Eleni	*Matrix Chambers (ORL)* ◇
Murray Rebecca	*Temple Tax Chambers* *
Sherry Michael	*Temple Tax Chambers* *
Thomas Michael	*Gray's Inn Tax Chambers*
White Jeremy	*Pump Court Tax Chambers* *
Band 3	
Brinsmead-Stockham John	*11 New Square (ORL)* ◇
Brown Edward	*Essex Court Chambers*
Brown Tim	*Temple Tax Chambers* *
Conolly Oliver	*Pump Court Tax Chambers* [A] *
Henderson James	*Pump Court Tax Chambers* [A] *
King Edmund	*Essex Court Chambers*
Macnab Andrew	*Monckton Chambers*
Ng Jern-Fei	*Essex Court Chambers* *
Singh Sarabjit	*1 Crown Office Row* *
Soares Patrick	*Field Court Tax Chambers (ORL)* ◇ *

◇ (ORL) = Other Ranked Lawyer.
[A] direct access (see p.11).
** Indicates set with profile.*

viduals and HMRC, in indirect tax cases. His areas of expertise include public procurement, EU sanctions and missing trader intra-community (MTIC) fraud matters. **Strengths:** "He has a really, really broad understanding of EU law." **Recent work:** He handled an ECJ case for the Revenue in which the interpretation of Kittel was tested in a variety of East European contexts.

JUNIORS

Peter Mantle An experienced indirect tax and EU law practitioner. His expertise involves remedies cases, including group litigation in the VAT context, and the representation of HMRC and private clients before UK and European institutions. **Strengths:** "Very thorough and well prepared." **Recent work:** He represented HMRC against Dixons Retail in a VAT case regarding the status of fraudulent payments for goods made with credit cards.

Valentina Sloane Often acts on behalf of the taxpayer, taking instructions from leading accountancy firms. He also has experience of representing the interests of the Revenue in significant cases. **Strengths:** "A leading light on both VAT and customs duty matters – she gets to know the important details of clients' businesses and provides advice which is highly practical and usable." **Recent work:** She was involved against HMRC in a continuing case concerning the tax status of gaming machines.

Raymond Hill An established expert on matters concerning VAT and indirect taxation more generally. He is especially well known for his work representing the Revenue's position before the ECJ. **Strengths:** "He has a calm demeanour and gets to the heart of the matter." "On his feet he's unflappable and is adept at handling interventions whether they be from the Bench or from his opponents." **Recent work:** He handled a case for the Treasury before the ECJ concerned with determining whether or not final salary pension schemes should be exempt from VAT with reference to special investment funds.

Andrew Macnab Concentrates his practice on a range of indirect tax areas, including VAT and customs and excise duties. He is particularly known for his work with the Revenue, but his workload also includes advising private clients on VAT matters. **Strengths:** "He is very experienced at working with government." **Recent work:** He represented HMRC in a challenge brought by Leeds City Council regarding the UK's three-year cap on repayment claims of overpaid VAT and its compatibility with EU law.

Pump Court Tax Chambers

See profile on p.852

THE SET

The indirect tax offering at Pump Court comprises "a deep legacy and really good people." This specialist tax set remains at the forefront of the Indirect Tax Bar, and offers both a strong range of skills and expertise in significant VAT cases. The breadth of tax knowledge on hand at the chambers provides clients with valuable insight into related tax areas. Members represent and advise HMRC and the taxpayer in complex, ground-breaking cases concerning VAT and other indirect taxes, such as landfill tax, gaming tax and stamp duty land tax (SDLT). Other areas of recent activity include exemptions and alleged abusive VAT schemes.

Client service: "They are extremely approachable, pragmatic and willing to work together to find the right solution to the problem. The clerks are a great asset to chambers and, overall, one gets a very comfortable feeling when dealing with chambers."

SILKS

David Milne QC (see p.673) Enjoys an extraordinary reputation as an indirect tax lawyer. He is often found acting for those involved in the most substantial and significant cases before the Supreme Court and ECJ. **Strengths:** "He is very experienced and knowledgeable, and well liked by the courts. He is trusted and very good at getting to the heart of the issue. **Recent work:** He successfully acted for Loyalty Management UK in its dispute with HMRC concerning VAT on Nectar Card redemptions.

Kevin Prosser QC (see p.700) Indirect taxation forms an integral part of his overall tax specialism. He is often instructed by leading accountancy practices, as well as notable law firms. **Strengths:** "A formidable advocate with an excellent grasp of technical issues." **Recent work:** He represented Wakefield College in the Upper Tribunal in an appeal considering if the costs of constructing a new building should be zero rated with regard to VAT.

Rupert Baldry QC (see p.542) Continues to represent HMRC, but now displays a broader practice working for the taxpayer on a range of indirect tax issues. His practice spans both the litigation and advisory contexts. **Strengths:** "He is very personable, puts clients at ease, but moreover has a huge intellect, and the knowledge and ability to see a problem through to a solution." **Recent work:** He acted for Northumbrian Water in a case considering whether or not an aggregates levy should be applied to the shifting of rock at a site.

Julian Ghosh QC (see p.607) A notable presence at the Tax Bar generally, who works right across the practice area. Indirect tax forms a strong part of his broad tax expertise and he is an authority on the interplay between UK and EU laws. **Recent work:** He represented Ocean Finance against the Revenue in a case concerning an alleged abuse of rights concerning its VAT structure.

Andrew Hitchmough QC A well-established expert on all matters concerning VAT, who has an enviable record of working on a variety of noteworthy cases. He is an experienced advocate who has regularly appeared before the Upper Tribunal. **Strengths:** "Andrew Hitchmough is outstanding, very much now the 'go-to' VAT barrister. He's very bright, very sound technically, very diplomatic and not arrogant – he listens. Calm and measured as an advocate, he takes time to make sure his point has got across." **Recent work:** He acted for McCarthy & Stone in a case concerning the recovery of VAT on items acquired for use in communal areas of retirement homes.

Roger Thomas QC (see p.736) An SDLT expert of some repute, who continues to act for clients involved in VAT cases, including arts and culture organisations. He has significant experience of appearing before the ECJ and the Supreme Court. **Strengths:** "He is the man to go to for cultural exemptions and the like." **Recent work:** He advised Prostate Cancer UK on the VAT status of the Movember campaign, especially with regard to the relationship between the UK charity initiative and the Australian concept owners.

JUNIORS

Penny Hamilton (see p.618) Has a broad indirect tax practice, encompassing VAT and a variety of other taxes, such as aggregates levy, landfill tax and climate change levy. She also handles customs and excise cases and MTIC fraud matters. **Strengths:** "She breaks everything down on paper and takes great care explaining things to the client." **Recent work:** She acted for TNT in a protracted case concerning the VAT status of bulk mail deliveries.

Jeremy White (see p.750) Has a first-class reputation for his work relating to customs and excise cases. He has an increasingly international practice due to his additional expertise in trade barriers. **Strengths:**

"He's just about the best in terms of knowing how customs or border force approach things." **Recent work:** He represented a consortium of seven appellants in a set of appeals concerning the designation of mobility scooters as motor vehicles or carriages for the disabled, and the customs duties implications of this.

Oliver Conolly (see p.577) Represents the interests of both the taxpayer and the Revenue in VAT cases and other disputes concerning indirect taxes, especially customs and excise issues. **Recent work:** Successfully represented HMRC in a case concerning customs duty levied on particular snack foods when an importer had failed to correctly complete the necessary paperwork.

James Henderson (see p.624) Has a fine reputation among leading accountancy firms who instruct him on a broad range of VAT-related cases. He regularly represents clients before a variety of major European and UK courts and tribunals. **Strengths:** "A highly capable barrister who is very thoughtful about the points of law that arise in a case." **Recent work:** He represented gaming company Peter Arnett Leisure in a case concerning the recovery of overpaid VAT after it failed to appeal within the designated timeframe.

Band 2

Essex Court Chambers

See profile on p.792

THE SET

This fine commercial chambers also offers strong tax expertise, and provides leading practitioners adept at handling a range of indirect tax cases. Its experienced group of standout individuals mixes acting for taxpayers with representing the Revenue in cases with UK and EU significance, before both domestic and European tribunals and courts.

Client service: "The chambers provide an excellent service and the clerks are very much part of that service." David Grief heads up the clerking team.

SILKS

Roderick Cordara QC Enjoys a stellar reputation for his abilities as an indirect tax barrister. He tackles international issues relating to indirect taxation in Asia and Australia, as well as Europe and the UK. **Strengths:** "He rapidly understands the issues before him and has an encyclopaedic knowledge of VAT that allows him to act quickly and with assurance to the benefit of his clients."

Paul Key QC Acts for taxpayers and the Revenue, and has an established practice handling VAT, excise and duties cases. His broader practice includes international and Commercial Court arbitration. **Strengths:** "His is very much a practical, hands-on approach. He talks to us and the client in language we understand and is keen to have meetings. He is also eager to resolve matters before they get to tribunal or court."

JUNIORS

David Scorey Has a broad international and domestic commercial practice, and handles a range of disputes including those concerning duties such as VAT and insurance premium tax. **Strengths:** "He is outstanding as he examines the evidence in great detail. His litigation skills are very good, and he has a very good understanding of VAT and European law."

Edward Brown Takes instructions from leading accountancy practices and law firms, and has an increasingly busy indirect tax practice that regularly sees him representing clients in the Court of Appeal, as well as the First-tier and Upper Tribunals. He also represents the Revenue. **Strengths:** "A class act. He is on the ball, works hard and always delivers." **Recent work:** He acted for HMRC in a case with BAA which concerned the possibility of recovering corporate acquisition costs after a contested takeover.

Edmund King Has a strong commercial chancery practice, which is augmented by his ability to take on significant VAT cases. He has acted for clients at all levels of the court system. **Strengths:** "He is very lively, and has lots of energy and enthusiasm. He is also very personable. He is a good person to have on your side; you can sense the confidence."

Jern-Fei Ng (see p.682) Maintains a broad practice that includes civil fraud and international arbitration, as well as related VAT matters. He also works on issues relating to Singapore. **Recent work:** Acted for Fitzwilliam College, Cambridge, in a tax planning case involving abuse of right claims and the doctrine on single/multiple suppliers.

Gray's Inn Tax Chambers

See profile on p.813

THE SET

Market sources acknowledge the presence of "some really good people" at this specialist tax set. Members act for the Revenue and the taxpayer, and are comfortable in handling cases both in the UK and abroad.

Client service: "They've been consistently good. The clerks are very efficient and are responsive in coming back and agreeing things quickly."

SILKS

Nicola Shaw QC (see p.719) Has recently forged a strong reputation for her general tax practice, and she represents HMRC and the taxpayer in indirect cases at various levels. **Strengths:** "She gives forthright views and is very technically aware. She is very, very approachable and puts things across to people who may not understand the technical issues." **Recent work:** She acted on behalf of Volkswagen Financial Services in a case considering if it is necessary for inputs to feature as cost components of a supply price in order to be designated as a deduction.

David Goy QC Maintains his indirect tax practice as part of his overall tax offering. He is an authority on VAT issues affecting property matters. **Strengths:** "Impresses with his mastery of the detail in a case."

JUNIORS

Conrad McDonnell Has a practice touching upon all contentious issues relating to VAT and stamp duty. He also has a healthy advisory practice, and regularly counsels large business clients including those in the insurance sector. **Strengths:** "He is very level-headed and has a good sense of what can be achieved for the client. He has a good sense of how the litigation process works." **Recent work:** He acted for BSkyB as part of an EU GLO concerning stamp duty levied on share issues.

Michael Thomas An acknowledged and established expert on tax relating to a wide range of property matters. **Strengths:** "He is very popular as he provides speedy, considered responses. He also comes back to us, tells us the risks and is positive."

Band 3

1 Crown Office Row

See profile on p.784

THE SET

This set maintains a strong reputation for acting on behalf of HMRC in noteworthy VAT cases, and continues to attract an increasing amount of work from the taxpayer. Members are active in a wide range of indirect tax cases and appear before the Administrative Court, Tax Tribunals and the European courts. Indirect tax strengths lie particularly in VAT, customs duty and landfill tax cases.

SILKS

Philippa Whipple QC Enjoys an excellent reputation for representing taxpayers and the Revenue in cases concerning indirect tax, which serves as part of her broader expertise across a range of areas, including general public law. **Strengths:** "She is a hard worker, a deep thinker, and an engaging and persuasive advocate. Judges and clients like her, as she chooses her juniors well and doesn't take rubbish points. Her skeleton arguments are straight to the point and the same is true of her advocacy." **Recent work:** She represented HMRC against Birmingham Hippodrome in a claim concerning overpaid output tax.

JUNIORS

Owain Thomas Regularly represents HMRC in a range of indirect tax cases. His areas of specialism include VAT, landfill tax and customs and excise issues. **Strengths:** "He is a big hitter. He is tenacious and really stands up for his client. Technically excellent and very diligent, he always gives you a good fight." **Recent work:** He acted on behalf of the Revenue against BAA in a case concerning input tax in a corporate takeover.

Sarabjit Singh (see p.722) Has an active practice in which he represents the interests of the Revenue and the taxpayer in front of tax tribunals at various levels. **Strengths:** "He gives prompt and thorough advice." "He is a favourite of the Revenue and is known for his forceful advocacy."

Thirty Nine Essex Street

See profile on p.797

THE SET

Members at this general public law set have a reputation for being heavily involved in the indirect tax practice area, and are especially strong on matters that set the VAT policy agenda. Members work in the domestic and European contexts, and receive instructions from taxpayers and the Revenue.

Client service: "The clerks are absolutely superb and very slick. They are very keen to please."

SILKS

Nigel Pleming QC Concentrates his practice on working with HMRC, although he also occasionally acts for the taxpayer. His workload is largely advisory in nature and mostly relates to VAT issues, especially in the context of tax avoidance. **Strengths:** "Bright, pragmatic and an extremely good advocate." **Recent work:** He acted for the Revenue in a case regarding VAT on the margin in car sales.

Alison Foster QC Comfortable representing the Revenue and the taxpayer in indirect tax cases, particularly those with a VAT element. **Strengths:** "She is absolutely excellent and everything you want in a silk. She is very approachable and clear, and adds insight." **Recent work:** She acted for the Revenue in a case consisting of a variety of judicial review applications relating to a Revenue decision denying an extra-statutory concession.

Timothy Lyons QC (see p.659) Handles a range of tax cases involving UK and EU issues, including those concerning VAT and customs. He has a notably international client list. **Strengths:** "A very good barrister who clearly knows his customs law." **Recent work:** He represented Targetti UK in its appeal concerning EU law provisions on anti-dumping duty as it relates to light-bulb imports from China.

Temple Tax Chambers

See profile on p.874

THE SET

This set of well-established general tax experts continues to offer clients a first-rate indirect tax practice, and has the ability to handle complex VAT cases. Members are comfortable working on a wide variety of challenging indirect tax matters, including stamp duty, SDLT and stamp duty reserve tax cases, most usually appearing on behalf of the taxpayer.

Client service: "The clerks are very responsive in terms of obtaining information and keeping us up to date."

SILKS

David Southern QC (see p.725) Has an advisory and litigation practice concentrating on general direct and indirect tax issues, including those concerning VAT. He is a noted authority on tax as it relates to derivative contracts and loan relationships. **Strengths:** "He is a very well-known figure in the field, and a very entertaining advocate." **Recent work:** He represented BAA in a case considering the recoverability of input VAT on professional advice fees involved in a company takeover.

JUNIORS

Rebecca Murray (see p.679) Has a growing reputation and has recently led in a number of significant and complex cases. She has a broad indirect tax practice, and has a particular area of specialism in the VAT principle of abuse and its interplay with tax avoidance. **Strengths:** "She appreciates what is going on with the clients, and provides practical and pragmatic solutions." **Recent work:** She represented BAA before the Court of Appeal in a case concerning the recovery of input tax incurred during a takeover.

Michael Sherry (see p.720) A general tax expert who represents clients in cases concerning indirect tax issues. He handles VAT matters relating to the education sector, and is also active in the areas of duties and property taxation.

Tim Brown (see p.558) Noted for his litigation experience relating to a wide variety of indirect tax issues. His matters include customs and excise duty, VAT and insurance premium tax cases. **Strengths:** "As he was previously employed as an Officer of HM Customs and Excise for many years he is fully familiar with HMRC law, regulations, policy, procedures and guidance. As a result he is able to take a broader view of HMRC tax investigations, and achieve the best possible outcome for our appellant clients." **Recent work:** Represented SHS International in a case to determine the tax status of amino acids imported for use in formulas for babies unable to take cow's milk as either food or medicine.

Other Ranked Lawyers

James Eadie QC (Blackstone Chambers) Enjoys an excellent reputation for his work representing the Treasury. He regularly acts for HMRC in a variety of tax contexts.

Sam Grodzinski QC (Blackstone Chambers) Acts for HMRC and taxpayers. He is especially adept at representing clients in cases concerning VAT and excise duty, particularly where they involve public law elements. **Strengths:** "What I really like about him is his responsiveness, and most importantly his ability to take complicated scenarios and simplify them. He focuses on the most important issues in a way that a client can understand." **Recent work:** He acted for the Revenue before the Supreme Court in a case concerning the VAT status of online hotel bookings.

Kieron Beal QC (Blackstone Chambers) Experienced in handling indirect tax cases before a range of tribunals and courts. His tax expertise is closely related to his specialisms in EU and competition law. **Strengths:** "He is technically brilliant, and can also be extremely tactical when handling litigation."

Patrick Soares (see p.724) (Field Court Tax Chambers) Concentrates his work on VAT and other indirect tax issues arising from property transactions. He is also known for his ability in cases relating to trusts and offshore tax. **Strengths:** "He has a wide knowledge of VAT and general tax, and is clearly used to litigating with HMRC."

Eleni Mitrophanous (Matrix Chambers) Concentrates her practice on acting for HMRC. Her work regularly includes cases with substantial EU law elements, including those regarding reasonable time limits. **Strengths:** "She is very, very capable, easy to work with and bright. She has a reputation as a tenacious advocate." **Recent work:** She represented HMRC in a Supreme Court case considering the VAT position of online accommodation bookings.

Jonathan Peacock QC (see p.691) (11 New Square) Regularly acts for clients in courts in the UK and in Europe. He represents the interests of both the Revenue and taxpayers such as financial institutions, corporate organisations and high net worth individuals. **Strengths:** "He is certainly one of the best advocates. He has a methodical approach to everything, and goes through things in conference and at court in a very clear and methodical way." **Recent work:** He represented Pollen Estate Trust Company in an appeal concerning the charity exemption from SDLT.

John Brinsmead-Stockham (11 New Square) Active in both litigation and advisory work relating to VAT. His work includes issues relating to medical services exemption, zero-rating and VAT relating to intermediaries. **Strengths:** "He is an outstanding young barrister. He is insightful, very articulate and very thorough." **Recent work:** He acted for Reed Employment in its attempt to recover a significant amount of overpaid VAT.

LONDON Private Client

Tax: Private Client London
Leading Sets
Band 1
Pump Court Tax Chambers *
Band 2
Gray's Inn Tax Chambers *
5 Stone Buildings *
Tax Chambers 15 Old Square *
Leading Silks
Star individuals
Massey William *Pump Court Tax Chambers* *
Band 1
Kessler James *Tax Chambers 15 Old Square* *
McCall Christopher *Maitland Chambers (ORL)* ◊ *
Prosser Kevin *Pump Court Tax Chambers* *
Band 2
Brandon Stephen *Tax Chambers 15 Old Square* *
Ewart David *Pump Court Tax Chambers* *
Flesch Michael *Gray's Inn Tax Chambers*
Ghosh Julian *Pump Court Tax Chambers* *
Leading Juniors
Star individuals
Chamberlain Emma *Pump Court Tax Chambers* 🄰 *
Band 1
Nathan Aparna *Devereux (ORL)* ◊ *
Whitehouse Christopher *5 Stone Buildings* *
Wilson Elizabeth *Pump Court Tax Chambers* *
Band 2
Lemos Marika *Devereux (ORL)* ◊ *
Rivett James *Pump Court Tax Chambers* *
Soares Patrick *Field Court Tax Chambers (ORL)* ◊ *
Vallat Richard *Pump Court Tax Chambers* 🄰 *
Band 3
Afzal Imran *Field Court Tax Chambers (ORL)* ◊ *
Davey Jonathan *Wilberforce Chambers (ORL)* ◊
Hardy Amanda *Tax Chambers 15 Old Square* *
Poots Laura *Pump Court Tax Chambers* 🄰 *
Richards Ian *Pump Court Tax Chambers* *
Sartin Leon *5 Stone Buildings* *
◊ (ORL) = Other Ranked Lawyer.
🄰 direct access (see p.11).
** Indicates set / individual with profile.*

Band 1

Pump Court Tax Chambers
See profile on p.852

THE SET

The private client service at Pump Court Tax Chambers remains the outstanding offering in the practice area. "Excellent all round," the chambers provides a comprehensive set of expertise in high-stakes private client tax matters arising from a variety of contexts. Notable areas of work remain trust matters, the representation of estate owners in relation to agricultural and business property relief, and employee incentive schemes including employee benefit trusts. **Client service:** "Counsel are generally commercial, knowledgeable and pleasant to deal with. The clerks and front desk of chambers are without doubt the best of any chambers I have dealt with. They support counsel, they support those instructing counsel and are more than happy to 'go the extra mile' to ensure quality of service is maintained and counsel and clients are happy."

SILKS

William Massey QC (see p.664) Enjoys a stellar reputation among solicitors and clients due to the high standards he sets in his private client practice. He is well known for his ability as an estate and tax planning adviser, and continues to be a leading expert on matters concerning agricultural and heritage property. **Strengths:** "A renowned expert on landed estates and country houses." "He is ahead of the pack on inheritance tax." **Recent work:** He represented the executors of Lord Howard of Henderskelfe in the Court of Appeal, arguing successfully against HMRC that proceeds from the sale of a notable painting were not subject to capital gains tax.

Kevin Prosser QC (see p.700) A well-respected member of the Tax Bar whose expertise is deployed right across the practice area. His private client work is often characterised by involvement in disputes relating to tax avoidance schemes. **Strengths:** "He's extremely bright and presents complex arguments in a coherent and straightforward manner." "He provides clear and direct advice." **Recent work:** He represented UBS in a dispute concerning the payment of bonuses, which included company shares, and their treatment as income tax.

David Ewart QC (see p.597) Has a well-developed advisory practice relating to personal tax matters, not least in the areas of trusts and inheritance tax planning. In addition, a significant proportion of his practice involves representing the Revenue in court and tribunals. **Strengths:** "He is a fountain of knowledge and his experience of working on the other side for HMRC can be invaluable." **Recent work:** He appeared for HMRC against Nicholas Barnes in the Court of Appeal in a case concerning Project Corbiere, a capital gains tax avoidance scheme.

Julian Ghosh QC (see p.607) Noted for his broad practice which covers both personal and corporate tax matters. He is comfortable representing the interests of HMRC and the taxpayer. **Recent work:** He represented HMRC against Aberdeen Asset Management in a case concerning the income tax treatment of bonuses paid in company shares.

JUNIORS

Emma Chamberlain (see p.568) A committed personal tax practitioner, with a background as a private client solicitor, who provides clients with a wide range of expertise relating to private client matters. She furnishes inheritance and capital gains tax advice for UK domiciles, and regularly provides trust guidance, often for those domiciled abroad. **Strengths:** "I had to instruct her on a matter that was so complicated that it made my nose bleed. Her advice was brilliant." **Recent work:** She successfully represented a high net worth individual living in Monaco in a residency case.

Elizabeth Wilson (see p.753) An experienced personal tax practitioner, whose work encompasses the various aspects of the practice area, including inheritance tax and capital gains tax. She also advises foreign domiciled individuals on offshore trust planning issues. **Strengths:** "She has a good grasp of tax issues affecting trusts." **Recent work:** She won an appeal on behalf of the Revenue in a case relating to potential relief due on National Insurance contributions.

Richard Vallat (see p.743) Provides a wide range of personal tax expertise in both the advisory and litigation contexts. His work includes cases and matters concerning income, capital gains and inheritance tax, and she is also adept at helping clients dealing with offshore trusts. **Strengths:** "He takes a sensible, practical approach, and is prepared to listen to what the clients want. He understands what works for clients and their businesses, and fully comprehends HMRC's approach."

Laura Poots (see p.696) Works with private clients to mitigate against tax losses incurred through capital gains, inheritance and further taxes, especially through the employment of offshore trusts and other alternative structures. She also possesses expertise in the area of domicile issues. **Strengths:** "She is responsive, clever and practical. Her opinions are provided in good time and address highly complex offshore tax issues in a methodical and comprehensible manner. She recognises that opinions are not requested simply as an academic exercise but will require practical application."

Ian Richards (see p.707) Concentrates solely on providing advisory expertise to notable non-domiciled ultra high net worth clients engaged in sport and the media, among other areas. She is particularly strong on issues relating to residency, offshore trusts and the sheltering of gains and profits.

James Rivett (see p.708) Has a rapidly expanding private client tax practice. He is an authority on tax law in relation to landed estates and heritage property, and is also an established expert on art law and its position in the tax landscape. **Strengths:** "He looks at things in a practical way and has a broad knowledge of tax law. He is particularly good on UK landed estates and inhereritance problems."

Band 2

Gray's Inn Tax Chambers
See profile on p.813

THE SET

This well-established set consists of tax specialists who continue to play a leading role at the Tax Bar in matters concerning private clients. Their expertise ranges across the private client spectrum, and they regularly represent ultra high net worth individuals. Members routinely tackle issues relating to offshore and domestic trust matters, and also offer impressive expertise in the areas of inheritance and capital gains tax.

Client service: "I have always found them to be very helpful and competent. The response times are very good."

SILKS

Michael Flesch QC Enjoys a significant reputation for his technical ability and his measured approach to matters. In addition, he is considered to be a leading expert in issues relating to the domicile status of private clients. **Strengths:** "He is so calm, so cool and collected, and his advice is absolutely solid. He is so charming and easy to deal with."

5 Stone Buildings
See profile on p.866

THE SET

A leading traditional chancery set, 5 Stone Buildings is also able to deploy impressive talent in the area of private client tax. Members' work arises in a range

of contexts and settings, and they provide advisory and litigation expertise in relation to domestic and international matters.
Client service: "They are very responsive and you can communicate with them." The senior clerk is Paul Jennings.

JUNIORS
Christopher Whitehouse (see p.751) Singled out by observers for the strength of his inheritance tax practice. He is also adept at matters concerning domicile status and trusts. **Strengths:** "Still at the top of his game in inheritance tax planning and someone with bright ideas. He is grounded, practical and a pleasure to work with."

Leon Sartin (see p.714) Has a broad private client practice, representing clients in matters concerning, or relating to, central issues in the practice area, such as inheritance tax and estate planning and trust work. **Strengths:** "He is very easy to deal with, as he is commercial and very responsive. He has the academic background and can translate that into practical advice."

Tax Chambers 15 Old Square
See profile on p.871
THE SET
This respected and well-known specialist tax set maintains a notable private client tax offering. Clients are provided with assistance in matters concerning offshore trusts and issues relating to domicile status, while additional expertise can be called upon in inheritance tax and estate planning and pensions work.
Client service: "The clerks have a very friendly approach. You feel they know you as an individual and value your instructions." Tony Hall is the senior clerk.

SILKS
James Kessler QC (see p.645) An authority on the intersection between tax and charity law. His work includes a variety of notable matters concerning offshore trusts, and he is regarded as an expert on domicile issues. **Strengths:** "He has an incisive mind and is very articulate. He has encyclopaedic knowledge and you get a very definite opinion."

Stephen Brandon QC (see p.555) Often acts in the interest of noteworthy high net worth individuals, both domestically and internationally. His work in such matters reflects his expertise in both direct and indirect tax in the private client sphere. **Strengths:** "He is immensely knowledgeable and coolly analytical. He gives time for discussion, and is able to debate a point and open himself up to other views. He produces carefully formulated opinions." **Recent work:** He represented a family in its challenge concerning the treatment of foreign income under UK law and its compatibility with EU law.

JUNIORS
Amanda Hardy (see p.619) Maintains a healthy private client practice that includes work concerning trust and inheritance matters. She is also active in the areas of pensions and domicile status. **Strengths:** "She is technically excellent in tax and trusts law, and has a real insight into how the Revenue works."

Other Ranked Lawyers

Aparna Nathan (see p.680) (Devereux) Has a strong advisory practice attending to the needs of high net worth individuals, as well as those who require assistance in matters concerning domicile status. **Strengths:** "She's extremely technically able and can deliver the advice in a understandable way."

Marika Lemos (see p.654) (Devereux) Acts for private clients in both an advisory and litigation capacity. Her matters often include a broad range of issues including, but not limited to, the structuring of onshore and offshore trusts, inheritance relief, pension planning and questions of client domicile status. **Strengths:** "She continues to really impress, especially on the tax/pensions crossover – she really understands how they fit together." **Recent work:** She was involved in a protracted case concerning Business Assets Taper Relief that recently settled.

Patrick Soares (see p.724) (Field Court Tax Chambers) An experienced tax practitioner with substantial expertise in the private client sphere. His workload includes assisting non-domiciled clients requiring advice on their offshore affairs. **Strengths:** "Very good on property and offshore work."

Imran Afzal (see p.532) (Field Court Tax Chambers) A genuine tax all-rounder, with experience of acting for clients across the Tax Bar. He is comfortable handling both advisory and dispute resolution work in both the domestic and international contexts. **Strengths:** "He grasps the nettle thoroughly and is able to cut through the law."

Christopher McCall QC (Maitland Chambers) Respected by clients and peers alike, he has vast experience of private client matters. He now concentrates his work in this area on the advisory side of the practice. **Strengths:** "He is incredibly speedy, he always tries to find his way around problems and his fees are reasonable and sensible."

Jonathan Davey (Wilberforce Chambers) Works in a range of private client contexts, including contentious and non-contentious estates matters. He is also experienced in working for HMRC in tax disputes concerning estates. **Strengths:** "He's very experienced and knows exactly what he is trying to achieve. He's also a fine cross-examiner." **Recent work:** Represented the Revenue against Icebreaker LLP in a case concerning the complex tax structures employed by a number of individuals of public repute, including Gary Barlow of Take That.

Contents:

LONDON

Telecommunications London	
Leading Sets	
Band 1	
Blackstone Chambers *	
Monckton Chambers *	
Band 2	
Brick Court Chambers *	
Leading Silks	
Band 1	
Carss-Frisk Monica	*Blackstone Chambers*
Rose Dinah	*Blackstone Chambers*
Turner Jon	*Monckton Chambers* *
Band 2	
Beard Daniel	*Monckton Chambers* *
Herberg Javan	*Blackstone Chambers*
Lowenstein Paul	*3 Verulam Buildings (ORL)* ◊
Pannick David	*Blackstone Chambers*
Read Graham	*Devereux (ORL)* ◊ *
Saini Pushpinder	*Blackstone Chambers*
Ward Tim	*Monckton Chambers* [A] *
Band 3	
Beal Kieron	*Blackstone Chambers*
Charlton Alex	*4 Pump Court (ORL)* ◊
Crow Jonathan	*4 Stone Buildings (ORL)* ◊ *
Demetriou Marie	*Brick Court Chambers*
Howe Timothy	*Fountain Court Chambers (ORL)* ◊ *
Rubin Stephen	*Fountain Court Chambers (ORL)* ◊ *
Smith Kassie	*Monckton Chambers*
Thompson Rhodri	*Matrix Chambers (ORL)* ◊ *
New Silks	
Bacon Kelyn	*Brick Court Chambers*
Leading Juniors	
Band 1	
Drake David	*Serle Court (ORL)* ◊ *
Holmes Josh	*Monckton Chambers* *
Kennelly Brian	*Blackstone Chambers*
Pickford Meredith	*Monckton Chambers* [A]
Band 2	
Chapple Malcolm	*New Square Chambers (ORL)* ◊ *
Howard Anneli	*Monckton Chambers* [A]
Lazarus Michael	*3 Verulam Buildings (ORL)* ◊
Levy Juliette	*Selborne Chambers (ORL)* ◊ *
Segan James	*Blackstone Chambers*
Woolfe Philip	*Monckton Chambers* *
Band 3	
Bates Alan	*Monckton Chambers* [A]
Ford Sarah	*Brick Court Chambers*
Jones Tristan	*Blackstone Chambers*
Lask Ben	*Monckton Chambers* [A]
Lavy Matthew	*4 Pump Court (ORL)* ◊ *
Lee Sarah	*Brick Court Chambers*
Lynch Ben	*Devereux (ORL)* ◊ *
O'Donoghue Robert	*Brick Court Chambers*
Palmer Robert	*Monckton Chambers* [A] *
Richards Tom	*Blackstone Chambers*
Up-and-coming individuals	
Gibson Nicholas	*Matrix Chambers (ORL)* ◊
Mussa Hanif	*Blackstone Chambers*
Osepciu Ligia	*Monckton Chambers* *

◊ (ORL) = Other Ranked Lawyer.
[A] direct access (see p.11).
** Indicates set / individual with profile.*
Alphabetical order within each band. Band 1 is highest.

Band 1

Blackstone Chambers

See profile on p.771

THE SET

Blackstone's telecoms team is made up of a number of seasoned barristers. Their wide public law expertise and regulatory know-how make them a leading choice in this sector. Recent high-stakes matters handled include the Frankovich cases and Competition Appeal Tribunal (CAT) mandates from key clients including Ofcom, BT, Colt and Cable & Wireless. Other cases undertaken include the Ethernet appeals and the mobile call termination case EE v Competition Commission.

Client service: "I like the set a lot, and they've got some standout clerks," led by Gary Oliver. "It is an entrepreneurial, energetic set of chambers."

SILKS

David Pannick QC A public law advocate nonpareil. His extensive, high-profile practice includes advising UK and international clients on matters in the telecommunications sector. **Strengths:** "He knows the industry forwards and backwards." **Recent work:** Advised HKT on a telecoms-related potential judicial review application.

Dinah Rose QC One of the most high-profile advocates of her age, and someone with recognised strength in telecommunications disputes. She acts for heavyweight clients on headline cases in the sector, and is praised for her convincing advocacy. **Strengths:** "As an advocate, she mixes charm and grit in equal measure to produce very persuasive results." "A universal force in public law." **Recent work:** Acted for a number of providers, including Cable & Wireless, as interveners in the Ethernet case, BT v Ofcom.

Pushpinder Saini QC Noted for his handling of headline telecommunications cases, he frequently represents Ofcom. Sources are quick to stress his well-prepared and methodical approach to cases. **Strengths:** "A quality opponent; he is a formidable and controlled public lawyer with a foothold in telecoms law." "Implicitly trusted by the court, he is a man who remains calm in the face of apparently anything." **Recent work:** Recently appeared in R v Secretary of State for Culture, Media, Olympics & Sport, handling a judicial review concerning telecoms provider access to the internet.

Monica Carss-Frisk QC An experienced barrister, known for her measured approach and composure in court. Her practice in the telecoms sector covers competition and regulatory cases. **Strengths:** "She's intellectually rigorous, but at the same time able to communicate complicated legal ideas to businesspeople." **Recent work:** Represented the claimants in a Frankovich case relating to the operation of GSM gateways and the compliance of domestic regulations with EU law.

Javan Herberg QC Commended for his work with Ofcom on high-profile cases. Clients appreciate his agile and strategic thinking in court. **Strengths:** "He is always very thorough and considered in his approach." **Recent work:** Represented Ofcom, as lead counsel, in appeals to the Supreme Court concerning BT's wholesale charges for non-geographic number ranges.

Kieron Beal QC Regularly appears in the CAT for major clients. His telecoms practice is supported by broader expertise in competition and European law. **Strengths:** "He's always good on his feet and understands the detail of the economics." "He always takes a good strategic approach." **Recent work:** Recently represented Colt in its appeal against an Ofcom decision relating to passive remedies in the leased line broadband market.

JUNIORS

Brian Kennelly Has great depth of experience of handling a range of major telecoms disputes. He is widely praised for his hands-on approach with lay clients and his impressive advocacy in court. **Strengths:** "A great telecoms specialist – we really value his opinion and he's great on his feet." **Recent work:** Represented Cable & Wireless in its challenge to the Isle of Man regulator alleging failure to prevent anti-competitive behaviour.

Hanif Mussa A junior with an increasing profile in the telecoms sector. He has picked up a number of high-profile mandates from Ofcom in recent times. **Strengths:** "A very effective and highly intelligent barrister, who is really carving a name for himself in this field." **Recent work:** Represented Ofcom in a number of appeals regarding its decision that BT had overcharged competitors for wholesale broadband services.

James Segan Has an increasing reputation for his skilful handling of fair, reasonable and non-discriminatory (FRAND) terms cases and is known for his work at the interface between competition and IP law. His practice also covers a variety of regulatory matters in the telecommunications sector. **Strengths:** "Outstanding in terms of his application of the law and his understanding of the area." **Recent work:** Advised and represented 118 118 in its appeal to the CAT concerning Ofcom's decision on call charges.

Tristan Jones A rising force in the telecoms sector, who has key expertise in competition law. He regularly acts for clients in the CAT. **Strengths:** "He is exceptionally well briefed in competition law, and allies that to a bright and personable style that makes him a pleasure to work with." **Recent work:** Acted for Cable & Wireless, Verizon and Virgin in appeals regarding decisions by Ofcom relating to Ethernet charges.

Tom Richards Well liked by peers and instructing solicitors, he has taken on increasingly important roles in regulatory disputes in the telecommunications field. Much of his work sees him challenging regulators. **Strengths:** "He represents exactly how a modern barrister should operate." **Recent work:** Represented Churchcastle as sole counsel in its challenge to a substantial fine imposed by PhonepayPlus. The case was favourably settled for the client.

Monckton Chambers

See profile on p.833

THE SET

The stellar reputation of the set in competition law gives it an edge in the telecoms field, and it represents a go-to group for those with disputes in the CAT. A number of its barristers are highly experienced in handling complex European law and competition law issues for telecoms clients. It has enjoyed extensive participation in the 08 numbers case and pay-TV cases, and its barristers have acted for Ofcom, BT and BSkyB.

Client service: "The set is very well clerked. David Hockney is very responsive and has a fantastic team. The clerks discuss things frankly and are never precious about giving you access to the barristers." "The set is very commercial, and very focused, right from the clerks through to the QCs."

SILKS

Jon Turner QC (see p.741) A leading figure in the telecoms field, who is acknowledged for his leading roles representing telecoms companies in the most significant regulatory disputes in the sector. **Strengths:** "One of the established stars of the Regulatory Bar, Turner has extensive experience in the telecoms field." **Recent work:** Instructed by solicitors for EE, Vodafone and Three in their challenge to a CAT decision regarding Ofcom's resolution of disputes between telecoms providers. The case was heard in the Supreme Court in February 2014.

Daniel Beard QC (see p.546) Lauded for his superior advocacy and his experience in telecoms, as well as competition and European law disputes more generally. He acts for a variety of clients in this field, and appears for both telecoms providers and the government. **Strengths:** "A heavy hitter who thinks strategically." "He is commercial and focuses on the key issues." **Recent work:** Instructed by BT in its appeal to the Supreme Court against the Court of Appeal decision in BT v Telefónica. The case concerned 08 numbers.

Tim Ward QC (see p.746) Regularly represents key clients BT and Vodafone in a range of regulatory disputes. He is a significant presence in the CAT and regularly handles EU law matters. **Strengths:** "I use him on cases which raise a public law issue – he's a very strong juridical review lawyer." **Recent work:** Acted as lead counsel for BT in the CAT. This case concerned Ofcom regulation on local loop unbundling.

Kassie Smith QC Has extensive expertise in telecoms and is the architect of a highly developed general regulatory practice. She is noted for her work handling telecoms matters with an IP element, and has recently handled cases raising FRAND issues. **Strengths:** "Incredibly accessible, proactive and really down to earth." "She has broad experience in telecoms and the broader competition field, and is destined to become one of the most sought-after QCs." **Recent work:** Acted for LIME BVI in judicial review proceedings arising out of the new regulatory regime in the British Virgin Islands. Challenges were brought to the regulator's decision on margin squeeze and dominance.

JUNIORS

Josh Holmes (see p.630) Regularly appears unled for Ofcom in the CAT. He also demonstrates experience acting in other jurisdictions and in European forums. Commentators particularly praise him for his written advocacy. **Strengths:** "A smooth operator with an encyclopaedic knowledge of this area." He "drafts like a dream" and is "capable of demolishing the other side step by step." **Recent work:** Successfully represented Ofcom in an appeal by Colt against the client's decision on passive remedies in business connectivity markets.

Meredith Pickford Accrues a wealth of positive feedback from peers and instructing solicitors. Pickford is lauded for his strength in handling complex economic issues that arise. Sky and TalkTalk are amongst the major clients he has represented. **Strengths:** "A formidable degree of experience and intellect, and his advocacy skills are excellent." "An economist by training – so he brings those analytical skills too." **Recent work:** Represented Sky and TalkTalk in the appeal of a CAT decision in relation to BT's overcharging of competitors for access to key telecoms products.

Anneli Howard A prominent competition lawyer, who is active for major clients on telecoms disputes. Recently, she has represented major clients including Ofcom and BT. **Strengths:** "A real competition law expert who is brilliant with clients." **Recent work:** Successfully defended Ofcom against Frankovich damages claims regarding implementation of the EC Telecoms Authorisation and EC Access Directives.

Ben Lask Handles significant regulatory and competition-related disputes in the telecoms field. He is commended by instructing solicitors for his responsiveness and accessibility. **Strengths:** "Very thorough in his analysis and highly practical in his advice to the client." **Recent work:** Represented Ofcom in judicial review proceedings brought by a provider of premium rate phone services, which was arguing that the regulation set by Ofcom was contrary to domestic and European law.

Robert Palmer (see p.689) Regularly appears for BT in significant regulatory disputes concerning regulators and service providers. Interviewees highlight his clear, direct and effective style of advocacy. **Strengths:** "He's really outstanding in terms of clarity and the succinct way in which he expresses himself." **Recent work:** Acted for BT in Colt's appeal to the CAT regarding Ofcom's decision not to impose passive remedies on BT. These remedies would have forced the client to allow access to its connectivity infrastructure.

Alan Bates Enjoys an increasing profile in utilities regulatory matters, and regularly handles telecoms cases. He acts on a range of cases concerning the Communications Act, and also has experience of handling EU law matters. **Strengths:** "He has a terrific manner and is super-smart – he brings something new to every case." **Recent work:** Represented BSkyB as an intervener in a case concerning Ofcom's dispute resolution duties under the Communications Act.

Ligia Osepciu (see p.687) Won praise from commentators for her recent representation of BT in the Supreme Court appeal BT v Telefónica. Sources identify her as a rising force in regulatory disputes in the telecoms sector, and specifically praise her for her modern and receptive approach. **Strengths:** "She always comes across excellently." **Recent work:** Acted as second junior for BT in BT v Telefónica, which concerned Ofcom's dispute resolution powers in the context of BT's decision to apply ladder pricing to 08 number calls on its network.

Philip Woolfe (see p.756) Enters the table this year following a raft of positive feedback, much of it relating to the strength of both his written work and his oral advocacy. **Strengths:** "He has extremely strong knowledge of telecoms, and can give concise advice very quickly." **Recent work:** Represented BSkyB and TalkTalk in their local loop unbundling case against Ofcom, which challenged the regulator's decision in respect of access to BT-owned infrastructure.

Band 2

Brick Court Chambers

See profile on p.774

THE SET

Brick Court barristers feature heavily in key cases in the telecoms field, often representing network providers and regulators, both at home and abroad. Telecoms competition cases are regularly handled by the barristers at the set, as well as matters concerning broadcasting and EU law issues. Nicholas Green QC, formerly of this set, and widely acknowledged for his work in the field of telecoms, was appointed to the Queen's Bench Division at the High Court in late 2013. Despite this the set maintains quality at both silk and junior level, and is a redoubtable player in the field.

Client service: Ian Moyler and Julian Hawes are the senior clerks at the set and are well recognised for their efficiency and open approach.

SILKS

Marie Demetriou QC Widely acknowledged for her expertise in EU and public law, and for her work before the CAT and higher courts. In telecoms, she has represented a variety of clients including consumers and sports authorities. **Strengths:** "She's smart and user-friendly, and performs well on telecoms competition matters." **Recent work:** Appeared in the CAT acting for the England & Wales Cricket Board in a case regarding the pay-TV dispute between BSkyB and Ofcom.

Kelyn Bacon QC Identified for her work on telecoms cases with a competition law element attached to them. Sources highlight her tenacity in court and recognise that she has established relationships with telecoms operators. **Strengths:** "She'll hang on and won't give in. A strong lawyer for telecoms and competition work generally."

JUNIORS

Robert O'Donoghue A key barrister for major clients such as Telefónica O2, and someone who also has experience of representing regulators. He frequently acts on competition-related disputes, and has particular expertise in abuse of dominance cases. **Strengths:** "A lawyer with a very sharp intellect, who is articulate and clear." "He's extremely responsive and client-aware. There's no ivory tower around him." **Recent work:** Acted for Irish regulator Comreg in a case brought by Vodafone challenging a mobile termination rate decision.

Sarah Ford Peers particularly applaud her for her work on behalf of BT. She has a strong and varied client base though and has handled numerous judicial review, EU and competition law cases. **Strengths:** "She's fantastic at case preparation and has a wonderful understanding of litigation." "She has a really detailed knowledge of the law." **Recent work:** Recently represented BT as junior counsel in its appeal from the CAT regarding an Ofcom decision to allow BSkyB to provide sports content to other telecoms providers.

Sarah Lee Noted for her extensive work for BT. She has a raft of significant disputes in the higher courts under her belt. **Strengths:** "A phenomenal advocate – she has a fine legal brain and is good on her feet." **Recent work:** Acted for long-standing client BT in the CAT on the Ethernet case concerning the Common Regulatory Framework.

Other Ranked Lawyers

Graham Read QC (see p.704) (Devereux) Has extensive experience of acting in both regulatory and commercial disputes. He is lauded for his long-standing representation of major client BT in high-profile cases. **Strengths:** "A tremendously commercial litigator." "He's a brutal cross-examiner, who is really, really tough." **Recent work:** Acted as lead counsel for BT in a long-running case looking at Ofcom's decision that the company had overcharged for Ethernet services by more than £150 million.

Ben Lynch (see p.659) (Devereux) Acts on major telecoms mandates alongside his work handling insurance and general commercial disputes. He has tackled a number of headline cases for key client BT. **Strengths:** "Extremely likeable and very hard-working – he's everything you want in a junior." **Recent work:** Praised for his work for BT in the Ethernet case, challenging Ofcom's decision regarding pricing and cost orientation.

Timothy Howe QC (see p.632) (Fountain Court Chambers) Recognised for his expertise across a number of practice areas. In telecoms, he represents major sector clients in domestic and multi-jurisdictional commercial disputes. **Strengths:** "He's a very clever but practical and commercially minded silk." "A deep thinker, who is highly collaborative in his approach and strategic in his thinking."

Stephen Rubin QC (see p.712) (Fountain Court Chambers) Has a varied practice, part of which sees him focusing on commercial disputes in the telecoms sector. He has a number of major international clients on his books. **Recent work:** Represented an international client in a dispute over the ownership of a telecoms group based outside the UK.

Rhodri Thompson QC (see p.737) (Matrix Chambers) Enters the table this year, having garnered praise for his representation of BT in the CAT and the higher courts. He is most well known for his work on regulatory and competition law issues. **Strengths:** "Calm, quick-witted and tough." "He has a fantastic grasp of the intricacies of the law and really understands the economic angle." **Recent work:** Recently represented BT in the three interrelated appeals regarding wholesale Ethernet pricing.

Nicholas Gibson (Matrix Chambers) Handles cases dealing with the interface between telecoms and competition law. Key instructions include those by the Treasury Solicitor, the Competition Commission and BT. **Strengths:** "He's carved a name for himself in the telecoms sector." "He's very hands-on, very friendly and very approachable." **Recent work:** Successfully represented the Secretary of State for Culture, Media & Sport in proceedings brought by operators of GSM gateways claiming that regulatory restriction on the devices contravened European competition law.

Malcolm Chapple (see p.569) (New Square Chambers) Provides advice to major telecoms clients on high-profile contentious and non-contentious matters. Also recognised for his work in IP, and its overlap with the telecoms sector. **Strengths:** "He is good at interpreting contracts and advising the client strategically."

Alex Charlton QC (4 Pump Court) Tackles commercial disputes with a technology component, and is identified by solicitors as a hands-on and tenacious advocate. **Strengths:** "Alex is very good at cross-examination and in terms of his overall strategy." **Recent work:** Acted on a significant dispute between a network operator and a mobile virtual network operator arising from charges for services provided by the former.

Matthew Lavy (see p.652) (4 Pump Court) A former software developer, lauded for his understanding of tech-heavy disputes. Sources are impressed by his advocacy skill. **Strengths:** "He's really happy to wade into the detail to understand the complexities of a case." "He has a clear mastery of technological issues." **Recent work:** Lavy was involved in a patent licensing royalties dispute relating to mobile telephone handsets.

Juliette Levy (see p.655) (Selborne Chambers) Known for her experience in property-related telecoms disputes. She regularly acts for landowners and is noted for her handling of cases involving network sharing issues. **Strengths:** "Her advice is clear, robust and helpful." "She has a strong commercial grasp of both the client's objectives and those of the other side – that's why clients love her." **Recent work:** Counsel to a network operator on a case raising issues of whether the client could share its network under the terms of its lease and the Electronic Communications Code.

David Drake (see p.590) (Serle Court) A litigator with a very diverse practice, who has experience of representing clients in the TCC. **Strengths:** "Very bright and commercial; he is particularly good on IT and telecoms disputes."

Jonathan Crow QC (see p.582) (4 Stone Buildings) A leading appellate barrister and one of the most talked-about barristers in practice today. In telecoms, he is best known for his work acting for major clients on significant public law and regulatory cases in the higher courts. **Strengths:** "He has a hugely impressive reputation across multiple areas of law." **Recent work:** Represented BT in the Supreme Court in its case against Telefónica regarding termination rates on 08 numbers.

Paul Lowenstein QC (3 Verulam Buildings) Has a broad commercial litigation practice, and is particularly noted for his expertise in technology-based sectors, such as IT and telecoms. **Strengths:** "A good, punchy advocate." "One of the big hitters from that set." **Recent work:** Recently advised a major international client on its obligations under a contract with a major telecoms provider and the potential consequences of termination of that contract.

Michael Lazarus (3 Verulam Buildings) Handles commercial disputes for telecoms clients. Sources highlight his intelligence and experience, and praise him for his handling of international matters. **Recent work:** Represented a major telecoms provider in its dispute with a customer regarding the applicability of termination fees.

TRAVEL: An Introduction

Contributed by 2TG – 2 Temple Gardens

Travel: International Personal Injury

The growth of international travel for work and pleasure and an ever-increasing awareness of recourse through litigation have meant that the number of personal injury claims relating to accidents abroad has proliferated in recent years. Whilst the details of a particular incident may appear depressingly familiar to the prospective claimant or defendant's solicitor (a road traffic accident, an accident whilst working abroad or an injury suffered in the grounds or swimming pool of a foreign hotel), the fact that the accident has occurred outside the jurisdiction may create a number of difficulties. In such cases, to the usual list of questions such as "Who to sue?" are added others such as "Can the claim be brought here?" and "Which law applies?"

In this context, the specific legislative schemes for package holidays and travel by air or sea remain important; some changes in these areas are highlighted below. However, an increasing proportion of claims relating to accidents abroad fall outside the scope of these schemes. In this context, identifying the court where a claim can or cannot be brought, and establishing which law applies, can be very significant: in some instances, it can mean the difference between winning and losing. Unsurprisingly, given their importance – and the fact that the law in this area is at a stage of rapid development – these issues are giving rise to a considerable volume of case law in the English courts and the CJEU.

Furthermore, the current law on jurisdiction in respect of accidents suffered abroad, combined with the advent of Rome II, has meant that English courts are being required to apply foreign law on a scale which was previously unimaginable.

In the current environment, specialist input from English and foreign lawyers is increasingly essential.

Jurisdiction, applicable law and related issues

The past year has seen further authority on the long-running issue of whether claims can be brought in the English courts in respect of accidents in countries not within the scheme of Regulation (EC) 44/2001 (and related schemes): see Wink v Croatia Osiguranje; Stylianou v Toyoshima; Pike v The Indian Hotel Company; Brownlie v Four Seasons Holdings; Young v Anglo American South Africa Ltd.

On the applicable law side the Courts have been no less active. Important cases include Cox v Ergo Versicherung, in which the Supreme Court considered the applicable law in fatal accident cases (including the territorial scope of the Fatal Accidents Act 1976); and Wall v Mutuelle de Poitiers, in which the Court of Appeal ruled on the scope of the applicable law under Rome II.

The judgment in Allen v DePuy has wide-ranging relevance; it gives further guidance on the temporal scope of Rome II in cases where the event giving rise to the damage and the damage are separated in time as well as determining the territorial scope of the Consumer Protection Act 1987.

Cases with foreign elements are also generating law of relevance to purely domestic cases. Nemeti v Sabre provides a cautionary illustration; the pitfalls arose due to the foreign elements in the claim but the resolution involved questions of English law (the proper interpretation of the Limitation Act 1980 and the CPR).

Package travel and carriage conventions

Looking forward, the European Commission's proposal for a revised Directive on 'Package Holidays and Assisted Travel Arrangements' continues to work its way through the EU legislative process, having had its second reading in the European Parliament. With its increased scope of application and its provisions relating to the insolvency of travel organisers, the revised directive is likely to have wide-ranging repercussions on the travel industry in the UK and, consequently, practitioners in this area.

Significant developments are also underway in the legislation applicable to carriage by sea and air. Of note are:

- the most recent amendments to the Athens Convention, which take effect in UK law from April 2014;
- the decision of the Supreme Court in Stott v Thomas Cook, which considers the interplay between the Montreal Convention and EU/national law; and
- the expected revisions to Regulation EC 261/2004 on air passenger rights: no date has yet been set for the implementation of the proposed changes, which are still under review, but the need for reform was underscored very recently in Jet2.com Limited v Ronald Huzar.

Conclusions

The fact that a personal injury claim has a foreign element can rapidly transfer an otherwise straightforward case into a minefield of difficult legal issues. In this context the value of specialist advice at an early stage cannot be overstated. There will be little or no cost saving by deferring the taking of such advice. Delay, on the other hand, can mean that the benefit of taking a particular position on jurisdiction or choice of law is lost forever.

With the advent of Rome II and the increasing scope for application of foreign law to a claim, obtaining advice from relevant foreign lawyers – often at an early stage in a claim – has become a necessity. A decision on whether to take a particular stance on applicable law can only properly be taken once the options are understood.

Travel: Regulatory and Commercial

On the regulatory side the revised package travel rules, referred to above, will clearly impact on operators, as will the new requirements on compulsory insurance in the revised Athens convention rules. The recent decision of the Supreme Court in Secret Hotels 2 v Revenue & Customs Commissioners on VAT liability in the context of supply of holidays through websites is also of particular note.

Contents:

LONDON

Travel: International Personal Injury London
Leading Sets
Band 1
1 Chancery Lane
3 Hare Court *
2TG – 2 Temple Gardens *
Band 2
Devereux *
Outer Temple Chambers *
Quadrant Chambers *
Leading Silks
Band 1
McDermott Gerard *Outer Temple Chambers*
Palmer Howard *2TG - 2 Temple Gardens*
Weir Robert *Devereux* *
Band 2
Browne Benjamin *2TG - 2 Temple Gardens* *
Stevens Howard *3 Hare Court*
Band 3
Block Neil *Thirty Nine Essex Street (ORL)* ◊ *
Dougherty Charles *2TG - 2 Temple Gardens* *
Killalea Stephen *Devereux* *
Ross John *1 Chancery Lane* *
New Silks
Russell John *Quadrant Chambers*
Leading Juniors
Band 1
Crowther Sarah *3 Hare Court*
Deal Katherine *3 Hare Court*
Doherty Bernard *Thirty Nine Essex Street (ORL)* ◊
Kinsler Marie Louise *2TG - 2 Temple Gardens*
McParland Michael *Quadrant Chambers*
Mead Philip *Old Square Chambers (ORL)* ◊
Prager Sarah *1 Chancery Lane* *
Woolf Eliot *Outer Temple Chambers* *
Band 2
Audland William *12 King's Bench Walk (ORL)* ◊ *
Harding Jack *1 Chancery Lane* *
Janusz Pierre *3 Hare Court*
Reeve Matthew *Quadrant Chambers*
Silvester Bruce *Devereux* *
Wyles Lucy *2TG - 2 Temple Gardens*
Young Andrew *3 Hare Court*
Band 3
Bradley Ben *Outer Temple Chambers*
Howells Katherine *Old Square Chambers (ORL)* ◊ *
McTague Meghann *2TG - 2 Temple Gardens* *
Saxby Dan *3 Hare Court*
Shah Bajul *XXIV Old Buildings (ORL)* ◊
Wijeyaratne Asela *3 Hare Court*
◊ (ORL) = Other Ranked Lawyer.
** Indicates set / individual with profile.*

Travel: Regulatory & Commercial London
Leading Sets
Band 1
Fountain Court Chambers *
Quadrant Chambers *
Leading Silks
Band 1
Crane Michael *Fountain Court Chambers*
Lawson Robert *Quadrant Chambers* *
Shepherd Philip *XXIV Old Buildings (ORL)* ◊
Band 2
Shah Akhil *Fountain Court Chambers* *
Thanki Bankim *Fountain Court Chambers* *
New Silks
Russell John *Quadrant Chambers*
Leading Juniors
Band 1
Kimbell John *Quadrant Chambers*
Reeve Matthew *Quadrant Chambers*
Band 2
Howells Katherine *Old Square Chambers (ORL)* ◊ *
Marland Timothy *Quadrant Chambers*
Phelps Rosalind *Fountain Court Chambers* *
Shah Bajul *XXIV Old Buildings (ORL)* ◊

The editorial is in alphabetical order by set name.

1 Chancery Lane

THE SET

1 Chancery Lane, "a very big player in travel law," has members who regularly act for claimants and defendants in some of the most high-profile travel litigation cases. The set particularly specialises in recovery actions against overseas suppliers and accident abroad claims. It offers unrivalled expertise in catastrophic injury abroad claims and its tenants are well versed in complex issues of liability and quantum.

Client service: "The clerks, led by Clark Chessis, are always willing to talk to you, flexible when you need them to be and very efficient."

SILKS

John Ross QC (see p.711) Head of chambers and a barrister who handles a variety of accident abroad cases for both claimants and defendants. His expertise in private international law and personal injury law complements his practice, and he has noted strength in RTA abroad cases. **Strengths:** "His level of knowledge of catastrophic cases is almost unsurpassed." "Excellent on tactics, he is incredibly astute." **Recent work:** Acted for the defendant in a case concerning an RTA in France. The matter involved complex issues of quantum.

JUNIORS

Sarah Prager (see p.698) Advises claimants and defendants on high-profile, complex personal injury abroad matters. She is especially highly regarded for her capabilities in package holiday claims. **Strengths:** "Excellent with clients, incredibly witty and insightful and someone who gets results." "If you have a practical dispute she is very tenacious; she is a true fighter." **Recent work:** Acted for the tour operator in the important Court of Appeal case Japp v Virgin Holidays. The matter concerned the application of British safety standards abroad.

Jack Harding (see p.619) Acts for and against foreign insurers, hoteliers, airlines, airports and tour operators on accident abroad cases. His expertise extends to multiparty litigation and claims arising from the application of the Montreal Convention. **Strengths:** "He pays very close attention to the detail; his pleadings and written work are second to none." "Very down to earth and approachable. He has technical expertise that is well beyond his years." **Recent work:** Acted for one group of claimants in litigation arising from an outbreak of norovirus on a cruise ship.

Devereux

See profile on p.785

THE SET

Members of Devereux act on a wide range of travel law matters, from food poisoning cases to claims arising out of fatalities. Its members appear for single and multiparty claimants as well as defendant travel agents, tour operators and insurers, and are noted for their expertise in catastrophic injury claims and applicable law matters.

Client service: Vince Plant leads a team that is "excellent," "very efficient" and "very responsive."

SILKS

Robert Weir QC (see p.748) Advises claimants and defendants on high-profile accident abroad cases. He is noted for his capabilities in cases concerning complex questions of jurisdiction and applicable laws. **Strengths:** "He is a heavyweight silk – his advocacy is outstanding and his written arguments are so clear." "He is razor-sharp in his analysis; he sees the issues and has a clear and forceful way of presenting issues in court." **Recent work:** Acted for the claimant in the landmark case of Wall v Mutuelle de Poitiers Assurances, which concerned the effect of French law on accidents abroad in light of Rome II.

Stephen Killalea QC (see p.646) Handles catastrophic injury abroad matters for claimants. He demonstrates particular expertise in cases concerning brain and spinal damage. **Strengths:** "He's got very good judgement, is well prepared and has an easy and relaxed manner with clients and opponents alike." "He's very clear and precise, and obviously knows his stuff inside out." **Recent work:** Represented Holly Raper, who sustained catastrophic injuries in a quad bike accident in Tasmania.

JUNIORS

Bruce Silvester (see p.720) Acts for claimants and defendants in cross-border personal injury litigation. He is notably strong in cases involving multiple claimants and issues arising from the Athens Convention. **Strengths:** "He's very forensic, good with experts, and demonstrates good attention to detail." "Pretty fearsome to come up against, he doesn't mince his words, is very thorough and is incredibly tenacious." **Recent work:** Acted for 205 claimants who fell ill during their stay on the 'Thomson Dream' cruise ship.

Fountain Court Chambers

See profile on p.804

THE SET

Fountain Court Chambers is highly regarded for its regulatory and commercial travel law work. Its members have a wealth of knowledge of aviation law, and regularly act for regulators, airlines and passengers. They have notable expertise in ATOL matters, and regularly handle cases concerning travel and holiday claims, as well as disputes arising in the field of carriage by air.

Client service: Alex Taylor leads a team that is "always looking to build a good long-term relationship" and is "efficient and very helpful."

SILKS

Michael Crane QC Handles regulatory and commercial travel law for airlines, manufacturers, airports and regulatory bodies. He is noted for his skill at handling product liability claims. **Strengths:** "Very good in court, he's poised and measured. He measures the temperature of a case well, and is an effective cross-examiner." **Recent work:** Acted for the claimant in Virgin Atlantic v Mitsubishi & Koito. This was a product liability claim by Virgin against its suppliers.

Akhil Shah QC (see p.717) Acts for airlines and tour operators in regulatory and commercial travel law cases. He is noted for his expertise in handling passenger claims arising from disruption to travel. **Strengths:** "He is excellent, extremely bright and very hard-working." "He understands the industry, is a good writer and has a perfect manner for judicial review proceedings." **Recent work:** Advised the claimant in the landmark case of Dawson v Thomson Airways Ltd. This concerned the correct limitation period to be applied to disruption claims under EU law.

Bankim Thanki QC (see p.735) Recommended for his regulatory and commercial travel practice. He brings a wealth of knowledge in aviation law to bear and frequently acts for airlines and regulators. **Strengths:** "A sound lawyer with a pleasant advocacy style; he is understated but is very effective." "He is a very good orator who is very bright." **Recent work:** Acted for Indian company GMR in a dispute relating to Maldives International Airport. The case concerned whether the cancellation of the project by the government was lawful.

JUNIORS

Rosalind Phelps (see p.692) Advises in regulatory and commercial travel law cases. She is highly regarded for her abilities in securing ATOL licences for airlines and for her advice on class actions. **Strengths:** "Very efficient; she's a good team player who cuts to the chase and finds innovative ways to get around situations." "Very bright, pragmatic and down to earth." **Recent work:** Advised Belfast International Airport in its £25 million contract dispute with Aer Lingus.

3 Hare Court

See profile on p.819

THE SET

3 Hare Court is a 'go-to' set for travel law, whose members act for claimants (including those involved in group actions) and defendants in personal injury abroad matters. They have notable expertise in handling matters concerning complex questions of applicable law and package travel regulations.

Client service: "The clerks, led by James Donovan, go the extra mile. They are friendly and accommodating and nothing is ever too much trouble."

SILKS

Howard Stevens QC Acts for claimants and defendants in cross-border litigation concerning personal injury abroad. He is noted for his capabilities in package travel cases. **Strengths:** "He really gets involved with the nitty-gritty and has a fantastic rapport with clients." "A very impressive advocate with great attention to detail, who can turn a judge around in a matter of hours." **Recent work:** Acted for the defendant in a claim arising from an accident involving a boat propeller during a snorkelling excursion.

JUNIORS

Sarah Crowther Handles a variety of personal injury abroad matters for claimants and defendants, including tour operators. She demonstrates particular expertise in cases concerning jurisdiction and applicable law. **Strengths:** "A very tenacious advocate, who is very persuasive and always thoroughly prepared." "She can be relied upon to provide robust and commercial advice, whilst also showing a caring and compassionate nature when meeting with lay clients." **Recent work:** Acted for the defendant in the high-profile case of Wink v Croatia Osiguranje. The matter involved novel questions of jurisdiction for English-based litigants.

Katherine Deal Acts for claimants and defendants in accident abroad claims. She is noted for her skill in tackling complex applicable law issues, package travel cases and catastrophic injury claims. **Strengths:** "Katherine is very bright, utterly fearless and a strident negotiator." "She is a tactician and a planner, who is always three moves ahead." **Recent work:** Successfully secured a £6 million award for a claimant who suffered a catastrophic brain injury following an RTA in Germany.

Pierre Janusz Advises claimants and defendants in personal injury abroad claims. He is well versed in Rome II and conflict of laws issues. **Strengths:** "Very clever, he's a thinking man's barrister," who "is on top of Rome II and conflict points." **Recent work:** Acted for the defendant in a complex applicable law case arising from an RTA in Portugal. The case involved UK-domiciled claimants.

Dan Saxby Advises on a wide range of matters relating to personal injury abroad, and is particularly noted for handling serious injury claims and cases arising from the Package Travel Regulations. **Strengths:** "Brilliant and hugely successful in court." "An extremely able advocate who does very well against silks."

Andrew Young Represents defendants and claimants in a wide range of personal injury abroad cases. He is recognised for handling group claims, gastric illness cases and accidents arising from adventure holidays. **Strengths:** "Massively intelligent, very good with clients and very good on his feet in court." "Highly experienced, he takes on difficult cases and wins them." **Recent work:** Acted for a claimant in a case which questioned whether a tour operator is responsible for an employee who is acting outside the course of employment.

Asela Wijeyaratne Handles a variety of personal injury abroad matters for claimants and defendant tour operators, travel agents, and air and cruise lines. Convention issues and jurisdictional matters represent particular strong suits. **Strengths:** "In court he is calm under pressure and thinks methodically; he's also very persuasive and never misses a thing." "Young, dynamic and ambitious." **Recent work:** Acted for the estate of an English holidaymaker who was killed when she drank limescale remover from a water bottle left in her room by a maid.

Outer Temple Chambers

See profile on p.842

THE SET

Outer Temple Chambers is recommended for its personal injury abroad practice, and has talented barristers at all level of seniority, whether they be silks or juniors. Members handle single and multi-party claims concerning anything from minor injuries to fatal illnesses. They have particular expertise in complex applicable law issues.

Client service: Paul Barton leads a team that is "very flexible and eager to help."

SILKS

Gerard McDermott QC Handles a wide range of personal injury abroad litigation, and is noted for his expertise in catastrophic injury matters. Commentators note that he handles a number of claims arising from the USA. **Strengths:** "Incredibly clever, he's very good with clients and a great team player." "He is charm itself; his advocacy is disarming, and he presents everything in a succinct, simple and crisp fashion." **Recent work:** Advised on Rome II issues in a case concerning an English tourist who became paraplegic after an accident in Spain.

JUNIORS

Eliot Woolf (see p.756) Handles a broad cross-section of personal injury litigation. He is highly regarded for his capabilities in group actions and cases involving gastric illness outbreaks. **Strengths:** "His eye for detail is fantastic. He is highly intelligent, highly analytical and his client care is the best I have seen." "A man who offers intellectual value, he's very charming and very good with judges." **Recent work:** Secured a £1.95 million claim against a tour operator. The claim was brought after an outbreak of illness at a hotel in the Dominican Republic.

Ben Bradley Represents single and multiparty claimants in a wide range of personal injury abroad cases. He is experienced in those clinical negligence claims that have a multi-jurisdictional element. **Strengths:** "He knows package holiday cases inside out and he's very good with clients." "Very good at turning work around quickly, he's knowledgeable, personable and a good advocate." **Recent work:** Acted in Skipp & 131 Others v Fred Olsen Cruises, a matter concerning multiple norovirus outbreaks aboard the 'Boudicca' cruise ship.

Quadrant Chambers

See profile on p.854

THE SET

Quadrant Chambers has members who act for claimants and defendants on a range of issues, from commercial disputes and regulatory matters through to fatal accident abroad claims. They are noted for their expertise in insurance-related travel matters.

Client service: "The clerks, led by Gary Ventura and Simon Slattery, think outside the box and assist clients on structuring claims management."

SILKS

Robert Lawson QC (see p.653) Acts primarily for tour operators and airlines in regulatory and commercial travel law disputes. He is highly regarded for his knowledge of commercial disputes involving airlines. **Strengths:** "The go-to guy for complicated aviation and Montreal issues, he has an easy manner and speaks to people in a way they understand." "He does very well in seeing the wood from the trees. He is a user-friendly QC with no airs and graces." **Recent work:** Acted for the defendant in Mehboob Travel Ltd and Others v Pakistan International Airlines. The case involved a multimillion-pound dispute about commission owed on ticket sales.

John Russell QC Advises in regulatory and commercial cases, as well as on personal injury abroad matters. He is recommended for his capabilities in group actions claims and regularly defends tour operators. **Strengths:** "One of the most fearsome, single-minded advocates I have ever come across." "Tremendously able, he's intelligent and articulate, and really knows his stuff." **Recent work:** Acted for the claimant in Olympic Holidays v Monarch Airlines. The case concerned the impact of terms under implied umbrella contracts.

JUNIORS

Michael McParland Acts in personal injury abroad claims, and is highly regarded for his expertise in high-value, complex applicable law cases. **Strengths:** "His grasp of complicated matters is second to none and he has an impressive ability to make the complicated incredibly simple." "He is incredibly knowledgeable and a tremendous advocate, who is a very powerful person to have on your side." **Recent work:** Acted for a claimant who was injured during a quad bike accident in Iceland.

John Kimbell Acts for multiparty claimants as well as tour operators and airlines in cross-border litigation. He is noted for his knowledge of jurisdiction and applicable law, and is particularly strong on cases involving the Montreal Convention. **Strengths:** "He stands out as someone who is both good legally and a strong advocate." **Recent work:** Successfully defended Thomas Cook in the Court of Appeal case Stott v Thomas Cook. The matter is a leading case on the scope and effect of the Montreal Convention.

Matthew Reeve Recommended for his wide-ranging travel practice. He has particular expertise in acting in claims arising from fatal air crashes. **Strengths:** "A charming advocate who strikes the right balance between robustness and politeness when handling difficult clients." **Recent work:** Advised on Cassley v GMP Securities Limited and Sundance, a case involving a fatal air crash in the Democratic Republic of Congo.

Timothy Marland Acts for claimants and defendants in regulatory and commercial matters. He is highly regarded for his knowledge of insurance matters and is often used in high-value aviation claims. **Strengths:** "He's good at giving strong, commercial, practical and down-to-earth advice." "He comes into his own in advocacy, as he is able to guide a court through complex case law in a very simplistic way and convey technical points that would otherwise take days at trial." **Recent work:** Represented the Turkish airline in Özlem Küpeli & 668 Others v Atlasjet. The case concerned a dispute over who was responsible for stranded holidaymakers following the collapse of Turkish Cypriot Airways.

2TG – 2 Temple Gardens

See profile on p.873

THE SET

2 Temple Gardens transfers its established reputation in personal injury law into the travel law sphere. Its members regularly represent claimants and defendants in cases concerning jurisdictional, insurance and personal injury issues. They have unrivalled expertise at all levels of call and are particularly highly regarded for their knowledge of conflict of laws issues.

Client service: "Senior clerk Lee Tyler leads a team that is ultra-efficient, always accommodating and competitive with rates."

SILKS

Howard Palmer QC Handles a variety of accident abroad matters for claimants and defendants. He is recommended for his expertise in cross-border disputes, in particular matters relating to Rome II. **Strengths:** "He's clearly very knowledgeable and very thorough, and his written advice is excellent." "A formidable leader and an excellent advocate who handled our case with outstanding competence." **Recent work:** Acted for a third-party defendant in a case concerning a ski accident in France which resulted in tetraplegia.

Benjamin Browne QC (see p.558) Head of chambers, he has a substantial personal injury abroad practice that spans multiple jurisdictions. Browne is highly regarded for his comprehension of complex issues concerning claims by foreign insurers and the question of discount rates in foreign jurisdictions. **Strengths:** "Very good with clients and very good when negotiating with the other side; he takes no prisoners." "His strength is his ability to consider extra-jurisdictional issues that arise in severe injury claims." **Recent work:** Acted for the defendant in the landmark case Wall v Mutuelle de Poitiers concerning assessment under Rome II.

Charles Dougherty QC (see p.589) Acts primarily for insurers in accident abroad cases. He has extensive experience of handling complex conflict of laws matters and cases involving the application of Rome II. **Strengths:** "A phenomenal legal brain, who slices up any problem, produces a solution and then argues it to the end of the earth." "He is able to respond quickly to every question or query thrown at him." **Recent work:** Acted for French insurers in a multimillion-pound claim arising from an accident abroad. The case involved complex issues on the scope of Rome II.

JUNIORS

Marie Louise Kinsler Acts for claimants and defendants in accident abroad cases and cross-border litigation. She is particularly well versed in cases arising from faulty products or accidents sustained in the course of employment. **Strengths:** "In terms of technical expertise specific to jurisdiction she is the number-one junior barrister in the country; she is phenomenal." "Fantastically efficient; she gets to grips with cases so quickly and immediately understands where the issues are." **Recent work:** Acted for the defendant in the significant case of Wall v Mutuelle de Poitiers, concerning the application of Rome II.

Meghann McTague (see p.669) Acts for claimants and defendant insurers and tour operators in accident abroad cases. She has notable expertise in package holidays claims and matters arising from the Montreal Convention and the Athens Convention. **Strengths:** "Down to earth, conscientious and hard-working." "She's excellent as she recognises what clients require. She is robust when required and sensitive when required." **Recent work:** Acted for a claimant who sustained serious injuries on a yacht in foreign waters. The case concerned complex jurisdictional issues.

Lucy Wyles Advises claimants and defendants on cross-border personal injury claims. She is recommended for her expertise in catastrophic injury abroad cases. **Strengths:** "A lawyer with a brilliant memory, she has a winning combination of being very clever and also very pragmatic in seeing the end game and what the clients are trying to achieve." "She's charming and personable, and knows her stuff inside out." **Recent work:** Acted for the defendant in a claim involving catastrophic brain injury arising from an industrial accident.

Other Ranked Lawyers

Neil Block QC (see p.551) (Thirty Nine Essex Street) Advises on cross-border personal injury litigation. He has notable expertise in acting for insurers and foreign defendants in accident abroad claims. **Strengths:** "He is very quick to get to the heart of the issue, and provides sound insight into complex cases." "He is responsive and is excellent on difficult questions of damages in a cross-border context." **Recent work:** Acted on Stylianou v Toyoshima, a case which involved complex jurisdictional matters.

Bernard Doherty (Thirty Nine Essex Street) Represents claimants and defendants in cross-border personal injury litigation. He is recommended for his ability to handle complex and high-value claims, including class actions. **Strengths:** "He is outwardly laid-back, but is very bright, works hard, is prompt in his responses and is easy to deal with." "Good on the international stuff – he's sensible and measured." **Recent work:** Advised on Saldanha v Fulton Navigation Inc. The case involved conflict of laws issues arising from an accident aboard a ship.

William Audland (see p.540) (12 King's Bench Walk) Advises claimants and defendants in personal injury abroad matters. He is noted for his expertise in conflict of laws cases. **Strengths:** "He has a really good, confident courtroom manner." "He is a really punchy advocate, who's fearless and will run his arguments as hard as they sensibly can be run."

Philip Shepherd QC (XXIV Old Buildings) Acts for claimants and defendants in regulatory and commercial travel law cases. He is recommended for his expertise in high-value contractual disputes, particularly those involving implied umbrella agreements. **Strengths:** "He quickly grasps the relevant issues and is markedly polished when presenting to clients. He provides clear, commercial advice in all forms and his drafting, in particular, is very impressive." **Recent work:** Acted for the defendant in Olympic Holidays v Monarch Airlines, successfully striking out a multimillion-pound claim for damages arising from an implied contract.

Bajul Shah (XXIV Old Buildings) Advises on all aspects of travel-related matters. He is noted for his expertise in disputes concerning airlines and tour operators. **Strengths:** "A very experienced junior with a wide and busy practice, who is user-friendly and hard-working." **Recent work:** Acted for the defendant in Olympic Holidays v Monarch Airlines. The case concerned complex questions on implied umbrella agreements.

Katherine Howells (see p.632) (Old Square Chambers) Has an extensive regulatory/commercial and personal injury abroad travel practice. She has particular expertise in accidents occurring at airfields or aboard aircraft. **Strengths:** "She is thorough, user-friendly, dogged and persistent – she doesn't give up." **Recent work:** Advised Storm Aviation in Donkers & BGV v Storm Aviation v Lufthansa CityLine. This was a claim in excess of EUR4 million, arising out of an explosion at Manchester airport.

Contents:

LONDON

Trusts London	
Leading Silks	
Band 1	
Barlow Francis	*Ten Old Square (ORL)* ◊ *
Boyle Alan	*Serle Court (ORL)* ◊ *
Brownbill David	*XXIV Old Buildings (ORL)* ◊
Green Brian	*Wilberforce Chambers (ORL)* ◊
Ham Robert	*Wilberforce Chambers (ORL)* ◊
Herbert Mark	*5 Stone Buildings (ORL)* ◊ *
Hinks Frank	*Serle Court (ORL)* ◊ *
Le Poidevin Nicholas	*New Square Chambers (ORL)* ◊ *
McCall Christopher	*Maitland Chambers (ORL)* ◊ *
Rajah Eason	*Ten Old Square (ORL)* ◊ *
Reed Penelope	*5 Stone Buildings (ORL)* ◊ *
Steinfeld Alan	*XXIV Old Buildings (ORL)* ◊
Talbot Rice Elspeth	*XXIV Old Buildings (ORL)* ◊
Taube Simon	*Ten Old Square (ORL)* ◊ *
Warnock-Smith Shân	*5 Stone Buildings (ORL)* ◊ *
Leading Juniors	
Band 1	
Child Andrew J	*3 Stone Buildings (ORL)* ◊ *
Dumont Thomas	*Radcliffe Chambers (ORL)* ◊
Hagen Dakis	*Serle Court (ORL)* ◊ *
Henderson William	*Serle Court (ORL)* ◊ *
Tucker Lynton	*New Square Chambers (ORL)* ◊ *
Wilson Richard	*3 Stone Buildings (ORL)* ◊ *
◊ (ORL) = Other Ranked Lawyer.	
** Indicates individual with profile.*	

Ranked Lawyers

Christopher McCall QC (see p.666) (Maitland Chambers) "A seasoned performer," who specialises in trusts, tax and charity law. He has a strong advisory practice, and has experience of advising in relation to offshore jurisdictions including the Cayman Islands, Channel Islands and Hong Kong. **Strengths:** "He has a very creative mind when it comes to traditional trusts work and a very sure grasp of traditional trusts and the taxation of them."

Nicholas Le Poidevin QC (see p.653) (New Square Chambers) Focuses his chancery practice on trusts, wills and estates. He has appeared in a number of courts in offshore jurisdictions including the Cayman Islands and the Isle of Man. **Strengths:** "Undoubtedly one of the top experts in the international trust arena." "Any superlative would not do him justice. His advice is superb, his drafting is elegant and he is tremendous in conference." **Recent work:** Acted in a Supreme Court dispute concerning the validity of mirror wills signed by the wrong spouses.

Lynton Tucker (see p.741) (New Square Chambers) Has extensive experience of handling trust disputes, and is often instructed on matters involving offshore jurisdictions such as Jersey, the Cayman Islands and Hong Kong. **Strengths:** "A man with an incredible knowledge of trusts law," he is "brilliant on the paperwork and knows the trusts world inside out."

David Brownbill QC (XXIV Old Buildings) Well equipped to handle all trusts matters, he has a practice that is heavily international in nature and dominated by contentious work. **Strengths:** "He combines all the ideal attributes of a barrister: he is a master of the technical law but also a major contributor towards strategy." "He has a fantastic knowledge of trusts law and a fantastic knowledge of all offshore jurisdictions." **Recent work:** Acted in a USD180 million claim regarding the insolvency of trusts arising from the liquidation of Kaupthing Bank.

Alan Steinfeld QC (XXIV Old Buildings) Receives extensive praise from peers and solicitors who describe him as a "leading choice of silk." He frequently appears in court in various offshore jurisdictions, including the British Virgin Islands (BVI), Cayman Islands and Bahamas. **Strengths:** "He is absolutely brilliant and my first choice for really complex, high-value work." "He's a grandee in this area, especially when it comes to offshore matters." **Recent work:** Acted in an appeal to the Chancery Division of the High Court for variation of a trust.

Elspeth Talbot Rice QC (XXIV Old Buildings) Frequently handles multimillion-pound trust disputes in various offshore courts. She is licensed to appear as an advocate in the Isle of Man and has been called to the Bar of the Eastern Caribbean. **Strengths:** "She is exceptional, has a superb legal brain and is a pleasure to work with." "I recommend her for contentious work: she can turn a court around." **Recent work:** Acted in a multimillion-dollar claim alleging that company assets held in a trust structure were held on trust for the claimant.

Francis Barlow QC (see p.543) (Ten Old Square) Head of chambers, he has extensive experience in contested trust and probate disputes and particular expertise in drawing up UK and offshore trusts. **Strengths:** "He has incredible in-depth knowledge of the intricacies of trust law at his finger-tips." "A fountain of knowledge on tricky trust issues and an excellent draftsman."

Eason Rajah QC (see p.702) (Ten Old Square) Undertakes chancery litigation and advisory work both in the UK and in offshore jurisdictions. He has extensive experience of drafting trusts and is an expert on succession planning. **Strengths:** "Has excellent client skills, is commercially aware and is a deft advocate." "Offers flexible and practical advice." **Recent work:** Appeared in the Court of Appeal in Jersey in a claim to recover £100 million of wrongly distributed trust property.

Simon Taube QC (see p.734) (Ten Old Square) Undertakes a broad range of chancery litigation and advisory work. He has particular experience in foreign and domestic trusts, and conducts cases in both the UK and abroad in other common law jurisdictions. **Strengths:** "Very able, bright and technical, he's both forceful and thoughtful." "An outstanding trusts lawyer with excellent depth of knowledge." **Recent work:** Successfully resisted a strike-out application on a dispute concerning breach of trust by a Swiss trustee. The case involved allegations of wrongful investment and the taking of secret profits.

Thomas Dumont (Radcliffe Chambers) Undertakes trusts work as part of his highly regarded chancery practice. He acts for trustees and beneficiaries in a range of trust disputes, often concerning multimillion-pound trust structures. **Strengths:** "One of the best names to have on your side." "His wealth of experience is invaluable when you're looking to get to the bottom of difficult technical questions." **Recent work:** Acted for infant beneficiaries in a successful £300 million application under the Variation of Trusts Act.

Alan Boyle QC (see p.554) (Serle Court) Has a broad commercial and chancery practice and is a noted expert on all trust-related matters. He has particular experience in trust issues relating to divorce. **Strengths:** "Highly impressive and astonishingly quick to develop a detailed understanding of a case and a client's needs." "Utterly dedicated to the client's cause and tirelessly hard-working."

Frank Hinks QC (see p.628) (Serle Court) Has a dedicated domestic and international trusts practice. He frequently provides advisory and litigation services to high net worth families. **Strengths:** "He really knows the inside out of trusts law and is really impressive." "He's a good collaborator, who is extremely good at turning the work around and very accessible."

Dakis Hagen (see p.616) (Serle Court) Has a highly regarded chancery and offshore practice. He is often instructed in divorce cases with a trusts or property element. **Strengths:** "He brings a good commercial approach and is technically sound." "He very much likes to be part of the team, and takes a genuine and real interest in matters. His commitment to the case really sets him apart." **Recent work:** Acted in Tchenguiz v Imerman, advising on the trusts elements of a highly publicised divorce.

William Henderson (see p.624) (Serle Court) Acts for private clients, trustees, trust companies and HMRC in disputes concerning domestic and international trusts. He also advises and represents the Attorney General in his role as junior counsel to the Treasury in charity matters. **Strengths:** "A great trusts lawyer," "he's one of the best around and as good as any silk." **Recent work:** Acted for the claimant in Pitt v Holt, a Supreme Court case resolving the position on the rule in Hastings-Bass and rescission on the ground of mistake.

Andrew Child (see p.571) (3 Stone Buildings) Frequently instructed on contentious trust and estate disputes, he has experience of acting at trial without a leader, and has been involved in a number of high-profile cases in recent years. **Strengths:** "One of the go-to names in trust litigation, who has, in particular, been involved in a lot of the important claims regarding removal of trustees." "Fast becoming one of the most feared opponent on the Chancery circuit, he's tough, strategic, sharp and smart." **Recent work:** Acted in Greaves v Stolkin, a dispute concerning the validity of a deathbed codicil in a will.

Richard Wilson (see p.753) (3 Stone Buildings) Tackles trusts and probate matters as part of his broad traditional and commercial chancery practice. He is particularly strong on the advisory side and frequently represents large corporate trustees. **Strengths:** "He's really creative: he genuinely thinks outside the box and comes up with some really clever ideas." "Richard is a team player who demonstrates a very high level of trust expertise and is not afraid to consider novel approaches to complex problems." **Recent work:** Represented the appellant trustees in Futter v HMRC, a case concerning the scope of the rule in re Hastings-Bass and the circumstances in which the court may set aside an exercise of discretionary power by a trustee.

Mark Herbert QC (see p.625) (5 Stone Buildings) Specialises in the law of trusts and tax. He has experience in offshore trusts and estate planning, and often assists with trust litigation in Jersey. **Strengths:** "He is one of the Rolls-Royces. One can only admire the way his trusts are put together." "He has a huge amount of experience and always has the ear of the court."

Penelope Reed QC (see p.705) (5 Stone Buildings) Has a broad chancery practice with a focus on trusts, wills and contentious probate. She is frequently instructed on high-value divorce cases involving property and trusts. **Strengths:** "Excellent with clients, very down to earth and hugely intelligent." "Very thorough, she gives clear and straightforward advice." **Recent work:** Acted in Green v Astor, a case concerning a contested Beddoe application by a beneficiary.

Shân Warnock-Smith QC (see p.746) (5 Stone Buildings) Handles a range of trust matters in the UK and internationally. She has been involved in a number of major trust cases in recent years involving offshore jurisdictions such as the Cayman Islands, the BVI and Bermuda. **Strengths:** "Excellent counsel, who is highly respected and very practical when dealing with clients on trusts disputes." "One of the 'stars' of the Chancery Bar. An absolute expert in Cayman law and lovely to deal with. She has bags of intellect and great emotional intelligence too." **Recent work:** Acted on a case in Bermuda concerning the recovery of billions of dollars of assets held in Bermuda purpose trusts.

Brian Green QC (Wilberforce Chambers) Receives glowing praise from peers and instructing solicitors, who value his experience in international trusts disputes. Commentators simply say he is "a go-to name for big trust cases." **Strengths:** "Outstanding, commercial, incisive, assertive and always the cleverest in the room, he's an exceptional asset to have on any case." "His mind works in an incredibly creative way: he is always trying to find a solution even when the odds are against him."

Robert Ham QC (Wilberforce Chambers) Focuses his litigation and advisory practice on trusts law. His experience includes handling tax law and professional negligence in relation to trusts. **Strengths:** "Remains a first choice for those seeking advice on offshore trusts. He is appreciated particularly for his calm, authoritative approach and the workable solutions which he invariably finds to complex issues." "An outstanding advocate and trusts technician, who is very popular with clients and solicitors." **Recent work:** Acted for Striker Trustees in a dispute in the Bahamas concerning the reinstatement of beneficiaries and the replacement of trustees in relation to a USD100 million trust.

RANKINGS AND COMMENTARY
SCOTLAND

Leading stables by number of rankings

Stables by number of rankings

Ranked in 12 practice areas
Axiom Advocates

Ranked in six practice areas
Ampersand

Ranked in three practice areas
Compass Chambers

Ranked in two practice areas
Arnot Manderson
Terra Firma Chambers
Westwater Advocates

Ranked in 12 practice areas

Axiom Advocates

Axiom Advocates' members are selected on merit, a policy which has enabled the stable to assemble a fantastic team of first-class legal minds. The stable has a universally high calibre of advocates, with 37 of its 44 members featuring in *Chambers UK*, who handle a multitude of practice areas. It is also home to some of the brightest lights at the Scottish Bar, including Richard Keen QC, a man with "a brilliant brain" who is rightly heralded as "the best commercial senior out there," as well as Julian Ghosh QC, who is "absolutely unique at the Tax Bar in Scotland," and the "absolutely first-class" Roddy Dunlop QC. Commentators note that "there is no doubt that Axiom is by far the leading public law stable," and its caseload bears this out, with its recent work including acting for the Lord President of the Council in an important case addressing the rights of prisoners to vote in European Parliament elections. Members also acted in a high-profile judicial review challenging the introduction of legislation imposing minimum unit pricing for alcohol in Scotland, and appeared in a Supreme Court case addressing the importance of mandated refugee status in asylum claims. The stable's advocates may make the headlines, but the unsung heroes behind its success are its stellar practice managers. Several sources told *Chambers UK*: "One of the main reasons for using Axiom is the clerking team led by Lesley Flynn."

Ranked in six practice areas

Ampersand

The Ampersand stable has been practising at the Scottish Bar as a group since 1981 and has earned a reputation for excellent client service. Sources are particularly keen to praise its clerking team, led by the experienced figure of Alan Moffat: "The service is very good in terms of the speed of responses and the knowledge of the advocates' practices and of who's there and who's available. The clerks are also good at making alternative suggestions, checking diaries and so on – they're just an excellent team." The stable covers a wide array of practice areas, and has particular strength in clinical negligence, insolvency, commercial and public law. It is home to a number of leading Scottish silks, including "outstanding advocate" Craig Sandison QC, David Sellar QC, a man with "unparalleled expertise in the Scottish market in corporate insolvency matters," and Robert Howie QC, who is "one of the cleverest advocates at the Scottish Bar."

Ranked in three practice areas

Compass Chambers

Compass Chambers is a clear market leader in Scotland for clinical negligence, personal injury, and health and safety work. It is home to a stellar collection of advocates, including Astrid Smart, a peerless junior in the clinical negligence field, and Peter Gray QC, who is acknowledged as the leading health and safety practitioner in Scotland and someone who is noted for his "silky smooth performance" in court. The stable's clerking team is "exceptionally helpful," and practice manager Gavin Herd is praised for "running a very efficient team."

Ranked in two practice areas

Arnot Manderson

Arnot Manderson's members undertake a broad range of work and are particularly highly regarded for their expertise in clinical negligence cases and tax matters. The stable boasts an array of high-quality advocates, but amongst its collection of stars there are some who shine particularly brightly, including the "absolutely brilliant advocate" Gerald Hanretty QC, the "elegant, concise and forceful" Jonathan Mitchell QC, and the peerless Iain Mitchell QC, who is Scotland's leading expert on IT law.

Terra Firma Chambers

Terra Firma Chambers is Scotland's leading property stable and is also highly regarded for its expertise in tax law. It scores particularly highly for its client service, and commentators are quick to praise the clerking team, noting that "in terms of speed, response times, knowledge of practices and making alternative suggestions, they're excellent." The stable has a host of noted advocates, chief amongst them "top-of-the-list, pure property expert" Roy Martin QC, who is the doyen of the Scottish Property Bar.

Westwater Advocates

Scotland's leading family law stable is blessed with "really gifted advocates; it is a privilege to listen to them analyse a case." This pioneering stable was the first at the Scottish Bar to become self-selecting, and is packed full of top-level practitioners, including the "passionate, tenacious and client-friendly" Sir Crispin Agnew of Lochaw Bt QC, and the excellent family law advocates Janys Scott QC and Ruth Innes.

Stars at the Bar

Ranked in seven practice areas

Roddy Dunlop QC: Axiom Advocates
The "absolutely first-class" Roddy Dunlop QC is one of Scotland's foremost advocates. He has wide expertise in media law, intellectual property, personal injury, clinical negligence, professional negligence, and public procurement to name but a few areas. "A standout advocate," he is "very robust, very persuasive, and very effective on his feet." He has appeared in many notable cases, and was instructed on behalf of the Scottish National Party in a defamation case concerning comments about a local councillor made by a property developer, successfully appealing against both an interim interdict and an appeal to the Supreme Court. As one instructing solicitor noted, "everyone wants Roddy Dunlop QC – it's a race to see who can get him first."

Ranked in five practice areas

Andrew Young QC: Arnot Manderson
Andrew Young QC is widely recognised for his expertise in personal injury, clinical negligence, and professional negligence matters. He is also highly regarded for his expertise in tax law, and was instructed on behalf of HMRC in its challenge to the validity of the aggregates levy in relation to EU competition law. His advocacy skills are applauded by his peers, with one noting that "he is just terrific and an excellent advocate; I'd worry if I were appearing against him."

Heriot Currie QC: Axiom
"One of the foremost advocates of his generation," Heriot Currie QC is "a formidable court performer" who "is extremely impressive when cross-examining witnesses in court." His phenomenal powers of advocacy are called into action across a wide range of commercial work, including IP, construction law and tax disputes. He is widely praised by solicitors as "he is very good at boiling difficult cases down to simple points." Currie acted for the defence in a high-profile dispute over the tunnel collapse at the Glendoe hydroelectric scheme.

Mark Lindsay QC: Axiom
Mark Lindsay QC's practice covers a wide range of commercial and public law cases. He is "a forensic, skilled and persuasive advocate," who is regularly instructed in significant cases such as Fleury Zoumbas v SSHD, a Supreme Court appeal regarding the UN Convention on the Rights of the Child. He also acted on behalf of the respondent in a Supreme Court case addressing the importance of mandated refugee status in asylum claims. A highly experienced and popular advocate, "he's like an old-fashioned silk in a good sense – he's a leading commercial lawyer and litigator who is prepared to take on cases that may be slightly outside of his comfort zone, but he will do the research he needs to do, apply his advocacy skills, and invariably be successful."

Ranked in four practice areas

Alastair Duncan QC: Axiom
Alastair Duncan QC has a wide-ranging commercial and public law practice, and is particularly noted for his expertise in professional negligence disputes. He draws considerable praise from his peers, who describe him as "a model senior to watch and learn from," and also impresses instructing solicitors as he is user-friendly and "does just feel like an extension of your team." He recently represented the Law Society of Scotland in connection with an appeal made by a solicitor suspended due to various allegations of misconduct. He also acted for a firm of solicitors accused of negligent misrepresentation by a financial institution.

Alistair Clark QC: Axiom
A high-profile commercial litigator who is also one of the Scottish Bar's leading defamation experts, Alistair Clark QC is "a very calm advocate who exudes confidence." One source noted that "if you have a complex, heavy-duty commercial matter in Scotland, it is hard to justify not going to him: he's got bags of experience, and is very talented both when it comes to consultation and when he's on his feet."

Craig Sandison QC: Ampersand
Craig Sandison QC's practice covers a wide range of commercial law. He is held up as one of the Scottish Bar's outstanding courtroom performers, with sources describing him as "an astute tactician and a brilliant advocate." Respectful peers say "he's a fantastic lawyer and a pain in the neck to you if he's your opponent." He is principally recognised for his focus on commercial contracts and real estate disputes, although he is also highly regarded for his expertise in professional negligence and IP matters.

David Sellar QC: Ampersand
With over 25 years' experience of company and insolvency work, David Sellar QC is a lawyer with "an encyclopaedic knowledge of insolvency law." He has "unparalleled expertise in the Scottish market in corporate insolvency matters," and impresses solicitors with the commercial nature of his advice: "He is considerate and aware of the commercial repercussions," and "is always willing to come off the fence and give definitive advice," commentators say.

David Thomson: Axiom
David Thomson is an experienced commercial litigator, whose practice encompasses real estate litigation, commercial contracts and insolvency disputes. His enthusiasm for the work in hand is remarked upon time and time again by solicitors, who value working with an advocate "who rolls his sleeves up and isn't shy of putting in the hours on a case." Other sources confirm that "he combines genuine expertise, a keen mind and a seriously impressive work ethic, making him hard to match at the junior Bar in Scotland."

Gavin Walker: Axiom
Gavin Walker's appeal was neatly summarised by one source who noted that "he has three very strong facets: he knows the law, he's very good in court and clients like him." His practice is focused principally on commercial contract litigation, construction and professional negligence, and he is also highly rated for his expertise in intellectual property disputes. He is "very personable and user-friendly," and impresses instructing solicitors with his drive and determination, with one suggesting that "if you give him something, he likes to get stuck in and he likes to win." He is increasingly instructed in high-profile matters, as exemplified by his appearance in a case concerning an attempt by the shareholders of Rangers International Football Club to interdict an annual club meeting.

J Gordon Reid QC: Terra Firma
Gordon Reid QC is a vastly experienced civil and commercial advocate whose practice is focused on real estate litigation, construction disputes, and agricultural landlord and tenant matters. Commentators agree that he is "one of the first names that rolls off the tongue if a QC is required for an agricultural matter in Scotland." He is recognised for his mastery of detail and "his innovative thinking," and is a top pick for any complex commercial property dispute.

James Mure QC: Axiom
James Mure QC is noted for his provision of "a consistently high standard of advice." He is praised by solicitors as "a very effective and efficient advocate," and he provides advice across a broad range of both commercial and public law matters. He is frequently instructed in high-profile cases and represented the Scottish Government in a judicial review challenging the ban on displays of tobacco products.

James W McNeill QC: Axiom
James McNeill QC is one of the Scottish Bar's leading experts on tax and pensions law. He is hailed by instructing solicitors for his user-friendly style, with sources describing him as "an incredibly efficient advocate," who is "straightforward to deal with."

Richard Keen QC: Axiom
Richard Keen QC is "one of the most sought-after QCs for commercial matters," and is regularly instructed in the Commercial Court, the Inner House and the Supreme Court. Recent Supreme Court cases include acting for the appellant in D L Morrison & Co v ICL Plastics, and acting for the respondent in Lloyds TSB Foundation v Lloyds Banking Group. He is "an outstanding advocate," whose charisma in the courtroom is readily acknowledged. Commentators are in awe of his "ability to grasp the key points and finer detail of complex appeals unbelievably quickly," and solicitors are especially quick to praise his "amazing ability to cut to the chase." He is a leading practitioner in administrative and public law, and is also a top-tier advocate for company and construction disputes.

Robert Howie QC: Ampersand
One of the leading commercial advocates in Scotland, Robert Howie QC is renowned for his expertise in construction disputes and for his knowledge of restructuring and insolvency law. He is lauded as "one of the cleverest advocates at the Scottish Bar," and he is frequently sought after by those instructing solicitors seeking "an inventive thinker" with "an amazing ability to come up with a left-field argument."

Ronald Clancy QC: Ampersand
Ronald Clancy QC is a civil litigator whose wide-ranging practice encompasses commercial law, personal injury, clinical negligence and media law disputes. He is hailed by his peers as "an excellent advocate" and "a fearsome opponent," whose "great courtroom presence" is much admired. He receives considerable acclaim for his "great 'bedside manner' with clients and lawyers alike," and has proven himself to be a team player, whose "collaborative, accessible and passionate" presence is welcomed by solicitors on cases of the highest complexity.

Contents:

ADMINISTRATIVE & PUBLIC LAW

Administrative & Public Law Scotland
Leading Stables
Band 1
Axiom Advocates *
Band 2
Ampersand *
Leading Silks
Band 1
Carmichael Ailsa J *Ampersand*
Drummond Lorna *Axiom Advocates*
Johnston David *Axiom Advocates*
Keen Richard *Axiom Advocates*
Lindsay Mark *Axiom Advocates*
Moynihan Gerry *Axiom Advocates*
O'Neill Aidan *Ampersand*
Wolffe James *Axiom Advocates* *
Band 2
Bovey Mungo *Hastie Stable (ORL)* ◊
Clark Alistair *Axiom Advocates*
Crawford Ruth *Axiom Advocates* *
Findlay James *Terra Firma Chambers (ORL)* ◊ *
Mitchell Jonathan J *Arnot Manderson (ORL)* ◊
Mure James *Axiom Advocates* *
Thomson Malcolm *Ampersand*
Leading Juniors
Band 1
Ross Morag *Axiom Advocates*
Webster Andrew G *Hastie Stable (ORL)* ◊
Band 2
MacGregor John *Axiom Advocates*
Pirie Chris *Hastie Stable (ORL)* ◊
Smith Jane *Ampersand*
Up-and-coming individuals
Byrne Daniel *Axiom Advocates* [A]
[A] *direct access (see p.11).*
◊ *(ORL) = Other Ranked Lawyer.*
* *Indicates stable / individual with profile.*

Band 1

Axiom Advocates

See profile on p.898

THE SET

Axiom Advocates is the pre-eminent public law stable at the Scottish Bar. It boasts an unrivalled roster of counsel, whose impressive depth of expertise spans the full range of public law matters. Commentators note that "there is no doubt that Axiom is by far the leading public law stable," and that the set's members are "invariably the first port of call for a tricky matter" in the area.

Client service: "The clerking is excellent – clerks are always available on the phone and one can have sensible discussions around fees."

SILKS

David Johnston QC Commands great respect for his broad practice, which takes in commercial and public law matters. He has appeared in a number of highly significant matters over recent years, including a case addressing the amenability to judicial review of decisions of the Upper Tribunal. **Strengths:** "An exceptionally fine lawyer, one of the intellectual stars of the Bar. He has a soothing manner, and the ear of the court." "He is one of the most intelligent, able people at the Bar."

Richard Keen QC Highly regarded advocate with extensive experience of public law principles. His practice focuses on the commercial side of judicial review, and particularly on cases with pronounced scientific or economic evidential elements. **Strengths:** "He has the ability to grasp the key points and finer detail of complex appeals unbelievably quickly, to marshal his arguments and to pitch his advocacy perfectly." **Recent work:** Represented the Scottish Information Commissioner in a case before the Supreme Court concerning whether its order to disclose information on pay structures at South Lanarkshire Council was in contravention of the Data Protection Act.

Mark Lindsay QC Typically acts for respondents in judicial review proceedings across a diverse range of public law issues. He is particularly experienced in cases challenging the decisions of local authorities and regulatory bodies. **Strengths:** "He is an excellent silk to work with. Technically excellent and very responsive to clients." "He is very good at explaining things without being bogged down in unduly complex issues." **Recent work:** Represented the Security Industry Authority in an appeal against its decision to revoke private security licences.

Alistair Clark QC A commercial litigator with considerable expertise in the principles of public procurement. Much of his public law practice is founded in damages claims against public bodies for having made unlawful decisions. **Strengths:** "He is a very calm advocate who exudes confidence. He gives very sound practical advice and does not get unsettled when the going gets tough." **Recent work:** Acted for Glasgow City Council in a damages claim founded on the contention that it had breached public procurement law.

Ruth Crawford QC (see p.580) Acts on behalf of Scottish government, UK government, local authorities and regulatory bodies in defending public law actions across a range of issues. She has particular expertise in prisoners' rights, welfare benefits and the public consultation duty. **Strengths:** "Whenever we want a very robust advocate we turn to her." "She's particularly strong on the planning elements of public law." **Recent work:** Acted for the Lord President of the Council in an important case addressing the rights of prisoners to vote in European Parliament elections.

Lorna Drummond QC A skilful advocate with a diverse public law practice. She is especially expert in questions of immigration, extradition and the powers of public authorities. **Strengths:** "She is widely regarded on the Bench as being outstanding. The judges listen to what she says." "She is a leading silk with a broad practice in public law." **Recent work:** Represented the petitioner in a judicial review challenging the decision to remove her from the country, on the basis that doing so after she has been identified as a victim of trafficking would be a violation of both her human rights and the Anti-Trafficking Convention.

Gerry Moynihan QC An experienced advocate whose public law practice is focused on acting for the government. He has particular expertise in the operation of human rights in public law actions. **Strengths:** "He has the ear of the court on any occasion he opens his mouth." "He is very able and experienced, and does a lot of work for the government." **Recent work:** Acted for the first respondent in a high-profile judicial review challenging the introduction of legislation imposing minimum unit pricing for alcohol in Scotland.

James Mure QC (see p.679) Attracts strong praise for work acting on behalf of government and local authorities. He is particularly expert in matters relating to planning and environmental decisions. **Strengths:** "He has a thorough, measured approach and is an extremely good advocate." "He gives a consistently high standard of advice in relation to matters of statutory interpretation." **Recent work:** Represented the Scottish government in a judicial review challenging the introduction of legislation prohibiting displays of tobacco products and their sale in vending machines.

James Wolffe QC (see p.755) Commands great respect for his broad public law practice, and is especially well regarded for his representation in matters concerning legislative competence, local government and the criminal justice system. Indicative of his standing in the market, he was elected dean of the Faculty of Advocates in 2014. **Strengths:** "He is extremely professional and thoughtful. He has the ear of the court and is prepared to push his client's position." "He's someone you're happy to have on your side, and you're dismayed if he's on the other." **Recent work:** Acted for Comhairle nan Eilean Siar in the first case addressing the Schools (Consultation) (Scotland) Act, and the powers vested by it in the Scottish government to close rural schools.

JUNIORS

Morag Ross Enjoys an excellent reputation for her intelligent and knowledgeable advocacy in public law matters. She represents both petitioners and respondents, particularly in relation to questions of freedom of information and the duties of local authorities. **Strengths:** "She possesses a rigorous intellect, gets to the heart of the matter quickly and is a delight to work with." "She is extremely clever, very capable and thoughtful but to the point." **Recent**

work: Acted successfully on behalf of the Scottish government in a judicial review challenging a decision of the Scottish Prison Service in connection to the transfer of a prisoner from Jersey, addressing the applicable rules and provisions to be taken into account.

John MacGregor Represents petitioners and respondents in a variety of issues within public law. He focuses particularly on issues arising in the context of immigration, public procurement, planning and mental health. **Strengths:** "He is absolutely fantastic. Petitioner work requires you to find the points yourself, something he is plainly capable of doing." "There is no doubt he is one of the very best public law juniors." **Recent work:** Acted for the Lord Advocate in the challenge to the alcohol minimum pricing legislation.

Daniel Byrne Acts for both sides in judicial review and statutory appeal proceedings covering a wide range of public law matters. His practice is characterised by an emphasis on issues related to immigration and human rights. **Strengths:** "He is about as intellectually able as they come." "He drafts extremely well, and very quickly." **Recent work:** Represented the petitioner in a successful judicial review challenging the practice of the Scottish government of writing letters to cover holes in reasoning given in refusing applications to leave to remain.

Band 2

Ampersand

See profile on p.896

THE SET

Ampersand enjoys a strong reputation in Scotland for the quality of its representation in public law matters on behalf of both petitioners and respondents. Its members are especially adept at handling proceedings with a pronounced commercial element, and those that deal with fundamental issues of human rights.

SILKS

Ailsa Carmichael QC Enjoys a strong reputation for her public law practice. She is especially interested in questions of human rights, freedom of information and the legislative competence of the Scottish Parliament. **Strengths:** "She is one of the best lawyers of her generation." "She is fantastic – she has the ear of the court." **Recent work:** Acted for the government in the judicial review challenge to legislation prohibiting tobacco displays and the sale of tobacco in vending machines.

Aidan O'Neill QC A leading figure at the Scottish Bar whose practice is dominated by public law matters. He is qualified to appear on both sides of the border, and focuses on issues relating to EU law, equality and human rights. **Strengths:** "He is very knowledgeable – he does a lot of public law work across a very broad range, and knows it inside out." "He's a great person to have on matters of constitutional and human rights law. There's very little he doesn't know in those areas." **Recent work:** Acted for the petitioners in a judicial review before the Outer House of the Court of Session addressing whether the Scottish Independence Referendum (Franchise) Act is compatible with international public law and the provisions of the ECHR.

Malcolm Thomson QC Well respected for his representation in judicial reviews and inquiries into matters related to planning. He is noted for his work in challenges to flood protection schemes. **Strengths:** "He's an excellent and very bright silk." "He's very experienced in the planning side of public law."

JUNIORS

Jane Smith Maintains a broad public law practice which dovetails with her commercial work. She appears for both sides in judicial review and statutory appeal proceedings, especially in relation to planning and insurance matters.

Other Ranked Lawyers

Jonathan Mitchell QC (Arnot Manderson) Well respected for his wide-ranging public law expertise, which has a particular focus on issues of civil liberties and human rights. He is also noted for his expertise in issues arising in the context of immigration, mental health and employment. **Strengths:** "He has a certain gravitas and presence in court. He is experienced, and with that comes confidence that you can rely on him in high-profile cases." "He is a class act, with a very wide range." **Recent work:** Represented the appellant in a Supreme Court case establishing that a greater weight should be given to the decisions and methodology of the UNHCR in asylum cases.

Mungo Bovey QC (Hastie Stable) Attracts strong praise for his abilities in handling public law proceedings, especially those with a pronounced human rights or immigration element. **Strengths:** "He is a go-to petitioner in matters relating to immigration."

Andrew Webster (Hastie Stable) Acts in his capacity as First Standing Junior for the Scottish government in a wide range of public law proceedings, including judicial reviews and statutory appeals. He is particularly experienced in matters relating to immigration and social security. **Strengths:** "He is regarded as a safe pair of hands for the government in significant cases."

Chris Pirie (Hastie Stable) Acts primarily on behalf of petitioners in public law proceedings arising in the context of professional discipline and equality. **Strengths:** "He is intellectually extremely able and a brilliant advocate."

James Findlay QC (see p.600) (Terra Firma Chambers) A dual-qualified practitioner whose reputation for public law expertise is growing at the Scottish Bar. He is especially expert in planning issues. **Strengths:** "He gives very good, pragmatic advice, and his advocacy is very eloquent." "He is very well grounded and has a lot of experience." **Recent work:** Represented the appellant in a case before the Supreme Court challenging the adequacy of reasons given by Scottish Ministers for their decision to approve the planning and development policy of Fife Council. The ruling clarified the meaning of adequacy in this context.

AGRICULTURE & RURAL AFFAIRS

Agriculture & Rural Affairs Scotland
Leading Silks
Star individuals
Agnew of Lochnaw Bt Crispin *Westwater (ORL)* ◊ *
Band 1
Reid J Gordon *Terra Firma Chambers (ORL)* ◊ *
Leading Juniors
Band 1
Maclean Iain *Terra Firma Chambers (ORL)* ◊ *
Sutherland Robert *Terra Firma Chambers (ORL)* ◊ *
Band 2
Cameron Donald *Westwater Advocates (ORL)* ◊ *
Band 3
Joughin Gail *Westwater Advocates (ORL)* ◊

Ranked Lawyers

Gordon Reid QC (see p.706) (Terra Firma Chambers) An expert in agricultural matters, his experience in this area includes rent review cases, partnership disputes and other matters related to the Agricultural Holdings Act. **Strengths:** "One of the first names that rolls off the tongue if a QC is required for an agricultural matter in Scotland." "He's just extremely thorough, extremely bright and extremely reliable."

Iain Maclean (see p.660) (Terra Firma Chambers) Handles the full breadth of both agricultural and crofting law. **Strengths:** "He has a first-class knowledge of agricultural and crofting law." **Recent work:** Instructed on a case concerning the use of common grazing land for the landing of light aircraft.

Robert Sutherland (see p.732) (Terra Firma Chambers) Covers a wide range of both crofting and agricultural law. He is regularly instructed in arbitrations concerning agricultural tenancy and contract disputes. **Strengths:** "He understands work in this area like nobody else because he does so much of it. He's very sensible in the sense that he has a very good judgement of when to fight, when to compromise, and what points to take." **Recent work:** Acting for the pursuer in Low v Betts, two related actions concerning a dispute over an agricultural tenancy and a dispute over right of access.

Sir Crispin Agnew of Lochnaw Bt QC (see p.532) (Westwater Advocates) A veteran advocate with considerable experience of acting on cases related to crofting, agricultural law and rural property law. **Strengths:** "He's very down to earth and approachable, and very good in consultation when explaining complex areas of law to clients; he also has gravitas and can help direct the client." **Recent work:** Successfully acted for the appellant in Bain v Crofting Commission, an appeal against the denial of an application for the assignation of crofts.

Donald Cameron (see p.563) (Westwater Advocates) Handles a wide range of matters relating to agricultural and environmental law, including acting on crofting cases and landlord and tenant work with respect to the Agricultural Holdings Act. **Strengths:** "He is very good with the clients; he comes across as very empathetic, and explains complex points in basic terms." **Recent work:** Acted for the respondent in Robin Feakins v Scottish Ministers, a case related to single farm payments.

Gail Joughin (Westwater Advocates) Acts on a wide range of cases concerning agriculture and rural affairs. She has considerable expertise of agricultural law, as well as experience on cases related to agricultural property. **Strengths:** "Gail Joughin does some good work in agriculture – she gets the job done."

CIVIL LIBERTIES & HUMAN RIGHTS

Civil Liberties & Human Rights Scotland
Leading Stables
Band 1
Axiom Advocates *
Band 2
Ampersand *
Leading Silks
Band 1
Carmichael Ailsa J *Ampersand*
Mitchell Jonathan J *Arnot Manderson (ORL)* ◊
O'Neill Aidan *Ampersand*
Band 2
Bovey Mungo *Hastie Stable (ORL)* ◊
Drummond Lorna *Axiom Advocates*
Band 3
Lindsay Mark *Axiom Advocates*
Poole Anna *Axiom Advocates* *
Leading Juniors
Band 1
Pirie Chris *Hastie Stable (ORL)* ◊
Webster Andrew G *Hastie Stable (ORL)* ◊
Band 2
MacGregor John *Axiom Advocates*
Up-and-coming individuals
Byrne Daniel *Axiom Advocates* [A]
Komorowski Julius *Terra Firma Chambers (ORL)* ◊ *
* *Indicates firm / individual with profile.*
◊ *(ORL) = Other Ranked Lawyer.*
[A] *direct access (see p.11).*

Band 1

Axiom Advocates
See profile on p.898

THE SET

Axiom Advocates is very well respected for the skilful and knowledgeable advocacy offered by its deep bench of advocates. Its members offer advice and representation to petitioners and respondents in a diverse array of issues within civil liberties, with particular expertise in the human rights elements of immigration, asylum, extradition and mental health.

SILKS

Lorna Drummond QC Centres her human rights practice on issues arising in the context of immigration, mental health and prison law. She has particular experience in cases concerning the voting rights of prisoners. **Strengths:** "She is a brilliant advocate in every way. She is up there with the best of them." "She has the ear of the court, and they know they can trust her." **Recent work:** She acted for the appellant in a case before the Supreme Court challenging the decision to remove the appellant and his family to the Congo, on the grounds it that it was contrary to his rights under Article 8 ECHR.

Mark Lindsay QC An accomplished public law practitioner whose work in human rights is typically rooted in immigration and asylum issues, and assessments of best interest for children. **Strengths:** "He is a forensic, skilled and persuasive advocate." **Recent work:** He acted on behalf of the respondent in a Supreme Court case addressing the importance of mandated refugee status in asylum claims.

Anna Poole QC (see p.695) Offers expertise in a range of human rights matters, including mental health and the rights of children and foster carers. She acts primarily on behalf of the government and public bodies. **Strengths:** "She is switched on to human rights issues, and is involved in a lot of cases for the Scottish government." **Recent work:** She acted on behalf of Renfrewshire Council as an interested party to a judicial review in the Court of Sessions, in which it was found the existing system of Child Protection Orders was incompatible with Article 8 ECHR.

JUNIORS

Daniel Byrne Attracts praise for his work representing both petitioners and respondents in a diverse array of human rights matters. He has particular experience in matters concerning the housing of asylum seekers. **Strengths:** "He's excellent, and has good judgement as to what arguments are sensible to run." **Recent work:** He represented the appellant in a hearing in the Inner House of the Court of Session challenging the use by the Scottish government of a Swedish language analysis company in coming to decisions on asylum.

John MacGregor Offers representation in a range of issues, including mental health, immigration and extradition. He acts on behalf of both respondents and petitioners. **Strengths:** "He is a robust and unflappable advocate." **Recent work:** He represented the Mental Health Tribunal for Scotland in a Supreme Court case that clarified provisions of the Mental Health (Care and Treatment) Act, and the correct approach to apply for a declaration of excessive security in the context of mental health detention.

Band 2

Ampersand
See profile on p.896

THE SET

Ampersand's advocates are instructed on a wide range of public law matters, very often involving arguments founded on Convention rights, in which area its members are highly skilled. They are especially experienced in the interaction of EU law and domestic law, equality and employment issues. Further areas of expertise include matters relating to the devolution settlement.

SILKS

Ailsa Carmichael QC Enjoys an excellent reputation for her work in civil liberties, which arises naturally from her broader public law practice. She has particular experience in issues emerging from Scottish devolution, and in prisoners' rights. **Strengths:** "She is very good at the old-fashioned art of persuasion. She goes into court, they listen to her and are persuaded – she wins marginal cases." **Recent work:** She acted for the petitioner in a judicial review in the Court of Session concerning whether there was a legitimate expectation that an immigration decision would be made by a certain date.

Aidan O'Neill QC Attracts considerable praise for his skilful advocacy and intellectual approach to novel legal issues, especially where there is a pronounced interrelation of EU and domestic law. He is admitted to practice at both the Scottish Bar and the Bar of England and Wales. **Strengths:** "He is prepared to take on extremely complex, difficult and even notorious work. He is intellectually impressive, and his advocacy skills are tremendous." "He is extremely hard-working and incredibly diligent." **Recent work:** He acted on behalf of one appellant in a joined hearing before the Supreme Court that addressed the question of whether preventing prisoners from voting in European elections violated their Convention rights.

Other Ranked Lawyers

Jonathan Mitchell QC (Arnot Manderson) Commands great respect for his civil liberties practice, which focuses on family and employment law, and commercial cases with a pronounced human rights element. He has particular experience in appellate matters. **Strengths:** "He is an elegant, concise and forceful advocate. I have a very high opinion of him." "He has a fierce intellect, is easy to get along with and is highly communicative." **Recent work:** He represented the appellant in a Supreme Court case concerning the duty incumbent on Scottish Ministers to implement a right of appeal against detention where there is excessive security.

Mungo Bovey QC (Hastie Stable) A well-regarded advocate known for his authoritative knowledge of asylum and extradition, as well as rights under Articles 6 and 8 of the ECHR. **Strengths:** "He's very intelligent, and very good on asylum and extradition issues." **Recent work:** He acted for the respondent in an appeal before the Supreme Court brought by the BBC challenging a decision of an earlier judicial review hearing allowing the respondent to anonymise his identity. The appeal was brought on the grounds it had violated the principle of open justice and the rights of the BBC under Articles 10 and 12 ECHR.

Chris Pirie (Hastie Stable) Enjoys a strong reputation as a leading civil liberties junior in Scotland. He primarily represents petitioners in relation to issues of professional discipline, criminal law and equality. **Strengths:** "He is reliable, diligent, very intellectually able and a brilliant advocate." "He is really good in submissions, being able to get points across in a concise fashion."

Andrew Webster (Hastie Stable) Acts for government departments on matters relating to the rights to privacy, family life and immigration. He has further experience in cases addressing the rights of convicted sex offenders. **Strengths:** "He's a real performer in court – well able to get up on his feet and persuade a judge."

Julius Komorowski (see p.648) (Terra Firma Chambers) Focuses his practice in human rights on issues relating to immigration, mental health and prison law. **Strengths:** "He's very earnest, very conscientious and extremely thorough, and he has a real sense of the legal landscape in a case." **Recent work:** He acted for the respondent in a judicial review of the decision to refuse leave to appeal against a ruling of the First-tier Tribunal to refuse an asylum claim founded on her rights under Article 8 ECHR.

CLINICAL NEGLIGENCE

Clinical Negligence Scotland
Leading Stables
Band 1
Ampersand *
Compass Chambers *
Band 2
Arnot Manderson *
Axiom Advocates *
◊ (ORL) = Other Ranked Lawyer.
* Indicates stable / individual with profile.
Alphabetical order within each band. Band 1 is highest.

Clinical Negligence Scotland	
Leading Silks	
Band 1	
Caldwell Marion	*Compass Chambers*
Dunlop Laura	*Hastie Stable (ORL)* ◊
Dunlop Roddy	*Axiom Advocates*
Ferguson Iain	*Axiom Advocates*
MacAulay Colin	*Arnot Manderson*
Maguire Maria	*Ampersand*
Smith Andrew	*Compass Chambers*
Band 2	
Anderson Rory	*Compass Chambers*
Bowie Simon	*Ampersand*
Cherry Joanna	*Arnot Manderson* *
Clancy Ronald	*Ampersand*
Duncan Alastair	*Axiom Advocates*
McLean Alan	*Hastie Stable (ORL)* ◊
Milligan Robert	*Compass Chambers*
O'Brien Susan	*Compass Chambers* *
Stephenson David	*Ampersand*
Young Andrew R W	*Arnot Manderson* *

Clinical Negligence Scotland	
Leading Juniors	
Star individuals	
Smart Astrid	*Compass Chambers*
Band 1	
Henderson Lisa	*Ampersand*
McGregor Malcolm	*Compass Chambers*
Sutherland Lauren	*Ampersand*
Band 2	
Hodge Margaret	*Westwater Advocates (ORL)* ◊
Lake Fiona	*Ampersand*
Mackenzie Euan	*Ampersand*
MacSporran Archie	*Ampersand*
Tait Arabella	*Arnot Manderson*
Band 3	
Forsyth Sandy	*Compass Chambers* *
Khurana Vinit	*Ampersand*
Paterson Chris	*Axiom Advocates*
Pilkington Ross	*Hastie Stable (ORL)* ◊
Pugh Richard	*Compass Chambers* *
Ross Douglas	*Ampersand*
Up-and-coming individuals	
Devaney Catherine	*Ampersand*

Band 1

Ampersand
See profile on p.896

THE SET

Continues to be recognised as one of the pre-eminent stables for medical negligence in Scotland. Both its senior and junior members consistently appear in market-leading cases, and it remains a go-to stable for high-value and complex cases.

SILKS

Maria Maguire QC A highly admired silk who acts for both claimants and defenders in complex brain injury and cerebral palsy cases. She also draws praise for her work on fatal accident inquiries. **Strengths:** "The first person you should go to for complex medical malpractice claims; she's top-class." "She is a brilliant advocate with a very good approach to clients."

Simon Bowie QC An experienced commercial practitioner who is frequently instructed on clinical negligence cases. He is noted for his work defending both medical institutions and individual medical practitioners. **Strengths:** "He is very calm, self-assured, reasonable and a very smooth advocate." "He keeps calm and always ensures that the client's best interests are kept centre-stage."

Ronald Clancy QC Clinical negligence forms a key part of his broader civil litigation practice. He is noted for his expertise in cerebral palsy claims, and has been instructed in claims brought before the GMC and NHS Tribunal. **Strengths:** "He focuses quickly on what really matters and commands respect in court. He also has a great 'bedside manner' with clients and lawyers alike."

David Stephenson QC Maintains a broad clinical negligence practice with noted expertise in obstetric claims. He has over two decades of experience in representing NHS bodies and medical defence unions. **Strengths:** "He is an incredibly accomplished performer in court." "He is one of the senior counsel at the Scottish Bar with the most experience of medical negligence work."

JUNIORS

Lisa Henderson Recommended for her work on cerebral palsy claims. She is also noted for her expertise in cases concerning spinal and brain injuries. **Strengths:** "Her attention to detail, compassion and practical means of problem solving are second to none."

Lauren Sutherland Frequently instructed by both pursuers and defenders across a wide range of clinical negligence cases. A highly experienced advocate, she has been instructed in a number of notable fatal accident inquiries. **Strengths:** "She has an apparently inexhaustible energy to prepare and argue some of the most ground-breaking cases."

Fiona Lake Principally recommended for her expertise on cases relating to birth injuries and brain damage. She is highly experienced across the full range of clinical negligence matters, and is instructed by both pursuers and defenders. **Strengths:** "She is incredibly clever; you really trust her ability to run the case."

Archie MacSporran Specialises in clinical negligence claims, especially complex cases concerning cerebral palsy and surgical negligence. He has also been involved in a number of mental health tribunals and fatal accident inquiries. **Strengths:** "He is a complete dream; a methodical advocate with a good eye for detail who gets to the heart of the matter quickly."

Euan Mackenzie Focuses his practice on complex and high-value clinical negligence cases. He acts on behalf of both pursuers and defenders across a range of claims. **Strengths:** "He is an extremely skilled and conscientious junior counsel who plays an invaluable role when pursuing high-value claims."

Douglas Ross Has a broad civil practice that encompasses some significant clinical negligence work. He is praised for his experience of matters relating to mental health. **Strengths:** "He is very clever and thoughtful. He appears a quite unassuming advocate, but is excellent on his feet." "You can't fault his analysis or advice."

Vinit Khurana A former doctor whose practice is focused on issues stemming from medical law, including mental health work and fatal accident inquiries. He is a vastly experienced clinical negligence practitioner, and is regularly instructed on behalf of both defenders and pursuers. **Strengths:** "He approaches every case meticulously and gives sound and helpful advice at all times." "He is a go-to counsel, who I would trust with any case no matter how big or small."

Catherine Devaney Focuses her practice on clinical negligence and personal injury claims. She has been instructed on a number of high-value cerebral palsy matters, and receives instructions from both pursuers and defenders. **Strengths:** "She gives mature and helpful advice in any case instructed and is a go-to junior counsel for a medical negligence case. "

Compass Chambers

See profile on p.899

THE SET

Compass Chambers' members operate across the full breadth of clinical negligence matters, and the depth of expertise of its advocates ensures it is one of the leading stables for clinical negligence in Scotland. Its members act for a wide range of clients, including NHS hospitals and medical defence organisations.

Client service: "Practice manager Gavin Herd runs a very efficient clerking team; they are willing to accommodate solicitors, and it feels like a very cohesive operation."

SILKS

Marion Caldwell QC Renowned for her detailed approach to complex medical negligence litigation on behalf of both pursers and defenders. She is noted for her expertise in cases concerning brain injuries. **Strengths:** "She is a fierce negotiator, with an excellent client manner." "She is very thorough; she totally immerses herself in the case."

Andrew Smith QC Widely praised for his advocacy on clinical negligence claims. He is experienced in high-value birth injury claims as well as patrimonial loss matters. **Strengths:** "He is an excellent counsel in court; he enjoys a challenge and gets good results."

Robert Milligan QC A personal injury and clinical negligence specialist with a focus on severe high-value actions regarding catastrophic injury or fatal claims. **Strengths:** "He is a walking oracle; he is very popular with the Bench." "He goes straight to the heart of the matter with speed and precision." **Recent work:** He was instructed on behalf of the pursuer in a claim concerning defective laser surgery.

Susan O'Brien QC (see p.684) Frequently instructed by both pursuers and defenders across a range of clinical negligence claims. She is noted for her expertise in cases concerning midwifery negligence and cerebral palsy in infants. **Strengths:** "She is absolutely marvellous; thorough, incredibly intelligent and simply a mind-bogglingly good advocate."

Rory Anderson QC A veteran medical negligence practitioner. Sources note that he is equally accomplished in his representation of both pursuers and defenders.

JUNIORS

Astrid Smart Receives an exceptional level of positive feedback confirming her position as a market-leading junior for clinical negligence. Her clinical negligence practice covers the gamut of claims, including negligent birth-induced cerebral palsy and other catastrophic injury claims. **Strengths:** "She has very good medical knowledge, and is on the level with the medical experts." "She has a wealth of experience in this area, particularly high-value and complex cases." **Recent work:** She was instructed by the pursuer in a high-value case concerning a misdiagnosis of cervical cancer.

Malcolm McGregor Has a broad civil litigation practice, of which medical negligence is a core focus. He is noted for his representation of medical professionals in complex clinical negligence claims. **Strengths:** "He is a strong defender's counsel; he always spots the weaknesses in the pursuer's case." "He takes a straightforward approach and gets straight to the heart of the matter."

Sandy Forsyth (see p.602) A former solicitor with a broad practice covering personal injury, insurance and clinical negligence work. He is experienced in acting on behalf of both pursuers and defenders. **Strengths:** "He is a detailed and efficient advocate who is very experienced in this area."

Richard Pugh (see p.700) Fast gaining an enviable reputation for his expertise on clinical negligence claims. He is already seen as a go-to advocate for high-value and complex cases. **Strengths:** "He is a rising star; he has a good grasp of complicated cases and an approachable manner." "It is lovely to see how well he interacts with clients." **Recent work:** He defended a health board against a pursuer's high-value claim concerning a wrongful diagnosis of HIV.

Band 2

Arnot Manderson

See profile on p.897

THE SET

Arnot Manderson's members cover a wide range of clinical negligence work, and are instructed on behalf of both pursuers and defenders in cases concerning negligence by doctors, dentists and nurses.

SILKS

Colin MacAulay QC Focuses on complex clinical and medical negligence claims. He is noted for his expertise on cases concerning catastrophic injuries. **Strengths:** "His extensive medical negligence experience ensures he can get to grips with complicated cases very quickly."

Andrew Young QC (see p.757) Has over two decades of clinical negligence and wider personal injury experience. He is highly regarded for his expertise in cases concerning catastrophic spine and brain injuries. **Strengths:** "His advice is pragmatic and measured. He has a calm and studied approach that reassures those he represents."

Joanna Cherry QC (see p.570) Returned to private practice from the Crown Office in 2011 and has since been instructed in a number of complex and high-value clinical negligence claims. She has also developed a strong reputation for her work on public and fatal accident inquiries. **Strengths:** "She has a real talent for mastering the detail and developing a thorough understanding of complex cases." "She is excellent; she works incredibly hard and covers all bases."

JUNIORS

Arabella Tait Handles both pursuer and defender work, often tackling cases involving catastrophic injury. She has considerable experience in medical, dental and nursing claims. **Strengths:** "She is an experienced junior, with a great grasp of complicated factual situations. She is clear in her advice to clients and tenacious in negotiations."

Axiom Advocates

See profile on p.898

THE SET

Axiom Advocates is going from strength to strength within the clinical negligence space, and its advocates are frequently instructed on complex and high-profile claims. The stable's members act for both pursuers and defenders, and are noted for their representation of bodies such as the MDDUS and the NHS Central Litigation Office.

SILKS

Roddy Dunlop QC One of the leading courtroom advocates in Scotland, his clinical negligence caseload forms a key part of his broader professional negligence practice. **Strengths:** "He is an excellent advocate with a strong grasp of the whole practice area."

Iain Ferguson QC Concentrates his practice on clinical and professional negligence matters. He has an impressive track record on complex obstetric claims and GP negligence claims. **Strengths:** "He has ferocious attention to detail, which he combines with robust and firm advocacy."

Alastair Duncan QC Maintains a broad practice that encompasses a variety of commercial and public law matters. He has developed considerable expertise in medical negligence cases. **Strengths:** "He is a model senior to watch and learn from." "He is very experienced and well versed in this whole practice area."

JUNIORS

Chris Paterson Has particular expertise in medical negligence claims, and is frequently instructed on behalf of dentists and GPs. **Strengths:** "He is obviously a person going places; he conducts negotiation fantastically." "He is very clear with clients and explains difficult issues clearly."

Other Ranked Lawyers

Laura Dunlop QC (Hastie Stable) Widely recommended for her clinical negligence expertise. She is also noted for her work in relation to high-profile public inquiries. **Strengths:** "She is an excellent senior counsel – very experienced, with high attention to detail. She is unflappable and gets very good results."

Alan McLean QC (Hastie Stable) Handles a wide range of commercial and reparation disputes for both pursuers and defenders. **Strengths:** "He has high attention to detail, is quick to respond, and deals with clients sensitively."

Ross Pilkington (Hastie Stable) Maintains a broad personal injury and clinical negligence practice. **Strengths:** "He has a great manner with clients – he's very professional, but he puts them at ease and they really feel he is on their side."

Margaret Hodge (Westwater Advocates) Acts on a wide range of clinical negligence cases. She draws praise for her expertise in delayed diagnosis of breast cancer claims. **Strengths:** "She is very thorough and looks at complex issues in great depth."

COMMERCIAL DISPUTE RESOLUTION

Commercial Dispute Resolution Scotland
Leading Stables
Band 1
Axiom Advocates *
Band 2
Ampersand *
Leading Silks
Star individuals
Keen Richard *Axiom Advocates*
Band 1
Clark Alistair *Axiom Advocates*
Currie Heriot *Axiom Advocates*
Ellis Nick *Westwater Advocates (ORL)* ◊ *
Howie Robert *Ampersand*
Martin Roy *Terra Firma Chambers (ORL)* ◊ *
Moynihan Gerry *Axiom Advocates*
Sandison Craig *Ampersand*
Wolffe James *Axiom Advocates* *
Band 2
Clancy Ronald *Ampersand*
Davidson of Glen Clova Neil *Axiom Advocates*
Duncan Alastair *Axiom Advocates*
Dunlop Roddy *Axiom Advocates*
Lake Jonathan C *Axiom Advocates*
Lindsay Mark *Axiom Advocates*
McNeill James W *Axiom Advocates*
Mure James *Axiom Advocates* *
Reid J Gordon *Terra Firma Chambers (ORL)* ◊ *
Sellar David *Ampersand*
Young Andrew R W *Arnot Manderson (ORL)* ◊ *
Band 3
Howlin Michael P *Hastie Stable (ORL)* ◊
MacNeill Calum H S *Westwater Advocates (ORL)* ◊ *
McBrearty Kenneth *Axiom Advocates* *
Weir Robert *Ampersand*
◊ (ORL) = Other Ranked Lawyer.
** Indicates stable / individual with profile.*

Commercial Dispute Resolution Scotland
Leading Juniors
Band 1
Borland Garry *Axiom Advocates* *
DelibegoviĐ-Broome Almira *Axiom Advocates*
MacColl Gavin L *Hastie Stable (ORL)* ◊
Richardson Martin H *Axiom Advocates*
Band 2
Barne Jonathan *Axiom Advocates*
Brown Jonathan *Westwater Advocates (ORL)* ◊
Higgins Roisin *Axiom Advocates* *
O'Brien Paul *Axiom Advocates* *
Robertson Eric W *Arnot Manderson (ORL)* ◊ *
Ross Morag *Axiom Advocates*
Band 3
McKenzie Alasdair *Axiom Advocates*
Ower Susan *Axiom Advocates* *
Paterson Chris *Axiom Advocates*
Smith Jane *Ampersand*
Thomson David *Axiom Advocates* *
Walker Gavin *Axiom Advocates*
Up-and-coming individuals
Duthie Euan *Axiom Advocates* *
McClelland Ross *Axiom Advocates* *

Band 1

Axiom Advocates

See profile on p.898

THE SET

Axiom Advocates remains the leading stable in Scotland for commercial dispute resolution and public law. The set has a unique depth of knowledge at both junior and silk level, and its members adopt an innovative approach to advice and counsel that appeals to clients. Other areas of focus include professional negligence, construction and contract disputes.

Client service: "The clerks are extremely good; the service there is among the best in the market."

SILKS

Richard Keen QC Regularly instructed by solicitors on matters before both the Supreme and Commercial Courts. He is widely accepted as a pre-eminent figure in Scottish commercial litigation, and is a go-to for complex cases involving large amounts of expert evidence. **Strengths:** "He's fantastic. He has a brilliant brain, and he prepares meticulously – not just in relation to the law, but he actually understands the client's background. He's just fantastic. He's the best commercial senior out there, with an amazing ability to cut to the chase. He's also absolutely incredible on his feet." **Recent work:** Represented ICL Tech in an action against Johnston Oils for contribution in relation to a high-value insurance claim.

Gerry Moynihan QC A veteran advocate frequently instructed by the Scottish government in judicial reviews. His expertise also extends to handling trust and professional negligence matters. **Strengths:** "A strong advocate who is also very user-friendly." "He is a superb advocate capable of explaining highly intricate issues in terms which are readily understood by clients and importantly by judges." **Recent work:** Acted on a construction contract dispute involving complicated quantum issues.

James Wolffe QC (see p.755) Has an excellent reputation in commercial matters, earning particular praise for his skill in handling high-value construction disputes. He is hugely experienced, and has handled high-profile matters before the House of Lords and the Supreme Court. **Strengths:** "You will struggle to find an advocate at the Scottish Bar who has a superior intellect." "He's an intellectual titan who provides sensible and pragmatic legal advice." **Recent work:** Instructed by the administrators of Buckie Shipyard in an action enforcing the shipbuilder's contractual lien.

Alistair Clark QC A standout practitioner with considerable experience in complex and high-profile cases. He is instructed across the full range of commercial dispute matters, earning particular recognition for his involvement in high-value cases in the media sector. **Strengths:** "If you have a complex, heavy-duty commercial matter in Scotland, it is hard to justify not going to him: he's got bags of experience, and is very talented both in consultation and on his feet." "He has an intellect that can assimilate a lot of complex information, and then produce an argument that people can understand. That's his strength." **Recent work:** Acted in Ted Jacobs Engineering Group v RMJM, an action concerning the recovery of documents in Section 1 proceedings.

Heriot Currie QC A leading commercial silk with a broad practice. He represents clients in matters including pensions claims and planning matters. He has been successful in a number of complex, high-value matters before the Supreme Court. **Strengths:** "He is one of the foremost advocates of his generation." "He is very good at making difficult cases boil down to simple points. A formidable court advocate." **Recent work:** Acted against James Wolffe QC in a payment action in the Commercial Court worth over £4 million. The case concerned the procurement of a waste treatment plant.

Alastair Duncan QC Handles high-value finance disputes, acting for major banking clients on cutting-edge matters. He is adept in appeals brought to the Court of Session, and masterful in representing a broad spectrum of professional clients in commercial matters such as partnership disputes. **Strengths:** "He is extremely thorough and pragmatic in his approach. He's a particularly user-friendly advocate." "He does just feel like an extension of your team." **Recent work:** Acted in a high-profile class action concerning allegations of contaminated residential land.

Roddy Dunlop QC Undertakes a broad range of general commercial matters. His stellar reputation stems from his experience of instructions on some of the most high-profile matters in Scotland, before courts at every level of the Scottish legal system. **Strengths:** "He is a calm advocate, but he possesses a sharp intellect. You know that you will get the best advice from him." "He's a no-nonsense silk who demonstrates first-class courtroom skills. He is not afraid to give robust advice." **Recent work:** Acted for the pursuer in seeking the disposal of litigation on the basis of error, in a matter with major implications for the concept of unilateral uninduced error.

Mark Lindsay QC Handles major commercial disputes covering an array of matters, including contractual, property and shareholder disputes. Solicitors appreciate his knowledge as both a qualified advocate in Scotland and a qualified barrister in England and Wales. He also has the experience of regular appearances before the House of Lords and the Supreme Court. **Strengths:** "He has the ear of the court, and is able to give an accurate prediction of how things are going to turn out. He ensures you spend time and money on the right things." "He's like an old-fashioned silk in a very good sense – he's a leading commercial lawyer and litigator who is prepared to take on cases that may be slightly outside of his comfort zone, but he will do the research he needs to do, apply his advocacy skills, and invariably be successful!" **Recent work:** Acted as counsel against Alistair Clark QC in a contractual dispute between Scottish Enterprise and RBS.

James Mure QC (see p.679) Regularly instructed for major commercial issues involving construction, environmental and professional liability disputes. He was previously First Standing Junior Counsel to the Scottish government, and has built up a solid reputation in the marketplace. **Strengths:** "He is an intellectual advocate who has the ear of the court." "He is exceptionally thorough, and very bright. His written work and oral submissions are both superb." **Recent work:** Represented CGIS in suing BT for a large claim relating to the dilapidation of a large commercial property.

Lord Davidson of Glen Clova QC Vastly experienced in litigation, arbitration and mediation. His specialisms include commercial contract claims and construction and engineering disputes. **Strengths:** "His delivery of submissions in court is concise and effective." "He is very much on the client's level, and fights their corner." **Recent work:** Acted for lenders in a series of cases brought against solicitors in the commercial court of the Court of Session.

Jonathan Lake QC Acts for high-profile commercial clients in a range of fields, primarily in litigation, but also advises on non-contentious issues that may arise. His areas of specialism include IP and niche matters such as actions for reduction. **Strengths:** "He's a very impressive advocate, thorough and eloquent." "He has an ability to understand hugely complicated legal arguments and principles, and explain it in a very user-friendly way."

James McNeill QC Earns praise for his expertise in cases related to trusts. He is a noted mediator and serves as a judge in the Courts of Appeal in Jersey and Guernsey. **Strengths:** "He's an incredibly efficient advocate – he's straightforward to deal with."

Kenny McBrearty QC (see p.666) Recognised for his skill across a range of commercial dispute matters, with particular experience in professional negligence, recovery and contract disputes. He is praised by solicitors as a highly user-friendly advocate. **Strengths:** "He is really collaborative in his approach, and works as a team member. He has good judgement." "His style, whether in consultation or in court, is very laid-back and understated – but very, very effective." **Recent work:** Acted for the pursuer in the Commercial Court against former employees and their new employers in relation to the use of confidential information and breach of restrictive covenants.

JUNIORS

Garry Borland (see p.553) Has a broad commercial practice and undertakes a range of work, including professional negligence, property, contracts and construction disputes. He has represented many major clients in disputes, such as BP, Balfour Beatty and ConocoPhillips. **Strengths:** "His thoroughness is exceptional. On his feet, he is exceptionally good, and always well prepared." "He has an ability to immerse himself in the detail of large cases, which makes him a great choice for cases of particular complexity." **Recent work:** Led by Richard Keen QC in a complex administrators challenge to a number of foreign property investments.

Almira Delibegović-Broome Specialises in commercial law disputes, with a particular proficiency in cases with complicated evidential hearings. She also has a strong reputation in the insolvency field, and has appeared alone before both the Scottish Appeal Court and the Supreme Court. **Strengths:** "She's very good tactically, and recognised as being in the top few juniors at the Scottish Bar." **Recent work:** Defended in an administrator's pre-insolvency transaction challenge, including bringing a challenge before the ECHR.

Jonathan Barne Acts for major institutions from the energy sector and high-profile banking clients. He has practised before courts of all levels in commercial disputes, and wins praise for his skilled handling of evidential hearings. **Strengths:** "He is a very experienced junior. He's attentive to the client's needs and commercially minded." **Recent work:** Represented Lloyds Banking Group in an Inner House appeal and an appeal to the Supreme Court. The matter concerned the interpretation of a covenant granted to a charity, and whether unforeseen changes to accounting standards will affect the percentage due to the charity.

Roisin Higgins (see p.626) A commercial litigator recognised for her expertise on IP matters. She is well versed in handling matters in arbitration, the Sheriff Court and the Court of Session. Commentators note that her prior career as a solicitor in major commercial firms in Edinburgh has given her superb client-handling skills. **Strengths:** "She is very user-friendly, and very good with clients."

David Thomson (see p.737) Practises exclusively in commercial and public law, and is known as a specialist in insolvency and property disputes. His experience encompasses regular appearances before the UK Supreme Court and the Court of Session. **Strengths:** "He is a hard-working and impressive advocate." "He is a very astute commercial lawyer." **Recent work:** Defended Forthflat against a claim by Morrison & Mutch Property Investments, in relation to remedies sought under the Companies Act.

Ross McClelland (see p.667) A former solicitor whose depth of commercial litigation experience belies his relatively junior year of call. He focuses on commercial dispute matters, and is regularly instructed in professional negligence and property claims. **Strengths:** "He impresses with the depth of his preparation. You expect a dedicated advocate, but he's just incredibly meticulous." "He's one of the best young juniors doing commercial work."

Euan Duthie (see p.592) Has a broad commercial practice covering a wide range of areas, including contractual and property disputes, in addition to handling professional negligence claims against professionals such as surveyors. He has also been instructed to represent insolvency practitioners in liquidation procedures. **Strengths:** "He is a sensible, solid commercial practitioner who is very good with clients." **Recent work:** Acted in the Court of Session in a dispute between Heritable Bank and Landsbanki, related to claims said to be extinguished under foreign insolvency.

Chris Paterson Has a broad commercial practice focused on professional liability matters. **Strengths:** "He is an approachable and pragmatic advocate." **Recent work:** Represented the petitioner against Dunbar Asset, seeking to have a European Enforcement Order reduced.

Martin Richardson Has a commercial practice focused on professional negligence and construction disputes. He is also instructed in financial services disputes on behalf of both pursuers and defenders. **Strengths:** "He's technically extremely able, but also able to translate that into good, solid commercial advice." "He is one of the juniors who garners a lot of respect from the Bench, particularly from the Court of Session." **Recent work:** Instructed on behalf of the shareholders of Rangers International FC in obtaining an interim interdict to delay an AGM.

Paul O'Brien (see p.683) A commercial litigator noted for his expertise in IP and insolvency law. He is an experienced advocate who regularly appears in the Court of Session commercial court. **Strengths:** "You can rely on him to provide you with a thorough analysis of the legal principles." "He has the ear of the court – he's not afraid to stand up against strong questioning or challenges." **Recent work:** Acted for Farstad Supply in a complex damages claim relating to a fire on board a ship.

Morag Ross Focuses on litigation relating to freedom of information, and has presented cases in the Supreme Court. She is praised for her work in public law and pensions litigation. **Strengths:** "She is excellent. Really bright and thorough." **Recent work:** Represented petitioners HFD Construction in a challenge against Aberdeen City Council relating to the selection of a preferred bidder for the sale of a council building.

Alasdair McKenzie Has considerable experience in construction disputes, including defect claims and liquidated damages. He has acted for a variety of professionals within the sector, such as employers and contractors. **Strengths:** "He's very thorough, and very good at turning work around quickly, and his considered strategy is combined with a commercial approach." **Recent work:** Instructed to act on behalf of an individual against RBS in a matter concerning a disputed collateral warranty.

Gavin Walker Focuses on professional liability, property and IP disputes arising from the construction sector. **Strengths:** "He has three very strong facets: he knows the law, he's very good in court, and clients like him." "If you give him something, he likes to get stuck in, and he likes to win." **Recent work:** Acted with Heriot Currie QC in opposition to shareholders of Rangers International FC in their attempt to interdict an annual club meeting and enforce their shareholder rights.

Susan Ower (see p.688) Specialises on matters which encompass both commercial and insolvency aspects. She is also regularly instructed in disputes regarding property and contracts. **Strengths:** "She discharges very difficult briefs with considerable ability." "She's a very effective examiner of witnesses, without being aggressive." **Recent work:** Acted for Search Consultancy in its action for recovery of confidential information and property.

Band 2

Ampersand

See profile on p.896

THE SET

A prominent stable offering commercial advice to a wide range of business clients. It is home to a number of vastly experienced commercial advocates, and these highly rated counsel work with clients across an array of disputes, including those relating to construction, insolvency, IP and professional negligence.

Client service: "The clerking, led by Alan Moffat, is very professional. The service is very good in terms of the speed of responses, the knowledge of the advocates' practices and of who's there and who's available, and even making alternative suggestions, checking diaries and so on – they're just an excellent team."

SILKS

Robert Howie QC Handles complex commercial cases relating to shipping litigation and insurance disputes. He receives regular instructions from high-profile international clients. **Strengths:** "His thoroughness and knowledge are second to none." "He is one of the cleverest advocates at the Scottish Bar. He's near the top of the pile in terms of quality commercial work."

Craig Sandison QC A veteran commercial silk who is regularly instructed in disputes relating to insolvency, IP, contracts and commercial property. **Strengths:** "He really is an outstanding advocate. He fights his corner extremely well for his clients." "He is tenacious and brilliantly clever."

Ronald Clancy QC Has a broad commercial practice covering a wide range of commercial disputes. He is also noted for his expertise in clinical negligence and personal injury claims. **Strengths:** "He is collaborative, accessible and passionate. He really fights his corner, and he is terrific to work with." "Has a highly developed sense of ethics, and is excellent with clients."

David Sellar QC Offers clients advice across a wide range of commercial matters. He is noted for his expertise in insolvency and company law disputes. **Strengths:** "He is a premier insolvency and corporate lawyer. He knows it inside out." "He's very good at commercial matters, and has a very good reputation."

Robert Weir QC Has a broad commercial practice and is particularly noted for his expertise in disputes arising within maritime law. He is a stellar advocate, and draws praise from peers for his skilled cross-examination. **Strengths:** "He has an amazing grasp of lots of different areas of law."

JUNIORS

Jane Smith Receives instructions on the most technically complex and challenging commercial matters. **Strengths:** "She is absolutely brilliant. She is quite often the junior of choice in the very big stuff, led by the very top silks."

Other Ranked Lawyers

Andrew Young QC (see p.757) (Arnot Manderson) Widely praised for his ability to provide advice that blends comprehensive legal knowledge and an understanding of the commercial realities facing the client. His practice encompasses a range of commercial disputes, including those relating to professional negligence, recovery and insolvency. **Strengths:** "He is well respected and well known, and has an extremely good command of commercial law." **Recent work:** Represented HMRC in its challenge to the validity of the aggregates levy in relation to EU competition law.

Eric Robertson (see p.709) (Arnot Manderson) Focuses on disputes arising from professional negligence, insolvency and commercial property. **Strengths:** "He's very easy to deal with and a joy to work with."

Michael Howlin QC (Hastie Stable) A true specialist in commercial litigation who is also highlighted for his expertise in insolvency and company law disputes. **Strengths:** "He's excellent. He understands the commercial side of it, and is very, very clever."

Gavin MacColl (Hastie Stable) A fantastic advocate with a tenacious and strategic style of advocacy. He has a broad practice encompassing matters related to property, insolvency and construction disputes, with a particular focus on contract law. **Strengths:** "He is client-focused, and goes the extra mile. He has the ear of the court and has outstanding legal skills." "He's very strong and has a good presence in court. He doesn't get ruffled, and is very thorough."

Roy Martin QC (see p.664) (Terra Firma Chambers) Handles high-value commercial matters, including fraud and partnership disputes. **Strengths:** "He is well regarded for his robust and thorough approach to cases – he's not one to shy away from a challenge." "He is a standout senior, particularly experienced in planning and property matters. Clients like him and he is well known in the Scottish commercial world as a go-to counsel." **Recent work:** Acted as senior counsel for North Lanarkshire Council in a Supreme Court matter against L Batley Pet Products. The matter arose from dilapidations and notice of lease termination.

Gordon Reid QC (see p.706) (Terra Firma Chambers) Noted for his expertise in a broad range of commercial matters, with a particular emphasis on real estate disputes. **Strengths:** "He's very knowledgeable, and extremely able in court." "He commands a great deal of respect for his attention to detail and his innovative thinking." **Recent work:** Acted in Calthorpe's Trustees v G Hamilton, a dispute over the title to commercial land in a quarry area.

Nick Ellis QC (see p.595) (Westwater Advocates) Has a broad commercial practice covering disputes relating to construction, engineering and commercial contracts. **Strengths:** "He is superb and regarded as a top-bracket advocate." "He really gets to grips with things, and gives his clients a real sense of direction." **Recent work:** Acted in Apolla Engineering v James Scott, a major engineering contract dispute arising before the UK Supreme Court.

Calum MacNeill QC (see p.660) (Westwater Advocates) Has a broad commercial practice that encompasses construction and employment law. **Strengths:** "He gets to grips very quickly with the technical aspects of a case." **Recent work:** Defended Euro Pools against a professional negligence claim by Country Leisure worth £2.8 million.

Jonathan Brown (Westwater Advocates) Has a broad commercial practice with considerable expertise in cases relating to professional discipline. **Recent work:** Acted in a dispute relating to the sale of RSM Tenon to Baker Tilly. He defended the attempt of both companies to enforce contractual restrictions on former RSM Tenon employees.

COMPANY

Company Scotland
Leading Stables
Band 1
Axiom Advocates *
Leading Silks
Band 1
Keen Richard *Axiom Advocates*
Sellar David *Ampersand (ORL)* ◊
Band 2
Currie Heriot *Axiom Advocates*
Howlin Michael P *Hastie Stable (ORL)* ◊
Leading Juniors
Band 1
Thomson David *Axiom Advocates* *

Band 1

Axiom Advocates
See profile on p.898
THE SET
Axiom Advocates is the leading stable for commercial law in the Scottish Bar, known as "the first port of call for commercial matters." Its members represent companies and individuals in corporate and contractual disputes in both public and private sectors. Barristers at Axiom also act in an advisory capacity, assisting with matters such as commercial petitions and corporate acquisitions.
Client service: "Lesley Flynn leads a very good clerking team. They are very helpful; it's very clear who does what."

SILKS
Richard Keen QC Acts on behalf of corporations and individuals. He specialises in commercial litigation, and is considered one of the Scottish Bar's leading advocates. **Strengths:** "He is very charismatic and an extremely strong courtroom performer." "He is one of the most sought-after QCs in commercial matters." **Recent work:** Acted for former Rangers FC director Paul Murray in a dispute regarding the football club's obligations surrounding its AGM.

Heriot Currie QC Handles a wide variety of matters, including construction, professional negligence and competition. He is very well regarded for representing companies and individuals in court, and also offers expertise in ADR. **Strengths:** "He has a gravitas about him. He is highly authoritative."

JUNIORS
David Thomson (see p.737) Practises in commercial litigation, including matters of insolvency, property and professional negligence. He is a highly respected junior with experience of matters involving government departments. **Strengths:** "He produces very helpful opinions indeed; he comes up with some novel lines of argument." "He is very busy and well instructed." **Recent work:** Acted for HM Secretary of State for Business, Innovation & Skills in a disqualification case against a former director.

Other Ranked Lawyers

David Sellar QC (Ampersand) Enjoys a reputation as a highly experienced adviser, especially on insolvency matters. He also makes applications to court on broader company matters. **Strengths:** "He is recognised as one of the leading experts in insolvency in Scotland." "He has made a name for himself through his expertise in company and insolvency work."

Michael Howlin QC (Hastie Stable) Specialises in company law and commercial litigation. He maintains his reputation for strong work in directors' and shareholders' disputes. **Strengths:** "He is very straightforward to work with, and a very effective cross-examiner."

CONSTRUCTION

Construction Scotland
Leading Stables
Band 1
Axiom Advocates *
Leading Silks
Band 1
Currie Heriot *Axiom Advocates*
Howie Robert *Ampersand (ORL)* ◊
Keen Richard *Axiom Advocates*
Reid J Gordon *Terra Firma Chambers (ORL)* ◊ *
Band 2
Ellis Nick *Westwater Advocates (ORL)* ◊ *
Wolffe James *Axiom Advocates* *
Leading Juniors
Band 1
Borland Garry *Axiom Advocates* *
Richardson Martin H *Axiom Advocates*
Band 2
Barne Jonathan *Axiom Advocates*
Broome Jonathan *Axiom Advocates*
McKenzie Alasdair *Axiom Advocates*
Walker Gavin *Axiom Advocates*
◊ *(ORL) = Other Ranked Lawyer.*
* *Indicates firm / individual with profile.*

Band 1

Axiom Advocates
See profile on p.898
THE SET
Axiom Advocates remains widely recognised as the leading set in Scotland for construction disputes and has an enviable list of expert advocates who have maintained a high-value caseload. This dominant stable acts on a wide range of construction and engineering matters, and is noted for its expertise on matters in the energy industry. The stable has also developed a reputation for handling construction cases with a professional negligence angle.
Client service: "The clerks, led by Lesley Flynn, are really proactive. They are the kind of clerks you can go to with a problem and they will give you a portfolio of counsel who are able to help."

SILKS
Heriot Currie QC One of the top construction advocates at the Scottish Bar. He has a broad range of experience across several commercial fields and continues to attract standout construction cases. **Strengths:** "He is very good on his feet. He is a heavyweight advocate." **Recent work:** Acted as lead QC for the defenders in a high-profile dispute over the tunnel collapse at the Glendoe hydroelectric scheme.

Richard Keen QC Recognised as a leader in construction. He is particularly praised for his advocacy style and brings a wealth of experience to complex and high-profile construction disputes. **Strengths:** "He is an outstanding advocate. He is very confident and has an easy style of presenting complex arguments to make them sound simple." "He is good at outlining his position to the court and dealing with points of reply." **Recent work:** Instructed in the major engineering dispute between SSE Generation and HOCHTIEF Solutions regarding the Glendoe hydroelectric tunnel collapse.

James Wolffe QC (see p.755) Known as a standout QC in the market, as supported by his election as the dean of the Faculty of Advocates. He acts on a range of construction disputes of significant value, and also attracts praise for his work involving European issues. **Strengths:** "He is one of the best commercial QCs in Scotland." **Recent work:** Successfully defended the enforcement of an adjudicator's award on grounds that the enforcement would be a breach of natural justice and of Convention rights.

JUNIORS
Martin Richardson Highly commended for his practical attitude, which sources attribute to the experience gained during his time as a solicitor. He has a dedicated following of solicitors and clients who instruct him on construction and construction-related professional negligence disputes. **Strengths:** "His written work is absolutely exemplary." "He has a very calm demeanour, commands a lot of respect and is very unflappable." **Recent work:** Instructed to pursue a £1 million technical defects claim against a contractor and other professionals relating to a social housing contract in Orkney.

Garry Borland (see p.553) Known as a go-to junior for complex construction work and as "one of the best junior counsel in the Scottish market." His practical, hands-on approach is praised by instructing solicitors as being particularly appropriate for adjudications. He also has a growing arbitration practice. **Strengths:** "He has strong technical skills and is an able and confident advocate." "He has a very thorough, analytical brain." **Recent work:** Acted in a dispute, valued at approximately £5 million, relating to defects at a large leisure facility.

Alasdair McKenzie Recognised as a strong construction junior by instructing solicitors. He acts on a broad range of construction disputes, such as defect and payment claims, for both defendants and pursuers. **Recent work:** Acted against fellow Axiom advocates in a social housing defects claim in Orkney, valued at £1 million.

Jonathan Barne Instructed in an increasing amount of big-ticket litigation. He is held in high esteem by senior peers for his construction work, as well as more general commercial cases. **Strengths:** "He has years of experience, and is an absolutely excellent advocate – and he's friendly as well!" **Recent work:** Instructed on behalf of an asbestos removal contractor in a defence and counterclaim following the rescinding of a contract by Marshall Construction.

Jonathan Broome A former solicitor now recognised by fellow advocates as a strong construction junior. The sheer volume of his industry knowledge is particularly noted by sources. **Strengths:** "He's incredibly bright and enthusiastic. He's good on tactics, and his specialist area is construction and he knows it inside out." **Recent work:** Acted for Halcrow Waterman on defending a significant claim by RBS for design flaws in the Gemini Building in Edinburgh.

Gavin Walker A former solicitor who acts regularly on behalf of construction companies as well as architects, surveyors and other professional practitioners. His extensive construction professional negligence work is well recognised in the market. **Strengths:** "He is very personable and user-friendly." "His written work is very thorough and I trust him fundamentally." **Recent work:** Defended a £10 million defects claim brought by the owner and tenants of an office block in Glasgow.

Other Ranked Lawyers

Robert Howie QC (Ampersand) A top advocate who attracts praise across the board for his diverse practice, which covers heavyweight building contract and engineering disputes. His technical and written skills are singled out for praise. **Strengths:** "A really great lawyer who is deserving of his great reputation and an opponent to be reckoned with." "He is very good at marshalling and dealing with legal arguments." **Recent work:** Acted for the pursuer against a civil engineering group in relation to a significant design and construction defects claim.

Gordon Reid QC (see p.706) (Terra Firma Chambers) Has a strong market reputation for his expertise in construction and property litigation. He is also a member of the English Bar and his expertise in Scottish construction law is often sought by solicitors practising in London. **Strengths:** "He is thorough and has a good reputation for attention to detail." "He quickly gets to grips with difficult issues."

Nick Ellis QC (see p.595) (Westwater Advocates) Has a broad practice encompassing construction contract and negligence cases, as well as wider commercial work. He receives consistent praise for his practical and user-friendly approach. **Recent work:** Acted for the respondent in a case concerning an engineering contract which reached the Supreme Court.

EMPLOYMENT

Employment Scotland	
Leading Silks	
Star individuals	
Napier Brian	*Hastie Stable (ORL)* ◊
Band 1	
MacNeill Calum H S	*Westwater Advocates (ORL)* ◊ *
Leading Juniors	
Band 1	
Hardman Alasdair	*Hastie Stable (ORL)* ◊
Band 2	
Cameron Donald	*Westwater Advocates (ORL)* ◊ *
Grant-Hutchison Peter	*Terra Firma Chambers (ORL)* ◊ *
McGuire Kenneth	*Westwater Advocates (ORL)* ◊
Stobart Alice	*Westwater Advocates (ORL)* ◊
Band 3	
Casey Juliette	*Westwater Advocates (ORL)* ◊ *
Hay David	*Westwater Advocates (ORL)* ◊ *
◊ (ORL) = Other Ranked Lawyer.	
** Indicates stable / individual with profile.*	

Ranked Lawyers

Brian Napier QC (Hastie Stable) Stands alone as the most highly regarded employment counsel at the Scottish Bar and remains the only dedicated specialist in this market. He appears in both English and Scottish jurisdictions on contractual breaches, discrimination and unfair dismissal cases, and is many clients' first choice for Employment Tribunal representation. **Strengths:** "He is highly technical, commercial and unflappable." "He has an extensive breadth of knowledge and great litigation skills." "You should instruct him where the creation of a novel argument or lateral thinking is required."

Alasdair Hardman (Hastie Stable) Noted for his strong business background and his commercially astute advice. He has worked on unfair dismissals, discrimination, contractual and trade disputes in addition to casework relating to zero hour contracts. **Strengths:** "He has a good style of advocacy and is clever at whittling down the main points." "He provides advocacy from an intellectual perspective." "He is highly recommended for the more complex matters."

Peter Grant-Hutchison (see p.614) (Terra Firma Chambers) Involved with employment law in a number of capacities, including as a judge and sheriff on the mental health tribunal. He has a wealth of experience in all matters relating to union work and has been instructed on a number of unfair dismissal cases in the education sector. **Strengths:** "He is very good with the client and down to earth."

Calum MacNeill QC (see p.660) (Westwater Advocates) Regularly instructed on cases involving interdict or damages actions by both solicitors and clients from the medical and local government sectors. Peers regard him as a commercial specialist with additional expertise in restrictive covenants, personal injury matters and constrictive disputes. **Strengths:** "If you wanted a commercial counsel you would use him." "He tests the mood and tailors his advice to where the conversation is going." **Recent work:** Instructed by Digby Brown on behalf of the GMB claimants in an equal pay case concerning more than 100 employees.

Donald Cameron (see p.563) (Westwater Advocates) Predominantly acts in contentious employment cases and frequently appears at both the EAT and the Inner House of the Court of Session. He has experience of employment disputes both north and south of the border, and handles a range of cases including unfair dismissals and issues surrounding the Equality Act. **Strengths:** "He is very organised and comes back with detailed lines of evidence." "His intellectual ability and good manner with clients continue to impress." **Recent work:** Represented employer Perry & Hamilton at the Inner House of the Court of Session where the Inner House reinstated the previous decision of the EAT regarding the subject of costs.

Kenneth McGuire (Westwater Advocates) An experienced advocate who maintains a strong general employment practice. He is regularly instructed in equal pay cases, and draws considerable praise for his ability to maintain a calm demeanour in difficult cases. **Strengths:** "He is a sensible and pragmatic advocate."

Alice Stobart (Westwater Advocates) Commended for her expertise in equal pay litigation and for the high-quality written work she produces for her clients. She frequently works on behalf of insurers and has also represented health boards in the recent past. **Strengths:** "Clients find her a pleasure to deal with." "She is someone to rely upon; she gets her preparation correct and produces good material."

Juliette Casey (see p.566) (Westwater Advocates) Has a strong practice that covers a range of different employment law areas. She undertakes significant work in European law and secures regular instructions on equal pay cases. She has additional experience in discrimination case law and frequently represents clients in unfair dismissal trials. **Strengths:** "She is very effective in a courtroom setting."

David Hay (see p.622) (Westwater Advocates) Represents both employees and employers in tribunal cases and is primarily known in the market for his contentious casework and involvement at the EAT. He receives instructions in employment disputes from a range of both public and private sector clients, including local authorities, NHS trusts and media groups. **Strengths:** "He is very good at analysing situations." "If you are looking for written work he is your man – he goes into a good level of detail."

FAMILY/MATRIMONIAL

Family/Matrimonial Scotland
Leading Stables
Band 1
Westwater Advocates *
Leading Silks
Star individuals
Scott Janys M *Westwater Advocates* *
Band 1
Dowdalls Catherine *Arnot Manderson (ORL)* ◇
Mitchell Jonathan J *Arnot Manderson (ORL)* ◇
Leading Juniors
Star individuals
Innes Ruth *Westwater Advocates* *
Band 1
Brabender Lynda J *Westwater Advocates* *
Jack David *Hastie Stable (ORL)* ◇
Speir John *Westwater Advocates* *
Band 2
Clark Marie H *Arnot Manderson (ORL)* ◇
Hayhow Robert *Westwater Advocates*
Loudon Mary *Westwater Advocates*
Malcolm Kirsty *Westwater Advocates* *
Wild Alison *Westwater Advocates* *
Band 3
Macfarlane Ross P *Mackinnon Advocates (ORL)* ◇
◇ (ORL) = Other Ranked Lawyer.
** Indicates firm / individual with profile.*

Band 1

Westwater Advocates

See profile on p.901

THE SET

With a high concentration of outstanding dedicated family law advocates, Westwater Advocates is widely known as the go-to stable at the Scottish Bar for family-related legal issues. Its members act on the full range of family cases, from high-value claims for financial provision post-divorce to child care cases. **Client service:** "They are really gifted advocates; it is exceptional to listen to them analyse a case. They're good with clients and the clerking is excellent."

SILKS

Janys Scott QC (see p.716) Sources praise her as an absolute authority on family law at the Scottish Bar. She regularly appears at the Inner House and Outer House of the Court of Session, and has made successful appeals to the Supreme Court. She has particular expertise in matters relating to child care and financial cases arising from family disputes. **Strengths:** "She has vast experience of the field, and is extremely knowledgeable and effective in court." "Her knowledge of the area is encyclopaedic and her memory is incredible."

JUNIORS

Ruth Innes (see p.635) Leads the pack when it comes to cases concerning divorce proceedings, cohabitation negotiations and child relocation matters. She handles the full range of family law issues, but is particularly highly noted for her expertise in high-value financial provisions in divorce cases. **Strengths:** "Her technical knowledge of the law is second to none. The judges all completely trust her." "Her attention to detail and her willingness to provide advice are first-class." **Recent work:** Acted on behalf of the husband in a high-value divorce proceeding resisting a claim for the provision of £20,000 a month to the wife.

Lynda Brabender (see p.554) Recommended for her niche expertise in cohabitation, adoption and children matters. She is a go-to lawyer in Scotland for both advisory and advocacy work, and is often instructed to lead on high-value divorce proceedings. **Strengths:** "A first choice in both financial provision and child-related cases on account of her excellent analytical ability, her pleasant and unflappable manner and her forensic skills." "She is a powerhouse of energy and ability."

John Speir (see p.726) Provides both advice and advocacy relating to child relocation, cohabitation and financial provision cases. **Strengths:** "He is able to think strategically, and doesn't lose sight of the client's objectives. He leaves no stone unturned." "He has an ability to look at a case from a different angle. He fights his client's corner." **Recent work:** Acted on the Whigham v Owen matter, a much-publicised Court of Session case that returned the largest award for a cohabitant in Scotland.

Mary Loudon A former solicitor who has developed a broad family practice at the Bar. Instructing solicitors are quick to praise her expertise in adoption and child protection work. **Strengths:** "She is very good with clients and on her feet."

Alison Wild (see p.751) A former solicitor noted for her empathetic client manner and strong advocacy skills. **Strengths:** "She has a very nice manner and is very knowledgeable and skilled." **Recent work:** Successfully represented the defender in a complex relocation case that involved a child abduction.

Robert Hayhow Has a broad practice covering a wide range of civil litigation. In the family law field he is noted for his considerable expertise on financial provision in divorce cases. **Strengths:** "He is meticulous in his preparation, reads everything thoroughly, gives excellent advice and is very straight-talking." "He is excellent in court, very resilient and assured. A great guy to have in your corner." **Recent work:** Acted in Whigham v Owen matter, a much-publicised Court of Session case that returned the largest award for a cohabitant in Scotland.

Kirsty Malcolm (see p.661) Has a broad family law practice encompassing high-value divorce cases, child abduction, adoption and residence disputes. She is developing expertise in complex cohabitation cases, an emerging niche in the family law practice area. **Strengths:** "She has a good knowledge and a firm grasp of the law." **Recent work:** Acted on a complex cohabitation dispute concerning the issue of time bar in respect of a claim under Section 28 of the Family Law (Scotland) Act 2006.

Other Ranked Lawyers

Catherine Dowdalls QC (Arnot Manderson) A specialist family law practitioner who appears in the Sheriff Courts across Scotland and has appeared at the UK Supreme Court in relation to Scottish appeal cases. She undertakes a wide range of family law claims, including financial provision on divorce, cases concerning provision for children, and cases relating to international child abduction. **Strengths:** "She has an excellent understanding of the law and of people, which is crucial. She is a welcome addition to the senior Bar." "She is outstanding. She makes even the most complicated things easy for clients." **Recent work:** She acted on a claim concerning financial provision for a former cohabitant, which was the first case of its kind decided at the Supreme Court.

Jonathan Mitchell QC (Arnot Manderson) Focuses his family law practice principally on high-value divorce cases. **Strengths:** "He really thinks outside the box. He provides very creative solutions."

Marie Clark (Arnot Manderson) Focuses her practice on the children side of family law. Solicitors and peers praise her measured approach and tenacity in pursuing a case. **Strengths:** "She is very straightforward and a sympathetic soul who has a lovely manner with clients. Underneath she is absolutely ruthless, which is the perfect combination."

David Jack (Hastie Stable) Covers a wide range of family law issues, including divorce provision, child abduction (both domestic and international) and child abuse. Sources praise his tenacious advocacy style and the depth of his experience. **Strengths:** "One of the best advocates in Scotland for child cases."

Ross Macfarlane (Mackinnon Advocates) Noted by peers for his innovative style in court and his considerable experience in child-related disputes, Macfarlane is a well-respected advocate in the family law arena. **Strengths:** "He is a highly creative advocate."

HEALTH & SAFETY

Health & Safety Scotland
Leading Stables
Band 1
Compass Chambers *
Leading Silks
Star individuals
Gray Peter *Compass Chambers* *
Leading Juniors
Band 1
Anderson Gavin *Westwater Advocates (ORL)* ◊ *
Smith Barry *Compass Chambers* *
Band 2
Duff Susan *Compass Chambers* *
Macleod Murdo *Compass Chambers* *

Band 1

Compass Chambers
See profile on p.899

THE SET

The stable has a specialist regulatory crime team that focuses on health and safety, environmental and corporate financial crime. It offers bespoke training sessions for firms and solicitors, in addition to annual conferences in Edinburgh, Glasgow and Aberdeen. Market sources believe the stable's unrivalled expertise ensures that it remains the market leader for health and safety work in Scotland.

Client service: "The clerks, led by Gavin Herd, are very flexible and amenable to commercial negotiation. There has never been an issue with fee agreements."

SILKS

Peter Gray QC (see p.614) Widely regarded as the pre-eminent regulatory advocate in Scotland, he has a history of representing prominent clients. He is noted for his expertise in regulatory issues in a number of industry sectors, including oil, construction and retail. **Strengths:** "He gives a silky smooth performance. He can walk the rope between the technical and legal aspects very well." "He has a wide understanding and is very user-friendly." **Recent work:** Advised SSE in relation to a potential prosecution regarding the death of a contractor by electrocution.

JUNIORS

Barry Smith (see p.723) Has a regulatory practice with a significant emphasis on health and safety, particularly in cases concerning fatalities. His expertise covers a range of industries, involving but not limited to cases arising from the agricultural sector and wind farms. **Strengths:** "He is good at responding to last-minute instructions." "He is a clever guy who is an excellent counsel from start to finish." **Recent work:** Advised the Scottish Fire & Rescue Service in relation to the death of a fire-fighter.

Susan Duff (see p.591) Primarily focuses on defence work, and acts for both corporate clients and individual defendants. She is particularly highly regarded for her expertise in cases relating to food safety. **Strengths:** "She is a formidable advocate."

Murdo Macleod (see p.660) Specialises in health and safety and general regulatory crime, with a caseload that includes high-profile work. **Strengths:** "He's very user-friendly and very good on his feet."

Other Ranked Lawyers

Gavin Anderson (see p.535) (Westwater Advocates) Exclusively acts for the defendant, and has a great reputation for handling cases relating to death and serious injury. His caseload is split between health and safety and environmental work. **Strengths:** "He is excellent in court." "He has the confidence of clients." **Recent work:** Acted on a case regarding a workplace injury suffered at an unsafe manufacturing plant.

IMMIGRATION

Immigration Scotland
Leading Silks
Band 1
Drummond Lorna *Axiom Advocates (ORL)* ◊
Lindsay Mark *Axiom Advocates (ORL)* ◊
Leading Juniors
Band 1
Bryce Joseph *Hastie Stable (ORL)* ◊
Caskie Alan *Hastie Stable (ORL)* ◊
Winter Stephen *Terra Firma Chambers (ORL)* ◊ *
Up-and-coming individuals
Byrne Daniel *Axiom Advocates (ORL)* ◊ 🅰
◊ (ORL) = Other Ranked Lawyer.
🅰 direct access (see p.11).
** Indicates stable / individual with profile.*

Ranked Lawyers

Lorna Drummond QC (Axiom Advocates) This dynamic immigration advocate makes her debut in the rankings on the back of her strong human rights and judicial review practice. She regularly appears in appeals at the Supreme Court and is also noted for her work on behalf of the Scottish government. **Strengths:** "Her great merit as an advocate is subtlety – she is able to see the complexities and she is someone who speaks really well in court." **Recent work:** Acted in Joy Balogun v SSHD, a judicial review relating to trafficking and the ECHR.

Mark Lindsay QC (Axiom Advocates) An experienced advocate whose expertise is called upon for the most complex of immigration matters. **Strengths:** "He is a great opponent to deal with. He is very able in court and fearless in his advocacy." **Recent work:** Acted in Fleury Zoumbas v SSHD, a Supreme Court appeal regarding the UN Convention on the Rights of the Child.

Daniel Byrne (Axiom Advocates) Has an extensive immigration and public law practice, which encompasses high-level appeals and judicial review matters. He also counsels the Scottish government and the Equality & Human Rights Commission. **Strengths:** "He is an absolute pleasure to work with – he is inventive, thorough and a great thinker."

Joseph Bryce (Hastie Stable) Has a broad immigration practice, and receives instructions from both petitioners and the government. He is noted for his expertise in refugee cases, and he founded LSA Brown's Refugee Legal Project. **Strengths:** "He is very experienced and utterly dedicated. He has enormous empathy with clients."

Alan Caskie (Hastie Stable) Covers a wide range of immigration and asylum issues. He is praised by market commentators for his experience in judicial reviews. **Strengths:** "He is a good advocate – his success rate is great. He recognises which cases are good to run."

Stephen Winter (see p.755) (Terra Firma Chambers) A talented barrister whose practice covers a wide range of immigration and public law matters.

INFORMATION TECHNOLOGY

Information Technology Scotland
Leading Silks
Band 1
Mitchell Iain G *Arnot Manderson (ORL)* ◊ *

Ranked Lawyers

Iain Mitchell QC (see p.674) (Arnot Manderson) Has a stellar reputation at the Bar for his expertise in open source software and public procurement. He is on the EC committee on cloud computing and represents the UK at the Council of Bars & Law Societies of Europe. **Strengths:** "He is very knowledgeable and good at having a multi-pronged approach. He can view a situation from a different point of view and see the opportunities." "He has both the hard and soft skills to do his job well." **Recent work:** He acted for a defendant in an alleged infringement of copyright case, which explored decompiling and unauthorised modification to software, and ownership rights to bespoke operating systems within the field of microprocessors.

INTELLECTUAL PROPERTY

Intellectual Property Scotland
Leading Stables
Band 1
Axiom Advocates *
Leading Silks
Band 1
Currie Heriot *Axiom Advocates*
Lake Jonathan C *Axiom Advocates*
Band 2
Mitchell Iain G *Arnot Manderson (ORL)* ◊ *
Sandison Craig *Ampersand (ORL)* ◊
Leading Juniors
Band 1
Higgins Roisin *Axiom Advocates* *
O'Brien Paul *Axiom Advocates* *
Band 2
Walker Gavin *Axiom Advocates*

Band 1

Axiom Advocates
See profile on p.898
THE SET
Axiom Advocates continues to be the dominant force of the Scottish IP Bar. Its silks and juniors consistently handle a variety of complex cases, ranging from trade mark and copyright infringements to patent disputes. It is the go-to stable for many, due to the user-friendly nature of its clerks and advocates, which has led to it being described as "one of the most commercial of the stables in Scotland."
Client service: "The clerks are good at getting back to you really quickly. They are very responsive in terms of getting costs and arrangements agreed."

SILKS
Heriot Currie QC Extremely well-regarded advocate with a vast amount of experience on sophisticated IP cases. He is particularly well known for his work on patent infringement matters. **Strengths:** "He is one of Scotland's leading silks and is very experienced in patent disputes." "He is extremely impressive when cross-examining witnesses in court."

Jonathan Lake QC Possesses an impressively broad IP practice, though he is especially renowned for his work on cases involving pharmaceutical and technology patents. He is universally well respected, and sources praise his "excellent eye for detail." **Strengths:** "He is a very good QC with a brilliant mind and excellent litigation instincts." "He is very good at simplifying complex cases. He produces excellent written work and is very sharp in court." **Recent work:** He represented Sky Broadcasting Group in various copyright cases brought against the owners of several licensed establishments.

JUNIORS
Paul O'Brien (see p.683) An experienced junior with considerable expertise across the full range of IP matters. He is noted for his meticulous approach and attention to detail. **Strengths:** "He is exceptionally well prepared in terms of being able to present in front of the judge." "He is very thorough, with good attention to detail, but he is also a practical and commercial advocate." **Recent work:** He acted for Girl Norma Shellfish in a passing off action brought against MacGillivray's Seafood, concerning the colour of the latter establishment.

Roisin Higgins (see p.626) Enjoys an enviable standing at the Scottish IP Bar, with recognised abilities in a whole host of cases including patent and trade mark disputes. **Strengths:** "She is very commercial and good at identifying clients' key objectives and tailoring her advice accordingly."

Gavin Walker A commercial advocate who is establishing a reputation for expertise in soft IP cases. **Strengths:** "He is quick to grasp complex matters and is good in court."

Other Ranked Lawyers

Craig Sandison QC (Ampersand) Proficient in handling a range of commercial matters, with IP being a particular area of focus. He is noted for his involvement in prominent patent and copyright infringement cases. **Strengths:** "He is razor-sharp, with a suitably aggressive approach." "His presentation of cases in court is persuasive. He has good advocacy skills."

Iain Mitchell QC (see p.674) (Arnot Manderson) Has a unique focus on IT-related IP matters. Recent work includes software licensing and copyright infringement cases. **Strengths:** "He is a very able advocate who likes to get his teeth into the challenging cases." **Recent work:** He represented Stepper Technology in a copyright infringement case involving the software used for the development of silicon chips.

MEDIA LAW

Media Law Scotland
Leading Silks
Band 1
Clancy Ronald *Ampersand (ORL)* ◊
Clark Alistair *Axiom Advocates (ORL)* ◊
Dunlop Roddy *Axiom Advocates (ORL)* ◊
Leading Juniors
Band 1
Campbell Ewen *Axiom Advocates (ORL)* ◊ *
Hamilton Duncan *Arnot Manderson (ORL)* ◊ *
* *Indicates stable / individual with profile.*
◊ *(ORL) = Other Ranked Lawyer.*

Ranked Lawyers

Ronald Clancy QC (Ampersand) Handles a range of civil and commercial disputes, and is particularly noted for his expertise at the intersection of human rights and media law. He is highly regarded for his work relating to freedom of the press. **Strengths:** "He has a great courtroom presence and really cares about his clients." "He is a fearsome opponent and a very good all-round advocate."

Duncan Hamilton (see p.618) (Arnot Manderson) Highlighted for his in-depth knowledge across the full breadth of media matters, he has experience handling issues relating to media coverage of court proceedings. He acts for high-profile individuals, newspapers and broadcasters, including the BBC. **Strengths:** "He has a media savvy other advocates struggle to match, and has a real gravitas in court." "He has a good knowledge of the issues and he knows exactly when to argue and when not to."

Alistair Clark QC (Axiom Advocates) Acts for companies and local authorities in high-value commercial litigation. He is esteemed for his depth of expertise in defamation and privacy matters. **Strengths:** "He is a very shrewd and practical lawyer." **Recent work:** He advised News Group Newspapers in relation to the motion for a new trial stemming from the defamation claim brought by Tommy Sheridan, for which he was awarded damages of £200,000 following a jury trial, but was subsequently convicted of perjury.

Roddy Dunlop QC (Axiom Advocates) He handles some of the most high-profile media matters in Scotland. He routinely acts for newspapers in defamation and breach of privacy claims. **Strengths:** "He's a standout advocate; very robust, very persuasive and very effective on his feet." "His knowledge and experience of media law is second to none." **Recent work:** He represented the Scottish National Party in a defamation case concerning comments about a local councillor made by a property developer, successfully appealing against both an interim interdict and an appeal to the Supreme Court.

Ewen Campbell (see p.564) (Axiom Advocates) Has developed a strong profile for his media work, and is noted for his handling contempt of court and defamation concerns. He regularly advises on issues relating to online blogging and the use of social media. **Strengths:** "He is very practical; he listens to what his clients want to achieve and not what he wants to achieve." "He is very easy to deal with and very approachable, while in court he is very effective." **Recent work:** He acted for the Scottish Daily Record and the Sunday Mail in a £1.37 million defamation claim brought by Mortons Rolls.

PENSIONS

Pensions Scotland
Leading Silks
Band 1
McNeill James W *Axiom Advocates (ORL)* ◊
Sellar David *Ampersand (ORL)* ◊
Leading Juniors
Band 1
Cunningham Greg *Westwater Advocates (ORL)* ◊

Ranked Lawyers

David Sellar QC (Ampersand) A veteran advocate well versed in representing clients before the Court of Session. His clients include those in the banking sector and local authorities, and he is praised for his commercial acumen and logical approach. **Strengths:** "He is always willing to come off the fence and give definitive advice." "He is consistent, and shows great clarity of thought. He is considerate and aware of the commercial repercussions."

James McNeill QC (Axiom Advocates) Receives instructions as both an advocate and a mediator in occupational pension scheme disputes. **Strengths:** "He stands out in pensions matters. He's very knowledgeable, and able to distil complex questions down to the essential issues." "His great depth of experience leads to sound, thoughtful advice."

Greg Cunningham (Westwater Advocates) Has a broad civil practice with a focus on pensions disputes. His recent instructions have seen him appear before the Commercial Court, Court of Session and the Sheriff Court, representing clients such as local authorities in Pensions Ombudsman claims. **Strengths:** "He made sure that everything was on time, to a really good standard. We were very happy with how he performed."

PERSONAL INJURY

Personal Injury Scotland
Leading Stables
Band 1
Compass Chambers *
Band 2
Ampersand *
Band 3
Westwater Advocates *
Leading Silks
Band 1
Caldwell Marion *Compass Chambers*
Clancy Ronald *Ampersand*
Hajducki Andrew *Westwater Advocates*
Hanretty Gerald *Arnot Manderson (ORL)* ◊
Mackay Ian *Compass Chambers*
Maguire Maria *Ampersand*
Milligan Robert *Compass Chambers*
O'Brien Susan *Compass Chambers* *
Primrose Graham *Ampersand*
Band 2
Bain Dorothy *Ampersand*
Clarke Geoff *Compass Chambers* *
Di Rollo Simon *Ampersand*
Dunlop Roddy *Axiom Advocates (ORL)* ◊
Grahame Angela *Compass Chambers* *
Ivey Gilmour *Westwater Advocates*
Shand Lesley *Compass Chambers* *
Smith Andrew *Compass Chambers*
Young Andrew R W *Arnot Manderson (ORL)* ◊ *
◊ (ORL) = Other Ranked Lawyer.
* Indicates stable / individual with profile.

Personal Injury Scotland
Leading Juniors
Band 1
Galbraith Amber *Compass Chambers* *
Lamont Gordon *Compass Chambers*
Lloyd Preston *Compass Chambers*
Love Steve *Compass Chambers* *
Mackenzie Neil *Arnot Manderson (ORL)* ◊ *
McGregor Malcolm *Compass Chambers*
Smart Astrid *Compass Chambers*
Band 2
Christine Kenneth *Compass Chambers*
Fitzpatrick Brian *Ampersand*
Henderson Lisa *Ampersand*
Mackenzie Euan *Ampersand*
Marney Christian *Ampersand*
Middleton Graeme *Compass Chambers* *
Pilkington Ross *Hastie Stable (ORL)* ◊
Pugh Richard *Compass Chambers* *
Tait Arabella *Arnot Manderson (ORL)* ◊
Wray Laura *Westwater Advocates* *
Up-and-coming individuals
Dawson Jamie *Ampersand*

Band 1

Compass Chambers
See profile on p.899

THE SET

Compass Chambers is the leading stable for personal injury work in Scotland. At both silk and junior level the stable possesses able and respected advocates active across a wide range of areas. Main areas of focus include catastrophic injury, industrial disease and employers' liability. In recent years Compass has expanded its bench to further its market expertise. Sources enthuse as to the quality and efficiency of the stable's clerking team, who consistently display a deep understanding of the specific requirements of instructing solicitors.

Client service: "There is not much I can't ask them to do in terms of sorting diaries out. The team, led by Gavin Herd, are exceptionally helpful."

SILKS

Marion Caldwell QC Widely respected for her work representing pursuers and defenders in high-value cases. Her areas of particular focus include brain injuries and occupational stress. She also has considerable experience of acting in fatal accident inquiries. **Strengths:** "Despite complications in the case she got a very good result." "She took the case by the scruff of the neck and was incredibly thorough."

Ian Mackay QC Regularly advises both pursuers and defenders in a range of complex cases, with special focus on industrial disease and catastrophic injury work. **Strengths:** "He is excellent, particularly in jury trials as he has a way with an audience."

Robert Milligan QC A renowned expert on claims relating to occupational stress and fatalities. He receives instructions from pursuers and defenders, and his practice also covers catastrophic injury and product liability. **Strengths:** "He is authoritative before the court – very thorough, very detailed." "He is probably the most academically gifted of the senior counsel in Scotland." **Recent work:** He defended Aberdeenshire Council in a case brought by an individual who was involved in a car crash and sought damages.

Susan O'Brien QC (see p.684) Focuses her personal injury practice on industrial disease, and catastrophic and psychiatric injury claims, in all of which she most frequently represents the pursuer. She is an experienced advocate with broader expertise in medical negligence cases and conducting judicial reviews. **Strengths:** "She is a formidable opponent for the other side." "She is not scared to go to court." **Recent work:** Successfully represented a subcontractor in a claim against Stewart Homes, which was found negligent following an accident that caused the pursuer serious injury.

Andrew Smith QC Earns acclaim for his work representing pursuers and defenders in high-value RTA and industrial disease cases. Brain injury matters are an area of particular expertise. **Strengths:** "He is always prepared to try out a new point." "He thinks outside the box."

Geoff Clarke QC (see p.572) Noted for his work handling industrial disease claims. He also has experience of working on Fatal Accident Inquiries (FAI). **Strengths:** "He explains things clearly and concisely in a way that the client can follow." "He is a good and tough negotiator." **Recent work:** Instructed in a £600,000 employment liability case in which the pursuer suffered an amputation and subsequent psychological trauma following an accident involving a JCB.

Lesley Shand QC (see p.717) Routinely represents pursuers and defenders. Her broad practice includes catastrophic injury cases and she also receives instructions in industrial disease litigation. **Strengths:** "She leaves no stone unturned." "Faultless preparation is the key to her success." **Recent work:** Acted in an RTA case in which the pursuer suffered severe injuries. She brought a claim against Zurich, the insurer of the driver involved in the accident, reaching a favourable settlement.

Angela Grahame QC (see p.613) Has a broad personal injury practice, with particular specialism in industrial disease and catastrophic injury cases. **Strengths:** "There are not many counsel as expert in the industrial disease area as her." "She'll fight your corner and your client's corner." **Recent work:** Acted for a pursuer who suffered a brain injury after an RTA.

JUNIORS

Gordon Lamont Has a brilliant reputation for his work in fatal accident inquiries. Other inquiry work he undertakes includes investigations concerning deaths in hospital and custody. **Strengths:** "He is a very safe pair of hands." "He's very good on his feet in court." **Recent work:** Represented a pilot who brought a claim against British Midland Regional after injuring his back accessing his cockpit chair. The case was settled.

Preston Lloyd A senior junior who primarily represents pursuers across the full range of personal injury cases. **Strengths:** "He has a firm grasp of all the legal technicalities." "He is an outstanding advocate."

Malcolm McGregor Regularly receives instructions on industrial disease cases, especially those related to asbestos. Instructing solicitors describe him as a very user-friendly advocate. **Strengths:** "He is straightforward and says it like it is." "He is a cool and calm character – he's fantastic at retaining his cool in negotiations."

Amber Galbraith (see p.605) Receives instructions from both pursuers and defenders in catastrophic injury and employment liability cases. She is also praised for her work on fatal accident inquiries. Sources enthuse about her empathetic approach with clients. **Strengths:** "She always has her clients' best interests at heart." "She is thorough, diligent and a pleasure to work with." **Recent work:** Successfully advised a pursuer in a case against an employer following an accident in the workplace.

Steve Love (see p.658) Has a broad practice covering RTAs, industrial disease and catastrophic injury cases. He is particularly noted for his niche expertise in motorcycle and aviation-related injuries. **Strengths:** "He provides advice that is practical but underscored by a deep understanding of the law." **Recent work:** Acted on behalf of a pursuer who claimed damages from Dundee City Council after sustaining an injury at a rugby coaching session.

Astrid Smart Has focused her practice on cases within the workplace, including accidents, occupational stress, industrial disease and employers' liability. She is an expert on European regulations concerning liability issues. **Strengths:** "She is wonderful with very distressed pursuers." **Recent work:** Represented a pursuer who suffered a serious injury at work involving a scissor lift.

Richard Pugh (see p.700) Noted by several sources for his representation of both pursuers and defenders, which is viewed by solicitors as a real strength. He regularly advises on complex, high-value catastrophic injury claims, and also appears routinely at FAIs. **Strengths:** "He makes clients and solicitors feel that he's working with them and lets everyone have their say." **Recent work:** He represented the National Park Authority in a case brought on behalf of a child who suffered serious head injuries after a fall.

Graeme Middleton (see p.672) Focuses on industrial accident and disease cases, and represents both pursuers and defenders. **Strengths:** "He is technically very good in court, and offers sound advice to clients."

Kenneth Christine Receives extensive instruction from pursuers. He has considerable experience of industrial disease cases, and also handles catastrophic and fatal injury cases. **Strengths:** "Nothing seems to faze him."

Band 2

Ampersand

See profile on p.896

THE SET

Ampersand has a large number of highly experienced personal injury advocates who offer excellent counsel on a broad range of matters, including industrial disease and brain and spinal injuries. A number of the stable's advocates are also experts in clinical negligence cases.

Client service: "When you call the clerks they are always willing to help out and are good at giving recommendations when certain individuals aren't available." Alan Moffat heads the team.

SILKS

Maria Maguire QC Draws praise for her tough negotiating style. She routinely represents both pursuers and defenders in complex high-value claims. **Strengths:** "She is robust and fearless: a tour de force."

Ronald Clancy QC Has a busy pursuer practice focusing on catastrophic injury cases, often stemming from RTAs. **Strengths:** "His experience from the Crown Office is a significant asset." "He prepares thoroughly and will not be fazed."

Graham Primrose QC Renowned for his high-profile work representing pursuers in helicopter crash cases. He is lauded by many as a very effective negotiator. His practice also includes advising clients on FAIs. **Strengths:** "He is very practical and straightforward with his advice." "He makes his clients feel at ease."

Simon Di Rollo QC Maintains a busy practice covering industrial disease and catastrophic injury cases. He is highly experienced in acting in FAIs. **Strengths:** "He has a wealth of experience – a real asset." "He cares for clients by being very measured and considerate." **Recent work:** Reached settlement in an industrial disease case whereby the pursuer developed cancer through exposure to wood dust at work.

Dorothy Bain QC Runs a broad practice, representing pursuers and defenders in liability and industrial disease cases. She is held in high regard by instructing solicitors for her client care skills. **Strengths:** "She cares about the case and is willing to go the extra mile." "She's incredibly hard-working and excellent with people."

JUNIORS

Brian Fitzpatrick Draws acclaim for his handling of catastrophic injury claims on behalf of pursuers. He has particular expertise in cases involving head and spinal injuries. **Strengths:** "He can be relied upon for excellence." "You can be confident that he will get the best possible settlement for his clients."

Lisa Henderson Splits her practice between clinical negligence and catastrophic personal injury work. She is a recognised authority on cerebral palsy cases. **Strengths:** "She prepares well and doesn't miss a thing."

Euan Mackenzie Advises both defenders and pursuers on high-value injury matters and is regularly instructed on fatal claims. **Strengths:** "He is extremely well prepared and thorough." **Recent work:** Represented a pursuer in a multimillion-pound claim following an RTA.

Christian Marney Has a broad practice that encompasses personal injury, professional negligence and employment cases. He has considerable experience of acting in FAIs. **Recent work:** Instructed on a case where a falling fence panel left the pursuer with brain damage. There was consideration as to whether the occupier of the premises could be held liable.

Jamie Dawson Routinely represents both pursuers and defenders in a broad range of case, including RTAs and industrial disease claims. **Strengths:** "He is a very good opponent."

Band 3

Westwater Advocates

See profile on p.901

THE SET

Westwater Advocates is the oldest stable at the Scottish Bar, and remains home to a number of the Bar's leading figures. Its advocates maintain mixed practices, and this is applauded by solicitors who value instructing established advocates who have not just considerable experience in personal injury cases, but also broader expertise in related areas such as clinical negligence.

Client service: Sheila Westwater is the principal clerk at the stable.

SILKS

Andrew Hajducki QC Offers counsel on a broad spectrum of matters, including high-value industrial disease and product liability cases. He maintains an excellent reputation for his strength in handling jury trials. **Strengths:** "He is one of the most talented QCs at the Scottish Bar." "He's completely unflappable and never seems to worry about anything." **Recent work:** Represented the pursuers in a fatal marine accident case.

Gilmour Ivey QC Enjoys a strong reputation in the market for his expertise in industrial disease cases. He regularly represents both pursuers and defenders. **Strengths:** "He is a strong advocate and a very safe pair of hands."

JUNIORS

Laura Wray (see p.756) Maintains a broad practice that includes industrial disease, RTAs and employers' liability cases. Solicitors value her experience of working for both pursuers and defenders. **Strengths:** "She doesn't just tell the client what they want to hear: she tells them what they need to hear." "Her work is always detailed and accurate." **Recent work:** Acted on behalf of a pursuer who suffered a brain injury following a car crash. The defenders admitted liability and a settlement of £285,000 was reached.

Other Ranked Lawyers

Gerald Hanretty QC (Arnot Manderson) Regularly instructed on high-value catastrophic brain and spinal injury cases. He also has considerable experience of handling FAIs. **Strengths:** "If you are ever in a very difficult position he is absolutely wonderful." "He is very tenacious and not frightened of a fight."

Andrew Young QC (see p.757) (Arnot Manderson) Focuses his busy practice on catastrophic injury cases. **Strengths:** "He is calm, measured and extraordinarily bright." "He cuts straight to the heart of the matter."

Neil Mackenzie (see p.660) (Arnot Manderson) Noted for his expertise in industrial disease cases. **Strengths:** "He is good with clients and extremely strong intellectually."

Arabella Tait (Arnot Manderson) Adept in advising both pursuers and defenders on cases across a broad range of claims, most notably on catastrophic injury proceedings. She also has an extensive clinical negligence workload. **Strengths:** "A great advocate with nerves of steel."

Roddy Dunlop QC (Axiom Advocates) Primarily represents insurers on catastrophic injury claims. **Strengths:** "He knows his stuff, and is pragmatic yet bullish." "He is an extremely able advocate."

Ross Pilkington (Hastie Stable) Has a broad practice that encompasses personal injury and both clinical and professional negligence work.

PLANNING & ENVIRONMENT

Planning & Environment Scotland	
Leading Stables	
Band 1	
Terra Firma Chambers *	
Leading Silks	
Star individuals	
Martin Roy	*Terra Firma Chambers* *
Band 1	
Agnew of Lochnaw Bt Crispin	*Westwater (ORL)* ◊ *
Armstrong Douglas	*Terra Firma Chambers* *
Thomson Malcolm	*Ampersand (ORL)* ◊
Wilson Ailsa	*Ampersand (ORL)* ◊
Band 2	
Campbell John D	*Hastie Stable (ORL)* ◊
Crawford Ruth	*Axiom Advocates (ORL)* ◊ *
Findlay James	*Terra Firma Chambers* *
Mure James	*Axiom Advocates (ORL)* ◊ *
Steele Gordon	*Terra Firma Chambers* *
Leading Juniors	
Band 1	
Burnet Alasdair J	*Terra Firma Chambers* *
Band 2	
McKay Marcus	*Ampersand (ORL)* ◊

◊ (ORL) = Other Ranked Lawyer.

** Indicates stable / individual with profile.*

Band 1

Terra Firma Chambers

See profile on p.900

THE SET

Terra Firma occupies an unquestioned position at the head of the Scottish Planning and Environment Bar, and is home to an unmatched roster of top-class silks and juniors. The set maintains a reputation for excellence in the field and sources point to its track record in advising and representing clients in sophisticated and heavyweight matters, with particular strength in issues arising from energy work.

Client service: "They're very good. In terms of speed, response times, knowledge of practices and making alternative suggestions, they're excellent." "They're absolutely superb – extremely switched on, highly responsive, and helpful to a huge degree."

SILKS

Roy Martin QC (see p.664) Recognised across the board as a leading light of the Scottish Planning and Energy Bar. He is praised for his singular breadth of experience and his handling of contentious and non-contentious matters for energy, retail and residential clients. **Strengths:** "He remains at the top of his game – he's still the leading planning QC in Scotland." "He stands out because you just know he'll be on top of it. His ability to grasp complicated issues is probably unparalleled."

Douglas Armstrong QC (see p.537) Acclaimed for his expertise in heavyweight matters across the infrastructure and energy fields. Sources note his impressive background in the environmental aspects of major developments. **Strengths:** "He thinks very strategically – there's always a game plan – and he gives very pragmatic, sensible advice." "He very quickly becomes part of the team. He's approachable, an excellent communicator and pretty damn brilliant on his feet." **Recent work:** He acted in Trump v Scottish Ministers, representing the developer in a challenge to a proposed offshore wind farm.

James Findlay QC (see p.600) Brings his impressive experience to bear on behalf of a diverse range of clients in a wide range of matters, with particular expertise in renewable energy work. He is highlighted for his courtroom presence and his strategic handling of complex matters. **Strengths:** "In a very short space of time he's confirmed himself as a go-to planning counsel – he's excellent in court, in inquiries and on opinion work." "He has tremendous court presence and he's very decent to deal with in terms of client handling." **Recent work:** He acted in the Druim Ba planning inquiry, representing the Highland Council and local residents in their objection to a Section 36 wind farm application.

Gordon Steele QC (see p.727) Receives significant acclaim for his handling of contentious work and judicial reviews. He enjoys an impressive reputation for his expertise in both energy and residential work, and is well recognised for his representation of developer clients. **Strengths:** "He's a good choice when faced with a difficult case." "He's great – very knowledgeable, an expert in planning and he can hold his own at inquiry and hearings."

JUNIORS

Alasdair Burnet (see p.561) Widely regarded as one of the leading juniors at the Scottish Planning Bar, marshalling his experience as a solicitor to represent developer and local authority clients in a range of complex matters. Sources note his deft handling of contentious work. **Strengths:** "He's an excellent senior junior, and very good on his feet." "His preparation for cases is very thorough." **Recent work:** He acted in Bova v Highland Council, appealing the Lord Ordinary's decision to refuse a judicial review into the refusal of planning permission to a housing development. He represented the developer.

Other Ranked Lawyers

Malcolm Thomson QC (Ampersand) Retains his standing as a clear leader in the field, with an enviable reputation for high-profile judicial reviews in the retail sector. Sources highlight his deft and surgical cross-examinations and his tactical mastery of complex matters. **Strengths:** "He's very professional and insightful, and his knowledge is unrivalled. He fills clients with confidence." "He has a really engaging style: clarity of speech, and an ability to break complex matters down into bite-size chunks and provide recommendations on strategy."

Ailsa Wilson QC (Ampersand) Enjoys an enviable reputation for her handling of major public inquiries and appeals, and is regarded across the board as one of the pre-eminent silks in the field. Among her areas of expertise are high-level residential matters, and she is well respected for her extensive experience in the sector. **Strengths:** "She's second to none when it comes to getting her head round complex issues of fact." "She's on top of her game at all times."

Marcus McKay (Ampersand) Receives widespread recognition for his breadth of expertise and his significant profile across the planning and energy sector. He is highly regarded for his handling of contentious work and appeals, with particular experience in acting on developments in the energy sector. **Strengths:** "He's superb – very good with clients and advice."

Ruth Crawford QC (see p.580) (Axiom Advocates) Centres her planning practice on the representation of public sector clients in major infrastructure and energy appeals and inquiries. She has an impressive track record in acting for the Scottish Ministers. **Recent work:** She acted in Upritchard v Scottish Ministers and the Fife Council, successfully representing the Ministers in a challenge brought by the pursuer against approval of the Fife Structure Plan.

James Mure QC (see p.679) (Axiom Advocates) Widely acclaimed for his breadth of expertise in commercial work and his skill in high-profile contentious matters. He is well known for his representation of local authority and governmental bodies, and enjoys an impressive reputation for work in the renewables and infrastructure sectors. **Strengths:** "He's a very effective and efficient advocate." **Recent work:** He defended Glasgow City Council against West Dunbartonshire Council's challenge to its grant of development permission to a third party.

John Campbell QC (Hastie Stable) Lauded for his depth of experience across the sector, receiving particular recognition as a go-to for strategic advice on wind farm developments. He is also well regarded for his deft advocacy. **Strengths:** "He knows the market inside-out." "He's just got huge experience."

Sir Crispin Agnew of Lochnaw Bt QC (see p.532) (Westwater Advocates) Operates at the forefront of the market, with formidable expertise in areas including renewable energy. His practice includes heavyweight experience in representing charities and clients in the agricultural arena in issues involving wind farms. **Strengths:** "He's hugely knowledgeable. He has vast experience in many areas of law, and it comes together to create effective advocacy." "He's passionate, tenacious and client-friendly – he's prepared to go the extra mile for a cause he believes in." **Recent work:** He acted in Sustainable Shetland v Scottish Ministers, a successful judicial review of a Section 36 consent for a wind farm made on the basis that the consent was given in breach of Birds Directive obligations.

PROFESSIONAL DISCIPLINE

Professional Discipline Scotland	
Leading Stables	
Band 1	
Axiom Advocates *	
Leading Silks	
Band 1	
Dunlop Roddy	*Axiom Advocates*
Lindsay Mark	*Axiom Advocates*
Band 2	
Duncan Alastair	*Axiom Advocates*
Leading Juniors	
Band 1	
Brown Jonathan	*Westwater Advocates (ORL)* ◊
Stuart Philip	*Ampersand (ORL)* ◊

Band 1

Axiom Advocates

See profile on p.898

THE SET

Axiom Advocates is regularly instructed in high-profile and complex professional discipline cases for a range of both regulators and regulated individuals. Although it has a particular presence in solicitors' disciplinary matters, it also receives regular instructions to act in both healthcare and police cases.

SILKS

Mark Lindsay QC His professional discipline practice is enriched by his commercial and public law experience. He receives regular instructions from the Scottish Legal Complaints Commission, and also acts on disciplinary matters in the healthcare sector. **Strengths:** "He can prepare and deliver robustly in writing and on his feet."

Roddy Dunlop QC Acts in a whole range of professional discipline matters, primarily on behalf of regulators. His practice encompasses complex cases in the policing, healthcare and legal sectors. **Strengths:** "Everyone wants Roddy Dunlop QC – it's a race to see who can get him first." **Recent work:** Represented the General Dental Council in resisting an appeal brought by a dentist who had been practising without insurance and had been struck off.

Alastair Duncan QC Regularly advises on regulatory cases in the legal sector, and receives instructions from both regulators and regulated individuals. **Recent work:** Represented the Law Society of Scotland in an appeal made by a solicitor who was suspended due to various allegations of misconduct.

Other Ranked Lawyers

Philip Stuart (Ampersand) Has extensive experience in medical law matters and acts predominantly for clients within the healthcare industry.

Jonathan Brown (Westwater Advocates) Held in high regard for his work in solicitors' disciplinary cases. He is instructed to both defend and prosecute, although his practice focuses on prosecuting for clients such as the Legal Defence Union and the Law Society of Scotland. **Strengths:** "He is very good at expressing the complex matters we have to deal with." "He provides well-ordered and carefully set-out written pleadings."

PROFESSIONAL NEGLIGENCE

Professional Negligence Scotland	
Leading Stables	
Band 1	
Axiom Advocates *	
Leading Silks	
Band 1	
Duncan Alastair	*Axiom Advocates*
Dunlop Roddy	*Axiom Advocates*
Ferguson Iain	*Axiom Advocates*
Hanretty Gerald	*Arnot Manderson (ORL)* ◊
Young Andrew R W	*Arnot Manderson (ORL)* ◊ *
Band 2	
Howie Robert	*Ampersand (ORL)* ◊
Lake Jonathan C	*Axiom Advocates*
McBrearty Kenneth	*Axiom Advocates* *
Murphy Laurence	*Arnot Manderson (ORL)* ◊
Sandison Craig	*Ampersand (ORL)* ◊

Professional Negligence Scotland	
Leading Juniors	
Band 1	
Barne Jonathan	*Axiom Advocates*
MacColl Gavin L	*Hastie Stable (ORL)* ◊
Richardson Martin H	*Axiom Advocates*
Band 2	
Broome Jonathan	*Axiom Advocates*
Marney Christian	*Ampersand (ORL)* ◊
McKenzie Alasdair	*Axiom Advocates*
Paterson Chris	*Axiom Advocates*
Walker Gavin	*Axiom Advocates*
Up-and-coming individuals	
Reid Paul	*Ampersand (ORL)* ◊

◊ *(ORL) = Other Ranked Lawyer.*

** Indicates stable / individual with profile.*

Alphabetical order within each band. Band 1 is highest.

Band 1

Axiom Advocates

See profile on p.898

THE SET

Axiom Advocates is a "top-notch commercial stable," pursuing and defending claims against professionals from a wide range of sectors. Its members have a wealth of expertise on the full range of professional negligence claims, including disputes involving solicitors, counsel and professionals in the financial and construction sectors. The set is consistently recognised by peers as a "centre of excellence."

Client service: "One of the main reasons to use Axiom is the clerking team led by Lesley Flynn. They go above and beyond, and do the legwork for you. They are very good at knowing who you like, matching stable strengths and accommodating your needs."

SILKS

Alastair Duncan QC Has a celebrated professional negligence practice. He is chiefly recognised in this field for his wealth of expertise in solicitors' negligence claims. **Strengths:** "Highly intelligent, meticulous in his preparation, and a skilled court performer, he is trusted by insurer and insured clients alike as a go-to silk." **Recent work:** Defended a firm of solicitors that was accused of negligent misrepresentation by a financial institution.

Roddy Dunlop QC Has a well-respected practice spanning a broad range of legal fields. He has extensive experience of defending professionals who are facing negligence claims. **Strengths:** "He is absolutely first-class." "He is very impressive on his feet in court." **Recent work:** Acted in Singh v Napier, successfully defending a senior counsel who was accused of negligence and discrimination by a former client.

Iain Ferguson QC Focuses his practice on professional and medical negligence claims, frequently advising on cases involving solicitors. He has significant expertise in medical negligence and is regularly entrusted with high-value obstetric claims. **Strengths:** "He has a brilliant forensic mind. He is good on the details and how to apply law." "He is very experienced and has a lot of gravitas." **Recent work:** He acted on Kirkton Investments v VMH, a claim brought against a firm of solicitors by a development company in relation to a housing development.

Jonathan Lake QC Has a varied practice, predominantly focused on handling commercial disputes. He has considerable experience of professional negligence cases, and is frequently retained to handle noteworthy claims against architects, surveyors and solicitors. **Strengths:** "He's excellent. He's not at all afraid of going into court – he relishes it." "He is superb on his feet and excels in complex matters."

Kenny McBrearty QC (see p.666) Highly regarded by peers for his expertise in both professional negligence and professional discipline. He receives regular instructions on complex claims involving solicitors, accountants and surveyors. **Strengths:** "He is a sharp tactician with an assured court manner. He has a great manner with both insured and insurer clients." "He's excellent. Very thorough, practical and commercial."

JUNIORS

Jonathan Barne Particularly well recognised for his work on construction-related disputes and professional negligence claims. He is frequently instructed on complex claims in the construction and legal sectors. **Strengths:** "He is technically very able and meticulous." "He is able to cut through the chaff to get to the heart of the matter. He's not just a good advocate – he has a commercial outlook and mind." **Recent work:** Instructed to pursue an architect's negligence claim relating to the extension of commercial premises where the main contractor of the project was insolvent.

Martin Richardson An experienced junior, particularly well known for his expertise in construction-related negligence claims, including disputes involving engineers and architects. He is also regularly instructed on cases involving professionals from the financial sector. **Strengths:** "He is certainly a go-to person for engineering negligence cases." "He goes the extra mile for the client and has an ability to understand the commercial imperatives of the clients." "He is extremely precise in his analysis and very persuasive on his feet." **Recent work:** Engaged by RBS to pursue an engineers' negligence claim concerning the design of an office building.

Jonathan Broome Has considerable expertise in construction law, having worked as a solicitor in this area for many years. He is particularly well regarded by peers and clients for his experience in professional negligence cases involving engineers. **Strengths:** "He is extremely diligent and goes the extra mile." "He's incredibly bright and enthusiastic. His specialist area is construction and he knows it inside out." **Recent work:** Defended a claim brought against engineers relating to alleged design failures of an office development in the centre of Edinburgh.

Chris Paterson Regularly acts on a range of negligence claims, including disputes involving solicitors, surveyors and individuals in the construction and medical sectors. **Strengths:** "He is very thorough and very good on the technical side of things." "He has many years of expertise in professional negligence claims as an advocate and solicitor." **Recent work:** Acted in Northern Rock v Bell & Scott on behalf of the defenders, who were accused of negligently advising a financial institution on a borrower's ability to pay off a loan.

Gavin Walker Frequently entrusted to pursue claims against professionals in the construction sector, including engineers, surveyors and architects. He has also acted on several high-value claims brought by financial institutions against valuers. **Strengths:** "He knows the law, he's very good in court and clients like him." **Recent work:** Acted for the Bank of Scotland on a negligence claim brought against surveyors arising from the valuation of a commercial development site.

Alasdair McKenzie Impresses peers and clients with his work pursuing and defending negligence claims arising in the construction sector. **Strengths:** "He is approachable and commercial. He is also technical but doesn't let it get in the way of resolving the case."

Other Ranked Lawyers

Robert Howie QC (Ampersand) Frequently acts on professional negligence disputes arising from construction projects. **Strengths:** "He has an amazing ability to come up with a left-field argument." "He is very bright, very able and an inventive thinker."

Craig Sandison QC (Ampersand) Has a broad commercial practice, with particular strengths in real estate litigation and IP, as well as undertaking noteworthy professional negligence work. **Strengths:** "He's one of these guys where you watch very carefully what you say: he exposes any weakness. He is one of the most able advocates." "He's a fantastic lawyer and a pain in the neck if he's your opposition."

Christian Marney (Ampersand) Has a significant professional negligence practice. He predominantly defends claims against solicitors and is frequently retained by the Law Society of Scotland professional indemnity insurer. He also handles notable claims involving construction and medical professionals.

Paul Reid (Ampersand) Focuses his practice on professional and medical negligence, personal injury and general commercial disputes. He is regularly instructed on claims involving solicitors and professionals in the construction industry. **Strengths:** "He is very bright but also very accessible." "He's up and coming. Definitely one to watch."

Gerald Hanretty QC (Arnot Manderson) Focuses his practice on high-value and sensitive professional negligence and personal injury claims, drawing praise from peers for his significant expertise in these areas. He predominantly acts on disputes involving solicitors and accountants. **Strengths:** "He is an absolutely brilliant advocate in court, very tenacious when needed."

Andrew Young QC (see p.757) (Arnot Manderson) Acts for both pursuers and defenders in professional and clinical negligence claims. He is praised for his expertise in solicitors' negligence cases, as well as disputes involving construction professionals. **Strengths:** "He is cerebral and has a good mind. He's a big presence."

Laurence Murphy QC (Arnot Manderson) Frequently retained to handle a broad array of negligence claims, including claims against solicitors, advocates, accountants, architects and surveyors. **Strengths:** "He is very tenacious and thorough." "He is very persuasive on his feet in court."

Gavin MacColl (Hastie Stable) Has a broad commercial practice with deep expertise in professional negligence claims. He frequently acts on claims involving professionals in the construction industry, as well as solicitors' negligence claims. **Strengths:** "He always takes a practical approach to matters; he doesn't just want to dazzle clients." "He's a pugnacious fighter for his clients." "He's excellent on his feet."

PUBLIC PROCUREMENT

Public Procurement Scotland
Leading Stables
Band 1
Axiom Advocates *
Leading Silks
Band 1
Clark Alistair *Axiom Advocates*
Mitchell Iain G *Arnot Manderson (ORL)* ◊ *
Mure James *Axiom Advocates* *
Band 2
Dunlop Roddy *Axiom Advocates*
Leading Juniors
Band 1
MacGregor John *Axiom Advocates*
Ross Morag *Axiom Advocates*

Band 1

Axiom Advocates
See profile on p.898
THE SET
Axiom Advocates' strength in administrative and public law feeds into the stable's excellent reputation for public procurement work. Its members act for both contractors and procuring authorities, and are equally comfortable acting in an advisory or advocacy capacity.

SILKS
Alistair Clark QC Acts for a number of public bodies, including city councils and government agencies, as well as for pursuers. He is a former academic with substantial experience of, and proven expertise in, acting for clients in the Court of Session. **Strengths:** "He gives clear advice, is extremely balanced, and has great experience of previously defending the government." "He is never ruffled; he exudes calm." **Recent work:** Advised Glasgow City Council on a third-party challenge for alleged breach of procurement law.

James Mure QC (see p.679) A former member of the diplomatic service, and a former first standing junior counsel to the Scottish government. He earns praise for his expertise in planning as well as public procurement.

Roddy Dunlop QC A widely respected practitioner whose user-friendly approach and stellar advocacy are valued by instructing solicitors. **Strengths:** "He is academically sharp and has a very good client-facing manner." "He is an aggressive litigator, but effective." **Recent work:** He acted as senior counsel in a motorway maintenance public procurement challenge against the Scottish Ministers.

JUNIORS
Morag Ross An experienced public procurement practitioner. She is regularly instructed by challengers to contract awards, and by public bodies such as higher education institutions. **Strengths:** "She is an excellent junior, very able and no-nonsense." "She is hugely experienced and knowledgeable in this area. Great to work with." **Recent work:** Acted for the pursuers in the high-profile Nationwide Gritting Services v Scottish Ministers case, concerning a challenge to the award for a contract to supply salt for de-icing.

John MacGregor Noted for his experience in advising on NHS matters and the provision of social services. **Strengths:** "He is very good with clients and very easy to communicate with, and explains complicated concepts clearly." **Recent work:** Acted for the defence in Glasgow Rent Deposit and Support Scheme v Glasgow City Council, a challenge to the award of a contract to provide homelessness services.

Other Ranked Lawyers

Iain Mitchell QC (see p.674) (Arnot Manderson) A highly respected Scottish silk whose core focus is on IT. His polished presentation style ensures he is a first port of call for potential procurement challenges. **Strengths:** "He is a mellow-toned, smooth and articulate advocate." **Recent work:** Advised on a possible challenge to a local authority's contract award for electronic traffic monitoring and enforcement.

REAL ESTATE LITIGATION

Real Estate Litigation Scotland
Leading Silks
Band 1
Martin Roy *Terra Firma Chambers (ORL)* ◊ *
McBrearty Kenneth *Axiom Advocates (ORL)* ◊ *
Reid J Gordon *Terra Firma Chambers (ORL)* ◊ *
Sandison Craig *Ampersand (ORL)* ◊
Leading Juniors
Band 1
MacColl Gavin L *Hastie Stable (ORL)* ◊
Thomson David *Axiom Advocates (ORL)* ◊ *
◊ (ORL) = Other Ranked Lawyer.
** Indicates stable / individual with profile.*
Alphabetical order within each band. Band 1 is highest.

Ranked Lawyers

Craig Sandison QC (Ampersand) Specialises in property law within his broad commercial practice. He is often involved in conveyancing and landlord and tenant matters. **Strengths:** "He is an astute tactician and a brilliant advocate."

Kenny McBrearty QC (see p.666) (Axiom Advocates) Handles rent reviews, commercial contracts and property-related professional negligence disputes. An experienced advocate, he handles the full range of property issues. **Strengths:** "He is an impressive advocate who is approachable and excellent with clients."

David Thomson (see p.737) (Axiom Advocates) Has focused his practice on commercial litigation and public law, and is highly regarded for his expertise on commercial property and leasing issues. **Strengths:** "He is a good advocate with a good brain who will roll up his sleeves and doesn't shy off putting in the hours on a case." **Recent work:** He acted for the liquidator of Letham Grange Development in an appeal to the Inner House regarding the reduction of a standard security.

Gavin MacColl (Hastie Stable) A go-to advocate for commercial property issues in Scotland. He has considerable experience in contractual disputes. **Strengths:** "He is commercial, personable and a fighter. He will work hard to secure a result."

Roy Martin QC (see p.664) (Terra Firma Chambers) Specialises in planning and property disputes and enjoys a strong reputation in the market. **Strengths:** "He is a top-of-the-list pure property expert." "He is a very well-known standout senior and clients like him."

Gordon Reid QC (see p.706) (Terra Firma Chambers) Handles agricultural, construction and land disputes. He is an experienced practitioner who handles a range of property issues including landlord and tenant and conveyancing. **Strengths:** "He is extremely able, clever and meticulous and is involved in very big property cases." "He is an impressive advocate with a good grasp of details."

RESTRUCTURING/INSOLVENCY

Restructuring/Insolvency Scotland
Leading Stables
Band 1
Ampersand *
Axiom Advocates *
Leading Silks
Band 1
Howie Robert *Ampersand*
Howlin Michael P *Hastie Stable (ORL)* ◊
Sellar David *Ampersand*
Band 2
McNeill James W *Axiom Advocates*
Leading Juniors
Band 1
Borland Garry *Axiom Advocates* *
DelibegoviĐ-Broome Almira *Axiom Advocates*
O'Brien Paul *Axiom Advocates* *
Thomson David *Axiom Advocates* *
Band 2
Ower Susan *Axiom Advocates* *
Summers Alan A. *Terra Firma Chambers (ORL)* ◊ *
Up-and-coming individuals
Dalgleish Graeme *Hastie Stable (ORL)* ◊
Duthie Euan *Axiom Advocates* *
◊ (ORL) = Other Ranked Lawyer.
** Indicates stable / individual with profile.*
Alphabetical order within each band. Band 1 is highest.

Band 1

Ampersand

See profile on p.896

THE SET

Ampersand's position as a top-tier insolvency stable is secured by its two market-leading insolvency silks. The stable is "extremely strong in technical insolvency cases" and remains a go-to for representation in litigious matters as well as for advice on non-contentious issues.

SILKS

Robert Howie QC A highly experienced advocate who focuses on insolvency cases arising out of the construction and shipping industries. **Strengths:** "He's very commercially and tactically minded." "His advice is always first-class, clear, well thought out and supported by detailed knowledge of case law."

David Sellar QC A popular choice for insolvency and company law in Scotland and one of the few dedicated insolvency specialists in the market. He is often instructed in an advisory capacity on complex and high-value insolvency cases. **Strengths:** "He is a highly regarded QC with unparalleled expertise in the Scottish market in corporate insolvency matters." "He has an encyclopaedic knowledge of insolvency law."

Axiom Advocates

See profile on p.898

THE SET

Axiom Advocates houses the largest concentration of experienced restructuring and insolvency advocates at the Scottish Bar. Advocates at the stable are instructed on some of the most significant and high-profile restructuring and insolvency cases in Scotland. Instructing solicitors praise the responsive clerking service and appreciate the transparency of the fee structure. Commentators note that "they have good quality throughout the levels from senior to new calls; you're always able to find someone to help you."

Client service: "They have a commercial, flexible approach." "The clerks know their stable inside out."

SILKS

James McNeill QC A highly regarded senior advocate with experience in insolvency matters pertaining to commercial, charitable and private trusts. **Strengths:** "He is an extremely experienced lawyer with a very good reputation for insolvency work."

JUNIORS

David Thomson (see p.737) A commercial specialist who is regularly instructed in disputes pertaining to insolvency law. He is frequently instructed on behalf of banks in corporate transactions and also by individuals in relation to personal insolvencies. **Strengths:** "He has a combination of genuine expertise, a keen mind and a seriously impressive work ethic that is hard to match at the junior Bar in Scotland." "He is experienced, knowledgeable and a determined counsel." **Recent work:** He was instructed by Burness Paull to act for the liquidator of Letham Grange Development in a successful appeal to reduce standard security due to gratuitous alienation.

Garry Borland (see p.553) A commercial law advocate with wide-ranging experience in insolvency and restructuring issues. He has a background in construction law and often acts on cases in the engineering and energy sectors. **Strengths:** "He is excellent in all respects: flexible, attentive to detail and impressive in court." **Recent work:** Instructed by DAC Beachcroft to act for the contractor's insurers in the Blythswood Square v Chard Construction case relating to an £11 million claim made against the insolvent construction company.

Almira Delibegović-Broome A standing junior to HMRC who receives regular instructions on high-profile administrations and liquidations. **Strengths:** "She is a real team player and a bright advocate." "She is invariably well prepared and adds greatly to the representation of the clients' interests in any case." "She has the most impressive mind. Her understanding of detailed statutory provisions is a great assistance." **Recent work:** She was instructed to advise a creditor of Rangers FC (in liquidation) in a case pertaining to the purchase of the club.

Paul O'Brien (see p.683) Began his career as a solicitor focusing on commercial litigation, and since being called to the Bar he has developed considerable insolvency expertise. **Strengths:** "He's a very analytical advocate, who is very responsive and comes back to you quickly. He's very user-friendly."

Euan Duthie (see p.592) Has extensive experience in dealing with a wide range of insolvency issues, including directors' disqualification disputes, administration litigation and warranty breach claims. **Strengths:** "He turns things around very quickly. He's always quick to respond and always willing to discuss things on short notice." **Recent work:** Acted on behalf of the administrators of Heritable Bank in relation to a dispute with the winding-up board of Landsbanki, its parent company in Iceland.

Susan Ower (see p.688) An emerging name in the insolvency field, proving her worth in her recent work on high-profile administrations and liquidations. She is instructed regularly by insolvency practitioners and financial institutions. **Strengths:** "She absorbs each experience and reflects it back the next time around. She is constantly gaining knowledge." "She is very able, very careful and measured. She's realistic about the prospects and not afraid of having the difficult conversations." **Recent work:** Represented Dunedin Building Company as a creditor in the administration of Station Properties, in relation to a £500,000 claim. The administrator's appeal to end the administration was refused and the case ended favourably for Dunedin.

Other Ranked Lawyers

Michael Howlin QC (Hastie Stable) Has a strong reputation for his high-quality non-contentious insolvency advice and has a wealth of experience in administrations and intricate insolvency matters. **Strengths:** "He is an advocate of choice in Scotland for complex technical opinion work." "He is very responsive and will go that extra mile to ensure that you get the advice you need in a tight timescale."

Graeme Dalgleish (Hastie Stable) A bankruptcy and insolvency specialist with a strong employment practice. He frequently undertakes personal insolvency cases arising from his employment work.

Alan Summers (see p.732) (Terra Firma Chambers) An advocate with a strong commercial practice who is noted for his expertise in contentious insolvency matters. **Strengths:** "He is a bright advocate and a real team player." "He is willing to explore the outer reaches of litigation strategy and gets stuck in."

TAX

Tax Scotland	
Leading Stables	
Band 1	
Arnot Manderson *	
Axiom Advocates *	
Band 2	
Terra Firma Chambers *	
Leading Silks	
Star individuals	
Ghosh Julian	*Axiom Advocates*
Band 1	
McNeill James W	*Axiom Advocates*
Band 2	
Currie Heriot	*Axiom Advocates*
Thomson Roderick	*Arnot Manderson*
Young Andrew R W	*Arnot Manderson* *
Leading Juniors	
Band 1	
Simpson Philip J D	*Terra Firma Chambers* *
Small David	*Arnot Manderson*
Band 2	
Artis Iain N J	*Westwater Advocates (ORL)* ◊ *
Francis Derek	*Terra Firma Chambers* *
◊ (ORL) = Other Ranked Lawyer.	
* Indicates firm / individual with profile.	

Band 1

Arnot Manderson

See profile on p.897

THE SET

This stable is home to a large group of experienced tax advocates, who frequently appear before the First-tier and Upper Tax Tribunals. It is one of the most respected stables in Scotland, and its members advise on a great variety of matters that require specialist tax knowledge, such as warranty enforcement, property valuation and professional negligence.

SILKS

Andrew Young QC (see p.757) Highly experienced at taking on tax matters, in addition to his noted private law practice. He has been instructed on tax disputes by HMRC, for which he has appeared in the Supreme Court. **Strengths:** "He is just terrific, an excellent advocate; I'd worry if I were appearing against him."

Roderick Thomson QC Noted for his expertise in commercial tax matters. He is experienced in going before VAT and tax tribunals, and has worked on some very high-profile tax issues. **Strengths:** "The go-to counsel when dealing with complex and unusual cases."

JUNIORS

David Small Previously worked as a tax partner at a Big Four accountancy firm, as well as being a former Inspector of Taxes. He has a very broad tax practice, and advises businesses and individuals on VAT, PAYE, capital gains tax, Stamp Duty Land Tax (SDLT) and inheritance tax issues, among others. **Strengths:** "Clients are impressed and reassured by the solid advice he gives; he is responsive, supportive and practical."

Axiom Advocates

See profile on p.898

THE SET

This stable houses a significant number of highly experienced tax advocates, who handle both transactional work and contentious matters. Its members are particularly active in the field of corporate tax.

SILKS

Julian Ghosh QC A tax specialist with a very broad practice, he is particularly noted for his work on corporate and European tax matters. **Strengths:** "He's very clever and very responsive, and explains complex issues thoroughly yet succinctly."

James McNeill QC Noted for his handling of tax matters for private clients. He is also well respected for work on corporate tax issues. **Strengths:** "He's an incredibly efficient advocate – he's straightforward to deal with."

Heriot Currie QC Takes on tax matters related to commercial transactions. He is particularly strong when it comes to VAT issues, and works on tax related to areas such as construction, IP and public procurement. **Strengths:** "He gives concise and focused advice."

Band 2

Terra Firma Chambers

See profile on p.900

THE SET

A well-respected stable that advises both businesses and individuals on tax matters. Areas of specialism include capital gains, income and inheritance tax on the personal side, while it assists businesses on VAT, corporation tax and capital allowances.

JUNIORS

Philip Simpson (see p.721) Advises on cross-border tax matters as well as those in Scotland and the UK. He is particularly skilled at advising business on the tax implications of reorganisations and corporate transactions, and is experienced at handling VAT litigation. **Strengths:** "He is excellent on indirect tax matters, offering clear, pragmatic advice." **Recent work:** Represented a client in a First-tier Tribunal against HMRC concerning the validity of a national insurance and income tax avoidance scheme.

Derek Francis (see p.603) Acts on tax issues relating to both Scottish and England and Wales trusts and executry. He is also skilled at taking on indirect and corporate tax matters, including those related to VAT, SDLT and capital gains tax. **Strengths:** "He is an excellent advocate with a good grasp of the finer points of tax and trust law." **Recent work:** Represented Butlers Ship Stores against HMRC in a notable case concerning whether warehouse keepers are indemnitors for excise duty if goods have been fraudulently diverted between duty suspended warehouses.

Other Ranked Lawyers

Iain Artis (see p.538) (Westwater Advocates) An experienced contentious tax specialist and a standing counsel to HMRC.

BARRISTERS' PROFILES

Leaders' Profiles in the Bar

ABBERLEY, Stephen
St Philips Chambers, Birmingham
0121 246 1600
sabberley@st-philips.com
Featured in Family/Matrimonial (Midlands)

Practice Areas: Stephen Abberley acts for parents, children and local authorities in public law children cases with humanity, imagination and determination. His particular interest is in cases involving disputed facts, when his forensic skills are to the fore. His experience encompasses child death, serious injury, fabricated illness and sexual abuse. Stephen has a strong practice in financial remedy on divorce/dissolution of civil partnership. He frequently represents professionals with significant pension and other assets.

Professional Memberships: FLBA; Association of Lawyers for Children.

Career: Called 2000 (Middle Temple).

ABRAHAMS, James
8 New Square, London
020 7405 4321
james.abrahams@8newsquare.co.uk
Featured in Intellectual Property (London)

Practice Areas: Barrister specialising in all areas of intellectual property law; including patents, copyright, design right, database right, registered designs, trade marks, passing off and confidential information. Recent cases include Rovi v Virgin Media (STB patents); Total v YouView (STB trade marks); IPC Media v Media 10 (retail trade marks); Microsoft v Motorola (patent/email protocols); PRS v B4U (music copyright); Coward v Phaestos (copyright in hedge fund software) HTC v Apple (smartphone patents); Liversidge v Owen Mumford (medical device patent); Numatic v Qualtex (passing off/vacuum cleaners); Motorola v RIM (mobile Internet patents); Nokia v IPCom (3G mobile communications); Wake Forest v Smith & Nephew and Mölnlycke v Wake Forest (medical device patent); Nokia v InterDigital (3G mobile telecommunications); Baigent v Random House (The Da Vinci Code copyright case); 19TV v Freemantle (copyright in Pop Idol and the X Factor); BHB v William Hill (database right in horseracing data); Halliburton v Smith (patents for oil well drill bits); IPC media v Highbury (copyright in magazine covers). For a comprehensive CV visit www.8newsquare.co.uk.

Professional Memberships: Intellectual Property Bar Association, Chancery Bar Association.

Career: Called 1997, Gray's Inn.

Personal: Born 1974. Educated at Bournemouth School; St Anne's College, Oxford (1995 BA Law, 1996 BCL).

ACTON DAVIS, Jonathan QC
Atkin Chambers, London
020 7404 0102
jad@atkinchambers.com
Featured in Construction (London)

Practice Areas: International and domestic arbitration, construction and engineering and professional negligence. Clients include government departments, most large construction companies, insurers and other commercial bodies. Recently finished his role as Leading Counsel to the Al-Sweady Inquiry, chaired by Sir Thayne Forbes.

Professional Memberships: TECBAR, Professional Negligence Bar Association, Combar, London Common Law Bar Association, Association des Juristes-Franco-Brittaniques.

Career: Called to the Bar 1977, Member of Bar Council 1993-98, Bencher of Inner Temple 1995; Queens Counsel, 1996. Assistant Recorder 1997, Recorder 2000. Chairman of Professional Conduct Committee of Bar Council 2001 and 2002; TECBAR certified adjudicator, Deputy High Court Judge 2008.

Personal: Born 15 January 1953.

ADAMS, Christopher
St Philips Chambers, Birmingham
0121 246 1600
cadams@st-philips.com
Featured in Family/Matrimonial (Midlands)

Practice Areas: Christopher has practised exclusively in the field of public child law since 1995. He acts on behalf of local authorities, parents, children and other family members and is frequently instructed in cases involving serious and medically complex injuries to children. He was head of the St Philips child-care team for three years and has spoken at conferences and seminars on various aspects of the law relating to children. Authorities include: C v Solihull MBC [1993] 1 FLR 290; Hereford and Worcester CC v S [1993] 2 FLR 360; Re C (A Minor) (Care Proceedings: Disclosure) [1997] Fam 76; Re G (Leave to Appeal: Jurisdiction) [1999] 1 FLR 771; A Local Authority v A & Others [2009] EWHC 1982 (Fam); Coventry CC v B, A, RK, KK [2012] EWHC 4014 (Fam).

Professional Memberships: FLBA; ALC; BAAF.

Career: Christopher was appointed as a Recorder in 2005 and is authorised to deal with family cases in both the private and public law jurisdictions. In 2013, he was authorised to sit as a Deputy High Court Judge in the Family Division.

ADAMS, Jayne
Ropewalk Chambers, Nottingham
0115 947 2581
jayneadams@ropewalk.co.uk
Featured in Personal Injury (Midlands)

Practice Areas: She has extensive experience in personal injury, clinical negligence, disease and fraudulent claims litigation, travelling throughout England and Wales. She is frequently invited to provide lectures in all of these areas, but particularly in the industrial disease field to both solicitor and insurer clients.

Professional Memberships: Personal Injuries Bar Association; Nottinghamshire-Medico Legal Society.

Career: Called in 1982; LLB, University of Birmingham.

ADAMSON, Dominic
Temple Garden Chambers, London
020 7583 1315
dominicadamson@tgchambers.com
Featured in Health & Safety (London), Personal Injury (London)

Practice Areas: Health and safety, personal injury and fatal accidents, product liability and consumer law.

Professional Memberships: HSLA and PIBA.

Career: Dominic has a broad health and safety practice representing duty-holders in health and safety prosecutions including those arising out of fatal accidents. He appears in related coroners inquests. Dominic deals with appeals against prohibition/improvement notices. He represents individuals and companies of all sizes including some of the largest operating in the UK. He advises non-UK based companies on their legal obligations and liabilities arising out of operations in the UK and vice versa. He has also represented duty holders in other regulatory prosecutions (e.g. environment, food safety, product safety). Dominic has acted in public inquiries and inquests arising out of public disasters (e.g. Southall and Ladbroke Grove Rail Crashes, Hillsborough). He has experience in the following industries/sectors: steel, rail, construction, motor and bicycle manufacturing, security, home and industrial appliance/equipment manufacturing, waste management, pollution, schools and child care, residential care, health, sports, leisure and food. Dominic's civil practice includes personal injury, fatal accidents and product liability (including dealing with product recall and related commercial disputes and insurance coverage issues). He acts for both claimants and defendants in catastrophic injury claims. He also has considerable experience of group injury litigation relating to defective products, occupational disease and foodstuffs.

Publications: Prosecuting and Defending Health and Safety Cases [2007 xpl] Sports Personal Injury: Law and Practice [2002 Sweet and Maxwell].

ADAMSON, Louisa
Becket Chambers, Canterbury
01227 786 331
clerks@becket-chambers.co.uk
Featured in Family/Matrimonial (South Eastern)

Practice Areas: Louisa represents all parties in cases involving neglect, physical or emotional harm of children including allegations of serious non-accidental injury and sexual abuse where there are concurrent criminal proceedings. Louisa regularly represents parents who may have substance abuse difficulties or suffer from mental health or learning difficulties. Private Law : representing clients who, after separation, have been unable to agree with which parent their children should live and how contact arrangements might best be managed. Louisa represents grandparents who are seeking either Contact or Special Guardianship Orders. Advising parents about applications involving other aspects of parental responsibility such as moving abroad or schooling. Financial disputes between former spouses or cohabitants involving not only properties, pensions and spousal maintenance applications but also financial provision for children, arguments about assets acquired either pre or post the marriage and cases where one of the parties has particular caring responsibilities towards a disabled child.

Professional Memberships: Family Law Bar Association, Family Mediators Association, Association of Lawyers for Children.

Career: Called to the Bar in 1994 Louisa is also a trained family mediator. She accepts instruction under the Direct Public Access scheme.

ADAMYK, Simon
New Square Chambers, London
020 7419 8000
simon.adamyk@newsquarechambers.co.uk
Featured in Chancery (London), Commercial Dispute Resolution (London), Company (London)

Practice Areas: Specialises in chancery/commercial litigation and advisory work. Represented former directors of Equitable Life Assurance Society in the society's multibillion pound claim, and acted for BTA Bank in its multibillion dollar international fraud claims. Has appeared in court in the British Virgin Islands and Privy Council and attended court in The Bahamas and the Isle of Man. Recent cases include: Bitel v Kyrgyz Mobil Tel (Isle of Man and Privy Council); Fortis Fund Services v Seward & Kissel (Bahamas and Privy Council); Stax Claimants v Bank of Nova Scotia; Equitable Life Assurance Society v Bowley; BTA Bank v Ablyazov (England and BVI); various other multimillion dollar commercial and other disputes in England, BVI, Jersey, Cayman Islands, Paris and Malta.

Professional Memberships: Member and former Treasurer, Chancery Bar Association; former member, Chancery Division Court Users' Committee.

Career: MA (Cantab); LLM (Harvard); Called to English Bar 1991; Called to Bar of Eastern Caribbean (BVI) 2006.

Personal: Gained a triple first Awarded highest mark in at University of Cambridge, being awarded the highest mark in the University in each of the three years of his law degree, and also a distinction (a 'starred first') in his first year. Attended Harvard Law School.

ADDY, Caroline
One Brick Court, London
020 7353 8845
ca@onebrickcourt.com
Featured in Defamation/Privacy (London)

Practice Areas: Defamation, confidence and privacy, harassment, advertising, contempt of court and media, freedom of information, data protection and all aspects of law relating to the communication of information or its restriction including human rights law and harassment.

Career: LLB (Euro) Hons Exon 1990. Called 1991, joined chambers 1992. Cases include: Cartus Corporation v Sidell & anr (2014) (libel injunction); LB Lambeth v Pead (2013) (Harassment, Breach of Confidence, Data Protection Act and Contempt of Court); Nowak v NMC and Guy's and St Thomas' NHS Trust (2013)(Harassment); O'Dwyer v ITV (2013)(Defamation); Iqbal v Mansoor (2011); Westminster NHS Trust v Shetreet (2010) (Breach of Confidence, Contempt of Court); Govei & anr v Ambrosiadou (2010); (Harassment/ Contempt) Khoury v Dahdah (2008), (Libel) Sheffield Wednesday Football Club and ors v Hargreaves (2007), Virdi v Associated Newspapers Limited (2007), Warren v (1) Hatton (2) BBC (2007), Stickland v Emap Metro Limited (2007), Guterman v Pemberton, Western Mail and Jones (2005), Morrison v Nord Anglia Educa-

tion Plc, and ors (2005), Downtex v Flatley (2003), Fox v Environment Agency and ors (2003), McPhilemy v Times Newspapers Ltd (2001-4), Melchett and Greenpeace UK v Glasgow Herald (2001), Sugar v News Group Newspapers Ltd and Mullery(2000), Arobieke v MGN Ltd and ors (2000), Tancic v Times Newspapers Ltd (1999). (Privacy/Confidence) Sorrell and Weber v Fullsix and ors (2007), Hughes v Carratu International PLC (2006). Acts for both claimants and defendants. Regularly advises major book and magazine publishers.
Publications: Contributor to Carter-Ruck on Libel and Privacy 6th edition; contributor to Arlidge, Eady and Smith on Contempt 4th Edition and supplement.
Personal: Lives in London. Languages French and German.

ADDY, Catherine
Maitland Chambers, London
020 7406 1200
cjaddy@maitlandchambers.com
Featured in Chancery (London), Company (London), Restructuring/Insolvency (London)
Practice Areas: Chancery and commercial litigation including: banking and financial services, company and insolvency matters, commercial contracts and other business related agreements (including partnerships), conflict of laws, property and other general equity and trust related matters. Appointed as Junior Counsel to the Crown (A Panel). She has particular expertise in insolvency related matters and is an appointed member of the statutory Insolvency Rules Committee. She is also a member of the Bankruptcy and Companies Court Users Committee and has provided expert insolvency and company law advice to international lawyers. Notably, she represented the Crown in Re Spectrum Plus, advised HM Treasury and the Bank of England in relation to Northern Rock, acted for the Secretary of State in the successful director's disqualification claim against Kevin Maxwell and for the successful non-executive directors in the failed director's disqualification proceedings brought by the Secretary of State in relation to the collapse of Farepak, and recently appeared in the Game appeal concerning administration expenses. She has also been instructed to represent the interests of the general unsecured creditors in various aspects of the Lehman Brothers' insolvency litigation and, as well as advising and appearing for officeholders of other well-known insolvent estates, she regularly acts for Crown Departments.
Professional Memberships: Chancery Bar Association; COMBAR; ILA; R3; International Associate Member of the American Bar Association; Insolvency Rules Committee; Bankruptcy and Companies Court Users Committee; Professional Practice committee and BARCO committee of the Bar Council.
Career: Called to the Bar 1998. Appointed Junior Counsel to the Crown (A Panel) March 2012 (B Panel 2007-2012, C Panel 2003-07). Chairman of the Young Bar (2004). Chairman of the Bar Conference (2007). Elected Member of the Bar Council (2001-07). Appointed Chancery Bar Association member of the Bar Council (2010-2012). Elected Hon. Treasurer of the Chancery Bar Association (2008-2012). Member of the Bankruptcy and Companies Court Users Committee (2012 to date). Appointed to serve on the Insolvency Rules Committee (2013 to date).

Publications: Contributor to Gore-Browne on Companies, Butterworths' Practical Insolvency, International Corporate Rescue and the Journal of International Business and Finance Law. Member of Jordan Publishing's Advisory Board for Insolvency.
Personal: MA, LLM (1st class) Cantab. Queen Mother Scholar of Middle Temple. Accredited advocacy trainer.

ADKIN, Jonathan QC
Serle Court, London
020 7400 7189
jadkin@serlecourt.co.uk
Featured in Chancery (London), Commercial Dispute Resolution (London), Offshore (London)
Practice Areas: Commercial and chancery litigation, civil fraud, trusts disputes (offshore and onshore), banking and finance, company and insolvency, and partnership.
Professional Memberships: Chancery Bar Association and COMBAR.
Career: Over the last few years Jonathan Adkin has appeared in a number of landmark commercial and chancery disputes including: Boris Berezovsky v Roman Abramovich (the much-publicised multi-billion dollar oligarch dispute), Re Glasgow Rangers (litigation arising from the collapse of the high profile football club), and Williams v Central Bank of Nigeria (the leading authority on limitation in dishonest assistance claims). In addition Jonathan has appeared in a number of high profile fraud cases including: the BCCI litigation, Jennington v Assaubayev (multi-million dollar claims in connection with a gold mining conglomerate), Central Bank of Ecuador v Conticorp ($150 million banking fraud claim), and Aviva v Darwin and Darwin (acting for the life insurers in the 'missing canoeist' case). His current partnership work includes acting in disputes arising from the collapse of Halliwells LLP. He has recently appeared in substantial offshore litigation in Gibraltar, the Cayman Islands, the Bahamas, and Bermuda.
Personal: Called 1997. Silk 2013. Called ad hoc to the bars of the Cayman Islands and Gibraltar. Educated at Balliol College, Oxford. Karmel scholar of Gray's Inn.

AFZAL, Imran
Field Court Tax Chambers, London
020 3693 3700
ia@fieldtax.com
Featured in Tax (London)
Practice Areas: Imran has a broad practice and has been involved in a range of domestic and international matters, acting for companies, private-clients and tax authorities. In addition to advisory work he is regularly involved in litigation. He is often instructed in high-profile and high-value matters, e.g. he has advised in relation to a multi-billion dollar settlement, he has assisted a foreign company in a matter involving over £1 billion, and he has been instructed by HMRC in relation to various partnership loss appeals.
Career: Imran was called to the Bar in 2008. In 2012 he was appointed to the Attorney-General's C Panel. In 2014 he founded Field Court Tax Chambers with three colleagues, having previously practised in another set of tax chambers.
Personal: Imran read Law at Oxford University as an undergraduate and postgraduate, coming top of the university on both occasions.

AGNELLO, Raquel QC
Erskine Chambers, London
020 7242 5532
clerks@erskinechambers.com
Featured in Pensions (London), Restructuring/Insolvency (London)
Practice Areas: Raquel Agnello QC is a sought-after specialist in insolvency, company and commercial litigation. She is a highly-regarded expert in the area of pensions and insolvency, in particular the 'moral hazard' provisions. She has led on many high profile cases on behalf of the Pensions Regulator, including on Nortel and Lehman in the Supreme Court. She has acted for the trustees of the Kaupthing Singer and Friedlander pensions scheme in their successful proceedings against the company in administration relating to the provability of the section 75 claim. In October 2012, she was named 'Barrister of the Year' at the Insolvency and Rescue Awards. In January 2012, she was selected as one of the 'Hot 100' by 'The Lawyer' and she was also shortlisted as Insolvency Silk of the Year by Chambers and Partners.
Professional Memberships: Chancery Bar Association. Insolvency Lawyers Association. Financial Services Lawyers Association.
Career: 1986; Silk: 2009; sits in the High Court part time as Deputy Registrar in Bankruptcy and also sits in the Companies Court; Bencher of the Inner Temple: 2011.
Personal: BA (hons) (Sussex), Diplome D'Etudes Juridiques Francaise; MCIArb. Fluent in French and Portuguese, working knowledge of Swedish.

AGNEW, Christine
2 Bedford Row, London
020 7440 8888
cagnew@2bedfordrow.co.uk
Featured in Crime (London)
Practice Areas: Cited by The Legal 500 and Chambers UK as a leading junior, Christine conducts the most serious and complex criminal cases as leading and junior counsel for both the defence and prosecution. She is a Grade 4 Prosecution Advocate for the CPS. Christine's practice covers the full range of criminal work and she has very considerable experience in relation to allegations involving murder, manslaughter, armed robbery, drug importations, kidnap and serious sexual offences. She has developed specialist expertise in relation to trials involving young offenders charged with all types of serious criminal offences. Christine has been instructed in a number of "baby-shaking" and infant non-accidental injury cases, which have involved extensive cross-examination of medical professionals, and dealing with expert medical evidence before juries. Christine is also regularly instructed in all types of fraud cases. She has represented defendants concerned in multimillion pound MTIC frauds. She also has significant experience of complex money laundering trials from simple cash to gold bullion and currency exchanges. She has a reputation as being an extremely hard working and able defence advocate who is exceptionally good with clients and achieves acquittals in the most difficult of circumstances. She is often first choice defence counsel for firms with private clients who demand an incisive and empathic advocate who can instil real confidence in the client. In addition to undertaking general crime work Christine also prosecutes for the Health and Safety Executive and the Environment Agency.Christine has been appointed to the A list for Specialist Regulatory Advocates in Health and Safety and Environmental Law and has prosecuted several fatality cases requiring detailed and specialist knowledge. She also has experience of coroners' inquests. Christine is authorised to accept instructions from members of the public in certain circumstances. She also appears before Police Disciplinary and Appeal Tribunals.
Professional Memberships: South Eastern Circuit. Criminal Bar Association. Association of Regulatory and Disciplinary Lawyers. Health and Safety Lawyers Association.
Career: Called 1992.

AGNEW OF LOCHNAW BT, Crispin QC
Westwater Advocates, Edinburgh
0131 668 3792
aofl@agnew.sol.co.uk
Featured in Agriculture & Rural Affairs (Scotland), Planning (Scotland)
Practice Areas: All aspects of rural property law including fishing law, environmental law and nature conservation; agriculture and CAP, agricultural landlord and tenant, crofting and wind & hydro renewable energy. Also acting in planning and environmental law applications and challenges, including acting in or defending planning appeals and judicial review challenges of planning and section 36 consent decisions. Local Authority law including licensing and special needs education & disability issues in education. Peerage and Heraldic Law. Knowledge of military issues having served in the Army 1962 to 1981 [Retired as Major].
Professional Memberships: Patron, United Kingdom Environmental Law Association [UKELA]; Chairman, Crofting Law Group; Agricultural Law Association.
Career: Called to Bar 1982; Silk 1995.
Publications: Agricultural Law in Scotland, Butterworths 1996; Connell on Agricultural Holdings (Scotland) Acts 7th Ed (with Donald Rennie WS) T & T Clark 1996 Variation and Discharge of Land Obligations, WGreen 1999 Crofting Law, T & T Clark 2000 Allan & Chapman, Licensing (Scotland) Act 1976 2nd to 5th Ed [with Heather Baillie, solicitor] Stair Memorial Encyclopaedia - Articles on Heraldy; Court of the Lord Lyon; Precedence; Scots law chapter in The Law of Trees, Forests and Hedges by Charles Mynors, 2nd Ed. Sweet & Maxwell 1912.

AHMAD, Mirza
St Philips Chambers, Birmingham
0121 246 7000
mahmad@st-philips.com
Featured in Administrative & Public Law (Midlands)
Practice Areas: Mirza practises from London, Birmingham and Leeds. He is nationally recognised as an expert in local authority law and employment law. He specialises in providing high quality advice and advocacy services in the areas of: judicial review, constitutional and governance issues; employment (including unfair dismissal, redundancy, TUPE, equal pay and discrimination); partnerships; procurement; land and property matters (including housing, planning and CPO); and personal injuries.
Professional Memberships: Chairman of the Bar Association for Local Government & the Public Services (since 1998); Member of The General Council of the Bar (since

1995, save for 1997), ALBA, ELA, PIBA and President of ACSeS (2009/2010).
Career: After being Called to the Bar in 1984 (Gray's Inn), Mirza spent over 26 years in local government. From 2000-11, he was the Chief Legal Officer and Corporate Director of Governance of Birmingham City Council, with leadership of 800+ staff. Mirza has an LLD (Hons), an LLM in Employment & Industrial Relations Law, and an MBA.
Publications: Mirza is the General Editor of two encyclopaedic publications: 'Local Authority Employment Law, Practice and Procedure'; and 'Knight's Guide to Public Procurement Law and Practice'.

AHMAD, Zubair
2 Hare Court, London
020 7353 5324
zubairahmad@2harecourt.com
Featured in Crime (London)
Practice Areas: A leading junior in serious and complex crime, appearing for both the defence and prosecution in some of the highest profile criminal and quasi-criminal cases. Has special expertise in homicide, terrorism, organised crime and fraud cases. Between 2010-2014 prosecuted high profile and complex cases including the trial of 20 defendants accused of murder – the largest joint enterprise murder trial to have taken place at the Central Criminal Court. Routinely engaged in high level National Security cases in the High Court, Administrative Court and SIAC. Also experienced in HM Treasury financial restrictions cases, and is involved in UN Sanctions and Justice and Security Act 2013 Closed Material Procedure cases in the High Court. Appointed to the A-G's Special Advocates panel in 2005, and in that capacity is regularly instructed by leading defence firms on behalf of their clients. Has acted as a Special Advocate in 20 different civil Terrorist / National Security cases in the High Court and SIAC (and in their subsequent appeals to the Court of Appeal). Acted as Junior Counsel for AF during 5 years of civil litigation against the SSHD which resulted in the landmark decisions of the House of Lords in MB & AF in 2007 and AF (No.3) in 2009 relating to Article 6 disclosure in National Security cases. He has been involved in many of the appellate cases involving terrorist Control Orders.
Career: Monitoree Treasury Counsel 2010-2014; CPS Advocate Panel: Grade 4 & Specialist Rape list; A-G's unified list of prosecuting counsel since 2006; A-G's Special Advocate panel since 2005; A-G's Special Counsel (PII) panel since 2004; List of Counsel for the defence and victims at the International Criminal Court since 2005.

AKKOUH, Tim
Erskine Chambers, London
020 7242 5532
takkouh@erskinechambers.com
Featured in Chancery (London), Commercial Dispute Resolution (London), Fraud (London)
Practice Areas: Called to the Bar in 2004, Tim's practice has in recent years focused on civil fraud and commercial litigation. Tim acts as junior counsel for the claimant in the BTA Bank litigation, which has generated important decisions including BTA v Ablyazov [2010] 1 WLR 976 (freezing order disclosure), BTA v A [2011] Bus LR D119 (pre-judgment receivers), BTA v Ablyazov (No 7) [2012] 1 WLR 1988 (practice on committal hearings), BTA v Ablyazov [2012] EWCA Civ 639 (discretion to refuse to hear contemnor), BTA v Ablyazov (No 8) [2013] 1 WLR 1331 (unless orders), BTA v Ablyazov (No 9) [2013] 1 WLR 1845 (recusal), BTA v Ablyazov (No 10) [2014] 1 WLR 1414 (injunctions against third parties). Tim maintains a commercial chancery practice, with an emphasis on insolvency, company and trusts law disputes. His reported decisions in these fields include Alhamrani v Alhamrani (2007-09, Jersey Royal Court), Gotham v Doodes [2007] 1 WLR 86, Halabi v Camden [2008] BPIR 370, Charity Commission v Framjee [2014] WLR(D) 340 and Setchim v Foreign Secretary [2014] EWHC 2218 (Ch). Member of Attorney General's B Panel of Counsel to the Crown.
Professional Memberships: Chancery Bar Association; COMBAR.
Publications: Co-author of Trusts Law (3rd ed, Palgrave Macmillan, 2013).
Personal: LLB (Lond), 1st class; LLM (Lond); married to Aimee; leisure interests include cricket and mountaineering.

AL-ATTAR, Adam
South Square, London
020 7696 9900
adamalattar@southsquare.com
Featured in Restructuring/Insolvency (London)
Practice Areas: Insolvency and restructuring, banking and financial services, and the law of trusts.
Professional Memberships: ILA, INSOL, COMBAR, Chancery Bar Association.
Career: Significant cases include the client money, priorities and surplus applications in Lehman Brothers; the client money applications and affiliate litigation in MF Global; litigation in the BVI and the Cayman Islands concerning Madoff feeder funds, including Primeo Fund; and the restructurings of IMO Carwash, Cattles, Drydock Dubai and The Co-operative Bank.
Publications: Contributor to The Law and Practice of Restructuring in the UK and US (first edition, OUP, 2011); Cross Border Insolvency (third edition, Bloomsbury, 2012); and European Debt Restructuring Handbook (first edition, Global Business Law, 2013).

ALDOUS, Grahame QC
9 Gough Square, London
020 7832 0500
galdous@9goughsquare.co.uk
Featured in Clinical Negligence (London), Personal Injury (London)
Practice Areas: Personal injury and clinical negligence, in particular catastrophic injury claims and claims involving maritime and foreign jurisdiction issues and complex and novel points of law. Cases include Marchioness Disaster; Simmons v Castle (general damages 10% uplift in Court of Appeal), Acori v Algol Maritime (Privy Council and Supreme Court of Gibraltar/ITWF Seaman's Contracts); Sansom v Metcalfe Hambledon (Court of Appeal: surveyors negligence); Hatswell v Goldbergs (Court of Appeal: solicitors negligence/clinical negligence), Johnstone v Whipps Cross Hospital (Court of Appeal: clinical negligence), Booth v Phillips (UK Admiralty Court Jurisdiction), Dickins v O2 (Court of Appeal: stress at work), Joshi v Toyo Tires (QBD Product Liability, defective tyre), Braganza v BP (Admiralty Court and Court of Appeal: death at sea). Also acts as a mediator.
Professional Memberships: PNBA, PIBA, Fellow of APIL.
Career: Called 1979, Recorder 2000, CEDR Accredited Mediator 2006, Silk 2008. Head of Chambers 2008-2013.
Publications: APIL Guide to Catastrophic Injury Claims, Kemp & Kemp Personal Injury Law Practice and Procedure, Work Accidents at Sea, Clinical Negligence Claims: A Practical Guide, Munkman on Employers' Liability, Applications for Judicial Review.
Personal: Ocean sailing, raced round Cape Horn in 1990 Whitbread Round the World Yacht Race and crossed South Atlantic in square-rig ship crewed with disabled/able bodied crew in the Norton Rose Sail the World Challenge, 2013. RYA/DOT Yachtmaster.

ALDRIDGE, James QC
Maitland Chambers, London
020 7406 1200
jaldridge@maitlandchambers.com
Featured in Chancery (London)
Practice Areas: Chancery/ commercial litigation, including matters involving contracts, property, professional negligence, company, insolvency and trusts.
Professional Memberships: Chancery Bar Association, COMBAR.
Career: Called to the Bar 1994. Queen's Counsel 2014.
Personal: Educated Rugby and Corpus Christi College, Cambridge. Lives in London.

ALEXANDER, Daniel QC
8 New Square, London
020 7405 4321
daniel.alexander@8newsquare.co.uk
Featured in Information Technology (London), Intellectual Property (London), Media & Entertainment (London)
Practice Areas: Barrister (QC) specialising principally in intellectual property, media and entertainment, information technology (IT Silk of the Year, 2007), EC and commercial law. Practice regularly involves cases with international and multi-jurisdicational aspects. Advocacy and advisory work in a wide variety of cases at all levels of UK courts and at the EPO, ECJ and General Court (CFI). Regular involvement in international arbitrations as counsel or arbitrator. Recent cases include: Fage UK Ltd v Chobani UK Ltd (Greek Yogurt), Actavis v Sanofi, HTV v Apple. For comprehensive CV visit the website at www.8newsquare.co.uk
Professional Memberships: Intellectual Property Bar Association (IPBA); Chancery Bar Association.
Career: Called to English Bar, 1988; QC, 2003; Deupty High Court Judge, 2006.
Publications: Joint author of 'Guidebook to Intellectual Property Law'; joint editor 'Clerk & Lindsell on Torts'; 'Encyclopaedia of UK & European Patent Law'; various articles and lectures.
Personal: Born: London, 1963. Education: BA Physics and Philosophy (Oxford University, 1985); DipLaw (1986); LLM (Harvard Law School, 1987); called to New York Bar (1988).

ALEXANDER, David QC
South Square, London
020 7696 9900
davidalexander@southsquare.com
Featured in Restructuring/Insolvency (London)
Practice Areas: Commercial, chancery, company, insolvency, banking, civil fraud and contentious trust work.
Professional Memberships: COMBAR, Chancery Bar Association.
Career: Called to the Bar in 1987 and made QC in 2006, David has a predominately litigation based practice covering a wide area of business and commercial law. He appears regularly in England, both in court in London at all levels as well as outside London. He has also acted in relation to many international cases including in the Bahamas (called to the Bahamas Bar ad hoc in 2011), Bermuda (called to the Bermuda Bar ad hoc in 1997 and 2013), the BVI, the Cayman Islands, Jersey and Gibraltar. David has been instructed in relation to many of the major recent insolvencies, including for the winding up Board of Landsbanki (in the Supreme Court) and the officeholders of the US arm of MF Global. A specialist and highly recommended trial lawyer, David has appeared in many major and lengthy trials, including the Maxwell saga, the KWELM litigation, the Thyssen litigation and the New Gadget Shop litigation. Most recently David appeared at both the trial and then in the Court of Appeal in Smithton v Naggar and in trust litigation in Bermuda.

ALEXIS, Fallon
QEB Hollis Whiteman, London
020 7933 8855
fallon.alexis@qebhw.co.uk
Featured in Crime (London)
Practice Areas: Fallon is an outstanding Barrister at QEB Hollis Whiteman, "a junior tenant, but she has a bright future" practicing in crime, fraud, and regulatory and professional discipline. She prosecutes and defends regularly in the Crown Court, and is recognised by colleagues and clients alike for the passion and dedication she puts into her caseload. "Fantastic written work. Great feedback from clients." Fallon's criminal work covers the full range of offences. She was recently instructed as led junior defending in a large fraud and money laundering case, which resulted in an acquittal on all counts. Fallon also receives instructions from HMRC in appeals before the First-tier Tribunal (Tax Chamber). She has gained experience in a bribery case, specifically in relation to a company's compliance with disclosure notices issued by the SFO and has experience of prosecutions brought by the OFT, having been seconded there for 11 months. Meticulous preparation, coupled with her legal knowledge, makes Fallon a highly accomplished lawyer. She is comfortable dealing with high-profile cases, as demonstrated by her role as junior counsel for the defence in the trial of Rebekah Brooks, instructed by Kingsley Napley LLP. Throughout the trial Fallon demonstrated the strong work ethic that she is rapidly becoming known for. Following Brooks' acquittal, Jonathan Laidlaw QC described Fallon and her fellow junior as 'fearsomely bright and intensely loyal'. Since joining QEB Hollis Whiteman in 2009, Fallon's reputation as a rising star has enabled her to gain experience far beyond her level of call.
Professional Memberships: Criminal Bar Association; Young Fraud Lawyers' Association; British Association for Sports and Law; Inner Temple's Qualifying Sessions Committee; Social Mobility Committee of The Bar Council; Association of Regulatory and Disciplinary Lawyers.
Career: Call 2008.

ALGAZY, Jacques QC
Cloisters, London
020 7827 4000
ja@cloisters.com
Featured in Employment (London)

Practice Areas: Jacques Algazy practices in employment, commercial, European, and public law. His robust advocacy wins praise in the directories. He regularly appears for major institutions, NHS Trusts and local authorities as well as appearing for individuals and trade union clients. He has experience of multi-party actions involving large numbers of litigants. Jacques' employment practice embraces Tribunal, High Court and appellate work and covers all areas of employment law, especially discrimination. He specialises in multi-jurisdictional (e.g. Tribunal and High Court) and cross-border litigation. Jacques regularly acts in restrictive covenant cases and associated areas of confidentiality and fiduciary duty. Jacques is well known for his expertise in the international aspects of employment law, statutory and contractual. He has appeared in a number of significant cases in the area of territorial jurisdiction including Lawson v Serco. Jacques also acts in employment cases in Northern Ireland and the Channel Islands. Jacques has appeared in a number of substantial claims in the medical field acting both for Doctors and NHS Trusts. Including successfully defending a 26 day race claim. Jacques also practices discrimination law in the field of goods and services. Jacques is a part-time Employment Tribunal Judge. His commercial litigation practice covers a broad range of commercial matters, especially cases with an international/EC dimension, including commercial agency and sale of goods and services. Jacques also acts in international arbitrations. Jacques acted in a partnership arbitration (injunction applications in England) arising out of a team move in Russia. He successfully acted in a ground-breaking case in which the minority shareholders of a company sued the majority who had bought them out and then sold the business on three weeks later at a substantially higher price. In a company dispute, Jacques succeeded in setting aside a transfer of shares on grounds of duress. Jacques' public law and regulatory work includes judicial review . See www.cloisters.com for more information.

Professional Memberships: ELA, ELBA and BEG.

Career: Part-time Employment Tribunal Judge. Called to Bar of Northern Ireland. Gray's Inn/ELBA advocacy trainer. Former lecturer in European and Company Law and legal adviser at European Commission (DGVI).

Publications: Jacques has published articles on EC law and employment law. He is regularly invited to provide training and lectures in the UK and abroad. This includes sessions for the ELA on international employment, a talk to Equality bodies in Budapest, training for European judges in Latvia, presenting a paper at a Colloquium for judges in Brussels, lecturing for the ILS and speaking at the Council of Employment Judges AGM(2013).

ALLARDICE, Miranda
5 Stone Buildings, London
020 7242 6201
clerks@5sblaw.com
Featured in Chancery (London), Family/Matrimonial (London)

Practice Areas: Extensive experience of Inheritance Act and probate claims, administration of estate issues, proprietary estoppel and undue influence. Miranda has expertise in Vulnerable Elderly and Capacity issues, together with Court of Protection work. An experienced Mediator with a thriving mediation practice in her areas of specialisation. Miranda also undertakes complex matrimonial finance claims; involving trust and company law aspects. Notable Cases include:Musa v Holliday [2012] EWCA 1268 Inheritance Act claim by cohabitee; Holliday v Musa [2010] WTLR 839 Domicile re Inheritance Act claim; H v Mitson [2010] WTLR 193 Inheritance Act claim by estranged adult child; Van Laetham v Brooker [2006] 2 FLR 495 Constructive Trust/Estoppel; Re Myers [2005] WTLR 851 Inheritance Act claim by an adult daughter.

Professional Memberships: Chancery Bar Association, ACTAPS, FLBA.

Career: Called 1982.

Publications: A key contributor to Jordans' Inheritance Act Claims; Law Practice and Procedure. Lectures for CLT,CPD and ACTAPS. She was an Advisory Group Member of the Law Commission Intestacy and Family Provision on Death Report.

ALLEN, Darryl QC
Byrom Street Chambers, Manchester
0161 829 2100
darryl.allen@byromstreet.com
Featured in Clinical Negligence (Northern), Personal Injury (Northern)

Practice Areas: Queen's Counsel specialising in personal injury and clinical negligence litigation. Personal injury - Advises and appears on behalf of claimants and defendants in catastrophic injury and high value fatal accident claims. Substantial experience of analysing difficult issues relating to local authority care and accommodation, large care claims and high value complex loss of earnings claims. Clinical negligence - Regularly instructed to advise and represent patients and their families in clinical negligence claims. Caseload covers a wide spectrum of medical accidents, including delayed diagnosis of cancer, delayed diagnosis of infant brain tumor, surgical errors (orthopaedic, general surgery, colorectal surgery etc.), birth trauma, hospital acquired infection, failure to diagnose and treat evolving cauda equine syndrome, failures in spinal anaesthetic technique leading to spinal cord injury, management of infant and grown up congenital heart conditions, community and hospital management of diabetes and diabetic complications, failures in psychiatric care (community and inpatient) leading to suicide/attempted suicide. Consistently recommended as a leading barrister in personal injury and clinical negligence work (Chambers and Partners/Legal 500).

Professional Memberships: PIBA and AVMA.

Career: Called 1995. Criminal Injuries Compensation Appeals Panel (2007). Recorder (Civil) (2010). Queen's Counsel (2014).

Personal: Born 1972. Education: Altrincham Grammar School for Boys and Leeds University (LLB (Hons)). Married with two daughters and two dogs. Completed New York and London Marathons and Ironman Lanzarote.

ALLEN, Neil
Thirty Nine Essex Street, London
0207 832 1111
neil.allen@39essex.com
Featured in Court of Protection (All Circuits)

Practice Areas: Particular interests in human rights, mental health and incapacity law, practising predominantly in health, personal welfare, financial and property matters in the Court of Protection. Reported cases include Re X [2014] EWHC 25 (COP DOL); P v Cheshire West [2014] UKSC 19 ("deprivation of liberty"); A LA v SY [2013] EWHC 3485 (non-marriages); P v M [2011] EWHC 2778 ("best interests"); Re MB [2010] EWHC 2508 (validity of DOLS authorisations); G v E [2010] EWHC 2512 (deputyship), [2010] EWHC 2042 (media), [2010] EWCA Civ 822 (Winterwerp), [2010] EWHC 621 (Articles 5, 8).

Professional Memberships: Liberty. Society of Legal Scholars

Career: Also a Lecturer at the University of Manchester.

Publications: Eg: 'Psychiatric care and criminal prosecution' (2013, CUP); 'The Right to Life in a Suicidal State' (2013) 36 IJLP 350; 'The opacity of sexual capacity' (2012) 2 ELJ 352; 'Criminal care: ill treatment and wilful neglect' (2012) 2 ELJ 71; 'Dare to care' (2011) 1(2) ELJ 167; 'The Bournewood gap (as amended?)' (2010) 18 Med LR 78-85; 'Saving life and respecting death: A Savage dilemma' (2009) 17 Med LR 262; 'Is capacity "in sight"?' (2009) JMHL 165; 'Restricting movement or depriving liberty?' (2009) JMHL 19.

ALLEN, Nicholas
29 Bedford Row Chambers, London
020 7404 1044
nallen@29br.co.uk
Featured in Family/Matrimonial (London)

Practice Areas: Matrimonial finance, children (private law), civil partnerships, cohabitation. Reported cases - M v W [2014] EWHC 925 (Fam); Sharland v Sharland [2014] 2 FLR 89,CA; S v S (Non-Disclosure) [2013] 2 FLR 1598; Marinos v Marinos (2007) 2 FLR 108; R v R (Divorce: Jurisdiction: Domicile) (2006) 1 FLR 389; A v B (Ancillary Relief: Property Division) (2005) 2 FLR 730; Currey v Currey (2005) 1 FLR 952; C v C (Costs: Ancillary Relief) (2004) 1 FLR 291.

Professional Memberships: Committee member - Resolution Dispute Resolution Committee (2011-date); Committee member - Complaints Committee of the Bar Standards Board (2005-07); Committee member - Family Law Bar Association (2003-08); Member - American Bar Association.

Career: Called to the Bar 1995. Admitted to the New York Bar 1998. Pupil Supervisor 2004. Trained as Collaborative Counsel 2009.

Personal: Education - Leeds Grammar School; Emmanuel College, Cambridge (MA, LLM); Harvard Law School, Cambridge, Mass, USA (Visiting Scholar 1995-96). Leisure Interests - watching Test Cricket.

ALLEN, Robin QC
Cloisters, London
020 7827 4000
clerks@cloisters.com
Featured in Employment (London)

Practice Areas: Employment, discrimination, European, human rights, local government and public law.

Professional Memberships: Recorder, Bencher Middle Temple, Chair of Bar Equality and Diversity Committee. Formerly legal adviser to Disability Rights Commission, Chairman the Employment Law Bar Association, founder member the Discrimination Law Association, and Chairman the Bar Pro Bono Unit.

Career: Head of Cloisters since 2002. Appeared in many leading employment, discrimination, public and human rights cases, including reported cases every year since 1978. Major advisory practice for public authorities, local government, specialist NDPBs and central government, on publicity powers and politically sensitive decisions. Very wide range of clients: from FTSE companies, trade unions, charities, to acting pro bono for individual and interventions and amicus briefs . Works frequently with the UK Equality Commissions. Extensive media work lecturing, writing and broadcasting including: Chairman of the Bar Conference in 2002, and the Home Office Publicity sub-committee for the launch of the Human Rights Act 1998. Full details see www.cloisters.com

Personal: Awards: Chambers and Partners Employment Law Team of the Year 2013. Chambers and Partners Employment Law Silk 2012 and 2008; Runner up Lawyer of the Year 2010; FT Innovative Barrister 2009; Equal Opportunities Review leading barrister; the Lawyer 'Hot 100'. Charity Award for the London Bombings Relief Charitable Fund 2006.

ALLEN, Rupert
Fountain Court Chambers, London
020 7583 3335
ra@fountaincourt.co.uk
Featured in Commercial Dispute Resolution (London), Professional Discipline (London)

Practice Areas: Since joining Fountain Court Rupert has been involved as part of a team in very heavy commercial litigation (such as the 77 day trial of Digicel's claims against Cable & Wireless) as well as a number of significant commercial cases in his own right and with a leader (including a number of cases in the Court of Appeal). Rupert also has substantial experience in the fields of regulatory law (particularly in relation to financial services and aviation) and professional discipline. His growing professional discipline practice has seen him regularly instructed (both as sole counsel and with a leader) by the Solicitors Regulation Authority in relation to high profile matters including contested interventions (and obtaining urgent injunctive relief to support interventions), proceedings before the Solicitors Disciplinary Tribunal and judicial reviews of the SRA's decisions. Rupert has also recently acted for the Financial Reporting Council, the Financial Conduct Authority and the Council of Licensed Conveyancers in relation to regulatory issues.

Professional Memberships: COMBAR, British Association of Sport and Law.

Career: MA (Law), Gonville and Caius College, Cambridge (First Class) BCL, Merton College, Oxford (Distinction) BVC, Inns of Court School of Law (Outstanding).

ALLEN, Scott
4 New Square, London
020 7822 2000
s.allen@4newsquare.com
Featured in Professional Negligence (London)

Practice Areas: Professional negligence, commercial litigation, construction, insurance.
Professional Memberships: PNBA, COMBAR, LCLCBA.
Career: Called in 2000.
Publications: Contributor to 'Human Rights in Civil Practice', Assistant Editor of Jackson & Powell on Professional Liability (co-authoring chapter on Information Technology Professionals).
Personal: Happily married, with identical twin boys, and an avid lover of all things sporting (especially tennis and surfing).

ALLEN, Tom
5 Paper Buildings, London
07977 071 969
ta@5pb.co.uk
Featured in Crime (London), Financial Crime (London)
Practice Areas: Expert in Domestic and International Criminal Law, including bribery, corruption, fraud, health and safety and homicide. -Appointed to HM Attorney General's list of Special Advocates -Appointed to the list of advocates at the International Criminal Court -Appointed to the list of advocates at the Special Tribunal for the Lebanon.
Professional Memberships: Member of the Criminal Bar Association Member of South Eastern Circuit Member of the Howard League.
Career: Year of Call: 1994.

ALLISON, David QC
South Square, London
020 7696 9900
davidallison@southsquare.com
Featured in Banking & Finance (London), Chancery (London), Commercial Dispute Resolution (London), Company (London), Financial Services (London), Restructuring/Insolvency (London)
Practice Areas: Specialises in business, commercial and financial law, with a particular emphasis on corporate restructuring, sovereign debt restructuring, banking, structured finance, commercial litigation and company matters. Recent cases include Lehman, ATU, Airwave, Stemcor, MF Global, Nortel, Bank of Ireland, European Directories, Stanford International Bank, Madoff, Landsbanki, Glitnir, Kaupthing, Woolworths, Almatis, Arcapita, Metronet, Northern Rock, Dewey & LeBoeuf, Deutsche Annington, PrimaCom, Nef Telecom, Biffa, Fitness First, NCP, Monier, Tele Columbus and Cattles. Extensive overseas practice which includes BVI, Cayman and Dubai (appearing in the first trial to come before the DIFC court).
Professional Memberships: COMBAR, Chancery Bar Association.
Career: Called to the Bar, 1998 (Middle Temple); Called to the Bar of the Eastern Caribbean, 2007; full registration under Part II of the DIFC Courts Register of Practitioners; Appointed Queen's Counsel, 2014.
Publications: Contributor to 'Gore-Browne on Companies'.
Personal: Educated at Downing College, Cambridge (MA Law, 1st Class Hons); Queen Mother Scholar (Middle Temple).

ALLSOP, Julian
Guildhall Chambers, Bristol
0117 930 9000
julian.allsop@guildhallchambers.co.uk
Featured in Employment (Western)
Practice Areas: Employment and Discrimination litigation in the Employment Tribunal and Civil Courts.
Professional Memberships: Lincoln's Inn, Employment Lawyers Association, Industrial Law Society, Employment Law Bar Association.
Career: Employment and Discrimination specialist who has a mainly Respondent based practice, representing Government Departments, Local Authorities, NHS Trusts and corporations of all sizes with particular expertise in complex whistleblowing, discrimination and victimisation claims. He also has a particular interest in contract based issues, including restrictive covenant cases, and enjoys a national practice.
Publications: Regular contributor to the ELA Briefing and Jordans Employment Law Portal.

ALTMAN, Brian QC
2 Bedford Row, London
020 7440 8888
baltman@2bedfordrow.co.uk
Featured in Crime (London)
Practice Areas: General specialisms are in criminal and regulatory work, but practice includes advising high net worth individuals, multinational corporations and has included a Middle Eastern Royal family. Has advised the Government on a wide variety of esoteric issues and private and corporate clients including a multinational corporation as regards allegations of a multi-million Euro fraud arising during a reverse takeover of a €1.7 billion part of its pan European business; a well known credit reference company during due diligence of a target company's data protection systems, bearing on issues of cybercrime and data protection; a national construction PLC on its POCA compliance; a significant victim of phone hacking; a household name company on issues of corporate governance; the Bar Council on the Bribery Act 2010 and its application to the Bar; LOCOG pre the 2012 Olympics on ticket touting offences online. Has defended in several difficult homicide cases. Has had instructions for the SFO in a high profile banking case, and for the CMA in a nationwide cartel case. Is currently instructed by CPS Counter-Terrorism Division to prosecute Moazzam Begg for terrorism offences allegedly arising from the conflict in Syria, as well as other cases arising out of the conflict in Syria, and is instructed by the CPS to prosecute the historic north Kent murder of Claire Tiltman. As Treasury Counsel prosecuted and advised in many serious and high profile cases of murder, medical and corporate manslaughter, health and safety, police misconduct, war crimes, official secrets and terrorism. Selective past high profile cases include: Downey (1982 Hyde Park bombing case where the abuse of process argument turned on whether Downey had erroneously received a comfort letter from Government in 2007 amounting to a promise not to prosecute); Naseer, Khalid and Ali (convictions of 2011 Birmingham terror bomb plotters); Desuze and Desuze (plea of guilty to the unlawful killing of 68 year old Richard Mannington Bowes during the 2011 summer riots in Ealing by 16 year old Darrell Desuze who punched him hard to the jaw, causing an unprotected fall on to his head, from which he died, in addition to pleas of guilty to violent disorder and to four burglaries during the same night's disturbances, and the later conviction of his mother for perverting the course of justice by destroying and disposing of the distinctive articles of clothing her son had been wearing that night); Bikubi and Bamu (murder of 15 year old Kristy Bamu, and attacks on two others of his siblings, on Christmas Day 2010 in the defendants' East London flat during days of a process of deliverance or exorcism, which was grounded in the belief that the children were practising on another child of the family a form of witchcraft or sorcery, known in the Congo as 'kindoki'); Bellfield (2002 abduction and murder of Milly Dowler and 2003/2004 murders of Amelie Delagrange and Marsha McDonnell, and 2004 attempted murder of Kate Sheedy); Sweeney (historic murders of two women in the Netherlands and London prosecuted under the auspices of Eurojust); Thomas, Alexander and Burke (convictions for manslaughter of Ian Baynham in Trafalgar Square in September 2009 following homophobic abuse); Gnango (murder of a Polish care worker who was killed in the crossfire of a gunfight between the defendant and another youth, where the defendant had not fired the fatal bullet and the victim had been the unintended target; this landmark case has now passed through a seven justice Supreme Court and a five judge Court of Appeal on issues of joint enterprise, accessory liability and transferred malice. The offender's murder conviction was restored on a prosecution appeal from the Court of Appeal); and Dixie (murder of Sally Anne Bowman).
Professional Memberships: South Eastern Circuit. Criminal Bar Association. Association of Regulatory and Disciplinary Lawyers.
Career: Called to the Bar by Middle Temple 1981. First Senior Treasury Counsel at the Central Criminal Court December 2010-June 2013. Senior Treasury Counsel at CCC 2002-2013. Junior Treasury Counsel at CCC 1997-2002. Recorder since 2003. Queen's Counsel 2008. Bencher of Middle Temple 2010.
Personal: King's College London (LLB (Hons), 1978), University of Amsterdam (Dip Eur Int, 1979).

AMAOUCHE, Sassa-Ann
29 Bedford Row Chambers, London
020 7404 1044
samaouche@29br.co.uk
Featured in Family/Matrimonial (London)
Practice Areas: Practice primarily focuses on financial remedy proceedings. A particular expertise in cases involving non-disclosure, multi-jurisdictional and business assets. Sassa's approach has been described as "robust" and "fearless" but always underpinned by the willingness to give unwelcome advice to her own clients. Notable cases include: N v N (BIIR: Stay of Maintenance Proceedings) [2012] EWHC 4282 (Fam), Moor J; Constantinides v Constantinides [2013] EWHC 3688 (Fam), Holman J.
Professional Memberships: FLBA
Career: Called 1996, Inner Temple.
Personal: King's School Canterbury; King's College London (1995 Law). Resides in London.

AMIRAFTABI, Roshi
29 Bedford Row Chambers, London
020 7404 1044
ramiraftabi@29br.co.uk
Featured in Family/Matrimonial (London)
Practice Areas: Almost exclusively in the field of children law. Private law children involving cases with an international element, in which questions of jurisdiction or enforcement of foreign orders arise, cases of child abduction (Hague and non-Hague), as well as international and internal relocation cases. Extensive experience in public law matters involving legally or factually complex issues, as well as those in which there are international issues, or where jurisdiction is challenged. Also instructed in applications concerning vulnerable adults, and those with mental incapacity in the Court of Protection, and in applications for forced marriage protection orders. Cases include: Re A (A Child) [2014] EWHC 604; A v A [2013] EWHC 3554; Re S (A Child) [2013] EWHC 1295; FQ v MQ [2013] EWHC 4149; L B Lewisham v DM (January 2012) (Family Law Journal); Re B (Children)(Relocation Jurisdiction)[2008] EWCA Civ 1034; Local Authority X v MM (no 2)[2007] EWHC 2003; Local Authority X v MM (an adult) & Anor (no 1) [2007] EWHC 2689.
Professional Memberships: Family Law Bar Association.
Career: Called 1993. Undertakes Public Access Cases.

AMOS, Tim QC
Queen Elizabeth Building, London
020 7797 7837
t.amos@qeb.co.uk
Featured in Family/Matrimonial (London)
Practice Areas: All aspects of family law, but predominantly international divorce/jurisdiction and family finance, married or unmarried, alive or dead (including claims under the Inheritance Act). Specially interested in Anglo-German cases and those with a foreign or international element. Fluent in German (including legal German) and has good professional French. Work experience in German Courts and German law firms. Standing Counsel to the Queen's Proctor (2001 - 08), a government appointment to advise the Treasury Solicitor on all matters of family law with a public interest element including the validity of foreign marriage and foreign divorce. Trained Collaborative Lawyer and the first family law collaborative QC. Resolution Mediator and private judge. Recent reported cases: Prest v Petrodel [2012] EWCA Civ 1395 and [2013] UKSC 34; Mittal [2013] EWCA Civ 1255 – Stays in non-B II R cases; T v T (Brussels II Revised: Art. 15) [2013] 2 FLR 1326 – European transfers; Kim v Morris [2013] 2 FLR 1197 – Divorce jurisdiction.
Professional Memberships: Family Law Bar Association and British German Jurists Association. Fellow of the International Academy of Matrimonial Lawyers (IAML).

ANDERSON, Gavin
Westwater Advocates, Edinburgh
07989 347 695
gavin.anders@btinternet.com
Featured in Health & Safety (Scotland)
Practice Areas: Gavin Anderson specialises in white-collar criminal law and regulatory matters, appearing regularly in the High Court of Justiciary, Sheriff Courts and Tribunals throughout Scotland. He is frequently instructed to act in health and safety prosecutions involving fatality or serious injury, environmental crimes involving pollution and waste management, as well as other forms of commercial crime, includ-

ing fraud, money laundering, bankruptcy, licensing, financial services and company director offences. He has been instructed for the defence in several prosecutions arising out of fatal road traffic accidents. He has acted in Fatal Accident Inquiry proceedings in relation to deaths in the workplace and in custody. Mr Anderson currently represents a number of commercial and public sector organisations in connection with health and safety prosecutions, including proceedings relating to a gas explosion, fatal exposure to hazardous chemicals, dangerous lifting operations, agricultural fatalities and hospital patient safety. He recently appeared for an appellant company which successfully challenged fines imposed in relation to environmental offences. He continues to lecture at CPD events in the areas of health and safety prosecutions and regulatory crime. Mr Anderson recently provided advice to a large multi-national company in relation to the Scottish aspects of a UK-wide police investigation and also to a financial services regulator in relation to the exercise of its investigative functions in Scotland. He has advised in relation to a variety of complex regulatory investigations undertaken by Police Scotland, the Health and Safety Executive, HM Customs & Excise, the Maritime and Coastguard Agency and the Scottish Environmental Protection Agency. A full Curriculum Vitae is available from Westwater Advocates (www.westwateradvocates.com).
Professional Memberships: The Fraud Advisory Panel, Health and Safety Lawyers' Association, Association of Regulatory and Disciplinary Lawyers, Proceeds of Crime Lawyers' Association, Faculty of Advocates Criminal Bar Association.
Career: LLB (First Class Honours) 1993; Diploma in Legal Practice 1994; solicitor 1996-2000; admitted to the Faculty of Advocates 2001.

ANDERSON, Lesley QC
Kings Chambers, Manchester
0845 034 3444
clerks@kingschambers.com
Featured in Chancery (Northern), Commercial Dispute Resolution (Northern), Partnership (Northern), Real Estate Litigation (Northern), Restructuring/Insolvency (Northern)
Practice Areas: All aspects of chancery and commercial litigation; corporate and personal insolvency; commercial contracts including joint ventures, distribution and agency contracts and share and asset sale warranty claims; company law especially shareholder disputes , directors' duties and breach of trust/fiduciary duty claims; directors' disqualification and directors' and employee duties (including restrictive covenants and confidential information); partnership; banking (especially secured lending and guarantees); commercial property and landlord and tenant; professional negligence (especially solicitors, accountants, surveyors and financial advisers); sale of goods, commercial torts and insurance.
Professional Memberships: Bencher of The Honourable Society of the Middle Temple Chancery Bar Association; Northern Chancery Bar Association; Northern Circuit Commercial Bar Association; member of the North and North Eastern Circuit
Career: University of Manchester 1984-89; Training Manager Norton Rose M5 Group 1989-91; Called to the Bar 1989; CEDR Accredited Mediator 2000; Year of Silk 2006; Recorder 2006; Authorised to sit as Deputy Judge of the High Court Chancery Division 2008; Master of the Bench of the Middle Temple 2011; Also a member of Hardwicke in London from 2011.

ANDERSON, Mark QC
No5 Chambers, Birmingham
0845 210 5555
man@no5.com
Featured in Commercial Dispute Resolution (Midlands), Company (Midlands), Professional Negligence (Midlands)
Practice Areas: Commercial dispute resolution. Companies, partnerships, share sales, shareholders' rights and directors' duties. Professional negligence for claimants.
Professional Memberships: Midland Chancery and Commercial Bar Association (Chairman). Chancery Bar Association. Professional Negligence Bar Association.
Career: QC 2010. Authorised to sit as Deputy High Court Judge, Chancery Division 2013.

ANDERSON, Nicholas
1 King's Bench Walk, London
020 7936 1500
nanderson@1kbw.co.uk
Featured in Family/Matrimonial (London)
Practice Areas: Practice in all areas of family law with a particular emphasis on matrimonial finance and children cases involving an international element, including international child abduction and jurisdictional disputes. Involved in re S before the Supreme Court in 2012. Recent experience of the registration and enforcement of European orders relating to children in England. Experienced in finance cases with a foreign dimension proceeding both in England and Wales and abroad and cases involving trusts and family companies. Also specialises in cases involving property and financial disputes between former cohabitees.
Professional Memberships: Member of FLBA and South Eastern circuit.
Career: Called 1995. Qualified as a mediator in 2008. Qualified as collaborative counsel in 2010.
Publications: Regular speaker at various conferences including those organised by Jordans and CLT, in Gibraltar and at various events organised by Resolution. Contributor to various publications, including the child abduction section on the PLC website.

ANELAY, Richard QC
1 King's Bench Walk, London
020 7936 1500
ranelayqc@1kbw.co.uk
Featured in Family/Matrimonial (London)
Practice Areas: Family and criminal law. Leading work undertaken in matrimonial finance including variation of trusts and conduct, Inheritance Act provision and in children work including wardship with international issues, international child abduction, adoption, child arrangements and in public law care proceedings, having acted for local authorities, parents, intervenors, guardians involving complex medical issues, and sexual, physical and emotional abuse including fictitious illness. Extensive experience in criminal cases including serious fraud, murder and manslaughter. Experienced mediator in children, finance cases, and early neutral evaluator in finance cases including in Jersey. Reported cases include K v K [2009] EWCA Civ 986; SK v WL 2011 All ER (D) 39; A (a child) (father:knowledge of child's birth) 2011 All ER (D) 205; Grubb v Grubb [2011] EWCA Civ 1486, [2012] EWCA Civ 398; Re L [2013] EWCA Civ 1481.
Professional Memberships: FLBA: SECircuit; Fellow IAML.
Career: Called 1970. QC 1993. Recorder 1992. Deputy High Court Judge (Family Division) 1995. Panel Deemster (IOM) 2007. Middle Temple Bencher.
Personal: Educated Queen Elizabeth Grammar School, Darlington, Bristol University (BA Honours Classics and Philosophy), Council of Legal Education.

ANGUS, Tracey QC
5 Stone Buildings, London
020 7242 6201
clerks@5sblaw.com
Featured in Chancery (London), Court of Protection (All Circuits)
Practice Areas: Probate and trusts, family provision, Court of Protection, charities and related professional negligence. Reported or noteable cases include: Curtis and others v Pulbrook [2011] EWHC (Ch) 167; Gill v Woodhall &amp v others [2009] EWHC 834 (probate, estoppel);[2009] EWHC 1370 (equity);[2009]EWHC 782 (undue influence); Holman v Hayes [2008] 1 FLR 1217 (trust of land); Kostic v Chaplin and others [2008] WTLR 655 (probate); P v G, P and P [2006] 1 FLR 431 (family provision); Burrell v Burrell [2005] STC 569 (trusts); Bayoumi v Women's Total Abstinence Union Ltd.[2004] Ch 46 (charitable land).
Professional Memberships: Association of Contentious Trust and Probate Specialists, Professional Negligence Bar Association, Chancery Bar Association.
Career: Called 1991. Silk 2012.
Publications: Heywood and Massey's 'Court of Protection Practice' (contributing with others); co-author of 'A Practical Guide to Inheritance Act Claims' (Law Society 2006).
Personal: MA Hons (Edin); Dip Law (City).

ANSELL, Rachel QC
4 Pump Court, London
020 7842 5555
ransell@4pumpcourt.com
Featured in Construction (London), International Arbitration (London), Professional Negligence (London), Property Damage (London)
Practice Areas: Construction, engineering and energy disputes: Specialises in high value and complex disputes in the TCC and in international and domestic arbitrations with particular experience in the UAE. Recent instructions include a broad range of construction and engineering projects ranging from oil pumping facilities in Africa to multi-use high rise developments in Dubai and road and specialist leisure facilities in the UK. Professional Negligence: Regularly acts on behalf of the professional indemnity insurers of building professionals in technically difficult disputes involving architects, engineers and surveyors. Insurance: Experience in general insurance and subrogated claims (with particular expertise in fire and business interruption claims).
Professional Memberships: TECBAR (Treasurer), COMBAR, PNBA, LCLCBA.
Career: Called to the Bar in 1995. Silk in 2014.
Personal: Educated at Downing, Cambridge (Law (first class)). Interests include supporting Wales and Saracens rugby union teams, supporting Middlesex and England cricket teams and the gym.

ANTROBUS, Simon
Crown Office Chambers, London
0207 797 8100
antrobus@crownofficechambers.co.uk
Featured in Consumer Law (London), Health & Safety (London), Inquests & Public Inquiries (London)
Practice Areas: Simon is regarded as one of the leading barristers in this country in the field of criminal regulatory law, ranging from corporate/individual manslaughter prosecutions, environmental crime, trading standards and all issues to do with retail/business compliance. He has defended corporate and individual defendants in the highest profile cases, such as the prosecution relating to the Buncefield oil refinery explosion, the Lion Steel corporate manslaughter, the defence of the fireworks organiser accused of causing a multiple fatality road accident on the M5 motorway and representing BP in the inquest relating to the terrorist attack on their Algerian oil refinery. He has also been particularly successful in defending directors faced by regulatory prosecutions, including gross negligence manslaughter. He is also a specialist in all matters relating to consumer and trading law, representing FTSE companies and SMEs in both criminal prosecutions, regulatory investigations and conducting judicial review proceedings on their behalf in relation to regulatory decision-making. The judicial review work has involved recourse to European legislation and the European Court of Justice. In this role Simon has also undertaken non-contentious work, advising upon the regulatory aspects of both product launches and recalls in this country for major food manufacturers and retailers.
Professional Memberships: Health and Safety Lawyer's Association.
Publications: The Criminal Liability of Directors for Health and Safety Breaches and Manslaughter (Crim L.R. 2013, 4, 309-322).

APPS, Katherine
Littleton Chambers, London
020 7797 8600
katherineapps@littletonchambers.co.uk
Featured in Administrative & Public Law (London)
Practice Areas: Equality, employment, public/administrative, human rights, civil liberties, trade unions, European, regulatory, disciplinary, medical, civil litigation, commercial.
Professional Memberships: ELBA, ALBA, BEG, ARDL.
Career: Call 2006. Treasury C Panel. MA (Hons) Cantab. LLM Harvard Law School. Bedingfield Scholar (Grays Inn). CV http://www.littletonchambers.com/barristers/juniors/katherine-apps.aspx. Cases include: R(MM) v SSWP [2014] 1 WLR 1716: reasonable adjustments judicial review; R(Peel) v Health and Safety Executive [2013] EWHC 1012(Admin): duties to consult in EU and domestic law; Halstead v Paymentshield Group Holdings [2012] IRLR 856: concurrent Employment Tribunal and High Court causes of action; R (G) v X School [2012] 1 AC 167: Article 6 ECHR and internal disciplinary hearings; W v M [2011] EWHC 2443 (COP): first application to withhold and withdraw life sustaining treatment from a person in minimally conscious state.
Publications: Contributed chapters to Industrial Action and Trade Union Recognition (2011, OUP); Equality Act 2010 (The Law Society). Sole Author articles include:

Damages claims against trade unions after Viking and Laval [2009] European Law Review 141. Major Impact: the practical effect Impact v MAFF could have on employment cases [2008] New Law Journal 875. Nationality Discrimination in football: FIFA's 6 + 5 Rule (2008) Solicitors Journal Vol 152 page 52.

ARDEN, Andrew QC
Arden Chambers, London
020 7242 4244
clerks@ardenchambers.com
Featured in Local Government (London), Social Housing (London)

Practice Areas: Housing; landlord and tenant; leasehold management; human rights, local government constitutional and administrative law, finance, regeneration and reorganisation; procurement and waste; public and administrative law. Accredited Mediator.

Professional Memberships: ALBA; HLPA; SHLA; Chartered Institute of Housing; Civil Mediation Council.

Career: Called 1974. Director, Small Health Community Law Centre 1976-78. QC 1991. Founded Arden Chambers (1993) as a centre for specialist practice primarily in housing and local government law. Has appeared in a large number of important housing cases - many in the House of Lords/Supreme Court - from the early homelessness cases of the 1980s through to the human rights cases of this century. His local government work includes the Crédit Suisse litigation, "Homes for Votes," audit cases and hearings, procurement, five local government inquiries/ reviews, and a wide range of other matters including land acquisition and disposal and waste. In the last few years alone, Andrew has been involved in a series of leading housing and human rights cases, including Manchester CC v. Pinnock [2010] UKSC 45; Hounslow LBC v Powell and other cases [2011] UKSC 8; Sims v Dacorum BC [2013] EWCA Civ 12 (Supreme Court decision forthcoming); R (CN) v LB Lewisham [2013] EWCA Civ 804; R (ZH) v LB Newham [2013] EWCA Civ 805 (Supreme Court decisions forthcoming) Andrew continues to appear in the most significant homelessness cases, including Ali v. Birmingham CC [2010] UKSC 8; Bubb v LB Wandsworth [2011] EWCA Civ 1283; LB Camden v Sharif [2013] UKSC 10. Other recent cases of note include R. (Enfield LBC) v Barnet Clinical Commissioning Group [2013] EWHC 3496 (Admin); Holt v Reading BC [2013] EWCA Civ 641 and Islington LBC v Unite Group Plc [2013] EWHC 508 (Admin).

Publications: Andrew is author/co-author of - among other works - Arden & Partington's Housing Law, Manual of Housing Law, Homelessness and Allocations, Local Government Constitutional and Administrative Law, Local Government Finance: Law and Practice. General Editor of Housing Encyclopedia, Housing Law Reports, Journal of Housing Law.

ARDEN, Peter QC
Erskine Chambers, London
020 7242 5532
parden@erskinechambers.com
Featured in Chancery (London), Company (London), Restructuring/Insolvency (London)

Practice Areas: Peter is a highly-regarded company law and commercial chancery Silk with particular expertise in large, complex insolvencies and restructurings, often with a cross-border element. Significant cases include: the Federal Mogul / T&N restructuring, Eurotunnel, the HIH litigation, the Baugur administration, Lehmans, the Landsbanki and Kaupthing insolvencies, Miss Sixty and other retail insolvencies, the TXU company voluntary arrangement, and the winding-up of Danka Business Systems and Travelodge. He is a member of Erskine Chambers which was named Insolvency Set of the Year in 2014.

Professional Memberships: Member of Association of Business Recovery Professionals; Member of the Chancery Bar Association.

Career: LLB (Lond); LLM (Cantab). Called to the Bar: 1983; Silk: 2006.

ARENTSEN, Andrew
Civitas Law, Cardiff
0845 0713 007
andrew.arentsen@civitaslaw.com
Featured in Personal Injury (Wales & Chester)

Practice Areas: Personal injury, clinical negligence and commercial dispute resolution. Andrew's Personal Injury practice has a particular focus on catastrophic, spinal and closed head injuries. This includes cases of employers liability, occupiers liability and road traffic accidents. Specialist advice is offered in claims with conflicting, complex medical evidence for example with orthopaedic, neurological or psychiatric disputes or where pain disorders are challenged. Work is divided between Claimant and Defendant and includes extensive experience at trial and in a pre trial advisory capacity of industrial disease litigation (including group actions) in the form of deafness, asbestosis, dermatitis, WRULD and HAVS. Clinical negligence work is for both Claimants and Defendant Trusts and has included injuries caused at birth, negligent surgical procedures and cases of mis-diagnosis.

Professional Memberships: PIBA.

Career: Cardiff High School. Corpus Christi College, Cambridge.

Publications: Butterworths Personal Injury Litigation Vol 1. Chapters include medical causation, clinical negligence. and professional negligence.

Personal: Married, 3 children. Lives Llanblethian Vale of Glamorgan. Interests: rugby, cycling, surfing and skiing.

ARKUSH, Jonathan
11 Stone Buildings, London
020 7831 6381
clerks@11sb.com
Featured in Chancery (London), Mediators (All Circuits)

Practice Areas: Jonathan Arkush deals with a wide range of commercial and chancery litigation and is a qualified and highly experienced mediator. Jonathan has conducted over 200 mediations concerning a wide range of disputes, including negligence, breach of contract, breach of trust, commercial and residential property, contested shares in property, boundary and neighbour disputes, family trusts and settlements, disputes between members of charitable and religious bodies, inheritance, wills and probate, sale of goods, employment and banking disputes. These often involve substantial amounts, frequently running into millions of pounds. Sitting as a Deputy Chancery Master helps to keep a firm hand on difficult situations and assess rival contentions tactfully and with impartiality and fairness. Jonathan received the ADRg Award 2006 and was cited as one of the Group's most successful mediators. Recent case highlight: Eaton Mansions (Westminster) Ltd v Stinger Compania De Inversion SA, Court of Appeal - Civil Division, May 18, 2011, [2011] EWCA Civ 607 which made a second trip to the Court of Appeal [2013] EWCA Civ 1308. For more information please visit the 'Barristers' section on www.11sb.com.

Professional Memberships: Chancery Bar Association; Combar; ADR Group; Mediation Panel - Property Bar Association; Association of Contentious Trust and Probate Specialists; Dispute Mediation.

Career: 1977 Call. Deputy Chancery Master. ADR Group mediator.

Publications: Author of the chapter Landlord and Tenant Disputes in ADR and Commercial Disputes (Sweet & Maxwell).

Personal: MA (Oxon).

ARLIDGE, Anthony QC
Red Lion Chambers, London
020 7520 6000
anthony.arlidge@18rlc.co.uk
Featured in Crime (London)

Practice Areas: Anthony Arlidge QC has appeared in many high profile criminal cases. He now concentrates on defending in serious criminal cases and disciplinary tribunals. Early examples include prosecuting Jeremy Bamber for multiple murders and successfully defending the Baroness de Stempel on a murder charge. More recently, he represented a GP charged with the murder of three patients, a severely disabled defendant in a case of historic sexual assaults against others with disabilities, and a gang-member for the multi-handed murder of an engineering student. He has recently published the 4th edition of his standard text book on Fraud. Anthony Arlidge's significant fraud practice includes successfully defending in Blue Arrow, Marconi and Butte Mining. He has prosecuted in disciplinary tribunals for Lloyd's of London and defended before the Stock Exchange, FIMBRA and General Medical Council disciplinary tribunals. He frequently appears in the Court of Appeal and the House of Lords in leading cases, including R v Lawrence (recklessness) and Prentice and Sulman (medical manslaughter). Recent reported appearances in the Court of Appeal include R v Killick and R v Armajit Singh.

Career: Double first class Degree in Law, Cambridge; 1962 Called to the Bar; 1981 Queen's Counsel; 2003 Treasurer, Middle Temple.

Publications: Arlidge and Parry on Fraud; Arlidge and Eady on Contempt of Court.

ARMSTRONG, Dean QC
2 Bedford Row, London
020 7440 8888
darmstrong@2bedfordrow.co.uk
Featured in Crime (London), Financial Crime (London)

Practice Areas: Having been called to the Bar in 1985, Dean spent six years specialising in corporate finance law. In 1991 he returned to practice at the criminal bar. Since then, he has established a reputation as an accomplished defence advocate, specialising in serious fraud, corporate and financial crime, and international drug trafficking, as well as murder and organised crime. His experience and ability in respect of the crossover of criminal and civil matters, such as confiscation, directors' duties and financial issues, are of great interest to specialist fraud firms, international firms, and those within the " Magic Circle". Dean has undertaken many cases in these fields with wide-ranging international elements. Dean has the experience and ability to deal with areas where civil litigation is the precursor to possible criminal proceedings, and where the institution of criminal proceedings has consequences for the defendant in the civil courts. He is at home in both jurisdictions which allows him to view matters with the widest possible perspective. Dean has experience outside of courtrooms in disciplinary matters and financial regulation, and is considered by the media as a "legal expert", and as such is often called upon by them for comment and debate. He is a regular guest commentator on Sky News and BBC News. He has been cited for the last 14 years as a leading junior at the Bar by the Chambers & Partners Guide, and has twice been nominated as "Junior of the Year in Crime". He has been instructed by the defence in many high-profile and sensitive cases including R v Darwin (the canoeist case); R v Asil Nadir and R v Tabak (the murder of Joanna Yeates in Bristol). He has advised in respect of the "Leveson Inquiry". Dean is currently instructed to represent an individual indicted in the criminal proceedings related to the investigation in to News International PLC, and the News Of The World newspaper. In April 2014, Dean was appointed Queen's Counsel.

Professional Memberships: Criminal Bar Association; South Eastern Circuit.

Career: MA (Cantab); Called 1985.

ARMSTRONG, Douglas QC
Terra Firma Chambers, Edinburgh
0131 260 5830
douglas.armstrong
@terrafirmachambers.com
Featured in Planning (Scotland)

Practice Areas: Principal areas of practice cover planning, environmental, property, local government, administrative, constitutional and licensing law. He has appeared at inquiries, hearings and challenges concerned with a wide range of matters including residential and retail development, landfill/ waste, mineral, flooding, roads, infrastructure, compulsory purchase, renewable energy generation proposals - including energy from waste proposals, enforcement notices, listed buildings and development plans. He has represented developers, planning authorities and special interest groups. Douglas advises on Development Plan policies, large infrastructure (including roads, rail and bridge) proposals and Environmental law issues. He has appeared in the Court of Session and Supreme Court at statutory appeals and judicial review.

Professional Memberships: Scottish Planning Local Government and Environmental Bar Group (Committee Member), Planning and Environmental Bar Association.

Career: Called Scotland 1990; QC 2005; called England and Wales 1999.

ARNFIELD, Robert
Ten Old Square, London
020 7405 0758
robertarnfield@tenoldsquare.com
Featured in Chancery (London)

Practice Areas: A substantial part of Robert Arnfield's practice involves trusts and tax (principally Inheritance Tax and Capital Gains Tax), wills, family provision, deeds of

variation and the administration of estates. However, he undertakes litigation, drafting and advisory work across the full range of Chancery and commercial work including commercial contracts, insolvency, all aspects of real property law, charities and professional negligence.
Professional Memberships: He is a member of the Chancery Bar Association, STEP and the Professional Negligence Bar Association.
Career: Called to the Bar 1996. Notable cases include: Chirkinian v Larcom Trustees Ltd [2006] EWHC 1917 (Ch) - Statutory demand set aside on appeal. Underlying issue involved trustee demands for repayment of loans from an employee benefit trust; Channon v Perkins & others [2005] EWCA Civ 1808 - Presumption that a will was duly executed applied on appeal notwithstanding contrary evidence of attesting witnesses; Penzer v Penzer (Chancery Division, Birmingham, HHJ Norris QC, 23rd March 2004) - Litigation over will construction, trust accounts and a claim under the Inheritance (Provision for Family and Dependants) Act 1975; Leadenhall Independent Trustees Ltd v Welham and another (Chancery Division, Park J., 19th March 2004) - Construction of a pension scheme trust instrument.
Publications: He is one of the editors of Mellows on Taxation for Executors and Trustees.

ARNOLD, Mark QC
South Square, London
020 7696 9900
markarnold@southsquare.com
Featured in Restructuring/Insolvency (London)
Practice Areas: Business and financial law, including in particular: insolvency and corporate restructuring, banking, company, chancery and professional negligence. Recent work includes Storm Funding (Lehman Pensions Quantum) (subject to appeal), Lehman (Waterfall), and the scheme of arrangement relating to Card Protection Plan Limited.
Professional Memberships: COMBAR, Chancery Bar Association.
Career: MA Cantab (Downing College, Cambridge); called to the Bar by Middle Temple (1988); appointed Queen's Counsel (2013).
Publications: Contributor to 'Company Directors: Duties, Liabilities and Remedies', edited by Simon Mortimore QC (OUP, 2013); Cross Border Insolvency, edited by Richard Sheldon QC (Bloomsbury Professional, 2012).

ARNOT, Lee
29 Bedford Row Chambers, London
020 7539 2448
larnot@29br.co.uk
Featured in Family/Matrimonial (London)
Practice Areas: All aspects of family law including public and private law applications under the Children Act 1989, Adoption and Children Act 2002 and Human Rights Act 1998; matrimonial finance; child abduction; property disputes between cohabitees and family members. Cases include: Re P (Finding of Fact) [2014] EWCA Civ 89; A&B v P Council [2014] EWHC 1128 (Fam); A County Council v E & Ors [2012] EWHC 4161 (COP); Re Y (Care Proceedings) [2013] 1 FLR 256; MA v RS (Contact:Parenting Roles) [2012] 1 FLR 1056; H (Children)(Sexual abuse: fact finding) [2011] EWCA Civ 525; A London Borough Council v K & others [2009] EWHC 850; Re H (Children) [2006] EWCA Civ 1875; Re M (Contact:Long-Term Best Interests)[2006]1FLR627; AvA (Shared Residence)[2004]1FLR1195; Roddy (A Child) (Identification: Restriction on Publication)[2004]2FLR949; C v Bury MBC [2002] 2FLR 818; Re:W (Minors) (Care Order: Adequacy of Care Plan)[2002]1FLR815.
Professional Memberships: FLBA. Member of Bar Standards Board (2006-2011). Committee Member FLBA (2004-2009).
Career: Called in 1990.
Publications: Articles include: 'Shared Parenting-the Clear Message from Re G' (2005) Family Law, vol.35 pp.718 (jointly with Emma Harte, Partner Alexiou Fisher Philipps).
Personal: Married.

ARTIS, Iain N J
Westwater Advocates, Edinburgh
0131 260 5701
iain.artis@westwateradvocates.com
Featured in Tax (Scotland)
Practice Areas: With a background in general private law, and commercial and insolvency practice, Iain Artis was in 2005 appointed standing junior counsel in Scotland to the Advocate General for Scotland specialising in work for HMRC. In that context he has appeared in a broad range of tax litigation, both direct and indirect, from the First Tier Tribunal to the Supreme Court, and in the employment tribunals on minimum wage and other employment matters. Outside tax, his practice is focused on litigation in areas such as insolvency, directors' liabilities, and contract.
Career: Graduated Law Edinburgh (1977); MBA Strathclyde (1995). Member, Faculty of Advocates. Called to the Bar in 1999 after twenty years in commercial management and company secretarial roles in the international defence, energy equipment, and wines & spirits industries. Experienced in the management of and dealings in intellectual property, joint ventures, the legal aspects of international distribution and sales arrangements, and compliance management.
Publications: Please see the Stable website at www.murraystable.com for recent articles and forthcoming seminars.
Personal: Gardening; clay target shooting; listening to music.

ASCROFT, Richard
Guildhall Chambers, Bristol
0117 930 9000
richard.ascroft@guildhallchambers.co.uk
Featured in Commercial Dispute Resolution (Western), Company (Western), Restructuring/Insolvency (Western)
Practice Areas: Company law (especially shareholder disputes/unfair prejudice petitions, directors' duties, unlawful distributions etc); insolvency (personal and corporate) including company director disqualification proceedings, Bankruptcy Restriction Orders and Debt Relief Restriction Orders, misfeasance claims (breaches of trust and breaches of duty), bankruptcy, transaction avoidance claims (voidable preferences, transactions at an undervalue, transactions defrauding creditors), administrations, voluntary liquidations, unlawful returns of capital, prohibited names (s 216 of the Insolvency Act 1986); commercial law (particular expertise in claims involving securing or resisting urgent pre-emptive relief (especially freezing and other injunctions); breaches of warranty and misrepresentation (typically in the context of share sale or franchise agreements); enforcement of post sale/employment restrictive covenants; professional negligence (solicitors, accountants); interference with goods (bailment, conversion).
Professional Memberships: Chancery Bar Association.
Career: LLB (Hons) (Otago, NZ); BCL (Oxon). Called to the Bar 1995; Barrister & Solicitor of the High Court of New Zealand 1990. Junior Counsel to the Crown (Attorney-General's Provincial Panel) 2002-. Has over 20 years advisory and advocacy experience and has appeared in courts at all levels including the House of Lords.
Publications: Contributor to Mithani: Directors' Disqualification.
Personal: Born Wellington, New Zealand. Educated NZ and Keble College Oxford. Leisure interests include shooting and opera.

ASHLEY-NORMAN, Jonathan
3 Raymond Buildings Barristers, London
020 7400 6400
jonathan.ashley-norman@3rblaw.com
Featured in Health & Safety (London), POCA Work & Asset Forfeiture (All Circuits), Financial Crime (London)
Practice Areas: Specialist in criminal and regulatory law in a business setting, both defending and prosecuting. Assistance at the investigation stage, advising on responding to law enforcement action and managing the investigation process (for example recent investigations into the pharmaceutical industry, and Caribbean holiday home alleged fraud). Prosecution advisory work in guiding and focusing investigations with a view to eventual successful disposal (for example fraudulent trading in insurance industry). Litigation advisory work, guiding interlocutory stages and pre-trial work, including disclosure strategies. Representation, both defence and prosecution, at all levels of courts and tribunals. Top defence work instructed by leading solicitors firms in fraud related and regulatory issues. Standing Counsel to DBIS, and A Panel prosecutor, regularly instructed by SFO, HSE, Office of Rail Regulation and other specialist prosecution bodies. Acts across a multiplicity of business areas in respect of a large range of law enforcement action. Specialism in restraint and confiscation. Judicial review. Inquests. First Tier Tribunal. Directors duties and disqualification. Increasingly instructed in civil litigation with a fraud or regulatory aspect.

ASHWORTH, Fiona
Kings Chambers, Manchester
0845 034 3444
clerks@kingschambers.com
Featured in Personal Injury (Northern)
Practice Areas: Personal Injury and chronic pain cases.
Professional Memberships: PIBA.
Career: Fiona Ashworth is a leading personal injury practitioner, specialising in chronic pain cases. Over the last 15 years, Fiona has developed specialisms in Chronic Pain Syndromes, Complex Regional Pain Syndrome, Chronic Fatigue Syndrome, Somatoform Pain Disorders, Fibromyalgia and Conversion Disorders. These conditions are often little understood and extremely challenging. Fiona has built up a deep knowledge of these chronic pain cases, working with medical experts of all different specialisms. She has been involved in hundreds of such cases, both at first instance and on appeal, acting for both Claimant and Defendant. She has lectured extensively over the country, run seminars and was invited to attend the Pain Summit at Westminster. She is considered to be a leading expert on chronic pain. Fiona sat on the Legal Services Commission Appeal tribunal for 15 years and was an external examiner for the City Law School and MMU. She was appointed as a Recorder sitting in crime in 2009 and in civil in 2014.
Publications: Solicitors Journal 17th July 2012 PI Brief Update Law Journal 14th January 2013 and 4th January 2014, UK Fibromyalgia Society February 2014.

ASHWORTH, Lance QC
Serle Court, London
020 7242 6105
lashworth@serlecourt.co.uk
Featured in Chancery (London), Commercial Dispute Resolution (London)
Practice Areas: Commercial litigation, insolvency, company/chancery, professional negligence. Recent cases include: QOGT v International Oil and Gas Technology [2014] EWHC 1628 (Comm) - termination of investment management contract; UK Power v Read [2014] EWHC 66 (Ch) - non-competition covenants and conspiracy, without notice injunctions; Credit Lucky Ltd v National Crime Agency [2014] EWHC 83 (Ch) - rescission of winding up order; Khoshkhou v Cooper [2014] EWHC 1087 (Ch) - exclusive supply agreement and minority shareholders petition; Mengiste v EFFORT [2012] EWHC 2782 - forum non conveniens, cross exmination of witnesses abroad; Emailgen Systems v Exclaimer Ltd [2013] EWHC 167 (Comm) - discharge of undertaking given in lieu of freezing injunction; Thursfield v Thursfield [2013] EWCA Civ 840 [2012] EWHC 3742 (Ch) - enforcing Michigan judgment, freezing order, contempt, committal, information order re trusts.
Professional Memberships: Chancery Bar; COMBAR; Midlands Commercial and Chancery Bar Association.
Career: Called 1987, Middle Temple; Recorder 2005; QC 2006; Mediator 2009.
Personal: Born 1964. Resides London. Educated at Oundle School; Pembroke College, Cambridge (MA). Trustee of the Access to Justice Foundation; Founder Trustee of the Medical Research Fund Coventry and Warwickshire; Member of Middlesex Lord's Taverners Committee.

ASWANI, Ravi
Stone Chambers, London
020 7440 6900
ravi.aswani@stonechambers.com
Featured in Shipping (London)
Practice Areas: All aspects of shipping and international trade including charterparty and bill of lading disputes, commodities, shipbuilding and ship sale and purchase, salvage and wreck removal. Ravi additionally has a wider commercial practice encompassing international commercial dispute resolution, insurance and reinsurance, and banking and finance. Ravi has had a busy year and is increasingly being instructed to appear alone against QC opposition. He has been particularly involved in international arbitration work, appearing in multiple arbitrations, in England and in Singapore, predominantly without a leader. He has also appeared in a number of related arbitration applications in court as well as appearing in the Admiralty Court and the Commercial

Court numerous times in litigation. Ravi represented without a leader an insurance company in a substantial marine insurance trial in the Commercial Court against a QC and a senior junior (Sea Glory Maritime v Al Sagr [2014] 1 Lloyd's Rep 14). Ravi is also instructed as junior counsel in a set of substantial consolidated arbitrations which have themselves resulted in multiple hearings in the Commercial Court (Konkola Copper Mines PLC v U&M Mining Zambia Ltd [2014] EWHC 2146 (Comm) and [2014] EWHC 2374 (Comm)). Ravi is increasingly developing an international perspective to his practice and has developed particular links with India, Singapore and the Middle East in the recent past.
Professional Memberships: British Maritime Law Association, Chartered Institute of Arbitrators (MCIArb), Commercial Bar Association, FDI International Moot Competition (College of Arbitrators), London Common Law and Commercial Bar Association, LCIA European Users' Council and Young International Arbitration Group, LMAA Supporting Member, UK India Business Council Next Generation Network, Worshipful Company of Arbitrators (Freeman).
Career: LLB (first class honours), UCL, 1999; Called to Bar of England and Wales, 2000; Judicial assistant in the Court of Appeal, 2001-02; Admitted to Register of Practitioners of the Dubai International Financial Centre Courts, 2008; CEDR Accredited Mediator, 2009; MCIArb, 2012; Deputy District Judge (Civil), 2013.

ATHERTON, Peter
Deans Court Chambers, Manchester
0161 214 6000
atherton@deanscourt.co.uk
Featured in Professional Discipline (The Regions)
Practice Areas: Peter Atherton is regularly instructed by the General Medical Council for his firm and sensitive handling of high profile cases before fitness to practise panels, certification appeal panels and the Administrative Court. He has extensive experience across a range of healthcare related litigation, Inquests, environmental regulation, health and safety and insurance litigation. He represented the claimant in the leading case on occupational stress (Hatton v Sutherland) and has represented parties in major Public Inquiries (Piper Alpha Disaster and Shipman). Peter is a Harvard trained mediator and is accredited by CEDR.
Professional Memberships: Association of Regulatory Lawyers, Professional Negligence Bar Association, Criminal Bar Association, Personal Injury Bar Association, Standing Council of Mediation Advocates, Association of Northern Mediators.
Career: LLB(Hons) Birmingham 1974 Called 1975 Northern Circuit Junior 1979 Chair of Young Barristers Committee (Bar Council) 1981 Recorder 1999 Junior Counsel to the Crown (Criminal Panel) 2001-11.

ATKINS, Mike
Crown Office Chambers, London
020 797 8100
atkins@crownofficechambers.com
Featured in Health & Safety (London)
Practice Areas: Specialist practice in criminal regulatory law with particular expertise in health and safety, inquests, consumer law, product safety, fire safety, environmental law, food safety and road traffic offences. Acts for companies, directors, employees and prosecuting authorities. Regularly instructed in cases of corporate and gross negligence manslaughter, health and safety prosecutions arising out of fatal and other serious accidents, and appeals against enforcement notices. Junior counsel for the acquitted Managing Director in the Lion Steel corporate manslaughter case. Junior counsel to the Coroner in the Lakanal House tower block fire inquests, which lasted 3 months. Secured the acquittal, after a 7 day jury trial, of a director charged with neglect after an employee was seriously injured in a bar cellar hatch fall. Experience of cases involving construction and demolition, work at height, manufacturing and technology, warehousing and logistics, waste management and recycling, mining and quarrying, asbestos, fire safety, gas and electrical safety, medical treatment, residential care, schools and nurseries and road traffic accidents. Reported cases include Wandsworth LBC v Covent Garden Market Authority (time limits in enforcement notice appeals) and Templeton Insurance Ltd v Motorcare Warranties Ltd (junior counsel on appeal against sentence for breach of High Court freezing order). Appointed to List B of the list of specialist regulatory advocates to prosecute on behalf of the Health and Safety Executive, the Environment Agency and the Office of Rail Regulation. Contributor to Westlaw Insight on food law.

ATKINS, Richard QC
St Philips Chambers, Birmingham
0121 246 7000
rpatkins@st-philips.com
Featured in Crime (Midlands)
Practice Areas: Specialises in serious crime and regulatory law, especially consumer law and trading standards and HSE cases (fatal accidents including corporate manslaughter). Defends and prosecutes in equal measure. Appeared in numerous murder cases, including gangland, sado-masochistic and matrimonial killings; gross negligence, unlawful act and diminished responsibility manslaughter cases; serious sex cases; and serious fraud including company, scrap metal and international boiler room fraud. Regularly appears in the Court of Appeal, most recently in R v Lewis [2013] EWCA Crim 776 (jury irregularities) and R v X [2013] EWCA Crim 818 (defining the Consumer Protection from Unfair Trading Regulations 2008 concepts of "commercial practice" and "transactional decisions" and giving guidance on mens rea and recklessness in relation to companies). An approachable and engaging advocate. Direct and Public Access work accepted.
Professional Memberships: Association of Health and Safety Lawyers; Association of Regulatory and Disciplinary Lawyers; Criminal Bar Association; Midland Circuit; Gray's Inn.
Career: Leader of the Midland Circuit. Fee-paid Judge of First-Tier Tribunal (Health Education and Social Care Chamber) (Mental Health) May 2014. Chairman Bar Conference 2014. Legal Chairman Financial Reporting Council Disciplinary Tribunal 2013. Silk 2011. St Philips Criminal Group Head 2011. Chairman Bar Council Member Services Board 2009. Recorder 2005.
Personal: King Henry VIII School, Coventry and St Catherine's College, Oxford University (MA, Jurisprudence). Chairman of the Governors of the Coventry School Foundation (Bablake and King Henry VIII Schools).

ATKINSON, Duncan
6KBW College Hill, London
020 3301 0910
duncan.atkinson@6kbw.com
Featured in Crime (London)
Practice Areas: Duncan has appeared as leader or junior in numerous homicide cases, including the murders of Milly Dowler and Carole Waugh. He has also appeared in cases of corporate and gross negligence manslaughter. Duncan has appeared as leader or junior in terrorist cases, including the 'fertiliser plot' case and a plot to kidnap a soldier. He is currently instructed in relation to allegations of phone hacking. Duncan has appeared in many cases of serious and complex fraud and corruption, including cases brought by the SFO and HMRC. He also has particular experience of various forms of "cybercrime". He has acted both in an advisory capacity and as an advocate in relation to health and safety legislation. He regularly appears in appellate work, including two recent appearances in the Supreme Court in relation to the definition of terrorism and assisted suicide. A more detailed profile is available on the 6KBW College Hill website (www.6kbw.com).
Career: Called in 1995; appointed Treasury Counsel in 2009; and made a Recorder in 2012.
Publications: Editor of EU Law in Criminal Practice; co-author of the Blackstones Guide to the Criminal Procedure Rules; contributor to Blackstones Criminal Practice and Fraud: Criminal Law and Procedure.

ATKINSON, Jody
St John's Chambers, Bristol
0117 921 3456
jody.atkinson@stjohnschambers.co.uk
Featured in Family/Matrimonial (Western)
Practice Areas: Family law: financial remedies on divorce, disputes between unmarried partners, child support agency, children act disputes. Chancery (wills and trusts): cohabitation disputes (constructive trusts), contentious probate, inheritance act claims, proprietary estoppel, tax advice in relation to the above.
Professional Memberships: Society of Trusts and Estate Practioners (STEP Full Member), Chancery Bar Association, Family Law Bar Association.
Career: BA Hons First Class, History (University of Bristol). MA Distinction, 18th Century History (York University). Barrister at Law, (Inns of Court School of Law).
Publications: The author of the sections on Child Support in Wildblood on Financial Provision in Family Matters and in the Westlaw Legal Encylopaedia: Insight on the Preparation of Wills, the Construction of Wills, Executors, Administrators, and Personal Representatives.
Personal: Interests: Music, swimming, BBQ, history, coins and banknotes.

ATKINSON, Timothy
One Brick Court, London
020 7353 8845
ta@onebrickcourt.com
Featured in Defamation/Privacy (London)
Practice Areas: Defamation, malicious falsehood, confidence, privacy, data protection, freedom of information and associated areas. Cases of note include Jackson v MGN; Ashby v Times Newspapers; McDonald's Corp. v Steel and Morris; Waple v Surrey CC; Isola v VOX; Garfoot v Walker; Cornelius v de Taranto; Alexander v Arts Council of Wales; Rakhimov v Jennings; Austin v Newcastle Chronicle and Journal; Multigroup Bulgaria v Oxford Analytica; Al Fagih v H H Saudi; Pell v Express Newspapers; Kearns v General Council of the Bar; Olafsson v Gissurarson; Ramis v Cutting Edge Press; Dressell v Guardian Newspapers; Schofield v Neish; McFadden v News Group Newspapers; Pinfield v H Bauer Publishing; NMT Medical v Wilmhurst; McLaughlin v Lambeth LBC; Theobald v Lincolnshire Media; Cammish v Hughes.
Professional Memberships: Human Rights Law Association.
Career: Called to the Bar 1988.
Publications: Co-author of Duncan and Neill on Defamation, 3rd ed; Editor of 'Atkin on Libel and Slander'; contributor to Arlidge, Eady & Smith on Contempt 4th Edition.
Personal: Education: St Pauls School, London and Balliol College, Oxford (Brackenbury Scholar).

ATRILL, Simon
Fountain Court Chambers, London
020 7583 3335
sa@fountaincourt.co.uk
Featured in Banking & Finance (London), Commercial Dispute Resolution (London), Fraud (London)
Practice Areas: Civil and commercial litigation including banking, financial services, insurance/reinsurance, civil fraud and professional negligence. Shortlisted for Chambers and Partners Banking and Finance Junior of the Year 2013. Recent cases include: JSC BTA Bank v Ablyazov; OFT v Abbey National and others (bank charges) (first instance to HL [2010] 1 A.C. 696); Group Seven Ltd v Sultana and others [2014] 1 W.L.R. 735 (freezing injunctions) and [2014] EWHC 2046 (Ch) (trial); interest rate swaps litigation; NatWest v Rabobank (four reported first instance judgments and CA); IBC v MAR [2010] 1 All ER (Comm) 112; various substantial confidential commercial arbitrations; payment protection insurance litigation; ICB v Akingbola; Arab Banking Corp v Saad [2010] EWHC 509 (Comm); Dhanani v Crasnianski [2011] 2 All E.R. (Comm) 799; various cases in Cayman Islands, Hong Kong and Trinidad and Tobago.
Career: Called 2005; Member COMBAR.
Publications: Legal Privilege and Mandatory Disclosure under the Proceeds of Crime Act 2002 [2005] LMCLQ; "Choice of Law in Contract: The missing Pieces of the Article 4 Jigsaw?" (2004) ICLQ; several in Cambridge Law Journal.
Personal: St Catharine's College, Cambridge (Double First); St John's College, Oxford (BCL, Distinction); University of Pennsylvania (LLM, summa cum laude).

AUBURN, Jonathan
Thirty Nine Essex Street, London
020 7832 1111
jonathan.auburn@39essex.com
Featured in Administrative & Public Law (London), Community Care (London), Education (London), Local Government (London)
Practice Areas: Jonathan practices in most areas of public law and judicial review, including Local Government law, Community Care, Mental Capacity, Education law, Healthcare law, Prisons, Inquests and Immigration. He has appeared in many leading cases in these areas, including, in the

last year, R (S & KF) v Secretary of State for Justice (2012) (human rights, relationship between Strasbourg and UK law), R (KM) v Cambridgeshire (2012 Supreme Court, community care, personal budgets), R (Al-Sirri and DD) v SSHD (2012, Supreme Court, immigration, Article 1F(c)) and R(SL) v Westminster (2012 Supreme Court, s.21 duty, whether services 'accommodation-related'). He has just published the co-authored text 'Judicial Review: Principles and Procedure' (OUP, 2013).
Professional Memberships: ALBA Secretary.
Career: LLB (West Aust), BCL (Oxon), D Phil (Oxon). Assistant to Lord Woolf, Lord Chief Justice, Junior Counsel to the Crown, Attorney General's Panel of Prosecution Advocates.
Publications: Publishes widely in public law, evidence and access to information, including Judicial Review: Principles and Procedure (2013, joint author), The White Book, Phipson on Evidence, Freedom of Information, Atkins Court Forms.

AUDLAND, William
12 King's Bench Walk, London
020 7583 0811
audland@12kbw.co.uk
Featured in Personal Injury (London), Travel (London)
Practice Areas: Travel law (personal injury, contractual, insurance, applicable law and jurisdictional matters); personal injury (including catastrophic injuries and accidents abroad); local authority liabilities (education and highways); professional negligence (clinical and solicitors); sports law (football, rugby, sailing, skiing, waterskiing, climbing); insurance.
Professional Memberships: PIBA, PNBA, TATLA, South Eastern Circuit.
Career: Called to the Bar in 1992, William won the Chambers and Partners UK Bar Award for Personal Injury/Clinical Negligence Junior Barrister of the Year 2013. He is also a qualified and accredited Mediator.
Publications: William is a Contributing Author of "Personal Injury Schedules: Calculating Damages" 3rd Edition, Bloomsbury Professional.
Personal: William obtained a BA in modern languages (Spanish and Portuguese) from Queen's College, Oxford, and subsequently a Diploma in Law (City University). He is reasonably fluent in Italian, is a keen skier, and enjoys ski touring, hockey and cycling.

AYLING, Tracy QC
2 Bedford Row, London
020 7440 8888
tayling@2bedfordrow.co.uk
Featured in Crime (London)
Practice Areas: Specialist Criminal Practitioner - Defence and Prosecution. Standing Counsel to HMRC from 1998 to 2005. Defends in serious sex cases, murder, and confiscation cases acting in some of the highest profile cases in the UK. Recent cases include gang murders, representing young gang members using knives and guns. Particular expertise in the ever-developing areas of child sex offending, grooming, and human trafficking. Leading defence counsel in Operation Bullfinch (very high profile, widely reported 2013 case concerning a gang of Asian men grooming and abusing very young girls over a period of many years in Oxford). Only the second case of its type. Advocacy trainer for the Inner Temple. Teaches a unique course on how to cross examine very young and vulnerable witnesses. Brought in to lead for the defence in a 2014 case involving 3 year old complainants and significant expert witness evidence. Leading specialist in matters of PII and disclosure. Extensive experience of cases concerning International Security and Government agencies requiring expert knowledge of the Regulation of Investigatory Powers Act 2000, including the legality of telephone intercept material. Appointed in 2010 as a Special Advocate for the Attorney General. Appears in the Special Immigration Appeals Commission.
Professional Memberships: Criminal Bar Association.

AYLOTT, Colin
Carmelite Chambers, London
020 7936 6300
colin.aylott@gmail.com
Featured in Crime (London), Financial Crime (London)
Practice Areas: A leading junior specialising in defending in complex fraud and serious crime. Advises and represents both individuals and corporate clients in all areas of commercial crime, money laundering and corruption. He practices internationally and is called to the Bar in the Turks and Caicos Islands.
Professional Memberships: Criminal Bar Association.
Career: "Recent high profile instructions include defending in the first SFO prosecution arising out of the LIBOR scandal and "Operation Elveden" (the News International trials). Current instructions include "Operation Spallation" (alleged corrupt HMRC officers), Operation Calluna (fraud by Diplomats), R v H (Film Tax fraud) and Operation Carp (carbon credit trader charged with in relation to trading).

AYRES, Andrew
Maitland Chambers, London
020 7406 1200
aayres@maitlandchambers.com
Featured in Banking & Finance (London)
Practice Areas: Banking and finance and financial services, civil fraud, commercial litigation and arbitration, partnership, trusts and offshore, chancery, property, company, insolvency and restructuring, professional liability and risk, regulatory, compliance and investigations, aviation finance, asset tracing, urgent injunctions and disclosure orders, equitable claims and enforcement, construction and engineering, energy and natural resources, funds and private equity, international trade, joint ventures, jurisdiction and service, media and entertainment, derivatives and structured products, TMT, and wills and estates.
Professional Memberships: COMBAR, Financial Services Lawyers Association, ChBA, Commercial Fraud Lawyers Association, ACTAPS, Association of Partnership Practitioners, Insolvency Lawyers Association and DIFC.
Career: Called 1996.
Personal: MA (Oxon).

BACHE, Nina
St Ives Chambers, Birmingham
0121 236 0863
nina.bache@stiveschambers.co.uk
Featured in Family/Matrimonial (Midlands)
Practice Areas: Family.
Professional Memberships: Family Law Bar Association.
Career: Nina is a specialist family law practitioner specialising in both public and private law. Public Law: Nina is regularly instructed by parents, Guardians, local authorities, other family members and interveners. She is known for her client-friendly approach and careful preparation. She is very experienced in care cases involving non-accidental injuries, sexual abuse, severe emotional abuse, chronic neglect, clients with learning difficulties and matters involving the Official Solicitor. She also has experience of cases involving expert evidence on the evaluation of children's ABE interviews and cross-examination of children. Nina also deals in adoption cases, including revocation of placement orders. Private Law: Nina is regularly instructed by parents, grandparents and Guardians acting for children. She has a sensitive and understanding approach to clients. She deals with difficult and complex Child Arrangements applications involving parents and non-parents, including cases involving complex psychological evidence, intractable contact disputes, and applications for removal from the jurisdiction.

BACON, Francis
Hailsham Chambers, London
020 7643 5000
francis.bacon@hailshamchambers.com
Featured in Professional Negligence (London)
Practice Areas: Francis specialises in professional negligence, regulatory and disciplinary work, and commercial insurance and commercial litigation both in the UK and overseas. He has appeared in many high profile cases in the High Court and Court of Appeal. His particular expertise is fraud and advising on coverage issues.
Professional Memberships: Professional Negligence Bar Association (PNBA).
Career: Called to the Bar in 1988. Karmel Commercial Scholar Gray's Inn. Recorder.
Personal: Educated Keele and Loughborough. Married with three children.

BACON, Nicholas QC
4 New Square, London
020 7822 2000
barristers@4newsquare.com
Featured in Costs Litigation (London)
Practice Areas: Nicholas Bacon QC is probably one of the best known silks in his specialised field of costs. He has been described as having 'probably the biggest costs practice at the Bar'. Nicholas undertakes high profile costs litigation work. He was retained in the Voicemail Interception Litigation for News International. He led the costs team for Trafigura in what was one of the largest costs claim in English legal history. He was retained by Lovells in the Three Rivers costs disputes and receives instructions from other magic circle firms. He is retained by Shell in the Bodo claims advising on all costs matters arising from the group claims. He has appeared in the Supreme Court, House of Lords Court of Appeal and has been retained in some of the most significant funding costs cases in the past decade. His costs practice is well juxtaposed to his professional negligence work with particular emphasis on solicitors' and barristers' negligence, both for and against solicitors and the Bar. He is co author of the Bar Handbook. His work includes regulatory and disciplinary work in respect of solicitors. He has been retained in some of the leading legal expense insurance cases and regularly advises the insurance industry in respect of funding and legal expense issues, coverage advice and policy terms. His move to 4 New Square reflects his increasing prominence in professional indemnity work. He is a member of the Civil Procedure Rules Committee and has been heavily engaged in the implementation of recent reforms recommended by Sir Rupert Jackson.
Professional Memberships: Professional Negligence Bar Association. Commercial Bar Association.
Career: Called to the Bar in 1992; to Queens Counsel in 2010.
Publications: He is the contributing editor to the section on Costs in Halsbury's Laws of England. He is contributing editor to the 'Green Book' - the Civil Court Practice where he edits the sections on Funding and Legal Aid. He is the co-author of The Bar Handbook. He is a contributing editor to Butterworths' Costs Service and the Civil Court Precedents.
Personal: Nicholas' outdoor passion is yachting. He is a qualified Yachtmaster. He is married with two young children.

BADGER, Christopher
6 Pump Court, London
020 7797 8400
christopherbadger@6pumpcourt.co.uk
Featured in Environment (London)
Practice Areas: Environmental crime and regulation; business crime and corporate defence. Specialist in corporate and regulatory investigations and providing early stage advice. Recent instructions include: Walker & Son (Hauliers) Ltd v Environment Agency [2014] 1 Cr. App. R. 30; [2014] Env L.R. 22 (leading authority on the statutory construction of "knowingly permit" in the Environmental Permitting Regulations 2007 and 2010); R v B (P) Ltd & others (8-handed environmental prosecution for waste offences involving multiple illegal sites); EA v WB Ltd (Counsel on behalf of 2 companies and their director in the largest prosecution for the illegal export of waste to date); EA v AA & others (leading Counsel in a 13-handed environmental prosecution for waste offences and water pollution).
Professional Memberships: UKELA, HSLA, ARDL, SEC, CBA.
Career: Lincoln College, Oxford. Called to the Bar in 2002. Appointed as 'A' List Counsel on the Attorney General's List of Specialist Regulatory Counsel in 2012.
Publications: Environmental Sentencing Referencer 2012; Contributor to Burnett Hall on Environmental Law 2013 (Sweet & Maxwell).

BAGCHI, Andrew
1 Garden Court Family Law Chambers, London
020 7797 7900
andrewbagchi@mac.com
Featured in Court of Protection (All Circuits), Family/Matrimonial (London)

Practice Areas: All forms of disputes relating to children. Ancillary relief. Disputes between co-habitees. Proceedings in relation to adult mental incapacity under the Mental Capacity Act 2005 and under the inherent jurisdiction of the High Court. Forced Marriage.
Professional Memberships: FLBA, Bar Council.
Career: Called to the Bar 1989. Joined 1 Garden Court 1996.
Personal: LLB Kings College London. Interests include golf, test cricket and electronica.

BAGOT, Charles
Hardwicke, London
020 7242 2523
charles.bagot@hardwicke.co.uk
Featured in Personal Injury (London)
Practice Areas: A specialist in personal injury, clinical negligence and civil procedure issues, Charles also sits as a Deputy District Judge and on Bar Disciplinary Tribunals. He represents claimants and defendants in high value claims usually arising from catastrophic brain injuries, spinal fractures and amputations as well as having a particular specialism in fatal accident cases. He represented the successful appellant/defendant in the notable secondary victim appeal: Taylor v A.Novo (UK) Ltd [2013] EWCA Civ 194. He is sought after by insurers for cases where fraud and exaggeration are suspected. He has advised an offshore insurer in various injury cases being litigated in the Caribbean and was lead counsel for an application for permission to appeal to the Privy Council. Amongst his claimant solicitor clients he is well known for being good at explaining complex matters to seriously injured clients and securing favourable settlements at JSMs. Charles is an accredited Inner Temple advocacy teacher. He regularly delivers seminars including recently at APIL and AvMA events as well as to insurer audiences.
Publications: Charles is on the Editorial Board of Kemp & Kemp: the Quantum of Damages.
Personal: Charles is fluent in French. He swam across the Solent in aid of the Samaritans.

BAILEY, James
New Square Chambers, London
020 7419 8020
james.bailey@newsquarechambers.co.uk
Featured in Chancery (London), Company (London), Restructuring/Insolvency (London)
Practice Areas: James Bailley's practice covers a range of commercial and chancery work focusing on personal and corporate insolvency, company law (especially minority shareholder disputes), commercial litigation and partnership matters. He has been called to the Cayman Islands Bar and has acted for Enron's liquidators in both the Cayman Islands and the United States. His work has also taken him to China, Japan, Italy and the Bahamas. Although some of his work has international aspects to it, much of his work takes place in the High Court in England. He has been involved in corporate insolvency matters such as the Comet administration and appeared in the recent leading company law decision in UPMS v Fort Gilkicker Limited which brought an end to the controversy pertaining to multiple derivative claims in English company law, their existence being affirmed.
Professional Memberships: Chancery Bar Association; COMBAR.
Career: Called to the Bar 1999. Called to the Cayman Islands Bar 2001. Elected Member of the Bar Council 2003-06.
Personal: Educated Winchester College; Brasenose College, Oxford - MA (Oxon), BCL. James is a passionate oarsman.

BAILIN, Alex QC
Matrix Chambers, London
020 7404 3447
alexbailin@matrixlaw.co.uk
Featured in Administrative & Public Law (London), Civil Liberties & Human Rights (London), Defamation/Privacy (London), Crime (London), Financial Crime (London)
Practice Areas: Specialist in fraud and crime; human rights and public law. Also instructed in extradition, media and public international law work. Financial crime: range of business crime cases, from corporate manslaughter and corruption to insider dealing and cartels. Clients include multinational corporations, senior business executives, regulators, prosecutors, city firms, professional bodies and foreign governments. Crime: from gross negligence manslaughter to official secrets and hacking. Human rights and public law: diverse practice, ranging from wealthy private clients, major shareholders, multinational corporations and FTSE companies to media organisations, regulators, public authorities, NGOs and publicly-funded individuals. 20+ cases in Supreme Court, House of Lords, Privy Council and European Court of Human Rights. Media practice: advising high-profile figures, editors, journalists and national newspapers on reputation management issues, production orders, witness summonses, reporting restrictions, contempt of court and other criminal offences. Public international law work includes genocide, rendition and violations of international criminal law. Experience of diverse jurisdictions.
Career: Called 1995. Silk 2010. Crown Court Recorder. Deputy High Court judge.
Publications: Contributing author to leading books on human rights, criminal justice and fraud. Numerous articles in national and legal press/journals.
Personal: Cambridge University. Previously a derivatives trader.

BAIN, Giles
New Court Chambers, London
020 7583 5123
gbain@newcourtchambers.com
Featured in Family/Matrimonial (London)
Practice Areas: Specialist Child Care lawyer, regularly instructed in complex disputes. Extensive representation of local authorities, within Greater London and outside of London. Substantial part of practice is as a result of being instructed by child care solicitors to represent parents, extended family and children. Recent Cases: Re W (fact finding: hearsay evidence) [2013] EWCA Civ 1374; Re S, K v The London Borough of Brent [2013] EWCA Civ 926; B (A Child) [2014] EWCC B55 (Fam) (17 January 2014).
Professional Memberships: FLBA.
Career: Called 1993, Lincoln's Inn. Tenant at New Court from 1995. Pupil Supervisor for over 10 years. Involved in providing CPD accredited seminars to professional and lay clients and training of social workers.
Personal: LLB (Hons) University of Hull. Avid follower of all sport.

BAKER, Christopher
Arden Chambers, London
020 7242 4244
christopher.baker@ardenchambers.com
Featured in Local Government (London), Social Housing (London)
Practice Areas: Local government, housing, landlord and tenant (public, social and private).
Professional Memberships: Administrative Law Bar Association; Housing Law Practitioners Association; Property Bar Association; Social Housing Law Association.
Career: Called 1984. Founder Member of Arden Chambers 1993. Illustrative recent cases include: Haile v Waltham Forest LBC [2014] EWCA Civ 792 - homelessness; Balog v Birmingham CC [2014] HLR 14 – homelessness; R (Alansi) v Newham LBC [2014] BLGR 138 - changes to housing allocation scheme, legitimate expectation; Ker v Optima Community Association [2013] 2 P & CR 19 - proportionality of eviction of Flexibuy tenant; R (Chatting) v Viridian Housing [2013] BLGR 118 - transfer of registered care home; R (W) v Birmingham CC [2012] BLGR 1 – eligibility criteria for adult social care; R (Birmingham Care Consortium) v Birmingham CC [2011] EWHC 2656 (Admin) – payment rates for residential care home placements; Karaj v Three Rivers DC [2011] EWCA Civ 768 – contracting-out of homelessness reviews; Mears Ltd v Leeds CC [2011] EuLR 596 & 764 – public procurement of housing repairs service; Morrison Facilities Services Ltd v Norwich CC [2010] EWHC 487 (Ch) – public procurement of housing repairs service; Ali v Birmingham CC [2010] 2 AC 39 - art 6 and homelessness appeals; Nessa v Tower Hamlets LBC [2010] HLR 37 – right to buy; R (Weaver) v LQHT [2010] 1 WLR 363 - whether RSL a public authority; R (Ahmad) v Newham LBC [2009] 3 All ER 755 - allocations scheme; Knowsley HT v White [2009] 1 AC 636 (tolerated trespassers and assured tenants); Riverside HA Ltd v White [2007] 4 All ER 97 (RSL rent increases).
Publications: Encyclopedia of Local Government Law (Sweet & Maxwell - contributor); Community Care Law Reports (LAG - editor); Halsbury's Laws of England (5th ed), vol 69, Local Government (Butterworths, 2009 - contributor); Local Government Constitutional and Administrative Law (Sweet & Maxwell, 2nd ed, 2008 - co-author); Local Government Liability Law (Sweet & Maxwell, 2007 - author); Housing Law: Pleadings in Practice (Sweet & Maxwell, 2nd ed 2003 - co-author).

BAKER, Philip QC
Field Court Tax Chambers, London
020 3693 3700
pb@fieldtax.com
Featured in Tax (London)
Practice Areas: All forms of revenue law, with particular specialisations in: international taxation (both corporate and private client, and government advisory work on taxation, with a particular interest in double taxation conventions); in European Union tax law; and in taxation and human rights (especially the European Convention on Human Rights).
Professional Memberships: Barrister, Grays Inn (1979), QC (2002); senior visiting fellow, Institute of Advanced Legal Studies, University of London; Committee Member, International Fiscal Association (British Branch); Member, Permanent Scientific Committee, International Fiscal Association; Member, International Tax Sub-Committees, Law Society and Chartered Institute of Taxation; Member, Exchequer Secretary's Forum for Tax Professionals.
Career: 1979-87, lecturer in law, School of Oriental and African Studies, London University. 1987-present, Barrister. Founder member of Field Court Tax Chambers, August 2014.
Publications: 'Double Taxation Conventions' (3rd edn, looseleaf, 2001). Editor, International Tax Law Reports.
Personal: Educated: Emmanuel College, Cambridge (MA); Balliol College, Oxford (BCL); University College, London (LLM); SOAS, London (PhD); London Business School (MBA). Married, three children. Awarded OBE, July 1997.

BAKER, Richard
7BR, London
020 7242 3555
clerks@7br.co.uk
Featured in Clinical Negligence (London), Personal Injury (London)
Practice Areas: Clinical negligence, personal injury, public law (inquests).
Professional Memberships: AvMA; APIL, Coroners Association of England and Wales, Royal Society of Medicine.
Career: Richard undertakes all types of clinical negligence, personal injury and public law (inquest) work. He has built up a specialist practice acting for claimants who have been caused to suffer catastrophic brain injuries as a consequence of clinical negligence but has also represented claimants in a broad range of claims involving health professionals, including cosmetic surgeons. In 2011 he was appointed an Assistant Deputy Coroner for South Yorkshire (Eastern District); he also regularly appears at inquests on behalf of interested parties, including inquests held in accordance with Article 2 of the European Convention and inquests held before juries. He has a particular interest in Fatal Accident claims and often represents parties through the inquest process and onto the conclusion of a subsequent civil claim. In addition to his busy Clinical Negligence practice Richard undertakes a wide variety of personal injury work, including workplace and road traffic accidents, accidents on the highway and in public places and claims arising from defective products. He acts on behalf of claimants and defendants and has experience of high value claims arising from catastrophic and non-catastrophic brain injuries. He regularly advises in cases where claimants have sustained spinal injuries or are exhibiting psychogenic symptoms.

BALA, Ruth
Gough Square Chambers, London
ruth.bala@goughsq.co.uk
Featured in Consumer Law (London)
Practice Areas: Ruth represents financial institutions on a broad range of consumer credit matters, including enforceability disputes and alleged mis-selling of investments and insurance. She also undertakes drafting and advisory work, including advising on compliance with the FCA Handbook and drafting requirements for the purposes of securitisations or acquisitions. In addition to financial services, Ruth also has experience in other consumer regulatory matters, both civil and criminal, including counterfeit goods and unfair commercial practices.
Career: Called in 2006. Successfully represented the lender in the leading case on alleged mis-selling of PPI: Harrison v Black Horse Ltd [2011]Lloyd's Rep IR 455 and was led by Nicholas Elliott QC in the Court of Appeal: Harrison v Black Horse Ltd [2012] Lloyd's Rep IR 521. Successfully represented the lender alone in the High Court, against Hodge Malek QC, in Conlon v Black Horse Ltd [2012] GCCR 11423, settled in June 2014, three days before expedited appeal to the Supreme Court due to be heard.
Publications: Author of the chapter 'Consumer Credit Law' in 'Consumer and Trading Standards: Law and Practice', Jordan (2013). Contributor to 'Advertising Law and Regulation', ed G. Crown, 2nd edn, Bloomsbury Professional (2010).
Personal: Read Classics at Oriel College, Oxford University.

BALDRY, Rupert QC
Pump Court Tax Chambers, London
020 7414 8080
clerks@pumptax.com
Featured in Tax (London)
Practice Areas: Specialising in tax including VAT and duties. Recent cases include FII GLO (Supreme Court); Sempra (House of Lords); Mars (House of Lords); Dextra (House of Lords); Jones v Garnett (House of Lords); Thin Cap GLO (Court of Appeal); Kellogg Brown & Root (Court of Appeal); Peter Clay Discretionary Trust (Court of Appeal); JD Wetherspoons (Upper Tribunal); Countrywide Estate Agents (Upper Tribunal); BT Pension Scheme (Court of Appeal); Hochtief (First-Tier Tribunal); Capital Cranfield (First-Tier Tribunal); Northumbrian Water (First-Tier Tribunal); Prudential Assurance (High Court).
Professional Memberships: Revenue Bar Association; London Common Law and Commercial Bar Association.
Career: Qualified 1987; junior counsel Attorney General's panel (1997-2005); Silk 2010.

BALDWIN, John QC
8 New Square, London
020 7405 4321
john.baldwin@8newsquare.co.uk
Featured in Intellectual Property (London), Media & Entertainment (London)
Practice Areas: Barrister (QC) specialising in all aspects of intellectual property, media and entertainment and information technology: including patents, trade marks, copyrights, confidential information, computer law, passing off, trade libel, EC law, data protection, restrictive covenants and restraint of trade. Recent cases: Fisher v Brooker (A Whiter Shade of Pale); Baigent v Random House (The Da Vinci Code), Evegate Publishing Ltd v Newsquest Media (southern) Ltd, A+E Television Networks LLC v Discovery Communications Europe Ltd. Fage UK Ltd v Chobani UK Limited (Greek Yogurt). For comprehensive CV and list of recent cases, visit Chambers' website at www.8newsquare.co.uk.
Professional Memberships: Intellectual Property Bar Association (IPBA); Chancery Bar Association.
Career: Called 1977, Gray's Inn; QC 1991; Recorder, 2004; Deputy High Court Judge, 2008.
Personal: Born 1947. Educated at Nelson Grammar School; University of Leeds (1968 BSc Agricultural Chemistry); St John's College, Oxford (1972 DPhil., 1972 Research Fellowship)., Inns of Court School of Law.

BALLARD, Briony
Serjeants' Inn Chambers, London
020 7427 5000
bb@3serjeantsinn.com
Featured in Inquests & Public Inquiries (London)
Practice Areas: Briony Ballard was called to the Bar in 2000. Briony specialises in clinical negligence and healthcare, Court of Protection, inquests and inquiries, police, professional discipline and regulatory and public and administrative law. An earlier edition notes that "she is both approachable and personable, she is known for having very good client care skills." Please click on the link to the Serjeants' Inn Chambers website for her profile, which sets out full details of her practice including relevant work of note.
Professional Memberships: Professional Negligence Bar Association, London Common Law and Commercial Bar Association, Liberty.

BALMER, Kate
Devereux, London
020 7353 7534
balmer@devchambers.co.uk
Featured in Employment (London)
Practice Areas: Kate practices predominantly in the fields of employment, discrimination and commercial law. She regularly represents clients in high value and multi-day claims involving all aspects of employment law. Kate's clients include FTSE 100 companies, international airlines, high street chains, banks, beauty brands, health care providers, charities and a wide range of public and private sector clients and private individuals.
Professional Memberships: ELA, ELBA, ILS, FRU, RBA.
Career: BA in Politics and History (First Class); Graduate Diploma in Law (Distinction); Bar Vocational Course (Very Competent); Called in 2009; appointed to the Attorney General's panel (C panel) in 2013.
Publications: Contributing author to Tottel's Discrimination Law (Bloomsbury Professional) and author of various articles including 'Fecitt & Ors v NHS Manchester: Whistleblowing' (ELA Briefing) and 'Bad Day At The Office' (Glamour Magazine).

BANERJEE, Lydia
Littleton Chambers, London
020 7797 8600
lbanerjee@littletonchambers.co.uk
Featured in Employment (London)
Practice Areas: Lydia's core areas of practice are commercial law, sports law and employment law. Lydia's commercial practice encompasses disputes including contractual interpretation, professional negligence and directors' duties. Lydia's sports law work covers work in relation to agency fee disputes, arbitrations and disciplinary proceedings. Lydia's employment work has a particular focus on disability discrimination but also incorporates all areas of tribunal disputes and high court action in relation to bonuses and restrictive covenants.
Professional Memberships: BASL, COMBAR, YFLA, ELBA, SEC, LCF.
Career: Called 2007, Middle Temple
Personal: Educated at Downing College, Cambridge, awarded Queen Mother Scholarship by Middle Temple and Senior Harris Scholar by Downing College. Listed in Who's Who of Britain's Young Entrepreneurs 2006 and Who's Who of Emerging Business Leaders 2007 and 2008. Trustee for charity Rafiki and Director of Kinson Pottery Ltd.

BANNER, Charles
Landmark Chambers, London
020 7430 1221
cbanner@landmarkchambers.co.uk
Featured in Administrative & Public Law (London), Competition/European Law (London), Planning (London)
Practice Areas: Administrative & public law; environmental law; European Union law; human rights; infrastructure, energy & natural resources; planning law; public law; public procurement; regulatory law.
Professional Memberships: Administrative Law Bar Association, Association of Regulatory and Disciplinary Lawyers; Bar European Group, Planning and Environmental Bar Association, UK Environmental Law Association, UK State Aid Law Association.
Career: Called to the Bar of England and Wales in 2004 and to the Bar of Northern Ireland in 2010. Regularly undertakes inquiry, tribunal, High Court and appellate work throughout England and Wales and also acts in litigation before the High Court of Northern Ireland. Has appeared in over 50 planning inquiries and over 40 reported cases, including 12 appeals in the UK Supreme Court / House of Lords (including as sole counsel for Heathrow Hub in the HS2 litigation), 4 cases before the CJEU (including as sole counsel for the UK on 2 occasions) and 4 cases before the UN Aarhus Convention Compliance Committee (all as sole counsel). Member of the Attorney General's B Panel of Junior Counsel to the Crown. ADR Group accredited mediator. College Lecturer in EU & Administrative Law at Oxford University (Oriel, Regent's Park and Lincoln colleges) since 2010. Ranked the No. 1 planning barrister in England & Wales under the age of 35 in Planning Magazine's annual survey of planning professionals for the last two years (2013 & 2014).
Publications: Editor of "The Aarhus Convention - A Guide for UK Lawyers" (Hart Publishing, forthcoming). Associate Editor of the "Encyclopedia of Planning Law and Practice" (Sweet and Maxwell, looseleaf) for 5 years from 2008-2013. Contributor to "Garner's Environmental Law" (LexisNexis Butterworths, looseleaf). Regular articles in leading journals - see profile on Landmark Chambers website for details.

BANNER, Gregory
Maitland Chambers, London
020 7406 1200
gbanner@maitlandchambers.com
Featured in Company (London)
Practice Areas: Main area of work is commercial chancery litigation, with particular emphasis on commercial litigation (with particular experience of natural resources disputes in the FSU), company law, shareholders' disputes, warranty claims, insolvencies, business disputes and related matters.
Professional Memberships: Chancery Bar Association, COMBAR.
Career: Called to the Bar in 1989; Junior Counsel to the Crown ('B' Panel) 1997-2004.
Publications: MA Cantab. Educated at Dulwich College and Trinity Hall, Cambridge. Personal interests include cycling, triathlon and skiing.

BARAN, Stuart
Three New Square, London
020 7405 1111
baran@3newsquare.co.uk
Featured in Intellectual Property (London)
Practice Areas: My practice focusses on intellectual property in all its aspects: patents, trade marks, copyright, designs and confidential information. I represent all types of clients from all sectors and in all fora, including all courts and proceedings at the UKIPO and EPO. Recent cases have included BSkyB v. Microsoft (SkyDrive), Resolution v. Lundbeck (citalopram), Comic v. Fox (GLEE), FH Brundle v. Perry (IPEC, threats), Cadbury v. Nestlé (CA, trade marks), Actavis v. Lilly (chemotherapy, UK and foreign patent laws, jurisdiction), Biocompatibles v. Biosphere (EPO), Coca-Cola "MASTER" (EU General Court), Merck v. ONO (patents, biotech), Teva v. Boehringer Ingelheim (patents, SPCs, pharmaceuticals), "TEAM GB" trade mark registration (for the British Olympic Assn), Idenix v. Gilead (sofosbuvir, antiviral drugs, patents), Timesource v. Ultimate Products (passing off, account of profits).
Professional Memberships: Inner Temple, AIPPI, IPBA.
Career: MChem Chemistry (Jesus College, Oxford: first class); DPhil (Oxford) Chemical Physics. GDL (City University: distinction); BPTC (BPP: Outstanding). Called July 2011.
Personal: Violinist and keen amateur cook.

BARCA, Manuel QC
One Brick Court, London
020 7353 8845
mb@onebrickcourt.com
Featured in Defamation/Privacy (London), Media & Entertainment (London)
Practice Areas: Media/ information law: defamation; privacy/ confidence; malicious falsehood; contempt of court; media/ literary copyright; passing off.
Career: Graduate trainee, Reuters 1984-85. Called: 1986 (Lincoln's Inn, Levitt Scholar). Joined 1BC 1987; QC 2011. Cases include: Pickering v Liverpool Daily Post (HL); John Major MP v New Statesman; Berkoff v Burchill (CA); Watts v Times Newspapers (CA); GMC v BBC (CA); Godfrey v Demon Internet; Upjohn v BBC; Peter Bottomley MP v Express Newspapers; British Coal v NUM; Barclay Brothers v BBC; Martin Clunes v Express Newspapers; Home Secretary v BBC; Marks & Spencer v Granada TV; ITN v Living Marxism; David Trimble MP v Amazon; Multigroup v Oxford Analytica; Elite Models v BBC; Skrine v Euromoney (CA); Steedman

v BBC (CA); Philip Green v Times Newspapers; Donal MacIntyre v Chief Constable of Kent (CA); Jimmy Nail v Newcastle Chronicle; Reuben Brothers v Time Inc; Conrad Black v Express Newspapers; Neil Lennon v Daily Record; Ricky Tomlinson v Associated Newspapers; Prince Turki Al-Saud v Paris Match; W v Westminster City Council; Roman Polanski v Condé Nast (HL); Paul McKenna v MGN; AG v BBC (Cash for Honours); Taranissi v BBC; Ajinomoto v Asda (CA); Hughes v British Airways; Baturina v Times Newspapers (CA); Prince Nayef Al-Saud v The Independent; Miller v Associated Newspapers (CA); PNM v Times Newspapers Ltd & anr (CA).
Personal: Educated: Wimbledon College; Cambridge University (Law, MA). Bilingual: English/Spanish. Fluent French. Working Italian & Portuguese.

BARCLAY, Robin
Outer Temple Chambers, London
robin.barclay@outertemple.com
Featured in Financial Crime (London)
Practice Areas: Robin Barclay has a specialist practice in international commercial fraud & financial crime. He acts for & advises senior professionals, entrepreneurs and corporate clients in high profile, sensitive & complex commercial disputes. He is routinely engaged in cross-border multi-agency civil, criminal & regulatory / professional disciplinary claims & investigations as well as internal corporate disputes & investigations.

BARDEN, Alex
Erskine Chambers, London
020 7242 5322
abarden@erskinechambers.com
Featured in Company (London)
Practice Areas: Alex is a specialist in company law, insolvency, and general commercial litigation and arbitration. Significant recent cases as a junior include the RBS Rights Issue litigation, the Alpstream case (a seven-week Commercial Court trial relating to security over aircraft), a number of high value, complex pieces of litigation arising from the insolvencies of Kaupthing Bank and of the Akai Electrical Group, and two Court of Appeal cases on the interpretation of the insolvency rules. He has also appeared in arbitrations relating to joint ventures and LLPs. He regularly appears as sole advocate in Commercial Court and Chancery Division litigation, and he was successful in a recent six-day Commercial Court trial (Paros v Worldlink). His corporate transactional practice includes cross-border mergers, joint ventures and reductions of share capital.
Professional Memberships: COMBAR, Chancery Bar Association.
Publications: Contributor to Buckley on the Companies Acts, Lightman and Moss on Receivers and Administrators (appointment of administrators) and Company Directors: Law and Liability (Insolvency).

BARLOW, Francis QC
Ten Old Square, London
020 7405 0758
francisbarlow@tenoldsquare.com
Featured in Chancery (London), Trusts (London)
Practice Areas: Francis Barlow's practice covers the full spectrum of Chancery matters, both contentious and non-contentious. As well as having particular expertise in drafting UK and offshore trusts and advising on their construction and effect and associated taxation issues, he has extensive experience in contested trust, probate and succession disputes.
Professional Memberships: Member of the Chancery Bar Association, STEP, ACTAPS and the Charity Law Association.
Career: Head of Chambers at Ten Old Square (2012 - date), Called to the Bar 1965, Silk 2006. Reported cases include:Re Q Trust [2010] Bda LR 26, [2011] WTLR 735 (Sup Ct of Bermuda) (appeared as amicus curiae to argue that a trust was not invalid as an illusory trust), Kershaw v Micklethwaite [2010] WTLR 413 (removal of executors; jurisdiction), Re Z Trust [2009] CILR 593 (Grand Court of Cayman Islands) (trusts: jurisdiction to confer administrative powers), Wyndham v Egremont [2009] WTLR 1473 (variation of trusts; extension of trust period; capital gains tax); Breakspear v Ackland [2009] Ch 32 (settlement; disclosure of letter of wishes; exercise of dispositive powers; conflict of interest), Thomas & Agnes Carvel Foundation v Carvel [2008] Ch 395 (will: jurisdiction to remove executrix; devastavit). Earlier reported cases: Sieff v Fox [2005] 1 WLR 3811 (avoidance of trust disposition under rule in Hastings-Bass and for mistake), Mitchell v Halliwell [2005] EWHC 937 (removal of executors; devastavit), Re DWS [2001] Ch 568, CA (murder, forfeiture and intestacy), Corbett v Newey [1998] Ch 57, CA (conditional wills), Re K [1985] Ch 85, CA (manslaughter, succession and relief from forfeiture).
Publications: Consultant editor of Williams on Wills, a contributor to the first and second editions of Thomas and Hudson's Law of Trusts, the third edition of International Succession (Garb and Wood) and to International Trust Disputes (Collins, Kempster, McMillan and Meek).

BARNARD, Jonathan
Cloth Fair Chambers, London
020 7710 6444
jonathanbarnard@clothfairchambers.com
Featured in Crime (London), Financial Crime (London)
Practice Areas: Regularly instructed to represent professional and corporate clients in high-profile criminal proceedings, complex financial matters, frequently with multi-jurisdictional aspects. He has represented the CEO of a billion pound company (reinsurance fraud, SFO prosecution); a company director (Market offences); a leading breast surgeon (fraud); a psychiatrist (rape); a solicitor (money laundering, SFO prosecution); a dentist (fraud) and a company director (MTIC fraud). Significant prosecution experience includes the largest Court Martial in British Military history, cases involving complex PII from Special Casework Directorate, electoral frauds, frauds within the City of London and numerous murders at the Old Bailey. Considerable experience at regulatory tribunals, including the GMC and the GDC, in serious and long running hearings e.g. Dr. Martin 2010. Has been instructed by the AADB (Accountancy and Actuarial Disciplinary Board), drafted representations to the City of London Police regarding tax evasion and financial irregularity in the football industry preventing charges. Represented an individual in successful plea agreement in the largest case brought by DEFRA, represented a Solicitor charged with laundering the proceeds of overseas executive corruption, represented a director of a company charged with corruption and international sanctions busting, advised ex-Icelandic banking executives, advised a former editor of a national newspaper in relation to the Leveson Enquiry and advised on a number of defamation maters. Advised Vincent Tchenguiz in judicial review of the search used by the SFO. Successfully represented an international property tycoon surrounding corruption charges in Turks & Caicos Islands. Represented a hedge fund manager before the Financial Services and Markets Tribunal re. market abuse. Looked after the interests of a national supermarket who became victims of a multi-million pound fraud scam. Successfully represented Eddy Shah over rape charges; advised healthcare company regarding potential fraud implications; successfully represented Victor Dahdaleh over international corruption allegations; advised a leading accountancy firm re potential money laundering. Acting for CEO of a raw materials company charged with conspiracy to defraud. Advising Raymond Kwok re corruption charges in Hong Kong. Advising individual in SFO investigation regarding Rolls Royce; Advising a national pharmaceutical company. Instructed to represent a former Senior Partner of accountancy firm over fraud charges in Gibraltar. Retained for former Barclays Senior Executive in SFO/FCA investigation. Continues to advise Thames Water. For further information please visit www.clothfairchambers.com.
Professional Memberships: Criminal Bar Association (member of the working party on plea negotiation in fraud trials), Association of Regulatory and Disciplinary Lawyers, sits on the Appeals Panel at the Legal Services Commission.
Career: 1997 - Called to the Bar
Personal: Edinburgh University 1988-92 MA (First Class, Hons).

BARNEY, Helen
No5 Chambers, Birmingham
0845 210 5555
hb@no5.com
Featured in Employment (Midlands)
Practice Areas: Helen practices exclusively in the field of employment and discrimination law. She has extensive experience (15 years) of advising and representing clients on employment law matters. She undertakes both claimant and respondent work, in the public and private sector. Clients include local authorities, NHS, police, multi-national companies, union and insurance supported Claimants. Helen started her career in employment law at a leading national firm of solicitors in 1999, joined Broadway House Chambers in 2002 and moved to the employment team at No5 Chambers in 2007.

BARNFATHER, Lydia
QEB Hollis Whiteman, London
020 7933 8855
lydia.barnfather@qebhw.co.uk
Featured in Professional Discipline (London)
Practice Areas: Lydia Barnfather is a leading practitioner in regulatory law and professional discipline. She prosecutes and presents complex, high profile and sensitive cases for regulatory bodies, many involving opposing Queen's Counsel. Lydia also has extensive experience in serious criminal cases including murder, sex abuse, fraud and drugs. She is on the Rape Specialist List. Lydia is expert in all aspects of conduct, performance and health and highly experienced in calling and cross-examining experts and dealing with vulnerable witnesses. Lydia has advised and appeared on appeals to the High Court (and formerly the Privy Council). Her dedication, thoroughness and high quality advocacy have ensured repeat instructions before the General Medical Council, General Dental Council, General Chiropractic Council, NHS England, and the Health and Care Professions Council amongst others. She advises on the most difficult areas of law and leads in-house training events for professional clients. Her recent landmark cases include the first criminal prosecution brought by the HCPC, the first test case for NHS England under the new regulations governing Performers Lists, and the follow-on appeal before the first-tier tribunal.
Professional Memberships: Association of Regulatory and Disciplinary Lawyers, Criminal Bar Association, South Eastern Circuit.
Personal: Call 1992; MA St Hilda's College, Oxford; CPE University of Westminster.

BARRETT, John
Kings Chambers, Manchester
0845 034 3444
clerks@kingschambers.com
Featured in Environment (Northern), Planning (Northern)
Practice Areas: Housing; waste disposal and management; minerals; major infrastructure projects; gas storage; highways; inquiries relating to substantial commercial and retail developments, including town centre redevelopments. John specialises in all aspects of town and country planning, environmental law, compulsory purchase and acquisition, local government, and highways. He has appeared as counsel in numerous UDP, Core Strategy and local plan inquiries and has worked extensively in the areas of waste disposal and management, minerals, highways and housing. Other significant inquiries include those relating to substantial commercial and retail developments, and major infrastructure proposals including underground gas storage.
Professional Memberships: Planning and Environment Bar Association, Administrative Law Bar Association.
Career: University: Manchester Metropolitan. Degree: BA (Hons) Law. Called:1982.
Publications: Former editor Encyclopaedia of Environmental Health - Sweet & Maxwell.

BARRETT, Joseph
11KBW, London
020 7632 8500
joseph.barrett@11kbw.com
Featured in Public Procurement (London)
Practice Areas: Joseph Barrett practises in public, commercial and employment law, with particular expertise EU procurement, State aid and competition litigation. Recent cases include: Covanta Energy Limited v Merseyside Waste Disposal Authority [2013] EWHC 2922 (leading case on interim relief in procurement litigation); R (Shepherd Offshore Ltd) v North Tyneside Council [2013] E.St.A.LQ 638 (EU State aid challenges to contract award decisions); R (LB of Lewisham) v Ofqual [2013] EWHC 211 (Judicial review of national GCSE results); and Bruton v Information Commissioner & Duchy of Cornwall [2012] 1 Info LR 17 (Constitutional test case establishing that the Prince of Wales' Duchy of Cornwall is a public authority).
Professional Memberships: Administrative Law Bar Association, Bar European

Group, Procurement Lawyers Association, UK State Aid Law Association.
Career: Called in 2009; 2009-2010 Judicial Assistant to the Deputy President of the UK Supreme Court; Appointed to the Attorney General's C Panel of Counsel in 2014.
Publications: Contributor to various texts and journals on public and employment law.
Personal: University of Glasgow, LLB (First Class Honours); Harvard Law School, LLM.

BARRY, Denis
5 Paper Buildings, London
020 7583 6117
dab@5pb.co.uk
Featured in Consumer Law (London)
Practice Areas: Substantial practice in consumer law and in general crime. Consumer law: Areas of specialisation include Trade mark and Copyright offences, Trading Standards and all Consumer offences, for which he is instructed by both defendants, companies, and local authorities. Regularly instructed in novel and complex consumer law proceedings; brought the first proceedings under Part VIII Enterprise Act 2002 (Stop Now Orders), and the first prosecution (for the OFT) under the Consumer Protection from Unfair Trading Regulations. Regularly acts in an advisory capacity on UK and EU regulatory consumer law for multinational companies, private prosecutors and individuals. Has particular experience on the overlap between EU law and UK criminal law (in the context of competition, environmental law and discrimination). Is available to undertake direct access cases. Regularly lectures on consumer law. Particular interest in new Consumer Rights Bill. General crime: Wide range of experience in defending and prosecuting all types of criminal cases. Grade 4 prosecutor. Specialist in confiscation. Particular expertise in homicide (including cases involving infant death), environmental cases, money laundering and cases involving gambling. Regularly instructed as leading junior counsel. Please see the 5 Paper Buildings website for additional details.
Career: Birmingham University LLB Warwick University LLM Called to the Bar 1996.
Publications: Denis has been commissioned by Oxford University Press to lead a team writing the Blackstone's Guide to the Consumer Protection Act (2015).

BARSAM, Talia
Devereux, London
020 7353 7534
barsam@devchambers.co.uk
Featured in Employment (London)
Practice Areas: All areas of employment law, including all areas of discrimination law, whistleblowing, unfair dismissal, equal pay, breach of contract, TUPE, restrictive covenants and jurisdictional issues. Particular expertise in complex disability discrimination claims and high-value sex discrimination claims. Clients include multinational corporations in the financial, technology, construction, retail and transportation sectors, public sector clients including NHS Trusts and trade unions and senior executives. Education and Professional Negligence.
Professional Memberships: ELBA, ELA, COMBAR, PNBA.
Career: Called 2006. Admitted to the New York Bar 2008. Member of the Equality and Human Rights Commission Panel of Approved Counsel since 2011.
Publications: Contributing author, "Discrimination Law" (Bloomsbury Professional (formerly Tottel Publishing)); Jordans Employment Law Service.
Personal: LLM New York University, BA Affiliate Law Cambridge University, BA English University of Birmingham.

BARTER, Isabel
2TG - 2 Temple Gardens, London
020 7822 1238
ib@2tg.co.uk
Featured in Professional Negligence (London)
Practice Areas: Isabel specialises in professional negligence including claims for and against accountants,archoitects, surveyors, solicitors and financial advisers. She acted in Mehjoo v Harben Barker and Harben Barker Trusts [2014] COA. Her practice also covers product liabiity, commercial dispute resolution, property damage insurance, travel and jurisdiction and commercial fraud.
Professional Memberships: PNBA, COMBAR.
Career: Called 2010 (Inner Temple). Major Scholar 2008 and 2009. Tenant at 2TG - 2 Temple Gardens since 2011.
Publications: "Narrowing the Scope: the limits of generalist accountants' duties after Mehjoo v Harben Barker Trusts and Trustees" (July 2014).

BARTLETT, Andrew QC
Crown Office Chambers, London
020 7797 8100
abartlett@crownofficechambers.com
Featured in Construction (London), Insurance (London), Professional Negligence (London), Property Damage (London)
Practice Areas: Arbitrations as at 2013-14 include: ICC (Paris) arbitration concerning power generation project in the Caribbean (chairman); ICC (Paris) arbitration concerning highway project (chairman, Ethiopian substantive law, French procedural law); insurance dispute concerning a UK highway project (sole arbitrator, Scots law); LCIA arbitration concerning a national defence project (chairman); ICC (Hong Kong) arbitration of claims and counterclaims arising from an international airport project in the Middle East (sole arbitrator); insurance dispute regarding explosion in refinery in USA (counsel, New York law). His principal areas of expertise are insurance; construction, engineering and energy; property damage; commercial contracts; professional negligence.
Professional Memberships: CI Arb (Member of Practice and Standards Committee 2006-12), COMBAR, TECBAR (Chairman 2007-10), LCIA (European Users' Council), Professional Negligence Bar Association, London Common Law and Commercial Bar Association, Society of Construction Law.
Career: Chartered Arbitrator; QC 1993; Head of Crown Office Chambers 2009-12; Member of arbitration panels of TECBAR, Institute of Chartered Accountants of England and Wales, and CI Arb; Adjudicator accredited by TeCSA and TECBAR; Deputy High Court Judge (England); Judge of the Upper Tribunal (Financial Services; Information Rights).
Publications: Author of the chapters on Arbitration and Adjudication in Emden's Construction Law; Articles include: Model arbitration award, (2000) 66 Arbitration 108; Client-Friendly Arbitration, (2000) 66 Arbitration 2; Dealing with Experts, TECBAR Review, summer 2012.

BARTON, Fiona QC
5 Essex Court, London
020 7410 2000
barton@5essexcourt.co.uk
Featured in Inquests & Public Inquiries (London), Police Law (All Circuits), Professional Discipline (London)
Practice Areas: police law; inquests and inquiries; public and administrative; professional discipline. Hillsborough Inquests [2014] – For South Yorkshire Police in the inquests into the Hillsborough Disaster. Nunn [2014] – Acting for Suffolk Constabulary in the Supreme Court concerning post-conviction disclosure obligations. Al Hilli Alps Murders [2013] – For Surrey Police in the family proceedings concerning care of the All Hilli children following the murder. A v B Constabulary [2013] – Test case concerning the vetting of police contractors. Powell v Chief Constable of West Midlands Police [2013] – Complex high value civil jury action. Icelandic Bank Collapse (Tchenguiz) [2012] – Successfully defended the actions of City of London Police re the arrest of Robert Tchenguiz in connection with his dealings with the collapsed bank. Cumbria Shootings Inquests [2011] – Represented Cumbria Police in the inquests into the deaths of Derrick Bird and his victims. 7/7 London Bombing Inquests [2010] – For City of London Police in the inquests into the deaths of the 52 victims. L v Commissioner of Police of the Metropolis [2009] UKSC 3 – Supreme Court test case on behalf of the Commissioner concerning the scope of Enhanced Criminal Record Certificate.
Career: Called to the bar 1986; Silk 2011.

BARTON, Zoe
Selborne Chambers, London
020 7420 9500
zoe.barton@selbornechambers.co.uk
Featured in Real Estate Litigation (London)
Practice Areas: Commercial and traditional chancery, specialising in property litigation, trusts and estates and related professional negligence.
Professional Memberships: Chancery Bar Association, Property Bar Association, Association of Contentious Trust and Probate Specialists, Charity Law Association.
Career: MA Hons (Edin), Dip Law (City) (Scholar). Called Gray's Inn 2003 (Scholar). Zoë is recognised by both Chambers & Partners and Legal 500 for her expertise in her principal practice areas. Her practice spans all areas of Chancery and she is frequently instructed in cases which involve fraud, or call for equitable remedies, including those which concern multiple jurisdictions. In the context of land, Zoë is regularly briefed by those with significant land portfolios, including regularly on behalf of Network Rail. She deals with both real property and landlord and tenant matters and regularly acts for lenders in claims arising in connection with mortgages. Her traditional chancery practice concentrates on breach of trust claims and private client work, including contentious probate, advisory work concerning the construction variation or rectification of wills and the administration of estates; she is instructed by both beneficiaries and trustees, including on behalf of numerous charities. Zoë draws on her considerable expertise in general commercial transactions, trusts and property issues to effectively handle complex and sophisticated professional negligence disputes on behalf of both claimants and defendants.

BARWISE, Stephanie QC
Atkin Chambers, London
020 7404 0102
sbarwise@atkinchambers.com
Featured in Construction (London)
Practice Areas: General commercial including all aspects of the law relating to the construction and civil engineering industry in litigation, arbitration and adjudication. Also has acted as adjudicator and arbitrator. Experience includes major road and tunnel construction, construction of railways, defects and locomotives, ship refurbishment, North Sea oil rig construction, Ladbroke Grove Rail Inquiry, LUL Piccadilly and Jubilee line upgrades, offshore wind farms and fully computer automated gantry cranes in Hong Kong as well as experience in various other disputes related to computer software. Practice also involves professional negligence in general and in particular of architects, engineers and surveyors. A further area of specialisation is procurement: has acted for central and local government, NHS Trusts (PFI agreements) and utility companies (acting under framework agreements). Experience of all major forms of contracts including NEC3.
Professional Memberships: TECBAR; Combar.
Career: Called to the Bar 1988. Joined Atkin Building in 1989. Took Silk 2006. Bencher Middle Temple 2010.
Personal: Educated at Bolton School and Cambridge University (Downing College). Fluent in French and German.

BASTIN, Alexander
Hardwicke, London
020 7242 2523
alexander.bastin@hardwicke.co.uk
Featured in Real Estate Litigation (London)
Practice Areas: A specialist in property-related litigation and advisory work including all aspects of commercial and residential landlord and tenant law (including breach of covenant, dilapidations, forfeiture, lease renewal and service charge disputes), real property (including adverse possession, boundaries, mortgages, nuisance, party walls, rights of way/easements and trespass as well as issues arising out of the sale of properties), trusts of land/co-ownership disputes, social housing (landlord & tenant aspects only) and property-related professional negligence.
Career: Educated at Eton College, Reading and City Universities and the Inns of Court School of Law. Called to the Bar in 1995. Six years at Francis Taylor Building, one year at Mayer Brown (employed barrister specialising in property-related litigation) and joined Hardwicke in 2002.
Publications: Samson v Gardner [2009] EWHC 3309 (QB) on constructive trusts and the presumption of advancement, The Governors of the Peabody Trust v Reeve [2008] EWHC 1432 (Ch) on the unilateral variation of a standard tenancy and Plantation Wharf Management Ltd v Jackson [2011] UKUT 488 (LC). OM Property Management v Hughes & Others [2012] UKUT 258 (LC) [2012] PLSCS 198.

BASU, Dijen
5 Essex Court, London
020 7410 2000
basu@5essexcourt.co.uk
Featured in Police Law (All Circuits)
Practice Areas: Public and administrative law, defending civil actions against the police, inquests and inquiries. Examples: R (Mackaill & ors) v IPCC & ors (the 'Plebgate' judicial review), R (Minter) v Hampshire Police [2014] 1 WLR 179, CA (extended sentences and sex offender registration), R (A) v Chief Constable of Kent [2013] EWCA Civ 1706, CA (Enhanced Criminal Record Certificates), R (M) v Hampshire Police [2012] EWHC 4034 (Admin) (search regime for sex offenders compatible with their human rights – to be heard by the Court of Appeal in November 2014), R (Mengesha) v Commissioner of Police of the Metropolis [2013] EWHC 1695 (Admin) ('kettling'), R (R) v Chief Constable of West Midlands Constabulary [2013] EWHC 2864 (Admin) (collection of DNA from historic offenders), Boardman v Nugent Care Society [2013] ICR 927, CA (teacher accused of assaulting a pupil), Aitken v Commissioner of Police [2012] ICR 78, CA (treatment of an officer with a mental illness).
Career: Called to the Bar 1994; Crown Court Recorder 2010; Attorney General's Panel of Special Advocates 2009; registered with the GMC to practise medicine 1992; M.B., B.S. degree (with distinction in surgery) from what is now Guy's, King's and St Thomas' School of Medicine 1991.
Personal: Private pilot's licence for both aeroplanes and helicopter.

BATES, John H
Old Square Chambers, London
020 7269 0359
bates@oldsquare.co.uk
Featured in Environment (London)
Practice Areas: Over the last 20 years John has acquired considerable experience in criminal and civil cases involving environmental work - although it is in the civil courts that John has been appearing in more recently. Barr v. Biffa [2011] EWHC 1003 (TCC) was a Group Litigation case of odour nuisance from a landfill with 152 Claimants. John did the legal advocacy for the Claimant which involved a detailed examination of the regulatory scheme in both English and EC legislation as the Defendant raised the defence of statutory authority. They also argued that compliance with the regulatory scheme was a 'reasonable use' of land for the law of nuisance. D's statutory authority argument was rejected but they succeeded on 'reasonable use.' The Court of Appeal overturned this decision and the case is being retried. Dobson v. Thames Water [2011] EWHC 3253 (TCC) was a Group Litigation nuisance case concerning odour and mosquitoes with over 1300 Claimants. John dealt with the mosquito case, cross examining expert witnesses and doing the opening and closing speeches on them. He was also involved in the detailed negligence claim in respect of the design and operation of the sewage treatment works and drafted the particulars of negligence. John also does water and drainage cases such as abstraction, flood defence or fishing rights.

BATES, Justin
Arden Chambers, London
020 7242 4244
justin.bates@ardenchambers.com
Featured in Social Housing (London)
Practice Areas: Housing, Property, Landlord and Tenant, Local Government. Justin has a particular interest in the LVT / First Tier Tribunal (Property Chamber) and has appeared in a number of important cases concerning leasehold property issues in the Upper Tribunal and Court of Appeal. He recently appeared (led by Andrew Arden QC) in the Supreme Court in CN & ZH v LB Newham and Lewisham; Sims v Dacorum BC, concerning homelessness accommodation, Protection from Eviction Act 1977, Art.8 and Art.1, First Protocol of the ECHR.
Professional Memberships: HLPA (Vice-Chair); PBA.
Career: BA (Hons) Oxford; LLM (Toronto). Called 2003. Reported/significant cases in 2013/14 include Burr v OM Property Management Ltd [2013] EWCA Civ 479 (led by Andrew Arden QC); Wynbay Ltd v (1) London RAP (2) Osman [2014] EWHC 172 (Admin); Trustees of the Green Masjid v Birmingham CC [2013] UKUT 355 (LC); Qdime Ltd v Bath Building [2014] UKUT 261 (LC); Columbia House Properties (No.3) Ltd v Imperial Hall RTM Co Ltd [2014] UKUT 30(LC).
Publications: Deputy General Editor, Encyclopedia of Housing Law; co-author "Leasehold Disputes"; co-author various Current Law Statutes Annotations, including Prevention of Social Housing Fraud Act 2013; contributor to "Local Government Constitutional and Administrative Law"; contributor to Halsburys Laws: Local Government.

BATES, Pascal
6 Pump Court, London
020 7797 8400
pascalbates@6pumpcourt.co.uk
Featured in Health & Safety (London)
Practice Areas: Prosecuting and defending regulatory prosecutions brought by national and local enforcement agencies – primarily health and safety but also railway, food, trading standards and environment: e.g. HSE v Marsh (2014), Defra/HSE v Pirbright Institute (2014), HSE v Green Partnership (2014), HSE v Basildon Hospital (2013), HSE v Leisure Connection (2013), FSA v Hook (2013), HSE v UK Power Networks (2013) – currently engaged in two multi-party major structural collapse cases, one involving design fault allegations and the other involving four fatalities. Confidential and strategic advice on regulatory and commercial matters, including recently advising on claims to arbitrate losses from trading standards seizures and allegedly botched mineshaft construction works. Inquests, including drowning, legionella infection and death in custody/hospital. Disclosure/PII in both civil and criminal contexts. General common and public law with an emphasis on statutory construction, especially with an international flavour, with recent instructions including rights to UK passports, the effect of transfer of a public body from England to Scotland, Iranian sanctions and US arms controls. Commercial contract and property: eg. Meretz Investments v ACP [2008] Ch 244, Haller v Deutsche Bank. Contested probate.
Career: MA (Cantab); called 1994; Standing Counsel to HSE & ORR; 'A' List for Environment Agency.

BATES, Richard
29 Bedford Row Chambers, London
020 7404 1044
r.bates@29br.co.uk
Featured in Family/Matrimonial (London)
Practice Areas: Matrimonial finance, particularaly interested in farming cases; children (private law).
Professional Memberships: FLBA.
Career: Called 1992.
Personal: Married to Victoria Francis with two young sons. Educated at Bedford School, University of Durham (BA Hons).

BATE-WILLIAMS, John
Temple Garden Chambers, London
020 7583 1315
jbw@tgchambers.com
Featured in Personal Injury (London)
Practice Areas: PI, fatal accidents, insurance, serious crime.
Professional Memberships: PIBA, CBA.
Career: The Senior Junior in TGC, John has a substantial Personal Injury, Fatal Accidents and Insurance practice. Described by the solicitor who advised Balfour Beatty to instruct him in the Hatfield Rail Crash case as a "pragmatic street fighter", he has acquired a reputation for sound judgment, realistic and practical advice and excellent advocacy. 70% of his practice involves the representation of insurers in high value claims, usually involving catastrophic head injuries or injuries of maximum severity. He has particular experience in exposing exaggerated and dishonest claims - in Harnett -v- Northover (January 2012) he succeeded in obtaining an Order requiring the Claimant to pay the entire costs of the action. His objective approach has ensured that he continues to receive a volume of instructions on behalf of Claimants in substantial and unusual claims including helicopter and powerboat accidents. In Dufosse -v- Melbury Events (December 2011) he persuaded the Court of Appeal to find Santa and an Elf responsible for the Claimant's downfall, and received The Times award for the Courtroom Joke of the Year. He was appointed a Crown Court Recorder in 2000.
Personal: Married with 2 children, lives in the Cotswolds. Recreations - tennis, skiing and travel, especially Australia and the South Pacific islands.

BATT, Charanjit
Queen Elizabeth Building, London
020 7797 7837
c.batt@qeb.co.uk
Featured in Family/Matrimonial (London)
Practice Areas: All aspects of private family law with an emphasis on financial matters (financial relief, Part III, and Schedule 1) and private law children (including relocation) cases. Has been instructed as a junior in a number of high value finance cases, including appearing in interlocutory hearings on her own against leading counsel, and has also been instructed as a junior in Children Act cases. Has a particular interest in cases with jurisdictional and/or international issues. Reported cases: Z v A [2012] 2 FLR 667 (with Lucy Stone QC).
Professional Memberships: FLBA; Bar Council member from 2006-2010
Career: LLB (University of Birmingham); LLM (UCL); and Internship at the Chambers of Parag Tripathi (Senior Advocate of the Supreme Court and former Additional Solicitor General) New Delhi.
Personal: Speaks Punjabi (native), Hindi (native), and conversational Urdu and Spanish.

BAXTER, Mark
5 Stone Buildings, London
020 7242 6201
clerks@5sblaw.com
Featured in Court of Protection (All Circuits)
Practice Areas: General Chancery practice with particular emphasis on wills and probate, trusts, estates and family provision, Court of Protection work and professional negligence related to all these areas. In the High Court and County Courts, Mark is increasingly instructed on behalf of both claimants and defendants in contentious probate and Inheritance (Provision for Family and Dependants) Act 1975 cases, and for both trustees and beneficiaries in applications concerning the administration and execution of trusts and estates. Recently, he succeeded in a 1975 Act claim on behalf of a co-habitant claimant where co-habitation was disputed. In the Court of Protection, Mark has recently been instructed in several contested attorneyship and deputyship applications, and contested statutory will applications (typically against a background of highly contentious family disputes) and is often instructed by the Official Solicitor.
Professional Memberships: Chancery Bar Association, Property Bar Association, the Denning Society.
Career: Called 2006.
Publications: Co-author of 'Risk and Negligence in Wills, Estates and Trusts' (OUP, 2009 and second edition, 2014). Regular contributor to professional journals. Lectures on all areas of his practice, particularly probate, tax, and Court of Protection matters.

BAYFIELD, Daniel
South Square, London
020 7696 9900
danielbayfield@southsquare.com
Featured in Banking & Finance (London), Chancery (London), Restructuring/Insolvency (London), Sports Law (London)
Practice Areas: Business and finance law (with an emphasis on insolvency, restructuring and banking) and general chancery and commercial litigation. Also sports law. Clients include the administrators of Lehman Brothers International (Europe), the administrators of MF Global UK, the FA Premier League and the Football League. Recent cases include: Re MF Global (UK) Ltd [2014] EWHC 2222 (Ch); Contrarian Funds LLC v Lomas [2014] EWHC 1687 (Ch); Re Lehman Brothers International (Europe) [2014] EWHC 704 (Ch); Pillar Denton Ltd v Jervis [2014] EWCA (Civ) 180; Re Magyar Telecom BV [2013] EWHC 3800 (Ch); Re Nortel / Re Lehman [2013] UKSC 52; Heis v MF Global Inc [2013] 1 WLR 903; HMRC v The Football League Ltd [2013] BCC 60; Lomas v JFB Firth Rixson Inc [2012] 2 Lloyds 548; Belmont Park Investments PTY Ltd v BNY Corporate Trustee Services Ltd [2012] 1 AC 383; BNY Corporate Trustee Services Ltd v Eurosail-UK 2007-3BL Plc [2011] 1 WLR 2524; Pearson v Lehman Brothers Finance SA [2012] 2 BCLC 151; Re Sigma Finance Corporation [2010] 1 All ER 571; Re Stanford International Bank Ltd [2011] Ch 33.
Professional Memberships: Chancery Bar Association; COMBAR.

Career: Called (Inner Temple) October 1998.
Publications: Contributor to Lightman & Moss: 'The Law of Receivers and Administrators of Companies' and Moss, Fletcher & Isaacs: 'The EC Regulation on Insolvency Proceedings'.
Personal: Magdalene College, Cambridge (MA).

BAZLEY, Janet QC
1 Garden Court Family Law Chambers, London
020 7797 7900
bazley@1gc.com
Featured in Family/Matrimonial (London)
Practice Areas: Private and public law children cases including those involving complex medical issues, cases with mental health issues, Court of Protection work, adoption, judicial review, cases with an international element, including abduction (Convention and non-Convention) and leave to remove. Family finance (including Schedule 1 applications, pre-nuptial agreements, private financial dispute resolution in Jersey.
Professional Memberships: The Family Law Bar Association (Committee member), The Association of Lawyers for Children; The Bar Council's Law Reform Committee (committee member).
Career: Called to the Bar (1980), Silk (2006), Recorder (Crime 2000, Family and Civil 2002). Joint Head of Chambers (2010).
Publications: Contributor to Halsbury's Laws (Children & Young Persons), co-author of Jordan's Applications under Schedule 1 of the Children Act (2010) and of Money Laundering for Lawyers.
Personal: Married with 3 children. Interests include languages (speaks French, German, Italian and Modern Greek), opera and travel.

BEALE, Anna
Cloisters, London
020 7827 4000
abe@cloisters.com
Featured in Employment (London)
Practice Areas: Anna is an employment and discrimination specialist. She acts for a wide variety of clients including individual claimants, trade unions, large public sector organisations and multinational companies. She is particularly known for her ability to communicate difficult legal concepts in a comprehensible way. Reported cases include: JP Morgan Europe Ltd v Chweidan [2011] IRLR 673 (CA: direct disability discrimination); Elstone v BP [2010] ICR 870 (EAT: extended the ambit of the whistleblowing legislation) and Wong v Igen Ltd [2005] ICR 931 (CA: junior counsel in the leading case on the burden of proof in discrimination claims). Anna is experienced in complex and high profile equal pay and discrimination litigation, having appeared as junior counsel in a national test case challenging the NHS job evaluation scheme and in the first cross-agency equal pay claim, comparing workers in the DVLA with male employees of the DSA. She is currently instructed on behalf of claimants in a number of related pregnancy/maternity discrimination claims. She also maintains a personal injury and clinical negligence practice, with ongoing involvement in complex spinal injury and meningitis claims.
Professional Memberships: Executive Committee Member, Industrial Law Society. Member of ELA, ELBA, IER, Bar Pro Bono Unit, ELAAS, HRLA and PIBA.
Career: Called to the Bar in 2001.
Publications: Co-editor of Discrimination in Employment: a claims handbook (LAG 2013); co-author of Age and Employment (European Commission 2011) and Employment Law and Human Rights (2nd ed, OUP 2007); contributor to Family Rights at Work (Jordans 2012).
Personal: Educated at Llanidloes High School and Magdalen College, Oxford (BA Jurisprudence 1st class).

BÉAR, Charles QC
Fountain Court Chambers, London
020 7583 3335
cbr@fountaincourt.co.uk
Featured in Administrative & Public Law (London), Commercial Dispute Resolution (London), Local Government (London), Public Procurement (London)
Practice Areas: Wide-ranging practice covering: general commercial litigation, judicial review, and public procurement. Commercial work includes: fraud, conspiracy, business sales/joint ventures, restitution, freezing and search orders, minority shareholder claims. Sector experience includes life sciences, aviation, telecoms and high-tech engineering. Practises in Commercial Court and Chancery Division, also Cayman Grand Court. Public law work is based in the Administrative Court and the appellate courts and includes numerous reported cases across fields varying from regulatory challenges to human rights. Also has significant experience of constitutional, financial and vires issues for local authorities, NHS trusts and other agencies. Regularly advises public bodies on major procurement issues. Also carries out employment work including post-termination injunctions (springboard, restrictive covenant, confidential information etc), bonus issues and strike litigation.
Professional Memberships: COMBAR, ALBA, ELBA.
Career: Called to the Bar 1986. QC 2003. Recorder 2003.
Personal: Born 1963. Magdalen College, Oxford, 1982-5 (1st Class Hons, Jurisprudence).

BEARD, Daniel QC
Monckton Chambers, London
020 7405 7211
dbeard@monkton.com
Featured in Competition/European Law (London), Telecommunications (London)
Practice Areas: Daniel Beard QC specialises in competition, EU, regulatory matters - including telecoms - and public law. He is widely regarded as one of the Bar's leading specialists in these areas and noted as a "first rate" advocate.
Career: He appears regularly in the High Court, Court of Appeal and Supreme Court, as well as doing a great deal of work in the specialist Competition Appeal Tribunal. He has acted in a large number of cases in the EU Court of Justice and General Court on a wide range of EU law matters. In addition he acts in arbitrations and on matters in other jurisdictions including in the Middle East, Singapore and Hong Kong. Recent work has included a large number of multinational competition damages actions, numerous regulatory (and other) judicial review cases and various appeals and interventions in the EU courts including representing the UK in relation to the accession of the EU to the ECHR. Prior to taking silk, Daniel was a member of the Attorney General's A Panel and standing Counsel to the Office of Fair Trading. He has developed vetting security clearance.
Publications: Daniel has written numerous articles on competition and public law. He was a founder of the Competition Law Journal.
Personal: MA (Hons) Cambridge (First Class) Bachelor of Civil Law (BCL), Oxford.

BEDFORD, Erica
Kings Chambers, Manchester
0845 034 3444
clerks@kingschambers.com
Featured in Costs Litigation (Northern)
Practice Areas: The law of costs.
Professional Memberships: Association of Cost Lawyers.
Career: University of Leeds LLB (Hons): 2003. Admitted as a Solicitor: 2010. Admitted as a Cost Lawyer: 2011. Call to the Bar: 2012.
Personal: Erica practices exclusively in the law of costs, with emphasis on costs arising from personal injury claims and commercial litigation. She regularly appears before Regional Cost Judges and in the SCCO. She is frequently instructed on appeal up to High Court level. She has particular specialism in the application of the various 'Distance Selling Regulations', arguments arising out of the fixed cost regimes, claims involving 'broken retainers', issues concerning the indemnity principle and procedural points of law. She frequently appears in CCMCs where costs are a particular concern. Additionally, she undertakes non contentious drafting and advisory work.

BEDFORD, Michael
Cornerstone Barristers, London
020 7242 4986
michaelb@cornerstonebarristers.com
Featured in Planning (London)
Practice Areas: Michael Bedford's practice covers all areas of town and country planning, environmental law, highways and compulsory purchase, including inquiries and hearings, examinations, advisory work, and High Court challenges. He also deals with related property matters including covenants, easements, public rights of way, and village greens. He acts for developers, landowners, and public sector clients, including via direct access. He has a substantial inquiry-based practice covering a full range of development projects. He has both promoted and resisted major housing schemes, retail proposals, waste developments, renewable energy schemes, and urban regeneration projects. His pracice extends across England and Wales. He has promoted a large number of development plans and is currently engaged in several DPD matters, housing and retail appeals, and a DCO examination. His practice embraces both large-scale infrastructure projects (including several new roads) and smaller developments in sensitive areas with heritage or environmental constraints. He is experienced in managing and co-ordinating large teams of expert witnesses and in cross-examining on a wide range of professional disciplines.
Professional Memberships: Planning & Environmental Bar Association.
Career: Called 1985.
Publications: Contributor: 'Gambling for Local Authorities - Licensing, Planning and Regeneration' (2010). Contributor: 'Environmental Law' (Burnett-Hall) (2012).
Personal: LLB (Hons) Lond. Barstow Law Scholarship. David Karmel Chancery Scholarship.

BEDWORTH, Georgia
Ten Old Square, London
020 7405 0758
georgiabedworth@tenoldsquare.com
Featured in Chancery (London), Court of Protection (All Circuits)
Practice Areas: Georgia has a very strong traditional chancery practice, which covers trusts, estates, property and probate work. Her practice has a bias towards trusts, estates and other private client matters, particularly those with a real property angle. In addition, Georgia often advises and appears in Court of Protection matters. Georgia acts in both contentious and non-contentious matters, advising frequently in litigation, on issues of construction as well as capital taxes planning and other issues, often in relation to multi-million pound trusts and estates. Chambers 2014 stated that she "excels in all areas of traditional chancery work" and "is fantastic at drilling down into the detail of a case" and she was described in the property section of the Legal 500 as being "extremely bright and tenacious".
Professional Memberships: Georgia Bedworth sits on two sub-committees of the Chancery Bar Association and is a member of the Property Bar Association.
Career: Georgia Bedworth was called to the Bar in 2001 after graduating from St. Hugh's College Oxford with 1st class honours degree in law and a distinction in the BCL. Georgia's recent cases include: Buzzoni and Others v Commissioners for HM Revenue and Customs [2013] EWCA Civ 1684; Fuller v Fuller [2005] All ER (D) 120 (Feb) (Revocation of grant of probate, mental incapacity); Turner v Turner [2006] All ER (D) 63 (Jul) (Grounds upon which a statutory demand may be set aside - relevance of a probate claim); Giles v Rhind (No. 2) [2008] EWCA Civ 118; [2009] Ch 191 (section 423 Insolvency Act 1986 and limitation).
Publications: Georgia is the joint author of the fourth edition of Rossdale on Probate and Administration of Estates (Wolters Kluwer 2008) and of Tolley's Inheritance Tax Planning, the first edition of which was nominated as the STEP private client book of the year. In addition, Georgia contributes to Fosters Inheritance Tax, one of the leading practitioner texts on that subject and is a joint author of Tolley's Trusts and Estates Practitioner's Guide to Mental Capacity. Georgia has written articles for the STEP journal, the Solicitors Journal and the Landlord and Tenant Review on diverse legal issues, most recently on Gifts with Reservation of Benefit.

BEECHAM, Sara
Five Paper, London
020 7815 3200
sarabeecham@fivepaper.com
Featured in Social Housing (London)
Practice Areas: Experience across the range of social housing and landlord and tenant work - including possession proceedings, succession claims, actions to restrain anti-social behaviour, disrepair claims, injunctive proceedings and cases involving public law and discrimination issues.
Professional Memberships: Social Housing Law Association.

Career: Called to the Bar 1999 (Middle Temple Astbury Scholar). Advises and represents public and private sector clients, including local authorities, registered providers of social housing and leaseholders. Sara regularly delivers seminars on current issues in housing law and has presented to numerous local authorities, in-house for solicitors and for professional associations in the housing field. Sara was appointed a Deputy District Judge in 2010. Sara was recently instructed as junior counsel for the social landlord in the Court of Appeal in Akerman-Livingstone v Aster Communities Ltd (formerly Flourish Homes Ltd) [2014] EWCA Civ 1081; a case concerning summary assessment of a disability discrimination defence in possession proceedings. An appeal by the tenant is pending in the Supreme Court.

BEER, Jason QC
5 Essex Court, London
020 7410 2000
clerks@5essexcourt.co.uk
Featured in Administrative & Public Law (London), Inquests & Public Inquiries (London), Police Law (All Circuits), Professional Discipline (London)

Practice Areas: Inquests and Inquiries, Police, Public & Administrative, Professional Discipline. Acted in the following public inquiries: Al-Sweady Inquiry, Leveson, Baha Mousa, Billy Wright, Rosemary Nelson, Legionella in Barrow-in-Furness, Hutton, Mubarek, Shipman, and Stephen Lawrence; the following inquests: Hillsborough, University of Manchester Radiation Inquests, 7/7 Bombings, Porton Down Nerve Gas Inquest, and New Cross Fire; the following JRs: Miranda (terrorist powers), GC & C (retention of biometric data), Children's Rights Alliance v Secretary of State for Justice (positive duties under ECHR); and the following police claims: Phone Hacking, Hayes v Merseyside Police (necessity of arrest), Howarth v Gwent Police (misfeasance), Richardson v West Midlands Police (necessity of arrest), Madeline McCann, Omagh Bombing, and Operation Ore.
Professional Memberships: ALBA, PIBA, ARDL.
Career: Called to the Bar 1992; Silk 2011; Previously Junior Counsel to the Crown (Common Law - A Panel). Developed Vetted. Recorder on SE Circuit.
Publications: "Public Inquiries" (OUP, 2011).

BEEVER, Edmund
St Philips Chambers, Birmingham
0121 246 2178
ebeever@st-philips.com
Featured in Commercial Dispute Resolution (Midlands), Employment (Midlands)

Practice Areas: Commercial litigation, including directors' duties. High Court commercial (contractual disputes; freezing and search orders) and employment (including Wright v Governing Body of Bilton High School and Another [2002] ICR 1463, Jaddoo v Birmingham City Council [2004] All ER (D) 410 (Oct)). Commercial springboard injunctions in insurance industry. Insolvency related disputes (SSTI v Blunt [2005] 2 BCLC 463, Re Blakemore and Son Ltd [2007] EWHC 963 (Ch)) and complex discrimination or dismissal cases. Regular clients include plc's, government departments and local authorities.
Professional Memberships: Chancery and Commercial Bar Association, COMBAR, Employment Lawyers Association.
Career: Head of Employment Group, St Philips Chambers. Accredited Advocacy Tutor. Attorney General Panel Counsel 1997, re-appointed 2007 and 2012. Appointed fee paid Employment Judge 2013.
Personal: Merton College, Oxford. Sport, family and property renovation.

BEGGS, John QC
Serjeants' Inn Chambers, London
020 7427 5000
jb@3sinn.com
Featured in Inquests & Public Inquiries (London), Police Law (All Circuits), Professional Discipline (London)

Practice Areas: John Beggs QC was called to the Bar in 1989 and took silk in 2009. John specialises in public and administrative, police, employment, inquests and inquiries and professional discipline law. An earlier edition notes that "he is probably the best cross-examiner outside the Criminal Bar" and that he is "extremely quick in his thinking, to the point and knows his stuff. If you want someone to win your case, he's the man." He was ranked as one of the 100 top silks by The Chambers Bar 100 2014. Please click on the link to the Serjeants' Inn Chambers website for his profile, which sets out full details of his practice including relevant work of note.
Professional Memberships: ARDL.
Publications: "Police misconduct, complaints, and public regulation", OUP, July 2009; "Public Order: Law and Practice" Blackstone's Practical Policing, with George Thomas and Susanna Rickard, OUP, 2012.

BEGLAN, Wayne
Cornerstone Barristers, London
020 7242 4986
wayneb@cornerstonebarristers.com
Featured in Local Government (London), Social Housing (London)

Practice Areas: Wayne Beglan undertakes most forms of local government work and also has a wide private client base. He has particular expertise in judicial review, housing, planning (housing, retail, waste, roads and s.106 agreements), regeneration, landlord and tenant, employment, procurement and contractual work for local authorities RPs, developers and corporations. He recently appeared on behalf of Welwyn HC in New Barnfield RERF inquiry, which is now under challenge by the developer in the high court. He has appeared in various tribunals; and has extensive experience in the high court and significant experience in the appellate courts.
Career: Called: 1996.

BELGROVE, Sophie
Devereux, London
020 7353 7534
belgrove@devchambers.co.uk
Featured in Employment (London)

Practice Areas: Specialises in all areas of employment law, advising and appearing in the EAT, the High Court and the Court of Appeal. Considerable experience of complex litigation, with particular expertise in relation to unfair dismissal, discrimination, equal pay, breach of contract, business transfers, restraint of trade, share schemes, bonus schemes and pensions. Clients include FTSE 100 companies, banks and building societies, dotcom companies, insurance companies, high street chains, airlines and airport authorities, charities and a wide range of public and private sector clients.
Professional Memberships: ELBA, ELA, COMBAR, LCLCBA.
Career: Called 2001; Middle Temple Benefactors Scholarship and Harmsworth Entrance Exhibition (2000).
Publications: Contributor to Jordans Employment Law Service.
Personal: BA (Oxon).

BELL, Laura
Devereux, London
020 7353 7534
bell@devchambers.co.uk
Featured in Employment (London)

Practice Areas: A client friendly barrister who provides robust and commercially astute advice. She leaves no stone unturned in her approach to advocacy and advisory work. Her persuasiveness and forensic approach to cross examination make her an obvious choice for difficult and sensitive cases. She has a wealth of experience representing claimants and respondents in all areas of employment law, in multi-day complex cases and at all levels of appeal. She also advises and represents parties in injunctive proceedings and contract claims in the High Court. Her clients include investment banks, airlines, global communication companies, large IT firms and sporting organisations. She also represents charities, local authorities and individual claimants.
Professional Memberships: ELA, ELBA, ILS, BASL, PIBA, APIL.
Career: BMus (Hons) First Class - University of Manchester & Royal Northern College of Music; Called, 2004 Lincoln's Inn; Lord Brougham Scholarship , Wolfson Scholarship, Hardwicke Entrance Scholarship, Sir Thomas More Bursary- Lincoln's Inn; Richard Isaacson Memorial Scholarship - Awarded for the highest Bar Vocational Course mark achieved by a new practitioner on the Northern Circuit.
Publications: Contributing Editor, 'Discrimination Law' (Bloomsbury Professional (formerly Tottel Publishing).
Personal: Professional violinist before coming to the bar. Enjoys art, sport and good food.

BENNETT, Miles
5 Paper Buildings, London
020 7815 3200
mb@5pb.co.uk
Featured in Consumer Law (London)

Practice Areas: Miles has specialised for the last 20 years in Consumer Law (criminal, regulatory and advisory) Trade Mark Infringement, Copyright theft, Health and Safety and inquests involving product safety issues. As well as acting as leading junior counsel in large scale consumer frauds he regularly appears in Case Stated, Judicial Review proceedings and the Court of Appeal in complex appellate work. Miles prosecutes for: the OFT, numerous Local Authorities nationwide and private prosecution organisations such as F.A.C.T Miles defends major Plc's in the retail sector, (in particular the supermarket sector) companies, directors and individuals. Recent Cases include the national prosecution of a major retailer over multi million pound allegations of misleading commercial practices in the promotion and sale of strawberries R (Birmingham CC) v Tesco Stores Ltd. He was involved in reviewing and advising the Olympic Development Authority in relation to their powers including seizure and forfeiture for "ambush marketing" during the 2012 Olympics. He also was junior counsel involved in securing the first acquittal of a company charged with corporate manslaughter since the statutory offence was created.
Professional Memberships: Member of HSLA.
Career: Called to the Bar 1986.
Publications: Several articles published in 'Trading Standards Law'. Frequent speaker at Trading Standards Conference. As well as a contributing editor in Kirk and Lewin's "Pink Book", one of the leading practitioner text books on Consumer Law.
Personal: Married (1991), two children, shooting, music.

BENNETT-JENKINS, Sallie QC
2 Hare Court, London
020 7353 5324
salliebennett-jenkinsqc@2harecourt.com
Featured in Crime (London)

Practice Areas: Cited on a number of occasions as a leading silk by The Legal 500 and Chambers UK and, prior to taking silk, as a leading junior. Appointed Queen's Counsel in October 2006 following a period of 8 years as Treasury Counsel, and has since become first choice defence counsel for firms with private clients who demand an incisive advocate with a mastery of detail, and who can instil real confidence in the client. Described as having a "thoroughly devastating style of cross examination which is a pleasure to watch". In silk, she maintains diverse defence practice ranging from murder to fraud and advisory work for multinational corporations in respect of computer crime, Health and Safety and Food and Drugs. Particular expertise in relation to trials involving young offenders, notably in homicide cases, as well as cases involving murder of infants in which an ability to assimilate medical evidence is of key importance. Sallie has recently concluded a number of "baby-shaking" and infant non-accidental injury cases, which have involved extensive cross-examination of medical professionals, and dealing with expert medical evidence before juries. She has also defended a number of celebrity clients in relation to allegations of violence and sexual assault, and is experienced in reputation management issues. She regularly comments for the national print and broadcast media. She also represents professionals accused of crime arising from their work. Sallie is increasingly involved in professional disciplinary work, and appears before the General Medical Council.
Career: Called 1984. Assistant Recorder 1998. Junior Treasury Counsel 1998. Recorder 2000. Silk 2006.

BENSON, Jeremy QC
Red Lion Chambers, London
020 7520 6000
clerks@18rlc.co.uk
Featured in Crime (London), Financial Crime (London)

Practice Areas: Jeremy is recommended by all who instruct him and consistently rated as a leading advocate by Chambers UK and the Legal 500. With an intuitive legal mind he is further an outstanding advocate and tactician. He has particular expertise in serious crime including homicide, complex fraud, trademark and copyright piracy and drug offences. He is adept at fact heavy,

multifarious cases such as those involving computer fraud, detailed scientific and medical evidence, multiple defendants, young defendants or those with psychiatric difficulties. He prosecutes and defends at the highest level. His expertise extends into the civil arena where he has developed a substantial regulatory and financial fraud practice. He appears regularly in Disciplinary Tribunals and on behalf of the HMRC in large scale VAT appeals.
Professional Memberships: CBA, Middle Temple Bencher. British Academy of Forensic Science. Teaches advocacy and the teaching of advocacy in the UK and abroad.
Career: Economics BA (hons). Head of Economics Department, Kings Heath School. Called 1978. Appointments: Recorder 1997. QC 2001.

BENTHAM, Daniel
Queen Elizabeth Building, London
020 7797 7837
d.bentham@qeb.co.uk
Featured in Family/Matrimonial (London)
Practice Areas: His practice is made up almost exclusively of family law, with a particular emphasis on financial cases (including cohabitation disputes and applications under Schedule 1 of the Children Act).

BENTLEY, Harry
2 Hare Court, London
020 7353 5324
harrybentley@2harecourt.com
Featured in Financial Crime (London)
Practice Areas: Harry is a criminal defence specialist whose principal area of practice is financial crime. He has substantial experience in cases of serious fraud both as led junior and junior alone. In addition to his clinical approach to large volumes of data he has excellent client care skills and ability to quickly recognise the issues in a case. He has experience in complex confiscation proceedings in both negotiating settlements and contested hearings. Recent cases include a £23m VAT carousel fraud, conspiracy to control prostitution with a related £1.8m money laundering, a £8m conspiracy to money launder, a £20m bank guarantee investment fraud, a £1.3m wine investment "boiler room" fraud, and a £500,000 football fraud with related money laundering. Harry is also currently instructed in a £5m land banking fraud (Operation Cotton) prosecuted by the FCA, a £32m biofuel fraud prosecuted by the SFO and a £300,000 confidence fraud involving over 80 victims. In addition he has significant experience in murder, drugs, money-laundering and other conspiracy prosecutions. His other areas of practice include regulatory prosecutions and tribunals, prison law, judicial review and road traffic prosecutions. He is the Secretary to the Kalisher Trust, named after the late Michael Kalisher QC (former head of chambers at 2 Hare Court). The Trust assists barristers at the start of their careers, and promotes diversity within the legal profession.

BERESFORD, Stephen
Ropewalk Chambers, Nottingham
0115 947 2581
stephenberesford@ropewalk.co.uk
Featured in Commercial Dispute Resolution (Midlands)
Practice Areas: He has wide experience of appearing in specialist and general higher courts and tribunals across a range of commercial and property and chancery matters. He is a frequently used accredited mediator and is head of the mediation team at Ropewalk Chambers. He focuses on ascertaining what both the professional and lay clients wish to achieve and then providing them precise advice and with a clear road map to achieve it.
Professional Memberships: Professional Negligence Bar Association; Planning and Environmental Bar Association; Commercial Bar Association; Midlands Chancery Bar Association.
Career: Called in 1976; LLB, University of Birmingham.
Personal: Away from the Bar, his interests include collecting antique firearms, playing jazz guitar, performing close-up magic and watching Leicester Tigers.

BERGIN, Terence
4 Pump Court, London
020 7842 5555
tbergin@4pumpcourt.com
Featured in Information Technology (London)
Practice Areas: Supply of computer systems; the licensing of software; internet, including domain name disputes and data protection. His clients have included the government, major software houses, local authorities and a public transport provider. Southwark v IBM [2011] EWHC 549 (TCC), Data Direct Technologies Ltd v M&S Plc [2009] EWHC 97 (Ch), Fujitsu Services Ltd v EDS Ltd (2007), TTI Team International Ltd v Axarte Ltd (2007), NEDDC v Anite Public Sector Ltd (2007), Serco Solutions Ltd v The Cabinet Office (2004), Foster v Fortis Clearing Bank Ltd (2004), Co-Operative Group (CWS) Ltd v International Computers Ltd (2003), SAM Business Systems Ltd v Hedley & Co [2002] EWHC 2733 (TCC), Psychometric Services Ltd v Merant International Ltd (2002), The Boots Company Plc v Amdahl (UK) Ltd (CA 2000), Anglo Group Plc v Winther Browne & Co Ltd (2000).
Professional Memberships: TECBAR, Society for Computers and the Law, PNBA, COMBAR.
Career: Called 1985.

BERKELEY, Iona
8 New Square, London
020 7405 4321
iona.berkeley@8newsquare.co.uk
Featured in Intellectual Property (London)
Practice Areas: Barrister specialising in all areas of intellectual property law, including patents, trade marks, copyright, database rights, registered and unregistered design rights, passing off, confidential information, and related areas, such as IP related contractual disputes (in particular International Arbitrations) and media and entertainment. Cases include Speciality European Pharma v Doncaster Pharmaceuticals (Pharmaceutical parallel importation/trade mark infringement case; Whirlpool Corp. v Kenwood (Trade Marks); EPI Environmental Technologies Inc v Symphony Plc (Confidential Information, contract, passing off); The Football Association Premier League v Panini (Copyright); Kirin-Amgen Inc. v TKT and Roche (Patents). For a comprehensive CV visit chambers website at www.8newsquare.co.uk.
Professional Memberships: Intellectual Property Bar Association (IPBA) and Chancery Bar Association.
Career: Called 1999, Middle Temple.
Publications: Iona Berkeley is co-author of Kerly's Law of Trade Marks and Trade Names (15th Ed) and co-author of Laddie Prescott and Vitoria on the Modern Law of Copyright and Designs (4th Ed).
Personal: Educated at South Hampstead High School; Trinity College, Oxford (1997 Biological Sciences); City University (1998 Dip Law); Inns of Court School of Law.

BERLIN, Barry
St Philips Chambers, Birmingham
0121 246 7000
bberlin@st-philips.com
Featured in Consumer Law (Midlands), Environment (Midlands), Health & Safety (Midlands)
Practice Areas: Senior practitioner in regulatory law - health and safety, environment, food safety and trading standards. Notable cases include: Formula One Autocentres v Birmingham City Council (1998) 163 JP 234; Davenport v Walsall MBC (1996) 28 HLR 754; Sterling Homes v Birmingham CC (1996) L.R. 121; Toys R Us v Gloucestershire CC (1994) 158 JP 338; Whirlpool (UK) Ltd & Magnet Ltd v Gloucestershire CC (1993) 259 S.P. 123; R v Newcastle Upon Tyne Magistrates Court Ex p. Poundstretcher Ltd [1998] COD 256; Birmingham City Council v Cadbury Limited (2007); Office of Rail Regulation v Network Rail Infrastructure Ltd (rail crash and derailment, 2011); Warwick DC v Merlin Entertainments Ltd (Warwick Castle fatality) [2013] 2 Cr. App. R.(S.) 36 CA; Environment Agency v Sellafield [2014] Env. L.R. 19 CA; HSE v BAE Systems Ltd (fatal body crushing, 2013); HSE v AETC Ltd (fatal head crushing case, 2013). Lectures to local authorities and government agencies.
Professional Memberships: Criminal Bar Association; Midland and Oxford circuit.
Career: BSc Hons (1980). Call 1981 Gray's Inn. 'A' List of Specialist Regulatory Advocates in health and safety and environmental law. Recorder Midland Circuit. Hon Lecturer MSc Environmental Health, Birmingham University.
Personal: Enjoys racing and theatre.

BERRAGAN, Neil
Kings Chambers, Manchester
0845 034 3444
clerks@kingschambers.com
Featured in Chancery (Northern), Commercial Dispute Resolution (Northern), Partnership (Northern), Restructuring/Insolvency (Northern)
Practice Areas: Neil practises almost exclusively in the specialist business courts (Mercantile, Chancery and TCC) in Manchester, Leeds & Liverpool, in London and on appeal from those courts. He specialises in commercial and chancery litigation, and is frequently instructed in urgent interim applications. His practice includes all types of business, company and shareholder disputes, insolvency, partnership, commercial fraud, sports law, and associated professional negligence. Recent cases include: EEW v PCRE [2014] (Merc), solar power plant dispute, urgent injunction application; Re Parkwood Holdings plc, scheme of arrangement and capital reduction; McGill v SEM & Bolton Wanderers FC & others [2014] (Merc), defending claims of fraud & conspiracy by football agent on behalf of club, officers and employees; Chairing appeals committee on behalf of the British Wrestling Association; R (May) v CIMA [2013] EWHC 1574 (Admin), successful application to quash finding of professional misconduct arising out of a charge of misuse of confidential information; CVS v Cooper [2013], successfully defending claim to set aside prior compromise allegedly obtained by fraud; Henning Berg v Blackburn Rovers [2013] EWHC 1070 Ch, unsuccessful attempt to withdraw admission of liability made by MD without authority of club owners; Re Bateson (Hotels) Ltd [2013] (Ch), successful application and appeal striking out allegations of unfair prejudice; Kammac plc v Hancox [2013] (Ch), successfully defending former factory manager against claims of fraud and theft; Templeton Insurance Ltd v Brunswick & Booth [2012] EWHC 3319 (Ch), successfully defending personal claim against trustee in bankruptcy; Smile Better Ltd v Travis Perkins [2012] (Merc), successful claim for breach of a series of marketing contracts; Waste Tec v H.W. Martin Waste Ltd [2012] EWCA Civ 859, successful claim and appeal on behalf of waste management licensees; Smith v Butler [2012] BCC 645 (CA), [2012] 1 BCLC 444, successfully defending interests of chairman and majority shareholder against unauthorised action by MD.
Professional Memberships: Northern Chancery Bar Association, Northern Circuit Commercial Bar Association, Chancery Bar Association, Professional Negligence Bar Association, Bar Pro Bono Panel.
Career: University: Oxford (Pembroke College); Degree: Jurisprudence (MA); Called: 1982 (Grays Inn).

BERRIDGE, Alison
Monckton Chambers, London
020 7405 7211
aberridge@monckton.com
Featured in Competition/European Law (London)
Practice Areas: Alison is a competition law specialist, with a strong merger control, behavioural antitrust and litigation practice. She has been instructed in a number of the key challenges under the merger and market investigation regimes, including BMI v CC and Ryanair v CC (I) and (II). Her recent advisory work has included advising Optimax on the CMA's second phase investigation of its acquisition of Ultralase, cleared on "exiting firm" grounds, and advising House of Fraser on the CMA's Competition Act investigation into the retail pricing of sports bras, resulting in a "no grounds for action" decision. She has also advised a number of competition authorities worldwide on merger and enforcement work.
Career: Alison joined Monckton from Allen & Overy, where she had a successful practice focusing on merger and behavioural antitrust work.
Publications: Co-author (with Alistair Lindsay) of The EU Merger Regulation: Substantive Issues (Sweet & Maxwell, 4th edition, 2012).
Personal: Call 2011 | (Solicitor) 1999; MA (Oxon).

BERRY, Anthony QC
9 Bedford Row, London
020 7489 2727
anthony.berry@9bedfordrow.co.uk
Featured in Crime (London)
Practice Areas: Mainly a defence practice since taking silk in 1994. Specialises in murder, fraud and other serious crime. His most recent cases include R v Lowe (2014, Liverpool Crown Court) the only one of seven defendants acquitted of murder; R v Shastri (2014, Old Bailey) acquitted of attempted

murder on judge's direction at conclusion of prosecution case; R v Wagner (2014, Chester Crown Court) acquitted of murder. In addition, represented Sgt Blackman (Marine A), at his court martial for murder of a Taliban insurgent in Helmand Province in Afghanistan. The deceased had been attacking a British outpost and was fired at from an Apache helicopter with 139 rounds of 30mm cannon. Sgt Blackman was tasked with conducting a battle damage assessment and, with members of his patrol, disarmed the severely injured individual. The issue was whether, when the captive had been removed to the side of the field, the defendant thought he was dead when he discharged his pistol into the man's chest. Also represented Sgt Blackman at his appeal when sentence was reduced (2014). Other cases in recent years include R v Taylor (2012, Old Bailey), acquitted of murder as part of gang attack on one man; R v Collier (2011, Old Bailey), acquitted of murder when client said to have shot victim at point blank range as part of a drugs vendetta; R v Watterson (2010, Isle of Man), young lady acquitted of murder of her boyfriend (convicted of manslaughter). Nicole Davis was acquitted of murder at her trial for racially motivated gang attack (2010, Bradford Crown Court). For various periods between 2008 and 2012 instructed by the DPP of Malawi to prosecute the Vice President of Malawi in the High Court sitting at Blantyre. He and another faced charges of conspiracy to murder the President of Malawi and High Treason, namely putting in place a scheme to overthrow the Government and kill members of the cabinet. Eventually, the case ground to a halt when the judges went on strike and, shortly thereafter, the President, Bingu Wa Mutharika died. Before that case had been engaged in R v Scard and others, the very long running Jubilee Line case (2005 to 2007, Old Bailey) in which client, a chartered surveyor, was alleged to be involved in a fraud involving wide ranging corruption arising out of the construction of the last line to be added to the London Underground. Defendant acquitted of all charges. Subsequently, defended one Charamboulous, an chartered accountant allegedly involved in substantial tax fraud (2011, Blackfriars Crown Court). In Liggins and Bonsor (Isle of Man, 2012) both clients were acquitted of an election fraud.
Professional Memberships: Member of Panel of Advocates at the International Criminal Court, Criminal Bar Association (Former Secretary), International Bar Association, European Criminal Bar Association, Association of Commonwealth Lawyers, Association of Military Court Advocates, Association of Fraud Lawyers.
Career: BA (Philosophy and Psychology), Lincoln College, Oxford. Called to the Bar 1976, Silk 1994 Head of Chambers from 1999. Former member General Council of the Bar. Bencher Gray's Inn 2000.

BERRY, James
Serjeants' Inn Chambers, London
020 7427 5000
jberry@3serjeantsinn.com
Featured in Police Law (All Circuits)
Practice Areas: James Berry was called to the Bar in 2006. James specialises in public and administrative, police, Court of Protection, employment, inquests and inquiries, professional discipline, clinical negligence and healthcare, product liability, civil liberties and human rights law. An earlier edition describes him as "a rising star" and notes that "he is meticulous and skilled in the fine detail" and that "he combines gentlemanly robustness with fierce intelligence." Please click on the link to the Serjeants' Inn Chambers website for his profile, which sets out full details of his practice including relevant work of note.
Professional Memberships: Treasury C Panel, ALBA, ARDL, ELBA, PNBA.
Publications: UK Police Law Blog (editor); Police Misconduct, Complaints and Professional Regulation (2nd ed, co-author, forthcoming; Medical Treatment: Decisions and the Law (2nd ed, co-author); Firearms Policing (forthcoming); Medical Law Reports (contributor).

BERTRAM, Jonathan
7BR, London
020 7242 3555
clerks@7br.co.uk
Featured in Clinical Negligence (London)
Practice Areas: Clinical Negligence, Personal Injury, Product Liability, Inquests and Employment
Professional Memberships: Association of Personal Injury Lawyers, Personal Injury Bar Association, Employment Lawyers Association
Career: Jonathan has built up a busy Claimant practice in clinical negligence cases. He has acted in cases concerning failure to diagnose and treat spinal injuries, cancer, liver disease, kidney disease and other similar conditions. He has advised in failed bariatric surgery and other weight loss claims. He has successfully pursued claims advanced on the basis of systemic failures by Trusts that have then led to injuries to patients, e.g. by failing to adequately staff maternity units. As Jonathan has gained in experience he has seen an increase in instructions relating to brain and birth injury cases. Jonathan also has a particular interest in inquest work and he frequently acts for bereaved families in cases where it is hoped that the evidence obtained during the inquest will assist with supporting a future clinical negligence claim. In addition to clinical negligence Jonathan undertakes a wide variety of personal injury and employment litigation. He has also recently developed a significant product liability practice, particularly in the field of metal-on-metal hip replacements.

BEX, Kate
2 Hare Court, London
020 7353 5324
katebex@2harecourt.com
Featured in Professional Discipline (London), Crime (London)
Practice Areas: Cited by The Legal 500 and Chambers UK as a leading junior, Kate is a highly regarded criminal advocate who both defends and prosecutes. She specialises in serious and complex crime especially offences of murder, firearms and fraud and is increasingly instructed as leading counsel alongside QCs. Kate also regularly undertakes professional disciplinary work, in particular before disciplinary panels and the High Court against the General Medical Council. Kate also appears before a number of other regulators, including the GDC and NMC, and sits as a Legal Assessor for the Health and Care Professions Council. Kate also has current experience of coroners' inquests and Courts Martial. Clients refer to Kate's reputation for "strong advocacy based on thorough preparation" and court room presence. Recent praise includes the endorsement that "she commands the respect of judges". Kate is authorised to accept instructions from members of the public in certain circumstances and from other authorised professionals. Kate is also an accredited mediator for alternative dispute resolution of civil and commercial disputes and is an associate member of ADR Chambers.
Career: Called 1992 (Inner Temple); 2007 Accredited Mediator for ADR (civil/commercial disputes). 2010 Legal Assessor HCPC.

BHOGAL, Kuljit
Cornerstone Barristers, London
020 7242 4986
kuljitb@cornerstonebarristers.com
Featured in Social Housing (London)
Practice Areas: Housing, community care, Court of Protection.
Professional Memberships: Founding supporter of Social Housing Lawyers Association (SHLA). Adminstrative Lawyers Bar Association, (ALBA), Property Bar Association (PBA), Association of Regulatory and Disciplinary Lawyers (ARDL).
Career: Called in 1998. Hardwicke Scholar, Lincolns Inn. LLB Law King's College, London 2.1 (Hons), 1994-97. Kuljit has established herself at the forefront of the social housing bar. Her practice includes housing, community care and Court of Protection work. She was instructed in Tachie v Welwyn Hatfield BC [2013] EWHC 3972 (QB); [2014] PTSR 66, a case which concerned the contracting out of homelessness functions. Kuljit is recognised for her thorough knowledge of the law, her exceptional advocacy skills and tactical awareness. She has an excellent understanding of her client's needs. Her practice covers policy advice; Kuljit has recently advised the Mayor on his Housing Strategy for London, anti-social behaviour (including ASBOs, ASBIs, committal applications, gang injunctions, closure orders in the Magistrates, County and Crown courts), homelessness, claims for possession (all grounds), housing management issues (including disrepair, contested successions, unlawful subletting, 'Right to Buy' disputes), unlawful eviction, benefit fraud and the investigation and prosecution of offences, houses in multiple occupation, service charge disputes, mental health and Equality Act 2010 points. Kuljit provides seminars and training to her wide client base and has recently delivered seminars on the new anti-social behaviour powers being introduced by the Anti-Social Behaviour, Crime and Policing Act 2014.
Personal: Enjoys travel, cookery and being a mum.

BHOSE, Ranjit QC
Cornerstone Barristers, London
020 7242 4986
ranjitb@cornerstonebarristers.com
Featured in Local Government (London), Real Estate Litigation (London), Social Housing (London)
Practice Areas: Ranjit has a varied practice, with particular specialism in the following: local government & public law; social housing; commercial landlord and tenant; licensing; civil litigation; property; rating and local taxation. He has strong links with local authorities, major private sector landlords and developers, and registered providers. His recent cases include: Sims v Dacorum DC (2014) (SC – housing and property, human rights); Evans v Wimbledon and Putney Commons Conservators (2014) (CA – easements over common land); Thompson v Oxford CC (2014) (CA – lap dancing); Superstrike v Rodriguez (2013) (CA - tenancy deposits); Bean Leisure v Leeds CC (2014) (Admin – lap dancing); Tachie v Welwyn Hatfield DC (2013) (Admin – public procurement, Teckal; contracting-out); BDW Trading v South Anglia (2013) (Chancery – service charges, QLTAs); Bristol CC Council v Digs (2014) (Admin – HMO licensing). Ranjit's current workload includes a number of property related negligence claims, many major service charge disputes, a licensing appeal over the largest nightclub in the UK, advice and representation across the breadth of local authority and registered provider functions and decision-making.
Career: B.A. University College, Oxford. Called to the Bar 1989, QC 2012.
Personal: Interests include running (slowly), DJing (semi-retired, but persuadable).

BICKERSTAFF, Jane QC
9 Bedford Row, London
020 7489 2727
jane.bickerstaff@9bedfordrow.co.uk
Featured in Crime (London)
Practice Areas: Prosecutes and defends in all areas of serious crime. Specialises in sexual offences, particularly in the defence of historical, multi complainant cases. Has a human touch and a real feel for the cross examination of children and vulnerable witnesses. Frequently lectures on all aspects of this subject. Regularly defends and prosecutes in murder cases with particular expertise in joint enterprise. Particular expertise in representing police officers before the Crown Court, supported by many years experience defending at police disciplinary tribunals. Throughout her career has also acted in cases of fraud and financial crime.
Professional Memberships: Executive Committee Member of the Criminal Bar Association. Member of South Eastern Circuit.

BICKFORD SMITH, James
Littleton Chambers, London
020 7797 8600
jbs@littletonchambers.co.uk
Featured in Employment (London)
Practice Areas: Commercial and employment law. In particular: 1) High Court litigation arising out of employment/fiduciary relationships, often involving injunctive relief applications (4 in first six months of 2014, 3 as sole counsel) or high value damages claims in the context of team moves (junior counsel for First Defendant in Marathon Asset Management litigation) 2) commercial litigation, especially in banking and finance field. Practice draws on substantial experience of high-value commercial litigation. Current areas of instruction include banking and finance litigation (swaps mis-selling, retail banking fraud claims, breach of mandate claims), contract litigation in the fashion and creative industries fields (recent clients include well-known designers, fashion agents and advertising agents), heavy civil fraud and in particular conspiracy claims 3) specialist work at interface of employment and chancery work. Much involved in 2013/4 in Partnership/LLP matters. Also led Defence of inventors subject to Chancery Division proceedings involving claims of

patent, design right, copyright and database infringement 4) statutory employment practice based on oral advocacy. Appears in Tribunal claims a) involving substantial reputational and other risks for Respondents (eg defending mid-Staffordshire NHS Trust following dismissal involving patient assault, defending FTSE 100 companies against discrimination claims). Also represents Claimants facing substantially-resourced Respondents, typically in Financial Services Sector (eg undertaking 5 day case against a QC for a former Managing Director working on a "Delta One" desk).
Professional Memberships: COMBAR, ELBA.
Career: Called to Bar in 2008 as mature entrant. Double First Class Honours (Balliol College). Masters and Doctorate. Former Lecturer at Oxford University. Also studied at Ecole Normale Supérieure.
Publications: Since 2012, monthly column A Practical View From the Bar, on civil procedure and litigation tactics, for the Practical Law Company.

BIGNELL, Janet
Falcon Chambers, London
020 7353 2484
clerks@falcon-chambers.com
Featured in Real Estate Litigation (London)
Practice Areas: All aspects of commercial and residential real property, landlord and tenant and related professional negligence and insolvency. Reported cases include: Stadium Capital Holdings (No 2) Ltd v St Marylebone Co Plc (damages for trespass); Sunberry Properties v Innovate Logistics Ltd (in administration) (alienation and the Insolvency Act); Norwich City Council v McQuillin (restrictive covenants); Leftbank Properties Ltd v Spirit Group (rent review/ arbitration); Simmons v Dresden (terminal dilapidations); Bakewell Management v Brandwood (easements).
Professional Memberships: Chancery Bar Association, LCLCBA, Property Bar Association, ARBRIX.
Career: MA (Cantab), BCL (Oxon). Called 1992. Recorder 2009. Member Chartered Institute of Arbitrators.
Publications: Author, Lewison's Drafting Business Leases; Co-Author, Registered Land Law and Practice under the LRA 2002; Co-Author; Registered Land: The New Law; Editorial Board, Landlord & Tenant Review; Former Contributor, Encyclopaedia of Forms & Precedents, Auctioneers, Estate Agents & Valuers and Fisher & Lightwoods Law of Mortgage.

BIRD, Andrew
5 St Andrew's Hill, London
020 7332 5400
andrewbird@5sah.co.uk
Featured in POCA Work & Asset Forfeiture (All Circuits)
Practice Areas: Fraud, asset forfeiture and confiscation, Judicial Review, overlap between civil and criminal jurisdictions.
Career: Andrew Bird read law at Cambridge and was called in 1987. He has been a tenant at 5 St Andrew's Hill (formerly 1 Harcourt Buildings) since 1989. He started with a broadly-based common law practice but from 1995 onwards concentrated on heavy crime and both the civil and criminal aspects of asset forfeiture. He has a particular interest and specialism in cases where the civil and criminal jurisdictions overlap. He has been involved in many of the appellate cases in cash forfeiture, including CCE v Muneka and UKBA v Angus, and edits Smith, Owen & Bodnar on Asset Recovery in this field. His civil recovery work includes the leading case of DARA v He & Chen. One of the few specialists in HMRC and UKBA condemnation, his work has included the Hoverspeed litigation and CCE v Newbury and recent work on high profile wildlife cases. His criminal work includes Montila (HL) and recent prosecutions of the online bank UMBS and of two land-banking frauds. In 2005 he was appointed Standing Counsel to the RCPO, and in 2008 Standing Counsel to the DWP. He is a Grade 4 CPS prosecutor and on the "A" Panels both for the SFO and the A-G's Treasury Panel for civil work. He has considerable experience in JR challenges to criminal process, including search warrants, such as the Faisaltex and Eastenders litigation, production orders and custody time limits. He regularly lectures and gives seminars in Asset Forfeiture, Money Laundering and Police powers.
Publications: Smith Owen & Bodnar on Asset Recovery (OUP).

BIRD, Simon QC
Francis Taylor Building, London
020 7353 8415
sbird@ftb.eu.com
Featured in Planning (London)
Practice Areas: Planning and environmental law.
Professional Memberships: Planning & Environment Bar Association. National Infrastructure Planning Association.

BIRTLES, Samantha
18 St John Street, Manchester
0161 278 1800
family@18sjs.com
Featured in Family/Matrimonial (Northern)
Practice Areas: Family Law - Children cases, particularly Care Proceedings.
Professional Memberships: Northern Circuit, Family Law Bar Association.
Career: Called in July 1989, Pupillage at 18 St John Street Chambers from Sept 1989 to Sept 1990. Barrister at 18 St John Street Chambers September 1989 to present.
Personal: Married, one son.

BISHOP, Edward QC
1 Chancery Lane, London
020 7092 2900
clerks@1chancerylane.com
Featured in Clinical Negligence (London), Police Law (All Circuits), Personal Injury (London)
Practice Areas: Edward's practice falls into four main areas of Practice Areas: personal injury, clinical negligence, police cases and human rights. Recent cases of note include Bedford v Bedfordshire CC [2013] (human rights & personal injury), Boyle v Commissioner of Police of the Metropolis [2013] CA (causation, procedure and personal injury), Saunders v Chief Constable of Sussex [2012] CA (causation and personal injury), Savage v South Essex Partnership NHS Foundation Trust [2010] (human rights and clinical liability), Van Colle v Chief Constable of Hertfordshire Police [2008] HL and Smith v Chief Constable of Sussex [2008] HL (police protection, negligence and human rights). He also appeared in the Court of Appeal in the widely reported case of Chittock v Woodbridge School concerning the duty of care of a school to a boy injured on a school skiing trip. He has a substantial practice representing both claimants and defendants in high value clinical negligence and personal injury cases.
Professional Memberships: Professional Negligence Bar Association; Personal Injuries Bar Association; London Common Law and Commercial Bar Association.
Career: Called to the Bar in 1985; Silk 2011.
Publications: Author of 'Recoupment of Damages' in the PIBA Handbook; author of 'Police Complaints Misconduct and Disciplinary Proceedings and Discipline' in Emergency Services Law and Liability; author of several chapters in 'Kemp and Kemp' and also on Editorial Board; Contributing editor of 'Pittaway & Hammerton: Professional Negligence Cases' and co-author of the chapter on accountants' negligence.
Personal: Educated at King's School, Canterbury and Pembroke College, Cambridge. Leisure pursuits include sport, music, travel, member MCC.

BLACKBURN, Elizabeth QC
Stone Chambers, London
020 7440 6900
elizabeth.blackburn@stonechambers.com
Featured in Shipping (London)
Practice Areas: Shipping; international carriage of goods; international trade/ finance; offshore construction and insurance disputes; damage to marine/ offshore installations; marine insurance and P&I Club issues; nuclear liability insurance; marine pollution (member UK delegation at IOPC Supplementary Fund Conference); collision, salvage; limitation, shipbuilding, particularly superyachts; arbitration; conflict of laws/ jurisdictional disputes; maritime heritage and wreck. Arbitrator in maritime and non-maritime disputes, including ICC arbitrations relating to commercial contracts, such as large scale supply contracts in the energy sector, shipbuilding and international trade disputes. Major cases: Abidin Daver; European Gateway; Kowloon Bridge; Goring; Volvex Hollandia; Freccia Del Nord; Captain San Luis; Iron Baron; Sea Prince; Nakhodka, MSC Rosa M; Freja Scandic; Ievoli Sun; St Jacques II; Margaretha Maria; Tricolor; Kaminesan/Hyundai No 105; Ken Explorer; Cristoforo Colombo; ECE; Sea Angel/ Tasman Spirit; Micoperi 30; A Turtle; Rocknes; MSC Chitra; Nordlake; Oliva; CMA CGM Libra; Barelli, Yusho Regulus, and major superyacht arbitrations (names confidential). TheTricolor, Kaminesan/Hyundai No 105, MSC Chitra, Barelli and CMA CGM are some of the largest casualty claims arising in the last decade).
Professional Memberships: Executive Committee of British Maritime Law Association, Commercial Bar Association; London Maritime Arbitrators' Association. Advisory Committee on Historic Wreck Sites (Dept of Culture). Executive Committee of London Shipping Law Centre. Bencher of Middle Temple.
Career: QC 1998. First instance arbitrator, Lloyd's Open Forum Arbitration Panel (2009). Named best in Shipping & Maritime at the Euromoney LMG Europe Women in Business Law Awards 2013. Member of the ICC Institute of World Business Law.

BLACKBURN, John QC
Atkin Chambers, London
020 7404 0102
clerks@atkinchambers.com
Featured in International Arbitration (London)
Practice Areas: John accepts appointments as arbitrator in domestic and international arbitrations over a variety of disputes, including engineering and oil and gas.
Professional Memberships: A bencher of the Middle Temple.
Career: Queen's Counsel in 1984, he practiced as counsel at the English bar and in international arbitration until 2006.
Personal: Born in 1954; Married with two grown sons; Educated at Rugby School and Worcester College, Oxford.

BLACKETT-ORD, Mark
5 Stone Buildings, London
020 7242 6201
clerks@5sblaw.com
Featured in Partnership (London)
Practice Areas: Barrister and arbitrator specialising in partnership, trusts, professional negligence, probate, ecclesiastical law and general Chancery litigation. Notable cases include: Wilson dec'd [2013] EWHC 499 (Ch); Manning v English [2010] EWHC 153 (Ch); Hopton v Miller [2010] EWHC 2732; Mary Gray Ritchie deceased [2009] EWHC 809; Olins v Walters [2009] Ch212 (mutual wills); Tann v Herrington [2009] EWHC 445 (partnership); Re St Peter's Draycott {2009}Fam 93(Court of Arches); Hopper v Hopper [2008] CA EWCA Civ 1417 (proprietary estoppel); M Young Legal v Zahid [2006] 1WLR 2562 CA, where Wilson LJ at para 31 refers to "Mr Blackett-Ord's excellent book"; Sandhu v Gill[2006] Ch 456 CA; Price v Williams-Wynn [2006] WTLR (for the claimant); Braymist v Wise Finance Co [2002] 2 AER 333 CA; Polly Peck plc v Nadir [1992] The Times 30.7.92 CA.
Professional Memberships: ACTAPS, STEP, APP, Chancery Bar Association and The Ecclesiastical Judges Association.
Career: Oxford University. Called 1974, Lincoln's Inn. Master of Bench Lincoln's Inn (2006) FSA (2006). Sits as an arbitrator. Fellow of the Society of Antiquaries, Chancellor of the Diocese of Leicester.
Publications: Author 'Partnership' (Butterworths 1997, 2nd ed 2002, 3rd ed (Tottel) 2007) 4th ed (Bloomsbury Law) 2012, co-authored with Sarah Haren. Editor 'Partnerships and LLP's' in Atkins Court Forms.

BLACKMORE, Sally
Ely Place Chambers, London
020 7400 9600
sblackmore@elyplace.com
Featured in Social Housing (London)
Practice Areas: Real property, landlord and tenant and housing; chancery; administrative and local government law; human rights.
Professional Memberships: ALBA, PBA, ChBA.
Career: Sally has appeared in the High Court, Court of Appeal, county court and property tribunal. In housing matters, she has particular expertise in dilapidations, unlawful eviction and harassment, and in possession matters involving public law and human rights issues (e.g. Optima Community Association v Ker [2013] EWCA Civ 579; Leicester City Council v Shearer [2013] EWCA Civ 1467). She has advised commercial and residential clients on – amongst other things – the construction of leases, easements and covenants, express and implied trusts. She has advised and represented applicants and local authorities in homelessness appeals and housing and com-

munity care judicial reviews. Other recent instructions include an acrimonious boundary dispute and a challenge to an authority's decision to revoke a prohibition order.
Personal: Sally studied English at the University of London and went on to obtain a Masters in Medieval Studies at the University of Bristol. She was an English language teacher in the UK, Greece, Estonia and Cameroon across a period of seven years before becoming a barrister. She has been a member of the Islington Legal Advice Centre since 2004.

BLAKE, Andrew
11KBW, London
020 7632 8500
andrew.blake@11kbw.com
Featured in Employment (London)
Practice Areas: Andrew's practice covers the full range of employment advice and litigation, with a particular recent focus on discrimination and whistleblowing claims in the Employment Tribunals. He has been instructed in a number of multiple equal pay claims in the public sector over the last decade, and is now seeing an increasing number of equal pay claims in the private sector. He also advises regularly on all areas of employment law including unfair dismissal, TUPE, collective consultation and working time, and acts for a wide range of employers and claimants. In the High Court, Andrew is often instructed on business protection and breach of contract claims. Recent appellate cases include: Cockram v Air Products UKEAT/0038/14/LA (claimant affirmed contract by giving long notice); Birdi v Dartford Visionplus Ltd UKEAT/0289/12/JOJ (adjournments due to the ill-health of a party); Prest v Mouchel Business Services Ltd UKEAT/0604/10 (selection of comparators in equal pay claims); Newcastle upon Tyne NHS Trust v Armstrong (No. 2) [2010] ICR 674, EAT (material factor defence in equal pay claims); National Amusements (UK) Ltd v Thomson UKEAT/0433/09 ('range of reasonable responses' in unfair dismissal claims); and Blackburn v Chief Constable West Midlands Police [2009] IRLR 135, CA (material factor defence in equal pay claims. Outside of the court room, Andrew is an accredited mediator, as well as an experienced party representative in negotiations and mediations.
Professional Memberships: ELBA, ELA.
Career: Called 2000.
Publications: Contributor to Tolley's Employment Law Handbook.
Personal: Cambridge University (BA), University of California Berkeley (LLM).

BLAKER, Gary
Selborne Chambers, London
020 7420 9500
gary.blaker@selbornechambers.co.uk
Featured in Real Estate Litigation (London)
Professional Memberships: Chancery Bar Association, Property Bar Association, Professional Negligence Bar Association.
Career: Gary has a Chancery practice with a strong emphasis on all aspects of property litigation and professional negligence. He has particular expertise in landlord and tenant, real property and property related professional negligence. He has appeared in numerous reported cases in recent years including H Waites Ltd v Hambledon Court Ltd [2014] EWHC 651 (Ch) (airspace above garages); Watson Farley & Williams [2014] EWHC 160 (QB) (whether a Greek lawyer was negligence in providing advice); Afia v Mellor LTL /12/13 (promissory estoppel claim relating to share purchase); Derek Hodd Ltd v Climate Change Capital Ltd [2013] WLR (D) 238 (identifying a misdescribed party to a contract); Rivercove Trustee Ltd v Euro Rubber Lines [2012] EWHC 2593 (TCC) (oil spill at a plastics factory); Kirby v Hoff LTL 14//2/11 non party costs orders.
Publications: Gary regularly provides seminars on property related matters and has written numerous published articles on the subject.

BLAKESLEY, Patrick
Crown Office Chambers, London
020 7797 8100
blakesley@crownofficechambers.com
Featured in Personal Injury (London)
Practice Areas: Patrick specialises in catastrophic and high-value personal injury claims, industrial disease, and inquests. He also practices in insurance, product liability and professional negligence. Personal injury He has particular experience with serious brain injury, paraplegia and tetraplegia cases; amputation claims; death and dependency; and all types of liability scenarios (including RTA, industrial and construction accidents, toxic exposures). He is happy to advise on jurisdiction and applicable law issues and limitation. He is regularly instructed on his own in multi-million pound claims. Disease : Asbestos and other toxic exposures, vibration and noise. Inquests : He has longstanding inquest experience and recently represented Kew Gardens in an Article 2 inquest into a death caused by a falling branch. Insurance: Patrick advises on insurance issues connected with personal injury claims, such as liability between EL, PL and motor insurers; European issues; insurance obligations and indemnities in construction contracts, and MIB/Article 75 issues. Product liability: Aligned with his personal injury practice, Patrick has substantial experience of product claims and enjoys getting to grips with technical and design problems. Professional negligence: Principally claims against solicitors, valuers and insurance brokers.
Career: Called to the Bar in 1993

BLAYNEY, David QC
Serle Court, London
020 7400 7122
dblayney@serlecourt.co.uk
Featured in Banking & Finance (London), Chancery (London), Commercial Dispute Resolution (London), Company (London), Partnership (London)
Practice Areas: General commercial and chancery litigation, particularly: commercial, banking, insolvency, companies, trusts, charities, contracts, professional negligence, joint ventures and partnerships. Particular specialism in financial, numerical and quantum issues. Major cases include: The RBS Rights Issue litigation; OFT v Abbey National (the bank charges litigation); Re Lehman Brothers International Europe (extended lien issues); Constantin Medien v Ecclestone (alleged bribery and conspiracy); Re Bradford & Bingley (banking); Re Bearwood College Trustees (charities); RBS v Winterthur (share sale warranties); Akkurate v Moschillo (directors duties); Credit Suisse v Ramot Plana (banking); Lemos v Coutts (trusts); Phillips v Symes (partnership/fraud); Re Continental Assurance (wrongful trading); SAAMCO (damages).
Professional Memberships: Chancery Bar Association, COMBAR.
Career: Called 1992. Silk 2013.
Personal: Born 1969. Educated at St Michael's (Jersey), Canford School and Lincoln College, Oxford (BA Law, 1st Class Honours). Married with two children. Interests include cycling, windsurfing, tennis and music.

BLOCH, Selwyn QC
Littleton Chambers, London
020 7797 8600
sbloch@littletonchambers.co.uk
Featured in Employment (London)
Practice Areas: Selwyn Bloch QC is a leading employment/commercial law Silk. He has appeared in numerous leading cases, including High Court employment disputes involving confidential information, team moves,economic torts, restrictive covenants, garden leave, fiduciary duties and wrongful dismissal. Cases include aspects of intellectual property, private international law, and sports law eg Tullett Prebon v BGC (confidential information, wrongful dismissal, fiduciary duties, restrictive covenants) and Duarte v Black and Decker (conflict of laws/restrictive covenants). Recent cases include QBE v Dymoke (springboard injunctions/team move); Caterpillar v Huesca de Crean(CA)(fiduciary duties/confidential information) and Halstead v Paymentshield (CA)(lifting stay of Court proceedings in favour of tribunal proceedings). Recent instructions include dispute (under Jersey law) regarding enforceability of "claw back" provisions in employee benefit scheme and arbitration relating to enforceability of anti-teams moves covenants (in LLP agreement). Substantial experience in discrimination, whistle-blowing, TUPE and unfair dismissal disputes.
Professional Memberships: Employment Law Bar Association, ELA and COMBAR.
Career: Silk 2000. Called 1982; joined current chambers that year. Employment Judge (part time) since 2000.
Publications: Co-author of leading textbook 'Employment Covenants and Confidential Information' (3rd edition 2009).
Personal: Interests include music, theatre, literature and sport.

BLOCK, Neil QC
Thirty Nine Essex Street, London
020 7832 1111
clerks@39essex.com
Featured in Clinical Negligence (London), Product Liability (London), Personal Injury (London), Travel (London)
Practice Areas: Principle areas of practice are professional and clinical negligence, insurance, contract, catastrophic injury, sports injury, group litigation and product liability. He has a particular expertise in claims arising out of accidents abroad (e.g. Stylianou v Yakamoto & Suncorps)Insurance (including policy coverage, avoidance/fraud and material loss claims eg McGregor v Prudential Assurance Co , ICF v NIG (a series of claims involving policy coverage issues, solicitors negligence, CFA and CCA issues)). Professional negligence (including solicitors, construction related professionals, accountants, surveyors and valuers, architects, stockbrokers and insurance brokers), group actions and similar(Hepatitis C, Toxic Sofas,Supertram, shipyards, organo-phosphates, Jimmy Savile), personal injury and disease (including sporting cases eg Smolden v Whitworth; Nolan, O'Neill v Wimbledon; Fashanu, Watson v British Boxing Board of Control, Allport v Wilbrahim (rugby referee)), catastrophic injury claims, clinical negligence (in particular paediatric brain damage, spinal injury, hospital associated infection), disaster litigation (eg Selby rail crash), product liability (eg Northwick Park drug trials, Scania 4 litigation, Sudan Red, Pollard v Tesco, Ide v ATB, Linkwise group action (toxic sofas), metal on metal hip cases).
Professional Memberships: Professional Negligence Bar Association, Personal Injury Bar Association, London Common Law and Commercial Bar Association, Bar Sports Law Group.
Career: Joint Head of Chambers. Called to the Bar in 1980; took Silk 2002. Bencher at Gray's Inn 2008. Accredited mediator.
Personal: BA (Hons), LLM (Exon).

BLUNT, David QC
4 Pump Court, London
020 7842 5555
dblunt@4pumpcourt.com
Featured in Information Technology (London)
Practice Areas: David Blunt practices principally in the Technology and Construction Court, dealing with IT & Telecommunications, construction, engineering, and other document-heavy disputes, as well as professional and other indemnity insurance claims. In addition he has a substantial arbitration practice and has a very broad experience of common law/ commercial work, including commercial contracts of all kinds, insurance/ reinsurance, banking. He is a Recorder, and sits as a Deputy High Court Judge, Deputy Judge of the Technology and Construction Court, arbitrator, adjudicator and mediator. He is also a Member of the Financial Reporting Council, Accountancy and Actuarial Discipline Board's panel of chairmen for Tribunals and Appeal Tribunals. He is the co-author of the chapter on Computer Consultants in 'Professional Negligence and Liability'.
Career: Called to the Bar 1967. Appointed recorder 1991. Took Silk 1992. Appointed Deputy Judge of the Technology and Construction Court 1993. Deputy High Court Judge 2003.

BLUNT, Oliver QC
Furnival Chambers, London
020 7405 3232
clerks@furnivallaw.co.uk
Featured in Crime (London)
Practice Areas: Entirely defence based practice specialising in murder, terrorism, and fraud and drugs cases. Currently instructed on behalf of three of the News International employees arrested in Operation Elveden. Also this year has successfully defended Mohanjit Bhatia in a multi million pound drugs conspiracy case and has also successfully defended three murder cases in the last year. Twice instructed on behalf of the British Boxing Board of Control in two appeals (Couch and Chisora). Murder and Violent Crime: In the course of the last twelve months has conducted a series of gang related murders at the Central Criminal Court. Previously conducted R v. Amoah and others (CCC, 2011, only murder/manslaughter acquittal in the first Victoria tube station murder trial), R v Peter Brown (Nottingham

CC, 2010, double murder), R v Peter Tobin (Chelmsford CC, 2009, convicted serial killer), R v Ian Davis (CCC, 2009, double murder trial), R v Khan (CCC, 2010, arson related double murder) and R v Imran Hussain (CCC, 2010, Tooting double murder). Has also represented such clients as William Cockram (the Millennium Dome Robbery trial), Patrick Smith (Murder 2001-2, CCC), John Taft (the beauty in the bath' murder trial, Liverpool CC, 1999), Syd Owen ('Ricky' of Eastender's, wounding, Snaresbrook CC, 1995), Michael Sams (kidnapping, blackmail, murder, Nottingham CC, 1993). Fraud: Recently appeared in R v Colwell and Sayers (Newcastle CC, 2009, multi-million pound mortgage and tax fraud). Has also represented William Casey, acquitted in a multi-million pound arson/insurance fraud (CCC, 1997), Kounnou, a £200 million shipping fraud (CCC, 2003), Devi Schahou in the Goldman Sachs trial (Southwark, 2004), and Dorian Morris, principal defendant in multi-million pound money laundering trial, acquitted (Kingston CC 2005). Sexual Crime: including high profile cases such as Richard Baker (DJ rapist, CCC, 1999) Drugs: recently appeared in R v. Cornick and others (Liverpool CC, 2010) conspiracy to import cocaine and cannabis, R v Faponnle and others (Blackfriars CC, 2010, heroin distribution), and R v Goren and others (CCC, 2008, Turkish heroin importation). Represented such clients as Paul Wyatt (Bolton CC, 2002-3), and R v Hillier and others (£150 million cocaine importation 1993). Terrorism: has acted on behalf of the Iranian Embassy and represented two members of the Consular Staff in separate terrorist trials at the CCC (Tabari Abcou/Fouladi). Appeared for the second defendant in R v Canning and Lamb (IRA trial, CCC, 1993), and in R v Shariff (21/7 trials, Kingston CC, 2007).
Professional Memberships: SE circuit, Criminal Bar Association.
Career: Called to the Bar 1974. Queen's Counsel 1994. Recorder 1991.
Personal: Born 8 March 1951. Married with four children. Member of Roehampton Club, Rossyln Park Rugby Club and Barnes Cricket Club.

BODNAR, Alexandra
Thirty Nine Essex Street, London
020 7832 1142
alex.bodnar@39essex.com
Featured in Construction (London)
Practice Areas: Specialist in construction, engineering and commercial disputes. Experience of complex, high-value international and domestic arbitration, as well as litigation and adjudication. Appears regularly in the TCC and the Commercial Court. Familiar with PFI contracts, bonds and guarantees, energy, nuclear, utilities, infrastructure, insurance and reinsurance (including coverage and avoidance), professional negligence, international trade, jurisdictional issues and competition law.
Professional Memberships: SCL, TECBAR, COMBAR, IBA.
Career: Called 2004, Inner Temple.
Publications: Contributor to Construction Contracts by Richard Wilmot-Smith QC (3rd Ed). Contributor to the UK chapter in The Projects and Construction Review (4th Ed).

BODNAR, Andrew
Matrix Chambers, London
020 7404 3447
matrix@matrixlaw.co.uk
Featured in POCA Work & Asset Forfeiture (All Circuits), Financial Crime (London)
Practice Areas: Specialising in asset recovery, fraud, money laundering and cases arising under the proceeds of crime legislation. Practice straddles the civil and criminal arenas, additionally including corruption, administrative law, insolvency, shareholder disputes, market manipulation and insider dealing, as well as other financial crime. Has appeared at all levels of court in the UK, as well as assisting with litigation in Jersey and appearing before the DIFC Court. Conversant with the proceeds of crime legislation of not just the UK but also of a number of common law jurisdictions. Appears for both the prosecution and defence, having prosecuted on the SFO's 'A' panel, and for both claimants and defendants. Co-editor of Smith, Owen and Bodnar on Asset Recovery, published by OUP. Lectures widely both in the UK and abroad. Ranked as amongst the leading lawyers in his field by a number of directories.
Professional Memberships: South Eastern Circuit; Criminal Bar Association; Administrative Law Bar Association; International Bar Association.
Career: Called to the bar 1995.
Publications: Editor 'Smith, Owen and Bodnar on Asset Recovery', published by OUP.
Personal: Educated King's College London.

BOEDDINGHAUS, Hermann
4 Stone Buildings, London
020 7242 5524
hb@4stonebuildings.com
Featured in Chancery (London)
Practice Areas: Company litigation and advice. Insolvency law. Commercial litigation.
Career: Hermann Boeddinghaus specialises in corporate and commercial disputes and insolvency law. He enjoys a busy litigation caseload, spread between the Chancery Division, the Commercial Court and international arbitration tribunals. Alongside this he has developed a substantial advisory practice. Hermann has represented Nigeria and Pakistan in major asset recovery claims against the families and associates of former rulers. Other clients have ranged from the world's largest banks to small family firms and individual entrepreneurs. He has built a reputation as a tough and persuasive advocate, much liked by his clients. Hermann began his career training as a solicitor with Slaughter and May, spending his first 6 months with Nigel Boardman. The firm's culture left a clear mark on his approach to practice: high standards in all aspects of his work, a readiness to go the extra mile, and an ability to see matters from his clients' perspective. Soon after qualifying he was called to the Bar. Within a week of commencing practice he appeared in his first reported case - Neuberger J's decision in Re Philip Alexander Securities & Futures Ltd. Hermann is adept at getting to grips with matters of a highly technical nature. His particular interest is in complex financial fraud; but he is equally at home in handling high value commercial arbitrations (construction, leisure, oil & gas, shipping). He has a strong academic background in science as well as law. Clients have repeatedly praised him for his rigorous attention to detail, tempered by a pragmatic, user-friendly approach. In 2013, Hermann was one of 200 junior barristers in England and Wales shortlisted for The Chambers 100 UK Bar.

BOND, Leisha
St Philips Chambers, Birmingham
0121 246 2148
lbond@st-philips.com
Featured in Family/Matrimonial (Midlands)
Practice Areas: Leisha is a matrimonial finance specialist. Her cases often run into millions of pounds and involve businesses, property portfolios, intervenors and large pensions. However she also acts in more modest asset cases where, although the capital is limited, the stakes can be high for the client (maintaining a roof over his/her head). She also appears in Children Act proceedings which are often complex and sometimes heard "back to back" with financial proceedings. Leisha also regularly undertakes Schedule One cases in relation to financial claims by unmarried parents as well as cohabitation disputes under TLATA. Leisha is renowned for her thorough preparation and penetrative cross examination. She has a reputation as a hard negotiator and a "fighter" where settlement is not in her client's best interest. She exudes confidence and has a good rapport with her clients, be they a multi-millionaire businessman or stay at home mum. Her results are extremely impressive.
Professional Memberships: Family Law Bar Association; Association of Lawyers for Children.
Career: University of Birmingham and Université de Limoges (Law and French Law) 2:i; Jules Thorne scholar Middle Temple; Called to Bar 1999. She regularly lectures to other legal professionals.
Personal: Married with a son.

BONE, Lucy
Littleton Chambers, London
020 7797 8600
lbone@littletonchambers.co.uk
Featured in Employment (London)
Practice Areas: Employment, commercial and disciplinary/regulatory law. Principal areas of practice include commercial disputes arising in an employment context, in particular all aspects of restrictive covenant disputes, unlawful competition including preparatory steps to compete and passing off, confidentiality disputes including issues in relation to social media, breaches of directors' duties and fiduciary duties, partnership and LLP disputes, and fraud and conspiracy. Particular experience in litigation concerning post-termination restraints and team moves, in applications for injunctive relief of all forms including springboard injunctions, and speedy trials. Predominantly involved in High Court and appellate litigation but also widely experienced in cases in the employment tribunals and EAT. Experience in employee injunctions to restrain dismissal etc. Regulatory practice especially in the healthcare field, including GDC, GMC, GOC and has appeared in internal disciplinaries and Fitness to Practice hearings. Employment Tribunal practice encompasses all forms of discrimination, maternity and parental rights, unfair dismissal including redundancy and whistleblowing, wrongful dismissal, transfer of undertakings and equal pay (experienced in both individual claims in the private sector and multiple complaints in the public sector), collective redundancies and strike injunctions. Recent reported cases include: Webber v. NHS Direct [2012] EAT; Whitmar Publishing Limited v. Gamage and Others [2013] EWHC 1881 (Ch); Clinisupplies v. Park [2012] EWHC 3209 (Ch).
Professional Memberships: ARDL, ELA, ELBA, COMBAR, EAT ELAAS Scheme. Barrister member of the Professional Conduct Committee of the Bar Standards Board since January 2013. Recently elected Management Committee Member of Employment Lawyers' Association.
Career: Called 1999, Queen Mother Scholar of Middle Temple.
Personal: Educated at St Paul's Girls' School and King's College London 1995-98 (LLB, LLM). Born 1974. Resides London.

BOON, Elizabeth
Crown Office Chambers, London
020 7797 8100
mail@crownofficechambers.com
Featured in Property Damage (London)
Practice Areas: Elizabeth specialises in property damage and construction, professional negligence, product liability, insurance, and general commercial litigation. In addition to drafting and advisory work, she has considerable experience of appearing as an advocate in court. She has regularly appeared in the High Court (particularly the TCC) and in the Court of Appeal. Elizabeth's experience ranges from acting both as a junior to other members of Chambers to acting in her own right in relation to property damage and construction claims. She is frequently instructed as junior counsel in multi-million pound claims in the TCC, and in addition to such work, Elizabeth advises on and appears at trial in her own right in smaller disputes, especially those relating to domestic construction and maintenance works. Recent work includes: Acting for local authority in relation to multi-million pound claim in the TCC arising out of fire damage to a timber framed building; acting for developer in relation to allegedly defective waterproofing to a luxury block of flats resulting in water ingress and associated damage; and acting for a mine management company in relation to a claim for damage caused to a railway track due to a landslip at a colliery.

BOOTH, Alexander
Francis Taylor Building, London
020 7353 8415
clerks@ftb.eu.com
Featured in Planning (London)
Practice Areas: Alex Booth has a practice encompassing all aspects of planning, compulsory purchase and environmental law. His practice also includes licensing and rating matters. He regularly appears on behalf of private and public bodies in the High Court, the Lands Tribunal and at Public Inquiries and has also appeared in the Court of Appeal and the Supreme Court. In addition, he advises clients in Commonwealth jurisdictions and has successfully brought judicial review proceedings in the Turks and Caicos Islands. Nationally significant infrastructure work includes promoting a Resource Recovery Facility on behalf of Covanta, and opposing the Able Marine Energy Park on behalf of Associated British Ports. Other cases of note include London Olympics Judicial Review and Compulsory Purchase litigation acting

on behalf of the London Development Agency; Compensation litigation connected with Crossrail, acting on behalf of corporate property investment claimants; Promoting compulsory purchase orders on behalf of National Grid Gas in South Wales; Statutory Reviews regarding planning enforcement in the Supreme Court and open cast coal mining in the Court of Appeal; Judicial Review of London Congestion Charging Scheme.

BORLAND, Garry
Axiom Advocates, Edinburgh
07739 638 941
garry.borland@axiomadvocates.com
Featured in Construction (Scotland), Restructuring/Insolvency (Scotland), Commercial Dispute Resolution (Scotland)
Practice Areas: Practice encompasses all areas of commercial law, specialising in commercial contracts, commercial property, company law and insolvency, construction and engineering, and energy.
Career: LLB (Hons), Glasgow University, 1st class (J Bennett Miller Prize winner in senior honours); BCL, St. John's College, Oxford, 1st class (Pirie-Reid scholar). Called to the Bar in 2000. Standing Junior Counsel to Her Majesty's Revenue and Customs, 2009-12.

BORRELLI, Michael QC
3 Raymond Buildings Barristers, London
020 7400 6400
michael.borrelli@3rblaw.com
Featured in Crime (London)
Practice Areas: Practice Areas: He has an exclusive practice defending in high profile, serious and complex crime, as well as an interest in other areas of quasi-criminal work, tribunals and disciplinary hearings, where his advocacy skills can be fully utilised. He is instructed to review and advise on appellate work and to conduct cases in the Court of Appeal. He has developed a reputation for his ability in cases requiring the examination and testing of experts' evidence. His extensive experience encompasses all areas of professional crime, and numerous homicide trials, and a variety of white-collar fraud work including banking fraud, duty evasion, and mortgage fraud. Recently he represented the wife of the former Governor of the Delta State, in Nigeria, in one of a series of money laundering trials, R v Theresa Ibori. Other recent and forthcoming work includes the Connors "slavery" trial, the Rachel Manning murder, an historic case that was the subject of a BBC Rough Justice Investigation that led to the re-trial and acquittal of the original defendant, the alleged diversion of £2million from the Copland Community School, and currently at Southwark Crown Court, Operation Cassandra, allegations of conspiracy to defraud over £30 million, corruption and money laundering, said to involve the Royal Bank of Scotland, Northern Rock, Barclays and other lending Institutions.

BOTT, Charles QC
Carmelite Chambers, London
cbott@carmelitechambers.co.uk
Featured in Crime (London), Financial Crime (London)
Practice Areas: 'A leading authority on all aspects of criminal and civil fraud, he has combined wide experience as an advocate and a background in civil, commercial and regulatory law to develop a extensive practice in fraud, money laundering and regulatory work: he has appeared in more than 80 serious fraud trials including many of the leading cases of recent years. He has represented politicians, solicitors, accountants and prominent figures in the city and insurance markets. He also undertakes a wide range of civil advisory work and litigation, specializing in the areas of financial regulation, money laundering and asset recovery. Represents both corporate and personal clients in dealing with the FCA and other regulatory authorities and has recent experience of substantial and complex civil recovery proceedings. Has advised on and drafted comparable legislation in other jurisdictions. Also has wide experience in cases of murder, terrorism, serious violence and drug trafficking and has appeared in two public enquiries.' Fraud clients include: a senior bank manager at Nat West (R v. Crowther 1991), a portfolio manager at BZW (R v. Borkum 1990), a leading importer of Indian films (R v. Jumani 1990), the Chairman of Boodles (R v. Shand 2002), the director of a re-insurance brokerage at Lloyd's (R v. Felstead 1997), the largest UK importer of tropical birds and parrots (R v. Hammond 1996), the principal sub-contractor on the Millennium Dome site (R v. McHale 2000), the managing director of a chain of employment agencies (R v. Strachan 1997), the owner of the Windmill Club (R v. Owide 2004), the auditor in the Jubilee Line Extension fraud (R v. Mills 2004/5), a Tower Hamlets councillor accused of financial corruption (R v. Uddin 2006) the director of a leading pharmaceuticals company (R v. F 2006-2008), the Chief Executive of a major psychiatric hospital (R v. Breeze 2009) and a number of solicitors and accountants . Other fraud work includes R v. Miller (1998) a prominent case about corruption in the City, R v. Stepnika and others (2000) money laundering by former Czech police officers,.R v. Headley (2002), laundering the proceeds of Europe's largest armed robbery.,R v. Zone (2003),test case on abuse of Local Authority Right to Buy scheme, R v. Baldar (2005), surgeon accused of obtaining NHS posts by deception. Re M (2007),FSA/French Stock Exchange insider dealing inquiry, R v. Thorne (2009), SFO Prosecution of leading UK car retailer. R v. R (2009/10), SFO Prosecution of investment fraud, R v JH (2012)Expatriates Ponzi fraud. Major revenue frauds include R v Koser (2008), R v Jones (2006/7), R v M (2010), R v YAM (2011) and R v PS (2012), amongst the largest modern MTIC trials. Has also defended a police officer charged under the Official Secrets Act (R v White), the Managing Director of 'Hustler' magazine in a pornography trial , the soldier responsible for the Sudbury Nursing Home siege(R v King), a Palestinian journalist charged with plot to bomb the Israeli Embassy (R v. Derbas 1996), a Leeds United footballer charged with serious assault (R v. Hackworth 2001, Bowyer, Duberry, Woodgate and others). Other recent work includes R v Ali (2008-21/7 terrorist case), R v Taylor (2008), the Woodhams Murder trial, R v Palmer (2009) the Colchester train manslaughter case, R v Faroqui (2011 - terrorist recruitment case) and R v Baroudi - doctor charged with manslaugter by gross negliegence, R v JW News of the World phone hacking case, R v G (ongoing) LIBOR manipulation case, R v D Deutsche Bank insider trading trial.
Career: Call: November 1979 Gray's Inn. Education: MA (Cantab).

BOULDING, Philip QC
Keating Chambers, London
020 7544 2600
pboulding@keatingchambers.com
Featured in Construction (London), International Arbitration (London)
Practice Areas: A "rock solid and hugely popular" Queen's Counsel specialising in construction, civil engineering and energy disputes and technology , who is a "a big international player with a great profile in Hong Kong and Asia in general." Practice comprises of domestic but principally international work, acting for a large number of clients in the Far East, particularly Hong Kong. Clients include local authorities, government departments, major national and international construction and engineering companies, energy and utility companies and direct access work from claims consultants involved in the construction industry. "Clever and cerebral"..."decades of experience"..."particularly acclaimed for his expertise in Hong Kong-based disputes"..."flexes his intellectual muscle on a regular basis in a wide array of complex international arbitrations." Chambers and Partners.
Professional Memberships: Dubai International Finance Centre Court (DIFC); Commercial Bar Association; Technology and Construction Bar Association.
Career: Called 1979; Queen's Counsel 1996. Admitted to Hong Kong Bar (ad hoc). Elected Master of the Bench of Gray's Inn 2004. Former Committee Member of TECBAR.
Publications: Consultant Editor to the Construction Law Reports; Contributor, Keating on Construction Contracts + supplement Ninth Edition.

BOURNE, Charles QC
11KBW, London
020 7632 8500
charles.bourne@11kbw.com
Featured in Administrative & Public Law (London), Immigration (London)
Practice Areas: Public law, human rights, employment, local government, immigration and public inquiries. Recent cases include: O'Brien v Ministry of Justice (judicial pension rights), R (SW Care Homes) v Devon County Council (care home fees, equality duties), Kiani v Home Office (Employment Tribunal closed material procedures), AHK and others v Home Secretary (High Court closed material procedures), Owen v HM Treasury (whistleblowing), the Baha Mousa Inquiry, R (Dulai) v Chelmsford Magistrates (trading standards, warrants), R (Lumba) v Home Secretary (unlawful detention), HJ (Iran) v Home Secretary (refugees, sexual orientation), Stagecoach Group v Transport Secretary (concessionary travel, EU law).
Professional Memberships: Human Rights Lawyers Association (former Chair), ALBA.
Career: Called 1991. QC 2014. CEDR accredited Mediator 2000. A Panel Treasury Counsel 2009. Recorder 2010. Accredited for Public Access.
Publications: Contributor to Tolley's Employment Law, Butterworths Civil Court Practice (the Green Book) and Civil Court Precedents. Author of "Civil Advocacy" (Cavendish).
Personal: Educated: UCS, London; Trinity College, Cambridge (MA, First Class); Université de Paris IV (Sorbonne) (Maitrise).

BOURNE, Colin
Kings Chambers, Leeds
0845 034 3444
clerks@kingschambers.com
Featured in Employment (North Eastern)
Practice Areas: Industrial Relations (individual and collective), employment, discrimination with a wide range of individual, trade union, public and private sector clients. Accredited CEDR mediator with wide experience of non-employment matters. Reported cases: Street v Derbyshire Unemployed workers' Centre [2004] EWCA Civ 964 [2004] IRLR 687 CA – the requirement for good faith when making protected disclosures. Miles v Linkage Community Trust [2008] IRLR 602 argued successfully for a nil award in a Working Time Regs case. Metropolitan Resources v Churchill Dulwich & others [2009] IRLR 700 identifying a service provision change under TUPE. 2006 Sturdy v Leeds Teaching Hospitals NHS Trust – 2009 ET highest ever injury to feelings award plus interest and aggravated damages plus indemnity costs. Leeds City Council v Woodhouse UKEAT/0521/08/DA – employee of Arms Length Management Organisation was contract worker for purposes of Race Relations Act 1976.
Professional Memberships: Employment Law Bar Association, Employment Lawyers' Association, Industrial Law Society, Association of Northern Mediators.
Career: 1973-81 Graphic designer/Art Editor, IPC Magazines; 1981-96 Trade Union Officer, National Union of Journalists; Called 1997 - 15 years previous employment law experience including European Works Councils.

BOURNE, Ian QC
Charter Chambers, London
020 7618 4400
ian.bourne@charterchambers.com
Featured in Crime (London)
Practice Areas: Ian was described in the Chambers Directory when a junior as 'capable of performing mental gymnastics at the drop of a hat'. Since taking silk in 2006 he has built up a formidable practice and has appeared in many of the major cases in recent times including in 2012 the successful representation of the City Broker in the largest ever FSA prosecution of insider dealing in Operation Saturn (R v Ali Mustafa and others) tried at the Southwark Crown Court. He regularly defends in murder, fraud, armed-robbery and substantial drug cases in equal measures. Recent cases include the "Harry Potter" murder, the £42 million Graf Diamonds robbery and a high-profile murder in the Cayman Islands.
Professional Memberships: Criminal Bar Association, South Eastern Circuit.

BOWES, Michael QC
Outer Temple Chambers, London
020 7353 6381
michael.bowesqc@outertemple.com
Featured in Financial Services (London), Financial Crime (London)
Practice Areas: Michael Bowes specialises in complex financial services work, financial crime and civil fraud, both in the UK and abroad. He acts for corporate and individual clients in major international and UK investigations and acts for the SFO, FCA, OFT and Lloyd's of London. He successfully prosecuted the FSA's first insider dealing case and has prosecuted several insider dealing

cases subsequently. He is instructed in the current LIBOR and FOREX investigations on behalf of a major financial institution and in several substantial cross-border corruption investigations. He receives instructions to advise overseas financial regulators and is instructed in overseas cases as an expert in English law. He is advising a major company in relation to EU sanctions against Russia. He is highly experienced in successfully leading large case teams in complex cases, both for the prosecution and defence.
Professional Memberships: Criminal Bar Association. Commercial Bar Association. Financial Services Lawyers Association. Western Circuit.
Career: Call 1980. Silk 2001. Deputy High Court Judge 2010. Recorder 2000. Bencher (Middle Temple) 2007.
Publications: Editorial Board, Blackstone's Criminal Practice 2011 -. Lissack & Horlick on Bribery (contributing author) 2011 (2nd ed.2014). Butterworth's Financial Services Law & Regulation (contributing author).

BOWHILL, Jessie
8 New Square, London
020 7405 4321
jessie.bowhill@8newsquare.co.uk
Featured in Intellectual Property (London)
Practice Areas: Barrister specialising in all areas of intellectual property law and related media law including; trade marks, passing off, copyright, design right, registered designs, database right, patents, malicious falsehood and confidential information. Recent cases include: Brian Belo v Lime Pictures (copyright in The Only Way is Essex (TOWIE)); University of Southampton v Mohtasham (copyright and malicious falsehood in the field of nuclear non-proliferation); Fisher v Brooker (HL - musical copyright in "A Whiter Shade of Pale"); Mitchell v BBC (copyright in TV programme "Kerwhizz"); ITV v TV Catchup (copyright in live-streaming of TV programmes); 19TV v Freemantle (copyright in the X Factor and Pop Idol); Peer Music v Termidor & Editoria Musica de Cuba (musical copyright); IPC Media v Highbury (copyright in magazine covers); A Khan Design v Horsley (designs in alloy wheels); IPC Media v Media 10 (Ideal Home trade mark); Fine & Country v Okotoks (trade mark/estate agents); Faberge v The Uri Group (Faberge trade marks); Julius Samann v Tetrosyl (Magic Tree trade marks); Cinpres v Melea (patent for gas injection technology); Conor v Angiotech (HL – patent for taxol-coated stents); Ranbaxy v Warner Lambert (pharmaceutical patent); Virgin Atlantic Airways v Premium Aircraft Interiors (patent for Virgin upper class seats).
Professional Memberships: Intellectual Property Bar Association, Chancery Bar Association.
Career: Called 2003, Gray's Inn.
Publications: Bullen & Leake; Jacob's Precedents of Pleadings. Contributor.
Personal: Classical pianist.

BOWLING, James
4 Pump Court, London
020 7842 5555
Jbowling@4pumpcourt.com
Featured in Construction (London)
Practice Areas: Principle areas of practice are construction, professional negligence, energy, commercial and insolvency.
Professional Memberships: Society of Construction Law, TECBAR, LCLCBA.

BOWSHER, Michael QC
Monckton Chambers, London
020 7405 7211
mbowsher@monckton.com
Featured in Construction (London), Public Procurement (London)
Practice Areas: Michael Bowsher has a diverse practice based around EU and commercial law. He has been a member of Monckton Chambers since 2001, having practised previously in Brussels (at Cleary Gottlieb) and in London. He is best known for his practice in regulated procurement and has appeared as counsel in many of the major UK procurement cases. For instance, he appeared for the claimant in the first major procurement damages case in England (Harmon v House of Commons) and successfully defended the first application for ineffectiveness (Alstom v Eurostar). He is involved in a range of other EU and competition/regulatory matters, as well as commercial disputes arising out of the same sorts of complex public contracts that give rise to procurement disputes. Michael continues to be appointed as arbitrator, mediator and expert by various institutions. Most of his appointments involve disputes concerning long term contracts in the public or utilities sector.
Career: Michael was called to the Bar of England and Wales (Middle Temple) in 1985 and became a QC in 2006. He was called to the Bar of Northern Ireland in 2000 and the Bar of the Republic of Ireland in 2012. He is a fellow of the Chartered Institute of Arbitrators, the European Law Institute and the Centre of European Law, King's College London. He is a visiting lecturer in EU public procurement law at King's College London and a bencher of the Middle Temple.
Personal: Michael is British and Canadian.

BOYD, Kerstin
Tanfield Chambers, London
020 7421 5300
kerstinboyd@tanfieldchambers.co.uk
Featured in Family/Matrimonial (London)
Practice Areas: All areas of family law with particular emphasis on matrimonial finance and cohabitee disputes. Regularly appears in high value matrimonial finance, but also deals with cases involving more limited assets where the search for a resolution can be equally challenging. Cases include W v W [2010] 2 FLR 985; L (a child)[2007] EWCA Civ 196; Foster v Foster [2003] EWCA Civ 565. Also practises in area of personal injury and clinical negligence.
Professional Memberships: Family Law Bar Association; Personal Injury Bar Association.
Career: Called 1979. BA (Law) Girton College, Cambridge.
Personal: Lives in London with her husband and 2 children.

BOYDELL, Edward
Pump Court Chambers, London
020 7353 0711
e.boydell@pumpcourtchambers.com
Featured in Family/Matrimonial (Western)
Practice Areas: Edward Boydell is head of the Family Finance team at Pump Court Chambers and is very well known for his expertise and long experience dealing with complex high net worth matters including cases concerning family businesses, farms, companies, trusts and also equitable co-ownership and TOLATA. Edward also regularly advises in personal injury cases particularly those concerning asbestos-related claims, complex road traffic accidents and traumatic brain injuries. He also has long experience in solicitors' negligence cases, particularly those concerning financial remedies or personal injuries. He has been regarded by Chambers and Partners as being in the top band of their "Leaders at the Bar" for many years and is also recommended in the Legal 500.
Professional Memberships: Family Law Bar Association, Professional Negligence Bar Association, Personal Injury Bar Association, Western Circuit.
Career: Called by Middle Temple in 1989. Appointed as a Recorder in 2005 to the Midland Circuit sitting in Civil and Family – including authorisation to deal with Public Law care cases and financial remedy appeals and applications. Edward also sits at the Central Family Court.
Personal: BEd (Hons) (Cantab), Dip Law (Westminster), married with two children. Lives in London.

BOYLE, Alan QC
Serle Court, London
020 7242 6105
aboyle@serlecourt.co.uk
Featured in Chancery (London), Commercial Dispute Resolution (London), Company (London), Fraud (London), Offshore (London), Trusts (London)
Practice Areas: Commercial and chancery litigation, contentious trusts, probate, civil fraud, company, insolvency and mediation. Recent cases include: Madoff (fraud), AB v MB (trusts), Lissack (contract), Lictor (insolvency), Masri (contempt), Centenary (company).
Professional Memberships: Chancery Bar Association, Commerical Bar Association, Commercial Fraud Lawyers Association, ACTAPS. Deputy High Court Judge.
Career: Royal Shrewsbury School, St Catherine's College Oxford (MA). Called to the Bar 1972. Silk 1991.
Publications: Editor and contributor, 'The Practice and Procedure of the Companies Court', Lloyds of London. Press.
Personal: Married, two daughters.

BOYLE, Gerard
Serjeants' Inn Chambers, London
020 7427 5000
gboyle@serjeantsinn.com
Featured in Clinical Negligence (London), Police Law (All Circuits), Professional Discipline (London)
Practice Areas: Gerard Boyle was called to the Bar in 1992. Gerard specialises in public and administrative, police, inquests and inquiries, clinical negligence and healthcare, professional discipline and personal injury law. An earlier edition notes that "his sense of humour, tenacity and excellent rapport with all he meets are just some of the reasons for his incredible effectiveness. He is considered one of the best forensic barristers by experts. He is a formidable opponent who is very strong in court." He was ranked as one of the top 100 juniors by the Chambers Bar 100 2014. Please click on the link to the Serjeants' Inn Chambers website for his profile, which sets out full details of his practice including relevant work of note.
Professional Memberships: Member of the Northern Irish Bar, PNBA, ARDL, LCLCBA, Bar Standards Board Panel of Prosecuting Counsel.

BOYLE, Matthew
Crown Office Chambers, London
020 7797 8100
boyle@crownofficechambers.com
Featured in Personal Injury (London)
Practice Areas: Principle areas of practice are personal injury and industrial disease, acting for both claimants and defendants. He specialises in catastrophic and brain injury work and has trial and round table settlement meeting experience of claims worth more than £10 million. He is also regularly instructed in complex or high value employers' liability and public liability claims. His disease practice encompasses asbestos, noise induced hearing loss, hand arm vibration syndrome, work-related upper limb disorders and stress at work cases. He also has a particular interest in claims for pure psychiatric injury and cases where fraud is alleged, including those featuring staged accident and phantom passenger scenarios. In the Court of Appeal his appearances have included Hartman v South Essex Mental Health & Community NHS Trust (the group stress appeals); Davies v Global Securities (the duty of care owed to a security contractor working in Iraq); Huscroft v P & O Ferries (civil procedure: the attachment of conditions to court orders); and Sutton v Syston Rugby Football Club (the standard of care owed by rugby clubs to their members). Sources have rated his forceful advocacy, clarity and personability.
Career: Called to the Bar in 2000 and joined Chambers in 2001.

BRABENDER, Lynda J
Westwater Advocates, Edinburgh
0131 226 5071
lynda.brabender@btinternet.com
Featured in Family/Matrimonial (Scotland)
Practice Areas: Family law - divorce, cohabitation, financial provision, contact, residence, relocation, child abduction, adoption, permanence orders, education, children's hearings, judicial review and devolution issues. First instance and appellate. Cases include: Glasgow City Council, Petitioners 2013 SLT 917 (judicial review, children's hearings); B v B 2012 Fam LR 65 (divorce, special circumstances); K v North Ayrshire Council 2012 SLT 381 (judicial review, education); O v Aberdeen City Council 2012 SC 60 (statutory interpretation); Principal Reporter v K [2011] 1 WLR 18 (unmarried fathers, human rights); Selkirk v Chisholm 2011 Fam LR 56 (cohabitation); Edinburgh City Council, Petitioner 2010 Fam LR 92 (permanence orders, devolution issue, statutory interpretation); Authority Reporter v S 2010 SC 531 (unmarried fathers, contact orders, human rights); Price v Baxter 2009 Fam LR 138 (husband and wife, revocation of wills, minutes of agreement); Savage v Purches 2009 SLT (Sh Ct) 36 (cohabitation, intestacy); Brown v Robertson 2009 Fam LR 13 (divorce, farming partnerships, dissolution, avoidance transactions); C v C 2008 SCLR 329 (international child abduction, for 11 year old, concealment, settlement); S v D 2007 SLT (Sh Ct) 37 (Council Regulation 2201/2003 (Brussels II bis), cross border proceedings Scotland and England); Clark v Clark (No 2) 2007 SLT (Sh Ct) 86 (division of farming partnership assets on divorce); and Treasure v McGrath 2006 Fam LR 100 (parental responsibilities and parental rights).
Professional Memberships: Member of the Scottish Civil Justice Council Family Law

Committee from 2014; Member of the Faculty of Advocates Disciplinary Tribunals from 2013; Faculty Council Member from 2010 to 2013; Committee Member, Advocates Family Law Association 2007 to 2014; Convener of the Additional Support Needs Tribunal for Scotland from 2005 to 2010.
Career: Called to the Bar in 2005; Solicitor in Scotland 1997-2004.

BRACE, Michael
Civitas Law, Cardiff
0845 071 3007
michael.brace@civitaslaw.com
Featured in Clinical Negligence (Wales & Chester), Personal Injury (Wales & Chester), Personal Injury (All Circuits)
Practice Areas: Michael is a personal injury and clinical negligence specialist. He has particular expertise in industrial disease claims most notably those in relation to asbestos exposure. His personal injury and clinical negligence practice encompasses high-value claims with a significant proportion of such work involving fatal claims and those in respect of catastrophic injury.
Professional Memberships: APIL, PIBA & AvMA.
Career: Called to the Bar 1991. General Provincial Panel of Treasury Counsel: 2000-07. Panel of Counsel for the Welsh Assembly Government: 2000-07. Michael is an ADR Group Accredited Mediator and a Pupil Supervisor.

BRADLEY, Matthew
Henderson Chambers, London
020 7583 9020
mbradley@hendersonchambers.co.uk
Featured in Product Liability (London)
Practice Areas: Commercial and civil law. Product liability and group actions, sale of goods and supply of services, financial services, consumer credit, insurance, professional negligence, product recall, property damage, insolvency, injunctive work, economic torts, international torts, conflicts of laws. Employment, including restrictive covenants and confidentiality cases and dual High Court/ET proceedings. Public procurement and public law. Property law. Health and safety. Has appeared in Chancery and QBD trials, Court of Appeal and EAT. Junior counsel in Sabril litigation (pharmaceutical product liability), petrol contamination litigation, public procurement and international tort claims. Further details: see chambers website.
Professional Memberships: COMBAR, HSLA, LCLCBA, ELA.
Career: Oxford University (French & German – 1st Class), Lord Woolf Scholar (Daily Telegraph/1 Crown Office Row); Hardwicke, Haldane & Thomas Moore Scholar (Lincoln's Inn); Phoenicia Scholar (Bar European Group). Called: 2004.
Publications: Author of "Product Recall in the EU" chapter in the International Product Law Manual 2011/12 (Kluwer). Various articles.
Personal: Married with children. Languages: French, German and Spanish.

BRADY, Jane
Cornwall Street Chambers, Oxford
01865 311 066
jane.brady@cornwallstreet.co.uk
Featured in Crime (South Eastern)
Practice Areas: Crime.
Professional Memberships: Criminal Bar Association, South Eastern Circuit, Thames Valley Bar Mess.
Career: Jane has thirteen years' experience as an Advocate with a busy criminal caseload. For nearly a decade she has enjoyed a successful practice in the Thames Valley, based in Oxford, where she both prosecutes (Grade 3 plus rape) and defends. Her competence and flair was recognised early in her career in Leeds, when at 2 years' call she was instructed to represent a 13 year old charged with murder. Jane's caseload is a mix of high-level criminal matters, often involving very young or vulnerable complainants and defendants, including: Serious violence; Conspiracies including Class A drugs; Arson; Fraud; Rape and serious sexual offences. Jane's languages and accounts background make her a natural and approachable expert in cases where interpreters and figures are involved. Her case preparation, fairness and good judgement have attracted favourable judicial comment, and she is known always to go the extra mile. She has only been to the Court of Appeal once on her own case, and has a 100% success rate there as a result. Jane is an Advocate, Junior of the Mess and active member of Chambers, who takes great pride in her profession and work.

BRAITHWAITE, Thomas
Serle Court, London
020 7242 6105
tbraithwaite@serlecourt.co.uk
Featured in Partnership (London), Real Estate Litigation (London)
Practice Areas: Commercial chancery litigation, including in particular real property, partnership, company, professional negligence and contractual disputes. Cases include Crown Estate v. Roberts [2008] Ch. 439 (CA), Amin v. Amin [2009] EWHC 3356 (Ch), Regus v. Epcot Solutions [2009] 1 All ER (Comm) 586, and Lictor v Mir Steel [2011] EWHC 3310 (Ch.).
Professional Memberships: COMBAR, Chancery Bar Association, Property Bar Association.
Personal: Born 1975. Educated at Clifton and Jesus College, Cambridge 1994-97 (MA double first class; George Long Prize for Civil Law, Hamson Prize for Obligations). Called to the Bar 1998 (Thomas More Bursar and Kennedy Scholar of Lincoln's Inn). Married, with one daughter.

BRANDON, Stephen QC
Tax Chambers 15 Old Square, London
020 7242 2744
s.brandon@15oldsquare.co.uk
Featured in Tax (London)
Practice Areas: All aspects of tax law for corporates and private clients. Particularly experienced in business taxation including international transactions, Treaty Relief, intangible financial assets, advising foreign domiciled individuals, entrepreneurs and on employee remuneration issues. Welcomes litigation and has conducted appeals to the First Tier and Upper-tier Tribunals (previously Commissioners/VAT Tribunals/ Transactions in Securities Tribunal) and up to the House of Lords and before foreign tax tribunals. Experienced at in-depth analysis of complex anti-avoidance provisions in negotiations with HMRC.
Professional Memberships: Fellow of the institute of Taxation. Member of Revenue Bar Association.
Career: Called to Bar in 1978, university lecturer before practising. Took Silk in 1996. Head of Chambers 2007 to date.
Publications: Publications include 'Taxation of Non-Resident and Migrant Companies' (Key Haven, 1989), 'Taxation of Non-UK Resident Companies and Their Shareholders' (2005) and numerous articles.
Personal: Married with one daughter. Lives in rural Northamptonshire and central London.

BRANNIGAN, Sean QC
4 Pump Court, London
020 7842 5555
sbrannigan@4pumpcourt.com
Featured in Construction (London), Energy & Natural Resources (London), International Arbitration (London), Professional Negligence (London)
Practice Areas: Commercial disputes focusing first and foremost on advocacy in both court and arbitrations. Particular expertise in construction, professional negligence and energy and natural resources disputes. Extensive experience of international arbitrations and cross-border litigation in London, Dublin, Paris, Geneva, the Middle East and the USA. Qualified mediator. Represents employers, contractors, professionals, insurers and various national governments.
Professional Memberships: Dually called to the Northern Irish Bar. Member of COMBAR, Technology and Construction Bar Association, London Common Law and Commercial Bar Association, LCIA Users' Council.
Career: BA (Oxon) in Jurisprudence. Called in 1994. Silk in 2009.

BRANSTON, Barnabas
5 Essex Court, London
020 7410 2000
branston@5essexcourt.co.uk
Featured in Police Law (All Circuits)
Practice Areas: Coroners' Inquests (on behalf of Chief Officers in police inquests and on behalf of Serco Home Affairs where there has been a death in custody) Civil Actions Against the Police (Defendant) in claims for assault, wrongful arrest/false imprisonment, malicious prosecution and misfeasance Regulatory and Disciplinary (presenting and legal advising before Police Misconduct Hearings, legal assessor in hearings before the Nursing and Midwifery Council) Health and Safety (defending alleged or actual breaches of the usual raft of regulations) Personal Injury (Claimant and Defendant) Public Law (on behalf of Chief Officers)
Professional Memberships: ARDL; PIBA.
Career: Called to the Bar in 1999; Infantry Officer (Welsh Guards, 1992-97).
Personal: Barney is married with three children, lives in Shropshire and his outside interests include sport and games (especially rugby and cricket), the Welsh Guards, and looking after his chickens, pigs and spaniel.

BRASLAVSKY, Nicholas QC
Kings Chambers, Manchester
0845 034 3444
clerks@kingschambers.com
Featured in Clinical Negligence (Northern), Personal Injury (Northern)
Practice Areas: Principal areas of practice: personal injury and clinical negligence litigation predominantly in cases of the highest value and complexity including road traffic, employers and public liability, military and recreational/transport cases, birth damage and other clinical negligence disputes. Particularly catastrophic injury litigation including neuro and spinal injury for claimants and major insurers. Also, regulatory and disciplinary cases for medical and other professionals and regulatory authorities. Health and safety cases. Chambers in Manchester, Leeds, Birmingham and London.
Professional Memberships: Personal Injury Bar Association.
Career: Birmingham University 1976-82; LLB (Hons) 1979; PhD 1982. Called 1983 (Inner Temple); Silk 1999; Recorder 2001. Deputy High Court Judge 2008. Head of Chambers and Head of Recruitment, Kings Chambers. Sports Resolution Panel (2012); Honorary lecturer School of Law, Manchester University 2012.

BRASSINGTON, Stephen
2 Hare Court, London
020 7353 5324
stephenbrassington@2harecourt.com
Featured in Professional Discipline (London)
Practice Areas: Stephen Brassington is rightly regarded as one of the leading juniors in the field of Professional Discipline and Regulation. A "class operator" who is "forthright and doesn't take any nonsense" (Chambers UK, 2013), "He is excellent – leaves no stone unturned and gets excellent results" (Chambers UK, 2014) and he "does the job brilliantly with great humour and charm" (Chambers UK, 2011). Also cited as a leading junior in this field by The Legal 500, which describes him as "Impressively effective", Stephen is in great demand to defend professionals whose fitness to practise has been called into question. "A natural advocate, who will go the extra mile to provide a good service to his client" (Chambers UK, 2010) Stephen has a significant practice representing Professionals at the GMC, GDC and other regulators, as well as in the Administrative / High Court and at Coroners' Inquests, and NHS England and Trust Disciplinary Hearings. He also advises on specialist register appeals, and accepts work on a direct access basis. He also represents such professionals in the criminal courts, where he has experience of cases involving murder, major fraud, money laundering and drug importation, amongst other offences, and particularly where such proceedings are concurrent with regulatory proceedings. He also undertakes work outside of the healthcare sector, and in particular is instructed by the Football Association to prosecute serious cases of misconduct. Stephen leads the 2 Hare Court team contracted to advise the National Council for Teaching and Leadership, and present complex and serious cases on their behalf involving the making of prohibition orders against teachers. Stephen also leads the 2 Hare Court Professional Regulation practice group.
Professional Memberships: ARDL; Criminal Bar Association.
Career: Called 1994 (Inner Temple).

BRAZIL, Dominic
1 King's Bench Walk, London
020 7936 1500
dbrazil@1kbw.co.uk
Featured in Family/Matrimonial (London)
Practice Areas: Matrimonial finance, children (private law) and often involved in matrimonial finance cases with equitable property claims by third parties and, most particularly, cases involving family trusts.

Recent cases of note: F v. F (Pre-Nuptial Agreement) [2010] 1 FLR 1743, F v. F (Divorce; Jurisdiction) [2009] 2 FLR 1496, N v. R (Injunction) [2009] 2 FLR 1496 and Rossi v. Rossi [2007] 1 FLR 790, RK v. RK [2011] EWHC 3910 (Fam).
Professional Memberships: FLBA.
Career: Worcester College, Oxford. CPE London Guildhall University. Astbury Scholar, Middle Temple.
Publications: Blackstones Guide to The Civil Partnership Act 2004.

BREDEMEAR, Zachary
1 Chancery Lane, London
020 7092 2900
zbredemear@1chancerylane.com
Featured in Real Estate Litigation (London)
Practice Areas: Zachary's practice covers all aspects of property litigation as well as professional negligence and commercial law. In the field of property law he has particular expertise and experience of commercial landlord and tenant work and is frequently involved in cases concerning forfeiture, tenant insolvency, dilapidations and business tenancies. His other property work includes restrictive covenants, easements, mortgages, joint ownership and vendor/purchaser disputes. Zachary has an extensive professional negligence practise, mostly dealing with claims against surveyors, architects and solicitors carrying out conveyancing or conducting litigation.
Professional Memberships: Chancery Bar Association; Professional Negligence Bar Association; Property Bar Association.
Career: Called to the Bar in 1996, Inner Temple.
Personal: Interests include cycling, theatre and watching Arsenal.

BREMNER, Jonathan
Pump Court Tax Chambers, London
020 7414 8080
clerks@pumptax.com
Featured in Tax (London)
Practice Areas: Jonathan practises in all areas of tax law. He advises on the major UK taxes and acts in tax appeals and tax-related litigation before the specialist tribunals and the higher courts. Recent cases include: the FII Group Litigation (Ch); Airtours v HMRC (Court of Appeal); Isle of Wight v HMRC (Upper Tribunal); Murray Group v HMRC (Upper Tribunal); Mehjoo v Harben Barker (Court of Appeal); MG Rover v HMRC (First-tier Tribunal); Aspinalls Club v HMRC (Court of Appeal); HMRC v Newey (CJEU).
Professional Memberships: Revenue Bar Association; VAT Practitioners Group; Chancery Bar Association.
Career: Called 2005 (Inner Temple); March 2011 – Appointed Junior Counsel to the Crown (C panel); March 2014 – Appointed Junior Counsel to the Crown (B panel).

BRENNAN, John
St Philips Chambers, Birmingham
0121 246 7000
jbrennan@st-philips.com
Featured in Chancery (Midlands), Commercial Dispute Resolution (Midlands)
Practice Areas: Broad range of commercial and chancery work; notably banking, commercial fraud, landlord and tenant, partnership, professional negligence, property, restraint of trade, trusts, and wills and probate. He aims to provide clear, reliable advice and a user friendly service.
Professional Memberships: Chancery Bar Association, Midland Commercial and Chancery Bar Association.
Career: Called 1996.
Personal: Born 1972. Educated at King Edward's School Birmingham and Jesus College, Oxford (MA, Modern History). Interested in politics, history and sport.

BRENNAN, Timothy QC
Devereux, London
020 7353 7534
clerks@devchambers.co.uk
Featured in Employment (London), Tax (London)
Practice Areas: Public and commercial law, including tax litigation and advice, judicial review, employment, professional discipline. Scores of reported cases in those fields, including many in House of Lords/UKSC as well as in Strasbourg and Hong Kong. Particular expertise in employment remuneration and its taxation.
Professional Memberships: Member of Revenue, Employment and Administrative Law Bar Associations, COMBAR.
Career: Call 1981 (Atkin Scholar of Gray's Inn). QC 2001. Elected Head of Chambers, 2013. Deputy High Court Judge (QBD, Administrative Court and Chancery Division) 2008. Bencher, Gray's Inn 2006. Recorder 2000. Judge, EAT 2002-04. Junior Counsel to Inland Revenue 1997-2001. Assistant Recorder 1997.
Publications: Contributing editor: 'Harvey: Industrial Relations and Employment Law' (LexisNexis), including division on Taxation of Employment Income.
Personal: Balliol College, Oxford, BCL MA. Trustee of London Welsh Trust. Interests include cycling and other sports, opera and choral music.

BRIDGE, Ian
No5 Chambers, Birmingham
0845 210 5555
ib@no5.com
Featured in Financial Crime (The Regions)
Practice Areas: Ian Bridge acts for companies and individuals facing allegations of fraud and money laundering. He prosecutes and defends and undertakes related civil work in the field of regulatory law. He works nationwide and internationally. Over a 25 year career he has been instructed in numerous high profile criminal and civil cases. "He is an excellent advocate as well as being good on the law - if there is a way through in any particular case Ian Bridge will find it." Over the last 15 years he has defended in numerous substantial tax frauds covering direct and indirect tax, excise duty, landfill tax, CIS scheme, film schemes and pension frauds. He has been instructed in numerous investment frauds, fraudulent importations and mortgage frauds. He has considerable experience of very substantial money laundering allegations. He has been instructed in a number of election frauds. He is regularly instructed in confiscation proceedings. He is instructed in the tax tribunals where he has been successful on behalf of Appellants facing allegations of knowing involvement in transactions connected to fraud. In regulatory law Ian Bridge is instructed in fatal and serious injury accident cases in the field of health and safety at work and road traffic. He has a particular expertise in defending allegations of causing death/serious injury by dangerous/careless driving. He is regularly instructed in inquests. He also has particular experience in healthcare cases arising from incidents in hospitals and care homes. He is instructed in all manner of other regulatory cases including professional discipline, trading standards and breach of copyright (alleged online piracy). He has lectured and produced training materials for corporate clients on the Bribery Act. He advises and represents companies and individuals facing regulatory investigation and is happy to assist in corporate disciplinary investigation procedures and advise on appropriate steps. He welcomes direct access clients.

BRIGGS, John
South Square, London
020 7696 9900
johnbriggs@southsquare.com
Featured in Restructuring/Insolvency (London)
Practice Areas: Insolvency – corporate, personal and international. Instructed in a number of high profile bankruptcies and insolvent partnerships in recent years including Asil Nadir, Jonathan Aitken, Mark Goldberg, Terry Ramsden, Jan Bonde Nielson, Kerry Katona and Sean Quinn.
Professional Memberships: COMBAR, Chancery Bar Association, Insolvency Lawyers' Association, INSOL International, INSOL Europe & R3.
Career: Called to the Bar of England and Wales (Gray's Inn) 1973; Jurist Linguist at European Court of Justice 1973-75; in practice as barrister 1976-to date; Deputy Bankruptcy and Companies Registrar of High Court 1989-to date; called to the Northern Ireland Bar 2011.
Publications: Joint senior author of 'Muir Hunter on Personal Insolvency' (Thompson, Sweet and Maxwell); joint author of 'Asset Protection Trusts' (Key haven); contributor to 'Rayden on Divorce' (18th ed Butterworths) - author of chapter on 'Bankruptcy, insolvency and ancillary relief', contributor to Cross Border Insolvency (Sheldon-Bloomsbury Professional).
Personal: Born 1949; resides London.

BRIGHT, Christopher QC
No5 Chambers, Birmingham
0845 210 0555
cb@no5.com
Featured in Clinical Negligence (Midlands), Personal Injury (Midlands)
Practice Areas: A leading personal injury/clinical negligence specialist, working nationwide for both claimants and defendants. Has specialised for many years in catastrophic brain injury, cerebral palsy/neonatal hypoglycaemia, cancer, spinal injury/surgery and high value fatal accident cases. Is highly regarded for his user-friendly and sensitive approach and for his expertise in complex claims involving issues of PCT/LA statutory care funding and periodical payments. Has been variously described as "first rate" and a "leading silk", "doing work countrywide", providing "well thought through, detailed advice" and "a helpful and considerate advocate", having "outstanding attention to detail", being "highly proactive and pragmatic" and "extremely busy". Is noted for his "considerable expertise", his "ability to handle the most complex matters" and being "able quickly to identify the legal issues involved in a case".
Professional Memberships: APIL/AvMA.
Career: Durham University BA Hons. Crown and County Court Recorder. Bencher of Gray's Inn. Regularly lectures to claimant and defendant solicitors/insurers and specialist organisations (such as the Spinal Injuries Association and Headway) upon subjects such as litigating head/spinal injury and cerebral palsy claims, Fatal Accidents Act litigation, the use of experts, statutory funding and periodical payments. Also lectures upon and chairs AvMA courses.
Personal: Interests: An old Mill in Tuscany and Gloucester Rugby Club.

BRIGHTWELL, James
New Square Chambers, London
020 7419 8000
clerks@newsquarechambers.co.uk
Featured in Chancery (London), Offshore (London)
Practice Areas: James Brightwell specialises in contentious and non-contentious private client work, including tax, the administration of estates, contentious probate, family provision, trustee applications, the variation of trusts, trusts of land and claims concerning professional liability in these areas. Much of his work involves offshore trusts and he has particular experience of claims for breach of trust and of issues concerning the removal of trustees. Recent cases include Alhamrani v Alhamrani (Jersey), Freeman v Ansbacher, BTA Bank v Stepanov, Schomberg v Taylor, Investec Trust (Guernsey) Limited v Oscatello, Alhamrani v Alhamrani (BVI).
Professional Memberships: Chancery Bar Association, ACTAPS.
Career: Called to the Bar 2000; Called to the Bar of the Eastern Caribbean in the British Virgin Islands; Deputy District Judge (Civil) 2010.
Publications: Co-author of Lewin on Trusts, 18th edition (19th edition forthcoming); Atkin's Court Forms, Nuisance, Halsbury's Laws, Income Taxation (forthcoming).
Personal: Born 1976. Educated in New Zealand; Emmanuel College, Cambridge MA, LLM. Lives in Yorkshire and London.

BRITTENDEN, Stuart
Old Square Chambers, London
020 7269 0300
brittenden@oldsquare.co.uk
Featured in Employment (London)
Practice Areas: Stuart is an employment law specialist with extensive experience acting for both sides in all aspects of individual and collective employment law at both first instance and appellate level. He regularly acts in complex/ high value claims and matters involving an equal opportunities dimension. Recent cases include: Anderson & Ors v LFEPA [2013] IRLR 459 CA (contractual interpretation of collective agreement, incorporation); HM Land Registry v Benson & Ors [2012] IRLR 373 EAT (indirect age discrimination/justification); Victoria & Albert Museum v Durrant [2011] IRLR 290 EAT (reason for dismissal/replacements); and Johnson Controls Limited v UKAEA first appellate authority on service provision changes where the activity is brought in-house under reg 3(1)(b)(iii) TUPE Regulations 2006.
Professional Memberships: ELBA, ELA Management Committee (2012-14), IER, ILS.
Career: Prior to joining Chambers, Stuart attained a Masters in Labour Law at the London School of Economics (LSE), and worked as an Employment Law Advisor to the British Dental Association (BDA). He has lectured in Labour Law at the LSE and has published in the employment field.

Publications: Tolley's Employment Law - co-author of Unfair Dismissal Chapter. Employment Precedents & Company Policy Documents - author of chapters on disciplinary/grievance procedures; trade union recognition; works councils. Munkman on Employer's Liability - author of 2 chapters. Westlaw Insight - author/co-author to 17 chapters.

BROMPTON, Michael QC
5 Paper Buildings, London
020 7583 6117
mjb@5pb.co.uk
Featured in Crime (London)

Practice Areas: Prosecutes and defends in serious and complex crime. His specialist fields include revenue fraud, insider trading and investment fraud, money laundering, drugs trafficking, confiscation and asset forfeiture. Formerly Standing Counsel to H.M. Customs and Excise, he has appeared in numerous high profile drugs cases and is prominent in the field of VAT fraud having appeared in many of the major cases of the past decade. He has also defended in numerous murders including, for instance, the alleged killing of a new-born baby by his mother and the contract killing of a solicitor's wife. His recent or pending cases include: a £130 million MTIC fraud (HMRC Operation Inertia); the prosecution of a management consultant for insider trading (instructed by the FSA); an £80 million carousel fraud (HMRC Operation Vex); a major investment fraud (instructed by the FCA); a multi-million pound mobile phone highjacking fraud; a £100 million bureau de change money laundering prosecution; the criminal investigation of an alleged tax avoidance scheme. He has lectured on tax and other serious fraud including, most recently, in LexisNexis webinars.

Career: Called Middle Temple 1973. Standing Counsel to H.M. Customs & Excise 1994-2003. QC 2003. Recorder of the Crown Court since 2006. Member of the Serious Fraud Office panel of Queen's Counsel. Head of Chambers 5PB, 2009-14.

BROOK SMITH, Philip QC
Fountain Court Chambers, London
020 7583 3335
pbs@fountaincourt.co.uk
Featured in Product Liability (London)

Practice Areas: Wide-ranging practice covers a broad spread of commercial and common law work with considerable experience of product liability issues. Instructed in (for example) HIV Haemophilia, Hepatitis C, Oral Contraceptives, MMR group litigation and PIP breast implants litigation. Wider commercial and general civil work undertaken includes banking disputes, financial markets, insurance/reinsurance, aviation, oil and gas, international arbitration work, anti-suit claims, competition, employment, professional negligence claims - particularly accountants' and solicitors', and all commercial fraud. Notable cases include the Jahre case (civil fraud, trusts). Extensive experience of offshore jurisdictions (particularly as regards financial services).

Professional Memberships: Common Law and Commercial Bar Association; South Eastern Circuit.

Career: Called to the Bar in 1982, joined Fountain Court Chambers in 1983, appointed QC in 2002.

Personal: Educated at the London School of Economics (BSc Mathematics - 1st Class Hons) and London University (MSc Mathematics - distinction). Born 6 March 1957. Lives in London.

BROOKS, Duncan
Queen Elizabeth Building, London
020 7797 7837
d.brooks@qeb.co.uk
Featured in Family/Matrimonial (London)

Practice Areas: Matrimonial finance (particularly international cases); private law children; family law-related common law (cohabitation disputes; professional negligence). Reported cases: Mittal v Mittal [2013] EWCA Civ 1255, [2014] 1 FLR 1514, Hope v Krejci & Others [2012] EWHC 1780 (Fam); [2012] All ER (D) 215 (Jul), K v L [2011] EWCA Civ 550 (with Lucy Stone QC), Re S (A Child) [2010] EWCA Civ 705, [2011] 1 FLR 183 (CA), Re B; Re S (Removal from Jurisdiction) [2003] 2 FLR 1043 (CA), GW v RW [2003] 2 FLR 108 (with Lewis Marks QC).

Professional Memberships: Family Law Bar Association; Resolution; International Bar Association.

Career: LLB Hons (Durham) 1999. Lord Justice Holker Award (Gray's Inn) 1999/2000. Bar Vocational Course (Inns of Court School of Law) 2000. Tenant at QEB since October 2001. Collaborative Lawyer (Resolution trained) since January 2009. Deputy District Judge Civil (2010). Family Arbitrator (MCI Arb) 2013.

Publications: Podcast for Jordans Publishing on businesses in matrimonial finance cases (2010). Freezing Orders and Orders to Set Aside Transactions [2007] Fam Law 1089.

BROOKS, Peter
9 Park Place, Cardiff
01685 721 172
peterbrooksb@rrister.wanadoo.co.uk
Featured in Personal Injury (Wales & Chester)

Practice Areas: Personal injury and clinical negligence specialist with particular interest in traumatic head injuries and severe multiple injuries. High Court, County Court (multi track) and CICA work undertaken. Joint settlement meetings and mediations in all PI cases may be held at Chambers by prior arrangement.

Professional Memberships: Personal Injury Bar Association, Welsh Personal Injury Lawyers Association.

Career: Called 1986. Undertakes legal expense insurance and collective/conditional fee funded work.

Publications: Numerous cited traumatic head, sports and other PI cases in the Law Reports, PIQR, Lloyds Medical Reports, Kemp, Current Law and Butterworths Personal Injury Service.

Personal: Liverpool University and Gray's Inn. Accredited Law Society personal injury lecturer for purpose of containing education. Recreational interests: Fine wine investment, philately, golf and country pursuits.

BROWN, Anne
Pump Court Chambers, Winchester
020 7353 0711
a.brown@pumpcourtchambers.com
Featured in Crime (Western)

Practice Areas: Formidable trial advocate with particular expertise in prosecuting and defending serious sexual violence and child abuse cases. Strong reputation for cases requiring skilful cross-examination, particularly of vulnerable witnesses, and meticulous consideration of unused material. Anne also defends senior and junior ranked military personnel in Court Martial hearings.

Professional Memberships: Criminal Bar Association, Forensic Science Society, American Bar Association, New York State Bar Association, JUSTICE.

Career: Called Middle Temple 2000, Called to the State Bar of New York on 27th June 2006, Pupil supervisor since 2008.

Personal: MA (Oxon) Jurisprudence 1998.

BROWN, Catherine
12 King's Bench Walk, London
020 7583 0811
chambers@12kbw.co.uk
Featured in Personal Injury (London)

Practice Areas: Catherine has a specialist personal injury and health and safety practice. She has particular expertise in public authority claims, including stress, education, highways, child abuse and property damage claims. She represents defendants in complex health and safety prosecutions and at inquests.

Professional Memberships: PIBA; PNBA; HSLA; SE Circuit; AWB.

Career: Called 1990 (Middle Temple); Recorder (Wales) (2008) (crime & civil); SE Circuit advocacy trainer (Keble); BSB Professional Conduct Committee. Interesting cases: R(Epping Forest DC) v Casterbridge Care and Education Ltd (2013); R(HSE) v Tennant (2013); R v Collier (2012); R(Herts CC) v Menna (2012); Armstrong v Keepmoat Homes Ltd (QBD 3/2/12); Thomas v Warwickshire CC [2011] EWHC 772 (QB); Rhiya Malin Inquest (2010); Harvey v Plymouth CC [2010] EWCA Civ 860; [2010] PIQR P18; Button v Caerphilly CBC [2010] EWCA Civ 1311; Maloney v Torfaen CBC [2005] EWCA Civ 1762; [2006] PIQR P21; Wallis v Balfour Beatty [2003] EWCA Civ 72.

Publications: Co-editor: Occupational Illness Litigation, Occupational Stress Chapter.

Personal: Nonsuch High School for Girls, Cheam; Birmingham University (B Com (Hons)); PCL (Diploma in Law).

BROWN, Christopher
Matrix Chambers, London
020 7404 3447
christopherbrown@matrixlaw.co.uk
Featured in Competition/European Law (London)

Practice Areas: EU/competition law; public procurement law; public law; sports law; commercial law. Recent cases include WM Morrison v MasterCard; WM Morrison v Visa (claims for damages arising from interchange fee arrangements), Somerfield v OFT and Co-operative Group v Office of Fair Trading (challenges to OFT's Tobacco decision), R (Sky Blue Sports and Leisure) v Coventry City Council (State aid challenge to financing of a sports arena); Singapore Airlines v Commission (acting for Commission in defence of its Airfreight cartel decision, General Court, pending), Stagecoach v Competition Commission (successful challenge to Preston Bus merger decision on Wednesbury unreasonableness grounds, CAT), R (Gallastegui) v SoS for the Home Department (challenge to ECHR compatibility of restrictions on long-term protest in Parliament Square, Div Ct).

Career: Called 2002; Referendaire, Competition Appeal Tribunal (2004-07); Barrister, Farrer & Co LLP (2007-09); Matrix Chambers 2009-.

Publications: Contributor, Bellamy & Child's European Union Law of Competition; Co-author, EU Competition Law: Procedure and Remedies (OUP); Co-author, Blackstone's Guide to The Human Rights Act 1998 (6th ed); Co-editor, Competition Law Journal; joint UK rapporteur, FIDE Congress, November 2010: "The Judicial Application of the EU Competition Rules".

BROWN, Edward QC
QEB Hollis Whiteman, London
020 7933 8855
edward.brown@qebhw.co.uk
Featured in Crime (London)

Practice Areas: Edward Brown QC has an outstanding practice in criminal law and related areas (disciplinary, regulatory, health and safety, inquests), chiefly at the Central Criminal Court where he was Senior Treasury Counsel for six years. He has prosecuted or defended in many of the most notable and sensitive cases, including terrorism, murder, 'shaken baby' deaths, corporate manslaughter, police and political corruption, firearms, export control evasion, fraud and rape. Examples include the Mark Duggan shooting; the 'cash for peerages' police inquiry, acting for the Labour Party (no charges were brought); the leading cases on the anonymity of witnesses (R v Mayers, R v Davis); R v Barot (the 'dirty bomber'); and the gang shooting of the five-year-old Thusha Kamaleswaran. He has advised Attorneys General on numerous cases, and has been consulted by the then Solicitor General (and has given seminars) on Deferred Prosecution Agreements. He gives lectures to young south London gang members on the consequences of gang violence.

Professional Memberships: He has been a member of the Criminal Bar Association steering party on involuntary manslaughter, CPS Steering Committee reviewing disclosure (resulting in the CPS Disclosure Manual), UN Detention Review Board, Kosovo.

Career: Silk 2008; call 1983.

Publications: He has written on joint enterprise in The Times.

Personal: University College of Buckingham; Université de Grenoble.

BROWN, Emma
No5 Chambers, Birmingham
0845 210 5555
eb@no5.com
Featured in Clinical Negligence (Midlands)

Practice Areas: All areas of clinical negligence for both claimant and defendant with particular experience of claims arising from general practice, emergency medicine, ophthalmology, oncology, obstetrics and gynecology. Increasing experience of complex brain injury and spinal injury claims. Extensive inquest practice acting for families, NHS Trusts, private care providers, H. M. Prison Service and the Ministry of Defence. Places a considerable emphasis on client care ensuring clients and witnesses thoroughly understand the nature of the proceedings, the prospects of success and the potential range of outcomes. Led regularly in high value, complex clinical negligence and personal injury claims. Trademarks include a thorough, straight-talking and practical approach to litigation.

Professional Memberships: Action against Medical Accidents, Personal Injury Bar Association, Coroner's Society.
Career: LLB (Dunelm) 2000. Called to the Bar 2001. Treasury Counsel 2008-12. Assistant Coroner for the District of Birmingham and Solihull 2014 onwards.
Personal: Married, two sons.

BROWN, Marc
St Philips Chambers, Birmingham
0121 246 7000
mbrown@st-philips.com
Featured in Commercial Dispute Resolution (Midlands), Restructuring/Insolvency (Midlands)
Practice Areas: Marc's practice comprises both general commercial and insolvency work. His practice encompasses the full spectrum of commercial disputes, with an emphasis on banking, financial and contractual disputes. Marc's insolvency practice is wide ranging, covering both personal and corporate insolvency. He acts for directors, companies and individuals as well as administrators, liquidators and trustees in bankruptcy. See for example Re: BTR (UK) Ltd [2012] EWHC 2398 (Ch) and Re: Care People Ltd [2013] EWHC 1734 (Ch). Marc has a particular interest in cases involving the determination of a debtor's Centre of Main Interests under the EU Insolvency Regulation (so-called "bankruptcy tourism" cases), see for example Re: Benk [2012] EWHC 2432 (Ch).
Professional Memberships: MCCBA.
Career: Marc studied law (jurisprudence) at Mansfield College, Oxford University. He was called in 2004 and then returned to Oxford University to undertake the Bachelor of Civil Laws, a postgraduate degree in law, in which he obtained the prestigious Vinerian Scholarship. Having completed pupillage at St Philips Chambers, he started practice in 2006. Marc appeared in the House of Lords early in his career in OBG v Allan [2007] UKHL 21, a case concerning the liability of invalidly appointed receivers, and the leading authority on the economic torts.
Personal: Marc's leisure interests include golf, mountainboarding and snowboarding.

BROWN, Robert
Arden Chambers, London
020 7242 4244
robert.brown@ardenchambers.com
Featured in Social Housing (London)
Practice Areas: Landlord and tenant, property, public law, and housing. He acts for local authorities, housing associations, private landlords and tenants. He appears in the County Court, High Court, LVT/FTT(PC) and has recently appeared in the Court of Appeal.
Career: BA (Hons), LLB (Hons). Called 2008. Awarded the Sir Louis Gluckstein Prize for Advocacy by Lincoln's Inn. He has previously worked in local government, the Civil Service, higher education and the Third Sector. Significant cases include Manchester v Pinnock [2010] UKSC 45 (as pupil, led by Andrew Arden QC; Jonathan Manning); Hounslow v Powell [2011] UKSC 8 (led by Andrew Arden QC; Jonathan Manning); Zafar v Goddard, Legal Action April 2011; and R (GCLC) v Greenwich [2012] EWCA Civ 496 (led by Jonathan Manning).
Publications: He has been an editor of the Housing Law Reports (Sweet and Maxwell) since 2012. He is a co-author of Judicial Review Proceedings - A Practitioner's Guide (LAG, 2013) and Current Law Statutes annotations for Localism Act 2011 and Local Government Finance Act 2012. He writes regularly for the Journal of Housing Law and is a headnote writer for the European Human Rights Reports. He also contributes to the RICS isurv service.

BROWN, Thomas
Cloisters, London
020 7827 4000
tb@cloisters.com
Featured in Employment (London)
Practice Areas: Tom specialises in employment and equality law, and has experience and expertise in wider partnership, commercial, regulatory, public law and human rights advice and litigation. He acts for companies, charities and public authorities, trade unions and individuals. He has substantial experience of appellate and High Court litigation without a leader. In addition to several high-profile trials, his significant appellate cases include UCU v. Stirling University (collective redundancy consultation), RR Donnelly Global v. Besagni (TUPE), Buckland v. Bournemouth University (breach of contract) and Thaine v. London School of Economics (apportionment of damages).
Professional Memberships: ELA, ELBA, ILS.
Career: Tenant at Cloisters since 2001; Judicial Assistant to Lord Bingham of Cornhill (2002—2003); secondment, commercial litigation department, Mallesons, Melbourne (2005); Associate, Federal Court of Australia (2005); secondment, Stewarts Law LLP (2012—2013).
Publications: Discrimination in Employment (Legal Action Group, 2013); Blackstone's Guide to the Equality Act 2010 (OUP, 2012); Family Rights At Work (Jordans, 2012).
Personal: Educated at the BRIT School, London; King Edward VI College, Nuneaton; Merton College, Oxford (first class honours; college and university scholar) and City University (DipLaw). Middle Temple and Pegasus scholar. Tom is a keen competitive oarsman.

BROWN, Tim
Temple Tax Chambers, London
020 7353 7884
tim@timothybrown.co.uk
Featured in Tax (London)
Practice Areas: All areas of VAT, customs duty, excise duty and investigations, including Capital Goods Scheme, charities, clubs and associations, construction, cross-border transactions, hotels and holiday accommodation, land and property, MTIC, partial exemption, penalties, zero-rating, BTI's, import classification, movement guarantees and warehousing. Recent cases include Roden v. HMRC, SHS International v HMRC, Magdalene College v. HMRC, TNT (UK) v. HMRC, ETOA v HMRC, Vehicle Control Services v HMRC.
Professional Memberships: Revenue Bar Association, Bar European Group.
Personal: Born April 1964. Captain England Schoolboys U18 football team 1981-82.

BROWNE, Benjamin QC
2TG - 2 Temple Gardens, London
020 7822 1203
bbrowne@2tg.co.uk
Featured in Clinical Negligence (London), Personal Injury (London), Travel (London)
Practice Areas: Personal injury - acting for both sides including liability from non ionising radiation, work related stress, defective components, riding accidents, criminal acts of employees and Fatal Accident Act claims. Clinical negligence - acting for both sides in cases involving catastrophic birth injury, negligent diagnosis and treatment, failure to recognise medical conditions, failure to safeguard suicidal patients and disputes over the correct approach to care. Travel - accidents abroad, Rome II, jurisdictional issues. Notable cases include Mirvahedy v Henley, House of Lords [2002] Animals Act, Mattis v Pollock, CA [2003] Vicarious Liability. Evans v Birmingham and the Black Country SHA, CA [2000] Liability: cerebral palsy. Williams v The Estate of Mr James McGarley Johnstone [RCJ QBD 2008] Limitation: section 33. Orchard v Lee, Randall and Governors of Corfe Hill School [CA 2009]:liability of children. Virgin Airways v Heathrow Airport [2011] Claim by a disabled US citizen injured in an accident at Heathrow: the Montreal Convention, jurisdiction and applicable law. Goldsmith v Patchcott and Roach [2012] PIQR P11(COA: Animals Act. Collier v Norton [2012]:highest reported PI case, Wall v Mutuelle de Poitiers [2013]: Approach to evidence under Rome II.
Professional Memberships: PIBA.
Career: Christ Church, Oxford. MA Jurisprudence.

BROWNE-WILKINSON, Simon QC
Fountain Court Chambers, London
020 7583 3335
sbw@fountaincourt.co.uk
Featured in Fraud (London)
Practice Areas: Has a general commercial practice, but specialises in particular in arbitration (domestic and international) and civil fraud, including the obtaining and discharging of interim relief. Practice also includes employment, insurance, professional negligence, banking, chancery, and professional discipline. Arbitration: Extensive experience of substantial international arbitration, including acting for Electronic Arts SA in an ICC arbitration relating to Italian distribution rights, the Government of India in an UNCITRAL arbitration pursuant to a Bilateral Investment Treaty against Bechtel, Enron and GEC relating to the Dabhol Power Plant, a Nigerian telecoms company in two arbitrations relating to a management agreement and call charges, a Cypriot company in a LCIA arbitration relating to the Russian manufacturing sector, and an ICC arbitration relating to petroleum products. Has also given evidence as a expert witness on English law in a Stockholm arbitration, and as an expert on English Arbitration law. Reported cases in the Commercial Court on the operation of the Arbitration Act 1996 include Econet Wireless Ltd v Vee Networks Ltd (discharge of injunction granted to support an arbitration), Vee Networks Ltd. v ESS (jurisdiction of arbitrators to consider a defence of set off), and Vee Networks Ltd v EWI (award set aside on the grounds of unfairness in the conduct of an arbitration). Also sits as an arbitrator. Fraud: Specialises in civil fraud including, in particular, injunctive relief relating to allegations of fraud. Recently obtained the discharge of search and seize and worldwide freezing orders on the ground of non-disclosure, and the discharge of an injunction preventing the completion of a billion dollar transaction on the ground of non-disclosure. In 2013 acted for the Secretary of State for Justice in a multi-million pound fraud claim, obtained judgment for a Nigerian bank in a fraud claim for over £500 million against its former chief executive, and as an expert on BVI Law in relation to claims in New York and Holland arising out of the Madoff fraud.
Career: Called to the Bar in 1981. QC 1998.
Personal: Educated at Oxford University.

BROWNHILL, Joanna
Five Paper, London
020 7815 3200
clerks@fivepaper.com
Featured in Social Housing (London)
Practice Areas: Social housing; Part time Judge of the Property Chamber (Residential Property); Leasehold Disputes; Real Property; and Judge of the First Tier Social Entitlement Chamber. Acting for both landlords (local authorities, social landlords, private individuals and companies) and tenants Joanna has a particular interest and expertise in: anti-social behaviour (including ASBIs and ASBOs in both the Magistrates and County Courts); possession proceedings; disrepair; disability discrimination; and service charge disputes. Joanna also has experience in real property matters including easements (rights of way etc.), and covenants. Joanna brings a wealth of experience and a balanced and practical viewpoint. She also has experience of representing clients at ADR.
Professional Memberships: Member of SHLA.
Career: Called to the Bar in 1997. Appointed as a part time Judge of the Property Chamber (Residential Property) (previously the Residential Property Tribunal Service), in 2011. Appointed as a part time Judge of the Social Entitlement Chamber in 2011.
Personal: 1996 MA Oxon (Lincoln College) - Jurisprudence.

BRUCE, Andrew
Serle Court, London
020 7242 6105
abruce@serlecourt.co.uk
Featured in Real Estate Litigation (London)
Practice Areas: Andrew has a commercial and chancery practice with a particular focus on property-related work. He is regarded as one of the leading senior juniors in real estate litigation and has been described as "an exceptional talent in the property sphere". In addition, Andrew is highly-rated for professional negligence work, acting for both claimants and defendants, in matters ranging from high-profile claims in respect of Old Master Paintings to claims against architects in respect of residential developments and claims against solicitors relating to international corporate transactions. Andrew also regularly acts in high-value commercial litigation and is a "skilful advocate" who is "effective in digging under the surface to uncover the real issues".
Professional Memberships: Property Bar Association (Committee member 2003-09); Chancery Bar Association; Professional Negligence Bar Association.
Career: Called to the Bar in 1992 (Hamsworth Exhibitioner and Benefactors' Scholar of the Middle Temple). Joined Serle Court from 3 Paper Buildings, Temple in 1999. Appointed Deputy District Judge in 2004 and Judge of the First-Tier Tribunal (Property Chamber) (part-time) (formerly Deputy Adjudicator to HM Land Registry) in 2008.

Personal: Honorary Legal adviser at Swanley CAB (2001-2012). Past captain of Leigh Cricket Club. Married with three daughters.

BRUNNING, Matthew
No5 Chambers, Birmingham
0121 606 0500
mb@no5.com
Featured in Personal Injury (Midlands)

Practice Areas: Matthew specialises in all aspects of personal injury and fatal accident work, representing Claimants and Defendants in equal proportion. His practice also encompasses clinical negligence and defending fraudulent claims. His personal injury practice covers high value and complex cases. He undertakes a significant number of brain and spinal injury cases, including in the CICA, as well as amputation, chronic pain and disease cases. He has extensive experience of multi-party construction and rail industry claims. He undertakes direct instruction work, particularly for insurers, and has acted for entities such as theme parks on a similar basis. Matthew also has extensive experience in the coroner's court, representing prisons, companies, health authorities and families before coroners and juries. Matthew has been defending fraudulent motor and other insurance claims for many years, lecturing to solicitors and major insurers on tactics to be adopted. Among his notable success was the first successful application for a non-party costs order against a credit hire firm, Farrell & Short v Birmingham City Council & DAMS. Matthew was instructed by several thousand successful Claimants in the sofa dermatitis group litigation.

Professional Memberships: Member of PIBA, AvMA & PNBA.

Career: Read Modern History at Worcester College, Oxford. Called to the Bar 1997. Appointed to the Attorney General's Regional Panel in 2007. DDJ 2013.

Publications: Contributing editor to Butterworth's Personal Injury Law Service.

BRYAN, Robert
One Paper Buildings, London
020 7353 3728
clerks@onepaper.co.uk
Featured in Crime (Western)

Practice Areas: Criminal law, local authority/regulatory law, health and safety, courts martial.

Professional Memberships: Western Circuit, CBA, Association of Military Court Advocates, POCLA, HSLA.

Career: Though practicing mainly on the Western Circuit Robert Bryan is happy to be instructed nationwide, and regularly appears off Circuit. As both Junior and Leading Junior his work covers the wide spectrum of serious crime including homicide, sex-offending, serious fraud and drug conspiracies. As Junior alone he has successfully defended attempted murder, and has both prosecuted and defended in a number of motor vehicle death cases. He is known for his expertise in 'document' and 'computer' cases. He was instructed as Junior Defence Counsel (with Karim Khalil Q.C) in an 'Anarchist Cookbook' terrorism case, described as being the largest collection of such material seized by the Police. He has a particular interest in the use of computers in the analysis, preparation and presentation of evidence. He has become somewhat of an authority on the use of Tablet Computers (particularly the iPad) by Advocates; he was selected by Wessex Crown Prosecution Service to be sent the first Digital Briefs. He now regularly receives Digital Briefs from the Crown Prosecution Service and Defence Solicitors; he is at the forefront of the use of new technology in Courts, and is very happy working electronically. Robert is instructed as a Leading Junior particularly in the areas of fraud (including mortgage fraud), money laundering, drug importation and duty evasion. He is often asked to advise and appear as an Advocate in the related subjects of confiscation, forfeiture and restraint (including when not originally instructed at trial). He has an interest in Health & Safety and other regulatory work. Robert is regularly briefed both to prosecute and defend in multi-complainant cases of sexual offending (including historic abuse cases and offences against children). He is on the Crown Prosecution Specialist Rape Panel. He appears before Military Courts (Courts-Martial and Summary Appeal Courts) both in the United Kingdom and abroad, instructed both by civilian solicitors and by AFCLAA. His advice is also sought post-conviction when he was not Trial Counsel; these cover the whole calendar of offences including murder, and including applications on behalf of prisoner's sentenced to Life Imprisonment for the reconsideration of their minimum term. Robert edits the Sentencing section of news@ONE and writes/administers the Chambers blog: onepaperblog Robert Bryan is known for being approachable and engaging well with clients; he has considerable experience of handling high-maintenance lay clients; he is particularly noted for sensitive handling of child witnesses, victims of sexual offences and other vulnerable adults, and generally for dealing with witnesses and juries with courtesy. As an Advocate he is known for his careful attention to detail and methodical approach to cases.

Publications: Criminal law today (Thomson Reuters)- regular contributor.

BRYANT-HERON, Mark QC
9-12 Bell Yard, London
020 7400 1800
m.bryantheron@912by.com
Featured in Crime (London)

Practice Areas: Criminal law – heavy fraud and serious general crime; Tax – instructed in the First and Upper Tier Tribunal in revenue fraud matters; Regulatory and professional discipline. Currently instructed in the phone hacking cases and an international corporate corruption SFO prosecution. Recent cases: the phone hacking case (R v Mulcaire, Coulson, Brooks & Others); prosecution of a senior police officer for misconduct in public office (R v Casburn); substantial VAT reclaim appeal (Electrical Environmental v HMRC); the prosecution of a large scale organised Trojan attack on internet bank account users (R v Kulibaba & Others); the successful defence of Akmal Khan, charged in connection with substantial trafficking of Class A drugs (R v Eze & Others); the prosecution of a £145 million revenue MTIC fraud (R v Sarwar & Others); the successful defence of a defendant charged in connection with the Heathrow Menzies robbery (R v Betts & Others) Advisory Work: a substantial advisory practice, advising in bribery and corruption matters, criminal confiscation, money laundering, cartel and office of fair trading matters, financial regulation, export licensing, and bankruptcy and liquidation related criminal liability. Formerly standing counsel to the Revenue and Customs prosecution office (2005-10). Recorder of the Crown Court.

Personal: MA Cantab (Clare College).

BRYNMOR THOMAS, David
Thirty Nine Essex Street, London
020 7832 1111
david.brynmor.thomas@39essex.com
Featured in International Arbitration (London)

Practice Areas: Practises as counsel and arbitrator in complex, high value international commercial litigation and arbitration, in particular in international trade and investment; joint-venture and other shareholder disputes; construction and engineering; major projects; and partnership disputes. Has significant experience of arbitration related litigation, including anti-suit injunctions in support of arbitration and challenges to awards. Sits as Presiding Arbitrator, co-Arbitrator and Sole Arbitrator in arbitrations under all rules, including those of the ICC, LCIA, DIAC and UNCITRAL. Has served as an emergency arbitrator, appointed by the ICDR. Is an Honorary Senior Lecturer in Construction law and Arbitration at Queen Mary University of London.

Professional Memberships: Trustee, Chartered Institute of Arbitrators; Member, ICC Commission on Arbitration and ADR; LCIA; ICDR Panel of Arbitrators. CEDR accredited mediator.

Career: Barrister (Middle Temple) (2011 to date); Partner in the International Arbitration Group of Herbert Smith (2000-11); Solicitor Advocate - 2001; Solicitor (England and Wales) - 1993; Law Society Finals (First Class Honours) - 1991; Common Professional Examination - 1990; MB, ChB (Bachelor of Medicine and Bachelor of Surgery), Edinburgh - 1987.

Publications: United Kingdom Chapter, The Projects and Construction Review (Fourth Edition) with Alex Bodnar; Interim Relief Pursuant to Institutional Rules Under the English Arbitration Act 1996, Arbitration International, Issue 4, pp. 405–409.

BUCHANAN, James
2 Hare Court, London
020 735305324
jamesbuchanan@2harecourt.com
Featured in Health & Safety (London), Crime (London)

Practice Areas: James is a versatile performer, recognised as a leader in criminal and regulatory fields. His true area of expertise is now workplace crime. He is acknowledged as 'an extremely diligent practitioner with meticulous attention to detail, who has a personable manner that endears him to professional and lay clients alike'. Criminal Regulatory -James' practice focuses on workplace crime, particularly in relation to health and safety matters. His work covers the full range of offences, from manslaughter to prosecutions under the HSWA arising out of fatal and non-fatal accidents. James has significant experience of the construction sector and is currently instructed in numerous cases involving fatalities and catastrophic personal injuries. He is a specialist defence practitioner with a reputation as a robust trial advocate and shrewd tactician. James also acts on behalf of interested parties in Coroners' Inquests. Crime -James has an established track record in the defence of professionals charged with serious and complex crime and acts in proceedings brought by the leading prosecuting authorities. He has appeared as leading counsel in numerous multi-handed trials, often involving serious organised crime and flowing from large-scale investigations run by, amongst others: the Serious Fraud Office; the Serious and Organised Crime Agency; HMRC; Trading Standards; Operation Trident and the Flying Squad.

Professional Memberships: Health and Safety Lawyers' Association; Association of Regulatory and Disciplinary Lawyers; Criminal Bar Association.

BUCK, William
St Philips Chambers, Leeds
0113 244 6691
wbuck@st-philips.com
Featured in Commercial Dispute Resolution (North Eastern)

Practice Areas: A commercial barrister who litigates across a wide spectrum of disputes and is instructed on high value cases in the High Court and in other jurisdictions such as the Isle of Man, Spain and the USA. Work undertaken includes shareholder/director disputes, guarantee claims, agency disputes, trust litigation, sale of goods, contracts for the provisions of services, partnership matters, construction, alleged restraints of trade, insurance, business sales, professional negligence and soft IP cases. He has a particular focus on banking and asset finance litigation and is regularly instructed by several of the largest financial providers in the market on multi-million pound disputes. A substantial aspect of this type of work is of an interlocutory nature, often on a without notice basis, and includes the obtaining of freezing orders, injunctions and orders for delivery up. Many of these cases have an international element to them, with recent cases involving the application of Spanish, German and Turkish law and where parties and/or assets are located outside of the jurisdiction. William's international practice predominantly relates to the financial services market and disputes concerning trusts. He has considerable appellant experience, regularly appearing before the Court of Appeal on a wide range of issues.

BUCKETT, Edwin
9 Gough Square, London
020 7832 0500
ebucket@9goughsquare.com
Featured in Police Law (All Circuits)

Practice Areas: Police disputes, personal Injury claims and property. Notable cases include London Borough of Camden v Gunby (2000) I WLR 465; Cummins v Shell International Manning Services Limited (2002) 3 AER 813; Burden v Harrods Limited (2005) P.I.Q.R 17; Kearney v Chief Constable of Merseyside [2006] LTL 23/11/06; Laurence v Commissioner of Police of the Metropolis (2006) EWCA Civ 425 the Queen (on the application of the Commissioner of the Metropolis)-v-Croydon Crown Court and Burrell [2007] EWHC 1792; R-v-Chief Constable of Hertfordshire Constabulary and Beck [2008] AER(D) 94; Gordon Taylor-v-Commissioner of Police [2009] Max Clifford-v-Commissioner of Police [2010]; Masterman-v-Commissioner of Police [2010] All ER (D) 72; Phillips-v-NGN [2010] All ER (d) 182; Andrew-v-NGN [2011] 108 LSG 22; Bryant, Prescott and others-v-Commissioner of Police [2011] All ER (D) 219; Boyle-v-Thompsons Solicitors

[2012] PNLR 17 and An Informer-v-A Chief Constable [2013] 2 WLR 694.
Professional Memberships: PNBA, PIBA, ALBA, Midland Circuit.
Career: Called 1988. Pegasus Scholar (Inner Temple) - Canada, 1990.
Publications: 'Preventative Orders' (Law Society Publishing) 2010 editor with Tom Little and Rob McAllister; Clayton & Tomlinson's 'Civil Actions Against Police', Sweet & Maxwell (2004) 3rd Edition, editor. Kemp & Kemp; Current Law, Journal of Personal Injury Law [JPIL], contributor.
Personal: Music and motorcycling.

BUCKINGHAM, Paul
Keating Chambers, London
020 7544 2600
pbuckingham@keatingchambers.com
Featured in Construction (London), Energy & Natural Resources (London), International Arbitration (London)
Practice Areas: Specialist in major construction, engineering and energy disputes, with particular interest and expertise in international arbitration work. He is a dually qualified chemical engineer/ Barrister after spending eight years with BP as a chemical engineer in the oil and gas industries. Has worked on a wide range of contentious matters involving international construction and engineering projects. Regularly acts for clients in court, domestic and international arbitration, adjudication and mediation hearings. Has experience at all levels of alternative dispute resolution, including dispute review boards, project appeal panels, and direct settlement negotiations.
Professional Memberships: CEng; FIChemE; IChemE Contracts Committee, responsible for the drafting of its standard forms of contract; Chairman of the IChemE Dispute Resolution Committee; Society of Construction Law; Technology and Construction Bar Association (TECBAR); Commercial Bar Association (COMBAR).
Career: Called to the Bar 1995, IChemE accredited arbitrator and adjudicator 2006.
Publications: Contributor to Construction Dispute Resolution Handbook and Keating on Construction Contracts; consulting editor to Construction Law Journal.

BUCKPITT, Michael
Tanfield Chambers, London
020 7421 5300
michaelbuckpitt@tanfieldchambers.co.uk
Featured in Real Estate Litigation (London)
Practice Areas: Property litigation in particular: Real property - all issues concerning real property including contracts for the sale of land, overage and options, easements, restrictive covenants and mortgages. Landlord and tenant - all areas of commercial and residential disputes including forfeiture, dilapidations, lease renewal, service charges, appointment of Managers and RTM. Enfranchisement - all aspects under the 1993 Act and 1967 Act.
Professional Memberships: Member of the Property Bar Association and Chancery Bar Association.
Career: Called 1988. Recommended for several years in Chambers & Partners, Legal Experts and Legal 500 for property work. Instructed by a variety of law firms on behalf of individuals and commercial clients (including developers, London Estates and clients with significant property portfolios) concerning disputes in the courts, the First Tier Tribunal (Property Chamber) and Upper (Lands) Tribunal and the Adjudicator to the Land Registry. (See www.tanfieldchambers.co.uk for further details).
Publications: Co-author: Service Charges and Management.
Personal: Born 1965 married with two children.

BUDDEN, Rosemary
Queen Elizabeth Building, London
Featured in Family/Matrimonial (London)
Practice Areas: Exclusively in family law specialising particularly in financial claims (including Schedule 1 applications and Trusts of Land Act applications) and private law children work. Reported cases: Schofield v Schofield [2011] 1 FLR 2129, CA In the matter of M-H (Children) [2006] EWCA Civ 499.
Professional Memberships: Family Law Bar Association, Lawyers' Christian Fellowship.
Career: St. Hilda's College Oxford (MA (Hons) Jurisprudence); Hardwicke Scholarship (Lincoln's Inn), called 2003.
Publications: Durable solutions – The collected papers of the Dartington Hall Conference" Edited by Rt. Hon Lord Justice Thorpe & Rosemary Budden, Jordans 2006.
Personal: Married with two children.

BUEHRLEN, Veronique QC
Keating Chambers, London
020 7544 2600
vbuehrlen@keatingchambers.com
Featured in Energy & Natural Resources (London), International Arbitration (London)
Practice Areas: Veronique Buehrlen QC has a wide ranging commercial litigation, international arbitration and advisory practise with special emphasis on complex energy disputes (onshore and offshore), construction, banking, insurance and civil fraud. Her strengths are meticulous preparation of complex highly detailed matters requiring penetrating and determined cross examination of expert and other witnesses. Having spent the first 19 years of her practise at Fountain Court, Veronique has a wealth of experience of the Commercial Court and international Arbitration. Since taking Silk in 2010, Veronique Buehrlen QC has conducted as Leading Counsel several major commercial hearings including a four week trial in the Commercial Court for Borealis AB, in respect of severe damage sustained following the delivery of contaminated LPG, a six week ICC arbitration in a dispute arising out of the construction and installation of a subsea pipeline used in the first gravity based structure for the regasification of LNG, an ICC arbitration concerned with the construction of a container port under FIDIC conditions of contract and a Commercial Court trial concerned with the lowering of a live subsea gas pipeline.
Career: Called 1991, Queen's Counsel 2010. Stage at the Legal Service and European Court of Justice. Fountain Court 1992-2011; Keating 2011.
Personal: 1st class Honours St Andrews University. City University CPE Distinction. Queen Mother's Scholar, Middle Temple. Bilingual French/English.

BUNYAN, Angus
2 Hare Court, London
020 7353 5324
angusbunyan@2harecourt.com
Featured in Crime (London)
Practice Areas: Established criminal and regulatory leading junior. Serious fraud, corruption and money laundering represent much of Angus' practice. Current cases include allegations of corruption between senior managers of HBOS and business leaders and he recently prosecuted allegations of market rigging and hidden referral fees within the insurance industry. Wider financial crime experience includes acting as independent Counsel to the FCA and appearing before the Tribunal regarding MTIC fraud. Routinely instructed in complex restraint and confiscation proceedings. Recently acted in the CA for the respondent opposing a private prosecutor's appeal against a refusal to grant a restraint order. Angus has a growing practice in defending environmental crime, having been junior Counsel to the EA in the largest waste case prosecuted by the Agency. He has recently successfully represented a major waste firm for breaching environmental permits and is currently instructed for a utility company facing prosecution for river pollution. He has appeared alone in cases of murder and attempted murder and has recently led for the Crown in a case involving the importation of large quantities of Cocaine into Heathrow.
Career: Called 1999, Lincoln's Inn, Wolfson and Hardwicke Scholar, CPS Grade 4 (including for fraud and organised crime), Specialist Regulatory Advocate (HSE, EA and ORR).

BURDEN, Angus
St Philips Chambers, Birmingham
0121 246 7000
eab@st-philips.co.uk
Featured in Chancery (Midlands)
Practice Areas: All aspects of contentious and non-contentious wills and trusts work including the validity of wills, breach of trust claims, will construction disputes, applications for the rectification of wills, and the removal of personal representatives/trustees. He has considerable experience in proceedings under the Inheritance (Provision for Family and Dependants) Act 1975, and claims against estates based on proprietary estoppel or constructive trust. He also undertakes Court of Protection work and professional negligence claims relating to wills and estates. His non-contentious work includes general issues arising in the administration of estates and trusts, including tax. Appeared in Perrins v Holland [2011] 2 WLR 1086.
Professional Memberships: Midland Chancery and Commercial Bar Association.
Career: Called 1994. Currently tenant at St Philips Chambers, Birmingham.
Personal: Educated at Exeter University (BA Hons, first class) and Bristol University (post graduate certificates in insolvency, restitution and company law).

BURGHER, Benjimin
Outer Temple Chambers, London
020 7353 6381
benjimin.burgher@outertemple.com
Featured in Employment (London)
Practice Areas: Commercial, employment, discrimination and professional negligence.
Professional Memberships: COMBAR, ELA, ELBA, EELA, PNBA, Fee Paid Employment Judge, DIFC Registered.
Career: Benjimin Burgher has significant experience of commercial employment related matters and professional negligence claims relating to the provision of legal services. Before joining Chambers Benjimin worked in-house as a barrister for over 2 years in a leading international law firm. Whilst there he advised on the employment implications of the London Underground PPP (JNP lines), Ashanti Goldfields IPO and collective redundancies at Continental Airlines. He is now regularly instructed to deal with sensitive discrimination and whistleblowing matters. His commercial experience includes advising on directors duties, restrictive covenants and the TUPE implications of business transactions. He has dealt with claims involving inducement of breach of contract, partnership disputes, breach of fiduciary duty and claims between companies arising from contract and interpretation of contract terms. In addition to first instance cases, he has experience of conducting cases in the Privy Council, Court of Appeal, High Court, EAT and Dubai International Financial Centre Court. Benjimin is standing counsel to a number of large companies and other organisations on commercial and employment matters. He is experienced in professional negligence matters relating to the provision of legal services and has been instructed in numerous claims for and against lawyers, involving SRA, LSC and Legal Ombudsman Scheme rules.
Publications: Articles in Employers Law, Employment Law Journal, Employment Law Briefing. Provides CPD lectures/webinars for training bodies.
Personal: Fatherhood, football, cycling, tennis and jazz.

BURKE, Trevor QC
3 Raymond Buildings Barristers, London
020 7400 6400
trevor.burke@3rblaw.com
Featured in Crime (London), Financial Crime (London)
Practice Areas: Has previously defended John Fashanu in the football corruption trial. Sol Campbell on an alleged assault. Nigel Benn on a serious assault. Terry Marsh on a student grant fraud and the Taylor sisters. Also defended Gary Glitter. Extensive experience in defending white collar fraud, recently defended Dr Padelis in a large fraud on the NHS. Also undertakes consumer protection/ trade description work, particularly experienced representing solicitors before the OSS. Spent lengthy period in the Cayman Islands achieving the acquittal of his client in the nine month Eurobank money laundering trial. Additionally, represented Peter Buck (of REM) on an air rage charge. Increasingly briefed in cases overseas. As well as the Cayman Islands, advises banking institutions in the United States, and undertakes appeal work in the Republic of Ireland. Regularly briefed in high profile cases including Patrick "Dutchy" Holland, who had been linked with the murder of journalist Veronica Guerin. More recently represented the footballer Marlon King. Advised a Premier Division football club during a long running tax investigation, all allegations were abandoned following written submissions to the prosecuting authority. Currently briefed in various criminal/regulatory and civil disputes in the Cayman islands. Advising in relation to a substantial civil dispute in New York, and will appear as lead advocate before a federal jury. Successfully defended Jay Patel in the long running metal market fraud trial at southwark. Successful pre-charge submissions on behalf of Jim Davidson on

allegations of historic sexual abuse. Recently secured the acquittal of Cheryl Carter (PA to Rebecca Brookes) in the Phone Hacking trial. Instructed for various Journalist facing trial for allegations of paying public officials whilst working at The Sun newspaper.
Professional Memberships: CBA, Member of South Eastern Circuit.
Career: Called 1981. Silk 2001.
Personal: BA (Hons) Law. Golf.

BURKILL, Guy QC
Three New Square, London
020 7405 1111
gb@3newsquare.co.uk
Featured in Intellectual Property (London)
Practice Areas: All intellectual property. He has been particularly active in technology-oriented patent cases involving, telecoms, computer hardware and software and electronics and also enjoys a more diverse practice in copyright, trade marks, and other IP. He has acted for many leading multinational companies in the telecommunication, computer, electronics, paper, chemical, pharmaceutical, aviation and other fields. Notable cases include Pavel v Sony (Walkman case); Hoechst v British Petroleum (chemical manufacture, account of profits); Discovision v Disctronics (CD mastering); Dyson v Hoover (vacuum cleaners, post expiry injunction); Sweeney v MacMillan (James Joyce's 'Ulysses', copyright and passing off); Glaxo v Dowelhurst (trade marks, parallel imports); Philips v Princo (writable CD; directors' liability), Schlumberger v EMGS (electromagnetic detection of subsea oil reservoirs); Qualcomm v Nokia, HTC v Apple, and Samsung v Apple (multiple aspects of mobile phone technology).
Professional Memberships: Intellectual Property Bar Association; Chancery Bar Association.
Career: Winchester College; Corpus Christi College Cambridge MA Degree, 1st Class Hons in Engineering (Electrical Option); called to Bar 1981; QC 2002.
Publications: Co-editor of 'Terrell on the Law of Patents' - 15th edition (2000), 16th edition (2006), 17th edition (2011).
Personal: Leisure interests include violin, opera, and (when time permits) programming.

BURLES, David
1 Garden Court Family Law Chambers, London
020 7797 7900
burles@1gc.com
Featured in Family/Matrimonial (London)
Practice Areas: Ancillary relief, property disputes between unmarried partners, private law children.
Professional Memberships: FLBA Member, Common Law Bar Association, Bar Sports Law Group. Member of the Legal Advisory Group to the Law Commission Cohabitation Law Project 2005-07, Deputy District Judge (2007).
Career: Cranleigh School. LLB (Hons) Bristol University. Called 1984 (Middle Temple). Joined 1 Garden Court in 1999 following a mixed family/common law practice at Goldsmith Building. Postgraduate Certificate in Sports Law (King's College) 1998.
Publications: Co-author of "Applications Under Schedule 1 to the Children Act 1989", Contributor to Halsbury's Laws (children - financial claims), Contributor to Butterworths Civil Court Precedents - ('children/family breakdown'). Articles in The Times, Family Law, Family Law Week, Solicitors Journal, New Law Journal.
Personal: Playing hockey, golf and some occasional cricket. Theatre.

BURNET, Alasdair J
Terra Firma Chambers, Edinburgh
0131 260 5830
a.burnet@terrafirmachambers.com
Featured in Planning (Scotland)
Practice Areas: Planning and judicial review, medical negligence and product liability. Appeared in Court of Session planning appeals in relation to airport, supermarket, wind farm and housing developments; and major public infrastructure inquiries - including proposed AWPR Aberdeen City Bypass; Intercontinental hotel development Haymarket, Edinburgh; and Road-to-Rail Waste Transfer Facility Portobello. Represented first petitioner to be granted a protective costs order in Scotland to challenge the National Planning Framework and Trump International in respect of its proposed golf course development in Aberdeenshire. Also experienced in Lands Tribunal compensation claims. Recent cases: Salvesen v Riddell (legislative competence of Act of Scottish Parliament); Patersons of Greenoakhill v Scottish Ministers (planning permission for minerals extraction); Carroll v Scottish Borders Council (appeal against Local Review Body); Trump International Golf Links Scotland v Scottish Ministers (planning permission for offshore wind farm); Pilkington Trustees v Scottish Ministers (major housing development); Bova v Highland Council (housing development); Tesco Stores Ltd v Aberdeen City Council (appeal against adoption of Local Development Plan); Bagmore Wind Ltd v Scottish Ministers (wind farm effect on SPA). Also instructed in general commercial disputes, medical negligence and product liability cases, including the Vale of Leven Hospital: C-difficile Outbreak Public Inquiry and for Merck Pharmaceuticals in relation to actions arising from the withdrawal of its painkiller "Vioxx" and Smith and Nephew in relation to their metal on metal hip replacement cases.
Professional Memberships: Scottish Planning Local Government & Environmental Bar Group (Secretary).
Career: Called to Scottish Bar 2006. Litigation solicitor McGrigors LLP, 1999–2005. Instructing solicitor in McTear v Imperial Tobacco Limited 2005 2 SC 1.
Personal: BA (Hons) (1994) University of Oxford, LLB (1996) & Dip LP (1997) University of Edinburgh.

BURNS, Andrew
Devereux, London
020 7353 3709
burns@devchambers.co.uk
Featured in Employment (London), Insurance (London)
Practice Areas: Commercial and common law, in particular insurance and reinsurance law and professional negligence. Employment law, particularly injunctions, trade disputes, restrictive covenants, CAC and discrimination claims. Andrew acted for major transport providers in relation to industrial action over Olympic Games bonuses and has prevented strikes in railways, telecoms, education providers and logistics companies. He has twice appeared in the Dubai IFC Court of Appeal. Reported cases include: Prophet v Huggett [2014] EWCA Civ 1013 (restrictive covenants); Morgan & King v Safran Group EWC/8/2013; Allen v TRW Systems [2013] IRLR 699 (incorporation of contractual terms); Durham v BAI [2012] 1 WLR 867 (Supreme Court 'EL Trigger' Litigation); Aviva Insurance v Brown [2012] Lloyd's Rep. IR 211 (insurance fraud); RMT v Serco [2011] ICR 848 (strike injunctions); Malone v British Airways [2011] ICR 125 and Russo v BA [2012] Eq LR 987 (BA Cabin Crew litigation); Horwood v Land of Leather [2010] Lloyd's Rep. IR 453 ('Toxic Sofas' insurance litigation); Bedfordshire Police v Constable [2009] Lloyd's Rep. IR 607 ('damages' in PL insurance); Tektrol v International Ins [2005] 2 Lloyd's Rep. 701 (policy exclusions); GMB v Amicus [2003] ICR 1396 (redundancy consultation); Jones v Post Office [2001] ICR 805 (disability justification); Jacobs v Coster [2000] Lloyd's Rep IR 506 (notification of insurance claims).
Professional Memberships: COMBAR, BILA, ELA, LCLCBA, ELBA.
Career: Called 1993, Middle Temple; Crown Court Recorder, 2009.
Publications: 'Law of Reinsurance' (OUP, 2012); 'Bloomsbury Discrimination Law', co-editor (2012); 'Bean on Injunctions' (Sweet & Maxwell, 2012), co-author; various New Law Journal articles.
Personal: Educated at Dover Grammar School and Downing College, Cambridge. Astbury Scholar, Middle Temple. Leisure interests: Scouting, water sports, drama and opera.

BURNS, Paul
Exchange Chambers, Liverpool
0151 236 7747
burns@exchangechambers.co.uk
Featured in Local Government (Northern), Social Housing (Northern)
Practice Areas: Housing law (including claims for possession, injunctions, demotion, unlawful eviction), all aspects of residential landlord and tenant law, community safety litigation (IPNA's, possession claims, gang injunctions, closure orders), all related human rights and public law challenges and drafting and advice relating to policies and procedures. Regularly instructed in high profile and test case litigation.
Professional Memberships: Member of Lincoln's Inn and The Northern Administrative Law Association. Sir Thomas More Scholar and Hardwicke Scholar (Lincoln's Inn).
Career: Called to the Bar in 1998 (Lincoln's Inn). Joined Exchange Chambers (1998). Registered Pupil Supervisor (2008). Head of the Local Government and Social Housing Department at Exchange Chambers (2010). Independent Counsel to Police Misconduct Panels (2010). Named one of the top 10 UK 'Future Stars of the Bar' by The Times and Barrister of the Year at the Liverpool Law Society Legal Awards.
Personal: Educated at St Mary's College Crosby, The University of Liverpool and The Inns of Court School of Law (London). Governor of St Mary's College Crosby (2003-2013) and Vice Chair of Governors (2011-2013). Appointed Non-Executive Director at Southport and Ormskirk Hospital NHS Trust by The Appointments Commission (2010). Appointed Senior Independent Director at Southport and Ormskirk Hospital NHS Trust (2012) and Chair of the Remuneration and Nominations Committee (2013).

BURROUGHS, Nigel
4 New Square, London
020 7822 2000
n.burroughs@4newsquare.com
Featured in Pensions (London)
Practice Areas: Pensions, commercial chancery litigation, civil fraud (including asset recovery), company and insolvency, real property, trusts, professional negligence.
Professional Memberships: Association of Pension Lawyers, COMBAR, PNBA.
Career: Called to the Bar in 1991; Called to the Bar of the Supreme Court of the Eastern Caribbean in 2006.

BURROWS, Michael QC
No5 Chambers, Birmingham
0845 210 5555
mpb@no5.com
Featured in Crime (Midlands)
Practice Areas: Michael is a highly-regarded criminal advocate instructed in some of the most serious and complex cases. Prosecution work includes R v Anslow and others (conspiracy to escape); R v Harrison and others (gangland shooting); R v Doe and others (defendants convicted on evidence from anonymous witnesses of killing a traveller whose body was not recovered); R v Kovvali (gross negligence manslaughter of patient by out of hours doctor); R v Ramnath (gross negligence manslaughter of patient by hospital doctor); and R v Jones and others (defendants convicted of serious drugs offences based on evidence of witness under SOCPA agreement). Defence work includes R v Gordon (mother charged with murder of child, Khyra Ishaq, who died of starvation; after 6 weeks of trial her guilty plea to manslaughter was accepted); R v X (young defendant with learning difficulties, ADHD and autism, charged with two manslaughters and arson; after 5 weeks of trial his guilty plea to a single count of reckless arson was accepted); and R v Garmson (instructed on appeal in one of the leading DNA cases).
Professional Memberships: CBA.
Career: Called 1979. Recorder 1997. Silk 2008.

BURROWS, Simon
Kings Chambers, Manchester
0845 034 3444
clerks@kingschambers.com
Featured in Administrative & Public Law (Northern), Court of Protection (All Circuits)
Practice Areas: Court of Protection-health and welfare, deprivation of liberty, medical treatment. Mental health: First tier and Upper Tribunal, nearest relative displacement, habeas corpus and damages claims. Interface between the Mental Health Act and the Mental Capacity Act (including DOLS). Human rights. Disability and equality. Clinical negligence (usually involving psychiatry- including suicides of patients); Inquests (suicide and homicide)- often involving mental health issues; Judicial Review- particularly mental health related including s.117 challenges, and commissioning issues. Regulatory, principally within the health and social care field. Significant cases: P v Cheshire West & Chester Council etc- Supreme Court authority on the meaning of deprivation of liberty in a health and social care setting; LCC v SG [2014] EWCOP 10- whether an adult can be deprived of her liberty whilst a resident in a children's home; TA v AA & Knowsley BC [2013] EWCA Civ 1661 (Court's obligation to review a case in

s. 21A application); MOJ v RB [2011] EWCA Civ 1608 (conditional discharge of restricted patient where deprived of liberty), GJ v Foundation Trust [2010] 3 WLR 840, (MHA/MCA interface) C v Blackburn with Darwen [2011] EWHC 3321 (Guardianship and DOLS). Also Munby, P's hearing on directions in Post-Cheshire cases (June 2014).
Professional Memberships: Inner Temple (1990), Northern Circuit (1992), North Eastern Circuit (2006).
Career: President of Mental Health Review Tribunal (2003-date) (from 2008 known as Tribunal Judge).
Publications: Author of Chapters on "Mental Health" and "Tribunals" in Judicial Review: Law and Practice (Second edition) (Jordans 2014). Volume on Mental Health Tribunals in Atkins Court Forms (Lexis Nexis, 2013).

BURTON, Frank QC
12 King's Bench Walk, London
020 7583 0811
burton@12kbw.com
Featured in Clinical Negligence (London), Personal Injury (London), Personal Injury (All Circuits)
Practice Areas: Frank was appointed as a Recorder in 1999 and a Deputy High Court Judge in 2010. He was Chairman of the Law Reform Committee of the Bar Council (2003-05) and the Chairman of PIBA (2004-06). He is a Bencher of Gray's Inn (2004). Frank was named 'Personal Injury Silk of the Year' 2005, 2006 and 2008 at the Chambers Bar Awards. Frank was awarded Star Individual status in Personal Injury in Chambers 2009, the first Barrister to achieve this rating. He was also described a leading Silk in Industrial Disease and Clinical Negligence. Frank is further recognised in The Chambers 100 as one of the best silks in his field.

BURTON, Paul
3 Stone Buildings, London
020 7242 4937
pburton@3sb.law.co.uk
Featured in Restructuring/Insolvency (London)
Practice Areas: Substantial experience in chancery and commercial litigation and arbitration including: corporate and personal insolvency, shareholder and joint venture disputes, asset and share sales, contentious private client work, fraud and asset recovery, domestic and international contractual disputes. Acts in multi-party and multi-jurisdictional proceedings. Frequently appears in urgent applications for domestic and international interim relief.
Professional Memberships: Chancery Bar Association. Commercial Bar Association. Member of the Chartered Institute of Arbitrators.
Career: Called Lincoln's Inn 1998. Accredited Mediator.

BUSUTTIL, Godwin
5RB, London
020 7242 2902
godwinbusuttil@5rb.com
Featured in Defamation/Privacy (London)
Practice Areas: Media law generally including defamation, privacy, confidence, data protection, reporting restrictions, contempt; also sports law and other regulatory work. Recent interesting cases include Dar Al Arkan v Al Refai, Johnston v League Publications Ltd, Euromoney Institutional Investor plc v Aviation News Ltd, Tamiz v Google Inc & Cammish v Hughes. For full case list and profile, see www.5rb.com.
Career: 1988-92 Jesus College, Cambridge MA, MPhil; 1992-3 City University, Dip Law; 1993-94 ICSL, London; 1994 called to the Bar (Lincoln's Inn; Mansfield and Hardwicke Scholar); 1999 Pegasus Scholar (USA); 2008 Accredited Mediator; 2012 Visiting Senior Fellow in Law, University of Melbourne, Australia.
Publications: Senior contributing editor of 'Gatley on Libel and Slander'; co-editor of Entertainment and Media Law Reports; co-author of 'The Law of Privacy and the Media' (1st & 3rd eds, OUP); contributed articles to Journal of Media Law and Entertainment Law Review.

BUTLER, Andrew
Tanfield Chambers, London
020 7421 5300
andrewbutler@tanfieldchambers.co.uk
Featured in Real Estate Litigation (London)
Practice Areas: All aspects of commercial and property litigation, with a particular emphasis on property-related professional negligence, construction, insurance and insolvency; development projects and joint ventures; commercial and residential landlord and tenant, boundary disputes and rights of way. Notable recent and ongoing cases include GenesisUKNet -v- Allianz Insurance (Merc Ct., insurance claim arising out of fire to warehouse), Smith v Eversheds (Ch Div, solicitor's undertaking given in context of subrogated mortgage indemnity claim), re 23-25 Lowndes Square (Ch Div, unfair prejudice petition brought by tenant shareholders in Management Company).
Professional Memberships: Property Bar Association, Professional Negligence Bar Association.
Career: Called 1993. Joined Tanfield Chambers (then 2nd floor, Francis Taylor Building) 1995. Head of Business & Commercial Practice Group. Accredited mediator.
Publications: Co-author, 'Service Charges and Management; Law and Practice', Tanfield Chambers 1st Edn 2006 and 3rd Edn 2013. Regular contributor to legal publications including Sols Journal and New Law Journal.
Personal: Educated at Harrow School and University College, Oxford (MA BA Classics). Married with two children. Hobbies: all sports especially cricket, rugby, and golf.

BUTLER, Michelle
Matrix Chambers, London
020 7404 3447
michellebutler@matrixlaw.co.uk
Featured in Crime (London)
Professional Memberships: Specialist in international law, crime and human rights. International law work spans proceedings at the International Criminal Court, International Criminal Tribunal for the Former Yugoslavia, Special Court for Sierra Leone, International Tribunal for the Law of the Sea and arbitral tribunals determining bilateral investment treaty claims under the ICSID, UNCITRAL and ICC rules. Domestic criminal work includes terrorism, extradition, fraud and general crime. Human rights work ranges from national security related proceedings (control orders and TPIMs), immigration (particularly complex asylum, deportation, and deprivation of citizenship cases), European Union sanctions work and cases before the Grand Chamber of the European Court of Human Rights. Former clients include Governments, Heads of State, leading political, military and business figures, corporations, public authorities, NGOs and individuals. In the UK has appeared before the Supreme Court, House of Lords, Privy Council and the Court of Appeal. Experienced in fragile environments having worked in Libya, Iran, Iraq, Nigeria, Pakistan, Sri Lanka, Georgia and throughout the former Yugoslavia.
Career: Admitted as a Solicitor (Australia) 2002. Called to UK Bar 2007. Appointed to Attorney-General's Public International Law 'C' Panel 2014.
Publications: Contributing author to leading books on human rights, international law and criminal justice.

BUTT, Matthew
3 Raymond Buildings Barristers, London
020 7400 6400
matthew.butt@3rblaw.com
Featured in Extradition (London), Inquests & Public Inquiries (London), Licensing (London), Professional Discipline (London), Crime (London)
Practice Areas: A criminal, extradition and regulatory practitioner with particular expertise in inquests, licensing law and professional misconduct. Prosecutes and defends in serious criminal cases. Acts at first instance and on appeal in extradition cases. Instructed in complex and high profile inquests, particularly those involving fatal shootings (recently represented the MPS "Flying Squad" Silver Commander at an inquest into a double shooting at Chandlers Ford, currently representing the MPS "Trident" Tactical Firearms Commander in the inquest touching the death of Mark Duggan). Regularly instructed to represent accused officers in police disciplinary hearings and appeals. Advises and represents on all matters connected with licensed activities, including gaming, alcohol, regulated entertainment, street trading, firearms and taxis before licensing committees and on appeal to the Magistrates' Court, the Administrative Court and the Court of Appeal. Clients include licensing authorities, the police, major national pub operators and festivals.
Career: Call, 2002, Lord Justice Holker Scholarship 2000, Atkin Scholarship 2002. Lead advocacy trainer (Gray's Inn). Pupil supervisor.

BYRNE, Garrett
4-5 Gray's Inn Square, London
020 7404 5252
gbyrne@4-5.co.uk
Featured in Environment (London)
Practice Areas: Principal areas of practice are environmental law, planning law, administrative law, police law and disciplinary proceedings. Extensive experience of all aspects of environmental law, including water pollution, water quality, sewers and drains, emissions trading, permitting, environmental impact assessment and strategic environmental assessment, contaminated land, flood protection, waste regulation and management, energy projects, nuclear, transport projects, highways and rights of way, nature conservation and nuisance. He is regularly instructed by industry, developers, the Environment Agency, local authorities and objectors and appears at environmental and planning inquiries. He appears in the High Court in judicial review proceedings and other challenges, and he has many years experience in police law appearing regularly at the police disciplinary tribunal both as advocate and legal assessor. He also prosecutes cases for the RCPO and DTI.
Professional Memberships: United Kingdom Environmental Law Association, Planning and Environmental Bar Association, founding member of Earthrights, environmental rights charity and public interest law firm, Criminal Bar Association.
Career: Called 1986, Recorder 2007, Member of the Bar Disciplinary Panel, Chairman of the Fulham Legal Advice Centre.
Publications: Editor, 'Disciplinary and Regulatory Proceedings' (3rd edition).
Personal: Educated at Wimbledon College and Bristol University. LLM in Environmental Law from Kings College, London.

CADE DAVIES, Lynsey
29 Bedford Row Chambers, London
020 7404 1044
lcadedavies@29br.co.uk
Featured in Family/Matrimonial (London)
Practice Areas: All aspects of family law including financial provision on the breakdown of marriage or civil partnership, reciprocal enforcement of foreign financial orders, issues relating to jurisdiction, foreign offshore trusts and disputes concerning trusts of land, private law children matters, inheritance act. Reported cases include: Shield v Shield [2014] EWHC 23; Shield v Shield [2013] EWHC 3525; Divall v Divall [2014] EWHC 95; Price v Price [2014] EWCA Civ 655; B v B [2010] All ER (D) 61 (May); D v D and Others & I Trust [2009] EWHC 3062 (Fam).
Professional Memberships: FLBA and Resolution.
Career: Called 2005, joined 29 Bedford Row in 2006 Inner Temple. Regular lecturer.
Personal: Queenswood School, Herts. University of Bristol (Law LLB). City University (Bar Vocational Course).

CALDECOTT, Andrew QC
One Brick Court, London
020 7353 8845
clerks@onebrickcourt.com
Featured in Data Protection (London), Defamation/Privacy (London)
Practice Areas: Defamation, privacy and breach of confidence, contempt of court, data protection, freedom of information, obscenity/ censorship and media-related law generally. Cases include: Hegglin v Google Inc (DPA, libel); Makudi v Baron Triesman (CA, libel, malicious falsehood, Parliamentary privilege); Rothschild v Associated Newspapers (CA, libel); Tesla Motors v BBC (CA, malicious falsehood, libel); Chris Cairns v Lalit Modi (CA, Twitter libel); Oriental Daily Publisher Ltd & anr v Ming Pao Holdings Ltd (Hong Kong Court of Final Appeal); El Naschie v MacMillan Publishing (libel trial); The Leveson Inquiry (representing Guardian News & Media, a core participant); Attorny General v News Group Newspapers & Mirror Group Newspapers (contempt); Spiller v Joseph (Supreme Court - libel - representing interveners Associated Newspapers Ltd, Times Newspapers Ltd & Guardian News & Media Ltd); R v D (C/A - Reporting Restrictions); Baturina v Times Newspapers Ltd (C/A - Libel); R v Morley & ors (CA reporting restrictions - MP's expenses trial); Sir Stelios Haji-Ionnou v Dixon & Regus Group (libel); AG v MGN Ltd (contempt); Tesco v Guardian (libel and malicious falsehood); AG v ITV Central (contempt); R v VAC (ex

parte BBFC) (judicial review, obscenity); Moyes v Rooney & Harper Collins (libel); X v Associated Newspapers (Anonimity); Morrisons v OFT (libel); Sir Martin Sorrell v FullSix SpA & anr (libel and privacy); X & Y v Person Unknown (privacy); The Law Society v Department of Constitutional Affairs (Civil Proceedure Rules); AG v Pelling (contempt); Armstrong v Times (CA - successfully reinstated plea of qualified privilege); Henry v BBC (libel, justification and qualified privilege); A v B and C (privacy injunction); AG v Express (contempt); Strachan v Gleaner Co Ltd (Privy Council - defendants successfully resisted claimants challenge); Green Corns Ltd v Claverley Group Ltd (privacy); Naomi Campbell v MGN (House of Lords - privacy/confidence); Bonnick v Gleaner Co Ltd (Privy Council - libel); King v Telegraph Group (libel/CFA's); Other cases of interest: The Hutton Inquiry - Lead counsel for the BBC; Reynolds v Times Newspapers (libel - qualified privilege); Venables v News Group Newspapers (confidence injunction to protect the identity of Jamie Bulger's killers).
Career: Called to the Bar 1975. Silk 1994. Inner Temple Bencher 2004. Head of Chambers since 2007. Appointed specialist adviser to House of Commons Joint Committee on the Draft Defamation Bill (2011).
Publications: Co-author of Halsbury's Laws, Defamation (2012); co-author of the section on Libel and Slander, Malicious Falsehood in Bullen & Leake, Precedents & Pleadings.
Personal: Educated Eton College and New College, Oxford. Lives in London.

CALDWELL, Peter
Dyers Chambers, London
020 7404 1881
clerks@dyerschambers.com
Featured in Extradition (London), Financial Crime (London)
Practice Areas: A specialist business defence advocate for fraud, extradition and regulatory cases. Peter is ranked as a leading financial crime practitioner and is regularly instructed as a leading junior in fraud trials. He has advised corporates, legal practices and overseas governments on anti-money laundering and anti-bribery compliance. In proceeds of crime he is typically instructed to protect the interests of parties affected by restraint, confiscation and receivership orders. His PoCA practice also comprises Part 5 civil recovery claims and associated cases before tax tribunals. He is also instructed in matters of commercial dispute resolution and civil fraud. Peter is also ranked as a leading extradition practitioner, instructed both for requested persons and foreign governments in complex and high profile cases. He has acted in landmark decisions shaping the law on extradition over the last 10 years, most recently with the first decision on the new forum bar. Peter's regulatory work encompasses trading standards, counterfeit goods, planning enforcement, and food safety, as well as professional disciplinary proceedings before the FCA, GMC, NCTL and FA.
Professional Memberships: Chatham House, ARDL, ALBA, IBA.
Career: Peter is a founding member of Dyers Chambers established in 1998. His web profile may be viewed here: www.dyerschambers.com/peter-caldwell_N38.html.

CALHAEM, Simon
29 Bedford Row Chambers, London
scalhaem@29br.co.uk
Featured in Family/Matrimonial (London)
Practice Areas: Provides advisory and advocacy work and specialises in complex high value financial work, particularly with an international element, including matrimonial finance, inheritance claims and civil disputes between family members. Cases include: AM v SS [2013] EWHC 4380; Wyatt v Vince [2014] 1 FLR 399; McRoberts v McRoberts - [2012] All ER (D) 12 (Nov), (Chd); Foster v Foster [2011] (2) CILR 89 (Cayman Islands Court of Appeal); V v V (Divorce: Jurisdiction) (Fam) [2011] 2 FLR 778; W v W (Financial Relief: Enforcement) [2011] 2 FLR 1268; K v B (Costs: Financial Relief) [2011] 1 FLR 1745; Bradley v Bradley (Security for Costs) [2008] 2 FLR 1433 (CA); A v B (Damages: Paternity) [2007] 2 FLR 1051, (QBD);Kimber v Kimber (Writ Ne Exeat Regno) [2006] EWCA Civ 706, CA; Rowe v Clarke, [2006] All ER (D) 124 (May); Crossley v Crossley (TLATA) [2006] 2 FLR 813, CA ;Rowe v Clarke (Probate), 149 Sol Jo LB 1450.
Professional Memberships: FLBA; London Common Law & Chancery Bar Association; The Denning Society.
Career: Called to the Bar of England & Wales 1999. Called to the Bar of the Cayman Islands ad hoc since 2011, Called to the Bar of Gibraltar ad hoc since 2013.
Publications: 'The Writ Ne Exeat Regno' Family Law, 'Express Trusts and Ancillary Relief' Family Law, 'Divorce and Recession' Family Law. Co-author of 'Divorce & Bankruptcy: A Practical Guide for a Family Lawyer'. Contributor to 'Duckworths Matrimonial Finance & Taxation (Bankruptcy)'. Contributor to Ross "Inheritance Act Claims and Challenges." Guest Lecturer - University of the West Indies (Barbados) 2013 -.
Personal: Sir Thomas Alleynes High School, Oxford University (MA) Lecturer and Moderator in Law (University of East London 1998 - 1999) Inns of Court School of Law, Sir Thomas More Scholar. Married, lives in London. Enjoys Yacht Racing.

CALLAN, Jane
Trinity Chambers, Newcastle upon Tyne
0191 232 1927
j.callan@trinitychambers.co.uk
Featured in Employment (North Eastern)
Practice Areas: Head of Trinity Chambers Employment Group - practises predominantly in employment and discrimination law. She has particular expertise in equal pay and discrimination cases. Instructed to represent claimants (including Trade Union backed claimants) and counts local authorities, health authorities and "blue chip" companies amongst her respondent clients. Instructed in high profile equal pay and discrimination cases. Jane has a particular interest in professional discipline and in acting for registrants appearing before regulatory bodies' panels. Administrative & Public Law - appeared for the North East Group of solicitors, intervenors in the high profile case of The Law Society v Legal Services Commission [2010] EWHC 2550 (Admin). First-tier Tribunal (Special Educational Needs and Disability), advised in cases involving schools admissions and exclusions. Expertise in discrimination law places her at a particular advantage in dealing with disability discrimination in the context of education, as does her knowledge and experience of public and education law.
Professional Memberships: Employment Law Bar Association; Industrial Law Society.
Career: Master's degree in Industrial Relations, London School of Economics 1983. Equality and Human Rights Commission Preferred Panel of Counsel. Junior Counsel to the Crown (Regional Panel. Fee-paid judge, First-tier Tribunal, Social Entitlement Chamber, Scotland.
Personal: Nee Woodwark.

CALLMAN, Jeremy
Ten Old Square, London
020 7405 0756
jeremycallman@tenoldsquare.com
Featured in Partnership (London)
Practice Areas: The broad range of work he undertakes includes partnership/LLP and business disputes, general contract and commercial law (including sale of goods), banking and building society law, professional negligence, insolvency and bankruptcy, landlord and tenant and real property. Jeremy regularly represents clients at arbitrations and mediations. Partnership Work: Jeremy has a strong reputation in partnership/LLP litigation. Additionally he acts on non-contentious partnership matters including updating and revising partnership and LLP agreements. He regularly advises managing partners on internal issues within partnerships/LLPs. He represents both firms and individual partners, from solicitors, accountants, hedge funds, doctors and dentists to recruitment consultants, architects, theatrical agents and farmers.
Professional Memberships: Association of Partnership Practitioners (Committee member 2008-2014), Chancery Bar Association, Property Bar Association, Professional Negligence Bar Association. Professional Standards Committee of the Bar Council 1994-98.
Career: Called to the Bar 1991. Reported cases include: Reinhard v Ondra (awaiting judgment, HC) - nature of members' interests in an LLP; Dr Shakarchi v Dr Muir (awaiting order of the court) - GP partnership dispute with injunctions sought; Eaton v Caulfield & Others [2013] EWHC 2214 (Ch) - scope of unfair prejudice relief to bring about discontinuance of proceedings (awaiting reporting); Paul Castledine v (1) RSM Bentley Jennison (2) RSM Bentley Jennison Ltd [2012] Bus LR (D77) – whether former partner retained a share in the goodwill of a substantial accountancy firm; Eaton v Caulfield & Others [2011] BCC 386 - Limited Liability Partnership: expulsion, unfair prejudice and just and equitable winding up; Capewell v Boulton LTL 6/11/2009 - Transfer of interests from one company to another in the context of an alleged partnership arrangement; Shaw v Finnimore & Watts [2009] All ER (D) 41 (Mar) - Alleged profit-sharing agreement; Horton (and others) v Brandish (and others) LTL 22/8/2005 - Estoppel and caution over land; Ridgeway Motors (Isleworth) Ltd v ALTS Ltd (2005) 1 WLR 2871 - Limitation and bankruptcy/insolvency; Ellis v Coleman LTL 10/12/2004 HC - Goodwill and construction of a partnership agreement; The Society of Lloyd's v Surman & others LTL 13/10/2004 HC - Enforcement of charging orders; The Society of Lloyd's v Bowman & others [2004] BPIR 324, CA, Thomas-Everard v Society of Lloyd's [The Times] 28 August 2003 HC - Bankruptcy and Lloyd's Names; Marsh v Sofaer & Griffinhoofe [2004] PNLR 24, [The Times] 10.12.2003 - Solicitor's negligence and duties of confidentiality; Partridge v Lawrence CA LTL 8/7/2003 - Construction of a deed and rights of way; Uddin v Ahmed [2001] 3 FCR 300 CA - Construction of a marriage contract; Adams v Attridge LTL 3/12/2001 - Confidentiality; Lafi Office & International Business SL v Meriden Animal Health Ltd (2000) 2 Lloyd's LR 51 - Conflict of laws; Tyler v Royal Borough of Kensington & Chelsea LTL 23/12/99 - Abuse of process and compromise; Venables v Mirror Group Newspapers [The Times] 9 December 1998, CA - Civil procedure.
Publications: He has written for The Sunday Times, The Mail on Sunday, The Solicitors Journal and the Journal of International Banking Law, the Association of Partnership Practitioners magazine 'A Propos Partnership' as well as appearing on Radio Four.
Personal: Beyond his practice, he is married with four children, and works with Norwood, a leading UK charity supporting children and families with learning disabilities. Member of the Garrick Club.

CALLOW, David
12 King's Bench Walk, London
callow@12kbw.co.uk
Featured in Personal Injury (Wales & Chester)
Practice Areas: Personal injury including high value catastrophic injury claims, industrial disease especially stress at work and asbestos related disease, general employers' liability, Road traffic and insurance including MIB and cover/ policy issues especially fraud/ staged accidents/ malingering, clinical negligence. Employment and Discrimination.
Professional Memberships: PIBA, ELBA, ELA, Wales Circuit.
Career: Called 1998, Pupil Supervisor, Deputy District Judge 2010.

CAMERON, Donald
Westwater Advocates, Edinburgh
donald.cameron@westwateradvocates.com
Featured in Agriculture & Rural Affairs (Scotland), Employment (Scotland)
Practice Areas: Advocate specialising in employment law and public law, as well as having a personal interest in agricultural and crofting matters. Recent cases include: Perry and Hamilton v EAT [2013] IRLR 544 (Inner House case concerning a costs award in the employment tribunal), Bagmoor Wind Ltd v Scottish Ministers [2012] CSIH 93 (planning appeal relating to Habitats/Birds Directives); Tayside Public Transport Co Ltd v Reilly 2012 SLT 1191 (appeal from EAT relating to strike-out orders in the employment tribunal); Seawell Ltd v Ceva Freight (UK) Ltd [2012] IRLR 802 (appeal in EAT relating to TUPE); Lord Advocate v B 2012 SLT 541 (vexatious litigant petition in the Inner House); and Angus Growers Ltd v Scottish Ministers [2012] Eu. L.R. 539 (agricultural subsidies case in the Scottish Land Court) and in the Inner House: [2012] CSIH 92.
Professional Memberships: Faculty of Advocates, Westwater Advocates; Member of the Faculty of Advocates Employment Law Group, Member of the Crofting Law Group; Member of the Scottish Public Law Group.
Career: Called to the Bar of England and Wales in 2002. Called to the Scottish Bar in 2005; Standing Junior Counsel to the Scottish Government 2009 to date.

Personal: Educated at University of Oxford (BA (Hons)), City University (Diploma in Law and Bar Vocational Course).

CAMERON, Gillon
Fourteen, London
020 7242 0858
clerks@fourteen.co.uk
Featured in Family/Matrimonial (London)
Practice Areas: Gillon practises in all areas of family law with an emphasis on financial disputes under Matrimonial Causes Act 1973, Schedule 1 Children Act 1989 claims for financial provision, and claims under Trusts of Land and Appointment of Trustees Act 1996. He is also frequently instructed to represent local authorities, parents and children in public law proceedings, as well as parents and children in private law proceedings. Reported cases include Re C (A Child) (Conduct of Hearings) [2006] EWCA Civ 144, Re K (Adoption: permission to advertise) [2007] 2 FLR 326; Oxfordshire County Council v X, Y & J [2010] EWCA 581 Civ.
Professional Memberships: FLBA, Lincoln's Inn.
Career: St Paul's School, London; Bristol University BA (Hons); Diploma in Law (City University); Lincoln's Inn Lord Bowen Scholar; Lincoln's Inn Lord Mansfield Scholar; Lincoln's Inn City University Scholarship; Called to the Bar 2002.
Publications: Frequent contributor to Family Law Week.
Personal: Passionate musician and footballer.

CAMMERMAN, Gideon
187 Fleet Street, London
020 7430 7430
clerks@187fleetstreet.com
Featured in Crime (London)
Practice Areas: Financial Crime, Regulatory and Disciplinary Law, Confiscation and Asset Forfeiture, Gambling.
Professional Memberships: Criminal Bar Association, Association of Regulatory and Disciplinary Lawyers.
Career: Called in 1996, Gideon has defended and prosecuted in many complex and high profile cases. Clients have varied from a well known online gambling company to "Anonymous" hacktivists to Irish Travellers accused of Slavery to a hedge fund manager accused of a $600m fraud. Gideon began his career prosecuting for a wide range of government organisations and remains on the CPS list for POCA, Fraud and SOCA. His focus has shifted to regulatory work (especially accountancy and gambling) and to the money orders associated with criminal litigation.
Publications: Contributing Editor of Chapter 4 "Frauds on Investors" in Butterworths "Fraud: Law, Practice and Procedure".

CAMPBELL, Alexis
29 Bedford Row Chambers, London
020 7404 1044
ACampbell@29br.co.uk
Featured in Family/Matrimonial (London)
Practice Areas: Core practice area is matrimonial finance with particular interest in: international disputes; offshore trusts; pensions; and companies. Extensive experience in high net worth cases, unravelling complex financial arrangements. Hard negotiator but sensible and pragmatic advice. Children practice focuses on private disputes with a focus on international relocation cases. Notable cases include: AS v JS & Others [2013] EWHC 1699 (Fam); Sharma v Sharma and others [2012] EWHC 2529 (Fam); Martin-Dye v Martin-Dye [2006] 2 FLR 901.
Professional Memberships: FLBA; Fellow IAML.
Career: Leeds University (LLB Hons). Called to the Bar 1990. Recorder 2010.
Publications: New Law Journal. Recent lectures on costs, pensions, divorce and company law.
Personal: Married with two children.

CAMPBELL, Douglas
Three New Square, London
020 7405 1111
clerks@3newsquare.co.uk
Featured in Information Technology (London), Intellectual Property (London)
Practice Areas: All types of intellectual property and information technology law including patents, copyright, designs, trademarks, passing off, trade libel and malicious falsehood, confidential information, franchising and licensing, entertainment and media, IT, and database rights as well as general litigation with a significant technical content. Experienced in arbitration and mediation. Acted as expert on UK intellectual property law in US District Court proceedings in the Southern District of New York.
Professional Memberships: IP Bar Association, Chancery Bar Association.
Career: First Class degree in Chemistry (with Distinction in Quantum Chemistry), Oxford University. Called to the Bar in 1993. Inner Temple Major Scholar. Pegasus Scholar at Mallesons Stephen Jaques, Melbourne, Australia in 1996. Member of Attorney-General's Panel of Junior Counsel to the Crown since March 2010. Appointed Civil Recorder in October 2010 and has sat in each of Central London County Court (both Civil and Chancery); Patents County Court; and Intellectual Property Enterprise Court. French and Japanese spoken, the latter to the Japanese Government's Grade 2 standard.
Publications: Terrell on the Law of Patents, Sweet & Maxwell.

CAMPBELL, Ewen
Axiom Advocates, Edinburgh
0131 226 5071
ewen.campbell@axiomadvocates.com
Featured in Media & Entertainment (Scotland)
Practice Areas: Ewen called to the Bar in 2013 after training and practising as a litigation solicitor with Levy & McRae. Since becoming an advocate, Ewen has been principally instructed in commercial and media related matters. He has provided advice in matters involving commercial (including construction) contracts, professional negligence, defamation, suspension and interdict, international private law, trademark infringement, nuisance and employment law. He has been instructed by a number of major media clients and has carried forward his experience as a solicitor in this area. He has also been instructed in a long running fatal accident inquiry. Ewen has appeared in proceedings in both the Court of Session (including the Inner House and Commercial Court) and the Sheriff Court. These appearances have included proofs, debates, fatal accident inquiries and successfully obtaining interim orders.

CAMPBELL, Oliver QC
Henderson Chambers, London
020 7583 9020
ocambellqc@hendrsonchambers.co.uk
Featured in Health & Safety (London), Product Liability (London)
Practice Areas: Health and safety, product liability, commercial litigation and environment. Awarded Health and Safety Junior of the Year at the 2012 Chambers UK Bar Awards. Instructed in many major health and safety and manslaughter cases including the prosecution arising out of the Hatfield train crash. He has also appeared in several major inquests, including inquests into the Potters Bar and Ufton Nervet rail accidents and the Marks and Spencer asbestos prosecution. He specialises in all aspects of product liability, including pharmaceutical claims, sales of goods claims, food and drink contamination claims, and property damage claims. He has particular experience of group actions/multi-party claims, including the OCENSA pipeline litigation, the Para Red and Sudan Red claims, the Lariam litigation and the Lloyds/HBOS litigation.
Professional Memberships: Committee member of the Health & Safety Lawyers Association.
Career: BA (Oxon). President of the Oxford Union (1990). Advocacy prize ICSL (1992). Called 1992. Member of the Bar Standards Board Centralised Examinations Board. Trustee of the Lambeth Law Centre. Appointed QC in 2014.
Publications: Contributor to Halsbury's Laws; Contributing editor to 'The Lawyer's Factbook' and to the 'International Product Law Manual'.

CAMPBELL, Stephen
No5 Chambers, Birmingham
0870 203 555
sgc@No5.com
Featured in Personal Injury (Midlands)
Practice Areas: Stephen Campbell is a personal injury specialist acting for both claimants and defendants. Recent experience includes cases of: Brain damage; paralysis; limb amputation; industrial disease; obstetric accidents and claims against the manufacturers of benzodiazepine drugs and their prescribing doctors. Stephen has been described in Chambers and Partners guides as having a "down to earth approach and someone you can trust completely" and "a standout for his expertise in brain injury and industrial disease". Stephen is regarded not only as a leading junior in the set but also a good team player who is thoroughly liked and respected by his peers.
Professional Memberships: PIBA.
Career: LLB (Hons) (Liverpool), recorder (both civil and crime).

CAMPBELL-TIECH, Andrew QC
Dyers Chambers, London
020 7404 1881
andrew.campbell-tiech
@dyerschambers.com
Featured in POCA Work & Asset Forfeiture (All Circuits), Crime (London)
Practice Areas: Recent confiscation cases include: the lawfulness of confiscation undertaken by a private prosecutor; Special Purpose Vehicles; off-shore trusts; confiscation in absentia; trade marks and the assumptions; enforcement notices and the assumptions. Recent restraint includes carbon credit fraud and money laundering. Recent fraud cases include Iran sanctions busting, banking and medical. Recent regulatory cases include trade marks; planning; RCVS, HCPC and UKCP. Recent criminal cases include alleged matricide by an epileptic.
Professional Memberships: CBA, ECBA.
Career: Head of Dyers Chambers 2008: QC 2003: Deputy Coroner 2011: Attorney-General Approved Counsel List A 2002: SFO Approved List QC: Recorder: 2001: Arbitrator: 1997, called 1978.
Publications: Recent publications include: 'Confiscation and Game Theory: Ahmad and Field'; 'The Proceeds of Crime Act 2002: a Quiet Revolution'; 'Restraint Orders: Prosecuting the Breach'; 'Too Many Murderers'; 'Lip Reading as Expert Evidence'; 'Stockwell Revisited: the Unhappy State of Facial Mapping'; 'The Future of Detention without Trial in the UK', 'A Corpse in Law' (Archbold News, Journal of the London Middle East Institute, Global Association of Risk Professionals, British Journal of Haematology, Local Government Journal, Dyers Newsletter).
Personal: Music, languages, chess & cycling.

CANBY, Fiona
Temple Garden Chambers, London
020 7583 1315
fionacanby@tgchambers.com
Featured in Health & Safety (London)
Practice Areas: Coroners and inquests, health and safety, personal injury. Cases include: Inquest into death of Sean Cunningham (Red Arrows pilot); Lakanal House Fire Inquest (HHJ Kirkham); Inquests into the London Bombings of 7 July 2005 (Hallett LJ) and R v Balfour Beatty (and others); the manslaughter prosecution arising out of the Hatfield train crash (Central Criminal Court and Court of Appeal). Particular expertise in long and complex inquests. Experienced in workplace fatalities; military and aviation inquests and prison/custody/detention deaths. Particular knowledge of the transport industry (rail; underground; cycle and surface transport); construction; manufacturing; glass and glazing; agriculture; packing; manual handling; work at heights; care homes; carbon monoxide and fire safety. Instructed in related personal injury claims. Instructed by motor insurers in claims for damage to train and track following road vehicle incursions onto the railway (Gilman v (1) UPS (2) Network Rail (2013)).
Professional Memberships: Member of the Health and Safety Lawyers' Association and PIBA.
Career: Called 2001; Middle Temple. Queen Mother Scholar and Blackstone Exhibitioner. Treasury Counsel (B Panel) since 2013.
Publications: Co-author of 'Prosecuting and Defending Health and Safety Cases' published by xpl.
Personal: Educated at Hull High School and Manchester University (1999 first class Hons Law).

CANEY, Michelle
St Ives Chambers, Birmingham
0121 236 0863
michelle.caney@stiveschambers.co.uk
Featured in Real Estate Litigation (Midlands), Social Housing (Midlands)
Practice Areas: Real Property, Landlord and Tenant, Social Housing.
Professional Memberships: Property Bar Association, Midlands Social Housing Law Association, Midland Circuit.

Career: Michelle Caney is a specialist property practitioner. In the commercial property sphere, she deals with breach of covenant claims, forfeiture, service charge disputes, business renewals, terminations and dilapidations. In the residential context, Michelle represents landlords and tenants in all areas of social housing, with particular expertise in complex cases involving mental capacity, disability discrimination and human rights issues. Her chancery practice includes boundary disputes, easements, nuisance, restrictive covenants, trusts and settlements, professional negligence (predominately of a property nature) and banking litigation.
Personal: Called to the Bar: 2004. Joined St Ives Chambers: 2005. Deputy Head of the Housing and Property Group: 2012. Deputy Head of the Civil Group: 2014. Recent cases include a complex trial in the High Court concerning a property development business in which judgment was secured in excess of £700,000.

CANNOCK, Giles
Kings Chambers, Manchester
0845 034 3444
clerks@kingschambers.com
Featured in Planning (Northern)
Practice Areas: All aspects of town and country planning with particular expertise in large housing projects, retail, renewable energy, infrastructure projects (underground storage of gas, strategic rail freight etc), commercial development, minerals and waste and Compulsory Purchase. Highways, rights of way and Village Greens (as advocate or Inspector). Judicial Review and Statutory Challenges, for developers or as Junior Treasury Counsel.
Professional Memberships: PEBA.
Career: Emmanuel College, Cambridge MA and LLM (Master Of Law), Lord Porter Senior Exhibition. Grays Inn Scholar 1998. Called to the Bar in Oct 1998.

CANNON, Josef
Cornerstone Barristers, London
020 7242 4986
jcannon@cornerstonebarristers.com
Featured in Licensing (London)
Practice Areas: Licensing, planning, housing, public law.
Professional Memberships: Institute of Licensing, ALBA, PEBA.
Career: Called in 2002. Active in all areas of licensing and gambling, with a particular specialism in SEV licensing: counsel for the successful respondent in KVP(Ent) Ltd v South Bucks DC on a JR challenge to a refusal to grant a SEV licence, and junior counsel in Bean Leisure (A) Trading Ltd v Leeds CC, a JR challenge to decisions to refuse SEV licences pursuant to a change in policy. Clients include operators, objectors, police, local authorities at the heart of developing licensing policy, and residents groups. Regular contributor to textbooks on licensing law and practice, member of the IoL and regular lecturer at their events; regular lecturer and trainer for local authorities.
Publications: Contributor to Kolvin, Licensed Premises: Law Practice and Policy (Bloomsbury, 2013) and Kolvin's Gambling for Local Authorities (IoL, 2007). Joint author of Atkin's Court Forms, Vol. 25: Licensing (LexisNexis, 2013).
Personal: Keen but limited cricketer; enthusiastic gourmand; runs (with others) a restaurant in South London in his 'spare time'.

CANNON, Mark QC
4 New Square, London
020 7822 2000
m.cannon@4newsquare.com
Featured in Construction (London), Insurance (London), Professional Negligence (London)
Practice Areas: Professional negligence (accountants, architects, engineers, financial advisers, insurance brokers, lawyers, Lloyd's agents and surveyors); insurance and reinsurance; construction and engineering; general commercial law.
Professional Memberships: Professional Negligence Bar Association (Chairman 2009-11); COMBAR, Chancery Bar Association; Tecbar; London Common Law and Commercial Bar Association.
Career: Educated at Lincoln College, Oxford 1980-83 (BA in Modern History) and Robinson College, Cambridge 1983-84 (Part 1B of Law Tripos). Called to the Bar in 1985. Silk 2008.
Publications: Co-author of 'Cannon & McGurk on Professional Indemnity Insurance' (OUP, 2010). Editor of 'Jackson & Powell on Professional Liability' since 3rd edition (1992).

CAPLAN, Jonathan QC
5 Paper Buildings, London
020 7583 6117
jc@5pb.co.uk
Featured in Health & Safety (London), Inquests & Public Inquiries (London), Crime (London), Financial Crime (London)
Practice Areas: Criminal and civil fraud, corporate liability, media law and contempt, public inquiries, disciplinary and regulatory, health and safety, corruption, money laundering and general criminal issues. Recent cases include: Successfully defending the former Managing Editor of the News of the World in the phone hacking trial (2013-2014). Representing the Department of Justice in Hong Kong in an appeal concerning letters of request to China (2013) and also in an appeal to the Court of Final Appeal concerning communications by defence lawyers with prosecution witnesses and the application of perverting the course of justice (2013). Advising in connection with a multi jurisdiction corruption investigation involving Asia and Europe. Representing Associated Newspapers in the Leveson Inquiry (2011-2012). Representing the SFO in a case involving the construction of section 501 of the Companies Act 2006 (2013). Representing a member of the Saudi Royal family in a libel case against Forbes magazine (2013-4). Advising a senior trader in connection with the LIBOR investigations (2013-2014). Recent reported cases include: AG v Mirror Group Newspapers (2012) 1 WLR 2408 (meaning of "impedence" in Contempt of Court Act); AG v Associated Newspapers (2011) 1 WLR 2097 (first internet contempt case); R v McQuoid Times Law Reports 23rd June 2009 (appeal concerning first FSA prosecution for insider dealing); FACT v Ashton (2013) All ER (D) 60 (June) (domestic infringement of BSkyB rights); R v Balfour Beatty (2007) Business Law Reports 77 (appeal concerning Hatfield Rail disaster); Alton Towers (2007) EWHC Admin 624 (noise nuisance case concerning theme park); R v N Limited (2008) 1 WLR 2684 (jurisdiction to entertain submission of no case before conclusion of prosecution case). Have appeared in many complex fraud cases here and abroad including Guinness ((1996) I Cr App Rep 463), Mirror Group pension, Barings Bank, Blue Arrow, Versailles and Langbar; also Allied Group ((2001) 1 HKLRD 599) and many other cases in Hong Kong as well as cases in Singapore ((1996) 1 SLR 161). Represented P and O Ferries after Zeebrugge disaster ((1991) 93 Cr App Rep 72), Great Western trains after Southall rail crash ((2000) QB 796), and Balfour Beatty after Hatfield disaster ((2007) BLR 77). Media cases include representing Saudi Prince in libel proceedings against Forbes magazine, Associated Newspapers in Leveson Inquiry, John Cleese in libel case against Daily Mail (2004) EMLR 37. Jimmy Nail in libel case against News of the World (2004) EWHC 647, and Channel 5 before OFCOM on premium telephone competitions.
Career: Recorder of the Crown Court; Master of the Bench of Gray's Inn; Co-Head of Chambers; former Chairman of the Public Affairs Committee of the Bar Council; Member of the Chartered Institute of Arbitrators; Member of the Adjudication Panel for the Dubai Media Authority.
Publications: Contributing editor to 'Fraud: Law, Practice and Procedure' (Lexis Nexis). Former Member of the Editorial Board of Journal of Criminal Law. Member of the Times Law Panel from 2009.

CAREY-HUGHES, Richard J QC
9 Bedford Row, London
020 7489 2727
clerks@9bedfordrow.co.uk
Featured in Crime (London)
Practice Areas: Richard Carey-Hughes QC is a highly experienced silk with a heavy criminal practice primarily centred at the Old Bailey. He specialises in all aspects of criminal law including murder, organised crime and serious fraud. He has a particular expertise in joint enterprise murder cases and successfully represented all four appellants in the leading case of R v A in the Court of Appeal; in this case the Vice President gave the judgment which is widely accepted as the most complete and authoritative rehearsal of the law relating to joint enterprise murder. Richard Carey-Hughes also appeared in the House of Lords in the appeals which restricted the automatic inclusion of police officers and prosecutors on juries. He was recently involved in the Court of Appeal in the current leading authority on legal professional privilege which effectively overturned a long line of criminal appeal authority on this complex topic. He was also recently involved n the reported appeal of Moore which is a leading authority on entrapment. His practice in financial crime is extensive and includes appearing in cases which involve solicitors and accountants as defendants and SFO prosecutions. He is a Recorder of longstanding and also a Bencher at Gray's Inn. He is the former holder of a Commercial Pilot's Licence and has extensive experience in aviation.
Professional Memberships: Recorder of the Crown Court 2000 Master of the Bench, Gray's Inn 2006 Former Secretary of the Criminal Bar Association of England & Wales 1996- 1999 Member of South Eastern Circuit Committee 1997-2003 Editor CBA Newsletter 1993-96 Founding Trustee Kalisher Scholarship 1998.
Publications: Editor CBA Newsletter 1992-96.

CARLILE OF BERRIEW, Alex QC
9-12 Bell Yard, London
020 7400 1800
a.carlile@912by.com
Featured in Crime (London), Financial Crime (London)
Practice Areas: Alex Carlile has extensive experience of cases involving fraud, regulation, judicial review and public policy. He has been involved in some of the largest commercial fraud cases of recent times. In a more general criminal setting, he has appeared in high profile Murder cases. He was for 9 years Independent Reviewer of Terrorism Legislation, and has extensive knowledge of the operation of government and Parliament. His knowledge of corporate activity includes long service as a non-executive director of a listed company. He is available for advisory work, inquiries and reviews, and for non-publicly funded contentious cases. He remains an active member of the House of Lords, has written several reports on issues related to criminal justice policy and has chaired numerous committees etc. He is a deputy High Court Judge and Recorder, a Master of the Bench of Gray's Inn, and Chairman of the Lloyd's Enforcement Board. He was called to the Bar in 1970 and became a QC in 1984. He is also a Director of SC Strategy Ltd, a boutique consultancy providing international strategic advice to governments, companies and individuals.

CARPENTER, Chloe
Fountain Court Chambers, London
020 7583 3335
cc@fountaincourt.co.uk
Featured in Professional Discipline (London)
Practice Areas: All areas of commercial law, (in particular arbitration, commercial litigation, banking, insurance and professional negligence) and disciplinary and regulatory work. Recent cases include: acting for the second defendant in Al Sulaiman v Credit Suisse and Plurimi [2013] EWHC 400 (Comm); acting for the claimant in Awal Bank BSC (In Administration) v Al-Sanea [2011] EWHC 1354 (Comm); acting for West LB in the litigation arising out of the Boxclever securitisation; acting for the appellant in Hilton v Barker Booth and Eastwood [2005] UKHL 8; the Miners Compensation cases; Law Society v Baxendale-Walker [2006] 3 All ER 675, [2007] 3 All ER 330, [2008] 1 W.L.R. 426; Thaker v SRA [2012] EWHC 432 (Admin); acting for the SRA (unled) in Lumsdon v LSB, BSB & SRA [2014] EWHC 28 (Admin).
Professional Memberships: COMBAR, ARDL.
Career: Called to the Bar 2001. Educated at Kings College London (LLB, 1st class, 1999) and Brasenose College Oxford (BCL, Distinction, 2000). Member of Fountain Court Chambers since 2002.
Publications: Joint author of The Law of Privilege, edited by Bankim Thanki QC (2nd edition, 2011, Oxford University Press).

CARPENTER, Jamie
Hailsham Chambers, London
020 7643 5000
jamie.carpenter@hailshamchambers.com
Featured in Clinical Negligence (London), Costs Litigation (London), Professional Negligence (London)
Practice Areas: A wide-ranging professional negligence practice involving claims against a variety of professions with a particular interest in limitation points. Clinical

negligence practice (claimant and defendant) involves all specialties and injuries of up to maximum severity. Costs practice involves all areas of costs law, including inter partes and solicitor-client disputes, costs orders and conduct, Part 36, fixed costs, funding arrangements, costs caps and estimates, wasted costs and costs against non-parties. Recent notable cases: "Right to Buy" managed litigation; Mount Eden Land Ltd v Speechly Bircham LLP [2014] EWHC 169 (QB); Flatman v Germany [2013] EWCA Civ 278; Simmons v Castle [2012] EWCA Civ 1288; Morgan v The Spirit Group [2011] EWCA Civ 68; Lane v Cullens [2011] EWCA Civ 547; Bowling & Co v Edehomo [2011] EWHC 393 (Ch); Khan v Solicitors Regulation Authority [2010] EWHC 1555 (Admin); Saunders v The Hearing Aid Council [2010] EWHC 629 (Admin); Cassidy v Stephensons & LSC [2009] EWHC 1562 (QB); R (Wright) v Secretary of State for Health [2009] 1 AC 739.
Professional Memberships: Professional Negligence Bar Association (PNBA).
Career: MA (Cantab), called to the Bar 2000.
Publications: Medical Law Precedents for Lawyers (contributor); Medical Law and Ethics at a Glance (contributor – in production).
Personal: Main interests: music, photography, cycling, rock climbing, Tottenham Hotspur FC.

CARR, Bruce QC
Devereux, London
020 7353 7534
carr@devchambers.co.uk
Featured in Employment (London)
Practice Areas: Employment law, commercial law, some tax and public law. Regularly instructed on behalf of both employers and trade unions, in particular in the EAT. Also frequently appears in interlocutory injunction applications, ranging from restrictive covenants to trade disputes. Substantial practice in discrimination, (including equal pay) transfer of undertakings and large scale redundancy matters. Frequently instructed by a range of government departments. Also instructed in inquiry work.
Professional Memberships: Employment Law Bar Association; Employment Lawyers Association; ILS, Recorder; Member, EAT User Group.
Career: Called 1986. Inner Temple.
Personal: Cambs High School for Boys, Cambridge. Hills Road Sixth Form College, Cambridge. LSE (BSc Economics) 1983, Central London Polytechnic (Dip Law) 1985.

CARTER, Martin
Kings Chambers, Manchester
0845 034 3444
clerks@kingschambers.com
Featured in Planning (Northern)
Practice Areas: All aspects of town and country planning, compulsory purchase, highways, towns and village greens, environment, together with administrative and public law and local government.
Professional Memberships: Planning & Environmental Bar Association; Administrative Law Bar Association; Northern Circuit; North Eastern Circuit.
Career: New College, Oxford MA (Oxon), BA (Jurisprudence) [First Class]; Member of MiddleTemple; Called 1992; Joined Chambers 1992; Appointed to Provincial Panel of Junior Counsel to the Crown.

CARTER, Peter QC
Red Lion Chambers, London
020 7520 6070
peter.carter@18rlc.co.uk
Featured in Crime (London), Financial Crime (London)
Practice Areas: Peter Carter undertakes criminal law prosecution and defence together with public inquiry work (appearing in and advising potential parties). The majority of his time is taken up with fraud cases, but he also appears in cases of terrorism, homicide, trafficking and sexual offences. FRAUD CASES: on behalf of the Financial Services Authority prosecuting a former Partner of Cazenove for offences of insider dealing (R v Calvert) and prosecuting an insider dealing case involving securities based on US stocks, which was achieved by collaboration between the FSA and the US authorities (R v Sanders & others); representing a defendant in a "carousel" fraud; acting for one of a number of pharmaceutical companies unsuccessfully prosecuted by the Serious Fraud Office as an alleged cartel (R v O' Neill and others - Operation Holbein); Doncaster City Council corruption case ('Donnygate'); Anglo-American; Jubilee Line; the Dome fraud; and on behalf of a senior police officer charged with money laundering. PUBLIC INQUIRIES: He is currently acting as counsel to an Inquiry in Trinidad and Tobago into failed pension and insurance companies. He advised some of those potentially involved in the Leveson Inquiry into phone tapping. TERRORISM: Peter was independent Counsel in Bourgass and others (the ricin case); acted for one of defendants in the 21 July 2005 attempted bombings trial, and for one of defendants in the "dirty bomb" plot (Barot and others) and represented a young man charged with neo-Nazi terrorism offences. TRAFFICKING: Peter was counsel for the appellants in R v O and R v N on human trafficking. Following those cases and a series of seminars he has conducted (jointly with Parosha Chandran of Pump Court Chambers, Pam Bowen of the CPS and Riel Karmy-Jones of Red Lion Chambers) he was appointed as a special adviser to the Joint Parliamentary Select Committee on the Modern Slavery Bill. HUMAN RIGHTS: Peter appears pro bono in Privy Council capital cases from the Caribbean, and has appeared in both the High Court and Court of Appeal of Trinidad and Tobago in a capital case remitted from the Privy Council. He represented the applicant in the Inter-American Court of Human Rights on the use of flogging as a penalty. He was one of the counsel instructed to produce an amicus brief on behalf of Members of Parliament in Rasul v Bush (concerning Guantánamo Bay). He frequently lectures on terrorism, the death penalty and human rights in criminal cases.
Professional Memberships: Criminal Bar Association; South Eastern Circuit; International Bar Association; Trustee, Fair Trials Abroad; Patron, Amicus; Member, Institute of Advanced Legal Studies; Member, British Institute of International and Comparative Law.
Career: LLB (UCL). Called 1974. Silk 1995. Bencher, Gray's Inn. Chair, Bar Human Rights Committee 2002-05. Chairman, Gray's Inn Advocacy and Continuing Education Committee 2008-09. Visiting Professor, Birkbeck, University of London.
Publications: 'Offences of Violence' (with Ruth Harrison), Sweet & Maxwell; The chapter on international criminal law in 'Human Rights Protection: Methods and Effectiveness' Frances Butler ed, published by Kluwer, 2001; contributing editor to 'A Practitioner's Guide to Terrorist Trials' published by 18 Red Lion Court, 2007; Article 'The Rule of Law' in (2009) 15 KHRP LR; contributed to a chapter in Human Trafficking Handbook : Recognising Trafficking and Modern-day Slavery in the UK', Chandran, P. ed. (Lexis-Nexis, October 2011).

CARTER, William
One Paper Buildings, London
020 7353 3728
williamcarter@onepaper.co.uk
Featured in Crime (South Eastern)
Practice Areas: Criminal Law, Health and Safety.
Professional Memberships: South Eastern Circuit, CBA.
Career: Will Carter has forged a reputation as an extremely able and knowledgeable barrister, prosecuting and defending in equal measure in serious criminal cases. He is regularly instructed in heavy fraud cases, both as junior and leading junior, where his meticulous approach and attention to detail are well known. He has wide experience of Revenue and Customs cases, in which he acts mainly for the defence. Will has appeared in a number of prosecutions of police officers for offences ranging from corruption to manslaughter. He is instructed as junior and leading junior in murder prosecutions and has particular experience of cases involving sudden death in infants and associated areas of medico-legal expertise. He has appeared in many cases involving charges of serious sexual misconduct, particularly where the allegations date back many years. His practice covers the full range of the criminal law. He has been a contributing editor of the practitioners' handbook Archbold for many years.
Publications: Contributing editor to Archbold.

CARTWRIGHT, Richard
Devereux, London
020 7353 7534
cartwright@devchambers.co.uk
Featured in Clinical Negligence (London), Personal Injury (London)
Practice Areas: Clinical negligence; personal injury (particularly neurotrauma and spinal injuries).
Professional Memberships: PNBA; AvMA.
Career: Clinical negligence: Recent claims include cerebral palsy claims defended on breach of duty and/or causation, missed diagnoses by GP or hospital (NHS and private) (of infection, cauda equina syndrome or post-surgical complications, of spinal tuberculosis, of recent infarction), spinal surgery, bariatric surgery, wrongful birth claims, and brachial plexus birth injuries. Personal injury: neurotrauma and spinal injury following road traffic accidents (eg. Smith v Finch (the cycling helmet case), Sahakian v McDonnell, and Jukes v Etti. In both areas: claims involving complex damages issues and oversea claimants (e.g. France, India, Australia and New Zealand): fatal claims (particularly those involving financial dependency arising from the deceased's business interests). One claim involving traumatic brain injury settled in 2012 for £16.6 million (including notional capitalised periodical payments).
Publications: JPIL article with Robert Glancy.
Personal: Leisure interests include Welsh(Lions) rugby, motor racing and skiing.

CARTWRIGHT, Sophie
Deans Court Chambers, Manchester
0161 214 6000
cartwright@deanscourt.co.uk
Featured in Administrative & Public Law (Northern), Professional Discipline (The Regions)
Practice Areas: Inquests; Court of Protection, Community Care Law; Administrative and Public Law; Professional Discipline; Healthcare; Regulatory Crime including Health and Safety and Care home regulation.
Professional Memberships: HSLA ARDL CoPPA CBA.
Career: Assistant Coroner. Regularly instructed by Local Authorities, NHS Trusts and Companies to represent at inquest and advise pre-inquest, particularly where systemic failings are alleged or Article 2 of the ECHR is engaged. Experience of conducting inquests in respect of deaths in custody representing operators of private prisons and prison escort staff. Judicial Reviews arising out of areas of practice, including representing Health Care Bodies (including Specialist Foundation Trusts; Clinical Commissioning Groups, where convention rights are engaged); Local Authorities and Doctors. Masters in Health and Safety and Environmental Law.

CASEMENT, David QC
Kings Chambers, Manchester
0845 034 3444
clerks@kingschambers.com
Featured in Chancery (Northern), Commercial Dispute Resolution (Northern), Company (Northern), Restructuring/Insolvency (Northern), Sports Law (The Regions)
Practice Areas: Company, Insolvency, Partnership, Commercial fraud, Trusts, Privacy and Confidentiality, Financial Services, Banking, Franchise Agreements, Entertainment, Media, Construction Disputes, Energy, Private International Law, Sport.
Professional Memberships: British Irish Commercial Bar Association (UK Chairman) Northern Circuit Commercial Bar Association (Chairman) Chancery Bar Association. Member of the Bars of England & Wales, Ireland and N Ireland.
Career: Called to the Bar 1992; Recorder 2005; Queen's Counsel 2008; Deputy High Court Judge 2013.

CASEY, Juliette
Westwater Advocates, Edinburgh
0131 260 5700
juliette.casey@westwateradvocates.com
Featured in Employment (Scotland)
Practice Areas: Specialises in employment law, sex discrimination and equality law, european law and human rights, commercial law and criminal law. Reported cases include: Kay v University of Aberdeen 102991/2011 (Disability discrimination under the Equality Act); Foley & Ors v Greater Glasgow Health Board S/114750/2006 (case on whether a Tupe-like transfer is subject to the 6 month time limit imposed by section 2ZA (3) of the Equal Pay Act); The City of Edinburgh Council v Wilkinson [2011] CSIH 70 (Inner House Intervention on behalf of the EHRC); North & Ors v Dumfries & Galloway Council, 2010 (Inner House Intervention on

behalf of the EHRC); Fowler, Adams & Ors v Glasgow City Council Case No 103930/2006 (Equal Pay); Dunn & Ors v Fife Council Case No 104702/2006 & Others (Equal Pay); Lynch & Ors v East Dunbartonshire Council Case Number 115961/2008 & Others (Plea of lis alibi pendens); Equal Pay Claims v North Lanarkshire Council Case Number S/107493/05 & Others; Lee Liddle v Brit Insurance Limited [2011] CSOH 145 (Credit Hire, Avizandum); Alexander Greenlees v Allianz Insurance plc [2011] CSOH 173 (Credit Hire, Avizandum); David Petrie and M Scott v Babcock Marine Cases 4105096/2012 and 4104435/2012 (Unfair Dismissal); Carol Webster v NPL Management Ltd Case 2336178/2013 (Material Factor Defence); Alistair Taylor v Paul Bonner 2013 Avizandum Sheriff Court (Consumer Credit); Glasgow City Council and Ors v Fox Cross and Ors 2014 CSIH 27.
Professional Memberships: Panel of Preferred Counsel for the Equality and Human Rights Commission; Industrial Law Society; Faculty of Advocates Employment Law Group; Faculty of Advocates Criminal Bar Association; Scottish Public Law Group; Scottish Human Rights Law Group; Justice Scotland; International Society for the Reform of Criminal Law.
Career: BCL and LLB, University College Cork; PhD in Equality and Criminal Law, University of Edinburgh; Called to the Bar in 2006; Member of The Honorable Society of King's Inns, Dublin in 2006; Tutored in Criminal Law, Jurisprudence and Constitutional Law at Edinburgh University.
Publications: Various articles in employment and criminal law including: 'The Right to Paid Annual Leave and Sick Leave: Exploring the Relationship and Extending the Right' in Employment Law Bulletin, Issue 98, August 2010; 'Ogden Six and the Civil Jury' in SLT Issue 35: 7-11-2008 229.
Personal: Member of the Scottish Chamber Orchestra Chorus.

CASSERLEY, Catherine
Cloisters, London
020 7827 4000
cc@cloisters.com
Featured in Employment (London)

Practice Areas: Catherine specialises in employment, human rights and discrimination law. She has particular expertise in disability discrimination, having worked as Senior Legal Adviser with the Disability Rights Commission, including in complex employment discrimination cases , and in services and public authority discrimination. She is regularly instructed by the Equality and Human Rights Commission, Law Centres, individuals, trades unions, public authorities and employers and appears in the Employment Tribunal, County Courts, High Court, Employment Appeal Tribunal, Court of Appeal and Supreme Court. She also advises disability organisations and the Equality and Human Rights Commission on a regular basis on litigation and legal policy issues - including on the UN Convention on the Rights of Persons with Disabilities and on the Equality Act 2010. She was also involved in the drafting of the Equality Act 2010 Codes of Practice on Services, guidance on the Public Sector Equality Duty and Education, and more recently on age and services. She has expertise in European discrimination law and has spoken and written extensively on both European and domestic discrimination legislation. Recent cases include: Hall and Preddy v Bull and Bull [2013] UKSC 73- first case to consider goods and servcies discrimination against a gay couple by Christian hotel owners; Finnigan v Chief Constable of Northumbria Police [2013] EWCA Civ 1191 Stott v Thomas Cook Plc [2012] EWCA Civ 66 ; Campbell v Thomas Cook [2013] EqLR 658 - first case where Equality Act 2010 applied to services outside the UK; Foster v Cardiff University Appeal No. UKEAT/0422/12/LA, ; Aylott v Stockton on Tees Borough Council [2010] EWCA Civ 910 - direct disability discrimination; SCA Packaging Ltd v Boyle [2009] UKHL [37] - definition of disability ; Royal Bank of Scotland PLC v Allen [2009] EWCA Civ 1213 ;
Professional Memberships: Director of the Discrimination Law Association: member of ELA and ELBA.
Career: Called to the bar in 1991; prior to returning to the Bar Catherine worked in Law Centres, as a Head of Trade Union legal department, and for a national disability organisation.
Publications: One of the editors of Discrimination in Employment : a claims Handbook (LAG: 2013) Chapters in Equality and Discrimination: the New Law (Jordans, 2010) and in Blackstones Guide to the Equality Act 2010 (2nd edition out).

CASTLE, Richard
1 King's Bench Walk, London
020 7936 1500
rcastle@1kbw.co.uk
Featured in Family/Matrimonial (London)

Practice Areas: Principal area of practice is all aspects of divorce and matrimonial finance, particularly cases involving international and jurisdictional issues and also those involving trusts and complex corporate structures. Has considerable experience of claims under Part III of Matrimonial and Family Proceedings Act 1984 (financial relief after a foreign divorce). Regularly advises in offshore jurisdictions and also in relation to cases involving the tracing of offshore assets. Also specialises in cohabitation disputes involving trusts of land and applications under Children Act 1989 Sch 1. Reported cases include: Evans v Evans [2013] 2 FLR 999, BJ v MJ (Financial Order: Overseas Trust) [2012] 1 FLR 667, Marinos v Marinos [2007] 2 FLR 1018 Bentinck v Bentinck [2007] 2 FLR 1, LK v K (No2) [2007] 2 FLR 729, and Pabari v Secretary of State for Work and Pensions [2005] FCR.
Professional Memberships: FLBA. South Eastern Circuit.
Career: Prince of Wales Scholar (Gray's Inn). Called to the Bar 1998.
Personal: Educated St Dunstan's College and University of Bristol (LLB).

CATTERMOLE, Rebecca
Tanfield Chambers, London
020 7421 5300
rebeccacattermole@tanfieldchambers.co.uk
Featured in Social Housing (London)

Practice Areas: All aspects of housing, landlord and tenant, anti- social behaviour, local government including human rights; and property.
Professional Memberships: Property Bar Association;Social Housing Law Association.
Career: Called to the Bar 1999. Advises and represents public and private sector clients including local authorities, RSLs and leaseholders. Reported Cases: Amicus Horizon Limited v Mabbott (1) Brand(2) Court of Appeal, 30 May 2012 (meaning of living as husband and wife in section 17(4) of the Housing Act 1988); Hyams v Wilfred East Housing Co-Operative Ltd [2007] 1 EGLR 89; Hastoe Housing Association Ltd v Ellis [2007] EWCA Civ 1238; (2008) HLR 25; Windsor & District Housing Association v Hewitt [2011] EWCA Civ 735.
Publications: Service Charges and Management: Law and Practice 3rd Edn (Sweet & Maxwell); Anti- Social Behaviour: Powers and Remedies (with Scott Collins), Sweet & Maxwell 2004; 2nd Edition, Sweet & Maxwell 2006; Contributor to the 5th Edition of Halsbury's Laws of England, Local Government Law, Vol. 69 (2009); and Contributor to Jowitts's Dictionary of English Law (2010) in Housing and Landlord and Tenant.

CAVANAGH, John QC
11KBW, London
020 7632 8500
John.Cavanagh@11kbw.com
Featured in Employment (London)

Practice Areas: Chambers & Partners Employment Silk of the Year 2009, and short-listed 2011. Principal areas of practice are employment law, and areas of commercial law, public law and human rights which overlap with employment law. In employment law particular emphasis on whistleblowing, discrimination and equal pay, TUPE, the European aspects of employment law, restraint of trade, wrongful dismissal, industrial disputes and large-scale redundancies. Has recently acted in O'Brien v Ministry of Justice, Ravat v Halliburton, and Russell v Transocean (all Supreme Court), Mattu v UHCW (CA), USA v Nolan (CA) and Woodford v Olympus Corporation.
Professional Memberships: Employment Law Bar Association (former Chair), Employment Lawyers Association, ALBA and COMBAR.
Career: Called 1985. Joined 11 King's Bench Walk 1985, QC 2001, Recorder 2005. Joint Head of Chambers 2013 -.
Publications: Formerly contributor to Harvey, Tolley's Employment Law and Butterworths 'Local Government Law'.
Personal: Educated: Warwick School; New College, Oxford (MA); Clare College, Cambridge (LLM) and University of Illinois. Married with four children. Lives in Harpenden.

CAYFORD, Philip QC
29 Bedford Row Chambers, London
020 7404 1044
pcayford@29br.co.uk
Featured in Family/Matrimonial (London)

Practice Areas: Family practice, bias towards ancillary relief. Some common law, entertainment and press injunctions. Court of Appeal decisions include Hague Convention and jurisdiction issues (Re R), leave to remove from the jurisdiction (Payne v Payne) [2001] 1 FLR 1052 CA, derivative shareholder action arising from breakdown of family owned company (Barratt v Duckett), setting aside consent orders (Muir), solicitors' conflict of duty (Davies), return of children to non - Hague jurisdictions (B v ELB), leave to remove Re J [2007] 1 FLR 2033, abductions (Re H [2007] 1 FLR 2007), Recusal & judicial humour (El Farargy [2007] EWCA), drawing inferences from non-disclosure (Mahon v Mahon [2008] EWCA Civ 901) and financial provision for Children (Morgan v Hill [2007] 1 FLR 1480). High Court decisions on Sch 1 applications (F v G [2005] 1 FLR 261) reinstating lump sum claim (Re G [2004] 1 FLR 997), big money footballers (Q v Q [2005] 2 FLR 640) costs of ancillary relief applications (RH v RH [2008] 2 FLR 2142) B v B [2010] 1AER D61 (offshore trusts); Re S (leave to remove costs) [2010] 1 FLR 834; PG v TW (No 1) Child: Financial Provision: Legal Funding [2012] EWHC 1892 (Fam); PG v TW (No 2) Child: Financial Provision) [2012]; Vince v Wyatt (striking out, delay, abuse of process) [2013] EWCA Civ 495. (Appeal to Supreme Court December 2014) Shield v Shield [2013] EWHC 23; [2014] EWHC 3525; [2014] EWCA. Other reported decisions on children cases, professional negligence, inquests, etc.
Professional Memberships: Middle Temple Bencher, FLBA Committee, Bar Standards Board Complaints Committee.
Career: Called 1975 with Blackstone Exhibition; joined 29 Bedford Row 1978. Silk 2002. Frequent lecturer.
Publications: Editor of FLBA's news letter, Family Affairs since 2007.

CHACKO, Thomas
Pump Court Tax Chambers, London
020 7414 8080
clerks@pumptax.com
Featured in Tax (London)

Practice Areas: Following 12 months pupillage Tom's tenancy began on 1st October 2009. Tom has a broad based tax practice covering all areas of revenue law, both advising (particularly in private client, employment and VAT) and litigating. Recent litigation has covered customs duties, VAT, general Tribunal procedure, and income tax. Recent cases include Murray Group v HMRC (the Rangers FC litigation), McCarthy and Stone v HMRC (both FTT and UT) and P J Wright (UT, concerning due process).
Professional Memberships: Revenue Bar Association.
Career: 2007 Called to the Bar (Inner Temple) 2008-09 Pupillage, Pump Court Tax Chambers 2009 Tenant, Pump Court Tax Chambers; 2011 2 month secondment at HMRC Solicitors Office.
Publications: Contributor to Ghosh, Johnson and Miller on the Taxation of Corporate Debt and Derivatives, Mortimore on Company Directors (2nd edition) and Halsburys (Stamp Taxes).

CHACKSFIELD, Mark
8 New Square, London
020 7405 4321
mark.chacksfield@8newsquare.co.uk
Featured in Intellectual Property (London)

Practice Areas: Mark practices in all areas of intellectual property law, with particularly strong expertise in major patent litigation. He has considerable experience in appearing as the sole advocate both at first instance and in the Court of Appeal, as well as in the EPO. Recent pharmaceutical and biotech cases include Genentech v. Hospira (Herceptin), Resolution Chemicals v H. Lundbeck (escitalopram/res judicata), Teva v Merck (efavirenz/quia timet actions), Eli Lilly v HGS (Neutrokine-α), Regeneron Pharmaceuticals v Genentech (Lucentis), Ranbaxy v AstraZeneca (Swiss-form claims/esomeprazole), and Convatec v Smith & Nephew (Durafiber wound care products). Mark has represented Nokia in the Interdigital, IPCom and HTC

litigations, as well as working with a number of other high profile telecoms companies. He has also appeared in both high tech and mechanical patent actions, including appearing alone in the leading Court of Appeal case on indirect infringement of Grimme Landmaschinenfabrik v Scott. Other areas of particular experience include media and entertainment, where Mark has represented broadcasters, record companies, picture libraries and well-known personalities in copyright and privacy claims, as well as acting in musical copyright actions concerning substantial hits.
Professional Memberships: Intellectual Property Bar Association (IPBA) and Chancery Bar Association.
Career: Called 1999, Middle Temple.
Personal: Born September 1974. Educated at Royal Grammar School, High Wycombe; Clare College, Cambridge University, BA (Double First) Natural Sciences (Zoology) Hurst Prize for Zoology.

CHAISTY, Paul QC
Kings Chambers, Manchester
0845 034 3444
clerks@kingschambers.com
Featured in Chancery (Northern), Commercial Dispute Resolution (Northern), Company (Northern), Partnership (Northern), Real Estate Litigation (Northern), Restructuring/Insolvency (Northern)
Practice Areas: Chancery and commercial litigation; insolvency - corporate and individual; commercial property; commercial landlord and tenant; professional negligence, director's disqualification; banking - recoveries, guarantees and securities; company - shareholder and boardroom disputes; commercial agents; breach of director and employee duties; partnership; commercial contracts – including joint ventures, share warranty and asset claims, distribution contracts and agency; sale of goods; commercial fraud and sports law.
Professional Memberships: Chancery Bar Association; Northern Chancery Bar Association; Northern Circuit Commercial Bar Association; COMBAR.
Career: University: Nottingham & Exeter College Oxford. Degrees: Law (LLB) (First Class) & BCL. Year of call: 1982 (Lincoln's Inn), Hardwicke and Cassell scholar. Recorder: 2000. Appointed QC: 2001. Official Appointments: Deputy High Court Judge (authorised to sit in Queen's Bench and Chancery Divisions) 2006. Called to Bar in British Virgin Islands and Bahamas 2009.

CHALMERS, Suzanne
Crown Office Chambers, London
020 7797 8100
chalmers@crownofficechambers.com
Featured in Insurance (London)
Practice Areas: Suzanne specialises in insurance, professional negligence and property damage. She acts in relation to all types of policy dispute (non-marine), including all risks, property damage, professional indemnity, personal injury and motor. She handles both coverage disputes and subrogated claims arising out of damage to property. She frequently deals with complex legal issues such as the operation of conditions precedent or warranties, proximate cause and double insurance. Her practice encompasses a wide range of claims for and against professionals, particularly solicitors and barristers, construction professionals and insurance brokers. She regularly acts in high-value property damage claims arising out of fire, flood or subsidence and has particular expertise in cases involving allegations of fraud. She also deals with complex personal injury litigation. She regularly appears as an advocate in the High Court (Queen's Bench Division, TCC and Commercial Court) as well as in the County Court. She has also appeared in the Court of Appeal. She recognises the importance of ADR and has considerable experience of conducting mediations and round table meetings.
Professional Memberships: COMBAR, LCLCBA, PNBA, TECBAR, PIBA.
Career: Barrister at Crown Office Chambers. Called to the Bar in 1995. Appointed as a Recorder in 2009.
Personal: Member of Gray's Inn. Suzanne read law at Magdalen College, Oxford (1994).

CHAMBERLAIN, Emma
Pump Court Tax Chambers, London
020 7414 8080
clerks@pumptax.com
Featured in Tax (London)
Practice Areas: Tax and trust advice for high net worth private clients. Specialist in capital taxation and adviser on all residence, domicile and remittance issues. Advises both HMRC and private clients. At the invitation of the Treasury in January 2013 she became a member of the Interim General Anti-Abuse Advisory Committee and worked with HMRC to produce the guidance and examples on private client taxation that were published in April. She sat on the consultation group that assisted in devising the statutory residence test. This was finally implemented in April 2013. Counsel for the taxpayer on the residence case of Glyn v HMRC FTT [2013]. Frequent tax counsel on divorce cases.
Professional Memberships: STEP Technical Committee, Chartered Institute of Taxation – Council member and member of Capital gains tax and Succession taxes committees. Fellow of the Chartered Institute of Taxation. Winner of outstanding achievement award from STEP
Career: Admitted as a Solicitor, 1986 Called: 1998.
Publications: Co-author of "Trust Taxation and Estate Planning" (4th Edition), Sweet & Maxwell (2014) One reviewer noted of 3rd edition : "I am confident that Winston Churchill would have forgiven me for misquoting him- albeit in context – when I say that never in the field of trust taxation was so much owed by so many to so few... this as is the case of all books produced by these two very clever lawyers, is a real tour de force." Co-editor of "Dymond's Capital Taxes" Co-author of "Pre-Owned Assets and Estate Planning (3rd Edition), Sweet and Maxwell, (2009) Co-author of Mirrlees Report IFS "Wealth and Wealth Transfer taxes" OUP 2009 Co-author of "Inheritance Tax Planning before 6th April 2008", Sweet and Maxwell (2008).

CHAMBERLAYNE, Patrick QC
29 Bedford Row Chambers, London
020 7404 1044
clerks@29br.co.uk
Featured in Family/Matrimonial (London)
Practice Areas: Barrister specialising in Financial Remedy, Private Law Children Applications, Inheritance Act Claims & Cohabitation. He also specialises in high net worth divorce (including Part III claims after foreign divorce), civil partnership and Schedule 1 claims and jurisdiction disputes. Particular interest in cases involving non-disclosure, trusts and businesses and cases with an international element. Cases include: SA v PA (Pre-marital agreement: Compensation) [2014] EWHC 392; H v H [2014] EWHC 760 (Fam); W v C (Financial Remedies: Appeal: Non-Disclosure) [2013] 2 FLR 115; Sekhri v Ray [2013] All ER (D) 350 (Jul); Lawrence v Gallagher [2012] EWCA (Civ 394); H v S [2011] EWHC B23 (Fam); Riding v Riding [2011] EWHC 3093 (Fam); Re G (Maintenance Pending Suit) [2007] 1 FLR 1674, CA; P v P (Inherited property) [2005] 1 FLR 576, FD.
Professional Memberships: FLBA.
Career: Called 1991, Inner Court. Appointed Silk 2010.
Personal: Clare College, Cambridge (MA Cantab); Bar School 91992 Scarman scholar).

CHAMBERS, Gaynor
Keating Chambers, London
020 7544 2600
gchambers@keatingchambers.com
Featured in Construction (London), Energy & Natural Resources (London)
Practice Areas: Energy, professional negligence, shipbuilding, environmental, sewage and wastewater treatment, as well as general construction and engineering matters ranging from procurement to final account claims. Previous career in building surveying. Experienced in advising on many standard forms, including the IChemE Red Book, MF/1, NEC and JCT contracts. Equally familiar with conducting disputes through the TCC, arbitration or adjudication. An experienced adjudicator (on the TECBAR and IChem E panels).
Professional Memberships: SCL and COMBAR.
Career: BSc (Hons) Building Surveying (1st); Called 1998; Public Access Training 2008.
Publications: Keating on JCT Contracts, Member of Editorial Team; Engineer's Dispute Resolution Handbook (Thomas Telford, 2006), author of chapter on dispute avoidance.

CHANDLER, Alexander
1 King's Bench Walk, London
020 7936 1500
achandler@1kbw.co.uk
Featured in Family/Matrimonial (London)
Practice Areas: Matrimonial finance, including claims involving third party interveners. Cohabitee claims under TOLATA and applications for financial provision under Schedule 1 to the Children Act 1989.
Professional Memberships: Family Law Bar Association, Chancery Bar Association, Member of the Chartered Institute of Arbitrators and Institute of Family Law Arbitrators.
Career: Called to Bar (Middle Temple, Benefactors' Scholar), 1995. Deputy District Judge (Civil) 2013, (Family) 2014; sitting on the South-Eastern Circuit. Panel Member of the Bar Tribunals and Adjudication Service (BTAS), 2013. Arbitrator in financial claims (MCIArb). Lectures with LexisNexis, Resolution, Thomson Reuters and Central Law Training.
Publications: Halsbury's Laws of England (Vol. 5(4)), Butterworths' Civil Court Precedents (Ancillary Relief), Jowitt's Dictionary of English Law. Recent articles include: "Bleak House II: The Interveners" [2013] Fam Law 821 "The Law Is Now Reasonably Clear: The Courts' Approach to Non-Matrimonial Assets" [2012] Fam Law 163, "Quantifying Shares in Jointly Owned Property: Stack v Dowden, Kernott v Jones", [2010] Fam Law 834. A full list of Alexander's publications can be found at www.familybrief.org.
Personal: Educated at King's School, Canterbury and Hertford College, Oxford (Modern History). Diploma of Law (City University). Married, living in Richmond with a steadily growing family.

CHAPMAN, Graham QC
4 New Square, London
020 7822 2120
g.chapman@4newsquare.com
Featured in Construction (London), Professional Negligence (London)
Practice Areas: Professional liability claims in a commercial context, commercial litigation and construction, engineering and environmental law. Professional liability work includes claims against lawyers, surveyors and valuers, architects and engineers, accountants and auditors, financial services professionals, and insurance brokers and agents. Also experience of professional disciplinary matters. Commercial practice spans the full range of commercial disputes including international arbitration and insurance and reinsurance work. In the construction field he has acted for and against contractors, architects and engineers in claims concerning projects both in the UK and overseas. International experience includes cases in BVI, Cayman, Channel Islands and Malaysia.
Professional Memberships: PNBA; COMBAR; TECBAR.
Career: BA (Oxon). (1st Class). Called to the Bar (Inner Temple) 1998 (Major Scholarship). Tenant 4 New Square 1999 to date.
Publications: Assistant editor to the 6th Ed. of 'Jackson & Powell on Professional Liability; contributing editor 'Construction Law Handbook'.
Personal: Educated Westcliff High School for Boys, Westcliff-on-Sea and Oriel College, Oxford (Scholar).

CHAPMAN, Jeffrey QC
Fountain Court Chambers, London
020 7583 3335
jpc@fountaincourt.co.uk
Featured in Banking & Finance (London), Commercial Dispute Resolution (London), Fraud (London)
Practice Areas: Commercial litigation including civil fraud, banking, international arbitration, insurance/reinsurance and professional negligence. Instructed in various long-running fraud proceedings in multiple jurisdictions (including MTN fraud proceedings [2014] EWHC 2046 (Ch) and the JSC BTA Bank litigation); professional negligence litigation relating to the collapse of Keydata Investments Limited; and also on behalf of the FSA. Acted in the successful Olympic stadium judicial review proceedings (acting on behalf of Leyton Orient FC) and advises on insurance coverage issues.
Professional Memberships: BSB PCC barrister pool member; COMBAR; CEDR Accredited Mediator.
Career: Law Commission 1986-89. Called 1989. British Virgin Islands Bar (1999). QC 2010.

Personal: BA First Class University of Sussex (1985); LLM First Class, Trinity Hall, Cambridge (1986).

CHAPMAN, John
Pump Court Chambers, London
020 7353 0711
j.chapman@pumpcourtchambers.com
Featured in Family/Matrimonial (Western)
Practice Areas: Family finance on the breakdown of marriage or civil partnership. Private law children disputes. Cohabitation cases.
Professional Memberships: FLBA (Treasurer Wessex region).
Career: Called 2003. Joined Pump Court Chambers after successful pupillage with Edward Boydell. Accredited pupil supervisor.
Personal: Married. Kings College London (BA Hons). BPP Law School London (PGDL & BVC).

CHAPMAN, Matthew
1 Chancery Lane, London
020 7092 2900
mchapman@1chancerylane.com
Featured in Personal Injury (London)
Practice Areas: Matthew Chapman practises primarily in the field of personal injury. His particular experience in travel and overseas accident claims sees him acting for claimants and defendants in cases pursued and defended under the Package Travel etc. Regulations 1992 and the international transport and carriage conventions. He regularly appears in matters that engage section 3 of the Judgments Regulation ('Odenbreit claims'), Part III of the Private International Law (Miscellaneous Provisions) Act 1995, the Rome I and II Regulations. In addition, he regularly appears for tour operators and other defendants in contractual and other recovery proceedings against foreign suppliers and his non-contentious practice includes advice on booking conditions and insurance contracts. Matthew's domestic personal injury practice includes employers' liability claims (including workplace stress), highways matters and occupiers' liability actions. While he acts regularly for both claimants and defendants, he has particular experience in acting for public bodies: local authorities, schools and hospitals. Matthew's reported cases include: Wall v Mutuelle de Poitiers Assurances [2014]; Brownlie v Four Seasons Holdings Incorporated [2014]; XYZ & YZA v Adventure Lifesigns & Gravesend Grammar School for Girls [2012]; Williams & Debling v Fred Olsen Cruise Lines Ltd [2011]; Cosmos Holidays Plc v Dhanjal Investments Limited [2009].
Professional Memberships: Professional Negligence Bar Association; Travel & Tourism Lawyers' Association (former Chairman); Personal Injury Bar Association; Bar Standards Board 'Mountfield Committee' on Financial Support for Entrants to the Bar (2002); Bar Council representative on Joint Academic Stage Board (2002 to 2012); Conciliator for the Passenger Shipping Association Conciliation Scheme(2005-10).
Career: Called to the Bar 1994; Inns of Court Pegasus Scholar (Australia) 1999.
Publications: 'Fraudulent Claims', Xpl Publishing 2007; 'The Fast Track and Personal Injury Claims', CLT Professional Publishing, 1999; Co-author (with Caroline Stack) of Chapter 15, 'Immigration Controls in the United Kingdom' in M J Finney and J Dixon (eds), Tolley's International Tax Planning (4th ed 2000). 'The Snail and the Ginger Beer: The Singular Case of Donoghue v Stevenson' (Widly, Simmonds and Hill 2009). Co-author, "Saggerson on Travel law and Litigation" (Widly,Simmonds and Hill 2013).
Personal: Cinema, reading.

CHAPMAN, Nicholas
29 Bedford Row Chambers, London
020 7404 1044
nchapman@29br.co.uk
Featured in Family/Matrimonial (London)
Practice Areas: Principal area of practice is Financial Remedy Applications including Financial Provision for Children, Pre and post-nuptial agreements, cohabitation disputes and Inheritance Act Claims. Also has experience of private law children and domestic violence work.
Professional Memberships: Family Law Bar Association.
Career: After completing a degree in Economics at UCL and a short service career as a Royal Naval Officer undertook Diploma in Law at City University and called to the Bar in 1990. Early career in general Common Law before specialising in Family Law since 1999. Collaborative Law trained and undertakes Public Access work. Has sat as Deputy District Judge on Western Circuit since 2000. Notable cases include: Yates v Yates [2013] 2 FLR 1070; V v V (divorce; jurisdiction) [2011] 2 FLR 778; Currey v Currey [2005] 1 FLR 952 & Matharu v Matharu [1994] 2 FLR 597.
Publications: Frequent Lecturer.
Personal: Married with three children. Lives in London and Dorset. Interests include cricket, national hunt racing and politics.

CHAPMAN, Richard
18 St John Street, Manchester
0161 278 1800
rchapman@18sjs.com
Featured in Commercial Dispute Resolution (Northern)
Practice Areas: Chancery and commercial law, including: real property, landlord and tenant, contract, company, trusts, partnership, insolvency, wills, intestacy, professional negligence, contract, banking, sale of goods.
Professional Memberships: Northern Circuit Commercial Bar Association (Committee Member), Northern Chancery Bar Association, Chancery Bar Association, Organisation of Jewish Lawyers, Mercantile Court Users Group (Committee Member).
Career: Called to the Bar in 1998. Junior Counsel to the Crown (Regional Panel) since 2002.
Personal: Educated at: The Manchester Grammar School; Brasenose College, Oxford (Jurisprudence; BA (Oxon); awarded the Somerset Iver Exhibition); Gray's Inn (awarded the Lord Justice Holker Award); Inns of Court School of Law.

CHAPMAN, Vivian R QC
9 Stone Buildings, London
020 7404 5055
vchapman@9stonebuildings.com
Featured in Agriculture & Rural Affairs (London)
Practice Areas: Property litigation with particular interest in law of commons and greens. His Report as inspector was upheld by the Supreme Court in R (Barkas) v North Yorkshire CC [2014] 2 WLR 1360 and was described by Lord Neuberger as an "excellent report prepared by Vivian Chapman QC". Described as 'a member of the Bar expert in the law of commons and greens' by Lord Hoffmann in Oxfordshire CC v Oxford City Council [2006] 2 AC 674 and as having "very extensive knowledge and experience of this area of the law" by HH Judge Waksman QC in R (Oxfordshire NHS Trust) v Oxfordshire County Council [2010] EWHC (Admin). Interesting cases include: R (Mann) v Somerset County Council [2012] (Green), Llewellyn v Lorey [2011] (CA: right of way), McLaren v Kubiak [2007] (Green: Jurisdiction of court), Hertfordshire v SoS [2006] (CA; rights of way; extinguishment), Fraser v Canterbury Diocesan Board of Finance (No. 2) [2006] 1 All ER 315 (House of Lords: School Sites Acts), Sangster v Biddulphs [2005] PNLR 33 (Partnership: professional negligence), R (Richards) v Pembrokeshire County Council [2005] BLGR 105 (Court of Appeal: judicial review ECHR art 6. and 1st Protocol art. 1.); Crest Nicholson Residential (South) Ltd v McAllister [2004] 1 WLR 2409 (Court of Appeal. Restrictive covenants); Fraser v Canterbury Diocesan Board of Finance (No 2) (2004) 148 SJ LB 149 (Court of Appeal. School Sites Acts); Massey v Boulden [2003] 2 All ER 87 (Court of Appeal: rights of way); Padgham v Rochelle (2003) WTLR 71, (2002) WTLR 1483 (undue influence); Bettison v Langton [2002] 1 AC 27 (House of Lords: rights of common); Carapeto v Good (2002) WTLR 801, 1305 & 1311 (probate); Fitzpatrick v Sterling Housing Association Ltd [2001] 1 AC 27 (House of Lords: Landlord and Tenant); Fraser v Canterbury Diocesan Board of Finance [2001] Ch 669 (Court of Appeal: Schools Sites Acts); Barclays Bank Trust Co Ltd v McDougall (2001) 2 WTLR 23 (trusts: construction of settlement); R v National Assembly of Wales ex p Robinson (2000) 80 P&CR 348 (public rights of way: deletion from definitive map). Frequently instructed by local authorities to chair public inquiries into applications to register new greens. Public inquiries in 2014: as inspector for Northamptonshire(2 inquiries) and as counsel in Surrey (2 inquiries) and Kent. Was the inspector in the cases of Sunningwell (House of Lords), McAlpine (High Court), Trap Grounds (House of Lords), Redcar (Supreme Court), Warneford Meadow (High Court) and Barkas (Supreme Court).
Professional Memberships: Lincoln's Inn (Bencher): Middle Temple: Chancery Bar Association: Property Bar Association: Recorder.
Career: Silk 2006.
Publications: Chancery Litigation Handbook (Jordans 2005). Town and Village Greens (2014).

CHAPPLE, Malcolm
New Square Chambers, London
020 7419 8000
malcolm.chapple
@newsquarechambers.co.uk
Featured in Intellectual Property (London), Telecommunications (London)
Practice Areas: Intellectual property, telecommunications and commercial.
Professional Memberships: Chancery Bar Association, Fellow of the Charted Institute of Arbitrators.
Career: Malcolm has a business litigation practice. He specialises in intellectual property litigation and contractual disputes. He appears regularly in the Chancery Division (including the IPEC), in the UKIPO Trade Mark Tribunal and on appeal therefrom before the Appointed Person. He has also acted for parties in Community registered trade mark disputes before both the General Court and the Court of Justice of the European Union. Recent cases include: Ross River v Waveley (breach of trust action) [2012] EWHC 81 (Ch); Shah v Three-N-Products Limited EU General Court T-313/10 and CJEU C-14/12 (trade mark opposition); Red Bull v Red Z [2012/13] (UKIPO and Appointed Person trade mark invalidity and opposition); Scott v West [2012] EWHC 1890 (Ch) (boiler room fraud); Mackie v Baxter [2012] EWHC 1890 (Ch) (boiler room fraud); SANI trade mark EU General Court T-523/12 (trade mark opposition); Pintorex v Keyvanfar [2013] EWPCC 36 (breach of confidence); Morse v Eaglemoss [2013] EWHC 1507 (copyright licensing dispute); FITZROY & MASON trade mark [2012/13] (UKIPO and Appointed Person trade mark invalidity and opposition); Norwich Pharmacal applications.
Publications: Intellectual property section of 'Law and the Business of Sport'.
Personal: Awarded BSc (first class) Aircraft Engineering. A Governor of Royal Star and Garter Home.

CHARBIT, Valerie
2 Bedford Row, London
020 7440 8888
clerks@2bedfordrow.co.uk
Featured in Crime (London)
Practice Areas: Valerie Charbit is a specialist advocate with considerable experience in both defending and prosecuting significant cases involving fraud, corruption, murder/manslaughter, health and safety, and other serious crime. Recent fraud cases include defending one of six solicitors charged with a £50 million mortgage fraud. In 2013 she was instructed to defend in the £200 million corruption and fraud involving [Halifax Bank of Scotland]. She prosecuted an accountant on a wide-ranging tax fraud against HMRC. She regularly acts for the Responsible Authority before the First Tier Tribunal (Mental Health) on restricted cases at Rampton Hospital involving a variety of mental health professionals on both sides. Valerie has also sat as a part-time judge for the First Tier Tribunal (Mental Health) since 2004. She is instructed to deal with appeals in both the Court of Appeal and the Upper Tier Tribunal. She is regularly instructed to defend and prosecute on murder/manslaughter cases. She has recently acted in cases where the defendant has Asperger's and is highly experienced in presenting and cross-examining on complex psychiatric evidence. Valerie has a growing reputation for cases involving mental disorder, diminished responsibility and other mental health issues, as well as cases involving vulnerable defendants or witnesses. In 2013 Valerie prosecuted and defended numerous rape cases involving children, domestic violence and historic sexual and other offences. She has been appointed to the A list for Specialist Regulatory Advocates in Health and Safety and Environmental Law and is also a Grade 4 Prosecution Advocate for the CPS, and has also been appointed to the CPS Fraud and Rape specialist panels. Valerie is legal adviser for disciplinary proceedings taken by the Association of Chartered Certified Accountants, the General Pharmaceutical Council and the Nursing and Midwifery Council. She is a chair for the Taxation Disciplinary

Board and an approved Advocacy Trainer for Middle Temple.
Professional Memberships: Criminal Bar Association; Association of Regulatory and Disciplinary lawyers; Health and Safety Lawyers Association; Mental Health Lawyers Association; South Eastern Circuit.
Career: Called 1992.

CHARLES, Henry
12 King's Bench Walk, London
020 7583 0811
charles@123KBW.co.uk
Featured in Clinical Negligence (London), Personal Injury (London)
Practice Areas: Personal injury, clinical negligence, legal professional negligence in respect of personal injury/ clinical negligence, health and safety and driving offences.
Professional Memberships: Personal Injury Bar Association; Professional Negligence Bar Association.
Career: Called 1987.
Personal: Enjoys both vintage and modern cars and horse riding.

CHARLWOOD, Spike
Hailsham Chambers, London
020 7643 5000
spike.charlwood@hailshamchambers.com
Featured in Professional Negligence (London)
Practice Areas: Professional negligence (especially lawyers, financial professions, insurance brokers and surveyors and valuers) and insurance law. Cases include: Zurich v Karim; Hobson v Ashton Morton Slack; Walker v Chruszcz; Polley v Warner Goodman & Streat (CA); Dubai Aluminium v Salaam (HL); Farley v Skinner (HL); Nationwide v Various Solicitors and numerous other lenders' claims; Asiansky v Khanzada; Guy v Mace & Jones; and Ikbal v Sterling Law. Spike has experience of managed and group litigation and large-scale mediation and so is well placed to deal with the issues to which such multi-party claims give rise. He has lectured widely on professional negligence.
Professional Memberships: PNBA; LCLCBA; SE Circuit.
Career: Called 1994; supervisor in Tort, Queens' College, Cambridge 1993-95.
Publications: 'Professional Negligence and Liability' (LLP, 2000): assistant editor and joint author of the chapter on barristers' negligence; 'Lloyds Law Reports: Professional Negligence', contributing editor 1999-2003; 'Cordery on Solicitors' (9th edition, looseleaf): previously a contributing editor; articles in the 'Solicitors' Journal' 1999-2007.
Personal: Education: Queens' College, Cambridge (MA (Hons) 1st Class). Leisure interests include walking, travel, wine, reading.

CHARMAN, Andrew
St Philips Chambers, Birmingham
0121 246 7000
acharman@st-philips.com
Featured in Chancery (Midlands), Commercial Dispute Resolution (Midlands)
See under Leaders at the Bar for profile.

CHAWLA, Mukul QC
9-12 Bell Yard, London
020 7400 1800
m.chawla@912by.com
Featured in Crime (London), Financial Crime (London)
Practice Areas: Defends and prosecutes in fraud and general crime. Professional discipline, particularly accountants and police officers. Currently instructed by the Serious Fraud as Lead Counsel in relation to LIBOR and by the CPS in a corruption trial involving a senior employee of the European Bank for Research & Development. Advising a number of individuals and companies in fraud investigations and acting for the Financial Reporting Council. In the last year he has defended in fraud and insider dealing cases and prosecuted an arms brokering case involving a huge quantity of weaponry from China to Nigeria. He has also acted in successful appeals against the revocation of shotgun, firearm and firearm dealers licenses. An accredited CEDR mediator and authorised to accept direct access work.
Professional Memberships: Criminal Bar Association and Founding Member of the Fraud Lawyers Association.
Career: Called (Gray's Inn) in 1983, appointed QC in 2001 and a Recorder of the Crown Court in 2007. Appointed Head of Chambers in January 2012. Vice-Chair - Gray's Inn Advocacy Training Committee
Personal: Born in Nairobi, Kenya on 31 May 1961. Educated at University College, London (LLB Hons).

CHEEMA, Bobbie QC
2 Hare Court, London
020 7353 5324
clerks@2harecourt.com
Featured in Crime (London)
Practice Areas: Bobbie Cheema is a well-respected Senior Treasury Counsel and Queen's Counsel who invariably attracts the respect of the court and her opponents. She relishes complex and demanding cases wherever the instructions originate from and has been instructed in many high profile cases in recent years. In silk she intends to make time to develop her defence practice as well as continuing to prosecute terrorism, serious fraud and homicide at the Central Criminal Court and country-wide. Bobbie Cheema is authorised to sit as a Deputy High Court Judge (Admin Court and QBD) and Crown Court Recorder. She is security cleared to DV level.
Professional Memberships: Criminal Bar Association and SE Circuit.
Career: Called 1989 (Gray's Inn). Attorney General's 'A' List. Serious Fraud Office list of preferred Counsel. Treasury Counsel at the Central Criminal Court 2006. Recorder 2006. Deputy High Court Judge 2010, Senior Treasury Counsel at the Old Bailey 2011, Queen's Counsel 2013.

CHEETHAM, Simon
Old Square Chambers, London
020 7269 0300
cheetham@oldsquare.co.uk
Featured in Employment (London)
Practice Areas: All aspects of employment and discrimination law, including industrial relations; represents both claimants and respondents in tribunals, High Court and on appeal; also professional disciplinary hearings (GMC, NMC etc) and pensions. Recent reported cases include Lock v British Gas [2014] IRLR 605, ECJ; I-Lab Facilities Ltd v Metcalfe [2013] IRLR 605, EAT; Commissioner of Police v Shaw [2012 ICR 464, EAT; and Wardle v Credit Agricole [2011] ICR 1290, CA. Recent work has included obtaining injunctions for and against trade unions, conducting high-profile internal investigations for universities and multi-day discrimination hearings.
Professional Memberships: Employment Lawyers Association, Employment Law Bar Association (Committee member), Industrial Law Society.
Career: Called to the Bar 1991. Fee-paid Employment Judge since 2002. Regularly lectures in-house and at conferences.
Publications: 'Equality and Discrimination: The New Law' (Jordans 2010); 'Age Discrimination: The New Law ' (Jordans 2006).

CHELVAN, S
No5 Chambers, London
0845 210 5555
sch@no5.com
Featured in Immigration (London)
Practice Areas: 2014 Legal Aid Barrister of the Year. Chelvan litigates, and provides advice on strategic litigation, from the First-tier Tribunal (Immigration and Asylum Chamber), up to and including the Supreme Court and the European Courts. Chelvan has a practice which spans the entire spectrum of immigration, asylum and nationality law, which is at the forefront of cutting edge litigation in the field. His practice additionally comes within the broader fields of civil liberties and human rights, and public law, specifically with respect to judicial review. His international work not only includes litigation, but also encompasses advisory work with practitioners, academics, the judiciary, the UNHCR, NGOs, the media and governments.
Professional Memberships: Preferred Panel List, Equalities and Human Rights Commission (April 2013 to date); ALBA; ILPA & BLAGG.
Career: Call: 14 October 1999, Inner Temple (Major Scholarship and Duke of Edinburgh Entrance Award). Tenant at No5 Chambers (January 2011 to date).
Publications: co-author with Harper et al "Same Sex Marriage and Civil Partnerships: the New Law" (Jordans, 2014).
Personal: Born 1 September 1974, Colombo, Sri Lanka. BSc (Soc Sci) Politics and Law (First Class) University of Southampton. LLM, Harvard Law School (Kennedy Memorial Trust Scholar). PhD Law (Candidate) (PT) King's College London.

CHENG, Serena
Atkin Chambers, London
020 7404 0102
scheng@atkinchambers.com
Featured in Construction (London)
Practice Areas: Serena is a commercial litigation and arbitration specialist with a particular emphasis on technically complex plant and utilities, construction and engineering, PFI and infrastructure disputes. She is regularly instructed to appear as both junior and sole counsel in the London TCC, in the District Registries and in domestic and international arbitration and has extensive experience of cross-examining both factual and expert witnesses. Recently reported cases : University of Brighton v. Dovehouse Interiors Ltd. (2014) 153 Con LR 147 (Adjudication – construction of conclusive evidence clause); Hillcrest Homes Ltd. v. Beresford & Curbishley Ltd. (2014) 153 Con LR 179, [2014] CILL 3506 (adjudication – jurisdiction to determine misrepresentation claims); Doosan Babcock Ltd v. Comercializadora de Equipos y Materiales MABE LDA [2014] BLR 33 (injunctive relief - performance bonds).
Professional Memberships: COMBAR; LCLCBA; SCL and TECBAR. Serena is an elected member of TECBAR's Management Committee.
Career: LLB (Hons) (London) 1999; called to the Bar of Lincoln's Inn 2000; Atkin Chambers 2001.
Publications: "Hudson's Building and Engineering Contracts", 12th Ed. (Sweet & Maxwell, 2010), contributing editor.

CHERN, Cyril
Crown Office Chambers, London
020 7797 8100
chern@crownofficechambers.com
Featured in Construction (London), International Arbitration (London)
Practice Areas: Dr Chern is a Barrister at Crown Office Chambers, London and specialises in engineering and construction projects in the United Kingdom, Europe, the Middle-East, South America, China, Singapore, and internationally with emphasis on the development and construction of both standard and PPP infrastructure projects. These include hydro-electric and nuclear facilities, facility and processing development, water treatment facilities, rail and roads projects, bridges, and tunnels. In addition to being a Barrister he is a trained Structural Engineer, Chartered Architect, Chartered Arbitrator, Accredited Mediator and Adjudicator.
Professional Memberships: Dr Chern is a Barrister at Crown Office Chambers, London and specialises in engineering and construction projects in the United Kingdom, Europe, the Middle-East, South America, China, Singapore, and internationally with emphasis on the development and construction of both standard and PPP infrastructure projects. These include hydro-electric and nuclear facilities, facility and processing development, water treatment facilities, rail and roads projects, bridges, and tunnels. In addition to being a Barrister he is a trained Structural Engineer, Chartered Architect, Chartered Arbitrator, Accredited Mediator and Adjudicator.
Publications: Dr Chern is also the author of numerous books relating to construction including: Chern on Dispute Boards – 1st and 2nd Editions (Wiley-Blackwell), 3rd Edition (Informa), International Commercial Mediation and The Law of Construction Disputes (Informa). He is also the co-author of Emden's Construction Law and its ADR and Dispute Boards section (LexisNexis). His newest books The Commercial Mediator's Handbook and Construction Delay and Damage are being published in early 2015.

CHERRY, Joanna QC
Arnot Manderson, Edinburgh
07710 769 081
joannacherry@amadvocates.co.uk
Featured in Clinical Negligence (Scotland)
Practice Areas: Clinical and Professional Negligence, Fatal Accidents and Public Inquiries, Personal Injury, Public and Administrative Law, Human Rights, Mental Health and Crime. She has extensive Appellate experience particularly in the UK Supreme Court where she lead for the Crown in the Sons and Grandsons of Cadder cases. She has also been instructed there in civil cases.
Professional Memberships: Trustee of the Scottish Council of Law Reporting; Chairperson of the Clark Foundation Legal Education Advisory Committee; Member

of the Faculty of Advocates Faculty Council and Convenor of the Faculty's Law Reform Committee.
Career: Edinburgh University; LLB Hons (1st class) 1988; Constitutional Law Honours Essay Prize Winner; Vans Dunlop Scholar; LLM 1989; Dip L.P. 1990; Scottish Law Commission research assistant; Tutor, University of Edinburgh; Brodies WS, Trainee and Solicitor; Called to the Bar 1995; Silk 2009; Standing Junior to the Scottish Government 2003-2008; Advocate Depute and Senior Advocate Depute 2008-2011.
Publications: Joint author and legal editor of Mental Health and Scots Law in Practice published by Greens (2nd edition). Joanna gives regular presentations on Clinical Negligence and Public Law. In 2010 she delivered a paper on "The Prosecution of Sexual Crime in Scotland" to the New South Wales Prosecutors' Conference. She has given evidence to the Justice Committee of the Scottish Parliament on behalf of the Faculty regarding law reform.

CHILD, Andrew J
3 Stone Buildings, London
020 7242 4937
achild@3sb.law.co.uk
Featured in Chancery (London), Offshore (London), Trusts (London)
Practice Areas: Specialises in contentious trust and estate litigation and civil fraud.
Professional Memberships: Chancery Bar Association, Revenue Bar Association.
Personal: King's College School Wimbledon, Sidney Sussex College Cambridge.

CHINN, Antony QC
9 Bedford Row, London
020 7489 2727
antony.chinnqc@9bedfordrow.co.uk
Featured in Crime (London)
Practice Areas: Crime and related matters. In addition to defending in a broad spectrum of serious criminal trials, clients who have sought advice or representation include television, film and music personalities, politicians, national media, a Formula One Team Principal, a former Formula One World Champion, his motor racing son, premiership footballers and supermodels. Cases of interest include representing a soldier accused of murdering an Iraqi civilian during the conflict in Iraq, representing a barrister on charges of child pornography and outraging public decency, and one of several defendants accused of conspiring to blow up airliners in 2006. Recently engaged in perhaps the largest MTIC fraud to be prosecuted.
Professional Memberships: Western and South Eastern Circuits; Criminal Bar Association.
Career: Assistant recorder 1996: recorder 2000. Tribunal Chairman: Motor Sports Association 2002.
Personal: Married. Two sons. Interests include motor racing, music and football.

CHISHOLM, Malcolm
1 Garden Court Family Law Chambers, London
020 7092 3700
chisholm@1gc.com
Featured in Court of Protection (All Circuits)
Practice Areas: Care proceedings and special guardianship, Court of Protection, private family law relating to children (residence, contact, leave to remove), adoption (international and domestic), child abduction, media injunctions in family and Court of Protection cases.
Professional Memberships: Family Law Bar Association, Association of Lawyers for Children.
Career: Called 1989 (Inner Temple). Joined 1 Garden Court Family Law Chambers in 2000. Appointed part time tribunal judge (Mental Health Tribunal) in 2004. Regular lecturer and podcaster. Reported cases include Re P (Parental Responsibility) [1998] 2 FLR 1996, CA, Re B (Abduction: False Immigration Information) [2000] 2 FLR 835, FD, Greenwich London Borough Council v. S [2007] 2 FLR 154, FD (Convention adoption order/habitual residence), Re LM (Reporting Restrictions: Coroner's Inquest) [2008] 1 FLR 1360, FD (Restrictions on publicity/Art 8/Art 10), Re A (A Child) (Adoption: Removal) [2009] 2 FLR 597, CA (Placement of children overseas for purposes of adoption), Re T (Care Order) [2009] 2 FLR 574, CA (Court's duties when presented with a proposed agreed order), X and Y v. Warwickshire County Council and B [2009] EWHC 47 (Wholesale breach of adoption rules in FPC), Re W (Adoption Order: Set Aside and Leave to Oppose) [2011] 1 FLR 2153 (Approach to be taken to late application to oppose adoption, SMBC v PR (SR Intervening) (Care Proceedings: Children's Evidence)(No 2) [2012] 1 FLR 852, FD: Court's approach to vulnerable witnesses, RC v CC [2013] EWHC 1424 (COP): withholding disclosure on behalf of adopted adult.
Personal: Born 1966. Educated at Sidney Sussex College, Cambridge (MA Law). Married with three children.

CHIVERS, David QC
Erskine Chambers, London
020 7242 5532
clerks@erskinechambers.com
Featured in Commercial Dispute Resolution (London), Company (London), Restructuring/Insolvency (London)
Practice Areas: David is a highly experienced, sought-after Silk who specialises in company law, corporate litigation and corporate restructuring/insolvency - onshore, offshore and internationally. He is known for the quality of both his advocacy and advisory skills. David has acted on many of the leading cases and transactions in these areas, including: Vodafone PLC – Verizon; Shire PLC; BHP Billton PLC (corporate advisory and schemes of arrangement); Jackson v Dear; Liverpool Football Club & RBS v Hicks & Gillett; Arbuthnott v Charterhouse (corporate litigation); Saad v PwC; Halliwells LLP (insolvency); and Validus Holdings v IPC (offshore).
Professional Memberships: Chancery Bar Association, COMBAR, ILA.
Career: Called: 1983. Silk: 2002. Admitted to the Bars of the following jurisdictions: British Virgin Islands, Bermuda and Cayman.
Publications: Contributor to Co-operatives that Work (Spokesman 1988); Practice and Procedure in the Companies Court (Lloyds of London Press 1997); The Law of Majority Shareholders Power, Use and Abuse (OUP 2008).
Personal: Born 1960. Educated Millfield School; Downing College, Cambridge.

CHOONGH, Satnam
No5 Chambers, Birmingham
0845 210 5555
ssc@no5.com
Featured in Planning (Midlands)
Practice Areas: Satnam specialises in planning, environmental and administrative law, and acts for developers, local authorities and government agencies. He appears at planning and associated inquiries, prosecutes and defends environmental and planning offences in the criminal courts, and appears both for appellants and respondents in applications for judicial review and statutory challenges in the High Court. Notable cases: represented HSE in nuclear power station inquiry; the Highways Agency in a six month MSA inquiry; Warwick District Council in two inquiries relating to Coventry Airport; Vale Royal and Neston Boroughs in 58ha waste recovery park inquiry and Helioslough in a 3.5million square feet rail-freight interchange inquiry; advised the local authorities affected by the Hinkley C new nuclear power plant. Acts regularly for national house builders and two of the "Big 4" national retailers. Judicial review and statutory challenges include those testing the meaning of conditions precedent; the duty to give reasons for planning consent; the meaning of the CIL regulations; proper application of the sequential test in retail cases; the meaning of appropriate and inappropriate development in the Green Belt.
Professional Memberships: Planning and Environmental Bar Association.
Career: LLB (Hons) (First Class) Warwick University 1990. DPhil (Oxon) 1994. Has served as Warwick University Research Fellow, Professor of Law at the Chinese University of Hong Kong and at Birmingham University.
Publications: Planning Law and Procedure (2000) (CCH Construction Law Manual).; The Meaning of Waste in EU Law (2006) (JPL); Development in Breach of Condition Precedent (2007) (JPL); New Planning Units, New Chapters in Planning History and Inconsistent Permissions (2009) JLP.

CHORFI, Camilla
Selborne Chambers, London
020 7420 9500
camilla.chorfi@selbornechambers.co.uk
Featured in Real Estate Litigation (London)
Practice Areas: Camilla specialises in chancery litigation, with expertise in the field of real property. As well as regularly appearing in the High Court and County Court, Camilla frequently appears before the First Tier Tribunal in land registration matters (formerly the Adjudicator to HMLR), on both HMLR referrals (typically applications concerning restrictive covenants, easements, adverse possession) and rectification of instruments. Camilla has extensive experience in a broad spectrum of residential and commercial landlord and tenant law, comprising opposed and unopposed 1954 Act claims, enforcement of leasehold covenants, consents and forfeiture. She advises landlords, tenants, administrators and mortgagees in relation to property related insolvency issues. Camilla's practice has an emphasis on mortgage related matters, and she is currently retained by a number of lenders in numerous professional negligence claims against both valuers and solicitors. Camilla has also been instructed on a number of complex trusts of land disputes.
Professional Memberships: ChBA, PBA (committee member), PNBA.
Career: Called 2008. Winner of the Lincoln's Inn Moot 2008. Hardwicke and Wolfson scholarships.
Personal: BA Classics (First); MA Classics (Distinction); LLB Law. Conversational French and Arabic.

CHOUDHURY, Akhlaq
11KBW, London
020 7632 8500
akhlaq.choudhury@11kbw.com
Featured in Data Protection (London), Employment (London)
Practice Areas: Procurement, information, employment and public law. Recent cases include: DWF LLP v Insolvency Service [2014] EWCA Civ 900 (Procurement, automatic suspension); Allan v Wandsworth LBC [2014] Eq LR 30 (Disability Discrimination), Esparon v Slavikovska UKEAT/0217/12, 8 May 2014 (National Minimum Wage), Romero Insurance Brokers v Templeton [2013] EWHC 1198 (Restrictive Covenants); BUQ v HRE [2012] I.R.L.R. 653 (Privacy Injunction); Keiller v University of East Anglia [2012] 1 Info LR 128 (FOI); Humphreys v Norilsk Nickel International [2010] IRLR 976 (Bonuses); OFCOM v Information Commissioner [2010] UKSC 3 (EIR); B2Net v HM Treasury [2010] Eu LR 471 (Procurement); BUAV v Home Office and Information Commissioner [2009] 1 WLR 636 (FOI); Corporate Officer of the House of Commons v Information Commissioner [2009] 3 All ER 403 (MPs' Expenses' case).
Professional Memberships: PLA, ELBA, ALBA, ELA.
Career: Called 1992. Recorder (SE Circuit) 2009. Appointed to Attorney General's A-Panel of Treasury Counsel March 2013.
Publications: Tolley's 'Employment Handbook' (1996-date), contributor. Information Law Reports, contributor.
Personal: BSc Hons, Physics (Glasgow); LLB Hons (1st Class) (London).

CHRISTIE, Aidan QC
4 Pump Court, London
020 7842 5555
achristie@4pumpcourt.com
Featured in Insurance (London), Professional Negligence (London)
Practice Areas: Principal areas of practice are insurance and reinsurance, professional negligence (including accountants, brokers, lawyers and financial advisors), insurance regulation and general commercial disputes.
Professional Memberships: COMBAR, London Common Law and Commercial Bar Association.
Career: Called to the Bar 1988, Silk 2008, Recorder 2009, Panel Deemster Isle of Man 2012.
Personal: BA (Oxon) Classics, MA (Cantab) Law.

CHRISTIE, Richard QC
187 Fleet Street, London
christie121@btinternet.com
Featured in Crime (South Eastern), Crime (London)
Practice Areas: Crime, civil liberties, fraud (crime), health and safety, inquests, POCA and asset and forfeiture.
Professional Memberships: Criminal Bar Association; South Eastern Circuit.
Career: Specialises in all areas of criminal work, particularly serious fraud, murder and cases requiring substantial client care.

Expertise in MTIC cases, both criminally and in the VAT tribunal. Recently defended in the hugely complicated historic axe murder of Private Eye Daniel Morgan: linked to the phone-hacking scandal, featured on Panorama and the longest pre-trial legal argument in English Criminal Law. Also prosecuted multi-million pound ten-handed excise fraud featured on ITV programme "Fiddles, Cheats and Scams". Both SFO's panels of approved Queen's Counsel (fraud and confiscation). Rough-justice cases and J.R. for Criminal Cases Review Commission. Trained with Touche Ross and Co. Those marked with a (P) below were prosecution briefs. (1) R v X (£40 million VAT fraud - extensive PII - D. an informant -acquitted); (2) R v Smith (Murder appeal based on fresh evidence); (3) R v Walpole (Conspiracy to import cocaine and cannabis (over one tonne); (4) R v Grady (Letters of Credit fraud on the Clearing Banks - acquitted); (5) R v Chapman (£16.75m MTIC VAT fraud); (6) R v Piggott (£44 million MTIC fraud - off-shore companies. Confiscation and ancillary relief proceedings - RCJ). (P). (7) R v Carine (Appeal - Southend airport conspirators (250kg of cocaine) (8) R v Bush (Appeal - murder) (9) R v Strain (Hydro carbons fraud and confiscation- Northern Irish criminal fraternity) (P). (10) R v Carter (Murder trial – complicated forensic evidence -successfully argued that there had been no killing at all - acquitted) (11) R v Duffy (Murder – successful diminished responsibility - battered mother to death with hammer) (12) R v Long (Serious fraud/arson trial - target criminal) (P) (13) R v Donnan (£35m MTIC money laundering and confiscation) (P) (14) R v Bodden (Murder - Cayman Islands – acquitted) (15) R v Nevers (Attacks on 9 women) (P) (16) R v Ahmed (Appeal: rape and kidnap - Islamic marriage. LPP, fresh evidence from LPP material) (17) R v Abu and others (3.5 month immigration fraud) (P) (18) R v Tambengwa (Murder and serious sexual offences on child) (P) (19) R v Small (Appeal - historic sexual offences. Conviction quashed. Re trial 2009 – acquitted) (20) R v Mahmood (Appeal – serious sexual offences. Appeal (quashed) – re-trial – 2nd appeal: acquitted) (21) R v Hale (Murder – missing victim. Note "By fire, by sea, by landsite, by acid." Front page Evening Standard and Sky News. Acquitted) (22) R v Rees (Murder, police corruption, 750,000 pp. of material, 5 month abuse of process; 5 previous enquiries. Acquitted); (23) R v Conroy (Ten-handed excise fraud and confiscation– organised crime) (P); (24) R v Briggs (£1 billion Cocaine importation, firearms - acquitted) (25) R v Hanson (Conspiracy to murder – contract killing - acquitted) (26) R v Gill (£38m carbon credit fraud) (27) R v Naqshbandi (£6m – crash for cash conspiracy to defraud) (28) R v Dudley (Gross negligence manslaughter - acquitted) (29) R v Durham (11 x conspiracy to rob CIT vans – 6/11 acquitted – large scale fit up alleged) (30) R v Beck (Murder) (31) R v Mohamoed – (Attempt murder/rape) (32) R v Yearsley (£ Multi-million confiscation) (P) (33) R v Tucker (rough-justice appeal – fresh evidence - ongoing) (34) R v Bensley (£24m MTIC fraud).

CHRISTOPHER, Julian QC
5 Paper Buildings, London
020 7583 6117
clerks@5pb.co.uk
Featured in Crime (London), Financial Crime (London)

Practice Areas: Julian Christopher QC has considerable experience in defending and prosecuting a wide range of general crime, with particular emphasis on tax fraud and organised crime; he has also applied the same analytical and advocacy skills to civil proceedings for fraud, confiscation of the proceeds of crime, inquests, and responding to third party witness summonses. Before taking silk he was Standing Counsel to the RCPO for five years, prosecuting cases involving the creation and promotion of tax evasion schemes, large scale drugs importation, diversion fraud and evasion of VAT or Anti-Dumping Duty. He is a member of the SFO's lists for both prosecution and proceeds of crime, and is also instructed by the OFT (re price fixing cartels). Recent cases include defending a lobster fisherman charged with importing 250kg of cocaine; defending a man who came to the rescue of the victim of a sexual assault and was charged with murder of her attacker; and prosecuting the promoters of a series of tax schemes which relied on false claims for tax relief on £200m of charitable donations. He teaches advocacy for Gray's Inn, and has been a contributing editor to Archbold since 2005.

CHUDLEIGH, Louise
Old Square Chambers, London
020 7269 0300
chudleigh@oldsquare.co.uk
Featured in Employment (London)

Practice Areas: Louise's practice includes employment, discrimination and regulatory work. She frequently appears in lengthy and complex sex, race, disability and trade union discrimination cases as well as large equal pay claims, often against leading counsel. Her practice encompasses all other aspects of employment law including, proceedings related to breach of contract, unfair dismissal and restrictive covenants. She regularly appears in the Employment Tribunals, the High Court and in the appellate Courts and has particular expertise in disputes involving professionals such as medical practitioners, police officers and teachers. Notable cases include: Birmingham City Council v Abdulla and others, a Supreme Court equal pay case and Chhabra v West London Mental Health NHS Trust, another Supreme Court case about the proposed disciplining of a doctor. Her regulatory work has included acting as a legal assessor as well as appearing as an advocate in professional disciplinary matters. She has often been instructed in internal disciplinary proceedings as both a representative and as legal adviser to panels. Louise is known to be a reliable and effective barrister as well as a strong advocate and good tactician.

Professional Memberships: ELBA, ELA

Career: Called to the Bar 1987 (England and Wales); 1989 (Bermuda); Fee paid Employment Judge since 2001; Certified mediator.

CLARE, Allison
Red Lion Chambers, London
chambers@18rlc.co.uk
Featured in Financial Crime (London)

Practice Areas: Allison has specialised in prosecuting, defending and advising upon complex fraud and confiscation over the last 15 years. Experience includes exchange traded funds, futures trading, other complex markets frauds, land banking, insider dealing, cartels, corruption, arms trading, investment frauds, conspiracy to defraud public planning authorities, energy procurement frauds, metal trading frauds, and Companies Act and Insolvency Act offences. Also undertakes regulatory work for OFGEM and GMC. Advised UBS in R v Adoboli and currently advises Lloyds Banking Group on large corruption case. Advised corporate and individuals on POCA, self-reporting and corruption responsibilities.

Professional Memberships: Criminal Bar Association; Fraud Advisory Panel; South Eastern Circuit; Bar Council, Professional Standards Committee (2002-05); Journal of Criminal Law Editorial Board.

Career: BA (Oxon); BCL (Oxon); Member of Red Lion Chambers since 1993.

Publications: Writer for major practitioner texts on fraud: "Montgomery & Ormerod on Fraud: Criminal Law and Procedure" (Oxford) and "Fraud: Law, Practice and Procedure" (LexisNexis).

CLARKE, Andrew QC
Littleton Chambers, London
020 7797 8600
ac@littletonchambers.co.uk
Featured in Employment (London)

Practice Areas: Leading employment and commercial lawyer, having successfully appeared in these areas before all relevant courts and tribunals. Expert in disputes relating to garden leave, restrictive covenants and confidential information, also company law (including directors' duties and minority rights), pensions, employment agencies and sport related matters. Appeared in numerous high profile cases on individual employment rights (wrongful dismissal, bonus issues, unfair dismissal and TUPE cases), all forms of discrimination, employment status, agency workers, equal pay (for NHS and local authority employers), restrictive covenants, garden leave, strike, leverage action and picketing injunctions. Clients include major corporations, public bodies, professional firms and senior employees, as well as leading sporting bodies, clubs and players. Sits as fee paid employment judge.

Professional Memberships: Employment Law Bar Association; Employment Lawyers Association; ILS; COMBAR; Bar Sports Law Group.

Career: Called to the Bar 1980, QC 1997, joined Littleton Chambers in 1981, joint Head of Chambers from 2006 to 2014.

Personal: Educated at Crewe County Grammar School, King's College London 1974-77 (LLB) and Lincoln College, Oxford 1977-79 (BCL). Leisure pursuits include playing and watching cricket and football.

CLARKE, Elizabeth
Queen Elizabeth Building, London
020 7797 7837
e.clarke@qeb.co.uk
Featured in Family/Matrimonial (London)

Practice Areas: Matrimonial finance.

Career: BA (Oxon).

CLARKE, Geoff QC
Compass Chambers, Edinburgh
0131 260 5648
geoff.clarke@compasschambers.com
Featured in Personal Injury (Scotland)

Practice Areas: Geoff took silk in 2008 after 14 years as a busy junior counsel and was immediately well instructed as a senior. He specialises in personal injury, professional negligence (including medical negligence) insurance, commercial and contract litigation. He also acts for many of Scotland's assessors in rating and valuation disputes. He is experienced in a wide range of civil litigation with a particular emphasis on advocacy ability and strong technical and scientific knowledge. He has a special interest in disease claims. He is involved in the teaching of advocacy skills and is an assessor of advocacy skills for the faculty. He has appeared in a number of inquiries and has a particular knowledge of health and safety issues. He is an accredited mediator and a certificated employment lawyer. Recent cases include – Reid v EWS Railways [2012] CSIH 16; 2012 GWD 11-216 – appeal to the Inner House on causation; Johnston v Amec [2010] CSIH 57 – appeal to the Inner House involving regulations 4 and 5 of power; Nugent v City of Glasgow Council [2009] CSOH 88 – a tripping case with consideration of the system for inspecting, reporting and repairing defects in pavements; Linda Henry v Rentokil [2008] CSIH 24 – appeal to the Inner House involving quantum of damages, Tummell Valley Leisure V Sudjic [2011] CSIH 82 – Inner House appeal concerning the rights of salmon fishing. See also 2010 SLT (Sh Ct) 170. In the recent past he has been involved in a major Commercial Reparation case which settled, on appeal, for several million pounds and in the past year has been involved in cases involving death caused by pulmonary embolism and the possible connection with leg trauma following a slip, a case involving potential secondary victim status for the claimant and amputation of the lower leg following collision with a turning articulated lorry. Decisions are awaited in all three cases.

Professional Memberships: Advocates Personal Injury Law Group; Mediation and Dispute Resolution Group; life member of the Royal Medical Society of Edinburgh.

Career: Edinburgh (1998 LLB Hons). Trainee and solicitor with Simpson & Marwick 1989 to 93; called to the Bar 1994; accredited mediator 2006. Lecturer in Delict at the University of Edinburgh 2008.

CLARKE, Ian
Selborne Chambers, London
020 7420 9500
ian.clarke@selbornechambers.co.uk
Featured in Real Estate Litigation (London)

Practice Areas: Ian is a chancery/commercial practitioner.

Professional Memberships: Chancery Bar Association; Property Bar Association; Professional Negligence Bar Association; Fellow, Chartered Institute of Arbitrators; Insolvency Lawyers' Association; Association of Contentious Trust and Probate Specialists.

Career: Ian continues to be ranked as a leading junior for his expertise in Professional Negligence, Commercial and Real Estate/Property litigation. He is "very strong on technical issues" and "has an extremely good manner with clients" and "gives advice which transcends pure legal opinion. He is a very tactical advocate." "He makes intelligent points, and he makes them eloquently. He's also extremely easy to deal with." He has "demonstrated his credentials in relation to property and insolvency over a period of years", with "excellent trial skills" and a "cerebral and knowledgeable" approach. During 2013, Ian was heavily committed in Madoff Securities v Raven, rated one of 2013's 'Top 10' pieces of commercial litigation by The Lawyer, successfully defending a claim for dishonest breach of fiduciary duty. His recent other instructions include a claim for dishonest assistance in breach of trust in the Court of Grand Cayman; instructions on behalf of lenders to recover substantial seven-figure sums from negligent solicitors and valuers; claims under a share sale agreement for breaches of warranty and claims to recover assets under the Insolvency Act 1986 on behalf of liquidators. As these cases indicate his practice involves substantial commercial contractual disputes, issues of fraud, trusts, insolvency and professional negligence (particularly that of solicitors and valuers). He also regularly undertakes instructions relating to land (especially on land registration matters, in which he has led other juniors), mortgages (on which he co-edits one of the two practitioner texts) and wills and probate. He is an accredited mediator and a part time Judge of the First-tier Tribunal (Property Chamber, Land Registration).

Publications: Wolstenholme & Cherry's Annotated Land Registration Act 2002 (2003 Sweet & Maxwell) co-author on The Law of Mortgages (2010, 3rd Edition, Sweet & Maxwell).

CLARKE, Patrick

Atkin Chambers, London
020 7404 0102
pclarke@atkinchambers.com

Featured in Construction (London)

Practice Areas: Construction, energy, information technology and professional negligence and disputes with a high technical content or concerning major projects generally.

Professional Memberships: TECBAR, Combar, SCL.

Career: Practicing in Atkin Chambers since completion of Pupillage in 1999.

Publications: Contributor-Hudson Construction and Engineering Contracts and "The Law of Contract" in the Construction Law Handbook published by Thomas Telford.

Personal: BSc Physics.

CLARKE, Sarah

Serjeants' Inn Chambers, London
020 7427 5000
sclarke@3serjeantsinn.com

Featured in Financial Services (London), Financial Crime (London)

Practice Areas: Sarah Clarke was called to the Bar in 1994. Sarah specialises in financial services, fraud, professional discipline and regulatory, public and administrative, inquests and inquiries and police law. She has particular experience of shaping complex litigation from an early stage. An earlier edition notes that "she's very good, very bright and very focused, and is strong in court. She's gleaned a lot of experience from being in-house at the FSA". Please click on the link to the Serjeants' Inn Chambers website for her profile, which sets out full details of her practice (including her time in the Enforcement Division and subsequently the Litigation Department of what was then the FSA) and relevant work of note.

Career: Recorder of the Crown Court: 2012, CPS Grade 4 Prosecutor (General Crime): 2012, SFO A Panel(POCA): 2013, CPS Grade 4 Specialist Fraud Panel: 2013, CPS Grade 4 Specialist Rape and Sexual Offences Panel: 2013.

Publications: Insider Dealing: Law and Practice, contributing author to LexisNexis and member of editorial board of LexisNexisPSL.

Personal: Member of Bar Standards Board and Vice-Chair of its Qualifications Committee, Member of Advocacy Training Council and Vice-Chair of its Training and Accreditation Committee, Member of Inner Temple Advocacy Training Committee, CPS Advocacy Assessor.

CLAY, Robert

Atkin Chambers, London
020 7404 0102
rclay@atkinchambers.com

Featured in Construction (London)

Practice Areas: Robert specialises in litigation and arbitration, domestic and international, in the construction, civil engineering, energy, oil and gas sectors. He handles cases for a wide range of clients, including governments, local authorities, main contractors, developers, manufacturers, energy companies, and professional firms. He has extensive experience in arbitration both domestically and internationally. He is regularly involved in arbitrations in foreign jurisdictions including Hong Kong, Singapore, and the Middle East, and in long running London arbitrations between non-UK parties. He is familiar with all forms of dispute resolution, including mediations (he is an accredited mediator) and expert determinations. He regularly acts in construction adjudications, both before adjudicators and in enforcement and other court proceedings. His practice has included numerous and frequent adjudications since the statute requiring adjudication first came into force.

Professional Memberships: TECBAR.

Career: Tenant at 1 Atkin Building since October 1990.

Publications: 1994 to 1998 Editor Building Law Reports, General Editor Hudson on Building Contracts, 12th Ed.

Personal: First Class in Ancient and Modern History, Oxford; Henry Fellow at Harvard. Interests include sailing. Rowed in the Oxford Boat Race crew.

CLAYTON, Richard QC

Kings Chambers, Birmingham
0845 034 3444
clerks@kingschambers.com

Featured in Administrative & Public Law (Midlands), Civil Liberties & Human Rights (Midlands)

Practice Areas: Principal areas of practice- public law, civil liberties and local government law. Advisory and litigation for and against public bodies- community care, data protection/FOI, public sector equality duties, education, local government (e.g. vires and powers, constitutional issues and standards), public procurement, healthcare, human rights, prison law, Privy Council/international work and regulatory work.

Professional Memberships: Deputy High Court Judge, Recorder, United Kingdom representative- Venice Commission (the Council of Europe's advisory body on constitutional law); Associate Fellow, Centre for Public Law, Cambridge University; former Chair of the Constitutional and Administrative Law Bar Association, Vice Chair, Liberty.

Career: Recent cases include Kennedy v Charity Commission (2014) (Supreme Court- Freedom of Information); R(McCallistair) v A-G of Turks and Caicos (2014) (TCI Court of Appeal- constitutional); R(Bridgerow) v Chester West (2014) (licencing); R(Littlefair) v Darlington(2013) (cuts case); R(May) v CIMA (2013) (regulatory). Many Supreme Court, House of Lords, Privy Council and Strasbourg cases. Clients include private individuals, NGOs, local authorities and PLCs. Richard is a member of both Kings Chambers (Birmingham) and 4-5 Grays Inn Square (London).

Publications: Joint author 'Law of Human Rights' (OUP).

CLAYTON, Richard QC

4-5 Gray's Inn Square, London
020 7404 5252
rclayton@4-5.co.uk

Featured in Administrative & Public Law (London), Civil Liberties & Human Rights (London), Local Government (London)

Practice Areas: Principal areas of practice are public law, civil liberties/human rights and local government law- wide range of advisory and litigation work for and against public bodies covering community care, data protection/FOI, discrimination and public sector equality duties, education, local government (e.g. vires and powers, constitutional issues and standards, elections), environmental, public procurement, healthcare, human rights, prison law, Privy Council/international work and regulatory/disciplinary work. (UK representative to the Venice Commission, the Council of Europe's advisory body on constitutional law; Associate Fellow at the Centre for Public Law, Cambridge University since 2001; Chair of the Constitutional and Administrative Law Bar Association (2008-10); Vice Chair, Liberty (2004-07). Recent cases include R(Southwest Care Homes) v Devon CC (2012) (community care); R(Condliff) v North Staffordshire PCT (2011) (CA- health care and Art 8); R(AF) v SSHD (2011)(CA- Bar Council intervention concerning costs in JR cases); R(Buckinghamshire CC) v Kingston [2011] EWCA Civ 457 (CA- consultation and community care); R(Rahman) v Birmingham CC [2011] EWHC 944 (Admin) (Public law equality duties and budget cuts); R(Lewis) v Permsimmon Homes [2009] 1 WLR 83 (CA bias and local government); S and Marper v United Kingdom (2009) 48 EHRR 1169 (Grand Chamber- DNA and Art 8); Huang v SSHD [2007] 2 AC 167 (HL); Panday v Virgil [2008] 1 AC 655 (Privy Council); Toussaint v A-G of St Vincent [2007] 1 WLR 2825 (Privy Council). Clients include private individuals, NGOs, local authorities and PLCs.

CLEGG, Richard

Selborne Chambers, London
020 7420 9500
richard.clegg@selbournechambers.co.uk

Featured in Real Estate Litigation (London)

Practice Areas: Richard specialises in commercial disputes, frequently of an international nature, and property disputes, often when arising as part of a commercial transaction. He is often called upon when issues of evidential or technical complexity arise (including in the context of fraud) or when creative strategic thinking is required. Disputes on which Richard acts are increasingly in the context of joint ventures, supply and distribution agreements, commodities, energy and other resources. Of recent note, Richard represented a foreign government in an ICSID investment arbitration concerning the construction of a gas pipeline; a case that considered for the first time a number of issues of importance to investors in infrastructure in foreign lands, including the enforcement of commercial arbitration awards through treaty arbitration. He is an author of the Practical Law Company's guidance in the UK and US on international arbitration, a registered foreign lawyer in Singapore, and has a working knowledge of Cantonese Chinese. Recent cases: Stickley v Barclays Bank (2013), LTL 9/5/2013, (Registrar Derrett); Fitzwilliam v Richall Holdings Services [2013] 1 P&CR 19; Represented a South Korean conglomerate in ad hoc arbitration proceedings in Singapore (2012); Twenty Two Clifton Gardens v Thayer Investments [2012] 2 EGLR 56; Michael Gerson (Leasing) v Greatsunny [2011] EWCA Civ 416 (CA); Represented a Japanese bank in SIAC arbitration proceedings in Singapore (2010).

Professional Memberships: Commercial Bar Association; Chancery Bar Association; International Bar Association; CIArb.

Career: Qualified Gray's Inn, 1999; Judicial Assistant to the Court of Appeal, 2000; Registered Foreign Lawyer, Singapore, 2007.

Publications: Author for the PLC International Arbitration service in the UK and US.

Personal: Languages: French (working knowledge); Cantonese Chinese (working knowledge).

CLEGG, Simon

St Philips Chambers, Birmingham
0121 246 7000
sclegg@st-philips.com

Featured in Commercial Dispute Resolution (Midlands)

Practice Areas: An experienced advocate and adviser in relation to commercial and business disputes involving contractual, banking, company, property and insolvency issues, as well as professional negligence.

Professional Memberships: COMBAR, Midlands Chancery and Commercial Bar Association.

Career: Called to the Bar in 1980. Spent three years working as a solicitor at Freehills in Sydney, Australia between 1988 and 1991.

CLEGG, William QC

2 Bedford Row, London
020 7440 8888
wclegg@2bedfordrow.co.uk

Featured in Crime (London), Financial Crime (London)

Practice Areas: Recently represented one of the acquitted defendants in the News of the World phone hacking trial. Frequently advises foreign governments, international corporations, trade unions and individuals in relation to all aspects of regulatory offences, compliance, corporate manslaughter and health and safety infringement. Also a specialist in advising and defending in cases of alleged fraud, corporate corruption and sanctions breaches frequently with international aspects to the case, acted in Balfour Beatty, B.E.A., Mabey and Johnson and Sainsbury. Often works in partnership with lawyers in other jurisdictions. A specialist in money laundering and restraint. Has appeared in over 125 cases in the Supreme Court, House of Lords, Administrative Court

and Court of Appeal which can be accessed using Lexis-Nexis search engine cases include R v Banfield & Banfield & Banfield [2013] EWCA 1394, R. (Rahndezfouli) b Crown Court at Wod Green [2013] EWHC 2998 (Admin), R. (on the application of Haligan) v Secretary of State for the Home Department [2012] AER (D) 178, R. (on the application of Robin Murray & Co.) v. Lord Chancellor [2011} AER (D) 102, R v Norris [2010] 1 AER (D) 88, R (on the application of Edwards) v CCRC {2008] AER (D) 110, R v Ali and Others 2006 1 CAR 8, R v Ramzan and Others 2007 1 CAR 10, R v El Kurd and Others 2007 1 CAR 30. Has practised extensively in The Hague and has advised in various countries in USA, Europe, the Middle East, West Indies and the Far East. Cases include Izodia plc; Brent Walker plc; Alliance Resources plc; Bute Mining plc; R v Smith (WSTC Merchant Bank); R v Smithson (The Arrows fraud); R v Alder (international bank fraud); R v Asil Nadir (Polly Peck); R v Hales (solicitors legal aid fraud). Cases of a more general nature include R v Serafinowicz (war crimes); R v Lee Clegg (British paragrooper accused of murder in Northern Ireland); R v Stone (Chillingden murders); R v Stagg (Wimbledon Common murder); R v Barry George (Jill Dando murder); R v Tabak (Joanna Yates murder); R v Varathadasan (Tamil Tigers); R v McMahon (UDA terrorists); R v Sawoniuk (war crimes); Prosecutor v Jelisic (war crimes the Hague); Prosecutor v Tadic (war crimes, The Hague); R v Duckenfield (Hillsborough Disaster). Has also been instructed in a lengthy public enquiry by the Medical Protection Society. Was a member of the standing committee of justice on fraud trials and prepared submissions to the Fraud Trials Committee chaired by Roskill (HMSO 1986).
Professional Memberships: Criminal Bar Association (Committee Member); South Eastern Circuit (Committee Member). Chairman Essex Bar Mess, 1997-2000.
Career: Called to the Bar 1972 and joined present chambers in 1973. Took Silk 1991. Appointed recorder 1992. Head of Chambers 1995.
Personal: Educated at Bristol University (LLB). Leisure pursuits include squash, cricket and wine. Born 5 September 1949.

CLEMENT, Joanne
11KBW, London
020 7632 8500
joanne.clement@11kbw.com
Featured in Administrative & Public Law (London), Civil Liberties & Human Rights (London), Community Care (London), Education (London), Local Government (London)
Practice Areas: Public law and human rights, all areas of local government law, particularly community care and education; EU and public procurement law; Court of Protection and information law. Recent cases include acting for the Attorney General in two devolution references concerning the legislative competence of the National Assembly for Wales (Attorney General's Reference on Local Government Byelaws (Wales) Bill 2012; [2013] 1 AC 792 and Agricultural Sector (Wales) Bill - Reference by the Attorney General for England and Wales [2014] UKSC 43; successfully challenging the abolition of full time nursery education for three year olds in R (West and others) v Rhondda Cynon Taff CBC [2014] EWHC 2134 (Admin); challenge to Secretary of State's allocation of €10 billion of EU structural funds in R (Rotherham MBC and others) v Secretary of State for Business, Innovation and Skills [2014] EWHC 232 (Admin) (Court of Appeal judgment forthcoming); successfully defending the Secretary of State in challenge to decision to convert failing school to an Academy in R (Governing Body of Warren School) v Secretary of State for Education [2014] EWHC 2252 (Admin); challenge to Secretary of State's policy of neither confirming nor denying whether extradition requests have been received in R (Manzarpour) v Secretary of State for the Home Department [2014] EWHC 1086 (Admin); acting for central Government in series of cases considering the impact of the Supreme Court's decision in Cheshire West and Chester Council v P [2014] 2 WLR 642; acting for Appellant in appeal under the Freedom of Information Act, seeking information held by the Foreign and Commonwealth Office concerning the UK's involvement in extraordinary rendition in All Party Parliamentary Group on Extraordinary Rendition v Information Commissioner and Foreign and Commonwealth Office [2013] UKUT 0560 (AAC); and R (Nicklinson) v Secretary of State for Justice and others [2012] EWHC 2381 (Admin); [2012] HRLR 32 (right to die case)
Professional Memberships: Administrative Law Bar Association.
Career: Called to the Bar 2002; Judicial Assistant to the Law Lords 2003-04; Appointed to Attorney-General's C Panel in 2007 and to B Panel in 2010; member of Welsh Government's Junior Counsel Panel.
Publications: "International Law in Domestic Courts: the Developing Framework" (2008) 124 LQR 388; contributor to Supperstone, Goudie & Walker on Judicial Review (5th ed, forthcoming); Coppel ed. Information Rights: Law and Practice (4th ed); Halsburys Laws of England – Judicial Review; Supperstone & Knapman, Administrative Court Practice.
Personal: Education at Ferndale Comprehensive School and Somerville College, Oxford (BA, BCL).

CLIFFORD, James
Maitland Chambers, London
020 7406 1200
jclifford@maitland.co.uk
Featured in Pensions (London)
Practice Areas: Specialises in pensions and trusts and has general commercial chancery litigation practice. Reported cases handled include: Briggs v Gleeds (Head Office), Honda Motor Group Ltd v Powell, Procter & Gamble v SCA, Dalriada Trustees Ltd v Foulds, MSM Consulting Ltd v United Republic of Tanzania, Trustees of Saffil Pension Scheme v Curzon, Barclays Bank v Holmes, ITS v Rowe, Polly Peck v Henry, Re Scientific Investment Pension Plan, Edge v The Pensions Ombudsman, Hood Sailmakers Ltd v Axford, Miller v Scorey, Process Developments Ltd v Hogg, Coloroll Pension Trustees Limited v Russell, Thrells Ltd v Lomas Nestle v National Westminster Bank, LRT v Hatt, Mettoy Pensions Trustees v Evans.
Professional Memberships: Association of Pension Lawyers (Member of APL's Legislative & Parliamentary Sub-Committee), COMBAR, Chancery Bar, Association Professional Negligence Bar Association, STEP, ACTAPS.
Career: Called to the Bar in 1984.
Publications: Contributor to 'Trust Law International', 'Trusts and Trustees', 'British Pensions Lawyer', and author of 'Pensions Title', 'Atkins Court Forms'.
Personal: Educated at Oxford University.

CLUTTERBUCK, Andrew QC
4 Stone Buildings, London
020 7242 5524
a.clutterbuck@4stonebuildings.com
Featured in Chancery (London)
Practice Areas: Company/commercial litigation including fraud; trusts (commercial); corporate insolvency; financial services. Recent cases include: Good v Onsette (beneficial interests in shares, forgery of electronic documentation); Citibank v Barclays (floating rate notes, noteholder rights), Aberdeen v Satyam (fraudulent financial statements, forum conveniens); re MK Airlines (insolvent liquidation - inadequate assets to meet winding up/administration costs); GEHC v Gray (fiduciary duties, oil technology); re Bell Group (bondholder rights, trustee directions).
Professional Memberships: COMBAR, Chancery Bar Association. Called to Bar in Cayman Islands and, for specific cases, in the Turks and Caicos Islands.
Career: Royal Marines; Called 1992.QC 2014.

COATES, Holly
Becket Chambers, Canterbury
01227 786 331
clerks@becket-chambers.co.uk
Featured in Local Government (South Eastern)
Practice Areas: Housing and land law – considerable experience in acting for and against Local Authorities in housing matters (in particular those involving anti-social behaviour), as well as adverse possession and TOLATA claims. Employment – regularly acts in claims involving unfair and/or wrongful dismissal, discrimination, redundancy and pay disputes including those against public sector employers. Family law – extensive experience of cases involving child arrangement orders, care orders and financial provision in the County Court and High Court.
Professional Memberships: South Eastern Circuit, Kent Bar Mess, Family Law Bar Association.
Career: Holly was called to the Bar in 2008. She joined Becket Chambers as a tenant in 2009 after completion of pupillage. Holly accepts instruction under the Direct Public Access scheme.

COCKINGS, Giles
Furnival Chambers, London
020 7405 3232
gcockings@furnivallaw.co.uk
Featured in Crime (London)
Practice Areas: Fraud and crime. A leading junior who is often prosecuted by silks having established a reputation for hard work and meticulous preparation. Having developed a defence and prosecution practice over the years in serious crime involving gangland murder (including over 30 major murder trials, reaching successful conclusions in 90%), armed robbery, white collar fraud, money laundering, company theft and drug importation, more recent years have been spent in serious commercial and complex fraud which is now his chosen specialty. Successfully defending both commercial solicitors and company directors within both the criminal and regulatory arenas. Specialisation within this area include FSA, banking fraud, insider dealing, MTIC, VAT, diversion, "boilerroom", advance fee, investment and corporate fraud, many of them involving both criminal and civil proceedings with cross-jurisdictional elements. Successfully defended in R-v-Knights & ors (SFO prosecution of 6 solicitors charged with £55 million mortgage fraud); Successfully defended in R-v-Doust & ors (FSA investigation into company director – international property investment fraud, Swedish credit unions and Spanish litigation); successfully defended in R-v-Khan (solicitor charged with Olympic development invoice fraud); successfully defended in R-v-White & ors (accountant charged with MTIC VAT fraud); R-v-N (stockbroker charged with hedge fund investment fraud); R-v-Debruin (successfully defended company director in diversion fraud); R-v-Connors (lead counsel in first "slavery case" to be prosecuted under new legislation). Recently defended company director in 6 month trial (£30 million property development fraud).
Professional Memberships: Hon. Soc Middle Temple; Criminal Bar Association; South Eastern Circuit.
Publications: Disclosure and the CPIA 1996.
Personal: DOB:1969; Educ: Bedford School; Higher Educ: Bsc (Hons) LLB (Hons) (London); Hon. Soc. Middle Temple.

COFFEY, John QC
3 Temple Gardens, London
020 7353 3102
jc@3tg.co.uk
Featured in Crime (South Eastern), Crime (London)
Practice Areas: Criminal law, including murder, fraud, money laundering, organised crime, serious sexual offences, drug related offences and court martial.
Professional Memberships: Called to the Bar in 1970, Silk 1996, Recorder 1989, Head of Chambers, Criminal Bar Association, South Eastern Circuit.
Career: An eminent London criminal silk, John Coffey is instructed consistently in the most high profile and complex cases. One of Her Majesty's Senior Treasury Counsel said "John Coffey QC., he's the silk I definitely do not want on the other side". Cases defended in the past year include R v RM & others - a 2 month murder trial involving the killing of a grandfather in his home during the course of a robbery; R v RSP - representing a graphic designer in a 'one punch' manslaughter trial; R v SB & others - a 5 week gangland murder and firearms case; R v X a high profile serious sexual offences case resulting in the defendant's acquittal of allegations of rape and other serious sexual offences; R v W & another - a murder case in Essex involving the killing of a young father. The defendant was acquitted of the murder allegation.
Personal: John is married with three adult sons.

COGHLIN, Thomas
Cloisters, London
020 7827 4000
tac@cloisters.com
Featured in Employment (London)
Practice Areas: Tom Coghlin specialises in employment and discrimination law, claims for injunctions to enforce restrictive covenants, trade union law and general common law. He has a wealth of experience of

first instance and appellate litigation. For full details see www.cloisters.com.
Professional Memberships: Employment Judge (fee paid). Institute of Employment Rights, Discrimination Law Association, ELBA, Industrial Law Society.
Career: Called 1998.
Personal: Educated at Worth Abbey and Worcester College, Oxford (MA, BCL). Married with 4 daughters.

COHEN, Edward
11 Stone Buildings, London
020 7831 6381
cohen@11sb.com
Featured in Chancery (London)
Practice Areas: Edward Cohen has a commercial and chancery litigation/arbitration and advisory practice including commercial contracts of all kinds; partnerships and LLPs; company (including shareholder disputes); personal and corporate insolvency; professional negligence; commercial property; and civil fraud. Within those areas his practice is wide-ranging in nature, enabling him to advise and act in individual cases involving different areas of law simultaneously. He has appeared in many reported decisions ranging from the House of Lords and Privy Council to the Court of Appeal and Courts of First Instance involving diverse legal issues. He is noted for combining an excellent legal brain with an extremely conscientious approach towards research and preparation; persuasively presented paperwork; forceful and astute advocacy; a user-friendly manner; a practical approach and a wealth of experience in a wide range of commercial and chancery work. He has been recommended as a leading Commercial Chancery practitioner in Chambers & Partners for several years. For further information about his practice and recent case highlights, please visit the 'Barristers' section on www.11sb.com.
Professional Memberships: Chancery Bar Association; Commercial Bar Association.
Career: Called to the Bar 1972. Recorder since 2000. Head of Chambers since 2004.
Personal: MA (Cantab). Working knowledge of French and Spanish.

COHEN, Samantha
9 Bedford Row, London
020 7489 2727
samantha.cohen@9bedfordrow.co.uk
Featured in Crime (London)
Practice Areas: Samantha is a shrewd tactician and a persuasive advocate. She has enjoyed a busy and substantial London practice for two decades. She is widely respected for her ability to question the most vulnerable witnesses: children, those with psychiatric disorders, those fearful of the criminal justice system. She is extremely good with lay clients in conference, putting the most nervous at ease and calming the more 'pugnacious'. She is a specialist organised crime and RASSO prosecutor and is a panel advocate for the Department of Business, Innovation and Skills. She is instructed to lead for the defence regularly in fraud cases where her diligent pre-trial preparation and meticulous cross-examination of expert accountants has impressed. As has her approach to pre-trial disclosure where her tenacity and perseverance have paid dividends for her clients. She provides timely, thorough and acute advice pre-trial (sometimes pre-charge for the Crown) on a range of issues, e.g. directing the professional client to an appropriate expert in a particular field such as blood pattern analysis, accountancy evidence or the significance of injuries. She has a particular interest in shaken baby cases and the complex, nuanced and frequently changing medical evidence relating the the diagnosis of Shaken Baby Syndrome from the classic 'triad' of injuries. A capable and approachable counsel who consistently impresses.

COLE, Edward
Falcon Chambers, London
020 7353 2484
cole@falcon-chambers.com
Featured in Real Estate Litigation (London)
Practice Areas: Real property, commercial, residential and agricultural landlord and tenant, easements and restrictive covenants, business tenancies and leasehold enfranchisement.
Professional Memberships: Chancery Bar Association; LCLCBA; Property Bar Association.
Career: Educated at Whitgift School; Jesus College, Oxford (MA 1978) (Classics) Mods and Greats; City University (Dip Law 1979); Called 1980 (Gray's Inn). Recorder 2010.
Publications: Contributor, Megarry on the Rents Act, 11th edn; specialist editor, Hill & Redman 'Law of Landlord and Tenant'; contributor, Halsbury's Laws, Vol 27, 'Landlord and Tenant'.

COLE, Nicholas
St Ives Chambers, Birmingham
0121 236 0863
nicholas.cole@stiveschambers.co.uk
Featured in Family/Matrimonial (Midlands)
Practice Areas: Family (Children and Finance) Regulatory (Environment, Health and Safety).
Professional Memberships: FLBA
Career: Head of Chambers since 2013, Recorder since 2009 (Crime; Family), Specialist List of Regulatory Advocates, List A, Regulatory: Nicholas Cole is an experienced regulatory barrister, appointed to the List of Specialist Regulatory Counsel, List A, for HSE/Environment Agency work. Whilst he is experienced in all areas of regulatory law, Nicholas is a nationally recognised specialist for his expertise in environmental law and animal health. He is regularly instructed by many Local Authorities and Government agencies and on behalf of companies and individuals facing prosecution. He has appeared in appeals to the Court of Appeal and in judicial review proceedings. Family: Nicholas has a substantial practice in all aspects of family law, notably in care proceedings where he is instructed by local authorities and on behalf of parents and children, frequently in the High Court, where he brings his previous scientific training to cases involving non-accidental injury. He has appeared in the Court of Appeal in a number of family cases and in the Administrative Court in related proceedings. He is also regularly instructed in financial remedy cases, often involving substantial assets, and where his attention to detail has been noted. Reported cases include: Nicholls v Nicholls [1997] 1WLR 314, CA - contempt; R (on the application of Langton & Allen) v DEFRA & Derbyshire County Council [2002] EnvLR 20 - judicial review; Re M (Children) [2007] EWCA Civ 1363 - parties bound by opinion of expert unchallenged at hearing; Re IH (A Child)(Permission to Apply for Adoption) [2013] All ER(D) 269 - foreign adoption.

COLEMAN, Richard QC
Fountain Court Chambers, London
020 7583 3335
rjc@fountaincourt.co.uk
Featured in Banking & Finance (London), Financial Services (London), Professional Discipline (London)
Practice Areas: Commercial dispute resolution (litigation and arbitration), banking and finance, financial services (including regulatory and disciplinary), professional negligence, civil fraud, professional discipline and employment. Noteworthy cases include acting for the Financial Conduct Authority in the PPI litigation, for the Office of Fair Trading in the test case on bank charges, for an international bank in the investigation into the manipulation of LIBOR and for the Guernsey Cells in the Arch-Cru litigation.
Professional Memberships: Commercial Bar Association.
Career: Called to the Bar 1994. MA Cantab (double first class honours). LLM (Yale). Member of New York Bar.
Publications: Contributor to Law of Bank Payments (Brindle and Cox, 4th ed.)

COLLETT, Ivor
1 Chancery Lane, London
020 7092 2900
icollett@1chancerylane.com
Featured in Professional Negligence (London)
Practice Areas: Specialises in insurance (including policy coverage and wording, insurance fraud and claims involving brokers and underwriting agents) and has extensive experience in professional indemnity/ negligence litigation across most professions, particularly in the fields of construction professionals, solicitors and barristers and financial/ insurance professionals, as well as related regulatory proceedings. Considerable amount of his practice is in the TCC. Commercial litigation. Also acts for public authorities and others, including PL, EL, personal injury litigation and inquests.
Professional Memberships: Professional Negligence Bar Association (Executive Committee since 2007); TECBAR; Chancery Bar Association; London Common Law & Commercial Bar Association; Personal Injuries Bar Association; Association of Regulatory and Disciplinary Lawyers; Member of the Bar Council since 2008; Member of Legal Services Committee of Bar Council.
Career: Called to the Bar 1995. TECBAR Accredited as Construction Adjudicator 2011. Lincoln College, Oxford (BA Hons).

COLLIER, Beatrice
5 Essex Court, London
020 7410 2000
collier@5essexcourt.co.uk
Featured in Police Law (All Circuits)
Practice Areas: Specialist in police law, public law and employment law. Notable recent police law work includes the ongoing Lynette White litigation. In the public law field her clients are government departments and police forces. She has a particular interest in judicial review claims involving mental health issues. Her recent employment work has focused on disability discrimination and whistleblowing claims.
Professional Memberships: Middle Temple, Member of Administrative Law Bar Association, Employment Law Bar Association.
Career: Degree in History and English 1998 (University of Cambridge), Degree in Law 2003 (University of Oxford), Called to the Bar 2004, Tenant at 5 Essex Court 2006, Attorney General's C Panel 2009-date.
Personal: Married with 2 daughters. Interests include Arsenal FC, contemporary art.

COLLINGS, Matthew QC
Maitland Chambers, London
020 7406 1200
m.collings@maitlandchambers.com
Featured in Chancery (London), Commercial Dispute Resolution (London), Company (London), Fraud (London), Offshore (London), Restructuring/Insolvency (London)
Practice Areas: Law experts single out three particular attributes for Collings: his advocacy ("He is charming and engaging in his manner, extremely deft in handling the judge and witnesses, and highly persuasive as a result."); his analytical skills ("He has exceptional analytical skills and the ability to think outside the box."); and his "user-friendly style" ("He has a direct, no-nonsense approach, and the ability to find creative new angles to a case."). Collings has had another busy year in his principal specialist areas: Company law, Restructuring and Insolvency, and Commercial Chancery. He has just appeared in the Supreme Court in the FHR case on constructive trusts, and will shortly be appearing in the Court of Appeal in the Pan Ocean cross-border insolvency. Collings' expertise and practice has an increasingly international flavour with cases in the Channel Islands and Hong Kong, and appearances in both Cayman (the Matador case on redemptions) and the BVI (most recently a successful trial and appeal in a shareholder dispute).
Professional Memberships: Chancery Bar Association, COMBAR, Insolvency Lawyers Association, INSOL International and Commerical Fraud Lawyers Association. Former Member, Insolvency Rules Advisory Committee.

COLLINGS, Nicholas
Atkin Chambers, London
020 7404 0102
nscollings@atkinchambers.com
Featured in Construction (London), Professional Negligence (London)
Practice Areas: Construction, engineering, energy, professional negligence, IT, international arbitration and commercial litigation.
Professional Memberships: TECBAR, COMBAR, SCL, CIArb.
Career: Called 1997.
Personal: LLB (Hons) Bristol.

COLLINGWOOD, Timothy
Serle Court, London
020 7242 6105
tcollingwood@serlecourt.co.uk
Featured in Chancery (London), Company (London)
Practice Areas: Practises across the broad range of the commercial-chancery spectrum, but with particular emphasis on litigation concerning issues in respect of business agreements and company, insolvency and international trusts matters. Tim has extensive experience of claims concerning breaches of duty, in particular in respect of directors or trustees, and of shareholder disputes. Prior to commencing practice in England, Tim was called to the bar in the Cayman Islands and practised as an attorney-at-law.

Professional Memberships: Chancery Bar Association, COMBAR.
Career: Called 1996. Called to the Bar of the Cayman Islands and practised as attorney-at-law in 1997.
Publications: 'Minority Shareholders: Law, Practice & Procedure'.
Personal: Born 1972. Educated at Royal Grammar School, Guildford; Magdalen College, Oxford (BA, BCL). Married with three children. Interests include cycling and water sports.

COLLINS, Ben
Old Square Chambers, London
020 7269 0300
collins@oldsquare.co.uk
Featured in Employment (London)
Practice Areas: Employment and equality, as well as public law and human rights. Particular expertise in the health sector, with huge experience of representing healthcare professionals and employers in employment, regulatory and disciplinary proceedings. Appears regularly in the High Court and tribunals in public sector and large commercial employment disputes. Leading expert in criminal injuries compensation. Extensive experience in military claims. Also a substantial practice in clinical negligence, personal injury, inquests and associated public law and human rights challenges. Notable cases (12 reported in 2013-14) include: Pollard/ Sheldon v CQC (Francis Inquiry whistle-blowers); Jones v FTT [2013] 2 AC 48; RS v CICA [2014] 1 WLR 1313; Oboh v SSHD [2014] 1 WLR 1680; Rogers v Deputy Commander [2013] UKEAT 455; the Discount Rate litigation; Al-Jedda v SSHD (as Special Advocate).
Professional Memberships: ELA, ELBA, ARDL, PNBA, PIBA, Justice.
Career: Called (Middle Temple) 1996. Attorney-General's A Panel. Special Advocate.
Publications: Contributing Editor to Professional Negligence and Liability (Informa).
Personal: Educated at King Henry VIII School, Coventry and Queens' College Cambridge.

COLLINS, Ken
29 Bedford Row Chambers, London
020 7404 1044
kcollins@29br.co.uk
Featured in Family/Matrimonial (London)
Practice Areas: Barrister specialising in family law (matrimonial finance and children) and cohabitation disputes.
Professional Memberships: FLBA, Resolution.
Career: Former Eurobond Trader. Called 1996, Inner Temple. Trained as Collaborative Counsel.
Personal: University of Sussex (LLB Hons, LLM International Commercial Law).

COLMAN, Andrew
2 Hare Court, London
020 7353 5324
andrewcolman@2harecourt.com
Featured in Professional Discipline (London)
Practice Areas: A leading junior of great intellect and experience, held in high esteem for his particular ability to cut through complex issues of fact or law in order to get to the heart of the matter, and his fairness and integrity. For the past ten years he has specialised exclusively in the field of professional discipline, deploying the skills previously honed in the highest levels of criminal advocacy to great effect in mounting submissions and cross-examining witnesses. He applies his expertise to the defence and presentation of disciplinary proceedings before the GMC, GDC and other regulators. He has been instructed in some of the most serious and complex Fitness to Practise hearings, for example, the GMC case against the former Chairman of the BMA. Having developed his expertise largely acting for regulators, he now spends most of his time defending. He is recommended as a leading junior in Professional Discipline by both The Legal 500 and Chambers UK (Band 1). The latter describes him as 'direct and incisive, very methodical, and his submissions are very focussed and effective'. He is also said to be commended as having 'an excellent manner with clients'. He appears regularly in the High Court, and lectures and writes articles on regulatory matters.
Professional Memberships: Association of Regulatory and Disciplinary Lawyers; Health and Safety Lawyers' Association.
Career: Year of Call: 1980
Personal: Fluent in Spanish, both oral and written.

COLTART, Christopher QC
2 Hare Court, London
020 7353 5324
christophercoltartqc@2harecourt.com
Featured in Crime (London), Financial Crime (London)
Practice Areas: Christopher Coltart QC took silk in 2014 following a highly successful junior career (Band 1 in Chambers & Partners and nominated for Criminal Junior of the Year 2012). He is described in the directories as "One of the brightest barristers at the criminal Bar" and someone who is renown for "fantastic advocacy and drafting". Christopher began his career as a City solicitor, specialising in commercial property litigation. His caseload comprised high value claims brought and defended by a variety of financial institutions including banks, pension funds and mortgage providers. Since coming to the Bar in 1998, Christopher has specialised in fraud and white collar crime. He is now head of the 2 Hare Court dedicated fraud team and defends in the most significant cases. Recent instructions include acting for a trader in the LIBOR scandal. Christopher also has an extensive regulatory practice. He has frequently appeared before the disciplinary tribunals of the General Medical Council, and has been involved in cases brought by a number of other regulators, including: the Security Industry Authority, the Solicitors Regulation Authority, the Medicines and Healthcare Products Regulatory Authority and the Financial Reporting Council. In addition to these core areas of his practice, Christopher also has significant experience of major inquest work. He represented a number of the bereaved families in the 7/7 inquest and is presently instructed on behalf of a witness in the inquest into the Hillsborough disaster.

COLTER, Lucy
4 New Square, London
020 7822 2047
j.barrass@4newsquare.com
Featured in Professional Negligence (London)
Practice Areas: Professional liability, construction claims and commercial litigation. Lucy acts for and against professionals in claims against lawyers, surveyors and valuers, often where there is a strong commercial and business element to the claim. Lucy's professional liability work is often in the construction and engineering context. She acts for and against construction professionals in claims against architects, contract administrators and quantity surveyors. She has considerable trial experience of final account disputes and acts for leading multinational construction service companies. Her practice also involves advising and acting in insurance matters (including coverage disputes). She has experience of arbitration in all aspects of her practice. Lucy has good experience of very complex and high value disputes as she has been led extensively by senior members of Chambers, and also has excellent trial experience as sole counsel.
Professional Memberships: COMBAR; PNBA. Lucy is the present chair of the Young COMBAR committee.
Career: MA Oxon, English Language & Literature; Called 2008 (Lincoln's Inn; Lord Brougham, Lord Mansfield and Lord Sheldon scholar).
Publications: Co-Editor: "Jackson & Powell on Professional Liability."

COLTON, Simon
One Essex Court, London
020 783 2000
scolton@oeclaw.co.uk
Featured in Commercial Dispute Resolution (London)
Practice Areas: Specialises in commercial litigation and arbitration, with particular experience of very large-scale litigation involving complex foreign law and other expert issues. Recent cases include Tchenguiz v Serious Fraud Office, Sabbagh v Khoury, Starbev v Interbrew and Berezovsky v Abramovich. Attorney-General's 'B' Panel. Regularly practises in cases requiring Italian and French language skills, reviewing documents and giving oral advice in those languages.
Professional Memberships: COMBAR. London Common Law and Commercial Bar Association.
Career: Called 1999, Inner Temple. Educated at St Paul's School, London; Trinity Hall, Cambridge (MA Hons). Also Université de Poitiers (Diplôme d'études universitaires juridiques francaises); Università per stranieri di Perugia (advanced course in Italian language, business and culture).
Personal: Born 1976, resides London.

COLVILLE, Iain
Arden Chambers, London
020 7242 4244
iain.colville@ardenchambers.com
Featured in Social Housing (London)
Practice Areas: All aspects of housing (public/social/private); landlord and tenant; planning and compulsory purchase and local government law.
Professional Memberships: HLPA, SHLA, PEBA.
Career: Called 1989. Join Chambers in 1997, having previously worked in local government legal service. Reported and significant cases in the last 12 months include: Temur v Hackney LBC [2014] EWCA Civ 877 (homelessness); R. (on the application of Bishop's Stortford Civic Federation) v East Hertfordshire DC [2014] EWHC 348 (Admin); [2014] B.L.G.R. 161; [2014] J.P.L. 852 (planning); Taylor v Spencer [2013] EWCA Civ 1600; [2014] H.L.R. 9; [2014] L. & T.R. 21 (landlord and tenant); Norbrook Laboratories Ltd v Carlisle City Council [2013] EWHC 1113 (Admin); (2013) 157(20) S.J.L.B. 35 (real property; planning); Kartikeya Solutions Ltd v Secretary of State for Communities and Local Government [2013] EWHC Admin (planning); Mansfield DC v Langridge [2013] EWHC Admin (landlord and tenant; disability); Aliya Sharif v London Borough of Camden [2013] UKSC 10 (led by Andrew Arden QC in the Supreme Court; appeared in the Court of Appeal as sole counsel for the local authority) (homelessness).
Publications: Blackstone's Civil Procedure (Oxford University Press) – sole contributor on the Homelessness Chapter between 2006 – 2010. A Guide to the Greater London Authority (Sweet&Maxwell, 2000) – co-author. Joint annotator of the Greater London Authority Act 1999 (Current Law annotations, 2000). A Guide to the Planning Process, Arden's Housing Library, (Lemos & Crane, 2000) – sole author. Human Rights Act 1998 A Practitioners Guide (Sweet & Maxwell, 1998) - contributor to Planning Chpt.

CONE, John
Erskine Chambers, London
020 7242 5532
jcone@erskinechambers.com
Featured in Company (London)
Practice Areas: John is a company law specialist. He has particular expertise in corporate reorganisations and reconstructions (including reorganisations of capital and schemes of arrangement – for both solvent and insolvent companies); takeovers, mergers and acquisitions; and Part VII banking and insurance business transfers. Notable matters include: Novac Group Plc (scheme of arrangement); Lloyds Banking Group and Citibank International/The Post Office (Part VII business transfers); and Netviewer AG (cross-border merger).
Professional Memberships: Chancery Bar Association. COMBAR. A Bar representative on the Law Society Company Law Committee, Member of the Law Reform Committee of the Bar Council, Bencher of the Middle Temple.

CONNOLLY, Barbara QC
7BR, London
020 7242 3555
clerks@7br.co.uk
Featured in Family/Matrimonial (London)
Practice Areas: All areas of family work with particular emphasis on complex public and private law children and adoption, including those with jurisdictional and international issues, relocation and abduction. Surrogacy and assisted reproduction, particularly those with an international element and concerning issues of parenthood and disputes following separation. Cases involving issues of medical treatment, including withdrawal of life sustaining treatment, both in the family court and court of protection, and other welfare/ best interests, financial and property applications in the court of protection.
Professional Memberships: Family Law Bar Association, Association of Lawyers for Children, International Bar Association, International Academy of Matrimonial Lawyers.
Career: Call 1986; Silk 2011.

CONNOLLY, Dominic
5 St Andrew's Hill, London
020 7332 5400
dominicconnolly@5sah.co.uk
Featured in Crime (London)

Practice Areas: Specialist criminal practitioner with experience in murder/manslaughter, organised crime, heavy fraud, serious sex offences and proceeds of crime.
Career: Prosecuted, as leading junior and alone, serious and high profile cases including murder, drug trafficking and serious sexual offences, particularly those involving historical allegations. As former Standing Counsel to RCPO, instructed in the most serious offences for Revenue and Customs and the Serious and Organised Crime Agency. Experience in fraud includes missing trader fraud, advance fee fraud, tax evasion and multi-million pound benefit fraud. Considerable experience in the restraint, confiscation and forfeiture of the proceeds of crime. Recent cases include Austin (murder of drug addict by street dealer), Milner (armed robbery of country house of high-profile entrepreneur by three armed men), Driscoll (prosecution of film director in a substantial vat fraud involving the creation of bogus invoices during the making of a horror film), Court (one of the largest fraud investigations ever carried out by the Kent Police), Rahmonov (prosecution of an internet banking fraud following an investigation by the Metropolitan Police's e-Crime Unit, local boroughs and the Specialist Crime Directorate, the first operation of its kind, working in collaboration with the financial services industry).

CONNOLLY, Joanne
9 St John Street, Manchester
0161 955 9000
joanne.connolly@9sjs.com
Featured in Employment (Northern)

Practice Areas: Joanne Connolly is pleased to act for both claimants and respondents. Her practice ranges from high profile / sensitive unfair dismissal and redundancy claims to the more complex multi-week discrimination, transfer of undertakings, whistle-blowing, working time and equal pay claims. She has particularly extensive experience in disability discrimination claims. Her work incorporates employment disputes in all areas including local government, education, banking, the police service, the legal profession and the NHS as well as business generally. She regularly handles cases involving groups of workers and is accustomed to the pressure of cases where there is a great deal at stake whether in terms of compensation, client expectation, number of employees affected or publicity. Joanne is regularly instructed by in-house solicitors as well as those in private practice. She is experienced at both first instance and appellate levels and has appeared in a number of reported cases. Joanne also acts in employment disputes in the County Court/High Court.
Professional Memberships: The Employment Lawyers Association.
Career: LLB (Nottingham). Called to the Bar in 1992. Awarded Council of Legal Education Studentship and Jules Thorn scholarship. Appointed Fee Paid Employment Judge November 2010.

CONNORS, Jess
Thirty Nine Essex Street, London
020 7832 1111
clerks@39essex.com
Featured in Construction (London)

Practice Areas: Jess Connors specialises in commercial, construction, insurance and oil & gas work, with a particular focus on international arbitration (including LCIA and ICC) and litigation. She also has substantial experience in financial services acting for and against various UK and other regulators and in professional negligence claims.
Professional Memberships: Professional Negligence Bar Association, TecBar, London Common Law and Commercial Bar Association.
Publications: A contributor to Nabarro's Local Authority Procurement (Butterworths, 2002) and Wilmot-Smith on Construction Contracts (2nd Edn).

CONOLLY, Oliver
Pump Court Tax Chambers, London
020 7414 8080
clerks@pumptax.com
Featured in Tax (London)

Practice Areas: Oliver specialises in all areas of taxation, direct or indirect, whether in an advisory capacity or in a litigation context. He has particular expertise in litigation and is regularly instructed by taxpayers, HMRC and NCA to appear before the First-Tier Tribunal, Upper Tribunal and higher courts. He has a particular specialism in tax related professional negligence disputes. he also has experience of litigating EU law issues. Recent cases include Macaw Properties Ltd v HMRC [2012] UKFTT 167 (TC) (First-Tier Tribunal, on commencement of trade for VAT purposes) and Jason Pope (deceased) v HMRC [2012] UKUT 206 (TCC) (Upper Tribunal, on meaning of interest for tax purposes); Tower Radio Ltd v HMRC (First-tier Tribunal); Robert Smith v HMRC (First-tier Tribunal); Fisher v HMRC (First-tier Tribunal); Christopher Lunn & Co (Adminitrative Court); Healy v HMRC (Upper Tribunal), Test Claimants in the FII Group Litigation v HMRC (High Court; Court of Appeal); Dong v NCA (First-tier Tribunal).
Professional Memberships: Revenue Bar Association; Professional Negligence Bar Association.
Career: Barrister since 2003. Lincoln's Inn; Appointed to Treasury C Panel in 2011.

CONSTABLE, Adam QC
Keating Chambers, London
020 7544 2600
aconstable@keatingchambers.com
Featured in Construction (London), Energy & Natural Resources (London), International Arbitration (London), Professional Negligence (London)

Practice Areas: Specialist in construction, engineering, energy, shipbuilding and technology disputes along with professional negligence and insurance claims related to these sectors. Extensive advocacy experience in the Courts of the UK, having appeared in the Technology and Construction Court (TCC), Commercial Court and Court of Appeal. Adam is regularly instructed in arbitration proceedings, both domestic and international, and has experience of proceeding under a variety of rules. He has considerable expertise in adjudication work, and all forms of ADR having represented clients in mediations, early neutral evaluations and expert determinations. Adam is also regularly appointed as adjudicator, arbitrator and independent expert.
Career: Called to the Bar 1995; appointed as Treasury Counsel 2002-07; MCIArb 2008; Inner Temple Advocacy Training Committee 2009; Construction Junior of the Year 2007 and 2010; Recorder of the Crown Court 2010; Queens Counsel 2011; Bencher of Inner Temple 2013.
Publications: Keating on JCT Contracts [Looseleaf & CD-Rom] Co-editor; Keating on Building Contracts (9th Edn) Contributor; Keating on NEC – Contributor; Construction Law Reports - Co-editor; "Construction Claims" and "Building Defects" (RICS Case in Point Series).

COOK, Ian
1 King's Bench Walk, London
020 7936 1500
icook@1kbw.co.uk
Featured in Family/Matrimonial (London)

Practice Areas: Ian Cook practices exclusively as a matrimonial finance barrister and has appeared in the list of leading juniors at the matrimonial finance bar in this publication for over 15 years. Previous years' editorial comments have included the following: "Perfect for the client who doesn't want to pay for a top silk but needs a junior of weight"; "seen as an imposing presence in court" affording clients the sense that "he will fight your corner, come what may"; "He instils confidence in clients by focusing on achieving the best outcome for them and never forgetting their anxieties"; "a purveyor of firm imaginative advice"; "technically very good and very good with clients as well - all round a class act".
Professional Memberships: FLBA.
Career: BA (Hons) 1st Class Philosophy, King's College London. CPE City of London Polytechnic.

COOKSLEY, Nigel QC
Old Square Chambers, London
020 7269 0300
cooksleyqc@oldsquare.co.uk
Featured in Personal Injury (London), Personal Injury (All Circuits)

Practice Areas: Principal area of practice for many years has been personal injury litigation on behalf of both claimants and defendants. He has acted as leading counsel in numerous multi-party actions. Areas of specialisation include brain and spinal injuries, industrial disease and stress. Other areas of practice include clinical negligence, professional negligence, product liability and regulatory compliance.
Professional Memberships: Former Chairman of the Personal Injuries Bar Association, Professional Negligence Bar Association, former member of the Civil Justice Council.
Career: Called to the Bar in 1975. Joint Head of Chambers.
Publications: Joint author of the Bar Council's guidance and standard documents relating to CFAs.
Personal: Educated at Felsted School and Cambridge University. Resides North Hertfordshire. Outside interests include sport, travel and writing.

COOPER, Ben
Old Square Chambers, London
023 7269 0300
cooper@oldsquare.co.uk
Featured in Employment (London)

Practice Areas: Employment and discrimination, labour law and professional discipline, in particular industrial action injunctions, doctors' disciplinaries, high court contractual claims, equal pay, complex discrimination, TUPE. Recent cases of note: Chakrabarty v Ipswich Hospital NHS Trust & another [2014] EWHC 2735 (QB) (doctor's disciplinary injunction); Airedale NHS Foundation Trust v McMillan [2014] EWCA Civ 1031 (contractual powers of employer under internal disciplinary appeal); Amey v Peter Symonds College [2014] IRLR 206 QB (strike pay deductions); Oxer-Patey v Commissioner of Police for the Metropolis [2013] EWHC 4715 (QB) (discrimination in pension scheme on grounds of legitimacy); Okoro & Okenwa v Taylor Woodrow [2013] ICR 580, CA (continuing act); Readman v Devon PCT [2013] IRLR 878, CA (redundancy pay); Gilgrove Ltd v Hay [2013] ICR 1139, CA (contractual interpretation); Unite v BA [2010] ICR 1316, CA (strike injunction)
Professional Memberships: Employment Law Bar Association; Industrial Law Society; Employment Lawyers' Association
Career: Called to the Bar – November 2000.
Personal: Born 1977. LLB (University of Birmingham, 1st class).

COOPER, Gilead QC
3 Stone Buildings, London
020 7242 4937
gcooper@3sb.law.co.uk
Featured in Art and Cultural Property Law (London), Chancery (London), Offshore (London)

Practice Areas: Chancery and commercial litigation, particularly contentious trusts and probate; removal of trustees; breaches of fiduciary duty and civil fraud; charities; real property; professional negligence; pensions; Court of Protection; partnerships; art and cultural property. A substantial proportion of his practice is in off-shore jurisdictions, particularly Hong Kong, the BVI, Bermuda and Caymann.
Professional Memberships: ACTAPS, APL, PNBA, CEDR Accredited Mediator.
Career: Christ Church, Oxford (1973-76); City University (1981); Freshfields (1985-89).
Publications: Palmer on Bailment (2009) 3rd edition, (Contributing Editor: Chapter on Limitation); Tolley's Pensions Law (Chapter on Winding-Up Pension Schemes).

COOPER, John QC
Crown Office Chambers, London
020 7979 8158
cooper@crownofficechambers.com
Featured in Health & Safety (London)

Practice Areas: Has been involved in most of the leading cases in the Regulatory field for many years including several pioneering Court of Appeal cases: Friskies Petcare, HTM, Willmott Dixon, Tangerine & Veolia, New Look, Upperbay, TDG and R v N & C some of which served to re define the parameters of the law. He was instructed and deposed as an expert witness in 2012 on Health and Safety law for DuPont in a commercial case in New York involving over $700M. In the last year he has appeared in the Court of Appeal in three further cases (EA v Red Industries HSE v Polyflor and HSE v London Waste) and in the Administrative Court (MWH v Wise) and although he has been regularly instructed to present a number of cases at appellate level he is equally known for his forensic skills as a trial lawyer. His breadth of practice includes health and Safety, Fire Safety, Environmental law prosecutions and Trading Standards cases where he represents directors of companies and companies involved in regulatory cases. In addition he advises and is consulted upon potential issues in non contentious work. He was instructed in the second corporate manslaughter trial in June 2012 (Lion Steel) successfully defending the Managing Director charged with gross negligence manslaughter. The Director was acquitted of all charges. He successfully defended Red Industries in a 5 week environmental law fish kill trial in 2014, all charges received not guilty verdicts. He is currently instructed in the Vauxhall helicopter crash, an electric gates Gross Negligence Manslaughter case in Manchester, the Claxton Engineering (4 Fatalities) case and both the Lindsey and Pembroke Oil refinery cases (Multi fatalities) in addition to many other cases involving corporate manslaughter, individual manslaughter against company directors and Health and Safety Prosecutions involving fatalities. He is a regular first choice counsel in fatality cases and serious safety cases where contested issues arise and defended in the longest running Health and Safety case (a 4 month asbestos trial at Winchester for Willmott Dixon 2011.) He was Chambers and Partners Health and Safety Junior of the Year 2010 and appointed Queens Counsel in 2014.

COOPER, Peter
St Ives Chambers, Birmingham
0121 236 0863
peter.cooper@stiveschambers.co.uk
Featured in Crime (Midlands)
Practice Areas: Crime.
Professional Memberships: Criminal Bar Association.
Career: Peter deals with heavyweight criminal work, defending and prosecuting. He regularly receives instructions in the most serious cases, including murder, manslaughter, rape, child abuse, firearms, drugs offences, and fraud. He has acted alone in several murder cases, and in many others led by Queen's Counsel. He has frequently appeared in the Court of Appeal, and has also dealt with appeals to the Administrative Court in criminal cases by way of case stated and judicial review. Cases 2013/2014: Peter prosecuted a 13 year old defendant for the rape of a three year old child. The young defendant was convicted, despite the evidence of the toddler victim being ruled inadmissible at trial. He successfully appeared in the Court of Appeal for one of the respondents in the consolidated appeal of R v Dlugosz, R v Pickering & others (mixed profile DNA evidence). He was junior counsel for the defence in the high profile and tragic child murder of 4 year old Daniel Pelka. He successfully defended a man charged, along with nine others, with conspiracy to import and to supply 60 kilos of cocaine. He led another counsel in the successful prosecution of a 16 year old defendant for the murder by stabbing of a fifteen year old boy. He was junior counsel for one of two defendants in a murder case where complex neuropathological evidence was in issue. The trial resulted in a hung jury.

COPELAND, Miles
Three New Square, London
020 7405 1111
copeland@3newsquare.co.uk
Featured in Intellectual Property (London)
Practice Areas: Intellectual property, Information Technology and commercial disputes involving the same; patents, trademarks, passing off, copyright, designs, confidential information, malicious falsehood. Advice, drafting and advocacy covering all these areas both in the UK and the EPO. Cases include Hospira v Novartis [2013] (zoledronate); HTC v Gemalto [2013] (computer software, mobile telephones); Nokia v HTC [2013] (mobile telephones); Resolution v Lundbeck [2013] (estoppel, privity); Fabio Perini v PCMC [2012], [2010] and [2009] (damages inquiry following mechanical patent trial and appeal); Eli Lilly v HGS [2012] (antibodies, Court of Appeal); Welland v Hadley [2011] (ostomy pouches, IPO entitlement proceedings, appeal to High Court); Ranbaxy v AstraZeneca [2011] (esomeprazole); Siemens v Seagate [2010] (hard disk reader); Nokia v IPCom [2010] (mobile telephones); Dr Reddy's v Eli Lilly [2010] (selection patents); Medeva's SPCs [2010] (vaccines, reference to CJEU); CSL/ University of Queensland's SPCs [2010] (vaccines, reference to ECJ); Edwards v Cook [2009] (heart valves).
Professional Memberships: Intellectual Property Bar Association (Hon Sec), Chancery Bar Association, IPSoc (society for junior IP practioners, committee).
Career: Called 2004, Lincoln's Inn, Gonville and Caius College, Cambridge (2002 MA Hons, Natural Sciences), ICSL.

COPLIN, Richard
Keating Chambers, London
020 7544 2600
rcoplin@keatingchambers.com
Featured in Construction (London), Professional Negligence (London)
Practice Areas: Specialist in the construction, engineering, energy and technology sectors. Qualified engineer and spent several years in industry before coming to the Bar. Acts for clients on claims in the English courts, particularly the Technology and Construction Court. Extensive experience of adjudication, arbitration in the UK and ICC arbitrations in Europe and the Middle East (including DIAC). Particularly well regarded for his work on professional negligence claims relating to engineers, architects, surveyors and valuers.
Professional Memberships: Commercial Bar Association; Society of Construction Law.
Career: BA in Engineering Science, Exeter College, Oxford 1989; Diploma in Law, City University 1996; Called to the Bar (Middle Temple) 1997; Pupillage, Keating Chambers 1997-98; Keating Chambers 1998.
Publications: Contributor - Keating on Construction Contracts Ninth Edition (2012). Has also contributed a chapter in "Construction Dispute Resolution Handbook" ed. Dr Gaitskell QC pub. Thomas Telford (2011).

COPPEL, Jason QC
11KBW, London
020 7632 8500
jason.coppel@11kbw.com
Featured in Administrative & Public Law (London), Civil Liberties & Human Rights (London), Data Protection (London), Competition/European Law (London), Local Government (London), Public Procurement (London)
Practice Areas: Specialist in public law, public procurement, EU law, information and human rights law, including judicial review, social security, pensions, data protection and freedom of information. Recent notable cases include Chester v Lord President (SC: EU and ECHR challenge to ban on voting by convicted prisoners); T v Greater Manchester Police (SC, disclosure of convictions on CRB checks); BY Developments v CGMA (TCC: use of expert evidence in procurement claims); Humphreys v HMRC (SC: splitting of social security child benefits between separated parents); JBW v MoJ (CA: service concession contracts and implied contract claims in procurement law); Greenwich CLC v Greenwich LBC (CA: impact of public sector equality duty on tender procedures); Varney v Hertfordshire CC (CA: disclosure of tender evaluation criteria, sub-criteria and weightings); St Prix v SSWP (SC: EU law rights of pregnant workers to social security benefits); Re Landsbanki (Icelandic Supreme Court: human rights challenge to change of insolvency priority order). Member of the Northern Ireland Bar.
Career: Called to the Bar: 1994; QC: 2013.

CORDREY, Thomas
Devereux, London
020 7353 7534
cordrey@devchambers.co.uk
Featured in Employment (London)
Practice Areas: Thomas has extensive experience in the High Court, County Courts, Employment Appeal Tribunal and Employment Tribunals (in England, Wales and Scotland). He has also appeared in the Court of Appeal acting for a specialist employment law firm in a test case in which he was led by Colin Wynter QC. Thomas' work in the complementary practice areas of professional negligence, insurance and personal injury frequently crosses over with his employment specialism and gives him expertise in handling employment claims outside the tribunal system. Thomas is a member of the Bar Council's Legislation & Guidance sub-group and is part of ELA's LEI working party. He is also a member of ELBA and sits on the Commercial Bar Association E&D committee. He writes widely on employment law both in journals and as a contributor to Bloomsbury Professional's leading practitioner text on discrimination law. Thomas has a particular specialism in religious discrimination and related human rights law and was called to give evidence to a Parliamentary Committee considering law reform in this area. He was featured in 'The Lawyer' commenting on the European Court of Human Rights' landmark decision in Eweida v British Airways.
Professional Memberships: ELBA, ELA, COMBAR, PNBA, PIBA.
Career: Called 2006; Lincoln's Inn Tancred Studentship and Hardwicke Scholarship.
Publications: Contributing author, 'Discrimination Law' (Bloomsbury Professional).
Personal: Thomas is vice chairman of the Lawyers' Christian Fellowship: "Seek justice, love mercy, walk humbly with God" (Micah 6:8).

CORNELL, Kate
5 Essex Court, London
020 7410 2000
clerks@5essexcourt.co.uk
Featured in Police Law (All Circuits)
Practice Areas: Police law, including civil claims for wrongful arrest, false imprisonment, malicious prosecution, discrimination, assault and misfeasance. Policy advice. Inquests. Police misconduct at first instance, PAT and judicial review stages. Human rights, particularly Article 2 and Article 8 issues. Discrimination cases. CLG, AJD, JAD v Merseyside Police (2013)Trial defending a claim for alleged wrongful disclosure of witnesses' identities to criminal defendants in a criminal trial. Claimants are currently appealing; R (on the application of Commissioner of the Police of the Metropolis) v Police Appeals Tribunal [2013] EWHC 4309 (Admin)Judicial review of PAT decision to reinstate a Special Constable; A & B v Chief Constable of Hampshire Police [2012] EWHC 1517 Successful strike out of a claim that the police had caused unauthorised disclosures of an informer's identity to be made during court hearings where the disclosures were protected by the core immunity applying to court proceedings; Metropolitan Police officer dismissed without notice for seriously mishandling 999 calls; Five Merseyside Matrix officers dismissed for gross misconduct following improper and unprofessional behavior during a search.
Professional Memberships: South Eastern Circuit; Association of Regulatory and Disciplinary Lawyers; Professional Negligence Bar Association; Proceeds of Crime Lawyers Association.
Career: Called to the Bar 2003.

CORNWELL, James
11KBW, London
020 7632 8500
James.Cornwell@11kbw.com
Featured in Data Protection (London), Education (London)
Practice Areas: Education, Data Protection and Freedom of Information, Administrative & Public, Local Government and Employment Law. Cases include: Information Commissioner v Niebel [2014] UKUT 255 (AAC); R (LV) v Secretary of State for Justice & Parole Board [2014] EWHC 1495 (Admin); R (Crawford) v Newcastle University [2014] ELR 110; R (Rotherham MBC) v Secretary of State for Business, Innovation & Skills [2014] EWHC 232 (Admin); Cabinet Office v Information Commissioner & Aitchison [2013] 2 Info LR 336, UT; Secretary of State for Energy & Climate Change v Friends of the Earth [2012] EWCA Civ 28; GC & JC v Tameside MBC [2011] ELR 470, UT; Miskovic & Blazaj v Secretary of State for Work & Pensions [2011] 2 CMLR 20, CA; Cheltenham BC v Laird [2009] IRLR 621; Kirklees Metropolitan Council v Radecki [2009] ICR 1244, CA; W v Staffordshire CC [2007] ELR 208, CA; J v Staffordshire CC [2006] ELR 141.
Professional Memberships: ALBA; ELBA; ELA.
Career: Called: 2002; Attorney General's 'B' Panel: 2012.
Publications: Tolley's Employment Handbook; Local Government Law; Halsbury's Laws of England – Judicial Review.
Personal: Educated: University College, Oxford (BA (Hons), PPE); University College London (MPhil, Philosophy); Brasenose College, Oxford (DPhil, Philosophy); City University (Diploma in Law).

CORSELLIS, Nicholas
QEB Hollis Whiteman, London
020 7933 8855
nicholas.corsellis@qebhw.co.uk
Featured in Crime (London)
Practice Areas: Nicholas Corsellis is a highly respected leading counsel specialising

in serious crime, ranging from murder to fraud, both prosecuting and defending. Professional and lay clients appreciate his direct and clear approach packaged with diplomacy and courtesy. Nicholas handles allegations of serious crime including murder, very high value drugs conspiracies and sexual abuse. He undertakes high-profile cases, for example representing the first defendant in R v O and others (the Victoria Station Murder). He also represented the first defendant in the £40 million Graff jewellery robbery (R v K), a Latvian serial rapist/murderer (R v D) and a 15-year-old contract killer (R v G). He has expertise in cases involving analysis and presentation of complex technical evidence such as the interpretation of all manner of forensic evidence (such as DNA, gunshot residue and blood spatter) as well as cell site and computer evidence. Nicholas acts in complex multi-million pound fraud cases, often with an international dimension. One example is R v S and others, a £5 million worldwide wine fraud. In the regulatory field, Nicholas acts for the International Tennis Federation and other governing bodies in arbitrations concerning professional tennis players, such as PTIOs v XXX.
Professional Memberships: Criminal Bar Association.
Personal: Call 1993; LLB (Hons); fluent French.

COSGROVE, Thomas
Cornerstone Barristers, London
020 7242 4986
tcosgrove@cornerstonebarristers.com
Featured in Planning (London), Professional Discipline (London)
Practice Areas: Planning, public and regulatory law (professional discipline).
Professional Memberships: PEBA, ALBA, ARDL, UKELA.
Career: Specialises in planning, environmental, public and administrative law and regulatory fitness to practise work. Detailed tactical knowledge of planning law and process. Extensive experience of planning inquiries and related statutory challenges throughout the country acting for private clients and planning authorities. Has recently been involved in major planning inquiries concerning nationally significant infrastructure projects for renewable energy provision. During 2013 and 2014 was instructed in one of the largest onshore wind farm inquiries in the UK. He has extensive experience of a wide range of planning areas including viability, climate change and renewable energy, housing, heritage assets and conservation, transportation and the delivery of major road infrastrusture, design, ecology and the natural environment. As well as major city developments, he has substantial experience of promoting and resisting development proposals in countryside areas of outstanding natural beauty, national parks and the green belt. He regularly appears in the High Court with specialist knowledge of judicial review procedure and statutory appeals. He has developed an additional specialisation in the area of professional regulatory law and in particular the fitness to practice procedures of various healthcare and legal regulators.

COTTAGE, Rosina QC
Red Lion Chambers, London
020 7520 6000
rosina.cottage@18rlc.co.uk
Featured in Crime (London)
Practice Areas: Rosina Cottage QC has a high-profile prosecution and defence practice in serious and complex cases: multi-handed fraud, murder and sexual offences. In the first half of 2014 she prosecuted in R v Max Clifford and defended in R v Mark Howes ("Dexter" copy-cat murder). In the second half of the year she has prosecuted 6 defendants in R v PT and others (historic child sexual offences) and is instructed to prosecute in R v R and others in a DWP fraud where, of the 8 defendants for trial this year, 6 are deaf. In 2013 she prosecuted R v Opemipo Jaji, a stranger rape of a child and R v Wendall Baker, a double-jeopardy re-trial of the rape of an elderly woman. In 2012 she defended in R v Cameron Rose, the alleged murder of a young child with complicated medical evidence. Rosina has defended and prosecuted various Revenue frauds, money laundering and significant confiscation proceedings. She has prosecuted multi-handed cases with demanding financial and/or overseas evidence. Rosina has a very strong reputation for her work in difficult and sensitive cases with very young children and extremely vulnerable people as witnesses and defendants. She has experience of all types of special measures, including intermediaries, and has defended and prosecuted in cases where defendants and/or witnesses had significant learning impairments, were on the autistic spectrum or suffered other mental health problems.
Professional Memberships: Committee Member and former Recorder of Southeastern Circuit Bar Mess; Chairman of the Central London Bar Mess; Circuit representative on the Criminal Bar Association.
Career: Queen's Counsel, 2011; Recorder, 2012; Bar Representative of the Council of the Inns of Court Disciplinary Tribunal.

COTTER, Mark
5 St Andrew's Hill, London
07973 622 183
markcotter@5sah.co.uk
Featured in Crime (London)
Practice Areas: Criminal law, with a particular emphasis on sexual offences, homicide, fraud and organised crime. Mark was first instructed as a leading junior in 2003; since then he has been instructed as a leading junior in a wealth of cases. He receives instructions from leading defence solicitors across London, the South East and the Midlands. He is also instructed by the London CPS and a number of specialist CPS rape units. He has recently been instructed to lead for the defence in a multi-handed murder case and was also recently privately instructed to defend the Non-Executive Director of an NHS trust in a multi-defendant heavy fraud. In his most recent heavy frauds, in which he acted for the Crown, he received unsolicited judicial commendations for the quality of his advocacy. Mark has also been involved in numerous celebrity cases. This year he successfully acted for the lead defendant in the high profile trial of four Brighton and Hove Albion Footballers accused of sexual offences. Mark's increasing reputation in cases involving sexual offences has resulted in the receipt of numerous private instructions over the past years, including a number of celebrity clients. Other examples of celebrity work include successfully defending in the Katie Price (AKA 'Jordan') nanny fraud and in the case of an Olympic diver facing assault charges. Mark also has particular experience of acting in cases involving medical professionals accused of sexual offences said to have been committed within a clinical setting.
Professional Memberships: Criminal Bar Association.
Career: Educated at Kingston University (LLB Hons 1992); the University of Wales, Cardiff College, (LLM 1993, Commercial Law); called 1994 (Middle Temple). Practice and career profile at www.5sah.co.uk.
Personal: Season ticket holder at Cardiff City Football Club, Friend of the Royal Opera House, Friend of the Imperial War Museum and Friend of the British Museum. Also a keen amateur cook.

COUGHLAN, John
No5 Chambers, Birmingham
07931 576 713
jco@no5.com
Featured in Clinical Negligence (Midlands), Personal Injury (Midlands)
Practice Areas: Clinical Negligence and Personal Injury.
Professional Memberships: PIBA, PNBA, AvMA.
Career: John's has a very well-developed clinical negligence and personal injury practice. He deals with claims of the utmost complexity and severity and regularly works alongside, and is instructed in cases against, Queen's Counsel. His detailed preparation enables him to bring the best out of his client's case. He is well-known for his robust advocacy, his intuitive handling of expert witnesses and his sensitive approach to the client.

COUSINS, Jeremy QC
11 Stone Buildings, London
020 7831 6381
cousins@11sb.com
Featured in Banking & Finance (London), Chancery (London), Professional Negligence (London)
Practice Areas: Jeremy Cousins QC practices in commercial, commercial chancery (including trusts and wills), professional negligence and property litigation and is continuously instructed in high-profile and/or high-value cases in these areas. He is well known for his particular expertise in banking and banking related disputes. His practice in these areas frequently involves him in Channel Islands work. His ability to deal with complex cases in a calm and measured way makes him a firm favourite among his clients. Over many years he has had substantial practices in the Midlands as well as London and from 2002-06 he was chairman of the Midland Chancery and Commercial Bar Association. In 2007 he was appointed to sit as a Deputy High Court Judge in the Chancery and Queen's Bench Divisions. On a regular basis he contributes articles to a number of leading publications. For a further insight in Jeremy's practice and case highlights, please visit the 'Barristers' section on www.11sb.com.
Career: Qualified 1977; QC 1999; assistant recorder 1996; recorder 2000; deputy High Court judge (Chancery, QB, Mercantile) 2007. Prior to 11 SB, Jeremy was a tenant at St Philips Chambers in Birmingham and Selborne Chambers in London.

COVER, Martha
Coram Chambers, London
020 7092 3700
clerks@coramchambers.co.uk
Featured in Family/Matrimonial (London)
Practice Areas: Children.
Professional Memberships: Family Law Bar Association Association of Lawyers for Children Human Rights Lawyers Association Liberty Gray's Inn.
Career: Called November 1979. Head of Chambers since January 2010. Martha Cover has been a child law specialist since 1990. She represents parents and children in cases of serious death and injury to a child. She has a particular interest in allegations of emotional harm where children are being brought up in unusual or false belief systems. She also specialises in international and domestic adoption, wardship, and intractable disputes between parents over contact and residence.
Publications: Martha regularly speaks and writes on children law matters. She has written for The Times and been interviewed on radio and television to discuss adoption and the wider policy issues affecting care proceedings.
Personal: Born and educated in Canada. BA University of Western Ontario, BA Law University of North London, LLM University of London. Married with three children.

COWTON, Catherine
Queen Elizabeth Building, London
020 7797 7837
c.cowton@qeb.co.uk
Featured in Family/Matrimonial (London)
Practice Areas: Matrimonial finance with an emphasis on complex financial cases involving substantial assets, trust structures, tax and valuation issues, and international jurisdictional disputes. Drafting pre-nuptial, post-nuptial and cohabitation agreements. Private law children applications (including applications to remove children from the jurisdiction).
Professional Memberships: Family Law Bar Association; Bar Pro Bono Unit.
Career: Magdalene College, Cambridge (MA (Hons) Law); Queen Mother's Scholar (Middle Temple); called 1995.
Publications: "Delight and Dole: The Children Act 10 years on" (edited with Lord Justice Thorpe).

COX, Jason
Ropewalk Chambers, Nottingham
0115 947 2581
jasoncox@ropewalk.co.uk
Featured in Clinical Negligence (Midlands), Personal Injury (Midlands)
Practice Areas: He specialises principally in high-value personal injury, clinical negligence, disease, counter fraud and regulatory defence work. He has a particular speciality in claims involving underground services damage. He is highly regarded for his formidable cross-examination skills and keen eye for detail. Many clients instruct him as an alternative to using Leading Counsel in catastrophic claims.
Professional Memberships: Personal Injuries Bar Association; Professional Negligence Bar Association; Nottinghamshire-Medico Legal Society.
Career: Called in 1992; LLB (Hons) 1st, University of Nottingham.
Personal: Away from the Bar, he lists his interests rugby and cricket (now only as a spectator), cycling and skiing (as a participant) and music (as both).

COX, Raymond QC
Fountain Court Chambers, London
020 7583 3335
rc@foutaincourt.co.uk
Featured in Banking & Finance (London), Insurance (London)

Practice Areas: Commercial disputes generally, including banking and finance, fraud, financial services, international arbitration, offshore, professional negligence, and regulatory. Serious Fraud Office, Queen's Counsel list (2009).
Career: Called to the Bar 1983, Silk 2002.
Publications: 'Law of Bank Payments', Brindle and Cox (4th ed., 2010); 'Private International Law of Reinsurance and Insurance', Cox, Merrett, Smith (2006); Contributor, 'Lloyd's Research Handbook on International Insurance Law & Regulation' (December 2011) and 'Professional Negligence and Liability', Simpson, (looseleaf).
Personal: Born 1959, BA (Oxon). 1st class, Eldon Scholar. Leisure includes odd theatre, cycling and making things in wood.

CRAIG, Aubrey
St Philips Chambers, Birmingham
0121 246 2165
acraig@st-philips.com
Featured in Intellectual Property (The Regions)

Practice Areas: An experienced practitioner whose practice in the field covers over 20 years in the UK as well as 10 years in the USA. His practice covers most aspects of UK, European and US IP law including copyright, database right, design right, trade marks, passing off and confidential information. He also acts and advises in relation to mechanical and electrical patents and UK, European and US patents for computer related inventions. Cases include: BSkyB v Digital Satellite Warranty Cover Ltd & Ors (trade mark infringement, passing off, infringement of database right, breach of confidence, joint tortfeasor liability); Schutz (UK) Ltd v Delta Containers Ltd (trade mark infringement and passing off, exhaustion of rights); Garrison Radio: Pool FM Trade Mark No.2328312 (opposition proceedings in the TM Registry O-117-06); Cyprotex Discovery Ltd v University of Sheffield (copyright ownership).
Professional Memberships: ChBA, IP Bar Association.
Career: 1977-87 New York, USA; admitted to New York State and US Federal Bars. 1987 to date Bar of England and Wales.
Publications: Electronic Disclosure (CIPA Magazine July 2007).

CRAIG, Nicholas
3 Verulam Buildings, London
020 7831 8441
ncraig@3vb.com
Featured in Commercial Dispute Resolution (London), Insurance (London), Shipping (London)

Practice Areas: Nicholas has a wide-ranging commercial practice encompassing all aspects of complex commercial disputes, with particular expertise in banking, civil/commercial fraud, shipping and commodities, aviation, insolvency and restructuring, insurance and reinsurance and professional negligence.
Professional Memberships: COMBAR.
Career: BA (Hons)(Lon)(1st Class): English Literature and Language M.Phil. (Oxon): Nineteenth century English literature Dip. Law (City) Call 1998.

CRAIL, Ross
New Square Chambers, London
020 7419 8000
ross.crail@newsquarechambers.co.uk
Featured in Agriculture & Rural Affairs (London), Real Estate Litigation (London)

Practice Areas: Wide-ranging experience in chancery and commercial matters; practice now principally focused on real property disputes, often with a public law flavour; a particular interest in rights of way (public and private), common land and town and village greens; instructed by local authorities as inspector to conduct public inquiries into applications for registration of new greens. Reported cases include Paddico (267) Ltd v Kirklees Metropolitan Council [2014] 2 WLR 300; R (Lewis) v Redcar and Cleveland Borough Council (No. 2) [2010] 2 AC 70; R (Oxfordshire & Buckinghamshire Mental Health NHS Foundation Trust) v Oxfordshire County Council [2010] LGR 631; R(Warden and Fellows of Winchester College) v Hampshire County Council [2009] 1 WLR 138; R(Godmanchester Town Council and Drain) v Secretary of State for Environment, Food and Rural Affairs [2008] 1 AC 221; Oxfordshire County Council v Oxford City Council [2006] 2 AC 674.
Professional Memberships: Chancery Bar Association.
Career: MA (Oxon) Literae Humaniores, Diploma in Law (City University). Called to the Bar 1986 (Lincoln's Inn).
Publications: Joint editor of 'The Law of Freedom of Information' (OUP). Contributor to the Rights of Way Law Review and member of its editorial board.

CRAMPIN, Peter QC
3 Stone Buildings, London
020 7242 4937
pcrampin@3sb.law.co.uk
Featured in Chancery (London), Charities (London), Real Estate Litigation (London)

Practice Areas: Chancery: property litigation and advice, trusts, charities, pensions, professional negligence.
Professional Memberships: ChBA; ACTAPS.
Career: Qualified as a solicitor in 1973. Called to the Bar in 1976. 2nd Junior Counsel to the A-G in charity matters 1988-93. Silk 1993.
Personal: Born 7 July 1946.

CRANGLE, Thomas
4 Pump Court, London
020 7842 5555
tcrangle@4pumpcourt.com
Featured in Construction (London)

Practice Areas: Construction and engineering, professional negligence, energy, technology and telecoms and insurance
Professional Memberships: TECBAR (committee member); Society of Construction Law; COMBAR; PNBA; Society for Computers and Law.
Career: Magdalene College, Cambridge MA (Law) 2001; Called to the Bar 2002.

CRAPPER, Sadie
Thirty Nine Essex Street, London
020 7832 1111
sadie.crapper@39essex.com
Featured in Fraud (All Circuits), Personal Injury (London)

Practice Areas: Personal injury and clinical negligence. Advises in all types of accident and injury claims with a particular emphasis on fraud. Experienced in all areas of accident-related fraud work including conspiracy to defraud cases, strike outs for fraudulent exaggeration (Summers v Fairclough Homes Limited) and committal proceedings (Fari v Homes for Haringay). Extensive experience in road traffic matters, workplace accidents and claims under the Protection from Harassment Act (Dowson v Chief Constable of Northumbria Police). Clinical negligence practice includes delayed diagnosis, obstetrics cases, negligent surgical treatment and cases arising from plastic surgery. Qualified mediation advocate adept at dealing with complex round table negotiations.

CRASNOW, Rachel
Cloisters, London
020 7827 4000
rc@cloisters.com
Featured in Employment (London)

Practice Areas: Rachel Crasnow has been consistently recommended as a leading employment junior for many years. She practices in all aspects of domestic & EU employment law, acting in high-profile cases in forums including the Supreme Court & CJEU. She undertakes a wide range of work from equal pay, working time & maternity rights to TUPE, internal disciplinary tribunals & collective rights. She is particularly recognised for her expertise in discrimination & human rights & her practice includes advising in goods & services cases. Rachel is regularly instructed in high value & complex trials by individuals, private companies, & public sector bodies. She is a trained mediator & is often instructed as counsel in difficult mediations. She also undertakes a range of regulatory & other civil work.
Professional Memberships: ELBA, ELA, DLA, Bar Pro-Bono Unit, ELAAS, HRLA.
Career: Notable recent work includes: O'Brien v MOJ - EAT Jan 2014 (judicial pension remedy); SC [2013] ICR 499 (part-time discrimination & judicial pensions), Dudley Council v Whitehead [2012] EAT (group action equal pay); Blackburn v Chief Constable of W.Midlands Police [2009] IRLR 135 CA (equal pay); Cadman v HSE [2007] 1 CMLR 16 ECJ (justifying equal pay); DTI v Rutherford [2006] ICR 785 HL (sex / age discrimination / EU law), Vince-Cain v Orthet [2005] ICR 374 (sex discrimination & tax); Goodwin v UK (2002) 35 EHRR 18 (transsexuals & human rights). Standing counsel to BPS for over 10 years. Counsel to 1999-2000 Turner Inquiry; instructed in the Climbie Inquiry. Long-term advisor at Camden Law Centre. Nominated for Employment Junior of the Year 2013. Sought after legal speaker & commentator.
Publications: Co-author/editor of Family Rights in Employment Law (Jordans 2012), co-author of Blackstone's Guide to the Equality Act 2010 (OUP 2010), co-author with Robin Allen QC of 'Employment Law and Human Rights' (2nd edition OUP 2007), editor of Bullen & Leake's Human Rights & European Law Sections. Previous editor of 'Educational Law Journal's Case Commentaries'. Writes for legal periodicals & responses to consultation papers.
Personal: Educated at Pembroke College, Oxford & City University, London. Middle Temple Diplock Scholarship 1993; Pegasus Scholarship 1999 (Human Rights & Equal Opportunities Commission, Sydney). Member of the Bar Council Equality & Diversity Committee; Chair of Bar Council Legislation & Guidance Group.

CRAVEN, Edward
Matrix Chambers, London
020 7404 3447
edwardcraven@matrixlaw.co.uk
Featured in Defamation/Privacy (London)

Practice Areas: Defamation, privacy and breach of confidence; reporting restrictions; data protection and freedom of information; human rights and judicial review; criminal law; public international law; commercial law and sports law. Notable recent cases include the Mobile Telephone Voicemail Interception Litigation; NGN Compensation Scheme; R (Miranda) v SSHD (seizure of journalistic material under Schedule 7 of Terrorism Act 2000); Liberty v GCHQ (challenge to legality of government mass interception and intelligence sharing programmes); Smith v Ministry of Defence (UKSC appeal regarding extra-territorial application of ECHR); R (Duggan) v SSHD (legality of post-incident conferring by police officers); Croatia v Serbia (ICJ Genocide Convention). Provides regular pre-publication/broadcast advice to national newspapers and BBC News.
Career: BA Law (First Class Hons), Trinity Hall, Cambridge University; BCL (Distinction), Brasenose College, Oxford University; Bar Vocational Course (Outstanding), Inns of Court School of Law. Judicial assistant at the Court of Appeal (2009); European Court of Human Rights (2010) and United Kingdom Supreme Court (2011-12). Lecturer in Administrative Law and European Human Rights Law at Oxford University (2010-11).
Publications: Contributing Editor to "Smith, Owen & Bodnar on Asset Recovery" (OUP) and "Criminal Justice and Human Rights" (Sweet & Maxwell). Regular contributor to the Inforrm media law blog.

CRAWFORD, Grant
Radcliffe Chambers, London
020 7831 0081
gcrawford@radcliffechambers.com
Featured in Chancery (London)

Practice Areas: General Chancery. Cases of note: professional negligence: Target Holdings Ltd v Redferns [1996] 1AC 421; company law and insolvency: Re: Phoenix Office Supplies Ltd [2003] 1 BCLC 76; Re: Bradley-Hole [1995] 1 WLR 1097; real property and trusts: de Bruyne v de Bruyne [2010] 2 FCR 251; Barnet LBC v Barnet FC (Holdings) Ltd [2004] EWCA Civ 1191; Carlton v Goodman, [2002] 2 FLR 259; State Bank of India v Sood [1997] Ch 276; family provision, probate and administration of estates: Shovelar v Lane [2011] EWCA Civ 802; Ghafoor v Cliff [2006] 1 WLR 3020; Re Hancock [1998] 2 FLR 346; charities: Re East Grinstead Working Men's Club [2011] WTLR 975; revenue: Lonsdale v Braisby (HMIT) [2005] STC 1049; limitation: Phillips & Co. v Bath Housing Co-operative Ltd [2013] 1WLR 1479.
Professional Memberships: Chancery Bar Association.
Career: Called 1974; accredited mediator 2011.

CRAWFORD, Ruth QC
Axiom Advocates, Edinburgh
0131 226 5071
ruth.crawford@axiomadvocates.com
Featured in Administrative & Public Law (Scotland), Planning (Scotland)

Practice Areas: Public and administrative law (including all aspects of Judicial Review), European Union law, planning and environmental law, public procurement (extensive advisory work and contentious litigation for economic operators and contracting authorities in respect of major procurement exercises) and professional negligence. Recent cases include British Telecommunications plc v Common Services Agency [2014] CSOH 44 (appeared for BT in first successful challenge in Scotland to a public procurement exercise), McGeoch v Lord President of Council [2013] UKSC 63, Uprichard v Scottish Ministers [2013] UKSC 21, M v Secretary of State for Work and Pensions [2013] UT (appeared for Secretary of State to successfully oppose appeal to vires of transition from income support to ESA), Wm Grant & Sons Distillers Ltd v Scottish Ministers [2012] CSOH 98 (appeared for SMs in this important case about relationship between consents udner the Electricity Act and Town and Country Planning (Scotland) Act), AXA General Insurance v Scottish Ministers [2011] UKSC 46 , KP and MRK v Home Secretary [2012] CSIH 18 (as amicus curiae, vires of a Rule of Court), and Comhairle Nan Eilean Siar v Scottish Ministers [2012] CSIH 6,[2013] CSIH 45.
Career: Faculty of Advocates 1993, Second Standing Junior Counsel to Scottish Executive 2002-08, Ad Hoc Advocate Depute 2006 to date, QC 2008. Appeared in the Supreme Court, House of Lords, Inner and Outer Houses of the Court of Session, Criminal Appeal Court, High Court of Justiciary, Upper Tribunal and Public Inquiries into major infrastructure and development projects. Written submissions to the European Court of Human Rights. On panel of counsel for Equality and Human Rights Commission. Member of Faculty Dispute Resolution Service as expert determiner. Advocate member of Access to Justice sub-committee Scottish Civil Justice Council.
Publications: Greens Planning Encyclopaedia, Section 75 Agreements, published 2010.

CRAWSHAW, Simon
Atkin Chambers, London
020 7404 0102
scrawshaw@atkinchambers.com
Featured in Construction (London)
Practice Areas: Simon has wide ranging experience in domestic courts, mediations and adjudications as well as domestic and international arbitrations conducted under various arbitral rules, including SIAC, HKIAC, ICC and UNCITRAL. He specialises in construction and engineering, energy, and professional negligence. Notable cases include: A claim related to the construction of a road tunnel in Gibraltar under a FIDIC form of contract (OHL v. Govt. of Gibraltar [2014] EWHC 1028); SIAC arbitration concerning the termination of a contract for the purchase of a large residential, commercial and retail development in Vietnam; Representing a company forming part of the consortium delivering the Manchester Tram project (Transport for Greater Manchester v Thales [2012] 146 ConLR 194); Appeal to the Privy Council from concerning the proper interpretation of certain statutory provisions (Presidential Insurance v St. Hill [2012] UKPC 33); Representing a member of the FIFA Executive Committee in libel proceedings brought against a prominent politician (Makudi v Lord Triesman [2014] 3 All ER 36).
Professional Memberships: TECBAR, LCLCBA, Combar, SCL
Career: MA (Oxon, 1st Class); LLB (London); Boulter Exhibition (Christ Church, Oxford), Marchant Scholarship (Lincoln's Inn); Called (England and Wales) 2005
Publications: Hudson's Building and Engineering Contracts, 12th Ed - contributing editor.
Personal: Private Pilot's Licence.

CREAN, Anthony QC
Kings Chambers, Birmingham
0845 034 3444
clerks@kingschambers.com
Featured in Planning (Midlands), Planning (Northern)
Practice Areas: Anthony's practice includes all areas of planning and environmental law and his particular strength is in high profile cases where excellence in advocacy is of great importance. Specialist expertise in large scale housing projects, retail, waste/minerals, renewables, heritage, highways and compulsory purchase. He is a visiting professor of planning law, University of Buckingham.
Professional Memberships: Planning and Environment Bar Association, Fellow of the Royal Geographical Society.
Career: Called 1987; silk 2006.

CRIDDLE, Betsan
Old Square Chambers, London
020 7269 0357
criddle@oldsquare.co.uk
Featured in Employment (London)
Practice Areas: All areas of employment and discrimination law and professional discipline, with particular expertise in doctors' disciplinary cases. Recent cases of note include Lim v Royal Wolverhampton Hospitals NHS Trust (2011), Kerslake v North West London Hospitals NHS Trust (2012) and Chhabra v West London Mental Health NHS Trust (2013).
Professional Memberships: ELBA, ILS, ELA.
Career: MA (Hons) Law, St John's College, Cambridge. Called to the Bar 2002.
Publications: Employment Precedents and Company Law Documents (Sweet & Maxwell); Employment Law Review (IER); Employment Tribunal Procedure (LAG).
Personal: Fluent Welsh speaker.

CRIDLAND, Simon
Serjeants' Inn Chambers, London
020 7457 5000
scridland@serjeantsinn.com
Featured in Clinical Negligence (London), Professional Discipline (London)
Practice Areas: Simon Cridland was called to the Bar in 1999. Simon specialises in clinical negligence and healthcare, professional discipline, product liability, inquests and inquiries and public and administrative law. An earlier edition notes that "his ability to get the information needed for a case... his thorough examination and cross-examination of experts are great" and that "he is incredibly eloquent, very tactically sharp and thinks of things that no one else has thought of. His advocacy works magnificently well." Please click on the link to the Serjeants' Inn Chambers website for his profile, which sets out full details of his practice and relevant work of note.
Professional Memberships: ARDL, PNBA, LCLCBA, ELBA.
Publications: "Gregg v. Scott: the lost chance of 'a loss of a chance'" Clinical Risk (2005) 11 138-141; Clinical Negligence (APIL) (contributor).

CRIGMAN, David QC
St Philips Chambers, Birmingham
0121 246 0200
dcrigman@st-philips.com
Featured in Crime (Midlands)
Practice Areas: Exclusively criminal practice, prosecuting and defending serious crime.
Career: Recorder since 1986. Originally a tenant of 1 Fountain Court, now merged with St Philips Chambers.
Personal: Likes indoor cycling, writing novels (first book published November 2006, second book published April 2008, third book published November 2009, fourth book published May 2011).

CROSS, James QC
4 Pump Court, London
020 7842 5555
jcross@4pumpcourt.com
Featured in Construction (London), Professional Negligence (London), Property Damage (London)
Practice Areas: James has an extensive and wide-ranging commercial practice with particular expertise in professional negligence (especially construction industry professionals), construction and engineering, insurance and product liability. "Meticulous" and a "cool, calm and collected performer" (Chambers UK 2012), James is recommended for his "superb grasp of technical detail", "commitment, high level of service and excellent response times" (Chambers UK 2009) and "commended for his thorough approach" (Chambers UK 2010).
Professional Memberships: COMBAR, LCLCBA, PNBA (Committee), TECBAR, SCL.
Career: Called 1985 (Gray's Inn) QC 2006.
Publications: Contributor to the Architect's Legal Handbook 9th ed. (Chapter on Architects' Liability).
Personal: Shrewsbury and Magdalen College, Oxford (MA, Jurisprudence).

CROSS, Tom
11KBW, London
020 7632 8500
tom.cross@11kbw.com
Featured in Data Protection (London), Education (London), Employment (London)
Practice Areas: Public, education, information, EU, employment, commercial.
Professional Memberships: ALBA, BEG, ELA.
Career: Called to the Bar in 2007. Judicial Assistant at the UK Supreme Court 2009-2010. Appointed in 2012 to Attorney General's C Panel of Counsel (Civil) and the Welsh Government's B Panel of Counsel. Recent cases include: JG v Lord Chancellor [2014] EWCA Civ 656; R (Abedin) v Secretary of State for Justice [2014] EWHC 78 (Admin); Manchester City Council v JW; [2014] UKUT 0168 (AAC); Bedale Golf Club Ltd v Revenue and Customs Commissioners [2014] UKUT 99 (TCC); R (Members of the Committee of Care North East Northumberland) v Northumberland County Council [2013] EWCA Civ 1740; Stadium Capital Holdings No 2 v Secretary of State for Communities and Local Government [2013] EWHC 3548 (Admin); R (SA) v London Borough of Camden [2014] ELR 29; R (Mehey and others) v Visitors to the Inns of Court [2014] ACD 39 [2013] EWHC 3097 (Admin); London Borough of Harrow v AM [2013] UKUT 157 (AAC); Information Commissioner v Dransfield [2012] UKUT 440 (AAC); Aderemi v London and South Eastern Railway Ltd [2013] EqLR 198; Woodford v Olympus Corporation (ET, May 2012); Independent Police Complaints Commission v Warner [2012] EWHC 271 (QB); R (on the application of Cheshire East Borough Councils and one other) v Secretary of State for the Environment [2011] NPC 92; R (on the application of Luton Borough Council & Others) v Secretary of State for Education [2011] EWHC 217 (Admin); R (on the application of Savva) v Royal Borough of Kensington and Chelsea [2010] EWCA Civ 1209; Bury Metropolitan Borough Council v Usman [2010] UKUT 406 (AAC); R (on the application of Boyle) v Haverhill Pubwatch [2009] EWHC 2441 (Admin); R (on the application of Bristol City Council) v Bristol City Magistrates Court [2009] EWHC 625 (Admin).
Publications: The Protections for Religious Rights (OUP: 2013). The Law of Regulatory Enforcement and Sanctions (OUP: 2011). Articles in The Times, Judicial Review, the European Advocate, the Education Law Journal.
Personal: Double 1st class degree from Oxford in Modern Languages (French and Spanish). CPE (City).

CROW, Charles
No5 Chambers, Birmingham
0121 606 0500
ctc@no5.com
Featured in Employment (Midlands)
Practice Areas: Charles undertakes a wide range of employment and discrimination work, advising and representing both Claimants and Respondents, including high value and multi day hearing work. He has extensive Tribunal and EAT experience, speaks publicly on a regular basis at Chambers and other events, and accepts instructions on a Direct Professional Access basis. Charles also has experience of injunction applications in the County and High Courts. Charles also practices in the fields of personal injury and costs, and is an accredited mediator. He is a member of the employment committee of the Birmingham Law Society. Recent cases: Dr Elaine Storkey v. Wycliffe Hall (unreported, Times 8th January 2008) Cpt. Mason v. Thomas Cook (Telegraph, 20 March 2009) – Hurley v Wye Valley NHS Trust (2011) (unreported) UKEATPA/0209/12/ZT Nazir & Aslam v. Asim [2010]ICR1225 Harber v. Kelly Residential UKEAT/0105/CEA Quashie v. Methodist Homes Housing Association [2012] ICR 1330 Heart of England v. Williams (unreported) UKEATPA/0105/13/RN.
Professional Memberships: ELA, PIBA and ELBA.
Career: Called 1999, Hardwicke Scholarship & Tancred Studentship, Lincolns Inn.
Personal: Married, with three (lively) sons.

CROW, Jonathan QC
4 Stone Buildings, London
020 7242 5524
j.crow@4stonebuildings.com
Featured in Administrative & Public Law (London), Banking & Finance (London), Chancery (London), Commercial Dispute Resolution (London), Company (London), Financial Services (London), Fraud (London), Offshore (London), Restructuring/Insolvency (London), Telecommunications (London)
Practice Areas: Company/ commercial litigation; administrative and public law; banking and finance; chancery (commercial); international trust work.
Professional Memberships: Administrative Law Bar Association; Commercial Bar Association; Chancery Bar Association; Insolvency Lawyers Association.
Career: Called 1981; Treasury Counsel 1994-98; First Treasury Counsel 1998-2006; Deputy High Court Judge 2001. Attorney General to HRH The Prince of Wales 2006. Court of Appeal Judge in Jersey & Guernsey 2011. Called to the Bar in the BVI, and also in Nevis, Bermuda and Cayman Islands for specific cases.
Publications: Annotated Companies Act 2006, OUP (contributing author).

CROWE, Cameron
36 Bedford Row, London
020 7421 8000
clerks@36bedfordrow.co.uk
Featured in Consumer Law (London)
Practice Areas: Consumer, trading standards and regulatory law spanning both criminal and civil jurisdictions. Prosecutes and defends the full spectrum of trading standards offences as well as representing parties in Enterprise Act proceedings. He is particularly noted for his expertise in relation to the Consumer Protection from Unfair Trading Regulations 2008, the Business Protection from Misleading Marketing Regulations 2008, the Trade Marks Act 1994 and the Enterprise Act 2002, as well as Fraudulent trading and money laundering. Recent cases include: prosecuting the largest ever 'rogue trader' prosecution brought by a local authority, obtaining an enforcement order against rogue building companies and advising several brands in relation to private prosecutions under the Trade Marks Act. Clients include local authorities, private companies and individuals. He is available to undertake work on a direct access basis. Visit the 36 Bedford Row website for more details.
Professional Memberships: Anti-counterfeiting Group, POCLA, Bar European Group.
Publications: Contributing editor of Consumer and Trading Standards: Law & Practice (Jordans 2013). Contributing editor of Modern Financial Regulation (Jordans 2013). Frequent lecturer at the annual Trading Standards Institute Conference. Has provided training to local authorities in relation to Consumer law, the Enterprise Act, Money laundering and Fraud.

CROWLEY, Jane QC
1 Garden Court Family Law Chambers, London
020 7797 7900
crowley@1gc.com
Featured in Family/Matrimonial (London)
Practice Areas: Family Finance Team, International & Private Child, Care & Adoption, Child Abduction, Local Authority Team, Human Rights Working Group, Family Related Crime, Court of Protection
Professional Memberships: Committee Member FLBA Association of Lawyers for Children.
Career: Jane's public law children practice includes cases involving complex physical injuries, including : - "baby shaking" - factitious illness - sexual abuse and incest - cases involving the death of children where both causation and likely perpetrator are in issue Jane has a particular interest in cases involving the unexplained death of a child and is known for the ease with which she disentangles complicated medical issues. She was involved in some of the early cases in which the legitimacy of statistical evidence to be applied to SIDS was challenged. She has experience in "honour based" killing/violence and forced marriage and has recently been involved in a lengthy case in which her client was also represented by a Special Advocate because of non disclosure of sensitive material. She is recognised as having considerable skill in representing learning disabled or otherwise vulnerable parents and parents with mental health difficulties. She has appeared in the only family cases to date in which evidence has been given through intermediaries. Her private law children work includes relocation, an area in which she has a particular interest. Jane represented Rhondda Cynon Taf in the Clwych Enquiry convened by the Children's Commissioner for Wales and subsequently undertook advisory work for the Commissioner. Jane's public law children practice includes cases involving complex physical injuries, including : - "baby shaking" - factitious illness - sexual abuse and incest - cases involving the death of children where both causation and likely perpetrator are in issue Jane has a particular interest in cases involving the unexplained death of a child and is known for the ease with which she disentangles complicated medical issues. She was involved in some of the early cases in which the legitimacy of statistical evidence to be applied to SIDS was challenged. She has experience in "honour based" killing/violence and forced marriage and has recently been involved in a lengthy case in which her client was also represented by a Special Advocate because of non disclosure of sensitive material. She is recognised as having considerable skill in representing learning disabled or otherwise vulnerable parents and parents with mental health difficulties. She has appeared in the only family cases to date in which evidence has been given through intermediaries. Her private law children work includes relocation, an area in which she has a particular interest. Jane represented Rhondda Cynon Taf in the Clwych Enquiry convened by the Children's Commissioner for Wales and subsequently undertook advisory work for the Commissioner. Jane's public law children practice includes cases involving complex physical injuries, including : - "baby shaking" - factitious illness - sexual abuse and incest - cases involving the death of children where both causation and likely perpetrator are in issue Jane has a particular interest in cases involving the unexplained death of a child and is known for the ease with which she disentangles complicated medical issues. She was involved in some of the early cases in which the legitimacy of statistical evidence to be applied to SIDS was challenged. She has experience in "honour based" killing/violence and forced marriage and has recently been involved in a lengthy case in which her client was also represented by a Special Advocate because of non disclosure of sensitive material. She is recognised as having considerable skill in representing learning disabled or otherwise vulnerable parents and parents with mental health difficulties. She has appeared in the only family cases to date in which evidence has been given through intermediaries. Her private law children work includes relocation, an area in which she has a particular interest. Jane represented Rhondda Cynon Taf in the Clwych Enquiry convened by the Children's Commissioner for Wales and subsequently undertook advisory work for the Commissioner.
Personal: Married, 2 children. Music, walking the Pembrokeshire countryside, Glamorgan Cricket Club, MCC Associate Member.

CULLEN, Edmund QC
Maitland Chambers, London
020 7406 1200
ecullen@maitlandchambers.com
Featured in Chancery (London), Commercial Dispute Resolution (London), Intellectual Property (London), Media & Entertainment (London), Professional Negligence (London)
Practice Areas: Has broad expertise in chancery and commercial litigation, with particular emphasis on the music, film and broadcasting industries, where he has acted for the major record companies, producers and broadcasters, as well as many leading artists, writers, composers and agents. Deals extensively with disputes over contractual and intellectual property rights in a wide variety of media. Also specialises in professional negligence in the legal and accountancy fields and in claims arising in the company/ insolvency context, including claims against directors, asset tracing and recovery and restitution.
Professional Memberships: Chancery Bar Association and COMBAR.
Career: Called to the Bar 1990. QC 2012.

CUNNINGHAM, Mark QC
Maitland Chambers, London
020 7406 1200
mcunningham@maitlandchambers.com
Featured in Chancery (London)
Practice Areas: Specialist chancery practitioner with a bias towards commercially orientated litigation. He has appeared in over 100 reported cases concerning: company law, directors' disqualification, personal insolvency, sale of land, landlord and tenant, rent reviews, easements, land registration, partnership, proprietary estoppel, copyright, passing off, entertainment law, the Inheritance Act, subrogation, the Court of Protection, the Copyright Tribunal, betting and gaming, VAT, winding-up, corporation tax, asset recovery, MTIC fraud, banking and solicitors. He has also been appointed as a DTI Inspector in relation to insider dealing matters. He appears regularly in the Cayman Islands and the BVI.
Professional Memberships: Chancery Bar Association, COMBAR.
Career: Called 1980. Appointed Junior Counsel to the Crown (Chancery), February 1992. Appointed Junior Counsel to the Crown 'A' Panel, 1999. Appointed Queens Counsel, 2001. Accredited mediator, 2002. Called to the East Caribbean Bar, 2005.
Publications: Contributor to 'Mithani: Directors' Disqualification'.
Personal: Educated at Stonyhurst College and Magdalen College Oxford (BA History). Born 6 June 1956. Lives in Buckinghamshire.

CUTRESS, James
Fountain Court Chambers, London
020 7583 3335
jc@fountaincourt.co.uk
Featured in Aviation (London), Banking & Finance (London), Commercial Dispute Resolution (London), Insurance (London), Professional Negligence (London)
Practice Areas: Specialises in commercial litigation and arbitration, with particular expertise in banking and finance, insurance and reinsurance, aviation, fraud/asset recovery, jurisdiction and conflict of laws, professional negligence and international and domestic arbitration.
Professional Memberships: Commercial Bar Association, London Common Law and Commercial Bar Association.
Career: Called 2000.
Publications: Co-Author of The Law of Privilege (ed B. Thanki QC, OUP, 2nd edition 2011).
Personal: Worcester College Oxford, BA (top first), BCL (first class); Harvard Law School LLM (Kennedy Scholar); Eldon Scholar.

DAINTY, Cheryl
Kings Chambers, Manchester
0845 034 3444
clerks@kingschambers.com
Featured in Commercial Dispute Resolution (Northern)
Practice Areas: Commercial dispute resolution (including agency, sale of goods, factoring/invoice discounting, enforcement disputes and interim relief/injunctions), banking and finance (including consumer credit and guarantees/indemnities), insolvency/asset recovery (corporate and personal, for office holders, creditors and debtors), company (including share and asset purchase agreements, minority shareholder petitions and directors' disqualification), partnerships and LLPs, professional negligence, mortgages, land registration.
Professional Memberships: Chancery Bar Association R3 Association of Business Recovery Professionals (Leeds and Manchester Womens' Groups) Northern Circuit Commercial Bar Association (Committee Member) Northern Chancery Bar Association Northern and North Eastern Circuits.
Career: 2004 BA (First Class Hons.) Law with Law Studies in Europe (German Law) (Corpus Christi College, Oxford) 2004-2007 Guest Lecturer (University of Wuerzburg and the University of Bonn, Germany) 2005-2006 Masters of Comparative Law (with a focus on comparative commercial law) (University of Bonn, Germany) 2006 Called (Inner Temple) 2010 - Junior Counsel to the Crown (Provincial Panel).

DANIELS, Iain
Ely Place Chambers, London
07973 670 553
idaniels@elyplace.com
Featured in Health & Safety (London), Police Law (All Circuits)
Practice Areas: Representing police forces, probation trusts, private prison and custody providers as well as claimants. Healthcare law: represents PCTs, NHS Hospital Trusts, private healthcare providers, nursing homes,

doctors, nurses and claimants in Court of Protection matters, inquests and medical negligence. Health and safety law: appears in cases involving all aspects of health and safety and fire safety legislation in the Court of Appeal, Administrative Court, Crown, Magistrates' and Coroners' Courts as well as PI/FAA/Clinical Negligence civil claims. Cases involving injuries and deaths relating to construction sites, large plant and machinery, warehouses and farms, asbestos and other hazardous substances as well as deaths and injuries within the healthcare, police and prison sectors. Appears on behalf of police forces, healthcare trusts, private prison providers and local authorities as well as multi-national corporate clients. Non-contentious work: advises on risk management policy and protocols. Lectures on regulatory and health and safety matters including prosecution and defence strategy, corporate manslaughter, fire safety legislation, RIPA and healthcare matters. Recent cases include: Houchin v Lincolnshire Probation Trust [2014] EWCA Civ 823; Wamala v Secretary of State for the Home Department [2014] EWHC 1503 (QB); Global Marine Drillships Ltd v La Bella [2014] EWHC 1230 (Ch); Brown (Widow and Executrix) v Hamid [2013] EWHC 4067 (QB); R. (on the application of Odigie) v Serco Ltd [2013] EWHC 3795 (Admin); R. (on the application of Commissioner of Police of the Metropolis) v Central Criminal Court [2013] EWHC 179 (Admin); (1) Commissioner of Police of The Metropolis (2) Serious Organised Crime Agency v (1) Times Newspapers Ltd (2) Michael Gillard [2011] EWHC 2705 (QB); Ahmad v (1) Brent London Borough Council (2) National Probation Service (London) (3) Ministry of Justice (4) Parole Board for England & Wales [2011] EWHC 80 (QB); R (Takoushis) -v- HM Coroner for Inner North London & Guy's & St. Thomas' Hospital NHS [2005] EWCA Civ 1440.
Professional Memberships: PIBA.
Career: Queen Mary's Grammar School, Walsall; Sheffield University LLB (Hons); called 1992 Lincoln's Inn.

D'ARCY, Eleanor
Kings Chambers, Leeds
0845 034 3444
clerks@kingschambers.com
Featured in Chancery (Northern), Restructuring/Insolvency (North Eastern)
Practice Areas: Chancery and Commercial Litigation; Insolvency – corporate and individual; Commercial Contracts; Company Law; Financial (especially guarantees and recoveries), Property (both real and commercial) and Professional Negligence arising within those areas.
Professional Memberships: Chancery Bar Association, Northern Chancery Bar Association, Northern Circuit Commercial Bar Association, R3 Yorkshire Women in Business Recovery Group (Committee Member).
Career: BA Classics, St. John's College, Oxford; Called: 2008 (Lincoln's Inn); Lord Haldane, Lord Denning and Wolfson Scholar.

DARLING, Paul QC
Keating Chambers, London
020 7544 2600
pdarling@keatingchambers.com
Featured in Construction (London), International Arbitration (London), Professional Negligence (London)
Practice Areas: Wide ranging expertise in the fields of construction, engineering, procurement, energy and commercial litigation, with a formidable reputation as an advocate in all types and levels of tribunals all over the world. Well known for his advocacy skills and in particular for cross-examining and arguing appeals. Has considerable experience of leading large teams in long and heavy cases. Regularly advises on both non-contentious and contentious aspects of bespoke and standard terms of Building and Engineering Contracts. Places particular emphasis on his commercial instincts and skills. Reputation as an advocate means that he is often instructed in areas of work outside of Chambers' case work, such as Sports, Sale of Goods and Bloodstock. Over sixty of his cases have been reported.
Professional Memberships: TECBAR; SCL (Member of Council 1999 to 2001); LCLCBA; PNBA; COMBAR.
Career: Called 1983; QC 1999; Bencher Middle Temple 2004; Construction Silk of The Year 2006; Head of Keating Chambers 2010.
Publications: Editorial Team, Keating on Construction Contracts - 8th Edition; Editorial Team, Keating on Building Contracts, 5th, 6th and 7th editions; Formerly Joint Editor, Construction Industry Law Letter.

DARWIN, Claire
Matrix Chambers, London
020 7404 3447
clairedarwin@matrixlaw.co.uk
Featured in Education (London), Employment (London)
Practice Areas: Claire specialises in employment, discrimination, education, public, information and commercial law. She has a broad advisory practice, and is frequently instructed in complex, high-value or high profile cases. Claire is one of the Attorney General's Junior Counsel to the Crown (C Panel). She has substantial experience of acting as sole counsel in the Employment Appeal Tribunal and Upper Tribunal. She has appeared as sole counsel in the Court of Appeal, and as junior counsel in two matters before the European Court of Human Rights.
Professional Memberships: Discrimination Law Association; Education Law Association; Employment Lawyers Association (ELA); Employment Lawyers Appeals Advice Scheme (ELAAS); Employment Law Bar Association (ELBA); Industrial Law Society.
Publications: Claire is co-author of the chapter on Discrimination in Employment in Bullen & Leake & Jacob's Precedents of Pleadings, 17th edition with 1st Supplement (December 2013), and the editor of the Practical Law Company's Guide to Discrimination in the Provision of Goods and Services. She is also co-author of the chapter on the Relationship between Freedom of Information and Data Protection in the Law Society's Freedom of Information Handbook (3rd edition, December 2012), and is a Contributing Editor of the Education Law Journal.

DASHWOOD, Alan QC
Henderson Chambers, London
020 7583 9020
adashwood@hendersonchambers.co.uk
Featured in Competition/European Law (London), Product Liability (London)
Practice Areas: The Law of the European Union and more particularly: all aspects of EU internal market regulation, including product liability, unfair commercial practices and the Services Directive; public procurement; veterinary and plant health legislation; competition law, including State aid; the interface between EU law and intellectual property law, including in the WTO context; the interface between EU law and the law relating to foreign direct investment; age and sex discrimination, the Working Time Directive and other EU-related aspects of employment law; all aspects of the law of EU external action, including trade, development co-operation and foreign, security and defence policy; EU anti- terrorism measures; the European Arrest Warrant and other EU Measures in the area of freedom security and justice; the Brussels 1 Regulation and the New Lugano Agreement.
Career: Called to the Bar 1969, entered private practice in 1997. Bencher, Inner Temple 2002. Appointed QC 2010. Previously, (1995-2009) Professor of European Law at Cambridge, now Emeritus; (1987-94) Director in the Legal Service of the Council of the EU, providing extensive experience of the EU Legislative process and of litigation in the CJEU. Professor (part-time) City University (2012).
Publications: Previously, Editor, Common Market Law Review and European Law Review. Co-author, Wyatt and Dashwood's European Union Law (6th ed). Co-editor, and principal contributor, The Future of the Judicial System of the European Union. Co-editor, and contributor, 'EU External Relations: Law and Practice.' Contributor to the Bar European Group's Practitioners' Handbook of EC Law.

DAVIDSON, Nicholas QC
4 New Square, London
020 7822 2000
n.davidson@4newsquare.com
Featured in Professional Negligence (London)
Practice Areas: Professional liability (particularly lawyers', investment managers/advisers' and financial services liability). Insurance (including professional liability cover) and general commercial cases, including corporate governance and computer litigation. Recently acted for the National Union of Mineworkers in its successful claim against Mr Arthur Scargill, and for Newcastle Airport in claims against executive directors and solicitors arising out of bonus payments; acting in swaps claims.
Professional Memberships: Professional Negligence Bar Association (Chairman 1997-99), British Insurance Law Association, Financial Services Law Association, Bar European Group, COMBAR, Chancery Bar Association, Society for Computers and Law; Member of the Chartered Institute of Arbitrators.
Career: Called 1974; joined present chambers 1999. Silk 1993. Deputy High Court Judge.
Publications: Contributor to Professional Negligence and Liability (ed. Simpson) (Informa, 2000).
Personal: Educated at Winchester 1964-69 (Scholar) and Trinity College Cambridge (Exhibitioner in Economics) 1969-72. Certificate of Honour, Bar Finals. Is a trustee of a defined benefit pension scheme.

DAVIDSON, Ranald
Serjeants' Inn Chambers, London
020 7427 5000
rdavidson@serjeantsinn.com
Featured in Clinical Negligence (London)
Practice Areas: Ranald Davidson was called to the Bar in 1996. Ranald specialises in clinical negligence and healthcare, professional discipline and regulatory, inquests and inquiries and public and administrative law. An earlier edition notes that "he is superb, very calm in the heat of battle and understands the issues in a case extremely well" and that he is "an approachable barrister, who is down to earth, responsive and sensible." Please click on the link to the Serjeants' Inn Chambers website for his profile, which sets out full details of his practice including relevant work of note.
Professional Memberships: Professional Negligence Bar Association, Association of Disciplinary and Regulatory Lawyers.
Publications: Consultant Editor Medical Law Reports; Contributor to forthcoming Atkins Sports Law text.

DAVIES, Andrew
Henderson Chambers, London
020 7583 9020
adavies@hendersonchambers.co.uk
Featured in Real Estate Litigation (London)
Practice Areas: Commercial and common law practice concentrating on business and insurance law, property, professional negligence, disciplinary and regulatory, finance and consumer, and civil claims involving police and other public authorities. Property expertise includes commercial and residential landlord and tenant, easements and covenants, dilapidations, co-ownership and beneficial interests, lease renewals, mortgages, undue influence, insolvency, boundary disputes, adverse possession, service charges, property related professional liability claims. Further details on Henderson Chambers' website http://hendersonchambers.co.uk
Professional Memberships: PNBA, COMBAR, ARDL.
Career: Worcester College, Oxford (1st class Hons). Called 1988. Legal assessor to NMC, GOsC, CIMA, I&FA. Deputy District Judge.
Publications: Butterworths Civil Court Precedents (editor, Professional Negligence); Clayton & Tomlinson's Civil Actions against the Police, 3rd edition (2003), editor.
Personal: Born 1966. Married with three children.

DAVIES, Angharad
30 Park Place, Cardiff
029 2039 8421
angharad@30parkplace.co.uk
Featured in Chancery (Wales & Chester)
Practice Areas: Traditional Chancery litigation specialising in contentious probate, administration of estates, trusts, Inheritance Act claims, as well as advisory work on the interpretation of wills and trusts. Particular interest in matters concerning land; from boundary disputes and easements to adverse possession and conveyancing concerns. Commercial Chancery work includes contractual claims, insolvency, landlord & tenant and professional negligence.
Professional Memberships: Chancery Bar Association, STEP, ACTAPS, SFE.
Career: Called in 2000, Lincoln's Inn.

DAVIES, Charlotte
Littleton Chambers, London
020 7797 8600
charlottedavies@littletonchambers.co.uk
Featured in Employment (London)
Practice Areas: Charlotte specialises in employment law and commercial litigation. Her employment practice includes matters involving restrictive covenants, confidentiality and directors' duties in addition to the

full range of statutory employment work. Her commercial practice covers contractual disputes, company disputes and civil fraud. Charlotte regularly undertakes appellate work, and has appeared in the Privy Council, Court of Appeal and EAT. Clients include a range of private and public sector organisations (including a number of FTSE 100 companies) as well as private individuals.
Professional Memberships: ELBA, COMBAR, LCLCBA.
Career: Called 2006, Lincoln's Inn.
Personal: Educated at St Hilda's College, Oxford University. Awarded Lord Mansfield and Lord Bowen Scholarships and Hardwicke Entrance Award by Lincoln's Inn.

DAVIES, Edward
Erskine Chambers, London
020 7242 5532
edavies@erskinechambers.com
Featured in Company (London)
Practice Areas: Edward is a specialist in company, commercial and corporate insolvency law. Recent cases: Hollis v Marylebone Cricket Club [2013] EWHC 3547 (QB) (application for an injunction to restrain the holding of a general meeting; Rothschild v Bumi Plc [2013] (unfair prejudice proceedings involving FTSE-listed mining conglomerate); Re Coroin Ltd [2012] EWHC 2343 (Ch) (Unfair prejudice and conspiracy claims concerning steps taken by Barclay brothers to take control of Claridge's, The Connaught and The Berkeley); Thomas v Jakes [2011] EWHC 2619 (Ch) (application to commit a company director for contempt of court); Michael Wilson & Partners Ltd v Emmott [2011] EWHC 1441 (Comm) (Challenge to an arbitration award under sections 68 and 69 of the Arbitration Act 1996); Stainer v Lee [2010] EWHC 1539 (Ch) (Permission to continue derivative claim).
Professional Memberships: COMBAR. Chancery Bar Association.
Career: Called 1998.
Publications: Company Directors: Law and Liability; Practical Law Company: Freezing injunctions case study.
Personal: Interests: Rugby, long distance running and birdwatching.

DAVIES, George
Temple Garden Chambers, London
020 7583 1315
gd@tgchambers.com
Featured in Fraud (All Circuits)
Practice Areas: George Davies has extensive experience of defending fraudulently induced, contrived and exaggerated insurance claims whether they arise from opportunism or are the product of sophisticated fraud rings. He also has had wide exposure to defending sham credit hire and LVI claims. His work covers all stages of litigation, from advising pre-issue to drafting pleadings and includes advocacy up to the level of the Court of Appeal. His experience of civil fraud proceedings includes the successful pursuit and continuance of freezing injunctions as well as full-blown contempt proceedings in the High Court. His recent Court of Appeal experience includes Ali v D'Brass [2011] EWCA Civ 1594.
Professional Memberships: PIBA, CBA, LCLCBA.
Career: Called: 1998, Admitted as Solicitor: 2002, Temple Garden Chambers: 2005 to date.
Personal: Interests include canine pursuits, running, hiking, history, family and the dramatic arts.

DAVIES, Jonathan
Old Square Chambers, London
020 7269 0339
davies@oldsquare.co.uk
Featured in Employment (London)
Practice Areas: Areas of specialism: atypical workers claims; Commercial Agents; Conflict of Laws/Territorial Jurisdiction; consultation rights; data protection/privacy in the workplace; discrimination; enforcement of contractual disciplinary procedures by way of injunctive relief; Equal pay; Human Rights; industrial relations and trade union affairs; maternity and paternity rights; misrepresentation claims in employment context; medical, dental health and care regulatory proceedings; National Minimum Wage; negligent references; Pay, Bonus and Commission Disputes; Protection from Harassment; restrictive covenants and business protection disputes; taxation in so far as it relates to employment disputes; TUPE; unfair dismissal; whistleblowing; Working Time regulations; wrongful dismissal. Recent reported cases are: Croesus v the Bradshaws [2013] EWHC 3685 QB (injunctive relief in business protection case); Greenwood v NWF Retail [2011] ICR 896, EAT (Employment Tribunal's duty to give reasons); Kulkarni v. Milton Keynes NHS Foundation Trust [2009] IRLR 829, CA (right to legal representation in internal disciplinary proceedings); Mezey v SW London & St George's Mental Health NHS Trust (No.2) [2010] IRLR 512 CA (enforcement of contractual disciplinary procedures by way of injunctive relief); Rice and Thompson v. Secretary of State for Trade and Industry [2007] ICR 1469, CA (workplace duties of care in negligence); McKie v. Swindon College [2011] IRLR 575, QBD (negligent references); GX Networks Ltd v. Greenland [2010] IRLR 991, CA (contractual commission dispute).

DAVIES, Sian
Cornerstone Barristers, London
020 7242 4986
siand@cornerstonebarristers.com
Featured in Community Care (London), Social Housing (London)
Practice Areas: Local government, social housing, community care, European Community law, immigration, human rights.
Professional Memberships: ALBA.

DAVIS, Adam QC
3 Temple Gardens, London
020 7353 3102
adqc@3tg.co.uk
Featured in Crime (London)
Practice Areas: Adam Davis QC has been involved in high profile cases throughout his career representing defendants such as Matthew Simmons in the "Cantona" case, Wayne Lineker and the Croydon Furniture Fire Case and prosecuting the eBay counterfeit golf club case. In Silk, he has successfully defended in the 2011 New Years Eve Hatton Garden Murder at the CCC and a Street Murder outside a Billericay Night Club. In 2013, he was instructed in a serious drug conspiracy, a £5m Confiscation and represented a Prisoner serving a life sentence charged with the historic murder of a cellmate. He also defended in a 5-month high profile conspiracy to traffic women into the UK for sexual exploitation. He is currently appearing in Operation Forbear a six-month trial at Liverpool Crown Court. In the next year he is due to defend a £200m confiscation and a four-month £30m money laundering case. He has appeared as an advocate in front of the British Boxing Board of Control on licensing matters, the Football League tribunal on transfer irregularities and other regulatory bodies and regularly advises Professional Athletes including current PGA European Tour Golfers and Sports Management companies. He is a Registered Lawyer with the Football Association. He sits as a Chairman on the "Very High Cost Cases Appeals Committee" and also undertakes single adjudicator appeals. He is an Independent Funding and Cost Assessor to the New Legal Aid Agency. He is an accredited lecturer on the Proceeds of Crime Act 2002 (Confiscation and Money Laundering) lecturing to solicitors and barristers, accountants and financial institutions. He advises companies on Money Laundering matters. He continues to act as Legal Adviser and Board Member for the Pro Touch Soccer Academy, a community based football organisation. He is a Non-Executive Director of Places For People PLC one of the largest residential property development, management and regeneration companies in the UK and a Board Member of a London religious organisation.
Professional Memberships: Criminal Bar Association, Central Criminal Court Bar Mess, South Eastern Circuit.
Career: Called 1985.
Publications: Employment Lawyers Association Briefing. Volume 11 Number 10 December 2004 (Money Laundering and the Proceeds of Crime).
Personal: Voluntary work as adviser and board director for the Pro Touch Soccer Academy. Leisure interests include Football, Golf, Cricket and Tennis.

DAVIS, Andrew
Crown Office Chambers, London
020 7797 8100
adavis@crownofficechambers.com
Featured in Personal Injury (London)
Practice Areas: Andrew specialises in personal injury and industrial disease, with a significant proportion of his work being catastrophic injury claims (both brain and spinal injuries, alone and with a Leader), fatal accident claims and chronic pain. He undertakes significant work in EL and PL claims and road traffic accidents. Industrial disease work includes including NIHL, mesothelioma, WRULD, VWF, HAVS, asthma, COSSH, dermatitis and display screen claims. He has extensive experience in advising and advocacy in cases of accidents abroad and accidents in this jurisdiction involving foreign nationals, including issues of jurisdiction and applicable law. He lectures widely on catastrophic claims and the Ogden Tables and is particularly interested in the practicalities of the law, maths and tactics of how the Tables are most advantageously deployed. He also undertakes commercial, insurance and related work. He appears in cases in litigation and mediation. He is particularly interested in matters with technical or scientific aspects. He is well accustomed to policy and coverage disputes of all types whether as freestanding claims or forming part of ongoing disputes. Reported cases include: Burton v Kingsbury, Crofts v Murton, Onay v Brown, Walton v Axa Belgium, OFT v Foxtons Ltd, Goad v Butcher and Smith v Bailey.

DAVIS, Carol
Littleton Chambers, London
020 7797 8600
cdavis@littletonchambers.co.uk
Featured in Employment (London)
Practice Areas: Employment, professional discipline and regulation, professional negligence and general commercial law.
Professional Memberships: ELA, ELBA and COMBAR.
Career: With a reputation for combining thoroughness to all details of the case and a commercial, costs-sensitive approach, Carol Davis is a sought after practitioner. She is praised for her careful attention to detail, her punchy and probing cross examination and her clear analysis of the law. Carol undertakes a wide range of advisory, court and tribunal work across all areas of employment law. Her forte lies in handling sensitive and challenging matters and she is regularly instructed in multi-day discrimination and whistleblowing cases. She also appears in employment related cases in the High Court (both led and alone) in interim hearings (often involving the seeking of injunctive relief to enforce restrictive covenants and the protection of confidential information) and at trial. Clients include major UK and multinational corporations, banking institutions and public authorities. Carol is also the Joint Head of Littleton Chambers' Disciplinary and Regulatory Group.
Publications: Author of 'Termination of Employment' with John Bowers QC; co-author of the chapter 'Dismissal With or Without Notice' in Butterworth Tolley's Termination of Employment (looseleaf) and author of numerous articles on aspects of employment law for a variety of journals. Carol is also Editor of Littleton Chambers' Insight into Disciplinary and Regulatory Law.
Personal: Education: Diploma in Law (1994-95); BA Hons in English literature, Sussex University (1991-94); interests include travel, theatre and her young family.

DAVIS, Glen QC
South Square, London
020 7696 9900
glendavis@southsquare.com
Featured in Financial Services (London), Restructuring/Insolvency (London)
Practice Areas: Insolvency and commercial law complicated by insolvency, particularly banking, financial services and insurance; company law and directors' duties; partnership; fraud and asset recovery.
Professional Memberships: Member, Chartered Institute of Arbitrators; Fellow, R3; Fellow, Society for Computers and Law; COMBAR (Chair, Africa Committee since 2007); Insolvency Lawyers Association; Financial Services Lawyers Association; INSOL Europe.
Career: Called to the Bar of England and Wales 1992; Member of Chambers at South Square since 1993; appointed Queen's Counsel 2011; called to the Bar of Gibraltar for specific cases; called to the Bar of the Eastern Caribbean Supreme Court in the British Virgin Islands; licensed to appear in the Courts of the Dubai International Financial Centre; experience of arbitrations as advocate and as arbitrator; CEDR-accredited mediator. Member, Insolvency Rules Committee (2002-12).
Publications: Editor, Butterworths Insolvency Law Handbook (since 1997); Insolvent Partnerships (1996); contributor to Company

Directors: Duties, Liabilities and Remedies (OUP, 2nd ed, 2013).
Personal: Married, four children; interests include contemporary art, Arsenal.

DAVISON, Richard
12 King's Bench Walk, London
020 7583 0811
davison@12kbw.co.uk
Featured in Personal Injury (London)
Practice Areas: Catastrophic and high value injury claims. Claims for harassment, including sexual abuse and child sexual abuse. Clinical negligence, especially birth injuries. Personal injury claims that have a 'cross-over' with employment law, e.g. bullying and stress at work, claims involving discrimination and disability. Employment law.
Professional Memberships: Personal Injury Bar Association, Professional Negligence Bar Association, Employment Law Bar Association.
Career: BA Jurisprudence, Corpus Christi College, Oxford. Fee-paid Employment Judge (1999), Recorder (2005), Treasury panel of special advocates (2009).
Personal: Married with 4 children. Away from work enjoys singing, tennis, sea-kayaking and wandering around art galleries.

DAVY, Neil
Serjeants' Inn Chambers, London
020 7427 5000
ndavy@serjeantsinn.com
Featured in Clinical Negligence (London)
Practice Areas: Neil Davy was called to the Bar in 2000. Neil specialises in clinical negligence, employment, professional discipline and regulatory law. An earlier edition notes that "he is an impressively tough negotiator" and that he is "brilliant with paperwork and excellent at complex, unusual cases which require lateral thinking." Please click on the link to the Serjeants' Inn Chambers website for his profile, which sets out full details of his practice including relevant work of note.
Professional Memberships: Professional Negligence Bar Association, London Common Law and Commercial Bar Association.

DAWSON, Adam
9 Gough Square, London
020 7832 0500
adawson@9goughsquare.co.uk
Featured in Personal Injury (London)
Practice Areas: Adam practices in all aspects of Personal Injury Litigation. He has a great reputation for his ability to put clients at ease, providing clear advice in a sensitive and effective way. Adam is tough court room advocate fighting hard for the best interests of his clients. Adam's varied practice this year has included: claim for PTSD following witnesses to the aftermath of a suicide; a significant six figure claim for future loss of earnings following a serious RTA; complex causation/liability case following the death of a client on board a cruise ship and many other six figures claims following RTA's or accidents at work.
Professional Memberships: Adam is a member of the APIL.
Career: University of Leeds (LLB Hons) 1995-98; Inns of Court School of Law 1999-2000 (BVC) (Queen Mother Scholar); 199 Strand 2000-05 and 9 Gough Square 2005-date.
Publications: Co - Author of: (a)'A Practical guide to Clinical Negligence" 9 Gough Square; and (b) "Road Traffic Claims, Liability", Jordans.
Personal: Adam lives in North West London with his wife and three young (and energetic) children. He is the Founder and Chair of Governors of a Primary School. Adam enjoys football and tennis (when he gets the time!).

DAY, Andrew
St Ives Chambers, Birmingham
0121 236 0863
andrew.day@stiveschambers.co.uk
Featured in Family/Matrimonial (Midlands)
Practice Areas: Family Finance.
Professional Memberships: Family Law Bar Association, Resolution, Midland Circuit, Birmingham Law Society.
Career: Andrew Day is an established family law specialist with extensive experience of dealing with financial and property disputes between married and unmarried partners, including particularly cases of significant legal or factual complexity, and high net worth. He is regularly instructed in cases involving significant on and off-shore trust assets, substantial pensions and businesses, in the High Court and in County Courts nationwide. He has a particular interest in applications for financial relief linked to, and family and property law issues arising in connection with, confiscation proceedings under both the Proceeds of Crime Act 2002 and earlier statutory regimes. Andrew's cases often involve, for example, the alleged concealment or dissipation of assets; nuptial agreements; significant pre-acquired, inherited or other non-matrimonial wealth; farming assets; businesses large and small; complex and valuable public service, Armed Forces or self-invested pensions; on- and off-shore trusts; jurisdictional issues; and substantial assets overseas.

DAY, Anneliese QC
4 New Square, London
020 7822 2036
a.dolby@4newsquare.com
Featured in Commercial Dispute Resolution (London), Construction (London), Insurance (London), Professional Negligence (London)
Practice Areas: Extensive experience of both domestic and international litigation in the commercial, construction, professional liability and insurance spheres. Won the prestigious Barrister of the Year Award by The Lawyer in 2014 due to her "extraordinary talent", eloquency and ability to explain complex issues to lay clients. A firm believer in seeking to bring added value to any case whatever her role. Thrives on the cut and thrust of advocacy but also brings commerciality to the issues she deals with.
Professional Memberships: COMBAR, SCL, TECBAR, PNBA, ChBA.
Career: MA (Cantab). Kennedy Scholar. Called to Bar (Inner Temple) 1996 (Princess Royal Scholarship). Joined Four New Square in 1997. Appointed to Treasury B Panel in 2005. Took silk in 2012. Appointed Non Executive Director of Legal Services Board from 1 April 2013. Became "Barrister of the Year" in The Lawyer 2014 Awards.
Publications: Editor of 'Jackson and Powell on Professional Negligence' and contributor to 'Civil Practice and Human Rights'.
Personal: Educated at the Edinburgh Academy, Clare College, Cambridge and Harvard University. Leisure interests: travel and bikram yoga. Speaks French and Spanish.

D'CRUZ, Rufus
Red Lion Chambers, London
020 7520 6000
rufus.dcruz@18rlc.co.uk
Featured in Crime (London)
Practice Areas: Rufus D'Cruz is an experienced leading junior who is instructed to prosecute and defend in serious, multi-handed criminal and regulatory work. Crime & Regulation: He specialises in complex fraud, including VAT, film tax credit, e-banking, corporate and mortgage fraud. He has particular expertise in money laundering, large-scale drugs offences and multi-million pound confiscation proceedings. In addition to financial crime, Rufus has extensive experience in prosecuting and defending cases of murder and significant experience and expertise in regulatory work, including Health and Safety offences, Environment Agency prosecutions and BIS prosecutions. He is particularly adept and experienced at representing and advising corporate clients, in relation to Health and Safety offences, Environment Agency offences, money laundering matters, production orders relating to special procedure material/LPP and in relation to corporate fraud. RUSSIA: Rufus has particular expertise, experience and insight in representing and advising clients based in Russia and the FSU, having studied Russian at university and lectured in Russia over many years. He has been instructed to advise clients in relation to the alternative criminal/regulatory remedies available to clients engaged in commercial litigation, in civil fraud cases involving allegations of unlawful enrichment and share dilution schemes. He brings to this work a unique combination of proficiency in the language, knowledge of the political and economic context and his experience of the interplay between commercial and criminal/regulatory remedies. He is a member of the British-Russian Law Association. Rufus has lectured on money laundering, confiscation, corporate manslaughter and cartel offences.
Professional Memberships: Bar Human Rights Committee; Criminal Bar Association; Liberty.
Career: 1991 - BA Hons, Russian, Birmingham; 1993 - Called to the Bar, Lincoln's Inn.

DE BONO, John QC
Serjeants' Inn Chambers, London
020 7427 5000
jdebono@serjeantsinn.com
Featured in Clinical Negligence (London), Police Law (All Circuits)
Practice Areas: John de Bono QC was called to the Bar in 1995 and took Silk in 2014. John specialises in clinical negligence and healthcare, inquests and inquiries, professional discipline, product liability, public and administrative and police law. An earlier edition notes that "he is highly rated by market sources for the combination of his strong intellect and his approachable nature" and "he is an incredibly gutsy fighter and a great strategist." John believes passionately in working with solicitors and clients as part of a team. He positively thrives on solicitors phoning to discuss any aspect of any case at any time. Please click on the link above to the Serjeants' Inn Chambers website for his profile, which sets out full details of his practice including relevant work of note.
Professional Memberships: PNBA.
Career: John is a clinical negligence specialist, regularly instructed by claimants and defendants (50/50) in cases of the highest value and greatest complexity, often against silks. Cases include cerebral palsy, wrongful birth, brain injury and spinal injury. He has a special interest in mental health and was counsel to the Broadmoor Inquiry, 2005-08, chaired by Robert Francis QC. John was invited to speak at the 2012 AVMA conference. He runs the 3SI/ Oxford Neurosurgery Medical Law Conference at Wadham College, Oxford each year. In police law John regularly presents police misconduct cases, sits as a legal adviser and acts for police forces in judicial reviews.
Publications: Various articles in legal and medical journals.

DE GARR ROBINSON, Anthony QC
One Essex Court, London
020 7583 2000
arobinson@oeclaw.co.uk
Featured in Banking & Finance (London), Chancery (London), Commercial Dispute Resolution (London), Company (London), Fraud (London)
Practice Areas: Practice covers an unusually broad range of commercial and chancery specialisations, including corporate litigation, investment disputes and complex commercial cases of every kind. Has considerable experience of international litigation, including jurisdictional disputes and cross border asset tracing, and frequently acts in international arbitrations. Has acted as an English law expert in proceedings in several jurisdictions. Sits as an arbitrator.
Professional Memberships: Chancery Bar Association, Commercial Bar Association and Commercial Fraud Lawyers Association. He has been called to the Bar in the BVI and The Bahamas and is registered as an advocate in the Dubai International Financial Centre Courts.
Career: Educated at University College, Oxford (Open Scholar and Gibbs Prize winner) and Harvard University (Kennedy Scholar). Called to the English Bar in 1987 (Denning Scholar and Hardwicke Scholar); took Silk in 2006.
Publications: 'The Legal Labyrinths of Leverage' (Legal Week, 16th July 2009); 'Wrotham Park damages' (Commercial Litigation Journal, January 2008).

DE MESTRE, Andrew
4 Stone Buildings, London
020 7242 5524
a.demestre@4stonebuildings.com
Featured in Chancery (London), Restructuring/Insolvency (London)
Practice Areas: Commercial litigation with particular emphasis on civil fraud and asset recovery; insolvency and company law including proceedings under the Insolvency Act 1986, directors duties, unfair prejudice petitions and other shareholder disputes; financial services and regulatory law including regulation in the Cayman Islands and Jersey. Leading cases include; Grupo Hotelero Urvasco v Carey Value Added [2013] EWHC 1039, 1732; Milsom & Ors v Ablyazov [2013] EWHC 1361 & [2011] EWHC 1846 and 955; Bourne v Charit Email Technology Partnership LLP [2010] BCLC 210, Carey Value Added SL v Grupo Urvasco SA [2011] 2 All ER 140, Real Estate Opportunities v Aberdeen Asset Managers (Jersey) Ltd; Mahme Trust Reg v Lloyds TSB Bank Plc [2006] EWHC 1321 and 1782; Re BCCI SA (Morris v Bank of America) [2003] EWCA Civ 425, The Arena Corporation v Schroeder [2003] EWHC 1089, HMC&E v

The Arena Corporation [2004] EWCA Civ 371; Secretary of State v Delfin International [2000] 1 BCLC 71.
Professional Memberships: Commercial Bar Association, Chancery Bar Association.
Career: Queen Mother Scholar of Middle Temple. Called March 1998. Joined 4 Stone Buildings in October 1998.
Publications: Contributor to OUP's 'Annotated Companies Acts'; Butterworths Journal of International Banking & Finance Law.
Personal: Educated at Sherborne School, Dorset and Magdalene College, Cambridge (MA).

DE VERNEUIL SMITH, Peter
3 Verulam Buildings, London
020 7831 8441
pdv@3vb.com
Featured in Commercial Dispute Resolution (London)
Practice Areas: Commercial litigation, banking litigation, company litigation, commercial fraud, international projects, conflicts of laws, insurance/reinsurance and professional negligence.
Professional Memberships: COMBAR, LCIA, CIARB, TECBAR.
Career: 2009- Fellow of the Chartered Institute of Arbitrators; 2008- Tenant at 3 Verulam Buildings; 1999-2008 Tenant at 2 Temple Gardens.
Publications: Contributor to Paget's Law of Banking (forthcoming edition), Contributor to the Encyclopaedia of Forms and Precedents (Banking) 6th Edition (2008). Contributor to European Civil Practice 2nd edition (2004).

DE WAAL, John QC
Hardwicke, London
020 7242 2523
john.dewaal@hardwicke.co.uk
Featured in Professional Negligence (London), Real Estate Litigation (London)
Practice Areas: John de Waal QC specialises in Chancery and commercial work with a particular focus on property litigation and property-related professional negligence. In the last three years John appeared, successfully, in the Court of Appeal on four occasions. The appeals included NYK Logistics v Ibrend [2011] 4 All ER 339, now the leading case on the meaning of vacant possession. His property work encompasses all aspects of real estate litigation (charges, covenants, easements), commercial landlord and tenant (lease renewal, dilapidations), with some agricultural and complex residential landlord and tenant work. John's professional negligence work is principally defendant, usually involving claims against solicitors or surveyors (instructed by most insurers and panel firms) with some claimant work as well. John is also a practising mediator and frequently instructed in property-related disputes.
Professional Memberships: Property Bar Association, Professional Negligence Bar Association.
Career: MA (Cantab); Called to the Bar 1992; Member of Hardwicke since 2009; CEDR Accredited 2002; QC 2013.
Publications: Contributor to Construction All Risks Insurance by Paul Reed QC, Sweet & Maxwell, 2014.

DEAN, Paul J
St Philips Chambers, Birmingham
0121 246 7000
pdean@st-philips.com
Featured in Partnership (Midlands)
Practice Areas: Specialisms: insolvency, banking and partnership. Practises from Birmingham and London. Recent insolvency cases include: Re Brown Bear Foods Ltd [2014] EWHC 1132 (Ch) (provisional liquidation instead of administration), Re Reflex Recordings Ltd [2013] EWHC 4514 (Ch) (costs - freezing injunction and administration order), Re Safehosts (London) Ltd [2013] EWHC 2479 (Ch), [2013] BCC 721 (provisional liquidation instead of administration), and Re James Dolman & Company Ltd [2010] EWHC 3950 (Ch) (undervalue, knowing receipt, constructive trust and restitution). Recent banking cases include: Nautch Ltd v Mortgage Express and Walker Singleton (Property Management) Ltd [2012] EWHC 4136 (Ch) (LPA receivers, equitable duty to borrower and global costs order), and Earles v Barclays Bank plc [2010] Bus LR 566 (electronic disclosure and costs). Other cases include: Wemyss v Karim and Douglas Wemyss LLP [2014] EWHC 292 (QB) (warranty/indemnity claim), Hamed v Stevens [2013] EWCA Civ 911 (conflicts of laws – foreign land), and Chahal v Mahal [2005] EWCA Civ 898 (partnership dissolution date).
Professional Memberships: MCCBA. Birmingham Law Society (member of Dispute Resolution Committee).
Career: Whitgift School. BSc Hons (1st class): 1991. PGDL: 1992-93. LPC (Commendation): 1993-94. Solicitor (Eversheds): 1996. Solicitor Advocate (civil): 2001. Called: 2001. Tenant 2002.

DEBATTISTA, Charles
Stone Chambers, London
020 7440 6900
charles.debattista@charlesdebattista.com
Featured in Shipping (London)
Practice Areas: Charles Debattista practises full time in shipping and international trade disputes. With full rights of audience before the courts, he works particularly in the areas of charterparties and bills of lading, commodities contracts and international trade disputes generally, including letters of credit. Since 2002 he has either acted as counsel or sat as arbitrator in over 200 arbitrations, under various institutional rules including LMAA, ICC, GAFTA and FOSFA rules, as well as in ad hoc arbitrations. Charles also has an advisory practice on all matters relating to international trade. He has sat as sole arbitrator, chairman and party-appointed. He has had a number of his Awards confirmed on referral to the Courts in England and has had a number of his publications cited by courts in England and elsewhere. Charles has written extensively in his areas of expertise and chaired the international drafting groups responsible for Incoterms 2000 and 2010. Charles is also a CEDR accredited mediator.
Professional Memberships: Baltic Exchange, Chartered Institute of Arbitrators, SCMA and a Supporting Member of the LMAA.
Career: Graduated in Law at the Universities of Malta and Oxford, where he was a Rhodes Scholar, Charles lectured at the University of Southampton until 2011, when he left as Professor of Commercial Law to devote himself entirely to his practice. Called 1978 (Malta); Called 2004 (England and Wales, Registered European Lawyer).
Publications: Bills of Lading in Export Trade, Tottel Publishing, third edition January 2009 (4th Ed in preparation); Ship Sales and the Singapore Sale Form [with F. Lorenzon], Lexis-Nexis, 2013; Maritime Law, Sweet and Maxwell, 2011, 2nd Ed, (3rd Ed forthcoming) co-author; Transfer of Property in International Sales (ICC-Paris, 2010), co-author; The Rotterdam Rules: A Practical Annotation, Informa 2009, co-author; Halsbury's Laws of England, vol 4, Carriage and Carriers; November 2008; Halsbury's Laws of England, vol 41, Sale of Goods and Supply of Services, 2005 Halsbury's Laws of England, vol. 43(2), Shipping and Navigation, 1997, with Hardy Ivamy.

DEIN, Jeremy QC
25 Bedford Row, London
07813 682 709
jdein@25bedfordrow.com
Featured in Crime (London)
Practice Areas: Huge experience in defending the gravest, most serious, complex and high-profile criminal cases. Unrivalled involvement in homicide cases over recent years, mainly at the Central Criminal Court. Recent notable murder trials include Mccluskie, the "Eastenders" killing and dismemberment case, Jeffs, the defrauding and murder of a millionaire London socialite, Joseph, the "Honeytrap" murder, Buck, the "shopping trolley" homicide. Also regularly instructed to defend in a wide variety of "celebrity" cases. Recent examples:Tulisa Contostavlos , former N Dubz star and X Factor judge (first ever stay of proceedings in non state agent entrapment case), Fielder Civil, Amy Winehouse's husband, Eric Joyce, Member of Parliament. Also instructed in such cases as Kanyare, the "fake Sheikh terrorist" case, B, Choudry , Attempted murder of a sitting MP, B, rape of a school teacher at School, S - a solicitor charged with perverting the course of Justice. Keen interest in legal issues and appellate work.
Career: Called 1982, Silk 2003, Sexual offences ticketed Recorder 2004, Judicial College Course tutor, former CBA Director of Education. Has written and lectured in UK and abroad, most recently in: Florida, Delhi, Seoul (South Korea), Hong Kong. Head of Crime Group, 25 Bedford Row.
Personal: Married, 4 children. Interests: Travel, gym, music (especially Salsa), reading, commentating on radio and all criminal justice related and Human Rights issues.

DELAHUNTY, Jo QC
4 Paper Buildings, London
020 7427 5200
jd@4pb.com
Featured in Family/Matrimonial (London)
Practice Areas: Jo was made Winner of the Jordans' Family Silk 2013', is identified as a 'Top Ranked Silk' by Chambers & Partners and ranked as a'Top Tier Silk' by the Legal 500. Jo is currently acting for 75 bereaved families in the Hillsborough Inquest,tasked with dealing with the adequacy of the emergency medical response and establishing whether better care could have saved lives. She is the only family silk chosen to act in the Inquest and is proud to work alongside her criminal and coronial silk colleagues. In a competitive and highly specialist silk field accross practice areas Jo has won a reputation for fearlesss advocacy allied with formidable tactical trial management. Within the Family Division Jo specialises in contentious child abuse cases at High Court level and above involving disputed medical evidence and scientific research. She excells in acting for parents/ carers alleged to have caused catastrophic injuries/ death to a child including TRIAD/NAHI allegations, FII cases, and acting for parent or victim/abuser child in sex cases involving intergenerational/inter-sibing abuse cases including genital mutilation and internet exploitation. Unravelling complex medical evidence and pushing the boundaries of scientific understanding of alleged NAI is her defining practice strength. Jo was the lead respondent counsel acting for the mother in the widely reported landmark TRIAD/Vit D case of L.B Islington v Al Alas (2012) 'the rickets case'. Cases in which she is instructed are regularly reported for their legal significance. The CoA praised the 'wise and responsible' decision of CAfcass in instructing her in RE A (2012). Jo has successfully transposed her public law forensic skills of tactical case and client management to complex and contentious private law disputes particulalry where issues of mental health and alcoholism are alleged to impact on capacity to parent.
Professional Memberships: FLBA, ALC, AWB, Resolution, INQUEST.
Career: Called 1986; Silk 2006, Recorder (Family) 2010, Bencher (Middle Temple) 2011. Mediator 2012, The Middle Temple Womens Forum (steering cmtte),Executive member Centre for Child and Family Reform 2012-. Recommended as a Leading Silk whilst ascending rankings in every edition of Legal 500 and C&P since her appointment: most recently described as 'absolutely superb ';a 'brilliant advocate who dissects extremely complex medical concepts with ease' ;noted for her 'sharp forensic eye and extraordinary memory'; 'razor sharp mind with a phenomenal work rate'; 'rapier like incisiveness'.
Publications: Re-litigation in Family Cases: Emerging Law and Practice' (Jan 2012 Fam Law 40); 'A Miscarriage of Justice corrected: the difference expert evidence can make to outcome' (Nov 2012 Fam Law 1344); In Defence of Experts'(Counsel August 2012 & the TEDR: the Experts and Disputes Resolver Vol 17 no 2 24); 'The Vitamin D and Rickets case: L B Islington v Al Alas) (2012) Fam Law 659; 'What price justice? Experts or Treating Clinicians? L B Islington v Al Alas 2012) Fam Law 126).

DEMPSTER, Jennifer
Red Lion Chambers, London
020 7520 6000
jenni.dempster@18rlc.co.uk
Featured in Crime (London)
Practice Areas: Jenni is a well-known and extremely able defence advocate specialising in fraud and general crime. Her practice comprises about 50% serious financial crime and 50% general heavyweight crime, including murder, rape and drug trafficking. She is regularly instructed as leading counsel in high-profile cases and has built up a loyal following of solicitors. She is known as an extremely hard worker and commands considerable respect among her peers for her jury handling and tactical acumen. Those who instruct her comment upon her excellent client management and the confidence she inspires in those she represents. She very frequently acts for defendants charged with rape and serious sexual offences, often where the allegations are historical. She spent three months of 2012 appearing as leading counsel for the first defendant in a multi-handed human trafficking and rape case. Later in 2012

she spent six weeks defending in a £20m conspiracy to defraud three London banks. In 2013/14 she successfully represented a number of defendants charged with rape/ sexual assault where the allegations dated back over 25 years. She has also appeared as leading counsel for an alleged serial rapist said to have committed offences in a number of European countries. In 2013 she defended in a multi-handed money laundering trial (& retrial) and defended in several cases where defendants were charged with conspiracy to pervert the course of justice (including one of whom was a serving police officer). In the spring of 2013 she acted for the defendant in a manslaughter case where a householder died during the course of a burglary. Between October 2013 and January 2014 she was instructed as leading counsel for the first defendant in a 10-handed rape & inciting child prostitution case at the Old Bailey. In March 2014 she represented one of five defendants charged with conspiracy to commit armed robberies across East London and Essex, a case which involved very extensive telephone and cell site evidence. Jenni is frequently instructed privately to defend in cases alleging possession of indecent images and has given lectures on this topic. Her practice encompasses both privately and publicly funded work. In July 2014 Jenni will represent a defendant charged with attempted murder (by shooting) at the Old Bailey. She is also instructed for the defence in a multi-million pound world-wide "social engineering" fraud (trial due to take place at Southwark Crown Court in late 2014). In January 2015 Jenni will represent the lead defendant in a fraud trial due to last several weeks at Southwark Crown Court relating to the collapse of a UK currency exchange business. Jenni is regularly instructed in fraud cases where the paperwork extends to over 50,000 pages. She is consistently recognised as a highly recommended leading junior and is now ranked in ChambersUK for eighth year running as a 'Leader at the Bar'.
Professional Memberships: Criminal Bar Association.
Career: Educated at Broughton High School, Edinburgh and London School of Economics LLB Hons). Called to the Bar 1993. Attended Diploma in Forensic Medicine and Science course in 2001.

DENISON, Simon QC
6KBW College Hill, London
020 3301 0910
simon.denison@6kbw.com
Featured in Crime (London)
Practice Areas: Simon Denison QC has just completed his term as Treasury Counsel after 13½ years, including nearly seven years as Senior Treasury Counsel. He has acted in many high profile, multi-handed and / or complex cases, including murder, manslaughter, firearms, gang related offences, robbery, kidnapping, human trafficking, serious sexual offences, drugs, human rights, European Law, fraud, corruption, cases involving issues of sensitive disclosure, national security, and terrorism, including cyber terrorism. He is Security Cleared. He has advised the Attorney General and appeared on his behalf in the Court of Appeal in many cases. Other advisory work has included advising prosecuting agencies pre- and post- charge on discrete issues of law, including statutory interpretation. He is on the SFO QC Panel. He is a member of the Cayman Islands Bar, where he appears for the prosecution and the defence. Examples of cases include R v Fadi Nasri and others (contract murder of woman special constable ordered by her husband), R v Leon Dunkley and others (gang murder of innocent 16-year-old girl by shooting into a pizza shop, involving anonymous witnesses), R v Hamilton and others (gang murder of 15-year-old Negus McLean who was chased on his bicycle and stabbed), R v RF (killing of sex worker by vulnerable defendant with mental health issues), R v Khan and others (cyber terrorism, including youngest convicted terrorist), R v Chentouf (mother hid bomb manual in her burka and considered turning her children into human bombs), R v Beach and others (Heathrow bullion robbery), R v Bellamy (paedophile sexual grooming), Attorney General's Reference No 16 of 2009 (firearms and assisting offenders, gun used in the gang murder of 11-year-old Rhys Jones), Attorney General's Reference Nos 4 – 8 of 2014 (firearms), R v Hanif and Khan (2014 CCRC reference to the Court of Appeal following finding by the ECHR of a violation of Article 6).
Career: Called in 1984. Corporate Finance Department at Kitcat & Aitken (Stockbrokers) 1984 – 1986. Tenant since 1987. Junior Treasury Counsel 2001 - 2007. Senior Treasury Counsel 2007 - 2014. Silk in 2009.
Personal: Tonbridge School, St Catharine's College, Cambridge. Keen sportsman.

DENNISON, Stephen QC
Atkin Chambers, London
020 7404 0102
sdennison@atkinchambers.com
Featured in Construction (London), Energy & Natural Resources (London), International Arbitration (London), Professional Negligence (London)
Practice Areas: Stephen is a leading specialist in the construction and civil engineering, energy and utilities, and the transport sectors together with related areas such as public procurement of infrastructure projects and insurance. He has conducted numerous substantial and complex cases in the High Court and in domestic and international arbitration, having extensive experience under the ICC, LCIA and SIAC rules. He is also frequently consulted to advise on and to represent clients in the resolution of disputes through alternative procedures including expert determination, mediation and adjudication. In addition to his experience as an advocate, Stephen has been appointed as an Adjudicator particularly with regard to high value infrastructure projects and retail developments, and also as an Expert. He has accepted invitations to determine or assist in the resolution of disputes through a process of expert determination as well as having been appointed as an expert on the Law of England and Wales in foreign proceedings.
Publications: Contributing Editor Hudson's Building and Engineering Contracts 12ed.

DENTON-COX, Gregory
4 Stone Buildings, London
020 7242 5524
clerks@4stonebuildings.com
Featured in Chancery (London), Company (London), Fraud (London)
Practice Areas: Chancery and commercial litigation including company law, civil fraud, tracing and asset recovery, shareholder disputes, international trusts, banking and finance, insolvency and restructuring and transfers of insurance business under Part VII of FSMA. Notable recent cases include: Napier Park v Harbourmaster (Court of Appeal), US Bank Trustees Ltd v Titan Europe (disputes concerning the construction of structured finance documents) Benedetti v Sawiris (Supreme Court) (claim to a shareholding in telecommunications holding company, payment on a quantum meruit), McKillen v Misland (shareholder dispute concerning ownership of London hotels).
Professional Memberships: Chancery Bar Association, COMBAR.
Career: Called to the Bar 2000. Junior Counsel to the Crown (C Panel) 2006-11.
Publications: Contributor to Atkin's Court Forms (Companies - General).

DENYER-GREEN, Barry
Falcon Chambers, London
020 7353 2484
clerks@falcon-chambers.com
Featured in Real Estate Litigation (London)
Practice Areas: Landlord and tenant, property law, compulsory purchase and compensation, planning and commons.
Professional Memberships: Hon-RICS; Honorary Fellow, College of Estate Management; Honorary Member of Central Association of Agricultural Valuers; Member of the DETR Compulsory Purchase Working Party 1998-2000; past Chairman of the Compulsory Purchase Association; Agricultural Law Association; Chancery Bar Association; LCLCBA: Property Bar Association.
Career: Educated at London University (LLB Hons 1973, PhD 1987); London School of Economics (LLM 1978); Called 1972 (Middle Temple).
Publications: Author, Compulsory Purchase and Compensation, 10th edn (2013); joint author, Development and Planning Law, 4th edn (2011); joint author, Law of Commons and Town & Village Greens, 2nd edn (2006); editor, Estates Gazette Law Reports (1987-2006); joint editor, Planning Law Reports (1987-2006).

DEVONSHIRE, Simon QC
11KBW, London
020 7632 8500
simon.devonshire@11kbw.com
Featured in Employment (London)
Practice Areas: Simon Devonshire QC practices in all areas of statutory and contractual/commercial employment law, but with a particular emphasis on (i) inter-business competition issues (Including confidential information, restrictive covenants and the poaching of employees in unlawful team moves), (ii) the attempted diversion of business opportunities by employee fiduciaries, and (iii) whistle-blowing and TUPE disputes. In the High Court, he is currently acting in a substantial fraud action, involving the alleged miss-sale of a freight forwarding business and on a number of team move disputes, and he recently acted: for the employee defendants in allegations of an unalwful team move raising issues of territoriality and jurisdiction; for Tullett Prebon in resisting claims by BGC that it unlawfully recruited one of BGC's serving employees; in a substantial claim involving alleged breaches of fiduciary duty and intellectual property rights by an employee who set up a friends reunite style website in Russia, in competition with his former employer; and in successfully resisting an attempt by 5 separate parties to set aside freezing injunctions for material non-disclosure. On the statutory front, Simon is handling a number of whistle-blowing disputes, arising particularly out of the financial services sector. He successfully defended a firm of solicitors against a claim that it had inherited TUPE liabilities for the employees of one of its competitors (which it had defeated in a competitive tender for legal services) in a decision upheld on appeal. He also acted for the Royal Cornwall Hospital Trust in its high profile 'whistle-blowing' dispute with its former Chief Executive. Recent reported and/or important cases include Thomson Ecology –v- APEM [2014] IRLR 184 (summary judgment and disclosure orders in team move cases), Allsop –v- Christiani & Nielsen Ltd (in Administration) [2012] UKEAT/0241/11/JOJ (limitation and jurisdiction in Wages Act claims); CEF Holdings -v- Mundey & Ors [2012] EWHC (QB) (the limits of springbaord relief and the obligations of a party moving the court without notice); BGC –v- Rees & Tullett Prebon [2011] EWHC 2009 (QB) (Tullett did not procure Rees to breach his contract of employment with BGC when recruiting him); Capital for Enterprise -v- Malik & Ors [2010] EWHC 343 (Ch) (disclosure obligations and freezing injunctions); Ward Hadaway –v- Love & Ors [2010] UKEAT/0471/09/SM (the winning of a contract to provide legal services to the NMC did not constitute a service provision change within the meaning of TUPE 2006, and the successful tenderer did not assume liability for the dedicated team of lawyers retained by his predecessor); New ISG –v- Vernon & Ors [2008] ICR 319 (a purposive construction should be given to reg 4(7) of TUPE 2006, so as to accord with the fundamental freedom of the employee to choose who he works for, and to permit and recognise the effectiveness of a post transfer objection where the employee does not know of the identity of the transferee or of his right to object pre transfer. In consequence, the transferee could not enforce post termination restrictive covenants against 'objecting' employees); Croke –v- Hydro [2007] ICR 1303 (an individual providing services through his own limited company to an end user via an employment agency was a worker for the purposes of the whistle-blowing provisions; and Bezant –v- Rausing & Ors [2007] EWHC 1118 (QB) (It was an abuse of process for a claimant (after his claims under employment law had failed) to seek to invoke the law of tort against directors and other professionals associated with his employment/dismissal, to seek to recover his alleged losses. Such conduct justified the making of an Extended CRO).
Professional Memberships: Employment Law Bar Association. ELA. LCLCBA.
Career: Called 1988. Appointed QC 2009.

DEW, Richard
Ten Old Square, London
020 7405 0758
richarddew@tenoldsquare.com
Featured in Chancery (London)
Practice Areas: Richard Dew's practice is focussed on wills, estates and trusts and related professional negligence. His practice is predominantly litigation, and he is frequently involved in large and complex claims. He also advises and represents in Court of Protection matters and provides expert advice in respect of tax and tax planning (principally capital taxation).

Career: Called to the Bar 1999. Notable cases include: Al-Sadi v Al-Sadi [2013] EWHC 2379, Goodman v Goodman [2014] Ch 186 Shovelar v Lane [2011] 4 All ER 669; Sutton v Sutton [2010] WTLR 115; Dibble v Pfluger [2010] EWCA Civ 1005; Lamothe v Lamothe [2006] EWHC 1387(CH) (Revocation and the testator's intention); Banks v National Westminster Bank plc and another [2005] All ER (D) 159 (Apr) Will ademption following loss of the testator's capacity); Clark v Clark [2004] All ER (D) 224 (Dec) (application for solemn grant of probate); Leadenhall Independent Trustees Ltd v Welham and another [2004] All ER (D) 423 (Mar) (pensions).
Publications: Richard is an author of a forthcoming edition of Parker's Modern Will Precedents, Tolley's Inheritance Tax Planning and the Trusts and Estate Practitioner's Guide to Mental Capacity. He has contributed to International Trusts Disputes and to the 25th edition of Ranking Spicer and Pegler's Executorship Law, Trusts & Accounts (Butterworths). Richard's published articles include: "2013 case round up" in TQR March 2014, Trusts and Disclosure, 2011 Private Client Business [2011] PCB 241-247; "Can TLATA 1996 be Interpreted as a Fiscal Bill?" Trusts and Estates Law & Tax Journal, May 2009, 11 (jointly with Gill Steel); "A Wasted Opportunity" (Trustee Exclusion Clauses) T.E.L. & T.J. (2007) No.83 January/February Pages 23-25; Equitable Compensation and Contributory Negligence in Trusts and Estates Law and Tax Journal January/February 2006; Banks v Natwest and Davenport in Trusts and Estates Law Journal July/August 2005; Property Sales under EPAs in Elderly Client Adviser September/October 2005.

DICKER, Robin QC
South Square, London
020 7696 9900
robindicker@southsquare.com
Featured in Banking & Finance (London), Chancery (London), Commercial Dispute Resolution (London), Company (London), Offshore (London), Restructuring/Insolvency (London)
Practice Areas: Specialises in commercial, business and financial law, including banking, commercial litigation, company, corporate restructuring and insolvency, professional negligence and disciplinary proceedings and civil fraud.
Professional Memberships: International Insolvency Institute (elected Founding Member), ILA, INSOL International, INSOL Europe, R3, LCIA, ICC, Commercial Bar Association, Chancery Bar Association , P.R.I.M.E. Finance Foundation (Expert).
Career: 1986: Called to the Bar (Middle Temple), 2000: Appointed Queen's Council.

DICKINSON, John FH
St John's Chambers, Bristol
0117 923 4700
john.dickinson@stjohnschambers.co.uk
Featured in Chancery (Western), Commercial Dispute Resolution (Western), Company (Western), Professional Negligence (Western)
Practice Areas: Chancery and general commercial litigation, with an emphasis on probate and wills, property, banking and pensions. Company law including shareholder disputes. Commercial landlord and tenant disputes. Insolvency. Partnership law, including the dissolution of partnerships relating to farming, solicitors and accountants. Contracts including sale of goods. Professional negligence in particular for solicitors, accountants and financial institutions.
Professional Memberships: Chancery Bar Association, ACTAPS, Professional Negligence Bar Association, Western Chancery and Commercial Bar Association, Chartered Accountant (ACA).
Career: Call 1995. Previously practiced as a Chartered Accountant for 5 years, latterly at Coopers and Lybrand in litigation support. Seconded to the Serious Fraud Office, including assisting the BCCI investigation. Counsel assisting Lord Penrose's Inquiry concerning Equitable Life.
Personal: Hobbies include tennis, surfing and skiing.

DIGNUM, Marcus
12 King's Bench Walk, London
020 7583 0811
dignum@12kbw.co.uk
Featured in Personal Injury (London)
Practice Areas: Marcus has developed a substantial personal injury practice involving both RTA and EL/PL work. He is instructed by both Claimants and Defendants and is frequently used by most of the leading large insurers. Recognised as a Leading Junior in Chambers & Partners, he is lauded for his "robust, realistic and very personal service." He combines "intellectual rigour, a commercial approach and great charm" to good effect on high-value catastrophic injury cases. Marcus deals with claims of the highest value, and whilst happy to be lead, is often instructed alone to represent his clients' interests against Silks and other senior Juniors. He has substantial experience of claims involving the most serious head and spinal injuries where awards are made or settlements reached of several million pounds. In addition, Marcus accepts instructions in most other areas of the common law, including in particular, contractual disputes, construction work, interlocutory relief and carriage of goods cases.
Professional Memberships: PIBA.
Career: BA (Classical studies) (First Class) University London. Called to the Bar in 1994.

DILWORTH, Noel
Henderson Chambers, London
020 7583 9020
clerks@hendersonchambers.co.uk
Featured in Product Liability (London)
Practice Areas: Consumer, Product Liability, Commercial, Financial Services, Health and Safety, Environment, Property, Employment.
Professional Memberships: ELBA, HSLA, COMBAR.
Career: Inner Temple Major and Princess Royal Scholar, Called to Bar 2001. Expertise in the field of insurance coverage disputes, particularly in the relation to property damage and product liability. Product Liability: Sabril group litigation (2006-2008); Seroxat (2010); Property / Commercial: Risegold Ltd v Escala Ltd [2008] EWCA Civ 1180, [2008] 1 EGLR 13, [2009] 1 P & CR D24; JS Bloor Ltd v Pavillion Developments Ltd [2008] EWHC 724 (TCC); Parkinson v Hawthorn [2008] EWHC 3499 (Ch) Merlo v Duffy [2009] All ER (D) 91 (Feb)Panayiotou v Nicolaou [2010] EWCA Civ 569; Cusack v Harrow London Borough Council [2013] UKSC 40; Administrative: R(Lin) v Barnet LBC [2007] EWCA Civ 132; R (B) v Barnet LBC [2009] All ER (D) 294 (Nov); K v G [2009] All ER (D) 128 (Oct). Employment: Coutinho v Rank Nemo DMS Ltd [2009] IRLR 672; Onwuka v Spherion Technology (UK) Ltd and ors [2008] All ER (D) 67 (Feb); Finney v Miles Platts Ltd, UKEAT / 0150 / 04; Peacehaven & Telscombe Help Service and Volunteer Bureau, UKEAT / 0461 / 03.

DINEEN, Maria
2 Bedford Row, London
020 7440 8888
mdineen@2bedfordrow.co.uk
Featured in Crime (London)
Practice Areas: Predominantly defence advocate specialising in heavyweight crime. Extensive experience of defending and prosecuting in cases involving allegations of murder/manslaughter; complex fraud; major drugs importations and supplies; violent crime; serious sexual offences and child cruelty. Particular expertise in dealing with vulnerable defendants and witnesses.
Professional Memberships: South Eastern Circuit; Criminal Bar Association; Fraud Lawyers Association; Association of Regulatory and Disciplinary Lawyers; Bar European Group.
Career: Varied, including newspaper journalism (covering mainly crime and the criminal courts). Called to the Bar 1997. Spent 10 weeks in Kingston, Jamaica in 2005 as volunteer (funded by chambers) assisting local attorneys in preparation and conduct of capital murder cases. Elected Member of Bar Council 1999-2002.
Personal: Born 29 October 1963. Lives in Suffolk.

DIXEY, Jonathan
5 Essex Court, London
020 7410 2000
dixey@5essexcourt.co.uk
Featured in Police Law (All Circuits)
Practice Areas: Police law, public and administrative law, inquests and inquiries, employment, professional discipline and regulatory law and personal injury. Jonathan acts on behalf of constabularies across the country in cases touching upon all areas of police law. Since 2011 he has acted on behalf of the Metropolitan Police Service in various aspects of its investigations into 'phone hacking' (Various Claimants v. News Group Newspapers Ltd. and Others ([2012] EWHC 2692 (Ch); [2013] EWHC 2119 (Ch) and others)). He has considerable experience in advising chief officers on policy and operational matters providing timely, practical advice often in high-profile, sensitive and complex cases (recent cases include Operation Weeting and Operation Yewtree). He has a particular interest and experience in the law relating to the disclosure and the sharing of information (R (L) v. Chief Constable of Kent Police [2014] EWHC 463 (Admin)). Recent inquests include: the Inquests into the deaths arising from the Hillsborough Stadium disaster (on behalf of the St John Ambulance), the Inquests into the London Bombings of 7 July 2005 (on behalf of the Commissioner of Police of the Metropolis) and the Inquest into the death of Dr Abbas Khan (on behalf of the Chief Coroner).
Professional Memberships: ALBA, ELBA, PIBA and the South Eastern Circuit.
Career: Called to the Bar 2007; Attorney General's C Panel of Counsel (appointed 2013).
Publications: 'The Employment Tribunals Handbook: Practice, Procedure and Strategies for Success' (3rd edition, 2011) with Alan Payne and John-Paul Waite.

DIXON, Clare
4 New Square, London
020 7822 2000
c.dixon@4newsquare.com
Featured in Professional Negligence (London)
Practice Areas: Clare's practice encompasses three main areas: professional liability, insurance and commercial litigation. She is regularly instructed to act for or against solicitors, surveyors, accountants, auditors, barristers and insurance brokers. At the cross over of her insurance and professional liability work come cases involving professional indemnity policies. Clare has advised both insurers and insureds on a variety of issues including policy interpretation, non-disclosure and fraud.
Professional Memberships: COMBAR, TECBAR, PNBA.
Career: MA (Oxon). Called to the Bar in 2002.
Publications: Editor of Jackson & Powell on "Professional Liability".
Personal: Clare read law at St Anne's College, Oxford University, where she was President of the Oxford Union. Leisure interests: travel, sailing and walking (particularly in the Yorkshire Dales).

DOBBIE, Olivia-Faith
Cloisters, London
020 7827 4070
ofd@cloisters.com
Featured in Employment (London)
Practice Areas: Employment, Discrimination and Public Law (human rights).
Professional Memberships: ELA, ILS and DLA.
Career: Olivia has a successful and dynamic practice with a focus on Employment Law, Discrimination and Human Rights. She regularly appears in Employment Tribunals, the High Court and the Employment Appeal Tribunal. She has also appeared as junior counsel in the Court of Appeal and Supreme Court in cases of great significance: the highly-reported judicial review regarding Gurkha soldiers' pensions against the Ministry of Defence and X v Mid Sussex CAB (on the issue of volunteers' rights under European and domestic anti-discrimination law). In her daily practice, Olivia has experience of a broad range of employment disputes and a sound appellate practice. She has a strong reputation for discrimination law (and in particular, disability discrimination) and is developing a thriving practice in High Court employment claims, specifically those entailing interim and final injunctions. Her trial skills are advanced beyond her year of call and she often runs complex multi-day trials. Olivia is very personable with clients, making her a very popular choice. She acts for a wide range of clients (from individuals to multi-national companies) and is able to appreciate the different priorities each may have, such as to achieve effective results that are specific to their needs.
Publications: Author of: Solicitor's Journal, Half Year Review, 2013: "Treated Equally", 3 chapters of the LAG book: "Discrimination in Employment" (2013), ELA Briefing, vol 18: "Exploring Combined Discrimination", Practice Notes on PLC online, Articles in Counsel Magazine.

DOBBIN, Clair
3 Raymond Buildings Barristers, London
020 7400 6400
clair.dobbin@3rblaw.com
Featured in Administrative & Public Law (London), Extradition (London), Inquests & Public Inquiries (London), Professional Discipline (London)
Practice Areas: Clair's areas of expertise are public law, human rights, extradition, public inquiries and inquests. Clair was first appointed junior Counsel to the Crown in 2004 and was appointed to the "A" panel of Treasury Counsel in 2014. She has appeared in numerous leading cases in the UK in recent years including important terrorist cases such as USA v Abu Hamza and USA v Babar Ahmad. She acted on behalf of the UK, before the European Court of Human Rights, in UK v Harkins and UK v Edwards on the issue of life imprisonment without parole. Other recent public law cases include litigation arising out of the "Plebgate" incident; Ismail v SSHD (application of Article 6 to the service of foreign judgments); Bats (Government of Mongolia Intervening) v FCO (special mission immunity) and T v SSHD (detention of children). She has a particular specialisation in criminal justice issues and the rights of children. She has very substantial public inquiry and inquest experience. Recent cases include the Baha Mousa Inquiry; the Alexander Litvinenko Inquest; the Mark Duggan inquest and the David Emmanuel Inquest.
Career: MA Hons (Cantab), Call 1999, Treasury 'C' Panel 2004; 'B' Panel 2007. "A" Panel 2014.

DOBIE, Lisa
1 Chancery Lane, London
020 7092 2900
ldobie@1chancerylane.com
Featured in Clinical Negligence (London), Police Law (All Circuits)
Practice Areas: Lisa specialises in defending civil actions against the police and in all aspects of clinical negligence, professional negligence, personal injury and coronial law. She has particular experience of representing public bodies. Cases include Omar Hadjarab v Oxford Radcliffe Hospital NHS Trust [2014] (inquest); Simson v Islington Council [2013] HC (highways act appeal under s.58); Zapello v Chief Constable of Sussex Police [2010] EWCA Civ 1417 (false imprisonment, necessity, costs appeal); Khalil v Plymouth Hospital NHS Trust and another [2013] HC (general civil restraint orders); Campbell v Dr Murty & others [2013] (capacity).
Professional Memberships: Personal Injury Bar Association, Professional Negligence Bar Association.
Career: University of Leeds First Class LLB, called to the Bar in 2006, Inner Temple.

DOCTOR, Brian QC
Fountain Court Chambers, London
020 7583 3335
bd@fountaincourt.co.uk
Featured in Commercial Dispute Resolution (London)
Practice Areas: Broadly-based commercial litigation and arbitration practice, specialising in cases requiring detailed examination of documents and cross-examination of witnesses. Many of Brian's cases involve allegations of civil fraud, and encompass complex factual and technical disputes. Brian has a hands-on approach to interlocutory matters leading up to trial, and gets heavily involved in the tactical and strategic decisions of major litigation. He has a wide experience of banking, insurance, competition and general commercial issues in the context of major litigation.
Professional Memberships: Commercial Bar Association.
Career: Solicitor in London 1978-80; South African Bar 1980-92 (took Silk in SA 1990); joined Fountain Court Chambers 1992 (took Silk in UK 1999).
Personal: BA, LL B (Witwatersrand) BCL (Balliol College, Oxford), Born 8 December 1949.

DOERRIES, Chantal-Aimée QC
Atkin Chambers, London
020 7404 0102
cadoerries@atkinchambers.com
Featured in Construction (London), Energy & Natural Resources (London), International Arbitration (London), Professional Negligence (London)
Practice Areas: Construction, energy and natural resources, professional negligence and shipbuilding.
Professional Memberships: Combar; International Committee of the Bar Council of England and Wales (Chairman - 2011-2014); TECBAR (Chairman 2010-2013);
Career: Called to the Bar 1992, Queen's Counsel 2008. Major Harmsworth Entrance Exhibition and Diplock Scholar, Middle Temple. Gertrude de Gallaix Achievement Award for Study of Law, FAWCO.
Publications: Joint editor of Building Law Reports; Contributing Editor of Hudson's Building and Engineering Contracts 12th edition.

DOLAN, Bridget
Serjeants' Inn Chambers, London
020 7427 5000
b.dolan@3serjeantsinn.com
Featured in Clinical Negligence (London), Court of Protection (All Circuits)
Practice Areas: Bridget Dolan was called to the Bar in 1997. Bridget specialises in Court of Protection, mental health, inquests and inquiries, public and administrative and clinical negligence law. An earlier edition notes that "she is a leading expert on capacity matters... providing well thought-out advice, is very pragmatic and is good at asking the right questions... a go-to for heavyweight medical cases." Please see the Serjeants' Inn Chambers website for her profile, which sets out full details of her practice including relevant work of note.
Career: Her PhD and previous career in forensic psychology give Bridget unique clinically based experience of complicated mental health issues which underpins her practice in the Court of Protection, the Civil and Admin Courts and in inquests and inquiries.
Publications: Inquest Law Reports (Editor); "Medical Treatment: Decisions & the Law", "The Mental Health Act Explained" (co-authored).

DOMENGE, Victoria
29 Bedford Row Chambers, London
020 7404 1044
vdomenge@29br.co.uk
Featured in Family/Matrimonial (London)
Practice Areas: Family Law with particular expertise in matrimonial finance and private law children cases. Reported cases include: N v F [2011] EWHC 586 Fam), M v M (Divorce: Domicile) [2011] 1 FLR 919; Re H (Contact Order) [2010] 2 FLR 866; M v M [2009] EWHC 1941 (Fam); Paulin v Paulin [2009] 2 FLR 354; RH v RH (Ancillary Relief: Costs) [2008] 2 FLR 2142; W (A Child) [2008] EWCA Civ 1181; El Faragy v El Faragy & Ors [2007] EWCA Civ 1149.
Professional Memberships: FLBA and Resolution.
Career: Called to the Bar 1993, Middle Temple. Trained in Collaborative Law. Public Access Barrister.
Personal: Educated at The Cheltenham Ladies College, University of Exeter (BA Hons), University of Westminster (CPT Postgraduate Law Diploma). Married with three children. Speaks good Spanish.

DONNELLAN, Christopher QC
36 Bedford Row, London
020 7421 8000
cdonnellan@36bedfordrow.co.uk
Featured in Crime (Midlands)
Practice Areas: Crime, Fraud, Health and Safety.
Professional Memberships: Criminal Bar Association, Midland Circuit.
Career: QC 2008.
Personal: Christopher Donnellan Q.C. has extensive experience in defending and prosecuting serious crime including murder, manslaughter, and death by dangerous driving. He has been described as having "an excellent brain and bedside manner" particularly relevant to his cases involving young and vulnerable witnesses and defendants. He has acted in complex, high profile cases of child abuse and historical sexual offences. He also has extensive experience in fraud, corruption, bribery, money laundering and confiscation. He has a particular expertise in health and safety cases involving death in the workplace and transport industry. He co-authored the response of the Bar to the Corporate Manslaughter Bill, and gave evidence to the House of Commons committee scrutinising the Bill. He was junior for the prosecution of the driver in the Watford train crash, and recently defended the owner of a haulage business responsible for the death of an HGV driver while exceeding the drivers' hours regulations.

DONNELLY, Kathleen
Henderson Chambers, London
020 7583 9020
kdonnelly@hendersonchambers.co.uk
Featured in Employment (London)
Practice Areas: Kathleen specialises in Commercial, Health Safety & Environment, and Employment Law. Her high profile cases include the OCENSA pipeline group action, the Stirling Mortimer fraud litigation, the Potters Bar Rail inquest and the Buncefield Oil Depot litigation. Her representative cases include Autoclenz and Westwood (employee and worker status), JB v African Development Bank (legitimate expectations in the international civil service), Back Office v Percival (corporate liability for contempt), and WXY v Burby (privacy harassment and injunctive relief). She has particular expertise in restrictive covenants, economic torts and complex discrimination claims.
Professional Memberships: Health and Safety Lawyers Association (HSLA), Employment Lawyers Association (ELA).
Career: BA Jurisprudence (Oxon), LLM Commercial and International Law (Cantab). Hardwicke Award (Lincolns Inn), Buchanan Scholar (Lincoln's Inn). Called to the Bar 2005.
Personal: Born 1979; resides London; dog owner; cake baker; fun runner.

DOUGHERTY, Charles QC
2TG - 2 Temple Gardens, London
020 7822 1200
clerks@2tg.co.uk
Featured in Commercial Dispute Resolution (London), Fraud (London), Insurance (London), Product Liability (London), Professional Negligence (London), Travel (London)
Practice Areas: Charles specialises in commercial law, in particular commercial fraud, banking, professional negligence, product liability, private international law (including travel) and insurance.
Professional Memberships: Commercial Bar Association (COMBAR); Professional Negligence Bar Association (PNBA); Commercial Fraud Lawyers Association (CFLA).
Career: BA, BCL (Oxon). Called 1997 (Middle Temple); QC 2013. Called to the Bar of the BVI and ad hoc to the Bar of Nevis. Prior to joining chambers, Charles was a management consultant and a law lecturer.
Publications: European Civil Practice, Sweet & Maxwell (2nd ed.), assistant editor.

DOUGHERTY, Nigel
Erskine Chambers, London
020 7242 5532
clerks@erskinechambers.com
Featured in Company (London)
Practice Areas: Company, insolvency and related areas of commercial law. Cases include: Ultraframe (UK) Ltd v Fielding [2005] EWHC 1638 (Ch); [2006] EWCA Civ 1133, Irvine v Irvine [2007] 1 BCLC 445; Kiani v Cooper [2010] BCC 463; Barclays Bank PLC v Nylon Capital LLP [2010] EWHC 1139 (Ch), [2011] EWCA Civ 826; and Eclairs Group Limited v JKX Oil & Gas Plc [2014] EWCA Civ 640.
Professional Memberships: Chancery Bar Association, COMBAR.
Career: Called 1993.
Publications: Contributor to "Company Directors: Law and Liability" (1998); Author (with Anne Fairpo) of "Company Acquisition of Own Shares" (6th ed).
Personal: Cambridge University: MA, LLM. Member of Gray's Inn.

DOUGLAS, Michael QC
4 Pump Court, London
020 7842 5555
clerks@4pumpcourt.com
Featured in Commercial Dispute Resolution (London), Information Technology (London), Professional Negligence (London)
Practice Areas: Professional negligence, information technology, insurance and commercial litigation. (Experience in other areas of law available on request from clerks). Michael Douglas QC's practice involves all areas of professional negligence including construction specialists and commerical and legal practitioners. In the information and technology field he advises on all commercial and legal aspects of IT contracts and appears in domestic and international arbitrations as well as the High Court.
Professional Memberships: COMBAR, TECBAR , PNBA, Society for Computers & Law, LCIA Users' Council.
Career: Called to the Bar in 1974. Queen's Counsel 1997. Recorder 1999.
Publications: Articles on implied terms and mandatory injunctions in Computers & Law magazine. Former editor of Atkins' Court Forms.

Personal: Educated at Westminster School and Balliol College, Oxford.

DOUGLAS, Zachary
Matrix Chambers, London
020 7404 3447
zacharydouglas@matrixlaw.co.uk
Featured in International Arbitration (London), Public International Law (London)

Practice Areas: Professor Zachary Douglas has a substantial practice before international courts and tribunals as counsel, expert witness and arbitrator, and also frequently appears before the English courts in cases with an international law element. Zachary has been instructed by States in relation to proceedings in the International Court of Justice and the Tribunal for the Law of the Sea. He has acted as counsel in a significant number of investment treaty arbitrations and commercial arbitrations under the ICC, LCIA, SCC, Swiss, UNCITRAL and ICSID Arbitration Rules and has served as an arbitrator in more than forty commercial and investment arbitrations under the same rules, including as president or sole-arbitrator in more than half of those. He has represented individuals and companies in proceedings before the European Court of Human Rights and has acted in dozens of cases before the Court of Arbitration for Sport, having formerly represented the International Olympic Committee. Zachary is fluent in Russian and French. He is the author of one of the leading treatises on investment treaty arbitration 'The International Law of Investment Claims' (Cambridge University Press, 2009) and major studies on topics such as state immunity, environmental law and financial crime.

DOUGLAS-JONES, Ben
5 Paper Buildings, London
020 7583 6117
bdj@5pb.co.uk
Featured in Consumer Law (London), Financial Crime (London)

Practice Areas: Complex, cross-jurisdictional fraud of all types, money-laundering, white-collar, regulatory, cyber and serious crime, consumer law, compliance, human rights, criminal intellectual property, civil fraud, asset recovery, JR and appellate work. As leader and junior, Ben defends and provides compliance advice to professional and corporate clients including public limited companies. He prosecutes for the Serious Fraud Office; CPS: Specialist Fraud Division, Organised and Special Crime Divisions, Appeals Unit, Proceeds of Crime Unit and Welfare Division (including medical regulation); and local authorities. Ben is a Level 4 specialist prosecutor on three panels: Fraud, Serious Crime and Proceeds of Crime (London, South East and Wales) and on the CPS Advocate Rape and Child Abuse List. Recent bribery and fraud: Bribery: Operation Vectorial (represented first person acquitted of Bribery Act offence); SFO v BH ($2.7Bn bribery). Fraud: Operation Valgus (mortgage; over 1,000 mortgages), Operation Festival (tax), Abacus Trading (invoice / banking); Operation Ernest (£110 million factoring fraud); Operation Militia (botnet cyber fraud); SFO v OB [2014] UKSC 23 (Contempt; Extradition; Restraint; Specialty; Boiler-room Fraud); and SFO Operation GLD01 [2014] EW Misc 5 (CrownC) (Scope of Conspiracy to Defraud; for first defendant: £170m case dismissed). Consumer: all areas, with emphasis on trademarks, copyright, criminal planning, food safety and environmental health. Recent human rights: Mateta and others [2014] 1 WLR 1516 (asylum defences) and R v L [2014] Crim LR 150 and R v Le [2013] QB 379 (human trafficking) and R (A) v Lowestoft Magistrates' Court [2013] EMLR 20 (privacy). Ben co-authored the CPS Guidance on Human Trafficking. Ben is also an attorney in Grenada.

Professional Memberships: Fraud Advisory Panel; Fraud Lawyers' Association; Gray's Inn accredited advocacy trainer.

Career: Called 1998.

Personal: LLB (Hons) (Reading); M Phil (Wales).

DOVAR, Daniel
Tanfield Chambers, London
020 7421 5300
ddovar@tanfieldchambers.co.uk
Featured in Real Estate Litigation (London)

Practice Areas: Landlord and Tenant (commercial and residential): Service charges, enfranchisement, dilapidations, '54 Act renewals, forfeiture. Real Property: easements, rights of way, covenants, boundary disputes, prescriptive rights, mortgages, trusts. Professional negligence: related to property transactions. Recent cases include R (on the application of O Twelve Baytree Ltd) v. Rent Assessment Panel [2014] EWHC 1229 (Admin), Furlonger v Lalatta [2014] EWHC 37 (Ch), Simpole v. Chee [2013] EWHC 4444 (Ch) and Paddington Basin Developments v Gritz [2013] UKUT 338 (LC).

Professional Memberships: Chancery Bar Association, Property Bar Association and Bar Pro Bono Unit.

Career: Called 1997. Appointed Judge First-tier Tribunal (Property Chamber) (2011).

Publications: Residential Possession Proceedings (9th ed Sweet & Maxwell). Megarry's Manual of the Law of Real Property (9th ed Sweet & Maxwell). Service Charges and Manaagement (3rd ed Sweet & Maxwell). Business Premises: Renewal and Possession (4th ed Sweet & Maxwell). Editor of Landlord and Tenant Review (Sweet & Maxwell). Editor of Property Litigation and Residential Tenancies (www.propertylawuk.net).

DOWDING, Nicholas QC
Falcon Chambers, London
020 7353 2484
dowding@falcon-chambers.com
Featured in Real Estate Litigation (London)

Practice Areas: All aspects of Chancery and real property law, commercial property litigation and arbitration.

Professional Memberships: Honorary member of the Royal Institution of Chartered Surveyors; Corresponding Member of RICS Dilapidations Practice Panel; Chancery Bar Association; LCLCBA; Property Bar Association.

Career: Educated at Radley College; St Catharine's College, Cambridge (BA 1978, MA 1982); called 1979 (Inner Temple); Silk 1997; Blundell Memorial Lecturer 1992, 1997, 2004, 2008 and 2013; Chambers and Partners Real Estate Silk of the Year 2005 and 2009; Chambers and Partners 100: UK Bar, 2013.

Publications: Joint Author, Dilapidations - The Modern Law and Practice; joint editor, Woodfall, Landlord and Tenant; general editor, Landlord and Tenant Reports.

DOWLEY, Dominic QC
Serle Court, London
020 7 242 6105
ddowley@serlecourt.co.uk
Featured in Chancery (London), Fraud (London)

Practice Areas: Commercial litigation, contentious trusts, fraud, insurance/ reinsurance, arbitration, banking and financial services/ regulation specialist.

Career: Called to the Bar and joined One Hare Court in 1983 (merged with Serle Court in 2000). QC 2002.

Personal: Educated at Oxford University 1977-80. Bacon Scholar of Gray's Inn: Barstow Law Scholar. Born 25 March 1958.

DOYLE, Louis
Kings Chambers, Manchester
0845 034 3444
clerks@kingschambers.com
Featured in Chancery (Northern), Restructuring/ Insolvency (Northern)

Practice Areas: Busy commercial chancery practice with significant insolvency, company law (especially shareholder and director disputes), financial (especially guarantees and recoveries) litigation emphasis. Instructed by office-holder, creditor, debtor and institutional litigants in addition to advising on transactions and re-structuring, together with disciplinary, regulatory and professional negligence work within area of expertise. Regularly appears in reported cases in areas of specialism. Particularly enjoys complex, tricky and/or challenging cases and dealing with matters at short notice. Accepts direct professional access and direct access instructions in appropriate cases.

Professional Memberships: Insolvency Lawyers' Association (full member), R3 (full member), Chancery Bar Association, Northern Chancery Bar Association, Professional Negligence Bar Association.

Career: LLB LLM (Birmingham). Admitted a solicitor in 1994. Called to the Bar: 1996 (Lincoln's Inn). Treasury Counsel (Provincial Panel) 2000-07.

Publications: Contributing Editor to Gore-Browne on Companies (Jordans, looseleaf). (Books) 'Insolvency Legislation: Annotations and Commentary' (with Professor Andrew Keay) (Jordans, 2014, 4th Edition); 'Insolvency Litigation' (Sweet & Maxwell, 2014, 2nd Edition); 'Company Voluntary Arrangements and Administration' (Jordans, 2010, 2nd Edition); 'Administrative Receivership: Law and Practice' (Sweet & Maxwell, 1995).

DRAKE, David
Serle Court, London
020 7242 6105
clerks@serlecourt.co.uk
Featured in Chancery (London), Fraud (London), Telecommunications (London)

Practice Areas: Chancery/ commercial litigation including civil fraud, telecommunications, professional negligence and corporate and personal insolvency.

Professional Memberships: Chancery Bar Association, COMBAR.

Career: Serle Court (formerly Thirteen Old Square) 1995 to date.

Publications: The Practice and Procedure of the Companies Court (1997), Minority Shareholders: Law, Practice and Procedure (4th ed, 2011).

DRAY, Martin
Falcon Chambers, London
020 7353 2484
dray@falcon-chambers.com
Featured in Real Estate Litigation (London)

Practice Areas: All aspects of real property law including landlord and tenant, adverse possession, options, easements and restrictive covenants. Reported cases include: No 1 Deansgate (Residential) Ltd v No 1 Deansgate RTM Co Ltd [2013] UKUT 0580 (LC) (right to manage); Dyer v Terry [2013] EWHC 209 (Ch) (adverse possession); Miller Properties Inc v Pastoll [2010] EWHC 2364 (Ch) (equitable charge); Donington Park Leisure Ltd v Wheatcroft & Son Ltd [2006] All ER (D) 94 (contract terms); Topplan Estates Ltd v Townley [2004] EWCA Civ 1369 CA (adverse possession); Dewar v Krestic Ltd [2004] All ER (D) 571 (boundary dispute, costs liability).

Professional Memberships: Chancery Bar Association; LCLCBA; Property Bar Association.

Career: Educated at Christ's Hospital; University of Bristol (LLB Hons 1991); called 1992 (Gray's Inn); Deputy Adjudicator to HM Land Registry (2008); Judge of the First-tier Tribunal (Property Chamber)(2013).

Publications: Contributor: Law and Practice of Charging Orders on Land (2013); Joint editor, Barnsley's Land Options, 5th edn (2009) and 4th edn (2005); Contributor: Fisher & Lightwood's 'Law of Mortgage', 11th edn (2001); ICSL Bar Vocational Course, Landlord and Tenant Manual; Landlord and Tenant Factbook, Chapter 10 (residential tenancies); New Law Journal Property Update; Sweet & Maxwell Localaw UK website.

DRAYCOTT, Natasha
5 St Andrew's Hill, London
020 7332 5400
natashadraycott@5sah.co.uk
Featured in Extradition (London)

Practice Areas: Natasha is a leading extradition barrister who acts on behalf of both foreign governments and requested persons under Parts 1 and 2 of the Extradition Act. Since 2012 she has appeared in over 200 appeals at the Administrative Court. She has acted successfully for both the Swiss and US government in cases involving people trafficking, complex cyber fraud in the sum of $70 million; USA v Konovalenko [2014] and drug importation. She appeared in Lumenica v Government of Albania [2012] a leading authority on powers of the Administrative court to extend time for service of appeals and was the only successful conjoined appeal; Poland v Demkowski. She has a busy Appellate practice and particular expertise in acting for Appellants raising Article 8 of the ECHR. She was the first practitioner to have an appeal allowed where the Appellant was a fugitive with only a partner in the UK, Poland v Sobieraj [2013]. She also acted in the landmark case Chmura v Poland [2013]. The first appeal to be allowed where the Appellant had no family. Recently she appeared before the Divisional Court in the leading authority on Lithuanian prisons; Alekynas & others [2014]. She is currently representing an Appellant raising Article 6 of the ECHR in an Albanian murder case.

DRAYCOTT, Simon QC
5 St Andrew's Hill, London
020 7332 5400
simondraycott@5sah.co.uk
Featured in Financial Crime (London)
Practice Areas: Criminal Fraud, Business Crime, Asset Forfeiture and Confiscation, Serious Crime and VAT Tribunal's
Career: Simon Draycott QC has a mixture of defence and prosecution work with the emphasis on defence work. He practices in a range of areas, particularly in serious fraud and other financial crime, in particular multi-jurisdictional asset tracing and money laundering. In 1995 he was appointed Standing Counsel to HM Customs and Excise. He became an assistant recorder in 1998 and a recorder in 2000. He took silk in 2002. He was appointed Head of Chambers at 5 St Andrew's Hill in 2003 which is one of the leading sets in relation to asset forfeiture and confiscation. Cases conducted for the defence include SFO -v–Hughes (Operation Steamroller) a £200 million pound boiler room fraud, R-v-Katcharian a multi jurisdiction investment banking fraud; R-v- Chemiel Successful defence in murder/manslaughter prosecution and R-v- Barso, successful defence, solicitor charged with fraud on insurers concerning 3rd party claims. Simon has been instructed to defend allegations of bribery and fraud in the Turks and Caicos Islands. He was retained by a property developer and also an ex cabinet minister in a large-scale corruption case. Simon was instructed to conduct the case for the prosecution in Operation Varlet, a £55 million MTIC carousel fraud, with 19 defendants and a VAT loss of £60 million on sales of £350 million. Operation Echogramme a sophisticated money laundering operation filtering criminal proceeds through Hong Kong via Gibraltar and through a solicitors account in the UK. This case has been successfully concluded. Simon has also successfully appeared several times in the VAT tribunal including: Blada Ltd –v- Commissioners for HMRC a case associated with an MTIC fraud resulting in a £4 million fraud against the UK government and Cotswold Computers Ltd –v- Commissioners for HMRC a £16.2 million input tax claim. Both cases were successfully concluded. Currently privately instructed defending a property developer accused of mortgage frauds through multiple companies over a number of years.

DREW, Jane
Coram Chambers, London
020 7092 3700
jane.drew@coramchambers.co.uk
Featured in Family/Matrimonial (London)
Practice Areas: Children, family finance, international. Handles all types of work concerning children with a special emphasis on children in local authority care, care proceedings especially non-accidental injury involving medical evidence, adoption, private children law, divorce, matrimonial property, family provision and inheritance. Also deals with cohabitees concerning real property disputes, cases under Section 14 of the Trusts of Land and Trustees Act 1996. Has dealt with numerous cases of sexual abuse and non-accidental injury. Regular lecturer and provider of seminars on cohabitees and public law children's work.
Professional Memberships: Family Law Bar Association. Middle Temple Association of Lawyers for Children British Association for Adoption and Fostering.
Career: Called to the Bar 1976. Deputy District Judge: Principal Registry.
Personal: Educated at Stevenage Girls Grammar School 1963-70, Trevelyan College, Durham 1971-74 and Inns of Court School 1974-76. Leisure pursuits include swimming, tennis and badminton. Born 6 June 1952. Lives in Knebworth.

DRISCOLL, Michael QC
Maitland Chambers, London
020 7406 1200
mdriscoll@maitlandchambers.com
Featured in Chancery (London), Real Estate Litigation (London)
Practice Areas: General commercial chancery (advisory and litigation) but in particular property related, partnership and company law, trust and mining law matters.
Career: Rugby and Cambridge (BA LLB).

DRUCE, Michael
Cornerstone Barristers, London
020 7242 4986
michaeld@cornerstonebarristers.com
Featured in Planning (London)
Practice Areas: Michael has considerable experience in all aspects of town and country planning, from advising at the pre-application stage to representation at the Inquiry and in the High Court. Acting for major developers, landowners and public sector clients, Michael has developed particular expertise in major infrastructure projects, housing (both open market and affordable), retail, employment, flood risk, listed buildings and conservation areas, historic environments, energy, aviation, enforcement notices, and CPO inquiries. Inquiries include: acting for Essex County Cricket Club at the Inquiry into the redevelopment of the Ford County Ground, Chelmsford involving the location within the Functional Floodplain of over 400 residential units required as enabling development to fund the upgraded cricket facilities; promoting new aviation facilities for General and Business Aviation at Elvington Aerodrome, York; appearing at the Barmoor, Moorsyde and Toft Hill windfarm appeals in Berwick-upon-Tweed; and promoting numerous Lidl foodstores in locations such as Oxford, Croydon, Ely, Leicester and Northfleet.
Professional Memberships: PEBA.
Career: MA (Cantab), called 1988.
Personal: Maried with 2 children.

DUCKWORTH, Peter
29 Bedford Row Chambers, London
020 7404 1044
pduckworth@29br.co.uk
Featured in Family/Matrimonial (London)
Practice Areas: Matrimonial finance, with a focus on high net worth divorces (£5m–£50m), typically where a business is involved. Cases: Dixon v Marchant (2008), Downing (2003), Dharamshi (2001), Hall v Simons (2000, HL), Jordan (1999), Thomas (1995), Hildebrand (1992).
Professional Memberships: Family Law Bar Association (ex-Treasurer); Chartered Institute of Arbitrators; Lawyers' Christian Fellowship.
Career: Called 1971, Middle Temple and Lincoln's Inn. Family arbitrator.
Publications: Matrimonial Property & Finance (loose leaf); articles and software.
Personal: LLB Hons (Manchester), MCIArb, LRAM. Directorships: EquityShare Ltd, Niche Capital Ltd, Xiros Ltd. Accomplished pianist.

DUFF, Susan
Compass Chambers, Edinburgh
07971 898 516
susan.duff@compasschambers.co.uk
Featured in Health & Safety (Scotland)
Practice Areas: Member of the Regulatory Crime Team at Compass Chambers. Susan is very experienced in acting for clients in all categories of crime both in negotiating resolution of cases in the best interests of clients and in conducting trials on clients' behalf. She specialises in defending regulatory prosecutions particularly Health and Safety, Food Safety, Environmental Offences, Fatal Road Traffic cases and Financial Crime. She is experienced in advising and appearing for appellants and respondents in relation to improvement/prohibition notices in civil proceedings under the Health and Safety at Work Etc. Act 1974; The Food Hygiene Regulations; Environmental Protection Regulations; and in proceedings under the Proceeds of Crime Act 2002. She is also experienced in representing the interests of parties at Fatal Accident Inquiries arising out of deaths at work, in custody and where it appears in the public interest that an Inquiry is held.
Professional Memberships: Health and Safety Lawyers Association, UK Environmental Lawyers Association, Association of Regulatory and Disciplinary Lawyers, Faculty of Advocates Criminal Bar Association
Career: Procurator Fiscal Depute 1992-1996, Principal Procurator Fiscal Depute 1996-2002, Called to the Bar 2003.

DUFFY, James
Fountain Court Chambers, London
020 7583 3335
jd@fountaincourt.co.uk
Featured in Banking & Finance (London)
Practice Areas: Broad commercial litigation and arbitration practice, including: banking and finance; civil fraud; aviation; insurance and reinsurance; and professional negligence. Significant recent cases: Barclays v UniCredit; Tchenguiz v Serious Fraud Office; Merrill Lynch, Dexia and UBS v City of Florence; Bmibaby v Durham Tees Valley Airport; Credit Agricole and FGIC v IKB; Office of Fair Trading v Abbey National and others; and American Reliable and CNA v Willis.
Professional Memberships: COMBAR
Career: Called 2005.
Personal: Christ Church, Oxford (BA, First; BCL, Distinction).

DUGGAN, Michael QC
Littleton Chambers, London
020 7797 8620
md@littletonchambers.co.uk
Featured in Employment (London)
Practice Areas: Michael specialises in commercial, sports regulatory and employment law. He regularly appears in the tribunals and EAT as well as County and High Court. He advises on contentious and non contentious matters and deals with all areas of discrimination, wrongful and unfair dismissal, redundancies and dismissals/variation of employment contracts arising out of re-organisations. He has particular experience of large scale wrongful dismissals. commercial agency cases and restrictive covenant cases in the High Court and discrimination, harassment, trade union law including labour disputes and whistle blowing and disability and stress cases in the Courts and Tribunals. His recent clients include financial institutions (Bank of England; Cantor Fitzgerald); Local Authorities (Kent, Swale, Leeds, Leicestershire, Bradford, Darlington, Stockton, East Lindsey); Universities (Cambridge, Trinity Hall, UKC, Leicester, Lincoln, Oxford); Police Constabularies and Local Authorities (Barnsley, Kent, Leeds, Lancashire, Nottingham, R.A.R.T.). He acts for both employers and employees. Cases include: Driskel v Peninsula Business Services Ltd [2000] IRLR 151 (harassment); Wall v BCAS [2004] IRLR 147 (age); Fitzgerald v UKC [2004] IRLR 300; The Scotts Co (UK) Ltd v Budd [2004] ICR 299 (sickness notice); Fulham FC v Tigana (Elias J - duties of fidelity), Intercall Conferencing Services Ltd v Steer [2007] EWHC 519 (QB) (restrictive covenants); Kynixa v Hynes & Ors [2008] EWHC 1495 (restrictive covenants); North Tyneside Primary Trust v Aynsley [1009] ICR 1333 (Tribunal strike outs); Abegaze v Shrewsbury College of Arts [2009] EWCA Civ 96 (CA – strike out); Da'Bell v. National Society for Prevention of Cruelty To Children [2010] IRLR 19 (Vento damages); GX Networks v Greenland [2010] IRLR 784 (Bonuses); RSA Consulting Ltd v Evans [2010] EWCA Civ 866 (agency); Gledhill v Bentley Designs (UK) Ltd [2010] EWHC B8 (commercial agency and fidelity); Shanahan Engineering Ltd v UNITE [2010] UKEAT 0411 (Protective awards); OTG Ltd v Barke & Ors [2011] IRLR 272 (TUPE); Halstead v Paymentshield Group Holdings Ltd [2012] EWCA Civ 524 (Stays); McCammon v Gillingham Football Club [2013] (discrimination), Gillingham Football Club Ltd & Anor v McCammon [2013] UKEAT 0559 (Unfair Dismissal, Reasonableness of dismissal); Ashcourt Rowan Financial Planning Ltd v Hall [2013] IRLR 637 (restrictive covenants); Shiret v Credit Suisse [2013] (age discrimination); Sunrise Brokers LLC v Rodgers [2014] EWHC 2633 (notice period and covenants). Also general commercial law including applications for interim injunctions and freezing orders and building and construction law, health and safety and professional negligence commercial agency. Regulatory/disciplinary issues concerning medical profession, sports and financial services. Education including SENDIST. Commercial agency.
Professional Memberships: ELA, ELBA
Career: Called 1984; Gray's Inn. Senior in Hall 2003. QC April 2014. Regular lecturer and writer. Past Committee member of ELA, London & SE Representative from 2004-8; ELA Training Committee and Gray's Inn Barrister's Committee.
Publications: Author The Modern Law of Strikes; Business Re-Organisations and Employment Law (FT Law & Tax)'; Termination of Employment of Directors (FT Law & Tax); Family Friendly Policies: A Handbook for Employers and Employees; The Law of Industrial Action and Trade Union Recognition (OUP 2nd edition 2010); Equal Pay, Law and Practice (Jordans March 2009). Law Guidance and Precedents series: Contracts of Employment, (two volumes) (4th Edition out Autumn 2014); Unfair Dismissal; Wrongful Dismissal (all now published by Duggan Press -see www.DugganPress.com). He writes regular employment bulletin and index available from Chambers website.

Personal: BA. BCL. LLM (First Class, Sidney Sussex College, Cambridge University). Holt Scholar of Gray's Inn. Married with three boys. Interests: music, guitar, mandolin, guitarviol, violin' renovating waterwheel in Norfolk. Director of Duggan Press Limited. Lives in Gray's Inn, Coton, Cambridge and Mundesley, Norfolk. His full cv and articles are at: http://www.littletonchambers.com/barrister.aspx?c=1033

DUNCAN, Hannah
Atkinson Bevan Chambers, 2 Harcourt Buildings, London
hduncan@2hb.co.uk
Featured in Crime (London)

Practice Areas: Hannah has a busy practice exclusively in criminal law. She acts in trials across the whole spectrum of criminal offences although is most frequently instructed to defend and prosecute serious sexual and violent offences, particularly those involving defendants or witnesses who are vulnerable through extreme youth, autism or mental health diagnosis. Recent examples: Junior counsel in gang related murder; junior counsel in 'London Riot' cases using cell site analysis and telephone evidence; sole counsel in multiple defendant/multiple complainant historic rape and sexual abuse; prosecuting historic rape where issues included 'false memory syndrome'; prosecuting case of sexual abuse where complainant was aged 4 at the time of giving evidence; defending in rape where complainant had mental health difficulties; defending youth in a sexual abuse case where complainant was five years of age; defending in rape where defendant and complainant were married and children were called as witnesses; prosecuting male rape; defending multi-handed large scale complex fraud; junior counsel in multi count rape of young complainant with autism and acute cognitive difficulties where defendant was a care worker; prosecuting 'scalping' case where female complainant suffered horrific scarring.
Professional Memberships: Criminal Bar Association, South Eastern Circuit and Western Circuit.
Career: Tenant of Atkinson Bevan Chambers since 2003.

DUNLOP, Rory
Thirty Nine Essex Street, London
020 7832 1111
rory.dunlop@39essex.com
Featured in Data Protection (London), Immigration (London)

Practice Areas: Immigration, Administrative and Public Law, Human Rights and Civil Liberties, Information Law, Environmental, Employment. Significant cases include: R (Akpinar) v Upper Tribunal [2014] EWCA Civ 937, NS (Kosovo) v SSHD [2013] EWCA Civ 408ST (Eritrea) v Secretary of State for the Home Department [2012] UKSC 12; G1 v Secretary of State for the Home Department [2012] EWCA Civ 867; FM v Secretary of State for the Home Department [2011] EWCA Civ 807; Abdi & Khalaf v Secretary of State for the Home Department [2011] EWCA Civ 242; AP v Secretary of State for the Home Department [2010] UKSC 26; AL (Serbia) v Secretary of State for the Home Department; R (Rudi) v Secretary of State for the Home Department [2008] UKHL 42; R (National Grid Gas plc) v Environment Agency [2007] UKHL 30.
Professional Memberships: Immigration Law Practitioners' Association; Human Rights Lawyers' Association; Bar Pro Bono Unit; Employment Law Bar Association; Free Representation Unit.
Career: Called 2001, Pegasus Scholar to European Court of Human Rights (2005), Attorney General's 'B' Panel of counsel; Attorney General's Freedom of Information panel; EHRC Panel.
Publications: Detention under the Immigration Acts: Law and Practice (OUP), forthcoming (author)

DUTHIE, Euan
Axiom Advocates, Edinburgh
07867 528 181
euan.duthie@axiomadvocates.com
Featured in Restructuring/Insolvency (Scotland), Commercial Dispute Resolution (Scotland)

Practice Areas: Commercial litigation, insolvency, public law, professional liability, property litigation and regulatory work. Appears regularly in Court of Session (particularly Commercial Court); has Inner House, Upper Tribunal, Lands Tribunal, Sheriff Court, disciplinary tribunal and arbitration experience. Recent cases include John G Sibbald & Son Ltd v Johnston [2014] CSOH 94 (professional negligence; negative prescription); Secretary of State for Business, Innovation and Skills v Hamilton [2014] CSOH 89 (director disqualification); HHG (Iraq) 2014 SLT 693 (immigration; rehabilitation of offenders); Hawthorne v Anderson [2014] CSOH 65 (solicitors' liability); British Telecommunications v Common Services Agency [2014] CSOH 44 (procurement); Mitchell v Great Lakes Reinsurance UK Limited 2013 SLT 393 (construction of insurance policy); Phimister v DM Hall LLP 2013 SLT 261 (surveyors' liability); and Winding-Up Board of Landsbanki Islands HF, Noter 2012 SC 209 (cross border insolvency, credit institutions).
Career: Solicitor, 2003-05. Lord Reid Scholar, 2005-06. Called to Bar, 2006. Legal Advisor, European Union Naval Force, 2012. Standing Junior to Advocate General, 2012 – date. Fee Paid Judge, First-tier Tribunal (Social Entitlement Chamber), 2014 – date.
Personal: Educated at University of St Andrews (MA (Hons), 1998); and University of Edinburgh (LLB 2000; Diploma in Legal Practice, 2001).

DUTTON, Timothy C QC
Maitland Chambers, London
020 7406 1200
Featured in Real Estate Litigation (London)

Practice Areas: Property related litigation and advisory work. Reported cases include: Meretz Investments NV v ACP [2007] Ch 197 (ChD); [2008] Ch 244 (CA); Legal & General v Expeditors International [2007] 1 P&CR 5 (ChD); [2007] 2 P&CR 204 (CA); Housden v Conservators of Wimbledon & Putney Commons [2007] 1 WLR 1171 (ChD); [2008] 1 WLR 1172 (CA); KPMG v Network Rail [2008] 1 P&CR 11 (CA); Heronslea v Kwik-Fit Properties [2009] Env. LR 28 (QBD); Norwich Union v Linpac Mouldings [2010] L&TR 74 (ChD); [2010] L&TR 183 (CA); Pittack v Naviede [2011] 1 WLR 1666 (ChD); Redcard v Williams [2011] 2 EGLR 67 (CA); Carey-Morgan v Sloane Stanley Estate [2012] 3 EGLR 38 (CA); Carey-Morgan v De Walden [2013] P&CR DG3 (UT); Cravecrest v 2nd Duke of Westminster WT [2014] Ch 301 (CA).
Professional Memberships: Chancery Bar Association; Property Bar Association.
Career: Called to the Bar in 1985. QC 2013.
Personal: Born 1962. Educated at Godalming Grammar School (1972-80) and Durham University (1981-84).

DYAL, Daniel
Cloisters, London
020 7827 4000
ddyal@cloisters.com
Featured in Employment (London)

Practice Areas: Daniel has a thriving practice in employment and equality law. He is renowned for the excellence of his judgment, client-skills and advocacy (both written and oral). Daniel has appeared in important and leading cases both at first instance and appellate level. He is an accomplished and experienced practitioner in all areas of employment law including: discrimination, TUPE, whistleblowing, unfair dismissal, bonus disputes and claims for injunctive relief.
Professional Memberships: ELBA, ELA, DLA.
Career: Called to the bar in 2006.

DYBLE, Steven
Red Lion Chambers, Chelmsford
01245 280 880
chelmsford@18rlc.co.uk
Featured in Crime (South Eastern)

Practice Areas: Steven Dyble practises from Red Lion Chambers' Chelmsford annexe. His practice covers all areas of crime with a particular emphasis on homicide, sexual offences (rape-accredited practitioner), drugs, money laundering and fraud. He regularly accepts leading briefs. Having prosecuted and defended for much of his career he now exclusively defends. He is instructed by most of the leading criminal firms of solicitors in East Anglia. He has a particular interest in assisted suicide. In addition to his mainstream criminal work he is also the crime columnist for The East Anglian Daily Times.
Professional Memberships: Criminal Bar Association; Essex Bar Mess; East Anglian Bar Mess.
Career: Education: University of West England; Called to the Bar, 1986.

DYER, Simon
Cloisters, London
020 7827 4000
sd@cloisters.com
Featured in Clinical Negligence (London), Personal Injury (London)

Practice Areas: Clinical negligence and personal injury.
Professional Memberships: PIBA.
Career: Simon Dyer was called in 1987 and has specialised in clinical negligence claims since 2000. He has specialised in personal injury claims since 1990. Simon is instructed in many high value cases. He is usually instructed as sole counsel and conducts hearings, conferences and roundtable meetings, as well as drafting complex pleadings, including large schedules and written advice. He is recommended for both clinical negligence and personal injury. Cases: Glasgow v Hillingdon Hospitals (2014) QBD 13/4/14 Smith v Bailey (2014) QBD 29/4/14 Parsons v Abertawe Bro Morgannwg (2014) QBD 28/4/14 H v K (2013) QBD 13/3/13 J K v P [2011] QBD B-S v L [2011] QBD Khudados v Hayden [Court of Appeal] [2008] C.P. Rep 12 NUM v UK Coal PLC [2008] IRLR 4 Hickman v Blake Lapthorn and David Fisher [2006] PNLR 20 Hartman v South Essex Mental Health and Community Care NHS Trust (Moore v Welwyn Components Ltd) [Court Of Appeal] [2005] ICR 782; [2005] IRLR 293; [2005] PIQR 255 Farrell v Southmead Health Authority [2001] Lloyd's Rep Med 458.

DYMOND, Andrew
Arden Chambers, London
020 7242 4244
andrew.dymond@ardenchambers.com
Featured in Social Housing (London)

Practice Areas: All areas of housing, landlord and tenant and local government law.
Professional Memberships: Housing Law Practitioners Association, Property Bar Association.
Career: Called to the Bar in 1991. Founder member of Arden Chambers in 1993. He advises and represents both public and private sector clients, including local authorities, PRPs, leaseholders, tenants and the homeless. Notable cases include: Islington LBC v Unite Group Plc [2013] EWHC 508 (Admin); Rochdale BC v Dixon [2011] EWCA Civ 1173; [2012] H.L.R. 6; Swindon BC v Redpath [2009] EWCA Civ 943; [2010] P.T.S.R. 904; Kilby v Basildon DC [2007] EWCA Civ 479; [2007] H.L.R. 39.
Publications: Publications: Co-author of: Manual of Housing Law (8th and 9th Eds); Current Law Annotations for the Housing Act 2004 and Housing and Regeneration Act 2008; Leasehold Valuation Tribunals – a Practical Guide. Deputy General Editor of the Housing Law Reports. An editor of Arden & Parington's Housing Law.

EARDLEY, Aidan
One Brick Court, London
020 7353 8845
ae@onebrickcourt.com
Featured in Data Protection (London), Defamation/Privacy (London)

Practice Areas: Defamation, privacy/breach of confidence, malicious falsehood, freedom of information, data protection, contempt of court and reporting restrictions, harassment, media-related human rights law. Notable/recent cases include: libel - Cruddas v Calvert & Ors [2014] EMLR 5 (CA), [2013] EWHC 2298; El Naschie v Macmillan Publishers Ltd [2012] EWHC 1809; Khader v Aziz [2010] 1 WLR 2673 (CA); Timtchenko v The Economist Newspaper Ltd (2009); Rath v Guardian News & Media Ltd (2008); Polanski v Conde Nast [2005] 1 WLR 637 (HL); privacy – WXY v Gewanter & Ors (2009-2013); Lord Browne v Associated Newspapers Ltd [2008] QB 103 (CA); Green Corns v Claverley [2005] EMLR 31; freedom of information - R(Evans) v Attorney-General [2014] EWCA Civ 254 (CA); Evans v Information Commissioner & 7 Government Departments [2012] UKUT 313 (AAC); Home Office v Information Commissioner (2013); Cobain v Information Commissioner (2011); HEFCE v Information Commissioner (2010); other – Ashley v CC Sussex [2008] 1 AC 962 (HL).
Professional Memberships: Human Rights Lawyers Association; London Common Law and Commercial Bar Association.
Career: Called 2002; Attorney General's 'B' Panel, 2011; Fee-paid Judge, First Tier Tribunal (Social Entitlement Chamber), 2013; Co-Author, Duncan & Neill on Defamation (3rd ed, 2009); contributor, Arlidge, Eady &

Smith on Contempt (4th ed, 2011 & supplement 2013).
Publications: Co-author, Duncan & Neill on Defamation, 3rd ed; Contributor, Arlidge, Eady & Smith on Contempt, 4th ed and supplement; Articles for The Times, Entertainment Law Review and other journals.
Personal: BA Hons (Oxon). DipLaw (City). Languages: good French, some Spanish and German.

EAST, William
5 Stone Buildings, London
020 7242 6201
clerks@5sblaw.com
Featured in Court of Protection (All Circuits)
Practice Areas: A traditional Chancery practice that incorporates a wide range of contentious and non-contentious work, with particular emphasis upon: trusts, wills, probate and the administration of estates, Court of Protection, capital taxes and estate planning, pensions, proprietary estoppel, claims under the Inheritance (Provision for Family and Dependants) Act 1975, real property and related professional negligence matters.
Professional Memberships: Bar Pro Bono Unit, Chancery Bar Association and the Lord Denning Society.
Career: Called in 2008.
Publications: Writes for several professional publications and frequently lectures on areas of his practice.
Personal: Educated at St John's College, Oxford (BA Hons) and City University, London.

EASTON, Jonathan
Kings Chambers, Manchester
0845 034 3444
clerks@kingschambers.com
Featured in Planning (Northern)
Practice Areas: Practises in all aspects of Town and Country Planning, with particular experience of section 78 and Development Plan Inquiries. Recognised by Planning Magazine as a leading planning barrister under 35 (2006). Notable cases include: Fordent Holdings Ltd v SSCLG [2013] EWHC 2844 (Admin); [2014] J.P.L. 226; Feather v Cheshire East BC [2010] EWHC 1420 (Admin); R. (on the application of P Casey (Enviro) Ltd) v Bradford MBC [2008] EWHC 2543 (Admin); [2009] J.P.L. 639. Also practises in environmental law and compulsory purchase.
Professional Memberships: Planning and Environmental Bar Association (PEBA).
Career: First Class Honours Degree in European Law (LLB) from Warwick University. Masters in Comparative and International Law (LLM) from European University Institute, Florence. Very Competent in Bar Finals, Inns of Court School of Law.
Publications: Author of the Housing Chapter in Judicial Review: Law and Practice (Jordans) (1st Edition).

EATON, Deborah QC
1 King's Bench Walk, London
020 7936 1500
deaton@1kbw.co.uk
Featured in Family/Matrimonial (London)
Practice Areas: All aspects of family law including matrimonial finance and private disputes relating to children.
Professional Memberships: Family Law Bar Association. Midland Circuit. International Academy of Matrimonial Lawyers.
Career: Called to the Bar (Inner Temple) 1985. Recorder 2004 - Family and Crime. Silk 2008. Bencher Inner Temple 2008. Deputy High Court Judge 2011.
Publications: Co-author and editor: 'Wildblood and Eaton: Financial Provision In Family Matters' (Sweet and Maxwell). Regular lecturer in matrimonial finance and children matters. Member of Jordans Advisory Board.
Personal: Born 28 March 1962, BSc (Hons) Psychology and Anthropology. Diploma in Law.

EATON TURNER, David
New Square Chambers, London
020 7419 8011
david.eatonturner
@newsquarechambers.co.uk
Featured in Chancery (London), Company (London), Restructuring/Insolvency (London)
Practice Areas: Company, insolvency and commercial law including reorganisations of capital, corporate and personal insolvency, commercial, company and chancery litigation, banking, civil fraud, asset recovery, directors' duties, unfair prejudice petitions and other shareholder disputes, agency, sale of goods, professional negligence. Cases include: Goldtrail Travel Ltd (in liquidation) v Aydin & Ors [2014] EWHC 1587 (Ch); Yam Seng Pte Ltd v International Trade Corp [2013] 1 Lloyd's Rep. 526 (Contract, obligations of good faith); Anglo Irish Bank Corp v Flannery [2013] BPIR 1; (bankruptcy); Raithatha v Williamson [2012] EWHA 909 (Bankruptcy, Pensions); Pioneer Iron & Steel Group Company Ltd; Phoenix (Contracts) Leicester Limited, [2010] EWHC 2375 (shareholders' rights); ltsalat International v Allied TC pie [2009] All ER (D) 141 (fiduciary duties, freezing and search orders); Dayman v Lawrence Graham [2008] All ER (D) 191 (professional negligence); BCCI v Bank of India (2005] 2 BCLC 328 CA (banking, insolvency, fraudulent trading); GHE Realisations Ltd [2006] 1 WLR 287 (insolvency, distributions by administrators); Royal Bank of Scotland v Sandra Fielding [2004] CA (banking, freezing orders); Mumbray v Lapper [2005] BCC 990 (shareholders, derivative actions).
Professional Memberships: Chancery Bar Association, COMBAR.
Career: Called to the Bar 1984.
Personal: Educated: Westminster School; Queen Mary College, University of London.

EDDY, Katherine
11KBW, London
020 7632 8500
katherine.eddy@11kbw.com
Featured in Education (London)
Practice Areas: Katherine practises in employment, education and public law.
In the employment field, she has acted for and against large financial institutions, local authorities, government departments, retailers and small charities. Her recent EAT cases include Croft Vets v Butcher [2013] Eq LR 1170, Somerset CC v Chambers (EAT, 25 April 2013, led by Daniel Oudkerk QC) and CVS Solicitors LLP v Van der Borgh [2013] EqLR 934. Katherine has a particular interest in public law work with an education element. She was recently involved in a judicial review challenge to a University's admissions decision, a challenge to the lawfulness of an academy order, and a disability discrimination claim brought by a pupil excluded from an independent school for violent behaviour.
Professional Memberships: ELA, ELBA, COMBAR.
Career: Called to the bar in 2009. Katherine is a member of the Attorney General's C Panel of Counsel and she also acts as Special Adviser to the States of Jersey government.

EDELMAN, Colin QC
Devereux, London
020 7910 8300
edelman@devchambers.co.uk
Featured in Insurance (London), International Arbitration (London), Professional Negligence (London)
Practice Areas: Principal areas of practice are insurance and reinsurance, professional negligence, energy disputes and commercial law. Recent reported cases include Axa v Nat West (insurance/professional negligence); Bedfordshire Police Authority v Constable (insurance); EL Trigger Litigation - Edwards, Akzo-Amec v Excess (insurance); Horwood v Zurich Insurance (insurance); Gater v Naftogaz (arbitration); Pearson Education v Charter Partnership (professional negligence); CGU v Astrazeneca (arbitration); Brit v Grant Thornton (insurance); Tesco v Constable (insurance); Mopani v Millennium (insurance); Teal v WR Berkley (reinsurance); Versloot Dredging v HDI Gerling (insurance); Zurich v International Energy (insurance).
Professional Memberships: Commercial Bar Association, Middle Temple and Midland Circuit.
Career: Called to the Bar: 1977; Tenant at Devereux Chambers: 1979; Assistant Recorder: 1993; QC: 1995; Recorder: 1996. Head of Chambers: 2002 - 2011; Bencher of Middle Temple: 2003; Director of Bar Mutual Indemnity Fund: 2007 (currently Chairman); Deputy High Court Judge: 2008 (currently authorised to sit in QBD & Commercial Court).
Publications: Editor of 'The Law of Reinsurance' (OUP). Contributor to 'Insurance Disputes' (LLP). Speaker at seminars on insurance and reinsurance topics.
Personal: Educated at Haberdashers' Aske's School, Elstree 1961-72 and Clare College, Cambridge 1973-76. Leisure pursuits include skiing, walking, badminton, Luton Town FC. Born 2 March 1954. Lives in London.

EDENBOROUGH, Michael QC
Serle Court, London
020 7242 6105
medenborough@serlecourt.co.uk
Featured in Intellectual Property (London)
Practice Areas: All aspects of intellectual property law and practice, in particular registered IPRs and the related unregistered rights. Over 100 reported cases since 2000, of which two thirds were appeals or judicial reviews. Instructed 'off-panel' by the UK IPO: eg acted for the Comptroller-General of Patents in Yeda Research (HLs, CA and PatCt), the Registrar of Trade Marks in General Cigars and Land Securities (both appeals to the ChD), and the UK Government in adidas (ECJ). Instructed in numerous appeals from OHIM to the General Court, and further appeals to the Court of Justice, Luxembourg, as well as direct Article 267 references to the Court of Justice (over 40 cases in all). Appeared before both the Legal and Technical Boards of Appeal in the EPO. Extensive experience in copyright and designs (both registered and unregistered, UK and Community). Advised and acted for CIPA (e.g. IP Translator, Case C-307/10), ITMA and AIPPI UK (e.g. R (otao Prudential) v Special Commissioner of Income Tax [2013] UKSC 1). Written two university textbooks: Lecture Notes on Intellectual Property Law and Organic Reaction Mechanisms: A Step-by-Step Approach.
Personal: MA (Natural Sciences) (Cantab.), DPhil (Biophysics) (Oxon.).

EDGE, Andrew
11KBW, London
020 7632 8500
andrew.edge@11kbw.com
Featured in Employment (London)
Practice Areas: Employment law, discrimination and commercial law. Regularly involved in High Court and appellate litigation. Andrew's practice covers all areas of employment law with an emphasis on whistleblowing, discrimination, TUPE, unlawful competitive activity (including springboard injunctions), bonus disputes, garden leave and the use of confidential information.
Professional Memberships: ELA, ELBA, and COMBAR.
Career: Called 2003, Major Scholar, Inner Temple.
Publications: Transfer of Undertakings (Sweet and Maxwell) and Butterworths Employment Law Practice and Procedure.
Personal: Educated at Colston's School Bristol and King's College London. Resides London.

EDGE, Charlotte
5 Stone Buildings, London
020 7242 6201
clerks@5sblaw.com
Featured in Chancery (London), Court of Protection (All Circuits)
Practice Areas: Chancery practice with an emphasis on litigation. Particular interest in contentious trusts and probate, family provision, removal of trustees and personal representatives, construction and rectification claims, Court of Protection work and pensions as well as professional negligence claims arising out of any of her practice areas. Also undertakes a range of non-contentious drafting and advisory work including capital taxes.
Professional Memberships: Chancery Bar Association.
Career: Called 2006.
Publications: Edits the "Powers and Duties of Pension Scheme Trustees" chapter of Tolley's Pensions Law, looseleaf. Writes and speaks regularly on all areas of her practice.

EDWARDS, Anthony
St Philips Chambers, Leeds
0113 244 6691
aedwards@st-philips.com
Featured in Construction (North Eastern)
Practice Areas: Anthony specialises in construction and engineering law. The combination of his legal and technical expertise as a Quantity Surveyor finds Anthony regularly engaged in complex disputes arising from building and engineering activities domestically and internationally. He has extensive experience in heavyweight matters such as power stations, processing plants, petro-chemical, roads, infrastructure, hospitals, dealing with breach of contract, delay & disruption, time extensions, prolongation, payment provisions, acceleration, loss of productivity, final accounts, conflict of laws and negligence actions against professional advisers including architects/engineers and surveyors. He often leads teams of professionals on complex cases. Anthony

regularly acts as both counsel and tribunal in arbitration, adjudication and mediation and often appears in the TCC. Anthony is a Chartered arbitrator and registered adjudicator and mediator on a number of panels and represents clients in ICC arbitrations. He advises clients on both non-contentious and contentious matters.
Professional Memberships: FIDIC, CIArb, LCIA, IChemE, CEDR, TECBAR, TeCSA, CIOB, ICE and ACE.
Career: Date of call: 1999, Middle Temple. Awarded the CIArb's Cedric Barclay Prize for the best International Arbitrators Award Writer of 2005.
Publications: Numerous articles in various law journals.

EDWARDS, Daniel
Dere Street Barristers, York
01904 620 048
d.edwards@derestreet.co.uk
Featured in Personal Injury (North Eastern)
Practice Areas: Dan has a nationwide practice encompassing a variety of complex and catastrophic claims, with a particular emphasis on industrial accidents and industrial disease work.
Professional Memberships: Personal Injury Bar Association.
Career: Called 1993. Recorder (Civil) 2008.
Publications: Charlesworth & Percy on Negligence (13th Edition) 2014. Associate Editor.

EDWARDS, Douglas QC
Francis Taylor Building, London
01992 555 659
clerks@ftb.eu.corr
Featured in Agriculture & Rural Affairs (London), Planning (London)
Practice Areas: Practice involves planning, compulsory purchase environment, administrative and local government, highway law and the law relating to town and village greens. He appears regularly for both appellants and local planning and other authorities at inquiries, in the Lands Tribunal and in the courts. Douglas Edwards planning inquiry practice has engaged a wide range of issues over the last year including major retail schemes, housing development, development of docks and proposed tall buildings. He represented the successful developers of a large retail park near Leeds as well as several large residential developments. He has considerable experience of planning enforcement both at inquiry and in the High Court in the context of injunction applications. He regularly advises and appears in respect of town/village green disputes and has had a number of notable and important successes for landowners in respect of such disputes. He is frequently asked to appear as inspector or to advise registration authorities in respect of these matters. He is regularly instructed by local planning authorities for complex enforcement cases and is noted for handling detailed factual disputes arising under ground (d) appeals and in lawful development certificate matters. He has considerable experience of gypsy and traveller work. Douglas regularly advises and appears in the Lands Tribunal on matters concerning compulsory purchase. He is a member of the Crossrail Panel of Counsel who appears and advises on compensation matters concerning that project. Douglas had been instructed on a number of listed building cases and has developed particular expertise in advising upon, and appearing at, inquiries in relation to enabling development proposals affecting listed buildings and in applying the guidance published by English Heritage concerning that subject. His other areas of specialism include mineral planning (in which he has recently had two notable successes, one for an appellant and one for a mineral planning authority) and also water and riverbank related development. He appeared recently in a controversial inquiry concerning the right to moor vessels temporarily on the River Thames.
Career: Called to Bar: 1992, QC: 2010.

EDWARDS, Heath
9 Park Place, Cardiff
02920 382 731
heath.edwards@9parkplace.co.uk
Featured in Crime (Wales & Chester)
Practice Areas: Crime, Fraud:Criminal, POCA work and asset forfeiture.
Professional Memberships: Criminal Bar Association.
Career: Heath Edwards is a criminal specialist with particular expertise defending and prosecuting large drug, money laundering and white-collar crime cases along with the associated restraint and confiscation proceedings. In recent years, he has defended in an NHS fraud and prosecuted for the Organised Crime Division in association with the Serious Organised Crime Agency (SOCA) and the Special Casework Unit of the CPS. He has also worked with and against the Confiscation Unit (CPS) and the Regional Assets Recovery Team (RART). Heath Edwards also continues to develop an appellate practice regularly being instructed to appear in the Court of Appeal (Criminal Division) for clients following trial or upon later referral after conviction and sentence.
Personal: Heath Edwards was educated at Warwick University and the Inns of Court School of Law. His interests include travelling the world and motorcycling.

EDWARDS, Peter
Devereux, London
020 7353 7534
edwards@devchambers.co.uk
Featured in Employment (London), Personal Injury (London)
Practice Areas: Practices in all areas of employment, discrimination and industrial relations law. Also practices in the field of personal injury and has been able to take full advantage of the increasing overlap between the two areas. Particular specialism in disability cases. Recent reported cases include: Autoclenz v. Belcher (Supreme Court); Rolls Royce v Unite (CA); and Craig v Transocean (Supreme Court). For a full list of reported cases see www.devereuxchambers.co.uk.
Professional Memberships: APIL; PIBA; ELBA; ELA; ILS.
Career: Scott Inquiry 1992-95.
Publications: Tottel Discrimination Law (Sexual Orientation and Religion/Belief); Jordans Employment Law (Whistleblowing); Jordans Employment Law Precedents.
Personal: The musical genius of Dolly Parton.

EKLUND, Graham QC
4 New Square, London
020 7822 2000
g.eklund@4newsquare.com
Featured in Insurance (London), Product Liability (London), Professional Negligence (London), Property Damage (London)
Practice Areas: Professional negligence; Product Liability; Insurance related matters, particularly fraudulent claims, policy construction and coverage issues, fire, explosion and disaster claims, including pollution and contamination. Personal injury, particularly serious injuries (tetraplegic, paraplegic and sports injuries). Reported cases include Jones & Marsh McLennan v Crowley Colosso (1996); Yorkshire Water v Sun Alliance (1996); John Munroe v LFCDA (1997); Chapman v Christopher (1998): Greatorex v Greatorex (2000); Beckett v Midland Electricity (2001); Cornhill Insurance v Stamp Felt Roofing (2002); James v CGU Insurance (2002); Johnson v Technitrack Europa (2003); Scottish & Newcastle v GD Construction (2003); Forrest & Sons v CGU Insurance (2006); Bartoline Ltd v Royal & Sun Alliance Insurance (2007); Meisels v Norwich Union Insurance (2007); Evans v Kosmar Villa Holidays (2007); Perrin v Northampton BC (2007); Kosmar Villa Holidays v Trustees Syndicate 1243 (2008); Harris v Perry (2009); Reilly v NIG (2009); Chubb Fire Ltd v Vicar of Spalding (2010); Seashell v Aviva (2011); Aviva v Brown (2011); Synergy v CGU (2011); Joseph Fielding Properties v Aviva (2011); Sharon's Bakery (Europe) Ltd v Axa (2012); Milton Keynes Borough Council v Nulty & Others (2012); Argos v Leather Trade House (2012); Hughes v Williams (2013); Mueller v Central Roofing (2013).
Professional Memberships: PNBA, PIBA, COMBAR.
Career: BA; LLB (Hons) (Auck). Barrister and Solicitor High Court of NZ; Solicitor Supreme Court of England and Wales (1979-84). Called 1984, Silk 2002.
Personal: Married, two children. Interests include music, theatre, sport.

ELKINGTON, Ben QC
4 New Square, London
020 7822 2000
b.elkington@4newsquare.com
Featured in Commercial Dispute Resolution (London), Insurance (London), Professional Negligence (London), Property Damage (London)
Practice Areas: Ben has a thriving practice centred on insurance, commercial disputes and professional liability. Insurance work involves all forms of coverage disputes (including fraud) and subrogated claims. Commercial work includes domestic and international litigation and arbitration. Professional liability work focuses on claims against insurance brokers, financial advisers, solicitors, barristers, accountants and surveyors. Ben acts for both claimants and defendants in equal measure, which gives him a real advantage when advising his clients and devising strategies to achieve their commercial objectives.
Professional Memberships: COMBAR, PNBA, LCLCBA.
Career: Called 1996 (Top of Bar Finals); Silk 2012. Previously admitted to the New York Bar and practised in New York with Sullivan & Cromwell.
Publications: Editor of Jackson & Powell on Professional Negligence, and Jackson & Powell Professional Liability Precedents.
Personal: Educated at Trinity College, Cambridge (BA, 1st Class Hons in Law 1993; MA 1997), and University of Virginia (LLM 1994). Lives in London with wife and four young children. Spends holidays on the Isle of Mull walking, fishing and playing golf.

ELLENBOGEN, Naomi QC
Littleton Chambers, London
020 7797 8600
ne@littletonchambers.co.uk
Featured in Employment (London)
Practice Areas: Employment, commercial and professional negligence law. In the employment field, deals with a wide range of employment litigation in courts, tribunals and mediation. Principal areas of court work include claims arising during the currency and on termination of the employment relationship, in particular: injunctions; misuse of confidential information; restrictive covenants and garden leave clauses; breaches of contract and fiduciary duty; bonus entitlements. Tribunal work (for claimants and respondents) includes all forms of discrimination (including equal pay claims); transfer of undertakings; whistleblowing; redundancy. Regularly appears in appellate courts and tribunals. Particular expertise in complex, sensitive discrimination claims. Provides representation in internal and professional disciplinary hearings. Conducts internal hearings in disciplinary matters. Experienced accredited mediator. Also provides representation in mediation. Lectures on substantive and procedural law in all specialist areas of practice. Reported cases include ESL Fuels Ltd v Fletcher & An'r [2013] EWHC 3726 (Ch): injunction to prevent the Defendant from trading, allegedly through misuse of a trade secret, refused; numerous appearances from 2008 onwards in the Court of Appeal and EAT addressing test issues in mass equal pay litigation across the country, e.g. North Cumbria University Hospitals NHS Trust v Fox & Potter (Fox Nos. 1 and 2 and Potter Nos. 1 to 3) and Hurst v Suffolk Mental Health Partnership NHS Trust [2009] IRLR 452 (CA). Other cases include: Macaulay & Others v Newham London Borough Council LTL 17/02/2012 (QBD): injunctive relief ending the suspension of five senior teachers refused; Koskinen v Health Professions Council & The Privy Council [2005] EWCA Civ 363 (CA): qualifying bodies and discrimination; LC Services Limited & Others v Brown & Kinesis Solutions Limited LTL 22/12/2003 (QBD): speedy trial following injunctive relief for breaches of fiduciary duty and misuse of confidential information; Dave v Robinska [2003] ICR 1248 (EAT): sex discrimination and partnerships; MITIE Managed Services Limited v French & Others [2002] IRLR 512 (EAT): TUPE – transferee's duty to provide benefit of substantial equivalence; Symbian Limited v Christensen [2001] IRLR 77 (CA): restrictive covenants, garden leave, breach of confidence; Camelot Group Plc. v Centaur Communications Limited [1998] IRLR 80 (CA): whistleblowing, breach of confidence, public interest in disclosure of the source of leaked information; Bradford & Bingley Building Society v Hatchwell & Draper [1997] EWCA 877 (CA): professional negligence, criteria for grant of permission to adduce expert evidence out of time; Sheffield v Pickfords Limited & An'r [1997] 16 Tr L 337 (CA): requirement to plead reasonableness of exclusion clause.
Professional Memberships: ELBA, COMBAR, PNBA, TECBAR.
Career: Called 1992 (Gray's Inn). Accredited mediator 2006. Appointed Queen's Counsel 2010. Barrister Vice-Chairman, Professional Conduct Committee of the Bar Standards Board 2011. Joint Head of Lit-

tleton Chambers 2014. Bencher of Gray's Inn 2014. Member of faculty, annual Advanced International Advocacy Course at Keble College, Oxford, promoting excellence in trial advocacy. Member of the Training & Accreditation Committee of the Advocacy Training Council.
Publications: General Editor, Butterworths Employment Law: Practice, Procedure & Precedents, Fifth Edition.
Personal: MA (Hons) Oxon. in Jurisprudence. Interests include sailing, travel, music and theatre.

ELLIOTT, Sarah QC
Doughty Street Chambers, London
020 7404 1313
s.elliot@doughtystreet.co.uk
Featured in Crime (London)
Practice Areas: Sarah Elliott QC took silk in 2014 at 17 years call after a highly successfully practice as a leading junior defending serious crime. She is recommended in both Chambers & Partners and the Legal 500. She has been described by solicitors as 'on the most wanted listed for heavyweight crime'; 'leaving clients reassured by her manner and juries persuaded by her arguments' ; and 'particularly adept at tricky mitigation matters'.
Career: Sarah has a proven track record in achieving successful outcomes for clients in complex, difficult and unusual cases involving homicides, multiple rape and other serious sexual offences including historic allegations, drug importations and supply, financial crime and money laundering, and in criminal appeals. She has been instructed in many high profile cases including (in 2014) the prosecution of trainee barrister Rhiannon Brooker for false allegations of rape; both prosecutions arising out of Operation Aeroscope (undercover police officer Mark Kennedy cases); Brian Dodgeon, university lecturer in possession of ecstasy taken by teenager who died; Gary Weddell, the Metropolitan police inspector who killed himself and his mother in-law whilst on bail for the alleged murder of his wife; and the trial of the leaders of SHAC, the campaign against Huntingdon Life Sciences.

ELLIOTT, Steven
One Essex Court, London
020 7583 2000
selliott@oeclaw.co.uk
Featured in Commercial Dispute Resolution (London), Fraud (London)
Practice Areas: Steven Elliott has a general commercial practice encompassing amongst others civil fraud including asset tracing and freezing, banking and financial services, company matters, restitution of tax, jurisdiction challenges and professional negligence. He has particular experience of handling large and complex commercial, financial and fraud matters, often spanning more than one jurisdiction. Steven regularly practices with and without a leader before all divisions of the the English superior courts, in arbitral matters, and in proceedings in other common law jurisdictions.
Career: Called to the Bar of the Eastern Caribbean (British Virgin Islands) (2007); Called to the Bar of England and Wales (2001); Judicial Assistant to the Lord Chief Justice (2000); Lecturer at St Catherine's College, Oxford (1998-2000); Called to the Bar of British Columbia (1997); Articles at Davis & Company, Vancouver (1996-97); Law Clerk to the British Columbia Court of Appeal (1995-96).
Publications: The Law of Rescission (2nd edn OUP 2014)(co-author); Snell's Equity (33rd edn Sweet & Maxwell 2014)(contributing editor); Restatement of the English Law of Unjust Enrichment (OUP 2012)(advisory committee); Restitution of Overpaid Tax (Hart 2013)(editor); and many articles on commercial and banking topics.
Personal: University of Oxford (Merton), DPhil; University of Toronto, JD Hons; Queen's University (Ontario), BA Hons. Lives in London.

ELLIOTT, Timothy QC
Keating Chambers, London
020 7544 2600
telliott@keatingchambers.com
Featured in Construction (London)
Practice Areas: Specialist in construction, engineering, energy and professional negligence work in those and related fields. Has been recognised for excellent advocacy skills ("renowned for skilfully demolishing the opposition whilst remaining a gentleman at all times") and his hands on approach to cases which has made him a popular choice with UK and overseas clients who include local and national governments, public authorities, developers, funding institutions, national and international contractors and sub-contractors, architects, surveyors and engineers. He has been involved in numerous reported cases. He now acts increasingly as arbitrator (both domestically and internationally), adjudicator and mediator.
Professional Memberships: Technology and Construction Bar Association (TECBAR); Commercial Bar Association (COMBAR); Society of Construction Law.
Career: Called 1975; Queen's Counsel 1992; ICC Arbitration Panel; LCIA Arbitration Panel; Law Society Panel of Arbitrators; HKIAC Panel of Arbitrators; KLRCA Panel of Arbitrators; CEDR Accredited Mediator; TECBAR accredited adjudicator.
Publications: Regular Legal Columnist for Building Magazine.

ELLIS, Nick QC
Westwater Advocates, Edinburgh
0131 226 2881
nick.ellis@westwateradvocates.com
Featured in Construction (Scotland), Commercial Dispute Resolution (Scotland)
Practice Areas: Civil Practice with particular expertise in contract and commercial law, personal injury and judicial review. Acted in the following cases: contract/commercial - Blyth & Blyth v Carillion, 2002 SLT 961; CSC Braehead v Laing O'Rourke, 2008 SLT 697; ANM Group v Gilcomston North, 2008 SLT 835; Wishart v Castlecroft 2009 SLT 812; Scottish Widows v Kershaw and Others 2010 SLT 1102; Luminar Lava v Mama Group 2010 SC 310; Apollo Engineering v James Scott 2012 SC 282 [2013] UKSC 37; Buchanan v Nolan [2013] CSIH 38. Personal injury - Mackie v AB2000, 2004 SC 334; Donaldson v Hays Distribution, 2005 SC 523; Matthews v Glasgow City Council, 2006 SC 349; Phee v Niddrie Castle Golf Club [2013] CSIH 18; Chinn v Cyclacel 2013 SLT 278. Judicial Review - Watt v Strathclyde Regional Council, 1992 SLT 324; Lloyds Pharmacy v National Appeal Panel, 2004 SC 703; Scotbeef Ltd v Palermo, 2006 SC 1; Apollo Engineering v James Scott, 2009 SC 525; Cooper v Forth Ports plc 2011 SLT 711.
Professional Memberships: Standing Junior Counsel to the Scottish Office / Ministers 1997-2002.
Career: Qualified solicitor 1981-89; Partner, commercial firm 1985-89; Called to the Bar in 1990; Took Silk in 2002.
Personal: Educated at the Royal High School in Edinburgh, LLB Edinburgh University 1979.

ELLIS, Peter
7BR, London
020 7242 3555
clerks@7br.co.uk
Featured in Clinical Negligence (London)
Practice Areas: Clinical negligence; personal injury; product liability; coroners' inquests.
Professional Memberships: Professional Negligence & Personal Injuries Bar Associations. Medico-Legal Society.Inquest Lawyers' Group. Faculty of Forensic & Legal Medicine, Royal College of Physicians of London. Centre for Dispute Resolution, Exchange Group. Society of Doctors in Law. Worshipful Society of Apothecaries. Coroners' Society of England & Wales.
Career: Former hospital doctor (MB. BS 1984, MRCP(UK) 1990). Former solicitor specialising in product liability and healthcare litigation at DAC Beachcroft LLP, London (Diploma in Law 1991, Solicitors' Final Examination 1992). Called to the Bar 1997 (Middle Temple). Qualified mediator (CEDR, 2000). Assistant Coroner, Outer London (South) (2000-08); Outer London (West) (2009 to date).
Publications: Author and editor of clinical negligence chapter in Butterworths' Personal Injury Litigation Service. Co-author of the Work Related Injury & Illness Litigation Handbook (XPL Publishing), winner 2004 Royal Society of Medicine/Society of Authors' Minty Prize, best medico-legal book.
Personal: Resides in London. Education: Royal Hospital School, Holbrook, Suffolk; St Mary's Hospital Medical School, London University. Interests: rugby, skiing, music, English literature, naval and military history.

ELLISON, Mark QC
QEB Hollis Whiteman, London
020 7933 8855
mark.ellison@qebhw.co.uk
Featured in Crime (London), Financial Crime (London)
Practice Areas: As First Senior Treasury Counsel, Head of Chambers Mark Ellison QC gained valuable experience in high profile terrorism, serious fraud and terrorist funding, official secrets, serious crime, corruption and public law cases. He now mixes private and public work across fraud, regulatory and criminal law. Mark carried out the independent review of undercover policing and possible police corruption connected to the Stephen Lawrence case. He recently represented Bruce Hall in the Alba Bahrain $40m corruption prosecution brought by the SFO; advised the CPS in connection with 'Plebgate; advised BP regarding the In Amenas inquest; acted for the prosecution in the murder of Stephen Lawrence; acted in the judicial review brought by the Tchenguiz brothers against the SFO; advised Google concerning Street View; defended in 'Marine Hose', the first OFT cartel prosecution under the Enterprise Act 2002; advised the Home Office in relation to the possible admission of intercepted communications as evidence; and has given public, international and domestic law advice relating to the alleged illegality of the Iraq war.
Professional Memberships: Public Access Bar Association; registered with the Bar Council - Public Access Directory.
Career: 2010 SFO Approved Counsel List; 2010 Deputy High Court Judge; 2006-2008 First Senior Treasury Counsel.
Personal: Silk 2008, call 1979; LLB (University of Wales).

ELVIDGE, John QC
Dere Street Barristers, York
0191 232 0541
j.elvidgeqc@derestreet.co.uk
Featured in Crime (North Eastern)
Practice Areas: Homicide: including multiple deaths, patricide, matricide and fratricide; causation issues – legal, factual and medical (e.g. alleged non accidental head injury leading to infant death); joint enterprise / secondary liability; killing by children and young people; partial defences of diminished responsibility and loss of control; gross negligence manslaughter. Organised crime: homicide; blackmail and kidnapping; conspiracies - fraud against financial institutions and insurance companies, supplying controlled drugs and medicines, money laundering; sexual offences against children; applications for trial by judge alone, by protected jury and for witness anonymity orders. Serious sexual offences: complaints against professionals; familial abuse; delayed complaints. Regulatory work, professional and police disciplinary hearings, licensing and high value personal injury claims.
Professional Memberships: Criminal Bar Association; North Eastern Circuit; Gray's Inn.
Career: 1988, called to the Bar; 2010, Queen's Counsel; pupillage at 2 Harcourt Buildings, Temple and its annex in York; from 1990, York Chambers; 2011, succeeded Gilbert Gray QC as head of chambers; 2011, head of Dere Street Barristers on merger of York and Broad Chare Chambers, Newcastle upon Tyne; 2014, Leader of the North Eastern Circuit.

EMANUEL, Mark
29 Bedford Row Chambers, London
020 7404 1044
memanuel@29br.co.uk
Featured in Family/Matrimonial (London)
Practice Areas: All areas of Family Law with particular expertise in high net worth financial remedy cases and private law children act matters. Reported cases include: M v M (Third Party Subpoena: Financial Conduct) [2006] 2 FLR 1253; Charalambous v Charalmabous [2004] 2 FLR 1093; M V M (Financial Relief: Substantial Earning Capacity) [2004] 2 FLR 236; Ganeshmoorthy v Ganeshmoorthy (ancillary relief: abuse of process) [2003] 3 FCR 167; Re A (children: shared residence) [2002] 1 FCR 177.
Professional Memberships: FLBA. The Association of District Judges.
Career: Called to the Bar 1985; Inner Temple. Deputy District Judge (County Court) 2000. Trained in collaborative law.
Personal: Educated at Stowe School. Trent Polytechnic; BA Law. Married with five children.

EMMERSON, Heather
11KBW, London
020 7632 8500
heather.emmerson@11kbw.com
Featured in Administrative & Public Law (London)
Practice Areas: Administrative and public law, human rights, local government, regulatory and information law. Heather is regularly instructed in high-profile and leading public law cases, including in 2014 the cases of (i) Stirling v London Borough of Haringey (an appeal heard by the Supreme Court in June 2014 relating to the law of consultation), (ii) Plantagenet Alliance Ltd v Secretary of State and others [2014] EWHC 1662 (Admin) (a judicial review claim heard by the Divisional Court concerning the burial of King Richard III in Leicester) and (iii) Francis v Secretary of State for Home Department [2014] EWCA Civ 718 (an appeal heard by the Court of Appeal relating to the Secretary of State's powers to detain foreign national prisoners and the scope of the tort of false imprisonment).
Professional Memberships: Administrative Law Bar Association, Association of Regulatory & Disciplinary Lawyers.
Career: Called to the Bar in 2009. Member of the Attorney General's C Panel of Counsel.
Publications: Contributor to Local Government Lawyer and Education and the Courts (McManus, 3rd edition).
Personal: Graduated from St Catharine's College, Cambridge with a First Class degree in Law.

ENGELMAN, Mark
Hardwicke, London
020 7691 0056
mark.engelman@hardwicke.co.uk
Featured in Intellectual Property (London)
Practice Areas: Mark Engelman has acted in numerous high profile cases: Adrian Jacobs against JK Rowling and Bloomsbury Publishing Plc for non-textual copyright infringement in the Harry Potter series; against Intel in the ECJ, defining the principle of trade mark dilution for Europe, and against Nanging Automobile Corporation over the rights to the badge MG on motor cars. Mark is praised for his encyclopaedic knowledge of the law and is incredibly commercial. He is also annually listed as one of the leading trade mark experts. He is author of Engelman's Intellectual Property Updates.
Professional Memberships: Mark was appointed to the Bench of Gray's Inn in 2009 and is a member of the Bar Council.
Career: Mark's experience comes from running businesses, having been the sole in-house counsel to Dunlop Slazenger and Head of IP for The Body Shop International Plc before joining Hardwicke. He is and has been standing counsel for a number of floated multi-national companies and SMEs, including as non-executive director of Alexander McQueen's haute couture operation as well as Specsavers, Monsoon and Oxford Brookes University to name a few. He also acts in international arbitrations.

ENGLAND, William
Carmelite Chambers, London
020 7936 6300
clerks@carmelitechambers.co.uk
Featured in Crime (London)
Practice Areas: A specialist-leading advocate with extensive experience in serious organised crime, including corporate fraud and market abuse. He also practices in both the regulatory fields and public inquiries. In matters of health and safety he has represented defendants in cases involving gross negligence manslaughter, and corporate manslaughter. He appeared for a core participant in the Baha Mousa Public Inquiry, chaired by Sir William Gage – an inquiry of national importance into the death of an Iraqi whilst in custody, and in the leading case of the successful defence of senior members of the Warwickshire Fire and Rescue Service for gross negligence manslaughter. He is a consultant at Prospect Law, (Winner of the Law Firm of the Year 2012, Business Green Leaders Awards). He advises corporate and individual clients on investigations into market manipulation, serious fraud, money laundering, and corruption. He also advises on restraint orders and asset recovery, and is recently instructed in cases in the US and Ukraine involving alleged fraud. He advises the FCA on legal professional privilege in relation to insider trading and improper disclosure. He has further represented clients in a number of other jurisdictions including Belize, Cyprus, Germany, Iraq, Kuwait, Afghanistan and Africa. He regularly appears in the Court of Appeal, including Attorney General's references and the Divisional Court.
Professional Memberships: He is a member of the CBA, FSLA, ARDL, AMCA and the CLBM.

EPSTEIN, Paul QC
Cloisters, London
020 7827 4012
pje@cloisters.com
Featured in Employment (London)
Practice Areas: Employment, discrimination, human rights and commercial: Paul has for many years been recognised as a leading employment and discrimination law specialist. He also specialises in commercial work. Paul combines an analytical approach with pragmatism and commercial acumen. Clients appreciate his willingness to work as part of a team, and his persuasiveness, clarity and forensic skills. He has worked for top 10 UK law firms, trade unions, public bodies, the EHRC and financial services institutions, as well as globally known rock and pop legends. Paul's recent work has been in the financial, insurance, banking, healthcare, local authority, charitable, legal, hospitality and education sectors. He has been instructed in some of Europe's largest ever equal pay cases, and some of the UK's leading discrimination cases. In the past year he has helped resolve problems involving direct and indirect discrimination, restrictive covenants, garden leave, partnership disputes, commercial contractual disputes, and privacy and anonymity orders. Recent Reported Cases: AB v Ministry of Justice [2014] All ER (D) 14 concerned with data protection and anonymity. Abdulla v Birmingham City Council [2012] ICR 1419 (SC); jurisdiction of the courts to entertain equal pay claims. Cordell v Foreign and Commonwealth Office [2012] ICR 280 (EAT); funded by EHRC, direct disability discrimination, reasonable adjustments, cost of adjustments. Lord Ashcroft v Foley and Ors [2012] EWCA Civ 423; [2011] EMLR 30 (HC); defamation claim by Lord Ashcroft against owner of Independent newspaper, editor and journalist over articles about Turks and Caicos. Joseph v Spiller [2010] ICR 642, [2010] EMLR 7 (CA); defamation case also raising employment agency arguments (in the Supreme Court now the leading case on honest comment). Re Al Mal Bank LLC, and Nazim Omara August 2010; case in the Qatar Financial Centre Civil and Commercial Court; concerning liquidation of bank (related judgment, No. 04/10, viewable at http://www.qfccourt.com/Judgement.php). Amnesty International v Ahmed [2009] ICR 1450, [2009] IRLR 884; a leading case on direct discrimination.
Professional Memberships: Chair, Employment Law Bar Association 2009-11; elected member ELA management committee 2012; elected Bencher, Middle Temple 2012; member ILS, ALBA.
Career: Balliol College, Oxford, History and Modern Languages, First, Exhibitioner. City University, Diploma in Law, Distinction. Visiting Lecturer, City University, 1988-90. Middle Temple Harmsworth Scholarship.
Publications: Tolley's Working Time; Bullen & Leake & Jacob's Precedents of Pleading; Butterworths Employment Law Guide; IRS Eclipse Competencies. Paul lectures widely, for bodies such as ELA, JUSTICE, the EU's judicial training college in Trier, Germany; he has lectured in France and the Netherlands, and has for many years been an advocacy trainer for Middle Temple.

ETHERINGTON, David QC
Red Lion Chambers, London
020 7520 6000
david.etherington@18rlc.co.uk
Featured in Crime (London), Financial Crime (London)
Practice Areas: Fraud and serious organised crime. David has always maintained a split between fraud work and serious organised crime and is an acknowledged leader in both fields. In 2013-2014 he successfully defended, leading Dafna Spiro, in the Canning Town Murder (in which a well known football agent was also a defendant) at the Bailey. He defended in a major immigration fraud at Canterbury Crown Court leading Umar Azmeh and in the Body on the Beach Murder case at Maidstone Crown Court. Other work included the successful defence both of historic sex abuse claims and death by driving cases at London Crown Courts. David has further murder cases and a major currency fraud trial coming up soon as well as cases in the Court of Appeal and the Supreme Court. David always enjoys travelling throughout England and Wales and, in 2013 and 2014, his cases have been located in both Kent and London.
Professional Memberships: Former Chairman of the Professional Conduct & Complaints Committee, Legal Services Committee and Professional Practice Committee of the Bar Council. Current Member of the South-Eastern Circuit, the Criminal Bar Association and the Ecclesiastical Judges' Association.
Career: Called to the Bar, 1979 (Middle Temple); Queen's Counsel, 1998; Recorder of the Crown Court, 2000; Bencher, Middle Temple, 2005; Head of Chambers, 2005-2012; Legal Assessor, General Dental Council; Chancellor, Diocese of Ipswich & St Edmundsbury (2009-), Deputy Chancellor, Diocese of Ely (2012-). David has had a long connection with film and television media advising on Kavanagh QC, Judge John Deed, The Jury and many other programmes and films.

ETIEBET, Peggy
Cornerstone Barristers, London
020 7242 4986
peggye@cornerstonebarristers.com
Featured in Social Housing (London)
Practice Areas: Social Housing, Administrative and Public Law, Community Care, Court of Protection, Local Government, Property.
Professional Memberships: Social Housing Law Association, Administrative Law Bar Association.
Career: Called to the Bar in 2001. Educated at Downing College Cambridge (MA). Peggy's strong practice in Social Housing is complemented by her expertise in the Administrative Court, principally for Community Care, and the Court of Protection. She is well known for her work involving the scope of local authorities' duties to unaccompanied minors and has appeared in the Supreme Court twice on these issues. She is regularly instructed by local authorities on a wide range of areas including homelessness, landlord and tenant, welfare disputes in adult and children social services, care disputes relating to those who lack capacity, disputes over cuts to services, issues regarding benefits and services owed to non-UK citizens and the scope of public sector equality duties. Peggy also has a thriving practice in property law - instructed by both local authority and corporate landlords in property and service charge disputes.
Personal: Peggy played water polo for Great Britain in 2013/14. She now coaches and does yoga instead.

EVANS, Andrew
St Philips Chambers, Birmingham
0121 246 7000
aevans@st-philips.com
Featured in Clinical Negligence (Midlands), Licensing (Midlands)
Practice Areas: Andrew's practice concentrates on clinical negligence, personal injury and licensing work. Clinical Negligence: cosmetic surgery; brain injury; urology; cardiology; paediatrics; oncology; gynaecology; general practice; orthopaedics; spinal surgery; dermatology; ophthalmology; general surgery; and nursing. Andrew's clinical negligence practice continues to expand each year and he is willing to accept instructions nationwide. Personal Injury: fatal accidents; industrial disease; accidents at work; road traffic accidents; low velocity impact; and personal injury fraud. Licensing: Andrew regularly appears before local authorities, the Magistrates' Court, Crown Court and Administrative Court in licensing matters. He receives instructions in matters relating to the Licensing Act 2003 (as amended) from major pub, hotel and sex establishment venue operators and local authorities across England and Wales. Andrew also accepts instructions in taxi licensing cases. Andrew is willing to provide training in all of his areas of expertise.
Professional Memberships: Member of PIBA, AvMA, IoL.
Career: Called 2000 (Lincoln's Inn) Hardwicke Scholar.
Personal: Dr.Challoner's Grammar School Amersham and University of Birmingham. Involved in historic motor sport, running, dismantling and attempting to re-assemble vintage and classic cars. Enjoys rugby and cricket.

EVANS, Catrin
One Brick Court, London
020 7353 8845
ce@onebrickcourt.com
Featured in Data Protection (London), Defamation/Privacy (London)
Practice Areas: Defamation, privacy, breach of confidence, harassment, contempt, reporting restrictions, data protection, FOIA, related media and human rights law. Recent cases of interest: Hegglin v Google Inc (2014) (DPA, libel); Rowland v Mitchell (2014) (libel); Weller v Associated Newspapers (2014) (privacy); Karpov v Browder (2013) (libel), Tamiz v Google Inc [2013] EMLR 14 (libel/internet), Bento v Bedfordshire Police (2012) (libel trial), Tesla Motors v BBC (2013) EWCA Civ 152; (malicious falsehood), Thornton v Telegraph Media Group (2011) (libel), Metropolitan Schools v Google Inc (2009) (libel), AG v Random House (2009) (contempt), Dept for Culture v Information Commissioner (2009) (FOIA), Haw v City of Westminster Mags Court (2007) (contempt), Lord Browne v Associated Newspapers (2007) (privacy), Cream Holdings v Banerjee (2005) (confidence/HRA), Campbell v MGN Ltd (2004) (privacy).
Career: Called to the Bar 1994.
Publications: Author, Atkins Court Forms title on 'Confidence, Privacy and Data Protection' (2002).

EVANS, Helen
4 New Square, London
020 7822 2000
hm.evans@4newsquare.com
Featured in Professional Negligence (London)
Practice Areas: Principal areas of practice are professional liability, general commercial, insurance (including policy and coverage) and property-related work. Helen's professional negligence practice focuses on solicitors, barristers, accountants, insurance brokers/agents, IFAs, surveyors and valuers (and includes substantial fraud claims). Helen is experienced in multi-party and group litigation. Notable cases include the TAG and CLE litigation, including Axa Insurance v Akther & Darby [2010] 1 WLR 1622.
Professional Memberships: PNBA, Chancery Bar Association, COMBAR, LCLBA. Member of Management Committee of PILARS and Member of Pro Bono Committee of Chancery Bar Association.
Career: Called to the Bar in 2001. Sits as Deputy District Judge.
Publications: Co-author of several articles (with Sue Carr QC) published in Tottel's Professional Negligence.
Personal: Born 1977. Educated at Redland High School for Girls, New College Oxford and Université d'Aix Marseille III, France. Lives London.

EVANS, Hugh
4 New Square, London
020 7822 2000
h.evans@4newsquare.com
Featured in Professional Negligence (London)
Practice Areas: Principal area of practice is Professional Negligence, in particular lawyers and financial professionals. Lawyers' liability claims include in particular: (1) defective business agreements especially those with a chancery flavour (e.g. Youlton v Charles Russell (2010), Fulham Leisure Holdings v Nicholson Graham Jones (2006), Mischcon de Reya v Barrett (2006)); (2) lost or bungled litigation of all types, including clinical negligence and personal injury claims (e.g. Miller v Garton Shires (2007)); (3) lenders claims and conveyancing (e.g. Boycott v Perrins Guy Williams (2011)); and (4) claims involving fraud, insurance and partnership issues (e.g. UCB v Soni (2011 and 2013), Goldsmith Williams v Travelers (2010), JD Wetherspoons v Van de Berg (2009), JD Wetherspoons v Jason Harris (2013)). Surveyors' claims include Paratus v Countrywide (2011). Also practises in Insurance (both in relation to professionals, and generally), clinical negligence and personal injury.
Professional Memberships: PNBA, COMBAR, ChBA.
Career: MA (Cantab), BCL (Oxon). Called to the bar 1987, in practice at these chambers from 1988.
Publications: An editor of Jackson and Powell on Professional Liability since 1992 and continuing, in particular of the solicitors' chapter; author of "Lawyers' Liabilities", 2nd edn 2002; numerous articles.

EVANS, Lee
Farrar's Building, London
020 7583 9241
levans@farrarsbuilding.co.uk
Featured in Personal Injury (London)
Practice Areas: Specialist personal injury practitioner, with particular emphasis in brain injury, spinal injury and amputation cases. Work includes workplace accident cases, road traffic accident cases and industrial disease cases.
Professional Memberships: Gray's Inn. Member of the General Council of the Bar's Summary Procedure Disciplinary Tribunal, the Inns of Court Disciplinary Tribunal and the General Council of the Bar's International Relations Committee. Grade A Advocacy teacher. Member of Gray's Inn's Education Committee. PIBA.
Career: Called to the Bar in 1996; Gray's Inn.
Publications: Contributor to editions of The Personal Injury Handbook, Kemp and Kemp and Munkman on Employers' Liability.
Personal: Married with three daughters. Interests include football, walking at the west coast of Scotland, fishing and southern Africa. Trustee of the Canon Collins Educational Trust for Southern Africa.

EVANS, Martin
The Chambers of Andrew Mitchell QC, London
020 7440 9950
me@33cllaw.com
Featured in POCA Work & Asset Forfeiture (All Circuits)
Practice Areas: Specialises in all aspects of the law relating to criminal and civil asset recovery and confiscation. Acts for prosecuting authorities, defendants and third parties in both civil and criminal matters. Experienced in handling restraint (including the restraint of UK assets pursuant to external requests), receivership and contempt proceedings in the Crown Court, the High Court (Administrative Court, Chancery Division and Family Division), Court of Appeal and Supreme Court. Particular interests include fraud, money laundering and corporate criminal liability on which he has written and lectured widely. Recently represented the Receiver in Barnes v Eastenders UKSC [2014] 26.
Professional Memberships: Proceeds of Crime Lawyers' Association.
Career: Called to Bar in 1989.
Publications: 'Corporate Criminal Liability' (co-author) Third Edition May 2013; 'Archbold' (contributing editor); 'Confiscation and the Proceeds of Crime' (contributing editor); 'Abuse of Process in Criminal Proceedings' (contributor).

EVANS, Philip
QEB Hollis Whiteman, London
020 7933 8855
barristers@qebhw.co.uk
Featured in Crime (London)
Practice Areas: Philip Evans has expertise in serious and complex crime and regulation, prosecuting and defending in high-profile criminal matters as both leader and junior. He successfully prosecuted in R v Ali Dizaei (the Metropolitan Police Commander convicted of perverting the course of justice). He defended Levi Bellfield at his five-month trial for multiple murders and attempted murders, and acted in R v Hutchinson-Foster, the case involving the man who supplied the gun sparking the London riots in 2011. He advises corporates and individuals on civil and criminal fraud, potential criminal liability, confiscation, compensation and related areas, including advising in a major criminal trial ongoing in India. A former national league rugby player, Philip has a prolific sports law practice, particularly regarding rugby, cricket and horse racing. He defended a Pakistani cricketer involved in match-fixing allegations and sits as a chairman on the RFU disciplinary panels. He regularly advises and acts on behalf of the Gambling Commission before its regulatory panel.
Professional Memberships: Criminal Bar Association, Association of Regulatory & Disciplinary Lawyers, British Association for Sport and Law, Public Access Bar Association, registered with the Bar Council – Public Access Directory.
Career: National Legal Advisor to the Innocence Network UK.
Personal: Call 1995. LLB (Hons) (University of Wales); MA (Southampton).

EVANS, Robert
Keating Chambers, London
020 7544 2600
revans@keatingchambers.com
Featured in Construction (London), Mediators (All Circuits)
Practice Areas: Specialist in construction, engineering and energy disputes and professional negligence work in the UK and abroad. Practice covers a wide variety of advisory work, drafting and advocacy, in the High Court and in arbitration. Acted for national and local governments, public authorities, contractors, sub-contractors, consultants, architects and engineers. Experience includes major defects claims arising out of design and build motorway contract; ICC arbitration over defects in container terminal; an arbitration in Mexico relating to a petrochemical plant and represented a major government department in an arbitration arising out of a long running dispute over a 25 year PFI contract.
Professional Memberships: Fellow of the Institution of Civil Engineers; Member of the Hong Kong Institution of Engineers; Fellow of the Chartered Institute of Arbitrators; Technology and Construction Bar Association (TECBAR); Commercial Bar Association (COMBAR); Society of Construction Law (Council Member); Member of the Institution of Civil Engineers and Engineer's Ireland Panels of Arbitrators, CEDR Accredited Mediator.
Career: Chartered civil engineer working for consultants and contractors in the UK and overseas (1981-89); Called to the Bar 1989.
Publications: Contributor, Keating on Construction Contracts Ninth Edition (2012); contributor, Keating on NEC3 2012; author of chapter on Mediation - Engineers Dispute Resolution Handbook 1st (2006) and 2nd (2011) editions.

EVANS, Stephen
Five Paper, London
020 7815 3200
stephenevans@fivepaper.com
Featured in Social Housing (London)
Practice Areas: Social housing, landlord and tenant, disability discrimination, administrative, local government, real property.
Professional Memberships: SHLA.
Career: Called 1992. Head of Property Practice Team. Represents landlords (particularly local authorities and registered providers) and tenants. Well-known for claims involving discrimination, dilapidations or medical vulnerability. Counsel for the local authority in LB Lewisham v Malcolm from County Court to House of Lords (disability discrimination). Notable other appellate decisions: IAM Group v Chowdrey (adverse possession), Church Commissioners v Meya (section 21 notices), LB Newham v Jones (ASBIs), Stroh v LB Haringey (occupiers' liability). Lane v RBKC [2013] EWHC 1320 (disability discrimination/Article 8). Also R(Bibi) v Camden LBC (allocations). Regular platform speaker at annual conferences and seminars.
Publications: Articles on the Equality Act entitled, Complete renovation or papering over the cracks? (guardian.co.uk) and The turning of the tide? (Property Law Journal). Co-author of legal chapter to RICS book 'Diagnosing Damp'. Contributor to 2010 College of Law DVD on overage claims.
Personal: MA (Cantab). Christ's College, Cambridge.

EWART, David QC
Pump Court Tax Chambers, London
020 7414 8080
clerks@pumptax.com
Featured in Tax (London)
Practice Areas: David Ewart Barrister specialises in all areas of Revenue Law including trusts and professional negligence. Cases include: BMBF v Mawson (House of Lords); Scottish Provident Institution v HMRC (House of Lords); Dr Beynon & Ors v HMRC (House of Lords); Trennery & ors v West (House of Lords); Deutsche Morgan Grenfell Group v HMRC (House of Lords); Marks & Spencer Plc v Halsey (ECJ); NEC Semi-Conductors v HMRC (House of Lords); Prizedome Ltd & Limitgood Ltd v HMRC (Court of Appeal); Pirelli Cable Holdings Ltd v HMRC (House of Lords); Vodafone 2 v HMRC (Court of Appeal); Mayes v HMRC (Court of Appeal); Philips Electronics v HMRC (Upper Tribunal); Astall & Edwards v HMRC (Court of Appeal); Bayfine v HMRC (Court of Appeal); Thincap GLO (Court of Appeal); FII GLO (Supreme Court); CFC GLO (High Court); Marks & Spencer v HMRC (Supreme Court); Anson v HMRC (Court of Appeal); AC v DC (Family Division); MJP Media v HMRC

(Court of Appeal); Lloyds TSB Equipment Leasing v HMRC (Court of Appeal); Chappell v HMRC (Upper Tribunal); Barnes v HMRC (Court of Appeal); EC Commission v UK (CJEU); Reed Employment Plc. V HMRC (Upper Tribunal); Prudential v HMRC (High Court).
Professional Memberships: Revenue Bar Association; Chancery Bar Association.
Career: Called 1987, Grays Inn. QC (2006).
Personal: Bridge, Golf.

EWINS, James
Queen Elizabeth Building, London
020 7797 7837
j.ewins@qeb.co.uk
Featured in Family/Matrimonial (London)
Practice Areas: James is an exceptionally talented senior junior with strong numeracy and client skills. His analytical prowess in legal and financial aspects of his work combined with an excellent bedside manner makes him a very popular choice. He is rated for his excellent grasp of complex domestic and international ancillary relief work. He has been described as exceptionally well-prepared and a superb negotiator and advocate. He typically conducts mid to high level financial remedy work, including at an appellate level, and is regularly pitched against other senior juniors and silks both in London and elsewhere.
Professional Memberships: He is a member of the FLBA.
Career: James read Jurisprudence at New College, Oxford.
Personal: Married, with four children; a keen sailor, skier and tennis player, with a couple of marathons under his belt; committed Christian with a personal interest and involvement in modern anti-slavery and human trafficking campaigns, having worked with bonded labourers in India for International Justice Mission during a sabbatical in 2009-1; specialist advisor to the Joint Select Committee on the Modern Slavery Bill (2014).

EYRE, Stephen
St Philips Chambers, Birmingham
0121 246 7000
seyre@st-philips.com
Featured in Chancery (Midlands), Commercial Dispute Resolution (Midlands), Real Estate Litigation (Midlands), Restructuring/Insolvency (Midlands)
Practice Areas: Commercial litigation, commercial property, chancery, contentious probate, insolvency/corporate recovery, and mediation in those fields.
Professional Memberships: Midlands Chancery and Commercial Bar Association. COMBAR. Ecclesiastical Judges Association. Chancery Bar Association.
Career: BA Jurisprudence (Oxon 1st Class 1979); BCL (1980); LLM (Cardiff 2010); called to Bar 1981; Recorder (2005); Tribunal Judge (Mental Health); Chancellor: Diocese of Coventry; Chancellor: Diocese of Lichfield; formerly Deputy Chancellor: Diocese of Southwell & Nottingham; accredited mediator (2006).
Personal: Educated Solihull School, New College, Oxford and Cardiff University. Member of the Country Land & Business Association.

FACENNA, Gerry
Monckton Chambers, London
020 7405 7211
gfacenna@monckton.com
Featured in Administrative & Public Law (London), Data Protection (London), Environment (London), Competition/European Law (London)
Practice Areas: Administrative law; EU law; competition law; regulatory proceedings, telecoms; information law and data protection; human rights; environmental law. An experienced advocate in the EU courts, domestic courts and specialist tribunals. Acts in a wide range of public law matters for and against public bodies, including commercial, competition and regulatory proceedings, environmental challenges and human rights cases. Specialist in EU law, including competition, telecoms, State aid, healthcare, environmental protection, fundamental rights, and free movement. Recent cases include: BT v BSkyB & Ofcom (competition in Pay TV); R (Optimus & Ordanduu) v PhonepayPlus (premium rate services and EU law); R (UK Power Networks) v Ofgem & Heathrow Airport (distribution / third party access); Browning v Information Commissioner v DBIS (use of closed evidence); British Aggregates Association v. HM Treasury (State aid and tax); C-202/13 McCarthy (EU citizenship and free movement); R (Long) v Ministry of Defence (human rights of service personnel); R (Kilgour) v Environment Agency (water framework directive); Birkett v Defra & IC (late exemptions in FOIA); R (Bailey) v London Borough of Brent (library closures).
Professional Memberships: Administrative Law Bar Association; Bar European Group; ComBar; Human Rights Lawyers Association; Planning & Environment Bar Association; UK Environmental Law Association.
Career: MA (Cantab.), LLB (Edin.), called to the Bar 2001. Member of the Attorney General's Panel of Counsel, Freedom of Information Panel and the Equality and Human Rights Commission's Panel of Counsel. Also a member of the Bar in Scotland (currently non-practising).
Publications: Contributing author to Information Rights: Law and Practice (Hart, 2014); Halsbury's Laws of England: Rights and Freedoms (LexisNexis, 2013); EU Competition Law: Procedures and Remedies (OUP, 2006); Law of State Aid in the European Union (OUP, 2004); and Law of the European Union Encyclopaedia (OUP, 2003).

FAGGIONATO, Marina
Queen Elizabeth Building, London
020 7797 7837
m.faggionato@qeb.co.uk
Featured in Family/Matrimonial (London)
Practice Areas: Marina's practice covers all aspects of private family law, including divorce, finance, private law Children Act (including Schedule 1 and relocation) and Hague Convention/child abduction cases. She has acted in a wide range of matters in courts up to and including the Court of Appeal (for example Re R (A Child) [2009] 2 FLR 819 CA and Re G (Abduction: Children's Objections) [2011] 1 FLR 1645 CA) and as a junior in both 'big money' see for example Luckwell v Limata [2014] EWHC 502 (Fam) and Children Act cases. Marina is a fluent French speaker with practical experience of family law in Paris and often acts in cross-border cases (for example EDG v RR [2014] EWHC 816 (Fam) and Divall v Divall [2014] EWHC 95 (Fam)) Marina also represents parents and carers at the Special Educational Needs and Disability Tribunal.
Professional Memberships: FLBA.
Career: Called 2006. Lord Denning & Eastham Scholar. Pupil & tenant at Queen Elizabeth Building.
Publications: Mental Health and Family Law, edited with the Rt Hon Lord Justice Thorpe, 2010.

FAIN, Carl
Tanfield Chambers, London
020 7421 5300
carlfain@tanfieldchambers.co.uk
Featured in Real Estate Litigation (London)
Practice Areas: Property and chancery practice with a focus on landlord and tenant. Work includes all aspects of commercial and residential including dilapidations claims, lease renewals, enfranchisement, RTM, appointment of managers and service charge disputes. Real property disputes including mortgage related claims and in particular LPA receivers, property related professional negligence, co-ownership, easements, restrictive covenants and boundary disputes. Cases include Yeung v Potel [2014] EWCA Civ 481 (easements), Christoforou v Standard Apartments Ltd [2013] UKUT 0586 (Administration charges), Rabiu v Marlbray Ltd [2013] EWHC 3272 (Ch) (sale deposits in respect of Hotel units), Barnard v Zarbafi [2010] EWHC 3256 (sale deposits), New Northumbria Hotel Ltd v Maymask (148) LLP [2010] EWHC 1273 (forfeiture and chattels), Idealview Ltd v Bello [2010] 1 EGLR 39 (rent review), FSA v Martin [2006] 2 BCLC 193 (s.380 FSMA proceedings).
Professional Memberships: Member of the Property and Chancery Bar Associations.
Career: MA (Jurisprudence), The Queen's College, Oxford. Called in 2001.
Publications: Contributed to 'Service Charges and Management: Law and Practice' 3rd Ed (Sweet & Maxwell).
Personal: Born 1979. Educated at Merchant Taylors' School, Northwood. Lives in London with his wife and two delightful daughters.

FANCOURT, Timothy QC
Falcon Chambers, London
020 7353 2484
fancourt@falcon-chambers.com
Featured in Agriculture & Rural Affairs (London), Real Estate Litigation (London)
Practice Areas: Principally real property based Chancery litigation, including commercial property, landlord and tenant, surveyors' and solicitors' professional negligence, conveyancing, building contracts, mortgages, easements and restrictive covenants, equity, trusts and insolvency. Other main area is commercial contracts.
Professional Memberships: Chairman, Chancery Bar Association (2012 - 2014), LCLCBA; Property Bar Association. Member of Bar Council 1996-2001; Vice-Chairman, Standards Committee, Bar Standards Board 2006-10.
Career: Educated at Whitgift School; Gonville & Caius College, Cambridge; Called 1987 (Lincoln's Inn; Bencher 2012); Silk 2003; Recorder 2009. Deputy High Court Judge 2013.
Publications: Author: 'Enforceability of Landlord and Tenant Covenants' (3rd ed 2014); General editor: Megarry's 'The Rent Acts' and 'Assured Tenancies' (1999); Contributor, Lightman & Moss, The Law of Administrators and Receivers.
Personal: Interests: Cricket; classical music.

FARMER, John
One Paper Buildings, London
020 7353 3728
clerks@onepaper.co.uk
Featured in Crime (South Eastern)
Practice Areas: Criminal law, Health and Safety, POCA.
Professional Memberships: CBA, South Eastern Circuit.
Career: John Farmer has vast experience as a specialist Criminal barrister. The geographic spread of his practice encompasses London, East Anglia and the East Midlands but he is engaged on very serious criminal matters on a nationwide basis. His practice embraces all serious criminal matters with an emphasis on top end violence, particularly murder and manslaughter, very serious sexual offences, heavy duty drug conspiracies and causing death by dangerous driving matters. He regularly prosecutes and defends numerous rapes, murders and drugs trials and prides himself in getting results quickly. Prosecuting and defending serious drugs cases and large scale commercial dishonesty has given John exposure to, and significant experience of Proceeds of Crime Act (POCA) matters. Of these cases, numerous matters have had confiscation values of £1 million and more. In two counties where John has prosecuted these offences have given rise to the biggest single recovery ever in each of the Counties. Over the years John has had experience of a wide range of regulatory work, notably Health & Safety matters, and his practice has given him considerable experience in dealing with a wide range of experts – a skill which is utilised across all practice areas.

FARRINGTON, Gemma
Stour Chambers, Canterbury
01227 764 899
gfarrington@stourchambers.co.uk
Featured in Family/Matrimonial (South Eastern)
Practice Areas: Family.
Professional Memberships: FLBA and ALC.
Career: Gemma specialises in Children Act 1989 proceedings, with her main interest in care proceedings. She is regularly instructed on behalf of parents, interveners and children in complex care proceedings where there are serious allegations involving suspected non accidental injury or sexual abuse. She is particularly experienced in long running fact finding hearings. She regularly represents adults with learning disabilities some of whom have required the Official Solicitor and assistance by way of an intermediary. Gemma is also experienced in contested adoption proceedings. She also undertakes complex private law work with cases involving serious allegations or suggestions of implacable hostility and parental alienation. Gemma has regularly appeared in the Higher Courts. Reported cases include: Re H (Child) [2003] EWCA Civ 369, LM (By her Guardian) v Medway Council, RM and YM [2007]1FLR 1698, Re K (Care Proceedings: Fact Finding) [2011] 2 FLR 199 [2011] 2 FLR 199 and H (Children) (Sexual abuse: fact finding) [2011] All ER (D) 69 (May).
Publications: 'Assessment of Parents within Care Proceedings' published by Jordan Pub-

lishing Ltd. This book was co-authored with Simon Johnson and published in 2014.

FAULKS, Edward QC
1 Chancery Lane, London
020 7092 2900
cchessis@1chancerylane.com
Featured in Clinical Negligence (London), Local Government (London), Personal Injury (London)

Practice Areas: Principal areas of practice: professional and clinical negligence; personal injury (including child abuse); education negligence; police claims; duties of care of public authorities; and human rights. He has been, or is involved in, group litigation arising out of retention of body parts, radiotherapy treatments, cardiac surgery errors, cervical cancer screening errors and child abuse. He appeared at every stage of the dyslexia litigation, (Phelps v London Borough of Hillingdon), culminating in the House of Lords in 2001. Reported cases include: Furnell v Flaherty (T/a) Godstone Farm & Health Protection Agency & Tanbridge District Council [2013]; Tracy v Cambridge University Hospitals NHS Foundation Trust [2012]; JGE v Trustees of the Portsmouth Roman Catholic Diocesan Trust [2012]; (1) AC (2) DC (3) TR v Devon County Council [2012]; An Informer v Chief Constable [2012]; OOO & Others v Commissioner of Police of the Metropolis [2011]; Furmedge & Others v Chester-le-Street District Council and Others [2011]; Stevenson (1) Hinton (2) Taylor (3) v Southwark London Borough Council [2011]; Everett & Anor v Comojo (UK) Ltd (T/A The Metropolitan & Others) [2011] CA; Clift v Slough Borough Council [2010] CA; VL v Oxfordshire County Council [2010]; Harvey v Plymouth City Council [2010] CA; A v Essex County Council [2010] SC; Maga v Archdiocese of Birmingham [2010]; Buckley & Ors v Chief Constable of Thames Valley Police [2009]; X&Y v Hounslow LBC [2009] CA; Peters v East Midland Health Authority [2009] CA; Adorian v Commissioner of Police of the Metropolis [2009] CA; Savage v South Essex Partnership NHS Foundation [2008] HL; Young v Catholic Care [2008] HL; Van Colle v Hertfordshire Police [2008] HL; Smith v Sussex Police [2008] HL; Ashley v Sussex Police [2008] HL.

Professional Memberships: Fellow of Chartered Institute of Arbitrators, Professional Negligence Bar Association (Chair, 2001-03), Personal Injury Bar Association, London Common Law and Commercial Bar Association.

Career: Called to the Bar 1973. Silk 1996. Recorder. Head of Chambers 1998-2007. Bencher of Middle Temple 2002. Special Adviser to Department of Constitutional Affairs on the Compensation Culture 2006. Life Peerage 2010. Minister of State at Ministry of Justice 2014.

Publications: Contributing editor of 'Liabilities of Local Authorities' (Morrell and Foster, 2009, 4th ed).

Personal: Educated at Wellington College and Jesus College, Oxford. Former literary agent. Leisure pursuits include theatre and cricket.

FEATHERBY, William QC
12 King's Bench Walk, London
020 7583 0811
featherby@12kbw.co.uk
Featured in Fraud (All Circuits), Personal Injury (London)

Practice Areas: Personal injury, clinical negligence, professional negligence. William's work is heavy personal injuries litigation, particularly trial work. He is featured in the Personal Injury Section of Legal Experts and as a leading Silk for personal injury in Chambers UK and The Legal 500. About two thirds of William's work is for insurance companies; the rest is for claimants, equally divided between union-backed and other work. The personal injuries work is a combination of accidents at work, industrial and occupational disease, road accidents and clinical negligence. William specialises in difficult medical issues, catastrophic injuries, industrial disease and fraud. William is also a specialist in proceedings for committal for contempt of court arising out of fraudulent cliams. He also has a regulatory practice.

Professional Memberships: Called to the Bar, 1978. QC, 2008. Recorder since 2002. Member of the Civil Procedure Rules Committee since 2008. PIBA; LCLBA.

Personal: Trinity College, Oxford (Scholar, MA).

FELDSCHREIBER, Peter
4 New Square, London
020 7822 2000
p.feldschreiber@4newsquare.com
Featured in Product Liability (London)

Practice Areas: Peter Feldschreiber is dually qualified as a barrister (Call Middle Temple 2000) and physician (BSc MBBS Kings College Hospital Medical School, Fellow Faculty of Pharmaceutical Medicine, Royal College of Physicians). He specialises and advises in all aspects of medical and healthcare law including healthcare products liability, pharmaceutical and medical devices regulatory law, clinical negligence, personal injury and medically related employment litigation. He has held appointments as Senior Medical Assessor and Special Litigation Coordinator to the Commission on Human Medicines, Medicines and Healthcare Products Regulatory Agency, Department of Health. Peter is Senior Specialist Advisor to the Faculty of Pharmaceutical Medicine. He is retained counsel to a number of solicitors and has experience of international litigation regarding drug induced injury.

Professional Memberships: He is on the Committee of Safety of Devices and the Code of Conduct Committee of the Association of British Health Industry.

Career: Medical Director, Cardiovascular and Anaesthetic clinical development Glaxo Pharmaceuticals 1981-91. Medical Director Europe, Procter and Gamble 1992-98. Senior Medical Assessor and Special Litigation Coordinator, MHRA, Department of Health, UK. Tenant Four New Square.

Publications: Peter has lectured and written extensively on pharmaceutical law and regulation; he is General Editor of the Law and regulation of Medicines, Oxford University Press and is consultant editor to Halsbury's Laws of England on Medicinal Products Law.

Personal: Enjoys fell walking, music and amateur dramatics.

FELTHAM, Piers
Radcliffe Chambers, London
020 7831 0081
pfeltham@radcliffechambers.com
Featured in Chancery (London), Court of Protection (All Circuits)

Practice Areas: Litigation, advice and drafting in: trusts, wills and probate, charity, private client (reported cases - Re Jimmy Savile, Connell v Creese (PC), Lake v Lake, Re East Grinstead Working Men's Club) - property/landlord and tenant (Gardener v Lewis (PC), Lloyds Bank v Hawkins (CA), Cork v Cork) - Court of Protection (Re W) - Estoppel (Pereira v Beanlands) - pensions (Moores (Wallisdown) v Pensions Ombudsman) - general contract (Colonial Fire v Harry (PC); Jawara v Gambia Airways (PC)) - Commercial Fraud (Indicii Salus v Chandrasekaran (CA)) - professional negligence/ mortgage fraud (allied surveyors v National home loans).

Professional Memberships: ACTAPS; Chancery Bar Association; Charity Law Association; STEP.

Career: BA (Cantab), Trinity College: George Long Prize for Jurisprudence; Called 1985: Uthwatt scholar of Gray's Inn.

Publications: Spencer Bower on Estoppel by Representation 4th ed (2004).

Personal: Married with three children; trustee of Fitzrovia Community Centre; trustee of the Ceasefire Centre for Civilian Rights.

FENN, Andrew
Atkin Chambers, London
020 7404 0102
afenn@atkinchambers.com
Featured in Construction (London)

Practice Areas: Specialises in domestic and international civil engineering, building, energy, shipbuilding, professional negligence and general commercial law matters. Has experience of domestic litigation and arbitration conducted under the ICC and LCIA rules. Represents contractors, private employers, professional advisors and insurers. Experience in engineering and construction includes disputes relating to airports, power stations, manufacturing plants and residential/ commercial developments. Experience in professional negligence includes claims involving architects, services engineers, quantity surveyors and project managers.

Professional Memberships: TECBAR, Combar, Society of Construction Law.

Career: Called 2007, Gray's Inn.

Publications: Hudson's Building and Engineering Contracts, 12th Ed. (Sweet & Maxwell, 2010) - contributing editor.

Personal: Educated St. John's College, Cambridge MA. Birkenhead Scholar of Gray's Inn. Interests include tennis, cooking, music.

FENWICK, Justin QC
4 New Square, London
020 7822 2000
j.fenwick@4newsquare.com
Featured in Commercial Dispute Resolution (London), Construction (London), Fraud (London), Insurance (London), Offshore (London), Product Liability (London), Professional Negligence (London)

Career: Justin Fenwick came to the Bar in 1981 and was appointed QC in 1993 (the most junior member of the Bar to be appointed as Silk in the 1993 list). He has sat as a Judge in both civil and criminal cases, having been made an Assistant Recorder in 1994, a Recorder in 1999 and a Deputy High Court Judge (Chancery and Queen's Bench Division) in March 2003. He was appointed a Deputy Judge of the Administrative Court in 2008. He was Head of Chambers at 4 New Square between 2000 and 2005 and has been a Bencher of the Inner Temple since 1997 and was Chairman of its Investment Sub-Committee between 2004 and 2011. He was Chairman of the Bar Mutual Indemnity Fund (the Bar's own Mutual Insurer) from 1999 until 2013. He is a Commissioner of the Royal Hospital Chelsea (home to the Chelsea Pensioners) since 2011 where he sits on the Remuneration Committee. He has an extensive offshore practice involving court appearances in Singapore, Dubai, BVI, Cayman, Bermuda, St Vincent and Nevis.

FERGUSON, Craig
2 Hare Court, London
020 7353 5324
craigferguson@2harecourt.com
Featured in Health & Safety (London), Professional Discipline (London), Crime (London), Financial Crime (London)

Practice Areas: A specialist defence advocate with a reputation for meticulous preparation, shrewd tactics, a thorough command of the law and penetrating cross-examination. His practice is now predominantly in defending directors and companies large and small, facing charges brought by the Health and Safety Executive, in professional and disciplinary matters and in fraud and business crime. Much of his work, both for individuals and companies here and abroad, is pre-charge and advisory in nature. Craig is described as "an excellent all-round talent" which is reflected in the fact that he is ranked as a leader in five practice areas. He regularly appears in inquests and is currently instructed to advise Statoil in the inquest into deaths during the terrorist attack at In Amenas, Algeria and to advise in the Hillsborough Inquests. Solicitors consistently praise him for setting the tone right at the outset, which instills confidence in professional and lay clients alike. For many years Craig has been cited as a leading junior in both the Chambers UK guide to the Bar, and the Legal 500, in all of his principal practice areas: Fraud, Crime, Professional Discipline and Health and Safety.

Professional Memberships: South Eastern Circuit; Criminal Bar Association; Association of Regulatory and Disciplinary Lawyers; Health and Safety Lawyers' Association.

Career: Called 1992. Recorder 2009.

FERGUSON, Eva
Hailsham Chambers, London
020 7643 5000
eva.ferguson@hailshamchambers.com
Featured in Professional Negligence (London)

Practice Areas: Professional negligence and liability and Clinical negligence. Eva has frequently been instructed in numerous complex and document heavy lender claims defending solicitors, valuers, and LPA receivers. She has wide experience of all aspects of solicitors' negligence claims and is currently acting on several high-value lost/mis-handled claims arising from clinical negligence and personal injury actions. Eva provides a comprehensive and realistic assessment of the case and believes that the sooner such advice is given, the better the value for money for the client. Eva acts for both claimants and defendants.

Professional Memberships: Member of PNBA and LCLCBA; Head of Hailsham's Pupillage Committee.

Career: BA History: First Class Honours - University of Durham, Hatfield College; Diploma in Law: Commendation - York College of Law; Postgraduate Diploma in Law:

Very Competent - ICSL; Diplock Scholarship, Middle Temple (1998).
Publications: Recently, Eva has provided professional negligence update talks to leading firms of solicitors specialising in that area.

FERNYHOUGH, Richard QC
Keating Chambers, London
020 7544 2600
rfernyhough@keatingchambers.com
Featured in Construction (London), International Arbitration (London)
Practice Areas: Experienced specialist in construction, engineering and energy law; arbitration both international and domestic. Appeared in many landmark cases in the field of construction law, including several notable cases in the House of Lords. Acted in countless heavy court cases and arbitrations on claims relating to a wide range of projects including airports, commercial properties, hotels, oil rigs, power stations, process plants, railways, and tunnelling projects. Recognised internationally as a leading commercial arbitrator who is well able to handle the heaviest and most technically complex disputes. Appointed on many occasions as either sole arbitrator, panel member or chairman by such bodies as the ICC, the LCIA the HKIAC, SIAC, the Kuala Lumpur Regional Centre, the Cairo Regional Centre for Commercial Arbitration and the Taiwan Arbitration Centre. Is a strong believer in delivering the award as soon as practicable after the conclusion of arbitral proceedings.
Career: LLB University College, London 1966; Called to the Bar (Middle Temple) 1970; Keating Chambers 1972; Called to the Bars of Hong Kong and Singapore; Queen's Counsel 1986; Deputy High Court Judge 1992; Approved Arbitrator, Hong Kong International Arbitration Centre 1999; Head of Keating Chambers 1997-2002.

FERRIS, Shaun
Crown Office Chambers, London
020 7797 8100
ferris@crownofficechambers.com
Featured in Personal Injury (London)
Practice Areas: His practice is based on product liability work and a broad range of personal injury work including, in particular, catastrophic and fatal injury claims, industrial disease claims (particularly asbestos and stress claims) and sports injury cases. He is also experienced in clinical negligence and professional negligence work. He is adept at working as part of a team, giving clear and imaginative advice and guidance on all aspects of any particular piece of litigation including all tactical and legal issues. He is also a skilled and robust performer in court whether at interlocutory hearings or at trial. He has considerable experience of conducting settlement negotiations at round table meetings or mediations in both high and medium value cases. He regularly appears against silks and is consistently recognised as a "leader at the bar" for personal injury work. Clients view him as a "market leader in large-loss claims" and value his "excellent advocacy skills" and "superb tactical appreciation". Recent cases include Uren v Corporate Leisure Ltd and MOD [2013] EWHC 353 QB, [2011] EWCA Civ 66 and [2010] EWHC 46 QB, Horner v Norman [2013] Lawtel 19-12-13 and Woodham v Turner [2012] EWCA Civ 375 and [2011] EWHC 1588 QB.

FETHERSTONHAUGH, Guy QC
Falcon Chambers, London
020 7353 2484
fetherstonhaugh@falcon-chambers.com
Featured in Real Estate Litigation (London)
Practice Areas: Real Estate Litigation, Arbitration.
Professional Memberships: RICS (Hon); CIArb; ARBRIX (Hon); Chancery Bar & Property Bar Association.
Career: Royal Green Jackets (1977 - 81); Barrister (1983 -); Queen's Counsel (2003 -).
Publications: Handbook of Rent Review, Commonhold, Litigation Practice.
Personal: Joint Head of Falcon Chambers.

FIELDSEND, James
Tanfield Chambers, London
020 7421 5300
jamesfieldsend@tanfieldchambers.co.uk
Featured in Real Estate Litigation (London)
Practice Areas: All aspects of property litigation, particularly commercial and residential landlord and tenant disputes. Emphasis on service charges, RTM and enfranchisement claims. Cases include: Daejan v Benson [2013] 1 W.L.R. 854 (service charges); Hatton v Connew [2013] EWCA Civ 1560 & 1681 (boundary dispute); Albion Residential v Albion Riverside [2014] UKUT 6 (LC) (RTM); BDW v South Anglia Housing [2014] 1 W.L.R. 920 (service charges); Paddington Basin v Gritz [2013] UKUT 0338 (LC) (service charges); Havering LB v MacDonald [2012] 3 E.G.L.R. 49 (service charges); 5 Felix Avenue v Pledream Properties [2011] L. & T.R. 20 (enfranchisement); McGlynn v Welwyn Hatfield [2010] H.L.R. 10 (possession and Art.8); Nailrile v Earl Cadogan [2009] E.G.L.R. 151 (enfranchisement); and CCE v Meya [2007] H.L.R. 4 (Housing Act 1988).
Professional Memberships: Member of the Property and Chancery Bar Associations.
Career: 1996 University of Newcastle LLB. Called 1997.
Publications: Co-author of 'Commercial Property Litigaiton' (Jordans); Contributor to 'Service Charges and Management: Law and Practice' (Sweet & Maxwell).
Personal: Born 1975. Keen interest in rowing.

FINDLAY, James QC
Cornerstone Barristers, London
020 7242 4986
jamesf@cornerstonebarristers.com
Featured in Environment (London), Licensing (London), Local Government (London), Planning (London)
Practice Areas: Principal areas of practice include local government, planning and environment, licensing and administrative law. Considerable experience in promoting and resisting planning applications, including windfarms, housing, retail and waste to energy facilities. Recent appearances include Welwyn Hatfield v Beesley (deceit and planning), Tesco v Dundee City Council (policy and sequential test) in the Supreme Court, Cherkley v Mole Valley in CA and the Cairngorms Campaign in the Inner House. Licensing work includes gambling and betting, hackney carriages as well as Licensing Act 2003/5 work.
Professional Memberships: PEBA; ALBA; NIPA, SPELG (Treasurer).
Career: Called 1984. QC 2008. Called in Scotland November 2008. Member of Terra Firma Chambers, Edinburgh, 0131 2605830 (Emma Potter).
Personal: Born 1961. Educated at Glenalmond and Magdalene College, Cambridge.

FINDLAY, James QC
Terra Firma Chambers, Edinburgh
020 7242 4986
jamesf@cornerstonebarristers.com
Featured in Administrative & Public Law (Scotland), Planning (Scotland)
Practice Areas: Specialist in planning and environment, licensing and local government law in both England & Wales and Scotland. Recent cases include Multilink Leisure Developments v North Lanarkshire Council (lease interpretation), Morge v Hampshire (resisting interim relief application), Welwyn Hatfield v SOSCLG (deceit and planning) and Tesco Stores Ltd v Dundee City Council (interpretation of policy and sequential test) – all in the Supreme Court. Acted in Garner and Roadsense with respect to PCO/PEO issues. Numerous other related Court cases. Likewise inquiries recent significant experience in windfarms, waste to energy facilities and coffee shops. Licensing work at all levels in both jurisdictions. Advises on all aspects of local authority law, including governance, elections, highways and procurement.
Professional Memberships: Scottish Planning Local Government & Environmental Bar Group, PEBA, UKELA.
Career: Called England 1984 - Scotland 2008. QC England 2008. Joint Head of Chambers of 2-3 Gray's Inn Square.
Publications: Contributing editor to the Waste on Land section of Volume 38 of Halsbury's Laws. Contributor to Kolvin Licensed Premises: Law and Practice. Various articles in JPL, SPEL and Judicial Review.

FIRTH, Matthew
Queen Elizabeth Building, London
020 7797 7837
clerks@qeb.co.uk
Featured in Family/Matrimonial (London)
Practice Areas: Matrimonial finance and private law Children Act cases.
Professional Memberships: Family Law Bar Association.
Career: Pupillage at QEB (1991-92); tenant at QEB since 1992.
Personal: Educated at Clifton College, Bristol, Pembroke College, Oxford (Literae Humaniores) and City University, London (diploma in law). Married with two children.

FISHER, Jonathan QC
Devereux, London
020 7353 7534
fisher@devchambers.co.uk
Featured in Financial Services (London), POCA Work & Asset Forfeiture (All Circuits), Tax (London), Financial Crime (London)
Practice Areas: Financial Services, Fraud, Proceeds of Crime, Tax, White Collar and Corporate Crime. Recent advisory work includes cases on money laundering, economic sanctions, market abuse, Ponzi fraud, bribery and corruption, international restraint of assets, tax avoidance & evasion investigations involving LDF and film schemes, Lloyds TSB (Verde) and LIBOR investigations. Recent Court cases include Wiese v UKBA, HMRC v Curran, Lunn v HMRC, SEC v Manterfield, Szepietowski v ARA. Advising and representing individuals, companies and Government agencies in High Court, First-tier Tribunal, Upper Tribunal, Crown Court and Appeal cases.
Professional Memberships: Include Administrative Law Bar Association, Commercial Fraud Lawyers Association, Criminal Bar Association, Financial Services Lawyers Association, Fraud Advisory Panel, Proceeds of Crime Lawyers Association, Revenue Bar Association, South Eastern Circuit.
Career: Called 1980, Silk 2003. Chartered Tax Adviser (Fellow). Accredited STEP practitioner. General Editor of Lloyds Law Reports: Financial Crime. Visiting Professor in Practice, London School of Economics. Standing Counsel (Criminal) to the Commissioners of Inland Revenue 1991-2003.
Publications: Regular contributor to books, legal journals and the media.

FISHER, Richard
South Square, London
020 7696 9900
richardfisher@southsquare.com
Featured in Chancery (London), Restructuring/Insolvency (London)
Practice Areas: Insolvency, company, banking, general chancery and commercial matters. Recent cases include Federal Mogul Asbestos Personal Injury Trust [2014] EWHC 2002 (Comm) (reinsurance declarations); Re Co-operative Bank Plc [2013] EWHC 4397 (Ch) (bank restructuring); Kemsley v Barclays Bank [2013] BPIR 839 (Ch) (injunctive relief in insolvency proceedings); BNY Corporate Trustee Services Ltd v Eurosail-UK 2007 [2013] 1 WLR 1408 (meaning of insolvency); Snoras Bank v Antonov [2013] EWHC 131 (Comm) (freezing injunctions and obligations to disclose information); SerVaas Inc v Rafidain Bank [2013] 1 AC 595 (sovereign immunity and debt enforcement).
Professional Memberships: COMBAR; Chancery Bar Association.
Career: Educated at University College London: LLB Law and French Law (1st), Universite d'Aix-en-Provence: Diplome de Droit Francais and St Edmund Hall, Oxford: BCL (1st).
Publications: Contributor to Halsbury's Laws (Insolvency); Sheldon, Cross-Border Insolvency.

FITZGERALD, Ben
QEB Hollis Whiteman, London
020 7933 8855
ben.fitzgerald@qebhw.co.uk
Featured in Crime (London)
Practice Areas: Ben FitzGerald prosecutes and defends in high-profile cases of serious crime and professional regulatory offending. He leads teams of lawyers in cases involving organised crime, large-scale fraud and homicide. He is a Grade 4 prosecutor for the CPS. He acts for corporate clients who require impeccable preparation and presentation in respect of criminal and regulatory allegations. He has successfully defended the UK's largest retailer against private criminal prosecution. He represents professionals charged with multi-million pound revenue fraud and has advised Thames Valley Police extensively on issues of legal privilege concerning a £35m alleged banking fraud on HBOS. Having served as First Junior Counsel to the Mid Staffordshire Public Inquiry, he has an in-depth understanding of public inquiry procedure and the operation of the NHS. He is regularly instructed by the General Medical Council to advise upon and prosecute some of its most serious cases.
Professional Memberships: Association of Regulatory & Disciplinary Lawyers, Public

Access Bar Association, registered with the Bar Council – Public Access Directory
Career: Ben has prior experience as a researcher for BBC Newsnight and Breakfast News and as a researcher/producer for Granada TV at Westminster.
Personal: Call 2000; MA (Trinity, Cantab); PGD Law (City).

FLANAGAN, Hugh
Cornerstone Barristers, London
020 7242 4986
hughf@cornerstonebarristers.com
Featured in Planning (London)
Practice Areas: Specialist in planning, environmental, and public law. Instructed by public authorities and developers on a range of significant proposals, both in inquiry and on judicial review in the High Court, Court of Appeal and Supreme Court. Particular experience in retail and residential development, transport infrastructure, and cases involving heritage and conservation issues. Inquiry work includes Pinewood Studios (major film studio development), Rushden Lakes (large scale out of town retail), Farnborough Airport (increase in aircraft movements) and Cineworld King's Road (prime London cinema and residential). Court work includes EU Plants v Wokingham DC (Court of Appeal - lawfulness of tree preservation order), Scottish Widows v Cherwell DC (High Court - judicial review of out of town retail), Garner v Elmbridge BC (Court of Appeal - heritage impact on Hampton Court Palace) and Gulliver's Bowls Club (Upper Tribunal Asset of Community Value). Member of the Attorney General's C Panel of Counsel.
Professional Memberships: Planning and Environmental Bar Association. Administrative Law Bar Association.
Career: Called 2008. Judicial Assistant to Lord Mance and Lord Kerr in the Supreme Court. Brasenose College, Oxford University (congratulatory first). Graduate Diploma in Law (distinction). Bar Vocational Course (outstanding).

FLANAGAN, Julia
Charter Chambers, London
07976 843 781
julia.flanagan@hotmail.com
Featured in Crime (London)
Practice Areas: Julia Flanagan is a very experienced defence advocate with a particular specialisation in serious sexual offending. Her practice covers the full spectrum of criminal work including homicide, large-scale fraud and serious drugs offences. She acts as both leading and junior counsel instructed privately and under the provisions of legal aid. She is accustomed to dealing with most difficult and sensitive cases involving highly vulnerable defendants and witnesses and the use of intermediaries in court. She recently participated in the pilot scheme for the pre-recorded video testimony of vulnerable witnesses. Recent cases include: R v V. Historical stranger rape in which there were numerous expert witnesses and extremely complex forensic evidence as a result of the defendant being an identical twin. R v F. Manslaughter in which the defendant was a child with significant learning and communication difficulties requiring the use of an intermediary throughout. R v F. Acted as leading counsel in lengthy and complex multi-handed fraud and conspiracy to commit misconduct in public office.
Career: Called to the Bar in 1993 from Lincoln's Inn.
Personal: Graduated from the London School of Economics.

FLENLEY, William QC
Hailsham Chambers, London
020 7643 5000
william.flenleyqc@hailshamchambers.com
Featured in Professional Negligence (London)
Practice Areas: Professional negligence, insurance, real property, mediation. Cases include: Nationwide BS v Davisons [2013] PNLR 12, solicitors/breach of trust; Hellard v Irwin Mitchell [2013] PNLR 8, barristers/waiver of privilege; Nationwide BS v Dunlop Haywards [2010] 1 WLR 258, contribution, solicitors and valuers; Pickthall v Hill Dickinson [2009] PNLR 10, limitation, abuse of process; Webster v Sandersons [2009] PNLR 37, no reflective loss principle, Taylor Walton v Laing [2008] PNLR II, professional negligence, abuse of process; Luke v Wansbroughs [2005] PNLR 2, barrister's negligence, loss of a chance; Luke v Kingsley Smith [2004] PNLR 12, contribution, loss of litigation; Direct Line Insurance v Khan [2002] LRIR 364, insurance, fraud; Ruparel v Awan [2000] Lloyd's Rep PN 258, solicitors' undertakings; Jenmain v Steed & Steed [2000] PNLR 616, CA, professional negligence - loss of profit; Matlock Green v Potter [2000] Lloyd's Rep PN 935, loss of business tenancy; Nationwide v Balmer Radmore [1999] PNLR 606, managed list of 400 lenders' claims; Mahoney v Purnell [1996] 3 All ER 61, undue influence: solicitors' duties.
Professional Memberships: Professional Negligence Bar Association (Vice Chairman 2011-2013; Co-Chair of annual lawyers' liability seminar 2007-10).
Career: Exeter College, Oxford (BA, BCL); Cornell University, USA (LLM). Called in 1988. QC 2010.
Publications: Flenley & Leech - 'Solicitors' Negligence and Liability' 3rd Edition, (2012); past contributor to 'Cordery on Legal Services '; original contributor to chapters 1 and 2 (general principles of liability and damages) of 'Professional Negligence and Liability' (2000); Assistant general editor, Lloyd's Law Reports: Professional Negligence (2000-03); co-author, 'The Mareva Injunction and Anton Piller Order' (1993).

FLETCHER, James
5 St Andrew's Hill, London
020 7332 5400
jamesfletcher@5sah.co.uk
Featured in POCA Work & Asset Forfeiture (All Circuits)
Practice Areas: Specialist in asset recovery and proceeds of crime, particularly in restraint, receivership,fraud,money laundering,confiscation and enforcement cases. Also acts in cash forfeiture,civil recovery, freezing injunctions and civil fraud litigation. James lectures regularly and contributes articles to a variety of publications. Over the past 12 months James has substantially increased his defence asset forfeiture practice acting in cash forfeiture proceedings, confiscation and enforcement cases; notably R v Terence Shepherd (enforcement of £1.25m confiscation order arising out of ticketing fraud). In the High Court he has acted in international contract and fraudulent misrepresentation claims. He obtained a £3m cash forfeiture order for the City of London Police and advised on asset recovery arising out of overseas bribery. Increasingly he appears in the Tax Tribunal and has experience in cases involving Search Warrants and Production Orders.
Professional Memberships: Proceeds of Crime Lawyers Association, Fraud Lawyers Association.
Career: Called 2000 (Middle Temple).

FLETCHER, Stephen
Dere Street Barristers, Newcastle upon Tyne
0191 232 0541
s.fletcher@derestreet.co.uk
Featured in Real Estate Litigation (North Eastern)
Practice Areas: Stephen has been a practising civil barrister since he was called to the Bar. His particular expertise lies in Chancery/Commercial and Employment law. Stephen has maintained a solid record of success at trial in recent cases, a selection of which includes: Successful recovery of damages and costs in team moves/restrictive covenants after fully contested High Court action; Enforcement of rent charges in respect of large residential estate; Damages and costs in professional negligence claim; Arbitration in agricultural partnership dispute; Contested business lease renewal; Contested probate claim; Boundary dispute. Stephen has also continued to steer cases to successful and advantageous conclusions for clients without trial in recent matters such as: Shareholder/share purchase and director disputes; Property rights disputes; Building disputes; Inheritance Act claims. In addition to the breadth and depth of his experience, Stephen attaches particular importance to achieving outcomes which provide real benefit to the client. In all cases he is committed to developing effective working relationships with both solicitors and lay clients.

FODDER, Martin
Littleton Chambers, London
020 7797 8600
mfodder@littletonchambers.co.uk
Featured in Employment (London)
Practice Areas: Principal area of practice is employment, all areas including wrongful dismissal/unfair dismissal, discrimination, equal pay, redundancy, transfer of undertakings, trade union law, restraint of trade and business secrets. Also professional negligence and general commercial dispute work. Reported cases include Cantor Fitzgerald v Wallace, Dan Tran v Greenwich Vietnam Community, Hinton v University of East London, Jackson v Ghost Inc, Neary v St Albans School, BP v Elstone. Mediator of employment and professional negligence disputes.
Professional Memberships: Employment Lawyers Association, Employment Law Bar Association, Industrial Law Society , Professional Negligence Bar Association.
Career: Call 1983.
Publications: 'Whistleblowing: Law and Practice', OUP (joint author); Atkin: Employment and Discrimination volumes, Butterworths, (joint contributor); 'Transfer of Undertakings', Sweet & Maxwell (contributor).
Personal: Educated University of London, (History, 1st class hons) City University (Dip Law) Cambridge University (LLM).

FORD, Charlotte
New Square Chambers, London
020 7419 8000
charlotte.ford@newsquarechambers.co.uk
Featured in Chancery (London)
Practice Areas: Charlotte specialises in trusts and estates work, both contentious and non-contentious, together with related insolvency and professional negligence matters. She has extensive experience both as junior and sole counsel. Her contentious probate and trusts work includes actions to remove or replace personal representatives, breach of trust claims, Inheritance Act claims, allegations of forgery and undue influence and questions of distribution in the case of a shortfall. Charlotte regularly advises on all aspects of the validity and construction of wills, together with issues arising in the administration of trusts and estates. Notable cases include Aeroflot v Gorbunova and others (the estate of Boris Berezovsky deceased) (dispute as to the representation of an estate), Charity Commission v Framjee (Dove Trust) (basis for the distribution of trust funds) and Davis v Smith (CA, severance of joint tenancy before death).
Professional Memberships: Chancery Bar Association.
Career: MA Hons Law, Downing College, Cambridge. Called Lincoln's Inn, 2007 (Denning Scholar).
Publications: Co-editor of Theobald on Wills; co-author of Williams, Mortimer & Sunnucks – Executors, Administrators and Probate.

FORD, Jeremy
9 Gough Square, London
020 7832 0500
jford@9goughsquare.co.uk
Featured in Personal Injury (London)
Practice Areas: Jeremy practices in all aspects of personal injury litigation. His specialism is in brain injury; catastrophic injury; and fatal accident cases, recently settling a brain injury case for in excess of £23 million. He has a particular interest in cases with a psychiatric component, including pain and somatoform disorders. He is known for his excellent client care skills and professional approach.
Professional Memberships: PIBA; PNBA; APIL (Secretary of the APIL Brain Injury Special Interest Group).
Career: University of Leeds, LLB (Hons), Inns of Court School of Law, BVC 1996, Lincolns Inn - Hardwicke Scholar.
Publications: Co - Author of: (a) APIL Guide to Catastrophic Injury Claims, 2nd Edition; (b) 'A Practical guide to Medical Negligence", 9 Gough Square; and (c) Road Traffic Claims, Liability, Jordans. Additionally, a contributing editor to 'Butterworths Personal Injury Litigation' on subject of Road Traffic Act 1988 and Motor Insurers' Bureau;
Personal: Jeremy lives on a farm in Norfolk with his wife and four children, enjoying cycling; tennis; and Taekwondo.

FORLIN, Gerard QC
Cornerstone Barristers, London
07947 136 349
gerardf@cornerstonebarristers.com
Featured in Health & Safety (London)
Practice Areas: Specialist in Health and safety, Corporate and Gross Negligence Manslaughter, Disaster litigation, Aviation, Railways, Shipping safety, Regulatory offences, Product liability, Healthcare, Commercial

fishing, Consumer crime, Corruption, Waste offences, Human rights and Inquests. Since taking silk he has been involved in over thirteen fatalities. He is described as a manslaughter specialist cases include acting for Balfour Beatty on the Hatfield crash. "one of the most compelling advocates that you could ever see in a courtroom." Been ranked in five areas in both the leading independent directories including: Health and Safety Crime Public Inquiries and Inquests Consumer Law and Environmental Law. Special Adviser to the Bar Council on the Corporate Manslaughter Bill, Standing Counsel to numerous PLCs, Unions and other agencies in the UK and abroad. Consultant to the Army and various Police Forces. Gerry has been involved in over 200 fatality cases and has appeared in many of the major cases in this field in the last ten years, including: Watford, Southall, Paddington, James Porter, Teebay, Barrow, Hatfield, Purley, Faversham, Britannia Air Crash, City of London Lift Case, a recent catamaran case in Greece an Inquest in the Falklands and many other Sporting, Aviation and Construction type cases. Recently involved in a major International Aircraft Disaster case. He has also acted in over 150 Jury Inquests both in the UK and overseas. Regular Presenter for the FCO and UN on Bribery and Corruption all over the World. He is also Bar Council Direct Access Licensed. See www.gerardforlin.com.
Publications: Visiting lecturer to numerous global universities. Has lectured or consulted in over 50 countries. Over 100 articles published. General Editor of Corporate Liability: Work related deaths and criminal prosecutions' (3rd Edition February 2014) Script adviser for TV. Appears on TV and radio as an expert. Also an actor
Personal: LSE LLB (Hons) LLM, Trinity Hall Cambridge M Phil, Diploma in Air and Space Law UCL. A panel member of the Royal Aeronautical Society Mediation/ Arbitration list. Member of Denman Chambers in Sydney. Also a tenant in Maxwell Chambers in Singapore. Called to the Bar in the BVI.

FORMBY, Emily
Thirty Nine Essex Street, London
020 7832 1111
emily.formby@39essex.com
Featured in Clinical Negligence (London), Personal Injury (London)
Practice Areas: Personal injury and clinical negligence. Advises in all types of accident and injury claims, both claimant and defendant including fatal accident claims and inquests. Specialising in catastrophic and high value claims often with multiple tortfeasors. Experienced in all types of workplace accidents including occupational disease and asbestos claims. Extensive road traffic claim expertise particularly cycling and highway claims. Clinical negligence experience includes delay in referral, diagnosis and treatment, obstetric cases, neurological disability and bariatric surgery. Highly experienced in complex issues of causation, material contribution and difficult damages calculations. As well as trial work, often involved in round table and negotiated settlements.
Professional Memberships: Personal Injuries Bar Association, Executive member and assistant secretary; Professional Negligence Bar Association.
Career: Call - 1993; Recorder of the Crown Court - 2009.
Publications: Kemp: Quantum of Damages, contributing editor; Kemp & Kemp: Practice & Procedure, contributer; Butterworths Personal Injury Litigation Service, section editor; PIBA Personal Injury Handbook 2007 (3rd Edn) - contributor.

FORSHAW, Simon
11KBW, London
020 7632 8500
Simon.Forshaw@11kbw.com
Featured in Employment (London)
Practice Areas: Employment law, commercial law, public law. Having a broad practice with an emphasis on employment and discrimination law, Simon is regularly instructed to appear in the High Court, the employment tribunals and at appellate level. Recently his practice (in employment law) has had a particular focus on litigation arising out of team moves (including interim relief), senior executive discrimination claims and equal pay claims.
Professional Memberships: ELA, ELBA and COMBAR.
Career: Called 2004, Gray's Inn. Recent notable cases include: Foster v. Bon Groundwork Limited [2012] IRLR 517; Ashby v. Birmingham City Council [2011] IRLR 473; Pinewood Repro Limited v. Page [2011] ICR 508; Willoughby v. CF Capital [2011] IRLR 198; Aon Limited v. JLT Reinsurance Brokers Limited [2010] IRLR 600.
Publications: Blackstone's Employment Law Practice (annually since 2009); Tolley's Employment Handbook (annually since 2010). Regularly writes articles for the Industrial Law Journal.
Personal: Educated at St. John's College, Southsea and St. John's College, Oxford. Resides London.

FORSTER, Tom
Red Lion Chambers, London
020 7520 6000
chambers@18rlc.co.uk
Featured in Crime (London), Financial Crime (London)
Practice Areas: Tom Forster concentrates almost exclusively on criminal defence work, particularly fraud, and associated professional disciplinary proceedings. For example, in recent months he has appeared for the defence in respect of a forthcoming major fraud trial and defended in a substantial firearms trial; he was instructed to defend in a high-profile 4-month mortgage fraud trial in 2014. He has also been instructed to prosecute serious and complex frauds: he was junior Counsel in the SFO's investigation into BAE Systems and recently appeared for the Central Fraud Group prosecuting corruption in the Gas & Oil Industry. He is a specialist in proceedings concerning the recovery of the proceeds of crime (both criminal and civil) and has recently represented a number of financial institutions (e.g. Bank of Scotland) as third parties in civil recovery proceedings. He has a large body of experience in bringing and defending actions for Judicial Review. In 2007 Tom was appointed as a Special Advocate (Senior and Junior Lists) by the Attorney General/Treasury Solicitor. Tom is often sought out to advise in cases involving Human Rights issues. He has frequently been invited to lecture on behalf of the British Institute of Human Rights.
Professional Memberships: Criminal Bar Association; Co-opted Member of the South Eastern Circuit Executive Committee; Bar Council's Race Relations Committee; Appointed Recorder, 2012.
Career: 1993 - Called to the Bar, Inner Temple.
Publications: Tom is a contributing author to 'Fraud: Law, Practice and Procedure' (LexisNexis, 2004).

FORSYTH, Sandy
Compass Chambers, Edinburgh
0131 226 5071
sandyforsyth@supanet.com
Featured in Clinical Negligence (Scotland)
Practice Areas: Civil practice with emphasis on personal injury and clinical negligence cases. Recent cases where judgements were issued include: Stewart v Trafalgar House Steamship Co Ltd & Ors 2013 SLT 834 (private international law; jurisdiction over foreign defendants); Pate v Stewart Homes (Scotland) Ltd [2013] CSOH 30 (proof on liability in brain injury case, issues of 'control' of construction workers); Anton v South Ayrshire Council & Ors 2013 SLT 141 (transfer of liabilities for occupational disease in local government); Burns v Boots UK Ltd 2012 Rep LR 124 (remission from Chapter 43 procedure); Kordakis v National Insurance and Guarantee Co Ltd [2012] CSOH 57 (proof or jury trial debate); and Matthews v Glasgow City Council 2006 SC 349 (Inner House appeal following conduct of proof in Sheriff Court - definitions of work and employees covered by the construction regulations).
Career: Litigation solicitor 1990-1998. Called to the Bar 1999. Speaker at numerous conferences and seminars on aspects of personal injury law.
Publications: Chapters on 'The Court' and on 'Procedure in Personal Injury Actions' in 'Court of Session Practice', edited by the late Lord Macfadyen, first published in 2006; Contributed the styles on Minutes of Tender to 'Green's Litigation Styles'.
Personal: Educated at Kelvinside Academy, Glasgow; LLB (Hons), University of Aberdeen 1989; DipLP, University of Glasgow 1990; BD (Hons), University of Glasgow 2008; MTh, University of Edinburgh 2010; PhD (Theology), University of Edinburgh 2014.

FORTE, Timothy
3 Temple Gardens, London
020 7353 32012
clerks@3tg.co.uk
Featured in Crime (London)
Practice Areas: Since 1996 Tim has specialised in lengthy, often high profile cases. Highlights include his first major case - an international $2 billion US Dollar Bond fraud. After the 11 month Operation Hobart case in 2005, Tim was instrumental in the successful appeals (instructed for all appellants) and in the abandonment of the retrial after complex and novel legal argument. In 2013, he acted in Dale Cregan & Others - the murder of two policewomen, involving grenades - as well as Operation Beath in Liverpool, "the largest ever multi-commodity drugs conspiracy in the UK". 2014 saw a £385 million, 200,000+ page MTIC fraud. Tim is almost exclusively instructed in complex and serious crime, specialising in murder, heavyweight fraud and drugs. Whether as a junior (alone or led) or, increasingly, as a leader, he has an excellent reputation among professional clients. An astute and intuitive lawyer, Tim identifies arguments often overlooked by others. His successful Judicial Review, ex parte Raeside, is now one of the leading cases in Custody Time Limits case law. His extensive technical expertise is much sought after in telephone intercept, audio surveillance and complex computer evidence cases. Tim is regularly instructed or recommended by previous clients or co-defendants. An accomplished appellate advocate, he is also increasingly instructed to take over Appeal or POCA cases. Tim also has an ever-growing private practice. He is fluent in German and has a working knowledge of French and Italian.
Professional Memberships: Justice, Liberty, Amnesty International, CBA, South Eastern Circuit.
Career: Called 1994.
Personal: Hockey, golf, cricket, music and literature.

FOSKETT, Rosanna
Maitland Chambers, London
020 7406 1200
rfoskett@maitlandchambers.com
Featured in Chancery (London)
Practice Areas: Commercial and chancery litigation (domestic and international), including business agreements and general contractual disputes, banking litigation, civil fraud and asset tracing, jurisdiction disputes/ conflicts of laws, company and insolvency, trusts and estates litigation, property litigation. Notable cases include: Lehman Brothers Waterfall application (construction of $2.25bn subordinated loan agreements/ questions about liability of members in insolvency), Dar Al Arkan Real Estate Development Co v Al Refai (multi-million dollar civil fraud/conspiracy/defamation claim involving conflicts of laws points), Eurofinance v Rubin (Supreme Court decision on Cross Border Insolvency Regulations 2006/enforceability of foreign judgments in insolvency context), Maloney v Filtons (sham lease/insolvency/ appointment of receivers), Alliance Bank v Aquanta Corp (civil fraud/asset recovery/jurisdiction challenge/conflict of laws), HMRC v Rochdale Drinks Distributors (Court of Appeal decision on insolvency/provisional liquidation/VAT fraud), Liverpool Football Club litigation (directors' duties/company meetings/anti-suit injunctions), Mackay v Ashwood Enterprises (Court of Appeal decision on costs made ex parte), Hart v Burbidge (undue influence/ademption/wills).
Professional Memberships: COMBAR, Chancery Bar Association.
Career: Called 2008.
Personal: Educated at Trinity College, Cambridge (MA – Double First; MPhil; Junior, Senior and Research Scholar) and City University, London (Distinction in Graduate Diploma in Law). Member of Lincoln's Inn (Hardwicke, Lord Bowen and Lord Mansfield Scholar).

FOSTER, Catherine
Crown Office Chambers, London
020 7797 8100
foster@crownofficechambers.com
Featured in Personal Injury (London), Personal Injury (All Circuits)
Practice Areas: Specialist areas are personal injury (with a particular interest in catastrophic injury litigation); occupational diseases (in particular claims involving asbestos related conditions, asthma, pneumoconiosis, cancers, carbon monoxide exposure, back injuries, upper limb

disorders, CTS HAVS, chemical exposure, NIHL, dermatitis, silicosis, DVT, Legionnaire's disease, food poisoning, norovirus and radiation exposure); clinical negligence; professional negligence and sexual abuse litigation. Has been involved in emerging areas of disease and abuse litigation over the past 20 years and is regularly instructed to advise on generic issues. Has been instructed in abuse claims involving the Catholic Church, other religious and secular organisations and on behalf of Local Authorities and foreign Governments over a wide range of complex issues. Recent reported cases: BCC HAVS Professional Negligence Litigation: Barnaby v Raleys Solicitors [2014] EWCA Civ 686; Philips v Haxton [2014] EWCA Civ 4; Nicholls v Ladbrokes Betting and Gaming Ltd [2013] EWCA Civ 1963; AB and others v Ministry of Defence 'The Atomic Veterans Litigation' [2012] UKSC 9 and ECHR application no. 61332/12; Peakstone Ltd v Joddrell [2012] EWCA Civ 1035; Baker v Quantum Clothing Group Ltd [2011] UKSC 17.
Professional Memberships: Membership of the Personal Injury Bar Association and the Professional Negligence Bar Association.

FOSTER, Charles
Serjeants' Inn Chambers, London
07980 610 322
cfoster@serjeantsinn.com
Featured in Clinical Negligence (London), Professional Discipline (London)
Practice Areas: Charles Foster was called to the Bar in 1988. Charles specialises in clinical negligence and healthcare, Court of Protection and professional and regulatory law. An earlier edition notes that "he always impresses, as he is able to advise really well on complicated cases where there are lots of papers involved. He provides tactical and practical advice." Please see the Serjeants' Inn Chambers website for his profile, which sets out full details of his practice including relevant work of note.
Professional Memberships: PNBA, Bar Human Rights Committee.
Publications: Numerous books and hundreds of articles and papers.

FOTTRELL, Deirdre
1 Garden Court Family Law Chambers, London
020 7797 7900
fottrell@1gc.com
Featured in Family/Matrimonial (London)
Practice Areas: Children Human Rights International Judicial Review Court of Protection.
Professional Memberships: Family Law Bar Association Association of Lawyers for Children Human Rights Lawyers Association Middle Temple.
Career: Deirdre Fottrell practises in all areas relating to children. She has particular expertise on surrogacy and alternative families and has appeared in a number of leading cases in these areas. In addition, she is a specialist in human rights law as it applies to children, having taught and published in that area before coming to the Bar. She has practised at all levels of court in the UK, including the Supreme Court, and has acted for clients before the European Court of Human Rights. She has wide experience in matters of international child law, including relocation, adoption, abduction and Brussels IIA. She is a visiting professor at the School of International Affairs at Columbia University, New York, and is a Council of Europe Expert on the European Convention. She also has a civil practice in the Administrative Court and represents children, foster carers and adopters in applications for judicial review arising out of the Children Act and Adoption legislation.
Publications: Publications include Halburys Rights and Freedoms, Sweet and Maxwell, April 2013.

FOX, Nicola
1 King's Bench Walk, London
020 7936 1500
nfox@1kbw.co.uk
Featured in Family/Matrimonial (London)
Practice Areas: Private law children work. Matrimonial Finance. Schedule 1. Cohabitant disputes.
Professional Memberships: Family Law Bar Association. Association of Lawyers for Children. Member of the South Eastern Circuit. Member of the Bar Pro Bono Unit (Panel).
Career: Family law barrister since 1996. Previous career as a child clinical psychologist. Specialising in matrimonial finance and private children law work. She has a particular interest in complex private law disputes and relocation matters. Deputy District Judge (Civil and Family).
Publications: Contributor to: Applications Under Schedule 1 (Jordans. Halsburys Laws - Children Law (5th reissue). Butterworths Civil Court Precedents - Matrimonial Finance.

FOY, John QC
9 Gough Square, London
020 7832 0500
jfoy@9goughsquare.co.uk
Featured in Personal Injury (London)
Practice Areas: John Foy QC specialises in serious personal injury and clinical negligence cases, occupational disease litigation and costs. Most of his cases nowadays are brain damage, paraplegics, amputations etc. He has appeared in many reported cases on these topics and has conducted occupational disease litigation since the 1970s. He acted for the coal miners in their ground breaking group litigation for respiratory disease which led directly to the setting up of the miners compensation scheme. He has expertise in costs, particularly in a personal injury/ clinical negligence context and has been involved in many of the leading cases in this area, including being instructed by APIL on behalf of its members in Myatt v NCB . He is a former chair and current member of the Bar Council CFA Panel. He was involved in the drafting of the original APIL/PIBA CFA and many subsequent CFAs and CCFAs. He has taught advocacy at Grays Inn, where he is a Bencher and sits as a Recorder trying criminal, family and civil cases. He is a judge of the Mental Health Review Tribunal.
Professional Memberships: PIBA; PNBA.
Career: Called and joined 9 Gough Square in 1969; QC (1998); recorder (2000); Judge of Mental Health Review Tribunal (2003); Bencher Gray's Inn (2004).
Publications: Articles in JPIL, APIL Newsletter and NLT on occupational disease and personal injury costs.
Personal: LLB (Hons) Birmingham University, 1967. Interests include most sports.

FRANCIS, Andrew
Serle Court, London
020 7242 6105
afrancis@serlecourt.co.uk
Featured in Real Estate Litigation (London)
Practice Areas: Specialist in restrictive covenants affecting freehold land, party walls and rights of light.
Professional Memberships: Chancery Bar Association. Property Bar Association.
Publications: Author of 'Restrictive Covenants and Freehold Land, a Practitioner's Guide', 4th Ed. (2013) (Jordans) and co-author of 'Rights of Light - The Modern Law' 2nd Ed. (2007) (3rd Ed. due November 2014) (Jordans). Private Rights of Way (Jordans) (2012).
Personal: Master of the Bench, Lincoln's Inn.

FRANCIS, Derek
Terra Firma Chambers, Edinburgh
07545 241 891
derek.francis@terrafirmachambers.com
Featured in Tax (Scotland)
Practice Areas: Barrister at Temple Tax Chambers. UK tax planning and litigation particularly trust, IHT, CGT, contentious VAT and excise duty. High-profile litigation concerning whether European principles of legal certainty and proportionality elide a circumspect taxpayer's liability for excise duty in intra-community transit diversion; cy pres scheme for major mixed public and private purpose trust partitioned into private and charitable. Derek has advised on Hastings-Bass/ Dundee Hospitals Board issues for pension trustees in a Barber equalisation context and for EBT trustees; on rectification with a view to averting IHT consequences of botched consensual trust restructuring; on construction/ rectification of deeds of major trust, inadvertently settlor-interested. Derek has drafted boiler-plate precedent trust styles for national firms.
Professional Memberships: Faculty of Advocates; Bar of England and Wales; Chartered Tax Advisor - Fellow of the Chartered Institute of Taxation; Society of Trust and Estate Practitioners.
Career: Advocate; Barrister; TEP; CTA (Fellow).
Publications: "Hastings-Bass and his Scottish Friends" S.L.T. 2008, 24, 161; "the Bonfire of the Charities – winding-up unregistered entities" S.L.T. 2011, 12, 63 Insolv. Int. 2011, 24(3), 38-44; "Personal Injury Trusts – the PITs?" Part 1, S.L.T. 2011, 15, 89-92; Part 2 S.L.T. 2011, 16, 95. Member Editorial Board of Foster's Inheritance Tax.

FRANCIS, Nicholas QC
29 Bedford Row Chambers, London
020 7404 1044
nfrancis@29br.co.uk
Featured in Family/Matrimonial (London)
Practice Areas: Principal area of practice is large money financial remedy applications, especially cases with an international element and cases involving trusts, including acting for international trustees and trust companies. Frequently instructed to advise upon and draft pre and post-nuptial agreements. Other main areas within practice include schedule 1 claims and family law-related professional negligence. Frequently chairs private FDRs and early neutral evaluation hearings.
Professional Memberships: Family Law Bar Association; International Academy of Matrimonial Lawyers; Chartered Institute of Arbitrators.
Career: BA Downing College Cambridge 1980; called to the Bar 1981; Recorder 1997; Silk 2002; Head of Chambers at 29 Bedford Row since 2002; Deputy High Court Judge 2011; Family Law Arbitrator 2012. Has appeared in a raft of reported cases over many years; cases include the largest reported Schedule 1 award and many leading family finance cases.
Publications: Numerous articles in 'Family Law'. Regular lecturer and Chair of Jordans and Butterworths Family Law Conferences and speaker at the International Trusts and Estates Litigation Conferences. Ancillary relief after Miller and McFarlane (Lime Legal). Editor and Co-Author of IAML publication "International Pre-nuptial Agreements" 2011.

FRANCIS, Robert QC
Serjeants' Inn Chambers, London
020 7353 0425
rfrancis@serjeantsinn.com
Featured in Clinical Negligence (London), Inquests & Public Inquiries (London), Professional Discipline (London)
Practice Areas: Sir Robert Francis QC was called to the Bar in 1973 and took silk in 1992. Sir Robert specialises in public and administrative, Court of Protection, employment, inquests and inquiries, clinical negligence and healthcare, professional discipline and public inquiries. Earlier directory commentary notes that he is "one of the outstanding silks of his generation", "a seasoned performer... forensically exceptional", "consistently impressive" and "a pleasure to work with." Please click on the link to the Serjeants' Inn Chambers website for his profile, which sets out full details of his practice including relevant work of note.
Professional Memberships: PNBA, LCCLBA, CBA.
Career: Chair: Freedom to Speak Up Review; Mid-Staffordshire NHS Foundation Trust Public Inquiry; Inquiry into care and treatment of Michael Stone; Inquiry into the care and treatment of Peter Bryan and Richard Loudwell. Counsel: Royal Liverpool Children's Hospital inquiry; Neale Inquiry; Bristol Royal Infirmary Inquiry; Rabone v Pennine Care NHS Foundation Trust [CA: human rights of mental health patient) R (Burke) v General Medical Council [(advance directives, life prolonging treatment); Airedale NHS Trust v Bland (persistent vegetative state); Cheatle v General Medical Council (impairment of fitness to practice); numerous multi million pound clinical negligence cases for claimants and defendants. Legal Assessor General Optical Council Professional Conduct Committee. Recorder.
Publications: Medical Treatment: Decisions and the Law (co-author).

FRASER, Peter D QC
Atkin Chambers, London
020 7404 0102
pfraser@atkinchambers.com
Featured in Construction (London), Professional Negligence (London)
Practice Areas: Peter specialises in construction and engineering disputes, both domestically in the United Kingdom and also internationally. He was appointed Queen's Counsel in 2009 and has appeared in a huge number and variety of cases, including those in various jurisdictions including Oman, The Bahamas, South Africa, Hong Kong, People's

Republic of China, Sweden, the United States and Bermuda. His practice includes both arbitration and also litigation in the specialist divisions of the High Court, the Technology and Construction Court and the Commercial Court. His client base includes governments, major infrastructure companies, civil engineering practices and transport authorities. This specialisation also encompasses professional negligence claims involving architects, engineers, construction managers and other construction professionals. He has advised on and appeared for parties involved in most of the major UK projects of recent years, including the Olympic Stadium and extensive railway infrastructure projects, refurbishment of national arts institutions, power stations, oil rigs and other energy infrastructure and hospitals.
Career: Called to Bar by Middle Temple 1989. Appointed Recorder of Crown Court 2002. Queens Counsel 2009. Called to the Bar in the Bahamas 2008. Member of the Rugby Football Union Anti-Drug and Disciplinary Panels.
Publications: Editor of the Building Law Reports 1991 to date. Author of 'How to Pass Law Exams' HLT Publications 1991. Past legal columnist of 'Building' magazine.
Personal: Educated Harrogate Grammar School and Cambridge University. LLM Cambridge University; MA in Law, Cambridge University. Open Exhibitioner and MacMahon Law Scholar of St John's College, Cambridge. Astbury Scholar of the Middle Temple.

FRASER, Vincent QC
Kings Chambers, Manchester
0845 034 3444
clerks@kingschambers.com
Featured in Environment (Northern), Local Government (Northern), Planning (Northern)
Practice Areas: All aspects of town and country planning with particular expertise in retail, renewable energy, major infrastructure projects, commercial development large scale housing projects, minerals and waste. Compulsory purchase and compensation. Highways and rights of way. Local government powers administration and finance. Education law. Election law. Licensing. Environmental protection, European Environmental provisions, contaminated land, drainage, water supply and sewerage, IPPC. Judicial review.
Professional Memberships: Planning and Environmental Bar Association, Administrative Law Bar Association, UKELA.
Career: University College, Oxford MA (1st Class), Open Scholar, Sweet & Maxwell Prize. Called Gray's Inn 1981, Holker Entrance Award, Reid Scholar, Band Prize. QC 2001, Recorder 2002, Deputy High Court Judge 2010.
Publications: Planning Decisions Digest (Sweet & Maxwell).

FRASER BUTLIN, Sarah
Cloisters, London
020 7827 4000
sfb@cloisters.com
Featured in Employment (London)
Practice Areas: Sarah is in constant demand in cases across the spectrum of employment and discrimination law. She is regularly instructed by the CPS and numerous NHS Trusts in their high profile employment disputes. Her robust but pragmatic client focus makes her a favourite for dealing with complex discrimination claims. Key cases: Junior counsel, Charles v Tesco Stores Ltd [2012] EWCA Civ 1128. Appeal relating to time limits. London Borough of Camden v. Pegg UKEAT/0590/11, [2012] EqLR 189. Successfully responding to an appeal relating to agency workers and discrimination provisions. Habashi v. Crown Prosecution Service [2010] EqLR 401 UKEAT/0554/10. Successfully responding to an appeal regarding the burden of proof and application of ACAS Code. Acting as junior counsel for a local authority in a mass equal pay claim, re-engagement on new terms and conditions and industrial action ballots.
Professional Memberships: Executive Committee member, Industrial Law Society. Editorial Board, ELA Briefing. ELBA.
Career: Called to the Bar, 2005. Affiliated Lecturer in Labour Law, University of Cambridge 2012 - present.
Publications: Highlight publications: Co-author with Deakin and McLaughlin, Equal pay, litigation strategies, and the limits of the law, Cambridge Journal of Economics Symposium June 2013. The UN Convention on the Rights of Persons with Disabilities: Does the Equality Act 2010 Measure Up to UK International Commitments? [2011] Industrial Law Journal 428, 40th Anniversary Edition on Equality. Co-author, "Judicial Review and the Human Rights Act" chapter, Judicial Review, Supperstone, Goudie and Walker, 4th edn. The National Minimum Wage: Under threat from an unlikely source? [2006] Industrial Law Journal 289.

FRASER-URQUHART, Andrew
Francis Taylor Building, London
07711 874 052
afu@ftb.eu.com
Featured in Planning (London)
Practice Areas: Andrew Fraser-Urquhart specialises in planning, environmental and compulsory purchase law. He was educated at St Catharine's College, Cambridge, securing first class honours in both History and Law. He was called to the Bar in 1993 as an Astbury Law Scholar of the Middle Temple. He was in practice at 4/5 Gray's Inn Square between 1993 and 2012 before moving to Francis Taylor Building in 2013. His planning practice encompasses all aspects of housing, retail, green belt and listed buildings and conservation. He also specialises in energy projects, both in minerals and mining and in renewables. He is the consultant editor of Halsbury's Laws volume on Mines, Minerals and Quarries. He has a further specialism in outdoor advertising. His work encompasses advisory work, inquiry work and High Court challenges, together with associated CPO procedures. He is also in demand as a lecturer and trainer and was given the prestigious task of Conference Summariser at the Oxford Joint Planning Law Conference in 2007. Andrew prides himself on his approachability, flexibility and quality of service. He is qualified to accept instructions directly from the public under the Direct Public Access.
Professional Memberships: PEBA, ALBA.

FREEDMAN, Clive
3 Verulam Buildings, London
020 7831 8441
cfreedman@3vb.com
Featured in Information Technology (London)
Practice Areas: Commercial work including information technology (in particular IT project disputes), building and engineering, professional negligence, banking, commercial fraud, company law, insurance, oil and gas, sale of goods and international trade, arbitration and ADR, electronic disclosure.
Professional Memberships: Chartered Institute of Arbitrators (Fellow), COMBAR, TECBAR, British Computer Society (Fellow), Society for Computers & Law (Trustee), Society of Construction Law, Adjudication Society, Arbitration Club, Franco-British Lawyers Association.
Career: Barrister at 3 Verulam Buildings. CEDR Accredited Mediator, Chartered Arbitrator, Fellow of the British Computer Society, Former Chair of the Disciplinary Panel of the British Computer Society, TECBAR Approved Adjudicator. Trustee of Society for Computers & Law.
Publications: Co-author of 4th Edition of Expert Determination (Kendall, Freedman and Farrell, Thomson Sweet & Maxwell, 2008), Contributor to Banking Litigation (edited by Warne and Elliott, Sweet & Maxwell, 1999, 2005, 2011) Contributor to Bullen & Leake Precedents of Pleadings (Sweet & Maxwell, 2001, 2004, 2008, 2012) - chapter on IT contract disputes, contributor to Electronic Evidence (Butterworths LexisNexis, 2012).
Personal: Interests include computer programming, bridge, skiing, horse-racing and bloodstock breeding.

FRIEDMAN, Danny QC
Matrix Chambers, London
020 7404 3447
dannyfriedman@matrixlaw.co.uk
Featured in Administrative & Public Law (London), Civil Liberties & Human Rights (London), Inquests & Public Inquiries (London), Crime (London)
Practice Areas: Specialist in crime, human rights, public law and humanitarian law.

FRIEDMAN, David QC
4 Pump Court, London
020 7842 5555
dfriedman@4pumpcourt.com
Featured in Construction (London), Professional Negligence (London)
Practice Areas: Principal area of practice covers all stages and all aspects of construction and engineering litigation and arbitration, both domestic and international. Also deals with professional negligence, particularly in relation to claims relating to professionals in the construction field and damage claims for 'Eurotorts'.
Professional Memberships: Technology and Construction Bar Association (former Chairman), Society of Construction Law, Society of Computers and Law, Professional Negligence Bar Association, LCIA Users' Council.
Career: Called to the Bar 1968. Tenant at 3 Paper Buildings 1970-92. Took Silk 1990. Joined Pump Court 1992. Appointed Recorder 1998. Appointed to act as Deputy Judge of TCC 2000. CEDR trained mediator 1999. Experienced arbitrator and adjudicator.
Personal: Educated at Tiffin Boys' School, Kingston-upon-Thames and Lincoln College, Oxford 1963-67 (MA, BCL).

FRIEL, John
Hardwicke, London
07970 961 047
john.friel@hardwicke.co.uk
Featured in Education (London)
Practice Areas: John Friel has been instrumental in shaping the law, and expanding the rights of parents and children throughout his career through his highly technical knowledge of the field. Following the publication of the draft Children's Schools and Families Bill, Educational Proposals, September 2012, John has been in the forefront of campaigning for substantial reforms. A number of amendments proposed by John were accepted. The Select Committee for Education, cited word for word from three representations settled by John. He has particular experience in public law issues concerning children, disability and mental health issues. He acts for private applicants, charities, independent schools, academies, maintained schools, governing bodies, and local authorities. He has won leading cases in the House of Lords, the Court of Appeal, the High Court and the Upper Tribunal. He has considerable understanding of expert issues and evidence, particularly in education, community care, disability and negligence related issues. John was Counsel for the parents in the case of S v Stanbridge Earls School, involving disability and sex discrimination and negligence.
Professional Memberships: Education Law Association, Administrative Law Bar Association, RSA, Constable Trust (Trustee), SOSSEN Trustee.
Publications: John regularly contributes chapters to books and has written on Education law and Special Educational Needs. He is due to publish a book on the new law.

FRYER-SPEDDING, James
9 St John Street, Manchester
0161 955 9000
commercial@9sjs.com
Featured in Chancery (Northern), Commercial Dispute Resolution (Northern)
Practice Areas: James Spedding specialises in chancery/commercial litigation and, in particular, professional negligence, trusts, probate and administration of estates, partnerships, real property, landlord and tenant, family provision, and commercial contract disputes.
Professional Memberships: Chancery Bar Association, Professional Negligence Bar Association, Northern Chancery Bar Association and Northern Circuit Commercial Bar Association.
Career: Called in 1994.
Personal: James Spedding studied law at King's College, London University (LLB (Hons), 1st Class) and then New College, Oxford (BCL, 1st Class). Chambers website - www.9sjs.com. Linkedin - http://uk.linkedin.com/in/jamesspedding.

FULLWOOD, Adam
Kings Chambers, Manchester
0845 034 3444
clerks@kingschambers.com
Featured in Administrative & Public Law (Northern), Civil Liberties & Human Rights (Northern), Court of Protection (All Circuits), Social Housing (Northern)
Practice Areas: Adam Fullwood's main areas of practice are public and administrative law (community care / adult social services, health care, medical treatment, mental capacity, housing, Inquests, prison and immigration),human rights law, Court of

Protection (welfare and property & affairs), public procurement and local government. Adam has a particular interest in the issue of statutory funding following compensation for catastrophic brain injuries.
Professional Memberships: Human Rights Lawyers Association The Constitutional & Administrative Law Bar Association Northern Administrative Law Association.
Career: He is a member of the Attorney General's regional panel. He is also a member of the Treasury Solicitor's Freedom of Information panel and the Equality and Human Rights Commission panel of Counsel.
Publications: Contributor to Community Care Law and Local Authority Handbook (2nd Edn) Jordans.

FURLONG, Richard
25 Bedford Row, London
020 7936 6300
rfurlong@carmelitechambers.co.uk
Featured in Financial Crime (London)
Practice Areas: He specialises in defending those accused of serious and complex fraud in criminal and related civil proceedings. His practice includes serious commercial and tax fraud of all types as well as corruption, money laundering, confiscation and restraint. He is often instructed privately and pre-charge. He also defends in other serious crime and undertakes regulatory, disciplinary and tribunal work. Accepts direct access where appropriate. Recent practice history available at Chambers website.
Professional Memberships: Criminal Bar Association.
Career: Called 1994. He was previously an investment analyst with Credit Lyonnais Securities. Educated Queens' College, Cambridge (MA, Economics).
Publications: Co-author of International Money Laundering & Terrorist Financing [Sweet & Maxwell], and Lexis PSL web content on the Bribery Act 2010. Also CPDCast podcasts on the Criminal Procedure Rules.
Personal: Interests include prosecuting offences under the Hunting Act 2004, advising and lecturing on fraud, bribery and money laundering.

FURST, Stephen QC
Keating Chambers, London
020 7544 2600
sfurst@keatingchambers.com
Featured in Construction (London), International Arbitration (London)
Practice Areas: Specialist in construction, engineering, energy, on-shore and off-shore plant, computer and technology related disputes along with professional negligence actions within these specialist areas. Regularly acts in complex cases of high-value in the UK High Courts and arbitrations, along with all forms of alternative dispute resolution. He also has a significant domestic and international practice as arbitrator and adjudicator, where he has developed a reputation for handling the most technically challenging cases. Recent appointments include arbitrations administered by the ICC, LCIA and DIAC. Accredited adjudicator and mediator of considerable experience.
Professional Memberships: LCIA, TECBAR, COMBAR, SCL.
Career: Called 1975; Queens Counsel 1991; Fellow of the Singapore Institute of Arbitrators 2003; Deputy Judge of TCC and recorder; approved arbitrator, Hong Kong International Arbitration Centre; Bencher, Middle Temple 2003.
Publications: Joint Editor Keating on Construction Contracts - Ninth Edition; Joint Editor, Construction Law Yearbook - 1994, 1995.

GAITSKELL, Robert QC
Keating Chambers, London
020 7544 2600
rgaitskell@keatingchambers.com
Featured in International Arbitration (London)
Practice Areas: Dual qualified engineer/lawyer specialist in construction, engineering and energy, particularly electrical, mechanical, and process engineering; instructed in numerous international and UK major disputes, (including frequent appointments as an arbitrator [including as Chairman of ICC tribunals] and Chairman of Dispute Boards) concerning, inter alia, complex projects (especially power stations), defence, computer facilities, chemical processing, food and drink production, oil and gas rigs, hospitals, motorways, bridges, tunnels, dredging, water treatment, airports, nuclear fuel processing and commercial property. Over 100 commercial, construction and intellectual property international arbitrations and over 100 mediations. CEDR accredited.
Professional Memberships: Chairman of the Joint IET/IMechE Committee on Model Forms (which produces the MF/1-4 suite of contracts); Technology and Construction Bar Association (Committee Member 1987-93); London Commercial & Common Law Bar Association (Committee Member 1987-2000); Commercial Bar Association (COMBAR); Singapore International Arbitration Centre 2006 (Fellow); CEDR Adjudication Panel.
Career: Called 1978; QC 1994; Vice President of the IEE (1998-2001); Senator of the Engineering Council (1997-2002), practised in UK and abroad as professional electrical engineer, Bencher of Gray's Inn. Recorder (part-time Judge); 2000-10; Chairman: ITER Nuclear Dispute Board.
Publications: Numerous publications on legal and engineering topics. Editor: 'Construction Dispute Resolution Handbook' (2nd Ed).

GALBRAITH, Amber
Compass Chambers, Edinburgh
0131 226 2881
amber.galbraith@compasschambers.com
Featured in Personal Injury (Scotland)
Practice Areas: Specialising in personal injury, clinical negligence and health and safety litigation, represents both pursuer and defender. Has extensive experience in conducting litigation in both the Court of Session and Sheriff Courts, including large-scale and complex litigation, fatal accident inquiries and public inquiries. Recent cases include: Anne MacKinnon v Thomas Hadfield [2014] CSOH 15 (proof on quantum); James Farmer v FTV Proclad [2013] CSOH 165 (proof on liability) John Cowan v Hopetoun House [2013] CSOH 9 (proof on liability); Fiona Dickie v Mohammadreza Khandani [2012] CSOH 122 (proof on quantum)
Professional Memberships: Representative of the Junior Bar on the Court of Session Personal Injuries User Group and Personal Injury Sub-Group of the Civil Justice Council Member of the Faculty of Advocates Professional Negligence Law Group.
Career: Admitted to Faculty of Advocates July 2005. Trained with Dundas & Wilson CS 1996 to 1998, then became prosecutor with COPFS. Part of Lockerbie trial team, and lead operational policy team in Crown Office. LlB (Hons) (Edinburgh Universtiy) (1995); DipLP (Edinburgh University) (1996); Diploma in Forensic Medicine (Glasgow University) (2001).
Publications: Trainer in legal courses for Health and Safety Executive, run by Warwick University, and has spoken at seminars organised by APIL and Compass Chambers.

GALBRAITH-MARTEN, Jason QC
Cloisters, London
020 7827 4000
JGM@cloisters.com
Featured in Employment (London)
Practice Areas: Hard work, dedication to the case, an ability to inspire confidence in clients and the expertise to persuade at all levels are just some of the attributes that have made Jason Galbraith-Marten QC one of the UK's pre-eminent labour and employment lawyers. He is especially valued for his ability to formulate a winning strategy in the most complex and challenging cases and to use the law creatively and imaginatively in pursuit of his client's best interests. Appointed Queen's Counsel in 2014 he is keen to play an ever greater role in the development of labour and employment law in the UK and internationally, representing a diverse range of clients. Over the past 18 months Jason has acted successfully for: East Midlands Trains to prevent hugely damaging industrial action; for a company providing security personnel in Afghanistan and Iraq to resist employment claims brought in the UK; for the Overseas Ship Holding Group Inc and the Ford Motor Company, both resisting claims brought under TUPE; and for Cambridge University and the University of Nottingham. He acted successfully for claimants against JP Morgan and Deutsche Bank in high value discrimination claims. He is currently representing over 4500 employees of Glasgow City Council in a class action challenging the job evaluation study used as the basis for pay and grading decisions and for several hundred former employees of IBM challenging as discriminatory changes to the company's final salary pension scheme. He is also acting for one of the most senior bank employees implicated in the LIBOR rate-fixing scandal.
Professional Memberships: Jason acts as a professional Mediator, was Chair of the Industrial Law Society from 2010 to 2013 and is a long-standing member of both the Employment Law Bar Association and the Employment Lawyers Association.
Career: Called to the Bar in 1991, Middle Temple Astbury Scholar. Inner Temple Pegasus Scholar to New Zealand in 1994. Chambers and Partners' Employment Junior of the Year 2009. Named as one of the 'Chambers 100' - the list of the top business lawyers in the UK - in 2014. Jason is also a Director of Assurety Ltd. an innovative witness training company.
Publications: Co-author of Bullen & Leake & Jacob's and of Butterworths Employment Law Guide. Contributor to Butterworths XpertHR online service.
Personal: The Campion School and Magdalene College, Cambridge.

GALLACHER, Kirsty
No5 Chambers, Birmingham
0845 210 5555
kg@no5.com
Featured in Family/Matrimonial (Midlands)
Practice Areas: Kirsty practises exclusively in family law, specialising in private and public law children matters and ancillary relief. Matters relating to children include all applications under Children Act 1989 and Adoption and Children Act 2002 with particular experience in applications to remove children from the jurisdiction. Kirsty regularly appears in complex care proceedings at all levels, including in the High Court, involving allegations of physical and sexual abuse, non- accidental injury, fabricated and induced illness and cases involving the death of a parent. Kirsty has particular expertise in jurisdictional matters and is instructed by Local Authorities to advise on the procedure concerning cases with an international element. Kirsty specialises in ancillary relief and is frequently instructed in cases involving substantial assets, third parties and foreign property. Kirsty's expertise includes cohabitation claims and applications under Schedule 1 of the Children Act 1989. Notable cases: Walsall MBC v KK & Anor [2013] EWHC 3192 (Fam).
Professional Memberships: Family Law Bar Association. Gray's Inn.
Career: Law LLB (Hons). Lecturers on the Post Qualified Social Work Course at Birmingham University.

GALLIVAN, Terence
Five Paper, London
07825 641074
terrygallivan@fivepaper.com
Featured in Social Housing (London)
Practice Areas: Principal practice areas (both contentious and advisory) landlord and tenant, property, service charge disputes, housing, homelessness.
Professional Memberships: HLPA, PBA.
Career: Terry was called to the Bar in 1981 after obtaining a first class honours degrees in law from the University of Durham and from the University Cambridge (in what is now known as the LLM). He studied at the University of California, Berkeley, as a Harkness Fellow. He specialises in landlord and tenant, housing, property, local government and public law and has appeared in a large number of leading cases in the House of Lords and the Court of Appeal in his specialist areas. He is regularly instructed in complex and difficult cases and has extensive experience as a trial advocate. He has a large advisory practice. Clients include local authorities, private registered providers of social housing and private individuals, both landlords and occupiers. Terry has significant experience of acting in disputes between Tenant Management Organisations and public authorities, including arbitration proceedings. He is authorised for direct access.

GALVIN, Kieran
Furnival Chambers, London
07971 581 367
kgalvin@furnivallaw.co.uk
Featured in Crime (London)
Practice Areas: Exclusively a defence advocate with a very detailed knowledge of police procedure and investigative techniques. Mr Galvin has tended to defend principally in the following areas: Serious Fraud Office cases and fraud cases gener-

ally, including those brought by the Inland Revenue as well as cases involving substantial undercover police operations and serious crime generally. In the last few years Mr Galvin has defended in major criminal cases by way of example- Operation Alpington- a Colombian 'supergrass' case and Operation Strait (the Bishops Stortford massacre) and Operation Kobus-a 14 month long investigation into a succesful businessman in the South West concerning allegations of perverting the course of justice, Operation Unbolt a £300 million money laundering case. Mr Galvin has defended in numerous fraud cases, two involving Chairmen of Football league clubs and others brought by the Special Compliance Office. Mr Galvin is an expert in cases involving the seizure of pre-cursor chemicals and has a detailed knowldge of ballistics evidence. He also has particular experience in confiscation cases, Customs cash seizure cases and resisting production orders. Regularly appears in front of the Police Appeals Tribunal. Mr Galvin has defended in many cases involving use of force and has a detailed knowledge of police disciplinary procedures. Mr Galvin is happy to accept instructions under the Direct Acces scheme. Mr Galvin is frequently instructed and advises before charges (criminal or disciplinary) are brought (most recently cases involving allegations of conspiracy to murder and conspiracy to defraud). Acts in Police Property Act matters and for individual officers at inquests. Undertakes a certain amount of pro bono CCRC work. Undertakes work on behalf of chemical supply companies now being targeted by SOCA. Regularly instructed by professionals to appear before disciplinary tribunals and inquests.
Professional Memberships: Criminal Bar Association.
Personal: Education: BA (Hons) Music (Newcastle University); LLB (Hons) (King's College, London). Personal interests include playing the piano (and listening-especially to Richter and Michelangeli), cycling and listening to music (Gesualdo, Mozart, Liszt, Bowling for Soup and Akon and Soft Cell), watching all sports particularly football (AFC Wimbledon), darts, cricket and boxing. Level 1 FA Coach. Spending time with my children.

GARLICK, Paul QC
Furnival Chambers, London
020 7405 3232
pgarlick@furnivallaw.co.uk
Featured in Extradition (London)
Practice Areas: Paul specialises in the fields of serious and corporate fraud (dealing with anti bribery and corruption regulation on an international basis); extradition (both in relation to requests made to the UK and also and also requests made to foreign states in the Commonwealth and the EU), human rights, EU criminal law, health and safety. Paul is an accredited mediator in commercial cases.
Professional Memberships: Extradition Lawyers Association; Supranational Environmental Justice Foundation (Founding Member and Vice President) ; International Academy for Environmental Sciences; Health and Safety Lawyers Association; European Criminal Bar Association.
Career: Paul was called in 1974 and took silk in 1996. Before taking silk, he was standing counsel to HM Customs and Excise. Since taking silk, his practice has become internationally based. He regularly advises and acts on behalf of international corporations in relation to anti-corruption regulation issues and other corporate criminal matters. Paul has extensive experience in extradition and has acted in several of the recent landmark extradition cases involving violation of human rights. He is one of the founding members and Vice President of the Supranational Environmental Justice Foundation in Venice and he is currently one of the experts appointed by the EU Commission to review and advise the EU Commission on European criminal law policy. Paul is an accredited mediator.
Personal: Paul is well known for his personable approach to cases and his ability to work as part of a team and to negotiate and mediate with regulatory and prosecutorial agencies. Having spent extensive periods working with international agencies such as the UN, the EU and the OSCE, he has a wealth of experience in dealing with international law issues on behalf of corporations and their officers and employees. The experience that he has gained in the international community has contributed greatly to his skills as a mediator.

GARNHAM, Neil QC
1 Crown Office Row, London
020 7797 7500
neil.garnham@1cor.com
Featured in Administrative & Public Law (London), Inquests & Public Inquiries (London)
Practice Areas: Principal areas of practice include judicial review and human rights, professional and clinical negligence, professional discipline, personal injury and public inquiries.
Professional Memberships: ALBA, HRLA, PNBA, PIBA, ARDL
Career: Called 1982; Junior Counsel to the Crown 1995-2001; Silk 2001; Recorder 2001; Junior Counsel to the Ladbroke Grove Rail Inquiry; Counsel to the Victoria Climbie Inquiry; Counsel for core participants in Baha Mousa, Leveson and Al-Sweady Inquiries; Bencher Middle Temple 2008; Deputy High Court Judge 2008. Member of the bar in the British Virgin Islands, an attorney in Trinidad and has conducted cases for both Claimant and Defendant in the Cayman Islands.
Personal: Educated Ipswich School and Peterhouse, Cambridge.

GARNIER, Edward QC
One Brick Court, London
020 7353 8845
eg@onebrickcourt.com
Featured in Defamation/Privacy (London)
Practice Areas: Defamation, malicious falsehood, contempt, reporting restrictions, breach of confidence, passing off, privacy and related human rights law. Cases of interest include: Loughran v Century Newspapers; Lord McAlpine v BBC, Lord McAlpine v ITV, Lord McAlpine v Sally Bercow, Lewis & Ors v R. Re Attorney General's Reference No. 15, 16 & 17 of 2012 [2012] EWCA Crim 1414 (01 June 2012); Thompson, Re Attorney-General's Reference No 103 of 2011 [2012] EWCA Crim 135 (10 February 2012); Rollings, R v [2012] EWCA Crim 86 (03 February 2012); A-G v Frail (2011) EWCA Crim 1570 Contempt of Court (Facebook jury contempt case, first case of its kind); Attorney General Reference No 18 of 2011 [2011] EWCA Crim 1300 (12 May 2011); Khan, R. v [2010] EWCA Crim 2880 (09 December 2010);R v Pyo, Anigbugu & McGee 2011 (CA) 3 separate "safe haven" rapes/sexual assaults on women in their home or workplace. Sentences increased respectively from 8 years to 15, 8 to 15, and from an extended sentence of 12 years 6 months to 14 years 6 months
Career: Called to the Bar 1976, Middle Temple; QC 1995; Bencher 2001. MP for Harborough since 1992; Knighted 2012; Solicitor General 2010-12; Shadow Attorney General 1997-2001 and 2009-10. Called to the Northern Ireland Bar 2010. Developed Deferred Prosecution Agreements (Section 45 and Schedule 17 of The Crime and Courts Act 2013) for use in cases of corporate bribery, money laundering and other economic crimes.
Publications: Contributor to Halsbury's Laws of England 4th ed Vol 45, Telecommunications & Broadcasting Law.
Personal: Wellington College, Berkshire; Jesus College, Oxford. Interests; Music, cricket, shooting, travel & history. Language, French.

GARRETT, Lucy
Keating Chambers, London
020 7544 2600
lgarrett@keatingchambers.com
Featured in Construction (London), International Arbitration (London), Professional Negligence (London)
Practice Areas: Impressive specialist practice in construction, engineering and energy, including all forms of marine and offshore construction. Her practice includes claims for and against professionals in these sectors and project-related issues such as insurance, bonds and guarantees. She is a popular and determined advocate with extensive experience in both the TCC and the Commercial Court (and won C&P Construction Junior of the Year 2013). Lucy is frequently instructed in international arbitration proceedings; her international work includes major infrastructure or energy-related projects, often in the Gulf and the Asia-Pacific region, but also in Africa and South America. She has wide experience of arbitrations conducted in accordance with the laws of civil code jurisdictions and with international parties and Tribunals. Lucy particularly enjoys disputes involving complex technical issues. Her approach is focused, practical and commercial.
Professional Memberships: SCL (UK and Hong Kong); TecBAR; ComBAR.
Career: Called 2001, Gray's Inn. Prince of Wales Scholar.
Publications: Keating on Construction Contractors (9th Edition); Keating on JCT Contracts; Keating on Offshore Construction (forthcoming).

GATTY, Daniel
Hardwicke, London
020 7242 2523
daniel.gatty@hardwicke.co.uk
Featured in Real Estate Litigation (London)
Practice Areas: Daniel Gatty specialises in property litigation including landlord and tenant, real property (especially easements, boundaries and covenants), land registration, mortgages and secured lending, enfranchisement. His practice also encompasses professional negligence (usually property related) and commercial/Chancery disputes. Recent reported cases include Mortgage Business plc v O'Shaughnessy [2012] 1 WLR 1521, Franks v Chief Land Registrar [2012] 1 All ER 326, Seeff v Ho [2011] PLSCS 102, Family Mosaic HA v Pimlico School HA [2011] All ER (D) 18 (Dec). Daniel has recently appeared in the Supreme Court in Scott v Southern Pacific Mortgages Ltd (judgment awaited at the time of writing).
Professional Memberships: Property Bar Association (formerly Secretary), Chancery Bar Association, Professional Negligence Bar Association.
Career: Called to the Bar in 1990. Sits as Judge of First Tier Tribunal (Property Chamber, Land Registration). ADR Group accredited mediator.

GAUNT, Jonathan QC
Falcon Chambers, London
020 7427 7307
gaunt@falcon-chambers.com
Featured in Agriculture & Rural Affairs (London), Real Estate Litigation (London)
Practice Areas: All aspects of commercial and residential landlord and tenant and property law, including easements, restrictive covenants, rent and rent review and property-related litigation.
Professional Memberships: Chancery Bar Association; LCLCBA; Property Bar Association.
Career: Educated at Radley College; University College, Oxford (BA); called 1972 (Lincoln's Inn); Silk 1991; Joint Head of Falcon Chambers since 1992; Bencher 1998; Deputy High Court Judge 2001.
Publications: Joint Editor, Halsbury's Laws 'Landlord and Tenant' volume, having re-written the chapters on repairing covenants, rent and rent review; joint editor, Gale on Easements 1997, 2002, 2008 and 2012 editions.
Personal: Interests: Golf, sailing.

GAVAGHAN, Jonathan
Ten Old Square, London
020 7405 0758
jonathangavaghan@tenoldsquare.com
Featured in Chancery (London), Partnership (London)
Practice Areas: Jonathan Gavaghan has a busy chancery and commercial practice. He has particular expertise in partnership/LLP, commercial and property litigation in both the High Court and arbitration. Company law (including breach of fiduciary duty claims and shareholder disputes) is a further area in which he specialises.
Professional Memberships: He is a member of the Chancery Bar Association, Property Bar Association and Association of Partnership Practitioners. He is a former Chairman of the Young Bar and has served two terms as an elected member of the Bar Council.
Career: Called 1992. Notable cases include: Patley Wood Farm LLP v Brake [2013] EWHC 4035 (Ch) (Arbitration/Partnership); Chaudhary v Yavuz [2013] Ch 239 (Constructive trusts, real property); Clarence House v Nat West Bank [2010] 1 WLR 1216 (virtual assignments); Manning v English [2010] Bus LR D89 (2010) (partnership); Re Claygreen Limited [2006] BCLC 715 (company law: pre-emption rights); Harris v Wallis [2006] All ER (D) 158 (security for costs); West Hampstead Management Co Ltd v Pearl Property Ltd [2002] 3 EGLR 55 (leasehold enfranchisement); Yeoman's Row Limited v London RAC [2002] All ER (D) 148 (landlord and tenant); R v Secretary of State for Environment, Transport and the Regions ex parte Spath Holme Ltd [2001] 2 AC 349 (public law/landlord and tenant); Loder-Dyer v Cadogan [2001] 3 EGLR 149

(leasehold enfranchisement); Spath Holme v North Western RAC [2001] 3 EGLR 30 (landlord and tenant); R v South Bank University ex p Coggeran [2000] ICR 1342 (public law/discrimination); Curtis v London RAC [1999] QB 92 (landlord and tenant); Globe Equities v Globe Legal Services [1999] BLR 232 (costs orders against third parties).
Personal: Jonathan Gavaghan studied law at Oxford University where he obtained a first class degree. Top of his year in Land Law, he subsequently obtained a BCL and returned to Worcester College Oxford as a visiting tutor in constitutional law.

GEEKIE, Charles QC
1 Garden Court Family Law Chambers, London
020 7797 7900
geekie@1gc.com
Featured in Family/Matrimonial (London)
Practice Areas: The law relating to children, including public and private law cases and abduction; complex residence cases and those involving relocation, representing local authorities, parents and guardians in public law and adoption cases, complex care cases involving fatalities, serious injuries, sexual and emotional abuse and cases where there is a conflict of medical evidence.
Professional Memberships: Member of FLBA committee. Association of Lawyers for Children. International Bar Association.
Career: Called 1985. Joined 1 Garden Court 1999. Silk 2006. Family Recorder 2006. Joint Head of Chambers 2013.
Publications: Contributor to Family Law. Specialist contributor to Rayden and Jackson on divorce and family matters. Contributor to Halsbury's Laws (children). Drafted training protocol for expert witnesses; run, jointly with senior consultant psychiatrists, training sessions for expert witnesses; drafted FLBA response to Government consultation on Expert Witnesses.
Personal: Interests: cycling, hill walking, theatre.

GEORGE, Sarah
St Philips Chambers, Birmingham
0121 246 7000
sgeorge@st-philips.com
Featured in Employment (Midlands)
Practice Areas: Sarah returned to the Midlands Bar in October 2010 following a career break living in the Far East when she co-wrote 'Discrimination in Employment'. Employment is now her sole specialty, principally appearing in the Employment Tribunal and advising on matters within that jurisdiction. She has a particular interest in discrimination law. She regularly handles multi-day cases which are complex both factually and legally. Her clients include public authorities such as NHS Trusts, universities and local authorities as well as individual and corporate employers. She represents both claimants and respondents.
Professional Memberships: ELA, ELBA.
Career: Called in 1991. Appointed as a fee paid employment judge in February 2011.
Publications: 'Discrimination in Employment' (Katherine Tucker and Sarah George) published by Thomson: Sweet & Maxwell (2006) and updated four times per year. Co-editor (with Katherine Tucker) of 'Equality Law Reports' published six times per year by Michael Rubinstein Publishing.
Personal: Sarah enjoys cycling, visiting the theatre and cheering on her local junior rugby team.

GHALY, Karim
Thirty Nine Essex Street, London
020 7832 1116
karim.ghaly@39essex.com
Featured in Construction (London), International Arbitration (London)
Practice Areas: Construction and civil engineering. Energy. Professional negligence. Insurance. Practice primarily consists of substantial construction, commercial or insurance disputes. Karim has acted in litigation and arbitration arising out of major projects in the United Kingdom, the Middle East, South America and South East Asia.
Professional Memberships: COMBAR, IBA, TECBAR.
Career: Oxford University 1995-98: First class honours degree in law. Called to the Bar in 2001.
Publications: Wilken and Ghaly, "The Law of Waiver, Variation and Estoppel", 3rd Edition, OUP. Contributor to "Construction Contracts" by Richard Wilmot-Smith QC, 3rd Edition, OUP.

GHOSH, Julian QC
Pump Court Tax Chambers, London
020 7414 8080
jghosh@pumptax.com
Featured in Tax (London)
Practice Areas: Julian Ghosh's practice covers all areas of taxation. He is particularly well known for his corporate tax work and that involving European taxation issues. Recent notable cases include Schofield v HMRC (Court of Appeal); Land Securities plc v HMRC (Upper Tribunal); Newey t/a Ocean Finance (CJUE); Aberdeen Asset Management Ltd v HMRC (Court of Session).
Professional Memberships: Revenue Bar Association; Bar European Group.
Career: Called 1993; QC 2006; Called to the Scottish Bar (1999); QC (Scotland) 2010. Academic positions: Visiting Professor, University of Leiden; Lector, Trinity College, Cambridge; Visiting Fellow, Fitzwilliam College, Cambridge; Judge of the First-tier and deputy Judge of the Upper Tax Tribunals.

GIBBON, Michael QC
Maitland Chambers, London
020 7406 1200
mgibbon@maitlandchambers.com
Featured in Chancery (London), Company (London), Restructuring/Insolvency (London), Tax (London)
Practice Areas: Commercial chancery practice, in particular for the Department of Business Innovation and Skills (formerly DTI) (company law, insolvency) and HM Revenue & Customs (insolvency, tax, trusts), as well as general commercial litigation. Cases include: In re Modern Jet Support [2005] 1 WLR 3880 (insolvency); West v Trennery [2005] 1 All ER 827 (tax, trusts); Schmidt v Rosewood [2003] 2 AC 709 (trusts); Euroafrica Shipping Lines v Zegluga Polska [2004] 2 BCLC 97 (company, commercial); Gamlestaden v Baltic Partners [2007] BCC 272 (company); Thomas and Agnes Carvel Foundation v Carvel [2008] 2 WLR 1234 (wills, trusts); DCC v HMRC [2011], 1 WLR 44 (tax, commercial).
Professional Memberships: Chancery Bar Association, COMBAR, Wales & Chester Circuit.
Career: Investment banker, then called to the Bar 1993, Junior Counsel to the Crown from 1999, on A Panel 2007-11, QC 2011.
Publications: An editor of the White Book.
Personal: Educated at Magdalen College Oxford (BA, 1st class); King's College Cambridge (MPhil).

GIBBONS, Ellodie
Tanfield Chambers, London
020 7421 5300
egibbons@tanfieldchambers.co.uk
Featured in Real Estate Litigation (London)
Practice Areas: Commercial and residential landlord and tenant, real property and associated professional negligence. Particular expertise in service charge disputes, leasehold enfranchisement, rights of first refusal and RTM. Cases include London Borough Camden v. 4767 Leaseholders, Unreported, 2014, FTT(PC)(Service charges, management charge); Money v. Cadogan Holdings Ltd [2013] UKUT 0211 (LC)(enfranchisement, valuation, value arising from the ability to release restrictive covenants); Westmacott v. Ackerman [2012] UKUT 415 (LC)(enfranchisement, houses converted into flats, valuation); Barrie House Freehold Limited v Merie Bin Mahfouz Company (UK) Limited [2012] EWHC Ch (enfranchisement, easements, injunctions); Palley v. London Borough Camden [2011] UKUT 469 (LC)(service charges, management costs); Calladine-Smith v. Saveorder Ltd [2011] EWHC 2501 Ch (lease extension, service of notices, Interpretation Act 1978); Sherwood Hall (East End Road) Management Company Limited v Magnolia Tree Limited [2009] UKUT 158 LC (enfranchisement, deferment rate, 88 year reversions).
Professional Memberships: Property Bar Association, Chancery Bar Association, Association of Leasehold Enfranchisement Practitioners.
Career: Lancaster Girls' Grammar School, MA (Law) Emmanuel College, Cambridge, Called 1999, Barrister of the Year, Enfranchisement and Right to Manage Awards 2011
Publications: Contributor to 'Service Charges and Management' 1st, 2nd and 3rd editions (Sweet & Maxwell) co-author 'Leasehold Enfranchisement Explained' (RICS).
Personal: Travel, dancing, skiing.

GIBBS, Georgina
36 Bedford Row, London
020 7421 8000
clerks@36bedfordrow.co.uk
Featured in Crime (South Eastern)
Practice Areas: Georgina specialises in defending and prosecuting in sexual offences, incorporating recent and historic familial and paedophile abuse, indecent images, and multi-perpetrator cases. Consequently, she is highly adept at handling vulnerable witnesses and defendants alike. She practices primarily in London, but also across the South Eastern and Midland Circuits. Her experience includes cases of murder, manslaughter, serious violence, death by dangerous, fraud, multi-defendant drugs cases and associated POCA proceedings. Those who instruct her remark upon her meticulous attention to detail, and her willingness to work exceptionally hard over and above the minimum required. Recent cases include being instructed as Leading counsel to prosecute a 10 handed drugs conspiracy, defending a hypnotherapist accused of sexual assault, and defending in a 4 handed conspiracy to commit armed robbery. She is also available to accept Direct Access instructions.
Professional Memberships: Immediate Past Recorder South Eastern Circuit 2011-2013, Junior of South Eastern Circuit 2012-2013. Member Criminal Bar Association. Appointed by Lord Justice Pitchford as a barrister panel member to adjudicate on barrister disciplinary hearings.
Personal: Warwick University LLB, and French law at Brodeaux University. Married with 2 children, living in Islington, London.

GIBBS, Patrick QC
3 Raymond Buildings Barristers, London
020 7400 6400
patrick.gibbs@3rblaw.com
Featured in Inquests & Public Inquiries (London), Professional Discipline (London), Crime (London), Financial Crime (London)
Practice Areas: Advice and advocacy at all stages of criminal and 'quasi-criminal' investigations, regulatory and disciplinary proceedings, deaths in custody, inquests and public inquiries. Recent notable work: Professional fraud; market abuse; murder/manslaughter; insider dealing; misconduct in public office; corruption; sanctions busting; police shootings; tax avoidance; money laundering. Recent inquiries: Litvinenko; Leveson; 7/7; Tomlinson; Saunders; De Menezes; Climbie. For more information go to www.3rblaw.com.
Professional Memberships: CBA; ARDL; FLA.
Career: Oxford 1981; City 1984; Called 1986; QC 2006.

GIBSON, Charles QC
Henderson Chambers, London
020 7583 9020
cgibson@hendersonchambers.co.uk
Featured in Environment (London), Health & Safety (London), Product Liability (London)
Practice Areas: Common law/commercial with an emphasis on product liability and insurance law (including group actions), health and safety, environmental law, professional negligence, insurance, disciplinary and regulatory law, sports law. Notable cases include: the Abidjan litigation; the Atomic Veterans litigation; the Buncefield litigation; the Seroxat litigation; the Sabril litigation; the Potters Bar Inquest; Borchard VMPC; Connelly v RTZ; Lubbe v Cape plc; Hodgson v Imperial Tobacco (the tobacco litigation); Bass Britvic v Terra; the Opren litigation; the Benzodiazepine litigation; Garland v West Wiltshire District Council; The Norplant litigation; the MMR litigation; group actions involving Prozac, Lariam, Minocin, Shiley heart valve, breast implants, drink contamination; the organo-phosphate litigation; the interest rate swap litigation; asbestos claims, mine radiation injury claims; other product liability cases for various manufacturers and producers; the Potters Bar Inquest; the King's Cross and Clapham Inquiries for the London Fire Brigade; the Severn Tunnel Inquiry.
Professional Memberships: PNBA. Common Law and Commercial Bar Association. Commercial Bar Association.
Career: Educated Wellington College; BA Hons Durham (Classics); Dip Law. Called to the Bar 1984. Author: 'Group Actions - Product Liability Law and Insurance'. CEDR Accredited Mediator. Recorder. Bencher of the Inner Temple. Head of Chambers.
Personal: Born 1960. Married with four children.

GIDNEY, Jonathan
St Philips Chambers, Birmingham
0121 246 7000
jgidney@st-philips.com
Featured in Employment (Midlands)
Practice Areas: Jonathan Gidney is a specialist employment practitioner with substantial experience in all aspects of employment law. He regularly appears in Employment Tribunals across the country and in the EAT. He undertakes complex multi-day discrimination proceedings (e.g. Ansar v Lloyds Bank Plc [2007] IRLR 211, CA) and has a proven track record in handling litigants in person in difficult cases and at putting his client's own witnesses at ease (including a recent instruction on a sex discrimination claim involving multiple allegations of rape). He has an exellent eye for detail, is always well prepared and has an effective advocacy style in Tribunal. In addition to his expertise in all types of discrimination, Jonathan undertakes all types of employment law, including TUPE, service provision change, redundancy and unfair dismissal. Jonathan regularly accepts instructions from local authorities, NHS Trusts, banks and large retail organisations.
Professional Memberships: Employment Lawyers Association; Employment Law Bar Association.
Career: Jonathan was appointed as an accredited CEDR Mediator in February 2004.
Publications: Connected Lender Liability, New Law Journal 24 May 1996; Walking the Reference Tightrope, New Law Journal 4 September 2001; Bias in Tribunal, ELA Briefing April 2009.

GILCHRIST, Naomi
St Philips Chambers, Birmingham
0121 246 0200
ngilchrist@st-phillips.com
Featured in Crime (Midlands), Health & Safety (Midlands)
Practice Areas: Naomi conducts a heavy weight practice in all areas of serious/ organised crime, criminal regulatory work and licensing. In serious/ organised crime, her work principally involves complex, high value fraud, business/ corporate crime, corruption and misconduct in public office, and homicide offences, including gross negligence/ corporate manslaughter. She is known and respected for her ability to deal with cases involving complex medical and scientific evidence. In the regulatory field, her experience is wide ranging and at all levels. She is regularly instructed to advise and appear on behalf of companies and individuals who are charged with offences under health and safety, food safety and product safety legislation, including fatal and serious injury cases. She is an experienced inquest advocate and also conducts hearings before disciplinary tribunals. She provides specialist advice in relation to RIPA 2000. Her approach is always professional and meticulous, but user friendly. Customer service is high on her list of priorities.
Career: Qualified as solicitor 1994; Called to the Bar 1996.

GILLETT, Emily
Erskine Chambers, London
020 7242 5532
clerks@erskinechambers.com
Featured in Chancery (London), Fraud (London)
Practice Areas: Emily has a broad commercial chancery practice, with experience in complex onshore and offshore litigation and arbitration. She was recognised as one of 10 'Stars at the Bar' by Legal Week in 2010, after only four years in practice. Emily has particular expertise in multi-jurisdictional commercial fraud cases (often with foreign law elements) and applications for interim relief (including freezing injunctions, receivership orders, search and seizure orders, disclosure orders, passport orders, and applications for cross-examination) as well as contempt applications. Her reported cases include: JSC BTA Bank v Solodchenko [2011] 1 WLR 888; JSC BTA Bank v Kythreotis [2012] 1 WLR 350; JSC BTA Bank v Ablyazov (No 9) [2013] 1 WLR 1845.
Professional Memberships: Chancery Bar Association; COMBAR.
Personal: Emily obtained a first class degree in Law and French Law from UCL (having spent her third year of study at Université Paris II where she gained a Licence en droit). Emily's leisure interests include horse riding and Formula One motor racing.

GILLIES, Jennie
4 Pump Court, London
020 7842 5555
jgillies@4pumpcourt.com
Featured in Construction (London)
Practice Areas: Principal areas of practice are construction and engineering disputes, with a particular emphasis on adjudication; professional liability claims (involving architects, engineers, accountants, surveyors and solicitors); general insurance, energy and IT disputes.
Professional Memberships: TECBAR, Society of Construction Law, Professional Negligence Bar Association and COMBAR.
Career: King's College Cambridge MA (History). Called to Bar 2000. Tenant at 4 Pump Court since October 2001.

GILLIS, Richard QC
One Essex Court, London
020 7583 2000
rg@oeclaw.co.uk
Featured in Commercial Dispute Resolution (London), Fraud (London), Restructuring/Insolvency (London)
Practice Areas: Richard has a broad practice, with a particular expertise in complex commercial cases where corporate issues arise in a litigation context. Following the near-collapse of the Icelandic banking system, he acted for the liquidators of Glitnir Bank and for creditors of Kaupthing Singer & Friedlander. He is a veteran of the Barings litigation, where he acted for the liquidators on their professional negligence claims against the bank's former auditors. In recent years he has been heavily involved in many of the large scale disputes arising from the privatisation of state assets in Russia and other CIS countries. He acted for the Part 20 Defendants in the long running TadAZ litigation (relating to an aluminium smelter in Tajikistan), represented joint-venturers in a Russian oil and gas investment, and acted for Boris Berezovsky in his high profile multi-billion dollar claim against Roman Abramovich regarding Sibneft and Rusal. As a consequence he has frequently litigated claims under foreign laws – including Russian, Tajik and Kazakh. He is currently acting for the directors of a collapsed Cayman hedge fund, and recently acted for parties disputing a controlling shareholding interest in the London Stock Exchange. In addition, Richard has substantial experience of financial services investigations and disciplinary proceedings. As well as appearing in the Senior Courts in England and Wales, he has wide experience of litigating before many other tribunals, having appeared in the European Court of First Instance, the Courts of Gibraltar, Cayman and the Isle of Man, and LCIA and Stockholm Chamber of Commerce arbitrations.
Professional Memberships: Chancery Bar Association and COMBAR.
Career: Called to the Bar in 1982. Took silk 2006. He has also been called to the Bar in the Isle of Man, Gibraltar and Cayman.
Personal: Educated at Sandbach School 1966-77; Balliol College, Oxford 1977-80 (BA) (first in law); Balliol College, Oxford 1980-81 (BCL). Born 1958. Lives in London.

GILLYON, Philip
Erskine Chambers, London
020 7242 5532
pgillyon@erskinechambers.com
Featured in Company (London)
Practice Areas: Company law, corporate insolvency, financial services. Cases include Re BSB Holdings Ltd [1996] 1 BCLC 155; Possfund Custodian Trustee Ltd v Diamond [1996] 1 WLR 1351; Re Exchange Travel (Holdings) Ltd [1996] 2 BCLC 524; Guinness Peat Group plc v British Land Company plc [1999] 2 BCLC 243 (CA); Banco Nacional de Cuba v Cosmos Trading Corporation [2000] 1 BCLC 813 (CA); Jarvis plc v PricewaterhouseCoopers [2000] 2 BCLC 368; Banca Carige v Banco Nacional de Cuba [2001] 2 BCLC 407; Re Joseph Holt Group plc [2001] 2 BCLC 604 (CA); Re Leyland Daf Ltd [2001] 1 BCLC 419 (Ch), [2002] 1 BCLC 571(CA); Re Anglo American Insurance Co Ltd [2002] BCC 715; P&P Design plc v PricewaterhouseCoopers [2002] 2 BCLC 648; Re Queens Moat Houses plc [2003] 1 BCLC 696 (CA); EIC Services Ltd v Phipps [2004] 2 BCLC 589; Re Queens Moat Houses plc (No 2) [2005] 1 BCLC 136; Sisu Capital Fund Ltd v Tucker (No 1) [2006] BCC 463; (No 2) [2006] BCC 577; Secretary of State for the DBERR v Amway (UK) Ltd [2008] BCC 713 (Ch), [2009] BCC 781 (CA); Royal Bank of Scotland plc v Hicks & Ors [2010] EWHC 2579 (Takeover of Liverpool Football Club); Jackson v Dear [2012] EWHC 2060 (Ch), [2014] 1 BCLC 186 (CA); S&K Group Ltd v Mortgage Agency Services No 1 Ltd [2014] EWHC (Ch).
Professional Memberships: Commercial Bar Association; Chancery Bar Association; Insolvency Lawyers' Association; Financial Services Lawyers Association; Middle Temple.
Career: Hymers College (1974-84); Downing College, Cambridge (1984-87). Called 1988. Joined Erskine Chambers 1989.
Personal: Born 1965. Lives in London.

GILROY, Paul QC
9 St John Street, Manchester
01619 559 000
paul.gilroy@9sjs.com
Featured in Employment (Northern), Sports Law (The Regions)
Practice Areas: Predominantly Employment-based practice. Senior Executive claims (for and against). High value Employment Tribunal claims (serious financial and/ or reputational issues and/or matters of precedent value for or against companies or trade unions). Class actions (for and against employers/employees). Restrictive covenants. Substantial claims with Employment/Sports overlap. Special interest in regulatory work (sport and non-sport; sitting and representing). Special interest in Public Inquiries (Ashworth Hospital/Harold Shipman).
Professional Memberships: ELA, ELBA.
Career: 2000: Part-time Chairman of Employment Tribunals (now Part-Time Employment Judge). 2006: Queen's Counsel. 2007: Member of Disputes Resolution Panel of SDRP (now Sport Resolutions (UK)). 2007: Specialist Member of the Judicial Panel of the Football Association. 2009: Member of the Appeal Board Chairman Panel of the Football Association. 2009: Retained by the League Managers Association to advise and act on behalf of football managers in relation to regulatory and employment matters. 2009: Legal Member of the National Anti-Doping Panel. Recent Work (Employment): Retained by Police Superintendents' Association in indirect age discrimination class action against 5 police forces on behalf of 22 Superintendents and Chief Superintendents forced to retire under Regulation A19 of the Police Pension Regulations (February 2013). Claims successful. Multi-million compensation now being pursued. Appointed by Vice Chancellor of a University of to conduct and chair 6 separate grievance hearings concerning senior academics. Advising leading UK "umbrella company" on business modelling to comply with National Minimum Wage and Working Time legislation. 30 day whistleblowing claim for NHS Chief Executive (part-heard). Secured £1.8m compensation for FD of a bank in whistleblowing claim. Succeeded in claim and then resisted appeal. Initial offer was £120,000. Recent Work (Sport): Retained by Scottish Gymnastics Association to conduct Independent Inquiry into issues resulting in loss of state funding. David O'Leary v Al Ahli (FC) (Court of Arbitration for Sport, Lausanne) (outcome pending). Chaired National Anti-Doping Panel in the matter of Tinklin (Drugs in Sport - Boxing). Chaired 2014 Commonwealth Games Selection Appeal Panel (England Table Tennis Squad). Unrivalled experience of (ie highest number of cases before) the Premier League Managers Arbitration Tribunal: (1) Alan Curbishley v West Ham United. (2) Burnley v Owen Coyle. (3) Martin O'Neill v Aston Villa. (4) Norwich City v Paul Lambert and Aston Villa. (5) Mark Hughes v QPR. (6) Nigel Adkins v Southampton. (7) Michael Laudrup v Swansea City. (8) Malky Mackay v Cardiff City. Unrivalled experience of football manager representation. Has acted in last two years for Brendan Rodgers, David Moyes, Sir Alex Ferguson, Roberto Martinez, Roy Hodgson, Alan Pardew, Steve Clarke, Alex McLeish, Harry Redknapp, Nigel Adkins, Tony Pulis, Mark Hughes, Chris Hughton, Martin O'Neill, Roy Keane, Paul Lambert, Malky Mackay, Tim Sherwood, Gus Poyet, Sean Dyche and Roberto Di Matteo.

GIROLAMI, Paul QC
Maitland Chambers, London
020 7406 1200
pgirolami@maitlandchambers.com
Featured in Chancery (London), Commercial Dispute Resolution (London), Company (London), Fraud (London), Offshore (London), Restructuring/Insolvency (London)
Practice Areas: Paul is a Deputy High Court Judge for the Queens' Bench & Chancery Divisions of the High Court. He

took silk in April 2002, having been one of the Junior Counsel to the Crown for about nine years. He appears in courts in England and Wales and in overseas jurisdictions and has given expert evidence of English law to foreign courts. His experience includes: commercial litigation (including fiduciary duties; rights over assets or property; charges and securities; financial instruments; and the acquisition or sale of businesses and shares): company (including technical company law issues, shareholder disputes; directors' duties and disqualification): insolvency and corporate recovery (including administration and voluntary arrangements; claims involving liquidators, administrators or trustees) and civil fraud. He is called to the bar in the BVI and Gibraltar and registered with rights of audience in the DIFC.

Professional Memberships: Chancery Bar Association; COMBAR; Insolvency Lawyers Association; Financial Services Lawyers Association.

Career: Called to the Bar, 1983. Junior Counsel to the Crown (Chancery) 1991-2000. QC 2002.

Personal: Born 5 December 1959. Educated St Paul's School London and Corpus Christi College, Cambridge. Lives in London.

GLANCY, Robert QC

Devereux, London
020 7353 7534
glancy@devchambers.co.uk

Featured in Clinical Negligence (London), Personal Injury (London)

Practice Areas: Specialises in all aspects of personal injury; clinical negligence and professional negligence.

Professional Memberships: PIBA.

Career: 2010 – A President, First Tier Tribunal Health and Safety Committee (Mental Health) for restricted cases 2008 – Appointed CEDR accredited mediator 1999 – Recorder 1999 – A President, Mental Health Review Tribunal 1997 – Appointed Silk 1993-1999 – Assistant Recorder.

GLASER, Michael

Fourteen, London
020 7242 0858
mglaser@fourteen.co.uk

Featured in Family/Matrimonial (London)

Practice Areas: Prior to his call to the Bar, Michael worked in finance for five years and then qualified as a commercial solicitor specialising in intellectual property law. He crossed over to the family Bar in 1998. Michael practices a wide range of family work including financial remedy, trusts and cohabitation disputes, public and private Children Act work, together with associated civil matters. Within his financial remedy work, which is the principal area of his practice, he specialises in cases which have an added dimension such as trusts, bankruptcy, partnerships and companies. Reported cases include F v F (S Intervening) (Financial Provision: Bankruptcy: Reviewable Disposition) ([2003] 1 FLR 911), in which a husband's bankruptcy was set aside and his award drastically reduced, due to his conduct, as well as Rossi ([2007] 1 FLR 790), in which an ancillary relief claim was successfully defended, in its entirety, due to delay and non-contribution to the marital acquest. Over the years, Michael has acted in a number of important reported cases including representing a husband in a 'big money' case involving wholly pre-acquired assets (R v R [2009] EWHC 1267 (Fam), a contested trusts of land case involving questions of sham transfers and illegality (Ashby v Kilduff [2010] EWHC 2034 (Ch)), a case where the Husband's assets were said to be tied up in a Jersey Trust (D v D and I Trust ([2011] 2 FLR 29) and a successful appeal to the Court of Appeal reducing a 'joint lives' maintenance order to a term order (N v N [2011] EWCA Civ 940). Michael continues to represent HRH Sheikh Ahmed bin Saeed Al-Maktoum [2011] EWHC B27 (Fam) in the first case dealing with whether an Islamic marriage performed in this country would be valid for the purposes of a nullity petition. The facts of the case make interesting reading, however, the court agreed that an Islamic marriage, whilst it may have significance for the parties involved, would not be a route for a purported wife to obtain the raft of financial remedies which can be applied for following a nullity petition. He has also successfully enforced an arbitration clause in a foreign pre-marital agreement where the assets were $140m (T v T [2012] EWHC 3462 (Fam)). His recent cases include (successfully) clarifying the law in the Court of Appeal regarding when orders can be set aside N v N [2014] EWCA Civ 314) and avoiding a Xydhias agreement being converted an order thus increasing his client's award by £2m. In addition to acting in high net worth cases, Michael frequently represents interveners in divorce matters (including acting for beneficiaries of trusts, such as children on settlement variations through the official solicitor), and parents involved in private law disputes including those with an international element such as relocation cases. As a result of his experience, both prior to being Called to the Bar, and whilst at it, Michael brings a breadth of experience to his work.

GLASGOW, Oliver

2 Hare Court, London
020 7353 5324
oliverglasgow@2harecourt.com

Featured in Crime (London)

Practice Areas: Oliver Glasgow was appointed Junior Treasury Counsel in 2009, and is included on the Attorney-General's list of approved counsel. He "courts high market esteem as one of the best juniors in the field" and was nominated for Criminal Junior of the Year 2011. He has a reputation for detailed preparation, exceptional advocacy and is "an especially good cross-examiner". He is recommended as a Band 1 leading junior by the Chambers UK guide, which describes him as "something special" and predicts his rise to the top is "all but certain". He divides his practice between working at the highest level in the criminal sphere and specialising in complicated and serious quasi-criminal and regulatory work – "his diligence and broad knowledge come to the fore in his busy practice". He regularly appears in high profile trials of the utmost gravity on behalf of the major prosecuting authorities and the principal defence solicitors – "he is hard working and fearless". His practice has seen an increasing emphasis on defending in regulatory and health and safety work, and inquests – his advocacy skills are "something special" and he is "commercial, hard-working and very approachable... and deals with extremely difficult clients very well".

Career: Called 1995 - Middle Temple. South Eastern Circuit.

GLASSBROOK, Alex

Temple Garden Chambers, London
020 7583 1315
ag@tgchambers.com

Featured in Consumer Law (London), Fraud (All Circuits)

Practice Areas: Consumer law (particularly credit hire), costs, insurance (particularly motor insurance fraud), personal injury.

Professional Memberships: Personal Injury Bar Association, Bar Human Rights Committee, International Committee of Bar Council, Trainer for Advocacy Training Council (international).

Career: Called 1995.

GLASSON, Jonathan QC

Matrix Chambers, London
020 7404 3447
jonathanglasson@matrixlaw.co.uk

Featured in Inquests & Public Inquiries (London), Product Liability (London)

Practice Areas: Jonathan has an eclectic and broad ranging practice including human rights, Inquests and Inquiries, public law, international law, asylum, extradition, mutual assistance, product liability and clinical negligence. He advised the Attorney General on the Hillsborough and David Kelly inquests. He appeared at the Azelle Rodney Inquiry and the Mark Duggan Inquest. He has a particular expertise in ECHR claims arising from Article 2 as well as claims from the Russian Federation. He has acted in a large number of national security cases in the Administrative Court, Special Immigration Appeals Commission (SIAC) and the Investigatory Powers Tribunal (IPT). Jonathan has also acted as a Special Advocate in SIAC and the Parole Board and as Counsel to the IPT. Jonathan is a Contributing Editor to the Butterworth's Personal Injury Litigation Service (and author of the sections on Product Liability and Psychiatric Injury) and is the co-author of the Blackstone's Guide to the Coroners and Justice Act 2009. In February 2007, Jonathan was appointed to the A Panel of Junior Counsel to the Crown which was the earliest date for such an appointment. He was appointed Silk in March 2013, one of the most junior in call to be appointed.

Career: Former Solicitor (Honours), Treasury A Panel, 2007-2013; QC 2013.

Personal: Maidstone GS, New College, Oxford.

GLEDHILL, Orlando

One Essex Court, London
020 7583 2000
og@oeclaw.co.uk

Featured in Commercial Dispute Resolution (London), Energy & Natural Resources (London), Fraud (London)

Practice Areas: A broad range of commercial litigation, arbitration and advice. Recently acted for Leonid Lebedev in London anti-suit proceedings brought by Viktor Vekselberg and Leonard Blavatnik in relation to proceedings in New York, gas companies CERT obligations, major French bank in disputes arising out of lending in Russia, various state-owned Chinese entities in energy sector arbitrations, the largest Mongolian bank in disputes with Tier 2 capital provider, financial advisory and trading house in trial against Barclays Bank concerning corporate acquisition, investment fund managers in claims by Fortress Investment Group, Deutsche Bank in trial concerning carbon credits, Investec Bank in claim by wealth management client. Advised FSA on PPI mis-selling, acted for Grangemouth CHP in litigation against Ineos, Glitnir Banki in freezing order proceedings against Jon Asgeir Johannesson, Woodside Energy in claim by Dana Petroleum re oil exploration offshore Kenya, Cenkos Securities in sub-agent's claim for fees on fundraising, The Bank of New York re structured investment vehicle security trust deed and advised the bankruptcy trustee of Lehman Brothers Treasury Co B.V.

Professional Memberships: Combar.

Career: Called 1998.

Personal: Born 1971. BA (Hons) Queen's University, Canada (First Class). MPhil, Corpus Christi College, Oxford. DipLaw, City University (Distinction).

GLEN, David

One Brick Court, London
020 7353 8845
dg@onebrickcourt.com

Featured in Data Protection (London), Defamation/Privacy (London)

Practice Areas: Defamation, privacy and breach of confidence, information law (including freedom of information and data protection), media-related public law and judicial review, contempt of court and reporting restrictions. Notable recent cases include: Dar Al Arkan & Bank Alkhair v Al Refai & ors (2014); Jon Gaunt v United Kingdom (2014); Jill Finney v Care Quality Commission (2014); Rothschild v Associated Newspapers Ltd (2013); Bob Crow v Boris Johnson (2012); Gee v Information Commissioner & BBC (2012); Various (Guardian News & Media) v News Group & Mulcaire (2012); R v Ofcom (ex parte Jon Gaunt) (2011); North London Central Mosque v Policy Exchange (2011); Budu v BBC (2010; Azad Ali v Associated Newspapers Ltd (2010); Taranissi v BBC (2009); Condoco Grand Cayman v KYC News (2008). Represented Guardian News & Media at the Leveson Inquiry and previously acted on behalf of the BBC in the Hutton Inquiry. Appointed to act as one of the Independent Scheme Barristers in the Voicemail Interception Compensations Scheme.

Career: Called 2002.

Publications: Contributor to Arlidge Eady & Smith on Contempt, 4th Edition and supplement; Atkin's Court Forms on Defamation.

Personal: University of Edinburgh (MA Hons History); Enjoys sport especially football, rugby, cricket, horseracing and Sunderland AFC.

GLENSER, Peter

9 Bedford Row, London
020 7489 2727
peter.glenser@9bedfordrow.co.uk

Featured in Licensing (London)

Practice Areas: Peter practices in licensing and defending serious rural regulatory proceedings and allied prosecutions in areas such as farming, meat production, hunting and fieldsports. He has an expert knowledge of firearms and firearms law and regularly acts for the appellant in firearms licensing matters, be it refusal or revocation of certificates or proceedings concerning the suitability of persons to be Registered Firearms Dealers. He also has an enviable reputation for defending service personnel before the Court Martial in the most complex, sensitive and difficult matters. His "sharp, analytical mind" enables him to cut through the most complex of issues to focus attention and

energy on the critical elements. Praised for diligent pre-trial preparation he provides timely, thorough and realistic advice pre-trial and throughout proceedings. He is regularly instructed to lead for the defence in all the areas in which he practices.
Professional Memberships: Peter is a member of the Agricultural Lawyers Association, the Association of Regulatory and Disciplinary Lawyers, the Criminal Bar Association and is on the Committee of the Association of Military Courts Advocates. Peter is on the Council of the British Association of Shooting and Conservation, he writes on legal matters for the Shooting Gazette and Gun Trade News. He is in high demand as a speaker at conferences and other events.

GLYN, Caspar QC
Cloisters, London
020 7827 4000
cg@cloisters.com
Featured in Employment (London), Sports Law (London)
Practice Areas: Caspar Glyn advises on contentious disputes and is a trial and appellate lawyer. He is ranked as a Leading Silk and is known as an "intellectual heavyweight", to be "consistently brilliant", is "fearsome in court", "scintillatingly intellectual", "an excellent cross examiner" and a "real fighter." His practice covers the whole width of the employment relationship, contractual (including injunctive relief) and regulatory sports' disputes and other linked contractual and commercial claims including civil fraud and breach of fiduciary duty. His work generally affects hundreds / thousands of employees, sets national precedents, are test cases, are of very high value, seriously affect the reputations of other employees or owners or the business itself or are a combination of these. Caspar is Chair of the Industrial Law Society, a trained mediator and sits as a Chairman of Football Association Arbitration Panels. To see Caspar's full profile please go to the Cloisters website www.cloisters.com
Professional Memberships: Chair of the Industrial Law Society, Employment Law Bar Association, Employment Lawyers Association.
Career: Called England and Wales 1992, Called Northern Ireland 2011, Silk 2012.
Publications: Co-author of Personal Injury section of Bullen & Leake, Personal Injury of Sweet & Maxwell's Fast Track Practice and a Section of the Personal Injury Handbook.

GLYNN, Stephen
9 Gough Square, London
020 7832 0500
sglynn@9goughsquare.co.uk
Featured in Personal Injury (London), Personal Injury (All Circuits)
Practice Areas: Personal injury: predominantly industrial disease and employer's liability work for claimants. In particular, asbestos-induced disease, HAVS and deafness work. Long experience of CICAP work, appearing in hearings nationwide. Catastrophic injury and substantial quantum cases. Niche child abuse claims practice. Experience also in bankruptcy and insolvency in the context of PI and prof neg claims. Clinical and professional negligence work. Substantial experience in trial and hearing advocacy.
Professional Memberships: Association of Personal Injury Lawyers, Personal Injury Bar Association, Professional Negligence Bar Association, Association of Child Abuse Lawyers.
Career: LLB (Hons) 2.1 Bristol University. Called to the bar: 1990.
Publications: General editor and co-author of 'Asbestos Claims, law practice and procedure', (2nd ed) general editor of 'Manual Handling Claims', series editor of 'Clinical Negligence Claims' (2nd ed), and general editor of 'Work Accidents at Sea'. Editor of APIL's Guide to Evidence, published by Jordans.
Personal: Interests: Motorbikes (wife permitting), his wife and children, food (eating as well as cooking it) and American crime novels (but not necessarily in that order).

GODDARD, Andrew QC
Atkin Chambers, London
020 7404 0102
agoddard@atkinchambers.com
Featured in Construction (London), International Arbitration (London)
Practice Areas: He specialises in the law of commercial obligations and professional negligence, particularly in the context of disputes concerning major construction and engineering contracts and IT projects. He has had much involvement in infrastructure, telecoms and energy disputes and has acted for main contractors, sub-contractors, professionals and employers, including national and foreign governments. Andrew has experience of PPP and PFI projects in the UK and various Commonwealth jurisdictions and is a Director of the Caribbean Procurement Institute. He has significant experience in international commercial arbitration and has appeared in many disputes referred to arbitration under the auspices of the ICC, the HKIAC, the LCIA and the LMAA and has recently acted in an Investor-State arbitration proceeding before the International Centre for the Settlement of Investment Disputes (ICSID). Related areas of law in which he has detailed knowledge and experience include ship construction and conversion, insurance and performance bonds.
Professional Memberships: He is a member of the IBA, LCIA, Combar, TECBAR, the Society of Construction Law and the Society for Computers and Law.
Career: Queen's Counsel 2003

GODFREY, Hannah
Cloisters, London
020 7827 4000
hg@cloisters.com
Featured in Clinical Negligence (London)
Practice Areas: Hannah specialises in clinical negligence and personal injury law including inquests. She is regularly instructed as sole counsel in a wide range of medical claims (with particular expertise in general surgery, plastic surgery and oncology), and as junior in maximum value catastrophic brain/spinal injury claims (including complex quantum claims requiring detailed excel workbook schedules of loss). She predominantly represents claimants. She has special interests in human rights issues, fatal accident claims and constructing damages claims for injured young people.
Professional Memberships: AVMA, APIL, INQUEST.
Career: BA Hons Cantab (First Class) 1999. PG Dip and BVC London 2001-2 (with internships at UNHCR (Geneva) and The AIRE Centre, London). Called to the Bar 2002 and undertook first six pupillage at Doughty Street Chambers, followed by second six at Cloisters and a judicial assistantship to Lord Justice Mummery. Hannah has been a tenant at Cloisters since 2004, and a pupil supervisor since 2012.
Publications: Contributor to 'Lewis and Buchan on Clinical Negligence'.
Personal: Hannah lives in Hampshire and is a keen amateur coastal skipper.

GOLDBERG, Jonathan QC
North Square Chambers, London
07831 586 273
jongold@btinternet.com
Featured in Crime (London)
Practice Areas: Appears in many high profile cases. Widely based trial and advisory practice focusing mainly on criminal, regulatory and common law. Undertakes a wide range of civil work also when leading specialist juniors. Has had the widest professional experience and exposure across a whole range of courts and tribunals. Noted first and foremost as a fearless fighter for his clients who possesses devastating cross-examination skills.
Professional Memberships: Admitted to the New York State Bar. Appearances and advisory work in The Caymans, Eire, Bahamas, Bermuda, Malaysia, Singapore, Botswana, Gibraltar and Hong Kong.
Career: Since early 2011 has seen no advantage whatever in being a member any longer of large conventional chambers and now practises solo (and more busily than ever) with his own dedicated clerk, Mr Gabriel Schleider. Recommends specialist juniors if appropriate from the select and talented list whom he has led (or sometimes opposed), and therefore knows well, over many years. Website www.GoldbergQC.com
Publications: Frequent appearances on Sky TV, CNN and Al-Jazeera TV on legal topics. Writes the "Ask the QC" column in The Jewish Chronicle . Advocacy lectures at www.legalpractitioner.co.uk/presentations/Advocacy1/testy-testy-5.html.
Personal: Married to Regina Skyer, a leading New York lawyer, 2 children, 2 stepchildren.

GOLDBERG, Simon
Trinity Chambers, Newcastle upon Tyne
0191 232 1927
s.goldberg@trinitychambers.co.uk
Featured in Chancery (North Eastern), Commercial Dispute Resolution (North Eastern), Employment (North Eastern)
Practice Areas: Head of Chambers' commercial litigation team, wide ranging Chancery and Commercial Practice encompassing advocacy/advisory work for clients, from individuals and small firms to PLCs and third sector organisations.Extensive experience of litigating in the Chancery and Queen's Bench divisions of the High Court, as well as dealing with cases before the Adjudicator to HM Land Registry and in arbitration. One of only a handful of local practitioners to be recognised nationally by the professional directories as a leading barrister in commercial litigation work, where his willingness to fight his clients' corner is regularly praised. extensive employment practice regularly instructed in disputes across the UK in the Employment Tribunal, the EAT and the High Court, often against Silks. He advises and represents employers and employees, and has over a number of years gained a national reputation for his discrimination and equal pay work. In the High Court, developed a niche practice in cases involving breaches of post termination restrictions and fiduciary duties, experienced in obtaining interim remedies for clients.
Professional Memberships: ELBA, Employment Law Association. Bar Pro Bono Unit. Registered Lawyer under The Football Association Football Agents Regulations External Examiner for Bar Professional Training Course.
Career: Appointed Junior Counsel to the Crown (Attorney General's Provincial Panel) 2007. Called 1999 by Middle Temple (Scholar and Exhibitioner).

GOLDRING, Jenny
5 St Andrew's Hill, London
020 7332 5400
jennygoldring@5sah.co.uk
Featured in Crime (London)
Practice Areas: Jenny is a highly experienced leading junior who specialises in cases of complex fraud. She is passionate about fraud work and is adept at mastering huge quantities of documents and distilling the key issues. She has a great deal of experience in cases with complex disclosure issues and also cross jurisdictional fraud. Jenny is instructed by both the Prosecution and Defence. She is on the CPS list and is also on the SFO (A panel) for both the General and Proceeds of Crime panels. She is an expert in MTIC fraud and is also instructed as leading Counsel in related proceedings in the VAT tribunal (First and Upper tier) on a regular basis. She is currently instructed in a number of multi million pound appeals. Jenny has conducted numerous fraud cases including mortgage fraud, insurance fraud, complex excise fraud, PAYE fraud, advance fee fraud. She recently represented the partner of a leading firm of Solicitors in a multi million pound allegation of fraud.
Professional Memberships: Fraud Lawyers Association, Criminal Bar Association, South Eastern Circuit.
Personal: MA Hons Jurisprudence (Oxford University).

GOLDSMITH, Jamie
One Essex Court, London
020 7583 2000
jgoldsmith@oeclaw.co.uk
Featured in Commercial Dispute Resolution (London)
Practice Areas: Practice covers a broad range of commercial and chancery disputes. Recent cases include Sukhoruchkin v Giebels (Ch Div, civil fraud and derivative actions), Gorgeous Beauty v Liu (Ch Div, civil fraud), Fortress v Blue Skye (Comm Ct- large financial fraud), Bank of Ireland v Jaffery (Ch- breach of fiduciary duty/banking), VTB v Nutritek (Ch- jurisdiction and governing law), RBS v Hicks (Ch- Liverpool FC takeover), Ferrero v Baskan Gida (Ch- conspiracy and other fraud claims), Conway v Ratiu (CA - libel/confidence/conflicts), United States v Phillip Morris (Comm Ct, CA - letter of request/privilege), M&S v Freshfields (Comm Ct, CA - conflicts of interest/confidence), BATCo v United States (Comm Ct, CA - privilege), IFC v DSNL (Comm Ct - equitable lien), Osco-Bingemann v DeJoria (Caribbean CA - shareholders agreement/estoppel).
Professional Memberships: LCL & CBA.
Career: Qualified 2002, Grays Inn. Educated at Westminster School, Gonville & Caius College (1996-2000, Cambridge Law

Tripos - First), Poitiers University (1998-99 - top mark in year for Droit Commercial), Bedingfield Scholar (2001, Grays Inn), College of Law (2002 - second in year).
Personal: French (fluent), German (basic).

GOLDSMITH, Joseph
5 Stone Buildings, London
020 7242 6201
clerks@5sblaw.com
Featured in Chancery (London), Court of Protection (All Circuits), Pensions (London)
Practice Areas: General Chancery practice, incorporating wide range of contentious and non-contentious work, with particular emphasis on trusts, wills, probate and administration of estates; capital taxes and estate planning; pensions; proprietary estoppel; family provision; real property; landlord and tenant; and related professional negligence matters. Particular interest in issues relating to incapacity and the MCA 2005. Appears regularly in the Court of Protection. Also practises in the field of ecclesiastical law. Notable cases include: IBM United Kingdom Holdings Ltd v Dalgleish [2014] EWHC 980 (Ch.); Sarjeant v Rigid Group Ltd [2012] EWHC 3757 (Ch.) and [2013] EWCA Civ. 1714, [2014] Pen. LR 143: Trustees of Lehman Brothers Pension Scheme v Pensions Regulator [2013] EWCA Civ 751; Re IBM Pension Plan [2012] EWHC 2766 (Ch); Hughes v Woolworths Group Pensions Trustee Ltd [2012] EWHC 905 (Ch); Re JDS [2012] EWHC 302 (CoP); Prudential Staff Pensions Ltd v Prudential Assurance [2012] EWHC 960 (Ch); Hapeshi v Allnatt [2010] EWHC 392 (Ch); DCM (Optical Holdings) Ltd v HMRC [2010] UKFTT 393 (TC); Re St Peter's Draycott [2009] Fam 93; Re Horley Town Football Club [2006] EWHC 2386 (Ch).
Professional Memberships: Chancery Bar Association; Property Bar Association, Ecclesiastical Law Society. Accredited Mediator.
Career: Called 2003.
Publications: Contributor to the wills and administration volume of Encyclopaedia of Forms and Precedents (2012 reissue), Tolley's Finance and Law for the Older Client, Dymond's Capital Taxes and Heywood and Massey's Court of Protection Practice.
Personal: Educated at Hereford Cathedral School; Brasenose College, Oxford (BA, Modern History); and City University.

GOLLANCZ, David
Keating Chambers, London
020 7544 2600
dgollancz@keatingchambers.com
Featured in Public Procurement (London)
Practice Areas: Public procurement and all aspects of public/private commercial transactions (commercial contract, public law, TUPE, pension rights, state aid and competition); employment law; judicial review. As solicitor, advised Nuclear Decommissioning Authority, Identity and Passports Service (ID Cards), National Policing Improvement Authority (IMPACT programme), DCSF (Academies programme), Department for Communities and Local Government (ECHR), BERR (state aids), Equality and Human Rights Commission (statutory Codes of Practice under Equality Act 2010). As barrister, has appeared on both sides in a number of procurement challenges and procurement-related judicial review, and has a substantial advisory practice. Notable cases include R (Nash)v Barnet London Borough Council [2013] EWCA Civ 1004, Corelogic Ltd v Bristol City Council [2013] EWHC 2088 (TCC), Pearson Driving Assessments Ltd v The Minister for the Cabinet [2013] EWHC 2082 (TCC). Appointed to Attorney-General's London Panel, 2014. Accredited for public access.
Professional Memberships: Procurement Lawyers Association; Technology and Construction Bar Association.
Career: Admitted solicitor 1990; Head of Public Procurement and Commercial team, Treasury Solicitors; Head of TUPE Task Force, Treasury Solicitors; Partner, EU Competition and Regulatory team, and Head of Public Sector at Field Fisher Waterhouse LLP. Called to Bar 2010. Post-graduate diploma in EC Law at UCL 2001; Post-graduate diploma in EU Competition Law 2009.
Publications: Frequent contributor to journals: PLC Public Sector; Law Society's Gazette; The Lawyer, Public Private Finance, Supply Management.
Personal: Lives in Islington, N London. Speaks French. Member of Bar Lesbian and Gay Group.

GOLLOP, Katharine
Serjeants' Inn Chambers, London
020 7427 5000
kgollop@3serjeantsinn.com
Featured in Clinical Negligence (London), Professional Discipline (London)
Practice Areas: Katharine Gollop was called to the Bar in 1993. Katharine specialises in clinical negligence and healthcare, professional discipline, employment and inquests and inquiries. An earlier edition notes that "she is a very formidable advocate and a shrewd tactician who isn't scared to make difficult decisions" and that she is "revered by clients for her strong-willed approach to litigation." Please click on the link to the Serjeants' Inn Chambers website for her profile, which sets out full details of her practice including relevant work of note.
Professional Memberships: PIBA, APIL, AVMA, ELA.
Personal: Gray's Inn Prince of Wales Scholar. St John's College, Oxford (BA First Class).

GOODALL, Patrick QC
Fountain Court Chambers, London
020 7583 3335
pjg@fountaincourt.co.uk
Featured in Banking & Finance (London), Commercial Dispute Resolution (London), Fraud (London), Insurance (London), Professional Negligence (London)
Practice Areas: Broad commercial litigation and arbitration practice, with particular expertise in banking and financial services, professional negligence, insurance and reinsurance, civil fraud and conflict of laws.
Professional Memberships: Commercial Bar Association (COMBAR); London Common Law and Commercial Bar Association; British Insurance Law Association.
Career: Called 1998. QC 2014. Junior Counsel to the Crown (A Panel) 2011-2014. Admitted as a solicitor 1997. CEDR accredited mediator.
Publications: Co-author of 'The Law of Privilege' (ed. Thanki, 2nd edition, Oxford University Press); Co-author of 'Law of Bank Payments' (eds. Brindle & Cox, 4th edition, Sweet & Maxwell); Contributor to Bullen & Leake & Jacob's 'Precedents of Pleadings' (17th edition, Sweet & Maxwell); Editor of 'Commercial Court Procedure' (Sweet & Maxwell).
Personal: Educated at Southampton University (LLB, First Class Honours) and Brasenose College, Oxford (BCL, First Class Honours).

GOODFELLOW, Giles W J QC
Pump Court Tax Chambers, London
020 7414 8080
gilesgg@pumptax.com
Featured in Tax (London)
Practice Areas: Practice covers the full range of advisory work on direct and indirect tax issues; particular areas of expertise cover corporate reorganisations, employee share incentive schemes, controlled foreign companies' legislation, tax warranty and indemnity claims, IHT and CGT planning for family-owned businesses, high net worth individuals and onshore and offshore trusts; substantial experience and expertise in advising on and negotiating compromises of Inland Revenue and Customs' investigation cases; Notable cases include R (Morgan Grenfell & Co Ltd) v Rounding (House of Lords); R (Carvill) v IRC (High Court); Blackburn v Keeling (Court of Appeal); Liverpool Archdiocesan Trustees v Goldberg (High Court); Carvill v Frost (Special Commissioners); Government of Mauritius v Maroussem and others (Privy Council); Smith v Smith (House of Lords); Raymond Stewart Partnership (High Court); Allen & Overy v Clark (High Court), Maco Doors & Windows v HMRC (House of Lords), Tower MCashback v HMRC (Supreme Court); Total People v HMRC (Court of Appeal); Euroceanica v HMRC (First-tier Tribunal); O'Neill v O'Neill (Family Division); FS Commercial v GLA (GLA Appeals Tribunal); Tower Radio Ltd v HMRC (First-tier Tribunal); Mehjoo v Harben Barker (QBD).
Professional Memberships: Revenue Bar Association; London Common Law & Commercial Bar Association (Treasurer), Professional Negligence Bar Association.
Career: Called to Bar, Middle Temple 1983; Senior Astbury Scholarship, Harmsworth Scholarship.
Publications: Co-author Inheritance Tax Planning with Andrew Thornhill QC and J Kessler (Longmans); co-author Financial Provisions & Taxation on Divorce with R Venables QC and Martin O'Dwyer (KeyHaven).
Personal: Born 1960; resides London.

GOODISON, Adam
South Square, London
020 7696 9900
adamgoodison@southsquare.com
Featured in Restructuring/Insolvency (London)
Practice Areas: Commercial, restructuring / insolvency, contract, banking and company law. Cases include: Re Wind Hellas; Re Primacom [2011] EWHC 3746 (Ch); Re Cortefiel [2012] EWHC 2998 (Ch); Re Seat Pagine; Re Iberotravel / Orizonia; Re Icopal; Re Apcoa Parking [2014] EWHC 1867 (Ch); Re Zodiac; Sandhu v Jet Star Retail Ltd [2011] EWCA Civ 459; Re Diwan (Court of Appeal, Dubai International Finance Centre); Re Globespan (Cartwright v Registrar of Companies) [2012] EWCA Civ 1159.
Professional Memberships: Chancery Bar Association, COMBAR, Insolvency Lawyers' Association.
Career: Called 1990; Bar Council member 1995-98 and 2004-2010.
Publications: Contributor to 'The Law of Administrators and Receivers of Companies' ROT chapter (Lightman and Moss, Sweet and Maxwell); 'Rowlatt on Principal and Surety' (Marks and Moss, Sweet and Maxwell); and 'Company Directors' (Mortimore, OUP).

GOODWIN, Deirdre
7BR, London
020 7242 3555
clerks@7br.co.uk
Featured in Clinical Negligence (London)
Practice Areas: Deirdre specialises in catastrophic clinical negligence where she acts for both claimants and defendants. She has significant expertise in cases arising from severe perinatal asphyxial brain damage, pre-natal diagnostics, Erb's palsy, paediatric neurological injury, major neurosurgical and orthopaedic iatrogenic injury, and delayed diagnosis of cancer and meningitis. Many of her cases involve complex causation issues and she has specialist knowledge in mental capacity matters. Deirdre has a reputation as a skilled advocate who has the ability quickly to distil the issues. She is known to be a strong negotiator with a keen intuition for an opponent's position and is proactive, turning round work speedily in order to maintain momentum in a case; this includes the preparation of meticulously pleaded schedules of loss in high value claims. Reported cases include Bolitho v City and Hackney Health Authority [1998] A.C. 238 HL; Murphy v Wirral Health Authority (1996) 7 Med LR 99. Approved settlements for claimants and defendants include claims where damages have exceeded £6 million. She has also been Visiting Counsel to the Cayman Islands Health Services Authority and lectures on medical law and ethics, clinical negligence and catastrophic injury claims. Deirdre also has extensive experience in all areas of personal injury practice, in particular catastrophic head injury, spinal trauma and Fatal Accident cases.
Professional Memberships: Professional Negligence Bar Association. Personal Injury Bar Association.
Career: LLB University College London 1972. Called 1974 (Grays Inn). Joined 7 Bedford Row as a tenant in March 2014 having previously been at 13 King's Bench Walk from 1984 to 2014.
Publications: Recent articles include: 'Capacity: Masterman-Lister and Bailey v Warren reconsidered' (2013) Personal Injury Law Journal, February 6-10. 'Mediation: An invitation to be ignored at your peril': The costs consequences of a refusal to mitigate six years after Halsey (2013) Personal Injury Law Journal, December 13/January 14 2-5. 'CPR: no procedural hiding place – the Mitchell effect': Discussion of the changing litigation landscape (2014) Personal Injury Law Journal, February 2 -7. 'Test of Capacity to conduct proceedings': Dunhill v Burgin (UKSC) (2014) Personal Injury Law Journal, April 10-14.
Personal: Languages: French and German. Interests include music and medieval history.

GOOLAMALI, Nina
2TG - 2 Temple Gardens, London
020 7822 1200
ng@2tg.co.uk
Featured in Personal Injury (London)
Practice Areas: Nina Goolamali has a very well established practice in catastrophic

injury and sports-related litigation. She is well known for her ability to defend in sensitive high value cases (regularly in excess of £1 million). She often acts unled in cases against Leading Counsel and is instructed by all the major EL, PL and Motor Insurers and Claims Handlers including AIG, Allianz Cornhill, Aviva, Chartis, Chaucer, Chubb, DAS, Ecclesiastical, Faraday, Groupama, Liberty, Liverpool Victoria, the MIB, NFU, NHSLA, Premier, Travelers & Zurich. Nina leads the 2TG Sports Team and holds a Post Graduate Diploma in Sports Law from King's College, London. She acts for players, teams and national governing bodies and her practice covers all major sports with a particular emphasis on motorsports (Formula 1, MotoGP, MotoCross, Speedway, Karting), rugby (union and league) and football.
Professional Memberships: LawInSport; British Association for Sport and Law; Personal Injury Bar Association; London Common Law and Commercial Bar Association; Professional Negligence Bar Association.
Career: Called to the Bar in 1995. Accredited Advocacy Trainer (Middle Temple).
Personal: MA Jurisprudence, Lady Margaret Hall, Oxford. Post Graduate Diploma in Sports Law, Kings College, London.

GORASIA, Paras
Kings Chambers, Manchester
0845 034 3444
clerks@kingschambers.com
Featured in Employment (Northern)

Practice Areas: Paras specialises entirely in employment and employment related litigation. He has particular experience in high value and/or sensitive disputes involving discrimination, whistleblowing, bonuses, illegitimate competitive activity (including breach of restrictive covenants), misuse of confidential information, unfair/wrongful dismissal and TUPE. Clients have included major UK and multinational corporates, charities and individuals.
Professional Memberships: Employment Lawyers Association, Employment Law Bar Association, Industrial Law Society, Chartered Institute of Arbitrators.
Career: Called July 2005 (Inner Temple). Judicial Assistant at the Court of Appeal to the then Master of the Rolls, Sir Anthony Clarke (now Lord Clarke) (January 2007). Pegasus Scholar to Hong Kong (October 2009). Appointed to the Panel of Counsel for the Equality and Human Rights Commission (February 2011). Appointed to the Welsh Assembly Government's Panel of Junior Counsel in Employment Law (October 2012). Appointed to the Attorney General's Regional Panel of Junior Counsel to the Crown (November 2012).
Publications: (1999-2002) University of Kent (LLB with First Class Honours); (2002-04) Exeter College, Oxford(BCL, MPhil); (2004-05) King's College London (LLM).

GOTT, Paul QC
Fountain Court Chambers, London
020 7583 3335
pag@fountaincourt.co.uk
Featured in Employment (London)

Practice Areas: Employment law and commercial law. Industrial relations law, especially injunctive work in relation to strike action. Treasury counsel "A" panel. Recent cases include: London Underground strike action 2011-2014, Royal Mail Privatisation 2013, British Airways plc v Unite [2010] IRLR 42 (injunction against 12-day cabin crew strike - Xmas 2009); BA v Unite (No.2) [2010] IRLR 809 (HC and CoA - injunction application to restrain May/June 2010 cabin crew strike); Network Rail v RMT [2010] EWHC 1084 (injunction to prevent 4-day national rail strike, Easter 2010); Metrobus v Unite [2010] ICR 173 (injunction against London bus strike, TULRA and Art 11 ECHR). Unite v easyJet [2010] TUR1/723 (CAC – resisting application for statutory union recognition). Muschett v HMPS [2010] IRLR 173 (CoA – race discrimination claims and temporary workers). Counsel for Solicitors Regulation Authority RA 2010-214. George v Royal Brompton & Harefield NHS Trust (ET and EAT 2010-2011 – alleged race discrimination, unfair dismissal and whistleblowing). Wheeler v Brixton plc (ET 2010 – alleged unfair dismissal of CEO of plc). Attorney General v Branch No.2 [2009] EWVH 673 (Noueiri anti-suit injunctions). Farm Assist v DEFRA [2008] EWHC 3079 (economic duress and legal professional privilege).
Professional Memberships: ComBar; Industrial Law Society; Employment Lawyers Association.
Personal: Education: 1979-86 Marple Hall Comprehensive, Stockport. 1986-89 MA Cambridge University, Downing College, Double First Class Honours. 1989-90 BCL Oxford University, Brasenose College, First Class Honours. Appointed as Junior Counsel to the Crown, July 1999. Appointed to Treasury 'A' Panel, April 2005. Re-appointed to Treasury 'A' Panel, February 2010. Appointed as Board Member to the Standards Board for England, February 2006 and re-appointed March 2009. Silk: 2012.

GOTTLIEB, David
Thomas More Chambers, London
020 7404 7000
clerks@thomasmore.co.uk
Featured in Crime (London)

Practice Areas: David Gottlieb has a heavyweight practice representing the individual against all forms of State power. He is often the client's last hope. He specialises in traditional, honest and fearless advocacy in the most difficult cases. He has consistently stood up for those who are not part of the establishment, particularly the weakest and most vulnerable members of society.
Career: David Gottlieb defended Michael Adebolajo (Mujaahid Abu Hamza) for the murder of the Woolwich soldier and secured a unanimous acquittal on the second charge of attempted murder of police officers. Other recent cases include successfully defending Selma Kabal (terrorism charges), the singer PJ Proby (fraud) and a young woman falsely accused of making up a rape claim to obtain UK citizenship. He has a long history of defending high profile terrorism, fraud and human rights cases.

GOUDIE, James QC
11KBW, London
020 7632 8500
james.goudie@11kbw.com
Featured in Administrative & Public Law (London), Education (London), Employment (London), Local Government (London), Public Procurement (London)

Practice Areas: Specialises in all aspects of employment law, public law and commercial law.
Career: Solicitor 1966-70. Called to the Bar Inner Temple 1970. Bencher; past President National Security Panel for Information Rights; Deputy High Court Judge, Queen's Bench and Chancery Divisions; past Chairman Law Reform Committee; General Council of the Bar; past Chairman Administrative Law Bar Association; past Chairman Bar European Group; member of the Football League Disciplinary Commission Panel of Arbitrators; Fellow of the Chartered Institute of Arbitrators; Fellow of the Society of Advanced Legal Studies. Member of Bar Eastern Caribbean Supreme Court (Antigua and Barbuda and Virgin Islands).
Personal: Educated at Dean Close School, Cheltenham and LSE (LLB Hons). FCI Arb. Governor of LSE.

GOUDIE, Martin
Charter Chambers, London
020 7618 4400
martin.goudie@charterchambers.com
Featured in Crime (London)

Practice Areas: Martin divides his practice between serious crime, regulatory and investigatory work. As a criminal practitioner he undertakes the full scope of grave and financial crime, defending and prosecuting in equal measure as Leading and Junior Counsel. Recent defence cases have included prosecutions brought by HM Revenue and Customs, the Department for Business, Innovation and Skills, the United Kingdom Border Agency and the Department for Education. Instructions are frequently received to provide advice and assistance prior to a charging decision having being made in cases ranging from serious frauds through to a roadblock shooting in Kabul. He is also instructed by the Crown Prosecution Service, including the Special Casework Unit (EAS Grade 4 and rape panel), and Civil Aviation Authority; this has included being asked to advise on jurisdictional issues, gathering evidence from overseas, prosecutions arising out of fatal crashes and appearing at Reg 6 appeals. Martin has been a member of the Attorney General's Panel of Special Advocates (DV security cleared) dealing with national security cases since 2005, and was junior Special Advocate in the applications brought by UK detainees in Guantanamo Bay, Binyam Mohammed and Shaker Aamer. He has contributed regularly to documents produced by groups of Special Advocates, including submissions to the Joint Committee on Human Rights, and was interviewed by Amnesty International as part of their investigations into the use of closed material proceedings in the UK. Earlier this year he appeared as the 'appointed person' at a closed hearing in respect of the £4.1 billion Thames Tidewater Tunnel project.
Professional Memberships: Criminal Bar Association, International Bar Association, South Eastern Circuit & Justice.
Career: Called 1996, Bencher 2014 - Inner Temple. Pegasus Scholar to Crown Law Office, Wellington, New Zealand - 1999.
Personal: Executive Committee of London Scottish (Rugby) Football Club.

GOUGH, Karen
Thirty Nine Essex Street, London
020 7832 1111
karen.gough@39essex.com
Featured in Construction (London)

Practice Areas: Specialises in the litigation and arbitration of building, engineering and professional negligence disputes. Also some banking and general commercial litigation. Long experience of most standard forms of building and engineering contracts, particularly FIDIC - acting as counsel, adjudicator and arbitrator (Past President of CIArb.). Also acts as party representative in domestic and international ADR processes.
Professional Memberships: Inner Temple; SEC; TECBAR; Fellow CIArb.; LCIA; International Arbitration Club; IBA; SCL; ICC UK, COMBAR.
Career: 1991: Fellowship of the Chartered Institute of Arbitrators; 1995: Panel Member CIArb.; 1998: Dip ICArb.; 1999: Chartered Arbitrator; 2001-02 President CIArb.; 2004: TECBAR Accredited Adjudicator; 2005: Panel Arbitrator/Adjudicator: CIArb. London Housing Panel, 2008 CEDR panel of "super adjudicators".
Publications: Contributing author to Bernstein's Handbook of Arbitration and Dispute Resolution Practice, 4th Edn, 2003, and to Wilmot-Smith on Construction Contracts, 2nd Edn 2010. Also writes and speaks regularly on construction law, arbitration, and ADR law and practice.

GOULDING, Jonathan
Gough Square Chambers, London
020 7353 0924
jonathan.goulding@goughsq.co.uk
Featured in Consumer Law (London)

Practice Areas: Consumer and regulatory law. He prosecutes, defends and advises in regulatory cases especially consumer protection, unfair trading, pricing, food safety and hygiene, food poisoning,food labelling,counterfeit goods, furniture safety, toy and product safety,animal by-products, pricing, health and safety and weights and measures. Jonathan has substantial experience in Enterprise Act 2002 proceedings for both claimants and defendants alike. He has been involved in several matters concerning the Consumer Protection from Unfair Trading Regulations 2008, including the two leading cases in the Court of Appeal Criminal Division.Consumer Credit licencing experience. His regulatory experience has seen him instructed in matters concerning such diverse matters as endangered species and the new scrap metal legislation Also appears on behalf of clients before such bodies as the The Traffic Commissioner and General Medical Council. His Clients include banks, food producers, national retailers, supermarkets and local authorities.
Professional Memberships: Food Law Group.
Career: Called to the Bar 1984.
Publications: Contibuting editor: author of Unfair Commercial Practices Chapter in 'Consumer and Trading Standards Law and Practice' ('the Pink Book'), Jordan (2013). Contributing editor: author of Financial Conduct Authority chapter in 'Modern Financial Regulation' ('the Blue Book', Jordan (2013).

GOURGEY, Alan QC
11 Stone Buildings, London
020 7831 6381
gourgey@11sb.com
Featured in Chancery (London), Commercial Dispute Resolution (London), Fraud (London), Information Technology (London)

Practice Areas: Alan Gourgey QC has an outstanding reputation in the field of commercial litigation as a litigator as well as an arbitrator and qualified mediator. His wide-ranging practice includes complex contract litigation, shareholder disputes, civil fraud

and IT law. He has acted in many substantial fraud cases ranging from bank to telecommunications fraud and has wide experience in securing pre-emptive remedies and cross-border issues. Recent cases include a $150 million unlawful means conspiracy claim for a Russian Bank and a £30 million claim for breach of share sale agreement. In IT his expertise extends to e-commerce and IT disputes, and he has acted recently for suppliers in relation to two of the largest Government IT projects. He is an experienced trial and arbitration lawyer with particular strengths in rapid assimilation and analysis of complex material, tactical guidance and forceful advocacy. Recent arbitrations including a $1 billion SCC arbitration concerning gas supply contracts, an ICC arbitration related to major infrastructure contract and UNCITRAL arbitration re off-shore mooring agreements. For more information on recent case highlights, please visit the 'Barristers' section on www.11sb.com.
Professional Memberships: Combar; Chancery Bar Association; ADR Group.
Career: Call: 1984 - Silk: 2003 - ADR Group accredited mediator.
Personal: LLB (Bristol).

GOURIET, Gerald QC
Francis Taylor Building, London
020 7353 8415
clerks@ftb.eu.com
Featured in Licensing (London)
Practice Areas: Gerald Gouriet QC was called to the bar in 1974. His first years were spent mainly in criminal defence work, which from its Old Bailey roots rapidly branched out into defending prosecutions brought under health and safety, environmental protection (principally noise abatement), Trade Descriptions and Planning legislation. In the mid 1980's he began to be instructed on a regular basis in Licensing cases, and by the time he left the UK to work in America (1991) he was regarded as one of the leading licensing juniors. He returned to practice at the Bar in 1999, and took silk in 2006. His recent appearances include successfully representing the AMLR to oppose the proposal by the Licensing Authority to impose an EMRO (Early Morning Restriction Order) in Blackpool and Paddy Power in their successful appeal against refusal by Newham Council to grant a betting premises licence. Recent clients include: Gaming: The Ritz Casino; The Empire Casino (LCI); Grosvenor Casinos (Rank); Gerald successfully obtained licences for the recently opened Hippodrome Casino (Leicester Square); Palace Casino (Great Yarmouth); Casino Red (Huddersfield). He has also acted for The Noble Organisation - amusement centres, bingo clubs and casinos; Luminar Leisure - casino applications in Bournemouth and Leeds; Lucinenne Barriere (French Casino Operators); Great Eastern Quays Casino; Group Partouche (French Casino Operators); Shipley Brothers - bingo clubs; and Caesar's Palace (Las Vegas). Betting: Paddy Power; Ladbrokes; Coral; William Hill; BetFred; Better Betting; Trafalgar Leisure (Newcastle). Alcohol & Entertainment: The BBC; Novus Leisure; Somerfield; Punch Taverns; John Lewis; Waitrose; The Cooperative Group; Mitchells & Butlers; Luminar Leisure; The Noble Organisation - "The Steak House" Leicester Square; The British Beer and Pub Association (BBPA); Gerald acted for the police in the revocation of the licence held by 'Syndicate Nightclub' in Blackpool and on their applications to revoke the licence for 'Spearmint Rhino' in London. Taxi Licensing: numerous local authorities, including Westminster, Kensington and Chelsea, Richmond, Chichester, Medway, Guildford; Transport for London, Shropshire Council, Coventry City Council (PHV and Hackney Carriage licensing); Berwick upon Tweed Council (redrafting Taxi Licensing Policy).
Publications: General Editor of Paterson's Licensing Acts.

GOWEN, Matthew
Red Lion Chambers, Chelmsford
01245 280 880
chambers@18rlc.co.uk
Featured in Crime (South Eastern)
Practice Areas: Matthew Gowen offers advice and representation in all areas of crime. He appears frequently as a leading junior both for the defence and the Crown in serious criminal cases specialising in financial crime and sexual offences. In that latter category he has represented a variety of professionals, including a large number of teachers as well as prison officers and medical professionals. He appears frequently as a leading junior both for the defence and the Crown in serious criminal cases including murder, corporate manslaughter, armed robbery, rape, drug conspiracy and large-scale fraud. He has also advised on and appeared in cases of regulatory crime, including Health & Safety, Trading Standards and Environmental matters. He also has an increasing experience of Road Transport law, including advising and appearing in cases prosecuted by VOSA and at Public Inquiries before the Traffic Commissioner. He has represented numerous interested parties at Coroner's Inquests, most notably the family of Stuart Lubbock, who died during a party at the home of entertainer Michael Barrymore. He is a Grade 4 Advocate (the highest rank) for the Crown Prosecution Service and a specialist rape prosecutor.
Professional Memberships: Criminal Bar Association; Southeastern Circuit.

GRAHAM, Charles QC
One Essex Court, London
020 7583 2000
cgraham@oeclaw.co.uk
Featured in Commercial Dispute Resolution (London)
Practice Areas: Charles Graham has particular expertise in share sale agreements, breach of warranty claims, accounting issues (including completion accounts and associated topics), complex questions of contractual construction, arbitration, banking, civil fraud, competition and EU law, financial services, insurance/reinsurance, joint venture/partnership, jurisdiction and conflict of laws, mediation/ADR, mergers, acquisitions and takeovers, oil and gas, energy and utilities, professional negligence and telecommunications and IT.
Professional Memberships: South Eastern Circuit, Commercial Bar Association.
Career: Called to the Bar in 1986 and joined Essex Court in 1987; QC 2003.
Personal: Educated at Wellington College 1974-79 and University College, Oxford 1980-84 MA Classics (First Class Honours). Born 1 April 1961. Lives in London.

GRAHAM, Thomas
New Square Chambers, London
020 7419 8000
thomas.graham
@newsquarechambers.co.uk
Featured in Chancery (London)
Practice Areas: Advice and litigation/arbitration in: company law, including shareholder disputes and claims by and against directors (particularly breach of fiduciary duty); commercial chancery; contract and commercial; insolvency; partnership; intellectual property including confidentiality, and media law. Appears regularly in the Chancery Division, Commercial Court, and Court of Appeal.Recent cases include: a Commercial Court trial concerning bribes; an LCIA arbitration construing a commercial/intellectual property contract; and appeals to the Court of Appeal concerning inadequate judicial reasoning, and challenging the conduct of administrators. Other notable High Court trials and/or Court of Appeal cases include a director's disqualification trial, and disputes concerning: the break-up of a London river-boat syndicate; ownership of a vintage car collection; stolen confidential commercial information; a film screenplay based on the life of a famous rock star; a guarantee - resulting in a personal, non-party costs order against the Claimant's director, a solicitor; beneficial ownership of company shares; and aircraft repairs in East Africa.
Professional Memberships: Chancery Bar Association; COMBAR, London Common Law and Commercial Bar Association.
Career: Called 1985. Gained wide and invaluable court-room experience in common law chambers before moving to commercial chancery chambers in 2000.
Personal: MA (Cantab), law. Based in London and Hampshire. Speaks non-fluent French and Spanish.

GRAHAM PAUL, Annabel
Francis Taylor Building, London
020 7353 8415
clerks@ftb.eu.com
Featured in Planning (London)
Practice Areas: Annabel Graham Paul has a practice encompassing all aspects of planning, compulsory purchase, environment, local government including rating and licensing, education, regulatory crime, ecclesiastical, and commons and greens. Major public inquiries include Hampden Fields, Aylesbury, the Ashton Vale to Bristol Temple Meads Bus Rapid Transit Scheme Transport & Works Act Order, Linton Wind Farm, Crystal Palace Park and Shepherds Bush Market Compulsory Purchase Order. Recent cases include R (McClellan) v Lambeth LBC [2014] EWHC 1964 (Admin), San Vicente v Secretary of State for Communities and Local Government [2014] 1 WLR 966, Wakil (t/a Orya Textiles) v Hammersmith & Fulham LBC [2014] Env LR 14. Sits as an Independent Inspector to conduct town and village green inquiries.
Publications: Contributor, Gadsden on Commons and Greens (Sweet & Maxwell, 2nd edition, 2011) and The Law of Regulatory Enforcement and Sanctions (OUP, 2011).

GRAHAME, Angela QC
Compass Chambers, Edinburgh
0131 260 5648
angela.grahame@compasschambers.com
Featured in Personal Injury (Scotland)
Practice Areas: Personal Injury; Public and Fatal Accident Inquiries; Clinical and Professional Negligence; Angela has a particular interest in claims for catastrophic injuries, including brain injury, and fatal claims; asbestos-related illness and harassment. Her considerable advocacy experience extends to the Court of Session, Sheriff Court and tribunals. She has appeared in public inquiries. She recently settled the first case in Scotland involving a woman who alleged she contracted mesothelioma as a result of washing her husbands overalls. Angela speaks regularly on the law and practice relating to personal injury, damages and clinical negligence.
Professional Memberships: Member of the Faculty Response Committee on the Criminal Justice (Scotland) Bill (2013); Member of the Faculty of Advocates' Board of Assessors (2007 to date); Member of the Faculty of Advocates' Response Review Group (2001 – 2003; 2007 to 2010); Faculty of Advocates' Representative on Employer Liaison Committee at Aberdeen University (2001 - 2003); Member of Disciplinary Rules: Investigating Committee (1999 – 2001); Curator of the Advocates' Library and Clerk to the Curators (1999 to 2001).
Career: Angela called to the bar in 1995 and took silk in 2009. She was appointed as a full time Advocate Depute in 2003 and promoted to Senior Advocate Depute in 2005. She was appointed as a Legal Member, Police Appeals Tribunal in April 2013.
Publications: Angela is a qualified Instructor and has taught advocacy skills to the Solicitors' profession; devils at the Faculty of Advocates; and at the University of Edinburgh. She has previously written articles in the Scottish Law Gazette, Juridical Review, Greens Civil Practice Bulletin; and Greens Reparation Bulletin.

GRANDISON, Myles
Dyers Chambers, London
020 7404 1881
myles.grandison@dyerschambers.com
Featured in Extradition (London)
Practice Areas: Public and international law. Myles is renowned as a leading extradition practitioner. He has been instructed by individuals, foreign governments and judicial authorities in a series of extradition cases which have helped shape the law on Convention rights. He has a particular interest in the interplay between domestic law and international obligations (see AT v. Luxembourg and Meizoso Gonzalez v. Spain). He has experience in cross-border financial crime and has advised on European restraint orders. In his public law work, Myles has successfully represented individuals in Judicial Review proceedings (see Klimeto v. Westminster Magistrates' Court) and applications for Habeas Corpus (see Netecza v. Governor of HMP Holloway). He also has a wealth of experience in Road Traffic law and has lectured on this subject.

GRANT, Gary
Francis Taylor Building, London
020 7353 8415
gary.grant@ftb.eu.com
Featured in Licensing (London)

Practice Areas: Licensing: acts for both premises operators and public authorities in numerous high profile licence applications, reviews, appeals and judicial reviews. Clients range from Spearmint Rhino to the Commissioner of the Metropolitan Police and include major nightclub/bar/lap-dancing operators, restauranteurs, leisure industry PLC's and public authorities. Also experienced in gambling, taxi, firearms and explosive licensing. He lectures and publishes widely in the fields of licensing and criminal regulatory law. REGULATORY & GENERAL CRIME: Acts in serious and often high profile criminal matters for both the defence and prosecution in all levels of tribunal from the Magistrates' Court to the House of Lords/Supreme Court and Privy Council. In addition to a wealth of experience in general crime, he has particular expertise in white-collar, corporate and regulatory offences (including planning, environmental, health and safety, corporate manslaughter and trading standards) as well as Proceeds of Crime, international and serious organised crime, serious and fatal road traffic cases.
Professional Memberships: Institute of Licensing; Criminal Bar Association.
Career: Called to the Bar 1994, Grays Inn; Recipient of the Sir Raymond Phillips MC Award (1994); Graded as 'Outstanding' by the Gray's Inn Advocacy Committee (1995).
Personal: Frequently appears as a legal analyst on national and international news channels.

GRANT, Marcus
Temple Garden Chambers, London
020 7583 1315
mg@tgchambers.com
Featured in Fraud (All Circuits), Personal Injury (London)
Practice Areas: Traumatic brain injury, spinal injury, chronic pain and insurance fraud (civil) specialist. Specialist in subtle brain injury and fibromyalgia / chronic pain litigation. Provides strategic advice to Insurers to combat fraud. Involved in many of the leading contempt cases and many of the leading subtle brain injury cases. Reported cases 2011/14 include: The Azimi Fraud cases - Lawtel - 13.02.14; Quinn Insurance v. Trifonovs Lawtel - 09.10.13; Liverpool Victoria v. Singh Lawtel 30.05.13; Samson v. Ali [2012] EWHC 4146; Mann v. Bahri [2012] Lawtel 02.04.12, Thompson & Fortis Insurance v. Middleton [2012] EWCA Civ 231, Liverpool Victoria v. Bashir [2012] EWHC 895 (Admin), Lane v. Shah [2012] ACD 1 (Admin), Nield v. Acromas v. Loveday [2011] EWHC (Admin), Vaile v. London Borough of Havering [2011] EWCA Civ 246.
Professional Memberships: PIBA.
Career: Called 1993, CEDR Mediator 2000, Direct Access Certified, Member of the Ogden Working Party.
Publications: Chronic Pain Society Journal, January 2012, 'The Times' Law Section (Credit Hire), 'Personal Injury Law Journal (Fighting Motor Fraud).
Personal: Interests include his young family, Andalucía, Headway, West London Churches Homeless Concern, the Athenaeum, Rachmaninov, tennis and Liverpool FC.

GRANTHAM, Andrew
Kings Chambers, Manchester
0845 034 3444
clerks@kingschambers.com
Featured in Chancery (Northern), Commercial Dispute Resolution (Northern)
Practice Areas: Agency (including commercial agency), banking, civil fraud and asset tracing, banking disputes, commercial arbitrations, company law (including shareholder actions), energy law, entertainment law, financial services law, insurance and reinsurance, partnership and LLPs, personal and corporate insolvency, professional negligence of accountants, solicitors and surveyors, sale and carriage of goods.
Professional Memberships: Northern Circuit Commercial Bar Association (Secretary), Chancery Bar Association, COMBAR, Northern Chancery Bar Association.
Career: Called to the Bar 1991, formerly lecturer in law Wadham College Oxford and King's College London.
Publications: Contributing Editor to Commercial Litigation Pre–Emptive Remedies (Sweet and Maxwell).

GRANT-HUTCHISON, Peter
Terra Firma Chambers, Edinburgh
0131 260 5830
peter.grant-hutchison@terrafirmachambers.com
Featured in Employment (Scotland)
Practice Areas: Peter specialises in employment law. He has a broad practice acting for both employers, employees, office holders such as police officers, chief constables and firemasters. He has undertaken complex Discrimination, Equal Pay Act and Transfer of Undertaking cases. He has appeared in all forums, including employment tribunals, employment appeal tribunals, the Inner House of the Court of Session and the House of Lords. He has acted in judicial mediations and appeared at Central Arbitration Committee hearings. Most recently he has been instructed in cases involving "whistleblowing" and questions of discrimination as a result of perceptions of disability.
Professional Memberships: Member of the Part Time Sheriffs Association; Member of the Council of Fee Paid Immigration Judges.
Career: LLB, Single Honours, MA Economics 1974-1979; apprentice then solicitor specialising in employment law 1978-1988; called to Bar in 1988; part time judge of the Social Entitlement Chamber 1988-date; member of the Competition Commission Appeals Panel 2002-2010; part time sheriff 2005-date; fee paid immigration judge 2003-date; member of Legal Panel for Equality and Human Rights Commission.
Publications: Architects Legal Handbook (Edition of Scottish Section on Employment Law and Health and Safety Legislation).
Personal: Born 1956. Educated at Dundee University. Chairman of Scottish Legal News.

GRAY, Justin
Trinity Chambers, Newcastle upon Tyne
0191 232 1927
j.gray@trinitychambers.co.uk
Featured in Family/Matrimonial (North Eastern)
Practice Areas: Specialist in: family; mental health; administrative and public law; Justin deals with all areas of family law; all areas of children law, including care proceedings, adoption and private disputes, with particular experience and interest in cases with an international element; ancillary relief, child maintenance, and co-ownership property claims; mental health and capacity law; forced marriage, "honour violence"; judicial review in family matters.
Professional Memberships: Family Law Bar Association; Chairman of the North East Family Law Bar Association 2014-2016; Bar representative on the Northumbria Local Family Justice Board;Bar representative on the Newcastle Courts Family Practitioner's Forum.
Career: Justin regularly contributes to Trinity's ongoing programme of family lectures and seminars. Topics have included interim care orders; Emigrating with children; Media attendance in family cases; Looked after children. The new Public Law Outline (PLO) (to Durham Law Society); The new practice following Re B-S and Re W; Court and presentation training for social workers.

GRAY, Peter QC
Compass Chambers, Edinburgh
0131 260 5661
peter.gray@compasschambers.com
Featured in Health & Safety (Scotland)
Practice Areas: Recently described by Legal 500 as "having a fabulous manner with clients and real gravitas before the courts" Peter Gray QC is a leading practitioner in regulatory crime, specialising in particular in health and safety, environmental and corporate financial prosecutions. In the fields of health and safety, and environmental crime Peter has been instructed to appear on behalf of corporate accused in the most serious prosecutions, statutory appeals and high profile Fatal Accident Inquiries in recent years and has been recognised by Chambers and Partners as "the top expert in the field" and by Legal 500 as "a leading authority in health and safety law, especially major industrial accidents". Representative cases include HMA v Transco plc(2005),HMA v CNR International(2008), The Stockline/ICL Public Inquiry (2008), Talisman Energy v HSE(2011),HMA v Maersk(2011), PF v Marks & Spencer plc(2011),Trident Offshore(The Bourbon Dolphin) v HSE(2012), HMA v Railcare Ltd(2012), PF v Taqa Bratani Ltd (2013), HMA v Svitzer Marine Ltd "The Flying Phantom"(2013),and the Superpuma Helicopter Fatal Accident Inquiry(representing BP)(2014). In the field of financial crime Peter specialises in corporate fraud, tax fraud, VAT evasion, and bribery and money laundering offences; much of his practice in this area is of an advisory nature provided at both national and international level. Recent instructions include HMA v Freeman(2008), Cell Trading Ltd v HMRC(2010), advising international company in relation to multi-million pound fraud committed by another in course of major commercial transaction (2011), AR Communications Ltd v HMRC (2011), advising major commercial entity regarding possible criminal activity relating to bribery by overseas agents(2012), and Re Abbott Group (2012)(first civil settlement achieved under self-reporting regime introduced by Crown post Bribery Act 2010).
Professional Memberships: Health and Safety Lawyers' Association, United Kingdom Environmental Law Association, Proceeds of Crime Lawyers' Association.
Career: Practiced at English Bar in London 1985-1992; called to Scottish Bar 1992; appointed Queen's Counsel 2002.

GREANEY, Nicola
Thirty Nine Essex Street, London
020 7832 1111
nicola.greaney@39essex.com
Featured in Community Care (London), Court of Protection (All Circuits), Professional Discipline (London)
Practice Areas: Professional discipline and all aspects of regulation including disciplinary hearings, legal assessing and appeals. Experience before a variety of regulatory tribunals, acting for registrants and regulators, including GDC, GOC, GCC, HCPC, BACP, RCVS, and SDT. Incapacity including decision-making about finances, medical treatment and social care of incapable adults. Particular interest in medical treatment and end of life issues and cases that have a cross-over with personal injury/clinical negligence, including deputies/management of awards. Public, administrative and human rights law including healthcare and community care. Also has a busy personal injury and clinical negligence practice, including group litigation. Notable cases include A Local Authority v H [2012] EWHC 49 (Fam), Buckinghamshire CC v RB Kingston v SL [2011] EWCA Civ 457, D County Council v LS [2010] EWHC 1916 (Fam), EM (Lebanon) v Secretary of State for the Home Department [2008] UKHL 64.
Career: Called to the Bar in 1999 and joined present Chambers upon completion of pupillage. Appointed to Treasury A Panel.
Publications: 'The Mental Capacity Act 2005: A Guide to the New Law', The Law Society (Editions 1 and 2), with Morris and Taylor.
Personal: Educated at New Hall, Cambridge, (BA (Hons) Law, part 1 French and German).

GREANEY, Paul QC
New Park Court Chambers, Leeds
0113 203 5501
paul.greaney@npc-l.co.uk
Featured in Crime (North Eastern), Sports Law (The Regions)
Practice Areas: Serious crime, principally homicide, financial crime and organised crime, including many high profile cases; regulatory crime including health and safety regulation and environmental health regulation; sports law in particular FA cases (eg. Suarez/Evra and Anelka/Quinelle); professional disciplinary proceedings including those concerning doctors and solicitors; police law; inquests, particularly those involving deaths in disasters (eg. leading counsel for the Police Federation in the Hillsborough inquests), in police custody, in hospital or in connection with medical treatment and those involving health and safety issues; public law, particularly claims relating to the criminal justice system, police law and coronial law.
Career: 1993 called; 1995 tenant at New Park Court Chambers; 2002 Attorney General's Panel of Advocates; 2010 Queen's Counsel; 2012 Head of the Criminal Team at New Park Court Chambers; 2012 Director of Advocacy Training North Eastern Circuit.

GREATOREX, Paul
11KBW, London
020 7632 8500
paul.greatorex@11kbw.com
Featured in Court of Protection (All Circuits), Education (London), Local Government (London)
Practice Areas: Public, employment and commercial law. Public law includes judicial review, human rights, public inquiries, and specialist areas include education, local government, immigration, mental capacity/ Court of Protection, planning and prisons. Employment practice covers advisory work as well as litigation in tribunals in England,

Wales and Scotland as well as in the civil courts and at all appellate levels up to the Supreme Court. Commercial practice consists of general litigation, including cross-border and international claims. Accredited under the Bar Public Access scheme so can be instructed by anyone.
Professional Memberships: ALBA, ELBA, PABA, PEBA.
Career: Called to the Bar 1999, Junior Counsel to the Crown (C and B Panel) 2005-2014. International experience includes spells with Richards Butler in Hong Kong, White & Case LLP in New York and Studio Pirola in Rome.
Publications: Co-author of 'Anti-Social Behaviour Law' (Jordans, 2nd edition, 2011) and contributing author to McManus, 'Education and the Courts' (Jordans, 3rd edition, 2012).
Personal: Educated at Christleton High School, Chester, Christ Church, Oxford and Université Panthéon-Assas (Paris II). Fluent in French, working knowledge of Italian and basic German and Czech.

GREEN, Alison
2TG - 2 Temple Gardens, London
020 7822 1200
agreen@2tg.co.uk
Featured in Insurance (London)
Practice Areas: Commercial practice, specialising in insurance and reinsurance, professional negligence private international law and arbitration. Reported cases include Novus Aviation v Onur Air [2009] (jurisdiction), Budgett Sugars v NU [2003] (products liability policy), Bestquest v Regency and Ecclesiastical Insurance Company [2003] (property/business interruption insurance), Stowers v GA Bonus [2003] (non-disclosure/commercial insurance) Sarwar v Allam [2002] (legal expenses insurance), Lonrho v ECGD [1996] (subrogation/insurance recoveries), Denby v Hellenic Mediterranean Lines [1994](jurisdiction/marine insurance).
Professional Memberships: COMBAR, BILA.
Career: University College London LLB, LLM, Robert Garraway Rice Pupillage Award, Belgian Government Scholarship to University of Louvain, law lecturer University of Surrey 76-78, tutor Queen Mary College 78 -79 and University College London 79-81, Vice President British Insurance Law Association, Vice Chair Bar Council Law Reform Committee, Chair BILA Charitable Trust, Law Commissions' insurance contract law panel member, Part - time Upper Tribunal Judge, mediator, arbitrator.
Publications: Editorial adviser, Insurance Contract Law, contributing author Insurance Law - An Introduction, contributing author Consumer Insurance Law, articles.

GREEN, David
Atlantic Chambers, Liverpool
0151 236 44 21
davidgreen@atlanticchambers.co.uk
Featured in Chancery (Northern), Real Estate Litigation (Northern)
Practice Areas: General chancery, particularly company and insolvency, landlord and tenant (commercial, residential and agricultural), dilapidations, service charges and rent review, partnerships and LLPs, real property (McLaughlin v Duffill [2010] Ch 1), boundaries, easements, restrictive covenants, options, mortgages and charges, wills, trusts, probate and estate administration (contentious and non-contentious), family provision, charities, professional negligence, Land Registry adjudication, highways and town and village greens. Advising, drafting and litigation undertaken in all those fields.
Professional Memberships: Northern Circuit, Chancery Bar Association, Northern Chancery Bar Association.
Career: Lancaster University LLB (Hons) 1992. Inns of Court School of Law. Called in 1993. Lincoln's Inn. Practised in Liverpool since 1994 and in present chambers since merger in 1996.
Personal: Seminars given to professional clients in a wide range of topics, most recently concerning Topical Issues for Landlords and Tenants, Proceeds of Crime Act 2002, Land Registration Act 2002, developments in the field of commercial landlord and tenant, contentious probate and family provision.

GREEN, Doré
2TG - 2 Temple Gardens, London
020 7822 1200
dgreen@2tg.co.uk
Featured in Property Damage (London)
Practice Areas: Professional indemnity, in particular construction professional, brokers' negligence and utilities; commercial insurance and product liability, in particular complex claims, coverage and indemnity, with a heavy insurance-based practice.
Professional Memberships: COMBAR. PNBA.
Career: Called 1994.
Personal: MA (Oxon). Mountaineering with notable first ascents in the wider ranges.

GREEN, Michael QC
Fountain Court Chambers, London
020 7583 3335
mg@fountaincourt.co.uk
Featured in Company (London), Tax (London)
Practice Areas: Principal areas of work are company, insolvency, civil fraud, financial services and tax including large scale commercial actions. With a background in commercial chancery chambers and many years on the Treasury A Panel before taking silk, Michael has extensive trial experience with a strong reputation for advocacy (both written and oral) and factual and expert cross examination. He also has substantial expertise in arguing complex legal issues in the appellate courts. Recent cases include: the high-profile successful defence of the directors in the Farepak disqualification case; Paycheck Services - the significant authority in the Supreme Court on de facto directorship; a number of cases for the FSA including Winterflood (in CA), Betton and judicial review case of Willford; huge transfer pricing litigation - Dixons (first to be tried) and AstraZeneca; instructed in huge tax case in Uganda; successful in winding up proceedings in the Cayman Islands; and instructed by court-appointed receiver in infamous Masri litigation which included an international arbitration.
Professional Memberships: COMBAR, Chancery Bar Association, Revenue Bar Association.
Career: Called 1987. Appointed Junior Counsel to the Crown (A Panel) in 1997 and a DTI Inspector in 1997. Silk 2009.

GREEN, Patrick QC
Henderson Chambers, London
020 7583 9020
pgreenqc@hendersonchambers.co.uk
Featured in Employment (London)
Practice Areas: Employment, Commercial, Economic Torts and Judicial Review. Recent leading employment cases include Shanks v Unilever (CA - employee patent compensation); Autoclenz v Belcher (SC - employee status); and Hospital Medical Group v Westwood (CA - worker status). Cases in the public eye include: Katharine Birbalsingh v St Michael and All Angels Academy (Teacher speaking at party conference); Dr Aisha Bijlani v Stewart & Others (barrister alleging discrimination); ABC News International Inc v Gizbert (journalist refusing work in war zones), and Pinnington v Governing Body of Ysgol Crug Glas (school nurse whistleblowing). Other leading employment cases include Jackson v Computershare (CA - TUPE); Lambe v 186K Ltd (redundancy and duty to decide issues) and Barke v SEETEC (lawfulness of providing additional reasons).
Professional Memberships: Middle Temple, ALBA, COMBAR, London Common Law and Commercial Bar Association, Bar European Group and Employment Law Bar Association.
Career: Magdalene College Cambridge 1989. Call 1990. CEDR Accredited Mediator 1997. Visiting Fellow at the LSE 2005. Treasurer of the IBA Mediation Committee 2012. Silk 2012.

GREEN, Robin
Cornerstone Barristers, London
020 7242 4986
clerks@cornerstonebarristers.com
Featured in Local Government (London), Planning (London)
Practice Areas: Planning; local government law; public and administrative law; property; highways.
Professional Memberships: ALBA; PEBA.
Career: Called 1992.
Publications: Principal contributor to the Housing title in the 'Encyclopaedia of Forms and Precedents', Volume 18; contributor on topics of local government land transactions, publicity and local government finance to Westlaw Insight; contributor to 'Licensed Premises: Law, Practice and Policy', 2nd ed, chapter 31 (Planning and other strategies).
Personal: LLB (London).

GREENHALGH, Jane
23 Essex Street, Manchester
Featured in Crime (Northern)
Practice Areas: Jane Greenhalgh is known as an experienced and highly competent junior with an extensive practice, instructed both by the Prosecution and Defence. Regularly involved in long running, notable and complex cases often generating much publicity. Now working from both the London and Manchester 23 Essex Street Chambers.

GRIFFIN, Nicholas QC
5 Paper Buildings, London
020 7583 6117
Featured in Inquests & Public Inquiries (London)
Practice Areas: Public law, public inquiries and crime, including fraud. His practice includes complex, often high profile litigation and he has particular experience in the conduct of large-scale proceedings. Cases include the Bloody Sunday Inquiry, the Rosemary Nelson Inquiry and the Guantánamo Bay litigation (Al Rawi & Others v The Security Service & Others). Represented a former News of the World Managing Editor in the Phone Hacking trial at the Central Criminal Court (R v Rebekah Brooks, Andrew Coulson & Others), who was acquitted in June 2014. He acts on behalf of a variety of clients from private individuals and organisations to soldiers, police officers and government departments and agencies.
Career: Called 1992 (England and Wales) and 2011 (Northern Ireland). Silk 2012.

GRIFFITHS, Peter QC
2 Bedford Row, London
07970 834 678
pgriffiths@2bedfordrow.co.uk
Featured in Financial Crime (London)
Practice Areas: Fraud Crime Restraint/Confiscation Sport/Regulatory Acts in some of the highest profile fraud and criminal cases in the UK. Listed for many years by Chambers and Partners in Fraud. Is a corporate fraud specialist and is regularly instructed to defend in complex and multi-handed fraud and money-laundering cases, frequently with a multi-jurisdictional aspect. High profile cases include successfully defending in what is acknowledged to be the SFO' costliest failure - "Operation Holbein" in which the SFO alleged that certain leading international pharmaceutical companies and their chief executives had formed a criminal cartel and had conspired to defraud the NHS by fixing the price and restricting the supply of antibiotics used by millions of people in this country. The case ran for three years during its complex interlocutory stages including going to the Court of Appeal on two occasions and also the House of Lords. Has been instructed to defend in MTIC-VAT frauds and also in money laundering cases including the "EK" £180 million case at Southwark. Was instructed to defend the head of what was said to be an eastern European criminal organisation who had removed millions of pounds from online customers of Barclays, HSBC, RBS and Lloyds using an extremely sophisticated "Trojan" virus described by the FBI as "arguably the most dangerous yet". Crime: Defends in a complete cross-section of heavy criminal cases throughout the country. These have included R v J (Newcastle) the notorious PC Sharon Beshenivsky murder trial, R v L and Others (Leeds) which was a double murder "Triad" case, R v T a London terrorist trial before Mrs Justice Rafferty, the four-month Johnson Matthey Gold Bullion Robbery Trial heard at Woolwich, the four-month Essex Contract Killing trial heard at the Central Criminal Court and the "Cobham Body-in-the-Wheelie-bin" murder trial in which the victim's body had been locked in a freezer for three years; this was again heard at the Central Criminal Court in 2010. Currently instructed to defend in the Stepping Hill Hospital 'insulin' murder and poisoning case due to commence in Manchester in January 2015 (estimated to last some 4 months). Sport/Regulatory Has advised and represented solicitors investigated and/or charged with misconduct including Re: D, a solicitor who acted in the multi-million pound transfer of an English international between two Premier League clubs who was alleged to have breached his professional regulations. Sports work includes acting as a member of the FA's Judicial Panel.

GROUND, Richard
Cornerstone Barristers, London
020 7242 4986
richardg@cornerstonebarristers.com
Featured in Planning (London)

Practice Areas: Specialises in planning, compulsory purchase, local government, town and village greens, property, judicial review and environment. He has extensive experience in particular in major planning inquiries, village green inquiries and high court challenges. He was voted one of the top 3 rated planning juniors in Planning. He has worked recently for Berwin Leighton, Herbert Smith Freehills Legal &General, Dentons and numerous Councils.
Professional Memberships: On committee of Planning and Environment Bar Association. Member of National Infrastructure Planning Association and Compulsory Purchase Association.
Career: Called 1994. MA(Cantab).
Publications: Significant contributor to Burnett-Hall on Environmental Law (3rd Edition).
Personal: Married with two children living in London.

GRUNDY, Nicholas
Five Paper, London
020 7815 3200
nicholasgrundy@fivepaper.com
Featured in Social Housing (London)

Practice Areas: Landlord and Tenant (residential and commercial); Chancery; Social Housing and Homelessness; Public Law, including Human Rights and Equality Act.
Professional Memberships: PBA; SHLA (Committee Member since 2008).
Career: Nick's reported and significant cases include: Francis v RB K&C [2003] EWCA Civ 443 (homelessness); Crest Nicholson v McAllister [2004] EWCA Civ 410 (restrictive covenants); Haringey LBC v Hickey [2006] EWCA Civ 373 (homelessness); Gallions HA v Various (>400 long lessees on Thamesmead Town Estate) LON/LVL/21-32/05 (variation of leases); Denton v Southwark LBC [2007] EWCA Civ 623 (homelessness); St Pancras HA v Leonard [2008] EWCA Civ 1442 (adverse possession/estoppel); Haringey LBC v Hines [2010] EWCA Civ 1111 (right to buy); Nzamy v Brent LBC [2011] EWCA Civ 283 (homelessness); Brent LBC v Shulem B [2011] EWHC 1663 (Ch) (residential service charges); Southwark LBC v Ofogba (2011) Case No 9PA37288 (water charges); Barnet LBC v Phoenix & Others (2012) (human rights); Obiorah v Lewisham LBC [2013] EWCA Civ 325 (homelessness); Chishimba v RB K&C [2013] EWCA Civ (homelessness); Southend-on-Sea BC v Armour [2014] EWCA Civ 231 (human rights) – permission to appeal to SC applied for; Aster HA v Akerman-Livingstone [2014] EWCA Civ 1081(equality and human rights) – D has permission to appeal to SC. These case show the breadth of Nick's practice; he is regularly instructed to represent public sector landlords in complicated cases.
Personal: MA (cantab); MSc (Loughbrough); Dip Law (Westminster).

GRUNWALD, Henry QC
Charter Chambers, London
020 7618 4400
henry.grunwald@charterchambers.com
Featured in Crime (London)

Practice Areas: All areas of criminal law.
Professional Memberships: Criminal Bar Association; South Eastern Circuit.
Career: 1972 call, Gray's Inn; Bencher, Gray's Inn; QC 1999. Known for his unflappability in court, Henry Grunwald is one of the most experienced criminal Silks in practice. He has defended in many high profile criminal cases at the Old Bailey and nationally, including. 1) the "witchcraft" murder of a young boy and the assault and torture of his siblings, 2) the honour killing of his daughter by a member of the Kurdish community, 3) one of the largest ever drug importations leading to one of the longest ever trials, 4) several large-scale fraud trials, and 5), most recently, the Bristol murder trial of a husband who killed his wife when under the influence of a cocktail of drink and drugs, taken in an attempt to commit suicide.
Personal: President, Board of Deputies of British Jews, 2003 to 2009. President Relate, North London. Vice-Chair National Holocaust Memorial Day Trust, 2005-2013. Chairman, National Holocaust Centre, 2012. OBE 2009.

GUEST, Peter
187 Fleet Street, London
07768 861 881
chambers@187fleetstreet.com
Featured in Financial Crime (London)

Practice Areas: High profile and client focused leading practice (exclusively defence) specialising in white-collar crime, money laundering, confiscation and other serious criminal cases, both in the Crown Court and the Court of Appeal. Recent work includes MG (cheating the Revenue), NB (duty fraud), DF (VAT evasion by firm of chartered accountants), NB (money laundering), EM (duty fraud appeal), MO (duty fraud appeal), GG (people trafficking), JG (duty fraud), RL (murder), JN (murder), DJ (contract murder), MN (confiscation), AS (armed robberies), DR (drug dealing police officer), AK (money laundering), AB (multi-kilo heroin dealing), CN (money laundering), DC (MTIC fraud and money laundering), SA (MTIC fraud), PM (duty fraud), BR (duty fraud), AH (money laundering), MN (confiscation appeal), JG (confiscation), MR (duty fraud), KC (professional armed kidnapping), WB (money laundering), S-T (duty fraud), JB (pervert justice), PB (kidnap, blackmail and false imprisonment), GM (confiscation), MD (duty fraud), RP (high-level cocaine dealing), TQ (mortgage fraud), MK (fraud), NM (MTIC fraud), NH (rape), PS (FSA insider dealing prosecution), DL (armed robberies), WY {money laundering) and TB (VAT evasion, cannabis supply and money laundering. Current work includes EJ (tax avoidance, conspiracy to defraud and money laundering), SJ (fraud and money laundering), YS (mortgage fraud), T (money laundering), AS (boiler room), SS (gangmaster), KH (duty fraud) and NR (MTIC fraud).
Professional Memberships: Criminal Bar Association.
Career: Called 1975. Recorder 2000.
Personal: Kingston Grammar School. Durham University. France.

GUN CUNINGHAME, Julian
Gough Square Chambers, London
020 7353 0924
jgc@goughsq.co.uk
Featured in Consumer Law (London)

Practice Areas: Consumer credit, mortgages, banking, financial services, estate agency, insurance, sale and hire of goods, misrepresentation, asset tracing, fraud, freezing injunctions, committal, undue influence, professional negligence, employment, real and leasehold property, housing, trusts of land and jointly owned property, limitation of actions, civil procedure and costs. Recently involved in litigation involving enforceability of credit card and loan agreements, misselling of payment protection insurance and unfair relationships in particular involving second charge and irresponsible lending. Counsel in Carey v HSBC [2009] EWHC 3417 (QB) [2010] Bus LR 1142, the test case on enforceability of credit card agreements and effect of unenforceability. Accepts instructions in all of the above areas as a Public Access barrister.
Career: Admitted as solicitor (1988); called to the Bar (1989); member of chambers of Frederick Philpott (1990); member of Gough Square Chambers (2003); Public Access barrister since 2010.
Publications: Atkins Court Forms on Landlord and Tenant and Trespass to Goods and Conversion.

GUNNING, Alexander QC
4 Pump Court, London
020 7842 1164
agunning@4pumpcourt.com
Featured in Commercial Dispute Resolution (London), Energy & Natural Resources (London), International Arbitration (London), Shipping (London)

Practice Areas: Domestic and international arbitration (including under ICC, LCIA, LMAA, UNCITRAL and trade association rules), shipbuilding/ offshore and energy-related construction projects, insurance and re-insurance, general commercial litigation, professional negligence.
Professional Memberships: COMBAR, LCLCBA.
Personal: King's College London, LLB (Hons), LLM (Commercial and Corporate Law), called to the Bar 1994, Queen's Counsel 2012

GUPTA, Mamta
No5 Chambers, Birmingham
0845 210 5555
mgu@no5.com
Featured in Clinical Negligence (Midlands)

Practice Areas: Principally Clinical Negligence work for both claimants and defendants in all areas plus Personal Injury work. Recent cases include: substandard spinal surgery causing tetraplegia, failure to carry out a caesarian section causing Erbs Palsy, failure to identify perforations in the bladder during salpingectomy causing serious injury. Mamta is also often instructed in gynaecological and obstetric matters as well as matters covering all areas of medicine in relation to primary and secondary Care. Mamta has an extensive inquest practice acting on behalf of families, Trusts and healthcare professionals and is increasingly led in high value and complex cases.
Professional Memberships: AvMA, Professional Negligence Bar Association, Personal Injury Bar Association,
Career: BSc [Hons] Pharmacology 2(i); Called to the Bar: 2004;

HABBOO, Camille
Fourteen, London
07976 151 634
chabboo@fourteen.co.uk
Featured in Family/Matrimonial (London)

Practice Areas: Children law specialist - public and private law. Instructed on behalf of Local Authorities, parents and children including complex cases of non accidental injury and sexual abuse.
Career: Recent reported cases involving sexual abuse include Re J (A child) 2014 EWCA Civ 875 acting on behalf of the child. The father successfully appealed findings of serious sexual abuse. Special mention was made of the Guardian's representatives' role where a parent was acting in person. The case highlighted the unfair process and the wrong balancing exercise undertaken by the Court particularly where there was no ABE interview or written narrative account of the allegations. That same case was reported as Re A (A Child) (Vulnerable Witness) 2013 EWHC 1694 where the Court determined the evidence of a very vulnerable witness could be received orally within the trial process with a range of special measures including the use of an intermediary and video link. Recent other cases include the successful opposition of the appeal against the findings of serious non accidental injury in respect of the earlier reported case of Re MR (a child) (Fact-Finding: physical injuries) 2012 EWHC 4258 (Fam) which was one of the first appeals to consider Re B-S (Children) 2013 EWCA Civ 1146.Camille also appeared for the Guardian in N v B v T&Y 2013 EWHC 820 (Fam) where the children's mother had been murdered by the father and the Court re-emphasised the guidelines to be followed in such cases.

HACKETT, Philip QC
4-5 Gray's Inn Square, London
020 7404 5252
phackett@4-5.co.uk
Featured in Financial Crime (London)

Practice Areas: Philip specialises in civil and criminal commercial fraud, international corruption, regulatory and disciplinary law, direct and indirect tax and associated areas such as sanctions, mutual legal assistance and asset tracing. Over the past 25 years he has been instructed in many of the leading cases including the most serious SFO investigations, FSA prosecutions for insider dealing and market manipulation, cartel prosecutions, HMRC prosecutions, enquiries and civil claims in respect of taxation matters and numerous HSE and manslaughter cases. The international aspects of his practice have resulted in experience of offshore matters in connection with BVI, the Channel Islands and Isle of Man and many European jurisdictions as well as US, Caribbean and Africa.
Career: Philip has acted in respect of many of the leading cases including; SIB (Isle of Man) (banking and audit); Arrows (property); Maxwell (pensions); three BCCI trials (banking and audit); Gooda Walker (insurance); Wickes (auditing); Merrion Re insurance (insurance); AIT (market manipulation; TransTec (audit); Kent Pharmaceuticals (cartel); Daily Mirror 'City Slickers' (market manipulation); Vantis (tax); Bouman (tax); Torex (audit); UKIP MEP expenses; Asil Nadir.

HAGEN, Dakis
Serle Court, London
020 7400 7156
dhagen@serlecourt.co.uk
Featured in Chancery (London), Offshore (London), Trusts (London)

Practice Areas: General commercial chancery, particularly trusts litigation (international and domestic, commercial and private client), fraud, asset tracing and business disputes. Significant cases include Walker v Egerton-Vernon, Tchenguiz v Imerman, Orconsult v Blickle in Bermuda, Charman v Charman and the Alhamrani litigation.
Professional Memberships: Chancery Bar Association; COMBAR.
Career: Called 2002.
Personal: Born: 1978. Educated at Peterhouse, Cambridge University (MA double first) and City University (Dip Law). Interests include history and music.

HALES, Sally-Ann QC
Red Lion Chambers, London
020 7520 6000
sally.hales@18rlc.co.uk
Featured in Financial Crime (London)
Practice Areas: Specialist in criminal law with a particular emphasis on corruption, fraud and white-collar crime. Instructed by defence and prosecution (SFO and Central Fraud Group). Acted in cases involving allegations of tax fraud, bank fraud, identity fraud, cartel offences, 'Ponzi' fraud, money laundering and VAT offences. First instructed by the SFO the Co-Operative Wholesale Society corruption case (1999-2003) has since been instructed in five further SFO cases. Currently instructed in two overseas corruption cases prosecuted by SFO; for defence in R v DK (Innospec) and for prosecution in R v B & others (Swift). Defended in R v Goldshield Group plc & others (Operation Holbein, 'pharmaceuticals') and aborted Operation Tangelo. Prosecuted for SFO in R v Afzal & others (Birmingham mortgage fraud). Recent cases include Operation Skijump, representing company director in large scale boiler room /carbon trading fraud and Operation Walrus, representing a company director accused of commercial mortgage fraud. Acting on behalf of the claimant in £15m claim in VAT tribunal. Advising jeweller in connection with civil insurance fraud. Sally-Ann is also instructed as 'Independent Counsel' to advise on LPP issues.
Professional Memberships: Elected as QC Representative to Criminal Bar Association Committee.
Career: Recorder, 2011; Queen's Counsel, 2012.

HALL, Matthew
Kings Chambers, Manchester
0845 034 3444
clerks@kingschambers.com
Featured in Real Estate Litigation (Northern)
Practice Areas: Land law (in particular easements, restrictive covenants, boundaries) Landlord and Tenant (commercial and acting in service charge / management disputes before the First Tier Tribunal (Property Chamber)). Also specialises in the law of succession and claims under the Inheritance (Provision for Family and Dependants) Act 1975. Significant Cases (from Court of Appeal): Ahmad v Secret Garden Cheshire [2013] 3 EGLR 42 (rectification of lease) Bradford v James [2008] EWCA Civ 837 (extrinsic evidence in construction of conveyance) Latimer v Carney [2007] 1 P & CR 213 (correct approach to assessment of damages in dilapidations claims) Tennant v Adamczyk [2006] 1 P & CR 485 (adverse possession).
Professional Memberships: Chancery Bar Association, Northern Chancery Bar Association.
Career: Year of call 1998 BA (Oxon) First Class in Law with Law Studies in Europe (French).

HALL, Melanie QC
Monckton Chambers, London
020 7405 7211
mhall@monckton.com
Featured in Tax (London)
Practice Areas: VAT.
Career: Melanie's cases have shaped the structure and boundaries of VAT and other indirect taxes. In recent months she has defended the legality of the very existence of VAT on hot takeaway food; the Aggregates Levy and the Landfill Tax. Over the years she has appeared in other key cases such as Mobilx, Southern Primary and the Mirror Group before the Court of Appeal and in cases such as Redrow, Eastbourne Radio Cars and Taxis and Dr Beynon before what is now the Supreme Court. She is also a well known and respected advocate in Luxembourg where she has argued cases before the European Court of Justice such as EC v UK on VAT Grouping, TNT, The Wellcome Foundation, Midland Bank, Abbey National, and Kretztechnik. There are very few areas of VAT upon which she has not advised. Although she acts for HMRC, she is frequently engaged by taxpayers, representing a broad range of household name clients which include local authorities, hoteliers, universities and charities (large and small), high street retailers, publishers, banks and other financial institutions, telecommunications providers, pharmaceutical companies, premier league football clubs and gambling operators.
Personal: QC BA (Dunelm).

HALL TAYLOR, Alex
4 New Square, London
020 7822 2000
a.halltaylor@4newsquare.com
Featured in Chancery (London), Financial Services (London), Fraud (London), Professional Negligence (London)
Practice Areas: Litigation and dispute resolution in core areas: commercial, professional negligence, chancery, financial, international and civil fraud work. Professional negligence claims both for claimants and defendants against solicitors, barristers, surveyors, accountants, tax advisers and financial services professionals (recent example Arrowhead Capital Finance Ltd v KPMG LLP [2012] 1801 (Comm) successful summary dismissal of $52m+ claim). Often acts in claims by or against fiduciaries (trustees, trust companies and administrators, directors, liquidators, receivers). Conducts or defends financial claims involving banking, financial products, pensions, tax and trusts disputes both on and offshore. Regularly appears in Chancery Division, Commercial Court, London Mercantile Court. Increasingly instructed as sole or lead junior counsel against senior silks. Frequently instructed to seek (and less frequently to defend) urgent injunctive and other pre-emptive relief, including freezing injunctions, search orders, Norwich Pharmacal and Bankers Trust orders, particularly in the Queen's Bench Division. Significant experience in handling complex, multi-party, document heavy litigation often requiring management of a team of more junior counsel. International work includes disputes from Africa to Fiji, from St Lucia to the Channel Islands, and from the BVI to Mauritius. Has appeared as sole counsel in a number of appeals to the Privy Council.
Professional Memberships: Professional Negligence Bar Association, COMBAR, Chancery Bar Association, London Common Law and Commercial Bar Association, South Eastern Circuit, Inner Temple.
Career: Education: Charterhouse School, Bristol University, College of Law, Inns of Court School of Law Inn: Inner Temple (Member 1994, Called 1996, Bencher 2012) Chambers: 11 Old Square (now Radcliffe Chambers) 1996-2001. Joined 4 New Square in 2001.
Publications: The "Property, Planning and Environment" chapter of Leigh-Ann Mulcahy's Human Rights and Civil Practice (Sweet and Maxwell, London 2001) the "Property, Planning and Environment" chapter of Leigh-Ann Mulcahy's Human Rights and Civil Practice (Sweet and Maxwell, London 2001).
Personal: Born in Sweden, early childhood spent in Singapore and Malaysia. Enjoys travel, particularly skiing. Speaks conversational French.

HALLAM, Jacob
6KBW College Hill, London
020 3301 0910
jacob.hallam@6kbw.com
Featured in Crime (London)
Practice Areas: Jacob is recognised as an expert in the conduct of substantial high-profile cases involving complex areas of fact, law and public interest in the Crown Court, High Court and Court of Appeal. Jacob's talents for the presentation of complex evidence at court, in his precise and measured courtroom manner, make him a persuasive advocate and impressive cross-examiner. He has appeared in many of the recent highest profile criminal trials in the country, involving homicide, diamond robbery, cybercrime and international criminal conspiracies. In addition to his work in the criminal courts, Jacob has developed an expanding practice in advisory work, judicial review, extradition, and libel law. For further information about Jacob's expertise and practice areas, please refer to the 6KBW College Hill website (www.6kbw.com).
Professional Memberships: Member of the Specialist Serious Crime Panel; member of the Faculty of Advocacy Teachers at Gray's Inn.
Career: Called in 1996; Junior Treasury Counsel to the Crown at the Central Criminal Court, 2014; Grade 4 CPS Prosecutor.

HALLIDAY, Patrick
11KBW, London
020 7632 8500
patrick.halliday@11kbw.com
Featured in Employment (London)
Practice Areas: Employment law, public law, procurement law.
Professional Memberships: ELBA; ELA; ALBA; APP; PLA, UKSALA.
Career: Called 2005, Gray's Inn. Former pupil to Sales J. Attorney General's B Panel of Counsel. Recent cases: R (Clulow) v Secretary of State for Work and Pensions [2013] EWHC 3241 (Admin): system for community care grants did not breach Article 14 of the ECHR; R (Moyse) v Secretary of State for Education [2012] EWHC 2758 (Admin), [2012] ELR 551 (leading case on enforced conversion of schools to academies); R (Williams) v Surrey County Council [2012] EWHC 867 (QB), [2012] Eq LR 656 (libraries and the public sector equality duty); Emmanuel v City & Hackney Teaching Primary Care Trust [2011] EqLR 1291 (equal pay, national test case on nurses, GMF 'market forces' defence made out); Baha Mousa Public Inquiry (2008 - 2011); Teva (UK) Limited v Heslip [2009] All ER (D) 277 (Jul) (EAT) (time limits); R (Hurst) v London North District Coroner [2007] UKHL 13 (article 2 ECHR and coroners' inquests).
Publications: Tolley's Employment Handbook (annually since 2007, EU law). 'Restitution and Public Bodies' (Judicial Review Vol 12 Issue 3). Lectures regularly on employment and procurement law. Joint editor of 11KBW's Procurement Law Newsletter.
Personal: Educated at Pembroke College, Cambridge (first class degree in Social and Political Sciences, Foundation Scholar) and City University (CPE, Distinction).

HALLIWELL, Mark
Kings Chambers, Manchester
0845 034 3444
clerks@kingschambers.com
Featured in Chancery (Northern), Commercial Dispute Resolution (Northern), Real Estate Litigation (Northern)
Practice Areas: General chancery and commercial law including contentious and non-contentious real property, landlord and tenant, rights of way, corporate and individual insolvency, charities, trusts, probate and the administration of estates, commercial arbitration and professional.
Professional Memberships: Chancery Bar Association, Northern Chancery Bar Association, Northern Circuit Commercial Bar Association.
Career: University: London School of Economics, degree: BSc (Econ), Called:1985 (Lincoln's Inn) Hardwicke scholar, Recorder 2003, Treasury Counsel (charities).
Publications: Distribution on Intestacy (FT Law and Tax).

HALPERN, David QC
4 New Square, London
020 7822 2000
d.halpern@4newsquare.com
Featured in Professional Negligence (London), Real Estate Litigation (London)
Practice Areas: Professional negligence and commercial Chancery litigation.
Professional Memberships: Chancery Bar Association (currently chairman of the International Subcommittee), COMBAR, Property Bar Association and Professional Negligence Bar Association.
Career: Since taking silk in 2006, David has continued to focus on his core areas of professional negligence and commercial Chancery work. He particularly relishes the challenge of acting for or against professionals in areas which call on his expertise in the underlying issues of property, company law, insolvency and accounts. He has wide experience of both litigation and mediation, as well as advisory work. He sits as a deputy judge of the Chancery Division and a Recorder, is a Bencher of Gray's Inn and an advocacy trainer for the Inn and has chaired disciplinary tribunals for the Bar Standards Board. He has been called to the Bar of Gibraltar.
Publications: Contributor to Jackson and Powell on Professional Liability (he edits the chapters on Auditors and Actuaries).

HAMER, Kenneth
Henderson Chambers, London
020 7583 9020
khamer@hendersonchambers.co.uk
Featured in Professional Discipline (London)
Practice Areas: Kenneth has substantial and wide ranging experience in professional conduct and competance matters. He regularly represents solicitors involved in disciplinary and regulatory cases. He has expertise in health care, legal, accountancy and financial aspects of professional discipline. He frequently lectures on fitness to practise issues. Copies of recent talks and other information about Kenneth are available on www.hendersonchambers.co.uk.
Career: Recorder of the Crown Court since 2000. He is a member of the prosecuting panel of the Bar Standards Board, a Legal Assessor for the General Medical Council, the Nursing & Midwifery Council and the General Dental Council. He is a former chairman of the Appeal Committee for the Chartered Institute of Management Accountants. In 2008 he spent six months advising the Financial Services Authority on various matters.
Publications: He is co-editor of the Assocation of Regulatory and Disciplinary Lawyers' newsletter. He is author of Professional Conduct Casebook published by Oxford University Press March 2013.

HAMILL, Hugh
12 King's Bench Walk, London
020 7583 0811
hamill@12kbw.co.uk
Featured in Personal Injury (London)
Practice Areas: Personal injury, clinical negligence, consumer credit, construction, health and safety. Recognised as a 'Leading Junior' in Personal Injury in Chambers Directory and the Legal 500. Hugh has an established practice acting predominantly for defendants but also for claimants in catastrophic injury claims. Areas of expertise include public/employers liability, catastrophic injury, brain and spinal injury, road traffic - fatal accident and serious injury claims including claims involving the Motor Insurance Bureau. Mental capacity - litigation capacity - Hugh successfully represented the defendants in Masterman- Lister the leading case in this area and is instructed in cases arising out of this decision. Fibromyalgia-chronic fatigue syndrome and cases of disputed causation. Defending health and safety prosecutions, insurance fraud/staged accidents/malingering.
Professional Memberships: PIBA LCLBA.
Personal: Lives in Oxfordshire. Married with two children.

HAMILTON, Duncan
Arnot Manderson, Edinburgh
07971 032 150
duncan.hamilton@advocates.org.uk
Featured in Media & Entertainment (Scotland)
Practice Areas: Specialises in defamation, privacy and media law and the only Junior Counsel at the Scottish Bar to be ranked in those areas in recent years. Instructed regularly for a range of national newspapers, broadcasters (including the BBC) and high profile individuals. He has appeared in a number of important recent cases (including the Supreme Court) redefining media coverage of court proceedings in Scotland and the leading defamation decision of the Inner House on qualified privilege, honest comment and defamatory meaning. His practice also includes personal injury, clinical negligence and public law. He is a Standing Junior to the Scottish Government.
Professional Memberships: Faculty of Advocates.
Career: Trained at leading Edinburgh firm before calling at the Scottish Bar. Previously a Member of the Scottish Parliament from 1999 to 2003. Served on six Parliamentary Committees, including the Justice Committee. Additionally, a weekly newspaper columnist for a number of national titles over the last decade including 'The Scotsman' and 'Scotland on Sunday'. In 2007-08, he served (part time) as a Special Adviser advising the First Minister of Scotland. In 2013 he was appointed as Standing Junior Counsel to the Scottish Government.
Publications: Contributor to 'Scots Law for Journalists' (Eighth Edition).

HAMILTON, Penny
Pump Court Tax Chambers, London
020 7414 8080
clerks@pumptax.com
Featured in Tax (London)
Practice Areas: Recognised in The Legal 500 and Chambers & Partners as a leading junior at the Tax Bar and voted Best in Tax Dispute Resolution in the Euromoney European Women in Business Law Awards, Penny Hamilton has extensive experience in advice and litigation and (including judicial review and references to the European Court of Justice) in VAT, landfill tax, aggregates levy, climate change levy, insurance premium tax, excise and customs duties, and the impact of European Community law. She advises clients in the commercial, retail, financial, property, education and charitable sectors on a wide range of issues. She served on the Consultative Committee of the Review of HMRC's Powers, Deterrents and Safeguards and the Tax Appeals Stakeholders Group. Cases include HMRC v Waste Recycling Group (Court of Appeal); Robinson Family Ltd v HMRC (FTT); London Borough of Richmond v Robinson (Kingston Crown Court, expert for the prosecution); TNT Post UK Ltd (Administrative Court & ECJ).
Professional Memberships: Fellow, The Chartered Institute of Taxation (President 2002-03); Tax Appeals Stakeholders Group; RBA; VPG; Bar European Group; Bencher of Grays Inn (2010).
Career: 1972: Called to the Bar (Gray's Inn); 1973-1975: Chambers at 12 Old Square, Lincoln's Inn; 1975-1987: Senior legal adviser to HM Customs & Excise; 1987-1989: Deloitte, Haskins and Sells (senior manager, indirect taxes division); 1989-2000: Partner in PricewaterhouseCoopers (and predecessor firms); 2000 onwards: Pump Court Tax Chambers; 2002: President of the Chartered Institute of Taxation; 2003: Voted "VAT Rat of the Year"; 2011: Voted "Best in tax dispute resolution", Euromoney European Women in Business Law Awards; 2012: CEDR accredited mediator; 2013 Member of the CEDR Mediation Panel.
Publications: Consulting Editor of Halsbury's Laws of England (VAT and Landfill Tax); Author (with Oliver Conolly) Hamilton on Tax Appeals (Bloomsbury 2010).

HAMMOND, Sean
2 Bedford Row, London
020 7440 8888
shammond@2bedfordrow.co.uk
Featured in Financial Crime (London)
Practice Areas: An experienced leading junior who specialises in advising and defending individuals and corporate clients facing allegations of fraud, money laundering, corruption and other white collar crime. He is often asked to provide advice to individuals and companies in pre-charge and ancillary matters such as compliance, financial services regulation, restraint proceedings and issues of disclosure and privilege. Much of his work involves parallel civil and criminal proceedings and he has considerable experience in this area. In recent years, he has defended in a number of high profile, complex cases brought by the Serious Fraud Office, Financial Services Authority (now FCA), HM Revenue and Customs and the Serious Organised Crime Agency. These included allegations of MTIC carousel fraud, VAT and tax fraud, diversion fraud, fraudulent trading, corruption of local government officials, money laundering, advance fee fraud, boiler room fraud and various offences under the Companies Act. In the regulatory and disciplinary field, he sits as a Panel Member of the Inns Conduct Committee (ICC), is a Legal Adviser to the Nursing and Midwifery Council (NMC), and regularly defends individuals before various tribunals such as the General Medical Council (GMC) and Solicitors' Disciplinary Tribunal (SDT). For further information, please visit www.2bedfordrow.co.uk.
Professional Memberships: South Eastern Circuit, Criminal Bar Association, Association of Regulatory and Disciplinary Lawyers.
Career: Called to the Bar 1991, Lincoln's Inn.

HANDYSIDE, Richard QC
Fountain Court Chambers, London
020 7583 3335
richardhandyside@fountaincourt.co.uk
Featured in Banking & Finance (London), Commercial Dispute Resolution (London)
Practice Areas: Commercial litigation, including banking and financial services, professional negligence, civil fraud, conflicts of laws, insurance/reinsurance, restitution and arbitration. Current / recent cases include Deutsche Bank v Unitech (LIBOR related issues); FSCS v Independent Financial Advisers (the Keydata litigation); JP Morgan v BVG (alleged mis-selling of a CDO); Dexia v Prato (interest rate swap; Italian public authority); Bull v Gain Capital (financial services; restitution).
Professional Memberships: COMBAR.
Career: Called 1993. QC 2009.
Personal: Born 1968. Bristol University (LLB Hons 1st Class) and Brasenose College, Oxford (BCL 1st Class).

HANIF, Saima
Thirty Nine Essex Street, London
020 7832 1111
saima.hanif@39essex.com
Featured in Financial Services (London), Professional Discipline (London)
Practice Areas: Saima has a specific expertise in financial services and professional discipline. She is particularly experienced in FCA regulatory investigations, mis-selling claims and banking disputes. She is currently representing the founder of Catalyst, Mr Roberts, in the Upper Tribunal, and is also acting for a claimant firm in a judicial review of a FOS decision, relating to the characterisation of tax mitigation arrangements. She has undertaken secondments in the Enforcement Division and General Counsel's Division of the FCA, the Bank of England and Clifford Chance. She acted for the successful claimant (as junior counsel to Hodge Malek QC) in the landmark High Court decision in Ford v FSA [2013]. In the Upper Tribunal, she represented a former UBS employee in Karan v FSA [2013], and a a mortgage broker Khan v FCA [2014]. She has also acted for a leading payday lender (as junior counsel) in a matter concerning the application of the CONC rulebook. She undertakes international work, in particular the Middle East. She has acted for clients (both individuals and institutions) before the DFSA and the DIFC Courts.
Professional Memberships: ALBA, FSLA.
Career: Tenant, 39 Essex Street. Secondments: FSA 2004; Financial Regulatory Department, Clifford Chance 2007; Financial Markets Law Committee (c/o Bank of England) 2008; FCA, General Counsel's Division 2013.
Publications: Prospectuses and Public Issues (Tolleys); Tribunal Practice (Jordans); Atkins Volume on Financial Services; Butterworths: Financial Regulation Service.
Personal: Oxford University: BA (Jurisprudence).

HANNA, Ronan
Atkin Chambers, London
020 7404 0102
rhanna@atkinchambers.com
Featured in Construction (London), Energy & Natural Resources (London), Professional Negligence (London)
Practice Areas: Specialises in construction, engineering, energy and natural resources, professional negligence and IT matters with experience of litigation, arbitration and other forms of dispute resolution. Represents developers, employers, professionals, contractors, sub-contractors, funders and insurers. Experience in engineering and energy disputes has included offshore renewables, oil / gas pipelines, combined power and desalination plants, railways, roads and stadiums. Regularly acts in professional negligence disputes involving architects, engineers, quantity surveyors and project managers. Recent IT experience includes major government infrastructure projects.
Professional Memberships: TECBAR, LCLCBA, Combar, Society of Construction Law.
Career: Called 2006 (England and Wales), 2011 (Northern Ireland).
Publications: Hudson's Building and Engineering Contracts, 12th Ed. (Sweet & Maxwell, 2010) - contributing editor.
Personal: BA (Oxon); BCL (Oxon).

HANNAFORD, Sarah QC
Keating Chambers, London
020 7544 2600
shannaford@keatingchambers.com
Featured in Construction (London), Public Procurement (London)
Practice Areas: Specialist in EU procurement, construction, engineering, energy and professional negligence in those and related fields. Sarah's recent case load has involved acting for various UK Government

departments on some of the highest profile and highest value disputes the UK Government has seen in recent times ranging from disputes for the Ministry of Justice for overpayments for electronic tagging services, the Ministry of Defence regarding the construction of a nuclear submarine facility and Section 68 Arbitration appeal arising out of a long running Arbitration regarding the design and construction of a substantial regeneration project. Sarah also has considerable expertise in disputes relating to party walls, rights of light and other easements, and has authored key publications on those subjects. In addition to her work as Counsel, Sarah Hannaford is a trained Mediator and accredited Adjudicator.
Professional Memberships: COMBAR; TECBAR; SCL; Procurement Lawyers Association.
Career: Called 1989; Queens Counsel 2008; TECBAR accredited Adjudicator 2004, trained mediator 2006.
Publications: Contributor-Keating on Construction Contracts Ninth Edition (2012). Party Walls RICS Books Case in Point Series (2004); Rights to Light - Case in Point Series (2008). Halsbury' s Fuel and Energy Volumes 19(1)-(3).
Personal: Working knowledge of French and Spanish.

HAQUE, Muhammed
Crown Office Chambers, London
020 7797 8100
haque@crownofficechambers.com
Featured in Personal Injury (London)
Practice Areas: Principle areas of practice are common law litigation (in particular professional / clinical negligence and personal injury), property damage (fire and floods), commercial disputes, insurance and insurance fraud and product liability (including product recalls). He is highly regarded for his user-friendliness with clients, his clear and focussed advice and his ability in Court. He is also known as one of the country's leading barristers in subsidence cases and has appeared or advised in most of the leading cases. His cases include the Marlie Farm litigation (QBD), Denness v East Hampshire (TCC); Robbins v LB Bexley (CA); Ghaith v Indesit (CA); MSL v Clearwell (QBD); Khan v Malik (Ch); Berent v Family Mosaic Housing (CA); Bell v LB Havering (CA); Ammah v Kuehne-Nagel (CA); Harrison v Derby (CA); Clark v Havering (QBD).
Professional Memberships: Personal Injury Bar Association London Common Law Bar Association Professional Negligence Bar Association TECBAR.
Career: Became a tenant at Crown Office Chambers in 1999. Lincoln's Inn Scholar, Advocacy Tutor and Scholarships Committee Member.

HARBAGE, William QC
36 Bedford Row, London
020 7421 8000
wharbage@36bedfordrow.co.uk
Featured in Crime (Midlands), Crime (London)
Practice Areas: Crime, fraud, regulatory.
Professional Memberships: Criminal Bar Association, British Association of Sports Lawyers, Midland Circuit.
Career: William Harbage QC is joint Head of Chambers at 36BR. Called 1983; Silk 2003. He specialises in criminal and regulatory law. In crime, he prosecutes and defends. His practice is mainly in cases of homicide but extends to all heavyweight and white collar crime including terrorism, cybercrime, fraud, money-laundering, confiscation, misconduct in public office, kidnapping, rape, and armed robbery. He has built up a particular expertise in cases with a medical or nursing element and is known for his thorough and conscientious approach. In regulatory law, his cases have involved Trading Standards, professional and sports disciplinary hearings, and the marketing of prescription medicines. He sits as Chairman of the Prescription Medicines Code of Practice Authority, the self-regulatory arm of the Association of the British Pharmaceutical Industry and as an Appeal Panel Chairman for the Rugby Football Union. Appointed to the London 2012 Olympic and Paralympic Games pro bono Legal Advice and Representation Service. Recorder since 1999. Registered to accept Direct Access clients. Door tenant 37 Park Square, Leeds.
Publications: "Losing it: the new defence to murder of Loss of Control"; Solicitors' Journal 8 Feb 2011, Vol 155 No5. Podcasts on "Loss of Control" and "Diminished Responsibility"; www.cpdcast.com.
Personal: Born 1960. Married, 3 children. MA Hons (Law) St.John's College Cambridge. 7th Gurkha Rifles.

HARDING, Ben
Kings Chambers, Manchester
0845 034 3444
clerks@kingschambers.com
Featured in Commercial Dispute Resolution (Northern)
Practice Areas: Ben Harding practises in all areas of commercial litigation and advisory work, including contractual disputes; banking and finance (including consumer credit, guarantees/indemnities, financial product mis-selling); insurance disputes (policy coverage and outlay recovery) construction contracts; factoring agreements; agency disputes (including commercial agency); franchise agreements; sale and supply of goods and services; company disputes; director/employee duties; share and asset purchase agreements; enforcement procedures; applications for injunctive relief (including freezing injunctions); personal and corporate insolvency; partnership disputes; and professional negligence (including solicitors, accountants, financial advisors, surveyors and construction professionals).
Professional Memberships: Chancery Bar Association Northern Chancery Bar Association Northern Circuit Commercial Bar Association British Irish Commercial Bar Association.
Career: 2002 - BA (Hons) Classics - first class (Balliol College, Oxford) 2003 – Major Scholar (Inner Temple) 2004 – GDL (City University, London) 2005 – BVC (BPP Law School, London); called to the Bar (Inner Temple).

HARDING, Jack
1 Chancery Lane, London
020 7092 2900
jharding@1chancerylane.com
Featured in Travel (London)
Practice Areas: Jack Harding specialises in travel law, holiday claims, claims for and against local authorities, general personal injury actions and professional negligence. He has a particular interest in the liability of air carriers under the Montreal Convention and EC Regulation 261/2004 and has written a number of articles on the topic. He is also the co-editor of the 5th Edition of Saggerson on Travel Law Litigation. His professional negligence practice includes work for and against solicitors, surveyors, architects, engineers and the medical profession. He is a regular contributor to the Travel and Tourism Lawyers' Association newsletter.
Professional Memberships: Personal Injuries Bar Association; Travel & Tourism Lawyers' Association; Professional Negligence Bar Association.
Career: Called to the Bar in 2004, Middle Temple.
Personal: Educated: Selwyn College, Cambridge (MA Law, 1st Class). Leisure pursuits: climbing, trekking, travel and cinema.

HARDING, Richard QC
Keating Chambers, London
020 7544 2600
rharding@keatingchambers.com
Featured in Construction (London), International Arbitration (London)
Practice Areas: Specialist in construction, engineering and energy arbitration relating to projects in the Middle East, representing contractors, employers and professionals in disputes under English and Middle Eastern laws (UAE, Egypt, Qatar, Kuwait, Jordan). Acted in matters relating to oil and gas, rail, commercial and residential premises, airports, roads, bridges, tunnels, dredging, marine structures, process engineering, power generation, mining and a theme park. Acted as leading counsel or arbitrator in numerous very substantial international disputes. In the UK, appears before the Technology and Construction Court.
Professional Memberships: International Bar Association; Technology and Construction Bar Association (TECBAR); Commercial Bar Association (COMBAR); Society of Construction Law (UK); founder Chairman of Society of Construction Law (Gulf); Law Society Panel of Arbitrators 2006; LCIA list of arbitrators; Tehran Regional Arbitration Centre list of arbitrators.
Career: Called 1992; Queens Counsel 2009.
Publications: Contributor - Keating on Construction Contracts Ninth Edition. Lectures on arbitration law and construction contracts to professional audiences in the UK and Middle East.
Personal: Languages: Arabic, German, Spanish, French, Persian.

HARDY, Amanda
Tax Chambers 15 Old Square, London
020 7242 2744
taxchambers@15oldsquare.co.uk
Featured in Tax (London)
Practice Areas: Amanda's practice falls broadly into two areas. Firstly, she has an increasingly busy litigation practice, having appeared, during her career to date, three times in the House of Lords, eight times in the Court of Appeal, once in the European Court of Justice and twice in the Privy Council as well as a number of appearances before the High Court and First and Upper Tier Tribunal (and the former Special Commissioners), she has recently been involved in litigation in most areas of direct and indirect tax, including trusts, capital gains tax, charities tax, income tax including the impact of European law on the taxation of foreign dividends, the nature of the source of interest and the tax aspects of divorce. She has also recently appeared in the Ugandan Tax Tribunal in a major oil tax dispute and in the First-tier Tribunal on the correct test for the source of interest, also successfully arguing that HMRC were not entitled to refer to unpublished special commissioners decisions. Secondly, Amanda's practice continues to involve a substantial amount of advice, planning and structuring work for individuals, corporations and particularly trusts including offshore domicile and residency issues, pension taxation issues and corporate reconstruction.
Professional Memberships: Revenue Bar Association, Chancery Bar Association (elected to the Chancery Bar Association Committee on 11 July 2012 and Chair of the Chancery Bar Association pro bono sub committee) Worshipful Company of Tax Advisors, Freeman of the City of London.
Career: Called to the Bar 1993.
Publications: Author of the International Guide to the Taxation of Trusts: United Kingdom, Author of Pensions Taxation (Forthcoming) Moderator of Taxation of Foreign Domiciliaries (online) by James Kessler Q.C. (www.foreigndomiciliaries.co.uk) Co-Author of Venables on Inheritance Tax Planning (3rd Edition) with Robert Venables Q.C.
Personal: Lives in Chelmsford with her husband and three daughters.

HARDY, John QC
3 Raymond Buildings Barristers, London
020 7400 6400
john.hardy@3rblaw.com
Featured in Extradition (London)
Practice Areas: Extradition, human rights, mutual legal assistance. Regularly appears in Supreme Court and House of Lords, frequent appearances in Divisional and Administrative Courts representing both foreign governments and defendants in extradition proceedings, as well as prosecuting authorities and defendants in domestic Judicial Reviews and cases stated. Also practises in serious crime, appearing for both prosecution and defence, money-laundering, professional and disciplinary tribunals, licensing. Recently represented a barrister at the CCC accused of VAT fraud.
Professional Memberships: Criminal Bar Association.
Career: Called 1988. Recorder of the Crown Courts 2002.
Personal: BA (Hons) Magdalen College Oxford. Diploma in Law.

HAREN, Sarah
5 Stone Buildings, London
020 7242 6201
clerks@5sblaw.com
Featured in Chancery (London), Court of Protection (All Circuits)
Practice Areas: Practice encorporating a wide range of Chancery work, both contentious and non-contentious, primarily comprising probate and the administration of estates, claims under the Inheritance Act 1975, trusts and related taxation, real property and landlord and tenant. Regularly appears in the Court of Protection as well as the High Court and county courts. She also has experience of litigation in the Cayman Islands.
Professional Memberships: Chancery Bar Association, ACTAPS.
Career: Wesley College, Dublin; University College, Oxford (1997 BA Hons Jursiprudence and 1999 BCL). Called 1999, Middle Temple.

Publications: Co-author of 4th edition of "Partnership"(Bloomsbury) with Mark Blackett-Ord, 2011.

HARGREAVES, Simon QC
Keating Chambers, London
020 7544 2600
shargreaves@keatingchambers.com
Featured in Construction (London), Professional Negligence (London)
Practice Areas: Specialising in construction, engineering, IT systems, transport, energy contracts and fires, including considerable experience of industry related professional negligence claims. Specialises in all forums including litigation, arbitration, adjudication and ADR as well as relief concerning pre-action disclosure, summary judgment, interim payment, strike out, security for costs, arbitration applications, injunctions and bond applications. Has considerable experience of heavy domestic and international cases being recently involved in claims arising from: the Magna Park fire; the London Underground transmission and radio upgrade project; a claim concerning turbine design for a nuclear power station; the Chancery Lane derailment; the Gerrard's Cross tunnel collapse; claims arising on Wembley Stadium and an ICC arbitration concerning a desalination plant in the Middle East.
Professional Memberships: Technology and Construction Bar Association (TECBAR); Professional Negligence Bar Association (PNBA); Commercial Bar Association (COMBAR) Society of Construction Law (SCL); Society for Computers and Law (SCL).
Career: Called 1991; Queens Counsel 2009; TECBAR Accredited Adjudicator, arbitrator, Dispute Resolution Board Member.
Publications: Assistant Editor, Construction Law Yearbook 1994, 1995 and 1996; Editorial team, Keating on Building Contracts 7th edition 2001; Has presented seminars to TECBAR, TeCSA, Chartered Institute of Arbitrators, firms of solicitors, developers and contractors.

HARPER, Mark
Kings Chambers, Manchester
0845 034 3444
clerks@kingschambers.com
Featured in Banking & Finance (Northern), Chancery (Northern), Commercial Dispute Resolution (Northern), Partnership (Northern)
Practice Areas: Commercial and Corporate Litigation including shareholder disputes, warranty claims, confidential information, restraint of trade, agency and sports related disputes. Partnership. Sports law, banking and finance litigation and professional negligence (solicitors, accountants and financial advisers).
Professional Memberships: Northern Chancery Bar Association; Northern Circuit Commercial Bar Association.
Career: Call 1993; Pupillage in present Chambers.

HARPUM, Charles
Falcon Chambers, London
020 7353 2484
harpum@falcon-chambers.com
Featured in Real Estate Litigation (London)
Practice Areas: 1. Land law in general but with particular reference to the following: (a) Conveyancing; (b) Land Registration; (c) Adverse possession; (d) Easements, profits, and covenants; (e) Commons, town and village greens; (f) Manorial rights; (g) Mines and minerals. 2. Issues concerning underwater land and issues involving water with particular reference to: (a) Mooring rights; (b) Rights of navigation; (c) Fishing rights; (d) Drainage; (e) Riparian rights.
Professional Memberships: (a) Chancery Bar Association; (b) Property Bar Association; (c) London Common Law and Commercial Bar Association.
Career: (a) Called to the Bar by Lincoln's Inn: 1976; (b) Taught law at Cambridge University: 1977 – 1993 (Fellow of Downing College, Cambridge:1977 – 2001; Emeritus Fellow: 2001 to date); (c) Law Commissioner for England and Wales (Head of Property and Trust Law Team): 1994 – 2001; (d) Bencher, Lincoln's Inn: 2001; (e) In practice at Falcon Chambers: 2001 to date; (f) LL.D, Cambridge University: 2003.
Publications: Numerous publications on property law, including many articles. In particular: Editor/author of Megarry & Wade's Law of Property , 6th, 7th and 8th editions, the 7th and 8th editions jointly with Judge Stuart Bridge and Professor Martin Dixon Co-author of Harpum and Bignell's Registered Land (2004) Editor and contributor to The Law and Practice of Charging Orders on Land (2013).
Personal: Main interests: classical music and foreign travel.

HARRIES, Mark
Carmelite Chambers, London
020 7936 6300
clerks@carmelitechambers.co.uk
Featured in Crime (London), Financial Crime (London)
Practice Areas: Principally criminal defence work in major crime as leading counsel nationwide, with a growing practice in regulatory and disciplinary work on behalf of individuals and professional bodies including the GDC, RICS & CWU. Significant experience in white-collar fraud and civil asset recovery actions complemented by substantial expertise in gangland crime and homicide. Instructed in Courts Martial in the UK and abroad, and in criminally related appellate work including judicial review. Direct access and pre-charge advice available in appropriate cases. Recent and current instructions include: In Fraud, Operations Evenbox (£300m tax evasion), Barber (DBiS long firm fraud), Bamburgh (multi-million £ mortgage fraud), Enigma (£200m money laundering), Iceman (wine investment fund fraud) and Vaulter (MTIC). In Crime, Operations Elveden (misconduct in public office), Diamond (gangland conspiracy to murder), Hayrack (corruption within Royal Household) and "P" (1970s sexual abuse in Midlands borstal).
Professional Memberships: University of London (LLB (Hons) 1994), Lincoln's Inn (call 1995), Criminal Bar Association, POCLA, ARDL, AMCA, Liberty. Advocacy Trainer and Pupil Supervisor.

HARRIS, Caroline
1 King's Bench Walk, London
020 7936 1500
charris@1kbw.co.uk
Featured in Crime (South Eastern)
Practice Areas: Caroline specialises in both criminal and family law. Criminal law: Caroline primarily acts for the defence and has experience up to and including successfully representing clients at the Court of Appeal. Caroline has expertise across the full range of criminal matters and is frequently instructed in; sexual offences, fraud, offences against the person and road traffic offences (including death by dangerous and death by careless driving). Caroline regularly acts for vulnerable defendants or those with mental-health difficulties. Caroline also represents professional clients, including police officers in disciplinary hearings.
In addition to conducting matters alone, Caroline has also acted as a led junior in complex and multi-handed cases. Family law: Caroline has experience in all areas of Family law. Caroline particularly specialises in acting for clients who require a barrister who understands both criminal and family law, for example in matters where clients are facing criminal charges that may impact on child arrangement orders.
Professional Memberships: CBA and FLBA.
Career: Bristol University (BA Mathematics and Philosophy) Nottingham Law School (CPE) Inns of Court School of Law (BVC) Called to the bar in 2004.
Publications: Contributor to Westlaw Insight.

HARRIS, Christopher
3 Verulam Buildings, London
020 7831 8441
christopherharris@3vb.com
Featured in Commercial Dispute Resolution (London), Energy & Natural Resources (London), International Arbitration (London)
Practice Areas: Commercial litigation and arbitration; investment arbitration; banking and financial services; energy and natural resources; commercial fraud; company and insolvency; professional negligence.
Professional Memberships: FCIArb; LCIA; ICC; Combar, IBA.
Career: Christopher Harris specialises in commercial litigation and arbitration and his work in both areas has been recognised by the directories for a number of years. In addition to his work as counsel in arbitrations under all of the main rules, Christopher has been appointed as arbitrator (sole, co-arbitrator and chairman) in more than ten disputes, principally under ICC and LCIA rules. One of the few investment arbitration specialists at the English bar, over the last ten years Christopher has been instructed in eleven such disputes including two ICSID annulment applications, as well as frequent advisory work. Christopher is above all an advocate, and has significant experience of both trial and appellate advocacy. Recent litigation highlights include TFL Management v. Lloyd's Bank [2013] WLR (D) 437 (Court of Appeal, first consideration of incidental benefit in the law of restitution); A v. B [2014] EWHC 1870 (Comm) (Commercial Court, first decision on meaning of s.70(2) Arbitration Act 1996); and Gul Bottlers v. Nichols PLC [2014] EWHC 2173 (Comm) (Commercial Court, £8.2m damages award for client in respect of Vimto licence). Christopher speaks French and German fluently and regularly uses both languages in his practice.

HARRIS, Lucinda
Devereux, London
020 7353 7534
harris@devchambers.co.uk
Featured in Employment (London)
Practice Areas: Specialises in all areas of employment law, including restrictive covenants and breach of confidence, breach of contract, wrongful and unfair dismissal, whistleblowing, discrimination, TUPE, national minimum wage and working time. She has a wide range of public and private sector clients, including FTSE 100 companies, banks, insurance companies, high street chains, hotels, airlines and charities, as well as governmental departments and agencies.
Professional Memberships: ELA, ELBA, ILS, COMBAR, PIBA.
Career: Called, Middle Temple 2004. Appointed to the Attorney General's Panel of Counsel (C Panel) in 2010. Member of the Equality and Human Rights Commission Panel of Approved Counsel since 2011. Judicial Assistant to Mr Justice Aikens (now Lord Justice Aikens) in the Commercial Court (2007-2008).
Publications: Contributing author, "Discrimination Law" (Bloomsbury Professional (formerly Tottel Publishing)); co-author, "Post-Termination Restraints" in "Managing People in a Legal Business" (Law Society).
Personal: LLM, Harvard Law School; MA Hons (First Class), Downing College, Cambridge University.

HARRIS, Luke
3 Stone Buildings, London
020 7242 4937
lharris@3sb.law.co.uk
Featured in Art and Cultural Property Law (London)
Practice Areas: Commercial chancery litigation and advice with a particular emphasis on claims involving chattels and bailment, trusts and estates, restitution and personal property (including the sale of goods). Luke specialises in claims involving art and antiquities and frequently acts for and against states, public bodies, museums, galleries, auction houses and private individuals in claims involving objects of cultural and artistic value. Luke's expertise in the field of personal property includes cases involving heirlooms, equity, trusts and entailed interest under settlements of land.
Professional Memberships: Inner Temple; Chancery Bar Association; COMBAR; PAIAM (Professional Advisors to the International Art Market).
Career: Called to the Bar, 2001; Member of 3 Stone Buildings, 2003.
Publications: Book contributions include: Taking it Personally: The Individual Liability of Museum Personnel (2011); Encyclopedia of Forms & Precedents (Sale of Goods) (2011); Palmer, Bailment (3rd edn, 2009). Luke has contributed articles in the field of commercial, chancery and personal property to Trusts & Trustees, Butterworths Journal of International Banking & Financial Law and Art, Antiquities & Law.
Personal: University College London (LLB Hons) (1997-2000); interests include: food and drink, travel, current affairs.

HARRIS, Miles
4 New Square, London
020 7822 2000
m.harris@4newsquare.com
Featured in Professional Negligence (London)
Practice Areas: Professional negligence, insurance, commercial litigation, accredited mediator.
Professional Memberships: PNBA, COMBar, BILA.
Career: Trinity College, Cambridge, Grays Inn's David Karmel and William Shaw

Awards for CPE and Bar. Has a strong practice in professional negligence (including lawyers, accountants, surveyors and insurance brokers), insurance and commercial litigation. Also practices as a mediator in these areas.
Publications: Authored series of Practice Notes for the Practical Law Company on Negligence and Insurance. Published in the Insurance Law Monthly, New Law Journal and Journal of Professional Negligence.
Personal: Sport (especially watching Northampton Saints, Town FC and CCC), Food & Drink, restoring home in Rutland.

HARRIS, Rebecca
QEB Hollis Whiteman, London
020 7933 8855
rebecca.harris@qebhw.co.uk
Featured in Professional Discipline (London)
Practice Areas: Rebecca Harris has been instructed in high-profile cases in professional discipline and serious crime, including related appellate work. She appears before a variety of regulatory and professional discipline tribunals and is frequently instructed both to advise and present cases before healthcare regulators. Examples include GDC v JT, involving a dentist struck off after a £1.4 million fraud. She appears and advises on behalf of regulators and registrants in appeals in the High Court (Admin), applications in the Family Division and other High Court proceedings. She advises on complex matters of law and procedure. She also has extensive experience of prosecuting and defending all types of criminal cases, including cases involving sensitive issues of disclosure. She prosecutes offences arising from misuse of social media and has specific expertise regarding young and vulnerable witnesses. Rebecca provides advocacy training for external agencies, and training in relation to law and procedure for healthcare regulators.
Professional Memberships: Association of Regulatory & Disciplinary Lawyers, Criminal Bar Association, British Association for Sport and Law, Fraud Lawyers Association, Public Access Bar Association, registered with the Bar Council – Public Access Directory.
Career: Call 1997.
Personal: King's College London (LLB); working knowledge of Spanish.

HARRISON, Caroline QC
2TG - 2 Temple Gardens, London
020 7822 1200
c.harrison@2tg.co.uk
Featured in Clinical Negligence (London)
Practice Areas: Clinical and lawyer's negligence. Catastrophic injury. Inquests. Medical research and product liability. insurance. Specialist in complex clinical and legal issues.
Professional Memberships: PNBA (Executive Committee member).
Career: Clinical negligence: Williams (Privy Council. Causation. Whether Bailey applies to indivisible and divisible injury. Whether need to prove doubling of risk if causation factors are sequential); Maytum (Causation. Obverse of Gregg v Scott. Delayed diagnosis breast cancer. 10-year survival always above 50%. Recurrence of metastatic disease. Poor prognosis); Thomas (Locked-in syndrome); Bint (Delayed diagnosis of anti-phospholipid antibody syndrome. Stroke in young man. Later leg amputation. Effect of under-anticoagulation c.f. atherosclerosis); Smith (Wrongful birth. Disabled child. Whether damages payable post-18 years). Lawyers negligence: Carter (Under-settlement of EL claim. Minor injury ultimately causing leg amputation. Failure investigate medical causation); Whitehead (Underlying wrongful birth claim. Novel issues: duty of care to father; when events after notional trial can be taken into account). Personal Injury: Merrett (Brain damage. £14m claim. Young man with pre-existing tetraplegia. Issues: scope of Sklair 'injury-on-injury damages'; non-delegable duty; vicarious liability for agency nurses); Scott (Head and leg injury to cyclist. No helmet. Contributory negligence. 'Bizarre presentation'. Difficult management issues. Psychiatric conversion disorder. £4m). Neve (Motor claim. Brain damage and vulnerable personality. £6m); Lyons (Psychiatric injury. Material contribution causation c.f. Jobling v Associated Diaries. Causation and physical injury where second accident prolonged effects of first). Medical Research and Product liability: PIP breast implants; Trans-vaginal and abdominal mesh claims; Consent in: experimental laser therapy; laparoscopic surgery by inexperienced operator. Member of: Gene Therapy Advisory Committee (to 2009); Human Genetics Commission (to 2012); National Research Ethics Advisory Panel (to 2012). Expert witness to House of Lords Science & Technology Committee (cloning, employment and insurance in genetics). Insurance: Willsher (£2m permanent health insurance claim. Discontinued at trial after cross examination exposed flaws in diagnosis of intractable depression).
Publications: Publications: Medical Ethics and Genetics, in Powers and Harris, Clinical Negligence (2008).

HARRISON, Christopher
4 Stone Buildings, London
020 7242 5524
c.harrison@4stonebuildings.com
Featured in Chancery (London), Company (London), Fraud (London)
Practice Areas: Commercial and chancery litigation; fraud and asset recovery; shareholder disputes; company law; insolvency and reconstruction; banking and finance.
Professional Memberships: Commercial Bar Association; Chancery Bar Association.
Career: Called to the Bar in 1988; Government Inspector (Insider-trading Inquiry, 1996); Government's 'B' Panel of appointed Counsel (1996-2003); Called to the Bars of the Cayman Islands and Turks and Caicos Islands for specific cases.
Publications: Author of the chapters on Shareholder Remedies (Derivative Claims and Unfairly Prejudicial Conduct) in Oxford University Press's 'Annotated Companies Legislation'.
Personal: Trinity Hall, Cambridge.

HARRISON, Nicholas
Serle Court, London
020 7242 6105
nharrison@serlecourt.co.uk
Featured in Chancery (London), Fraud (London), Offshore (London)
Practice Areas: Commerical chancery and commercial fraud, including international trust litigation.
Professional Memberships: Chancery Bar Association, COMBAR.
Career: Continuous full time practice at the English Bar and between 1999 and 2001 at the Bermuda Bar, working full-time on the Thyssen litigation. Experienced in International Litigation, including in Jersey, the Isle of Man and the Caribbean. Specialises in very large cases.
Personal: Education: Winchester and Oxford. Leisure interests: hiking, music, a variety of sports. Chairman of Blackheath Cricket Club. Married with two children.

HARRISON, Philomena
Maitland Chambers, London
020 7406 1200
pharrison@maitlandchambers.com
Featured in Real Estate Litigation (London)
Practice Areas: All aspects of property litigation including commercial property, landlord and tenant, other real property claims eg. mortgages, easements, restrictive covenants, conveyancing, related professional negligence and insolvency. Also general chancery litigation. Recent cases include: Blueco v BWAT and Prudential [2014] EWCA Civ 154 (options and pre-emption rights); Schyde Investments v Cleaver [2011] CA (standard conditions of sale), Tetra Pak v Oracle Corporation UK (2011) ChD (injunction), SMQ v (1) RFQ (2) MJQ (2008) EWHC 1874 (beneficial ownership and proprietary estoppel), Prudential Assurance Company v Ayres and Grew [2008] EWCA Civ 52 (claim against former tenants under an authorised guarantee agreement); Tamares v Fairpoint (2006) EWHC 3589 (Ch); (2007) EWHC 212 (Ch) (right to light claim); Donnelly v Weybridge [2006] EWHC 348 (TCC) (Unilateral notices); Wormall v Wormall (2004) EWCA Civ 1643 (proprietary estoppel); Corbett v Halifax Plc and Deakin [2003] 1 WLR 964 (exercise of power of sale by mortgagee); Amec Developments v Jury's Hotel Management [2001] 1 EGLR 81 (assessment of damages in lieu of an injunction for breach of a restrictive covenant); Cottingham v Attey Bower & Jones (professional negligence claim) [2000] PNLR 557.
Professional Memberships: Property Bar Association, Chancery Bar Association and Professional Negligence Bar Association.
Career: Called to the Bar in 1985.
Personal: Born 1960. University College London BA (Hons) Classics (First); City University Dip Law. Lives in London.

HARRISON, Richard
Devereux, London
020 7353 7534
harrison@devchambers.co.uk
Featured in Insurance (London)
Practice Areas: Specialises in commercial litigation and arbitration, with particular emphasis on insurance, reinsurance and professional negligence of the legal profession, construction professionals, accountants, tax advisers, financial services and insurance claims handlers, adjusters and brokers. Cases in 2014-15 include Rathbone Brothers v Novae in the Court of Appeal (coverage dispute re liability of professional trustee and subrogation issues); defending a group action alleging negligent tax advice in relation to geared Enterprise Zone tax schemes; defending accountants against claim for over £50m arising from client fraud; numerous claims involving issues of notification, aggregation, avoidance and fraud; advising re FCA regulation, TOBAs, binding authorities and claims management contracts.
Professional Memberships: COMBAR, LCLCBA, BILA.
Career: Robinson College, Cambridge 1987-90. Lincoln's Inn Sunley Scholar. Called 1991.
Personal: Partial to fine wine.

HARRISON, Richard QC
1 King's Bench Walk, London
020 7936 1500
rharrison@1kbw.co.uk
Featured in Family/Matrimonial (London)
Practice Areas: Specilaises in complex matrimonial finance disputes, prenuptial agreements, international forum disputes, international child abduction, international relocation and other private law children disputes. Acted in a number of leading cases including five cases in the Supreme Court and the House of Lords.
Professional Memberships: Family Law Bar Association, International Bar Association, International Academy of Matrimonial Lawyers. Member of reunite Legal Working Group.
Career: Called 1993.
Publications: Consultant editor of Hershman and McFarlane Children Law and Practice and of Jordans International Child Law Portal.
Personal: Emmanuel College, Cambridge; City University. Fluent Spanish, proficient French.

HARRISON, Sarah
St Philips Chambers, Leeds
0113 244 6691
sharrison@st-philips.com
Featured in Chancery (North Eastern)
Practice Areas: Specialises in probate, trusts and associated capital taxation issues. Sarah has extensive experience in dealing with contentious probate disputes, family provision claims, Court of Protection work, will constructions and directions applications involving executors and trustees. She also deals regularly with all aspects of non contentious probate and trust work, including drafting wills and settlements, the variation of wills and settlements, and the termination of trusts. Sarah acts for solicitors throughout the country and is happy to provide in-house seminars on request.
Professional Memberships: Chancery Bar Association, Northern Chancery Bar Association.
Career: Call 1989 (Certificate of Honour). Lincoln's Inn Student of the Year.

HARRY, Timothy
Maitland Chambers, London
020 7406 1200
clerks@maitlandchambers.com
Featured in Real Estate Litigation (London)
Practice Areas: Property litigation, professional negligence and chancery commercial work.
Professional Memberships: PNBA, Chancery Bar Association, Property Bar Association, COMBAR.
Career: Called 1983. Lecturer, Hertford College, Oxford, 1983-88. Called to the Bar, 1983, Hong Kong 1992. Member of Hong Kong Bar Association (c/o Gilt Chambers). Member of Hong Kong Government Panel for civil matters. Called to the Bar of the Eastern Caribbean 2009. Registered lawyer, Dubai International Finance Centre. Called to the Bar of Samoa 2013. Accredited mediator.
Publications: Contributing editor Hill &; Redman's 'Landlord & Tenant', Snell's 'Equity', Sweet & Maxwell's 'Land Registration Act

2002'; contributor to 'Lloyds Professional Negligence Law Reports'; LLP's 'Professional Negligence and Liability'; and Sweet & Maxwell's 'Hong Kong Civil Justice Reform Practice Manual'.
Personal: Educated Monmouth School; Law (1st Class), BCL (Oxford).

HART, Joseph
Deans Court Chambers, Manchester
0161 214 6000
hart@deanscourt.co.uk
Featured in Crime (Northern), Environment (Northern)
Practice Areas: Joseph Hart's practice is predominantly defence work, but he is also a grade 4 CPS prosecutor and member of the specialist rape panel. He is on the government's national list of special regulatory advocates in health and safety and environmental law and he has a significant environmental law practice focussing on environmental offences. He practices in all areas of crime, regulatory crime, and associated regulatory areas such as professional discipline and inquests. He also regularly practices in the British Overseas Territories.
Professional Memberships: Criminal Bar Association; Advocate of the Supreme Court of St Helena; Approved Counsel for the Falkland Islands; member of the Institute of Licensing; and the International Bar Association.
Career: Member of Deans Court Chambers since 2000. Locum Crown Counsel St Helena 2010.
Personal: Joseph read Jurisprudence and French at Corpus Christi College, Oxford. He speaks Italian and French fluently; and has basic German. Joseph regularly attends the International Bar Association Conferences, and was recently selected to be a member of the Bar Council's 2012 trade delegation to China.

HARWOOD, Richard QC
Thirty Nine Essex Street, London
020 7832 1111
richard.harwood@39essex.co.uk
Featured in Environment (London), Local Government (London), Planning (London)
Practice Areas: Planning, environmental, public law, compulsory purchase, local authority administration, finance and standards, historic environment, art law and Parliamentary work. Acts for developers, landowners, public authorities, interest groups and private individuals. Major court cases include Mellor (CJEU); Heard, RWE v Milton Keynes (planning policy); Dale Farm (enforcement, travellers); Champion, SAVE Britain's Heritage (Environmental Impact Assessment); Holder, Newlyn Dean (Green Belt); Majed (legitimate expectation); Hirose (private nuisance); Woolley (species protection); Elvington (statutory nuisance); Burkett, Berky (time limits); Hethel (wind farms). Other recent work includes environmental and planning inquiries, development consent orders, environmental crime and promoting development plans. Parliamentary work includes three hybrid Bills and drafting private members Bills. Art work is for owners, auction houses and regulators.
Professional Memberships: Fellow, Society for Advanced Legal Studies. Member, PEBA, ALBA, CPA, ELF, NIPA, Professional Advisers to the International Art Market and UKELA.
Career: Jesus College, Cambridge MA, LLM. Silk 2013. Former Deputy Chair, Advisory Panel on Standards for the Planning Inspectorate. Environment/Planning Junior of the Year 2011 (Chambers Bar Awards). Short-listed Barrister of the Year 2006 (Lawyer Awards). OBE 2014.
Publications: Author, 'Historic Environment Law'(2012, Supplement 2014), 'Planning Enforcement'(2013); case editor, 'Journal of Planning and Environment Law'; co-author, 'Contaminated Land', 'Planning and Compulsory Purchase Act 2004'.

HATTAN, Simon
Serle Court, London
020 7242 6105
shattan@serlecourt.co.uk
Featured in Banking & Finance (London), Chancery (London), Financial Services (London), Fraud (London)
Practice Areas: Commercial chancery litigation, including in particular commercial fraud and breach of fiduciary duty, trusts litigation, banking and finance, professional negligence and contractual disputes. Also significant experience in regulatory and disciplinary proceedings, especially those related to the financial services industry. Cases include: Alhamrani v Alhamrani (BVI Commercial Court, Court of Appeal + Privy Council), RBS Rights Issue Litigation (ongoing), Alhamrani v Alhamrani (Jersey Royal Court - breach of trust and fiduciary duty), ACKO v Van Bom (fraud) RBS v Winterthur (breach of warranty, fraudulent misrepresentation), Hoben International v Horton and others (breach of fiduciary duty, breach of confidence), Charter v City Index (knowing receipt), FSA v Legal & General (FSMA Tribunal), Philips v Symes (partnership/fraud), FSA v CSFB International (regulatory proceedings).
Professional Memberships: COMBAR, Chancery Bar Association, Commercial Fraud Lawyers Association, Financial Services Lawyers Association.
Career: Called 1999. Previously worked in international financial markets.
Personal: BSc(Hons); Dip Law(Distinction), City University, London.

HAUGHEY, Caroline
Furnival Chambers, London
020 7405 2232
mandcbraid@mac.com
Featured in Crime (London)
Practice Areas: Crime, regulatory, coroners inquests and public enquiries.
Professional Memberships: Middle Temple, CBA, member of the Northern Ireland Bar, member of the Bar Standards Professional Conduct Committee, Kalisher Trust Trustee, Approved for Direct Access.
Career: Regarded as an excellent leading junior with an ability to deal with voluminous and or complex cases. Carolines' defence practice is focused on murder, serious violence, drugs and fraud. She has particular expertise in areas of complex forensic evidence: LCN DNA, entomology, causation etc. A Grade 4 prosecutor who regularly appears against Queens' Counsel and with a growing reputation in the prosecution of novel law cases including: slavery (R -v- Khan, R -v- Balira, R-v- Motroc), bribery (R -v Patel) RIPA (R -v- Beeckman). Caroline is an expert in Human Trafficking and associated offences and both advised the government on this area as well as giving evidence to the Inter Parliamentary Committee on the Modern Day Slavery Bill. Caroline has significant appellate court experience having appeared in the leading authorities on firearms, expert evidence and LCN DNA and is able to provide consultancy advice on all areas of crime and regulatory work: health and safety, pharmaceuticals, veterinary, GOC, GMC, SRA etc with particular experience in homicide cases (Corporate Manslaughter etc).
Publications: Regular contributor to CBA and Bar Council publications and committees.
Personal: Wycombe Abbey. Trinity College, Dublin (LLB).

HAWES, Neil
Charter Chambers, London
neil.hawes@charterchambers.com
Featured in Financial Crime (London)
Practice Areas: Serious Fraud, Financial Crime and Regulatory. Neil specialises in all aspects of commercial fraud and associated financial and regulatory work. He is very experienced in defending large scale prosecutions brought by the SFO, FCA and CMA. Regularly instructed from an early stage in the investigative process he gives clear and practical strategic guidance. He is consistently sought after and instructed by large corporations and national firms of solicitors. He has acted in some of the most serious fraud cases in the recent decade, including: British Airways Director in the BA / Virgin price fixing criminal prosecution – the first and only contested cartel prosecution to date – OFT); A Director of a national pharmaceutical company in Op Holbein (the NHS Pharmaceutical price fixing case – SFO); A individual in an advanced fee fraud (the 'Lord' Davenport case – SFO); an Individual charged in Op Tabernula - Largest alleged FCA prosecuted insider dealing case; A Director in a pensions fraud; A Director accused of corruption for MOD contracts; A Director in the IKEA fraud (SFO) [R v. H House of Lords re disclosure]; A Director in the Landfill tax fraud (SFO); A Director in a fraud on the Department of Education (CPS National Casework) and Directors in MTIC frauds, recently Op Vaulter (HMRC/CPS). He regularly advises individuals and corporates on issues concerning corporate investigations, bribery, corruption, cartels, fraud, whistleblowing, self reporting and now DPA's. Neil also appears in serious crime cases, including murder and manslaughters.
Professional Memberships: Criminal Bar Association, The Fraud Lawyers Association
Career: Called to the Bar 1989, Silk 2010. Joint Head of Chambers.

HAY, David
Westwater Advocates, Edinburgh
07812 064 062
david.hay@westwateradvocates.com
Featured in Employment (Scotland)
Practice Areas: All areas of employment law, with experience in equalities issues (including sex discrimination, race discrimination, disability discrimination, age discrimination and equal pay), TUPE, unfair dismissal (including constructive dismissal), redundancy, working time and restrictive covenants. David is routinely instructed for hearings in the employment tribunal across Scotland and in the employment appeal tribunal (including London) for appeals. He also has experience in arguing employment appeals in the Inner House of the Court of Session without a leader. David undertakes an element of other civil work (elements of property law, contract law and administrative law) in the Sheriff Court and Court of Session.
Professional Memberships: Committee Member, Faculty of Advocates Employment Law Group.
Career: Qualified as a solicitor in 2005. Called to the Bar in 2008. Tutor in Delict at Edinburgh University 2007-2009. Tutor for WS Society's PCC Course for trainee solicitors 2007-2010. Member of the Panel of Preferred Counsel for the Equalities and Human Rights Commission in Scotland. Faculty of Advocates Instructor in Advocacy for the training of devils (pupils) since 2013.
Personal: Educated University of Glasgow LLB (Hons) (2001); Glasgow Graduate School of Law, Diploma in Legal Practice (2002). David's hobbies include tennis and playing the clarinet.

HAYMAN, George
Maitland Chambers, London
020 7406 1200
ghayman@maitlandchambers.com
Featured in Chancery (London), Fraud (London)
Practice Areas: Commercial litigation and arbitration; commercial fraud; media, entertainment and sports law. George's practice covers heavy contractual disputes of all kinds (often involving a major international element or the media industry), civil fraud and asset tracing, property disputes, and insolvency. He has extensive advocacy experience in the Commercial Court, Chancery and Queen's Bench Divisions of the High Court, and has appeared on numerous occasions in the Court of Appeal. He has also been called to the Bar of the Eastern Caribbean Supreme Court (BVI) and appears in litigation there. Cases include JSC BTA Bank v Ablyazov (commercial fraud), Cadogan Petroleum v Tolley (fraud), JSC BTA Bank v Solodchenko (summary judgment, fraud), Bleasdale v Forster (fraudulent misrepresentation), BERR v Sullman (directors' disqualification re Claims Direct), R v Johnstone (House of Lords, criminal trade mark offences), National Sporting Club v Professional Cricketers' Association (England Cricket team's sponsorship), and Affinity v Federation of International Cricketing Associations (joint venture sponsorship agreement).
Professional Memberships: Chancery Bar Association, COMBAR, Intellectual Property Bar Association.
Career: Called to the Bar 1998; Called to the Bar of the Eastern Caribbean Supreme Court (BVI) 2013.
Personal: Cambridge University, MA Law.

HAYNES, Matthew
St Ives Chambers, Birmingham
0121 236 0863
matthew.haynes@stiveschambers.co.uk
Featured in Family/Matrimonial (Midlands)
Practice Areas: Matthew practises in family law, including public and private law, matrimonial and cohabitation/trusts of land cases. He also undertakes Inheritance Act 1975 claims. He has represented companies and third party interveners in financial relief cases. Matthew also practises in commercial and chancery, including: real property, wills and probate, family provision, trusts, boundary disputes, professional negligence and landlord and tenant. He also undertakes common law and personal injury work. Recently reported cases: GR-v-SR [2013] All ER (D) 230 (nuptial variation of a company in a Petrodel context) and Moore-v-Holdsworth

[2010] EWHC 683 (Ch) (family provision). Other cases: Kynnersley-v-Wolverhampton City Council [2008] WTLR 65 (validity of residuary gift to council employees) and Re. M [2003] All ER (D) 125 (CA) (residence case).
Professional Memberships: FLBA, PIBA, Midland Chancery & Commercial Bar Association.
Career: Qualifications: MA (Oxon.) Oxford University.
Publications: Contributor to Family Law and The Conveyancer.

HAYS, William
6KBW College Hill, London
020 3301 0910
william.hays@6kbw.com
Featured in POCA Work & Asset Forfeiture (All Circuits)
Practice Areas: Will Hays acts in Chambers' core practice areas, but particularly in crime, proceeds of crime and public law. His ability as an advocate was recently recognised by the Divisional Court, which described his written and oral advocacy as being of "conspicuous quality". In asset forfeiture he has extensive experience of restraint and confiscation, appearing at all levels up to and including the Supreme Court. Will advises on the enforcement of overseas forfeiture orders and has been retained by an 'Arab Spring' government on this issue. Will is currently instructed by the NCA in a number of substantial civil recovery claims. In public law, Will appears in judicial review claims. He frequently represents the Home Office and HMRC in the Tax Tribunal. Will accepts instructions in complex fraud, bribery and corruption. He is currently instructed by the SFO in a substantial allegation of corporate corruption for which criminal proceedings will commence shortly. For further information, please refer to the 6KBW College Hill website (www.6kbw.com).
Career: Called in 2006; Attorney General's Panel for Civil Litigation (Panel C); SFO Panel of Counsel (Panel C); CPS Prosecutor (Level 2).
Publications: Contributor to "Millington and Williams on the Proceeds of Crime" (OUP).

HAYWOOD, Jennifer
Serle Court, London
020 7242 6105
clerks@serlecourt.co.uk
Featured in Partnership (London)
Practice Areas: General commercial and chancery litigation practice, including partnership, company, insolvency, trusts and civil fraud. Cases include Republic of Djibouti & Ors v Boreh & Ors (fraud), Aeroflot v Berezovsky & Ors (fraud), Fiona Trust v Privalov (fraud, arbitration), Secretary of State for Health v Norton & Ors (restrictive practices), Barnes v Tomlinson (breach of trust) and Experience Hendrix LLC v PPX Enterprises Inc (damages for breach of contract). Numerous partnership disputes, particularly law firms and financial services. CEDR accredited mediator.
Professional Memberships: Chancery Bar Association, COMBAR, Association of Partnership Practitioners, ACTAPS.
Career: MB BCh (Cantab), Dip Law (City University). Called 2001.

HEAD, Peter
11 Stone Buildings, London
020 7831 6381
head@11sb.com
Featured in Chancery (London)
Practice Areas: Peter Head is a commercial and chancery litigator with particular expertise in commercial fraud, banking, oil & gas, shareholder claims, corporate & personal insolvency and arbitration. Notable cases include: Rosserlane v Credit Suisse (sale of largest onshore oil and gas field in Azerbaijan); an oil and gas dispute against a State (UNCITRAL); Bank of Moscow v Kekhman (breach of WFO, committal proceedings, bankruptcy of non-EU debtor); Investors' claim arising out of the Madoff fraud (ICC); VTB v Skurikhin (commercial fraud, s.25 CJJA 1982); Jenington v Assaubayev (fraud claims relating to the sale of a gold mining conglomerate); Cadogan v Tolley (alleged bribery in relation to oil and gas business in Ukraine); Westminster v Nilon (BVI jurisdiction dispute arising out of Nigerian joint venture); Investment dispute with connected proceedings in Singapore, Mauritius and India (LCIA). For more information please visit the 'Barristers' section on www.11sb.com.
Professional Memberships: COMBAR, Chancery Bar Association, Commercial Fraud Lawyers Association.
Career: Called 2008.
Personal: Canford School, Magdalene College Cambridge (Music and English); Webber Douglas Academy (drama); College of Law (LLB). Former Mansfield and Eastham Scholar of Lincoln's Inn.

HEAL, Madeleine
New Square Chambers, London
020 7419 8000
madeleine.heal
@newsquarechambers.co.uk
Featured in Intellectual Property (London)
Practice Areas: Madeleine is a specialist advocate in all aspects of commercial and intellectual property law; and in media, entertainment and sport. In addition to patent, trade mark, copyright and design right infringement actions, Madeleine appears in commercial cases with technical, media, entertainment, branding and trade secrets/breach of confidence aspects. She appears in the Patents Court, IPEC, the Court of Appeal and offshore. She is one of the few IP counsel who combines a commercial practice with cases across the IP spectrum. She is quick off the mark to assimilate complex technical and commercial information and assess prospects for obtaining interim injunctions, search and freezing order relief, particularly cross border, in appropriate cases. Madeleine is known for identifying her client's best case and fighting their corner to the end although always with an eye for early commercial resolution. Madeleine is currently working on a High Court patent infringement action relating to an agricultural device, in a large offshore copyright action involving copyright in a database, lists of LinkedIn 'connections' and other social media accounts, and in patent infringement litigation in Hong Kong. She is instructed on appeal for the appellants in the continuing dispute with Island Records over copyrights in Bob Marley's No Woman No Cry and other compositions. Her past cases include Beecham Group v Norton Healthcare; ITV Broadcasting v TV Catchup; Future Investments v FIFA; Jules Rimet Ltd v The Football Association; Building Product Designs Ltd v Sandtoft; Wolters Kluwer (UK) Ltd v Reed Elsevier; Miss World Ltd v Channel 4; Christian Louboutin v New Blossom; Nautech v CSS; Crocker Enterprises v Giordano Poultry-Plast; and Healey Sports Cars (Switzerland) Limited v Jensen Cars Limited. She has also recently acted in commercial judicial review actions for clients in the telecoms, broadcasting and healthcare sectors.
Professional Memberships: Chancery Bar Association; Intellectual Property Bar Association; European Patent Lawyers Association; British Association for Sport and Law.
Career: Called to the Bar in 1996.
Personal: LLM London School of Economics – IP, Restitution, International Business Transactions and EU Competition Law. She follows F1 and all performances of Shakespeare.

HEALY, Alexandra QC
9-12 Bell Yard, London
020 7539 4861
a.healy@912by.com
Featured in Crime (London)
Practice Areas: Alexandra has a broad criminal practice with extensive experience in all aspects of criminal law. Fraud - She has considerable experience in complex fraud, insider dealing and corruption cases. Current instructions include defending a journalist in Operation Elveden; defending in criminal proceedings involving allegations of mortgage fraud and corruption (which relate to the landmark civil case involving the aggregation of professional indemnity insurance claims Godiva Mortgage Ltd v Travelers Insurance) and advising the SFO in relation to an alleged fraud in respect of football apprenticeship schemes. Recent instructions include the successful prosecution of R v Downes & MacDonald (a substantial international boiler room fraud), the successful defence of Hossain in R v Sanders & ors (an FSA insider dealing prosecution which involved ground breaking liaison with US agencies) and securing acquittals in R v Shepherd & ors (Beijing Olympics ticketing fraud), and R v Ravjani & others (a £100 million MTIC fraud). General Crime She has acted in high profile murder cases, has extensive experience of cases involving sexual offences and vulnerable witnesses and has regularly undertaken trials involving allegations of drugs, firearms and violence. Cases include and the successful prosecution of R v Sithole (arson murder of a 6 year old child following the defendant's extradition from South Africa). R v H (a child sex abuse case involving 6 complainants – included the cross-examination of an autistic victim through an intermediary). R v Bedi (Court of Appeal successfully appealed imposition of IPP); R v Chenery-Wickens (murder of BBC makeup artist); R v Khalisadar & ors (conspiracy to pervert the course of justice); R v Jaggs (killing of daughter of Harrow school master); R v Dennis & ors (misconduct in a public office); R v Edwards (murder); R v Fox & ors (Heathrow robbery); R v Thompson ('black widow' murder). She was instructed to act as independent counsel to review legally privileged material in the 'Cash for Honours' investigation.
Professional Memberships: Criminal Bar Association. Director of the Bar Mutual Indemnity Fund.
Career: Call 1992; Queen's Counsel (2011); Recorder of the Crown Court (2010); Joint Chair Bar Remuneration Committee (2012); Secretary of the Criminal Bar Association 2007-08.
Personal: Cambridge University (MA Cantab).

HEALY, Sandra
7 King's Bench Walk, London
020 7910 8300
sandra.healy@7kbw.co.uk
Featured in Energy & Natural Resources (London), Shipping (London)
Practice Areas: A broad commercial practice with advocacy experience (both as sole counsel and as part of a counsel team) in the Commercial Court and in arbitration. Particular expertise in: (i) shipping and international trade - experience of a broad range of cases including charterparty and cargo, commodities, ship sale and purchase, shipbuilding and admiralty; (ii) energy - experience of onshore and offshore projects and an on-going instruction on a major arbitration claim concerning gas fields in the Middle East; (iii) insurance - experience of marine and non-marine policies; (iv) jurisdiction and other interlocutory applications including those involving urgent injunctive relief, anti-suit injunctions, jurisdiction challenges and arbitration applications.
Professional Memberships: COMBAR; LCLBA; Supporting member LMAA; London shipping Law Centre – Young Maritime Professionals Association.
Career: Downing College, Cambridge University BA (Hons). Called to the Bar in 2007.

HEATHER, Christopher
Tanfield Chambers, London
020 7421 5300
cheather@tanfieldchambers.co.uk
Featured in Real Estate Litigation (London)
Practice Areas: Landlord and tenant (commercial, residential, enfranchisement and lease renewals), mortgages, boundaries, easements and associated professional negligence. Cases include: Merie Bin Mahfouz Company (UK) Ltd v Barrie House (Freehold Ltd) (collective enfranchisement, leases back, telecoms); Hauser v Howard De Walden Estates Ltd [2013] UKUT 597 (LC) (flying freeholds, enfranchisement, relativity); Rey-Ordieres v Lewisham LBC [2013] UKUT 14 (LC) (service charges, PFI); Helman v John Lyon [2013] 16 E.G. 106 (disclaimer, insolvency, enfranchisement); Griffin v Bromley LBC (long leases, housing benefit regulations); Point West London Limited v Rothschild Trust (Bermuda) Limited [2012] EWCA Civ 884 (stay of execution); Beech v Kennerley [2012] EWCA Civ 158 (abandonment of easements); Barrie House Freehold Ltd v Merie Bin Mahfouz Company (UK) Limited [2012] EWHC Ch (enfranchisement, easements, injunctions); Hilmi Associates Limited v 20 Pembridge Villas Freehold Limited [2010] EWCA Civ 314 (enfranchisement, companies, notices); Hughes v Borodex Limited [2010] EWCA Civ 425 (assured tenancies, tenant's improvements); Hanoman v Southwark LBC [2009] 1 WLR 1367 (HL) [2009] 1 WLR 374 (CA) (right to buy/sanctions for delay).
Professional Memberships: Chancery Bar Association, Property Bar Association, ALEP, Bar Pro Bono Unit.
Career: Barrister of the Year, Enfranchisement and Right to Manage Awards 2010;

Thorne Scholar, Middle Temple; Hewett Comprehensive School, Norwich, and Girton College, Cambridge.
Publications: Contributor to Service Charges and Management: Law and Practice (3rd Ed).
Personal: Running, swimming and photography.

HEATON, Laura
29 Bedford Row Chambers, London
020 7404 1044
lheaton@29br.co.uk
Featured in Family/Matrimonial (London)
Practice Areas: Matrimonial finance, Schedule 1 Children Act 1989, cohabitation disputes under Trusts of Land and Appointment of Trustees Act 1996, pre and post nuptial agreements and children matters (private law). Also works as collaborative counsel and mediator in all of these fields. Reported cases include: Re C (Financial Provision) [2007] 2 FLR 13, Q v Q (Ancillary Relief: Periodical Payments) [2005] 2 FLR 640.
Professional Memberships: Family Law Bar Association. Resolution (Barrister representative on Dispute Resolution Committee).
Career: Educated at Northgate High School, Ipswich and Clare College, Cambridge (MA). Called to the Bar in 1998. Middle Temple. Trained as Collaborative Counsel and Mediator. Public Access Barrister.
Publications: Co-author of: 'Cohabitation and Trusts of Land' pub. Thomson Sweet and Maxwell - second edition pubished December 2009.
Personal: Born 1 May 1975. Leisure pursuits include yoga, Indian classical dance, singing and watching sport. Married with children.

HEDWORTH, Toby QC
Trinity Chambers, Newcastle upon Tyne
0191 232 1927
t.hedworthqc@trinitychambers.co.uk
Featured in Crime (North Eastern)
Practice Areas: Judicial Review, Regulatory and Serious crime. Specialising in international terrorism, major professional crime, money laundering, confiscation proceedings including proceeds from organised crime. Conspiracy to murder, rob and the importation and distribution of controlled drugs on an international level. Fraud and white-collar crime. Currently instructed on what has been described as the UK's largest mortgage fraud. Substantial and complex contested caseload; including conduct of the first ever prosecution for membership of a proscribed organisation, defended in alleged al Qaeda Ricin plot, represented alleged leader of al Qaeda cyber-terrorism plot (involving protracted and detailed p.i.i. hearings centring on issues of both national security and government decision making processes), and represented white supremacist who manufactured Ricin, multiple murders and gangland murders, historical sex abuse, dentist accused of major fraud on NHS. Prosecution of multi-million pound armed robberies and drugs importation/supply conspiracies, al Qaeda extradition hearings and Bermudian murder appeal. Inquests involving alleged unlawful killing by the police, and police disciplinary proceedings.
Professional Memberships: CBA; Justice.
Career: Called 1975. Head of Chambers since 1999. Recorder 1995. QC 1996. Appointed by the Department of Energy and Climate Change to hear Carbon Reduction Commitment Energy Efficiency Scheme (CRC) Appeals.

HEER, Deanna
5 Paper Buildings, London
07976 284 578
dh@5pb.co.uk
Featured in Health & Safety (London), Crime (London)
Practice Areas: Deanna prosecutes and defends serious crime and health and safety offences. She has been appointed Junior Treasury Counsel from July 2015 and is an 'A' list advocate for the HSE. She also appears before the Coroner's Court and professional disciplinary tribunals. Deanna regularly appears in homicide cases, including joint enterprise murder, gangland killings, unlawful act manslaughter and cases of so-called Shaken Baby Syndrome. She also has many years experience prosecuting serious organised crime including large scale drugs importations and money laundering. Deanna also specialises in health and safety law. She was instructed in the leading case of Tangerine Confectionary Ltd and Veolia (UK) Ltd [2011] EWCA Crim 2015 and regularly appears in cases brought against corporate defendants in respect of allegations of gross negligence manslaughter and statutory breaches resulting in death in a wide range of industries.
Professional Memberships: Criminal Bar Association, South Eastern Circuit, Health and Safety Lawyers Association.
Career: Called 1994; Recorder 2009.

HELME, Ian
One Brick Court, London
020 7353 8845
ih@onebrickcourt.com
Featured in Defamation/Privacy (London)
Practice Areas: All aspects of media and information law including defamation, breach of confidence and privacy, data protection, harassment, contempt and all related human rights law. Cases include: Hegglin v Google Inc; Untulmus & ors v Collett & ors; Karpov v Browder; Cairns v Modi; Waterson v Lloyd; Lord McAlpine v ITV; Voicemail Interception - News International; Lait v Evening Standard Ltd; R v VAC (ex parte BBFC); Rath v Guardian Newspapers Ltd; Taranissi v BBC; Oldham Online Ltd v Rochdale Online Ltd; Financial Times v United Kingdom.
Career: Called 2005, Middle Temple; judicial assistant to Lord Justice Waller, Vice President of the Court of Appeal, Jan-Jun 2007.
Publications: Contributor to 4th Edition of Arlidge, Eady & Smith on Contempt and supplement; Co-Author of Carter-Ruck on Libel & Privacy; Co-Author of Atkins Court Forms Defamation title 2011 issue; contributor to edition of Halsbury's Laws Libel & Slander title.
Personal: Pembroke College, Cambridge (BA Hons Law First Class).

HENDERSON, James
Pump Court Tax Chambers, London
020 7414 8080
clerks@pumptax.com
Featured in Tax (London)
Practice Areas: James Henderson advises on all the major UK taxes. His work covers corporate tax, VAT, private client, customs duties and insurance premium tax. He regularly presents cases in the Tax Tribunals and higher courts. James also undertakes professional negligence work involving a tax aspect.
Professional Memberships: Revenue Bar Association; London Common Law and Commercial Bar Association.
Career: Called 1997, Gray's Inn; joined Pump Court Tax Chambers after completing Pupillage in 1998; Appointed Junior Counsel to the Crown "B" Panel 2012.
Personal: Born 1974; resides London.

HENDERSON, Neil
4 Pump Court, London
020 7842 5555
clerks@4pumpcourt.com
Featured in Shipping (London)
Practice Areas: Shipping and international trade: cargo claims, charterparty disputes, arrests, demurrage and demurrage timebars, bunker disputes, shipbuilding disputes, sale and purchase, marine insurance, commodity sales. Commercial litigation and arbitration: private equity, shareholder disputes, banking, insolvency, director disqualification, general contractual disputes. High Court applications in support of arbitration, including freezing injunctions and Chabra injunctions, anti-suit injunctions, inspection orders, jurisdiction disputes, security for costs and applications under ss.57, 67, 68 and 69 of the Arbitration Act 1996. Extensive experience of LMAA, ICC and LCIA arbitrations.
Professional Memberships: COMBAR, London Common Law and Commercial Bar Association, Young Maritime Professionals, Young Shipping Professionals (Greece). Direct and Public Access qualified.
Career: Before joining the Bar, Neil worked as an analyst in the corporate finance departments of JPMorgan and Flemings investment banks for over two years during which time he completed a wide range of deals including acquisitions, disposals, IPOs and private equity financings.
Personal: First class degree in Medieval and Modern History at the University of Birmingham. Japanese language and history at Hitotsubashi University, Tokyo. PgDL (distinction) and BVC (outstanding) at the College of Law. Institute of Shipping Law, Short Course. Outside of work, Neil windsurfs, sails yachts (RYA day skipper) and dinghies, snowboards and bicycles.

HENDERSON, Simon
4 Pump Court, London
020 7842 5555
shenderson@4pumpcourt.com
Featured in Construction (London), Information Technology (London), Professional Negligence (London)
Practice Areas: General commercial law, particularly in the field of IT, construction, energy and related professional negligence and insurance. Also handles professional negligence for and against accountants, legal professionals and surveyors.
Professional Memberships: COMBAR, TECBAR, London Common Law and Commercial Bar Association.
Career: Called to the Bar in 1993.
Personal: BA (Durham) (Philosophy - 1st Class). Dip Law (City University).

HENDERSON, William
Serle Court, London
020 7242 6105
whenderson@serlecourt.co.uk
Featured in Chancery (London), Charities (London), Trusts (London)
Practice Areas: Trusts and estates, charities and probate plus associated public law and professional negligence claims. Cases: Joint Stock Co Aeroflot v Berezovskaya [2014] EWCA Civ 431; Ferguson v. HMRC [2014] UKFTT 433 (TC); Pitt v. Holt [2013] UKSC 26 [2013] 2 AC 108; Wood v Gorbunova [2013] EWHC 1935 (Ch) [2014] 1 B.C.L.C. 487; Helena Housing Ltd v HMRC [2012] EWCA (Civ) 569 [2012] 4 All E.R. 111; Gudavadze v. Kay [2012] EWHC 1683 (Ch) [2012] W.T.L.R. 1753; R. (on the application of Independent Schools Council) v Charity Commission [2011] UKUT 421 (TCC); [2012] Ch. 214; Attorney General v Charity Commission [2012] UKUT 420 (TCC); [2012] W.T.L.R. 977; Re Kostic [2007] EWHC 2298 and 2909 (Ch).
Professional Memberships: Chancery Bar Association. ACTAPs. STEP.
Career: 1968-72 St Paul's School London; 1973-77 Trinity College Cambridge - BA in Natural Sciences (Pt I) and Law (Pt I). Junior counsel to the Treasury in Charity Matters.

HENDY, John QC
Old Square Chambers, London
020 7269 0360
hendyqc@oldsquare.co.uk
Featured in Employment (London), Professional Discipline (London)
Practice Areas: John's practice is predominantly in the field of industrial relations and employment. He specialises, in particular, in collective aspects of labour law. He has also appeared at a number of significant Public Inquiries and Inquests, usually for the bereaved and injured. He occasionally undertakes professional disciplinary work. He also has international work, notably for the Irish Congress of Trade Unions and the International Trade Union Confederation. He is Standing Counsel to a number of UK unions. His impressive list of reported cases can be found in his CV at www.oldsquare.co.uk He was the Legal 500 Employment Silk of the Year for 2013, and is recognised as a leading silk in employment by the Legal 500 and Chambers & Partners. The latter's entry for 2013 describe him as the "absolutely excellent" John Hendy QC, who is a "terrific fighter" and an "authoritative silk" respected by opposing counsel, instructing solicitors and members of the judiciary.

HENLEY, Christopher
Carmelite Chambers, London
020 7936 6300
clerks@carmelitechambers.co.uk
Featured in Crime (London)
Practice Areas: Chris Henley specialises in fraud, terrorism, homicide and other serious crime. He regularly acts as leading counsel in high profile and demanding cases. He has led in trials prosecuted by HMRC, the SFO, the Department for Business Innovation and Skills, SOCA and the Counter-Terrorism Unit of the CPS. He has defended in a series of significant trials, including the Damilola Taylor case (junior counsel for the first defendant), the 21/7 terrorism trial (attempts to detonate explosive devices on the London transport system), the Daniel Morgan murder trial (notorious murder of a private investigator linked to corruption in the Met; proceedings stayed as an abuse), Operation Munda (terrorist plot to groom vulnerable individuals for 'jihad'), Operation Iridescent (fundraising for Al Shabaab), Operation Savate (Income Tax and VAT fraud in the

construction industry). He has recently successfully defended the first application brought by the CTU to seize a convicted defendant's home under the Terrorism Act. He is currently acting in ongoing proceedings involving allegations of terrorism in Syria, for the Head of a Prep School facing allegations of historic child cruelty, and in proceedings involving allegations of corruption by HMRC officers.
Professional Memberships: Grays Inn (call 1989), CBA Executive Committee, Pupil Supervisor, Fraud Lawyers Association, Liberty, the Labour Party.

HENRY, Annette QC
Furnival Chambers, London
020 7405 3232
ahenry@furnivallaw.co.uk
Featured in Crime (London), Financial Crime (London)
Practice Areas: Annette has been consistently recognised as a leading defence specialist throughout her career and displays a formidable commitment to her cases combined with an outstanding rapport with clients. She is regularly instructed in the most serious and complex fraud and financial crime cases, but continues to successfully combine these areas of practise with heavyweight drugs and murder/manslaughter cases. Typically she represents individuals with additional, unusual and challenging features personal to them or within the proceedings against them. Notable cases: Currently instructed in the largest most complex HMRC carbon credit fraud; Choudhury & others - Highly sophisticated immigration fraud; Khurshid - International fraud against major mobile airtime providers; Benelabed - International money laundering operation; Shah & Others -1st insider dealing ring prosecution; Melbourne & McQuoid - 1st insider dealing FSA prosecution; Reeves - Counter surveillance expert in multi million pound missing trader fraud. Other notable cases: Campbell - Indiscriminate gang related shootings at nightclub; Kovacs - International human trafficking ring; Brown - Conspiracy to supply firearms and manufacture ammunition from prison; Oppong - Triple shooting; Roffey - Attempted murder of victim with motor neurone disease; Cooke - Manslaughter by 7 year old riding quadbike; Securitas Robbery - Largest reported robbery in legal history.
Professional Memberships: Member FSLA and ARDL, Former Mental Health Review Tribunal (President), Mental Health Act Commissioner (and inpatient deaths investigator).
Career: Called 1984; LLB (Hons) Manchester. Queen's Counsel.
Publications: 'Mental Health Law Referencer' (Sweet and Maxwell).

HENRY, Edward
QEB Hollis Whiteman, London
020 7933 8855
barristers@qebhw.co.uk
Featured in Crime (London)
Practice Areas: A leading specialist defence junior with a silk-type practice, Edward Henry has been recommended in legal publications over many years and described as 'an excellent advocate with a phenomenal brain'. Edward's practice encompasses all forms of serious crime, business crime and regulatory matters. Edward is also asked to advise on professional negligence and liability in the context of criminal claims. Edward is widely regarded for his expertise in matters involving experts and disclosure. His cross-examination of an expert, following extensive analysis of her evidence in previous cases, led to her being abandoned in other prosecutions and he was invited to speak on Newsnight about the case. His capacity to 'think outside of the box' means he often argues novel and successful points of law. His client care and empathy is described as 'very strong'. Edward has been instructed to act in over 40 murder trials, cases of terrorism (both IRA and Islamicist), serious sexual assault, drugs, money laundering, immigration fraud, people trafficking and firearms. His recent fraud and financial cases include the successful defence of a former CEO of The Money Portal on a £60 million pension fraud and advising on appeals as a second opinion post conviction. Edward has considerable regulatory experience, defending police, solicitors and medical professionals. Edward has a passion for advocacy and the criminal justice system. He is asked to speak by a variety of media outlets. He gives seminars on various aspects of law and is highly sought after as a mentor by Pegasus scholars from the USA, Australia and New Zealand.
Professional Memberships: SEC, CBA Representative on Bar Council, ARDL, Justice, Public Access Bar Association, Release, Fine Cell Work.
Career: Called 1988. Exhibitioner of Jesus College,Cambridge BA(Hons)(Cantab). Dip Law(City University).
Personal: Family, art, music, singing, dancing. Trustee of "Release".

HENTON, Paul
Quadrant Chambers, London
020 7583 4444
paul.henton@quadrantchambers.com
Featured in Aviation (London)
Practice Areas: Paul acts in a range of commercial disputes; with particular focus on shipping; international trade; commodities; energy; shipbuilding; banking; aviation and insurance; and related interlocutory matters including jurisdictional challenges, freezing orders and anti-suit injunctions. Reported cases include The "Astipalaia"[2014] EWHC 120 (Admlty) (damages; loss of oil major approvals); Taurus Petroleum v Oil Marketing Company of Iraq [2014] 1 Lloyd's Rep 432 (commercial enforcement; letters of credit; State immunity); Vitol v Sterling Oil Trading [2012] EWHC 3108 (Comm) (dispute under long-term oil supply contract and related financing agreements);the 'CENK KAPTANOGLU' [2012] 1 Lloyd's Rep 501 (Charterparty dispute; economic duress); The 'PRINCESS 7' [2011] EWHC 3940 (Comm) (Marine insurance; jurisdiction; conflict of laws; claims settlement clauses); Invertec v de Mol Holdings [2009] EWHC 2471 (Share sale; fraudulent misrepresentation); appeal from Wilhelm Finance v Ente Administrador Del Astillero Rio [2009] EWHC 1074 (Shipbuilding; jurisdiction; State Immunity); National Westminster Bank v King [2008] 2 WLR 1279 (Banking; jurisdiction); the 'REMMAR' [2007] 2 Lloyd's Rep. 302 (Ship sale and purchase; arbitration procedure; misrepresentation). Currently acting as junior counsel for insurers in a US$1.6 billion patent infringement liability insurance tower dispute.
Career: LLB (UCL); LLM (Cantab), 1st Class. Called 2004, Inner Temple (ranked "outstanding").

HEPPINSTALL, Adam
Henderson Chambers, London
020 7583 9020
aheppinstall@hendersonchambers.co.uk
Featured in Professional Discipline (London)
Practice Areas: Common law practitioner who specialises in a broad range of areas including professional discipline, group actions, health and safety, personal injury, public law, product liability and employment law. He is Junior Counsel to the Crown (A Panel) and as such has a public law practice as well as public inquiry and coronial law experience (particularly in the health sector). He appeared for the GMC in the Professor Sir Roy Meadow proceedings and before the Shipman Inquiry. He acts for solicitors, health professionals, surveyors and accountants before their disciplinary bodies. He has wide regulatory experience, has represented companies in health and safety and local government regulatory prosecutions, has dealt with financial services/consumer credit/trading standards enforcement proceedings, has advised on and appeared in regulatory appeals in relation to data protection and freedom of information and is an expert on fire safety regulation and associated enforcement proceedings.
Professional Memberships: ARDL, ELBA, PBA, COMBAR, LCLCBA.
Career: Called 1999, Middle Temple; Judicial assistant to Otton and Buxton LJJs in 2000; Junior Counsel to the Crown since 2004.
Publications: Contributor Vol 37 Halsbury's Laws; He is the co-author of 'The Manual of Employment Appeals', Jordans, 2008.
Personal: Married.

HERBERT, Douglas
Ropewalk Chambers, Nottingham
0115 947 2581
douglasherbert@ropewalk.co.uk
Featured in Personal Injury (Midlands)
Practice Areas: He specialises in personal injury and professional negligence, particularly clinical negligence, cases. He prides himself upon his good and friendly manner with clients, which is coupled with his rigorous, clear and focused approach to the issues involved in the claim.
Professional Memberships: Personal Injuries Bar Association; Professional Negligence Bar Association.
Career: Called in 1973; LLB, University of Bristol; Recorder on the Midland Circuit.
Personal: Away from the Bar, his interests are family golf, rugby, travel and music.

HERBERT, Mark QC
5 Stone Buildings, London
020 7242 6201
clerks@5sblaw.com
Featured in Chancery (London), Charities (London), Trusts (London)
Practice Areas: An experienced specialist in the law of trusts and tax whose practice covers all aspects of the law relating to settlements, wills, charities and occupational pension schemes, including probate, family provision and breach of trust litigation as well as less contentious applications under the Trustee Acts and the Variation of Trusts Act 1958. Particular experience in capital taxation, the taxation of settlements and estates, charities and offshore trusts. Also handles pensions work, both advisory and litigation. Important cases include Mettoy Pension Trustees v Evans [1990]; Re Christy Hunt Pension Fund [1991]; Fitzwilliam v IRC [1993]. Hamar v Pensions Ombudsman, R v Opra ex p Littlewoods (1997); Edge v Pensions Ombudsman (1999); Espinosa v Bourke (1999). Sieff v Fox [2005]: Re Wedgwood Museum Ltd [2011]; Shergill v Khaiva [2014].
Professional Memberships: Chancery Bar Association; Revenue Bar Association. Member of the executive committee of the Trust Law Committee.
Career: Called to the Bar 1974. Tenant at 17 Old Buildings 1975-77 before joining Queen Elizabeth Building in 1977. At present Chambers since 1991. Took Silk 1995. Accredited mediator since 2002. Deputy High Court judge of the Chancery Division. Commissioner of the Royal Court of Jersey.
Publications: Co-editor of 'Whiteman on Capital Gains Tax'. Other publications include 'The Drafting and Variation of Wills'.

HESLOP, Martin S QC
2 Hare Court, London
020 7353 5324
clerks@2harecourt.com
Featured in Licensing (London), Crime (London)
Practice Areas: Martin Heslop QC is recognised as one of the leading experts in crime, health & safety and gaming & licensing at the bar today. He is cited in the Legal 500, Chambers UK and legal experts as such, with recent commentary stating he is, "A truly brilliant advocate with no discernable weaknesses", "In the super league", "Held in high regard by his peers", "A thorn in any opponent's side", "Punctilious in his presentation" and, "A fine silk whose standing as an excellent criminal lawyer is seen further to complement his gaming practice" He spent 9 years as Treasury Counsel, prosecuting the most serious and complex cases but unusually maintained a very significant defence practice during that period being in demand to defend in many of the major criminal trials at the time. In Silk, this has continued, enabling him to enjoy a diverse practice of the highest profile in the areas of crime, health & safety, gaming and licensing. In Crime, he has represented both the Crown and the defence in cases varying from murder and terrorism to international fraud. In Health & Safety, he represents well-known major companies both in the United Kingdom and abroad and regularly lectures on the implications of new legislation in this field. In Gaming & Licensing, he is regularly instructed by the leading operators and his achievements are confirmed by unsolicited comments in numerous legal publications. Most recently, he has succeeded in obtaining Stage 1 licences against significant opposition for casinos in Stratford and Milton Keynes on behalf of Aspinals. In addition, he is frequently instructed of cases outside the jurisdiction, in particular the Channel Islands and the Caribbean.
Career: Called 1972 (Lincoln's Inn), Junior Treasury Counsel 1987, First Junior Treasury Counsel 1991, Senior Treasury Counsel 1992, Recorder 1993, Queen's Counsel 1995.
Personal: Sailing, travel, photography, wine and good food.

HEWITT, Alison
5 Essex Court, London
020 7410 2000
hewitt@5essexcourt.co.uk
Featured in Inquests & Public Inquiries (London)

Practice Areas: Inquests / Coronial law; Public / Administrative law; Police law; Personal Injury; rofessional discipline. For many years Alison had a broad based common law practice, specialising in personal injury and employment law and acting regularly for the Treasury Solicitor. In 2002 she represented two Coroners at the Shipman Inquiry and since then she has developed a particular expertise in coronial law. She has acted as "Counsel to the Inquest" in a number of lengthy and complex cases, including the inquest into the death of Ian Tomlinson, who died following contact with the police at the G20 riots. She represents a wide range of clients at inquests and in related judicial review, including Police Constabularies, private prisons, doctors and NHS Trusts, care homes and families. Alison is also an experienced Assistant Coroner and has conducted cases involving deaths in custody, deaths in detention under the Mental Health Act and deaths resulting from poor clinical care and treatment.Since moving to 5, Essex Court in 2012 Alison has developed an ever-growing Police law practice. She regularly represents and advises Constabularies in relation to civil claims, judicial review proceedings and disciplinary matters. She also acts as Legal Adviser to the General Dental Council.
Professional Memberships: The Coroners' Society of England and Wales; PIBA.
Career: Called to the Bar 1984; Assitant Coroner 2007; Legal Advisor to the General Dentist Council 2004.

HEYWOOD, Mark QC
No5 Chambers, Birmingham
0845 210 5555
silks@no5.com
Featured in Crime (Midlands)
Practice Areas: Described as a silk clients "would instruct without hesitation," Mark Heywood both prosecutes and defends major criminal offences. Commercial Fraud: Operation Foamy - multi-million pound "boiler room" fraud investigated by FSA. R v Al Haq & others – Alteration of title deeds at Land Registry allowing fraudsters to use victims' homes as collateral for loans. Operation Fraxwood - multi-million pound tax and VAT fraud. Operation Acumen - contract pricing fraud on a police authority. Corruption, Misconduct in Public Office: Operations Wasp & Spoke – lengthy undercover investigation and prosecution of corrupt police officer supplying operational intelligence to criminals. R v Morgan - police officer soliciting corrupt payment to end a case. R v "D" - prosecution of a member of Special Forces. R v Lee & others – corruption and theft of tank and other armoured vehicle equipment from MoD. Homicide, Firearms: Operation Usk (jnr) -'missing body' killing. Multi-handed 4-month trial involving anonymous witnesses. Operation Precept – Drug gang "turf" shooting R v Grant & Wheeler – machine gun at gang violent disorder. Sexual Offences: R v Kaci & others - human trafficking from Eastern Europe. R v Ali & others, R v Khan - rapes of vulnerable victims groomed by gangs. Regulatory Offences: Health & Safety fatalities, Pollution (noise and toxic substances) Planning enforcement.
Professional Memberships: Criminal Bar Association.
Career: QC 2012. Prior to taking silk, appointed to the Attorney General's "A" list of prosecuting counsel.

HIBBERT, William
Henderson Chambers, London
020 7583 9020
whibbert@hendersonchambers.co.uk
Featured in Consumer Law (London)
Practice Areas: Consumer law, in particular finance, consumer credit, banking, mortgages and financial services. In the wider field of consumer protection, regulatory law including legislation on unfair contract terms, unfair commercial practices, pricing, advertising, distance and doorstep selling, pyramid selling, package holidays and timeshare. Also food, food labelling, medicines and cosmetics. Cases include OFT v First National Bank [2002] 1 AC 481 (Unfair Terms in Consumer Contracts Regulations); Wilson v First County Trust [2002] QB 74 (CA), [2004] 1 AC 816 (HL)(Declaration of Incompatibility under HRA regarding irredeemable unenforceability under CCA); OFT v Lloyds TSB Bank [2005] 1 AER 843 (QB), [2006] 2 AER 821 (CA), [2008] 1 AC 318 (HL) (Lender's liability under s.75 CCA for credit card transactions financing foreign transactions); Goshawk v Bank of Scotland [2006] 2 AER 610 (Wording of prescribed notices of cancellation rights under CCA); Conister Trust v Hardman and Co [2009] CCLR 4 (Solicitor's liability for client's litigation funding agreement); Meah v GE Money Home Finance Ltd [2013] EWHC 20 (Ch) (Mortgagee's liability for valuation of repossessed property).
Professional Memberships: COMBAR,Food Law Group, Consumer Credit Forum.
Career: Called to the bar 1979.
Publications: The Law of Consumer Credit and Hire, OUP 2009.
Personal: Born 1957. Educated: Charterhouse; Worcester College, Oxford.

HICKEY, Alexander
4 Pump Court, London
020 7842 5555
AHickey@4pumpcourt.com
Featured in Construction (London), Energy & Natural Resources (London), International Arbitration (London), Professional Negligence (London)
Practice Areas: Construction, energy and waste management, technology and other commercial disputes both domestic and international. Professional negligence claims involving construction professionals, solicitors and valuers. Alex is regularly involved in trials and arbitrations (ICC, LCIA, DIAC). He has a string of reported cases in relation to adjudication, and several reported cases to his name in the House of Lords, Court of Appeal and the High Court.
Professional Memberships: TECBAR (committee 2001-04); COMBAR; SCL.
Career: Called 1995 (Lincoln's Inn). Judicial assistant to the Court of Appeal (1997).
Publications: Adjudication section of Lexis PSL.
Personal: Educated at Christ Church, Oxford, where he read Jurisprudence and was a choral scholar (1991-94), and Hereford Cathedral School. Married with two children.

HICKS, Edward
Radcliffe Chambers, London
020 7831 0081
ehicks@radcliffechambers.com
Featured in Real Estate Litigation (London)
Practice Areas: Chancery, court of protection and commercial practice, specialising in: land, landlord and tenant, trusts, wills and probate, family provision, commercial, consumer credit and insolvency. Cases include: Di Marco v Morshead Mansions Ltd [2014] EWCA Civ 96 Re Devillebichot [2013] EWHC 2867; Log Book Loans Ltd and Nine Regions Ltd v Office of Fair Trading (1st Tier Tribunal) CCA/2009/0010 and 0011.
Professional Memberships: Chancery Bar Association.
Career: MA Cantab (Magdalene College), BLC, Called to bar in 2004.
Publications: Contributor to Atkins Court Forms (education). Seminars include: A practical approach to risk management in trusts and estates litigation 2011 (STEP/Connect 2 Law); Challenging the Validity of Wills 2011 (Connect 2 Law); Protecting Gifts from Challenge 2010 (Solicitors for the Elderly).
Personal: Born 1981; resides London.

HICKS, Martin QC
2 Hare Court, London
020 7353 5324
martinhicksqc@2harecourt.com
Featured in Crime (London), Financial Crime (London)
Practice Areas: Martin Hicks QC is widely regarded as a leading silk who specialises in the defence of crime (domestic and international), fraud, and all forms of business regulation (especially planning, trading standards, and health and safety). Described by this guide as "a fantastic advocate, whom juries love, he fights relentlessly for his clients", and "able to relate to clients from all spheres of society, he is often first choice counsel for many of the major defence firms, and he appears across the UK. He advises and appears for individual defendants, corporate clients and their directors and officers. He also acts on behalf of professionals such as accountants, solicitors and others who face proceedings arising out of their work. Martin appears in cases involving murder, serious violence, drugs importation and related money laundering, blackmail, and other offences. He is particularly requested for complex cases, or those involving high-profile individuals. He is also instructed in terrorism cases both in the UK and the Caribbean. Martin appears regularly in the Court of Appeal and is instructed to advise on appeal or provide 2nd opinions in appropriate cases. Throughout his career Martin has also specialised in cases involving fraud and other forms of wrong-doing, and these have formed a substantial part of his practice. He has experience of VAT and MTIC fraud, residential and commercial mortgage fraud, banking and boiler room fraud, insurance fraud, advance fee fraud, Ponzi schemes, bribery and corruption, money laundering, and others. He also has extensive experience of POCA and related proceedings including confiscation, restraint and asset forfeiture. Martin is authorised by the Bar Council to accept instructions on a direct access basis in appropriate cases.

HIGGINS, Gillian
9 Bedford Row, London
07957 351 458
gillian.higgins@9bedfordrow.co.uk
Featured in Crime (London)
Practice Areas: Gillian Higgins is regarded as a leading lawyer in international criminal law (ICL). Her courtroom advocacy is recognised as being of the highest class. Gillian specialises in offences of genocide, crimes against humanity and war crimes. Her notable cases include Prosecutor v Kenyatta (ICC); Prosecutor v Cermak (ICTY); Prosecutor v Milosevic (ICTY); Prosecutor v Nahimana (ICTR); Prosecutor v Musema (ICTR); and Osmanoglu v Turkey (ECHR). Gillian lectures and provides consultancy on fair trial rights. She has also advised on defence issues before the State Court of BiH in Sarajevo and Cambodia's ECCC.
Professional Memberships: Gillian is a founding member of the International Criminal Law Bureau (ICLB) and the founder of "ARC" (Advice, Representation and Cases), which provides advice on taking cases to the African Court on Human and Peoples' Rights.
Publications: She edits and writes for the ICLB blog, nominated in 2011 by Lexis Nexis as 'Blog of the Year'. She also reviews Oxford University Press ICL publications.

HIGGINS, Nichola
Doughty Street Chambers, London
020 7404 1313
n.higgins@doughtystreet.co.uk
Featured in Crime (London)
Practice Areas: Nichola's in depth knowledge of fraud and corruption comes having defended, investigated and prosecuted complex and challenging overseas corruption prosecutions. Combining her experience with a tactical mind and commercial awareness she is regularly instructed to advise on the Bribery Act, corruption investigations both internal and external, fraud matters, pre and post charge, and compliance procedures.
Career: Recent instructions include: Advising a French blue-chip (CAC40) multi-national on its Bribery Act obligations for six months in 2014; SFO v Dahdaleh and Hall, an international conspiracy to corrupt involving the payment of €30 million of alleged bribes over an eight year period; SFO v Shephard and Steele, an equity partner in a City law firm conspired with a client to cheat a private Swiss bank of €22 million; SFO v Messent, the payment of overseas bribes by a London reinsurance company to high ranking officials in Costa Rica.
Publications: Contributor to 'Bribery: A compliance handbook', Bloomsbury Professional, 2014.
Personal: Nichola is appointed to the Serious Fraud Office 'B' Panel and is a fluent Spanish speaker. She was selected by Legal Week as a rising star of the Bar in 2012 and named in The Lawyer's 'Hot 100' in 2013.

HIGGINS, Roisin
Axiom Advocates, Edinburgh
07739 639 083
roisin.higgins@axiomadvocates.com
Featured in Intellectual Property (Scotland), Commercial Dispute Resolution (Scotland)
Practice Areas: Intellectual property law; commercial law; commercial contracts; commercial property; construction. Reported cases: Verathon Medical (Canada) ULC v Aircraft Medical Ltd. [2011] CSOH 60 (patent infringement, revocation and amendment): Bayer Cropscience KK v Charles River Laboratories & Anr. 2011 SLT 145 (patent infringement, 'springboard' account of profits); East Dunbartonshire Council v Gladedale (Northern Division) Ltd. [2012] CSIH 1, [2011] CSOH 56 (property dispute/breach of contract); City Inn Ltd. v Shepherd Construction Ltd. [2010] BLR 473, [2008] BLR 269 (construction law/delay claim);

Martin Hines & Anr. v King Sturge LLP 2011 SLT 2, 2009 SLT 763 (professional negligence/duties of care); Castle Inns (Stirling) Ltd. (t/a Castle Leisure Group) v Clark Contracts Ltd. [2009] CSOH 174 (construction law/delay and loss of profits); Cala Management v Messrs A & E Sorrie (A Firm) [2009] CSOH 79 (property dispute/missives).
Professional Memberships: Committee Member, TIPLO.
Career: Roisin has particular expertise in the field of intellectual property law, including patents, trade marks, copyright, passing off, breach of confidence, design rights and plant variety rights. She also has significant experience in commercial litigation, including commercial and construction contract disputes and property litigation. She appears predominantly in the Court of Session, both at first instance and in appeals, though has also appeared in the sheriff court and at arbitration. She gives regular lectures and seminars in the field of intellectual property law and is a door tenant at 8 New Square, Lincoln's Inn.
Publications: 'Confidentiality, Counselling and the Law in Scotland' (2006) (with Tim Bond and Alan Jamieson).

HIGGO, Justin
Serle Court, London
020 7242 6105
jhiggo@serlecourt.co.uk
Featured in Chancery (London), Commercial Dispute Resolution (London), Fraud (London)
Practice Areas: Specialist in commercial and chancery litigation and advice. In particular domestic and international commercial fraud and pre-emptive remedies, domestic and international trusts, arbitration, company and banking. Recent cases include: Chambal Fertilizers & Chemicals -v- Trafigura & Ors, JSC BTA Bank -v- Ablyazov & Ors, Fiona Trust -v- Privalov in the Commercial Court; Orb ARL -v- Ruhan; Aeroflot -v- Berezovsky & Ors, Labrouche -v- Frey & Ors, Bank of St Petersburg -v- Arkhangelsky, CCE Ltd -v- Corry & Ors and Uddington -v- Browne in the Chancery Division; international arbitrations; ongoing substantial litigation in the Channel Islands; Wahr-Hansen -v- Monsen in the Cayman Islands.
Professional Memberships: Chancery Bar Assocation, COMBAR.
Career: Called February 1995.

HILL, Jonathan
8 New Square, London
020 7405 4321
clerks@8newsquare.co.uk
Featured in Intellectual Property (London)
Practice Areas: Barrister specialising in all areas of intellectual property law and related commercial, IT and media law including; trade marks, passing off, copyright, patents, design right, registered designs, database right, and confidential information. Recent cases include: Shanks v Unilever (inventor's claim to fair share of benefit from patent licensing for blood glucose testing); D Jacobson v Crocs (registered designs in Crocs shoes); Blue Gentian v Tristar (validity of patent for expandable hose); Magical Marking v Ware & Kay (professional negligence allegedly arising from handling of an IP claim); Polo/Lauren Co (Community trade mark appeal); Quick Draw v Global Live Events (film finance, copyright and performer's rights infringement, relating to Michael Jackson tribute concert); BMW v Round & Metal (registered designs and trade marks); Nintendo v Playables (copy-protection circumvention devices); BMS Computer Solutions v AB Agri (mill control software); Zipher v Markem (patent infringement); Best Buy v Worldwide Sales (threats of trade mark infringement proceedings).
Professional Memberships: Intellectual Property Bar Association; Chancery Bar Association; Lincoln's Inn.
Career: Called 2000. Awarded Kennedy, Mansfield, Major CPE and Hardwicke scholarships during qualification. Judicial Assistant, Court of Appeal (2002).
Publications: Atkins Court Forms - Patents
Personal: Studied Physics and Philosophy, Oxford (1st).

HILL, Mark QC
Francis Taylor Building, London
020 7353 8415
mark.hill@ftb.eu.com
Featured in Civil Liberties & Human Rights (London)
Practice Areas: Religious liberty, ecclesiastical law, public law, costs, ADR.
Professional Memberships: PNBA; PIBA; HRLA; Ecclesiastical Law Society; Western Circuit.
Career: Specialist in ecclesiastical law, religious liberty, judicial review and costs. Recorder; Chancellor of Dioceses of Chichester and Europe; Deputy Chancellor of York and Blackburn; Legal Assessor, General Medical Council; Honorary Professor of Law, Cardiff University; Extraordinary Professor, University of Pretoria; Member, Legal Advisory Commission, General Synod; Co-Chair of BIMA (Belief in Mediation and Arbitration). Cases: President of Methodist Conference v Preston (2013) Supreme Court; Eweida v UK (2013) ECtHR; Shergill v Khaira (2012) Court of Appeal; Church of Jesus Christ of Latter-day Saints v UK (2011) ECtHR; R v Twaite (2010), Court Martial Court of Appeal; Sant Baba Jeet v Eastern News Group (2010), QBD; Holliday v Musa (2010), Court of Appeal; R (HM Coroner for Eastern London) v Secretary of State for Justice (2009) Admin Ct; R (Madden and Finucane) v Secretary of State for Northern Ireland (2006) Admin Ct; PCC of Aston Cantlow v Wallbank (2004) HL; Re Blagdon Cemetery (2002) Ct of Arches.
Publications: 'Religion and Discrimination Law in the European Union' (2012); 'Religion and Law in the United Kingdom' (2011); 'Ecclesiastical Law' (3rd ed, 2007); 'Religious Liberty and Human Rights' (2002); 'English Canon Law' (1998); together with numerous articles in legal periodicals. Contributing editor, 'Jowitt's Dictionary of English Law' (3rd ed, 2010) and 'Butterworths Costs Service' (2011). Consultant Editor, Ecclesiastical Law Journal.

HILL, Max QC
Red Lion Chambers, London
020 7520 6000
max.hill@18rlc.co.uk
Featured in Crime (London)
Practice Areas: Max Hill is the Head of Red Lion Chambers. He defends in cases of murder and serious fraud. He appears for the defence at the Central Criminal Court. During 2013-14 he defended in several multi-defendant Murder trials, a major money laundering trial and a tax evasion case. He was previously instructed for the defence in the long-running SFO pharmaceutical cartel case R v O'Neill and others. He has also conducted the prosecution of many of the most serious terrorism trials of recent years, including R v Bourgass and others (the ricin conspiracy), R v Ibrahim and others (the 21/7 bombers), R v Ali and others and R v Girma and others (the 21/7 follow-on trials), as well as other terrorism trials involving Syria, Baluchistan and Somalia. He was also instructed in R v Preddie (the second set of trials concerning the killing of Damilola Taylor). He appeared for the Government in the Binyam Mohamed case in the Adminstrative Court. He acted for the Metropolitan Police Service in the Inquests into the 7th July London tube bombings.
Professional Memberships: Chairman of the Criminal Bar Association 2011-12; Chairman of the Kalisher Trust 2014-.
Career: Crown Court Recorder, 2005; Queen's Counsel, 2008.

HILL, Michael
Trinity Chambers, Newcastle upon Tyne
0191 232 1927
m.hill@trinitychambers.co.uk
Featured in Clinical Negligence (North Eastern)
Practice Areas: Qualified as a dental surgeon and practised dentistry for 15 years before coming to the Bar in 2004, he therefore has a unique understanding of clinical negligence claims acting for both Claimants and Defendants. Operating from Chambers in Newcastle and Teesside, Mike accepts instructions from across the UK. Also prepared to review certain cases on a pre-CFA basis. His clinical negligence, dental negligence and personal injury practice has recently included: advising a professional defence society/indemnifier upon a high value orthopaedic and anaesthetic negligence claim; advice in cases of severe drug reaction; advice in catastrophic injury overlying schizophrenia and alcohol dependency; advising upon claims against clinicians now out of the jurisdiction; coroners inquests; several personal injury claims arising from accidents on ships; costs disputes.
Professional Memberships: Professional Negligence Bar Association; North of England Medico-legal Society; Gray's Inn; North Eastern Circuit.
Career: Member, Bar Council Pupillage Portal Review Group; visiting lecturer and tutor to MSc in Conscious Sedation in Dentistry at the University of Newcastle upon Tyne; visiting lecturer to the Postgraduate Institute of Medicine and Dentistry at the Northern Deanery; Trinity Deputy Director of Pupil Training; Trinity Deputy Equality and Diversity Officer.

HILL, Rebecca
5 St Andrew's Hill, London
020 7332 5440
rebeccahill@5sah.co.uk
Featured in Extradition (London)
Practice Areas: Rebecca is an extradition expert having specialised in the field since 2007. She has extensive experience in prosecuting and defending requests at first instance and on appeal, as well as advising individuals at risk of extradition. Her breadth of experience is an asset in understanding cases from all angles and identifying innovative and novel points in the best interests of her clients. Whilst Rebecca has particular expertise in identifying and arguing points arising from the European Convention on Human Rights, Rebecca is also skilled in conducting technical and procedural arguments. Rebecca's strength lies in her ability to identify and efficiently convey the most complex legal arguments whilst retaining an approachability which puts clients, particularly those most vulnerable, at ease. Recent cases include Art 3 cases for the Appellants Parker v Argentina [2013] EWHC 226 and Agardi v Hungary [ongoing] and Netecza v Hungary [2014] EWHC 2098, a habeas application for the Respondent.

HILL, Thomas QC
Thirty Nine Essex Street, London
020 7832 1111
thomashill@39essex.com
Featured in Planning (London)
Practice Areas: Thomas Hill QC has more than 25 years' experience in the fields of planning, environmental, compulsory purchase and related administrative law. He is regularly instructed at public inquiries and in the High Court, acting for a wide variety of developers, local authorities and third party clients. His practice has for many years encompassed advocacy and advisory work in relation to major infrastructure - with particular emphasis on the airport (runway and terminal expansion), port (container port proposals, HROs and harbour dues litigation) and energy sectors (biofuels, EfW, wind and solar energy). He is also very familiar with the full range of issues relating to residential development (including both bringing forward strategic greenfield sites and complex brownfield redevelopment opportunities). Recent instructions include on-going appeal and advisory work for several UK airports, for Birmingham City Council on its Development Plan, numerous section 78 appeals for residential developers and housing associations, as well as appeal and advisory work for many private individuals, with particular emphasis on projects with complex design issues in London.
Professional Memberships: Planning and Environmental Bar Association Administrative Law Bar Association.
Career: Called to the Bar 1988, Year of Silk 2009.

HILL, Timothy QC
Stone Chambers, London
020 7440 6900
timothy.hill@stonechambers.com
Featured in Shipping (London)
Practice Areas: Timothy Hill QC has a broad commercial practice with particular expertise in all aspects of: shipping and maritime law including charterparties, bills of lading, contracts of affreightment etc., ship finance, shipbuilding, ship sale and purchase, collisions and salvage; international trade (CIF, C&F, FOB etc), sale of goods (domestic and international), commodities; marine insurance including hull, war risks, loss of use, mortgagees' interest, cargo, P&I etc; non-marine insurance; commercial litigation including joint ventures, distribution agreements, commercial agencies, and shareholders' agreements; banking and finance with particular expertise of the ISDA Master Agreement; arbitration (practice and procedure) and civil fraud. Timothy Hill QC also sits as a commercial Arbitrator and acts as a Mediator. He is recommended in Chambers & Partners and Legal 500 as a leading silk for both shipping and commodities and in Legal Experts for commercial litigation.

He is noted in these leading directories as an 'eminently respected' and 'excellent silk', a 'real star and advocate for the client' and for his involvement in 'heavyweight cases'.
Professional Memberships: COMBAR; LMAA Supporting Member; British Maritime Law Association; Chartered Institute of Arbitrators; CEDR-accredited mediator.

HILLIER, Nicolas
9 Gough Square, London
020 7832 0500
clerks@9goughsquare.co.uk
Featured in Personal Injury (London)
Practice Areas: Personal injury and professional (clinical and legal) negligence litigation, predominantly employers' liability and road traffic accident claims. Considerable experience in high value catastrophic injury and Fatal Accident Act work. Reported decisions of interest include Verlander v Rahman [2012] EWHC 1026 (serious brain injury claim about which there was substantial disagreement between the medical experts both as to consequences and, particularly, Mental Capacity), Connery v PHS [2011] EWHC 1685 (a Complex Regional Pain Syndrome developing as a consequence of a whiplash injury); Hardisty v Aubrey [2006] EWCA Civ 1196 (road traffic accident claim - the Court of Appeal reversing a finding of fact made erroneously by the trial judge upon an incomplete assessment of the totality of the evidence on the issue); Harris v BRB (Residuary) Ltd [2006] PIQR P10 (noise induced hearing loss claim - appeal on issues of noise exposure and use of hearing protection); Godbold v Mahmood [2006] PIQR Q5 (high value brain damage claim including a substantial periodical payments award); Pirelli General Plc v Gaca [2004] I WLR 2683 (employer's liability claim - appeal on issue of deduction of insurance receipts); Edmonds v Lloyds TSB Bank plc [2004] EWCA 1526 (employer's liability claim - appeal on issue of failure to mitigate loss).
Professional Memberships: PIBA; APIL.
Career: Called to the Bar in 1982. Joined Chambers in 1983.
Personal: LLB (Hons). Lives in London. Leisure pursuits: an energetic and demanding family, a general interest in most sports - now a (long!) retired rugby player, more recently a struggling golfer and still an all weather surfer!

HILLIER, Victoria
Civitas Law, Cardiff
0845 071 3007
victoria.hillier@civitaslaw.com
Featured in Administrative & Public Law (Wales & Chester)
Practice Areas: Victoria is regularly instructed to advise and represent local authorities and housing associations on a wide spectrum of housing claims including possession, anti social behaviour injunctions and the homelessness provisions. She specialises in claims raising issues under the Equality Act 2010 and is currently defending a number of claims for discrimination, victimisation and harassment against public bodies. Her practice also encompasses licensing appeals, planning matters and judicial review in the aforementioned areas. She has represented Police Authorities in a number of high profile inquests including deaths in custody and a double fatal shooting. This compliments Victoria's significant practice in defending civil actions against the Police, which incorporates unlawful arrests, false imprisonment, misfeasance in public office and employer liability claims. Victoria also has a busy personal injury practice.
Professional Memberships: Victoria was delighted to be appointed onto the Attorney General's List of Counsel and Welsh Assembly Government Panel in 2012. She receives regular instructions in this capacity on personal injury matters and a wide range of public law issues.
Career: Called to the Bar in 2005.
Personal: Victoria enjoys travelling, skiing, cycling, dancing and attending the gym.

HILLMAN, Gerard
Carmelite Chambers, London
020 7936 6300
ghillman@carmelitechambers.co.uk
Featured in Financial Crime (London)
Practice Areas: Complex fraud, confiscation, corporate liability, asset recovery, regulatory, health and safety, disciplinary tribunals and VAT and Duties Tribunal.
Professional Memberships: Criminal Bar Association, Gray's Inn, Inner Temple.
Career: Silva (multi-million pound fraud committed over long period by IFA); Suleman (multi-million pound MTIC fraud); Odia (£4m international advanced fee fraud); Coombs (principle defendant in multi-million pound duty evasion fraud); Ferrigan (SFO prosecution of a solicitor charged with a series of mortgage frauds valued in excess of £50 million); Breeze (chief executive of a private psychiatric hospital acquitted of multi-million pound fraud on NHS); Akinwolemiwa (accountant acquitted of fraud and money laundering); Poole (significant fraudulent trading by company director); Roope (SFO prosecution of multi-million pound international advance fee fraud); Vidgeon (SFO prosecution of £7 million boiler room fraud); Miah (major immigration fraud); Choudhury (multi-million pound boiler room fraud); Khan (£10 million pound mortgage fraud); Chahal (£15 million bank fraud); Bridden (£16 million money laundering proceeds of MTIC fraud); Zec (£15 million duty evasion); Smith (£15 million duty evasion); Bondswell (investment fraud by non regulated individual promoting CFDs / derivatives); Farrier (company fraud on the European Social Fund and the European Regional Development Fund); James (£15 million VAT fraud); Director of the Asset Recovery Agency v R. (asset recovery through the civil courts).

HILL-SMITH, Alexander
New Square Chambers, London
020 7419 7000
alex.hill-smith
@newsquarechambers.co.uk
Featured in Chancery (London)
Practice Areas: Property work including for large retail and industrial groups together with property-related professional negligence. Also does more general company and commercial work. Recent cases include Deir v Sheikh Fahad Al Athel and others[2011] EWHC 354, Thomas and others v Capita Trustees Limited and others [2012],Giles v Tarry [2012] EWCA Civ 837 and Martin Penny v Swift Advances Plc [2012].
Professional Memberships: Chancery Bar Association, Property Bar Association.
Career: Called to the Bar, Grays Inn, 1978 (Holt Scholar); Recorder 2005 to date, South Eastern Circuit, Civil and Crime.
Publications: Section on solicitors' negligence in Sweet & Maxwell Professional Negligence encyclopaedia. Article on "Rights of parking" in the Conveyancer commended by Lord Scott in the House of Lords in Jameson v Moncrieff. Article on Fraud and Land Registration in The Conveyancer, 2009.
Personal: Born 1955. Lives in London.

HINCHLIFFE, Thomas
Three New Square, London
020 7405 1111
hinchliffe@3newsquare.co.uk
Featured in Intellectual Property (London)
Practice Areas: All aspects of contentious intellectual property, with a particular emphasis on patent litigation in the pharmaceutical, biotechnology and mobile telephony fields. Recent notable cases include: Teva v AZ [2014]; Philips v Nintendo [2014]; AGA v Occlutech [2014]; HTC v Nokia [2014]; Janssen v Abbvie [2014]; Samsung v Apple [2013]; Glenmark v Wellcome [2013]; Generics v Yeda [2012]; Merck v Sigma [2012]; Warner-Lambert v Teva [2011]; Gedeon Richter v Bayer [2011]; Datacard v Eagle Technologies [2011]; Abbott v Medinol [2010]; RIM v Motorola [2010]; Scinopharm v Eli Lilly [2009]; Generics UK v Daiichi [2009]; Actavis v Merck [2008]; Generics v Lundbeck [2008]; Qualcomm v Nokia [2008]; Conor v Angiotech [2007].
Professional Memberships: Intellectual Property Bar Association; Chancery Bar Association.
Career: Called to the Bar 1997.
Personal: Brasenose College Oxford (1995 MA, Chemistry).

HINES, James
3 Raymond Buildings Barristers, London
020 7400 6400
james.hines@3rblaw.com
Featured in Extradition (London), Crime (London), Financial Crime (London)
Practice Areas: James Hines practises in crime, commercial fraud and extradition, principally defending. With over 30 years experience he specialises in cases which have both criminal and commercial/civil aspects particularly those with an international element. In 2012 James represented Silvio Berlusconi by live television link from London to his trial in Milan for offences of making corrupt payments to a UK based solicitor. He is currently instructed by the Serious Fraud Office in the LIBOR manipulation investigation. James has defended in numerous SFO trials and in several insider dealing cases, James is also instructed by the Competition and Markets Authority on cartel matters. In crime he has acted as both leading and junior counsel in all areas including international money laundering, corruption, murder, robbery, drugs. James has been practising in the field of extradition for many years Notable cases include Bermingham, Derby and Mulgrew "The Nat West Three" and the Tollman case. He has appeared in the Commercial Court and in the Court of Appeal Civil division on issues of contempt and self-incrimination, and in the QBD in respect of Civil Recovery arguing abuse/double jeopardy. He regularly provides strategic advice to clients during the investigation stage and specialises in acting for third parties in respect of witness summons, SFO s.2 notices and international cooperation (MLA). For some years he acted as outside criminal counsel for Microsoft.
Professional Memberships: Justice; Criminal Bar Association; Fraud Lawyer Association; Commonwealth Lawyers Association; Association of Regulatory & Disciplinary Lawyers. Extradition Lawyers Association, Proceeds of Crime Lawyers Association.
Career: LLB; Call 1982 Gray's Inn; Elected Member of the Bar Council, CBA Committee Member, Member of the Professional Practice Committee and the International Committee of the Bar Council.

HINKS, Frank QC
Serle Court, London
020 7242 6105
fhinks@serlecourt.co.uk
Featured in Chancery (London), Offshore (London), Trusts (London)
Practice Areas: Domestic and international trusts (including expert evidence) in relation to offshore jurisdictions including Hong Kong, Cayman, Bahamas, Bermuda and Jersey: Re Nina Wang Dec'd [2013] Hong Kong; BQ v DQ [2011] Bermuda; St. George v Hayward [2010] Bahamas; Brown v Executors of HRH Princess Margaret [2008] Re Ojjeh Trusts [1993] (Cayman Islands); Re 1995 and 1996 Trusts [1998] Washington State; Wight v Olswang [1999] (trustee exemption clauses); Flemmer v HRO [2000] Colorado. Re Chan Settlement (2001) (Hong Kong); Topham v Charles Topham Group Ltd (2002) (Rescue of tax freezer scheme); Partnership law: Kerr v Morris [1987]. Real property including landlord and tenant and commons: Crown Estate Commissioners v Roberts [2008]; Roberts v Swangrove Estates Ltd [2008]; Earl of Macclesfield v Beechwood Estates Company (2003) Proprietary estoppel; Mid-Glamorgan CC v Ogwr BC [1995] (commons). Dugan-Chapman v Grosvenor Estate Belgravia [1997] (leasehold enfranchisement), National Trust v Ashbrook [1997] (commons). Inspector and counsel in town and village green inquiries. Chancery and commercial litigation.
Professional Memberships: STEP, Chancery Bar Association, Association of Contentious Trust and Probate Specialists.
Career: Called to Bar in 1973. Joined present Chambers in 1974.
Personal: Educated at Bromley Grammar School; St Catherine's College, Oxford. BA 1st Class Hons; BCL 1st Class Hons.

HITCHCOCK, Patricia QC
Cloisters, London
020 7827 4000
phitchcock@cloisters.com
Featured in Clinical Negligence (London), Personal Injury (London)
Practice Areas: Clinical negligence, catastrophic injury, inquests, medical law, related administrative law and regulatory matters. Mediator, CEDR accredited 2003. Highlight case list on www.cloisters.com.
Professional Memberships: Action Against Medical Accidents (AvMA) Lawyers Group and Inquest Project; Bar Pro Bono Group; Inquest; Professional Negligence Bar Association; Personal Injury Bar Association; Centre for Dispute Resolution (CEDR) Exchange; Civil Mediation Council; MIND Legal Network.
Career: Non-fiction book editor for 10 years in UK and USA. Elected 'Mother' of the NUJ chapel at Hutchinson Books, discovered taste for advocacy. Called to the Bar 1988. Initial common law practice dominated by criminal defence (over 100 Crown Court trials), plus

personal injury, employment, discrimination and education law. Specialised in medical law 1996. Busy High Court and Appeals practice; regularly instructed in major multi-million pound cases on both liability and quantum, especially brain and spinal injury; cancer; psychiatric negligence; fatal accidents. Took silk 2011.

Publications: Co-author, Butterworths Personal Injury Litigation Service Division VI: Limitation (to 2014); Division XV: Claims of the Utmost Severity (forthcoming). Chapter author (Experts) for Clinical Negligence, ed. Lewis and Buchan (Bloomsbury Professional). Various articles.

Personal: Married to a sculptor, two adult children.

HOCKMAN, Stephen QC

6 Pump Court, London
020 7797 8400
qc@shed31.demon.co.uk

Featured in Environment (London), Health & Safety (London), Local Government (London)

Practice Areas: Principal areas of practice are regulatory, environmental, planning and administrative law. Regularly instructed by corporate and individual clients and by national and local government bodies in regulatory, environmental and health and safety matters.

Professional Memberships: Planning and Environment Bar Association, Administrative Law Bar Association, Health and Safety Lawyers Association.

Career: Called to the Bar in 1970 and began to practice at 6 Pump Court in 1971. Appointed Recorder 1987. Took Silk 1990. Leader SE Circuit, January 2001-December 2003. Chairman of the Bar Council, 2006. Visiting Professor of Law at City University.

Publications: Blackstone's Planning Practice.

Personal: Educated at Eltham College, London (1955-65) and Jesus College, Cambridge (1966-69). Born 4 January 1947. Lives in London, Peterborough and Paris.

HOCKTON, Andrew

Serjeants' Inn Chambers, London
020 7427 5000
ahockton@serjeantsinn.com

Featured in Clinical Negligence (London), Professional Discipline (London)

Practice Areas: Andrew Hockton was called to the Bar in 1984. Andrew specialises in clinical negligence and healthcare, professional discipline and regulatory, inquests and inquiries, Court of Protection and public and administrative law. An earlier edition notes that "he is a real star - not only a pleasure to work with but highly intelligent and unflappable with it." Please click on the link to the Serjeants' Inn Chambers website for his profile, which sets out full details of his practice including relevant work of note.

Professional Memberships: PNBA, COMBAR.

Publications: Law of Consent to Medical Treatment, Clinical Negligence: Powers & Harris 4th Ed (2003, Sweet & Maxwell) (Chapter on Consent).

Personal: City University: Diploma in Law, Balliol College, Oxford: BA (Classics scholarship), fluent in Spanish.

HODGETTS, Elizabeth

St Philips Chambers, Birmingham
0121 246 7000
ehodgetts@st-philips.com

Featured in Employment (Midlands)

Practice Areas: Practises exclusively in employment law. Clients include government bodies, local authorities including Birmingham City Council, universities, schools and private sector employers. Practice includes the full range of discrimination claims, equal pay claims, protected disclosure claims, and collective consultation work including s.189 TULCRA claims and large scale amendment of contractual terms. Regularly undertakes multi-week hearings, including, in 2014, two three week cases defending a major public sector employer against claims of race discrimination brought by groups of employees following successive competitive redundancy selection exercises. Cases include Birmingham City Council v Wetherill [2007] IRLR 781 (CA) and, in 2008-10, as leading junior instructed on behalf of Birmingham City Council, a high value group action arising out of the implementation of Single Status and measures designed to implement equal pay, including s.189 TULCRA claims brought by four trade unions, together with claims for unfair dismissal and breach of contract brought by over 1000 employees.

Professional Memberships: Employment Lawyers Association.

Career: Call 1998; appointed to Attorney General's Regional Panel of Counsel in 2012.

Publications: Contributor to 'Discrimination in Employment' Tucker and George (Sweet and Maxwell).

Personal: University of Oxford (Mansfield College) BA (Hons) MA Oxon (Exhibitioner).

HODGSON, Jane

Five Paper, London
020 7815 3200
janehodgson@fivepaper.com

Featured in Social Housing (London)

Practice Areas: Experience across the range of social housing and landlord and tenant work including: possession proceedings, succession claims, actions to restrain anti-social behaviour, disrepair claims, injunction proceedings, service charge disputes, homelessness appeals and judicial review.

Professional Memberships: Constitutional and Administrative Bar Association, Property Bar Association, Social Housing Law Association, London Common Law & Commercial Bar Association, Association of London Welsh Lawyers.

Career: Called to the Bar 2000. Advises and represents public and private sector clients, including local authorities, registered providers of social housing, private landlords, leaseholders and tenants.

Publications: Harassment and Anti-social Behaviour title of Atkin's Court Forms (2nd Ed), Vol 21 (2006 issue).

HODIVALA, Jamas

2 Bedford Row, London
020 7440 8888
jhodivala@2bedfordrow.co.uk

Featured in Professional Discipline (London)

Practice Areas: Regularly defends in the GMC, GDC and GOC, as well as representing police officers and sportsmen in disciplinary proceedings. Has gained considerable experience defending complex criminal cases (particularly fraud, bribery and corruption) and is able to skilfully cross-examine on highly specialised and detailed areas of expertise. Professional Discipline cases include: defending a practitioner facing 118 separate allegations arising from a Performance Assessment and successfully avoiding a finding of deficient professional performance; using expert psychological evidence in disciplinary proceedings to demonstrate that a practitioner had falsely confessed to an offence of dishonesty for which she had accepted a police caution, thereby avoiding any adverse sanction; avoiding a finding of "impairment" where an elderly patient had swallowed a metal hand file that a dental practitioner had accidentally dropped into her mouth; avoiding dismissal in a case where a police officer had not declared the fact she had been overpaid £60,000 over a period of 7 years and representing a cricketer in proceedings relating to spot-fixing. Also experienced in Judicial Review proceedings, including commercial judicial review of regulators' decisions.

Career: Called 1998.

HOGARTH, Andrew QC

12 King's Bench Walk, London
020 7583 0811
hogarth@12kbw.co.uk

Featured in Personal Injury (London)

Practice Areas: Specialist in industrial law, employment law and personal injuries with a particular interest in all forms of psychiatric damage litigation. Interesting cases include the stress cases of Veakins v Kier Islington, Hatton v Sutherland, Barber v Somerset County Council, Hartman v Southend and Bristol City Council v Deadman; the personal injury cases of Owens v Noble, Cooke v United Bristol Healthcare NHS Trust, Fairchild v Glenhaven and Page v Smith (Nos 1 and 2), the costs case of Drew v Whitbread, the insurance case of BT plc v Royal Mail group and numerous reported employment law cases including Marshalls Clay v Caulfield, Byrne Brothers v Baird and Bunce v Postworth.

Career: MA (Cantab). Called to the Bar 1974. Joined 12 King's Bench Walk in 1975. Head of Chambers at 12 King's Bench Walk since 2005.

Publications: Author: 'Asbestos Disease Litigation' (Butterworths 2004). Contributor: Munkman on Employers' Liability 14th, 15th and 16th Editions and PIBA handbook.

HOLBECH, Charles

New Square Chambers, London
020 7419 8000
charles.holbech
@newsquarechambers.co.uk

Featured in Chancery (London)

Practice Areas: Trusts, wills, probate, tax, court of protection, real property, landlord and tenant.

Professional Memberships: STEP, ACTAPS, Chancery Bar Association.

Publications: Halsbury's Laws of England, Inheritance Tax. Williams, Mortimer & Sunnucks, Executors, & Probate, 20th Ed., Ch. 50, Taxation of Personal Representatives.

HOLBROOK, Jon

Cornerstone Barristers, London
020 7242 4986
jonh@cornerstonebarristers.com

Featured in Social Housing (London)

Practice Areas: All aspects of social housing, property and public law (including community care and Court of Protection). Jon Holbrook built up a tenant-based practice during his 12 years at Garden Court Chambers and after two years at Hardwicke Building he joined Cornerstone Barristers in 2006 where he is now instructed mostly by landlords, local authorities and community care providers.

Professional Memberships: Administrative Law Bar Association (ALBA). Property Bar Association (PBA). Social Housing Law Association (SHLA). Jon instigated the formation of SHLA in 2005, an organisation he chaired until 2008.

Career: Before being called to the Bar in 1991 Jon was a local authority housing advisor and tenancy relations officer at Westminster City Council.

Publications: General Editor of the Housing & Property Law Review. Consultant Editor of the Journal of Community Care Law.

HOLDCROFT, Matthew

5 Essex Court, London
0207 410 2000
holdcroft@5essexcourt.co.uk

Featured in Police Law (All Circuits), Professional Discipline (London)

Practice Areas: Public law, tortious actions, discipline and regulatory work and human rights. Matthew's practice includes work for both public authorities and private clients. Recent high profile work includes appearing in the Hillsborough and Raoul Moat inquests, the PC Harwood (Ian Tomlinson) discipline hearing and advising in relation to aspects of the Jimmy Savile investigation. Matthew's advisory work covers a wide range of areas from safety and security of nuclear installations, fatal accidents, shootings, police actions (all aspects), personal injury litigation and regulatory and disciplinary investigations and hearings. Recent public law cases include, R (on the application of the Chief Constable of West Yorkshire) v Independent Police Complaints Commission [2013] EWHC 2698 (Admin), R (on the application of Commissioner of Police of the Metropolis) v Police Appeals Tribunal [2013] EWHC 1684 (Admin), R (on the application of Lee) v Chief Constable of Essex [2012] EWHC 283 (Admin) and R on the application of L v Commissioner of Police of the Metropolis and the Secretary of State for the Home Department and Liberty [2009] UKSC 3.

Professional Memberships: ALBA, PIBA, ARDL.

Career: Called to the Bar in 1998.

Publications: Matthew regularly writes articles for a number of publications and lectures on all areas and aspects of his practice.

HOLL-ALLEN, Jonathan

Serjeants' Inn Chambers, London
0207 457 5000
jholl-allen@3serjeantsinn.com

Featured in Clinical Negligence (London), Professional Discipline (London)

Practice Areas: Jonathan Holl-Allen was called to the Bar in 1990. Jonathan specialises in clinical negligence and healthcare, professional discipline, inquests and inquiries, police and employment law. An earlier edition notes that "he is an excellent advocate. Commentators say that he is highly professional, very steady and adept at advising across a range of issues" and that "he is very knowledgeable and thorough in his approach. He spends time on cases and puts in a lot of hard work - you can trust his advice." Please click on the link above to the Serjeants' Inn Chambers website for his profile, which sets out full details of his practice including relevant work of note.

Professional Memberships: PNBA, ARDL.

Publications: Principles of Medical Law (co-author of chapter on Regulation of Healthcare Professions); Contributing Editor to Medical Law Reports since 1999.

HOLLAND, Charles
Trinity Chambers, Newcastle upon Tyne
0191 232 1927
c.holland@trinitychambers.co.uk
Featured in Commercial Dispute Resolution (North Eastern), Licensing (North Eastern)
Practice Areas: Busy and well-established chancery/commercial practice, with particular emphasis on business and property matters. He aims to provide pragmatic, business-focused resolutions to disputes, with advice delivered promptly in user-friendly terms. Well known nationally as a specialist licensing advocate and has acted in a large number of licensing applications relating to a wide range of venues and events. Many years' experience in lap dancing applications, now regulated as Sexual Entertainment Venues. Frequently appears in firearms matters. Active taxi licensing practice representing both operators and local authorities. Practice involves a significant amount of work in the Administrative Court, where Charles also conducts public law Judicial Review cases largely concerning local authorities.
Professional Memberships: North Eastern Circuit; Institute of Licensing; Chancery Bar Association.
Career: Junior Counsel to the Crown (Provincial Panel) 2003-2007. A workshop leader on the Bar Vocational Course at Northumbria University. Regularly presents seminars to local authority clients on licensing and social housing matters.

HOLLAND, Jordan
5 Stone Buildings, London
020 7242 6201
clerks@5blaw.com
Featured in Court of Protection (All Circuits)
Practice Areas: General Chancery practice with an emphasis on contentious probate, family provision, trusts and property disputes and professional negligence related to all areas in which he practises. Regularly instructed for both claimants and defendants, Jordan has significant trial experience. He recently appeared for the successful claimant in Watts v Watts [2014] EWHC 668 (Ch) where he proved a will to be a forgery. His Court of Protection practice is especially strong and he acted for the successful applicant in Re M (N v O&P) [2013] WTLR 681 and in Re BM [2014] All ER (D) 178. He has a particular expertise in art and cultural property matters, having successfully appeared in Avrora Fine Arts Investment v Christie, Manson & Woods Ltd [2012] PNLR 35. He frequently acts for dealers, collectors, galleries and institutions, often in cases involving an international element. Jordan also has a notable offshore practice, especially in the Channel Islands.
Professional Memberships: Chancery Bar Association, PAIAM (Professional Advisors to the International Art Market), Institute of Art and Law.
Career: Called 2009.
Publications: Regular contributor to specialist journals. Lectures on all areas of his practice, including Court of Protection and art and cultural property matters.

HOLLINGTON, Robin QC
New Square Chambers, London
020 7419 8000
robin.hollington@newsquarechambers.co.uk
Featured in Company (London), Offshore (London), Restructuring/Insolvency (London)
Practice Areas: Principal areas of work are company law, shareholder disputes, insolvency and chancery litigation - in UK and abroad: including Cayman Islands, BVI and Hong Kong. He has appeared in many leading cases in his field in the Court of Appeal, House of Lords/Supreme Court and Privy Council, and has much experience of litigation with strong cross-border and asset-protection features (including appointment of provisional liquidators), most recently the long running UK High Court litigation concerning Beppler & Jacobson Limited and Cayman litigation concerning the NYSE-listed company, Ambow Education Holding Ltd.
Professional Memberships: Chancery Bar Association; MCIArb; Bencher of Lincoln's Inn.
Career: MA (Oxon) Jurisprudence 1977; LLM (University of Pennsylvania) 1978; Called to the Bar 1979; QC 1999; Recorder 2004; Deputy High Court Judge 2013; Head of New Square Chambers 2010-2014.
Publications: Author of 'Shareholders' Rights' (Sweet & Maxwell, latest edition 7th ed 2013); 'Oppression of Minority Shareholders - Reflections on Blisset v Daniel' Denning Law Journal 2007 Vol 19 p 5.
Personal: Educated at Haileybury and University College, Oxford. Married with one son; principal leisure interests: tennis and golf.

HOLMES, Josh
Monckton Chambers, London
020 7405 7211
jholmes@monckton.com
Featured in Competition/European Law (London), Telecommunications (London)
Practice Areas: EU, Competition and Telecommunications.
Career: Josh is a senior junior with a practice that covers all aspects of EU law, competition law and regulatory dealing. He is twice winner of the Chambers Competition/EU Junior of the Year award (in 2011 and 2013) and is recognised by Chambers UK as a leader in his fields of practice. He appears regularly before regulators and Courts in the UK and EU, and advises a wide range of clients from major multinationals to small firms and regulators in a number of jurisdictions.
Personal: MA (Oxon) – first class; BCL (Oxon); LLM Harvard.

HOLTHAM DEN BESTEN, Ruth
Serle Court, London
020 7242 6105
rdenbesten@serlecourt.co.uk
Featured in Chancery (London), Commercial Dispute Resolution (London), Company (London), Fraud (London)
Practice Areas: Commercial and chancery litigation; civil fraud; personal and corporate insolvency; professional negligence (solicitors). Cases include BTA v Ablyazov & Ors; Re Coroin; Belltrey Corporation v Newcote International; Lexi Holdings v Pannone & Partners; Lexi Holdings v Luqman and SFO v Lexi Holdings (fraud); Lesini & Ors v Westrip Holdings Ltd (company) Kamos Finanz v SLEC (commercial); Addax Bank v Wellesley LLP; Mobilx Ltd v HMRC (VAT fraud); the TAG Litigation (professional negligence and insurance); Al-Rawas v Pegasus Energy Limited (injunctive relief).
Professional Memberships: Chancery Bar Association, Commercial Bar Association.
Career: Jesus College, Oxford; City University, London (Dip Law); 2001-02 McCarthy Tetrault (Canada, Fox Scholarship); 2002-03 Peters & Peters.

HOLWILL, Derek
Hailsham Chambers, London
020 7643 5000
derek.holwill@hailshamchambers.com
Featured in Clinical Negligence (London), Professional Negligence (London)
Practice Areas: Professional and clinical negligence. Also commercial and insurance litigation; and general common law work. Cases include Nationwide v Davisons (CA - mortgage lender's claim against solicitors for breach of trust); Mulcahy v Castles (CA – alleged under-settlement claim against solicitors); McManus Seddon Runhams v European Risk (CA - block notification to professional indemnity insurers); Short & others v Sigma (group claim for investment losses against IFAs); Wolstenholmes v Hockleys (solicitors' contribution claim against valuers in multiple claims); Mortgage Express v Connells (multiple mortgage lender's claims against valuers) Watkins v Jones Maidment Wilson (CA - limitation - application of Sephton); Law Society v Sephton & Co (HL - limitation; accrual of cause of action in negligence); Abbott v Will Gannon & Smith (CA - limitation; architects); Abbey National v Gouldman (contribution claims); Tippet v Guys and St Thomas' (clinical negligence – cerebral palsy claim); TSB v Robert Irving and Burns (CA - conflicts of interest).
Professional Memberships: Professional Negligence Bar Association (PNBA).
Career: Called 1982.
Personal: Leisure pursuits include Lindy Hop and scuba diving.

HONEY, Richard
Francis Taylor Building, London
020 7353 8415
clerks@ftb.eu.com
Featured in Agriculture & Rural Affairs (London), Environment (London), Local Government (London), Planning (London)
Practice Areas: Richard Honey practises in public and environmental law, with particular specialisms in judicial review and High Court challenges, infrastructure projects, compulsory purchase, compensation and land valuation, and commons and village greens. Recent work includes DCOs, HS2, Crossrail, Olympics, Thameslink, West Coast Route Modernisation, airport expansions, highway schemes and wind farms. Environmental work includes contaminated land, protected habitats and species, civil liability for pollution and environmental crime. Acts as party representative in mediation and sits as an inspector in village green cases. Recent cases include: Manchester Ship Canal [2014] UKSC 40, Ramac v Kent CC [2014] UKUT 109 (LC), R (Eaton) v Natural England [2013] Env LR 37, Colman v SSCLG [2013] JPL 1351, Mata v SSCLG [2013] JPL 545, Koumis v SSCLG [2013] JPL 215, Listing Officer v Callear [2013] RVR 34, Harringay Meat Traders v SSCLG [2013] PTSR 436.
Professional Memberships: Planning and Environment Bar Association, Administrative Law Bar Association, Bar European Group, UK Environmental Law Association, Environmental and Planning Law Association of Northern Ireland, Compulsory Purchase Association, National Infrastructure Planning Association.
Career: Called to the Bar at Inner Temple (2003) and Northern Ireland (2013). Attorney General's panel of junior counsel to the Crown. Visiting lecturer, King's College London. Chartered Surveyor. Fellow of the Chartered Institute of Arbitrators.
Publications: Editor, Gadsden on Commons & Greens. Editor, Journal of Planning & Environmental Law. Contributor, Law of Regulatory Sanctions and Enforcement. Contributor, Burnett-Hall on Environmental Law.

HOOD, Nigel
New Square Chambers, London
020 7419 8000
nigel.hood@newsquarechambers.co.uk
Featured in Chancery (London), Fraud (London)
Practice Areas: Commercial/Chancery litigation with a particular emphasis on civil fraud, breach of fiduciary duty and various forms of interim asset protection and recovery (including freezing, search and disclosure orders). As part of his civil fraud practice, Nigel has appeared in several of the largest fraud cases in recent years, recently appearing as Junior Counsel for the Claimant, JSC BTA Bank in its widely reported 45 day Commercial Court fraud trial in which it recovered damages exceeding $2b: JSC BTA Bank v Ablyazov & Others [2013] EWHC 510. During the last year, Nigel has also represented the Defendant in a £100 million cross border fraud/conspiracy claim and the Claimant in a $10 million deceit/breach of trust and conspiracy claim involving bogus financial instruments. Nigel's commercial litigation practice includes LCIA arbitrations, contractual disputes, unfair prejudice and other shareholder actions, actions against directors and trustees, claims involving guarantees and indemnities, professional negligence claims and insolvency matters. Other recent notable cases include: CMCS Common Market Commercial Services v Taylor [2011] PNLR 17; Shah v Shah [2010] EWHC 313, [2011] 1 P.&C.R. DG19 (CA); 4ENG v Harper & Others (No. 2) [2010] 1 BCLC 176; 4ENG v Harper & Others [2009] Ch 91; Portsmouth City Football Club Limited v HMRC [2010] EWHC 75 (Ch); Independent Trustee Services Limited v GP Noble Trustees Limited [2009] EWHC 161 (Ch); Zabihi v Janzemini [2009] EWCA Civ 851 (CA), [2008] EWHC 2910 (Ch). Islamic Investment Company of the Gulf (Bahamas) Ltd v Symphony Gems NV [2008] EWCA Civ 389.
Professional Memberships: Chancery Bar Association.
Career: Nigel was called to the Bar in 1993.

HOOPER, Ben
11KBW, London
020 7632 8500
ben.hooper@11kbw.com
Featured in Administrative & Public Law (London), Civil Liberties & Human Rights (London), Data Protection (London)
Practice Areas: Public and human rights law, regulatory law and information law. Recent / ongoing cases include Kennedy v. Information Commissioner (Supreme Court), R (Barclays) v. Lord Chancellor (Supreme Court), ITV v. Pensions Regulator

(Court of Appeal) and Liberty and others v. GCHQ and others (Investigatory Powers Tribunal). Particular interest in regulatory work - acting for and against regulators - and in commercial judicial review more generally. Extensive information law practice covering data protection, data breaches, PECR, Article 8 privacy rights and surveillance / RIPA, including in the telecommunications sector.
Professional Memberships: Constitutional and Administrative Law Bar Association; Association of Regulatory and Disciplinary Lawyers; Procurement Lawyers Association.
Career: Called to the Bar in 2000. Appointed to the Treasury A Panel in 2012 (previously on both the B and C Panels).
Publications: "Proportionality and the form of law" (2003) 119 LQR 426; contributor to Supperstone, Goudie & Walker on Judicial Review.
Personal: Balliol College, Oxford (scholar; First Class Hons Physics and Philosophy) and City University (Dipl in Law). Also a professional sculptor.

HOPKINS, Adrian QC
Serjeants' Inn Chambers, London
020 7353 0425
adrianhopkinsqc@serjeantsinn.com
Featured in Clinical Negligence (London), Professional Discipline (London)
Practice Areas: Adrian Hopkins QC was called to the Bar in 1984 and took silk in 2003. Adrian specialises in clinical negligence and healthcare, inquests and inquiries and professional discipline and regulatory law. An earlier edition notes that he has "the ability to really drive a case through to maximise the return for a client" and "the great capacity to make the difficult straightforward." Please click on the link to the Serjeants' Inn Chambers website for his profile, which sets out full details of his practice including relevant work of note.
Professional Memberships: PNBA, LCLCBA.
Publications: Contributing editor of Medical Law Reports.
Personal: 1980-83 St. Peter's College, Oxford University (Exhibitioner 1980-83) BA (Hons) in Jurisprudence.

HOPKINS, Robin
11KBW, London
020 7632 8500
robin.hopkins@11kbw.com
Featured in Data Protection (London)
Practice Areas: Information rights specialist (data protection, privacy, FOI, EIR) also practising in public and local government law. Co-edits the Information Law Reports and Panopticon blog. Teaches privacy and data protection at University of Winchester. Regularly acts for the Information Commissioner. Has appeared in leading data protection cases e.g. Southern Pacific Personal Loans [2013] EWHC 2485 (Admin) (commercial insolvency); Edem [2014] EWCA Civ 92 (Court of Appeal on definition of 'personal data'). Appeared in leading data breach, privacy and monetary penalty cases, e.g. Niebel GIA/177/2014 (privacy and direct marketing). Highly experienced in information-sharing, subject access requests, surveillance, data protection compensation claims. Regularly appears in leading and high-profile FOI and EIR cases, e.g. IPSA [2014] UKUT 33 (AAC) (MPs' expenses); Lend Lease (EA/2013/0162) (property developer's financial viability assessment); APPGER [2012] 1 Info LR 258 (security services, international relations; extraordinary rendition); Thornton (High Speed 2; ministerial veto).
Professional Memberships: LCLBA; Ecclesiastical Law Society.
Career: Called 2008; Treasury C Panel.
Publications: Co-edits Law Society's Freedom of Information Handbook (2012); 'expert commentator' at Freedom of Information Journal.
Personal: Grew up in South Africa; came to UK (Exeter College, Oxford) as a Rhodes Scholar; degrees in finance, PPE, theology.

HOPPER, Stephen
5 Paper Buildings, London
020 7583 6117
sjh@5pb.co.uk
Featured in Financial Crime (London)
Practice Areas: Stephen's practice is a mixture of criminal defence, criminal prosecution and professional discipline. His work covers the full range of criminal offences with particular emphasis on financial crime. Recent cases have included the prosecution of an NHS Cancer trust fraud (leading junior), £80 million missing trader fraud, large scale benefit fraud and £12 million organised excise fraud. In addition to his criminal work, Stephen appears at hearings before the disciplinary tribunal of the Association of Chartered Certified Accountants.

HORNE, Michael
Serjeants' Inn Chambers, London
020 7427 5000
mh@serjeantsinn.com
Featured in Clinical Negligence (London)
Practice Areas: Michael Horne was called to the Bar in 1992. Michael specialises in clinical negligence and healthcare, professional discipline, inquiries and inquests and Court of Protection. An earlier edition notes that "he is an immensely experienced and knowledgeable clinical negligence counsel and a particularly impressive negotiator" and that "he has stacks of confidence and experience, and grasps the issues in a case very quickly." Please click on the link above to the Serjeants' Inn Chambers website for his profile, which sets out full details of his practice including relevant work of note.
Professional Memberships: PNBA, LCLBA.
Publications: LS Law Medical reports, contributing editor.

HORNE, Wilson
Kings Chambers, Manchester
0845 034 3444
clerks@kingschambers.com
Featured in Real Estate Litigation (Northern)
Practice Areas: All aspects of property law with a bias towards commercial work. Extensive experience of planning and construction law. Particular non-contentious experience of planning clawback and overage. Commercial law including construction, banking, partnership/shareholder, and sports disputes, particularly agency disputes. Extensive experience of Premier League and FA arbitrations. Professional liability within the above practice areas, with a particular emphasis on lawyers, surveyors, construction professionals and accountants. Dispute resolution experience includes extensive trial work in Court/arbitration, and mediation.
Professional Memberships: Chancery Bar Association, Northern Circuit Chancery Bar Association, Northern Circuit Commercial Bar Association.
Career: University of Leeds LLB (Hons), Called 1992 (Lincoln's Inn). Regularly accepts direct access and licensed access instructions.

HORNETT, Stuart
Selborne Chambers, London
020 7420 9500
stuart.hornett@selbronechambers.co.uk
Featured in Chancery (London), Real Estate Litigation (London)
Practice Areas: Stuart practice comprises commercial chancery, property and professional negligence.
Professional Memberships: Chancery Bar Association; Property Bar Association.
Career: Stuart has reported cases in all fields and regularly acts and advises in large and complex commercial and property matters. Recent cases include: JSC BTA Bank v Solodchenko & Ors; Kearns Brothers Ltd v Hova Developments Ltd [2012] EWHC 2968 (Ch) (property and joint venture dispute); Westcoast (Holdings) Ltd v Wharf Land (Subsidiary No.1) Ltd [2012] (CA) (shareholder dispute); National Westminster Bank Plc v Alfano [2012] EWHC 1020 (QB) (acting for bank on guarantee claim; United Marine Aggregates Ltd v GM Welding & Engineering Ltd [2012] EWHC 779 (fire and insurance warranty claim), pending in CA.

HOUGH, Jonathan QC
4 New Square, London
020 7822 2000
j.hough@4newsquare.com
Featured in Consumer Law (London), Inquests & Public Inquiries (London), Insurance (London)
Practice Areas: Principal areas of practice are: insurance and reinsurance; professional liability; commercial and consumer law; administrative law. Within the field of insurance law, work ranges from substantial coverage disputes to litigation and arbitration between insurers, reinsurers, brokers and coverholders. Experienced with most classes of risk, including: general commercial liability; property; motor; professional indemnity; legal expenses; trade credit; D&O; title insurance; employers' liability; personal accident; financial risk. Non-contentious drafting work, including policy wordings and binding authority agreements, is also covered. Professional liability practice covers mainly solicitors, barristers, financial professionals, insurance brokers, surveyors / valuers. Public and administrative law practice involves judicial review and advisory work covering local government, professional discipline and commercial regulation. Special expertise in the law relating to coroners. Acting as counsel to the inquiry in the following major inquests: Hillsborough Stadium Disaster; Diana, Princess of Wales; de Menezes (Stockwell Shooting); Potters Bar and Grayrigg rail disasters; explosion on the nuclear submarine HMS Tireless. Special expertise in the law of consumer credit, and has appeared in several of the leading recent appellate cases in the field. Notable recent cases include: Coles v Hetherton (RSA motor claims lead cases) [2013] Lloyd's Rep IR 9; Network Rail Infrastructure v Conarken Group [2012] 1 All ER (Comm) 692; Persimmon Homes v Great Lakes Reinsurance [2011] Lloyd's Rep IR 101; Parkinson Engineering Services v Swan [2010] PNLR 17; R (Lewis) v HM Coroner for Shropshire [2010] 1 WLR 1836; Heath v Southern Pacific Mortgages [2010] Ch 254; Temple Legal Protection Ltd v QBE Insurance (Europe) Ltd [2009] Lloyd's Rep IR 544.
Professional Memberships: PNBA; LCLCBA; ALBA; COMBAR.
Career: Called to the Bar 1997. Took silk 2014.
Publications: Contributing editor of Jackson & Powell on Professional Liability (7th edn.).
Personal: Educated at Bradford Grammar School and St Hugh's College Oxford (first in classics). Queen Mother scholar, Middle Temple. Graded outstanding on Bar course.

HOWARTH, Simon
Hailsham Chambers, London
020 7643 5000
simon.howarth@hailshamchambers.com
Featured in Professional Negligence (London)
Practice Areas: Professional negligence (especially concerning lawyers, financial advisers, accountants and construction professionals), commercial litigation, construction and insurance law (including coverage issues and subrogated recovery actions). He is recognised as a leading junior in professional negligence work. He is admitted to practice in the Republic of Ireland, and in the DIFC in Dubai.
Publications: He is a lecturer to solicitors and insurers on his specialist areas and has contributed articles to several professional journals including the Law Society Gazette. He is the co-author of the chapter on Insurance Brokers in Ter Haar and Levene on Construction Contracts and Construction Insurance.
Personal: Education: Grays Inn Mould Scholar and Advocacy Prize; Magdalen College Oxford.

HOWE, Martin QC
8 New Square, London
020 7405 4321
martin.howe@8newsquare.co.uk
Featured in Information Technology (London), Intellectual Property (London), Media & Entertainment (London)
Practice Areas: Barrister (QC) specialising in Intellectual Property, Information Technology and European Union law both relating to IP and other fields such as free movement of goods and services and regulatory and public law. Many high technology cases, with particular emphasis on computing, information technology and internet fields; also extensive experience in biotechnology/ genetic engineering cases. Regular appearances in the ECJ, Luxembourg, and the European Patent Office, Munich. Recent cases include: RFU v Viagogo (UK Supreme Court), SAS v WPL (ECJ Grand Chamber and Court of Appeal), Nintendo v PC Box (ECJ on reference from Milan). For comprehensive CV visit website at www.8newsquare.co.uk.
Professional Memberships: Intellectual Property Bar Association (IPBA); Bar European Group (BEG); The Intellectual Property Lawyers Organisation (TIPLO).
Career: Called 1978. QC 1996. Worked for IBM (UK), computer and engineering contract programmer 1976-78. Member, govt Commission on a Bill of Rights for the UK, 2011-12.
Publications: Halsbury's Laws on Trade Marks, 'Trade Names and Designs'; 'Russell-Clarke and Howe on Industrial Designs' (6th, 7th and 8th edn).

Personal: Born 1955. Educated at Trinity Hall, Cambridge (1977 BA Engineering and Law, 1979 MA).

HOWE, Timothy QC
Fountain Court Chambers, London
020 7583 3335
th@fountaincourt.co.uk
Featured in Banking & Finance (London), Commercial Dispute Resolution (London), Energy & Natural Resources (London), Fraud (London), Insurance (London), International Arbitration (London), Professional Negligence (London), Telecommunications (London)

Practice Areas: Specialising in domestic and international commercial litigation and arbitration, with particular expertise in: banking and financial services, energy and natural resources, oil and gas, international cross-border disputes, insurance and reinsurance, corporate mergers, acquisitions and disposals, joint ventures, telecoms, professional negligence and civil fraud and asset recovery. Recent cases include LIBOR litigation against global investment banks, Lehman Brothers Administration, Madoff fraud proceedings; Icelandic banking crisis; UK Bank Charges litigation; Box Clever securitisation; Masri Yemen oil & gas litigation; 9/11 WTC & Hurricane Katrina reinsurance claims; Eurotunnel restructuring; litigation relating to AIG, Enron, Parmalat, Polly Peck, Split Capital Trusts, UK pension mis-selling, Film Finance insurance, the PA LMX spiral, and HIH Group; US Asbestos & Pollution losses in the London insurance/reinsurance markets.
Professional Memberships: COMBAR Executive Committee (since 2000). CEDR Accredited Mediator (2004). Chairman, Bar Council Member Services Board (2008). ISDA Credit Derivatives Determinations Committee Pool Member (since 2011).
Career: Called 1987. Bermudian Bar 1998. Queen Mother's, Harmsworth, Astbury Senior Scholarships, Middle Temple, Silk 2008.
Publications: Co-author, 'Law of Bank Payments', 'Commercial Court Procedure'.
Personal: St Paul's School, Magdalen College, Oxford (1st Class Hons 1985). Languages: French and Italian.

HOWELL WILLIAMS, Craig QC
Francis Taylor Building, London
020 7353 8415
chw@ftb.eu.com
Featured in Planning (London)

Practice Areas: Craig Howell Williams QC specialises in planning, environment and related areas of public law. He is acknowledged as one of the leading practitioners in the field and has acted in some of the most high profile cases. He represents developers and operators, local authorities, third parties and others at public inquiries and in a range of other tribunals. He is regularly involved in large planning and /infrastructure schemes including proposals for new settlements, urban extensions, airport expansions, road and rail projects, reservoirs and also in employment, leisure, retail and other commercial development projects. His experience encompasses many different legislative regimes, including: heritage and listed buildings, compulsory purchase and compensation, applications under the Wildlife and Countryside legislation, advertisement regulations and aggregates levy. In court he served as Junior Treasury Counsel (B Panel) and has appeared in a number of significant cases. He is also a CEDR Accredited Mediator.
Professional Memberships: Planning and Environment Bar Association; UKELA, Parliamentary Bar Mess; National Infrastructure Planning Association; Compulsory Purchase Association; Chartered Institute of Arbitrators; RICS Mediation Panel; Chartered Institute of Arbitrators.
Career: Called to Bar: 1983, QC: 2009. MCIArb (2013). DCLG Planning Services Mediation Panel (2013). Lead Assistant Commissioner to the Boundary Commission for England (2013). Junior Counsel to the Crown (B Panel) (1993-99). Chairman of the London Luton Airport Consultative Committee (S35 Civil Aviation Act 1982) (1999-2002). Accredited Mediator (CEDR 2005), RICS Mediation Panel (2010).

HOWELLS, Chris
Civitas Law, Cardiff
0845 071 3007
christopher.howells@civitaslaw.com
Featured in Employment (Wales & Chester)

Practice Areas: Chris specialises in employment law. He is experienced at conducting cases across the spectrum of employment law issues ranging from routine unfair dismissal claims to discrimination claims on all of the prohibited grounds. Chris is also regularly instructed to deal with sometimes complex TUPE cases, particularly involving insolvent employers.
Professional Memberships: Employment Lawyers' Association; PIBA; Wales and Chester Circuit.
Career: Called to the Bar in 1999. Chris joined Civitas Law, Cardiff in 2010 as a member of their Employment and Personal Injury Practice Groups. Appointed to the Equality and Human Right Commission Preferred Counsel Panel during 2010.
Personal: Educated at Atlantic College; UCL (LLB); Cambridge (MA). Leisure interests include football and water sports. Chris is fluent in French.

HOWELLS, James QC
Atkin Chambers, London
020 7404 0102
clerks@atkinchambers.com
Featured in Construction (London), Energy & Natural Resources (London), Information Technology (London), International Arbitration (London)

Practice Areas: Construction, engineering and IT disputes both domestic and international with experience of litigation, arbitration and other forms of dispute resolution. Experience in engineering disputes has included a number of energy-related cases involving, amongst other things, oil and gas production platforms and rigs, FPSOs, gas storage caverns, combined power and desalination plant, power station/dams. Extensive experience of domestic and international infrastructure projects include metro and heavy rail, roads and airports. IT experience includes commercial and technical disputes in respect of projects ranging from small to medium size commercial systems and software to major government infrastructure projects. International arbitration experience in building, engineering and IT disputes in Hong Kong, Thailand, Russia, Oman, Continental Europe, Philippines, Indonesia, Australia, UAE, South Africa, Channel Islands, India and Tanzania.
Professional Memberships: TECBAR, LCLCBA, Combar, Society of Construction Law, Society for Computers and Law.
Career: Silk 2014.
Publications: Editor of 'Building Law Reports', Contributing Editor of Hudson's Building and Engineering Contracts 12th edition.
Personal: MA (Cantab), BCL (Oxon).

HOWELLS, Katherine
Old Square Chambers, London
020 7269 0300
khowells@oldsquare.co.uk
Featured in Travel (London)

Practice Areas: Specialises in personal injury, travel and aviation. Extensive experience acting for both claimants and defendants in fast and multi-track cases. Particular focus on high-value road traffic or workplace accidents together with occupiers and public liability claims. Involved in multi-party litigation, claims involving the MIB, fatal accident and high value head and spinal cord injury claims. Particular specialist knowledge of and interest in travel and aviation matters including accidents overseas, claims under the Package Travel Regulations, Montreal Convention passenger injury and delay and baggage claims, accidents on board aircraft or at airports or airfields and delayed and denied boarding and downgrading claims under European Regulation No. 261/2004. Also experienced in dealing with aviation maintenance disputes and IATA Ground Handling Agreements.
Professional Memberships: PIBA, TATLA.
Career: Called to the Bar in 1994.

HUBBARD, Mark
New Square Chambers, London
020 7419 8000
mark.hubbard
@newsquarechambers.co.uk
Featured in Chancery (London), Fraud (London), Offshore (London)

Practice Areas: Commercial and traditional chancery litigation and advice, offshore/international litigation, civil fraud, financial business crime, trust, estates and company law cases, asset tracing and insolvency. Mark has particular experience of litigation in the Bahamas, the Isle of Man, Guernsey and Jersey and . He is the author of thea new international practitioners' text book, Protectors of Trusts (Oxford University Press, 2013). His recent reported and interesting cases include Rusant v Traxys Far East [2013] All ER (D) 236 (Dec) (insolvency, arbitration); Mosley v Popely [2013] WTLR 521 (dishonest assistance), Davenport v Cream Holdings [2012] EWHC 787 (ch) (share valuation, abuse of process), Re Nordea Trust Company [2010] WTLR 1393 (duties of trustees) and Howell v Lees-Millais (2009) 2 P & CR D60 (construction of trusts). In 2009 he also He appeared in the Manx criminal case R v Baines & anor (money laundering, involving the transfer of $175m) and acted in the well-known high-value Jersey contentious trust case Alhamrani v Alhamrani. Mark's earlier cases include A v B [2007] 1 All ER 591 (Comm) (arbitration, trusts), Soutzas v Asombang [2008] All ER (D) 16 (injunctions), X v A [2006] 1 WLR 741 (powers of trustees); Grace v Biagioli [2006] BCC 82 CA (unfair prejudice), Malcolm v Benedict Mackenzie [2005]1 WLR 1238 CA (pensions, insolvency, human rights), the Poyiadjis litigation, e.g. AG v Poyiadjis [2003-05] MLR 198, where Mark represented Manx trustees in a complex high value trust and fraud claim; Union Discount v Zoller [2002] 1 WLR 1517 CA (commercial contracts) and Carr-Glynn v Frearsons [1997] 2 All ER 614 CA (professional negligence, wills).
Professional Memberships: Chancery Bar Association, COMBAR, STEP, ACTAPS, Commercial Fraud Lawyers Association.
Career: Called 1991. Licensed Advocate of the Isle of Man Bar since 2003 on case by case basis. Member of Bar Standard's Board Prosecuting Panel. Lectures internationally on trusts, conflicts of laws and related topics.
Publications: Protectors of Trusts (OUP 2013), 1st edition of a new international practitioners work. When 'fraud' does not unravel all: the limits of the doctrine of dishonest assistance in a breach of trust and the decision in Mosley v Popley, Trusts & Trustees (2013) 19 (10): 992-995. More about Schmidt, TQR June 2014.
Personal: Married with two children.

HUBBLE, Ben QC
4 New Square, London
020 7822 2032
b.hubble@4newsquare.com
Featured in Insurance (London), Offshore (London), Professional Discipline (London), Professional Negligence (London)

Practice Areas: Professional liability claims and disciplinary proceedings involving accountants and auditors, actuaries, directors, insurance brokers, lawyers and tax advisers, as well as general commercial litigation (both onshore and offshore), particularly banking, financial services and insurance. Substantial expertise in multi-party litigation, post credit crunch claims and tax schemes.
Professional Memberships: Professional Negligence Bar Association (vice chair), COMBAR , Chancery Bar Association.
Career: Called to the Bar in 1992. Appointed QC in 2009. Appointed Head of Chambers in 2013. Nominated for Chambers & Partners' Professional Negligence QC of the Year for 2012 and 2013. Chambers & Partners' Professional Negligence Junior of the Year in both 2006 and 2008.
Publications: Chapter on insurance brokers in 'Jackson & Powell: Professional Liability Precedents' (Sweet & Maxwell).
Personal: BA Hons (Oxon). Leisure interests: family, skiing and football.

HUCKLE, Theodore QC
Civitas Law, Cardiff
0845 071 3007
theohuckleqc@civitaslaw.com
Featured in Clinical Negligence (Wales & Chester), Personal Injury (Wales & Chester), Personal Injury (All Circuits)

Practice Areas: Theo is an acknowledged leader at the PI Bar with expertise in trial preparation, appellate advocacy and ADR, especially mediation. He specialises in catastrophic injury (spinal/head injury/clin neg), and disease claims. Particular expertise in complex quantum issues (eg loss of chance, Ogden 6/7/8) including preparation of detailed spreadsheet schedules for service and tactical analysis. Significant experience in constitutional and public law, human rights, fraud and professional negligence. ADR Group-accredited Mediator.
Professional Memberships: PIBA Executive since 2002; APIL; WPLHRA; HRBA; CBA.
Career: Theo is Counsel General for Wales. He has appeared in the Supreme Court 5 times in 3 years, including Baker-v-Quantum[2011]. He practises throughout England

& Wales from chambers in Cardiff. QC 2011. Bencher, LIncoln's Inn 2012. Founder member of Civitas as the first specialist civil chambers in Wales in 2008. Treasury Panel (Civil) 1995-2005; NAW Civil Panel and Clinical Speedy Resolution Scheme Panel 1999-2006; SFO Panel 2002-07.
Publications: Major publications: Butterworths' PI Litigation Service (Editor); Munkman: Employer's Liability (Noise Induced Hearing Loss); Future Loss in Practice: Periodical Payments &Lump Sums (2007). Sweet & Maxwell: Occupational Illness Litigation (Vibration Injuries Editor).
Personal: Education: Jones's WestMon School, Pontypool. Jesus College, Cambridge, BA, LLM (International), MA, Titular Exhibitioner. Lincoln's Megarry Scholar & Hardwicke Scholar 1984-85.

HUGHES, David
9 Bedford Row, London
020 7489 2727
david.hughes@9bedfordrow.co.uk
Featured in Crime (London)
Practice Areas: A widely experienced leading junior, specialising in serious crime including murder, terrorism, fraud, cyber crime, drugs, sexual offences and confiscation (including international mutual legal assistance). In the past year he has been involved in a number of high profile murder and/or terrorism cases (including the murder of Lee Rigby) and cases requiring a detailed knowledge of scientific evidence (including the first trial involving the use of genotyping of Chlamydia in relation to sexual offences and the appropriate interpretation of mixed profile DNA). He has acquired a detailed knowledge and expertise, on behalf of both prosecution and defence, in relation to computer fraud including phishing, vishing, pharming, the use of Trojans and other malware such as SpyEye and Zeus programmes. His extensive experience as an advocate is reflected in the complexity and seriousness of the cases in which he is instructed and the detailed preparation and research (of facts, law and expert evidence) required to seek a successful outcome to proceedings.
Professional Memberships: Criminal Bar Association.

HUGHES, Gwydion
9 Park Place, Cardiff
02920 382 731
clerks@9parkplace.co.uk
Featured in Chancery (Wales & Chester), Commercial Dispute Resolution (Wales & Chester)
Practice Areas: General commercial, chancery and administrative work including company law and insolvency, land law, probate and trusts, inheritance and family provision, local government, planning, landlord and tenant and professional negligence as well as public inquiries. Handles advisory and advocacy work for the Public Services Ombudsman for Wales.
Professional Memberships: Chancery Bar Association, Wales Commercial Law Association (Treasurer), Wales & Chester Circuit Specialist Court Bar Association (Secretary).
Career: Called 1994, Appointed to the National Assembly for Wales Commission's panel of counsel for real property and commercial work, Honorary Counsel to the Welsh Books Council.
Personal: Educated at Llanidloes High School and University of Wales College Cardiff (LLB). Fluent in Welsh.

HUGHES, Paul
Kings Chambers, Manchester
0845 034 3444
clerks@kingschambers.com
Featured in Costs Litigation (Northern)
Practice Areas: The Law of costs, personal injury. Paul is an experienced costs practitioner with particular expertise in procedural law and the costs of actions based on negligence (such as personal injury, clinical negligence, etc), including group litigation. He is an experienced cross-examiner, and is frequently instructed to deal with disputes concerning conduct, misconduct, wasted costs and non-party (third-party) costs orders. In 2013 he has been heavily involved in assisting firms with managing the transition to the post-Jackson world, having given business advice and undertaken substantial non-contentious work in this regard. Paul also advises on managing 'broken retainers' and resolving disputes concerning the indemnity principle, both from the paying party's point of view and the receiving party's point of view. Paul has appeared before the Courts from the County Court to Court of Appeal and has experience of advising on claims for costs in excess of £1m.
Professional Memberships: Member of the Personal Injury Bar Association, Fellow of the Association of Costs Lawyers (FACL).
Career: St Catherine's College, Oxford, BA Jurisprudence, Year of Call - 2001 (Middle Temple).
Publications: Paul has, since early 2005, contributed to the Costs Brief for the New Law Journal.

HUGHES, Ruth
5 Stone Buildings, London
020 7242 6201
clerks@5sblaw.com
Featured in Court of Protection (All Circuits)
Practice Areas: Ruth has a busy Traditional Chancery practice which focuses on trusts and estates claims and Court of Protection litigation. She also has a broader, more commercial practice acting for the Crown, especially HMRC. She regularly appears in the High Court and has appeared in the Court of Appeal. She particularly enjoys claims involving equitable remedies, for example, proprietary estoppel, mutual wills and injunctions. Ruth is frequently instructed by the Official Solicitor in statutory will/gift claims, particularly where there is an element of complexity. For example, relating to taxation of cross border issues. She is happy to undertake cases which have a personal welfare or mental health aspect.
Professional Memberships: Chancery Bar Association, Property Bar Association, ACTAPS.
Career: Called 2007. MA Cantab. Attorney General's C Panel. Accredited mediator.
Publications: Assistant editor of the Elder Law Journal.

HUGHES, Simon QC
Keating Chambers, London
020 7544 2600
shughes@keatingchambers.com
Featured in Construction (London)
Practice Areas: Specialist in litigation, arbitration and advisory work in connection with energy and natural resources; construction and engineering and related commercial dispute work for both UK and international clients. Extensive experience of very substantial cases where the governing law is not English. Experience of disputes where the law of the following countries governed the contract: France, Germany, Ghana, New Zealand, Trinidad & Tobago, Uzbekistan, Georgia, Azerbaijan, Portugal, Singapore, Hong Kong, Romania, Italy. Regularly acts in TCC and Commercial Court litigation, adjudication and mediation, and domestic and international arbitrations predominantly in the Far and Middle East, with experience of various parts of the Caribbean and South America. Disputes relating to various power generation, utilities, process plants, shipbuilding, mining and other construction and engineering projects. In-depth experience, both advisory and litigation, of energy work (construction and operation of power stations and off shore platforms and rigs; oil and gas drilling and transportation; construction, operation and decommissioning of nuclear power plants together with disputes about spent fuel management). Significant experience of litigation overseas, particularly in New Zealand and the Caribbean. Called to the Bar in New Zealand -- to conduct a very large power plant dispute for Rolls-Royce plc -- and more recently called to the Bar in Trinidad & Tobago, in order to represent companies in the Court of Appeal. Simon has particular experience and expertise in the FIDIC standard forms, on which he has written and lectured extensively, in addition to FIDIC disputes being a core part of his practice.
Professional Memberships: Society of Construction Law; TECBAR; COMBAR.
Career: Called 1995; Queen's Counsel 2011.
Publications: Understanding the New FIDIC Red Book: a clause-by-clause commentary Simon Hughes QC & Jeremy Glover; Contributing Editor - Keating on Construction Contracts 9th Edition (2012); former Contributing Editor - Chitty on Contracts.

HUGHES, William QC
9-12 Bell Yard, London
020 7400 1800
w.hughes@912by.com
Featured in Crime (London)
Practice Areas: Criminal law specialist. Prosecution and Defence of Serious Crime including, Homicide and related, Serious Offences, Organised Crime, Serious and Complex Fraud and Confiscation. Wide experience of Coroner's Inquests, Inquiries, Professional Discipline and other Tribunals (see www.9-12bellyard.com for details).
Professional Memberships: Elected Recorder of the South Eastern Circuit (2004-06), Executive Committee Member (2001-08) Elected member of the Criminal Bar Association Committee (2006-09) Committee Member of the Fraud Lawyers Association Committee Member of the Association of London Welsh Lawyers Treasurer and Trustee of the Criminal Bar Association's Kalisher Scholarship Trust Advocacy Trainer for the Honourable Society of Gray's Inn.
Career: Called (Gray's Inn) 1989, Queen's Counsel 2013.

HUGH-JONES, George QC
Serjeants' Inn Chambers, London
020 7427 5000
ghugh-jones@serjeantsinn.com
Featured in Professional Discipline (London)
Practice Areas: George Hugh-Jones QC was called to the Bar in 1983 and took silk in 2010. George specialises in professional discipline, clinical negligence, inquests and inquiries and public and administrative law. An earlier edition notes that "he always has the answer, according to impressed sources, who value his charming manner and his ability to give clear straightforward advice" and that he is "a tenacious advocate who goes the extra mile." Please click on the link to the Serjeants' Inn Chambers website for his profile, which sets out full details of his practice including relevant work of note.
Professional Memberships: PNBA.

HUMPHRIES, Michael QC
Francis Taylor Building, London
020 7353 8415
clerks@ftb.eu.com
Featured in Planning (London)
Practice Areas: Michael Humphries specialises in all aspects of property development law, but is particularly well known for his infrastructure planning and compulsory purchase work, where he has acted in relation to some of the largest and most important projects in recent years. Michael is currently acting for the promoters of a large number of Nationally Significant Infrastructure Projects and his experience encompasses the energy, transport, water, wastewater, ports and airports sectors. Michael is the Treasurer of the National Infrastructure Planning Association and the General Editor of Bloomsbury's National Infrastructure Planning Service. Michael is also a Visiting Fellow at Cambridge University giving occasional lectures on national infrastructure planning. Michael is also a leading practitioner in compulsory purchase and compensation law and was a founder of the Compulsory Purchase Association, for which he has been recognised as an honorary member. Michael is the Senior Editor of Bloomsbury's 'Compulsory Purchase and Compensation Service'. In 2013 Michael was Chambers and Partners Environmental and Planning Silk of the Year.
Professional Memberships: National Infrastructure Planning Association - treasurer; Joint Planning Law Conference committee - member; Planning and Environment Bar Association - member; Compulsory Purchase Association – honorary member; Anglo-American Real Property Institute - past chair.
Career: Called 1982 (Inner Temple); QC 2003.
Publications: General Editor – Bloomsbury's National Infrastructure Service. Senior Editor – Bloomsbury's 'Compulsory Purchase and Compensation Service'.
Personal: Chiltern Edge School; University of Leicester (LLB); Inns of Court School of Law. Born 1959; resides London. Enjoys spending time with family in France – married with three children.

HUMPHRYES, Jane QC
3 Raymond Buildings Barristers, London
020 7400 6400
jane.humphryes@3rblaw.com
Featured in Crime (London)
Practice Areas: Preparation and presentation at all stages of criminal and 'quasi-criminal' investigations. Recent notable work: historic and current allegations of serious sexual abuse including rape and child complainants; land banking fraud and

money laundering; murder, manslaughter, firearms, and violence. Jane's exacting standards both in and out of court leave her clients, both professional and lay, confident in their representation. She is a 'consummate professional'. For more information go to www.3rblaw.com.
Professional Memberships: Criminal Bar Association.
Career: Called 1983, Recorder 1999, QC 2003.

HUNTER, John
Kings Chambers, Manchester
0845 034 3444
clerks@kingschambers.com
Featured in Administrative & Public Law (Northern), Planning (Northern)
Practice Areas: John practises across the field of administrative and public law and, in particular, planning and environmental law, housing law, prison law, immigration and asylum law, discrimination and human rights. From 2004-5 John was judicial assistant to Lord Rodger and Lord Nicholls in the House of Lords. John acts for a mix of public authorities, developers, individuals and interest groups across these areas.
Professional Memberships: PEBA, ALBA.
Career: Kings Chambers (2003-present), Judicial Assistant, House of Lords (2004-5), The Queen's College, Oxford University (1995-2000).

HUNTER, Robert
Devereux, London
020 7353 7534
hunter@devchambers.co.uk
Featured in Personal Injury (London)
Practice Areas: Rob's practice has three major strands: (i) mainstream personal injury work in cases of serious injury or fatality; (ii) higher value clinical negligence claims; (iii) instructions as junior counsel in catastrophic injury cases. Rob has experience of the full spectrum of serious injuries, especially brain, spinal, and orthopaedic injuries of the utmost severity (including amputation). He has substantial expertise in fatal claims and has acted his cases involving, for example, deceased wealth creators, a departure from the conventional dependency calculation, disregarded benefits, and apportionment issues. Rob is also instructed in asbestos-related disease claims, especially if quantum is complex; in high or maximum severity claims arising from accidents abroad; and in group actions brought on behalf of poorly holiday makers.
Professional Memberships: PIBA.
Career: Called 2000 (Gray's Inn); happily in practice on the Northern Circuit until 2007; now contented in London.
Publications: Contributing Editor to Butterworth's Personal Injury Service; author of numerous practice notes for LexisNexis PSL, including the catastrophic claims section.
Personal: Married with one child (so far). Jazz addict, amateur economist and fresh air obsessive.

HUNTER, Winston QC
Byrom Street Chambers, Manchester
0161 829 2100
winston.hunter@byromstreet.com
Featured in Clinical Negligence (Northern), Personal Injury (Northern)
Practice Areas: Practice Areas: General common law with particular expertise in insurance, contractual disputes, professional negligence and catastrophic injuries. In respect of the latter, particular expertise in advising and handling claims of particular complexity where issues of insurer liability, public authority funding and third party indemnities is concerned. Regular appearances in the Court of Appeal and Supreme Court in cases spanning all areas of speciality. Specialist areas: personal injury, employment, insurance, commercial disputes. Recent notable cases: Personal injury litigation: recent cases: Sowden v Lodge [2004] Court of Appeal, Crookdale v Drury [2004] Court of Appeal, Hartman v South Essex Mental Health & Community Care NHS Trust [2005] Court of Appeal, Tinsley v Sarker (2005) 18th January, Smith v Wright and Beyer [2001] Court of Appeal. Commercial Litigation: Huktra NV v Huktra UK [2003] Court of Appeal, Tameside MBC v Barlow Securities [2001] Court of Appeal. Employment: Eastwood and Williams v Magnox plc [2004] House of Lords, Consignia v Burkett [2003] Court of Appeal. Insurance: Whitlam v Hazel (for Lloyds Syndicate 260) [2004] Court of Appeal. Churchill Insurance Co Ltd v Benjamin Wilkinson,Tracey Evans v Equity Claims Ltd [2010]+ [2012] Court of Appeal and [2011]Courts of Justice of the European Justice. [2011] Murphy v MPS in the Courts of Justice of the European Union.
Professional Memberships: Founder Member and Committee of the Northern Circuit Commercial Bar Association, Member of the Technology and Construction Bar Association, Member of the Personal Injury Bar Association, Member of the Professional Negligence Bar Association.
Personal: Married with three children. Enjoys cricket, wine, shooting and reading.

HUNTLEY, Clare
9-12 Bell Yard, London
020 7400 1800
c.huntley@912by.com
Featured in Crime (London)
Practice Areas: Defends and prosecutes in general crime and fraud, with specialism in financial crime including complex e-banking fraud, corruption, multi-million pound money laundering and tax fraud. Clare has particular experience in prosecuting and defending serious organised crime including murder, conspiracy to assist unlawful immigration, conspiracy to rob and intellectual property crime. Clare is regularly instructed in cases alleging offences of rape and serious sexual offences. This specifically includes defending in cases concerning allegations of multiple-complainant familial historic sexual abuse.
Professional Memberships: Vice-Chair and founding member of the Fraud Lawyers Association; Criminal Bar Association.
Career: Appointed to: CPS Specialist Fraud Panel (2013); CPS Serious Crime Group/ Terrorism Panel (2013); CPS Advocate Panel at Level 3 (2012); List of Specialist Rape Prosecutors (2012); List of Specialist Regulatory Advocates in Health and Safety and Environmental Law (2012). Called in 2000 (Gray's Inn).
Personal: Lives in London. Leisure interests include cookery, theatre, photography and running. Educated at the University of Warwick.

HURST, Andrew
2 Hare Court, London
020 7353 5324
andrewhurst@2harecourt.com
Featured in Professional Discipline (London)
Practice Areas: Andrew has considerable experience in the Regulatory field – appearing for well over ten years as a respected and highly competent advocate at the GMC and the GDC, and more recently for other Regulators, particularly the NCTL. He has considerable experience of the whole range of healthcare cases: clinical, research, probity, sexual impropriety, health, performance and conviction cases. He is well regarded as a respected and committed defence practitioner at both the GMC and GDC. He has recently achieved a considerable number of positive results at the Interim Orders stage for practitioners in difficult circumstances. Andrew is well respected for his preparation, analysis, calm and persuasive style before Panels, and is well regarded for his quiet but highly effective advocacy. He also maintains a Crown Court criminal practice centered on defence work, with particular emphasis on defending sexual / abuse allegations (including those involving children and vulnerable witnesses). It is said his style is well suited to achieving good results with Juries and in mitigation. His careful attention to the drafting of Defence Case Statements has often reaped benefit, including the discontinuation of cases (including rape) before trial. Beyond that he is just at home across the range of criminal offences. Appointed Recorder in 2009 he remains dedicated to first-class advocacy with impeccable client relationship skills.
Professional Memberships: Association of Regulatory and Disciplinary Lawyers; Criminal Bar Association; Professional Negligence Bar Association.
Career: Call: 1992 (Former Solicitor in City practice).

HUSSAIN, Riaz
Atkin Chambers, London
020 7404 0102
rhussain@atkinchambers.com
Featured in Construction (London), International Arbitration (London), Professional Negligence (London)
Practice Areas: Specialist in construction, engineering, energy disputes and international arbitration. Relative to his level of call he has an increasing amount of experience advising on and appearing as sole counsel in high value construction and general commercial claims. Riaz has experience of general commercial disputes and particular expertise in construction and engineering, energy, transport and professional negligence disputes. He has appeared as Counsel in both domestic and international arbitration (Caribbean, American, Middle East, Turkey, Russia, Far East, Europe and Africa). Recent international arbitrations have been under UAE law; Trinidad and Tobago law; Russian law and Swiss Law. He regularly appears as Counsel in English High Court litigation and advises on other forms of ADR such as mediation and adjudication. Riaz has represented Government Ministries, Local Authorities, Builders, Employers in all sorts of Projects including PFI Projects, Architects, Engineers, Surveyors, aviation and transport companies, residential owners, and technology professionals in construction disputes and investors, companies and business consultants amongst others in general commercial disputes.
Professional Memberships: Combar; TECBAR; SCL; LCLCBA.
Career: University College, London (LLB First Class); called to the Bar 2001.

HUSSAIN, Tasaddat
Broadway House, Bradford
01274 722 560
clerks@broadwayhouse.co.uk
Featured in Administrative & Public Law (North Eastern)
Practice Areas: Asylum and Immigration. Sports Immigration.
Career: Asylum/immigration - fresh claim refusals, certifications, challenging removal directions, delay in processing claims, refusals of immigration claims where there is no right of appeal (eg Article 8); Cart challenges to decisions of the Upper Tribunal; Asylum support – refusal of s4 or s95 support where no right of appeal to the AST, the appropriateness of accommodation, refusals of local authorities to support under s21 NAA 1948; UASC - disputes regarding: claimed and assessed age, type of support provided namely s17 or s20 CA 1989: entitlement of children leaving care services: disputes between local authorities regarding responsibility for UASC; Unlawful detention; Prison law - delay in treatment/coursework provision, recategorisation, unlawful detention, licence condition challenges. Mental Health - disputes between PCTs/local authorities regarding who has responsibility for s117 aftercare, transferring clients to unsuitable facilities. Azimi-Moayed Iran (Rev.1) [2013] UKUT 197 NN (Zimbabwe) CG [2013] UKUT 198 HM (Article 15(c)) Iraq CG [2012] UKUT 00409 MK (Iraq) CG ([2012] UKUT 00126 PR (Sri Lanka) [2011] EWCA Civ 988 TR v SSHD [2011] EWHC 557 (Admin) PRH v LSC [2011] EWHC 1323 (QB) Jia Fu Zhang v. SSHD [2008] EWHC 3050 (Admin) JT (Cameroon) [2008] EWCA Civ 878".

HUTCHINGS, Martin QC
Wilberforce Chambers, London
020 7304 2940
mhutchings@wilberforce.co.uk
Featured in Real Estate Litigation (London)
Practice Areas: Real estate litigation.
Professional Memberships: Property Bar Association; Chancery Bar Association.
Career: Martin has a broad property law practice covering both contentious and non-contentious matters and professional liability in related areas. He has acted in many recent high profile cases covering all aspects of property litigation. Martin is known for his ability to understand clients' commercial objectives and for providing rapid and practical advice. He has particular experience in commercial landlord and tenant matters including business tenancies; dilapidations; insolvency related lease issues, and consent for alienation. Martin also regularly appears in and advises on real property cases. He has a wealth of recent reported cases. They concern such diverse areas as restrictive covenants; development agreements; easements; commercial lease interpretation and land registration. He is consistently praised for his advocacy, including for his cross examination skills (see e.g. Chambers & Partners (2013)) In 2013 he was successful in 4 separate property cases in the Court of Appeal concerning: easements; construction of a confidentiality agreement; issue estoppel

and dilapidations. He regularly advises on and acts in arbitrations and mediations.

HUTTON, Alexander QC
Hailsham Chambers, London
020 7643 5000
alexander.hutton
@hailshamchambers.com
Featured in Clinical Negligence (London), Costs Litigation (London), Professional Discipline (London)
Practice Areas: Medical law: clinical negligence, medical disciplinary proceedings, inquests/tribunal work; the law of costs. Particular interest in cases involving complex medical issues. Has also appeared in many of the leading cases in costs over the past few years. Cases include Meiklejohn v St George's Healthcare NHS Trust [2014] EWCA Civ 120 [2014] Med LR (what a clinician has to tell a patient about comparative risks of different treatment options), Solomon v Cormwell Group; Oliver v Doughty [2012] 1 WLR 1048 (where a low value RTA claim settles pursuant to a Part 36 offer whether fixed costs or standard basis costs apply), Marcus v Medway PCT [2011] PIQR Q4; [2011] Med LR 560 (the correct costs order where a clinical negligence claimant recovers a tiny fraction of claim but the defendant had not made a Part 36 offer), Gloucestershire CC v Evans (CA) [2008] 1 WLR 1883 (lawfulness of a no win, reduced fee CFA with success fee), Tankard v John Fredericks and others [2009] 1 WLR 1731 (lawfulness of the Accident Line scheme), Jenkins v Young Brothers [2006] 1 WLR 3189 (assignment of conditional fee agreements), R (Factortame) v Secretary of State for Transport (costs) [2003] QB 381 (CA) (the legality of contingency fees), Malkinson v Trim [2003] 1 WLR 463 (CA) (costs when a solicitor acts in person), Lownds v Home Office [2002] 1 WLR 2450 (CA) (the leading case on proportionality of costs under the CPR), South Coast Shipping v Havant Borough Council [2002] 4 All ER 779 (disclosure on costs assessment under the Human Rights Act), Roberts v Bro Taf Health Authority [2002] Lloyds Rep Med 182 (the principles of damages where failed sterilisation leads to a brain damaged baby).
Professional Memberships: PNBA, AvMA.
Career: Called 1992. Junior Counsel to the Crown (B Panel) 1999-2005. Assessor for High Court costs appeals. Recorder of the Crown Court (2009). QC 2012.
Personal: Education: University of Bristol (First Class Honours in Politics).

HUTTON, Louise
Maitland Chambers, London
020 7406 1182
lhutton@maitlandchambers.com
Featured in Banking & Finance (London), Chancery (London), Fraud (London)
Practice Areas: General commercial and commercial chancery litigation: in particular, fraud, insolvency, banking and finance litigation (including fund litigation), company and trusts and estates litigation. Cases include ITS v GP Noble Trustees & Ors (claims arising from pension fraud); RBS v Highland (applications for anti-suit injunctions to restrain proceedings in Texas); Interactive Investor v City Index (claims arising from conduct of wind down period of white label trading arrangements); EIIB v AHAB (claim for sums due under an Islamic financing facility; defence based on alleged fraud of Maan Al-Sanea); JPMorgan v Wockhardt (claim, involving issues overn non-reliance clauses, for sums due under rang accrual derivatives transactions); HSBC v 5th Avenue Partners, So v HSBC (negligence and other claims arising from bank fraud of Lib Dem donor Michael Brown); Birley v Anor v Birley & Ors (proceedings relating to the validity of the late Mark Birley's will); Shalson v Russo (fraud, tracing, sham trusts and contempt of court).
Professional Memberships: Chancery Bar Association, COMBAR, ACTAPS, Commercial Fraud Lawyers Association (Committee Member).
Career: Called 1998.

HYAMS, Oliver
Devereux, London
020 7353 7534
hyams@devchambers.co.uk
Featured in Education (London)
Practice Areas: Education; employment (including in particular public sector pensions); discrimination; professional disciplinary matters and related areas such as the regulation of care homes; public law (including local government administrative law). Reported cases include: Hagen v ICI Chemicals & Polymers Ltd [2002] IRLR 31; S v Brent London Borough Council [2002] ELR 556; Qua v John Ford Morrison [2003] ICR 482, McCabe v Cornwall County Council [2005] 1 AC 503; Barke v SEETEC [2005] ICR 1373; R (O) v Governing Body of Parkview Academy [2007] ELR 454; R (Siborurema) v Office of the Independent Adjudicator [2008] ELR 209; R (Hill) v Bedfordshire County Council [2008] ELR 660; Kovats v TFO Management LLP [2009] ICR 1140; Governing Body of X Endowed School v SENDIST [2009] IRLR 1007; YKK Europe Ltd v Heneghan [2010] ICR 611; Pothecary Witham Weld v Bullimore [2010] IRLR 572; R (M) v Independent Appeal Panel of Haringey [2010] ELR 218; Parmar v East Leicester Medical Practice [2011] IRLR 641; Abramova v Oxford Institute of Legal Practice [2011] ELR 385; Hill v Governing Body of Great Tey Primary School [2013] IRLR 274; President of the Methodist Conference v Preston (Formerly Moore) UKSC 29; [2013] ICR 833, R(Rudewicz) v Ministry of Justice [2013] QB 410.
Professional Memberships: ALBA; ELBA; ELA. Currently Chair of the Education Law Association.
Career: Called 1989. Appointed part-time Chairman of Employment Tribunals (now Employment Judge) in July 2000.
Publications: 'Law of Education' (2004, Jordans, second edition); 'Employment Aspects of Business Reorganisations' (2006, Oxford University Press); 'Employment in Schools - A Legal Guide' (2007, Jordans, second edition); Consultant Editor for the Education title of 'Halsbury's Laws' (2011).

I'ANSON BANKS, Roderick
48 Bedford Row (Partnership Counsel), London
020 7430 2005
rciab@partnershipcounsel.co.uk
Featured in Partnership (London)
Practice Areas: Exclusively partnership and LLP law. Has specialised in this area since the late 1970s. Handles all aspects of partnership/LLP law, including the drafting and review of agreements, advising on structural issues and strategic advice and representation in disputes, arbitrations and mediations. Particular expertise in partner extractions and removals, garden leave and repudiation disputes in LLPs. Acts for solicitors, accountants, and other professional firms, as well as hedge fund managers and numerous financial and commercial institutions, particularly when involved in limited partnership or corporate partnership ventures.
Professional Memberships: Lincoln's Inn; Association of Partnership Practitioners; Country Land and Business Association.
Career: Called to the Bar 1974 and joined 3 Stone Buildings, (Chambers of DR Stanford). Set up 48 Bedford Row in 1991, as the only chambers specialising exclusively in partnership/LLP law. CEDR Accredited Mediator, 1993. Acted as a consultant to the Law Commission on its reviews of partnership law and limited partnership law (1999 - 2003). Lectures widely on partnership related subjects.
Publications: Editor of 'Lindley & Banks on Partnership'; author of 'The Encyclopedia of Professional Partnerships'.
Personal: Educated at Westminster School 1965-69 and University College London 1970-73. Leisure pursuits include reading and films. Born 5 December 1951. Lives in Beare Green, Surrey.

INNES, Ruth
Westwater Advocates, Edinburgh
07776 182 470
ruth.innes@westwateradvocates.com
Featured in Family/Matrimonial (Scotland)
Practice Areas: Family law, particularly financial provision, cohabitation and international and cross-border child issues. Reported cases include Carroll v Carroll 2005 FamLR 99 (jurisdiction); H v H 2006 FamLR 59 (international child abduction); Clark v Clark 2006 FamLR 90 (financial provision on divorce); C v C 2008 FamLR 28 and 96 (international child abduction); Bain v Bain 2008 FamLR 81 (financial provision on divorce); Smith v Smith 2009 FamLR 39 (financial provision on divorce); Watt v Watt 2009 FamLR 62 (financial provision on divorce); Steel v Steel 2010 SLT 1085 (financial provision on divorce); Selkirk v Chisholm 2011 FamLR 56 (cohabitation); M v M 2011 FamLR 24 (financial provision on divorce, trusts); S v S 2011 FamLR 86 (adoption - removal of child from the UK); G v G 2012 SLT 2 (international child abduction), Simpson v Downie 2011 Fam LR 145; 2013 SLT 178 (cohabitation) and W v W 2013 Fam LR 85 (financial provision on divorce).
Professional Memberships: Member of Advocates' Family Law Association.
Career: Solicitor until 2004. Called to the Bar in July 2005.
Publications: Reporter for Session Cases 2006-2014.
Personal: LLB (Hons) with German Law, Aberdeen University.

IRWIN, Gavin
Dyers Chambers, London
020 7404 1881
gavin.irwin@dyerschambers.com
Featured in POCA Work & Asset Forfeiture (All Circuits), Financial Crime (London)
Practice Areas: Gavin is a specialist fraud and regulatory crime practitioner. In the last 12 months, in addition to advising on restraint orders in a complex consumer protection fraud and representing individuals charged with advance fee, mortgage and VAT frauds, he has: continued to advise in sensitive disputes involving sanctions and export licensing, with a particular emphasis on Iran; offered practical advice to law firms on business risk and compliance with ABC, AML and sanctions law and regulations; represented individuals in professional conduct and discipline matters before regulatory tribunals and the High Court; and, defended in extradition proceedings brought by Peru, Turkey and numerous Part 1 countries for serious criminal offences including terrorism, fraud, drug trafficking and murder.

ISAAC, Nicholas
Tanfield Chambers, London
020 7421 5300
nisaac@tanfieldchambers.co.uk
Featured in Real Estate Litigation (London)
Practice Areas: All aspects of property litigation, but particular interest and experience in commercial and residential leases, boundaries, party walls and rights of way. Recent cases include Patel v Peters [2014] EWCA Civ 335 (party walls), Emmett v Sisson [2014] EWCA Civ 64 (rights of way) Stannard v Gore [2012] EWCA Civ 1248 (Rylands v Fletcher fire case); Reeves v Blake [2010] 1 WLR 1 (party walls).
Professional Memberships: Chancery Bar Association, Property Bar Association.
Career: Called 1993. Joined Tanfield 2006.
Publications: Author of "The Law and Practice of Party Walls" - Property Publishing March 2014, contributor to "Service Charges and Management: Law and Practice" Sweet & Maxwell 2nd Edition 2009, co author of "Easements and Other Rights" - RICS publishing March 2008.
Personal: Married with two children. Hobbies include skiing (including ski touring), hillwalking, climbing, cycling, and golf.

ISAACS, Barry QC
South Square, London
020 7696 9900
barryisaacs@southsquare.com
Featured in Restructuring/Insolvency (London)
Practice Areas: Barry specialises in reconstruction and insolvency, banking and finance, commercial litigation/arbitration, and company law. He is an Associate of the Society of Actuaries and has particular expertise in insurance matters and cases of financial complexity. He was named as Chambers and Partners Insolvency/Restructuring QC of the Year 2013. In recent years, Barry has appeared in numerous substantial and high-profile cases in the Supreme Court/House of Lords (eg Lehman Brothers/Nortel, Rubin/New Cap Reinsurance, Sigma Finance, Mainstream Properties, Three Rivers v Bank of England), in the Court of Appeal (eg Woolworths, Davenham Trust, FKI v Stribog, Golden Key, Whistlejacket Capital, OT Computers), and at first instance, including several major trials and arbitrations. Other recent cases of note include APCOA Parking, Lehman (Waterfall Application), MF Global (Hindsight Application), Travelodge, Punch Taverns, Monarch Point Fund (BVI), Lehman Re (Bermuda), BTA Bank v Ablyazov, AWAL Bank and Kaupthing.
Professional Memberships: Associate of the Society of Actuaries.
Career: Queen's Counsel 2011; called to the Bar of the BVI 2011, England and Wales 1994; investment manager, Societe Generale 1991-93; strategy consultant, Bain & Company 1989-91. MA (Harvard), MA (Oxon).

Publications: Contributor to Company Directors: Duties, Liabilities and Remedies (OUP, 2009).

ISAACS, Elizabeth QC
St Ives Chambers, Birmingham
0121 236 0863
elizabeth.isaacs@stiveschambers.co.uk
Featured in Family/Matrimonial (Midlands)
Practice Areas: Family: Child Care Court of Protection.
Professional Memberships: FLBA ALC.
Career: Elizabeth is an engaging and knowledgeable family silk with substantial expertise in all areas of public and private child law and welfare issues relating to vulnerable adults, including a strong appellate practice. Particular interests include child death and serious physical injury, sexual abuse (including historical abuse) insulin poisoning, fabricated and induced illness (FII), judicial review, human rights issues relating to children, residence and contact arrangement disputes, same-sex and LGBTQ parenting issues, surrogacy and parental order applications, parental alienation, child abduction, and leave to remove from the jurisdiction. Elizabeth is renowned for her ability in quickly identifying the practical implications of complex cases. She has an established reputation for compassionate client care, excellent advocacy and forensic preparation, and a pragmatic and tactical approach.
Publications: Clarke, Hall & Morrison on Children – contributing editor from 2014 Family Court Practice (Jordans) – contributor from 2014 Social Work Decision Making: A Guide for Child Care Lawyers (2nd ed 2012) (co-author) Challenging and Defending Local Authority Childcare Decisions: A Practical Guide (2013) (co-author).

ISAACS, Paul
Broadway House, Leeds
0113 246 2600
pi@broadwayhouse.co.uk
Featured in Family/Matrimonial (North Eastern)
Practice Areas: Family law - matrimonial finance.
Career: With a vault of experience underpinning his practice, Paul Isaacs is the barrister of choice in difficult ancillary relief applications in the North. He is known nationally as a first-rate advocate and his qualities as an advocate are matched by his intellect and ability to conquer the most complex briefs. He remains at the forefront of ongoing developments in the law of ancillary relief and is regularly instructed in cases involving pre and post nuptial agreements, inherited wealth, overseas assets, consent orders and Barder events. He was appointed Recorder in 1995 and brings judicial experience to his busy practice at the bar.

ITEN, Corinne
Pump Court Chambers, London
020 7353 0711
c.iten@pumpcourtchambers.com
Featured in Family/Matrimonial (Western)
Practice Areas: Corinne Iten practises in all areas of family law, as well as TLATA, Inheritance Act and related matters of property law. She has a special interest in public law and is regularly instructed on behalf of local authorities, parents and children. She increasingly deals with complex cases, including those where there are allegations of non-accidental injury, parental alienation, factitious induced illness or sexual abuse.
Professional Memberships: Family Law Bar Association (co-opted committee member).
Career: Corinne has been a tenant at Pump Court Chambers since 2007 after joining as a pupil in 2006. She was called to the Bar in 2006 (Inner Temple). Corinne read Linguistics at University College London (BA in 1996, PhD in 2000) and held post-doctoral positions at UCL and Carlton University, Ottawa, between 2000 and 2003.
Personal: Corinne grew up in Switzerland and is a native speaker of German. She also speaks French. In her spare time she sings in a choir and enjoys long-distance walking and cycling.

IVILL, Scott
2 Hare Court, London
020 7353 5324
scottivill@2harecourt.com
Featured in Crime (London)
Practice Areas: Scott Ivill is ranked as a leading criminal barrister by both Chambers UK and the Legal 500. Described as a "Premier League" advocate, he is extremely popular with both professional and lay clients alike. He is instructed by leading defence solicitors to represent those charged with a wide range of the most serious and complex criminal offences, appearing both as leading junior and junior counsel. Scott has significant experience in grave crimes, including murder, armed robbery, large-scale drug conspiracies, serious violence, firearms, and money laundering. He has particular interest in multi-handed cases, large-scale fraud and organised crime. He also undertakes confiscation cases and related Proceeds of Crime Act matters. In addition, he has extensive experience of appellate work in the Court of Appeal and also accepts instructions to advise upon, and appear in, cases involving judicial review proceedings arising from criminal matters. Scott regularly accepts instructions in privately funded cases, including road traffic matters, and has acted for a number of high-profile clients. He also accepts instructions in Health & Safety and other regulatory crime cases, and all types of professional disciplinary work, particularly the defence of accountants and other financial professionals.
Professional Memberships: Criminal Bar Association; Member of Gray's Inn.
Career: Called in 1997. LLB (Hons) 2:1; Rodney Bax QC Scholar Grays Inn; Inns of Court School of Law, London.

JACKLIN, Susan QC
1 Garden Court Family Law Chambers, London
020 7797 7900
jacklin@1gc.com
Featured in Family/Matrimonial (Western)
Practice Areas: Family Finance, ToLATA and Inheritance Act Susan's practice includes all forms of family disputes arising from relationship breakdown and death, with particular emphasis on high net worth claims involving complex issues, such as multiple businesses, trusts, hidden assets, third party claims. She has been instructed in numerous farming cases across the West Country, Wales and the Midlands.
Professional Memberships: Chairman of the Family Law Bar Association 2014, Vice Chairman (Family) Bar Council Remuneration Committee, Western Circuit Committee.
Career: Susan has specialised in Family Law for 25 years and has vast experience of dealing with a wide range of people and cases on the Western Circuit and also in London, Birmingham and South Wales. Her practice includes the full range of family finance work and children. In private law disputes she is able to advise and represent clients on finance and children issues. Clients value the continuity of relationship between the two forms of dispute. Although the main focus of Susan's practice is financial claims she has extensive experience of dealing with disputes regarding the welfare of children including numerous applications for leave to remove children from the jurisdiction.
Personal: Walking, particularly along the sea cliffs in Cornwall, travel, entertaining and all things cultural.

JACKSON, Andrew
St Philips Chambers, Birmingham
0121 246 7000
ajackson@st-philips.com
Featured in Crime (Midlands)
Practice Areas: Andrew Jackson is an established and respected criminal practitioner. He defends and prosecutes in all cases across the criminal calendar. He defends in cases of homicide and sexual offences, and has particular expertise in cases involving child witnesses, with and without intermediaries. He defends in all cases involving dishonesty, including corporate insolvency. He has vast experience in cases involving the possession, production and supply of all forms of controlled drugs. He defends in all cases of violence and in cases of malfeasance in public office. He has the requisite experience and knowledge of all forms of restraint and confiscation. He also defends in cases alleging breaches of the health and safety and trading standards legislation. Andrew is a Grade 4 prosecution advocate with an attendant practice. His overall experience is such that, allied with persuasive and focussed advocacy, he can represent people powerfully and effectively.
Professional Memberships: Member of the Criminal Bar Association.
Career: Called to the Bar in 1986.

JACKSON, Claire
Kings Chambers, Leeds
0845 034 3444
clerks@kingschambers.com
Featured in Restructuring/Insolvency (North Eastern)

JACKSON, David
St Ives Chambers, Birmingham
0121 236 0863
david.jackson@stiveschambers.co.uk
Featured in Crime (Midlands)
Practice Areas: Crime.
Professional Memberships: Criminal Bar Association.
Career: David has defended in all types of cases, including murder, serious sexual and violence offences and armed robbery. He is a Level 4 prosecutor and, as such, is instructed to prosecute and defend the most serious cases including homicide, rape and armed robbery. He is also briefed in many serious sexual cases involving children as victims. David is also instructed to give a pre-charge advice on a number of serious cases which include sexual offences and infant/child deaths. He has been instructed in a Serious Organised Crime Agency case as prosecution junior in a multi-handed large scale conspiracy to import drugs. He has recently received a Chief Constable's commendation having successfully prosecuted a gang for firearms and drugs offences. Has a keen eye for detail. He is particularly good at client care including, where necessary, sensitive handling of vulnerable witnesses.

JACKSON, Hugh
Selborne Chambers, London
020 7420 9500
hugh.jackson@selbornechambers.co.uk
Featured in Commercial Dispute Resolution (London), Professional Negligence (London)
Practice Areas: Commercial chancery practice centred on land and finance, trade, business and technology. He has an extensive track record in loss recovery in professional negligence and title reconstruction, fraud, tracing and asset recovery including related freezing orders. Particular experience of the preparation, presentation and control of multiple claim/multiple defendant managed cases.
Professional Memberships: Hugh sits as a Judge of the First Tier Tribunal, Property Chamber. He is also an accredited mediator.
Career: He is counsel of choice for many institutional lenders in loss recovery claims and claims against professionals. His knowledge and expertise in both the business of lending money, backed with real property security and the complex issues concerning recovery of loss by litigation, ranges across the BTL investment, retail, sub-prime and bridging finance industries. Also claims against auditors, tax advisors and private client claims. He has been retained by leading lending institutions to advise as to the drafting of terms governing their relationships with "panel" solicitors and valuers. Hugh has extensive experience also in land and title disputes and, in particular, mortgage fraud in the context of title to Registered Land together also with the aspects of rectification and indemnity connected with such disputes. His practice extends also to shareholders' remedies and commercial disputes. Recent and reported cases: Horn v Commercial Acceptances [2012] EWCA Civ 958 (construction of loan agreement and associated trust deed); Ibrahim v Barclays Bank Plc, Court of Appeal [2012] 2 Lloyd's Rep 13 (CA) (Discharge of debtor's liability by creditor recovering an amount equivalent to the debt from a bank that had provided a standby letter of credit); Paragon Mortgages Ltd v McEwan-Peters [2011] EWHC 2491 Commercial Court (guarantees / indemnities in buy-to-let lending; Unfair Relationships provisions of Consumer Credit Act 1974); Horn v Commercial Acceptances Ltd [2011] EWHC 1757 (Ch) (meaning of good faith in the context of a commercial contract) Paragon Mortgages Ltd v Hyett 29.11.10; Ch Div (Manchester) (non- applicability of Unfair Relationships provisions of Consumer Creditor Act 1974 to guarantee / indemnity); Midland Packaging v HW, Chartered Accountants [2010] EWHC 1975 (QB) (professional negligence in inheritance tax advice).

JACKSON, Judith QC
Maitland Chambers, London
020 7406 1200
jjackson@maitlandchambers.com
Featured in Real Estate Litigation (London)
Practice Areas: Commercial and residential real estate litigation, commercial landlord and tenant including rent reviews and

dilapidations, leasehold enfranchisement, restrictive covenants, solicitors' professional negligence and Human Rights Act aspects of real estate litigation. For a list of leading cases please refer to Judith's webpage at www.maitlandchambers.com. Judith also acts as a mediator and arbitrator and provides seminars.
Professional Memberships: Chancery Bar Association, Professional Negligence Bar Association, Property Bar Association.
Career: LLB (London), LLM (London). M Res 2012 (Birkbeck, London). Called to Bar (1975). QC (1994). Bencher of Lincoln's Inn (2001-). Director of Bar Mutual Indemnity Insurance Fund Ltd (1999-2009).
Personal: Spanish and Latin American Cultural Studies, trekking in the Andes.

JACKSON, Matthew
Hailsham Chambers, London
020 7643 5000
matthew.jackson
@hailshamchambers.com
Featured in Clinical Negligence (London), Professional Negligence (London)
Practice Areas: Specialises in professional negligence, especially solicitors' negligence and clinical negligence, and general insurance work. Matthew acts mainly for defendants, on instructions from professional indemnity insurers, the NHSLA, MPS, and MDU. In the clinical field, he has dealt with claims arising from many different areas of medical practice, including obstetrics, paediatrics, orthopaedics, spinal surgery, neurosurgery, vascular surgery, general surgery, cardiology, oncology, radiology, radiotherapy, microbiology, anaesthesia and histopathology. In the professional negligence field, he has extensive experience of defending mortgage lender claims against solicitors and valuers, and with claims arising out of the VWF compensation scheme. He has also acted for barristers, accountants, receivers, architects and insurance brokers. Recent significant cases include Leigh v London Ambulance Service [2014] Med LR 134 (Globe J), where a 17 minute delay in the arrival of an ambulance was held to have made a material contribution to the development of the claimant's psychiatric illness; Ganz v Childs & Ors [2011] EWHC 13 (QB) (Foskett J), a claim involving catastrophic brain damage which his client successfully defended on causation grounds; and Cabvision v Feetum & Ors [2009] EWHC 3400 (Ch) (Norris J), where his solicitor clients successfully resisted a multimillion pound claim.
Professional Memberships: Professional Negligence Bar Association (PNBA).
Career: Educated at Winchester College (scholar) and Trinity Hall, Cambridge (scholar). Called to the Bar in 1986.

JACKSON, Rosemary QC
Keating Chambers, London
020 7544 2600
rjackson@keatingchambers.com
Featured in Mediators (All Circuits)
Practice Areas: Building on the expertise gained in 30 years of practice as a barrister specialising in construction, engineering, professional negligence and commercial/contract law, Rosemary has acquired a first class reputation as an international commercial mediator. With 13 years of experience as a mediator of all kinds of international and domestic commercial disputes, Rosemary has successfully mediated disputes up to £200m, and between up to 8 parties. Very experienced in case-management of lengthy, complex and multi-party mediations. Mediation and conciliation experience includes disputes relating to transportation infrastructure, oil and gas, energy, party wall awards, insurance, copyright, proceeds of crime, and competition law, as well as disputes under PFI, PPP, FIDIC, JCT, ICE, NEC and IChemE contracts. On both CedrSolve and TECBAR Mediator and Adjudicator panels and named as a panel adjudicator in contracts. Frequently appointed as adjudicator.
Professional Memberships: Technology and Construction Bar Association, Commercial Bar Association, Society of Construction Law, Society of Construction Arbitrators.
Career: Called 1981, CEDR Accredited 2001, Crown Court Recorder 2002, Queen's Counsel 2006.
Publications: "Mediation, And Some Tips For Getting The Best Out Of It" and "Mediation: Some Do's and Don'ts".

JAMAL, Isabel
8 New Square, London
020 7405 4321
isabel.jamal@8newsquare.co.uk
Featured in Intellectual Property (London)
Practice Areas: All areas of intellectual property law, including patents (particularly in the pharmaceutical and telecommunications industries) trade marks, copyright, passing off, registered and unregistered design rights and confidential information. Recent career highlights include: a) representing Actavis in Actavis v Sanofi (in which Actavis successfully invalidated Sanofi's SPC) and in Actavis v Eli Lilly (in which Actavis successfully sought a declaration of non-infringement); b) representing ZTE against Vringo in an on-going telecoms patent dispute (in which ZTE successfully defended an application by Vringo to deal with FRAND as a preliminary issue); c) appearing as sole counsel for the successful patentee in Lizzanno Partitions Limited v Interiors Manufacturing Limited (a patent infringement and invalidity dispute); d) appearing as junior counsel for the successful defendant in Evegate Publishing v Newsquest Media (a trade mark and passing off dispute); and e) appearing as junior counsel for the successful patentee in Regeneron v Genentech (a biotech patent dispute which went to the Court of Appeal).
Career: Called 2008; Lincoln's Inn.
Personal: First class Masters degree in Physics and Philosophy from Oxford University. Several major scholarships during degree, law conversion and bar vocational courses. Prize-winning public speaker (competed at a regional and European level).

JAMES, Alun
Temple Tax Chambers, London
020 7353 7884
clerks@templetax.com
Featured in Tax (London)
Practice Areas: Tax and VAT. Business and corporate tax advice; clearance work and planning for transactions and reorganisations; structuring through LLPs; employment-related securities. Professional clients mainly accountants. Litigation undertaken at tribunal level and in the higher courts. Lectures extensively nationwide.
Professional Memberships: Also a member of Exchange Chambers, Liverpool and Manchester.
Career: Called to the Bar 1986 and joined Temple Tax Chambers in 1988.
Publications: Co-author of 'Taxation of Companies and Company Reconstructions' (Sweet & Maxwell).
Personal: Scholar of St John's College, Oxford (BA, Hons 1st Class (Jurisprudence), BCL). Born 13 May 1964.

JAMES, Grahame
Carmelite Chambers, London
020 7936 6300
ghjames200@msn.com
Featured in Crime (London)
Practice Areas: Since being called in 1989 he has practised exclusively as a defence advocate in all areas of the criminal law. He is instructed as Leading Junior in serious and complex cases across the criminal spectrum, with emphasis in fraud, drugs and serious violence. He has significant experience in white collar fraud, representing both professional and personal clients in such matters as fraudulent trading, banking, factoring and HMRC fraud, money laundering, Trademark violations and identity fraud. He has worked in asset protection and forfeiture, and high value POCA disputes both here and abroad. Recent cases include operation Savate, a multi-million pound fraud on the Revenue, R v Q- a large scale banking/factoring fraud, R v D- involving £7.5m fraudulent trading and R v R- an international identity fraud ring supplying boiler room frauds. He is also instructed in serious organised crime including homicide, serious violence, drugs and sexual offending. Recent Leading cases include R v Ahmed- the largest and longest prosecution in the UK of child grooming, R v R - murder trial after botched robbery, R v M - a large scale drugs conspiracy run from prison, R v G – Diamond robbery/kidnapping and attempted murder, and R v K- a Russian mafia syndicate.
Professional Memberships: Criminal Bar Association, Gray's Inn (1989), South Eastern Circuit.

JARMAIN, Stephen
1 King's Bench Walk, London
020 7936 1500
sjarmain@1kbw.co.uk
Featured in Family/Matrimonial (London)
Practice Areas: Domestic and international family finance, private and international children, child abduction.
Professional Memberships: FLBA, International Society of Family Law.
Career: 2013 Reported Case: HB v PB, OB [2013] EWHC 1956 (Fam) 2011 International Family Law Exchange Placement, Houston, Texas; sponsored by American Bar Association 2009 Reported Case; Re S and O (Temporary Removal from Jurisdiction) [2009] Fam Law 114 2008 International Bar Association and College of Law: Practice Diploma in International Human Rights Law and Practice.
Publications: Contributor, "Key Authorities", Family Law (forthcoming); Contributor, "Cases That Shook the World"; Contributor, "Applications under Schedule 1 of the Children Act 1989"; Contributor, "Family Law Journal"; Contributor, FamilyLawWeek.co.uk.
Personal: A particular interest in foreign travel and culture. Hobbies include football: playing, watching and refereeing (as a qualified FA referee) and musical interests, playing the saxophone and electronic organ.

JEANS, Christopher QC
11KBW, London
020 7632 8500
christopher.jeans@11kbw.com
Featured in Employment (London), Sports Law (London)
Practice Areas: Specialises in employment law and discrimination and sports law. Recent cases include: CD v ST (European Court) Cristal v Manchester Health Trust X v Mid-Sussex CAB (SC); Geys v Societe Generale (SC); Andrew Coulson v News International (CA and HC); Proactive Sports Management v Wayne Rooney and others, (CA) ; Wardle v Credit Agricole (CA and EAT); Williams v British Airways, (European Court, SC two hearings , CA, EAT and ET) Audit Commission v Haq (EAT and CA) Keane v Sunderland FC O'Neill v Aston Villa, Keegan v Newcastle FC (Arbitration Tribunal) Bateman v Asda Stores (ET and EAT); Law Society v Office for Legal Complaints and OLC (HC); Ainsworth Stringer v HMRC (European Court and HL); Chagger v Abbey National (CA and EAT); Middlesbrough v Matthews (EAT); Surtees v Middlesbrough (1 and 2 (EAT and CA); Grundy v British Airways (1 and 2 (EAT and CA); Cumbria County Council v Dow, Slack and others (1 and 2, CA and EAT), EB v BA (2 and 3 EAT); O'Hanlon v HMRC (CA); Derbyshire v St Helens (HL and CA).
Professional Memberships: Employment Lawyers Association, Employment Law Bar Association.
Career: 1974-77: LLB degree at King's College, London. 1977-79: BCL degree at St John's College, Oxford. 1980: called to the Bar (Gray's Inn). Since 1983 has practised full time at the Bar, specialising in employment law, discrimination and sports law at chambers of Lord Irvine QC (now Chambers of James Goudie QC). Bencher Gray's Inn (2007). Former part time Chairman/ Judge Employment Tribunals 1998-2008. Recorder from 2009. President Commonwealth Secretariat Arbitral Tribunal.
Personal: Main interests: sport (especially football and cricket), travel, theatre, cinema. Arctic and world travel.

JEFFORD, Nerys QC
Keating Chambers, London
020 7544 2600
njefford@keatingchambers.com
Featured in Construction (London)
Practice Areas: Specialist in construction, engineering and energy disputes, and domestic and international arbitration (ICC, LMAA, HKIAC, DIAC). Practice covers a wide spectrum of advisory work, drafting and advocacy related to domestic and international standard form and bespoke contracts; including PFI contracts; professional negligence claims (architects, engineers, surveyors, valuers); bonds and guarantees and financing arrangements. Nerys' work is principally contentious and she has been involved in disputes arising out of a wide range of projects from the construction of substantial commercial, residential and public developments (including schools, hospitals and museums) to major engineering and infrastructure projects (including roads, tunnels, underground and overground stations, water treatment and sewage plants), off-shore work, shipbuilding, energy recovery and power generation projects.

Professional Memberships: SCL (Former Councillor and Chairman); TECBAR (former Committee Member); COMBAR.
Career: Called 1986; Queens Counsel 2008; Nominated as Construction Junior of the Year, Chambers Bar Awards 2005; Recorder; MCIArb; TECBAR accredited adjudicator.
Publications: Contributing Editor - Keating on Construction Contracts Ninth Edition.

JELF, Simon
48 Bedford Row (Partnership Counsel), London
020 7430 2005
sjelf@partnershipcounsel.co.uk
Featured in Partnership (London)
Practice Areas: Exclusively partnership and LLP law. Deals with a wide variety of partnership/LLP matters, from the drafting of agreements to the resolution of disputes, whether involving litigation, mediation or negotiation. He has wide experience in issues surrounding retirement and expulsion, including contested expulsions, the enforceability of restrictive covenants and arguments relating to repudiation (in LLPs) and dissolution (in traditional partnerships) on behalf of both individual partners and firms. His clients include both large and small firms of solicitors, accountants and other professionals, as well as a range of other businesses. He has particular expertise in medical partnerships within the NHS.
Professional Memberships: Association of Partnership Practitioners.
Career: Called to the Bar (Gray's Inn) 1996. Law Commission 1996-98, principally involved with the review of partnership law. Joined 48 Bedford Row (Chambers of Roderick I'Anson Banks) in 1999. Lectures widely on partnership and LLP related subjects.
Publications: Contributor to the 'Encyclopedia of Professional Partnerships'.
Personal: Educated at John Taylor High School, Burton-upon-Trent, and University of East Anglia. Leisure pursuits include property renovation and golf. Lives in Buckinghamshire.

JENKINS, Alan
Serjeants' Inn Chambers, London
020 7427 5000
ajenkins@serjeantsinn.com
Featured in Professional Discipline (London)
Practice Areas: Alan Jenkins was called to the Bar in 1984. Alan specialises in professional discipline and regulatory law. An earlier edition notes that "he is without doubt one of the best barristers in the field in terms of client care, advocacy and the ability to assimilate masses of documents and present an effective case." Please click on the link to the Serjeants' Inn Chambers website for his profile, which sets out full details of his practice including relevant work of note.
Professional Memberships: CBA, HSLA, ARDL.

JENKINS, Catherine
1 Garden Court Family Law Chambers, London
020 7797 7900
jenkins@1gc.com
Featured in Family/Matrimonial (London)
Practice Areas: Child care law, with a particular emphasis on public law children proceedings, care and adoption. Advising and representing local authorities, parents and children. Often instructed in care proceedings involving serious allegations of sexual abuse or non accidental injury.
Professional Memberships: Member of the FLBA, Association of Lawyers for Children.
Career: BA (Joint Hons) Keele University, called to the Bar in 1990 (Middle Temple). At 1 Garden Court since pupillage.
Publications: Contributed to EC Legal Systems An Introductory Guide (Family law England and Wales) Butterworths.
Personal: Interests include Sailing, Theatre and Arsenal Football Club.

JEWELL, Matthew
One Paper Buildings, London
020 7353 3728
matthewjewell@onepaper.co.uk
Featured in Crime (Western)
Practice Areas: Criminal law, regulatory law.
Professional Memberships: Western Circuit (Committee Member since 2008), CBA (Committee Member 2005-08), Member of the General Council of the Bar (2006-08).
Career: Matthew Jewell's practice includes criminal prosecution and defence matters, covering in particular serious fraud and regulatory law but also drugs and violence offences. He is regularly instructed as a leading junior in place of a silk. He has a particular interest in cases involving sensitive disclosure issues, and those involving the use of covert surveillance. He is finding himself increasingly instructed at pre-charge stage for early advice, advising upon disclosure, and forming a case plan through negotiation and the best possible use of correspondence. His experience from over twenty years in practice is highly sought for tactical advice in particular – Matthew is known as an adept tactician. Matthew can cut through legal jargon and complicated points of law to communicate with clients in language they can easily understand. This skill is particularly appreciated by clients with no experience of the criminal justice system, as is his attention to detail and service ethic – something borne out by the legal directories, where professional clients praise his "exceptional service". Matthew Jewell is also a Pupil Supervisor.

JINADU, Abdul
Keating Chambers, London
020 7544 2600
ajinadu@keatingchambers.com
Featured in Construction (London)
Practice Areas: Specialist in construction, engineering and energy disputes, and domestic and international arbitration, covering a wide spectrum of advisory work, drafting and advocacy, related to standard form and bespoke contracts; contractors' sub-contractors' and employers' claims; professional negligence claims (architects, engineers, surveyors and valuers). Acts for construction and engineering companies, government organisations, corporations, public utilities, local authorities, consultancies, architects and engineers. Significant cases have involved oil and gas; facilities pharmaceutical plants, hospitals, mining, marine construction, major projects, local authority cases and major construction projects. Advises in adjudication and has acted for clients at all stages of the process up to the Court of Appeal where he has appeared successfully in reported decisions both enforcing and resisting enforcement of adjudicators decisions, also advises on ADR.
Professional Memberships: TECBAR, COMBAR, SCL, CIArb.
Career: Called 1995, TECBAR Accredited Adjudicator 2004, Public Access Training 2004.
Publications: Contributor - Keating on Construction Contracts Eighth Edition (2006) and First Supplement (2008). Contributor - Keating on Construction Contracts Ninth Edition (2012). Editorial Board LexisNexis PCL.
Personal: Fluent Yoruba.

JOHN, Benjamin
Maitland Chambers, London
020 7406 1200
bjohn@maitlandchambers.com
Featured in Chancery (London), Commercial Dispute Resolution (London), Fraud (London)
Practice Areas: Commercial and chancery litigation, frequently involving a major international or jurisdictional element, encompassing business agreements and general commercial disputes, civil fraud and asset tracing, conflicts of laws and jurisdictional issues, banking, company matters (including insolvency), claims against fiduciaries & trustees and property disputes. Particular experience of claims for and against sovereign states. Notable current and recent cases include: Slocom v Tatik Inc & Sibir Energy [2014] (EWCA), [2012] (Ch) (fraud & sham claims; interference with contractual relations; claims under s. 423); Panagopoulos v Lloyds Bank [2014] (Comm) (complex derivative mis-selling); Terra Raf Traiding v Assaubayev [2013] (Comm) (alleged fraud connected to sale of oil & gas assets); Dar al Arkan v Al Refai [2013] (Comm) (conspiracy and blackmail claims); Re the Estate of X [2013] (Hong Kong dispute relating to the estate a Hong Kong billionaire); Re D [2012] (Admin) (global relief freezing billions involving veil-piercing issues); NML Capital v Argentina [2011] (UKSC), [2010] (EWCA), [2009] (Comm) (sovereign immunity); JSC BTA Bank v Ablyazov [2011] (EWCA), (Comm) (the massive fraud claim relating to the Kazakh bank); Yukos Capital v Rosneft [2011] (Comm) (enforcement of arbitral awards arising from the Khodorkovsky affair; act of state); Wirecard AG v Shepherd [2011], [2010] (QB) (the Beijing Olympics ticket fraud).
Professional Memberships: COMBAR, Chancery Bar Association, FSLA
Career: Called 2002.
Personal: University College, Oxford (Chemistry, First Class Honours) and City University (CPE, Distinction); Major and Princess Royal Scholar of Inner Temple; winner of the 3VB Prize for best overall performance (CPE, 2001); winner of the Barstow Prize Scholarship (Bar School, 2002).

JOHN, Laura Elizabeth
Monckton Chambers, London
020 7405 7211
ljohn@monckton.com
Featured in Competition/European Law (London), Data Protection (London)
Practice Areas: Laura is a highly sought after junior who has particular expertise in Competition, Information, and Environmental law. Recent work includes: Competition law: Welsh Ministers v Reckitt Benkiser; Welsh Ministers v Servier; National Grid Electricity Transmission v ABB and others; BCL Old v BASF; Emerson Electric v Morgan Crucible.; Information law: Webber v IC [2013] UKUT 648 AAC (deceased persons' medical records); Oliver v IC and Police Service of Northern Ireland EA/2014/0011 (investigation into the Omagh bombing); Mercer v IC and Ministry of Defence EA/2013/0250 (legal advice on whether the regime of the Sovereign Base Areas in Cyprus is compatible with the ECHR); Corke v IC (personal data in National Archive file containing correspondence between the Prime Minister and Jimmy Saville); Eastleigh Borough Council v IC (EA/2013/0069) (development of local development plan); Breeze v IC and NHS Business Services Authority (EA/2013/128); Breeze v IC and Crown Prosecution Service (EA/2013/0053) and (EA/2012/0152) (documents created in the course of an investigation into alleged fraud); Environmental law: European Low Fares Airlines Association v Secretary of State for Energy and Climate Change; United Utilities v Manchester Ship Canal Company and others [2014] UKSC 40. She is direct access qualified, and can accept instructions directly from clients.
Career: BCL (European and Comparative Law), Brasenose College, Oxford (2004); BA (Hons) Jurisprudence, Brasenose College Oxford (2003). Called in 2007; Inner Temple Inn. Before being called to the Bar, Laura worked in DEFRA on the Animal Welfare Act 2006.
Publications: Updates Editor, for the leading EU Competition law text, Bellamy & Child European Union Law of Competition (7th Ed, OUP, 2013); and contributor to the chapter on NCA enforcement in Bellamy & Child 7th Edition.

JOHNS, Alan
Maitland Chambers, London
020 7406 1200
ajohns@maitlandchambers.com
Featured in Real Estate Litigation (London)
Practice Areas: Specialises in all types of property litigation. Recent cases in the Court of Appeal and the High Court include Parkin v Alba Proteins Ltd (2014) (nuisance/prescription/limitation) Newbold v Coal Authority (2013) (£100m claim for mining subsidence), Docker v Rose (2013) (question of construction), Wilkinson v Kerdene Ltd (2013) (enforceability of freehold covenants), Pavledes v Hadjisavva (2013) (rights of light and availability of declaratory relief), Ansa v Towerbeg & Ford (2012) (forfeiture/consent to sublet) Avocet Industrial Estates LLP v Merol Ltd & Tudor Rose International Ltd (2012) (validity of break notice), Cleaver & Ors v Schye Investments Ltd (2011) (standard condition of sale unfair), Milebush Properties Ltd v Tameside Metropolitan Borough Council (2011) (construction and enforceability of s.106 agreement), Extra MSA Services Cobham v Accor UK (2011) (termination of agreement for hotel premises at new M25 service station). Also appears in the County Court and the Upper and First-tier Tribunals.
Career: Called to the Bar in 1994. Part-time tutor at Magdalen College, Oxford during 1996 and 1997.
Personal: Helston School, Cornwall. Magdalen College, Oxford. Member of Philosophy Football Football Club.

JOHNSON, Edwin QC
Maitland Chambers, London
020 7406 1200
ejohnson@maitlandchambers.com
Featured in Real Estate Litigation (London)

Practice Areas: Practice Areas: Property, chancery and commercial litigation and advisory work. In particular commercial and property disputes, general landlord and tenant (including leasehold enfranchisement) and professional negligence (solicitors, surveyors, valuers, architects, other construction professionals, accountants and insurance brokers), conveyancing, mortgages, easements, restrictive covenants, trusts, insolvency, commercial contracts, building and construction work, insurance work and competition law. Recent cases of interest include, in the House of Lords and Supreme Court, Boss Holdings v Grosvenor (meaning of a house in leasehold enfranchisement), Earl Cadogan v 26 Cadogan Square Ltd (rights of lease extension), Earl Cadogan v Pitts (enfranchisement valuation), and Day v Hosebay (meaning of a house), and in the Court of Appeal, John Thomas v Ken Thomas Ltd (forfeiture in relation to company voluntary arrangement), Shell v Total (recovery of economic loss in negligence and nuisance), Kutchukian v John Lyon (valuation assumptions in a collective enfranchisement); Kim v Chasewood (proprietary estoppel), and at first instance, Malmesbury v Strutt & Parker (surveyors negligence), Hotgroup v RBS (exercise of break clause), and Extra MSA v Accor (taking advantage of own wrong in conditional contract).
Professional Memberships: Chancery Bar Association, Professional Negligence Bar Association, Property Bar Association.
Career: Called to the Bar 1987. Queen's Counsel 2006. Real Estate Junior of the Year (2005), Silk of the Year (2012 & 2013), Chambers Awards.

JOHNSON, Jeremy QC
5 Essex Court, London
020 7410 2000
johnson@5essexcourt.co.uk
Featured in Administrative & Public Law (London), Inquests & Public Inquiries (London), Immigration (London), Police Law (All Circuits)
Practice Areas: Public law, human rights, civil liberties, malfeasance, public inquiries. Acts in all cases involving the police (both for and against the police), including claims for judicial review, private law actions, and advisory work. Instructed in numerous public inquiries and long running inquests, including the Al Sweady Inquiry, the Hutton Inquiry, the Billy Wright Inquiry, the Inquests into the deaths of Diana, Princess of Wales and Dodi Al Fayed, and the Hillsborough Inquests.
Professional Memberships: ALBA, PIBA.
Publications: Police Law Reports, Halsbury's Laws (Police).

JOHNSON, Laura
1 Chancery Lane, London
020 7092 2900
ljohnson@1chancerylane.com
Featured in Clinical Negligence (London), Police Law (All Circuits), Personal Injury (London)
Practice Areas: Laura specialises in clinical negligence, personal injury, police law, professional negligence and other insurance related claims, public law and malfeasance claims. She acts for claimants and defendants, but has particular experience representing public bodies including government departments, local authorities, the police and NHS Trusts. Cases include Boyle v Cmr Police of the Metropolis [2013] HC; Bristol Alliance Ltd Partnership v (1) Williams (2) EUI Ltd [2012]CA; R (Burke) v Independent Police Complaints Commission (Defendant) & Commissioner of Police for the Metropolis (IP) [2011] (police complaints); Dunn v Gloucestershire County Council [2013] (brain injury case); Onwuama v London Borough of Ealing [2008] (issue estoppel); Pennington v Surrey County Council [2006] CA (employer's liability); D v East Berkshire Community Trust [2005] HL (duty of care of social workers).
Professional Memberships: Personal Injuries Bar Association (Executive Committee); Professional Negligence Bar Association; Administrative Law Bar Association; London Common Law and Commercial Bar Association.
Career: Called to the Bar in 2001, Grays Inn. Judicial Assistant to the Law Lords 2003-04. Appointed Assistant Coroner for East London in April 2014 as a part-time judicial role.
Publications: Contributor - Atkins Court Forms 'Personal Injury' 2007; research assistant - De Smith, Woolf and Jowell's Judicial Review of Administrative Action 2007.
Personal: Educated Withington Girls' School, Manchester and St Anne's College, Oxford.

JOHNSON, Paul
Kings Chambers, Manchester
0845 034 3444
clerks@kingschambers.com
Featured in Mediators (All Circuits)
Practice Areas: Paul's sole area of specialisation is mediation. He mediates a wide range of disputes: banking, charities, competition, commercial, contractual, construction and engineering, costs, employment, fraud, inheritance and trusts, insolvency, intellectual property, local government, matrimonial/family, partnership, personal injury, professional negligence, property, shareholders, regulatory.
Professional Memberships: CEDR Solve, Consensus Mediation, Sport Dispute Resolution Panel and member of the Bar Council ADR Committee.
Career: Qualified as a solicitor in 1990. Joined Pannone LLP in 1992; he was a Partner from 1995 to 2006. Paul transferred to the Bar in 2006, joined Kings Chambers and is Head of their Mediation Group.

JOHNSON, Zoe QC
QEB Hollis Whiteman, London
020 7933 8855
zoe.johnson@qebhw.co.uk
Featured in Professional Discipline (London), Crime (London)
Practice Areas: Zoe has immense experience in the most demanding crime. She prosecutes complex homicide and terrorist cases including the Real IRA and Islamic fundamentalists. Following R v Harris and Others (Court of Appeal) she has particular expertise in matters with a medical element and acts in "shaken baby syndrome" and sudden infant death cases; she was instructed in the first ever FGM (female genital mutilation) prosecution. She advises pre-charge and is experienced in managing strategy and leading teams in large cases. She advises the Attorney General and appears for him in the Court of Appeal. Much of her work has an international dimension. Zoe defends and prosecutes in all types of fraud and financial crime brought by the SFO, CPS and HMRC. Before becoming Treasury Counsel she was instructed in corporate crime, large-scale drug importations and other inter-jurisdictional cases. Zoe acts for either regulator or regulated in most health and medical regulatory councils, notably the General Medical Council, and has advised the Accountancy and Actuarial Discipline Board on procedure.
Professional Memberships: Criminal Bar Association; founder member, Bar Disability Panel; Association of Regulatory & Disciplinary Lawyers; Public Access Bar Association.
Career: Call 1990. Junior Treasury Counsel 2005. Recorder 2009. Senior Treasury Counsel 2011. Silk 2012.
Publications: Presentations/papers include Cleaning up cosmetic surgery (Society of Ethics and Law), Prosecuting baby shaking cases (Regulatory Law).
Personal: BA (Oxon); Dip Law (City University)

JOHNSTON, Christopher QC
Serjeants' Inn Chambers, London
020 7427 5000
cjohnstonqc@3serjeantsinn.com
Featured in Clinical Negligence (London), Court of Protection (All Circuits), Product Liability (London)
Practice Areas: Christopher Johnston QC was called to the Bar in 1990 and took silk in 2011. Christopher specialises in clinical negligence and healthcare, product liability, Court of Protection, public and administrative, inquests and inquiries, professional discipline, police and employment law. An earlier edition notes that "he is quite superb" and "he has fantastic client care skills and he's very clever. He's a star." Please click on the link to the Serjeants' Inn Chambers website for his profile, which sets out full details of his practice including relevant work of note.
Professional Memberships: NI Bar, PNBA, co-chair of the PNBA Clinical Negligence Conference.
Publications: Medical Treatment: Decisions and The Law (editor); Product Liability Introduction JPIL (2012); Medical Law Reports (contributor).

JOLLY, Schona
Cloisters, London
020 7827 4000
sj@cloisters.com
Featured in Employment (London)
Practice Areas: Schona has a strong equalities practice with employment and human rights specialism across all fields including commercial. She is an acknowledged expert in all areas of discrimination law and complex whistleblowing claims, including in multiple-claimant equal pay claims and county court/High court actions, as well as protection of harassment claims, TUPE and civil liberties matters. She is particularly experienced in crossover matters and has appeared in a number of high profile cases, such as, most recently, Carol Howard v Metropolitan Police which was widely covered in the national press, as well as the landmark Supreme Court case Jivraj v. Hashwani whose effects have been felt in the employment, equality and commercial arbitration worlds. She represents both claimants and respondents/defendants at all court and tribunal levels, including high profile public, private and corporate employers, trade unions, national charities and housing associations, the Equalities and Human Rights Commission, as well as individuals. She is known for her skilled advocacy, detailed knowledge of the law as well as her practical and common sense approach both with clients and the courts. She advises various NGOs on international law and discrimination topics. She is also a qualified mediator.
Professional Memberships: Elected Executive Committee member of the Bar Human Rights Committee, Council member of JUSTICE,ELBA, ELA, Discrimination Law Association, Lawyers for Liberty, Advocates for International Development, Oxfam International Lawyers Network.
Career: Called to the Bar 1999; Licence Speciale (European Law)at University of Brussels; BA Jurisprudence, Magdalen College, Oxford.
Publications: Contributor to LAG Discrimination in Employment Handbook 2013; Co-author of LAG Age Discrimination Handbook 2006; 2004 co-author Consultation paper for Age Concern: Addressing Age Barriers: An international comparison of legislation against age discrimination in the field of goods, facilities and services. Author of frequent professional articles. Former co-editor Sweet & Maxwell European Human Rights Reports.
Personal: Legally fluent in French. High level Spanish, Hindi, Punjabi, Basic Arabic.

JONES, Charlotte
Crown Office Chambers, London
020 7797 8100
jones@crownofficechambers.com
Featured in Clinical Negligence (London)
Practice Areas: Charlotte has experience of all types of clinical practice. She represents Claimants and Defendants in claims which include the following areas: Obstetric claims: claims on behalf of babies brain damaged at birth and now suffering cerebral palsy; shoulder dystocia resulting in brachial plexus injury; third degree tears resulting in incontinence and other complications; anaesthetic awareness during delivery; twin to twin transfusion; feto-maternal haemorrhage; unrelated maternal condition affecting mode of delivery. Gynaecology: termination of one of twin fetuses; bladder damage through failure to catheterise; ureteric and bowel injury. Oncology: late diagnosis of breast cancer, mismanagement of cervical disease; delay in recognition of a childhood neck tumour presenting as benign lumps. Anaesthetic cases: complications arising from the administration of general anaesthetic including massive brain damage. Orthopaedic: hip replacement surgery, hip revision with prosthetic breakage, laminectomy with no spinal stabilisation. Neurosurgery: failure to recognise and treat subdural haemorrhage, delay in treating head injury with major causation argument; spinal surgery with resulting paralysis. Colorectal surgery: failure to fashion a defunctioning colostomy, treatment of anal fissure, incontinence following obstetric damage. Paediatric: late diagnosis of childhood diseases including meningitis. Cosmetic and other elective surgery: breast reconstruction including following mastectomy and considerable experience of high value brain damaged baby.

JONES, Elizabeth QC
Serle Court, London
020 7242 6105
ejones@serlecourt.co.uk
Featured in Chancery (London), Commercial Dispute Resolution (London), Media & Entertainment (London), Mediators (All Circuits), Offshore (London)

Practice Areas: Wide ranging litigation practice, both in the chancery fields of company, insolvency, property and trusts, and in a wide range of commercial disputes, such as fraud, sale of goods, banking, financial services, entertainment, railway industry, and contractual disputes in many different business areas. Also regulatory work in the City and in relation to solicitors. Mediator.
Professional Memberships: Chancery Bar Association, COMBAR, ACTAPS.
Career: Called to the Bar 1984. Silk 2000.

JONES, Gillian
Red Lion Chambers, London
020 7520 6000
gillian.jones@18rlc.co.uk
Featured in Crime (London), Financial Crime (London)
Practice Areas: Known for meticulous preparation, mastery of her material, easy manner and excellent advocacy skills, Gillian is a strong leading junior. Crime and fraud: Specialising in both defence and prosecution of serious crime and fraud, she has acted in cases including murder, organised crime, major drug importation, money laundering, insider dealing, serious sexual offences and a wide spectrum of fraud offences. She is regularly instructed as a leading junior defending and prosecuting alongside Queen's Counsel. She is instructed by defence solicitors and prosecuting/investigating bodies such as the Financial Conduct Authority, Serious Fraud Office, Medicines and Healthcare Products Regulatory Authority, CPS Serious Crime Directorate and Central Fraud Group. Gillian is on the Attorney General's List of Prosecuting Pounsel - Panel B, the Serious Fraud Offices' List - Panel A and CPS specialist panels for Fraud, Rape, Organised Crime and Confiscation/Asset Recovery. Regulatory: Gillian also appears in VAT appeals before the First Tier Tax Tribunal, in Judicial Review proceedings and is currently on the developmental list for the General Medical Council. She regularly conducts restraint, confiscation and cash forfeiture proceedings. Advisory work includes City law firms re money laundering obligations / compliance procedures and anti-corruption issues, as well as acting as independent counsel advising on LPP issues. Current instructions: by the Serious Fraud Office in the first criminal prosecutions arising out of alleged libor manipulation; by the Financial Conduct Authority in relation to allegations of insider dealing; as leading junior in a prosecution investigated by the MHRA into the sale of unlicensed medicines over the Internet and defending a number of cases involving historic sexual abuse. Recent cases: R v Ali Mustafa & others - longest and most complex FSA prosecution to date of insider dealing ring, tried over four-month period; R v Islam and others – joint enterprise murder; R v C – defence counsel in Kurdish mafia related case involving blackmail, rape and firearms; R v MacDonald & others – defence counsel in large scale 'Boiler Room' fraud and money laundering involving mis-selling of 'Penny Shares' and Carbon Credits; R v Gillespie & Others - international conspiracy to import counterfeit prescription drugs (for treatment of serious disease, e.g. cancer) to UK wholesale market on massive scale - first case of its type tried in UK; R v Chambers & others - defence counsel in large-scale multi-handed cheat on the Revenue (tax); HMRC v Amitel Ltd (VAT Tribunal) - wholesale trader in mobile phones and CPUs alleged to be linked to MTIC fraud; R v Owen & others - defence counsel in multi-handed allegation of conspiracy to defraud representing head of procurement for an NHS trust - case dubbed 'jobs for mates'; R v Thorne & others - leading counsel for first defendant prison governor of HMP Downview, allegation of misconduct in public office - 'sex for favours' case; R v Edwards & Others - lead defence counsel for first defendant, international drug gang trial involving importation of cocaine on massive scale; R v Ali & Ali - revenge murder trial; R v Parkins - defended foster carer of 30 yrs, alleged to have assaulted and drugged baby in her care. Gillian was instructed by the Milan Prosecutors' Office to conduct mutual legal assistance proceedings in the corruption case of Silvio Berlusconi and David Mills.
Professional Memberships: Criminal Bar Association; South Eastern Circuit; Association of Regulatory and Disciplinary Lawyers; International Society of the Reform of Criminal Law.
Career: Called to the Bar 1996. Appointed Recorder of the Crown Court 2012. Experienced in lecturing and conducting training seminars on developments in criminal law.
Publications: Chapter contributor to Rook and Ward "Sexual Offences Law & Practice", Sweet & Maxwell and "Fraud Law, Practice and Procedure", Lexis-Nexis; Contributing Editor to "Archbold Magistrates Court Criminal Practice", Sweet & Maxwell; Articles include Parliamentary Brief (Right to trial by jury in fraud cases); Contributor to "Gynaecology: Towards better care of the female victim of sexual assault", used in training of forensic gynaecologists and contributor to Legal Network TV (College of Law) training DVDs on developments in criminal law.

JONES, Jennifer
Atkin Chambers, London
020 7404 0102
jjones@atkinchambers.com
Featured in Construction (London)
Practice Areas: Jennifer maintains a wide ranging practice with experience in domestic courts, international and domestic arbitrations and mediations and adjudications. Her main areas of specialisation are construction and engineering, energy, and professional negligence. Jennifer is also well versed in jurisdictional and conflicts issues and in the construction of guarantees and bonds. Recent decisions: Platform Funding v Anderson & Associates (2012, alleged negligence of a surveyor where the underlying transaction had been procured by fraud); Towsey v Highgrove Homes (2012, proper approach to winding up a company following an adjudicator's decision); Vossloh Aktiengesellschaft v Alpha Trains (2010, proper construction of a guarantee); Rust Consulting v PB (2010, indemnities, issue estoppel).
Professional Memberships: TECBAR, Combar, SCL.
Career: Called to Lincoln's Inn in 2003; MA(Oxon) Law with Law Studies in Europe.
Personal: Good command of French.

JONES, John Richard QC
Carmelite Chambers, London
020 7936 6300
clerks@carmelitechambers.co.uk
Featured in Financial Crime (London)
Practice Areas: "Fraud work has lead into regulatory work with several high profile trials involving Health and Safety work and trading standards. Trading standards case recently concluded at Wolverhampton Crown Court resulted in the dismissal of all charges a court order prevents wider reporting." All aspects of serious fraud including money laundering, insider dealing, financial services and M.T.I.C. including R v Cox & others (Operation Divert). Other notable recent fraud cases include: R v Aspin (& Others) Commercial Fraud/Tax Evasion; R v Forsyth: S.F.O. prosecution concerning a major computer fraud; R v Jackson (& Others) Rail track Safety Fraud case; R v Bowes: Fraudulent share floatation. R v Brown (and others) SFO prosecution concerning the affairs and supplies of IKEA. R v Cahill (and others) SFO prosecution concerning a phoenix type fraud within various supply companies concerned with the supply of mobile phones (non MTIC) and airtime agreements. R v Mawdesley a fraud concerning both criminal and regulatory breaches of the FSA regulations. The criminal aspects concerned the abuse and ultimately theft of investor funds. Has considerable experience of both UMBS and FCIB related issues. Has recently concluded the Countries largest mortgage fraud defending one of six Solicitors accused of participation in fraud by false valuations and fraudulent conveyancing. (Client Knights was acquitted). The case was known by the operational name BMIF1 and was prosecuted by the S.F.O. Presently retained in several high profile fraud cases including a Boiler Room fraud. Recently concluded the defence in trial 1 of Operation Vex (Van Laarhoven, Donnelly and others) in which he defended the alleged "shadow director" of the MITEK Group and the FCIB. Retained for the defence in Operation Steamroller which concluded in Southwark in May 2013 and in a Hawala Bank fraud and alleged money laundering concerning the alleged laundering of £200 million in alleged ciminal proceeds.
Professional Memberships: A member of the Criminal Bar Association.
Career: Since taking Silk in 2002 (aged 42) has increasingly specialised in fraud based work.

JONES, Jonathan QC
No5 Chambers, Birmingham
0845 210 5555
jjo@no5.com
Featured in Clinical Negligence (Midlands), Personal Injury (Midlands)
Practice Areas: Clinical negligence: cerebral palsy claims; obstetrics; gynaecology; surgical errors; cosmetic surgery; paediatrics; optical negligence; oncology; general practitioners; nursing practice; human rights; inquests. Personal Injury: catastrophic brain injuries; severe spinal injuries; amputations; fatal accidents; industrial disease; asbestos claims; deafness claims; CICA claims; road traffic accidents and accidents at work.
Professional Memberships: AVMA PIBA.
Career: Called 1994. Silk 2013.
Personal: Born 1970. Educated at Bedford School, St Andrews University (Economics MA) and City University (Diploma in Law).

JONES, Mark
Stone Chambers, London
020 7440 6900
mark.jones@stonechambers.com
Featured in Shipping (London)
Practice Areas: Mark Jones has a broad commercial practice, encompassing general commercial work, banking, insurance and reinsurance, shipping, and the sale and carriage of goods (international and domestic). His work covers all aspects of international trade, whether it be the carriage of goods, the sale of goods, or the related financial and insurance transactions. His expertise extends to all corners of the shipping industry, from charterparties to salvage, from cargo claims to collisions, from ship finance to performance guarantees, and from marine insurance to general average. He acts in arbitrations both in London and abroad, and appears regularly in the English Courts. He also provides expert evidence on English maritime law for use in foreign proceedings. Over the years, he has appeared in a number of leading shipping cases, such as the 'ATLANTIK CONFIDENCE' (Court of Appeal), the 'ALEXANDROS T', the "MSC NAPOLI", the "STARSIN" (House of Lords) and the "SEA ANGEL" (Court of Appeal). He has been consistently recommended in the well-known legal directories as a leading barrister for shipping, where he has been noted for his particular expertise in shipbuilding and ship sale and purchase disputes and described as a "very knowledgable, sharp minded and skilful barrister" with a "great analytical mind" who has "a good understanding of front line litigation" and pays "phenomenal attention to detail and gives prompt and pragmatic advice."
Professional Memberships: COMBAR; LCLBA; BMLA; supporting member LMAA.
Career: BA (Hons) - Oxford University; 1998-2000 - Ince & Co; 2000 - Called to the Bar (Lincoln's Inn, Kennedy Scholar).

JONES, Nicholas David
Civitas Law, Cardiff
0845 0713 007
ndj@civitaslaw.com
Featured in Clinical Negligence (Wales & Chester), Personal Injury (Wales & Chester)
Practice Areas: Practiises in high value personal injury litigation. Acts on behalf of Claimants and Defendants (including Central Government and the Welsh Government). Caseload consists of catastrophic injury claims: traumatic brain injuries, spinal cord injuries (tetraplegia and paraplegia) and upper and lower limb amputations. Cases have included Claimants in a persistent vegetative state, minimally aware and locked in. Also included those who have sustained injuries abroad. Involved in litigation where orthopaedic and psychiatric injuries and pain syndromes remove or substantially reduce the ability to work as well as asbestos related litigation. Fatal Accident Act claims and appeals against the Criminal Injuries Compensation Authority also form an important part of work. Practises in significant cases of clinical negligence. Caseload includes negligence arising out of: birth; anaesthesia; consent to treatment; negligence in diagnosis (missed, delayed and wrongful; including cancer misdiagnosis); GP practice; nursing care; prescriptions; surgery (including injury to spinal cord).
Professional Memberships: PIBA.
Career: Junior Counsel to the Crown (Provincial Panel): appointed in 2000; reappointed in 2003; reappointed in 2007. Junior Counsel to the Attorney General's Panel of Prosecution Advocates (Health and Safety and Environmental): appointed in

2002; reappointed in 2006;reappointed in 2012. Junior Counsel to the Counsel General of the Welsh Government: appointed in 2000; reappointed in 2003; reappointed in 2009 (specialist field of Personal Injuries law); reappointed in 2012 (specialist field of Personal Injuries law). Mediator (civil and commercial).

JONES, Nigel QC
Hardwicke, London
020 7691 0050
nigel.jones@hardwicke.co.uk
Featured in Construction (London), Insurance (London), Professional Negligence (London)

Practice Areas: Joint Head of Chambers. Consistently recommended by legal directories as a leading silk in his four areas of specialist practice: commercial litigation, insurance and reinsurance, construction, and commercial professional negligence. Nigel is a highly experienced adviser and trial and appellate lawyer. He is instructed by some of the country's leading and most specialist solicitors for national and international clients including: clearing banks, private banks and building societies; Lloyd's syndicates and leading insurers such as Ace, RSA, QBE, Liberty and MarketForm; major utility companies such as EDF Energy and UK Power Networks; local authorities and the FSA Ombudsman; national housebuilders (e.g. Barratt & Bellway), listed companies and high-profile sports clubs and sportsmen. He is a highly experienced mediator and commercial arbitrator.
Professional Memberships: ADR Chambers (UK) Ltd; Commercial Bar Association; Franco-British Lawyers Society; Institute of Arbitrators; London Commercial Law and Commercial Bar Association; Professional Negligence Bar Association; Technology and Construction Bar Association.
Career: Qualified 1976; QC 1999; mediator and arbitrator (and former Recorder).

JONES, Philip QC
Serle Court, London
020 7242 6105
pjones@serlecourt.co.uk
Featured in Chancery (London), Commercial Dispute Resolution (London), Company (London), Fraud (London), Partnership (London), Professional Negligence (London), Restructuring/Insolvency (London), Tax (London)

Practice Areas: Company and partnership law; insolvency; commercial fraud; Chancery (trusts and property litigation); financial services; professional negligence; competition; tax and VAT litigation; public law.
Professional Memberships: Chancery Bar Association; COMBAR.
Career: Junior Counsel to the Crown (Chancery) 1994, Junior Counsel to the Crown (A Panel) 1999.

JONES, Richard
1 Garden Court Family Law Chambers, London
020 7797 7900
jones@1gc.com
Featured in Family/Matrimonial (London)

Practice Areas: Richard's practice is concentrated on cases involving children both in the public law field and in private law proceedings. His private law work includes disputes relating to contact and residence as well as leave to remove applications. Richard's practice has developed a particular focus on International Child Abduction, representing both Applicants and Defendants in cases relating to both Hague and non Hague Convention countries. In the public law arena, Richard represents the full range of parties be it for a local authority, the parents or guardian and has undertaken a wide variety of cases dealing with allegations of serious sexual abuse and NAI. Of late Richard has engaged in many cases involving applications for Special Guardianship Orders. Richard's breadth of experience in care cases has enabled him to be instructed in Court of Protection cases before the High Court.
Professional Memberships: FLBA, FMA - Family Mediators Association, Association of Lawyers for Children.
Publications: The Inherent Jurisdiction of the High Court in light of Re SA: Court of Protection; Nova Law, Mediation in the Context of Child Abduction: Nova Law, Mediation in International Family Law Disputes: International Family Law.
Personal: History, Theology and the Arts.

JONES, Seán QC
11KBW, London
020 7632 8500
sean.jones@11kbw.com
Featured in Employment (London), Sports Law (London)

Practice Areas: Sean specialises in Employment and Sports law. His employment practice is broad. He acts for individuals, trade unions, employers' federations, international banks, airlines, public and private utilities, hospitals, universities, firms of solicitors, television and other media companies, local authorities, technology and computer companies and charities. He advises upon and litigates claims across the full range of employment issues including unfair and wrongful dismissal (including 'whistle-blowing' dismissals), race, sex, disability, sexual orientation and religious discrimination, equal pay and transfer of undertakings. He specialises in high value claims of particular complexity. His Sports practice is principally focused on football cases. He has represented a number of Premier League and other teams in manager and player disputes and for managers in disputes with their clubs.
Professional Memberships: ELBA, ELA, COMBAR, Discrimination Law Association, Industrial Law Society, British Association for Sport and the Law.
Career: Called to the Bar and joined Chambers in 1991. Appointed a Fee-paid Employment Judge in 2011 and took silk in 2012.
Publications: Tolley's Employment Handbook (general editor).
Personal: Educated at Colchester Royal Grammar School 1977-84 and Worcester College, Oxford 1985-89 (BA Hons in Jurisprudence, BCL). Born 9 July 1966. Lives in Wimbledon.

JONES, Timothy
No5 Chambers, Birmingham
0845 210 5555
tj@no5.com
Featured in Planning (Midlands)

Practice Areas: Tim Jones has extensive experience in planning advocacy, appearing at all levels from inquiries (development-control, development-plan, CPO and transport) to the House of Lords and the European Court of Human Rights for both developers and LPAs. He also works as part of teams dealing with major s106 and highway agreements. Cases include Barnsley v SSCLG, Buckley v UK, Butler v BANES, Chapman v UK, Sainbury v Greenwich, R v Sandwell ex parte Wilkinson, R (Bleaklow) v Peak District NPA, R (CPRE) v Swindon, R (Jones) v North Warwickshire, R (Maxwell) v Wiltshire, Wychavon v SSE, Wyre Forest v SSE. His writings and talks include EU environment law, the relationship of human rights to planning, highway agreements, housing, law reform and Gypsies. He has taught European law in several countries for the Council of Europe, US State Department and Ministries of Justice. He is a member of the Bars of Ireland and Northern Ireland, FCIArb (UK & International Arbitration) and an accredited mediator.

JORDAN, Ruth
Serle Court, London
020 7242 6105
rjordan@serlecourt.co.uk
Featured in Restructuring/Insolvency (London)

Practice Areas: Chancery and commercial litigation; company and insolvency (including directors' disqualification); probate, property, charities, tax and trusts (offshore and domestic) litigation; fraud and injunctive relief; financial services and judicial review. Acted in Pitt v Holt [2013] UKSC 26 and [2011] EWCA Civ 197; Ardagh Group v Pillar Property [2013] EWCA and [2012] EWHC 3649; Oceania v Willard Clarke [2013] UKPC 3; Reid v HMRC [2012] UKUP 338; Re Mercury Tax Group (In Administration) [2010] EWCA 1379; Re Stakefield [2010] EWHC 2518 and 3175; R v Save Guana Cay [2009] UKPC 44; Klincke v HMRC [2009] UKFTT 156; Harding v HMRC [2008] EWCA 1164; Smith v HMRC [2008] WTLR 147; Re City Trucks Ltd [2008] BCC 76; Re TXU, Sisu v Tucker [2006] 1 All ER 167.
Professional Memberships: Chancery Bar Association, COMBAR.
Career: Called to the Bar 2001. Seconded to the FSA (splits investigation) 2003-04. Junior Counsel to the Crown (Attorney General's C Panel) 2007.
Personal: BA (Trinity College Dublin), MPhil, PhD (Cambridge), PgDL (City).

JORY, Richard QC
9-12 Bell Yard, London
020 7400 1800
r.jory@912by.com
Featured in Crime (London)

Practice Areas: Defends and prosecutes in cases of fraud and serious crime. Particular experience and knowledge in complex fraud. Richard has been instructed by a variety of prosecuting authorities including CPS Central Fraud Group [and the former Revenue and Customs Prosecutions Office as their Standing Counsel], the CPS Organised Crime Division and the Serious Fraud Office. He has been instructed by the defence in allegations of serious fraud and financial crime in an advisory capacity and at trial. He has been lead counsel in high profile cases involving tax evasion, money laundering, drug trafficking, bribery and corruption. He has experience in dealing with foreign jurisdictions in obtaining and using evidence in UK courts. Richard has lectured on topics including money laundering, obtaining evidence from abroad, Abuse of Process, disclosure and confiscation.
Professional Memberships: Criminal Bar Association, Fraud Advisory Panel, Fraud Lawyers Association.
Career: Called 1993 (Middle Temple, Gottlieb Award), Standing Counsel to the Revenue and Customs Prosecutions Office 2008-2011, CPS advocate panel level 4 for London and the South East, and specialist level 4 for Fraud and Organised Crime. Member of the Conduct Committee of the Bar Standards Board, 2006-2011. Queen's Counsel 2013.
Personal: Born 22nd April 1967. University of Reading (Modern History and International Relations). Richard is a member of the Howard League for Penal Reform and Justice, and a Board trustee director of 'Outside Chance'.

JOSEPH, Paul
No5 Chambers, Birmingham
0845 210 5555
pj@no5.com
Featured in Commercial Dispute Resolution (Midlands)

Practice Areas: Commercial Litigation, Costs, International Arbitration, Insurance and Insolvency. Paul has a particular interest in the area of Costs and has recently appeared in the Court of Appeal for the Government on a costs matter. Notable cases include Tibbles -v- SIG PLC [2012] EWCA Civ 518 (operation of CPR Part 3.1(7)) and G -v- Hull City (applicability of the SCCO Guidelines to detailed assessments). He is often instructed on appeals on costs issues as well as on detailed assessments themselves.
Career: Paul qualified as a solicitor in 1992 and then worked for 9 years in the commercial litigation department of the firm now known as Squire Sanders. He then spent 4 years working as an Attorney-at-Law in the Cayman Islands. In 2005, he transferred to the Bar and joined No 5 Chambers.

JOURDAN, Stephen QC
Falcon Chambers, London
020 7353 2484
clerks@falcon-chambers.com
Featured in Agriculture & Rural Affairs (London), Real Estate Litigation (London)

Practice Areas: Real property, commercial, agricultural and residential landlord and tenant, conveyancing, mortgages, solicitors' and surveyors' professional negligence, environmental contamination, insolvency aspects of real property, contractual disputes relating to property and agriculture. Acts as arbitrator and independent expert in property related disputes.
Professional Memberships: Chancery Bar Association; LCLCBA; Property Bar Association.
Career: Educated at Haberdashers' Aske's Boys' School; Trinity College, Cambridge (MA Law 1984, 1st); Qualified Solicitor 1987; called to the Bar 1989 (Gray's Inn); Deputy Adjudicator to HM Land Registry 2008 - 2013; Silk 2009; recorder (Civil) 2010; Deputy High Court Judge (Chancery) 2013, Judge of First Tier Tribunal (Property Chamber) Land Registration Division 2013.
Publications: Adverse Possession (2nd ed. Bloomsbury 2011); Consultant Editor or "Boundaries" in vol 4 of Halsbury's Laws (5th ed 2011).

KAMM, Rachel
11KBW, London
020 7632 8500
rachel.kamm@11kbw.com
Featured in Data Protection (London), Education (London)

Practice Areas: Public law, including a wide range of education, information, immigration, community care and local

government issues. She is registered on the public access scheme, was appointed to the Attorney-General's 'C' Panel of Junior Counsel to the Crown on 1 March 2011 and sits as a fee-paid Judge of the First-tier Tribunal (Social Entitlement Chamber). Recent cases include: Kennedy v Charity Commission [2014] UKSC 20, [2012] 1 Info LR 137R (access to information and human rights); O'Brien v. Ministry of Justice (No. 2) [2014] IRLR 440 (discrimination); (Afework) v LB Camden [2013] EWHC 1637 (Admin) (mental health after-care); Information Commissioner v Dransfield and Devon CC [2012] UKUT 440 (AAC), [2013] 1 Info LR 360 (vexatious requests for information); R (RB) v Devon CC and Devon PCT (2013) EqLR 113 (public sector equality duty); R (Moyse) v Secretary of State for Education and the Interim Executive Board of Downhills School [2012] EWHC 2758 (Admin), [2012] E.L.R. 551 (conversion of maintained school to academy).
Publications: Halsbury's Laws of England (volume 61, Judicial Review, Fifth Edition), Administrative Court Practice (OUP, 2008), and Administrative Court Digest (Sweet & Maxwell). Posts on 11KBW's information and education blogs (www.panopticonblog.com; www.education11kbw.com). Tweets as @kamm11kbw.

KANE, Adam
Carmelite Chambers, London
07749 347 225
avkane@hotmail.com
Featured in Financial Crime (London)
Practice Areas: Criminal defence specialist across high-value white collar crime, in complex cases often involving multiple complainants. Frequently acts for company officers and professionals, in investigations in the Financial Services sector, market-rigging and regulatory offending, HMRC evasions, commercial and residential property fraud, Public Sector fraud and money laundering. Current cases include R –v Harper & Others – bribery and corruption of the Privy Purse & Treasurers Office of the Royal Household, Operation Hornet –£35 million bribery and corruption case involving HBOS executives and turnaround consultancy , Operation Bellum – abuse of position and fraud conspiracy, for Nat West business banking manager, Operation Kyrenia – fraud on NHS by perfusion scientists. Recent caes include Operation Pursuit – a £7 million commercial property fraud, Operation MFB – a £300 million MTiC fraud, Operation Nanobot – conspiracies to defraud the Revenue and to launder proceeds of a fraud upon DEFRA, Operation Steamroller – a $100 million investment fraud, Operation Groat – fraud upon the NHS by dental practice, and Operation Raiment – conspiracies to defraud management receivers and liquidators.
Professional Memberships: Criminal Bar Association, Administrative Law Bar Association, South Eastern Circuit.
Career: BA (Oxon), CPE, Grays Inn.

KAPILA, Rachel
3 Raymond Buildings Barristers, London
020 7400 6400
rachel.kapila@3rblaw.com
Featured in Extradition (London), Licensing (London)
Practice Areas: Criminal, licensing, extradition and regulatory practitioner, with a growing practice in sports law. Criminal law: Prosecution and defence, as led junior and alone, with increasing focus on fraud and financial crime. Experienced extradition practitioner, advising and acting for defendants and requesting states/judicial authorities, at first instance and on appeal. Licensing: Advises and represents licensees/applicants, local authorities and interested parties in all matters connected with licensable activity, including gambling, liquor, regulated entertainment, child performance/stage licensing, street trading and taxi licensing; extensive appellate and public law practice in these areas. Professional discipline: Particular expertise in representing police officers at misconduct hearings; also experience appearing before the Solicitors Disciplinary Tribunal. Regulatory law: Advises and appears in proceedings arising out of a variety of regulatory regimes, including health and safety, fire safety, food safety and trading standards prosecutions. Extensive inquest practice, with focus on inquests involving investigations into the actions of the police. Developing practice in sports law, with particular interest in disciplinary and anti-corruption work.
Career: BA Hons (Oxon) Jurisprudence; Postgraduate Certificate in Sports Law and Practice (Distinction, 1st in order of merit); Bar Vocational Course (Outstanding, 1st in order of merit); Appointments: British Swimming Judicial Appeal Panel (2012).

KARAS, Jonathan QC
Falcon Chambers, London
020 7353 1261
clerks@falcon-chambers.com
Featured in Agriculture & Rural Affairs (London), Planning (London), Real Estate Litigation (London)
Practice Areas: All aspects of land law, extending from litigation and advice concerning leases, transfers, development agreements and rights over land to the law of planning and compulsory purchase, highways and waterways, manorial rights, commons and greens.
Professional Memberships: Chancery Bar Association; Property Bar Association; Planning and Environmental Bar Association; Compulsory Purchase Association.
Career: MA (Oxon); Called 1986; Supplementary Panel of Junior Counsel to the Crown(Common Law)(now the 'B' Panel)1995-2000; 'A' Panel of Junior Counsel to the Crown 2000-2006; Silk 2006.
Publications: Subject editor of Hill and Redman's law of Landlord and Tenant; author (with David Elvin QC) of Unlawful Interference with Land second edition (2002); contributing editor to the Compulsory Acquisition title (1996), editor of the Distress title (2000, 2007 re-issues), the Forestry title (2007 and 2009 re-issues) and co-editor of the Perpetuities and Accumulations title (2013)' Blundell Memorial Lecture (2007) on the award of damages in lieu of injunctions and (2014) on "negotiating damages".

KARIA, Chirag QC
Quadrant Chambers, London
020 7583 4444
chirag.karia@quadrantchambers.com
Featured in Shipping (London)
Practice Areas: Commercial law, including shipping, commodities, joint ventures, share purchase agreements and commercial arbitration. Cases: DC Merwestone (2014) (CA) (insurers' fraudulent device defence & A1P1 of Human Rights Convention); Crudesky [2014] 1 Lloyd's Rep 1 (CA)(demurrage; novus actus; restraint of princes); Proton v. Orlen [2014] 1 Lloyd's Rep 100 (whether CIF sale concluded; description vs. quality); DC Merwestone [2013] 2 Lloyd's Rep 131 (Com.Ct)("perils of the sea" & Inchmaree insurance cover; fortuity requirement; privity defence); Lehmann Timber [2013] 2 Lloyd's Rep 541 (CA)(recoverability of lien exercise costs; loss of lien); Ratna Shradha [2013] EWCA Civ 746 (CA)(US$60 million oil cargo dispute between Sudan and South Sudan; state immunity); Arbitration (2013)(recoverability of pure economic loss in tort); ICC Arbitration (subsea blowout preventer supply); Qatar Star [2011] 1 Lloyd's Rep 350 (effect of standard anti-technicality clause); The Sylvia [2010] 2 Lloyd's Rep 81 (remoteness of damages after Achilleas); Socol 3 [2010] 2 Lloyd's Rep 221 (deck cargo indemnity; negligence); Choil v Sahara [2010] EWHC 374 (Comm)(recoverability of hedging losses).
Professional Memberships: COMBAR; State Bar of California.
Career: Called 1988, Lincoln's Inn (Denning Scholar); Queen's Counsel 2012; MA(Cantab.), Slaughter & May Prize (top 1st in Law at Cambridge University); LL.M. (UC Berkeley), Harkness Fellow; Attorney practising in California(1990-2000).
Publications: Joint Editor, "Butterworths Commercial Court and Arbitration Pleadings".

KARIM, Sam
Kings Chambers, Manchester
0845 034 3444
clerks@kingschambers.com
Featured in Administrative & Public Law (Northern), Civil Liberties & Human Rights (Northern), Court of Protection (All Circuits)
Practice Areas: Sam is a leading junior practitioner in arbitration (domestic and international), information law, public and administrative law and human rights law, regulatory law, public procurement and state aid law, Court of Protection and mental health. He is a member of the Attorney General's regional panel of Treasury Counsel.
Professional Memberships: Member of the Attorney General's Regional Panel. Member of the Executive Committee of the Administrative Law Bar Association (ALBA). Northern Administrative Law Association (NALA), Acting Chair. Director of Manchester Public Law Pro-Bono Scheme.
Career: LLM(Lond.), LLB(Hons), PG Dip Laws, MCIArb Call in 2002 (Grays Inn).
Publications: Joint author and editor of "Public Law Online" and the book 'Judicial Review: Law & Practice' with Mrs Justice Patterson.

KAY, Dominic
Crown Office Chambers, London
020 7797 8100
kay@crownofficechambers.co.uk
Featured in Health & Safety (London)
Practice Areas: Consistently ranked in Band 1, former 'Junior of the Year' and listed in the 2014 'Bar 100'. One of the Country's leading health & safety barristers who spends the vast majority of his time defending high profile regulatory prosecutions brought against corporate and individual defendants. Significant experience in manslaughter prosecutions, both corporate manslaughter (having defended Lion Steel Limited in 2012), and cases involving allegations of individual gross negligence manslaughter. His work includes cases concerning the construction, leisure, agriculture, care and retail sectors, and those involving educational establishments, public bodies and the emergency services and typically involves multi-fatalities and accidents involving complex machinery. Undertakes large number of inquests into health and safety and workplace related deaths. Highly experienced in cases concerning the deaths of children. Described in 2014 'Bar 100' as "renowned for his top level Health & Safety work...a barrister with a nationwide practice...with a strong grasp of clients' commercial and legal requirements and excellent communication skills. He is very confident before the Bench and when handling opponents." Highly experienced defending environmental prosecutions, including those concerning large-scale pollution incidents, permitting offences, waste escapes and licence infringements. His consumer work includes cases concerning food, toy and general product labeling and safety.

KAY, Steven QC
9 Bedford Row, London
020 7489 2727
steven.kayqc@9bedfordrow.co.uk
Featured in Crime (London)
Practice Areas: Steven Kay QC leads 9 Bedford Row's International Team. He is a leading international criminal lawyer, with a global reputation who has been in many of the landmark cases that have established modern international criminal law. He has represented Heads of State, leading Military figures and civilians in high profile international trials. His cases demonstrate the depth of experience and the quality of the work for which he has been hired (OTP v. Tadic; OTP v. Musema; OTP v. Milosevic; OTP v. Cermak; OTP v. Kenyatta; ECHR Beslan case against Russia). Other advisory work not in the public domain is confidential. He has developed an impressive team at 9BRi to meet the unique challenges these cases present in whatever part of the world they may arise. Steven is experienced in advising clients at the crisis stage of an international situation by setting out their options and guiding their responses, whilst also making the preparations necessary for future litigation. International cases are complex and demanding, they require a careful exercise of judgment and a thorough understanding of the issues involved so that a case is ready for trial. Experience has shown that good systems for the collection and management of evidence are necessary and he assembles a highly able team to perform these tasks. The presentation of that material is then crucial and it is here where his advocacy is able to make the difference in a clear, understandable and accurate presentation of a case either through the questioning of witnesses or speeches. Steven is currently Co-Chair of the IBA War Crimes Committee. For full details, see http://www.9bedfordrow.co.uk/members/Steven_Kay_QC and www.9bri.com.
Professional Memberships: International Bar Association, S.E. Circuit.
Career: Called to the Bar 1977, QC 1997, Secretary CBA 1993-96, Co-Chair IBA War Crimes Committee 2013-, Founder European Criminal Bar Association 1998, Founder International Criminal Law Bureau 2008 see www.internationallawbureau.com.
Publications: Contributor to 'Commentary on The Rome Statute of the International

Criminal Court', OUP 2002. Westlaw UK Insight: International Criminal Justice.
Personal: Educated Epsom College; Leeds University.

KEE, Peter
Becket Chambers, Canterbury
01227 786 331
clerks@becket-chambers.co.uk
Featured in Local Government (South Eastern)
Practice Areas: Peter has a general common law practice. His practice includes employment, discrimination, housing (in particular anti-social behaviour), customs (condemnation and cash forfeiture), crime and inquests. Peter also has extensive experience of licensing (both at committee and appeal stages).
Professional Memberships: South Eastern Circuit, Criminal Bar Association, Kent Bar Mess.
Career: After completing pupillage Peter joined the Treasury Solicitor's Department where he worked for six years and was involved in a variety of roles including litigation, drafting and advisory work. He spent three years as a part-time volunteer with Toynbee Hall Legal Advice Centre. He went with Voluntary Service Overseas to the Pacific for four years – two years as an assistant public solicitor in the Solomon Islands and two years as a provincial government legal officer in Papua New Guinea. He went back to university in 2006 to take a LLM degree in Human Rights and Civil Liberties. He spent four years with the Refugee Legal Centre in London and Dover. He joined Becket Chambers in 2004. He accepts work under the Direct Public Access scheme.

KEELING, Adrian QC
No5 Chambers, Birmingham
07711 749 643
afk@no5.com
Featured in Crime (Midlands), Police Law (All Circuits), Professional Discipline (The Regions)
Practice Areas: Adrian specialises in regulatory, criminal, and professional discipline work. He has a practice at the highest level nationally and locally. He specialises in the most complex and difficult of cases. He has the ability to understand intricate facts, and then convey them sympathetically with the advocacy skills of an established silk. He is a very effective advocate. He is described as "an excellent tactician, charming with juries and offering brilliant client care". His recent casework has included; Operation Elveden instructed by News International, "Plebgate", numerous high value frauds, other "white collar crime", the leading authority on Misconduct in Public Office, gross negligence manslaughter, as well as contract killing and other murders. In Regulatory work he has particular experience in professional misconduct, inquests and professional regulatory work. He has huge experience in police work and has had extensive success in professional misconduct hearings, and trials throughout the length and breadth of the country. In addition he has been instructed in some of the most high profile Inquests of recent times. He prides himself on his relations with clients.
Professional Memberships: Member of the Criminal Bar Association. Member of the Association of Regulatory and Disciplinary Lawyers.

KEITH, Benjamin
5 St Andrew's Hill, London
020 7332 5400
benkeith@5sah.co.uk
Featured in Extradition (London)
Practice Areas: Ben is a Barrister specialising in Extradition, Serious Fraud, Human Rights and Public Law including the challenge of INTERPOL Red Notices. He leads the 5SAH extradition team. He was voted Judicial Review Barrister of the Year by Acquisition International Magazine. He has a developed expertise in political corruption cases and in particular requests from former soviet states especially: Russia, Ukraine, Azerbaijan, Kazakhstan and Moldova.
In 2014 he was successful in the case of Government of Ukraine v Kononko [2014] EWHC 1420 (Admin) which related to the BTA Bank (Kazakhstan) v Mukthar Ablyazov litigation; where the prosecution was found to be an abuse of the court's process.
Career: Ben has considerable experience of EAW cases including cases of murder, rape, people trafficking, terrorism and complex fraud. Ben has a busy Appellate practice and has recently appeared for the Appellants in the leading authorities in the Divisional Court on Latvian Prisons: Brazuks and others v Latvia [2014] EWHC 1021 (Admin); Romanian Prisons: Florea v Romania [2014] and the taking into account of personal and Family life in: Goman v Poland [2013] EWHC 3606 (Admin) and Baturo v Poland [2014] EWHC 710 (Admin).
Personal: Ben lectures in Human Rights at the University of London.

KEITH, Hugo QC
3 Raymond Buildings Barristers, London
020 7400 6400
hugo.keith@3rblaw.com
Featured in Administrative & Public Law (London), Extradition (London), Inquests & Public Inquiries (London), Crime (London), Financial Crime (London)
Practice Areas: Described as 'a fabulous silk' and as having 'an outstanding reputation', Hugo is recognised as one of the legal profession's leading QC's. He was a member of the 'A' Panel of civil Treasury Counsel for 8 years, during which time he regularly appeared on matters of public and criminal law both on behalf of Government departments and as amicus curiae before the High Court, Court of Appeal and House of Lords. He has appeared in 14 cases before the House of Lords/Supreme Court. He won the Chambers and Partners award for criminal barrister of the year 2008, and took silk in 2009. He has been instructed in some of the most high profile cases of recent years. He represented The Queen in the Inquest into the death of Diana, Princess of Wales, and Malcolm Calvert in the Cazenove insider dealing case. He was then appointed leading Counsel to the Inquests into the London Bombings of 7 July 2005 and, subsequently, appeared in the Leveson Inquiry on behalf of Rebekah Brooks and in the Tchenguiz action against the SFO. Notable cases in 2013 included the Gary McKinnon case, the Shrien Dewani extradition (in which he successfully represented the Republic of South Africa), the Inquest into the death of Mark Duggan (Hugo represented the Metropolitan Police Commissioner), the Inquest into the death of Alexander Litvinenko (on behalf of Boris Berezovsky), the Hermitage Capital affair, and the SFO investigation into LIBOR.

KELLER, Ciaran
Maitland Chambers, London
020 7406 1200
ckeller@maitlandchambers.com
Featured in Chancery (London), Commercial Dispute Resolution (London), Real Estate Litigation (London)
Practice Areas: Commercial and chancery litigation and arbitration (domestic and international), including business agreements and general contractual disputes, banking and financial services litigation, civil fraud and asset tracing, property litigation, energy and minerals, jurisdiction disputes, company and insolvency matters, fiduciaries, professional negligence and claims for and against sovereign states. Notable cases include: Yukos Capital v Rosneft [2014] (Comm – enforceability of annulled arbitral awards); Value Discovery Partners v New World Value Fund Partners [2014] (ECSC – construction of articles of association); Cifal Groupe v Meridian Securities [2013] (Comm – jurisdiction challenge); Yukos Capital v Rosneft [2012] (CA - act of state, issue estoppel); Favor Easy Management v Wu [2012] (CA – civil fraud); NML v Argentina [2011] (Supreme Court - sovereign immunity); Crossco v Jolan [2011] (CA - constructive trust, proprietary estoppel); Star Energy v Bocardo [2010] (Supreme Court – trespass by oil pipelines); Crest Nicholson v Akaria [2010] (CA - contractual formation); Mentmore International v Abbey Healthcare [2010] (CA – test for summary judgment); Lindsay v O'Loughnane [2010] (QBD – civil fraud), North Principal Investments v Greenoak Renewable Energy [2009] (Ch – interests in an offshore wind farm); Howell v Lees-Millais [2009] (construction of trustees' power of appointment); IPCO v NNPC [2008] (CA - partial enforcement of a New York Convention award); Langston v Cardiff City FC [2008] (Ch - dispute over loan notes); Barclays Bank v Guy [2008] (Ch – enforceability of charge over fraudulently transferred property); Gamlestaden v Baltic Partners [2007] (Privy Council – unfair prejudice); Meretz Investments v ACP [2007] (CA - unlawful means conspiracy, inducing breach of contract); Donegal International v Zambia [2007] (Comm – bribery, sovereign immunity); Wembley National Stadium v Wembley (London) [2007] (Ch – dispute relating to Wembley Stadium).
Professional Memberships: Commercial Bar Association; Chancery Bar Association; Financial Services Lawyers Association.
Career: Formerly a Member of HM Diplomatic Service (serving at the United Nations and the British Embassy, Lisbon). Called to the Bar 2004.
Personal: Educated at Cheadle Hulme School and Brasenose College, Oxford (MA, 1st Class Honours; Gibbs Prize, John House Prize, Shell Prize; Open Scholarship), City University (Distinction) and the Inns of Court School of Law (Barstow Scholarship, Sweet & Maxwell Company Law Prize). Member of Lincoln' s Inn (Hardwicke, Lord Haldane, Lord Mansfield and Megarry Scholarships; Buchanan Prize; Sir Louis Gluckstein Advocacy Prize).

KELLY, Brendan QC
2 Hare Court, London
020 7353 5324
brendankellyqc@2harecourt.com
Featured in Crime (London), Financial Crime (London)
Practice Areas: Described by the leading industry directory as having "a phenomenal court presence", Brendan Kelly QC's practice focuses on the provision of advice and advocacy in cases of fraud, serious crime, and regulatory law. According to The Legal 500, "His charming style of advocacy makes him a huge hit with both judge and jury". As well as representing individuals, he is also sought out by regulated professionals for cases arising in the workplace. He also regularly advises and represents corporate clients, as well as their individual directors and officers (both in the UK and abroad), in all aspects of business crime. Throughout his career Brendan has been cited as a leader in fraud. He is well experienced in matters involving MTIC and VAT issues, Ponzi schemes, land banking, carbon credit, FOREX / currency exchange, advance fee, boiler room and mortgage frauds. He advises on money laundering, and ancillary proceedings including asset forfeiture, restraint and confiscation. Brendan is also an acknowledged specialist in the law of bribery and corruption, and lectures and trains extensively in this area in the UK, US and other jurisdictions. Alongside his fraud practice, Brendan is requested for serious criminal trials, often involving high-profile defendants; recent instructions include representing the defendant charged with the murder of Welsh schoolgirl, April Jones, as well as the son of a notable Conservative MP who was charged with a serious of offences of violence. He also undertakes regulatory law, and appears for pharmacists who face proceedings brought by their regulatory body, and also appears on behalf of police officers in such cases. Brendan also represents sports professionals, and recent work has included appearing for a racehorse trainer and a Formula One racing driver. Brendan is also authorised to accept instructions to advise individuals and corporate clients on a Direct Access basis.
Career: Called 1988; Recorder 2003; Queen's Counsel 2008.

KELLY, Emma
St Philips Chambers, Birmingham
0121 246 7000
ekelly@st-philips.com
Featured in Real Estate Litigation (Midlands)
Practice Areas: Real estate litigation, commercial and residential landlord and tenant, land registration, beneficial interests in property, and professional negligence in property matters.
Professional Memberships: Property Bar Association; Midland Chancery and Commercial Bar Association.
Career: Called 1997; tenant at 1 Fountain Court, Birmingham until merger with St Philips in 2002; appointed Deputy District Judge (Civil) in 2010; qualified for public access instruction in 2010. Emma regularly participates in Chambers' external seminar programme.
Personal: Educated at University of Sheffield 1993-96 LLB (Hons); Inns of Court School of Law 1997. Emma enjoys time with her young family, skiing, gardening and travel.

KELLY, Geoffrey
Pump Court Chambers, London
020 7353 0711
g.kelly@pumpcourtchambers.com
Featured in Family/Matrimonial (Western)

Practice Areas: Specialises in all areas of family finance litigation. In particular he deals with financial remedies upon divorce or dissolution of civil partnerships, applications under Schedule 1 of the Children Act 1989, property disputes between cohabitees and disputes regarding children. Regularly appears in the Central Family Court (previously the Principal Registry of the Family Division) as well as on Circuit. Reported cases: Bhura v Bhura [2014] EWHC 727; In Re B (A Child) 2011 [2011] EWCA Civ 1001; Fytche v Wincanton Logistics Plc [2004] UKHL 31, [2004] ICR 975; I v N [2003] EWHC 327; A etc v Times Newspapers [2002] EWHC 2444, [2003] 1 FLR 689; R v Headley [1996] TRT 173.
Professional Memberships: Family Law Bar Association, Personal Injury Bar Association.
Career: Called Middle Temple 1992, Recorder of the Crown Court since 2009.
Personal: LLB (Hons), LLM Queen Mary & Westfield College London. Married with children, he enjoys running, fishing and coaching rugby.

KELLY, Mark
No5 Chambers, London
07966 283 120
mrk@no5.com
Featured in Financial Crime (The Regions)
Practice Areas: Defence advocate- specialisations- large scale fraud (international dimension / tax / internet / VAT / education /advance fee / boiler house etc); niche practice in complex / historical sexual assaults; Substantial experience in disciplinary tribunals (for example:police; osteopaths / GMC). Particular interest in disclosure issues / confiscation. National practice/ Accredited mediator / Available for Public Access or Direct Access work. Very interested to utilise skills in foreign jurisdictions (working knowledge of French).
Professional Memberships: Bar European Group; Criminal Bar Association.
Career: Previous experience working as stagiaire in DGIV European Commission in Brussels- also studied European Law at College of Europe in Bruges, Belgium and French at Summer school at Sorbonne in Paris, France.

KELLY, Sean
St Philips Chambers, Leeds
0113 244 6691
skelly@st-philips.com
Featured in Chancery (North Eastern)
Practice Areas: Specialises in Chancery and commercial law including banking, company law, financial services, insolvency, partnerships and LLPs and professional negligence. Sean Kelly is regularly instructed in large scale disputes relating to the ownership and management of companies and partnerships and those relating to business and company sales. His professional negligence practice includes claims against accountants, architects, financial advisers and solicitors. Sean Kelly has a science background and regularly conducts cases involving technical issues. He has been conducting claims relating to interest rate swaps since 1999 and appeared in the only case to date won by the customer. Since mis-selling became widely recognised, he has become a leading specialist in this area and is now involved in over 50 claims on behalf of customers.

Professional Memberships: Chancery Bar Association. Association of Partnership Practitioners. Professional Negligence Bar Association.
Career: Date of Call: 1990 Gray's Inn

KELSEY, Katherine
1 King's Bench Walk, London
020 7936 1500
kkelsey@1kbw.co.uk
Featured in Family/Matrimonial (London)
Practice Areas: Katherine Kelsey specialises in the following areas of Family Law: Financial Remedies: Advising and acting in all areas of matrimonial finance. Experience in dealing with complex cases involving the assertion of third-party interests and intervenors. Other Financial Relief: Advising and acting in relation to claims brought under the Trusts of Land and Appointment of Trustees Act 1996 and Schedule 1 of the Children Act 1989. Private Law Children: Advising and acting in all areas of private law proceedings. Experience in dealing with complex cases involving internal and external relocation and intractable contact disputes. ADR: Katherine is also a qualified mediator and collaborative lawyer.
Professional Memberships: Family Law Bar Association; South Eastern Circuit.
Career: Call: 2003.
Personal: Education: Ilford Ursuline High School; Greyfriars Hall, University of Oxford - BA (Hons) Jurisprudence.

KELSEY-FRY, John QC
Cloth Fair Chambers, London
020 7710 6444
nicknewman@clothfairchambers.com
Featured in Crime (London), Financial Crime (London)
Practice Areas: Practices largely high profile defence, especially Corporate and Business crime eg. Blue Arrow, R v Regan (co-op corruption case), R v Stiedl (pensions funds), R v Stovold (Local Authority Financing). Notable cases include; advised defendant subject of a Hong Kong Department of Justice investigation into market abuse/ insider dealing, represented the defendant in a FSA Crown Court Prosecution, successful half time submission, prosecuted on behalf of the FSA in an insider dealing trial, Dougall the leading authority on sentencing executive level whistle blowers, represented a director of Mabey and Johnson in the sanctions busting investigation. Acted for a former director of iSoft in criminal proceedings, continues to advise re FSA investigation. Notable cases in crime: R v Serafinowicz and R v Sawoniuk (war crimes), R v Smith (KGB Spy), R v Donald and Cressey (police corruption/ Panorama case), R v Charlie Kray, R v Jane Andrews, R v Coutts (necrophiliac murder), Mohammed Al Fayed (deposit box), R v Bukhari (arms case involving FBI). Recent notable cases include; successfully represented Kieren Fallon; Steven Gerrard; secured an acquittal for Harry Redknapp over allegations of tax evasion. Represented a Saudi Prince charged with Murder. Successfully represented an international property tycoon surrounding corruption charges in Turks & Caicos Islands. Advised real estate company Walshaw Moor regarding a dispute with Natural England. Represented former Energy Secretary Chris Huhne charged with perverting the course of justice. Advised ex News International Chief Executive Rebekah Brooks re phone hacking. Acting for Olympus Corporation during SFO investigation and subsequent charges. Advising an individual in SFO investigation regarding Rolls Royce. Acting for former Senior Executive of Barclays in SFO/FCA investigation. Representing Raymond Kwok over corruption charges in Hong Kong. Libel, has been instructed in the following matters; Turcu (Beckham kidnap), Paul McKenna, Wayne Rooney, Sharon Stone, Roman Polanski, Max Mosely, Sir Stelios (founder of Easyjet), Craig Bellamy. Advised The Times Newspaper. For further details please visit www.clothfair-chambers.com.
Professional Memberships: Criminal Bar Association.
Career: Called to the Bar 1978. Treasury Council (Junior and Senior) 1992-2000. QC 2000. Founder member of Cloth Fair Chambers 2006.

KEMBER, Richard
9 Park Place, Cardiff
029 2038 2731
clerks@9parkplace.co.uk
Featured in Chancery (Wales & Chester)
Practice Areas: Richard specialises in chancery, commercial and employment work. His chancery practice is split between land and wills, trusts and probate disputes. He advises and represents clients in all disputes over land, including TOLATA claims, and appears in the specialist courts and tribunals for these matters. His contentious probate caseload includes inheritance and family provision and court of protection matters.
Professional Memberships: Wales and Chester Circuit, PIBA, ELA.
Career: Richard has practised on the Wales and Chester Circuit since 1994.
Personal: Richard read law at Balliol College, Oxford.

KEMP, Edward
Littleton Chambers, London
020 7797 8600
ekemp@littletonchambers.co.uk
Featured in Employment (London)
Practice Areas: Ed is a trial and appellate lawyer specialising in employment law, discrimination law and related areas. Ed has appeared as an advocate (whether unled or part of her larger team) in every level of court and tribunal all the way up to the Supreme Court. He recently appeared for the successful appellant in the Supreme Court in Verma v. Barts and the London NHS Trust [2013] IRLR 567. Ed's industry expertise spans both the public sector (local government, police force, doctors) and the private sector, including cases for or against senior executives and financial institutions. Ed has particular expertise in all discrimination strands, whistle-blowing, complex contractual interpretation points, cases with an international element or ground-breaking points at the interface between domestic and European law. Ed is regularly instructed on cross-over work, for example: discrimination in goods and services litigation, professional negligence and breach of contract claims in the County Court and in the High Court. Ed has recently acquired full rights of audience before the DIFC Courts in Dubai and he is co-head of the International Opportunities Committee at Littleton Chambers.
Professional Memberships: ELBA, ELA, DLA, ELAAS, PIBA, A4ID.
Career: Called to the Bar 2005; Inner Temple Exhibitioner and Sir Joseph Priestly Scholar; LLM, University College London; Maîtrise en Droit, Université de Paris I (Panthéon-Sorbonne); LLB, King's College London.
Personal: Ed speaks French.

KENDRICK, Julia
Crown Office Chambers, London
020 7797 8100
kendrick@crownofficechambers.com
Featured in Health & Safety (London)
Practice Areas: Specialist practice in criminal regulatory law with particular expertise in health and safety, inquests, fire safety, residential care, trading standards, product safety, environmental law, food safety, road traffic offences. Acts for companies, directors, employees. Regularly instructed in health and safety prosecutions arising out of fatal and other serious accidents. Experience of cases involving construction sites, work at height, residential care, fire safety, medical treatment, gas and electrical safety, waste management and recycling; mining and quarrying, COSHH, schools, printing, road traffic accidents. Recently instructed in cases involving: death of four ground workers crushed while erecting reinforced steel; drowning of dementia patient following escape from care home; death of two fire fighters in high-rise block; occupational asthma from inhalation of reactive dyes; paralysis from burns sustained in explosion at work; neonatal death after failure to administer anti-D medication during pregnancy; self-immolation of mental health patient; aquaplaning fatality; asphyxiation from paint stripper fumes; noise-induced hearing loss; carbon monoxide fatality; fall from scaffolding; fatal radiator burns at care home; printing press hand injuries; maternal death during child birth; smoke asphyxiation due to poor fire safety maintenance; death from involuntary movement of crushing machinery due to ground fault; electrocution on construction site; sale of non-compliant tobacco products.

KENT, Michael QC
Crown Office Chambers, London
020 7797 8100
kent@crownofficechambers.com
Featured in Personal Injury (London), Personal Injury (All Circuits)
Practice Areas: He acts for claimants and defendants in a range of complex matters, including disease cases and catastrophic and psychiatric injury claims. He regularly advises on insurance coverage disputes (particularly those relating to employers' and public liability claims). He has acted in a number of test or group actions including contaminated blood products, the Camelford water pollution cases, CJD from human growth hormone, asbestos-related pleural plaques, industrial deafness in Midlands clothing industries , dermatitis from contact with chemicals in furniture (the Linkwise/ Eurosofa litigation), claims by veterans of UK atom bomb tests in 1950s; historic child abuse cases; claims by some 18,000 claimants alleging injury from factory fire (Sonae Group Litigation).
Professional Memberships: London Common Law and Commercial Bar Association (Chairman 2011-13) Administrative Law Bar Association Tecbar London Court of International Arbitration He is a Deputy

High Court Judge (Queen's Bench Division and Administrative Court) and Recorder. He has sat as a legal assessor on GMC committees. He is a Bencher of the Middle Temple.

KENYON, Flavia
3 Temple Gardens, London
020 7353 3102
fk@3tg.co.uk
Featured in Crime (London)
Practice Areas: Serious organised crime, fraud, public access.
Professional Memberships: Lincoln's Inn, Criminal Bar Association.
Career: Flavia was born in Romania, educated at Oxford University and called to the Bar in 2005. She is the only British criminal barrister fluent in Romanian, and has become the 'go-to' lawyer amongst the UK's Romanian community. However, her practice goes well beyond that. She has recently been instructed as leading junior in a case of people trafficking for exploitation. She regularly appears as sole and led junior in complex multi-handed cases of fraud, including cyber fraud, fraudulent trading, ponzi schemes, conspiracies to defraud and money laundering. She also defends in cases of people trafficking, rape and serious violence. Flavia has been instructed in cases before the European Court of Human Rights. She also provides advisory work for the Romanian Embassy and other related bodies. Flavia is respected amongst her peers as a fiercely articulate and determined advocate whose meticulous preparation coupled with intellectual flair, ensure she masters the most complex of briefs.
Publications: "Deportation: Two views on Kluxen" - feature article in Archbold Review, Issue 6, July 2010.

KERR, Tim QC
11KBW, London
020 7632 8500
tim.kerr@11kbw.com
Featured in Education (London), Public Procurement (London), Sports Law (London)
Practice Areas: Judicial review, sports law, sitting as an arbitrator, education law, employment law, local government, public procurement law, disciplinary tribunals. Sits as arbitrator, mainly in domestic and international sports disputes and disciplinary tribunals. Undertakes investigations into allegations against public officials.
Professional Memberships: Administrative Law Bar Association; Employment Law Bar Association; Editorial Advisory Board of the International Sports Law Review. Member of the FA Premiership panel of arbitrators and the Sport Resolution UK National Anti-Doping Tribunal. Chairman of the International Cricket Council Doping Hearing Panel.
Career: Appointed Silk April 2001. Chairman of Employment Tribunals 2001-06. Sits as a Deputy Judge of the Chancery Division and a recorder in criminal cases.
Publications: Sports Law (co-author) (2nd edition, 2012). Various journal articles.
Personal: Runner of four marathons and keen Chelsea supporter. Married with three children. Working languages: French, German and Spanish.

KESSLER, James QC
Tax Chambers 15 Old Square, London
020 7242 2744
kessler@kessler.co.uk
Featured in Charities (London), Tax (London)
Practice Areas: Revenue law. James Kessler QC is particularly interested in foreign domiciliaries, offshore entities of all kinds, and trusts, wills and charities. Other interests include prosecution of tax crime in complex cases, particularly along the avoidance/evasion faultline, and freedom of information.
Professional Memberships: Revenue Bar Association. Member of the Bar of Northern Ireland.
Career: Called to the Bar 1984. QC 2003.
Publications: James is the author of three major works: Taxation of Non-Residents and Foreign Domiciliaries (13th ed, 2014). Drafting Trusts & Will Trusts (12th ed 2014). Taxation of Charities and Non-Profit Organisations (9th, ed 2013). There are at present nine foreign-law editions of Drafting Trusts and Will Trusts: Drafting Trusts and Will Trusts in Australia. Drafting Trusts and Will Trusts in the Channel Islands. Drafting Trusts and Will Trusts in Canada. Drafting Trusts and Will Trusts in New Zealand. Drafting Cayman Islands Trusts. Drafting Trusts and Will Trusts in Northern Ireland. Drafting Trusts and Will Trusts in Singapore. Drafting Trusts and Will Trusts in Scotland. Drafting Trusts in the British Virgin Islands.
Personal: Interests: cinema, jogging.

KHALIL, Karim QC
One Paper Buildings, London
020 7353 3728
karim.khalil@onepapercjsm.net
Featured in Crime (South Eastern)
Practice Areas: Karim Khalil QC is Head of Chambers at One Paper Buildings, working mainly in London and the South East, although he is being instructed increasingly across the country. He is equally in demand for defence and prosecution work and has been instructed in most of the high profile and high value matters to arise on Circuit in recent years, including those relating to significant Police informants. Karim was called to the Bar in 1984, became one of the youngest Recorders, and took Silk in 2003 before prosecuting Ian Huntley & Maxine Carr (Soham murders). He covers a diverse range of work, including murder, sexual offences, drug trafficking, serious fraud (including Revenue, Customs & Excise and MTIC), Health & Safety, and Sport law. As a Cambridge University graduate he can call upon the finest experts when considering new challenges, making him a leading Silk in the cross examination of scientific experts in many fields (including pathology, neuropathology, genetics, palynology and mineralogy). His opinion is sought in significant "cold case reviews". He represents appellants before the VAT Tribunal (usually following assertions of VAT/MTIC fraud); he is instructed in significant POCA proceedings and has undertaken criminal and civil litigation relating to company fraud plus civil claims against the police and prison service. He represented a Cambridge College against the HSE. Karim has promoted computerised presentation of evidence in Court, writes the chapter on Confiscation Law in "Fraud: Law Practice & Procedure" and is a member of many professional bodies, including the British Academy of Forensic Sciences (to whom he presented the keynote speech on "The Science of the Soham Murders").
Professional Memberships: SE Circuit, SE Circuit Liaison Committee (Chairman), CBA, Norwich Bar Mess, Cambridge Bar Mess (Chairman), three years on the Professional Conduct and Complaints Committee, Bar disciplinary Tribunal member.
Career: Cheadle Hulme School (Manchester), Queen's College (Cambridge), called to the Bar 1984, Assistant Recorder 1997, Recorder 2000, Queen's Counsel 2003.
Publications: Fraud: Law, Practice and Procedure - chapter on confiscation.
Personal: Married with two sons. Member of Hawks Club and Okeford Duck Golf Society; alto sax in The Eye; lacrosse player now turned to tennis and golf.

KHAN, Ashraf
2 Bedford Row, London
020 7440 8888
akhan@2bedfordrow.co.uk
Featured in Crime (London), Financial Crime (London)
Practice Areas: Serious Crime Complex Fraud Professional Discipline Regulation and Compliance Civil Recovery and Asset Forfeiture Alternative Dispute Resolution.
Professional Memberships: Chartered Institute of Arbitrators Accredited Civil & Commercial Mediator Registered Lawyer under The FA Football Agents Regulations Registered Practitioner with Dubai International Finance Centre (DIFC) The Honourable Society of the Middle Temple Midland Circuit Junior (October 2011-October 2012) Criminal Bar Association.
Career: Ashraf has a national defence practice which includes a case load of some of the biggest and most complex criminal/fraud cases seen in recent times. His extensive experience of high profile litigation in this area covers a wide spectrum of cases; including homicide, firearms, serious sexual offences, large scale organised crime involving price fixing, corruption, cartel, trafficking, money laundering and high value serious fraud. He is often instructed at the earliest stages of major investigations so clients have the benefit of his advice and assistance during what is often a critical stage in a criminal inquiry. International crime and regulatory law are also a key part of Ashraf's practice. He is appointed to the defence panel at the International Criminal Court (ICC), a registered lawyer with the Football Association and approved to conduct cases at the Dubai International Finance Centre (DIFC), where he advises and represents corporate bodies and individuals in relation to regulatory breaches or complex commercial disputes. Ashraf also offers a high-quality, relevant and sensitive mediation service. He has a wealth of litigation experience and is able to deal with the most complex legal and factual issues in the context of a Mediation. Members of the Public and Businesses can now instruct Ashraf directly under the Bar Council's Direct Access Scheme to provide advice, assistance and representation in a wide range of Criminal and Civil matters. Please contact Chambers and speak directly with John Grimmer or Paul Rodgers for further enquiries.

KHAN, Zarif
Dyers Chambers, London
zarif.khan@dyerschambers.com
Featured in Crime (London)
Practice Areas: Exclusively a defence practitioner in serious crime including murder, terrorism, sexual offences and fraud, frequently under VHCC contracts. His caseload in recent years has attracted considerable media attention both nationally and internationally, from Rochdale and Oxford Sex grooming cases to the murder of Shafelia Ahmed. Zarif combines his jury friendly advocacy style with excellent relationship skills, communicating effectively with both his lay and professional clients. Zarif has a reputation with solicitors for handling the most difficult and challenging defendants. Zarif is also actively sought out by lay and professional clients from around the Country on the basis of recommendations and his reputation. As a result Zarif's practice expands the country. More recently Zarif has developed a Professional Discipline practice where because of the criminal background he is ideally suited to appear before the various professional bodies. His most recent appearances have been before the Medical Practitioners Tribunal Service (MPTS) representing a Doctor and the High Court and Nursing and Midwifery Council (NMC) on behalf of a nurse.
Professional Memberships: Criminal Bar Association, South Eastern Circuit.
Career: Called to the Bar 1996 (Lincoln's Inn).
Personal: Languages - Urdu and Punjabi (Fluent).

KHAYUM, Zulfikar
Atkin Chambers, London
020 7404 0102
zkhayum@atkinchambers.com
Featured in Construction (London)
Practice Areas: Zulfikar practices across all areas of construction, engineering, IT and energy sectors in both the domestic and international context. He has experience of dealing with matters in litigation, arbitration, adjudication and mediation. He represents employers, architects, contractors, sub-contractors, developers, funders, insurers and others. He is often asked to advise on tactical as well as legal issues. Zulfikar has appeared in a number of court hearings as junior counsel as well appearing as sole counsel at various applications and hearings, including trial. He has further advised and acted in arbitrations conducted under various arbitral rules and governing laws in different jurisdictions. Recent experiences include major hearings in the Bahamas, Singapore and Hong Kong and a large domestic dispute concerning a waste processing facility.
Professional Memberships: TECBAR, LCLCBA, Combar, Society of Construction Law.
Career: Called 2006.
Publications: Hudson's Building and Engineering Contracts, 12th Ed. (Sweet & Maxwell, 2010) - contributing editor.
Personal: LLB (Hons); BCL (Oxon).

KILCOYNE, Paul
Temple Garden Chambers, London
paulkilcoyne@tgchambers.com
Featured in Personal Injury (London)
Practice Areas: Paul has an established practice and strong reputation in personal injury and clinical negligence work. He has a special interest in military claims and is instructed by Royal British Legion Panel solicitors and the Forces Law organisation. He is experienced in catastrophic injury claims, industrial disease, deafness claims and work related upper limb disorders. He also represents interested parties at Inquests involving military or hospital deaths. His clinical negligence practice extends to all areas of medical practice including birth

injuries, plastic surgery, dental surgery and consent issues.
Professional Memberships: APIL PIBA ARDL.
Career: Birmingham University LLB (Hons). Lincoln's Inn called 1986 (Hardwicke Scholar). Legal Assessor to the Nursing & Midwifery Council. Legal Adviser to the General Dental Council. Legal Adviser to the General Optical Council. For a full and up to date account of Paul's practice and reported cases please refer to his web-site entry at www.tgchambers.com
Publications: Regular features in the Journal of Personal Injury Law (JPIL).

KILLALEA, Stephen QC
Devereux, London
020 7353 7534
killalea@devchambers.co.uk
Featured in Health & Safety (London), Personal Injury (London), Travel (London)
Practice Areas: A substantial personal injury practice specialising in catastrophic brain and spinal injuries. Considerable experience of industrial accidents, including offshore accidents, commercial diving and accidents on ships and catastrophic accidents occurring abroad. A leading health and safety practice representing companies and individuals in criminal prosecutions by the HSE and other enforcement authorities. (Further details see Chambers website www.devereuxchambers.co.uk).
Professional Memberships: Personal Injuries Bar Association; Association of Personal Injury Lawyers; Health and Safety Lawyers Association.
Career: Called to the Bar 1981. QC 2006.
Publications: Co-author 'Health and Safety The Modern Legal Framework' (2nd Edition) Butterworths 2000. Author of Sections on Construction Regulations and Divers and Offshore Installations (Personal Injury Factbook) Gee & Co 1998.
Personal: Lives in Sussex.

KILVINGTON, Simon
Byrom Street Chambers, Manchester
0161 829 2100
simon.kilvington@byromstreet.com
Featured in Personal Injury (Northern)
Practice Areas: Acts for both Claimants and Defendants in serious and complex personal injury and clinical negligence cases, including catastrophic brain and spinal injuries, amputations and severe psychiatric damage. Acts for Claimants in asbestos-related injury and industrial disease claims and has appeared in many of the leading cases in recent years, including: IEG v Zurich [2014] (Supreme Court); National Grid v McDonald [2014] (Supreme Court); Collins v Secretary of State for Business, Innovation and Skills [2014] (Court of Appeal).
Professional Memberships: PIBA.
Career: Hertford College, Oxford. Called 1995.

KIMBLIN, Richard
No5 Chambers, Birmingham
0845 210 5555
rk@no5.com
Featured in Environment (Midlands), Planning (Midlands)
Practice Areas: Planning, public, environmental and regulatory law.
Professional Memberships: Chair of the United Kingdom Environmental Law Association. PEBA; ALBA.
Career: BSc (Dunelm); PhD; Junior Counsel to the Crown (London Panel). Richard Kimblin is acknowledged in planning, environmental and energy/infrastructre as a leading junior. He has completed a range of cases on the application of the Framework: R (oao) Holder v Gedling BC [2013] EWCA - material considerations in energy proposals; R (oao) Gate v SSfT [2013] EWHC 2973- development consent orders; Cotswold District Council v SSCLG [2013] EWHC 3719 (Admin) - meaning of 'persistent under delivery'; South Northamptonshire DC v SSCLG [2014] EWHC 573 (Admin) - evidence base for housing land supply requirement; policies for the supply of housing; Hampton Bishop PC v Herefordshire Council [2014] EWCA; R (oao) CBRE (Lionbrook) v Rugby BC [2014] EWHC 646 - retail planning policies and the NPPF; R (oao) Timmins/Lymn v Geldling BC [2014] EWHC 654 (Admin) - Green Belt and NPPF; Ashdown Forest LLP v Secretary of State for Communities and Local Government & Wealden DC [2014] EWHC 406 core strategy policy restrained by reason of impacts on a SAC/SPA.
Publications: Interpretation of Planning Policy after Tesco [2012] JPL 9, 1045 – 1052.

KING, Henry
Fountain Court Chambers, London
020 7583 3335
hk@fountaincourt.co.uk
Featured in Banking & Finance (London), Financial Services (London)
Practice Areas: General commercial litigation and arbitration practice, with a particular emphasis on banking and financial services. Notable cases include acting for Deutsche Bank in Deutsche Bank v Sebastian Holdings [2013] EWHC 3463 (Comm), for the Central Bank of Trinidad & Tobago in the CLICO Enquiry, for the Bar Council in R (Prudential) v HMRC [2013] UKSC 1, for John Pottage in Pottage v Financial Services Authority [2013] Lloyd's Rep FC 16 and for the Bank of England in Three Rivers [2006] EWHC 816 (Comm).
Professional Memberships: Institute of Chartered Accountants in England and Wales, Commercial Bar Association, Association of Regulatory and Disciplinary Lawyers, Russian and CIS Arbitration Network.
Career: ACA 1996, Called to the Bar of England and Wales 1998, called to the Bar of the BVI 2011, ad hoc call to the Bars of the Cayman Islands and of Trinidad and Tobago, Junior Counsel to the Crown (B panel).
Publications: Contributor to: The Law of Privilege (ed B. Thanki QC, OUP, 2nd edition 2011); Bullen & Leake & Jacob's Precedents of Pleadings, specialist contributor on Restitution (Sweet & Maxwell, 17th edition 2011); Information Rights: Law and Practice (ed. P Coppel QC, Hart Publishing, 4th edition 2014).

KINNEAR, Jonathan S QC
9-12 Bell Yard, London
020 7400 1800
j.kinnear@912by.com
Featured in Financial Crime (London)
Practice Areas: Specialises in cases of real financial complexity in criminal, civil, regulatory and tribunal jurisdictions. He also deals with complex confiscation and restraint issues at both first instance and all appellate levels. His highlights in the last year include representing: the FRC in regulatory cases against the CEO and auditors of Farepak, the failed Christmas saving club; HMRC in Megantic Services Limited, the longest ever case before the First Tier Tax Tribunal, relating to £40 million of tax; the CPS in Operation Inertia, obtaining confiscation orders in excess of £30 million; the SFO in an investigation relating to the embezzlement of funds from Ukraine by former government ministers and the laundering through major financial institutions; advising the officers of multi-national companies in respect of money laundering investigations.
Career: Called (Gray's Inn) in 1994 and Northern Ireland (1996), appointed QC in 2012, Deputy District Judge in 2004 and a Recorder of the Crown Court in 2009.
Personal: Educated at Methodist College, Belfast and Newcastle University.

KINNIER, Andrew
Henderson Chambers, London
020 7583 9020
akinnier@hendersonchambers.co.uk
Featured in Local Government (London), Product Liability (London), Public Procurement (London)
Practice Areas: Product liability: acting for defendants in group and unitary actions, particularly relating to pharmaceutical products, medical devices and motor vehicles. Public, administrative and local government law, and, in particular, public procurement and state aid: advises central government, local and other public authorities on a broad range of matters including powers, finance, social services, education, waste, civil contingencies and anti-terrorism. Health & safety law: represents corporate clients in respect of regulatory prosecutions, civil proceedings and inquests.
Professional Memberships: ALBA; BEG; Procurement Lawyers' Association; UK State Aid Law Association; Public Law Wales; South Eastern Circuit, Wales and Chester Circuit.
Career: Educated at Sidney Sussex College, Cambridge (1991-95) (BA 1st Class Honours; MA); Called 1996 Middle Temple (Queen Mother-Fox Major Entrance Scholarship). Junior Counsel to the Crown (A Panel 2011-), (B Panel 2008-11); Junior Counsel to the Welsh Government (Public Law Panel 2009-2012); Junior Counsel to the Welsh Government (Public Law - A Panel, 2012-).
Publications: Contributor - Halsbury's Laws of England (Vol 37); Specialist Contributor - Bullen & Leake Precedents & Pleadings (15th-17th editions); Specialist Contributor - Kluwer's Manual of International Product Law (1st and 2nd editions).

KIRBY, PJ QC
Hardwicke, London
020 7242 2523
pj.kirbyqc@hardwicke.co.uk
Featured in Commercial Dispute Resolution (London), Costs Litigation (London)
Practice Areas: Commercial fraud, banking, professional negligence, employment, costs. PJ's practice covers a wide range of commercial dispute resolution but many of the disputes in which he acts involve allegations of fraud. Has acted for and against many banks on professional negligence actions and in general banking and secured lending disputes. Particular interest in restrictive covenant employment cases, including injunctions, and misuse of confidential information. Costs expertise in particular in relation to enforceability of CFAs.
Professional Memberships: PNBA, LCLCBA, ELA, ELBA.
Career: Former solicitor. Deputy District Judge. Bar Council appointed High Court costs assessor. Silk (2013).
Publications: Skiing, watching Chelsea, spending time with family (2 out of 3 normally at the same time).

KIRK, Anthony QC
1 King's Bench Walk, London
020 7936 1500
akirkqc@1kbw.co.uk
Featured in Family/Matrimonial (London)
Practice Areas: Anthony Kirk has particular expertise in children cases, public and private, as well as in the field of international child abduction. He is used to assimilating large quantities of complex medical material relating to brain and skull injuries, as well as cases involving fabricated illness. He has been instructed in the most difficult of adoption cases.
Professional Memberships: Anthony is a member of the South-Eastern circuit, an Honorary Life Vice-President of the FLBA, an affiliate member of Resolution, a member of the FMA, the ALC, and a Fellow of the IAML. He is a member of the Bar Council ADR Group, a Fellow of the RSM and a Bencher of Gray's Inn.
Career: He was called to the bar by Gray's Inn in 1981 and was awarded scholarships by the Inn in recognition of the highest marks awarded in the Bar Final examinations. He joined chambers at 1kbw in 1982. He is a Chairman of the Children Group, the Head of the DRS Team and the Deputy Head of Chambers. He has sat on numerous Committees established by the MOJ to include, most recently, the Mediation Task Force chaired by David Norgrove.
Publications: Anthony continues to give presentations and lectures on aspects of family law whenever able to do so. Within the past 12 months he has addressed numerous conferences both internally and at the request of others nationwide.
Personal: Mediation in private law children cases continues to form a substantial part of his work, away from the court arena. Anthony qualified as a mediator with FMA in April 1998 and was one of the first members of the family Bar to do so. He was particularly pleased to be short-listed for Family Law ADR Practitioner of the Year 2014 by Jordans Publishing. Away from practice Anthony is sometimes reminded that he is a reasonably competent pianist and (when the occasion demands) still an accomplished organist.

KIRK, Jonathan QC
Gough Square Chambers, London
020 7353 0924
gsc@goughsq.co.uk
Featured in Consumer Law (London)
Practice Areas: Consumer.
Professional Memberships: Bar European Group, POCLA, the Food Law Group, the Anti-Counterfeiting Group and the CBA.
Career: Jonathan Kirk QC has spent most of his career advising and representing parties in litigation concerning consumer law and financial regulation. In 2013 he advised and represented several companies on misleading pricing issues following Part 8 enforcement action by the OFT or trading standards departments. He advised and represented companies in relation to the food mis-selling scandals, food labelling, ticket re-selling

and private car parking enforcement. He also advised the Trading Standards Institute, National Trading Standards Board and several regional trading standards groups on consumer law and enforcement issues. In 2012 he advised the Olympic Delivery Authority on the enforcement of advertising and trading standards regulations at the 2012 London Olympics and Paralympics. He lectures widely on EU consumer and trading standards law. He was appointed as counsel at the United Nations in 2005 and Queen's Counsel in 2010. Notable cases: Torfaen CBC v Douglas Willis Ltd [2013] UKSC 59 (Supreme Court): food standards and minimum durability labelling; R v X Limited [2013] EWCA Crim 818 (Court of Appeal): first consideration of the meaning of 'commercial practice' under the Consumer Protection from Unfair Trading Regulations 2008 ('CPUT'); Birmingham CC v Tesco Stores Limited [2013]: pricing under CPUT (strawberries); Cheshire East v Salsa Enterprises Limited and Sean Ellman [2013]: defence of company accused of breaching CPUT by selling 'legal highs'; R v Blake [2013]: defence of managing director of finance company prosecuted for breach of financial conduct provisions; OFT v First Step Finance Limited [2013]: representation of company in relation to the revocation of consumer credit licence; House of Cars Ltd v Derby Car and Van Rental [2012]: first private prosecution under CPUT; East Riding of Yorks v UK Parking Control Ltd [2012] (CC, HC (QBD) and CofA). first trading standards enforcement of CPUT in private car parking enforcement; R (LOCOG) v Sportsworld Limited, Events International Limited and International Corporate Events Limited [2012]: defence of national ticket sales company prosecuted under the provisions 2006 Olympic Act; Brighton & Hove CC v Towers Property Developments Ltd [2011] EWHC (Ch): first Part 8 EA 2002 and CPUT trading standards enforcement against land banking company.
Publications: He is the General Editor of the consumer law textbook: Consumer and Trading Standards: Law and Practice (the Pink Book) and the General Editor of Modern Financial Regulation.

KISSER, Amy
Queen Elizabeth Building, London
020 7797 7837
a.kisser@qeb.co.uk
Featured in Family/Matrimonial (London)
Practice Areas: Amy's practice encompasses all aspects of private family law, including divorce, finance (for married parties after an English or foreign divorce; for unmarried cohabitees and for unmarried parents), and private law children matters. She has a particular interest in cases involving a foreign or international element (including jurisdictional disputes) and complex financial cases involving company, trust and tax issues. Amy has experience in all levels of tribunal up to and including the Supreme Court, and recently acted as Tim Amos QC's junior in the Supreme Court in Prest v Petrodel Resources Limited [2013] EWCA Civ 1395.
Professional Memberships: Family Law Bar Association.
Career: Oxford University (MA Jurisprudence (First Class)). Oxford University (BCL Bachelor of Civil Law (Distinction)). BPP (BVC (Outstanding)). Called 2009. Pupil and tenant at Queen Elizabeth Building.
Publications: 'Search Orders and Preservation Injunctions After Imerman' [2011] Fam Law 54 ; 'Appealing an Order Out of Time in Proceedings for a Financial Remedy' Practical Law Practice Note; 'Setting Aside an Order in Proceedings for a Financial Remedy' Practical Law Practice Note.

KISSIN, Clare
One Brick Court, London
020 7353 8845
ck@onebrickcourt.com
Featured in Defamation/Privacy (London)
Practice Areas: Defamation, privacy and confidence, malicious falsehood, harassment, reporting restrictions, contempt of court, data protection, freedom of information and media-related human rights law. Provides regular pre-publication advice to publishing houses and national newspapers. Recent cases of interest include: Makudi v Triesman [2014] 2WLR 1228; R v Marine A & ors [2013] EWCA Crim 2367; R v Dale Cregan [2013], R v Webber [2013] (opposition to reporting restrictions); Makudi v Triesman [2013] EWHC 142 (QB), McLaughlin v London Borough of Lambeth [2012], Ibrahim v Swansea University [2012] EWHC 290 (QB) (libel claims); and WXY v Gewanter & ors [2012] EWHC 496 QB (privacy and harassment claim).
Professional Memberships: Human Rights Lawyers Association.
Career: Called 2009, Middle Temple. Intern at Article 19: the Global Campaign for Free Expression, 2007. Parliamentary researcher for Simon Hughes MP, 2007 - 2008. Intern at UN ICTY, 2008. Pegasus Scholar to Washington D.C, 2011. Media Law Tutor at Kings College London, 2012 - 2013. Expert contributor on UK FCO and EU project "Promoting Legal Reform for the Protection of Media in China", 2012 - 2014.
Publications: Contributor to Arlidge, Eady and Smith on Contempt, 4th Edition (2011) and supplement (due 2013); co-author of Halsbury's Laws of England, vol 32 defamation (2012).
Personal: Pembroke College, Cambridge (2004 - 2007, MA (Cantab), law; Willoughby Prize, Searle Prize); The City of Law School (2008-9, BVC, Outstanding; Queen Mother Scholarship). Hockey player.

KITSON, Justin
Selborne Chambers, London
020 7420 9500
justin.kitson@selbornechambers.co.uk
Featured in Real Estate Litigation (London)
Practice Areas: Justin is a commercial-chancery barrister specialising in property litigation, property related professional negligence, commercial disputes and copyright and licensing.
Professional Memberships: Property Bar Association; Chancery Bar Association; Professional Negligence Bar Association.
Career: Called Gray's Inn 2000 (Prince of Wales Scholar). In addition to a multitude of property and chancery cases, notable highlights in 2012/13 have included his instruction in (i) a commercial dispute involving the demerger of an organisation worth more than £150 million, (ii) copyright litigation arising from the disputed ownership of one of the most famous pop songs from the late 1970s, and (iii) a licensing dispute involving one of the world's largest software manufacturers. Solicitors instructing Justin commend him for his exceptional client handling skills and ability to cut quickly to the pertinent issues and offer forthright, practical and tactical advice. He has been variously described in the directories as "a barrister with real presence", a "very forceful advocate", "a brave and tough advocate who is great on cross-examination", and somebody who has "the ability to absorb huge volumes of paper and give advice extremely quickly."

KNIGHT, Christopher
11KBW, London
020 7632 8500
christopher.knight@11kbw.com
Featured in Administrative & Public Law (London), Data Protection (London)
Practice Areas: Christopher practises in administrative and public law, data protection and information law, education law and employment law. Recent cases include: Kennedy v Charity Commission [2014] UKSC 20; Adegbola v Marks & Spencer [2013] EWCA Civ 1808; R (Zacchaeus 2000 Trust) v Secretary of State for Work & Pensions [2013] EWCA Civ 1202; R (London Borough of Lewisham) v AQA, Edexcel and Ofqual [2013] EWHC 211 (Admin); Harrod v Chief Constable of West Midlands Police (2014, ET); Camden LBC v Information Commissioner & Voyias [2012] UKUT 190 (AAC); R (Camelot) v Gambling Commission [2012] EWHC 2391 (Admin). He regularly appears in the Information Rights and Gambling jurisdictions of the First-tier Tribunal. He has a wide experience of regulatory work and of local government law in areas ranging from community care and mental health to setting up academy schools and special educational needs.
Professional Memberships: ALBA, ELA, ELBA, ARDL.
Career: Called to the Bar in 2008. Judicial Assistant at the UK Supreme Court 2009-2010.
Publications: Bradley, Ewing & Knight, Constitutional and Administrative Law (2014); Blakeley, Knight & Love, The New Tribunals Handbook (2011); contributor to: The White Book, Supperstone, Goudie & Walker on Judicial Review and Tolley's Employment Law Handbook.

KNIGHT, Heidi
Serjeants' Inn Chambers, London
020 7427 5000
hknight@serjeantsinn.com
Featured in Clinical Negligence (London), Product Liability (London)
Practice Areas: Heidi Knight was called to the Bar in 2001. Heidi specialises in clinical negligence, personal injury, product liability and group litigation and inquests and inquiries. An earlier edition notes that she "is well liked for her charming manner with clients" and is "an extremely helpful, very intelligent barrister with a keen interest in product liability in all its forms. An excellent team player, she's an absolute trooper." Please click on the link to the Serjeants' Inn Chambers website for her profile, which sets out full details of her practice including relevant work of note.
Professional Memberships: PIBA, PNBA and AVMA.
Personal: 1999 MA (Cantab); BA (Law, First Class Honours) Senior Scholar, Fitzwilliam College; Cambridge College Prize for Distinguished Performance.

KNOX, Christopher
Trinity Chambers, Newcastle upon Tyne
0191 232 1927
c.knox@trinitychambers.co.uk
Featured in Crime (North Eastern), Family/Matrimonial (North Eastern)
Practice Areas: Christopher Knox has a particular interest in criminal defence, in particular heavy cases and prosecution (CPS and HM Revenue and Customs). He is recognised for his wide level of advocacy experience. In crime he has dealt with homicides, including as a leader. He is regularly instructed as a leader in serious crime and financial cases. He also has a particular interest in cases involving informants. Christopher also has an extensive ancillary relief practice, in particular large money cases. Christopher has extensive experience of dealing with high value and complex ancillary relief proceedings, including those involving business and insolvency. He has an appetite for more problematic cases and is a determined advocate. Christopher has dealt with disciplinary and regulatory matters. He has a particular interest in business and financial cases across the spectrum. He has wide tribunal advocacy experience, for example the Transport Tribunal, tax, disciplinary hearings etc. Christopher also deals with personal injury and common law matters – he is always interested in the unusual ranging from clinical negligence, catastrophic injury to actions against the police.
Professional Memberships: FLBA, CLBA. AMCA.
Career: Kings School, Tynemouth. Durham University. Recorder 1996. External moderator on the BVC since 2008 for the BSB.

KOHLI, Ryan
Cornerstone Barristers, London
020 7242 4986
ryank@cornerstonebarristers.com
Featured in Planning (London), Social Housing (London)
Practice Areas: Landlord and Tenant (including Social Housing), Administrative and Public law, Planning and Licensing.
Professional Memberships: Administrative Law Bar Association, Social Housing Law Association and Association of Regulatory & Disciplinary Lawyers.
Career: Ryan was awarded an MA from St Edmund Hall, Oxford University where he read law between 2002-05. He was called to the Bar in 2006 (Inner Temple) having achieved the grade of "Outstanding" in the Bar Vocational Course (BPTC). He has quickly developed a successful practice at the bar and was appointed to the Attorney General's Panel of Counsel (C Panel) in March 2012. He regularly represents and advises clients in a range of landlord and tenant matters; planning inquiries; licensing appeals; resisting applications for judicial review and in statutory planning appeals.
Publications: J Findlay QC and R Kohli, When does a tree preservation order protect [2008] JPL 615.
Personal: Ryan was born in Arlington, Texas and educated at The Glasgow Academy and Oxford University. He enjoys the theatre, cinema, travel and good restaurants.

KOLINSKY, Daniel
Landmark Chambers, London
020 7430 1221
dkolinsky@landmarkchambers.co.uk
Featured in Administrative & Public Law (London), Local Government (London), Planning (London)
Practice Areas: Dan Kolinsky specialises in public law, planning, environmental and local government. His clients include individuals, pressure groups, NGOs, commercial bodies, local and central government. He has a busy specialist practice in non-domestic rates acting for ratepayers, valuation officers and billing authorities across the full spectrum of rating cases including rateability and exemption issues, valuation cases and enforcement cases. He frequently acts as an advocate in the High Court and Court of Appeal, at public inquiries and before the Upper Tribunal. He was called to the Bar in 1998. He is a member of the Attorney General's A panel. He is a CEDR accredited mediator.

KOLVIN, Philip QC
Cornerstone Barristers, London
020 7421 1807
philipk@cornerstonebarristers.com
Featured in Licensing (London)
Practice Areas: Licensing of leisure economy, gambling and sex establishments. Acts for industry, local authorities, trade bodies, regulators and communities from committees to Supreme Court.
Professional Memberships: Head of Cornerstone Barristers; Patron, Institute of Licensing; Chairman, Purple Flag Advisory Board.
Career: RGS Newcastle upon Tyne, Balliol College Oxford, called to Bar 1985, QC 2009.
Publications: Licensed Premises: Law, Practice and Policy (2 ed); Gambling for Local Authorities: Licensing, Planning and Regeneration (2 ed); Sex Licensing; Saving Open Space; Atkins Courts Forms on Licensing; Encyclopedia of Forms and Precedents on Licensing; Halsburys Laws on Protection of the Environment and Public Health.

KOMOROWSKI, Julius
Terra Firma Chambers, Edinburgh
0131 260 5697
julius.komorowski
@terrafirmachambers.com
Featured in Civil Liberties & Human Rights (Scotland)
Practice Areas: Advocate specialising in administrative and public law, human rights, asylum and immigration, and employment. He has extensive experience appearing for and against the UK Government. He has also appeared for and against local authorities, and against the Scottish Ministers. His cases include HS (Algeria), Pet 2011 SC 324 (UN Convention on the Rights of the Child); LE (Turkey), Petitioner [2011] Imm AR 245 (Home Office policy held to be inconsistent with EU law); Scottish Ministers v MHTS (JM) 2012 SC 225 (mental health) and MGW, Petitioner [2014] CSOH 104 (Home Office entitled to find failed asylum-seekers could be returned to Iraq).
Professional Memberships: Member of Scottish Public Law Group steering committee.
Career: Called Advocate in 2008. Law Clerk to the Lord Justice Clerk (2011/2012) and to the Lord President (2012/2013). Standing junior counsel to the Advocate General from 2013.
Personal: University of Glasgow LLB (1st Class Hons) (Dr John MacCormick Prize); GGSL (Dip LP); Lord Reid Scholar.

KORN, Anthony
No5 Chambers, Birmingham
0845 210 5555
ak@no5.com
Featured in Employment (Midlands)
Practice Areas: Anthony's practice ranges from the straightforward unfair dismissal case to complex TUPE, whistleblowing, discrimination and equal pay issues representing both Claimants and Respondents. He has worked in the health and education sectors dealing particularly with disability discrimination and reasonable adjustment issues, TUPE, redundancy and age discrimination. He has considerable experience in representing employers faced with difficult litigants in person. Anthony is a contributor to Blackstone's Employment Law Practice and Jordans Employment Law Manual. He is the co-author of Employment Tribunal Remedies (4th edition-OUP 2011). Reported cases include: Landmark Brickwork Ltd v Sutcliffe [2011] IRLR 976 (enforceability of restrictive covenants and springboard injunction), Smith v Gardner Merchant [1998] IRLR 510 (sex discrimination and harassment), Kent County Council v Mingo [2000] IRLR 90 (disability discrimination, reasonable adjustments to redundancy policy and compensation issues), Rossiter v Pendragon plc [2005] IRLR 256 (TUPE and constructive dismissal), Nationwide Building Society v Benn and ors [2010] IRLR 922 (TUPE and constructive dismissal),Korashi v Abertawe Bro Morgannwg University Local Health Board [2012] IRLR 4 (PIDA, and Racial discrimination) and White and Todd v Troutbeck SA[2013] IRLR 286 (employment status).

KOVALEVSKY, Richard QC
2 Bedford Row, London
020 7440 8888
rkovalevsky@2bedfordrow.co.uk
Featured in Crime (London), Financial Crime (London)
Practice Areas: Crime, fraud: Richard Kovalevsky is a specialist in fraud and money laundering. He advises companies and directors on a wide range of potentially criminal issues both nationally and internationally and represents them in these matters. His substantial high-profile defence practice includes numerous prosecutions by the Serious Fraud Office, Financial Services Authority and Revenue and Customs and he has extensive experience in diversion, tax, VAT fraud, fraudulent trading, Companies Act offences, large scale money laundering and confiscation proceedings. Jurisdictions in which he advises include Bermuda, the British Virgin Islands and the United States. Criminal: Richard is frequently instructed in cases involving complex issues of public interest immunity or with extensive forensic issues requiring the cross-examination of expert witnesses. He has considerable experience in advising clients who have exposure to multi-jurisdictional issues.
Professional Memberships: British Virgin Islands Bar; CBA.
Career: LLB Hons (Manchester University); 1983, Called to the Bar; 2003, Queen's Counsel.
Publications: www.thebriberyact.com

KRAMER, Adam
3 Verulam Buildings, London
020 7831 8441
akramer@3vb.com
Featured in Banking & Finance (London), Commercial Dispute Resolution (London), Energy & Natural Resources (London), Fraud (London), Insurance (London)
Practice Areas: The full range of commercial disputes, especially civil fraud, banking, professional negligence, insurance/reinsurance and energy. Major current and recent cases in the public domain include the RBS 2008 Rights Issue dispute, BP Oil International Ltd v Bankers Petroleum Albania Ltd (oil dispute), Renaissance Capital Ltd v African Minerals Ltd (investment bank commission dispute), Challinor v Juliet Bellis & Co (investor dispute).
Professional Memberships: Society of Legal Scholars, COMBAR, Bar Pro Bono Unit.
Career: Lecturer at Durham University (2000-3); Tutor at University College Oxford (2003-4); called by Gray's Inn (2004); 3VB pupillage (2004) then tenancy (2005).
Publications: Sole author of The Law of Contract Damages (Hart Publishing, 2014). Contributor to Paget on Banking.
Personal: Educated at Manchester Grammar School, University College Oxford (BA Law, first class) and McGill University, Canada (LLM). Current interests include cooking, painting with oils and running.

KREISBERGER, Ronit
Monckton Chambers, London
020 7405 7211
rkreisberger@monckton.com
Featured in Competition/European Law (London)
Practice Areas: Widely recognised as a leading senior junior Competition and EU Law. Particular expertise in sport, pharmaceutical and healthcare sectors. Key cases include: T-472/13 Lundbeck 'pay for delay'; T-111/08 MasterCard v Commission (interchange fees); T-38/11 Cathay Pacific v Commission (air cargo surcharges appeal); AXA v CMA (private healthcare appeal); NHS v Reckitt Benckiser (Gaviscon follow on claim); Chemistree v Roche (2011) EWHC 1579(ch); Intercare Direct v Pfizer; BAGS v AMRAC (Turf TV) :High Court (2008) EWHC 2688(ch): Court of Appeal (2009) EWCA CIV 750; CDI v OFT (construction recruitment appeal) (2011) CAT 8; Ballast Needam v OFT (construction cover pricing appeal) (2011) CAT3; Inntrepreneur v Crehan (2006) UKHL 38; C-58/08 Vodafone v UK (challenge to Roaming Regulation).
Career: Called 1999. Senior Associate in EU/Competition Department of Herbert Smith Freehills from 1998-2005. Judicial assistant to Lord Justice Buxton in the Court of Appeal in 2000. Qualified as Solicitor Advocate. Joined Chambers in 2005. Member of Attorney General's B Panel of Junior Counsel to the Crown since March 2011.
Publications: Ronit is a contributing editor to the 7th edition of Bellamy & Child, The European Community Law of Competition. She is a regular contributor to various EU/competition publications and frequent speaker on competition issues.
Personal: MA (Oxon) 1995, BCL (Oxon) 1997

KREMEN, Philip
Selborne Chambers, London
020 7420 9500
philip.kremen@selbornechambers.co.uk
Featured in Real Estate Litigation (London)
Practice Areas: Philip is a leading senior junior in property litigation.
Professional Memberships: Chancery Bar Association.
Career: A substantial proportion of Philip's work is property related, covering property litigation and advice in all areas of landlord and tenant, conveyancing, restrictive covenants, easements, options and property related professional negligence claims. In addition, Philip also has considerable experience in civil fraud work and asset recovery that has involved him in overseas work on a regular basis. Philip is noted in the Legal 500 as a leading property litigation junior. He is also commended in Chambers Guide 2006 as an outstanding litigator and for bringing to all cases a sensible commercial approach, providing all clients with advice of a clear and pragmatic nature. Recent cases include: Group Seven Ltd v Allied Investments Corporation Ltd and others [2013] EWHC 1423 (Ch), (the court considered whether the fraud exception to legal professional privilege applied to all of the documents held or generated by solicitors under a joint retainer); Good Harvest Partnership v Centaur Services Ltd [2010] NPL 22 (whether original guarantor's guarantee of assignee is enforcable under 1995 Covenants Act); Fenton Properties Inc. v 41 Arundel Gardens Ltd (LTL 19.12.05) Peter Smith J. (local authority's letter outlining items that an inspector had found required attention was not a notice under the Housing Act 1985 s.352 and the specifications in that letter were not sufficient to found an order for specific performance) Mount Cook Land Ltd v Joint London Holdings Ltd (2005) EWHC 507 Court of Appeal ("victualler" in user clause in lease was not restricted to licensed victuallers and so use of premises as a sandwich shop was prohibited) Luiz Vicente Barros Mattos Junior v MacDaniels Ltd (LTL 24.6.05) Lawrence Collins J. (amendments allowed to particulars of claim where the amended particulars of claim did not add new causes of action but were based on the same legal and factual basis as the existing claim and the amendments raised matters which were arguable at trial) Norman Hill & Terence Welford v Transport for London [2005] Ch 378 Rimer J. (sense of the word "first" in the phrase "first accrued to the Crown" in the Limitation Act 1980 Sch.1 para.12 was "earlier" or "previously" and not "originally". Paragraph 12 provided a complete code for possession claims brought by persons claiming through the Crown, whether the right of action accrued originally to the Crown or only so accrued earlier).

KUBIK, Heidi
St Philips Chambers, Birmingham
0121 246 0200
hkubik@st-philips.com
Featured in Crime (Midlands)
Practice Areas: Heidi has built up an extensive practice in all areas of serious crime. She has particular expertise in sex cases and cases of dishonesty and violence at all levels, including those involving expert paediatric evidence regarding serious injuries/death of children. She has been led in several high profile murders including a six month mur-

der trial concerning the death of a toddler (R v Shuttleworth, July 2013). She has successfully defended in a conspiracy concerning a bank robbery and is currently instructed to defend in a shooting. She conducts cases involving gang related crime, anonymous witnesses and undercover officers from the Counter-Terrorism Unit. She has a reputation for getting results through effective cross examination and persuasive advocacy. Heidi is experienced in dealing with young and/or vulnerable defendants, or those suffering from mental disability, in a sympathetic manner. She can explain complex issues in simple terms and can give strong advice when necessary. She is particularly adept at dealing with difficult clients in a non-confrontational way. She is approachable and capable of adapting her style to suit the case in hand. Grade 4 prosecutor.
Professional Memberships: CBA.
Career: Nottingham University Law BA (Hons). Lectureship at Leicester University 1991-92. Called 1993.

KYNOCH, Duncan
Selborne Chambers, London
020 7420 9500
duncan.kynoch@selbornechambers.co.uk
Featured in Chancery (London)
Practice Areas: Duncan is a chancery barrister specialising in commercial and property litigation.
Career: Called Gray's Inn 1994. Duncan's general Chancery practice involves commercial contracts, sale of goods, company disputes, insolvency, civil fraud, asset tracing/recovery. His expertise encompasses all aspects of real property with particular emphasis on commercial and residential landlord and tenant (including insolvency); property trusts, easements and boundaries; professional negligence claims against solicitors and surveyors. Duncan is known as a combative advocate. Recent cases include: Nelson's Yard Management Co v Eziefula, CA [2013] EWCA Civ 235 (judge's improper exercise of discretion as to costs where a claimant discontinues an action where there has been a material change in circumstances during the course of the action); Re Branchempire Ltd [2011] EWCA Civ 106 (liquidator's powers and duties to approve a settlement which is opposed by the main creditor); Acre 1127 Ltd (In Liquidation) v De Montfort Fine Art Ltd [2011] EWCA Civ 87 (what conduct by a party to a contract was sufficient to be repudiatory, thereby discharging the innocent party from his obligations under a contract); De Bruyne v De Bruyne [2010] EWCA Civ 519 (fiduciary obligations of constructive trustees for family shares intended to be settled on grandchildren).

LADENBURG, Guy
3 Raymond Buildings Barristers, London
020 7400 6400
guy.ladenburg@3rblaw.com
Featured in Professional Discipline (London), Crime (London)
Practice Areas: Prosecutes and defends fraud and serious crime, and practises across a range of regulatory areas. Currently instructed in the 'Celtic' SFO prosecution as junior defence counsel for an insolvency silk, and in Operation Cotton on behalf of a solicitor. Recent fraud cases for the defence as led junior and junior alone include the Copland School fraud, the Vantis tax fraud, the Appleguild diamond fraud and the Iran Investment Corporation fraud. Also prosecutes and defends in heavy criminal cases and also those involving serious sexual offences, including as prosecution counsel in two recent cases involving historical allegations of child rape, and defence counsel for two historic family abuse cases. Other specializations include the full range of Licensing work for applicants, appellants, local authorities and police; the representation of police officers from forces across the country in criminal trials, misconduct hearings, inquests and inquiries; advising Police forces and regulatory authorities across a range of regulatory areas.
Career: Called to the Bar 2000.
Publications: Co-author with Simon Farrell Q.C and Nick Yeo of Blackstone's Guide to the Fraud Act (2006).
Personal: Charterhouse and St. Hugh's College Oxford (1st Class BA Hons).

LAIDLAW, Jonathan QC
2 Hare Court, London
020 7353 5324
jonathanlaidlawqc@2harecourt.com
Featured in Health & Safety (London), Crime (London), Financial Crime (London)
Practice Areas: Jonathan Laidlaw QC has consistently been rated by Chambers UK as one of the "star silks" practising in this country and he is listed as a "leading silk" by The Legal 500. The directories speak of "an extraordinarily able advocate with great style who can deal with the most difficult of cases with the greatest of ease", of "lethal cross-examination skills and a mean way with closing speeches" and of him being "quite outstanding in his conduct of a case". Since his appointment as Queen's Counsel he has been described as "one of country's leading silks" with "advocacy skills right out of the top drawer". Jonathan Laidlaw QC's practice is predominantly in fraud and business crime, in defending directors and companies facing charges brought by the HSE and in professional, regulatory and disciplinary matters. Much of his work, both for individuals and companies here and abroad, is pre-charge and advisory in nature. Jonathan Laidlaw QC has also appeared in major Inquests and in sporting tribunals. Recent instructions include acting for Rebekah Brooks; for the Football Association in the Hillsborough Inquests; for Fluor, Hugo Boss and Koch Industries in fatality cases; for the Princes Sporting Club who faced a charge of corporate manslaughter; for Highland (the Texas based hedge fund); for Aviva; for JC Decaux; and for a number of individuals and financial institutions facing SFO, FCA and CMA investigations.

LAIRD, Francis QC
St Philips Chambers, Birmingham
0121 246 0200
flairdqc@st-philips.com
Featured in Crime (Midlands)
Practice Areas: Specialises in high profile and complex criminal cases. He has vast experience of cases involving allegations of homicide, organised crime, serious fraud and serious sexual offences, and is regarded as an outstanding jury advocate. Notable cases include: R v Hawkins, a complex baby shaking murder; R v Newstead, a high profile murder of an autistic woman whose body was left by a rail track in Rugby; R v Turner, the infamous M40 murder of a Hells Angel; R v Toor, the attempted murder of the "Living Guru" of the Namdhari sect of Sikhism which attracted worldwide media interest; R v Rich, a conspiracy to import £1 billion of cocaine from Colombia; R v Warwick, a multi-million pound fraud by employees of the West Midlands Police; R v Cox, a large and complex internet fraud; R v Morris and Ward, an allegation of "gang rape" by two international sportsmen; and R v P, a rape by a pupil of the Royal Ballet School.
Professional Memberships: Midland Circuit; Criminal Bar Association.
Career: Called to the Bar in 1986; QC 2011; Recorder of the Crown Court 2010.

LAKHA, Abbas QC
9 Bedford Row, London
020 7489 2727
abbaslakhaqc@mac.com
Featured in Crime (London)
Practice Areas: Abbas Lakha QC is a defence specialist, with a wide-ranging practice in all areas of serious and complex litigation. He is particularly noted for his extensive experience in advising and representing Individuals and Corporations in Regulatory and Criminal Proceedings both in the Courts and before Tribunals. His principal expertise relates to the defence of individuals who are prosecuted in relation to allegations of Financial Crime. Abbas has appeared in many of the country's most high profile fraud trials which frequently have international dimensions. He is regularly instructed to advise at the pre-investigative stages of cases. He is highly respected for his courtroom advocacy skills, his attention to detail on case preparation and his negotiating skills. He has experience of representing high profile individuals for whom reputation management is a significant concern. R v Malik Blackburn, Murder; R v Gathani, Fraud - MTIC Fraud £100m; R v Goddard, Fraud - MTIC Fraud £80m; HMRC v Sunico and the Harwanis, High Court - Commercial Fraud - £40m; Atlantic Electronics v HMRC VAT Tribunal.
Career: Called to the Bar 1984 and took Silk 2003.

LAKIN, Tracy
St Ives Chambers, Birmingham
0121 236 0863
tracy.lakin@stiveschambers.co.uk
Featured in Family/Matrimonial (Midlands)
Practice Areas: Family, Court of Protection. Tracy practises in public law and private law Children Act applications. She is experienced in all aspects of proceedings in the County Court, High Court and Court of Appeal. She has also been led in the High Court and the Court of Appeal.
Career: She represents Local Authorities, Children's Guardians, parents (including adults acting under a disability) and children (including older children with the ability to instruct in their own right). Her cases have involved death of children, serious non-accidental injury, shaken baby syndrome, sexual abuse (including cases where parents have been falsely accused of sexual abuse by the other parent) and chronic neglect. Her particular strength is in fact finding hearings where her past experience as a Criminal/Crown Court advocate offers some advantages. She also has a particular interest/expertise in cases involving Fabricated/Induced Illness. Tracy also practices in Court of Protection with a particular interest in forced marriage and deprivation of liberty cases and has appeared in the Court of Protection in Birmingham on such matters.

LAMB, Maria
One Paper Buildings, London
020 7353 3728
marialamb@onepaper.co.uk
Featured in Crime (Western)
Practice Areas: Criminal law.
Professional Memberships: Western Circuit, CBA.
Career: Maria Lamb is a Criminal Law specialist with particular emphasis on serious sexual offences, serious offences of violence and large scale drugs matters. She acts on behalf of the prosecution and defence although due to her reputation finds her practice more biased in terms of defence matters. Maria was Called to the Bar in 1984 and has practiced on the Western Circuit since taking tenancy. She was appointed a Recorder in 2006. Recent matters include a conspiracy to murder case involving an entire family, a large scale drug importation, a serious sexual abuse case involving children and a "Baby-Shaking" murder where she secured an acquittal. At a time where many Criminal Law practitioners seek to diversify into quasi-criminal practice areas Maria is one of a rare breed - the true specialist who still enjoys a caseload of exclusively serious and complex Criminal Law.

LAMBERT, Nigel QC
Carmelite Chambers, London
0207 936 6300
nlambert@carmelitechambers.co.uk
Featured in Crime (London)
Practice Areas: Specialist defence practice in all criminal courts and Courts Martial in all areas of serious and complex crime including commercial fraud, money laundering, homicide, extreme violence, people trafficking, serious sexual offences and large scale drug cases. Has had a considerable number of money laundering, murder and other cases stayed as an abuse of the process. Has particular expertise representing both young and/or vulnerable offenders and in cases where there are young Prosecution witnesses. R v Wragg £20m loss to Revenue and Customs carousel fraud, R v Simpson successful abuse argument in carousel fraud R v Lombardi year long trial of international banking fraud, R v Chipping off-shore accounts Income Tax fraud R v Agidi successful abuse argument in money laundering case following extensive fraud and corruption at highest political level in Nigeria. Operation Vaulter - MTIC fraud involving contra trading and off-shore operations in Dubai. R v Xin Li successfully defended in money laundering case connected to the largest ever seizure of counterfeit DVDs in Western Europe. R v Butt street gang murders of two brothers stayed as an abuse following witness collusion. R v Calero-Guevera successfully defended a blind man charged with murder by multiple stabbings. R v Fathers successfully defended an educationally sub normal woman charged with torture and murder by drowning R v T successfully defended a young offender with Aspergers Syndrome charged with raping two young females. R v F successfully defended a13 year old boy charged with rape of step-sister. R v R 16 year old assassin in drive by gang land shooting R v Lewington successful abuse argument in historic sexual abuse case. R v M rape of step-daughter between ages of

8-12. R v Fitzpatrick charged with conspiracy to blackmail re Huntingdon Life Sciences and international drug companies. R v Rothery - conspiracy to supply 1.5 tons of cocaine.. R v Shah and Others – conspiracy to cheat/ importation of drugs large number of commercial imprtations. Duty loss approx £6m. R v Hadfield and Others Successfully defended in high profile and maximum security trial concerning Manchester rival family feuds culminating in gunshot and hand grenade murders. [Codefendant Dale Cregan who shot dead two female police officers]. R v Krezolek. man accused of the murder of his four year old step-son – Daniel Pelka.. Allegations of chronic starvation, imprisonment and long term violence. R v Gacek and Others, mother accused of causing or allowing the death of her seven week old baby.
Professional Memberships: South Eastern Circuit, Criminal Bar Association.
Career: Call 1974 Gray's Inn, Recorder 1996, Queen's Counsel 1999, Bencher 2004, Head of Chambers 2009 -2014.
Personal: Member of the Garrick Club and MCC.

LAMBERT, Sarah
1 Crown Office Row, London
020 7797 7500
sarah.lambert@1cor.com
Featured in Clinical Negligence (London), Costs Litigation (London)
Practice Areas: Clinical and dental negligence, personal injury, professional discipline, inquests, costs.
Professional Memberships: PIBA, PNBA.
Career: Called 1994. Grays Inn Scholar. Recorder 2012. Deputy Costs Judge SCCO 2013. Clinical negligence: Cutting v Islam 2014 EWHC 720 (QB); Cairns v Medway NHS Trust 2014; Appleton v Medway NHS Foundation Trust 2013; Watson v David Ross RCJ 6 March 2012; Wright v Basildon & Thurrock University Hospitals NHS Foundation Trust 2011; Chipchase v Marsh, 9 July 2010. Professional Discipline: GDC v Dr Stephenson 2013, 2014; GMC v Dr McLaverty 2012; GMC v Dr Steele 2011; GMC v DrMellor 2010; GDC v Bal Sharma 2010. Costs: Cutting v Islam [2014] EWHC 1515 (QB) Marcus v Medway [2011] EWCA Civ 750 Fortune v Roe [2010] EWHC 90180 (Costs); Cullen & Anor v Chopra [2007] EWHC 90093 (Costs); Arkin v Borchard Lines Ltd & Ors [2005] EWCA Civ 655; Cafane v London Borough of Lambeth [2004] EWHC 90042 (Costs); R (on the application of) v Governing Body of JFS &Anor (Rev 3) [2009] UKSC 1; Smith v Havering Hospitals NHS Trust [2003] EWHC 9002 (Costs);
Publications: Westlaw UK online encyclopaedia; Jowitt's Dictionary of Law; Sweet and Maxwell Personal Injury Handbook.

LAMONT, Calum
Keating Chambers, London
020 7544 2600
clamont@keatingchambers.com
Featured in Construction (London), International Arbitration (London), Public Procurement (London)
Practice Areas: Calum commands a broad commercial practice with particular specialisms in construction, engineering, shipbuilding, procurement and energy disputes, together with related insurance, bonds and professional negligence matters. Calum has extensive experience in the Middle East (particularly in the UAE and Qatar) and Korea.
Professional Memberships: Society of Construction Law; Technology and Construction Bar Association (TECBAR); Commercial Bar Association (COMBAR); Procurement Lawyers Association.
Career: MA History (Double First Class), St. Catharine's College, Cambridge University (2000); M.Phil. Historical Studies, St. Catharine's College, Cambridge University (2001); Diploma in Law/CPE (Distinction), City University (2003); Bar Vocational Course (Outstanding), Inns of Court School of Law (2004); Pupillage, Keating Chambers (2004); Keating Chambers (2005); TECBAR committee (2009-); TECBAR accredited Adjudicator (2011); TECBAR accredited Mediator (2011).
Publications: Contributor, Keating on Construction Contracts - Ninth Edition (2011). Consultant Editor, Construction Law Reports. Joint Author of three RICS Case in Point Series publications: Construction Claims, Contract Administration and Building Defects.

LANCASTER, Roger
Kings Chambers, Manchester
0845 034 3444
clerks@kingschambers.com
Featured in Planning (Northern)
Practice Areas: Residential development and inquiries; retail schemes; comprehensive development schemes including commercial and leisure development; highways, noise and air quality; conservation, listed buildings and enabling development schemes; compulsory purchase; High Court section 288 applications and judicial review.
Professional Memberships: PEBA.
Career: Solicitor 1975-2002; Bar 2002.

LANDER, Richard
Kings Chambers, Manchester
0845 034 3444
clerks@kingschambers.com
Featured in Real Estate Litigation (Northern)
Practice Areas: Established practice covering most aspects of chancery and commercial law. Particular emphasis on real estate litigation (commercial and residential), and associated areas including professional negligence, banking, Inheritance Act claims and corporate and personal insolvency. Extensive experience before courts of all levels up to the Court of Appeal, and before the Adjudicator to HM Land Registry.
Professional Memberships: Chancery Bar Association, Northern Chancery Bar Association.
Career: Educated University of Cambridge, Tancred and Hardwicke Scholar of Lincoln's Inn Called 1993, pupil at current Chambers 1994.

LANE, Andrew
Cornerstone Barristers, London
020 7421 1824
andrewl@cornerstonebarristers.com
Featured in Social Housing (London)
Practice Areas: Social Housing.
Professional Memberships: Chartered Institute of Housing; Social Housing Law Association; Constitutional and Administrative Law Bar Association.
Career: Since coming to the Bar in 1999 Andy has established himself at the forefront of the Social Housing Bar. His recent and successful involvement in cases such as Byrne v Poplar HARCA [2012] EWCA Civ 832; [2012] HLR 33; Corby Borough Council v Scott; West Kent Housing Association v Haycraft [2012] EWCA Civ 276; [2012] HLR 23; Swan Housing Association v Gill [2013] EWCA Civ 1566 and Sims v Dacorum Borough Council [2013] EWCA Civ 12; [2013] HLR 14 (judgment awaited from the Supreme Court) is testimony to this fact and he continues to be instructed by the leading solicitors in the social housing field. He is known for his instinctive client care skills, thorough knowledge of the law, tactical awareness and exceptional advocacy skills. His practice covers all areas of social housing law from possession and injunction work, through to welfare reform, Human Rights Act 1998, oppression and Equality Act 2010 work alongside general policy, council tax and tenancy work for private registered providers. Andy is also an established speaker at seminars and conferences.

LANE, Lindsay
8 New Square, London
020 7405 4321
lindsay.lane@8newsquare.co.uk
Featured in Intellectual Property (London), Media & Entertainment (London)
Practice Areas: Specialises in all areas of IP and media and entertainment. Recent patent cases include: Mylan v Gedeon Richter (emergency contraception); Schutz v Werit (which went to the Supreme Court on the issue of repair); Generics v Yeda (pharmaceutical for treating MS). Recent copyright/ database right cases include: Football Dataco v Stan James and Football Dataco v Sportradar(concerning rights in football data, both referred to the CJEU). Recent breach of confidence cases include: Wade v BSkyB (television format); Force India v 1 Malaysia Racing Team (trial and appeal on liability and quantum relating to F1 cars). Recent trade mark/passing off cases include: A&E Television Networks v Discovery Communications (TV channel names); 32Red v WHG (inquiry as to damages). For a comprehensive CV visit www.8newsquare.co.uk
Professional Memberships: Intellectual Property Bar Association (IPBA); Chancery Bar Association.
Career: Called 1996.
Publications: 'The Modern Law of Copyright and Designs' (Butterworths, Fourth Edition).
Personal: Educated: Newnham College, Cambridge (1992 BA (Hons) Natural Sciences and Law); European University Institute, Florence (MA in Comparative, European and International Law).

LANGDALE, Rachel QC
7BR, London
020 7242 3555
clerks@7br.co.uk
Featured in Family/Matrimonial (London)
Practice Areas: Children Act proceedings (both public and private law), including cases which involve the scrutiny of medical evidence and medical treatment issues. International disputes surrounding the residence of children, forced marriage cases, and relocation cases involving the Hague Convention and Brussels II Revised Regulation. Instructed in Public Inquiries, most recently Mid Staffordshire NHS Foundation Trust Public Inquiry (2010 – 2012).
Professional Memberships: Bencher Middle Temple, JUSTICE (independent charity, working to advance access to justice, human rights and the rule of law), Member of the Professional Practice Committee of the Bar Council (2009 onwards), Family Law Bar Association.
Career: LLB (Hons) (1983-86;) MPhil (Cantab) (1986-87). Called to the Bar:1990. Silk: 2009.

LANGDALE, Timothy QC
Cloth Fair Chambers, London
020 7710 6444
timothylangdale@clothfairchambers.com
Featured in Crime (London), Financial Crime (London)
Practice Areas: Principal area of practice is all aspects of criminal law with an emphasis on high profile, serious crime cases and commercial fraud. Practice involves both prosecution and defence work in these areas. Notable past cases include Alexander Howden, BCCI, Birmingham Six (final appeal), Judith Ward, Hillier (Swindon Town FC fraud), Darius Guppy, MTM, Landhurst Leasing, Derek Goldsmith, Stephen Hinchliffe, Hatfield Rail Crash, SSL case (medical fraud) and prosecuting in the Sarah Payne case. Also instructed in high profile libel cases i.e. Kieren Fallon v News Group Newspapers and Hatton v Frank Warren. Successfully defended Col. Mendonca, the highest ranking British Officer to face a Court Martial which concluded 2007. Successfully represented company charged with corporate manslaughter in a three month trial. He has represented the 'Suffolk Strangler' Steven Wright. R v Agis, high profile acquittal in health and safety corporate manslaughter prosecution. Three month GMC hearing in relation to the deaths of multiple patients; represented a company (Mabey & Johnson Ltd) in the first successful SFO corporate plea agreement. Represented the interests of Col. Mendonca at the public enquiry into the death of an Iraqi civilian in military custody. More recently, advised one of the largest international private equity firms re the implications of the Bribery Act. Successfully represented various doctors, most recently Dr Nikkhah and Dr Kokkarne, all of whom were charged with manslaughter by way of gross negligence. Acted in GMC case for Dr Keilloh, disciplinary proceedings into the death of an Iraqi detainee in the custody of British soldiers. Acted for Dr Islam over charges of sexual assault. Advised an internationally renowned retailer in relation to copyright infringements. Secured an acquittal for one of the defendants in the 'Vantis' tax fraud trial. Instructed to represent a company director in a SFO investigation into a national sports retailer. Represented Andy Coulson, the former editor of the News of the World, in the phone hacking trial. For further details please visit www.clothfairchambers.com.
Career: Called to the Bar 1966. Silk 1992.

LANGLEY, Charles
2 Bedford Row, London
020 7440 8888
clangley@2bedfordrow.co.uk
Featured in Crime (London)
Practice Areas: Recognised as a leading defence junior in crime. Instructed in serious and complex cases both as leading and junior counsel. Extensive experience in cases involving murder, manslaughter, drug conspiracies, robbery, kidnap and sexual offences. Wide-ranging fraud practice including computer hacking and multi-million pound abuses of the film tax credit and carbon credit trading schemes.

Detailed knowledge of money laundering and confiscation provisions. Strong appellate practice, regularly asked to advise on appeals where no grounds have previously been found. Specialist in road traffic and driving cases, often defending high-profile clients. Frequently representing insurers in cases involving fatalities. Recent notable cases include: R v Al-Issa (defended lead conspirator in the first Film Tax Credit and VAT prosecution by HMRC); R v Cox (double murder appeal, commended by the court for representing the applicant "admirably"); R v Crittenden (large-scale building fraud, the only one of six defendants to be acquitted); R v Patel (multi-jurisdictional carbon credit trading fraud); and R v Maule (large scale people and sex trafficking across Europe). See www.2bedfordrow.co.uk for full profile.
Professional Memberships: Criminal Bar Association, Central Criminal Court Bar Mess and South Eastern Circuit.
Career: Called 1999 (Middle Temple)
Publications: Contributor to Legal Network Television's CPD programme.

LANGRIDGE, Niki
Coram Chambers, London
020 7092 3700
niki.langridge@coramchambers.co.uk
Featured in Family/Matrimonial (London)
Practice Areas: Family Finance, Mediation, Dispute Resolution.
Professional Memberships: Family Law Bar Association.
Career: Niki was called to the Bar in 1993 and specialises exclusively in family work, her practice being entirely financial remedies on divorce and related family finance work. Her financial work covers all levels but, in particular, she deals with medium to high income and asset cases and matters that contain complex legal or factual issues.

LAPRELL, Mark
18 St John Street, Manchester
0161 278 1800
clerks@18sjs.com
Featured in Personal Injury (Northern)
Practice Areas: Personal injury and especially catastrophic injuries, road transport law. Reported cases include; Faunch v O'Donoghue & Anor [2013] EWCA Civ 1698; A B and Others v Tameside & Glossop Health Authority [1997] PNLR140 and Gorringe v Calderdale MBC [2004] UKHL 15; Road Transport: Skills Motor Coaches [2001] AER289, V. I v York Pullman [2001] RTR18, Attorney General's Reference [2001] 2 Cr App Rep. 22, Yorkshire Traction Company v Vehicle Inspectorate [2001] RTR34, Vehicle Inspectorate v Bruce Cook Road Planing Limited [2000] RTR90, Vehicle Inspectorate v Nuttall [1999] RTR264. Defended a number of major death by dangerous driving cases and a gross negligence manslaughter case. Appears in the Transport Tribunal and before Traffic Commissioners.
Professional Memberships: Northern circuit. FLBA. PIBA.
Career: Pupillage 1979-80 with Rodney Klevan. Assistant Recorder 1997. Recorder 2000.
Personal: Born 1956. Bradford Grammar School 1966-74; Magdalen College, Oxford 1975-78. Married 1984; two children.

LARKIN, Sean QC
QEB Hollis Whiteman, London
020 7933 8855
sean.larkin@qebhw.co.uk
Featured in Professional Discipline (London), Crime (London), Financial Crime (London)
Practice Areas: Sean Larkin provides specialist advice and advocacy at all stages of criminal and regulatory, with a particular emphasis on financial and serious crime and regulatory or disciplinary breaches by individuals (particularly professionals) and companies. He is described as 'incredibly bright and industrious' and 'absolutely superb'. Selected Times Lawyer Of The Week. Recent cases include: Operation Cotton (FCA's largest case), Gul (landmark Supreme Court decision on definition of terrorism), Dr Pandya (GP accused of FGM), defence of a former CEO for £52m pension fraud; defence of company director accused of laundering £900m, defence of company for workplace death. Sean's experience includes: advising, pre-charge through to representation or prosecution at trial, a variety of professionals (including lawyers, doctors, dentists, police officers, directors, IFAs, accountants and insolvency practitioners) in a wide variety of criminal, regulatory and disciplinary offences. He regularly speaks at conferences and conducts training sessions on a variety of legal topics.
Professional Memberships: CBA, ARDL, FSLA, HSLA, Justice.
Career: Called 1987. Silk 2010.
Publications: 'Fraud. Law Practise and Procedure'. Co-author of many reports for the Criminal Bar Association, including those relating to conspiracy, sentencing, and bail, Offences Against the Person Act, bail and human rights.
Personal: Family, music, sport.

LASCELLES, David
Littleton Chambers, London
020 7797 8600
dla@littletonchambers.co.uk
Featured in Commercial Dispute Resolution (London), Company (London)
Practice Areas: Claims relating to the performance and termination of high-value commercial contracts; claims arising out of the sale of shares and businesses; shareholder and LLP membership disputes; commercial fraud disputes; and director and senior employee disputes.
Career: David specialises as an advocate and adviser in commercial and company law disputes. In addition to his extensive trial and interim applications experience, including in jurisdiction disputes, David has acted in arbitrations including under the ICC and LCIA rules. David has been recommended in Chambers and Partners for some years as a leading commercial junior with previous editions commenting that David "regularly handles complex briefs as sole counsel…has an excellent grasp of legal issues, is incredibly diligent and has good client skills. Definitely someone you want on your team," and that he is "highly impressive… with excellent analytical skills…a brilliant young advocate who inspires confidence with his exemplary client manner and comprehensive and commercial advice." He has also been singled out as a junior star at the commercial bar by Legal Week magazine. Prior to coming to the Bar, David took a Double First in law from Cambridge University and a Masters in Law from Oxford University.

LASOK, Paul QC
Monckton Chambers, London
020 7405 7211
plasok@monckton.com
Featured in Competition/European Law (London), Public Procurement (London), Tax (London)
Practice Areas: Paul Lasok QC is considered by many of his peers as a heavy weight in EU law where his main areas of work include agriculture, competition, public & administrative law, public procurement, telecommunications, state aid, trade law (anti-dumping) and VAT & Customs Duties. He advises and represents private clients, including public companies and NGOs, as well as public sector bodies, including government departments, in litigation before the European Courts and English courts and in proceedings before regulatory authorities (including the EU Commission).
Career: 1994 QC; 1985-1987 private practice in Brussels, specialising in EU law; 1980-1985 legal secretary to Advocate-General J-P Warner and Advocate-General Sir Gordon Slynn, Court of Justice of the European Communities which included drafting the Advocate-General's Opinions in cases before the European Court. Areas covered included administrative law, agriculture, Brussels Convention, competition, customs law, free movement of goods, free movement of persons, freedom to provide services, industrial and commercial property, right of establishment, social security, State aids, taxation; 1979 trainee, Legal Service of the Commission of the European Communities (October to December); 1977-1979 pupillage in London.
Personal: MA in Law (Jesus College, Cambridge, 1972-1975), LLM in European Legal Studies (Exeter University, 1975-1977), Council of Legal Education (Bar finals, 1976-1977), PhD (Exeter University, 1986).

LATHAM, Kevin
Kings Chambers, Manchester
0845 034 3444
clerks@kingschambers.com
Featured in Costs Litigation (Northern)
Practice Areas: Kevin is an experienced costs practitioner with a busy nationwide practice. Having specialised in costs litigation throughout his career at the bar, Kevin has been highly sought after to provide business advice in light of the recent reforms to civil litigation. He is regularly instructed to advise and represent both paying and receiving parties in all aspects of inter-partes costs litigation involving complex matters of law and fact. Whilst maintaining a strong personal injury practice, Kevin's trial skills are an asset in solicitor/own client disputes or matters requiring robust cross-examination such as wasted and third party costs orders. Kevin's advisory services are well sought after with clients impressed by his thorough yet clear advice both in writing and in conference. Kevin's experience as a law costs draftsman and at a national firm of Solicitors prior to commencing pupillage enable him to provide first class service in cases where an appreciation of the 'bigger picture' is required. Kevin is frequently instructed in cases involving high value claims for costs in commercial claims, fatal accident claims and multiple party actions. He regularly appears in the SCCO, County and High Court and has experience in the Court of Appeal.
Professional Memberships: Northern Circuit Personal Injury Bar Association Middle Temple (Call 2007).
Career: LL.B (Hons), University of Hull 2006; BVC, Manchester Metropolitan University 2007; Called to the bar by the Honourable Society of the Middle Temple 2007.
Publications: "Following Protocol" Personal Injury Law Journal P.I.L.J. (2010) No.86 June Pages 9-14 (An article highlighting the salient factors of the new RTA Protocol); Kevin also contributed to Dr Mark Friston's seminal text: "Civil Costs: Law and Practice" (Jordans).

LATIMER, Andrew
Kings Chambers, Leeds
0845 034 3444
alatimer@kingschambers.com
Featured in Chancery (Northern), Commercial Dispute Resolution (North Eastern)
Practice Areas: Chancery and commercial litigation, directors' duties, shareholders' remedies, insolvency, partnership, restrictive covenants, confidential information, passing off, enforcement of securities and associated professional negligence. Significant cases: Maresca v Brookfield [2013] EWHC 3151, Linfoot v Adamson [2012] BPIR 1033, Eskape v Route [2011] EWHC 1635, Hitachi v V12 [2009] EWHC 2432, ICI v TTE Training [2007] EWCA Civ 725, Stansfield v AXA [2006] EWCA Civ 88, Thane v Tomlinson [2006] EWHC 1182, Anglo-Eastern v Kermanshahchi [2003] BPIR 1229 (trial), [2002] EWCA Civ 198 (interim appeal), South Coast v Axisa [2002] All ER (D) 123, Lunnun v Singh Times 19.7.99, R v CLE ex parte Nightingale, Latimer and Toms, Times 5.5.94.
Professional Memberships: Chancery Bar Association, Northern Chancery Bar Association.
Career: BA (Oxon), 1st Class in Law (1993). Bachelor of Civil Law (1994).
Publications: Contributor to 'Commercial Litigation: Pre-Emptive Remedies' (Sweet & Maxwell).

LATTIMER, Justine
St Ives Chambers, Birmingham
0121 236 0863
justine.lattimer@stiveschambers.co.uk
Featured in Court of Protection (All Circuits)
Practice Areas: Family, Court of Protection.
Career: Justine is a senior family law barrister who specialises in Child Protection. She is highly experienced in serious and complex cases such as those involving sexual abuse, serious physical injury or factitious illness. She has a reputation for client care and in particular for her sensitive approach to clients with mental health difficulties or learning disabilities. Justine has spearheaded the inception of the Court of Protection Group in chambers and, together with other members, has helped establish the team within the region.

LAUGHLAND, James
Temple Garden Chambers, London
020 7583 1315
jameslaughland@tgchambers.com
Featured in Costs Litigation (London), Fraud (All Circuits), Personal Injury (London)
Practice Areas: Aims to provide pragmatic and clear advice as swiftly as possible. Instructed regularly by leading solicitors such as Irwin Mitchell, Leigh Day & Co, Kennedys

& DWF to act in substantial personal injury litigation, whether for the claimant or the defendant. Frequently involved in defending fraudulent RTA claims. With respect to costs, instructed in cases concerning the recoverability of ATE premiums post-LASPO or heavy detailed assessments; regularly appearing in the SCCO and county courts nationwide. Accepts instructions by Direct Access. Contributor to Cook on Costs and Westlaw UK Insight.
Professional Memberships: Personal Injury Bar Association.
Career: 1987-90: University of Kent at Canterbury: BA (Hons) Law.
Publications: Contributor to Cook on Costs and Westlaw UK Insight.
Personal: Lives in London.

LAURENCE, George QC
New Square Chambers, London
020 7419 8000
clerks@newsquarechambers.co.uk
Featured in Agriculture & Rural Affairs (London), Chancery (London), Real Estate Litigation (London)
Practice Areas: Practice encompasses countryside law (including five cases in the Supreme Court in 2014-15) public law, hybrid bills in Parliament and property litigation (including landlord and tenant, judicial review and planning). Has recently appeared in major Crown Court litigation relating to regulatory offences under section 28P Wildlife and Countryside Act 1981. Has appeared frequently before opposed Bill Committees in both Houses of Parliament. Acted for the Corporation of London and British Land in connection with their petition to include an additional station at Liverpool Street for the Crossrail project. In the last 12 years has appeared frequently in the House of Lords (now the Supreme Court), Court of Appeal and at first instance, often in cases public rights of way and on village greens and, latterly, securing their deregistration or considering the impact of the Growth and Infrastructure Act 2013. Cases include: Supreme Court: Betterment (No 2) [2014], Paddico [2014], Barkas [2014], Lewis [2010]. House of Lords: Godmanchester [2007]; Oxfordshire [2006]; Beresford [2004]; Sunningwell [2000]. Court of Appeal: Newhaven [2013]; Trailriders v Dorset [2013]; Cash [2012]; Fortune [2012]; Leeds Group [2011] and [2010]; Winchester College [2008]; Smith [2008]; Betterment (No 1) [2008]; Ford-Camber [2007]; Ashbrook [2003]; Trevelyan [2001]; Masters [2000]. First instance: Andrews (No 2) [2014]; Malpass [2012]; Mann [2012]; MJI (Farming) Ltd [2009] and Kidner [2009] (final appeal). Newhaven and Dorset are due to be heard in the Supreme Court in November and January 2015. PTA to the Court of Appeal has been granted in Andrews (No 2).
Professional Memberships: Parliamentary Bar, ALBA, PESA, Property Bar Association, Environmental Law Foundation, Bencher of Middle Temple since 1999, Fellow of Institute of Advanced Legal Studies.
Career: Called to the Bar 1972. Joined 9 Old Square 1973; current chambers January 1991. Silk 1991. Former Deputy High Court Judge and Recorder (resigned to pursue career as advocate). Bencher of the Middle Temple (1999).
Personal: Educated at University of Cape Town 1966-68 (BA) and University College, Oxford 1969-71 (MA). Rhodes Scholar. Harmsworth Scholar. Frequently writes, lectures and appears on educational TV channels. Leisure pursuits include sport and theatre. Born 15 January 1947. Lives in London.

LAVENDER, Nicholas QC
Serle Court, London
020 7242 6105
nlavender@serlecourt.co.uk
Featured in Banking & Finance (London), Commercial Dispute Resolution (London)
Practice Areas: Commercial litigation and arbitration, including banking and finance, insurance and reinsurance, trust litigation, arbitration, professional conduct and human rights. Recent cases include: The Weissfisch litigation in the Bahamas; Ener-G Holdings Plc v Hormell [2012] 1 All ER (Comm) 466; JP Morgan Chase Bank v Springwell [2008] EWHC 1186 (Comm); A v B [2007] 1 Lloyd's Rep. 358 and 487; Weissfisch v Julius [2006] 1 Lloyd's Rep. 716; FSA investigation into Shell's reported oil and gas reserves; Hollywood 4 & 5 film finance litigation; and arbitrations in England and overseas, ad hoc and under UNICITRAL, LCIA and CIArb rules. Human rights: various cases before the European Court of Human Rights.
Professional Memberships: Commercial Bar Association; Professional Negligence Bar Association.
Career: 1989: call. 1990-2000: 1 Hare Court. 2000 to date: Serle Court. Silk 2008.

LAVY, Matthew
4 Pump Court, London
020 7842 5555
mlavy@4pumpcourt.com
Featured in Information Technology (London), Telecommunications (London)
Practice Areas: Commercial litigation and arbitration with a particular focus on IT, telecoms and other-technology related disputes (including software copyright and licensing).
Professional Memberships: COMBAR, TECBAR, SCL, LCLCBA, PNBA, BILA, BCS.
Career: MA (Cantab) Music; PhD (Cantab) Musicology; Called 2004.
Publications: Contributing editor to 'Professional Negligence & Liability' published by Informa - Chapter on Computer Consultants.

LAW, Charlotte
Kings Chambers, Manchester
0845 034 3444
clerks@kingschambers.com
Featured in Clinical Negligence (Northern)
Practice Areas: Clinical Negligence Personal Injury Coroners' Inquests Practises predominantly in the field of clinical negligence, dealing with cases of surgical and pharmaceutical negligence, dental negligence, misdiagnosis and delayed diagnosis in primary and secondary care. Has particular experience in cases involving obstetrics and gynaecology, general surgery, orthopaedic injury, hand and plastic surgery (cosmetic and therapeutic) and general practice. Also practises in personal injury, specialising in cases of severe injury arising from employer's liability, public liability, product liability and road traffic. Has particular experience in claims brought on behalf of military personnel. Appears regularly in the Coroner's Court representing bereaved families, in particular following deaths in hospital and residential nursing homes. Also represents applicants to the Criminal Injuries Compensation Authority and Armed Forces Compensation Scheme.
Professional Memberships: PIBA.
Career: University: Cambridge MA Classics PgDL College of Law, Guildford BVC BPP Law School, London.

LAWRENCE, Anne
4-5 Gray's Inn Square, London
020 7404 5252
clerks@4-5.co.uk
Featured in Education (London)
Practice Areas: Anne has extensive experience in all areas of education and community care law. She has a specialism in SENDIST cases including First Tier and Upper Tribunal Appeals (formerly statutory appeals to the High Court) - reported cases including: FS (Re T) v LB Bromley (SEN) [2013] UKUT 0529 (AAC)]; Camden LBC v FG (SEN) (2010) UKUT 249 (AAC); Hampshire CC v TP (2009) UKUT 239 (AAC); SV (1) SENDIST (2) Solihull MBC (2007) EWHC 1139 (Admin) Anne's practice includes UT Appeals concerning SEN assessment, statementing and provision, and school exclusions, and Judicial Reviews of s19 failures to provide education, breach of Article 2 Protocol 1, failure to provide services and provision. Anne works primarily for parents across the range of SENDA Tribunal Appeals. More broadly Anne has been involved with exclusion and School Admissions Appeals. In the area of Higher Education law Anne's practice includes disciplinary and academic appeals, student fitness to practise cases, hearings and appeals, and complaints to the OIA. Anne also has wide experience in advising in education contract and negligence matters involving independent schools and university/college courses, and educational negligence claims against schools and LEAs. In the area of community care law Anne has advised in numerous cases involving children and adults and brought numerous applications for judicial review arising out of the failure of local authorities to carry out assessments, provide services or comply with statutory duties, regulations and guidance. Whilst most settle during preliminary stages reported cases include R (on application of O) v Lewisham LBC (2008) EWHC 3503 (admin); R (M) v LB Hackney (2014) (24th July 2014) which also engaged with post Jackson and Mitchell guidance on compliance with CPR rules, PDs and court orders.
Professional Memberships: (ELAS) (HRLA) Member of Lincoln's Inn.
Career: Anne worked for a number of years in education as a teacher, assistant SENCO and a lecturer in special education. She worked in East London and Zimbabwe before working for the British Council in Southern Africa lecturing in special educational needs in teacher training colleges and developing policies and procedures for the identification, assessment and monitoring of children with SEN and those marginalised and excluded because of socio- economic, health and race reasons.

LAWRENCE, Patrick QC
4 New Square, London
020 7822 2154
p.lawrence@4newsquare.com
Featured in Professional Discipline (London), Professional Negligence (London)
Practice Areas: Professional negligence; regulatory and disciplinary proceedings; insurance; commercial litigation. Patrick Lawrence acts in cases concerning solicitors, barristers, auditors, valuers, insurance brokers, financial advisers and pension consultants. Many of his cases involve allegations of fraud and the prospect of cross-examination. He appeared in the Supreme Court on an appeal in which the immunity of expert witnesses was removed. In the disciplinary/regulatory field he is instructed on both sides in cases concerning auditors, lawyers and insolvency practitioners. Other areas of practice include sports law (he obtained an order restraining a jockey from riding in the Derby on the eve of the race) and aspects of public law, in particular relating to political activity and funding (he appeared for the successful appellant in R v Electoral Commission in the Supreme Court).
Professional Memberships: PNBA; Combar; ChBA.
Career: BA Oxon (PPE); called 1985; QC 2002.
Publications: Co-author of the Solicitors Negligence section in Lloyds looseleaf.

LAWS, Eleanor QC
6 Pump Court, London
020 7797 8400
eleanorlaws@6pumpcourt.co.uk
Featured in Crime (South Eastern), Crime (London)
Career: Eleanor Laws QC defends in cases involving young and vulnerable witnesses, in particular serious violence (including murder) and serious sexual offences. Notable cases include highly publicised sex trafficking cases. These include the Oxford sex trafficking case, acting as Specialist Advisory Counsel in the Jersey Child Abuse cases, cases arising out of the recent North Wales Children's Homes Inquiry, cases involving historic allegations, abuse by professionals and in numerous other high profile sex cases. She regularly trains the profession. She is an External Advocacy Trainer for CPS Grades 2-4, and recently assisted in compiling a training programme for the treatment of vulnerable witnesses as part of the launch of the Advocate's Gateway. She is part of HHJ Rook QC's Working Group whose task is to develop advocacy training for cases involving sex offences and vulnerable witnesses and defendants. She has lectured to the Criminal Bar Association and members of the South East Circuit on False memory, Advocacy in cases involving vulnerable witnesses, and Disclosure in criminal cases. Appointed by COIC to Chair the Bar Disciplinary Tribunal Hearings; Elected Committee Member (Criminal Bar Association).
Publications: Eleanor Laws QC has written the Sexual Offences Referencer, considered to be the most widely used practitioner guide to Indictments & Sentencing in sex cases dating back to 1950.

LAWSON, Daniel
Cloisters, London
020 7827 4000
dl@cloisters.com
Featured in Personal Injury (London)
Practice Areas: Personal injury, clinical negligence and insurance law. Undertakes the full range of personal injury work, with special expertise in complex public and employer's liability cases. Has acted in a wide variety of clinical negligence claims. Insurance work focuses upon disputes as to

policy construction and avoidance for non-disclosure or misrepresentation.
Professional Memberships: PIBA; APIL.
Career: Called to Bar in 1994.
Personal: Education: Balliol College, Oxford (BA Hons PPE); Birkbeck College, London (MA).

LAWSON, Robert QC
Quadrant Chambers, London
020 7822 1454
rob.lawson@quadrantchambers.com
Featured in Aviation (London), Product Liability (London), Travel (London)
Practice Areas: All aspects of commercial litigation, international arbitration and advisory work, including insurance coverage. In particular in relation to aviation, travel and product liability. Significant recent court cases include: Rogers v Hoyle [2014] 3 WLR 148; Huzar v Jet2.Com Ltd [2014] EWCA Civ 791; Global 5000 Ltd v Wadhawan [2012] 2 All ER (Comm) 18; R (Kibris Turk Hava Yollari) v Secretary of State for Transport [2011] 2 All ER (Comm) 340.
Professional Memberships: FRAeS, Fellow of the International Academy of Trial Lawyers, MCIArb, European Air Law Association, LCIA, COMBAR.
Career: BA (Oxon), Dip Law (City). Called 1989. CIArb accredited Mediator 2005. QC 2009. Chairman RAeS Air Law Group.
Publications: Contributor to Halsbury's Laws of England title 'Aviation', volume 2(3), 4th Edition Reissue (2003).

LAZARIDES, Marcus
Queen Elizabeth Building, London
020 7797 7837
m.lazarides@qeb.co.uk
Featured in Family/Matrimonial (London)
Practice Areas: Specialises in all aspects of family law; in particular financial remedies and private law children cases, both on his own and as a junior to a variety of leading Counsel. Frequently appearing against more experienced counsel, including Queen's Counsel and ranked as a leading junior in Chambers and Partners. Important cases include: Jones v Jones [2011] EWCA Civ 41, J v J [2009] EWHC 2654 (Fam) and G v G (Matrimonial Property: Rights of Extended Family) [2006] 1 FLR 62.
Professional Memberships: Family Law Bar Association.
Career: Queen Mother's Scholarship, Middle Temple (1998-99). Called 1999. Pupillage at QEB (1999-2000). Tenant at One Garden Court (2000-04). Tenant at QEB since 2004.
Personal: Educated at Brasenose College Oxford (DPhil), came to the bar late from a background in academia. Married with four children.

LAZUR, Thomas
Keating Chambers, London
020 7544 2600
tlazur@keatingchambers.com
Featured in Construction (London), Energy & Natural Resources (London)
Practice Areas: Specialist in construction, engineering and energy disputes. Work is split evenly between litigation in the Technology and Construction Court and international arbitration. Domestic work covers the full range of issues arising out of construction projects of varying size and complexity. International arbitration experience generally involves larger projects in the energy industry, such as the construction and operation of offshore drilling rigs. He is a Member of the CIArb, a TECBAR accredited Adjudicator, an experienced mediator, and an Advocacy Trainer for the Inner Temple.
Professional Memberships: MCIArb, IBA, TECBAR, COMBAR, SCL, Inner Temple.
Career: Called to the Bar 2005; Keating Chambers 2006; MCIArb 2013.
Publications: Keating on Construction Contracts 9th Edition - Contributor; Keating on NEC3 - Contributor; Bullen & Leake & Jacob's Precedents of Pleadings - Co-author of Construction section.

LE FEVRE, Sarah
3 Raymond Buildings Barristers, London
020 7400 6400
sarah.lefevre@3rblaw.com
Featured in Health & Safety (London), Licensing (London)
Practice Areas: Specialist practitioner in licensing, regulatory, inquest and public law with extensive expertise in criminal law. Licensing: instructed to advise and represent licensees, applicants, police and licensing authorities on all matters connected with licensable activity, including gambling, alcohol, entertainment of all kinds, street trading and taxis with extensive appellate and High Court practice. Regulatory: List 'A' Specialist Regulatory Advocates in Health and Safety and Environmental Law (HSE/EA/ORR); instructed by enforcing authorities, companies and individuals to advise and represent in civil, criminal, administrative and coronial proceedings, with particular expertise in railway and fire safety and environmental and water law. Inquests: instructed by bereaved families, employers, premises operators, enforcing authorities and police to advise and represent at inquests and in related High Court and civil proceedings. Criminal law: prosecution and defence as led junior and alone, with particular focus on cases involving police and vulnerable defendants.
Career: MA (Hons) Cantab (Anglo-Saxon, Norse & Celtic); LLM Public International Law (Distinction); 4 years multiple licensee in Somerset; trained actor (Poor School).

LE POIDEVIN, Nicholas QC
New Square Chambers, London
07525 245 087
nicholas.lepoidevin@newsquarechambers.co.uk
Featured in Chancery (London), Offshore (London), Trusts (London)
Practice Areas: Contentious and other trust and probate work (including the first probate case in the highest court for decades); property; conflicts of laws; associated professional negligence. Work from Channel Islands, Isle of Man and Caribbean. Cases: Marley v Rawlings [2014] 2 WLR 213, SC (executing crossed wills: construction and rectification); Re A Trust [2012] SC (Bda) 72 Civ, Bermuda (jurisdiction clause in trust); Re Bernstein [2010] WTLR 559 (scope of Variation of Trusts Act 1958); Gomez v Vives [2009] Ch 245, CA (jurisdiction of English court in trust disputes); Alhamrani v Alhamrani, Jersey (breach of trust; longest case ever in Jersey; points reported e.g. 2007 JLR 44); Gregson v HAE Trustees Ltd [2008] 2 BCLC 542 (liability of directors of trust company); Close Trustees (Switzerland) SA v Vildosola (2008) 10 ITELR 1135 (trustees' retention for litigation costs); Wingate v Butterfield Trust (Bermuda) Ltd [2008] WTLR 357 and 543, Bermuda (beneficiary's right to information; costs); Howell v Lees-Millais [2007] All ER (D) 64 (Jul), CA (Beddoe application; recusal); X v A [2006] 1 WLR 741 (power of advancement); Re Schmidt [2004] WTLR 887, Isle of Man (revocation of letters of administration); Re Q Trusts [2001] CILR 481, Cayman Islands (trustees' powers); Don King Productions Inc v Warren [2000] Ch 291, CA (partnership and trust).
Professional Memberships: Society of Trust and Estate Practitioners; ACTAPS; Chancery Bar Association.
Career: MA, LLB (Cantab). Called to Bar 1975. Commons Commissioner 2003. Bencher of Lincoln's Inn 2006. Recorder 2009. QC 2010.
Publications: Lewin on Trusts, 18th ed. (2008 + 3rd supplement 2012). A Practical Guide to the Transfer of Trusteeships (contributor). Sham Transactions (contributor). A Portrait of Lincoln's Inn (contributor). Articles on the law of trusts.
Personal: Educated at Trinity Hall, Cambridge. Interested in legal history.

LEABEATER, James
4 Pump Court, London
020 7842 5555
clerks@4pumpcourt.com
Featured in Construction (London), Energy & Natural Resources (London), Professional Negligence (London), Shipping (London)
Practice Areas: Insurance and reinsurance, professional negligence, construction, shipping, shipbuilding and offshore construction disputes; commercial disputes including arbitration, commercial fraud, interim relief and conflicts of law.
Professional Memberships: COMBAR, Professional Negligence Bar Association, TECBAR.
Career: MA (Oxon) Modern History; called to the Bar 1999; tenant of 4 Pump Court from October 2000. Called generally to the Bar of the Cayman Islands.
Publications: Co-author of "Civil Appeals: Practice & Procedure" (Sweet & Maxwell 2010) and author of chapter on professional indemnity insurance in 'Architect's Legal Handbook'.

LEARMONTH, Alexander
New Square Chambers, London
020 7419 8000
alexander.learmonth@newsquarechambers.co.uk
Featured in Chancery (London)
Practice Areas: Succession, trusts, property, Court of Protection and professional negligence in related cases. Succession includes mutual wills, secret trusts, rectification, lost wills and Inheritance Act claims, will construction and other problems in estate administration. His property work encompasses land registration, easements, mortgages, adverse possession, leasehold enfranchisement and business tenancy renewal. Important cases include: Marley v Rawlings (Supreme Court, rectification of wills); Ashkettle v Gwinett (ChD, probate), Kell v Jones (ChD, rectification of wills), Bradshaw v Taylor (CA, proprietary estoppel); Swain-Mason v Mills & Reeve (CA, professional negligence, amendment); Gotham v Doodes (CA, limitation); French v Barcham (ChD, occupation rent); Vale v Armstrong (ChD, undue influence); Green v Somerleyton (CA, easements).
Professional Memberships: STEP, ACTAPS, Chancery Bar Association (committee), Bar Council (2007-09, 2013 - date, Young Barristers' Committee Chairman 2009).
Career: BA Hons Oxon, Jurisprudence (college exhibitioner). Called Lincoln's Inn, 2000 (Tancred award).
Publications: Co-editor of Theobald on Wills. Contributor to: Williams, Mortimer & Sunnucks; Probate Practitioners' Handbook.

LEE, Jonathan
Keating Chambers, London
020 7544 2600
jlee@keatingchambers.com
Featured in Construction (London)
Practice Areas: Barrister with professional background in electrical and electronic engineering and specialist legal practice at the Technology and Construction Bar since 1995. Practice covers advocacy and advisory work acting for clients in litigation, domestic and international arbitrations, adjudications and mediations. Typical disputes have related to energy sector, transport infrastructure, hospitals, computer software and telecommunication equipment. Instructed by public sector and private sector clients, including: central and local government departments, commercial project funders, employers, contractors and associated professionals. Also instructed in claims on financial bonds and guarantees associated with engineering and construction cases. Accepts appointments as arbitrator, adjudicator, and mediator.
Professional Memberships: Institution of Engineering and Technology; Technology and Construction Bar Association; Commercial Bar Association; The Society of Computers and Law; The LCIA and Chartered Institute of Arbitrators.
Career: Called 1993, trained mediator and accredited adjudicator 2005, recorder 2009.
Publications: Chapter Author - Construction Dispute Resolution Handbook Second Edition (2011); Researcher - Keating on Construction Contracts Eighth Edition (2006) and First Supplement (2008).

LEE, Krista
Keating Chambers, London
020 7544 2600
klee@keatingchambers.com
Featured in Construction (London)
Practice Areas: Krista specialises in engineering and construction disputes. She has a BSc in engineering and enjoys complex technical disputes. Her experience covers all sectors of the industry including energy, mining, infrastructure, telecoms, utilities, entertainment venues, factories, hotels and housing both in the UK and overseas, onshore and offshore. She regularly acts for professional indemnity insurers and has acted for and against some of the world's leading engineering, architectural, project management and consultancy firms. Krista is an experienced advocate and has conducted trials, applications and sought injunctions in the Technology and Construction Court, Commercial Court and Chancery Division. She is familiar with all forms of ADR including mediation, adjudication, expert determination and dispute resolution boards. Krista is a fellow of the Chartered Institute of Arbitrators and Chartered Arbitrator. She has acted as sole arbitrator in ICC and other arbitrations. As counsel, she has conducted arbitrations pursuant to the ICC, UNCITRAL, LCIA and other ad hoc rules. Krista has worked with all the major forms of contracts including JCT, FIDIC, ICE, ACE, IMechE, LOGIC and RIBA. She has a particular interest in NEC3 and was the assistant

editor and a major contributing author to Keating on NEC3.
Professional Memberships: CIArb, LCIA, TECBAR, SCL, ICC.
Career: MA, BCL (Oxon), Call 1996, BSc, Chartered Arbitrator, TECBAR Adjudicator and Arbitrator.

LEE, Michael
11KBW, London
020 7632 8500
michael.lee@11kbw.com
Featured in Employment (London)
Practice Areas: Michael practises in employment, commercial and public law. He frequently advises on injunctive relief and restraint of trade issues. His recent work includes acting in Lonmar Global Risks Ltd v West & Ors and advising on an application to set aside service in a claim under section 212 of the Insolvency Act 1986. He is also currently instructed in a breach of confidence claim. Michael recently appeared in the EAT in Keppel Seghers UK Ltd v Hinds. In the Employment Tribunal his recent cases include a 2 week disability discrimination hearing for a university and a 5 day whistleblowing claim acting for a Finance and Operations Director. Michael also undertakes a broad range of public law work, recent cases including R (Newby) v Food Standards Agency and Patel v London Borough of Hackney Group (the first appeal to the First-Tier Tribunal (General Regulatory Chamber) under the Assets of Community Value (England) Regulations 2012).
Professional Memberships: COMBAR, ELA, ELBA, ALBA.
Career: Called to the bar in 2009.
Publications: Tolley's Employment Law Handbook.
Personal: Graduated from St Catharine's College, Cambridge with a First Class degree in Law.

LEECH, Stewart QC
Queen Elizabeth Building, London
020 7797 7837
s.leech@qeb.co.uk
Featured in Family/Matrimonial (London)
Practice Areas: Stewart specialises in ancilliary relief and cohabitee disputes, generally involving high net worth individuals with complex financial arrangements. He is regularly instructed on behalf of trustees. His cases often have an international dimension and frequently involve jurisdictional issues. He is also experienced in private law children applications. He is bilingual in French and English and has a particular interest in cross-channel cases. He routinely drafts and advises on nuptial agreements.
Professional Memberships: Family Law Bar Association; International Academy of Matrimonial Lawyers; Franco - British Lawyers Society.

LEEK, Samantha QC
5 Essex Court, London
020 7410 2000
leek@5essexcourt.co.uk
Featured in Inquests & Public Inquiries (London), Police Law (All Circuits)
Practice Areas: All areas of police and government law, including civil actions, judicial review, inquests, advice on policy.
Professional Memberships: Member of the Administrative Law Bar Association and Personal Injuries Bar Association.
Career: Particular expertise in inquests arising out of deaths in police and prison custody and the police use of firearms.She has represented police forces and police officers in numerous recent high profile inquests / civil claims including – Hillsborough, Mark Duggan, Azelle Rodney, Ian Tomlinson, Jean Charles De Menezes. Has represented numerous government departments, including the MOD and Home Office, in inquests and civil claims arising out of the death of individuals during training sessions or whilst on duty.Called in 1993; Treasury C Panel 1999;Treasury B Panel 2003; Treasury A Panel 2009; Silk 2012.

LEGARD, Edward
Dere Street Barristers, York
01904 620 048
e.legard@derestreet.co.uk
Featured in Employment (North Eastern)
Practice Areas: Specialist Employment Practitioner covering all major aspects of employment and equality law. A strong appellate practice with regular appearances before both CA and EAT. Caseload comprises a broadly even split of Respondent and Claimant work. Cases include Powell v OMV Exploration Ltd [2014] IRLR 80 (Langstaff P), Barnsley MBC v Yerraklava [2012] IRLR 78; Woods v Pasab [2013] IRLR 305, CA; Horizon Recruitment Limited v Vincent [2010] ICR 491; B & C v A [2010] IRLR 400; Kimberley Group Housing Ltd v Hambley & Os [2008] IRLR 682; Flett v. Matheson [2006] IRLR 277, CA; Ramsay v. Walkers Crisps [2004] IRLR 754.
Professional Memberships: Employment Law Bar Association.
Career: Called to the Bar 1996. Head of Employment Team, Dere Street Barristers. Mediator since 1999. Fee paid Employment Judge since 2010.
Personal: Highly experienced commercial mediator with a strong track record of success.

LEGGE, Henry QC
5 Stone Buildings, London
020 7242 6201
hlegge@5sblaw.com
Featured in Art and Cultural Property Law (London), Chancery (London), Offshore (London), Pensions (London)
Practice Areas: Henry's practice includes a broad range of Chancery work, but with particular emphasis on cases involving trusts, estates, pension schemes and art. In recent years, he has appeared in a number of high profile trust disputes both onshore and offshore (eg Gorbunova v Berezovsky) as well as appearing in some of the largest pensions cases of the last few years (eg BT, IBM, Nortel). He has acted in numerous trustee and beneficiary disputes, claims in breach of trust and asset recovery claims. As well as domestic trust and estate disputes, he has considerable experience in advising and acting in offshore jurisdictions and in cases involving offshore structures (including foundations and other civil law structures). He has appeared and advised in a number of significant cases in which complex offshore structures were under attack (for example, Berezovsky, Stow and Tchenguiz-Imerman) and is very familiar with the principles of law and tactical issues involved. He has also advised extensively on non-contentious trust issues, both domestic and offshore, including commercial trusts and securitisation structures. Henry spent much of his early years in practice defending solicitors and actuaries in negligence proceedings and he has continued to advise and appear in negligence claims for both claimants and defendants since that time. Over the years he has acted in a broad range of cases and is used to dealing with complex issues of tax, actuarial practice, investment or accounting should they arise. He has an additional area of expertise in disputes involving works of art and chattels. In recent years he has appeared in many of the most significant cases in this niche area, including Avrora v Christies, in which he acted for the successful Claimant.
Professional Memberships: CBA, APL, STEP, PAIAM, the Trust Law Committee.
Career: BA Oxford, called to the Bar 1993. Silk 2012.
Publications: "Pension Schemes" in "Company Directors: Duties, Liabilities and Remedies" (OUP); Consulting Editor to "Subrogation" by Mitchell and Waterson (OUP); various articles on the law of chattels, trusts and multi-jurisdictional succession.

LEIPER, Richard
11KBW, London
020 7632 8500
richard.leiper@11kbw.com
Featured in Employment (London)
Practice Areas: Litigation in the High Court and in employment tribunals, and appeals, including claims concerning directors' and employees' duties, protection of confidential information and post-termination restrictions, and claims concerning discrimination, whistleblowing and TUPE. Cases include Makdessi v Cavendish [2013] EWCA Civ 1539 (penalty clauses; permission to appeal to SC) [2013] EWCA Civ 1540 (applications to commit); Clements v Lloyds Banking plc [2014] ICR D22 (causation in discrimination); Macleod v Mears Ltd [2014] EWHC 2191 (QB) (discretionary bonus); Farnon v Devonshires [2011] EWHC 3167 (QB) (claim of solicitors negligence); Rabobank v Docker [2011] EqLR 580 (race discrimination); Lonmar Global Risks Ltd v West [2011] IRLR 138 (business protection); Merrill Lynch v Chunilal [2010] EWHC 1467 (Comm) (jurisdiction dispute); Redcar & Cleveland BC v Bainbridge [2009] ICR 133 (equal pay); Park v Korean Residents Association [2008] EWHC 866 (QB) (injunctive relief and trial challenging the election of the association chairman); Ogilvy & Mather Ltd v Oktobor Ltd [2007] EWHC 1285 (QB) (trial in commercial dispute concerning the termination of production contract): Commerzbank AG v Keen [2007] ICR 623 (UCTA in employment contracts); IGEN v Wong [2005] ICR 931 (burden of proof in discrimination); Clark v Nomura International [2000] IRLR 766 (rational bonus awards).
Professional Memberships: Employment Law Bar Association (Chair); Employment Lawyers Association; European Employment Lawyers Association; Industrial Law Society; Financial Services Lawyers Association.
Career: Called 1996.
Publications: Contributor to Tolley's 'Employment Handbook'.
Personal: Birmingham University (LLB); Keble College, Oxford (MJur).

LEMON, Jane
Keating Chambers, London
020 7544 2600
jlemon@keatingchambers.com
Featured in Construction (London), Energy & Natural Resources (London), International Arbitration (London), Professional Negligence (London)
Practice Areas: Specialist in litigation, arbitration and ADR for the construction, engineering, energy, shipbuilding, facilities management and technology sectors. Built a reputation as a fine advocate with a "famed intellectual prowess" who "is remarkable for the sheer hard work she puts into a case". She has acted in complex domestic litigation in the Technology and Construction Court as well as multi-million pound international arbitrations. Recent cases include projects involving highway construction, tunnelling , gas storage facilities, wind farms and semi submersible oil rigs. She is also an accredited adjudicator.
Professional Memberships: Technology and Construction Bar Association (TECBAR); Commercial Bar Association (COMBAR); The Society of Construction Law (SCL).
Career: Called 1993; public access training 2008; TECBAR accredited adjudicator.
Publications: Contributor, Keating On Construction Contracts - Ninth (2012), Eighth and Seventh Editions; Joint Author with Coulson J Section of Architects and Engineers for Professional Negligence and Liability LLP (2000).

LEMOS, Marika
Devereux, London
Featured in Tax (London)
Practice Areas: Specialises in all aspects of tax litigation (direct and indirect taxes). Also accepts instructions: in the context of commercial litigation, trust and pensions disputes, Variation of Trust Act applications and professional negligence cases where tax is involved. On the advisory side, her clients include UK and international trustees and individuals. Areas of specialism: structuring onshore and offshore trusts, farms, businesses and charities; UK and cross-border estate planning; deeds of variation; domicile and the remittance basis; residence of individuals, corporates and partnerships; funds and incentive structuring; unwinding EBTs; disposals of businesses; immunities from tax; property holding structures; taxation of pensions; etc.
Professional Memberships: On Attorney General's C Panel. Member of the Revenue Bar Association, the VAT Practitioners Group, the Chancery Bar Association, and the International Fiscal Association. On the Bar Pro Bono Unit's panel.
Career: Practising barrister since October 2005. Nominated for the Bar Pro Bro Bono Award 2013.
Publications: Co-author of the 5th and 6th Editions of McCutcheon on Inheritance Tax; Principal Editor of Whiteman & Sherry on Capital Gains Tax; Regular contributor to a number of professional publications including Tolley's Property Taxation, Taxation, Tax Journal, Private Client Business, Gray's Inn Tax Chambers Review, etc.
Personal: Read languages at St John's College, Cambridge; Vice President of LALCF, a charity set up to relieve poverty, promote education and support sustainable development on Oinousses, Greece.

LEVENE, Simon
12 King's Bench Walk, London
020 7853 0811
levene@12kbw.co.uk
Featured in Personal Injury (London), Personal Injury (All Circuits)
Practice Areas: Personal injury; clinical negligence; solicitors' negligence; health and safety; product liability; group litigation; MIB; CICA. Experience of all aspects of personal injury work, with particular emphasis on fatal accidents; occupational injuries; occupational and industrial diseases, including in particular asbestos-related diseases, deafness, asthma and eczema. Particular expertise in complex quantum issues, drafting schedules and counter schedules in cases of utmost severity. Extensive experience of all aspects of clinical negligence, including birth related trauma, obstetrics and gynaecology, spinal surgery and trauma and orthopaedics.
Professional Memberships: PIBA, PNBA, LCLCBA. Ogden Committee. Industrial Injuries Advisory Council.
Publications: Editor of Kemp & Kemp: 'Facts and Figures'; 'Ogden Tables'; 'PIBA Personal injuries Handbook'. Author of 'Damages', 'Heads of Claim' and 'Causes of Action'.

LEVY, Jacob QC
9 Gough Square, London
020 7832 0500
jlevy@9goughsquare.co.uk
Featured in Clinical Negligence (London), Personal Injury (London)
Practice Areas: All aspects of personal injury and clinical negligence work, particularly cases involving gynaecological, serious spinal, orthopaedic and brain injuries. From misplaced swabs to spinal injuries to birth accidents; as with his approach to personal injury work his motto used to be: "No case too big-no case too small." However the passage of years and attainment of Silk has caused him to recalibrate this to; "Big, Bigger and Bigger Still...oh my!". The bulk of his personal injury work comprises slippers, trippers, snippers, lifters, wheezers, stressers, backers, headers and rear-end shunters - now all of considerable value and with catastrophic consequences. He also deals with Professional Negligence cases; specifically personal injury and clinical negligence claims that have gone awry.
Professional Memberships: PIBA, PNBA.
Career: LLB (Hons) London (LSE) 1984. Called July 1986 and joined 9 Gough Square following pupillage there with John Foy QC and HHJ John Reddihough.
Personal: Family prevents anything much other than supporting failing football team and watching late night TV whilst over-eating pizza. Otherwise fanatical film and music buff and gig-goer. Byline: 'Eat football, sleep football - practice PI and Clin Neg'. And munch cheesecake - as long as the wife isn't looking. And settle Schedules of Loss - endlessly. Oh, and being the Gigmeister General - so long as the wife allows him to watch old re-formed, re-warmed Punk, New Wave and Blues.

LEVY, Juliette
Selborne Chambers, London
020 7420 9500
juliette.levy@selbornechambers.co.uk
Featured in Chancery (London), Telecommunications (London)
Practice Areas: Juliette is a chancery commercial practitioner. She also has a particular expertise in telecommunications law and regulation.
Professional Memberships: Chancery Bar association; Society for Computers and Law; International Bar Association; Women in telecoms and Technology.
Career: Called 1992: Juliette is recognised as leading junior in telecommunications, and chancery commercial work. Juliette undertakes a wide variety of commercial, telecommunications law and regulation and chancery work (including civil fraud, asset freezing orders, equitable doctrines and remedial trusts), both litigation and advisory at first instance and appellate levels. Juliette was retained in the Arqiva litigation against Everything Everywhere and Orange arising out of their recent joint venture for the creation of a single network. She has also been retained in the Pinnacle Development fraud/breach of contract action ad in the past was retained in the long running Dadourian Group fraud action. Juliette's telecommunications experience covers regulatory, commercial and Code-related issues and all telecommunications sectors, both stakeholder and regulatory/licensing, ranging from network operators and mast site providers, to content providers, Ofcom and PhonepayPlus.

LEVY, Neil
Guildhall Chambers, Bristol
0117 930 9050
neil.levy@guildhallchambers.co.uk
Featured in Banking & Finance (Western), Commercial Dispute Resolution (Western), Restructuring/Insolvency (Western)
Practice Areas: Neil specialises in banking litigation and advising on financial transactions. He has particular experience of domestic banking transactions having worked as part of the Lloyds Bank in-house legal team from 1987-1992. His field of expertise also covers professional negligence in financial transactions, insolvency and commercial disputes. Neil is a contributor to Paget's Law of Banking, Penn & Shea's Law of Domestic Banking, and the editor of Bank Notes, a website of recent banking related cases. Notable cases in 2013/2014 include Tidal Energy Ltd v Bank of Scotland [2014] EWCA Civ 1107 (31 July 2014) where Neil was successful in resisting a claim relating to a Chaps Payment and representing Lloyds TSB in TFL Management Services Ltd v Lloyds Bank Plc [2013] EWCA Civ 1415. Neil also worked with Stephen Davies QC and John Virgo on the Guardian Care Homes Libor Battle.
Professional Memberships: Chancery Bar Association; Western Circuit.
Career: Called to the Bar 1986. In-house counsel Lloyds Bank 1987-92.
Publications: Contributor Paget's Law of Banking, 13th edn (2007) & The Law & Practice of Domestic Banking (Penn & Wadsley), 2nd edn (2000); Editor banknotesuk.com.

LEWERS, Nigel
12 King's Bench Walk, London
020 7583 0811
lewers@12kbw.co.uk
Featured in Personal Injury (London)
Practice Areas: Personal injury, in particular liability of local authorities, employer's liability, road traffic accidents and liability for animals, especially horses. Cases of catastrophic injury. Clinical negligence. Motor insurance especially claims involving the MIB.
Professional Memberships: Personal Injury Bar Association; Professional Negligence Bar Association; London Common Law & Commercial Bar Association; South Eastern Circuit.
Career: In practice since 1987. Former prosecutor on behalf of the Bar Standards Board. Former member of Executive Committee of Personal Injury Bar Association.
Publications: General Editor, Kemp & Kemp Personal Injury, Law, Practice and Procedure.
Personal: Graduated in Jurisprudence from Magdalen College, Oxford. Married with four children.

LEWIS, Christopher
Atkin Chambers, London
020 7404 0102
clewis@atkinchambers.com
Featured in Construction (London), Energy & Natural Resources (London), Information Technology (London), International Arbitration (London)
Practice Areas: Construction, engineering, energy, technology and related matters.
Professional Memberships: TECBAR, Combar, LCLCBA, Society for Computers and Law, SCL.
Career: Tenant at Atkin Chambers since 1999. Some-time tutor of Law at Wadham College, Oxford and LSE; former Judicial Assistant to Lord Woolf MR.
Publications: Editor of Building Law Reports, Contributor to Hudson's Building and Engineering Contracts 12ed.
Personal: MA, BCL (Oxon).

LEWIS, David
Hardwicke, London
020 7242 2523
david.lewis@hardwicke.co.uk
Featured in Commercial Dispute Resolution (London)
Practice Areas: David Lewis has a wide-ranging commercial litigation practice including commercial contract, domestic and international arbitration, commercial agency law, franchising, civil fraud, sales of good and services, employment law with a commercial dimension, and injunction/ interim relief proceeding. Appears as an advocate in all levels of Court, adjudications, mediations and other forms of ADR. He is frequently instructed in complex commercial disputes, for example advising litigation funders in Harcus Sinclair (a firm) v Buttonwood Legal Capital and others [2013] All ER (D) 134 (Oct); [2013] EWHC 2974 (Ch); VTB Capital Plc v Nutritek International Corp & Ors [2012] EWCA Civ 808 (20 June 2012), but other areas of particular experience include trade, construction, professional negligence and insurance.
Professional Memberships: COMBAR; London Common Law and Commercial Bar Association; ELBA; ELA.
Career: Sheffield University LLB (Hons) 1996. Called to the bar (Lincoln's Inn) 1997.

LEWIS, Jonathan
4 Pump Court, London
020 7842 5555
jlewis@4pumpcourt.com
Featured in Construction (London)
Practice Areas: Jonathan Lewis specialises principally in construction and construction based professional negligence disputes in litigation, arbitration and adjudication acting for employers, contractors and professionals. Recent cases have concerned a range of construction and engineering disputes including port wall construction, railway signalling, sewerage and water contracts, steelwork design causing catastrophic building collapse, drainage, power stations and bridges. He has considerable expertise in adjudications with a number of reported decisions in this area. In addition, Jonathan has expertise in insolvency law and has previously been named Barrister of the Year at the Insolvency and Rescue Awards. He is often instructed in construction cases where an insolvency issue arises as well as having a broader insolvency practice.
Professional Memberships: Chancery Bar Association, COMBAR.
Career: Called to the Bar in 1996.
Personal: LLB, Manchester University.

LEWIS, Meyric
Francis Taylor Building, London
020 7353 8415
meyric.lewis@ftb.eu.com
Featured in Planning (London)
Practice Areas: Meyric specialises in all aspects of planning (including environmental assessment) and compulsory purchase both at inquiries and in the courts, up to the Court of Appeal and the Supreme Court. Clients range from substantial developers to public authorities and individual developers or objectors. He is frequently reported in the specialist law reports in notable cases. His court practice ranges from judicial and statutory review in the higher courts to prosecutions and other regulatory proceedings in the Crown Court and Magistrates' Court. He has particular experience in proceedings relating to planning enforcement, statutory nuisance and land contamination. Other specialisms include: residential, commercial and retail development, local development frameworks, licensed premises, listed buildings and conservation areas, highways, major infrastructure projects, compulsory purchase and compensation, trees, enforcement notices and injunctions.
Professional Memberships: Administrative Law Bar Association; Compulsory Purchase Association; Planning and Environmental Law Association.
Career: Called to Bar 1986. B Panel Counsel for the Secretary of State 1995-2001 defending planning decisions in the High Court.
Publications: Many articles including Expediency in Enforcement [2003] JPL 1106 and The New Procedures for Planning Challenges in the High Court [2008] JPL 1720.

LEWIS, Paul QC
Farrar's Building, London
020 7583 9241
chambers@farrarsbuilding.co.uk
Featured in Crime (Wales & Chester)
Practice Areas: Criminal law - both prosecution and defence. Regularly works in Wales, London and the Midlands, but also appears nationally. Particular specialisation in homicide and serious fraud. Cases include R-v-Joel Smith (The "Toni Anne Byfield" double murder case;) R-v-Osbourne and others (professional "contract killing" of a drugs rival;) R-v-Riches (historic allegation of murder of a baby 30 years earlier;) R-v-Stewart and others ("torture murder" by fire of an abducted youth;) R-v-Morrissey and others (robbery and murder at a Worcestershire Post Office;) R-v-Abu Hamza (the "Khyra Ishaq" starvation case.) Recent cases include R-v-Crooks and others (convictions of five appellants for alleged "gangland murder" quashed by Court of Appeal upon arguments

based upon non-disclosure of Prosecution material.) Successfully represented the acquitted principal defendant in the trial of R-v-Beckford and others (triple murder case arising from the Birmingham Riots of 2011.) Also works in sports law.

Professional Memberships: Bencher of Gray's Inn. Leader of the Wales and Chester Circuit, January 2014 to December 2016.

Career: Graduate of Leicester University (LLB) Called 1981; Assistant Recorder 1998; Recorder 2000; QC 2001.

Personal: Married, with two children. Lives in London and South Wales. Interests include sport (especially rugby and cricket;) music and travel.

LEWISON, Josh

Radcliffe Chambers, London
020 7831 0081
jlewison@radcliffechambers.com

Featured in Charities (London)

Practice Areas: Traditional and commercial chancery including charities, trusts, wills and succession, real property, insolvency and related professional negligence.

Professional Memberships: Chancery Bar Association, Charity Law Association.

Career: Westminster School and Downing College, Cambridge (MA, Cantab). Hardwicke and Denning Scholarships (Lincoln's Inn). Called to the Bar in 2005.

LEY-MORGAN, Mark

Serjeants' Inn Chambers, London
020 7427 5000
mlm@serjeantsinn.com

Featured in Police Law (All Circuits), Professional Discipline (London)

Practice Areas: Mark Ley-Morgan was called to the Bar in 1994. Mark specialises in public and administrative, police, employment, inquests and inquiries and professional discipline law. An earlier edition notes that "he is an excellent jury advocate with a very persuasive court technique that certainly goes down well with both judge and jury" and that "he is an extremely astute lawyer, who is very intelligent and personable, his ability to win over a jury is incredible." Please click on the link to the Serjeants' Inn Chambers website for his profile, which sets out full details of his practice including relevant work of note.

LIDDELL, Richard

4 New Square, London
020 7822 2000
r.liddell@4newsquare.com

Featured in Professional Negligence (London), Sports Law (London)

Practice Areas: Wide-ranging practice with particular experience and expertise in the following areas: (i) professional liability (ii) sport (iii) commercial litigation and (iv) construction and engineering. Rick specialises in all fields of professional liability, with particular emphasis upon barristers and solicitors, construction professionals, valuers and surveyors, accountants and auditors, IFAs and insurance brokers. Rick has been involved in numerous high-profile cases, including Co-op v Birse (CA, 2014), Aspect v Higgins (CA, 2013), Mengiste v Endowment Fund (CA, 2013), Elvanite v AMEC (TCC), Linklaters Business Services v How Engineering Services Ltd & Ors (TCC) and The Innovator Litigation (substantial multi-party Commercial Court litigation). He has also a busy sports practice and his cases have spanned the following sports: athletics, basketball, boxing, football, horseracing, rowing, rugby union, and shooting. He is instructed in both sports commercial disputes and sports disciplinary matters.

Professional Memberships: British Association for Sport and Law; COMBAR; PNBA; TECBAR; Chancery Bar Association; LCIA.

Career: MA (Cantab); LLM. Called to the Bar (Middle Temple) in 1999 (Major Scholarship). Tenant at 4 New Square 2000 to date.

Personal: Educated at Eastbourne College; Pembroke College, Cambridge University. Married with two children. Supports Sunderland AFC!

LIDINGTON, Gary

11 Stone Buildings, London
020 7831 6381
lidington@11sb.com

Featured in Commercial Dispute Resolution (London), Real Estate Litigation (London)

Practice Areas: Gary Lidington specialises in the full range of commercial, commercial chancery and real estate litigation, including related professional negligence disputes. Gary's commercial work includes company and shareholder disputes, contractual claims and partnership matters, much of which has a strong fraud or multi-jurisdictional element. He also has a growing oil and gas practice, both in the English Courts and in international arbitration. His property practice extends to all areas of real property and both commercial and residential landlord and tenant work. He also has a well-developed and highly regarded professional negligence practice in particular in respect of solicitors, accountants, financial professionals and valuers. For further details of Gary's practice please visit 'the Barristers' section on www.11sb.com.

Professional Memberships: COMBAR, Chancery Bar Association.

Career: Notable cases include: UNCITRAL arbitration relating to an oil and gas dispute (2013-14); Bank of Scotland v Pereira & Pains [2011] EWCA Civ 241 (fraud, leading authority on setting aside judgment/appealing when a party does not turn up to trial); Nessa v Khatun (2011) (complex dispute re allegations of fraud, undue influence, forgery, mis-representation); Close Invoice Finance Ltd v Pile [2009] 1 FLR 873 (relevance of Art 8 ECHR to enforcement of charging orders); Dartmouth Court Blackheath Ltd v Berisworth Ltd [2008] EWHC 350 (a leading case on the scope of pre-emption rights under Landlord & Tenant Act 1987).

LIGHTFOOT, Jeremy

Stone Chambers, London
020 7440 6900
jeremy.lightfoot@stonechambers.com

Featured in Shipping (London)

Practice Areas: Jeremy Lightfoot has a broad commercial litigation and arbitration practice, appearing regularly in arbitrations (both in London and abroad) and in the High Court. He has particular expertise in all aspects of shipping and maritime law, including charterparties, shipbuilding, international trade and commodities, ship sale and purchase, enforcement of foreign judgments and arbitral awards, freezing injunctions, contracts of affreightment, collisions, groundings, unsafe ports/berths, piracy, marine insurance, cargo contamination, sale of goods, ship management agreements, marine insurance, general average, demurrage, arbitration appeals, civil fraud and jurisdictional disputes.

Professional Memberships: COMBAR; London Common Law and Commercial Bar Association; Lincoln's Inn.

Personal: Jeremy studied law at Oxford University and was called to the Bar in 2006. Jeremy's leisure interests include motorsport in all its guises.

LIGHTMAN, Daniel

Serle Court, London
020 7242 6105
dlightman@serlecourt.co.uk

Featured in Chancery (London), Commercial Dispute Resolution (London), Company (London), Restructuring/Insolvency (London)

Practice Areas: General chancery, commercial, company and insolvency litigation. Recent cases include: Eckerle v Wickeder Westfalenstahl GmbH [2014] Ch 196 (re-registration of a plc as a private company); Apex Global Management Ltd v Fi Call Ltd [2014] BCC 286 (unfair prejudice petition); Petrodel Resources v Prest [2013] 2 AC 415 (piercing the corporate veil); Bamford v Harvey [2013] Bus LR 589 (derivative claim); Serious Organised Crime Agency v Perry [2013] 1 AC 182 (Proceeds of Crime Act); Re Dunstans Publishing Ltd [2012] BCC 515 (rectification of company register).

Professional Memberships: Chancery Bar Association, COMBAR, ACTAPS, Insolvency Lawyers' Association.

Career: Called to the Bar 1995.

Publications: Author of Chapter 3 (derivative claims) and co-author of Chapter 8 (s.994 procedure) of Minority Shareholders: Law, Practice & Procedure (5th Ed. forthcoming, 2015); co-author of Chapters 14, 15 and 31 of Lightman & Moss, 'The Law of Receivers and Administrators of Companies' (5th Ed. 2011). Other publications include: 'Unfair Prejudice Petitions: long-range missiles for minority shareholders' (BJIB&FL, Dec 2013); 'Petrodel Resources Ltd v Prest: where are we now?' (Trusts & Trustees, Nov 2013); 'A Drafting Enigma' (NLJ, 17 August 2012); 'Two Aspects of the Statutory Derivative Claim' (LMCLQ, Feb 2011); Cricket Grounds from the Air (2nd Ed. 2010).

Personal: BA Lit. Hum. (First Class), Magdalen College, Oxford; Dip. Law (Distinction) City University, London. Hardwicke, Mansfield and Denning Scholar of Lincoln's Inn.

LIMB, Christopher

18 St John Street, Manchester
0161 278 1800
climb@18sjs.com

Featured in Clinical Negligence (Northern)

Practice Areas: Practice is almost exclusively clinical negligence. Claimant counsel in the seminal Court of Appeal decision of Naylor v Preston HA in 1987, fundamentally altering the conduct of clinical negligence cases. Subsequent Court of Appeal cases have included Forbes v Wandsworth HA in 1997 (limitation) and Gouldsmith v Mid-Staffs Trust in 2007 (causation). The entire spectrum of clinical negligence work is undertaken, including many current cerebral palsy cases. Recent cases have included; cancer, intestinal, brain, eye, Erbs palsy, CPA cases relating to prostheses/devices, vascular surgery, pressure sores, orthopaedic, spinal and wrongful birth. He has great experience at all stages of preparation, conferences and settlement meetings, as well as hearings. Contributing author Jordans Personal Injury.

Professional Memberships: PNBA, PIBA, NCMLA. APIL - Clinical Negligence Conference Organiser.

Career: Called 1975. Tribunal Judge in Primary Health Lists and SEN.

Personal: Born 1953. 2 adult sons. Choral singing, rugby league, wine, France and walking are among the many interests he has insufficient time for.

LIMB, Patrick QC

Ropewalk Chambers, Nottingham
0115 947 2581
patricklimbqc@ropewalk.co.uk

Featured in Personal Injury (Midlands), Personal Injury (All Circuits)

Practice Areas: He specialises principally in disease, all aspects of personal injury, clinical negligence and regulatory defence work. He is highly regarded for his work in test litigation and group actions and is an experienced appellate advocate to Supreme Court level. Sure-footed on law and procedure, he provides strategic thinking, commercial nous and seeks to serve each client by leading as an effective team-player.

Professional Memberships: Personal Injuries Bar Association; Professional Negligence Bar Association; Health and Safety Lawyers Association; Discrimination Lawyers Association; Nottinghamshire-Medico Legal Society.

Career: Called in 1987; Silk: 2006; Called to the Gibraltar Bar 2010; MA (Cantab) Law, Pembroke College, Cambridge; Accredited Mediator; Head of Ropewalk Chambers: 2012 – present. He was awarded Barrister of the Year by Nottinghamshire Law Society in 2014.

LINTOTT, David

Cornerstone Barristers, London
020 7242 4986
davidjl@cornerstonebarristers.com

Featured in Social Housing (London)

Practice Areas: David is a public law specialist working primarily in areas of local government, planning and social housing. He has appeared in some of the most significant housing cases in recent years and has related expertise in human rights and EU law. He is a highly experienced and knowledgeable advocate with extensive experience of the Court of Appeal and High Court where he has successfully represented many local authorities, his cases include London Borough of Wandsworth v NJ [2013] EWCA Civ. 1373; Falis Ibrahim v London Borough of Wandsworth [2013] EWCA Civ. 20; Chaoui El Goure v Royal Borough of Kensington and Chelsea [2012] EWCA Civ 670 CA; Bubb v Wandsworth LBC [2011] EWCA Civ 1285; Adel William v Wandsworth London Borough Council [2006] EWCA Civ 535 C.A; Lomotey v Enfield [2004] EWCA Civ 627 C.A.

Professional Memberships: ALBA, PEBA

Career: David was called to the Bar in 1996, after completing a law degree at Cambridge University.

Personal: David has a keen interest in ecology and arboriculture and has been involved in conservation of large carnivores as a founder member of the Slovak Wildlife Society since 1998.

LISSACK, Richard QC
Outer Temple Chambers, London
020 7353 6381
law@rlqc.com
Featured in Financial Services (London), Health & Safety (London), Inquests & Public Inquiries (London), Financial Crime (London)

Practice Areas: For full details of Richard Lissack's practice please visit www.rlqc.com. Richard is now instructed in most of the landmark regulatory/criminal cases: Barclays Bank in £10.7b Qatar capital raise FCA and SFO [UK] and DoJ and SEC [US]; HP $11b Autonomy takeover FRC and SFO [UK] and DoJ and SEC [US]; JP Morgan Chase $6b London Whale case FCA [UK] and DoJ and SEC [US]; Eastern European energy corporation $100b corruption and fraud case SFO and Civil claim [UK]. He is also instructed in the International FX investigations of major foreign banks and the LIBOR rigging charges against a senior European trader in a foreign bank. Richard Lissack QC has for several years has been recognised by the legal directories as a leading Silk across multiple areas of law, this year it is 13 - Banking and finance, administrative and public law: public inquiries, crime, employment, financial crime, financial crime: corporates, financial services, fraud: criminal, health and safety, inquests and public inquiries, civil liberties and human rights, personal injury and professional discipline and regulatory law. Furthermore in the last twelve months he has been retained by over 20 solicitors who have been recommended as 'leaders' in the legal directories. Testimonial 1: Tim Russ, Partner Clarke Willmott: "Richard is almost unique in that he combines a number of qualities rarely found in a silk: He's very accessible, quick to respond and able to digest complex data and cut straight to the heart of a case and formulate original strategies. He is full of energy and leads a legal team with a light touch, whilst managing to make lay clients feel reassured and confident. No mean feat." Leading solicitors quoted in the key legal directories have variously described him as " A force of nature", "QC of choice in any big case", "a truly exceptional talent", "a standout silk", "a true leader", and "in a league of his own" They add that he combines "forensic brilliance, a tactical approach and first-rate legal analysis" with "excellent client care" and a "charming, personable" manner that "puts clients at ease" and makes him "a joy to work with". He is noted for being "a very strong, persuasive and excellent advocate.", for his "breathtaking advocacy" and for being "very intelligent and creative in undermining another side's case". He is also praised for "an amazing ability to grasp and analyse a vast body of information" allowing him to "get to the nub of the issue" whilst explaining complex legal points "entirely without pomposity" and for his "very strong tactical judgment and a good rapport with the court, and being excellent with clients,". Richard's practice is mainly high-profile complex litigation, with a strong corporate slant, often combining regulatory and fraud/criminal practice. His areas of expertise include: Anti-corruption legislation / Bribery Act; Commercial fraud; Corporate killing; Employment law; Health and safety law; International banking and finance; International financial services; Proceeds of crime; Public Inquiries; Regulatory breaches. Richard frequently works in overseas jurisdictions, including New York, Abu Dhabi, the British Virgin Islands, Italy, Switzerland, Luxembourg and Hong Kong. He has been admitted to the New York Bar (as a Foreign Legal Consultant), the Eastern Caribbean Bar and the Dubai International Financial Centre. Testimonial 2: Kevin Bridges, Partner, Pinsent Masons LLP: "Richard Lissack QC is the go to barrister in the field of health and safety and the best Leader I have instructed. His ability to direct a team of lawyers is inspiring, ensuring that solicitors and barristers work seamlessly together as part of a team, always playing to their strengths. His creativity ensures that clients receive a first class service leaving no possible stone unturned in getting the best result achievable. As a tactician, there is none better than Richard; no problem appears too difficult or issue too complex. As an advocate, Richard is superb on his feet, reading the mood of the judge and jury; and using this to deliver the best strategic advice on trial tactics. As well as being an exceptional barrister, Richard is great to be around. He puts junior lawyers and clients at ease, and respects the views and opinions of the partners instructing him".

Professional Memberships: Bencher, Inner Temple; Member Chartered Institute of Arbitrators; Financial Services Lawyers Association (Board Member); Human Rights Lawyers Association; Commercial Bar Association; International Bar Association; Employment Law Bar Association; Bar European Group; Health and Safety Lawyers Association; American Counsel Association; Federal Bar Council of New York. Richard is also in the register of public access-accredited barristers.

Career: Called 1978, QC 1994 aged 37; QC Bar of the Eastern Caribbean 2002; Recorder 1993 onwards; New York Bar 2007; Northern Ireland Bar (QC) 2008; 2008 Dubai International Financial Centre Courts; 2008 Bencher of Inner Temple.

Publications: Co-authored Lissack and Horlick on Bribery, LexisNexis. Contributing editor, Public inquiries, Oxford University Press. Financial Services Law and Regulation, LexisNexis. Richard has written and contributed to numerous articles for legal/ business publications and is regularly called upon to provide expert commentary for national newspapers and radio.

Personal: Richard has three daughters and when not in court he rides, goes to the theatre, sails off the coast of the Cornwall and acts as an Ambassador for Action Aid and a Patron and Development Board member of RADA.

LITTLE, Tom
9 Gough Square, London
020 7832 0500
tlittle@9goughsquare.co.uk
Featured in Crime (London), Financial Crime (London)

Practice Areas: Principal area of practice is criminal and criminal fraud work. Tom has particular expertise in cases involving complex expert and telephone evidence. In addition Tom's practice comprises police law, inquests and Judicial Review cases linked to criminal investigations.

Professional Memberships: Criminal Bar Association, Administrative Law Bar Association and South Eastern Circuit.

Career: Called to the Bar in 1997. Appointed as a Special Advocate by the Attorney General in 2009 and as Junior Treasury Counsel at the Central Criminal Court in 2012 and in 2014 to the Attorney General's Civil 'A' Panel. Appointed by the Lord Chancellor as member of the Criminal Procedure Rule Committee from 2004-11. Secretary of the Criminal Bar Association (2008-09). He also sits as a Judge in the Crown Court having been appointed a Recorder in 2012.

Publications: Joint author of 'Preventative Orders: A Practical Guide' (2010).

LIVESEY, Bernard QC
Hailsham Chambers, London
020 7643 5000
bernard.liveseyqc
@hailshamchambers.com
Featured in Professional Negligence (London)

Practice Areas: Commercial, construction, defamation, insurance and professional liability litigation and arbitration. Bernard's core practice covers insurance (the construction of policies, coverage issues, non-disclosure and fraud) and the mainstream of professional liability (esp. of barristers and solicitors; building professionals; accountants; brokers and valuers). His special expertise is as a tactician and advocate, esp. in cross-examination of witnesses, lay, expert and technical. Recommendations in directories include "an ingenious and lateral thinker", "a devastating cross-examiner", "a respected practitioner who fills the court with 'a real feeling of crunch'" and "sharp, precise and clear…everything you want in a silk, good on paper and nifty on his feet". Leading cases include: Minkin v Cawdrey Kaye Fireman Taylor [2012] EWCA Civ. 546 (entitlement of solicitor to recover costs); Islamic Investment Co of the Gulf v Cains Advocates [2012] (scope of duty of advocates for negligence and alleged conspiracy to inflict loss); Eminence Property Developments v Heaney [2010] EWCA Civ (construction of contract for sale of property); Fitzpatrick Contractors v Tyco (2008/9 - £18m delay disruption and defects claim); Jones v Associated Newspapers (2007 - defamation, Pt 36 costs); Hibbert Pownall Newton v Whitehead & Searle (CA. 2008 - solicitors, scope of retainer); Dayman v Lawrence Graham (2008 - solicitors, scope of duty); Reader v Molesworths (CA 2007) solicitors, scope of duty; Talisman v Norton Rose (CA 2006 - property, evaluating lost chances); Moy v Pettman Smith (HL 2004 - barrister's liability for negligent settlement advice; Pickersgill v Riley (PC 2004 - scope of solicitor's duty); Kapur v J.W. Francis & Co (CA 1999 - insurance broker's liability); Kumar v AGF (1998 - construction of PI policy); Spring v Guardian Insurance (HL 1995 - negligent references). As a Deputy High Court Judge he has dealt with and given judgment in diverse specialist areas including: Hunter Kane v Watkins (directors' duties); RDF Media Group v Alan Clements (employment); Tann v Herrington (partnership); Land Securities v Fladgate Fielder (tort of abuse of process) and a wide variety of property, planning, insolvency and commercial disputes.

Professional Memberships: COMBAR; PNBA; ChBA.

Career: Silk 1990; Deputy High Court Judge (ChD & QB) 1998; Bencher of Lincoln's Inn 1999.

LIVESEY, Kate
4 Pump Court, London
020 7842 5555
clerks@4pumpcourt.com
Featured in Construction (London), Professional Negligence (London)

Practice Areas: Common law and commercial litigation/ arbitration, particularly: construction (incl. shipbuilding/ offshore construction), insurance, professional negligence (incl. accountants, brokers, construction professionals, IFAs, lawyers and valuers) and procedural challenges (conflict/ bias/ jurisdictional/ ECHR). Awarded Professional Negligence Junior of the Year 2012. Reported cases include: Browning v Brachers [2005] PNLR 44 & [2004] PNLR 28 (solicitors' negligence -- lost litigation chance); P (A Barrister) v Bar Council [2005] 1 WLR 3019 (disciplinary tribunal conflict/bias); Smith v Kvaerner Cementation Foundations [2007] 1 WLR 370 (judicial conflict/ bias); Sumukan v Commonwealth Secretariat - ss.67/68/69 arbitration appeals: (2007) 2 Lloyd' s Rep 87(CA) (validity of s69(1) exclusion agreement); (2007) 1 Lloyds Rep 370 (Comm), (2008) 1 Lloyds Rep 40 (CA) (ss67/68 appeals - defective appointment); R ex p. Heather Moor & Edgecomb v FOS (2008) Bus LR 1486 (CA) (whether FOS to determine complaints according to law); FOS v Heather Moor & Edgecomb (2009) 1 All ER 328 (CA) (lawfulness of FOS case fee); Cooperative Group Ltd v John Allen Associates Ltd (2012) 28 Const LJ 27 (engineers' negligence); Attrill & Ors. v Dresdner Kleinwort Ltd & Commerzbank AG (bonus claims): [2011] IRLR 613 (CA – Part 24); [2012] IRLR 553 (QBD); and [2013] IRLR 548 (CA).

Professional Memberships: BILA, COMBAR, LCLCBA, PNBA, TECBAR, YIAG.

Career: BA Cambridge (Double 1st), Dip. Law (City), called 2001.

LLOYD-JONES, John QC
36 Bedford Row, London
020 7421 8000
jlloyd-jones@36bedfordrow.co.uk
Featured in Crime (Midlands)

Practice Areas: John Lloyd–Jones QC is a trial strategist, dedicated to the forensic analysis of evidence and passionate about the in-court examination of witnesses. Appointed QC in 2013, John has spent his first year in Silk building on his reputation as one of the most highly experienced, in–demand junior barristers defending and prosecuting on the Midland and South Eastern Circuits. 2013-2014 has seen John advise Solicitors and private clients on discrete issues of privilege, confidentiality, costs and disclosure involving multi-national third parties. John was also instructed to prosecute a £3m VHCC fraud and has prosecuted and defended in four high profile East Midlands murders.

Professional Memberships: Midland & South-Eastern Circuits. Criminal Bar Association. British Association of Sport & Law. CEDR Accredited Mediator.

Career: After serving as an Officer in the Coldstream Guards for 3 years, John was called to the Bar in 1993 winning the Evered ver Heyden Foundation Prize for Advocacy. He was Head of the Criminal Team in Chambers 2011-14 and appointed Queen's Counsel, on his first application, in March 2013.

Personal: Born 1965. Eton College, Durham University & Polytechnic of Central

London. Married with 2 children & living in the East Midlands.

LOFTHOUSE, Simon QC
Atkin Chambers, London
020 7404 0102
slofthouse@atkinchambers.com
Featured in Construction (London), International Arbitration (London), Professional Negligence (London)
Practice Areas: Practice covers international and domestic arbitration and litigation acting both for and against governments, public and private corporations worldwide. He is familiar with and has advised on the standard domestic and international construction and engineering contracts, as well as advising on their revisions. The types of disputes he is instructed in frequently involve complex engineering, construction, technology, IT or energy projects particularly those requiring detailed cross examination on technical issues, delay or allegations of professional negligence against architects, engineers, quantity surveyors and other professionals. The disputes are wide ranging but include oil and gas platforms, emission abatement process software disputes, large commercial and residential developments, M&E works, piling operations onshore and offshore, construction of roads, pipe laying, tunnelling, track installation/repair, pumping stations, coastal defences and effluent, power stations, utilities, chemical plants, and airport terminals.
Professional Memberships: Commercial Bar Association; Technology and Construction Bar Association; registered adjudicator. Qualified to appear in the DIFC, Dubai.
Career: Called to Bar of England and Wales in 1988. Recorder 2003. Advocacy teacher for Gray's Inn. Silk 2006. Chair of Professional Conduct Committee of the Bar 2011- ; Member, Bar Standards Board 2011-.
Publications: Articles editor Current Law (Sweet and Maxwell) between 1989-94. Contributes generally to professional publications such as Building Magazine and lectures worldwide on issues relating to international arbitration, construction and engineering disputes.
Personal: LLB (Hons) (Lond); Enjoys squash and skiing. Married. Lives in London.

LOMNICKA, Eva
4 New Square, London
020 7822 2000
eva.lomnicka@kcl.ac.uk
Featured in Consumer Law (London), Financial Services (London)
Practice Areas: Advisory work on consumer credit law and financial services regulation, reflecting publications.
Professional Memberships: FSLA (Advisory Board and Treasurer); COMBAR; SLS. Bencher (Academic), Middle Temple.
Career: Professor of Law, King's College London. Called to the Bar 1974. Adviser to UK delegation to UNCITRAL convention on receivables financing (1997-2001 Vienna and New York); on DTI's steering group leading to the Consumer Credit Act 2006 (2002-06).
Publications: (1) General Editor, Encyclopaedia of Consumer Credit Law; (2)Author, The Financial Services and Markets Act 2000: An Annotated Guide; (3)Co-editor, Lomnicka and Powell, Encyclopaedia of Financial Services Law; (4) Contributor, Palmer's Company Law (Part 11); (5) Co-author, Modern Banking Law; (6) Co-author, The Law of Security and Title-based Finance; (7) Contributor, Chitty on Contracts (Chap.38); (7) Contributor, Financial Services Law (Chap. 17).
Personal: Born 17 May 1951; 1969-73 Girton College, Cambridge (MA, LLB; Chancellor's Medal). Married with three children.

LORD, David W QC
3 Stone Buildings, London
020 7242 4937
dlord@3sb.law.co.uk
Featured in Insurance (London), Offshore (London)
Practice Areas: Principal areas of practice are commercial and chancery law. Work includes insurance and reinsurance, company law, insolvency and media and entertainment. Acted in Fairfield Sentry v Migani, RP Explorer V Chilukuri, The Seashell of Lisson Grove v Aviva, Weaverig Macro Fixed Funbd Ltd v Peterson, Cherney v Deripaska, Aspinall's Club Ltd v Al-Zayat, Freakley v Centre Re (T&N), BIA v Prince Jefri, KCM v Coromin, British Horseracing Board v Victor Chandler Intrernational Ltd, Feasey v Sun Life, Henderson v Merrett, Deeny and Others v Gooda Walker Ltd and Re MC Bacon Ltd amongst others. Recently heavily involved in hedge fund litigation (involving amongst other Madoff and Weavering) in various offshore jurisdictions in particular the Cayman Islands and the British Virgin Islands.
Professional Memberships: Middle Temple, Lincoln's Inn, Chancery Bar Association, COMBAR. Called to the New York Bar (FLC, BVI Bar and on an ad hoc basis to the Cayman Bar. Member of the Chartered Institute of Arbitrators.
Career: Called to the Bar in 1987 and became a tenant at 3 Stone Buildings in 1988 and Queen's Counsel in 2009.
Personal: Educated at King's School Rochester 1971-81 and Bristol University 1982-86 (LLB Hons). Leisure pursuits include most sports, especially skiing, tennis and golf. Born 28th September 1964. Lives in London.

LOVE, Steve
Compass Chambers, Edinburgh
0131 226 5071
steve.love@compasschambers.com
Featured in Personal Injury (Scotland)
Practice Areas: Extensive civil and criminal court practice dealing principally with all aspects of personal injury, clinical negligence and regulatory crime. Substantial experience in high value cases involving catastrophic injury and claims arising out of accidents at work, road traffic accidents (particularly those involving motorcycles), accidents on board aircraft and industrial injury/disease. Also significant experience: advising and appearing for companies and individuals in relation to prosecutions under the Health and Safety at Work Etc. Act 1974 and related statutory regulations; advising and appearing for appellants in relation to improvement/prohibition notices served under HSWA 1974, the accused in prosecutions under the Road Traffic Act 1988 and parties at Fatal Accident Inquiries.
Professional Memberships: Health and Safety Lawyers' Association: Association of Regulatory and Disciplinary Lawyers.
Career: Aberdeen University 1983 – 1987: LLB/DLP; Partner Simpson & Marwick WS 1994 – 1997; Partner Ledingham Chalmers, Solicitors 1997 – 1999; Admitted to Faculty of Advocates in 2001.

LOVEDAY, Mark
Tanfield Chambers, London
020 7421 5300
markloveday@tanfieldchambers.co.uk
Featured in Real Estate Litigation (London)
Practice Areas: Residential and commercial property issues. Extensive experience of leasehold enfranchisement and management, service charges, business tenancies, easements and boundaries. Significant cases include: Filering v Taylor (forfeiture), re: Palmeiro (fixtures), Berthon Boat v Hoods Sailmakers (business tenancy renewal), Stapel v Bellshore Property Investments (service charges), Riaz v Masaku (indemnity), WX Investments v Begg (rent review), Smith v Titanate (licence/business tenancy), Talisman v Norton Rose (professional negligence - business tenancy), Buckley v Bowerbeck (service charges), Weir v Area Estates (2010, rescission of auction contract), Howard de Walden v Broome (2011, individual lease extension), Arnold v Britten (2012, 'stepped' service charges), John Lyons Estate v Jackson (2012, leasehold enfranchisement valuation) Kutchukian v John Lyons Estate, CA (2013, leasehold enfranchisement break clause), Alamouti v John Lyons Estate (2014, leasehold enfranchisement valuation).
Professional Memberships: Property Bar Association, Chancery Bar Association, Chartered Institute of Arbitrators, Association of Leasehold Enfranchisement Practitioners.
Career: Career: Called 1986. Judge, First-tier Tribunal (Property Chamber). Barrister of the Year, Property Management Awards 2011-12.
Publications: Publications: Editor, Service Charges and Management, Law and Practice (Sweet & Maxwell). Editor, Rent Review: A Surveyor's Handbook (RICS). Column on residential property law in the The Times newspaper every Friday.

LOWNDS, Peter
2 Hare Court, London
020 74353 5324
peterlownds@2harecourt.com
Featured in Crime (London)
Practice Areas: A former Slaughter and May solicitor he is a specialist in defending in complex and substantial cases that have frequently made national news. His practice encompasses fraud, terrorism and other serious crime. He is currently acting for a Russian banker in a corruption case involving funding applications by oil and gas companies from the Former Soviet Republics and for a client accused of involvement in a City based fraud involving diamond selling. He regularly appears in major cases involving domestic and international acts of terrorism. These include a widely reported case involving incitement to murder over the internet by the media wing of al-Qaeda in Iraq. He is very experienced in defending in cases involving fatal violence, often in the context of alleged organised crime or gang related activity. In a particularly high profile case he successfully defended a pilot of a helicopter charged with manslaughter following an airfield fatality. He has conducted many rape trials and recently obtained an acquittal for an actor who appeared in War Horse. He has a particular interest in criminal cases involving communication over social media and issues of privacy and data protection and recently represented a man charged over the prohibition of the publication of images of the murderers of James Bulger.
Career: Called 1998 (Grays Inn). Direct Access Course 2010.

LUCKING, Adrienne QC
36 Bedford Row, London
020 7421 8000
alucking@36bedfordrow.co.uk
Featured in Crime (Midlands)
Practice Areas: Adrienne both prosecutes and defends in the most serious and complex cases of homicide, violence and sexual offences. Her practice includes organised crime involving multi-million pound drug importation and firearms. She has substantial expertise in cases involving mentally disordered and dangerous offenders, as well as the very young. Adrienne is particularly sought after by prosecutors in cases involving the need for Counsel who inspires confidence in vulnerable defendants and witnesses. She is noted for her sensitive but firm handling of emotive issues in cases. Defence solicitors rely on her experience in the representation of clients with serious mental health issues and learning difficulties charged with grave offences, facing life sentences or hospital orders with restrictions. She regularly deals with complex medical and scientific issues ranging from the phylogenetic analysis of viral DNA in HIV, ageing of fractures and odontology to more obscure issues such as friction co-efficients.
Professional Memberships: Criminal Bar Association, Professional Negligence Bar Association.
Career: Called in 1989 and a tenant at 36 Bedford Row since 2007. Appointed a Recorder on the Midland Circuit 2009 and authorised to try serious sexual offences since 2013. Appointed a member of the Independent Rugby Judiciary in 2013. Appointed Queen's Counsel 2014.
Personal: Adrienne lives in rural Leicestershire and has a passionate interest in National Hunt racing and Rugby Union. She is a horse owner and is married to a farmer. Her other interests include classical music.

LYKIARDOPOULOS, Andrew QC
8 New Square, London
020 7405 4321
andrew.lykiardopoulos@8newsquare.co.uk
Featured in Intellectual Property (London)
Practice Areas: Barrister(QC) practising in all areas of intellectual property law. He regularly appears in the High Court, Court of Appeal and at the EPO. He has also been involved in cases both before the UK Supreme Court and the Court of Justice of the EU. He has been described by the legal directories as "indisputably one of the best advocates at the junior IP Bar" and as being "a remarkable advocate with excellent client handling skills". Andrew was awarded "IP Junior of the Year" by Chambers & Partners in 2012. Recent cases include NLA v. Meltwater & PRCA, Servier v. Apotex, Swarovksi v Leica, Seitz v. KHS Corpoplast, Assos v. Asos, Sanofi v. Actavis and HTC v. Apple. A full CV is at www.8newsquare.co.uk
Professional Memberships: Member of the Chancery Bar Association, AIPPI.
Career: 1994-2000:IP solicitor at Bristows, 2000-04: Partner at Bristows, 2004 onwards: called to the bar and practising at 8 New Square. Appointed QC 2014.

LYNCH, Adrian QC
11KBW, London
020 7632 8500
adrian.lynch@11kbw.com
Featured in Employment (London)
Practice Areas: Principal area of practice is employment law, covering the full gamut of that specialism including unfair and wrongful dismissal, sex, race and disability discrimination, trade union law and restrictive covenants. Has appeared in the European Court of Justice in Luxembourg as well as before the Commission and Court of Human Rights in Strasbourg. Adrian also practises in public law. Adrian represented the Secretary of State for Health in successfully resisting before the Newcastle Upon Tyne Employment Tribunal what would probably have been the largest equal pay challenge ever which concerned a major reorganisation within the NHS affecting over one million employees, see Ms Hartley and Others v Secretary of State for Health and Others. Thereafter Adrian has represented the Secretary of State for Health in a number of other, post Hartley, equal pay matters. Adrian also successfully represented the Royal Mail in the EAT and Court of Appeal in connection with the scope and meaning of regulation 13 of TUPE, and successfully represented Parkwood Leisure Ltd in the European Court of Justice in proceedings concerned with the scope of the contractual rights which transfer under TUPE.
Professional Memberships: Gray's Inn.
Career: Called to the Bar in 1983 and joined 11KBW in 1984. Took Silk in 2000, prior to which he was a member of the Attorney General's Panel of Junior Counsel (Supplementary Panel). Appointed recorder in 2002. Member of the Equal Opportunities Commission's Panel of Barristers and member of the Employment Panel of the City Disputes Panel's Employment Service.
Publications: As an academic teaching at King's College London between 1971-84, published a number of articles and book reviews, including publications in the 'Law Quarterly Review'. Author of the chapter on settlements in employment law in David Foskett QC's work 'The Law and Practice of Compromise' in the most recent edition of that work.
Personal: Jelf medallist 1971 at King's College, London.

LYNCH, Ben
Devereux, London
020 7353 7534
lynch@devchambers.co.uk
Featured in Commercial Dispute Resolution (London), Insurance (London), Professional Negligence (London), Telecommunications (London)
Practice Areas: Commercial Dispute Resolution, Insurance, Professional Negligence and Telecommunications. Recent cases: "... Limited v ... Limited" [2014] very high value solicitors' professional indemnity insurance aggregation dispute, acting for insurer, led by Colin Edelman QC; "A v B" [2014] multi-million pound solicitors' professional indemnity year of attachment arbitration (acting alone); "A v B" [2014] complicated and high value IFA / Court of Protection professional negligence claim; "A and B v X and ... QC" [2014] barrister's negligence claim, acting alone for leading QC; BT v Ofcom "Ethernet" case [2013] led by Rhodri Thompson QC, Graham Read QC and Sarah Lee; "A v B" [2013] large, high-value notification and aggregation case (acting alone); very high value Jordanian energy / insurance dispute (acting alone) [2012]; BT v Ofcom "PPC" case [2012] EWCA Civ 1051, led by Christopher Vajda QC, Andrew Burrows QC (Hon) and previously by Graham Read QC; "... Ltd v 5 Defendants" [2011-2012] complicated insurance brokers' negligence and insurance claim (acting alone); Nouri v. ... (A Firm) and 2 Others [2010] 50 EG 64, Sephton limitation issues: successful on own in Court of Appeal; Flexsys America L.P. v. XL Insurance Company Limited [2010] Lloyd's Rep. IR 132, led by Colin Wynter QC; Telecommunications case [2009] up to £90 million claim, led by Graham Read QC; multi-million pound barristers' negligence claim [2009], led by George Bompas QC; The Welsh Rugby Union Limited v. ... (A Firm) [2007], led by Colin Edelman QC; "Mr ... v. ... QC" [2007] barrister's negligence claim acting for leading QC, led by Andrew Burns; ERC Frankona v. American National [2006] Lloyd Rep IR 157, led by Colin Wynter QC.
Professional Memberships: LCLCBA (committee member),PNBA (co-opted committee member), COMBAR, Bar Pro Bono Unit.
Career: Astbury Scholar, Middle Temple. Columbia Law School, LLM (Stone Scholar). Inns of Court School of Law (Very Competent). Balliol College, Oxford, BA (Hons) Law (Top First in College, Paton Scholar). King's College School, Wimbledon.
Publications: MacGillivray on Insurance Law, upcoming second supplement to 12th Edition (2014), first supplement to 12th Edition (2013), 12th Edition (2012), and 2nd Supplement to 11th Edition (2011); "Discriminate without prejudice" (2004) 154 NLJ 1038; "Pleading Fraud: the Insurer's Alternative" (2004) 154 NLJ 502 with Andrew Burns; and "What will happen to the QC Clause in Insurance Contracts if the rank of QC is abolished?" Corporate Counsel Magazine 2003.
Personal: Languages: working French. Interests: family, fly fishing, proper sports, modern art, opera.

LYNCH, Jerome QC
Charter Chambers, London
020 7618 4400
jerome.lynch@charterchambers.com
Featured in Crime (London)
Practice Areas: His practice is predominantly serious crime: white-collar offences, fraud, corruption, Companies Act offences, murder "gangland and honour killings" and "terrorist" offences. Important cases include; Lim (the Grobbelaar Trial, alleged match fixing), Geoff Knights (Gillian Taylforth's partner) case dismissed on the sole ground of adverse publicity, FA v Segers (alleged bung) and FA v Burtenshaw (alleged bung with George Graham), Brian Brendon Wright (the "laundryman") '£3500m cocaine importation, 'Arms to Iran', professional assassination of a 'supergrass', the Royal Blackmail case. He has undertaken work in the Caymans, Bermuda and Ireland. He is registered to receive work by direct access.
Professional Memberships: CBA, Bencher of Lincoln's Inn.
Career: University of Lancashire, BA(Hons). Silk 2000.
Personal: Television: Channel 4 - two eight-part series of 'Nothing But The Truth' - moral questions set against a court room scene; 'Crime Team' a team of investigators are set the task of solving real murders in the 19th century; Judge in People's Court (ITV1); Roy Marsden's Incident Room (ITV West); cameo roles for Sky and other newsrooms. Recently involved in a film "The All Together" starring Danny Dyer and Martin Freeman and has produced other ventures.

LYONS, Timothy QC
Thirty Nine Essex Street, London
020 7832 1111
timothy.lyons@39essex.com
Featured in Tax (London)
Practice Areas: Timothy has a broad practice within the commercial and public law groups at Thirty Nine Essex Street. His tax work covers indirect and direct taxation in the UK and in other jurisdictions including Hong Kong. He also advises on customs and trade related duties and deals with other financial and regulatory matters. He is regularly involved in cases involving EU law, ranging from disputes over specific directives or regulations to those concerning, for example, the fundamental freedoms and state aid. Known also for his private client and trust work, his clients include commercial entities, financial institutions, private individuals and trustees, as well as a number of European tax authorities and other public sector bodies. Recent cases include an anti-dumping duty appeal (Targetti UK Ltd v HMRC: ongoing) and the representation of trustees in a number of contentious matters. Other reported cases include BUPA, heard together with Halifax plc v CCE [2006] ECR I-1609 (VAT input tax and abuse); Case C-296/95 The Queen v CCE, ex parte EMU Tabac SARL [1998] ECR I-1605 (excise duty on cross-border movements of goods); R v Dimsey [2002] 1 AC 509 (human rights and UK tax).
Professional Memberships: Bar European Group, Chancery Bar Association, Revenue Bar Association, International Fiscal Association, STEP's Cross-Border Estates Group and EU Committee. Member of the EU Savings Directive Group assisting the European Commission in the review of the EU Savings Directive.
Career: Called 1980 (Inner Temple), Lincoln's Inn (1994), QC 2003. Visiting Professor London School of Economics and Porto University. Assistant Editor, British Tax Review (European Law).
Publications: Publications include: EC Customs Law (OUP, 2nd ed, 2008); European Cross-Border Estate Planning (Sweet & Maxwell) General editor. State Aid, Tax and Abuse of Law in Prohibition of Abuse of Law: A New General Principle of EU Law? (Hart Publishing, 2011); regular contributions to the British Tax Review.
Personal: LLB (Bristol) LLM and PhD (London).

MACDONALD, Alison
Matrix Chambers, London
020 7404 3447
alisonmacdonald@matrixlaw.co.uk
Featured in Administrative & Public Law (London), Civil Liberties & Human Rights (London), Police Law (All Circuits), Public International Law (London), Crime (London)
Practice Areas: Diverse international and domestic practice. Alison has extensive international arbitration experience, including both advocacy and advisory work: she is instructed as counsel in a number of ongoing ICSID arbitrations and annulment proceedings, and has advised governments, companies and individuals on arbitration, environmental and trade law matters. She has also acted as counsel in a number of significant inter-State disputes, including ongoing proceedings between Mauritius and the United Kingdom. She has a particular interest in the intersection between international arbitration and public international law, and is a contributor to the latest edition of The Law of State Immunity. Alison also appears regularly in the English courts, including in cases with a criminal dimension. She is experienced in issues of fraud, corruption, and their domestic and international law consequences. She also has an extensive practice in public law for a wide range of clients, civil liberties work, and civil claims arising out of complex criminal cases.
Career: Cambridge University, Law (top first of the year); Oxford University, BCL. Called 2000.
Publications: Edits or contributes to a range of leading textbooks on international law, human rights, and criminal justice.

MACDONALD, Alistair QC
St Philips Chambers, Birmingham
0121 246 1600
amacdonald@st-philips.com
Featured in Family/Matrimonial (Midlands)
Practice Areas: Alistair specialises in the law relating to children, concentrating on complex cases in the High Court and the appellate courts, including proceedings for judicial review and cases in the Court of Protection. Alistair is a recognised expert on children's rights. He has particular experience in dealing with cases under the Children Act 1989 involving complex medical issues and in dealing with complex appeals under the children and adoption legislation.
Professional Memberships: He is a member of the Family Law Bar Association, the Association of Lawyers for Children, and the British Agencies for Adoption and Fostering.
Career: Called to the Bar 1995; recorder 2009; Silk 2011.
Publications: Alistair is the author of the hardback practitioner text 'The Rights of the Child: Law and Practice' (2011 Family Law) and its companion volume 'The Rights of the Child: Annotated Materials' (2014 Family Law). Alistair is the general editor of 'Clarke, Hall & Morrison on Children' (LexisNexis). He is a member of the editorial board of the journal 'Child and Family Law Quarterly'. Alistair is a contributing author for the Family Court Practice (Family Law).

MACDONALD, James
3 Verulam Buildings, London
020 7831 8441
jmacdonald@3vb.com
Featured in Banking & Finance (London), Commercial Dispute Resolution (London)
Practice Areas: Regularly instructed in major commercial disputes, often with a banking aspect to them. Substantial experience of investment and retail banking. Recent instructions include: a US$8bn Commercial Court claim relating to FX derivatives and prime brokerage, a substantial LIBOR/EURIBOR claim, a claim involving credit ratings for structured notes; a $200m LCIA arbitration; a $160m Appeal relating to commodity derivatives (SCB v CPC); a major application in the Lehmans insolvency (Excalibur No. 1 Plc v LB Refinancing No. 3 Ltd); and the substantial claim brought by Centrica against Accenture in relation to the

British Gas customer billing system. Past instructions include JP Morgan v Springwell (a $700m claim brought against JP Morgan for allegedly negligent investment advice); ALS v Honeywell (a £3.5 billion claim in relation to a failed automotive development project); and involvement in aspects of the "bank charges" litigation.
Professional Memberships: COMBAR, Inner Temple.
Career: Called to the bar in 2005.
Publications: Contributor to Butterworths Journal of International Banking and Financial Law; Paget (forthcoming).
Personal: Educated Magdalen College, Oxford. Interests include music, cooking and cricket.

MACHELL, John QC
Serle Court, London
020 7242 6105
jmachell@serlecourt.co.uk
Featured in Chancery (London), Commercial Dispute Resolution (London), Partnership (London)
Practice Areas: General commercial/chancery dispute resolution and advisory work, particularly partnership, LLPs, trusts, fraud, company and insolvency.
Professional Memberships: Association of Partnership Practitioners, Chancery Bar Association.
Career: University of Southampton 1988-92 LLB (1st Class). Serle Court (formerly 13 Old Square) 1994 to date.
Publications: 'The Law of Limited Liability Partnerships' (2009) Bloomsbury Professional.
Personal: Married with two children.

MACKENZIE, Neil
Arnot Manderson, Edinburgh
07714 094 006
neilmackenzie@amadvocates.co.uk
Featured in Personal Injury (Scotland)
Practice Areas: Neil has specialised in the areas of professional negligence and industrial disease, and is predominantly instructed as junior counsel in complex, high value medical negligence actions. He acts for both pursuers and defenders across a range of subject matter that includes neurosurgery, general surgery, obstetrics and orthopaedics. Neil also deals with a large volume of other reparation claims. He is regularly instructed in industrial disease actions, in particular concerning asbestos. His experience of solicitor's negligence cases is extensive. In medical negligence and industrial disease actions, Neil must often deal with complex and difficult issues of causation. Overlaps in the law of causation in disease cases, medical negligence cases and cases alleging product liability involve further complexity.
Career: Neil was called to the Bar in 1999. He is a CEDR-accredited mediator. He was invited to join and contribute to the Faculty's sub-committee considering the Scottish Government's proposal for no-fault compensation for medical injury. Neil was invited to visit Malawi in December 2012, along with David Young QC, to assess the need for and possibility of advocacy training as part of a Scottish Government-funded aid programme. Following his visit, Neil gave evidence to the Cross-party Group on Malawi at the Scottish Parliament on 5 June 2013.

MACKINNON, Lucy
Hailsham Chambers, London
020 7643 5000
lucy.mackinnon@hailshamchambers.com
Featured in Clinical Negligence (London)
Practice Areas: Medical law, clinical negligence, medical disciplinary and regulatory and personal injury claims. Lucy has wide experience in all areas of medical law. She acts for both claimants and defendants in clinical negligence claims against NHS Trusts and private clinicians and hospitals. Her disciplinary and regulatory work includes representing practitioners in proceedings before the NMC, GMC, HCPC and GCC. Lucy advises NHS Trusts on issues such as disclosure and disability discrimination and regularly attends inquests. Lucy also specialises in all areas of personal injury work, including credit hire and fraud.
Personal: Education: Admitted to the New York Bar in June 2004; New York Bar Exams, Central Law Training (2003-04); Bar Vocational Course (Very Competent), BPP Law School (2002-03); Lucy was awarded the Sir Thomas More Bursary by Lincoln's Inn; University of Reading, LLB Law (Hons) (2:1) (1999-2002).

MACLEAN, Iain
Terra Firma Chambers, Edinburgh
0131 260 5830
iain.maclean@terrafirmachambers.com
Featured in Agriculture & Rural Affairs (Scotland)
Practice Areas: Advocate specialising in land and property law, encompassing commercial property and estates/rural property and associated private client matters.
Professional Memberships: Member of the Scottish Government's European Union Agricultural Subsidies Appeals Procedure External Advisory Panel (2005-09); member of the Scottish Law Commission's Advisory Group on the Law of Succession; founder member and former office bearer of Trustbar (The Trusts, Fiduciaries and Executries Bar Group).
Career: Iain Maclean was legal assistant to the Lord President of the Court of Session before calling to the Scottish Bar in 1994. He has appeared in the Outer and Inner Houses of the Court of Session, the Land Court, Lands Tribunal and the Lyon Court and in sheriff courts across Scotland. He has an extensive Opinion practice in the areas of law in which he specialises.
Publications: Contributor, Greens Annotated Rules of the Court of Session.

MACLEOD, Murdo
Compass Chambers, Edinburgh
0131 260 5648
murdo.macleod@compasschambers.com
Featured in Health & Safety (Scotland)
Practice Areas: Murdo specialises in regulatory crime - particularly in the fields of corporate financial, environmental and health and safety prosecutions - and in public inquiries and inquests. He is regularly instructed by commercial and institutional clients, both for trials where he is described in Legal 500 as being "very high quality" and "highly skilled", and in an advisory capacity. In 2014 he represented Eurocopter in the Superpuma fatal accident inquiry. Between 2005 and 2010 he served as Counsel to the Billy Wright inquiry, a major public inquiry (the first under the Inquiries Act 2005) into the murder of a prominent paramilitary prisoner and the management of HMP Maze. Murdo has considerable experience in criminal law having served as Crown Counsel and Senior Crown Counsel. He is a practising member of the English Bar (Temple Garden Chambers) and sits as a part-time Sheriff. Representative cases include: Re Super Puma Inquiry, 2013-14 (representing helicopter manufacturer); Re Rangers FC, 2014: (representing City law firm in on-going financial inquiry); HMA v Coulson, 2014 (representing former editor in forthcoming perjury case); HMA v S, 2013 (advising turbine manufacturer in health and safety case); FCL v HMRC, 2013 (advising export company re HMRC decision on customs warehousing facility); TB v DECC, 2012 (advising oil company in appeal against offshore pollution enforcement notice); HMA v K Ltd, SC Ltd, F Ltd, 2011-12 (representing three companies in a series of landmark prosecutions for breaches of EU fishing regulations and in associated Proceeds of Crime Act proceedings); Re Billy Wright inquiry, 2005-2010 (counsel to the inquiry); HMA v Megrahi and Fhimah, 1999-2001 (junior counsel for second accused in Lockerbie/Pan-Am bombing trial).
Career: Admitted to Faculty of Advocates 1994 (appointed Queen's Counsel 2008); Crown Counsel 2001-03; Senior Crown Counsel 2004-05; Counsel to Billy Wright inquiry 2005-10; called to Bar of England and Wales (Middle Temple) 2011; Special Counsel 2011; part-time Sheriff 2011; UK delegate to the CCBE Criminal Law Committee 2012.

MACNEILL, Calum H S QC
Westwater Advocates, Edinburgh
0131 226 2881
calum.macneill
@westwateradvocates.com
Featured in Employment (Scotland), Commercial Dispute Resolution (Scotland)
Practice Areas: Calum MacNeill QC has a busy practice in commercial litigation, building and construction, professional (including medical) negligence and employment law. As a senior his practice has developed from these core areas to include equality law, civil recovery of the proceeds of crime, disciplinary hearings and professional regulatory work. Active as a mediator in commerical conflicts. Participant in the Faculty of Advocates Dispute Resolution Service. Legal member of the Police Appeals Tribunal. Teaches advocacy skills within the Faculty and externally.
Career: Called to the Bar in 1992. Advocate depute 1998-2001. Standing Junior to the Scottish Ministers 2003-06. Took Silk in 2007.
Personal: Educated at Robert Gordon's College, Aberdeen. University of Aberdeen - LLB (Hons) 1985, Dip LP 1986.

MADGE-WYLD, Sam
Arden Chambers, London
020 7242 4244
sam.madge-wyld@ardenchambers.com
Featured in Social Housing (London)
Practice Areas: Residential and commercial landlord and tenant, property, local government law. He acts for private landlords, tenants/applicants, local authorities and housing associations.
Professional Memberships: Administrative Law Bar Association, Housing Law Practitioners Association and Property Bar Association.
Career: Since being called to the Bar in 2008, and joining Arden Chambers in 2009, Sam Madge-Wyld's noteworthy cases include R (Enfield LBC) v Enfield CCG & Others [2013] EWHC 3496 (Admin); Birmingham CC v Lloyd [2012] EWCA Civ 969 [2012] HLR 44, R (W) v Birmingham CC [2011] EWHC 1147 (Admin); (2011) 14 CCL Rep 516 and R (H) v Birmingham CC [2010] EWHC 3752 (Admin).
Publications: Co-author of Quiet Enjoyment (LAG, 7th Edition, 2012) and Housing Law Casebook (LAG, 6th Edition, forthcoming). Contributor (2014-) to Encyclopedia of Local Government Law (Sweet and Maxwell) and Defending Possession Proceedings (LAG, 7th Edition, 2010). Assistant Editor (2012-) of Local Government Finance: Law and Practice (Sweet and Maxwell). He has had articles on housing and local government law published in the New Law Journal, Solicitor's Journal, LAG, Inside Housing, Judicial Review, Journal of Housing Law and Local Government Lawyer.

MAGARIAN, Michael QC
Dyers Chambers, London
020 7404 1881
michael.magarian@dyerschambers.com
Featured in Crime (London)
Practice Areas: Exclusively defence silk known for his tenacity and for standing shoulder to shoulder with his clients. Specialises in gang murder cases eg in 2014 led at the CCC in R v Degoze (a Tottenham multi-handed stabbing) and R v Walczyk. In July 2014 acted for a police Superintendent charged with misconduct in a public office. In recent years other notable murder cases include R v Hummerstone (an especially brutal murder on a drug dealer) and R v Mann (murder of a sex offender in gaol by a man already serving life for another double murder). Last year appeared in front of the LCJ in the new guideline case on life imprisonment and IPP's (R v Edwards). In more recent past appeared in the Damilola Taylor murder.
Professional Memberships: Criminal Bar Association.
Career: Called 1988 1st class honours Trinity College Cambridge 1987. Gray's Inn Karmel and Prince of Wales scholar.

MAGEE, Samuel
2 Bedford Row, London
020 7440 8888
clerks@2bedfordrow.co.uk
Featured in Crime (London)
Practice Areas: Habitually recommended as a leader at the Criminal Bar, Sam Magee is a specialist criminal law practitioner dealing with heavyweight criminal matters in Northern Ireland and England. Having acted in some of the most high profile murder and white collar fraud cases in recent years (including the Midsomer Murder trial and the Vantis Fraud trial) Sam is highly sought after to defend and prosecute all manner of complex criminal matters. Sam is regularly instructed to advise and act in HMRC and SFO prosecutions dealing with complex fraud investigations having experience in multi-million pound VAT, boiler room, insider dealing, MTIC, investment scheme and share dealing frauds. Sam is also regularly instructed to act in Health & Safety prosecutions and has experience in cases of Corporate Manslaughter. He is instructed to act in inquests (including matters of Health

and Safety), sports and medico-legal disciplinary tribunals. Sam can accept instructions by direct access. A full profile is available at www.2bedfordrow.co.uk and www.barlibrary.com.
Professional Memberships: Bar Library of Northern Ireland. CBA.
Career: Called (E&W) 2003 (Inner Temple Duke of Edinburgh Scholar). Called (NI) 2006. Inner Temple Advocacy Trainer 2011.
Personal: Irish Football Association Disciplinary Committee Chairman. Ulster & Ireland Rugby.

MAKEPEACE, Peter

Dere Street Barristers, York
01904 620 048
p.makepeace@derestreet.co.uk
Featured in Crime (North Eastern)
Practice Areas: Peter Makepeace has practised exclusively in Criminal law since 1994 and has extensive experience of defending and prosecuting in all areas of serious crime. He is a grade 4 prosecutor. Peter has frequently acted as leading Junior in multi counsel cases. Areas of Special experience include Homicide and other serious violence, Fraud, serious and large-scale drug conspiracies, sexual offences, the importation and distribution of medicines, and a growing expertise in computer-related law culminated in the first prosecution for fraud of a peer to peer, bit torrent music file sharing site. Peter has developed a particular reputation in cases requiring sensitivity of approach either through the nature of the offence or the vulnerability of witnesses, victims or the accused etc. He is acknowledged to have an exhaustive approach to case preparation and manages his diary to ensure serious cases are afforded the proper case management they require. Peter also accepts private instructions in the field of licensing and regulatory offences.

MALCOLM, Alastair R QC

One Paper Buildings, London
020 7353 3728
clerks@onepaper.co.uk
Featured in Crime (Western)
Practice Areas: Serious crime, fraud, financial regulatory law.
Professional Memberships: Member of the Inner Temple, Western Circuit, CBA and Temporary Member of the Cayman Islands Bar (2000, 2003-06 and 2008-13).
Career: Alastair Malcolm's practice covers every aspect of serious crime, from murder to fraud via serious sexual offences and armed robberies. Having started his career on the Western circuit, Alastair's reputation has grown to the extent that he is now instructed to appear in courts around the country and as far afield internationally as the Caribbean. For 9 years he was junior standing counsel for the Inland Revenue on the Western Circuit appearing in cases which involved the whole range of Revenue Offences from the simple misuse of "lump" exemption certificates to complicated tax evasion schemes. He was part of the prosecuting team in the Revenue case against Swindon Town Football Club. In 2004/2005 he successfully defended the first defendant in the US$350 million Cash-4-Titles money laundering case in the Cayman Islands.
He has experience defending in "Baby-Shaking"murder cases, most recently (2014) securing an acquittal in R v Hunt at Exeter.

MALCOLM, Kirsty

Westwater Advocates, Edinburgh
07986 591 079
kirsty.malcolm@westwateradvocates.com
Featured in Family/Matrimonial (Scotland)
Practice Areas: Family law with a particular focus on financial provision on divorce, cohabitation, adoption and permanence orders, international and cross border child issues and adults with incapacity. Reported cases include: Clarkson v Clarkson 2008 S.L.T. (Sh Ct) 2 [financial provision on divorce– setting aside agreement]; B v B 2009 S.L.T. (Sh Ct) 249 [jurisdiction]; Simpson v Downie 2011 Fam L.R. 145 [cohabitation- time bar]; Murdoch v Murdoch 2012 S.C. 271 [financial provision on divorce – competency issues]; City of Edinburgh Council v C 2012 Fam LR 132 [permanence order with authority to adopt]; Gow v Grant 2011 S.C. 618 and 2013 SC (U.K.S.C) 1 [cohabitation- lifetime claim, and statutory interpretation]; Kerr v Mangan 2013 Fam LR 38 [cohabitation- claim on death re foreign property]; H's Guardian v H 2013 SLT (Sh Ct) 31 [divorce, Adult with Incapacity]; Cameron v Lukes 2014 GWD 7-144 [cohabitation – appeal]; Douglas v Bell 2014 Fam LR 2 [cohabitation – relevancy and time bar]; McIntyre v Stewart 2014 Fam LR 7 [cohabitation – pleadings and time bar]; TCM v AFMM 2014 Fam LR 11[pensions on divorce – statutory interpretation].
Professional Memberships: Advocates Family Law Association 2006-present, Faculty of Advocates Family Law Reform Sub Committee.
Career: Solicitor for 17 years specialising in family law. Called to Bar June 2007.
Publications: Cohabitation (2nd edition) Thomson/W.Green [2011]; Editor Litigation Styles Lexis Nexis/Butterworths Scottish Family Law Service 2007-present.
Personal: LLB (Hons) Aberdeen; Dip LP, Glasgow. She continued her connection with Glasgow University as Senior tutor/Course Designer, for their new Diploma in Legal Practice, Family Law Elective – 2010/11.

MALEK, Hodge M QC

Thirty Nine Essex Street, London
020 7832 1111
hodge.malek@39essex.com
Featured in Banking & Finance (London), Commercial Dispute Resolution (London), Energy & Natural Resources (London), Financial Services (London), Fraud (London), Professional Discipline (London), Financial Crime (London)
Practice Areas: Specialises in Commercial law, including arbitration, accountancy, banking, company, energy, financial services, fraud, insurance, securities, professional negligence and shipping. Hodge Malek routinely acts for both the regulators and banks in the financial sector. He acts for firms and individuals in relation to the Financial Conduct Authority and the SRA, both in disciplinary and regulatory matters. He has been advising on potential mergers in the financial services sector in the light of the current crisis. He advises banks on a large range of activities, including litigation and regulatory matters. In 2011, he acted for the Financial Ombudsman Service in relation to the challenge by the BBA in respect of PPI and is currently retained to conduct the appeal in the Supreme Court on unfair relationships in the context of PPI. He is also advising in relation to LIBOR. Hodge Malek has a substantial practice in commercial fraud, both in civil proceedings and criminal proceedings in the UK and Internationally. Hodge has travelled extensively on cases abroad to jurisdictions such as Europe, Caribbean, the Middle East and Asia. His experience of Middle Eastern (Islamic law jurisdictions), civil law (Europe) and common law jurisdictions (Commonwealth) is probably unparalleled at the bar. He is a member of the bar of the British Virgin Islands and has been called to other bars for specific cases, such as the Isle of Man (insider dealings on NASDAQ and letters of request) and Gibraltar (dealing in shares on Lisbon Stock Exchange). He has appeared in the Tribunal de Commerce and Cour d'Appel in Paris on a number of cases.
Professional Memberships: Bar Sports Group ALBA COMBAR PEBA Franco-British Lawyer Society.
Career: Date of call: 1983 Gray's Inn Year of silk: Recorder (2004), appointment to Serious Fraud Office list of QCs (2009), Member of Inns of Court Conduct Committee (2010), Chairman of Competition Appeal Tribunal(2013).
Publications: General editor of Phipson on Evidence(17th ed 2010), joint author of Disclosure (4th ed 2012), contributor to Atkins Court Forms(Administrative Court, Disclosure and Human Rights volumes)And Mithani, Directors Disqualification.

MALLALIEU, Roger

4 New Square, London
020 7822 2000
r.mallalieu@4newsquare.com
Featured in Costs Litigation (London)
Practice Areas: Costs and civil procedure, professional negligence (including clinical negligence), solicitors regulatory, commercial.
Professional Memberships: LCBA.
Career: Roger's practice focuses primarily on all aspects of costs and technical civil procedure issues and more generally on issues relating to the professional conduct of solicitors. He has appeared in many of the leading cases, including Mitchell v NGN and is instructed regular in complex and high value costs cases, including in High Court and Court of Appeal appeals in a range of technical issues. He has considerable experience of all aspects of costs law, including solicitor-client costs, group litigation, the costs of office holders, the drafting of agreements and general inter partes costs and in civil procedure rule issues including in relation to relief from sanction, Part 36 and similar matters. He also is instructed in wider cases concerning solicitor's duties, including in professional negligence matters, disciplinary cases and cases concerning the duties of professional deputies.
Publications: Roger is a regular contributor to a range of publications.

MALTZ, Ben

Five Paper, London
020 7815 3200
benmaltz@fivepaper.com
Featured in Social Housing (London)
Practice Areas: Social Housing, Landlord and Tenant, Leasehold Enfranchisement, Real Estate Litigation, Professional Negligence.
Professional Memberships: Property Bar Association.
Career: Called to the Bar by Lincoln's Inn in 1998. Commenced pupillage at 9 Stone Buildings. Tenant at Five Paper since 2000. Regularly advises and represents numerous local authorities, registered providers of social housing and private sector landlords. Particular expertise in relation to service charge disputes having appeared for the landlords on two recent appeals before the Upper Tribunal: Southern Land Securities Ltd v. Hodge [2013] UKUT 0480 (LC) and Red Kite Community Housing Ltd v. Robertson [2014] UKUT 0134 (LC).
Publications: "Liability of the Negligent Surveyor", Estates Gazette. Recent articles include "An LVT Lifeline for Landlords", Estates Gazette.

MALYNICZ, Simon

Three New Square, London
020 7405 1111
malynicz@3newsquare.co.uk
Featured in Intellectual Property (London), Media & Entertainment (London)
Practice Areas: Specialising in all aspects of intellectual property including trade marks, registered and unregistered designs, passing off, copyright, IT/software, media/ entertainment, confidential information and patents. Recent cases include: Interflora v M&S, Woolley v Ultimate Products, Zee TV v Zeebox, Healey Sports Cars, Nestle v Cadbury (Colour Purple), Nestle v Cadbury (Kit-Kat), Chartered Institute of Patent Attorneys (IP Translator), Total v YouView, Lush v Amazon, Comic Enterprises v Fox, Enterprise v Europcar, SAS Institute, Football Dataco, UPC Telekabel. For full list of recent and reported cases, see chambers website at www.3newsquare.co.uk/html/simonmalynicz.html.
Professional Memberships: IPBA, ChBA, ITMA, Bar Pro Bono Unit.
Career: Appointed Junior Counsel to the Crown (A Panel) in March 2014. Previously Junior Counsel to the Crown (B Panel) 2008-2013. BA (Sydney) LLB Hons (Lond.) MA (New School, NY). First class honours in law.
Publications: Joint author of "Gurry on Breach of Confidence" 2012, OUP. Joint author of previous editions of "IP in Europe", Sweet & Maxwell, and "Modern Law of Trade Marks", Butterworths.

MANLEY, David QC

Kings Chambers, Manchester
0845 034 3444
clerks@kingschambers.com
Featured in Environment (Northern), Planning (Northern)
Practice Areas: Planning; environmental law; law of commons, highways and compulsory purchase. Appears on a weekly basis as an Advocate at Public Inquiries in respect of a very broad range of planning and environmental issues including renewable energy projects; strategic and local housing development; waste and rendering issues. Adviser to British Nuclear Fuels. David regularly sits as an Inspector on town/village green issues as well as a representative of landowner and interest groups. He appears in the High Court regularly in respect of judicial review matters. His client base comprises a broad range of nationally known companies.
Professional Memberships: Planning and Environmental Bar Association; UK Environmental Law Association.
Career: Leeds University BA (Hons). Called 1981 (Inner Temple. Head of Planning in Chambers.)

MANNING, Colin
Littleton Chambers, London
020 7797 8600
cmanning@littletonchambers.co.uk
Featured in Mediators (All Circuits)
Practice Areas: Principal areas of practice are general Commercial and business law, specialising in commercial contract disputes including computer litigation (involving the supply and implementation of computer systems, networking and associated intellectual property rights), also professional negligence, Media and entertainment, employment, Company shareholder, partnership, construction and landlord and tenant and general property disputes. Mediating in all these areas.
Professional Memberships: COMBAR, London Common Law and Commercial Bar Association. CEDR accredited mediator. Fellow of the Chartered Institute of Arbitrators. Chair of the Bar Council ADR Committee. Member of the Advisory committee of the Civil Mediation Council.
Career: Called to the Bar, Gray's Inn, 1970; CEDR accredited mediator, 1997; Fellow of the Chartered Institute of Arbitrators, 2001, Recorder, 2000; Bencher, Gray's Inn, 2003; Chair of the Bar Council ADR Committee, 2012, Board Member of the Civil Mediation Council. Mediation and advocacy trainer.
Publications: Main contributor to "Civil Appeals, Practice and Procedure".
Personal: Educated at University College London (LLB Honours).

MANNING, Jonathan
Arden Chambers, London
020 7242 4244
jonathan.manning@ardenchambers.com
Featured in Local Government (London), Social Housing (London)
Practice Areas: All aspects of local government and public law (including human rights and equality issues), housing (public/social, private), landlord and tenant, anti-social behaviour.
Professional Memberships: HLPA; ALBA.
Career: Called 1989 (2nd in year). Founder member, Arden Chambers. Advises, represents, trains public and private sector clients including local authorities, PRPs, leaseholders, tenants, applicants. Recent work includes advising on: library closure proposals, charges for special police services, additional and selective licensing schemes, and council tax reduction schemes. Notable recent cases include: R (SG) v Secretary of State for Work & Pensions (2014, Supreme Court - benefit cap challenge for Shelter as intervener); Beech v Birmingham CC [2014] EWCA Civ 830 (tenant's notice to quit not vitiated by undue influence or absence of mental capacity assessment); Birmingham CC v Rafiq and others (2014, Birmingham County Court - 9-handed gang injunction concerning two factions of a drugs and firearms gang); Swan HA v Gill [2013] EWCA Civ 1566 (public sector equality duty); R (MA) v Secretary of State for Work & Pensions [2013] EWHC 2213 ("bedroom tax" challenge - for Shelter and Birmingham CC as Intervener/Interested Party); Birmingham CC v James [2013] EWCA Civ 552 (gang injunctions, human rights); R (Buckley) v Sheffield CC [2013] EWHC 512 (Admin)(council tax reduction schemes, consultation, public sector equality duty); Birmingham CC v Ashton [2012] EWCA Civ 1557(anti-social behaviour, appeal against suspension of possession order); Birmingham CC v Lloyd [2012] EWCA Civ 969, Corby BC v Scott [2012] EWCA Civ 276, Birmingham CC v Frisby (heard with Hounslow LBC v Powell) [2011] UKSC 8, Manchester CC v Pinnock [2010] UKSC 45(art.8 defences, possession claims); R (Greenwich Community Law Centre) v Greenwich LBC [2012] EWCA Civ 496 (third sector funding, public sector equality duty); Maswaku v Westminster CC [2012] EWCA Civ 669; El Goure v Kensington and Chelsea RLBC (homelessness, notification duties); A2 Dominion Homes v Godfrey (heard with Places for People v Sharples) [2011] EWCA Civ 813(debt relief orders and possession claims); R (East Devon) v Boundary Committee [2009] EWCA Civ 238; R (Shrewsbury & Atcham BC) v Secretary of State [2008] 3 All ER 548 (local government reorganisation, powers, consultation.
Publications: Co-author: 'Blackstone's Guide to the Anti-Social Behaviour Act 2003' OUP 2004; 'Local Government Constitutional and Administrative Law', Sweet & Maxwell 2007. Author: Judicial Review Proceedings: A Practitioner's Guide, 3rd ed LAG 2013.

MANSELL, Jason
7BR, London
020 7242 3555
clerks@7br.co.uk
Featured in Financial Services (London), Financial Crime (London)
Practice Areas: Jason provides strategic advice and representation to firms and individuals facing investigation and potential criminal prosecution by the SFO and prosecution and/or disciplinary action by FCA and other regulatory bodies. A formidable advocate, Jason has acted for firms and individuals in connection with over 70 FCA/FSA regulatory investigations and associated proceedings. He also acts for individuals and corporates in some of the more high profile and complex criminal prosecutions. Many of his cases result in no formal public action. Jason is currently acting for a PLC in relation to a referral to the SFO under the Bribery Act and for three individuals in connection with the investigations by both the SFO and FCA in relation to the alleged manipulation of LIBOR. Past cases include FSA-v–Verrier, FSA-v-Gower and he recently persuaded the FCA not to issue a Decision Notice against a CEO accused of market abuse. Previous criminal instructions include R-v-Littlewood (insider dealing), R-v-Whelan (market manipulation) and R-v-Norton Healthcare (price fixing). Jason also advises firms on compliance issues under anti-money laundering and anti-bribery legislation.
Professional Memberships: Association of Regulatory and Disciplinary Lawyers, Financial Services Lawyers Association, Criminal Bar Association.
Career: Called 1991, Lincoln's Inn.

MANSFIELD, Gavin QC
Littleton Chambers, London
020 7797 8600
clerks@littletonchambers.com
Featured in Employment (London)
Practice Areas: Employment discrimination law and commercial litigation, principally involving the commercial aspects of the employment relationship. Areas of practice include contractual disputes (wrongful dismissal, bonus claims, restrictive covenants and garden leave), breach of confidence and fiduciary duties, all aspects of statutory employment law, partnership disputes, shareholder and joint venture disputes. Recent cases include UK Power Reserve Ltd. v Read [2014] EWHC 66 Ch, Baker Tilly UK Holdings Ltd. v Clough [2013] EWHC 3616 QB, 3616 Spaceright v Baillavoine [2012] IRLR ICR 520 CA, Caterpillar Logistics Services Ltd. v Huesa de Crean [2012] IRLR 410 CA.
Professional Memberships: Employment Law Bar Association (Vice-Chairman), Employment Lawyers Association, Industrial Law Society, COMBAR.
Career: Called 1992 (Middle Temple). QC 2013. Regular lecturer and writer on employment law topics.
Publications: Editor of Blackstone's 'Employment Law Practice'; contributor to Brearley & Bloch "Employment Covenants and Confidential Information" (3ed 2009); 'Essential Facts: Disability Discrimination for Providers of Goods, Facilities and service' (2003).
Personal: Education Nottingham High School; Jesus College, Cambridge.

MANZONI, Charles QC
Thirty Nine Essex Street, London
+852 224 81801
charlie.manzoni@39essex.com
Featured in International Arbitration (London)
Practice Areas: As a qualified mechanical and electrical engineer, Charlie worked in the International Development Department of a multinational blue-chip industrial company for five years before qualifying as a lawyer and entering private practice. His legal practice in London initially concentrated on the technology and engineering industries, and their related disputes, including professional negligence and insurance. For the last 10 years Charlie's work has involved mainly international litigation, arbitration and mediation across a broad spectrum of commercial work. He acts as counsel in the High Courts of London and Hong Kong, in international and domestic arbitrations, acts as a mediator and conciliator in cross-border disputes and regularly sits as a sole arbitrator or as part of a three man tribunal.
Professional Memberships: Institution of Mechanical Engineers. TECBAR. Society of Computers and Law. London Common Law and Commercial Bar Association. Hong Kong International Arbitration Centre. Dubai International Arbitration Centre, Kuala Lumpur Regional Centre for Arbitration; London Court of International Arbitration.
Career: Qualified and practised as a mechanical engineer before qualifying for the Bar in 1988.

MARGOLIN, Daniel
Maitland Chambers, London
020 7406 1200
dmargolin@maitlandchambers.com
Featured in Chancery (London), Real Estate Litigation (London)
Practice Areas: Commercial chancery; company and insolvency litigation (including DDQ proceedings); property litigation; professional negligence and disciplinary proceedings; tax; trusts, charities and succession litigation. Reported cases include Megtian v HMRC (MTIC fraud); Late Editions (MTIC fraud); Domain Dynamics (Holdings) v HMRC (CGT; EIS deferment relief); Dawsongroup v HMRC (whether appellant was investment company within ICTA 1988 s130; whether costs of de-listing from Stock Exchange were expenses of management within ICTA 1988 s75); Gouldson v HMRC (Seafarers' Earnings Deductions; whether vessel was ship or offshore installation); Worby v IR (challenge to tax assessments in insolvency proceedings); HMRC v Benton-Diggins (phoenix trading); Re Oxford Pharmaceuticals (preference claim; misfeasance); Secretary of State for BIS v Aaron (DDQ; regulated investment services company; mis-selling; regulatory breaches); HMRC v Millichap (VAT; application to reverse liquidator's decision on proof; extension of time; insolvency set-off); Croatia v Serbia (public international law; land registration); Day v Day (resulting trusts; right to buy discount; costs); R (Cameron) v HMRC (judicial review; Seafarers' Earnings Deduction; withdrawal of concessionary treatment; legitimate expectation); ACCA v Koumettou (appointment of replacement insolvency officeholder); Anglo-German Breweries v Chelsea Corporation (fraud; piercing corporate veil); Re Teathers (surrender of lease; dilapidations; measure of damages); Fabb v Peters (negligence and misfeasance claims against administrators; civil restraint orders). Particular experience of property disputes relating to the Electronic Communications Code.
Professional Memberships: Chancery Bar Association; COMBAR; PNBA.
Career: Called to the Bar 1995; Junior Counsel to the Crown Panel C 1999, Panel B 2005, Panel A 2010.
Publications: Mithani: Directors' Disqualification (Contributing Editor); The Electronic Communications Code – an introduction for property litigators (Author); Bankruptcy and ancillary relief: what is the court's approach where the debtor may be using bankruptcy to frustrate an ancillary relief claim within divorce proceedings? (Author).
Personal: Born 1972. Educated at Balliol College, Oxford (Scholar; Coolidge Pathfinder; BA 1st class honours, 1993). Karmel Entrance Award and Prince of Wales Scholarship, Gray's Inn. Married, one daughter, one son.

MARKHAM, Hannah
36 Bedford Row, London
020 7421 8000
hmarkham@36bedfordrow.co.uk
Featured in Family/Matrimonial (London)
Practice Areas: Hannah's stellar practice sees her very often pitched against leading Silks and principally in the High Court or Court of Appeal. She appeared – successfully – in the Supreme Court in Re B [2013] UKSC 33. Expert in all areas of children law, her Public Law cases include the most complex care cases, involving sexual abuse, child or parent death, factitious illness, cases with linked criminal proceedings, honour-based violence, forced marriage and media restrictions. In Private Law she is fast developing a significant niche practice in cases involving same-sex parenting disputes, and in particular cases in which surrogacy or gamete donation are involved. She has a number of recently reported cases involving international elements, including the groundbreaking Article 8 decision in Ms L v Ms C [2014] EWFC 1 and the successful Article 15 application in Leicester City v S [2014] EWHC 1575 (Fam). She also has a busy and successful practice in family-related judicial review cases.

Professional Memberships: FLBA (committee member for 3 years), ALC, Herts FJB.
Career: Call: 1998. Hannah has a Masters Degree in Latin American Studies and Spanish. Hannah speaks good Spanish and conversational French.
Personal: Long distance running and travel.

MARKS, Lewis QC
Queen Elizabeth Building, London
020 7797 7837
l.marks@qeb.co.uk
Featured in Family/Matrimonial (London)
Practice Areas: Specialist in big-money financial provision and international family law, and has appeared in many of the leading authorities. Often instructed to draft prenuptial (and postnuptial) agreements. Reported cases include: Y v Y [2012] EWHC 2063 (Fam); WF v HF [2012] 2 FLR 1212 (Fam); Z v Z (No.2) (Financial Remedy: Marriage Contract) [2012] 1 FLR 1100; W V W (Divorce Proceedings) [2011] 1 FLR 372; H v H [2010]1 FLR 1864; Marano [2010] 1 FLR 1903; M v M (Costs) [2010] 1 FLR 256; Spencer [2009] 2 FLR 1416; P v P [2008] 2 FLR 1135; Moore [2007] 2 FLR 339; H v H [2007] 2 FLR 548, Sorrell [2006] 1 FLR 497, Miller [2006] 1 FLR 151, OS V DS (Oral Disclosure: Preliminary Hearing) [2005] 1FLR 675, Wermuth (No.2) [2003] 1 FLR 1029; Pearce [2003] 2 FLR 1144; GW v RW [2003] 2 FLR 108; White [2000] 2 FLR 981.
Professional Memberships: Family Law Bar Association; elected as Fellow of the International Academy of Matrimonial Lawyers in 2004.
Career: Educated BNC, Oxford (BA Juris). Called 1984, Silk 2002. Head of Chambers since 2010.
Publications: Editorial Board of FLBA publication 'At A Glance' from 1996 - present. Occasional contributor to Family Law and other journals, and frequent speaker at conferences and seminars.
Personal: Born 1961, lives in Essex, married with four (adult) sons. Enjoys eating, walking, jazz, country and western music, watching cricket and musicals, but not necessarily simultaneously or in that order.

MARRIN, John QC
Keating Chambers, London
020 7544 2600
jmarrin@keatingchambers.com
Featured in Construction (London), International Arbitration (London), Professional Negligence (London)
Practice Areas: Queen's Counsel and Arbitrator with over 35 years' experience as a specialist in construction, engineering, energy, technology and software sectors as well as disputes arising from PFI projects and from the rail industry. As Counsel appears principally in the UK High Court, Court of Appeal and before various global arbitral tribunals. As an advocate, he is "measured and thorough" and "his ability to forecast the way a case is going to go is second to none" (Chambers and Partners). An accomplished arbitrator with "an aura of enormous authority whether it be as adjudicator, arbitrator or mediator" and "excellent technical ability" (Chambers & Partners). Appointed regularly as chairman and tribunal member, by the ICC and centres such as the DIAC, the SIAC and the LCIA, and under UNCITRAL rules. Globally recognised authority on the analysis of delay claims.
Professional Memberships: LCLCBA; Society of Construction Law; Commercial Bar Association; TECBAR; London Court of International Arbitration; HKIAC Panel of Arbitrators.
Career: Call 1974; Queen's Counsel 1990; Deputy High Court Judge 2008; Fellow, Chartered Institute of Arbitrators (FCIArb); Bencher of the Inner Temple; CEDR Accredited Mediator. Head of Keating Chambers 2005 to 2010.

MARSDEN, Andrew
St John's Chambers, Bristol
0117 923 4700
andrewmarsden@stjohnschambers.co.uk
Featured in Chancery (Western), Commercial Dispute Resolution (Western), Company (Western), Partnership (Western)
Practice Areas: Specialising in company, partnership, agency and commercial litigation. His expertise includes contractual disputes of all types, shareholder disputes, directors' duties, disputes between partners and commercial agency disputes. He is also a fully qualified and experienced mediator. Andrew has been described as 'commercial, user friendly and accessible', 'one of the best pound for pound commercial barristers in town' and as a 'deeply impressive barrister who prepares fully, is fantastic with documents and is commercially minded'.
Professional Memberships: Commercial Bar Association; Chancery Bar Association.
Career: Called 1994; formerly a solicitor with Freshfields.
Publications: Shareholder Protection from Unfair Prejudice: Case and Statute Citator 2013 Commercial Agents: Case and Statute Citator 2013.
Personal: Skiing, the piano, triathlon and Cognac.

MARSHALL, Andrew
Red Lion Chambers, London
020 7520 6000
chambers@18rlc.co.uk
Featured in Financial Crime (London)
Practice Areas: Andrew Marshall has conduct of the most difficult cases across a wide range fields. His practice reflects his considerable legal, technical and advocacy abilities, particularly in specialist regulatory, criminal and quasi-criminal areas: health and safety and environmental, pharmaceutical, fraud - particularly international and City-based, money laundering and organised crime.
Professional Memberships: Criminal Bar Association.
Career: Called, 1986; Recorder, 2003; Standing Counsel to Attorney General (Crime), 2005 and previously on C, B then A lists. Presently: Director of Edmonds, Marshall McMahon (a ChambersUK-listed solicitors' firm); approved counsel for the UK government's Regulatory Panel (A List), the Serious Fraud Office (A List), CPS lists (Grade 4 and specialist lists) and Financial Conduct Authority.

MARSHALL, Philip QC
1 King's Bench Walk, London
020 7936 1500
pmarshall@1kbw.co.uk
Featured in Family/Matrimonial (London)
Practice Areas: Mostly 'big money' matrimonial finance. Counsel in the House of Lords in White v White (2000), Mark v Mark (2005) and Miller v Miller; McFarlane v McFarlane (2006). Trained mediator.
Professional Memberships: National Vice Chairman of the Family Law Bar Association (FLBA); Fellow of the International Academy of Matrimonial Lawyers (IAML); Associate member of Resolution; Vice Chairman of Gray's Inn Advocacy & CPD Committee.
Career: Called 1989. QC 2012.
Personal: Merchant Taylors School, Liverpool University (LLB).

MARSHALL, Philip QC
Serle Court, London
020 7242 6105
PMarshall@serlecourt.co.uk
Featured in Banking & Finance (London), Chancery (London), Commercial Dispute Resolution (London), Company (London), Fraud (London), Offshore (London), Professional Negligence (London), Restructuring/Insolvency (London)
Practice Areas: Commercial fraud (BTA Bank v Ablyasov; Aeroflot v Berezovsky; Bank of St. Petersburg v Arkhangelsky; Constantin Medien v Ecclestone; AWG v Morrison; Cala Cristal v Al-Borno; Canada Trust v Stolzenberg; Berry Trade Ltd v Moussavi; Zhakarov v White; NatWest v Rabobank; Lexi Holdings v Luqman); insolvency (Re Nortel Networks; Re Woolworths PLC; BIM v Maxwell; Re: Murjani; Haig v Aitken); banking (BTA Bank v Ablyasov; NatWest v RaboBank; Wahda Bank v Arab Bank and Sirius v FAI Insurance); company (Re Coroin Ltd; Re MT Realisations; Oystertec v Fraser); commercial litigation and arbitration, (Tchigirinski v Orton Oil; Shanshal v Al-kishtaini; Torkmain v Nomura; Fiber Technologies v Moscow Oil Refinery); professional negligence (Brown v GRE; Peach Publishing v Slater; David Lee v Coward Chance; Goose v Wilson Sandford; Bradcrown v Kidd Rapinet; Lexi Holdings v Pannone; Lexi Holdings v DTZ).
Professional Memberships: Chancery Bar Association, Insolvency Lawyers Association.
Career: Queens' Cambridge; Harvard Law School. Former fellow of Queens' Cambridge. Recorder and Deputy High Court Judge (Chancery and Queen's Bench, Commercial/Mercantile Court); Bencher Lincoln's Inn. Publications: Joint editor of 'The Practice and Procedure of the Companies Court'; Contributor to Insolvency and Company Chapters of 'Civil Appeals' (Sir Michael Burton Ed.).

MARSHALL-ANDREWS, Robert QC
Carmelite Chambers, London
020 7936 6300
clerks@carmelitechambers.co.uk
Featured in Financial Crime (London)
Practice Areas: Commercial Fraud Trials, Category One: All save one of the Johnson Matthew trials: Bannerjee, Sethia (2), Lakhiani and Golecha and Choraria – (probably the seminal case in banking fraud). Barlow Clowes (for crabtree). DPR Futures (for Deller) – The largest Futures fraud to be tried. Stewart – Managing Director Cobbold Roach. Investment Fraud. Stafford – Duputy Leader Derbeyshire CC. Local Authority Finance. Duralite/PPR – (for Malcolm Johnson) – Probably the largest and most complex case ever undertaken by the SFO. Enerty Capital – Stock Exchange. Alleged fraudulent Rights issue. Regina v Dhillan – House of Lords – Mortgage Fraud. In addition to these high profile cases the majority of his practice concerns serious investment, mortgage and revenue frauds mainly in London but also on the Midland and Oxford and Northern Circuits. R v El Kurd (Seminal case on money laundering) – Ct of Appeal; R v Palmer and ors (for Parrott) frontline MTIC fraud; R v Tickle and ors (Operation Catrina) Diversion fraud and Abuse of Process; R v Sthankiya, collapse of Ciro Citterio Group – Abuse of Process. R v Oliver and ors (MTIC fraud – successful abuse application). R v Harrison (Blackmail case relating to Huntindon Life Services – successful dismissal application). R v Naveed Shaikh (Copywright Fraud). R vs. Keith Bennett (April to July 2009) – Southwark Crown Court Successful defence of B a mobile phone exporter and domestic trader (buffer and broker) in the largest MTIC/Carousel fraud then prosecuted, with a total value of over £1bn. R v Thurlbeck and anor – Watford Crown Court Successful defence of 2nd Defendant (a police officer) on corruption allegations involving the supply of NCIS information to the News of the World. R v Minto & Others, Basildon CC. Successful defence of last major fraud case undertaken by DTI R v Singh & Others, Portsmouth CC. Successful defence of alleged massive conspiracy to counterfeit/pass off Microsoft products. R –v- R & others – Kingston Crown Court Acting for a defendant in a £100 million VAT fraud involving the supply of mobile telephones. R –v- M & others (Operation Ukraine) – Cardiff Crown Court Successful defence of M in case concerning an alleged fraudulent acquisition tax scheme and the evasion of £15 million of VAT. The system employed for the alleged fraud involving the VAT 414 scheme for the importation of cars into the UK is alleged by the Crown to mirror the system employed by MTIC/carousel fraud with missing traders. The client was acquitted by the jury in September 2011. 2012 – R v Doshanj and others at Southwark Crown Court – successful defence of second defendant, B on 110m carbon credit fraud: 2013 – R v Graham and others at Southwark Crown Court – successful defence of W former CEO of the iSoft Company on FSA prosecution for stock exchange fruad.
Career: 1967. Recorder 1982. Silk 1987 (Bencher 1996). Deputy High Court Judge.

MARTIN, Bradley
2TG - 2 Temple Gardens, London
0207 822 1200
bmartin@2tg.co.uk
Featured in Clinical Negligence (London)
Practice Areas: Clinical negligence (claimant and defendant); personal injury; professional discipline (GMC; GDC; CIPFA; ICAEW); product liability. Notable cases include: Myodil litigation for Glaxo; Lariam cases for GPs; PIP Hydrogel breast implant litigation; PIP Silicone breast implant litigation; Barry v NHSLA (QBD London 09/05/02 - cord prolapse at home - ambulance liability); The Royal Victoria Infirmary & Associated Hospitals NHS Trust v B (A Child) [2002] Lloyd's Med LR 282 (CA) (life expectancy/multipliers); Reynolds v North Tyneside Health Authority [2002] Lloyd's Med LR 459 (QB); P v T [2004] Lloyd's Rep Med 537 (QB); Bailey v Northfield (Manchester CC 2009 - misdiagnosis of acute ischaemia - amputation); Nicholas v Imperial College NHS Trust [2012] EWHC 591 (QB); R v Royal National Orthopaedic Hospital NHS Trust [2012] EWHC 492 (QB); Ecclestone v Medway NHS Foundation Trust [2013] EWHC 790 (QB); Helps v Nottingham University Hospitals NHS Trust (Nottingham CC 2014 - standard of care in revision ileostomy).

Professional Memberships: LCLCBA; PNBA; PIBA; ARDL.
Career: Research assistant to the Federal/Provincial/Territorial Review of Liability Issues in Health Care at the University of Toronto (1987/8); Tutor in tort law at Leicester University (1988/9); Barrister in private practice (called 1990).
Personal: Resides in Hove; plays guitar, bass, banjo, ukulele.

MARTIN, Dale
Littleton Chambers, London
07814 967 352
dmartin@littletonchambers.co.uk
Featured in Employment (London)
Practice Areas: Dale Martin is one of the UK's top juniors specialising in employment law. Increasingly instructed by blue chip firms, his practice focuses on injunctions, restrictive covenant matters, fiduciary duties of directors and senior employees, contractual disputes and statutory employment matters. Having successfully resisted an injunction at the interim stage, Dale acted for the Defendants at trial in the restrictive covenant dispute in Romero Insurance Brokers Ltd v. Templeton [2013] EWHC 1198 (Sir Raymond Jack sitting as a High Court Judge), a case that figured heavily in the insurance press and followed on from his appearance with David Reade QC in the important springboard case of QBE v. Dymoke [2012] IRLR 458. Dale is currently advising and appearing in respect of a number of multiple party injunctions and related damages claims. Dale also has particular experience in work concerning City financial employers/employees including bonuses and other contractual issues. He acted for the bank in the appeal in Portnykh v. Nomura International plc [2014] IRLR 251. He is currently involved in a number of matters relating to the LIBOR and EURIBOR scandal. Added to that, Dale carries out top end statutory employment work, for example, important or high profile discrimination matters (in 2014, Dale is acting for a number of law firms defending their own claims), multiple working time/holiday pay and contract claims for large employers (he is currently dealing with a multiple of over 300 arising out of BA v. Williams and Lock v. British Gas and is advising blue chip clients on others), appearance at trial in a recent multiple claimant/multiple respondent TUPE matter arising out of an insolvency and multiple equal pay claims (with John Bowers QC). Dale's recent appellate work also includes his second successful defence, in a levy dispute, of an Employment Tribunal Judgement in his client's favour before the High Court: Online Design & Engineering Ltd v. ECITB [2013] EWHC 287 (see also [2010] EWHC 2776).
Professional Memberships: Employment Law Bar Association; Employment Lawyers Association; COMBAR.
Career: Called 1997 (Inner Temple).

MARTIN, Roy QC
Terra Firma Chambers, Edinburgh
0131 226 5071
roy.martin@terrafirmachambers.com
Featured in Real Estate Litigation (Scotland), Commercial Dispute Resolution (Scotland), Planning (Scotland)
Practice Areas: Specialist in planning, commercial, and administrative law. Has appeared in many of the most significant planning inquiries to have taken place in Scotland, including the Braehead and Gyle retail inquiries, the Harris superquarry inquiry, the proposed Gartcosh gas-fired power station inquiry and the Princes Street Galleries inquiry. Has acted for the promoter and objector in a number of transport schemes to have come before the Scottish Parliament, including the Stirling-Alloa-Kincardine Railway Bill, the Glasgow Airport Rail Link Bill and the Edinburgh Trams Bill. In England, acted for the developer in relation to an appeal under the Channel Tunnel Railway Link Act concerning the redevelopment of St Pancras Station. In 2009 and 2010 represented pensions advisers in relation to claims of alleged failure to equalise retirement dates and acted for Trump International in respect of their property and golf course development in Balmedie, Aberdeenshire. In 2008 acted as Counsel to the Inquiry into the explosion at the ICL Plastics Factory in Glasgow set up under the Inquiries Act 2005. In 2010 he acted for pension trustees in two cases concerning amendment to company pension schemes.
Professional Memberships: Scottish Planning Local Government & Environmental Bar Group; Planning & Environmental Bar Association.
Career: Called Scotland 1976; QC Scotland 1988; Called England & Wales 1990 (Lincoln's Inn); QC England & Wales 2008; Vice-Dean of the Faculty of Advocates 2001-04; Dean of the Faculty of Advocates 2004-07; member of the Judicial Appointments Board for Scotland 2007-10; honorary Professor of the University of Glasgow School of Law since 2006; Called Northern Ireland 2010; Chairman of Terra Firma Chambers.
Publications: Author of the chapter on public local inquiries in the Scottish Planning Encyclopaedia.

MARVEN, Robert
4 New Square, London
020 7822 2000
r.marven@4newsquare.com
Featured in Costs Litigation (London)
Practice Areas: Robert Marven is a specialist in all aspects of costs law. He is also an expert on the law concerning the funding of litigation. He has been instructed in a range of high profile cases in the Court of Appeal, the High Court, the Senior Courts Costs Office and the County Court. Robert's practice includes: costs issues arising from high value litigation; conditional fee agreements and contingency fee agreements; commercial funding for substantial disputes; legal expenses insurance and 'after the event' insurance; fixed costs; costs budgets and estimates; costs capping; as well as wasted and non-party costs orders. Robert acts for a wide range of clients including PLCs and public bodies, solicitors, major insurers, funders, claims management companies and individuals. He is often brought into major litigation to advise and to present submissions on specific costs issues. Robert provides strategic advice on matters of commercial importance to insurers, solicitors and others involved with the management and funding of litigation. He provides strategic advice on matters of commercial importance to insurers, solicitors and others involved with the management and funding of litigation. His cases include: Tasleem v Beverley [2014] CP Rep 25, Light on Line Ltd v Zumtobel Lighting Ltd [2013] 1 Costs LR 129; Letts v Royal Sun Alliance plc [2012] 3 Costs LR 591; Joyce v West Bus Coach Services Ltd [2012] 3 Costs LR 540; Legal Services Commission v F [2011] 5 Costs LR 740; Rybak v Langbar International Ltd [2011] PNLR 16; Sulaman v Axa and Direct Line [2010] 3 Costs LR 391; Tankard v John Fredericks Plastics Ltd [The Accident Line Protect test cases] [2009] 1 WLR 1731, [2009] 4 All ER 526; Crane v Canons Leisure Centre [2008] 1 WLR 2549, [2008] 2 All ER 931, Days Healthcare UK Ltd v Pihsiang Machinery Manufacturing Co Ltd [2006] 4 All ER 233.
Career: MA (Cantab). Called to the Bar 1994.

MASSARELLA, David
Cloisters, London
020 7827 4000
dm@cloisters.com
Featured in Employment (London)
Practice Areas: David's work covers the full range of employment and discrimination law at first instance and appellate levels. He represented the successful claimants in two of the most high-profile of recent pregnancy discrimination cases (Tantum v Travers Smith [2013] EqLR 736 and Gregory v Her Majesty's Forces). He has appeared in leading cases on sexual orientation discrimination (Bivonas LLP v Bennett [2012] EqLR 216), amendment (Redhead v London Borough of Hounslow [2012] EqLR 628), disability discrimination (Meikle v Nottinghamshire County Council [2005] ICR 1) and indirect sex discrimination (Hardy and Hansons v Lax [2005] ICR 1565 CA). He has considerable experience defending long-running discrimination and whistleblowing cases. Recent respondent clients have included local authorities, major retailers, charities and banks.
Professional Memberships: DLA, ELBA, ILS, Bar Pro Bono Unit and ELAAS.
Career: David read Modern Languages at Magdalen College, Oxford (BA Hons, 1st Class). Before being called to the Bar in 1999 he worked as a director in theatre and opera, including four years with the Royal Opera House. He is on the board of Actors Touring Company and has previously been a trustee of Southwark Citizens Advice Bureaux and a member of the Executive Committee of the Discrimination Law Association.
Publications: He contributed chapters to the 2012 Jordans book on Family Rights in Employment and the 2013 LAG book on Discrimination in Employment.

MASSEY, William QC
Pump Court Tax Chambers, London
020 7414 8080
clerks@pumptax.com
Featured in Agriculture & Rural Affairs (London), Tax (London)
Practice Areas: Practice covers all areas of personal and corporate taxation, with an emphasis on tax appeals and other tax-related litigation, private client and trust and estate tax planning and heritage and agricultural property. Recently involved in a number of trust variations under the Variation of Trusts Act 1958. Cases include Application to vary the undertaking of A and B (Special Commissioners); Marquess of Hertford and others v IRC (Special Commissioners); Lloyds TSB (PRs of Antrobus) v IRC (Special Commissioners); Lloyds TSB (PRs of Antrobus) v IRC (Lands Tribunal); Arnander v IRC (Special Commissioners); McCall v HMRC (Northern Ireland Court of Appeal); HMRC v Trustees of the Nelson Dance Family Settlement (High Court); Executors of Lord Howard of Henderskelfe v HMRC (Upper Tribunal); HMRC v Executors of Lord Howard of Henderskelfe (Court of Appeal).
Professional Memberships: Revenue Bar Association; London Common Law and Commercial Bar Association; Chancery Bar Association; Western Circuit.
Career: Called 1977, Middle Temple; QC 1996, Tax Committee Historic Houses Association; Bencher of Middle Temple 2004.

MASTERS, Dee
Cloisters, London
020 7827 4000
deemasters@cloisters.com
Featured in Employment (London)
Practice Areas: Dee Masters is a leading barrister who specialises in all areas of discrimination law. She works predominantly in the employment field although she also undertakes work in relation to discrimination in the provision of education, goods, facilities and services. She is regularly instructed in a range of cases across the spectrum of employment and discrimination disputes including unfair dismissal, whistle-blowing, race, sex, age and disability discrimination, flexible working, maternity/pregnancy rights, TUPE and breach of contract. Her clients include multinational companies, banks, charities, universities, NHS trusts and local authorities conducting court hearings and advisory work. She also represents senior employees in a diverse range of sectors from sales to banking. Dee is also instructed by the Equality and Human Rights Commission in cases that are at the cutting edge of discrimination law. For example, she appeared in the Supreme Court in Seldon v Clarkson, Wright and Jakes and is currently advising on the lawfulness of gender segregation in universities. Dee is also drafting the Supplement to the ban on age discrimination in goods, facilities and services on behalf of the Equality and Human Rights Commission. She has advised the Northern Ireland Equalities Commission and the Northern Ireland Children's Commission on proposals to ensure that in Northern Ireland age discrimination is outlawed for people under 18 in conjunction with Robin Allen QC.
Professional Memberships: ELA, ELBA, ILS.
Career: Notable cases include: Shaw v CCL Ltd [2008] IRLR 284, Bainbridge v Redcar & Cleveland Borough Council [2008] ICR 238, Redcar & Cleveland Borough Council v Bainbridge [2009] ICR 133, Potter v North Cumbria Acute NHS Hospitals [2009] IRLR 176, Potter v North Cumbria Acute NHS Hospitals [2009] IRLR 900, Wilson v HSE [2010] ICR 302 and Seldon v Clarkson Wright & Jakes [2012] ICR 716.
Personal: Education at University College, London (LLB) and the London School of Economics (LLM) specialising in employment law.

MATHER, James
Serle Court, London
020 7242 6105
jmather@serlecourt.co.uk
Featured in Partnership (London)
Practice Areas: General commercial chancery dispute and advisory work, particularly civil fraud, LLP and partnership, company, insolvency and trusts.

Professional Memberships: Association of Partnership Practitioners, Chancery Bar Association.
Career: Called 2006. Junior Counsel to Department of Business, Innovation and Skills for directors' disqualification proceedings, 2009. Junior Counsel to the Crown (Attorney General's C Panel), 2011.
Personal: Gonville and Caius College, Cambridge, Harvard University (Kennedy scholar); City University, London (Dip. Law).

MATTHEWS, Claire
One Paper Buildings, London
020 7353 3728
clerks@onepaper.co.uk
Featured in Crime (South Eastern)
Practice Areas: Criminal law.
Professional Memberships: South Eastern Circuit, CBA, Cambridge & Peterborough Bar Mess.
Career: Claire Matthews works across the South Eastern Circuit, with an exclusively criminal law practice. Her practice is almost equally divided between prosecuting and defending, and she is regularly instructed in cases involving expert evidence, complex third party issues, and cases with a particular emphasis on infant death/serious injury/neglect. Another large part of her practice are cases including armed robbery, serious violence, firearms, child abuse, serious sexual offences, major drugs, and mental health cases. Latterly Claire has also been instructed as junior counsel in cases of murder, attempted murder, manslaughter, firearms offences, serious fraud and money laundering. She has recently both prosecuted and defended parents/guardians in murder and manslaughter cases of alleged 'Shaken Baby Syndrome', and has a professional interest in medico-legal evidence.

MAUGHAM, Jolyon
Devereux, London
020 7353 7534
maugham@devchambers.co.uk
Featured in Tax (London)
Practice Areas: Jolyon has a predominantly litigation based practice in the fields of direct and indirect tax. He has particular expertise in 'scheme' transactions, intangible property, legitimate expectation, film financing and employment taxation. He holds the distinction of being the only specialist tax counsel appointed by the Attorney-General to the "A" Panel of Junior Counsel to the Crown. Recent notable cases include Icebreaker [2014] UKFTT 416 (TC), Eclipse Film Partners No 35 v HMRC [2014] EWCA Civ 184 & [2013] UKUT 639 (TCC) and Vaccine Research Limited Partnership [2013] UKFTT 73 (TC).
Career: Called 1997. Junior Counsel to the Crown (A Panel). Revenue Bar Association representative on the Bar Council. Member of the Bar Council Equality and Diversity Committee.
Personal: LLB European Legal Studies (Durham and Katholieke Universiteit Leuven), First; MA Birkbeck, Distinction.

MAWREY, Eleanor
9 Gough Square, London
020 7832 0500
emawrey@9goughsquare.co.uk
Featured in Financial Crime (London)
Practice Areas: Criminal law, in particular fraud/financial crime. Eleanor has been instructed in a number of high profile cases, most notably as junior counsel for the FSA (now FCA) in the successful prosecution of R v Joseph, a case which attracted one of the highest sentences for insider dealing to date. She was also instructed in the linked case of R v Mustafa and others. Eleanor is currently Junior Counsel in a sensitive pre-charge case for the SFO, where she appears on their B list, having previously acted for them in R v Khatab and Others (a Ponzi scheme). She is a Grade 3 CPS Prosecutor (including Fraud Specialist Panel), appearing frequently in benefit and revenue cases. Eleanor also regularly defends. Her work frequently involves POCA matters whether restraint or confiscation and ancillary orders such as SCPOs. Other recent cases: R v Wade and Others (Rail ticket fraud), R v Mohammed (benefit fraud), R v Q (complex confiscation hearing held in camera).
Professional Memberships: Bar Council member (2006-2011, 2013-2015) CBA committee member (2006-15)and its Director of Equality and Diversity , Remuneration Committee member (2006-12), Equality and Diversity Committee 2012-15.
Career: Called to the Bar in 2001. SFO B list and CPS Grade 3, Fraud Specialist Panel Grade 3. Direct Access.

MAWREY, Richard QC
Henderson Chambers, London
020 7583 9020
rmawreyqc@hendersonchambers.co.uk
Featured in Consumer Law (London), Information Technology (London)
Practice Areas: Main areas of practice are commercial law and local authority work. Commercial work includes contracts, leasing, finance and credit law, financial services, computer law and commercial drafting. Local authority work covers contracts, public procurement, public liability, finance, employment, passenger transport, local taxation, land development, housing, community services and computer problems.
Professional Memberships: London Common Law and Commercial Bar Association, Local Government Planning and Environmental Bar Association, Tecbar.
Career: Called to the Bar 1964 and joined present chambers 1965. Appointed assistant recorder 1981. Took Silk 1986. Appointed recorder 1986 and Deputy High Court Judge 1994, Election Commissioner 1994.
Publications: Author of 'Computers and the Law', Blackstone's 'Guide to the Consumer Credit Act 2006', Butterworths 'Commercial and Consumer Law Handbook'. Specialist editor contract and business law section of Butterworths' 'Civil Court Precedents', 'Bullen & Leake & Jacob's Precedents of Pleadings',Goode's 'Consumer Credit Law and Practice' and 'Encyclopaedia of Banking'.
Personal: Scholar of Rossall School and Exhibitioner of Magdalen College, Oxford (BA Jurisprudence 1963, First Class Honours, and Eldon Scholar of Oxford University 1964, MA 1967). Born 20 August 1942. Lives in London.

MAXWELL, David
St Philips Chambers, Birmingham
0121 246 7000
dmaxwell@st-philips.com
Featured in Employment (Midlands)
Practice Areas: David's practice encompasses Employment Tribunal, EAT, High Court and Court of Appeal litigation. Specialising in complex, lengthy and high value discrimination claims, he also accepts instructions in professional regulatory and disciplinary matters. David is frequently instructed by a wide variety of private sector respondents, including banks and other blue chip companies. He often acts on behalf of public employers including government departments, local government, the police and fire authorities. Recent cases include Davies v Sandwell MBC [2013] IRLR 374 CA.
Professional Memberships: ELBA; ELA.
Career: Called 1994. Attorney General's Treasury Counsel Panel. Fee-paid Employment Judge.

MAY, Charlotte QC
8 New Square, London
020 7405 4321
charlotte.may@8newsquare.co.uk
Featured in Intellectual Property (London), Media & Entertainment (London)
Practice Areas: Barrister(QC)practising in all areas of intellectual property and media law. She has particular experience in biotech patent litigation including Eli Lilly v Janssen Alzheimer's Immunology (immunotherapy for Alzheimer's) and Intervet v Medinol. She has also appeared in chemical patent actions such as Smith & Nephew v Convatec (silverised wound dressings) and mechanical patent cases including Abbott v Medinol (stents) and Liversidge v Abbott (injecting devices). She has a niche practice in SPCs with experience as the sole advocate in the High Court, Court of Appeal and/or CJEU in a range of cases including Yissum, Gilead, Astellas, DuPont, Neurim, Merck, Generics v Synaptech, Novartis v Actavis, AstraZeneca and GSK. Charlotte has a strong reputation for copyright, trade mark and media and entertainment cases. Recent examples include A&E TV v Discovery (dispute over satellite channel name); ITV v TV CatchUp (copyright infringement of TV programmes streamed over the internet); FAPL v QC Leisure (copyright infringement of Premier League football matches); BDO Stichting v Banco d'Oro (dispute over mark BDO); L'Oreal v eBay (online use of trademarks as keywords). For a comprehensive CV visit www.8newsquare.co.uk
Professional Memberships: Intellectual Property Bar Association (IPBA); The Intellectual Property Lawyers Organisation (TIPLO); ITMA Designs Committee.
Career: Inner Temple, 1995.
Personal: Born 1971. Educated at The Abbey School; Brasenose College, Oxford (1993 Biochemistry); City University (1994 Dip Law); Inns of Court School of Law. Appointed QC 2014.

MAYHEW, Alice
Devereux, London
020 7353 7534
mayhew@devchambers.co.uk
Featured in Employment (London)
Practice Areas: Specialist in employment litigation and advisory work involving restraint of trade, whistleblowing, all types of discrimination, equal pay, business transfers, wrongful and unfair dismissal, industrial action and breach of contract claims. She has extensive experience of acting for a wide variety of clients such as airlines, banks, local authorities, media, telecommunications and police forces as well as senior employees. Undertakes multi day complex cases before the employment tribunal, county court and high court as well as all levels of appeal (often being instructed for the first time at appellate level).
Professional Memberships: ELBA, ELA (Member of the training committee).
Career: Called 2001, Inner Temple Major Scholarship, Pegasus Scholarship, Ede and Ravenscroft Prize for Student of the Year and Duke of Edinburgh Award.
Publications: Contributor to Bloomsbury Discrimination Law and Jordans Employment Law Service.
Personal: LLB Exeter, LLM Cambridge. Enjoys swimming, Yoga and going to the beach in Norfolk.

MAYNARD, Matthew
St Ives Chambers, Birmingham
0121 236 0863
matthew.maynard@stiveschambers.co.uk
Featured in Family/Matrimonial (Midlands)
Practice Areas: Matthew Maynard is a family law specialist, whose practice encompasses both children work and financial remedy applications.
Career: Children: Matthew's practice, both at first instance and appeal, is heavily weighted towards complex public law proceedings involving allegations of the utmost severity, including: non-accidental injury, sexual abuse, FII (Fabricated or Induced Illness) and Female Genital Mutilation. Within the sphere of non-accidental injury, Matthew's experience includes cases involving brain injury, retinal damage, fractures (including high numbers, with various fracture windows) and suffocation. Additionally, he has extensive experience of cases involving the inherent jurisdiction of the High Court and Wardship. He often appears against leading counsel in his own right. Matthew also accepts private law instructions with an international element, such as abduction and international relocation and contact disputes. Matthew's domestic private law practice primarily involves proceedings where serious allegations of harm are a live issue. Finance: Matthew's financial remedy practice includes applications for financial orders on divorce and Schedule 1. He represents clients in cases ranging from moderate to high value, including business assets.

MAYNARD-CONNOR, Giles
Exchange Chambers, Manchester
0161 833 2711
maynardconnor
@exchangechambers.co.uk
Featured in Chancery (Northern), Restructuring/Insolvency (Northern)
Practice Areas: Chancery and commercial litigation with emphasis on insolvency (corporate and personal), company, corporate fraud, professional negligence and banking. Notable cases include Zavvi Retail Ltd, Beloit Walmsley Ltd, The Phone People, The Accident Group and Kwik Save (corporate insolvencies), Ultraframe (UK) Ltd v Fielding & Others (corporate fraud) and Solar Energy Savings Ltd (public interest winding up).
Professional Memberships: Chancery Bar Association, Northern Chancery Bar Association, Northern Circuit Commercial Bar Association, R3 and Bar Pro Bono Unit.
Career: Called to Bar 24 November 1992. Junior Counsel to the Crown (Provincial Panel). Accredited mediator. Also member of 13 Old Square, Lincoln's Inn.
Personal: University of Lancaster. Leisure interests: football, motor racing, rugby union, travel, film and dining.

MAYO, Simon QC
187 Fleet Street, London
020 7430 7430
simonmayo@187fleetstreet.com
Featured in Crime (London), Financial Crime (London)
Practice Areas: Simon Mayo specialises in serious and complex crime. He has particular experience in the full spectrum of serious fraud work, including, tax frauds and frauds centred on the financial markets. He is regularly instructed for the defence in large and complex fraud cases. His experience and expertise in this field is also called upon by specialist prosecution agencies. He has been appointed by the SFO to both the prosecution and proceeds of crime specialist panels. He also acts for the FCA in relation to the investigation and prosecution of malpractice and fraud in the financial services sector. He has appeared in money-laundering cases arising out of the operation of mainstream and alternative banking systems. In the field of general crime, he has gained a wealth of experience in homicide cases and is regularly instructed on behalf of the defence and the prosecution. Simon also appears for defendants before a number of professional and sporting disciplinary bodies. He advises individuals and corporate bodies on a wide range of issues affecting director and corporate liability.
Professional Memberships: Criminal Bar Association (six years as elected member of executive committee).
Career: Call 1985. QC 2008. Recorder 2009.
Publications: Regular author of articles on recent developments in criminal law.

MCATASNEY, Philippa QC
Furnival Chambers, London
07860 933 389
pippa@leach.plus.com
Featured in Crime (London)
Practice Areas: Philippa McAtasney QC is an experienced, leading London criminal barrister who has a wide ranging practice. She has an excellent record in both prosecuting and defending in cases concerning murder, manslaughter, serious sexual offences, violent crime and fraud. She has a specialist practice in police discipline work and has represented many police officers at all ranks both at tribunals and in the Crown Court. In addition, she has acted for several businesses prosecuted under Health and Safety at Work legislation. For notable cases see www.furnivalchambers.co.uk
Professional Memberships: Philippa is a Bencher of Lincoln's Inn and a qualified advocacy tutor. She is a member of the South Eastern Circuit and the Western Circuit. She is also a member of the Criminal Bar Association, the Surrey and South London Bar Mess and the Sussex Bar Mess.
Career: Philippa went to University at the London School of Economics and Political Science. She was called to the bar in 1985 and took silk in 2006.
Personal: Philippa is married and has two daughters.

MCBREARTY, Kenneth QC
Axiom Advocates, Edinburgh
0131 226 5071
kenny.mcbrearty@axiomadvocates.com
Featured in Professional Negligence (Scotland), Real Estate Litigation (Scotland), Commercial Dispute Resolution (Scotland)
Practice Areas: Commercial law; professional negligence; property litigation; professional discipline; sports law. Cases include Salvesen v Riddell 2013 SC (UKSC) 236; Ruddy v Chief Constable, Strayhclyde Police [2012] UKSC 57; BH and KAS v Lord Advocate and Scottish Ministers [2012] 3 W.L.R. 151 (Supreme court decision application to ECtHR now pending); ICL Inquiry; Junior Counsel to the Inquiry, chaired by Lord Gill under the Inquiries Act 2005; extensive experience of dealing with a wide variety of commercial disputes, for example, Ahmad v The Rangers Football Club Limited; particular interest in the misuse of confidential information and related wrongs, and in the ex parte recovery of documents and property prior to litigation (for example, Search Consultancy Ltd v BE-IT Resourcing Ltd); significant experience in professional negligence, in particular, in relation to solicitors, accountants and surveyors (for example, McCann v Waddell & Mackintosh [2014] CSOH 15A).
Career: Qualified as a solicitor 1994; Called to the Bar 2000; standing junior counsel to the Scottish Government from 2006-2013; appointed silk 2013.
Personal: Fluent in Spanish

MCCABE, Louise
St Philips Chambers, Birmingham
0121 246 1600
lmccabe@st-philips.com
Featured in Family/Matrimonial (Midlands)
Practice Areas: Louise is a specialist in financial remedy proceedings and inquests. She conducts cases covering all aspects of matrimonial finance including financial remedies, trusts of land, Schedule 1 of the Children Act and Inheritance Act applications. She represents husbands, wives and intervenors and is regularly involved in cases of high net worth and those involving complicated and technical issues, expert evidence, business and other valuations, third party interests, and assets subject to trust. She has conducted financial cases involving children with separate representation, and conducted a number of cases arising out of the breakdown of same sex relationships. She regularly appears as an advocate in inquests, with particular experience in prison deaths.
Professional Memberships: FLBA.
Career: Durham University BA (Hons) in Law. Called to the Bar 1996. Appointed as an Assistant Deputy Coroner in 2009, and as a Deputy District Judge in 2013.

MCCAFFERTY, Jane
11KBW, London
020 7632 8548
jane.mccafferty@11kbw.com
Featured in Employment (London)
Practice Areas: Employment and commercial law with particular experience in business protection litigation involving team moves, restrictive covenants, misuse of confidential information, breach of fiduciary duty and contractual disputes. Jane's practice frequently involves multi-jurisdictional disputes and complex, high value litigation in financial services and regulated markets. Recent cases include an arbitration between members of a LLP in the asset management sector and acting for the successful claimants in the high profile team poaching / conspiracy claim Tullett Prebon v BGC [2011] IRLR 420.
Professional Memberships: Employment Lawyers Association, Employment Law Bar Association. COMBAR.
Career: Called to the Bar in 1998.
Personal: Educated at Foyle and Londonderry College and Newnham College Cambridge (BA Hons in Law, LLM).

MCCAFFERTY, Lynne
4 Pump Court, London
020 7842 5555
clerks@4pumpcourt.com
Featured in Construction (London), Information Technology (London), Professional Negligence (London)
Practice Areas: Construction, engineering, energy and technology disputes and professional negligence. Acts for employers, contractors and professionals in a wide range of construction litigation and arbitration (domestic and international) and adjudication proceedings (substantive and enforcement). She regularly appears in the TCC. Recent cases have involved the multi-million pound refurbishment of a private hospital, the design of lifts at commercial premises, major works to a water main in Central London, the onshore and offshore refurbishment of a jack-up rig, a multi-million pound dispute relating to the largest civil IT system in the world, and large commercial residential developments.
Professional Memberships: TECBAR (Secretary), Society of Construction Law, Society for Computers and Law, COMBAR, PNBA.
Career: BA (Oxon) English - 1st Class; Diploma in Law (City University) - Distinction; Called to the Bar 1997; Judicial Assistant to the Court of Appeal (1999), TECBAR Accredited Adjudicator.
Publications: Civil Appeals: Principle & Procedure (Co-author), Sweet & Maxwell; A Practical Guide to Adjudication, for the Practical Law Company.

MCCALL, Christopher QC
Maitland Chambers, London
020 7406 1200
mccallqc@aol.com
Featured in Chancery (London), Charities (London), Offshore (London), Tax (London), Trusts (London)
Practice Areas: Specialises in trust and charity law. Has appeared in numerous appeals in the House of Lords, Privy Council and Court of Appeal and in foreign courts: has regularly addressed specialist associations and seminars and written in legal journals.
Professional Memberships: Trust Law Committee, STEP, ACTAPS, Chancery Bar, and Charity Law Associations.
Career: Called to Bar Lincoln's Inn, November 1966. Took Silk, April 1987. Bencher 1993. 2nd Junior Counsel to the Inland Revenue in Chancery Matters 1977-87. Junior Counsel to the Attorney General in Charity Matters 1981-87. Practised at 7 New Square Lincoln's Inn 1967-94, subsequently 13 Old Square (now Maitland Chambers). Member of Bar Council 1973-76. He was until 2013 a member of the Executive of the Trust Law Committee and in that capacity took part in numerous initiatives in the sphere of trust law reform.
Personal: Born 3 March 1944. Married 1981, no children. Educated Winchester College (Scholar), Magdalen College, Oxford (Demy): 1st class, Mathematical Moderations 1962 and Finals 1964. Eldon Law Scholarship: 1966. Trustee of British Museum 1999-2004.

MCCANN, Claire
Cloisters, London
020 7827 4000
cm@cloisters.com
Featured in Employment (London)
Practice Areas: Claire McCann specialises in employment, equality and public law. She is instructed by magic circle firms, law centres and high street solicitors as well as the EHRC. She has a particularly strong reputation for her equality work, including non-employment discrimination cases and judicial reviews. She is also instructed in High Court employment-related litigation concerning restraint of trade and director's duties. Claire has a strong advisory practice and is a sought-after junior in complex and high profile litigation. She is particularly regarded for her tenacity in court, her sharp cross-examination skills, her meticulous preparation and her ability to put clients at ease. She gives sound, commercial advice and is quick to respond.
Professional Memberships: ELA, ELBA, DLA, HRLA, ILS, Bar Pro Bono Unit and ELAAS.
Career: Claire joined Cloisters in 2000 having worked as a consultant for the Public Law Project where she co-authored a publication on Access to Health Records. In 2005, she worked in the Human Rights Team of the Crown Law Office in New Zealand.
Publications: Claire is a contributor to the LAG Handbook on Discrimination Law (2013). She is co-author of the 2004 Consultation paper for Age Concern: "Addressing Age Barriers: An international comparison of legislation against age discrimination in the field of goods, facilities and services". Claire contributes articles to legal journals and she lectures widely on employment law and has filmed contributions for Legal Network TV.
Personal: Education at Wadham College, Oxford BA in English and French; Modern Languages (1st Class) and City University (Dip Law). Wadham College Scholar (1995/1996). Inner Temple Major Scholar (1998) and Princess Royal Scholar (1999). Pegasus Scholarship (2005).

MCCANN, Sarah
Hardwicke, London
020 7242 2523
sarah.mccann@hardwicke.co.uk
Featured in Construction (London), Professional Negligence (London)
Practice Areas: Practises in Hardwicke's commercial and insurance divisions, with a particular specialism in construction and engineering and professional indemnity disputes. Construction work covers the whole range of disputes arising on residential, commercial and industrial developments, including disputes involving loss and expense/ delay, design and build, public liability, street works, procurement and contaminated land. Considerable experience advising the electrical distribution industry. Acts in all manner of professional negligence and indemnity work in a diverse range of areas including the construction, legal, financial and property sectors. Appears as an advocate in all levels of Court and in domestic and international arbitrations, adjudications and mediations and is an accredited mediator and adjudicator.
Professional Memberships: TECBAR, Society of Construction Law; Adjudication Society; COMBAR; Chancery Bar Association; London Common Law and Commercial Bar Association (Secretary).

Career: LLB (Law and German) First Class 2000, Called to the Bar (Lincoln's Inn) 2001, Lincoln's Inn Eastham, Wolfson and Hardwicke Scholar and Everard ver Heyden Foundation Prize for the BVC, Barrister at Hardwicke 2002 to date, CEDR Accredited Mediator 2011, MCIArb 2011, TECBAR Adjudicator 2013.
Publications: Contributor to Construction All Risks Insurance by Paul Reed QC (2014) and CMS Cameron McKenna Insurance Broking Practice looseleaf.

MCCARTHY, Hui Ling

Gray's Inn Tax Chambers, London
020 7242 2642
clerks@taxbar.com

Featured in Tax (London)

Practice Areas: Predominantly VAT, business and corporate taxation. In particular, matters involving accounting issues, alleged avoidance or abuse of rights, and proportionality or human rights arguments. Appears regularly in significant, high-value cases, including: Supreme Court – WHA. Privy Council – NTA v MSI. Court of Appeal – Esporta; Equity Trust (Singapore); MJP Media; Drummond; Underwood. Upper Tribunal/ High Court: R(Derrin Bros); Dhanak; Bosher; Telfer v Sakellarios; Tameside MBC v VO; Smith. First-tier Tribunal – Hawksbridge (aka Icebreaker 2); Project Blue; African Consolidated Resources; Hills; Wiltonpark; Xerox; Zetland Trust; Allchin; Vardy; Weiser; Curran; Enersys. Also acted in a variety of other disputes involving tax issues including professional negligence actions, media tion, Land Registry and Companies Court proceedings.
Professional Memberships: CEDR-accredited mediator; Chartered Institute for Securities and Investment (MCSI); ATT; Chair of the CIOT's Tax Tribunal's Working Group.
Career: Called 2005, Inner Temple. Tax Junior of the Year - Chambers Bar Awards 2013. Finalist, Young Practitioner of the Year (STEP Private Client Awards, 2013). Rising Star Indirect Tax (Indirect Tax Awards, 2012). 40 under 40 (Tax Journal, 2011). Shortlisted, Taxation's Rising Star (Taxation Awards, 2009). Formerly a corporate finance analyst at a US investment bank.
Personal: Mathematics BSc (dunelm).

MCCARTNEY, Kevin

5 Paper Buildings, London
020 7583 6117
km@5pb.co.uk

Featured in Professional Discipline (London)

Practice Areas: Kevin is instructed in professional discipline and healthcare regulation cases, with particular expertise in community pharmacy regulation. He is regularly instructed by the leading solicitors to represent pharmacists facing proceedings before the Fitness to Practice and Appeals Committee's of the General Pharmaceutical Council. Kevin also regularly appears before the Fitness to Practice Panel of the General Medical Council and Police Misconduct Panels.
He has been instructed to act for solicitors appearing before the Solicitors Disciplinary Tribunal and appeared for ILEX when their disciplinary proceedings were challenged by way of Judicial Review. Kevin frequently acts for NHS England and healthcare professionals with regard to the regulation of both the performers and pharmaceutical lists: dealing with both fresh applications for inclusion and allegations of misconduct made against existing contractors. He is instructed in statutory appeals arising out of all of the above. Kevin has previously been instructed to act as legal chair for disciplinary committees set up by PCT's (NHS England) and has acted as legal chair for British Fencing.
Professional Memberships: Association of Regulatory and Disciplinary Lawyers. Criminal Bar Association.
Personal: Married with two children.

MCCLELLAND, James

Fountain Court Chambers, London
020 7583 3335
jm@fountaincourt.co.uk

Featured in Administrative & Public Law (London), Banking & Finance (London), Commercial Dispute Resolution (London), Financial Services (London), Professional Discipline (London)

Practice Areas: James practises in commercial, public and regulatory law with a particular focus on banking, jurisdictional disputes, judicial review and the regulation of legal and financial services. In recent years James has appeared in numerous complex, commercial and regulatory disputes both in arbitration and across the full range of domestic courts up to and including the Supreme Court. A number of those cases have involved multi-billion pound liabilities and/or regulatory outcomes of industry-wide significance. James also appears in a wide range of shorter matters ranging from extradition proceedings to tax tribunal appeals and disciplinary prosecutions. James has substantial experience as a sole advocate both at trial and on appeal (including the Court of Appeal and Divisional Court). In 2011 James was named by Legal Week as one of ten "Stars at the Bar". James is one of the Attorney General's Counsel to the Crown (B Panel).
Professional Memberships: COMBAR, ARDL, ALBA, YPLG.
Career: 2004: called to the Bar. Appointed to Attorney General's C Panel in 2009 and to the B Panel in 2012.
Publications: Contributing author of Brindle & Cox on The Law of Bank Payments.

MCCLELLAND, Ross

Axiom Advocates, Edinburgh
ross.mcclelland@axiomadvocates.com

Featured in Commercial Dispute Resolution (Scotland)

Practice Areas: Ross has a broad practice focusing mainly on commercial disputes. He has particular interests in property litigation and professional negligence. Recent cases include Prow v Argyll & Bute Council [2012] CSOH 77, [2013] CSIH 23 (rent review notices, whether time of the essence) and Abram v British International Helicopters [2013] CSOH 69, [2014] CSIH 53 (dismissal for delay).
Professional Memberships: Faculty of Advocates, 2011 to date
Career: Admitted to the Faculty of Advocates in 2011. Commercial litigation solicitor, Maclay Murray & Spens, 2001-10. Trainee solicitor, 1999-2001.
Personal: LLM (First Class) University of Cambridge (Jesus College, Foundation Scholar); LLB (Hons) (First Class) University of Aberdeen (Cruickshank Medal). Enjoys skiing and golf.

MCCLUGGAGE, Brian

9 St John Street, Manchester
0161 955 9000
brian.mccluggage@9sjs.com

Featured in Employment (Northern), Personal Injury (Northern), Fraud (All Circuits)

Practice Areas: Catastrophic injury; Insurance issues in personal injury and liability cases; Fraud and exaggeration issues; Professional Negligence; Disability Discrimination. Practice is now predominantly in high value personal injury work and insurance law. Cases often involve technical and/or insurance points or allegations of dishonesty. Ongoing claims include a £20 million+ property damage case, costs appeals and serious injury cases involving Chronic Regional Pain Syndrome, amputations, 'nervous shock' and high value Fatal Accidents Act claims. Representing families of 2010 Birmingham riot murder victims.
Professional Memberships: Personal Injury Bar Association; British Insurance Lawyers Association; Employment Lawyers Association.
Career: Attorney-General's Panel of Regional Counsel (2002); Fee paid Employment Judge (2010).
Personal: Football, tennis, economics.

MCCORMICK, William QC

Ely Place Chambers, London
020 7400 9600
wmccormick@elyplace.com

Featured in Defamation/Privacy (London)

Practice Areas: Defamation and Privacy. Chancery and Commercial. Property. Personal injury.
Professional Memberships: PNBA. PIBA. BASL.
Career: Defamation/Privacy work includes Cooper v ANL(jury award of £65,000 for an individual accused of masterminding the Millbank riots); Tesla Inc v BBC (CA) suing Top Gear for mis-representing performance of electric car; McAlpine v Bercow (twitter libel); Fox v Boulter (action by former defence secretary); McGrath v Prof Dawkins (comment thread on website); MPS & SOCA v TNL (suing to restrain use of leaked reports); Ecclestone v Khyami (privacy claim and dispute over ownership of Lambourghini). Commercial work. Disputes over the ownership or sale of businesses and the misconduct of directors and employees. Cases over banking and investment advice including: a claim by a software "start- up" for losses due to the wrongful termination of an overdraft facility; claims for mis-selling of investments in AIG; mis-selling of interest rate hedging products; mis-selling of tax efficient "film funding" schemes. Serious personal injury work: obtained substantial awards for a teenage girl severely brain damaged after walking out from behind a parked car ; a boy who suffered serious burns from electricity arcing to his fishing rod when he trespassed across a railway, and a man who walked into the path of a bus.

MCCREDIE, Fionnuala QC

Keating Chambers, London
020 7544 2600
fmccredie@keatingchambers.com

Featured in Construction (London), Public Procurement (London)

Practice Areas: Specialist in procurement, construction, engineering, energy, environment and professional negligence related claims, and instructions regarding health and safety, and insurance disputes. Practice covers a wide range of advocacy, advisory and drafting for both domestic and international clients. Advocacy expertise has led to regularly acting for clients in all the UK Courts including, the TCC, High Court, the Court of Appeal and before arbitrators, adjudicators, tribunals and in mediation. Recent work includes numerous appearances in early and specific disclosure in procurement cases; advising contracting authorities and challengers in procurement disputes; advising in relation to standard and bespoke contracts, PFI and facilities management disputes, repudiation, termination, loss and expense claims and retrospective delay analysis, including comparative delay analysis methodologies.
Professional Memberships: Procurement Lawyers Association, Technology & Construction Bar Association; Professional Negligence Bar Association; Society of Construction Law; Commercial Bar Association.
Career: Manchester University - Bsc (Hons) Geography 1986; Brunel University - MA Public & Social Administration 1990; Middlesex Polytechnic Business School - CPE 1991; Called to the Bar (Middle Temple) 1992; 3 Serjeants' Inn to 2008; Keating Chambers 2008; Bencher, Middle Temple 2010. Queens Counsel 2013.
Publications: Keating on Construction Contracts 9th Edition, 2012 – Contributor.

MCDONALD, George

4 New Square, London
020 7822 2000
g.mcdonald@4newsquare.com

Featured in Costs Litigation (London)

Practice Areas: George has extensive experience of commercial litigation, with a real emphasis on costs and professional liability. George is particularly at home arguing complex points of costs law and has been instructed on some of the seminal costs cases, both on his own account and as a junior (recently including, for example, Elvanite v AMEC Earth & Environmental (UK) Ltd with Anneliese Day QC on costs budgets and Assaubayev v Michael Wilson & Partners, Ltd with Nicholas Bacon QC). George regularly attends detailed assessments (and appeals therefrom), both inter-partes and solicitor-client, and enjoys dealing with the specific and detailed issues which arise.
Professional Memberships: PNBA, COMBAR.
Career: BA (Oxon) (1st class). Worcester College Scholar. Called to the Bar (Lincoln's Inn) 2007 (Hardwicke and Shelford Scholar). Joined Four New Square in 2007.
Publications: Contributing editor to Butterworths Costs Service, author of Lexis Nexis PSL Costs Practice Notes.
Personal: Qualified USPTA tennis coach and keen sportsman.

MCDONNELL, Constance

3 Stone Buildings, London
020 7242 4934
cmcdonnell@3sb.law.co.uk

Featured in Chancery (London), Court of Protection (All Circuits)

Practice Areas: Chancery litigation specialising in contentious trusts and probate, Inheritance Act claims, administration claims, removal of personal representatives, real property and proprietary estoppel. Constance also appears in the Court of Protection (property and affairs).

Professional Memberships: Chancery Bar Association, STEP, ACTAPS.
Career: Called in 2000 (Lincoln's Inn).

MCGEE, Andrew
2 Bedford Row, London
020 7440 8888
amcgee@2bedfordrow.co.uk
Featured in Health & Safety (London)
Practice Areas: Andrew has a heavyweight Health and Safety practice both defending and prosecuting (he is a List A prosecutor for the HSE and others). His work covers corporate and gross negligence manslaughter, as well as HSWA and regulatory offences. He often advises at an early stage in investigations and prosecutions and in relation to enforcement proceedings. He has considerable experience in representing interested parties at inquests, acting for police officers, clinical and other professionals, companies and individuals. Andrew also undertakes work in the First Tier Tribunal in health care matters, which complements his very busy practice in the area of professional discipline - eg work before the General Optical Council, the General Medical Council, the General Dental Council etc. Andrew's criminal work and experience is extensive (both prosecution and defence) across the whole range of criminal offences (murder , serious assault, sexual offences, public order, drugs, firearms, fraud and financial crime) in all courts (from the magistrates to the Supreme Court and Privy Council). He is regularly instructed by the Registrar of Criminal Appeals to act for unrepresented appellants. Andrew also acts for clients in environmental regulation and crime. He is regularly instructed on a direct access basis in all courts, including the Court of Appeal.

MCGHEE, John QC
Maitland Chambers, London
020 7406 1200
jmcghee@maitlandchambers.com
Featured in Commercial Dispute Resolution (London), Real Estate Litigation (London)
Practice Areas: John McGhee has wide experience in a broad range of chancery and commercial litigation including banking, commercial fraud, landlord and tenant, professional negligence, company and property disputes. Recent cases include: The Buncefield Litigation [2009] EWHC 540 (Comm) (nuisance and negligence claims arising from explosion at oil terminal); Menolly Investments v CEREP [2009] EWHC 516 (Ch) (specific performance of development agreement and construction of building contract); Progress Property Company v Moorgarth Group [2010] UKSC 55 (whether undervalue transaction ultra vires company or in breach of directors' duties); Scottish Widows v BGC International [2012] EWCA Civ 698 (rectification of lease); Re Game Station [2014] EWCA Civ 180 (scope of administration expenses).
Professional Memberships: Chancery Bar Association, COMBAR, Property Bar Association.
Career: University College Oxford 1980-83 (MA).
Publications: General editor of Snell's 'Equity' 33rd edn.

MCGRATH, Elizabeth QC
St Philips Chambers, Birmingham
0121 246 1600
em@st-philips.com
Featured in Family/Matrimonial (Midlands)
Practice Areas: Liz has specialised in family law for over 20 years. She acts for high net worth clients in ancillary relief proceedings and her vast Children Act experience spans both private and public law. This broad range of expertise enables her to provide a complete service for those involved in emotionally challenging litigation. In her ancillary relief practice, Liz has experience of cases involving private limited companies and partnerships, valuable property and pension portfolios, and farming interests. In private law work, she deals with all applications arising under s.8 of the CA, Schedule 1 applications and cases involving complex jurisdictional issues, including surrogacy. Liz regularly appears in the High Court representing Local Authorities, parents and Guardians. Recent care cases have involved fatal injuries, serious sexual abuse, factitious illness and parents with profound disabilities. Liz is approachable and possesses considerable inter-personal skills which enabled her to lead the family group at St Philips for a number of years. Solicitors and clients alike appreciate her down to earth approach to cases and her ability to cut through complex evidence to find a sensible way forward for her lay clients.
Professional Memberships: Association of Lawyers for Children; Family Law Association; British Agencies for Adoption and Fostering.
Career: Called 1987. Silk 2014.

MCGUINNESS, John QC
9-12 Bell Yard, London
020 7400 1800
j.mcguinness@912by.com
Featured in Financial Crime (London)
Practice Areas: Serious Fraud; Corruption; Asset Confiscation; Judicial Review and other Appellate work (criminal, regulatory and public law); First & Upper Tier Tax Tribunal; Homicide; Taxis & Local Authority licensing; Chairs Home Office Disciplinary Tribunals. Prosecutes and defends in Serious Fraud Office cases. Regularly instructed by Financial Conduct Authority, HM Revenue and Customs, CPS Appeals Unit Special Crime & Counter Terrorism Division and local authorities. Recent cases include: AM v DPP, 2013 [Court of Appeal (Civil Division): proposed assisted suicide by claimant with 'locked-in syndrome']; R v Wise & Doyle, 2012 [Court of Appeal (Criminal Division): football banning orders]; R v Wilmot, 2011 [Southwark CC: £26 million 'boiler room' fraud]; R v Marrache & Others, 2014 (Concluded a 9 month prosecution on behalf of the Attorney General resting in convictions of two partners of law firm of £40million fraud on clients and banks).
Professional Memberships: Criminal Bar Association
Career: Called 1980 (Licoln's). 1992-2001: Standing Counsel to the Department of Trade & Industry, South Eastern Circuit; 2001: QC; 2002-present: Recorder of the Crown Court. Appointed to SFO QC panels for (1) prosecution and (2) proceeds of crime.

MCKECHNIE, Stuart
9 Gough Square, London
020 7832 0500
clerks@9goughsquare.co.uk
Featured in Personal Injury (London)
Practice Areas: Stuart has extensive experience in the field of personal injury and clinical negligence work but specialises in high value catastrophic claims involving complex issues and multiple experts. He in instructed by many of the leading catastrophic injury firms nationwide with most of his practice based in the High Court. In 2013 Stuart represented claimants in cases with a combined value of over £40 million. Stuart is the co-author of the APIL Guide to Catastrophic Injury Claims and 1 of only 3 Barrister members of the editorial working party of the Judicial College Guidelines for the Assessment of General Damages in Personal Injury Cases. In 2011 Stuart was awarded the title of Personal Injury Barrister of the Year at the Proclaim National Personal Injury Awards. He was shortlisted for this award again in 2013. In 2012 Stuart was shortlisted for the Chambers & Partners Personal Injury & Clinical Negligence Junior of the Year Award.
Professional Memberships: PIBA, APIL.
Career: University of Nottingham 1993-96. Called to the Bar 1997. Inner Temple Scholar.
Publications: Co-author of the APIL Guide to Catastrophic Injury Claims published by Jordans. Contributing Editor to 'Kemp: Personal Injury Law, Practice and Procedure' on the subject of Periodical Payment Orders and 'A Practical Guide to Clinical Negligence Claims by 9 Gough Square'. Member of the editorial working party of the Judicial College Guidelines for the Assessment of General Damages.
Personal: Spending time with his wife and young son. Sport, particularly football and cricket. Good food and drink.

MCKONE, Mark D
Sovereign Chambers, Leeds
0113 245 1841
mark.mckone@sovereignchambers.co.uk
Featured in Crime (North Eastern)
Practice Areas: Mark McKone's practice is exclusively criminal, both defence and prosecution. He undertakes mainly serious sexual offences, fraud and serious violence. He is a Grade 4 prosecutor and is on the rape and serious crime panels. He has significant experience in multi-handed cases, with considerable experience in criminal appeals. He also has accountancy experience. He undertakes public access motoring offences, particularly those involving exceptional hardship. He has a reputation for very early preparation, and for being friendly and approachable.
Professional Memberships: Criminal Bar Association, North Eastern Circuit, Criminal Law Week.
Career: Called 1988. Pupillage and tenancy at Sovereign Chambers. Recorder of the Crown Court. Grade 4 Prosecutor. Rape panel and Serious Crime panel.
Personal: Married with three children. Keen sportsman.

MCLAREN, Michael QC
Fountain Court Chambers, London
020 7583 3335
mm@fountaincourt.com
Featured in Aviation (London), Commercial Dispute Resolution (London), Professional Discipline (London)
Practice Areas: Broad spread of commercial and regulatory work, particularly aviation, regulatory/disciplinary, insurance, professional negligence and civil fraud/trusts. Cases include: Aviation – ACG v. Olympic (2014, CA, issue estoppel), Tarom v. Jet2.com (2014, CA, causation), ACG v. Olympic (2013, CA, certificate of acceptance); Shaker v. Vistajet (2012, aircraft deposit); Tandrin v. Aero Toy Store (2010 frustration; 2009 jurisdictional challenge); Fujitsu v. Bax (2005, air waybills). Insurance – British Credit Trust v. UK Insurance (2004 credit insurance); KlerKitwear (2001 suspensive conditions). Other commercial – Russian Commercial Bank v. Khoroshilov (2011, discharge of injunctions); Power v. Open Text (2009 life assurance trust); Mbasago v. Logo (HL/CA 2006 Equatorial Guinean coup); Investment Invoice Financing v. Limehouse (CA 2006 assignment/security for costs). Solicitors' regulatory – Dennison v. SRA (CA 2012, dishonest solicitor); Patel v. SRA (2012 solicitor providing banking facilities); Faniyi v. SRA (2012 solicitor's non-appearance at SDT); SRA v. Davis (2011 SDT costs); Virdi v. Law Society (CA 2010 challenge to SDT procedure); Casson v. Law Society (2009 insolvency/IPS). Solicitors' fraud – Law Society v. Habitable Concepts (2010 recovery of trust monies).
Professional Memberships: COMBAR.
Career: Called 1981, Fountain Court Chambers 1982, Silk 2002.
Personal: Christ's College Cambridge (MA Law, 1st).

MCLOUGHLIN, Kevin
Temple Garden Chambers, London
020 7583 1315
kevin.mcloughlin@tgchambers.com
Featured in Health & Safety (London)
Practice Areas: Health and Safety, Coroner's Inquests, road traffic prosecutions and personal injury litigation. In health and safety prosecutions, Kevin represents companies, individuals, healthcare providers, Local Authorities and insurers. Appeared for the defence at Manchester Crown Court in respect of a hospital prosecuted for a safety offence, which was acquitted after a 6 day trial and recovered its legal costs. Prosecutes health & safety offences for Local Authorities in both the crown court and magistrates courts. At Inquests, acts for families, TUs, motorists, employers, NHS Trusts, Local Authorities and insurers. Represents both claimants and defendants in personal injury compensation claims. Retained by companies to advise and train on health and safety issues.
Professional Memberships: Coroners Society; Institution of Occupational Safety & Health (IOSH); Personal Injuries Bar Association.
Career: Qualified originally as a solicitor over 25 years ago. Formerly a Partner in DLA Piper and Eversheds. National Head of DLA's Insurance, Marine and Aviation Group for many years. Regularly sits as an Assistant Coroner in four Coronial jurisdictions, dealing with workplace fatalities, deaths involving Article 2 ECHR, road traffic, and medical cases. Previously a university law lecturer. Chartered Safety & Health Practitioner (CMIOSH).

MCMULLAN, Manus QC
Atkin Chambers, London
020 7404 0102
mmcmullan@atkinchambers.com
Featured in Construction (London), Energy & Natural Resources (London), International Arbitration (London), Professional Negligence (London)
Practice Areas: Barrister specialising in commercial disputes with an emphasis on construction and engineering, energy and natural resources, information technology,

professional negligence and insurance matters. Acts both in the United Kingdom and internationally in court and arbitration. Represents developers, employers, professionals, contractors, sub-contractors, funders and insurers. Winner of construction barrister of the year (junior) 2006, 2008 and 2009. Nominated professional negligence barrister of the year (junior) 2007. Very experienced in high value and multi-party disputes, as well as those which are extremely technical in nature. Fluent Spanish and competent French.
Professional Memberships: Combar, TECBAR.
Career: Called 1994. QC 2010.
Publications: Editor: 'Technology and Construction Law Reports' (Sweet and Maxwell).
Personal: BA Oxon (1st Class).

MCNAMARA, Andrew

Ropewalk Chambers, Nottingham
0115 947 2581
andrewmcnamara@ropewalk.co.uk
Featured in Social Housing (Midlands)
Practice Areas: He practices primarily in personal injury related claims and housing matters. He acts for Claimants and Defendants across the range of cases, drawing on over twenty years' experience both as a practitioner and holder of judicial appointments.
Professional Memberships: Personal Injuries Bar Association; Professional Negligence Bar Association; Housing Law Practitioners' Association.
Career: Called in 1992; BA (History), University of Southampton; LLB, University of Leeds; Assistant Coroner, Nottinghamshire: including deaths at work; in hospital, including intra/post operatively; in the residential/nursing care environment; in prisons/detention; and as a result of road traffic collisions; Judge of the First Tier Tribunal (Property Chamber): The Residential Property Chamber is charged with hearing cases regarding fair and market rents; leasehold enfranchisement; service charges; fitness to manage residential property and licences; mobile homes; and right to buy. He is an Accredited Mediator.
Personal: Away from the Bar, his interests are reading, cinema and running. He is passionate about music and is the drummer in two bands.

MCNAMARA, Stephen

Kings Chambers, Manchester
0845 034 3444
clerks@kingschambers.com
Featured in Clinical Negligence (Northern)
Practice Areas: Stephen practises principally in the field of clinical negligence, acting predominantly for Claimants. His cases span the areas of surgical and pharmaceutical negligence, misdiagnosis and delayed diagnosis, dental negligence, inappropriate treatment and failure to obtain informed consent, amongst others. Stephen is well used to dealing with complex areas of breach of duty and causation and is regularly instructed in high-value cases in which significant future losses are claimed. He is experienced in leading and managing a large team of experts during such cases. Stephen has particular experience of claims involving suicide arising as the result of negligent psychiatric treatment, including claims advanced under the Human Rights Act 1998. He regularly attends inquests on behalf of families and other interested parties in such cases and had developed an in-depth knowledge of the application of Article 2 ECHR to inquest proceedings, both in relation to jurisdictional issues and its effect on the scope of inquiry. Stephen also has considerable experience of cases arising as the result of negligent cosmetic surgery and is adept at dealing with the often difficult medical, legal and emotional issues which such cases involve. Stephen also practises in the field of personal injury, acting for both Claimants and Defendants in claims for serious injury arising from accidents in the workplace, on the highway and on private premises, and those caused by defective products and road traffic collisions.
Professional Memberships: Gray's Inn Personal Injury Bar Association Northern and North Eastern Circuits.
Career: Year of Call: 2008 University: London School of Economics and Political Science Degree: BSc Government (2:1) Awards: Anthony Bessemer Clark Scholarship (Graduate Diploma in Law) Goldie Award (Bar Vocational Course) St James' Chambers Award (for highest advocacy results on the Bar Vocational Course at Manchester Metropolitan University).

MCNEILL, Jane QC

Old Square Chambers, London
020 7269 0300
mcneillqc@oldsquare.co.uk
Featured in Employment (London)
Practice Areas: Employment, discrimination under domestic and European law, all areas of common law and statutory employment rights; high value claims, including those involving psychiatric/psychological injury. Cases include: Williams v. British Airways; Yapp v Foreign and Commonwealth Office; Chhabra v North West London Mental Health Trust; Haq v Audit Commission; Michalak v Mid Yorks Hospitals NHS Trust; Gutridge v. Sodexo; Gibb v. Maidstone & Tunbridge Wells NHS Trust; Grundy v BA; Kapur v Barclays; Preston v Wolverhampton Healthcare NHS Trustees. Also practises in personal injury, clinical negligence and mediation.
Professional Memberships: Employment Law Bar Association; Industrial Law Society; Employment Lawyers' Association; Personal Injuries Bar Association.
Career: Called 1982; QC since 2002; fee-paid employment tribunal judge since 2000; Mediator since 2002; Recorder (Civil) since 2006; Joint Head of Chambers since 2009.
Publications: Editor of 2nd Equality and Diversity Code for the Bar.
Personal: BA Hons (Oxon); Dip Law (City University); Member of Advisory Board, City Law School; Council Member of ACAS. Reasonably fluent Italian and French.

MCPHERSON, Graeme QC

4 New Square, London
020 7822 2000
l.stewart@4newsquare.com
Featured in Professional Discipline (London), Professional Negligence (London), Sports Law (London)
Practice Areas: Principal areas of practice are (1) professional liability (in particular claims involving accountants and auditors, solicitors and barristers, financial service professionals and sports agents), (2) professional discipline (3) sports law and discipline, and (4) commercial litigation, including insurance, finance services and bloodstock litigation. Recent important cases include: Professional Negligence: Coulthard v Neville Russell (CA) [auditors' duty of care towards company directors]; Barex Brokers v Morris Dean (CA) [valuers' duty of care to assignee of a loan]; Flannery v. Halifax Estate Agency (CA) [duty of a judge to give adequate reasons]; IAICL v Cook (CA) [scope of auditors' duty of care towards third party]; University of Keele v PWC (CA) [construction of an exclusion clause in accountants' retainer]; Keydon Estates v Eversheds (Ch) [measure of damages in solicitors' negligence claims]; Glyn v McGarel-Groves (QB) [scope of duties owed by treating and supervising vets]; Shawton Engineering v DGP (CA) [scope of cover provided by a design & build PII policy]; Hickman v Blake Lapthorn (QB) [duties of barrister when advising on settlement]; Sunderland Mutual Marine v Wiseman (Comm Ct) [conflict of laws within UK]; Hedrich v Standard Bank (CA) [wasted costs application against solicitor arising from a disclosure exercise]; Fulham Leisure Holdings v Nicholson Graham Jones (CA) [claim against solicitors arising from sale of Fulham AFC]; TAG (QB) [claims arising out of collapse of The Accident Group]; Kidsons v Various Underwriters (CA) [test for 'notification' under a PII policy]; Webster v Sandersons (CA) [damages in a professional indemnity claim for reflective loss]; Gill v Humanware (CA) [wasted costs jurisdiction in Employment Tribunals]; Spreadex v Barnes (Ch) [claim against solicitors arising from drafting of a gambling arrangement]; Fonexco v Manches (QB) [obligations of a solicitor in a jurisdiction race]; Zurich v Brown & Barnes (Ch) [construction of Solicitors MTCs]; Nahum v Citibank N.A. (Comm Ct) [obligations of a bank performing 'best execution']; Thomas v Capita (Ch) [film finance litigation]; Mengiste v EFFORT (CA) [recusal of Judge; wasted costs]; Redstone Mortgages v B Legal (Ch) [solicitors' obligations towards mortgagee client]; AIB v Mark Redler & Co (SC) [breach of trust against solicitors; measure of compensation for breach of trust] Sport: Nicky Henderson, Aidan O'Brien, Howard Johnson, CASELA PARK, Jim Boyle, Mahmood Al Zarooni, Gerard Butler, Grand National 2014 (BHA Disciplinary Panel & Appeal Board) [corruption, doping, sporting disrepute]; Whittaker (FEI Inquiry) [doping]; Mullins v Jockey Club (Admin Ct) [amenability of sporting bodies to judicial challenge]; Arachi v Fallon (CA) [injunction to prevent jockey from riding in Derby]; Burton v British Shooting (Olympic selection dispute); Sports Mantra v Force India (F1 sponsorship dispute) Professional Discipline: RCVS v Jones & RCVS v Auerbach (RCVS Disciplinary Panel) [disgraceful conduct]; BSB v McCarthy (Bar Disciplinary Tribunal) [dishonesty]; Hedrich v Standard Bank (CA), Gill v Humanware (CA), Mengiste v EFFORT (CA) [wasted costs].
Professional Memberships: PNBA, COMBAR, ChBA, BASL, ADRL.
Career: MA (Cantab). Called (Gray's) 1993 - scholar & winner ver Heyden de Lancey prize. Joined Four New Square (formerly 2 Crown Office Row) in 1993. Silk 2008.
Publications: Editor of 'Jackson & Powell on Professional Liability' (7th edition).
Personal: Educated at Canford School, Wimborne and Emmanuel College, Cambridge. Leisure interests: Training and riding NH racehorses.

MCTAGUE, Meghann

2TG - 2 Temple Gardens, London
020 7822 1200
mmtague@2tg.co.uk
Featured in Travel (London)
Practice Areas: Meghann is a personal injury barrister with particular expertise in travel and foreign claims. She has extensive experience of dealing with complex litigation involving choice of law and jurisdiction disputes. Meghann is regularly instructed in foreign claims arising out of road traffic accidents, disease cases, fatal accidents and catastrophic injury cases. She has dealt with numerous claims under both the Athens and Montreal Conventions and regularly advises on cases arising out of the Package Travel, Package Holiday and Package Tours Regulations 1992.
Professional Memberships: Personal Injury Bar Association, British Association for Sport and Law.
Career: Meghann was called to the Bar in 2004. She completed her pupillage and spent the first five years of her career at Deans Court Chambers in Manchester before moving to London in 2009 and joining 2 Temple Gardens. Before coming to the Bar, Meghann worked as a management consultant in the Sport and Leisure industry.
Publications: Meghann regularly contributes to a range of publications and gives seminars both in-house for solicitors and insurers and also in chambers on new developments in this area.

MEACHIN, Vanessa

St Philips Chambers, Birmingham
0121 246 1600
vmeachin@st-philips.com
Featured in Family/Matrimonial (Midlands)
Practice Areas: Vanessa has been practising in family law since being called to the Bar in 1990. Her practice includes public law, private law, financial remedy proceedings and Court of Protection cases. Financial remedy proceedings: Vanessa regularly appears in complex cases involving business interests, inheritance, conduct and intervener applications. Her financial experience extends to cases relating to applications under Schedule 1 of the Children Act 1989 and under the Trusts of Land and Appointment of Trustees Act 1996. Private law: Vanessa has a wide ranging experience of child arrangement orders (previously residence and contact), specific issue/prohibited steps orders and applications to remove the child from the jurisdiction. Public law: She regularly appears in the High Court acting for parents, children and local authorities. Her cases range from factitious illness, complex medical cases to those of chronic neglect. Vanessa also accepts public access instructions in relation to financial remedies and private law.
Professional Memberships: Association of Lawyers for Children; Family Law Bar Association; British Agencies for Adoption and Fostering.
Career: Regularly lectures for Jordans; Recorder on the South Eastern Circuit (family, public/private and civil); Head of St Philips' Family Finance Team.

MEADE, Richard QC
8 New Square, London
020 7405 4321
richard.meade@8newsquare.co.uk
Featured in Information Technology (London), Intellectual Property (London), Media & Entertainment (London)
Practice Areas: Barrister specialising in all aspects of Intellectual Property, with particular experience in biotechnology, pharmaceutical, telecommunications and electronics patent litigation. For a comprehensive CV and list of recent cases, visit 8 New Square website at www.8newsquare.co.uk.
Professional Memberships: Intellectual Property Bar Association (IPBA); The Intellectual Property Lawyers Organisation (TIPLO). CEDR Accredited Mediator.
Career: Called 1991. Appointed QC 2008. Sits as a Recorder and Deputy High Court Judge.
Personal: Born 1966. Educated at William Ellis School; University College, Oxford (BA Law).

MEADWAY, Susannah
Ten Old Square, London
020 7405 0758
clerks@tenoldsquare.com
Featured in Chancery (London)
Practice Areas: Susannah Meadway's practice encompasses advisory, drafting and litigation work in the fields of trusts and associated taxation, wills, probate and the administration of estates, pensions, family provision, Court of Protection matters and charities.The core though of Susannah's practice is non-contentious trust and estate work, and in particular: assisting trustees and beneficiaries to achieve their aims for the future administration of their trusts (whether those aims be for tax efficiency, flexibility, the inclusion of particular persons as beneficiaries, or otherwise); putting right mistakes which have occurred in trust documents (including wills), whether the mistake has been made by the settlor, the testator or the trustees; the re-arrangement of trusts, whether by use of applicable powers in the relevant trust instrument, or in the absence of such powers with the approval of the Court.
Professional Memberships: Susannah is a member of STEP and the Chancery Bar Association.
Career: Called to the Bar 1988. Notable cases include Re Segelman [1996] Ch 171 (will rectification and validity of a charitable gift); Re Bell [2002] WTLR 1105 (will rectification); Healey v Brown [2002] WTLR 849 (mutual wills); Bartlam v Coutts [2006] WTLR 1165 (settlement rectification); Numerous successful applications under the Variation of Trusts Act 1958, including applications to extend perpetuity and accumulation periods, and to re-arrange trusts in a tax efficient manner.
Publications: The Wills and the Executors titles in Halsbury's Laws of England (joint editor); Williams on Wills (joint editor); Mellows: Taxation for Executors and Trustees (joint editor); The Probate and Family Provision title in Atkin's Court Forms (editor); Foster's Inheritance Tax (contributor); Tolley's Practitioner's Guide to Contentious Trusts and Estates (co-author); Perpetuities and Accumulations Act 2009 (Trusts and Trustees 2010).

MEDCROFT, Nicholas
Wilberforce Chambers, London
020 7306 0102
nmedcroft@wilberforce.co.uk
Featured in Financial Services (London), Financial Crime (London)
Practice Areas: Nicholas Medcroft has a broad commercial practice, with an emphasis on banking and financial services, civil fraud disputes and professional liability. He is regularly instructed in major commercial disputes, especially those with a financial services or civil fraud/breach of trust element. He has particular experience of financial services regulation. Much of his professional liability work is in the field of financial professional negligence/misconduct. He is recommended as a leading junior in The Legal 500 and Chambers and Partners, where he is described as "very user-friendly" and "'extremely bright and phenomenally hardworking". Notable cases include Stone Consultants v NatWest, Shah v HSBC Private Bank (the leading case on the conflict between a bank's duties to its customers and its duties under POCA), FSA v Alexander (the first market abuse case to be brought by the FSA in the Chancery Division) and Financial Reporting Council v Deloitte (arising from the collapse of the MGR Rover Group - one of The Lawyers' Top 20 cases of 2013).
Professional Memberships: COMBAR, Chancery Bar Association, Financial Services Lawyers Association.

MEHRZAD, John
Littleton Chambers, London
020 7936 5055
jmehrzad@littletonchambers.co.uk
Featured in Employment (London), Sports Law (London)
Practice Areas: Employment, Commercial and Sport.
Professional Memberships: Employment Law Bar Association, Employment Lawyers Association, Industrial Law Society, British Association of Sport and Law, Commercial Bar Association, Bar European Group, London Irish Lawyers Association, Free Representation Unit, Bar Pro Bono Unit.
Career: Called at Inner Temple in 2005. Appointed FA arbitrator, member of sports advocacy section of the London 2012 Olympic Games Pro Bono Legal Advice and Representation Service and Glasgow 2014 Commonwealth Games, panel of preferred Counsel for Equality and Human Rights Commission. Notable cases include: Charlesworth v. Amey PLC UKEATPA/0326/13/MC; Tavistock School v. Richards UKEAT/0244/13/SM; Seaco & Ors. v. Buss Capital & Ors (QBD) 2012; Rubicon LLP & Ors v. Attias & Ors (Ch D) 2012; Stuart v. London City Airport Ltd. UKEATPA/1651/11/MAA; Blazevic v. Hayashibara International Inc. UKEATPA/0738/11/CEA; Bullimore v. Pothecary Witham Weld Solicitors & Hawthorne [2011] IRLR 18; Humphreys v. Norilsk Nickel International (UK) Ltd. [2010] IRLR 976; Hunt v. Legal & General Resources Ltd. UKEATPA/1531/10/DM; Parsons v. Burworth Estates (a firm) UKEAT/0547/08/MAA. Awarded Inner Temple Major Scholarships (GDL and BVC) and BEG Peter Duffy Scholarship.
Publications: Selection Challenges, World Sports Law Report, April 2014; Age and Disability issues in Playing Contracts, World Sports Law Report, January 2013; Fixed Term Contracts in Sport, World Sports Law Report, November 2012.
Personal: Studied at Keble College, Oxford University; University of Nantes, France; Trinity College, Dublin; BPP Law School, London. Speaks working French; intermediate Italian, German and Farsi. Leisure interests include sport, in particular rowing and football; history; politics; travel.

MEHTA, Nikhil
Gray's Inn Tax Chambers, London
020 7242 2642
nm@taxbar.com
Featured in Tax (London)
Practice Areas: Specialising in both UK and Indian taxes. All forms of taxation in both advisory and litigious areas including acting for corporates, partnerships, financial institutions, entrepreneurs, private equity and hedge funds, high net worth non-doms, particularly of Indian origin. Subject-matter includes M&A, group reorganisations, financial instruments, cross-border structuring for both corporates and individuals, advice on UK structures for individuals coming to the UK, employee taxation, tax risk management, and contentious work from correspondence to advocacy.
Professional Memberships: IBA, IFA, Institute for Fiscal Studies, Revenue Bar Association, Chancery Bar Association.
Career: 1977-1980: Tax advocate in Mumbai, India; 1981-83: Inland Revenue's Solicitor's Office; 1983-2002: Linklaters (tax partner since 1989 and Head of the India Business Group from 1992); 2002-2009: tax partner, Cleary Gottlieb Steen & Hamilton LLP; 2010 onwards: Gray's Inn Tax Chambers.

MEHTA, Sailesh
Red Lion Chambers, London
020 7520 600
sailesh.mehta@18rlc.co.uk
Featured in Environment (London), Health & Safety (London)
Practice Areas: Sailesh has prosecuted and defended in some of the most important environmental and health & safety cases, and has helped to shape environmental prosecution policy over the last 20 years. He has been awarded the highest ranking in the Regulatory and CPS Lists of Prosecution Counsel. He is Counsel of choice in cases involving a complex, novel or difficult aspect of regulatory law. He is instructed by a number of regulatory bodies, often in high-profile cases: the Environment Agency (recently as leading Counsel in a series of law-defining cases involving international pollution); the Health and Safety Executive (instructed in a number of fatality cases attracting media interest); Fire Brigades (prosecuting in 2013 a double fatality case which was said to the fire brigades' most complex case of the year). Sailesh lectures on all aspects of regulatory and criminal law and has been cited in legal directories as "a real heavyweight", "a charismatic advocate" and a leader in his field. In the past, he has been "Lawyer of the Week" in The Times newspaper and The Lawyer magazine, "Lawyer of the Month" in the BLD and was the Society of Asian Lawyers' "Lawyer of the Year".
Career: Called 1986 (Lincolns Inn); Recorder of the Crown Court.
Publications: Editorial Board Member of "Mithani: Directors' Disqualification".

MEICHEN, Jonathan
St Philips Chambers, Birmingham
0121 246 7000
jmeichen@st-philips.com
Featured in Employment (Midlands)
Practice Areas: Jonathan has always specialised in employment law and has a busy practice in the employment tribunal. He is an experienced tribunal advocate who has appeared in a diverse range of cases. Jonathan regularly acts in more complex or lengthy claims. He is instructed by large employers, PLCs, government departments and local authorities and also represents a variety of claimants, often via trade unions. In addition, he has been instructed by the Equality and Human Rights Commission. Jonathan undertakes appeal work and is frequently asked to advise in cases at an early stage. He believes in working as part of a team and seeks to work closely with professional and lay clients in order to achieve the best possible result at tribunal. Jonathan has particular experience of employment issues in the education sector. He appeared in the important EAT case of BCC v Emery [2014] E.L.R. 203 concerning the power of a governing body to dismiss a teacher, and is currently undertaking an investigation into allegations of serious misconduct against a prominent head teacher.
Career: Called 2006. Appointed to the Attorney General's Panel of Counsel in 2012.
Personal: Interests include music, football and skiing.

MELLOR, James QC
8 New Square, London
020 7405 4321
james.mellor@8newsquare.co.uk
Featured in Intellectual Property (London), Media & Entertainment (London)
Practice Areas: Barrister (QC) with wide ranging Intellectual Property, Media and Entertainment and Information Technology Practice. Specialist in electronics, mechanical and pharmaceutical patent cases. Has an extensive Trade Marks practice and is co-author of Kerly on Trade Marks. Recent cases include JW Spear & Sons Ltd and Mattel inc v Zynga (trademarks), Performing Right Society Ltd v B4U network (Europe) Ltd (copyright), Football dataco Ltd v Yahoo! UK Ltd (database rights). For a comprehensive CV visit 8 New Square website at www.8newsquare.co.uk
Professional Memberships: Intellectual Property Bar Association (IPBA). Former Member of the Disability Panel of the Bar Council. Chancery Bar Association.
Career: Called 1986. Prior work experience in a variety of engineering disciplines in the UK, France, Germany, Somalia, the Congo and Iraq.
Publications: 'Kerly on Trade Marks' 13th & 14th edns, 'The Trade Marks Act 1994 - Text and Commentary', Bullen, Leake & Jacob.
Personal: Born 1961. Educated at Rugby School; King's College, Cambridge (1983 BA, MA Engineering and Production Engineering, 1985 Law (1st Class).

MELTON, Christopher QC
Byrom Street Chambers, Manchester
0161 829 2100
christopher.melton@byromstreet.com
Featured in Clinical Negligence (Northern), Personal Injury (Northern), Personal Injury (All Circuits)

Practice Areas: Personal injury, clinical negligence and industrial disease.
Professional Memberships: PNBA, PIBA, NCMLA, AvMA. Trustee of the T and N Asbestos Trust and retained Counsel for the US DII Asbestos Trust.
Career: Chris Melton QC was called in 1982 and took Silk in 2001. He sits as a Recorder. His main areas of practice are in personal injury and clinical negligence, focussing on severe, catastrophic and fatal injury cases at first instance,in the Court of Appeal and in the Supreme Court. Although he is increasingly involved in cases at appellate level, with 5 appearances in the Court of Appeal and 3 in the Supreme Court in recent years, his cross examination skills mean he is always in demand as a trial lawyer.
Personal: A keen runner, cyclist, skier and soccer player.

MELVILLE, Elizabeth
Old Square Chambers, London
020 7269 0300
melville@oldsquare.co.uk
Featured in Employment (London)
Practice Areas: All areas of employment law, predominantly within the healthcare, education and business sectors. Undertakes both adversarial work in the employment tribunals and other courts and non-contentious disciplinary work including conducting investigations, chairing internal disciplinary hearings and representing parties in internal proceedings or before external disciplinary bodies.
Professional Memberships: Employment Law Bar Association, Industrial Law Society, Employment Lawyers Association.
Career: BA Oxon. Called to the Bar 1994. Spent two years at City law firm Simmons & Simmons between 1996-97 before returning to the Bar. Initially practised in fields of personal injury, clinical negligence and employment law. From 2003 has specialised in the field of employment law.
Personal: BA Oxon, French and History. Interests: travel, yoga, cooking.

MENDOZA, Colin
Devereux, London
020 7353 7534
mendoza@devchambers.co.uk
Featured in Personal Injury (London)
Practice Areas: All aspects of personal injury work for claimants and defendants; high value personal injury claims including fatal accidents, catastrophic brain damage, spinal injury, severe orthopaedic injuries leading to amputation, scarring and psychiatric damage. Clinical negligence (including spinal surgery, dental and veterinary). Health & Safety criminal proceedings. Experienced in ADR/mediation. Colin was appointed in 2008 as a Tribunal Judge of the Criminal Injuries Compensation Appeal Tribunal.
Professional Memberships: Personal Injury Bar Association; Professional Negligence Bar Association; Association of Personal Injury Lawyers; The British Academy of Forensic Sciences.
Career: Haberdashers' Aske's School, Elstree; University of Kent (1982 BA Law); Cambridge University (1984 LLM).
Publications: Sometime instructor and examiner at the Inns of Court School of Law, and contributor to the School's Manuals on the skills of opinion writing and drafting skeleton arguments.
Personal: Jazz, touch rugby, water-skiing.

MENDOZA, Neil
Selborne Chambers, London
020 7420 9500
neil.mendoza@selbornechambers.co.uk
Featured in Real Estate Litigation (London)
Professional Memberships: Fellow of the Chartered Institute of Arbitrators, Chancery Bar Association, Property Bar Association, Professional Negligence Bar Association, London Common Law and Commercial Bar Association.
Career: Neil is a highly accomplished commercial litigator whose practice substantially involves disputes in a business context. He provides friendly, pragmatic and plain-speaking advice and is known as a tenacious advocate who does not flinch or back off under pressure. In a particularly difficult case, one Chancery Judge remarked that the client should be grateful to Neil for his 'dogged and determined advocacy". He is particularly noted for his speed in dealing with paperwork and working within tight deadlines. Many of Neil's cases involve land and property issues and, from the development of his practice over the years, he has extensive practical experience in commercial landlord and tenant, general property litigation including conveyancing, easements, boundary and development disputes. He is more than familiar with professional negligence issues involving solicitors and surveyors and in dealing with general commercial contract litigation. A list of notable cases appears on Neil's entry on the Selborne Chambers' website and include claims concerning the "Pallant v Morgan equity", the approach of the Court of Appeal to procedural irregularity, solicitors' negligence, breach of trust and section 61 of the Trustee Act 1996, limitation in trust cases, the Trusts of Land and Appointment of Trustees Act 1996, enforcement of settlement agreements, misrepresentation, restrictive covenants, the Access to Neighbouring Land Act 1992, disability discrimination and many other, and varied, topics. Comfortable in the High Court and Court of Appeal, Neil welcomes instructions from new contacts and is happy to discuss matters on a casual basis prior to receiving formal instructions.

MEREDITH-HARDY, John
Farrar's Building, London
020 7583 9241
jmeredithhardy@farrarsbuilding.co.uk
Featured in Personal Injury (London)
Practice Areas: Personal Injury- Accidents at work including factories, oilrigs, workshops, shops and offices; Occupational disease including asbestos related conditions; Road traffic accidents involving heavy goods vehicles, cars and motorbikes; Employment and holiday accidents abroad whilst on-land and on-ship; Nervous shock; Brain injury, cerebral palsy and spinal injuries of the utmost severity; Complex injuries resulting in lifetime care and therapy, adaptive housing and ancillary services; CICA claims of the utmost severity; Fatal accidents. Professional negligence- Actions against medical professionals for clinical negligence; Actions against solicitors for breach of duty in the conduct of personal injury, clinical negligence and commercial disputes; Actions against mortgage brokers, architects, surveyors, accountants and IFAs for failing to discharge their duties towards their client. For details of commercial, insurance indemnity, general common law and notable cases see Farrar's Building's website

Professional Memberships: Personal Injury Bar Association; Professional Negligence Bar Association; Public Access work accepted; Accredited mediator.

METHUEN, Richard QC
12 King's Bench Walk, London
020 7583 0811
methuen@12kbw.co.uk
Featured in Personal Injury (London)
Practice Areas: Personal injury; clinical negligence.
Professional Memberships: PIBA and PNBA.
Career: Called 1972; QC 1997; Head of chambers 2000-05; appointed MIB arbitrator 2001; recorder 2002 and to the Ogden Committee 2004. Experienced mediator (ADR accredited) and leads the 12 Mediation Team. His success rate over the past two years exceeds 85%. He specialises in evaluative mediations.

MEYER, Birgitta
11 Stone Buildings, London
020 7831 6381
meyer@11sb.com
Featured in Restructuring/Insolvency (London)
Practice Areas: Birgitta has a strong chancery commercial practice with a particular specialism in all insolvency matters, both corporate and individual, where she is regularly instructed on challenging cases. She is recommended by Chambers & Partners as a leading insolvency junior. Her particular strengths are her ability to deal with complex mathematical calculations as well as her skill to grasp the legal and factual issues raised by difficult cases quickly. For further details of Birgitta's practice please visit the 'Barristers' section on www.11sb.com.
Professional Memberships: Chancery Bar Association.
Career: Call 1992, BA (Cantab).

MIAN, Naeem
2 Hare Court, London
020 7353 5324
naeemmian@2harecourt.com
Featured in Crime (London)
Practice Areas: Naeem Mian is regularly instructed in the most complex and high profile of cases. Having secured high profile acquittals in the past in cases such as the 7/7 tube bombing, he is now frequently instructed as leading counsel. His exclusively defence based practice continues to go from strength to strength. In addition to cases of murder, complex multi-defendant fraud and large scale drug offences, his current terrorism related instructions include leading briefs on behalf of one of the two defendants in the unprecedented so called "secret terrorism trial" and separately; leading in the defence of a young British student accused of involvement in the funding of terrorism in Syria. Naeem also frequently appears for both individuals and organisations seeking a robust defence in other tribunals including Regulatory, Professional Discipline, Inquests and alleged breaches of Health and Safety. As is illustrated by his broad practice, Naeem is seen as a talented and highly sought after all rounder by those who instruct him. Whilst being totally committed to pursuing the best interests of his clients, his relaxed and approachable style immediately puts both professional and lay clients at ease.

MICHAEL, Simon
No5 Chambers, Birmingham
0845 210 5555
slm@no5.com
Featured in Clinical Negligence (Midlands), Personal Injury (Midlands)
Practice Areas: Catastrophic, fatal and multiple personal injuries and clinical negligence, for claimants and defendants. Simon's experience includes brain, birth and spinal injuries, and injuries of maximum severity arising from accidents on the roads, at work and in hospitals. Most of his cases are high value (highest to date £9m). He also acts in professional negligence claims involving the negligent conduct of personal injury and clinical negligence litigation. Commentators state that "he has many strengths. He is meticulous, fosters fantastic relationships with lay clients, and has the ability to work extremely well as part of a team with instructing solicitors" and this "ingenious and dynamic" lawyer is "easily equivalent in terms of ability to the silks in this field".
Professional Memberships: PNBA, PIBA.
Career: Educated at Hendon County Grammar School, King's College, London University. Called 1978. Visiting laws lecturer 1978-81. Bar Pro Bono Award Winner 2001. Former chair and trustee of the Road Victims Trust (charity giving psychological, practical and legal support to those bereaved or suffering life-changing injury on the roads).
Personal: Simon is a part-time novelist, screenwriter and parent of four. His favourite pastime is fronting a scratch blues and soul band.

MICHELL, Paul
Cloisters, London
020 7827 4000
pm@cloisters.com
Featured in Employment (London)
Practice Areas: Leading junior Counsel for high-value and complex dismissal, discrimination, whistle-blowing, EqPA, TULRA and TUPE claims, and related contract/ director disputes. Regularly acts in cases where breach of covenant, database rights, fiduciary duty, confidentiality or other commercial wrongdoing is alleged, and injunctive relief is sought. Praised in directories and by clients as "a brilliantly skilled advocate"; "feisty tough and creative"; "top employment counsel... intelligent, articulate and highly personable", and "one of the barristers that clients return to most often". See Paul's entry at www.cloisters.com for more details. Acts as an adjudicator of grievances brought by senior employees, and as a Designated Independent Person investigating alleged wrongdoing by senior local authority staff. Named 'Lawyer of the Week' in The Times. Appeared in BBC documentary 'See You in Court', May 2011. Clients include the BBC, Belgo, British Red Cross, Danielle Lloyd, EHRC, the Elders Foundation, the Football Association; the GMB, the Premier League; RNIB, Royal Ballet School, Trevor Horn CBE, the TUC and several major higher education and financial institutions. Recent landmark cases include Hainsworth v. MoD [2014] EWCA Civ 763, CA; X v. Mid Sussex CAB [2013] IRLR 146, SC, Kulikauskas v. Macduff Shellfish [2011] ICR 48, EAT, CJEU; EBR Attridge v Coleman [2010] ICR 242 (EAT), and Coleman v Attridge Law [2008] ICR 1128 (ECJ).
Professional Memberships: ELBA, ILS, ELA.

Career: 2013- Appointed Visitor for Loughborough University, and part time Employment Judge.
Publications: Author of Bullen & Leake & Jacob's Precedents of Pleadings (Employment Tribunal Proceedings and High/County Court).
Personal: Highgate School; Downing College, Cambridge (BA, English); City University (Dip Law).

MIDDLETON, Graeme
Compass Chambers, Edinburgh
0141 434 0451
graeme.middleton
@compasschambers.com
Featured in Personal Injury (Scotland)
Practice Areas: Specialising in personal injury/industrial disease, professional/clinical negligence, property damage (pursuing and defending); health and safety/road traffic crime. Extensive experience in Court of Session and Sheriff Courts, including complex, high-value claims. Recent cases: Dickson v Kinsman [2013] CSOH 111 – road accident, operation of "agony rule"; Cowan v Hopetoun House [2013] CSOH 9 – occupier's liability, Pursuer fell over unlit/unmarked "Ha Ha" at stately home; Reid v EWS Railways 2010 GWD 28-592; 2012 GWD 11-216 – difficult causation issue re foot condition; Brand v Transocean 2011 GWD 14-336 - arguing for "loss of employability" award instead of Ogden "multiplier x multiplicand"; Hodgkinson v Renfrewshire Council [2011] CSOH 142 – PUWER case regarding "suitability" of park gate which struck Pursuer when opened; Patterson v Grattan 2011 SLT (Sh Ct) 2 - Sale of Goods Act case, resolved by "best evidence" rule; Blair v Axa Insurance [2009] - construction of travel insurance policy, paralysed Pursuer claiming 'permanent total disability'; HMA v Abernethy Trust – outdoor adventure centre prosecution (fatality); HMA v Sanctuary Housing Association – care home prosecution (fatality); HMA v Faulds – death by careless driving (2012).
Professional Memberships: Member of the Faculty of Advocates Professional Negligence Law Group.
Career: LL.B (Hons) & DIPLP (Aberdeen University 1988 to 1993); Solicitor (1993 to 2002); admitted Faculty of Advocates 2003.
Personal: Spoken at seminars for Law Society of Scotland and Compass Chambers; lectured Court of Session Practice at Glasgow University.

MIDGLEY, Andrew
Old Square Chambers, Bristol
020 7269 0300
clerks@oldsquare.co.uk
Featured in Employment (Western)
Practice Areas: Andrew is a discrimination law specialist, with particular expertise in high value discrimination claims. He has a special interest in disability discrimination and his practice incorporates the Special Educational Needs and Disability Tribunal (SENDIST). His broad experience includes all forms of discrimination, bullying and harassment claims, employment contracts, restrictive covenants and references, employment status, illegality and immigration status, business reorganisations, redundancies and TUPE, industrial relations, working time and breach of contract claims. He is instructed by Government departments, NHS trusts, local authorities, the Metropolitan Police, Unions and insurance companies to appear in the Employment Tribunal, the Employment Appeals Tribunal, the county court and High Court. He delivers seminars in relation to new legislation and case law for the ELA and professional clients.
Professional Memberships: Employment Lawyers Association, Discrimination Law Association, Employment Law Bar Association, Industrial Law Society.
Career: Andrew was called to the bar in 2000, having graduated from ICSL in the top 8% of the year. He was appointed to the Attorney General's Regional Panel of Counsel in 2010.

MILFORD, Julian
11KBW, London
020 7632 5000
julian.milford@11kbw.com
Featured in Data Protection (London), Employment (London)
Practice Areas: Employment, public law, information law.
Professional Memberships: ELBA, ALBA.
Career: Julian was called to the bar in 2000. His areas of practice are employment law, public law and information law. He regularly acts for both claimants and respondents in employment disputes in the Employment Tribunal, the High Court, the Employment Appeal Tribunal and the Court of Appeal, including business protection cases, where his clients include major companies, banks, local authorities, police forces, unions, and healthcare providers. Julian also undertakes advisory and judicial review work in the field of public law, appearing in a wide range of judicial review cases, including commercial and regulatory judicial review challenges. He has undertaken a number of high profile cases in the data protection and freedom of information field, including acting in challenges to the Intelligence Agencies by civil liberties organisations arising out of Edward Snowden's disclosures, and freedom of information cases concerning letters between The Prince of Wales and Government Ministers, Cabinet minutes relating to the Hillsborough disaster, and records of conversations between Tony Blair and George Bush. Julian is a member of the Attorney General's A Panel of Treasury Counsel.
Publications: Contributor to Tolley's Employment Law Handbook.
Personal: Pianist.

MILLER, Andrew QC
2TG - 2 Temple Gardens, London
020 7822 1260
amiller@2tg.co.uk
Featured in Insurance (London), Property Damage (London)
Practice Areas: Commercial disputes, with a particular focus on the energy sector, domestically and internationally. Domestic and international construction disputes, with significant experience of arbitrations in (among others) Brunei,Singapore and the Philippines. Property damage, especially arising from floods, fires, explosions and subsidence. Insurance and reinsurance: coverage disputes, policy construction, fraudulent and exaggerated claims. Professional negligence: particularly claims against architects, engineers, surveyors, other construction professionals and insurance brokers. Recent cases include representing major UK Oil and Gas Project Management company in a US$53m claim arising out of the drilling of a prospective well in West Africa; an ICC Arbitration acting for insurers of a power plant in Albania; a recovery action arising out of flood damage to £75m private residence in London. Recent reported cases include: Mueller v Central Roofing [2013] EWHC(fire); Brit Inns Ltd v BDW Ltd [2012] EWHC (recovery of subrogated loss); Caterpillar Logistics Services (UK) Ltd v P Huesca de Crean [2011] EWCA (restraint of trade); EL Policy Trigger Litigation [2010] EWCA Civ (policy construction); Axa Seguros S.A de C.V v Allianz Insurance Plc [2011] EWHC (reinsurance); Scottish Coal v Royal and Sun Alliance Insurance PLC & Ors [2008] EWHC (change of risk); Buncefield Litigation [2009] EWHC (subrogated recovery).

MILLER, Christopher
Fourteen, London
020 7242 0858
cmiller@fourteen.co.uk
Featured in Family/Matrimonial (London)
Practice Areas: Practices exclusively in Family Law and areas related to the breakdown of family relationships. Christopher undertakes all aspects of public and private law children work, often in cases where the most serious types of allegations are considered by the Court and complex medical/expert evidence has been filed (eg death of, or serious injury to, a child or where the involvement of a paedophile 'ring' is suspected). He has also developed specialism in cases involving an international element (e.g. leave to remove applications, cases where the child or adult party's immigration status is a relevant consideration or where it is proposed that children should be placed by the state in a foreign jurisdiction). He has been instructed in a number of cases to apply for, or to resist, applications for Judicial Review and/or the grant of injunctions pursuant to s7 of the HRA 1998. Usually these instructions have been provided in the context of related public law children litigation. He also regularly represents high net worth clients in financial remedy cases and appears in cases that involve issues such as assets abroad, trusts, linked POCA proceedings and complex business assets. In addition to his busy caseload, Christopher has presented numerous lectures and workshops on diverse topics such as: Leave to Remove, Petrodel v Prest, circumventing nuptial contracts, forensic testing in relation to alcohol misuse and court skills for non-legally-qualified professionals.
Professional Memberships: FLBA, Lincoln's Inn.

MILLER, Richard QC
Three New Square, London
020 7405 1111
clerks@3newsquare.co.uk
Featured in Intellectual Property (London)
Practice Areas: Specialist in patents, trade marks, passing off, design rights, breach of confidence, restrictive covenants and all other aspects of intellectual property, including EU law relating to Intellectual Property. Also appears in the European Patent Office on behalf of applicants and opponents for European patents.
Professional Memberships: Intellectual Property Bar Association, Chancery Bar Association, Bar European Group, The Intellectual Property Lawyers Organisation (TIPLO), International Association for the Protection of Industrial Property (AIPPI), American Bar Association, American Intellectual Property Law Association.
Career: Called to the Bar 1976. Appointed QC 1995. Bencher (Middle Temple) 2007. Head of Chambers, Three New Square 2012- . Chairman, Middle Temple Finance Committee & Member of Executive Committee 2012- . Chairman, Intellectual Property Bar Assocation 2005-11. Co-chairman, EU Law Committee (formerly European Committee) of the Bar Council 2009-11. Member, General Council of the Bar 2006-11. Member, Professional Practice Committee of the Bar Council. Member, Patents Sub-group of the Council of the Bars and Law Societies of Europe (CCBE). Observer, UK Council, International Association for the Protection of Industrial Property (AIPPI),
Publications: "TERRELL on the Law of Patents", co-editor 14th-17th editions (1995-2011).
Personal: Educated: Charterhouse 1966-70; University of Sussex 1971-74, BSc (Chemical Physics); College of Law 1974-76.

MILLIKEN-SMITH, Mark QC
2 Bedford Row, London
07973 111 736
mmilliken-smith@2bedfordrow.co.uk
Featured in Professional Discipline (London), Sports Law (London), Crime (London), Financial Crime (London)
Practice Areas: Recognised by Chambers UK and The Legal 500 as a leading silk in Crime, Financial Crime, Professional Discipline and Sport. Trial lawyer with extensive experience as advisor and advocate across a wide range of criminal, commercial and regulatory matters. Regularly advises corporate and individual clients nationally and internationally pre and post charge, in criminal as well as quasi-criminal matters, including bribery, corruption, money laundering, restraint, market abuse, insider dealing, match fixing and murder/manslaughter. Substantial regulatory and disciplinary practise before, inter alia, healthcare and financial services regulators. Significant and high profile sports law practise in cases before the disciplinary arms of sporting governing bodies. Please see 2 Bedford Row website for full details.
Professional Memberships: South Eastern Circuit, Criminal Bar Association.
Career: Called 1986. Recorder of the Crown Court 2004. Queen's Counsel 2006.
Personal: Married with two children. Educated at Wellington College and Bristol University. Interests include sport (whenever possible), particularly cricket, golf, rugby and football.

MILLS, Ben
St Philips Chambers, Birmingham
0121 246 0200
bmills@st-philips.com
Featured in Consumer Law (Midlands), Crime (Midlands)
Practice Areas: Ben enjoys a thriving practice working predominantly in regulatory crime (fraud, counterfeiting, consumer protection and health and safety law), other serious crime and associated complex confiscation proceedings. At the core of his practice is an acute attention to his client's best interests and a tireless commitment to his cases. He was Junior Counsel in R v X [2013] EWCA Crim 818, the leading authority on the CPUT Regulations 2008 and the application of recklessness to corporate entities. He is one of a small number of expert Counsel instructed nationally in cases

focusing on the activities of "loan sharks". These predominantly involve Consumer Credit Act offences, blackmail and large scale fraud/money laundering. During the House of Lords expenses scandal, he was instructed to advise a Life Peer in all pre-charge matters and police interviews. His client was not prosecuted. He was nominated for Birmingham Law Society's Barrister of the Year 2013.
Career: Called 2000; Law Commission Research Assistant 2000-2001; joined St Philips Chambers 2001; appointed to the Attorney General's Unified List of Prosecuting Advocates (Panel B); Level 3 CPS prosecutor.
Publications: Contributing Editor: 'Consumer and Trading Standards: Law and Practice', Jordans, 2013.
Personal: Semi-professional soul/jazz musician and keen sportsman.

MILLS, Simon
Five Paper, London
020 7815 3200
simonmills@fivepaper.com
Featured in Commercial Dispute Resolution (London)
Practice Areas: Simon works in banking and commercial finance, insolvency and asset recovery. He works with banks, financial institutions, companies and insolvency practitioners and has wide experience of recovering money under financial and security instruments or following commercial fraud. He is the Leader of the Commercial Team at Five Paper.
Professional Memberships: COMBAR.
Publications: 'Salinger on Factoring' (4th ed., Sweet & Maxwell 2006). This is recognised as the leading textbook on receivables financing in the UK (joint editor). "Goode on Proprietary Rights and Insolvency in Sales Transactions" by Prof. Sir Roy Goode (3rd ed., 2009) (sole editor). This important book deals with the nature of proprietary rights that can arise in the context of contracts for the sale of goods, both domestic and international. It contains a penetrating analysis of the following topics: (i) Concepts of ownership, possession and sale, (ii) Acquiring title to oil, gas, minerals and precious metals, (iii) Buying through an agent, (iv) Dealings in warehoused goods and goods in transit, (v) Reservation of title and tracing rights in goods, products and proceeds.

MILNE, David QC
Pump Court Tax Chambers, London
020 7414 8080
clerks@pumptax.com
Featured in Tax (London)
Practice Areas: Specialises in both direct and indirect tax, especially litigation and dispute resolution; recent cases of note include Westmorland Investments v MacNiven (House of Lords); Marks & Spencer plc v HMRC (House of Lords and ECJ); CCE v Mirror Group (ECJ); Sinclair Collis v CCE (House of Lords and ECJ); R v Dimsey & R v Allen (House of Lords); BMW (ACT Class IV GLO) v Inland Revenue (ECJ); Peterson v CIR (NZ) (Privy Council); Telewest Communications v CCE (Court of Appeal); Mars UK Ltd v Small (House of Lords); British Telecommunications plc v HMRC (House of Lords); Newcastle United FC v HMRC (High Court); Marks & Spencer plc v HMRC (2) (ECJ); Spearmint Rhino v HMRC (High Court); Newnham College, Cambridge v HMRC (House of Lords); Brunel Motor Company Ltd v HMRC & Ford (Court of Appeal); TNT v HMRC & Royal Mail (ECJ); Philips Electronics (UK) Ltd v HMRC (ECJ); Gaines-Cooper v HMRC (Court of Appeal); LMUK v HMRC (ECJ and Supreme Court); CCJ v Jamaica (Privy Council); British Film Institute v HMRC (Upper Tribunal); Med Hotels v HMRC (Supreme Court); Greene King v HMRC (Upper Tribunal); Wheels v HMRC (First-Tier Tribunal; ECJ); HMRC v Marks & Spencer (Group relief) (Supreme Court); Wildfowl & Wetlands Trust v HMRC (First-tier Tribunal); Kumon Educational (First-tier Tribunal).
Professional Memberships: Revenue Bar Association; VAT Practitioners' Group; London Common Law & Commercial Bar Association; Chancery Bar Association; Honorary Fellow of Chartered Institute of Taxation 2009.
Career: Called 1970, Lincoln's Inn; QC 1987; Recorder 1994-2006.

MILNER, Alexander
Fountain Court Chambers, London
020 7583 3335
anm@fountaincourt.co.uk
Featured in Aviation (London), Commercial Dispute Resolution (London)
Practice Areas: Commercial litigation and arbitration. A Russian speaker, Alexander has appeared in several of the most significant recent cases to emerge from Russia and the CIS, such as Bank St Petersburg v Arkhangelsky (where he obtained a rare anti-enforcement injunction in the Court of Appeal), Mezhprombank v Pugachev, Berezovsky v Abramovich, BTA Bank v Ablyazov, and Tajik Aluminium Plant v Ermatov, as well as numerous confidential ICC and LCIA arbitrations involving Russian parties. He also has wide experience of aviation, including leasing, financing, insurance, injunctive relief and claims under the Montreal Convention and EU Regulations). Recent cases include Virgin Atlantic v KI Holdings, Aerotransleasing v Polet Airlines, ACG Acquisition v Olympic Airlines. Other specialisms are civil fraud, banking and financial services, conflicts of law and jurisdiction, and EU law and competition.
Professional Memberships: Russian and CIS Arbitration Network; COMBAR.
Career: Called 2006.
Publications: Liability for negligent investment advice following extraordinary market turmoil (Journal of Professional Negligence, 2013); Advantages and disadvantages of arbitration CIS disputes in Western Europe (Transnational Dispute Management, 2012); Regulation EC 261/2004 and 'extraordinary circumstances' Air and Space Law, 2009).
Personal: King's College, Cambridge (BA Modern and Medieval Languages, first class with distinction, first in university; choral scholar).

MILSOM, Chris
Cloisters, London
020 7827 4035
cmi@cloisters.com
Featured in Employment (London)
Practice Areas: Employment (ET and High Court), Equality, Personal Injury, Public law.
Professional Memberships: ILS, ELBA, ELA, DLA, BHRC.
Career: Chris enjoys an employment and discrimination practice which goes from strength to strength. He has developed a niche appellate practice: in a period of 18 months alone he will have made 13 appearances in the EAT and 6 in the CA. He wins consistent praise from solicitors and clients alike for his specialist expertise and his user-friendly style. His practice encompasses the full gamut of employment disputes and clients vary from FTSE 100 companies to migrant workers. Chris is regularly instructed by the EHRC and solicitors of the highest calibre. His oral and written arguments have recently been described by the EAT as "a tour de force." Highlight cases include: Griffin v Plymouth Hospital NHS Trust (CA, judgment awaited); Hainsworth v Ministry of Defence [2014] EWCA Civ 763, Taiwo v Olaigbe [2014] ICR 571, Jessemey v Rowstock Ltd [2014] ICR 550, JJ Food Service Ltd v Zulhayir [2014] C.P.Rep.15, Lemonious v Church Commissioners [2013] All ER(D) 199 and XX v UKBA [2012] EqLR 94. For further information please see http://www.cloisters.com/barristers/chris-milsom.asp.
Publications: Family Rights at Work (Jordans, February 2012).
Personal: Walking, theatre, travel and cricket.

MIRCHANDANI, Siân
4 New Square, London
020 7822 2036
s.mirchandani@4newsquare.com
Featured in Professional Negligence (London)
Practice Areas: All aspects of commercial practice including professional liability, construction, insurance, reinsurance, including claims against lawyers (solicitors and barristers), architects and engineers, insurance brokers and agents, surveyors and valuers, accountants, financial services professionals, land management agents, estate agents, clinicians and veterinary surgeons, including coverage and indemnity disputes, insolvency, fraud and dishonesty.
Professional Memberships: COMBAR, TECBAR, PNBA, SCL, ChBA.
Career: Siân studied Veterinary Medicine at Cambridge University and worked as a Junior Fellow at Bristol Veterinary School and then in practice before coming to the Bar and joining chambers in 1998. Sian has a particular interest in claims involving technical and scientific knowledge and this has led to a strong construction and engineering practice acting for employers, contractors, sub-contractors and construction professionals in a wide range of construction disputes including arbitrations and adjudications. She has particular experience in claims concerning subsidence, design & construction of farm buildings and swimming pool claims. She is a TECBAR accredited adjudicator.
Publications: Former editor of Clinical Negligence chapter of Jackson & Powell on Professional Liability.
Personal: Educated in Swansea, S Wales; University of Cambridge (MA, Vet MB); City University, London (CPE); Inns of Court (Bar). Divorced with two daughters. Hobbies: running, swimming, yoga, reading, riding.

MISHCON, Jane
Hailsham Chambers, London
020 7643 5000
jane.mishcon@hailshamchambers.com
Featured in Clinical Negligence (London)
Practice Areas: Principal area of practice is clinical negligence (on behalf of both claimants and defendants) dealing with cases of widely diverse medical specialties. Jane also represents healthcare professionals in disciplinary and regulatory cases. She has chaired nine independent inquiries into homicides by psychiatric patients and in 2010 chaired an independent inquiry into histopathology services in Bristol. Cases: Farraj v King's Healthcare NHS Trust & Cytogenetic Services Ltd [2010] 1 WLR 2139; Ndri v Moorfields Eye Hospital NHS Trust [2006] EWHC 3652; Peet v Mid-Kent Healthcare Trust [2002] 1 WLR 210; Re R-B: [2000] Lloyds Rep Med 87; Clarke v South Yorkshire Transport Ltd [1998] PIQR 104 CA; McAllister v Lewisham & North Southwark HA [1994] Lloyds Law Reports Med 343.
Professional Memberships: Professional Negligence Bar Association (PNBA).
Career: Call: 1979. Accredited mediator.
Publications: Ten Independent Inquiry reports.
Personal: BA (Hons) Oxford University.

MISRA, Eleena
Littleton Chambers, London
020 7797 8600
emisra@littletonchambers.co.uk
Featured in Employment (London)
Practice Areas: Employment (Tribunal and High Court), Professional Discipline & Regulation and Judicial Review.
Professional Memberships: ELBA, ELA, ARDL, PNBA and ILS. Approved Panel Counsel of the Equality and Human Rights Commission. Bar Council Law Reform Committee.
Career: Eleena has undertaken a significant amount of complex, high value employment work in the ET and High Court. She is considered to be a specialist in injunctive relief, especially in the healthcare and education sectors. Eleena holds a medico-legal qualification (DipFSM) and accepts inquest instructions. Eleena is often instructed in cases requiring expertise in internal and external dispute resolution and is particularly well known for her work in sensitive discrimination claims in respect of all protected characteristics. Recent instructions include a high profile religious discrimination appeal concerning a Christian paediatrician and a multi-million pound sex discrimination claim against a foreign bank. Eleena is also the Head of Littleton's Disciplinary & Regulatory team and regularly accepts instructions to undertake work spanning all of her complementary practice areas.
Publications: Eleena is the author of Procedure in Civil Courts and Tribunals. She has co-authored Atkins on Employment and Equal Opportunities and is one of the authors of Blackstones Employment Law Practice 2014. Eleena is a standing editor of Bath Publishing Employment Cases Update.

MITCHELL, Andrew QC
Fountain Court Chambers, London
020 7583 3335
aem@fountaincourt.co.uk
Featured in Banking & Finance (London), Commercial Dispute Resolution (London), Financial Services (London), Insurance (London)
Practice Areas: Specific expertise in banking; civil fraud; commercial contract; (re)insurance and professional negligence, in particular in the Commercial Court, as well as in international arbitration and foreign jurisdictions including the BVI, IoM, Channel Islands and Singapore. Recent high profile cases include the interest rate swaps litigation, in which Andrew represents a number of banks; he appeared successfully at first instance and in the Court of Appeal in Green

& Rowley v RBS (the only such case so far to be taken to trial). He defended the board of Safeway against Competition Act fines (Court of Appeal), and has successfully prosecuted on behalf of the FCA market abuse charges against a fund manager and brokers (Chaligne & Sejean). He acts for Barclays in relation to the PPI litigation, having also acted in the retail Bank Charges Litigation (House of Lords), the Consumer Credit test cases relating to the enforceability of credit card agreements, and in the McKillen/Barclay Brothers Claridges litigation. Andrew acts in relation to the Arch Cru investment litigation in Guernsey and London, and has advised in connection with the Keydata litigation. He has represented litigants in relation to a number of credit crunch related matters concerning e.g. Citi; RBS; BarCap; UBS; West LB; Lehmans and Deutsche Bank. Recent complex insurance and PI cases include claims for substantial hurricane damage to US oil refinery; Korean shipbuilding guarantee litigation; broker negligence cases; mining/commodities litigation; E&O coverage claims arising from the construction of fertilizer plants in Qatar; and D&O claims arising from hedge fund fraud.
Professional Memberships: COMBAR.
Career: Called 1992. QC 2011.
Publications: Contributing Editor to 'Commercial Court Procedure' (Sweet & Maxwell).
Personal: Educated at Cambridge University (1987-90, MA) and Oxford University (1990-91, BCL). Harmsworth Scholar of Middle Temple. Born 1968.

MITCHELL, Andrew QC
The Chambers of Andrew Mitchell QC, London
020 7440 9950
clerks@33cllaw.com
Featured in POCA Work & Asset Forfeiture (All Circuits), Financial Crime (London)
Practice Areas: Pre-eminent in civil and criminal asset forfeiture, confiscation and restraint, specialises in financial crime, commercial wrongdoing corruption and receivership. Advised and represented prosecuting authorities, defendants, receivers and third parties in the Crown Court, High Court, Court of Appeal (civil and criminal), House of Lords and UK Supreme Court on all aspects of the restraint, management and confiscation of property. Advises domestically and internationally, professionals and multinationals on the practice and procedure in relation to money laundering regulations and legislation, compliance, fraud, corruption and civil commercial wrongdoing. Recently successfully represented cross-appellants in the UK Supreme Court in the ground-breaking case on apportionment of benefit in multi-handed cases. Lead prosecutor in the SFO "Innospec" corruption case against individuals and is Lead Counsel in the investigation and prosecution of politicians and attorneys relating to multi-millions of bribery and corruption in property developments in the Turks & Caicos.
Professional Memberships: Chairman of Proceeds of Crime Lawyers' Association.
Career: Called to Bar 1976, Queen's Counsel 1998. Recorder [Crime & Civil]. Speaker/lecturer/consultant to UN, Commonwealth Secretariat, ESAAMLG, APG and IMF. Recently chaired committee, drafting model provisions (on behalf of international organisations). Conducts training and capacity building workshops for prosecutors and judiciary in Africa, Asia, the Caribbean and the Pacific.
Publications: Confiscation and the Proceeds of Crime - co-author; 'Administrative Court Law and Practice' - contributor.

MITCHELL, David
Ely Place Chambers, London
020 7400 9600
dmitchell@elyplace.com
Featured in Employment (London)
Practice Areas: Employment, public, media and defamation, commercial.
Professional Memberships: ELBA, ELA, ILS, ALBA, BHRC.
Career: Attorney General's B panel (2012). Employment: wide-ranging Tribunal and High Court practice representing Claimants and Defendants/Respondents. Public: predominantly Defendant practice. Currently instructed in a number of applications under the Terrorist Asset Freezing etc Act 2010 on behalf of HM Treasury. Libel: Claimant and Defendant practice - cases include Lord McAlpine v Sally Bercow.

MITCHELL, Iain G QC
Arnot Manderson, Edinburgh
07739 638 999
iainmitchell@amadvocates.co.uk
Featured in Information Technology (Scotland), Intellectual Property (Scotland), Public Procurement (Scotland)
Practice Areas: Iain is an experienced litigator, dual qualified in Scotland and England, with strengths in business and commercial law, European law, information technology and intellectual property, public procurement, employment law and judicial review. He has appeared in over 60 reported cases, including two in the House of Lords: Moncrieff v Jamieson 2007 1 WLR 2620 (the leading modern case on servitudes and easements) which definitively established the easement of parking in the laws of both Scotland and England; and Clarke v Fennoscandia Ltd 2008 SC (HL) 122, which concerned the enforcement of a foreign decree allegedly obtained fraudulently in the US Third Circuit. He acted in Grant Estates Ltd v RBS, the first Interest Rate Swap Agreement mis-selling case in Scotland and one of the first in the UK. He is currently appearing in a large number of similar cases in both Scotland and England, and is a leading member of QA legal, an international grouping of barristers, solicitors, financial experts and others who are pre-eminent in this field.
Career: Iain was called to the Scottish Bar in 1976, and took silk in 1992. He was accredited as a mediator by the Mediation Bureau (Scotland) in 1997 and by Mediation Forum Ireland in 2007. He is a member of the Scottish Council for International Arbitration and sat on the bench as a Temporary Sheriff from 1992 to 1997. He was called to the English Bar in 2012 and is an associate member of Tanfield Chambers. He is the UK representative on the IT Committee of the CCBE and a member of the IT panel of the Bar Council. He is also Chairman of the Scottish Society for Computers and Law and a Liveryman of the Worshipful Company of Information Technologists.
Publications: His appointments include an honorary lectureship at the Institut für Informations-Telekommunikations- und Medienrecht at the Westfälische Wilhelms-Universität Münster. He is joint editor of the International Free and Open Software Law Review, and his other publications include contributions to 'Electronic Evidence' (Butterworths), 'The International Free and Open Source Lawbook' (Open Source Press), and 'Free and Open Source Software: Policy, Law and Practice' (Oxford University Press) as well as frequent articles in academic journals and national newspapers.

MITCHELL, Keith
The Chambers of Andrew Mitchell QC, London
020 7440 9950
kam@33cllaw.com
Featured in Financial Crime (London)
Practice Areas: Criminal/civil fraud and confiscation.
Career: Keith has long been recognised for his expertise in fraud and white collar crime and has been consistently ranked as a leader in his field in all fraud sections of the top legal directories, Chambers UK and the Legal 500. He was named UK White Collar Crime Barrister of the Year for 2012 by Acquisition International and again in 2013 when he won UK White Collar Crime Defence Barrister of the year. He has been described as " superb with clients and popular with juries", " a talented practitioner who knows his way around fraud cases." His practice encompasses major SFO, VAT and MTIC frauds as well as business, financial and other white-collar crime matters. It has been said that "his ability to sift through heavy paperwork and present a cogent argument in court is the envy of many". He has appeared in the 'Jockey Club' case and in Operation Exhort 'cash for crash', and in Operation Vaulter MTIC fraud the largest ever contra trading and offshore operation based in Dubai. One source said of him: "He is just superb. He's always involved in the biggest cases in the country and he has a great touch with the clients." Previous legal directories have said of Keith, that "apart from having the brains and personality to deal with the most complex fraud cases, Keith Mitchell is also the type of barrister who takes the time to go through everything with his clients". He has been "recognised as being one of the main players specialising in VAT and fraud". Keith is also known "for his great client care skills and flair when it comes to case management" and his "flamboyant" style as an advocate. He is leading in Operations Vaulter, Galion and Barber and has recently been instructed in Operation Enbourne a 'Green Belt' land bank investment fraud and Operation Cactus Hent the North West SIPP fraud.

MITCHELL, Paul
Hailsham Chambers, London
020 7643 5000
paul.mitchell@hailshamchambers.com
Featured in Professional Negligence (London)
Practice Areas: Professional negligence, insurance, general commercial litigation, disciplinary. Recent cases of interest: Hermann v Withers [2012] EWHC 1492 (Ch); Hazelhurst v Solicitors Regulation Authority [2011] EWHC 462 (Admin); Eminence v Heaney [2010] EWCA Civ 1168; West Wallasey Car Hire v Berkson & Berkson & Anor [2010] PNLR 14.
Professional Memberships: Professional Negligence Bar Association (PNBA).
Career: Called 1999. Hardwicke, Mansfield, Denning Scholarships from Lincoln's Inn; Pegasus Scholar from Inns of Court.
Publications: Joint author then editor of chapter on limitation in Lloyd's Professional Negligence and Liability (looseleaf); contributed chapter on conveyancing in second edition of Flenley & Leech on solicitors' negligence (Tottel, 2008).
Personal: Educated King's Col. Cambs (BA (1st), PhD); SOAS (MA); married, two daughters.

MITCHELL, Peter
29 Bedford Row Chambers, London
020 7539 2464
pmitchell@29bedfordrow.co.uk
Featured in Family/Matrimonial (London)
Practice Areas: All aspects of the law governing financial relationships between family members, including the drafting and implementation of pre- and post-nuptial agreements, financial provision on relationship breakdown (upon divorce under the Matrimonial Causes Act 1973 and Part III of the Matrimonial and Family Proceedings Act 1984, generally under TLATA 1996 and for children under the Children Act 1989, Schedule 1) and associated issues relating to jurisdiction, companies, family trusts, offshore trusts and other family wealth-holding structures. Cases include: Agbaje v. Agbaje [2010] 2 FLR 1900 (UKSC), C v. C [2011] 1 FLR 434 (HC) and S v. S (Non-Disclosure) [2013] EWHC 991 (Fam) – currently pending in the Court of Appeal.
Professional Memberships: FLBA.
Career: Called in 1996, Inner Temple, Trained as Collaborative Counsel.
Personal: Royal Academy of Music LRAM. Kings College London LLB.

MITCHESON, Thomas QC
Three New Square, London
020 7405 1111
mitcheson@3newsquare.co.uk
Featured in Intellectual Property (London)
Practice Areas: All aspects of intellectual property law, including regular EPO and CJEU appearances. Cases include Norowzian v Arks (copyright, CA); Arsenal v Reed (trademark, CJ and CA), Collag v Merck (confidential information), GSK v Apotex (pharmaceutical patent, CA), Sir Robert McAlpine v Alfred McAlpine (passing off), Pozzoli v BDMO (mechanical patent, CA), CoreValve v Edwards (medical device patent, CA), Lundbeck v Teva (patent sufficiency, HL), L'Oreal v eBay (trademark, CJEU), Medeva's Patent (SPC, CA and CJEU), Schutz v Werit (definition of "making", SC), MedImmune v Novartis (antibody technology, CA), Lilly v HGS (industrial applicability, SC; SPC, CJEU), Bayer v Genentech (VEGF antagonists, CA), Cadbury v Nestle (3D trademark, CJEU), Lilly v Janssen (antibody for Alzheimer's), Hospira v Genentech (anti-HER2 antibody), Lush v Amazon (trademark, online trading), Krka v AZ (enquiry as to damages), Actavis v Lilly (non-infringement of foreign patents), ISCC (patentability of stem cells, CJEU), Servier v Apotex (SC).
Career: Internship at Cold Spring Harbor Laboratory, USA 1990-91. Trinity College, Cambridge, 1991-94, First Class Hons Natural Sciences. City University (Dip-Law), 1995 (Distinction). Called to the Bar 1996. Standing Counsel to the Comptroller General for Patents Designs and Trade Marks 2009-2014. QC 2014.
Publications: 'Two Genes in Saccharomyces Cerevisiae Encode a Membrane Bound Form of Casein Kinase-1' Wang, Vancura, Mitcheson and Kuret (1992).

MODGIL, Sangita
Carmelite Chambers, London
020 7936 6300
sangitamodgil@yahoo.co.uk
Featured in Crime (London)
Practice Areas: A highly regarded Defence advocate instructed to represent those charged with a wide range of the most serious crimes and appears as both Leading and Junior counsel. She is known for her attention to detail and willingness to work exceptionally hard whenever required to. She has significant experience in multi handed cases in which the allegations have included murder, armed robberies, kidnap, drug conspiracies, fraud and the full range of sexual offences including child abuse cases and cases involving paedophile rings. She is particularly valued for her skill in representing those who are inexperienced with the criminal court system including the young or mentally vulnerable. Recent cases include R v Iqbal (multi-handed allegation of Conspiracy to Defraud) R v Connolly (defendant alleged to have been member of a paedophile ring), R v MT (representing young defendant in a joint enterprise gang murder), R v Knight (Conspiracy to commit Armed Robberies of banks), R v RJ (allegations of GBH and Rape). R v Reddan (Kidnap case based on phone and cell site evidence), R v Hussain (Fraud and Rape of numerous complainants).

MOERAN, Fenner QC
3 Stone Buildings, London
020 7242 4937
clerks@3sb.law.co.uk
Featured in Chancery (London), Fraud (London), Pensions (London)
Practice Areas: Fenner Moeran QC specialises in chancery and commercial litigation, including particularly civil fraud, pensions, financial services, insurance and insolvency litigation.
Professional Memberships: Chancery Bar Association, ComBar, APL.
Career: Called to the English Bar: 1996. QC: 2014. Called to the Bar of Northern Ireland: 2012.
Publications: Tolley's 'Pensions Law' contributor. Palmer on Bailment (3rd edition) contributor.
Personal: Bristol University, City University, ICSL.

MOFFETT, Jonathan
11KBW, London
020 7632 8500
jonathan.moffett@11kbw.com
Featured in Administrative & Public Law (London), Education (London), Local Government (London)
Practice Areas: Jonathan is a leading public law junior, with a practice that has a particular emphasis on the fields of education law, local government law, regulatory law, environmental law, and human rights and civil liberties. He has a particular expertise in the interface between public law and human rights, and regularly lectures on public law issues. Jonathan acts for individuals, charities, companies, NGOs, central and local government bodies, regulators and other public bodies; as a member of the Attorney-General's A panel, he is regularly instructed to represent central government departments on their most difficult public law matters, ranging across topics including human rights, immigration, planning, prisons, revenue, schools and healthcare.
Professional Memberships: Administrative Law Bar Association, Planning and Environmental Law Bar Association, Employment Law Bar Association. Career: Called 2009; appointed to the Attorney-General's A Panel of counsel to the Crown, 2009; appointed to the Welsh Government's A Panel of counsel, 2012; appointed to the Equality and Human Rights Commission's panel of counsel, 2011.
Publications: Co-author of Judicial Review: Principles and Procedure (OUP, 2013); editor of Atkin's Court Forms – Administrative Court (Butterworths, 2007); contributing author to Education and the Courts (Jordans, 2003); contributing author to Halsbury's Laws of England – Local Government (Butterworths, 2001).

MOGER, Christopher QC
4 Pump Court, London
020 7842 5555
cmoger@4pumpcourt.com
Featured in Commercial Dispute Resolution (London), Insurance (London), Licensing (London), Professional Negligence (London)
Practice Areas: Commercial litigation and international arbitration with particular emphasis on arbitrations involving China, insurance, professional negligence, and regulatory and disciplinary proceedings.
Professional Memberships: LCLBA; COMBAR; PNBA, LCIA Users' Council, Member of the HKIAC, KLRCA & CIETAC Panels of Arbitrators.
Career: Called 1972; Silk 1992; recorder 1993; FCIA 1997. Deputy Judge of High Court 1999. Trained mediator and Member of ADR Chambers, International. Member of Panel of Chairmen of Lloyds Disciplinary Tribunal 2001, Commissioner, Alderney Gambling Control Commission 2014, Member Arbitration Chambers Hong Kong.

MOHYUDDIN, David
Exchange Chambers, Manchester
0161 833 2722
mohyuddin@exchangechambers.co.uk
Featured in Chancery (Northern), Restructuring/Insolvency (Northern)
Practice Areas: Insolvency (all types, including public interest winding up and directors disqualification both for and against the Secretary of State/Official Receiver); commercial litigation (fraud and deceit allegations, obtaining urgent injunctive relief); professional negligence (both for and against professionals) company and shareholder disputes (including enforcement of directors' duties); asset recovery (both within and outside insolvency regimes); sports-related litigation.
Professional Memberships: Chancery Bar Association; Northern Chancery Bar Association (Secretary); Northern Circuit Commercial Bar Association; Association of Business Recovery Professionals (Fellow); Insolvency Lawyers' Association.
Career: Called by Lincoln's Inn in 1999. Joined Exchange Chambers in 2001. Also at 13-14 Old Square, Lincoln's Inn. Accredited Mediator. Junior Counsel to the Crown (Regional Panel) since 2007.
Personal: Interests include skiing (instructor); rugby union (spectator), golf (beginner) and politics (armchair).

MOLD, Andrew
Wilberforce Chambers, London
020 7306 0102
amold@wilberforce.co.uk
Featured in Chancery (London), Offshore (London), Pensions (London)
Practice Areas: Chancery, commercial, pensions, trusts and related areas. Frequently instructed in international work.
Professional Memberships: Chancery Bar Association, COMBAR, APL, ACTAPS.
Career: MA (1st Class), St John's College, Cambridge; LLM, Harvard Law School.
Publications: Frequent author of articles and papers on all subjects within his practice areas.
Personal: Secretary of the Bar Lawn Tennis Society.

MOLYNEUX, Brent
29 Bedford Row Chambers, London
020 7404 1044
BMolyneux@29br.co.uk
Featured in Family/Matrimonial (London)
Practice Areas: Matrimonal finance.
Professional Memberships: Family Law Bar Association.
Career: Called to the Bar, February 1994.
Personal: Born 31 December 1968. Educated at Birkenhead School, Christ Church, Oxford (BA) and City University (Dip Law).

MONTY, Simon QC
4 New Square, London
020 7842 2000
s.monty@4newsquare.com
Featured in Professional Discipline (London)
Practice Areas: Professional liability litigation; professional regulation; commercial litigation; mediation and arbitration.
Professional Memberships: Professional Negligence Bar Association; Chancery Bar Association; COMBAR; London Common Law & Commercial Bar Association; Western Circuit.
Career: LLB Hons 1981 (Manchester University); Called to the Bar 1982 (Middle Temple); Silk 2003; Master of the Bench, Middle Temple 2004; Recorder (Civil) 2010; accredited mediator 2009; Board Member, Bar Standards Board 2006-11; Independent Reviewer, Architects Registration Board 2010; Deputy High Court Judge, Chancery Division 2013; Advocacy Training Council (Accreditation & Training Committee Member) 2014.
Publications: Jackson & Powell, 'Professional Liability Precedents' (Contributing Editor, 'Solicitors' and 'Appeals' chapters).

MOODY-STUART, Thomas
8 New Square, London
020 7405 4321
tom.moodystuart@8newsquare.co.uk
Featured in Information Technology (London), Intellectual Property (London), Media & Entertainment (London)
Practice Areas: Intellectual property, copyright, designs, patents, trade marks, passing off trade secrets, media and entertainment, information technology, data protection, advertising standards. Sole advocate in numerous High Court and Court of Appeal cases, has also appeared before EPO, CJEU and UK Supreme Court. Recently significant cases include Hearst v. Avela (the Betty Boop character merchandise case)and Vestergaard Frandsen v. Bestnet (substantial inquiry as to damages concerning misuse of trade secrets)
Professional Memberships: ChBA, IPBA, TIPLO.
Career: Middle Temple, 1995.
Publications: Editor Kerly's Law of Trade Marks and Trade Names, Butterworth's Encyclopedia of Patent Law.
Personal: Born 1970. Educated Shrewsbury School, Gonville & Caius College Cambridge. Double First, Natural Sciences Tripos (Biological), Part II Genetics. Queen Mother's Fund Scholarship, Middle Temple.

MOON, Angus QC
Serjeants' Inn Chambers, London
020 7427 5000
amoon@serjeantsinn.com
Featured in Clinical Negligence (London), Professional Discipline (London)
Practice Areas: Angus Moon QC was called to the Bar in 1986 and took silk in 2006. Angus specialises in clinical negligence and healthcare, Court of Protection, employment, inquests and inquiries, professional discipline and public and administrative law. An earlier edition notes that he is "a huge presence in cout", "a suave and articulate silk who is able to advise pragmatically whilst maintaining the confidence of his clients" and "one of the top rated silks at this set." Please click on the link to the Serjeants' Inn Chambers website for his profile, which sets out full details of his practice including relevant work of note.
Professional Memberships: ELA, ELBA, LCLCBA, PNBA.
Publications: General Editor: Medical Law Reports.

MOONEY, Giles
9 Gough Square, London
020 7832 0500
gmooney@9goughsqare.co.uk
Featured in Personal Injury (London)
Practice Areas: Giles' practice encompases all aspects of serious Personal Injury with a balanced claimant/defendant split. He has a particular interest and speciality in Animals Act claims (and has been involved in several Court of Appeal cases on the subject) and claims arising from defective products. Giles also has a busy clinical negligence practice acting for claimants and defendants in cases involving serious and catastrophic injuries. Giles also acts for claimants and defendants in contract/commercial and business disputes.
Professional Memberships: Personal Injuries Bar Association, Professional Negligence Bar Association.
Publications: Contributing editor to "Guides to Road Traffic Accident Claims" (Jordans). Contributing editor to "Guide to occupational Illness Claims" (Jordans). Contributing editor to 9 Gough Square publication - "Guide to Clinical Negligence Claims".
Personal: A very keen, but increasingly less effective, cricketer and show jumper.

MOORE, Martin QC
Erskine Chambers, London
020 7242 5532
clerks@erskinechambers.com
Featured in Company (London)
Practice Areas: Martin is a leading Silk for company law litigation and advice, corporate finance, financial services, and insolvency. He has particular expertise in corporate transactions and reorganisations, and schemes for transfer of insurance and banking business (Part VII transfers). Significant cases and transactions include: Pfizer/Astra-Zeneca; Barclays Bank plc,

Co-op Bank plc, Glencore / Xstrata, Invesnys plc, Vodafone / Verizon, Re TDG plc and Liberty International plc. Significant Part VII transfers include: Commercial Union Life Assurance Company Ltd (reattribution of inherited estate); Direct Line Insurance plc; Aviva International Limited; (large scale general insurance reorganisations); Prudential Assurance Company (domestication of Hong Kong branch) and long-term business reorganisations for Friends Life Group and Phoenix Group. Insolvency cases include: Lehmans Brothers International; Setchim v Secretary of State for Foreign and Commonwealth Affairs. General corporate litigation includes: Thermodynamics Inc v Turbotec Products plc (breach of duty, unlawful return of capital) and Bumi Resources plc (s.994 unfair prejudice petition). He has written two published opinions for the FRC on the True and Fair requirement, has advised on Bermudan, Hong Kong and Channel Islands law and has given expert evidence in the United States and Australia.
Career: BA (Oxon). Year Qualified: 1982. Lincoln's Inn. QC 2002.
Personal: Born: 1960.

MOORE, Miranda QC
5 Paper Buildings, London
020 7583 6117
mm@5pb.co.uk
Featured in Crime (London)
Practice Areas: A specialist in serious fraud and organised crime. Has particular experience in hi-tech and computer hacking cases. . Lead counsel in murders, white collar crime, money laundering and fiscal frauds (including frauds on the NHS). Since taking silk she has increased her defence practice and deals with a variety of cases including historic sexual abuse, rape, murder, and fraud. Currently prosecuting trials arising from the SFO investigation into JJB Sports Ltd. Experienced in cases involving sudden deaths of infants and is recognised as a leader in cases involving young or vulnerable witnesses (including the use of intermediaries). In the last year she has successfully defended a number of teenage gang related murder cases, and high profile "mercy" killings as well as a series of historic abuse cases and baby shaking allegations. Currently lead counsel in the prosecution of Dave Lee Travis arising out of Operation Yewtree.
Professional Memberships: Criminal Bar Association, South Eastern Circuit, Bencher of Lincoln's Inn.
Career: Called to the Bar 1983. QC 2003. Lecturer in Hi-Tech Crime; Mobile Phone Forensics and Case Presentation. Member of the Home Office Digital Forensics Specialist Group.
Personal: Business Studies Degree Class 1 Aston University.

MORAN, Andrew
Serle Court, London
020 7242 6105
amoran@serlecourt.co.uk
Featured in Fraud (London)
Practice Areas: Civil fraud (domestic and international): Barlow Clowes International Ltd. v International Trust Corp. and others [2006] 1 W.L.R. 1476, P.C. (accessory liability); Intrigue Shipping Inc. and others v H. Clarkson & Co. Ltd. and others (shipping fraud). Professional negligence: Winterthur Swiss Insurance Co. and anr. v The Accident Group Limited and others (professional negligence litigation concerning the collapse of the Accident Group A.T.E. scheme). Insurance: Cayman General Insurance Co. Ltd. v Crawford Adjusters (Cayman) Ltd. and others (insurance and breach of fiduciary duty claim in the Cayman Islands). Enforcement of judgments and jurisdiction: Nechi Investments v Papadopoulos & Bright; Shetty v Al Rushaid [2011] EWHC 1460 (Ch), Regulation 44(2001 Art 612).
Professional Memberships: Commercial Bar Association, Commercial Fraud Lawyers Association.
Career: LLB (Lond) 1st class; BCL (Oxon); called 1989.

MORAN, Vincent QC
Keating Chambers, London
020 7544 2600
vmoran@keatingchambers.com
Featured in Construction (London), Energy & Natural Resources (London), International Arbitration (London), Professional Negligence (London)
Practice Areas: Specialist in the fields of construction, engineering, energy (particularly wind farms) and technology disputes with vast experience of professional negligence and insurance matters in those and related fields, both domestically and internationally. Advocacy expertise covers all the UK Courts including the TCC, High Court, international and domestic arbitration, professional disciplinary boards, Court of Appeal and also the House of Lords where he has acted in professional negligence actions relating to construction professionals. A large part of his caseload over the last two years relates to wind farms disputes. He also has extensive experience in alternative dispute resolution.
Professional Memberships: PNBA; TECBAR; COMBAR; SCL.
Career: Called 1991; Queen's Counsel 2011.
Publications: Contributor - Keating on Construction Contracts 9th Edition (2012); Keating on JCT Contracts [Looseleaf & CD-Rom] Member of Editorial Team 2006-09; Editor of Chitty on Contracts - 29th and 30th Edition (Chapter on Construction Law); Researcher, Keating on Construction Contracts - Eighth Edition (2006).

MORGAN, James
St Philips Chambers, Birmingham
0121 246 7000
jmorgan@st-philips.com
Featured in Chancery (Midlands), Commercial Dispute Resolution (Midlands), Restructuring/Insolvency (Midlands)
Practice Areas: Chancery/commercial litigation, including all aspects of personal and corporate insolvency. Cases of note: Top Brands v Sharma [2014] EWCA Civ 761 (standing to challenge status as creditors); Re Casa Estates [2014] BCC 269 (meaning of "insolvency"); Masters v Furber [2014] BPIR 263 (IVAs and injunctions); Re GP Aviation [2014] 1 WLR 166 (meaning of "property"); Nautch v Mortgage Express [2012] EWHC 4136 (Ch) (mortgagees/receivers); Re BXL Services [2012] BCC 657 (appointment of administrators); Cathie v SSBIS [2012] EWCA Civ 739 (CDDA); Re Stealth Construction Ltd [2012] 1 BCLC 297 (preference); Hill v Stokes [2011] BCC 473 (appointment of administrators); Irwin v Lynch [2011] 1 WLR 1364 (amendments and limitation); Bolsover DC v Ashfield [2011] BPIR 7 (council tax and winding up); Dennis Rye Ltd v Bolsover DC [2010] 4 All ER 1140 (cross claim on winding up petition); Crooks v Newdigate [2009] EWCA Civ 283 (settlements and assignments).
Professional Memberships: Midland Chancery and Commercial Bar Association.
Career: Jesus College, Cambridge, MA (Cantab). Inner Temple Major Scholar (1995). Called 1996. Junior Counsel to the Crown (Provincial Panel). Pupil master. Recorder (County Court).
Personal: Married with two children. Enjoys wine, golf and skiing.

MORGAN, Jamie
Trinity Chambers, Newcastle upon Tyne
0191 232 1927
j.morgan@trinitychambers.co.uk
Featured in Employment (North Eastern)
Practice Areas: Commercial and Chancery -County Court, in multi-track and fast track cases, and the High Court in relation to commercial disputes. Commercial practice also has a significant Chancery element. He has significant experience of disputes involving trusts of the family home, Trusts of Land and Appointment of Trustees Act 1996 ('ToLATA'), residential landlord and tenant- including easements boundary disputes and matters relating to covenants. Insolvency - in relation to individual and corporate insolvency. Employment - high value unfair dismissal claims, encompassing conduct, redundancy and TUPE related dismissals. High value discrimination cases, achieved significant success in representing Claimants in pregnancy related discrimination claims. National practice in equal pay litigation, and is instructed in multi-week hearings involving multiple Claimants, and has frequently appeared against Silks. Professional Discipline and Fitness to Practise -cases involving individuals who are the subject of professional disciplinary proceedings and in particular acting for registrants in fitness to practise hearings. PI - both Claimant and Defendant work. Costs -disputes acting on behalf of both Claimants and Defendants. Instructed in costs budgeting and assessment hearings.
Professional Memberships: Employment Lawyers Association.
Career: LLB (Dunelm), University of Durham. Awarded Very Competent, BVC, BPP (London). Inner Temple Exhibitioner

MORGAN, Richard QC
Maitland Chambers, London
020 7406 1119
organ@maitlandchambers.com
Featured in Commercial Dispute Resolution (London), Fraud (London)
Practice Areas: Richard has a broad commercial chancery practice, quite often with significant international elements and issues concerning disputes about jurisdiction and the grant of freezing orders. Recent cases have involved a dispute arising from the collapse of the Red October steel works in Volgograd, the value of a St Petersburg shopping centre, the alleged embezzlement of US$1.1 billion from a Kazakh bank, the collapse of an offshore collective investment vehicle, and an alleged fraud committed by directors against a listed gas company. Richard has experience working with lawyers in a number of other jurisdictions, has appeared in the Cayman Islands and the BVI, and has been called for cases in the Isle of Man.
Professional Memberships: Chancery Bar Association, COMBAR, Commercial Fraud Lawyers Association.
Career: Called 1988, QC 2011.
Publications: 'International Asset Chasing and Tracing' in Insolvency Bulletins and 'Litigation Strategies aimed at Swelling Assets' in Butterworths Practical Insolvency.
Personal: Born 1963. Interests include science, rowing and travel.

MORGAN, Sarah QC
1 Garden Court Family Law Chambers, London
020 7797 7900
morgan@1gc.com
Featured in Family/Matrimonial (London)
Practice Areas: All aspects of the law relating to children: Public Law: Care and adoption. Represents Local Authorities; parents; guardians; competent children. Particular interest in cases involving death and serious non-accidental injury; complex and controversial medical evidence; mental health issues. Significant experience of cases attracting media interest and requiring reporting restrictions. Private Law: disputes between parents and other significant adults in respect of children. Applications in relation to living arrangements for children including domestic and international relocation issues.
Professional Memberships: Committee member of the FLBA, Member of the FLBA and ALC, Member and Past Council Member of the Medico-Legal Society.
Career: Recorder (Crime) 2009 (Family) 2011 Silk 2011 Experienced speaker both at Chambers seminars and as an invited guest speaker to external events including FLBA events and Experts' conferences.

MORIARTY, Stephen QC
Fountain Court Chambers, London
020 7583 3335
sm@fountaincourt.co.uk
Featured in Aviation (London), Commercial Dispute Resolution (London), Insurance (London), Professional Negligence (London)
Practice Areas: A very broad commercial litigation and advisory practice, with particular emphasis upon banking and financial services matters; professional negligence disputes; insurance and reinsurance disputes, international commercial arbitrations, and joint venture and shareholder disputes, as well as large contractual disputes of a commercial nature more generally.
Professional Memberships: Chairman of Commercial Bar Association: 2011-2012, London Common Law and Commercial Bar Association.
Career: Brasenose College Oxford (BA, 1977; BCL and Vinerian Scholarship, 1978). Fellow and Tutor in Law, Exeter College Oxford, and University Lecturer in Law in the University of Oxford:1979-1986. Called to Bar and joined Fountain Court Chambers, 1986. QC, 1999.
Publications: Editor of Insurance Chapter in Chitty on Contracts 26th edition (1989) and 27th edition (1994). Contributor to Laundering and Tracing O.U.P. 1995 (Chapter entitled Tracing, Mixing and Laundering dealing with the tracing of laundered monies through bank account). General Editor (with Raymond Cox) Commercial Court Procedure (Sweet & Maxwell).

MORLEY, Stephen
Serjeants' Inn Chambers, London
020 7427 5000
SMorley@3serjeantsinn.com
Featured in Police Law (All Circuits)
Practice Areas: Stephen Morley was called to the Bar in 1996. Stephen specialises in public and administrative, police, inquests and professional discipline law. An earlier edition notes that "he is always very approachable, highly experienced" and "impresses with his understanding of case law and its practical application." Please click on the link to the Serjeants' Inn Chambers website for his profile, which sets out full details of his practice including relevant work of note.

MORRELL, Roxanne
Carmelite Chambers, London
020 7936 6300
rmorrell@carmelitechambers.co.uk
Featured in Crime (London)
Practice Areas: Specialises in defending as leading and junior counsel in complex fraud and serious organised crime and homicide. Defended in cases of the highest gravity including E (100 million pound investment fraud), B (allegations of 1.5 million fraud involving a business set up to exploit disabled employees and the government pursuant to the "back to work programme"), S (£51 million pound trademark fraud), B) £1 billion conspiracy to import Cocaine), B (£53 million Tonbridge Securitas robbery and kidnapping), B (Murder and dismemberment of the body), T (Contract killing involving prison intercepts) and L (Attempted murder of police officer by shooting). In last year successfully defended in a 5 month trial involving £24 million MTIC fraud. Wide range of experience in the appellant courts, including an AG Reference to the HOL and proceedings involving the overturning of acquittals pursuant to the statutory removal of the double jeopardy rule which also involved police applications to recover all lost prosecution papers following the acquittal from the defence solicitors.

MORRISON, Matthew
Serle Court, London
020 7242 6105
mmorrison@serlecourt.co.uk
Featured in Fraud (London)
Practice Areas: Commercial Chancery litigation with a particular emphasis on civil fraud, company and insolvency litigation (especially claims against directors) and offshore and domestic trust litigation. Cases include Carlyle Capital Corporation & Anr v Conway & Ors; Isis Investments Limited (in liquidation) v Kaupthing Bank Int; BTA v Ablyazov & Ors; Alhamrani v Alhamrani.
Professional Memberships: Chancery Bar Association; Commercial Bar Assocation.
Career: St John's College, Oxford (Jurisprudence (MA (Oxon.)), Bachelor of Civil Law); Attorney at Quin and Hampson (now Mourant Ozannes), Cayman (2005-06); formerly Junior Counsel to the Secretary of State for Business, Innovation and Skills.
Publications: Chapters on Directors' Liabilities in Insolvency and Disqualification of Directors in Butterworths Corporate Law Service; PLC Practice Notes on Trustees' Duties of Skill and Care, Claims against Directors, and Minority Shareholder Rights and Remedies.

MORSE, Malcolm
St Philips Chambers, Birmingham
0121 246 7000
mmorse@st-philips.com
Featured in Crime (Midlands)
Practice Areas: Malcolm has developed an exclusively criminal practice since the 1980's after a generalist beginning. His practice consists of three quarters of prosecutions for crime including serious fraud, violence and sexual cases, and one quarter defending in the same areas. He has acquired some expertise in confiscation and money laundering cases, about which he has lectured. He has appeared twice for the Crown in the House of Lords, firstly in DPP v P in which he proposed the necessary change in the law of evidence preceding the Criminal Justice Act 2003, and secondly in R v Hinks in which the question concerned appropriation in Theft Act cases.
Career: Called 1967. Practised first at Fountain Court, now St Philips following its merger in 2002. Recorder of the Crown Court since 2001 with authorisations in crime, civil, private and public family law (retired June 2014).
Personal: Born 1944. Queens' College Cambridge. Inner Temple Scholarship. Leisure interests include theatre, cinema, art and history.

MORT, Justin QC
Keating Chambers, London
020 7544 2600
jmort@keatingchambers.com
Featured in Construction (London), Energy & Natural Resources (London)
Practice Areas: Specialist in disputes arising out of construction, process engineering, energy (on-shore and off-shore), mining and natural resources, and infrastructure projects. Recent experience includes a number of instructions arising from projects relating to the London Olympics in 2012, Crossrail, and various renewable energy projects including wind farms and waste to energy projects. Recent reported cases of interest include Parkwood Leisure Ltd v Laing O'Rourke Wales and West Ltd, U&M Mining Zambia Ltd v Konkola Cooper Mines plc, Atkins Ltd v Secretary of State for Transport, and Alstom Power Ltd v SOMI Impianti S.r.l. He regularly acts in TCC litigation, international arbitrations, and in adjudication and equivalent processes. Justin also has particular experience of injunction proceedings in a range of contexts; he prepared the relevant section in the 9th edition of Keating on Construction Contracts. He is familiar with most standard forms of contract including NEC (2nd and 3rd editions), and forms published by JCT, ICE / ICC, and FIDIC. He has appeared in numerous cases arising under the Housing Grants, Construction and Regeneration Act 1996, both relating to adjudication enforcement and the Act generally.
Professional Memberships: SCL; TECBAR; LCIA; King's College Construction Law Association; COMBAR.
Career: Called to the bar (Middle Temple) 1994; Public Access Training 2008; took silk in 2014; TECBAR Accredited Adjudicator.

MORTIMER, Sophie
1 Chancery Lane, London
020 7092 2900
smortimer@1chancerylane.com
Featured in Clinical Negligence (London), Police Law (All Circuits)
Practice Areas: Sophie specialises in police law, clinical negligence, and personal injury. She has a particular interest in representing police forces in civil claims and at inquests. Recent cases include: Nicholson v Commissioner of Police for the Metropolis (false imprisonment, necessity of arrest) (May 2013); Kyriacou v Commissioner of Police for the Metropolis (assault, false imprisonment, malicious prosecution) (2013); Alanov v Chief Constable Sussex Police (trespass, false imprisonment, assault) [2012] EWCA Civ 234; Alanov and Alanova v Chief Constable Sussex Police (a separate claim arising from the previous case, arising out of a different incident involving allegations of trespass, false imprisonment, assault) (2012), Oliver v Commissioner of Police for the Metropolis (false imprisonment, assault and malicious prosecution) [2012]; Inquest into the death of David Ainsworth (representing Chief Constable of Wiltshire and Wiltshire Police Authority at the inquest into the death of the force's Deputy Chief Constable) (2012) ; Inquest into the death of Cassandra Hassanovic (representing Chief Constable of Sussex Police in respect of death of Mrs Hassanovic who was murdered by her husband).
Professional Memberships: Personal Injuries Bar Association.; Professional Negligence Bar Association.
Career: Called to the Bar in 1996, Lincoln's Inn.

MORTIMORE, Simon QC
South Square, London
020 7696 9900
simonmortimore@southsquare.com
Featured in Restructuring/Insolvency (London)
Practice Areas: Barrister specialising in insolvency law, banking, corporate and commercial law. Recent work includes Apcoa Parking, major Guernsey unfair prejudice proceedings, European Directories, acting for many parties in Lehmans and Icelandic bank insolvencies, noteholders in Sigma (House of Lords) and Cheyne Finance, the administrators of Innovate (Court of Appeal), the Australian liquidators of HIH (House of Lords) and the T&N pension trustees in Federal-Mogul, and the liquidators and administrators of Barings. Substantial involvement in almost all the major insolvencies of the last 20 years (BCCI, Maxwell, Olympia & York etc). More than 70 reported cases.
Professional Memberships: ILA (Insolvency Lawyers Association), R3, INSOL, Chancery Bar Association, COMBAR.
Career: Qualified 1972, Inner Temple; QC 1991; mediator, CEDR accredited 1997 end Court of Appeal panel member 2003; member ACCA disciplinary panel 2003-07; deputy bankruptcy registrar at the High Court 1987-99; admitted to the Bar of the British Virgin Islands and for specific cases to the Bars of Bermuda and The Cayman Islands.
Publications: Mortimore, "Company Directors: Duties, Liabilities and Remedies" (OUP, 2nd ed, 2013).
Personal: Born 1950, resides London.

MORTON, Keith QC
Temple Garden Chambers, London
020 7583 1315
kmorton@tgchambers.com
Featured in Health & Safety (London), Inquests & Public Inquiries (London)
Practice Areas: Inquest, public inquiries, health and safety law and related proceedings. Significant cases include: R v Balfour Beatty and Geoconsult (1999) (Heathrow tunnel collapse), R v Lord Condon and Sir John Stevens (2003) (death of police officer), R v Thames Trains (2004) (Paddington rail crash), R v Southampton University Hospital (2006), R v Office of the Commissioner of Police for the Metropolis (2007) (prosecution arising out of the Stockwell shooting), R v Bulmer and Nalco (2008) (outbreak of legionnaires disease in Hereford), R v Costain Ltd (2009), R v Cotswold Geotechnical Ltd (2011) (first prosecution under the Corporate Manslaughter and Corporate Homicide Act), R v Dalkia Ltd (2011), R v BAM Construction (2012), R v Austin & McLean and Esso (2013). He has extensive experience of public inquiries (such as the Ladbroke Grove Rail Inquiry, the D Inquiry and Mid-Staffordshire NHS Foundation Trust Inquiry) and inquests (for example, the 7/7 London Bombings, work related deaths, deaths in custody, military including inquest into the deaths of six Royal Military Police soldiers in Iraq, an air crash at RAF St Mawgan). More generally, he has a common law practice with a particular focus on employment and administrative law and is accustomed to dealing with complex civil litigation.
Professional Memberships: Justice, Administrative Law Bar Association, Health and Safety Lawyers Association.
Career: Called to the Bar Lincoln's Inn 1990; Treasury Counsel B Panel (1997-2003), A Panel (2003-08) (2009 - 2011). Silk 2011.
Personal: Educated at University of Hull, City University. Interests include theatre, art, music, architecture, cycling.

MOSER, Philip QC
Monckton Chambers, London
020 7405 7211
pmoser@monckton.com
Featured in Competition/European Law (London), Public Procurement (London), Tax (London)
Practice Areas: European law; public procurement; commercial law; VAT. Recent cases include: Recall v DCMS [2014] CA (telecommunications – Francovich damages); Delaney v SoS for Transport [2014] CA (MIB – Francovich damages); Ibero Tours [2014] ECJ (travel agents' margin scheme); Abdulrahim v Council [2013] ECJ (UN sanctions); Gestmin v Credit Suisse [2013] Comm Crt (bank – duty of care); Bonik EOOD [2012] ECJ (input VAT carousel fraud); Indigo v Colchester Institute [2011] (public procurement). Older cases include: Lonsdale (commercial agents' compensation); 'Metric Martyr' litigation; Factortame.
Professional Memberships: Bar European Group; UKAEL; European Circuit; ELI Fellow.
Career: Called 1992; former research associate, Centre for European Legal Studies, University of Cambridge; accredited Mediator 2003; Silk 2012.
Publications: Editor, 'The European Advocate'; co-editor, 'European Law Reports' and 'Making Community Law' (2008).
Personal: MA(Cantab) in Law. Fluent German.

MOSES, Stephen
Furnival Chambers, London
020 7405 3232
smoses@furnivallaw.co.uk
Featured in Crime (London)

Practice Areas: Crime.
Professional Memberships: Criminal Bar Association; South Eastern Circuit; Gray's Inn.
Career: "Stephen Moses is a class act" according to senior members of the judiciary. "He has developed a first class criminal practice". Stephen is regularly instructed in large scale and high profile cases at the Central Criminal Court and beyond. He is increasingly instructed in recent years as a leading junior in matters of serious fraud, manslaughter, attempted murder, serious and organised violence, complex money laundering offences and large scale drugs conspiracies. His impressive catalogue of recent high profile cases include:- R v Gary Dobson (2012) [the murder of Stephen Lawrence]; R v Peter Blake (2011), defending the first defendant in the landmark first "judge alone" trial; as well as representing the "mastermind" in the much publicised conspiracy to rob Securitas in Tonbridge of £53 million - the largest cash robbery in history (R v Lea Rusha). Stephen was also instructed in 2012 to represent the principal defendant in a multi-handed conspiracy to produce £17 million of counterfeit currency, as well as being instructed to defend in Operation Eaglewood: a multi-million pounds money laundering conspiracy, said to be the largest case prosecuted by the CPS Special Casework Division.

MOTRAGHI, Nadia
Old Square Chambers, London
21 7269 0300
motraghi@oldsquare.co.uk
Featured in Employment (London)
Practice Areas: Nadia specialises in employment law and professional discipline. In employment, her practice spans the Tribunal, High Court and all levels of appeal including the Supreme Court. She acts for employees and employers in every area of employment law including discrimination of all types, wrongful dismissal, whistleblowing, TUPE, breach of contract, trade union cases, and injunctions (industrial action, restrictive covenants, MHPS). Nadia regularly represents in high value and complex lengthy discrimination and whistleblowing cases as well as in large multiple Claimant cases. Her clients span include public sector (NHS, local government), private sector (especially banking, technology and retail), individuals and trade unions. In professional discipline, she appears before a variety of regulators especially in healthcare and at internal hearings and at all levels of appeal. Notable recent work includes Uddin v GMC [2012] (Admin); Maggs & Johnson v NMC [2013] (Admin); Kapadia v GMC [2014] (Admin); Whether acting alone, leading or being led, Nadia is a sought after junior barrister.
Professional Memberships: ARDL, ELA, ELBA, ILS.
Career: St John's College, University of Oxford (MA Jurisprudence); Harvard Law School (LLM, Frank Knox Fellow, Deans Award); College of Law (BVC Outstanding; Bedingfield Scholar, Ede & Ravenscourt Prize for Student of the Year). Prior to joining Chambers, Nadia worked for the Law Commission, the European Roma Rights Centre, and held a number of part-time teaching posts including at Kings College London and Harvard University. Currently a Barrister Member of the Bar Disciplinary Tribunal.

MOTT, Richard
One Essex Court, London
020 7583 2000
rmott@oeclaw.co.uk
Featured in Banking & Finance (London), Commercial Dispute Resolution (London)
Practice Areas: Richard has a broad commercial litigation and arbitration practice, including civil fraud, banking, energy, financial services / regulatory and general commercial disputes. Recent cases include Tullow Uganda Ltd v Heritage Oil and Gas Ltd (first instance ([2013] EWHC 1656 (Comm)) and Court of Appeal; $313m claim arising out of the sale of petroleum rights in Uganda), Sloane House Ltd v Fleury (civil fraud; obtained initial freezing order, then summary judgment and committal order), acting in a very substantial LCIA arbitration arising out of a dispute between shareholders in one of the world's largest aluminium companies, Mainfirst Austria GmbH v US Bank Trustees Ltd (dispute between investment adviser and trustee to a note issue), Weavering Capital (UK) Ltd v Peterson & Ors [2013] EWCA Civ 71 (fraud by CEO of collapsed hedge fund; appeared as sole counsel before Court of Appeal), Desmond v Credit Suisse International (misselling claim in respect of a swap contract), Jeremy D Stone Consultants Ltd v National Westminster Bank Plc [2013] EWHC 208 (Ch) (civil fraud / restitution claim arising out of a Ponzi scheme), and Barclays Bank Plc v Svizera Holdings BV (freezing order; US$38m claim under facility agreement).
Career: Called 2006. Christ's College, Cambridge (BA, History – First Class); City University (CPE – Commendation); Inns of Court School of Law (BVC – Outstanding).

MOUNTFIELD, Helen QC
Matrix Chambers, London
020 7404 3447
helenmountfield@matrixlaw.co.uk
Featured in Administrative & Public Law (London), Civil Liberties & Human Rights (London), Education (London), Employment (London), Local Government (London)
Practice Areas: Barrister specialising in public law, human rights, discrimination, education and employment. Recent notable cases include: Smith v Secretary of State for Defence (Supreme Court - jurisdiction of ECtHR); R (London Borough of Lewisham) v Ofqual, Edexel & Ors (Divisional Court: successful defence of education regulator); Burnip v DWP (Court of Appeal: use of international law in national court); R(F) v DPP (Divisional Court: challenge to non-prosecution of rape); R(MA) v DWP (bedroom tax challenge). R(Woolas) v General Election Court (election petition and judicial review challenge to election court); R(G) v Governing Body of X School (Supreme Court - article 6 and professional discipline); R(Hurley & Moore) v Secretary of State for Trade & Industry (challenge to legality of university tuition fee increase); R(E) v Governing Body of JFS (Supreme Court - discrimination law and legality of admissions policy of Jewish faith school); R(RB & Othman) v SSHD (House of Lords - deportations with assurance); Stec v UK (Grand Chamber ECtHR - discrimination and social security); Pedro v DWP (EU citizens' directive); Ladele v London Borough of Islington (religious discrimination); Bracking v Minister for Disabled People and R(Elias) v Ministry of Defence (public sector equality duties). Other notable cases on www.matrixlaw.co.uk.
Professional Memberships: Administrative Law Bar Association; Employment Law Bar Association; Employment Law Association; Bar European Group; Human Rights Lawyers' Association; Industrial Law Society.
Career: Called 1991; Silk 2010; Gray's Inn; Recorder 2009; Deputy High Court Judge Administrative Court 2013. Master of the Bench Gray's Inn. Treasury A Panel (until 2010); Special Advocate; Member of Equality and Human Rights Commission panel. Lectures widely in UK and abroad, including at Harvard, NYU, Oxford, Cambridge and for the Judicial Studies Board. Chambers Bar Awards Human Rights and Public Law Junior of the Year 2009; short listed for The Lawyer Magazine Barrister of the Year 2010.
Publications: Include 'Blackstone Guide to Human Rights Act 1998' (6th edition), editor of the Human Rights section of the White Book.
Personal: Magdalen College Oxford (BA Hons History 1st class); City University (Diploma in Law); King's College London (Postgraduate Diploma in EU Law); Holker Scholar and Reid Scholar of Gray's Inn.

MOXON BROWNE, Robert QC
2TG - 2 Temple Gardens, London
020 7822 1200
rmoxonbrowne@2tg.co.uk
Featured in Insurance (London), Professional Negligence (London), Property Damage (London)
Practice Areas: Described by Chambers and Partners as "an amazing courtroom presence" who is "completely bulletproof", Bob is recognised as a leader of the Bar in Professional Negligence, Insurance and Property Damage. Heading the Professional Negligence Group at 2 Temple Gardens, he is an authoritative advocate with huge experience of indemnification and other insurance issues. His reputation is for an informal, hands on style, and robust advocacy. An amiable and relaxed manner belies a capacity for meticulous attention to the detail of complex cases, and, when necessary ferocious cross-examination. He works for and against accountants, solicitors, valuers and surveyors, as well as construction industry professionals, especially in cases about the allocation of responsibility within multi-disciplinary teams. Bob's background is in insurance law, with long experience of subrogated recoveries in cases involving fire, flood and other catastrophic events, policy construction questions and repudiation for fraud. He retains a special interest in life and critical illness issues,and is often counsel of choice for insurers and reinsurers interested in these risks. Bob's impressive record of appearances in reported cases, many of them landmark Court of Appeal authorities in his areas of specialisation, attest to the depth and width of his experience, and the success which he enjoys as a top-rated Queen's Counsel.
Professional Memberships: ORBA, Professional Negligence Bar Association, CLBA, COMBAR.
Career: Called to the Bar 1969, QC 1990. Recorder 1992. Deputy Judge of the Technology and Construction Court 1993. Deputy Judge of the High Court 1999.
Personal: Born 1946. Educated Gordonstoun School, University College Oxford (BA).

MUIR, Nicola
Tanfield Chambers, London
020 7421 5300
nicolamuir@tanfieldchambers.co.uk
Featured in Real Estate Litigation (London)
Practice Areas: Real property, commercial and residential landlord and tenant, enfranchisement, property tribunal cases, mortgages and property related professional negligence. Nicola has had 3 reported Upper Tribunal (Lands Chamber) cases in the last year - Jastrzembski v Westminster City Council [2013] UKUT 0284; Triplerose Ltd v Bishun [2013] UKUT 0257 (LC) and Tibber v Buckley [2014] UKUT 74 (LC).
Professional Memberships: Property Bar Association, Association of Leasehold Enfranchisement Practitioners (ALEP).
Career: Barrister at Tanfield Chambers since October 2012, Barrister at Hardwicke Building August 1999 to October 2012, solicitor from 1991 to 1998.
Publications: Co-author of Tanfield on Service Charges and Management:Law and Practice, 3rd Edition. Nicola has regular column on the Estates Gazette. Recent Articles: "Back to the Future - The Retrospective variation of leases of flats under the Landlord and Tenant Act 1987", Estates Gazette 23rd July 2013; "PRS - is more regulation needed", Estates Gazette 23rd November 2013; "Is an end to the crystal ball gazing in sight?", Estates Gazette 11th January 2014; "Curing Defective Leases under the Landlord and Tenant Act 1987", L & T Review 2014, 18 (1), 12-14; "Section 21 Notices - An End to the Quest for "The Last Day of a Period of the Tenancy", L & T Review 2014, 18 (2), 51-53; "Leasebacks - What is the Landlord Entitled To?", L & T Review 2014, 18(3), 102-104; "Reliance on the tribunal's expertise", Estates Gazette 5th July 2014.

MULCAHY, Leigh-Ann QC
4 New Square, London
020 7822 2000
l.mulcahy@4newsquare.com
Featured in Insurance (London), Product Liability (London), Professional Negligence (London)
Practice Areas: Insurance law (with a particular emphasis on employers, public, professional and product liability insurance and issues related to asbestos and environmental liabilities). Professional liability (especially lawyers, financial services professionals and accountants). Product liability (including pharmaceuticals, medical devices, commercial products and food. Civil fraud. Public and human rights law including commercial/regulatory judicial review. Costs. Inquiries. Mediation. Has appeared in three cases before the House of Lords and Supreme Court (The Employers Liability Insurance Trigger Litigation; The Atomic Veterans Litigation and Medcalf v Mardell [2003] AC 120) and she is now acting on a further Supreme Court appeal (International Energy Group Ltd v Zurich). Has recently acted in a high value commercial arbitration arising out of an IT dispute, appeared in the Miners' Knee Litigation in the Court of Appeal and in the PIP Breast Implant Litigation. She acted in an international fraud case on behalf of the Central Bank of Trinidad and Tobago. Cases include: International Energy Group Ltd v Zurich [2013] EWCA Civ 39; Davies v Secretary of State for Energy and Climate Change [2012] EWCA Civ 1380; Durham v. BAI and ors [2012] 1 WLR 867 (SC); AB v. Ministry of Defence [2012] 2 WLR 643 (SC);

R (McVey) v Secretary of State for Health (2010) Med LR 204 and [2010] EWHC 1225; Leonard v Byrt [2008] EWCA Civ 20; Bezant v Rausing [2007] EWHC 1118; Russell Young and Co, v Kevin Brown [2008] 1 WLR 525, CA; the Inquest into the death of L/Cpl Hull in Iraq from US friendly fire (2007); R (Lord Chancellor) v Chief Land Registrar [2006] QB 795; Phillips v. Symes (No 2) [2005] 1 WLR 2043; R (Ministry of Defence) v. Wiltshire and Swindon Coroner [2006] 1 WLR 134; Medcalf v Mardell [2003] AC 120, HL.
Professional Memberships: COMBAR; Professional Negligence Bar Association; Administrative Law Bar Association; BIICL Product Liability Forum.
Career: MA (Cantab); LLM (Osgoode); Dip. EC Law (London). Called to Bar 1993. Appointed QC 2009. Treasury Counsel - A Panel 2006-2009. CEDR accredited mediator. Also called to Bar of Republic of Ireland.
Publications: Editor 'Jackson and Powell on Professional Liability'; Consulting Editor 'The Law and Regulation of Medicines'; General Editor 'Human Rights and Civil Practice'.

MULHOLLAND, Helen
Kings Chambers, Manchester
0845 034 3444
clerks@kingschambers.com
Featured in Clinical Negligence (Northern)
Practice Areas: Principal area of practice is clinical negligence, with experience and interest in: obstetrics and gynaecology; general surgery; delay in diagnosis of cancer; orthopaedic injury; psychiatric injury and cases involving children and protected parties. Also practises in personal injury, specialising in cases of multiple serious injury and with a particular interest in cases involving brain injury.
Professional Memberships: Professional Negligence Bar Association, Personal Injury Bar Association.
Career: University: Birmingham BA (Hons) Italian and French; CPE (Chester); BVC (ICSL); Inn: Middle Temple.

MULLEN, Jayne
St Ives Chambers, Birmingham
0121 236 0863
jayne.mullen@stiveschambers.co.uk
Featured in Family/Matrimonial (Midlands)
Practice Areas: Matrimonial Finance.
Professional Memberships: Deputy District Judge (Family) 2010 Deputy District Judge 2002.
Career: Jayne specialises in complex ancillary relief cases with many years experience in analysing business accounts and complex pension provision, providing comprehensive advice at all stages of the proceedings. Jayne enjoys finding solutions to complex and difficult cases, whether this is as a result of limited resources or the fair division of substantial assets and incomes, businesses, farms, trusts and assets outside of the jurisdiction. She is noted for her pragmatic and sensible approach, explaining complex legal principles and finances to clients to enable them to be fully involved and in control of the decision making process.

MUMFORD, David
Maitland Chambers, London
020 7406 1200
dmumford@maitlandchambers.com
Featured in Banking & Finance (London), Chancery (London), Commercial Dispute Resolution (London), Company (London), Fraud (London), Offshore (London), Partnership (London)
Practice Areas: Commercial and chancery litigation, including business agreements and general commercial disputes, civil fraud, company and partnership matters (including insolvency), professional negligence, and claims against trustees and other fiduciaries. Notable cases include: Bumi (shareholder and other claims concerning the UK-listed mining enterprise); Red October (jurisdiction challenge in debt and conspiracy claims against Russian steel works); Berezovsky v Abramovich, Hine & ors (various actions involving the famous Russian oligarch); Masri v Consolidated Contractors (alleged conspiracy to evade judgment debts); Jennington v Assaubayev (fraud claims in connection with the sale of a gold mining conglomerate); Cadogan Petroleum v Tolley (fraud and bribery claims in connection with a gas exploration business); Lehman Brothers (concerning the administrators' liability for rent); Cinnamon v BCP (claim against a Portuguese bank about a mortgage securitisation); Equitable Life v Bowley & Ors (acting for former Managing Director and Appointed Actuary in claims arising out of the collapse of the Society); In re the Buncefield Incident (acting for commercial property owners in claims arising out of the oil terminal explosion); Marlwood v Kozeny (acting for US investors in fraud claims concerning the privatisation of the Azeri oil industry); Scottish & Newcastle v PwC (defending professional negligence claims against management consultants) and Gregson v HAE Trustees Limited (successfully resisting a 'dog-leg' claim against directors of a trust company for breach of trust).
Professional Memberships: Chancery Bar Association and COMBAR.
Career: Called in 2000.
Personal: Born 6 March 1975. Educated King's College School and Magdalen College, Oxford (MA Classics, 1st Class Honours). Former Mansfield Scholar and Denning Scholar of Lincoln's Inn.

MUNRO, Joshua
Hailsham Chambers, London
020 7643 5000
joshua.munro@hailshamchambers.com
Featured in Costs Litigation (London)
Practice Areas: Main areas of practice: costs and professional negligence. Cases include: Joyce v Darby [2014] EWCA Civ 677; Saigol v Thorney Limited [2014] EWCA Civ 556; Haynes v Department for Business Innovation and Skills [2014] EWHC 643 (QB). French v Carter Lemon Camerons [2013] P.N.L.R. 2; Minkin v CKFT [2012] 3 All E.R. 1117; Letts v Royal Sun Alliance Plc [2012] 3 Costs L.R. 591; Gossage v Bishton [2012] EWCA Civ 717; Lord Coleridge v Sotheby's [2012] EWHC 370 (Ch); Kynaston v Carroll [2011] EWCA Civ 1699; Scurfield v Revenue & Customs Commissioners [2011] UKFTT 532 (TC); Lake v Hunt Kid Law Firm [2011] 6 Costs L.R. 948; Webb v Macdonald [2010] Lloyd's Rep. P.N. 287; Boyd & Hutchinson v Foenander [2004] B.P.I.R. 20.
Professional Memberships: PNBA; LCLCBA.
Career: Called 2001; Lecturer in contract and tort law, University of East London, 2002-06.
Publications: Contributor to the Solicitors' Journal, Butterworths Costs Newsletter, LexisNexis Insight.
Personal: Education: Lady Margaret Hall, Oxford (BA (Hons) 1st Class). Fluent Italian, some French and Spanish. Leisure interests include swimming and music.

MURE, James QC
Axiom Advocates, Edinburgh
07739 639 212
james.mure@axiomadvocates.com
Featured in Administrative & Public Law (Scotland), Public Procurement (Scotland), Commercial Dispute Resolution (Scotland), Planning (Scotland)
Practice Areas: James Mure is a founding member of Axiom Advocates, and was formerly First Standing Junior Counsel to the Scottish Government (2007-2009). Now a leading silk in public and commercial law, he is particularly known for his work for public authorities in planning, environmental and contractual disputes, human rights, EU law and FOI. With experience in a range of high-profile cases, James appears regularly in the Inner House of the Court of Session, and in the Supreme Court. Recent cases include: Trump v Scottish Ministers [2014] SLT 406 (wind farm dispute); Walton v Scottish Ministers [2013] PTSR 51 (roads order appeal); Salvesen v Riddell [2013] HRLR 23 (agricultural holdings and Convention rights); Angus Growers Ltd v Scottish Ministers 2013 SLT 611 (recognition of producer organisation for EU subsidy); Martin v Most 2010 SC (UKSC) 40 (legislative competence of Scottish Parliament); Eba v Advocate General for Scotland [2012] 1 AC 710 (judicial review of Upper Tribunal); Multi-Link Leisure Developments Ltd v North Lanarkshire Council [2011] 1 All ER 175 (construction of option to purchase in commercial lease); M v Scottish Ministers [2012] 1 WLR 3386 (statutory construction); Axa General Insurance Ltd, Petitioners [2012] 1 AC 868 (human rights and legislative competence); Crieff Highland Gathering Ltd v Perth and Kinross Council 2011 SLT 992 (rescission of lease); R (F) v Home Secretary [2011] 1 AC 331 (human rights and sex offenders' registration); Imperial Tobacco Ltd, Petitioners 2013 SC (UKSC) 153 (legislative competence of Scottish Parliament).
Career: Faculty of Advocates (called 1995; QC 2009).
Personal: Clare College, Cambridge (MA Hons); University of Edinburgh (LLB); Formerly Member of HM Diplomatic Service. Enjoys music, travel and theatre.

MURPHY, Melissa
Francis Taylor Building, London
020 7353 8415
melissa.murphy@ftb.eu.com
Featured in Planning (London)
Practice Areas: Melissa's practice is focused on planning and real estate matters. She has extensive experience of providing advice and representation in relation to planning appeals, compulsory purchase and compensation and related public law challenges. She offers realistic and sensitive advice to both public and private sector clients in order to provide solutions to legal problems concerning land.
Professional Memberships: Member of the Planning and Environment Bar Association, the Constitutional and Administrative Law Bar Association, the Compulsory Purchase Association and the National Infrastructure Planning Association."
Career: Queen Mother Scholar (Middle Temple), called in 2001.

MURRAY, David
Fountain Court Chambers, London
020 7583 3335
dm@fountaincourt.co.uk
Featured in Banking & Finance (London), Commercial Dispute Resolution (London)
Practice Areas: Commercial litigation including banking, financial services, insurance/reinsurance, aviation, sale of goods, conflict of laws, financial regulation, civil fraud and professional negligence. Recent notable cases include: Tigris International NV v China Southern Airlines Co Ltd [2013] EWHC 2211 (Comm) (aviation/sale of goods); A.H. Baldwin and Sons Ltd v Al-Thani [2012] EWHC 3156 (QB) (sale of goods/freezing injunctions); Injazat Technology Fund v Najafi [2012] EWHC 4171 (Comm) (anti-arbitration injunctions); Deutsche Bank AG v Petromena ASA [2013] EWHC 3065 (Comm) (jurisdiction under Lugano Convention); Stone & Rolls Ltd v Moore Stephens [2009] UKHL 39, [2009] 1 AC 1391 (auditors' negligence and the illegality defence); Safeway Stores Ltd v Twigger [2010] EWCA Civ 1472; [2011] 2 All ER 841 (recoverability of indemnity in respect of criminal penalties). Other recent experience and current instructions include various substantial confidential commercial arbitrations in London and overseas; a heavy and complex Commercial Court dispute arising out of a CDO transaction; and a variety of financial mis-selling claims.
Professional Memberships: COMBAR. Authorised to practise in the Dubai International Financial Centre.
Career: Called 2004. Internship at ICC, Paris, Oct-Dec 2005; Pegasus Scholar, Hong Kong, Sep-Dec 2007.
Personal: Christ Church, Oxford: BA 2001 (First), BCL 2002 (Distinction). Vinerian Scholarship 2002; Eldon Scholarship 2004.

MURRAY, Rebecca
Temple Tax Chambers, London
020 7353 7884
clerks@templetax.com
Featured in Tax (London)
Practice Areas: Rebecca advocates and advises in all areas of direct tax (corporate and private client) and VAT on matters ranging from multi-billion pound transactions to small complex issues. She frequently conducts cases in the First Tier Tribunal and Upper Tribunal and appeared unled for HMRC in procedural hearings for the 2 most significant tax avoidance cases of 2013 (Tower MCashback and Eclipse). Her impressive diverse practice has won her 3 awards, Taxation's Rising Star 2013, Tax Journal 40 under 40 2012/13 and STEP's Young Practitioner of the Year 2013/14 finalist. Her book "Tax Avoidance" (Sweet & Maxwell, November 2013), described as "excellent coverage of extremely hard areas of law", is now in its 2nd edition. Pro bono work: advocate to the Upper Tribunal in Donaldson, involving HMRC's automated system for daily penalties; Cases for the Bar Pro Bono Unit and LITRG on tax credits.
Professional Memberships: Secretary, Revenue Bar Association; Chartered Institute of Tax (Corporate Tax Committee); Society of Trusts and Estates Practitioners.
Career: Called 2001. ATT (2002), CTA (2003), CTA Fellow (2013), TEP (2013).
Publications: "Tax Avoidance" (Sweet & Maxwell, November 2013); CCH British Tax Guide on Corporation Tax 2007/8; Articles.

Personal: Sporty, highly competitive.

MURRAY, Stephen J
18 St John Street, Manchester
0161 278 1800
family@18sjs.com
Featured in Family/Matrimonial (Northern)

Practice Areas: Family law (matrimonial finance, cohabitee disputes, private law children, applications under the inheritance (Provision for Family and Dependants) Act 1975.

Professional Memberships: Family Law Bar Association.

Career: Stephen originally pursued a career with the Derbyshire Constabulary. After two years in the police service he left to go to university; graduated with a law degree from Leicester University in 1985 and was called to the Bar in 1986 having come in the top eight per cent in the Bar Finals and won two separate scholarships. For many years now Stephen has specialised in matrimonial finance (with a particular emphasis on complex financial remedy cases for high net worth clients involving issues such as trusts and company valuations) and related fields, particularly applications under the Inheritance (Provision for Family and Dependants) Act 1975 and cohabitation disputes. Stephen enjoys and continues to accept instructions in private law children cases.

Personal: Called to the Bar 1986. Received the Inner Temple Profumo Award and The Skinners Company Award. Published an article entitled "Ancillary Relief Trial Bundles - An Ignored Art" in the April 2011 Edition of Family Law.

MUSGRAVE, Caroline
Cloisters, London
020 7827 4000
cmusgrave@cloisters.com
Featured in Employment (London)

Practice Areas: Caroline Musgrave specialises in employment and discrimination law with particular expertise in equal pay, sex, age, race and disability discrimination, TUPE, maternity/pregnancy rights and breach of contract. Caroline also maintains a practice in personal injury and clinical negligence.

Professional Memberships: ELA, ELBA, ILS.

Career: Called in 2008, Caroline is highly regarded for her strategic approach, personable style and excellent witness handling. Notable cases include the equal pay litigation of Barry v University of Wales Trinity St David in which Caroline represented 18 male workers (caretakers and tradesmen) who successfully claimed equal pay with female workers (secretaries and library assistants). In Wendy Williams v MOD Caroline represented the most senior serving nurse in the RAF in her successful claim of both direct and indirect sex discrimination.

Personal: After graduating from Clare College, Cambridge, Caroline worked as a relief and development professional for six years in the UK, Pakistan, Indonesia and Rwanda. Since being called to the bar, she has remained interested in international law and in 2013 spent three months as a visiting fellow at the Harvard Law School Project on Disability focusing on how the UN Convention on the Rights of Persons with Disabilities can be used to further the rights of the disabled.

MYHILL, David
Crown Office Chambers, London
020 7797 8100
myhill@crownofficechambers.com
Featured in Clinical Negligence (London)

Practice Areas: Specialist civil practice, with particular expertise in disputes involving professionals accused of negligence (including clinical negligence, as well as surveyors, accountants, brokers, IFAs and solicitors), property damage claims, and general commercial and insurance litigation. Clinical negligence practice involves regular instructions in high value claims for Claimants, NHS Trusts and privately insured Defendants, with regular trial experience. Property damage practice involves a particular emphasis on subrogated claims involving fires, floods and subsidence. Insurance work includes coverage disputes, claims involving fraud, and interpretation of all forms of non-marine policies. Commercial practice incorporates wide-ranging disputes concerning the sale of goods and supply of services, with an emphasis on disputes concerning IT contracts, and claims for commission arising out of estate agency contracts. Regularly acts in settlement negotiations including mediations and round table meetings. Highly experienced in representing parties at oral hearings, including trials, applications, and inquests.

Career: MA (Cantab), Called 2006.

Publications: David has presented talks on the effect of the decision in The Achilleas [2008] UKHL 48 and also on limitation periods for contingent losses.

MYLONAS, Michael QC
Serjeants' Inn Chambers, London
020 7427 5000
mmylonasqc@3serjeantsinn.com
Featured in Clinical Negligence (London), Court of Protection (All Circuits), Professional Discipline (London)

Practice Areas: Michael Mylonas QC was called to the Bar in 1988 and took silk in 2012. Michael specialises in clinical negligence and healthcare, Court of Protection, health and safety, human fertilisation and life sciences, inquests and inquiries, personal injury, product liability, professional discipline and regulation, public and administrative and sports law. An earlier edition notes that "he is never daunted by a fight and shows complete understanding and compassion to clients" and "he is blindingly brilliant in conference and at trial. His preparation is second to none... He is extremely good on his feet in court and at cross-examination - he's the best I've met. He goes in like a machine gun." Please click on the link to the Serjeants' Inn Chambers website for his profile, which sets out full details of his practice including relevant work of note.

Professional Memberships: PNBA, AVMA, ARDL, HSLA, LCLCBA.

Publications: Medical Treatment: Decisions and The Law (Co-author), Medical Law Reports (2000 - 2010), APIL Clinical Negligence.

NAGPAL, Deepak
1 King's Bench Walk, London
020 7936 1500
dnagpal@1kbw.co.uk
Featured in Family/Matrimonial (London)

Practice Areas: Divorce and Matrimonial Finance. Interesting cases include: Sharbatly v Shagroon [2014] 2 FLR 209; CR v MZ [2013] EWHC 295; Shagroon v Sharbatly [2013] 2 WLR 1255; Gordon v Stefanou [2011] 1 FLR 158; JKN v JCN [2011] 1 FLR 826; W v W [2011] 1 FLR 372; Granatino v Radmacher (formerly Granatino) [2011] 1 AC 34; S v S (Hemain Injunction) [2010] 2 FLR 502; S v S (No 2) (Ancillary Relief Application to Set Aside Order) [2010] 1 FLR 993; Miller Smith v Miller Smith [2010] 1 FLR 1402; Crossley v Crossley [2008] 1 FCR 323; Charman v Charman [2007] 2 FCR 217; McFarlane v McFarlane [2006] 2 AC 618; Mark v Mark [2006] 1 AC 98; Moore v Moore [2005] 1 FLR 66.

Professional Memberships: Commitee Member of the Family Bar Association; Member of the LexisPSL Family Consulting Editorial Board; Member of the South Eastern Circuit.

Career: Called in 2002 (Lincoln's Inn). Hardwicke Scholarship; Lord Mansfield Scholarship; Megarry Scholarship. Treasury counsel.

Publications: Co-editor of Jackson's Matrimonial Finance; Advisory Editor of the Family Court Reports.

Personal: Educated at Loughborough Grammar School and Christ Church, University of Oxford. MA (Oxon) Jurisprudence (1st Class); BCL. .

NAJIB, Shakil
St Philips Chambers, Birmingham
0121 246 7000
snajib@st-philips.com
Featured in Company (Midlands), Partnership (Midlands)

Practice Areas: Shakil specialises in commercial and chancery law with a particular emphasis on company, insolvency and partnership litigation. He has significant experience in dealing with all aspects of corporate and personal insolvency including voluntary arrangements, administrations, administrative and other receiverships, liquidations, bankruptcies, the adjustment of prior transactions, recovery of corporate assets and misfeasance claims. His company law practice includes claims arising from breach of directors' duties, derivative claims, shareholders' disputes and acting for directors and the Secretary of State in directors' disqualification proceedings. Shakil handles all types of partnership disputes, including preliminary disputes as to the existence, constitution and dissolution of partnerships, post dissolution accounts and enquiries, partnership retirements and evictions, and the construction and enforcement of partnership deeds. He is regularly instructed in a broad range of contractual and commercial disputes and has particular experience of claims arising from the sale and supply of goods and services, and the enforcement of guarantees and other securities.

Professional Memberships: Chancery Bar Association; COMBAR; Midlands Commercial and Chancery Bar Association.

Career: Called (Lincoln's Inn) 1999. Appointed to the Attorney General's Regional Panel of Counsel 2010.

Personal: LLB University of Birmingham, LLM (Corporate and Commercial Law) The London School of Economics (Distinction).

NAMBISAN, Deepak
Fountain Court Chambers, London
020 7842 3779
dn@fountaincourt.co.uk
Featured in Commercial Dispute Resolution (London), Fraud (London)

Practice Areas: Broad commercial and civil practice, with particular expertise in: all areas of commercial law, particularly fraud, aviation, banking, insolvency, insurance/reinsurance, professional negligence; regulatory law, including Law Society, financial services, City regulatory work and disciplinary tribunals; employment law; administrative and public law; entertainment, music and sports law; conflict of laws and multi-jurisdictional issues.

Professional Memberships: New York Bar; ICC; LCIA; COMBAR; LCLCBA; South Eastern Circuit; British Association for Sport & Law, British Insurance Law Association; British Russian Law Association.

Career: Called 1998; Gray's Inn Prince of Wales Scholar; Junior Counsel to the Crown (B Panel).

Publications: Editor, Commercial Court Procedure (Sweet & Maxwell); Co-author, Chapter 23 on Directors & Officers, Professional Negligence & Liability (2005, LLP); Co-author, Director' & Officers' Liability Insurance (2008, LLP).

Personal: King Edward's School; The Williston Northampton School; Christ's College, Cambridge; Exeter College, Oxford; Harvard Law School.

NATHAN, Aparna
Devereux, London
020 7353 7534
downes@devchambbers.co.uk
Featured in Tax (London)

Practice Areas: Tax law, tax planning for high/ ultra high net worth individuals (especially non-domiciliaries), offshore structures, estate planning, ATED Related planning; application of GAAR; corporate tax planning with a focus on residence and permanent establishment issues; disguised remuneration. Aparna also has a busy litigation practice. Most notable cases include Moyles et al v HMRC ("Working Wheels" - structured avoidance scheme); Boyle v HMRC (structured avoidance scheme); Berry v HMRC (structured avoidance scheme); Professional Golfers Association v HMRC (whether PGA is an eligible body); Lord Howard of Henderskelfe v HMRC (whether Reynolds portrait is a wasting asset).

Professional Memberships: Chartered Institute of Taxation - Chair - Capital Gains Tax Sub Committee; member Succession Taxes Sub Committee;Revenue Bar Association; Chancery Bar Association; Addington Society -Honorary Secretary;Worshipful Company of Tax Advisers.

Career: Private practice at at Devereux Chambers from August 2014. Previously in private practice at Gray's Inn Tax Chambers.

Publications: McCuthceon on Inheritance Tax (6th ed.); Grundy & Nathan on Offshore Business Centres (8th ed.); Mellows on Taxation for Trustees and Executors (Non-resident Trusts Chapter); Regular contributor to professional journals.

Personal: Member of the Education Committee of Bharatiya Vidya Bhavan, London (Indian Institute of Culture).

NATHAN, David QC
5 St Andrew's Hill, London
020 7332 5400
wayne@5sah.co.uk
Featured in Crime (London)

Practice Areas: For over twenty five years he has led for the defence in numerous serious and high profile cases across the criminal spectrum, beginning with the Brinks Matt and Security Express robberies in the 1980s, and later, for example, the defence of Ronnie O'Sullivan Senior for murder, the Panorama police corruption trial, and the trial at Southwark Crown Court which finally exposed the London City Bond as informants and led to the quashing of a number of convictions in the Court of Appeal. Since taking Silk in 2002, he has conducted over fifty murder trials, as well as several of importing and supplying Class A drugs, complex fraud, serious sex and violence, blackmail, armed robbery, firearms, and internet crime. Many of these have involved the cross-examination of expert witnesses—forensic scientists, cell-site and hand writing experts, pathologists, psychiatrists, and consulting engineers. Although based in London and the South East, he has also conducted many cases in the Midlands, the West Country, Leeds and Manchester, and is currently due to appear in homicide cases at the Old Bailey, Lincoln, and Birmingham. Apart from crime, he has also undertaken tribunal work and a fact finding in the Family Division of the High Court.

NAWBATT, Akash
Devereux, London
020 7353 7534
nawbatt@devchambers.co.uk
Featured in Employment (London), Tax (London)

Practice Areas: Employment: Recent cases include - Crossland v OSC Group [2014] EWCA Civ 576 (Disability Discrimination); Lockwood v DWP [2013] IRLR 941 (Age Discrimination); Fox v BA [2013] ICR 51 (Loss of a chance) and R (Sharon Shoesmith) v SoS for Education [2011] ICR 1195 (JR challenge of summary dismissal). Tax: Recent cases include - McLaren Racing Ltd v HMRC [2014] STI 2288 (Deductibility of Regulatory Fine); John Mander Pension Scheme Trustees v HMRC [2014] 1 WLR 2209 (Consequences of withdrawal of approval); Mertrux Ltd v HMRC [2013] STC 2199; (Taxation of termination payment); Kuehne & Nagle Drinks Logistics v HMRC [2012] STC 840 (Earnings from employment); and R (Gaines-Cooper) v HMRC [2012] 1 All ER 1048 (Residence).
Career: Called 1999. Judicial assistant to the House of Lords (2001-02). Junior Counsel to the Crown: C Panel (2004-08); B Panel (2008-2012); and A Panel (2013 - 2018).
Publications: Contributing Editor to 'Harvey on Industrial Relations and Employment Law'.

NEALE, Fiona
Hailsham Chambers, London
020 7427 5000
fiona.neale@hailshamchambers.com
Featured in Clinical Negligence (London), Professional Discipline (London)

Practice Areas: Fiona specialises in clinical negligence claims and disciplinary cases. She has extensive experience acting for claimants and defendants in a wide range of cases including numerous high value claims. Her professional disciplinary work includes cases before the General Medical Council and at the General Dental Council. Fiona is highly experienced in cases involving medical ethics (consent in the context of drug trials) and inquests (coroner`s court, families, trusts and medical defence organisations).
Career: Called 1981; CLE (Bar Finals, 1980-81); King's College, London (LLB Hons 2:1, 1977-80); King Edward VI High Schools for Girls (1969-76).
Publications: Co-author of chapter, Limitation, in APIL's book 'Clinical Negligence', published April 2008; 'How to litigate cerebral palsy claims', London, May 1996.

NEAMAN, Sam
Littleton Chambers, London
020 7797 8600
sneaman@littletonchambers.co.uk
Featured in Employment (London)

Practice Areas: Employment lawyer "with a strong commercial leaning". "A real fighter", best known for his employment/commercial crossover work. Heavy High Court injunction practice, principally freezing, search and seize, 'team move' and restrictive covenant injunctions. Expertise and experience covers all courts including Supreme Court. Regularly instructed in high profile/high value cases, particularly in the sectors of insurance, broking, banking and finance, the media, IT, and sport. Specific expertise in the NHS/medical sector where he acts for doctors and Trusts in the High Court, tribunals, and GMC/internal disciplinary processes. In the employment tribunal Sam specialises in high profile/complex whistleblowing claims, discrimination, TUPE, and working time issues. House of Lords cases include Johnson v Unisys [2003] 1 AC 518 and Fourie v Le Roux Ors [2007] UKHL 1 (freezing injunction) as well as numerous reported cases in the Court of Appeal, High Court and EAT. Significant practice in banking and commercial litigation, including claims worth over £1 billion. Regularly instructed by High Street Banks and other financial institutions, with particular experience in SWAP/interest rate hedge mis-selling cases. Also recognised as a leading individual in sports law. High profile cases have included boxing, Formula 1, and premiership football, rugby union and rugby league.
Career: Called to the Bar 1988. Former legal advisor to the Amateur Boxing Association of England. Accredited mediator (2003).
Publications: Co-author of "Security for Costs and Other Court Ordered Security" (Jordans, 2010).
Personal: Educated at Oxford University (MA Hons) and City University (Dip Law). Leisure pursuits include boxing (former boxer - Oxford University double blue and Member of Angel ABC 1986-91) and playing drums in jazz and blues bands. Former drummer with top UK R&B band, the Burke Brothers. Married with two children.

NEISH, Andrew QC
4 Pump Court, London
020 7842 5555
aneish@4pumpcourt.com
Featured in Insurance (London), Professional Negligence (London)

Practice Areas: General commercial law. Principal areas of practice are insurance and reinsurance and professional negligence (especially brokers, lawyers and accountants).
Professional Memberships: COMBAR, London Common Law and Commercial Bar Association, LCIA Users' Council
Career: Called 1988. Silk 2009.
Personal: MA (St Andrews), Dip Law (City). Admitted in the BVI, MCIArb, Trained Mediator.

NELSON, Michelle
Red Lion Chambers, London
020 7520 6000
chambers@18rlc.co.uk
Featured in Crime (London)

Practice Areas: All areas of crime, both defending and prosecuting. Particular experience in homicide, often involving young defendants. Experience in prosecution of serious and complex fraud, money laundering and restraint and forfeiture. Appointed Junior Treasury Counsel in 2009. Defence work has included defending in capital murder cases in Jamaica and advising on behalf of appellants in Privy Council appeals.
Career: Treasury Counsel, 2009; Called to the Bar of Turks and Caicos Islands, 2014; Criminal Bar Association; South Eastern Circuit. Charities: Prison Reform Trust, Scene and Heard and Ekaya (Vice Chair).

NEUBERGER, Edmund
Atkin Chambers, London
020 7404 0102
eneuberger@atkinchambers.com
Featured in Construction (London)

Practice Areas: Practice covers general commercial disputes with particular specialisation in construction and engineering, IT, professional negligence, insurance and PFI related matters. Edmund has advised on and appeared for parties involved in a wide range of disputes from major commercial construction contracts, railway infrastructure projects, energy infrastructure projects, waste PFIs to professional negligence and domestic building projects. Edmund has been instructed by insurers, developers, employers, professionals, contractors, sub-contractors and government. Edmund is experienced with most standard forms of contract, including NEC3. Edmund appears frequently in the High Court, as well as County Courts, and has broad experience of a range of dispute resolution procedures including litigation, arbitration, adjudication and mediation, as well as sitting as an adjudicator.
Professional Memberships: TECBAR, LCLBA, Society of Construction Law, Combar and CEDR (Adjudication Panel member).
Career: MEng (Oxon), Called to Bar by Lincoln's Inn 2008.
Publications: Contributing Editor of Hudson's Building and Engineering Contracts, 12th edition.

NEVILLE, Stephen
Gough Square Chambers, London
020 7353 0924
stephen.neville@goughsq.co.uk
Featured in Consumer Law (London)

Practice Areas: Has specialised in financial services, consumer credit and general contract for 25 years. Provided compliance reviews for many of the largest business and portfolio sales in the consumer lending sector over the last decade. His clients include a wide range of banks, lenders, debt acquirers and retailers, for whom he has drafted CCA related documentation, and is now advising on the technical issues arising from transition to FCA regulation. He is also active in loan enforcement and contract litigation: cases include - Airbus v Withey [2014 - Mercantile court trial of £1.5m secret commission claim], Carey v HSBC [2010] Bus LR 1142 [represented OFT: test case on enforceability of creditcard agreements], McMillan v Range [2004] 1 WLR 1858 (CA) [definition of credit], Rahman v Sterling Credit [2001] 1 WLR 496 (CA) [extortionate credit bargains], and Swindle v Harrison [1997] 4 AllER 705 (CA) [solicitor loan to client].
Career: St John's College, Cambridge MA(Hons)Law. Called to the Bar 1986.
Publications: Co-author of 'The Law of Consumer Credit and Hire' (OUP 2009) and 'Atkins Court Forms: Consumer Credit' (2009).

NEWMAN, Anya
St Ives Chambers, Birmingham
0121 236 0863
anya.newman@stiveschambers.co.uk
Featured in Social Housing (Midlands)

Practice Areas: Social housing.
Career: Anya Newman has developed a strong reputation in the field of housing and property law and prides herself on her ability to understand her client's objectives and give practical advice, enabling clients to achieve the best possible outcome in the most efficient manner. Anya frequently undertakes possession claims involving complex succession arguments or human rights and Equality Act 2010 elements. She is a specialist in anti-social behaviour litigation, and undertakes judicial review work as well as frequently advising on homelessness issues. Anya is currently being lead in a ground breaking cross-county injunction application to prevent car cruising and its associated issues across the Midlands.

NEWMAN, Catherine QC
Maitland Chambers, London
020 7406 1200
cnewman@maitlandchambers.com
Featured in Chancery (London), Company (London), Fraud (London), Offshore (London)

Practice Areas: Principal area of work encompasses business and commercial chancery litigation including all forms of business agreements, breach of contract, breach of trust, equitable remedies, restitution, corporate insolvency, partnership, loans and security, civil fraud and asset recovery, trusts litigation, and professional conduct and professional negligence. Acted in large insolvencies eg. Madoff, Maxwell Communications Corporation, BCCI and at all stages of the local authority interest swaps litigation (for the London Borough of Hammersmith & Fulham). Recent reported cases include Robert Tchenguiz v SFO [2014] EWHC 2379; JSC v Ablyazov [2014] EWCA Civ 602; Intesa Sanpaolo v Regione Piemonte [2013] EWHC 1994; JD Wetherspoon v Jason Harris [2013] 1 WLR 3296; Sycamore Bidco v Sean Breslin [2013] EWHC 583; Sycamore Bidco v Sean Breslin [2012] EWHC 3443; Boghani v Nathoo [2011] 2 All ER (Comm) 743 : [2011] 2 BCLC 704 : (2011) 108(32) LSG 17 : [2012] Bus LR 429; HMRC v Uddin [2010] EWHC 1799; Liquidators of Madoff Securities v Yacht Bull Corp [2010] EWHC 133; J D Wetherspoon v Van de Berg; [2009] 16 EG 138 (CS); John Curtis v Lockheed [2008] 1 CLC 219, Gamlestaden Fastigheter v Baltic Partners [2007] UKPC 26; J D Wetherspoon v Van de Berg [2007] PNLR 28.
Professional Memberships: Chancery Bar Association, COMBAR, ACTAPS, PNBA, IBA.
Career: Called to the Bar 1979; to the BVI Bar 2011; QC 1995. Assistant Recorder 1998. Recorder 2000. Lieutenant-Bailiff of the Royal Courts of Guernsey 2001-14. Deputy

High Court Judge 2008. Registered to appear in the DIFC (Dubai).
Personal: Educated at Convent of the Sacred Heart High School 1965-72 and University College, London. (LLB 1st Class Hons 1978). Harmsworth Scholar of the Middle Temple 1979-80.

NEWMAN, Peter
1 King's Bench Walk, London
020 7936 1500
pnewman@1kbw.co.uk
Featured in Family/Matrimonial (London)
Practice Areas: Matrimonial Finance and Divorce; Financial Provision for children; Trusts of Land; Private children law and child abduction.
Professional Memberships: Member of the Honourable Society of the Inner Temple; Member of the Family Law Bar Association; Member of the South Eastern Circuit; Member of the Sussex Bar Mess.
Career: Peter Newman specialises in matrimonial finance. Peter has appeared at all levels, including the Court of Appeal and the Supreme Court. He is frequently instructed in complex and high value disputes, both appearing on his own or led by Queen's Counsel. In addition Peter advises and acts in other family finance work, such as Trust of Land disputes between cohabitants and applications for financial provision for children pursuant to Schedule 1 of the Children Act 1989. Peter also acts in child abduction cases, and private law children disputes.
Personal: Peter is married and has a young son. He lives in South London.

NEWSOM, George
Guildhall Chambers, Bristol
0117 930 9000
george.newsom@guildhallchambers.co.uk
Featured in Agriculture & Rural Affairs (Western)
Practice Areas: George Newsom is a national expert on restrictive covenants. He is a specialist property, estates and farms barrister, and a mediator and arbitrator. He accepts instructions from solicitors, other professionals and direct from clients. His areas of expertise include real estate (land) litigation, tribunals, and arbitrators; dispute resolution and mediation; covenants, titles, easements and registration; options, leases and tenancies; farms, businesses, developers, private estates and partnerships; boundaries, walls, fences, rights of light, drainage and ways; public and private rights; commons and highways; planning appeals and enforcement; environment and nuisance; compulsory purchase and compensation; local authority property, church property, charities, clubs; co-ownership, shared property, and family trusts; inheritance provision, wills, intestacy and probate; surveyors, valuers and professional negligence.
Professional Memberships: Chancery Bar Association, Chartered Institute of Arbitrators.
Career: MA (Oxon), Barrister since 1973, ADR Accredited Mediator, Fellow of the Chartered Institute of Arbitrators, Part-time Regional Judge of the First-tier Tribunal (Property Chamber, Agricultural Land and Drainage). Recent cases include Shephard v Turner (Tribunal and Court of Appeal) substantially clarifying criteria for modifying covenants and of considerable importance to developers and objectors.
Publications: Preston & Newsom's 'Restrictive Covenants affecting Freehold Land' (now 10th Edition, 2013); Newsom's 'Faculty Jurisdiction of the Church of England'.

NEWTON, Katharine
Old Square Chambers, London
020 7772 5524
newton@oldsquare.co.uk
Featured in Employment (London)
Practice Areas: Katharine practices almost exclusively in the field of employment law, and appears regularly in the employment tribunal, the High Court and the appellate courts, including the Court of Appeal. Katharine acts for both employers and employees in every area of employment law including discrimination of all types, victimisation, unfair and wrongful dismissal, whistleblowing, TUPE, breach of contract, restrictive covenants, wages and trade union and industrial disputes. Katharine also has considerable experience of conducting lengthy, complex and high value discrimination claims, including many lasting in excess of 20 days. Katharine's experience encompasses a wide range of sectors, but she has particular expertise in acting for Banking and Financial Institutions (including well known high street banks), NHS Trusts, High Street retailers, Higher Education Institutions as well as Claimants holding both senior and junior roles. In addition, Katharine has particular expertise in conducting claims in the civil courts arising out of discrimination in the provision of goods and services.
Professional Memberships: Employment Lawyers' Association; Employment Law Bar Association; Industrial Law Society; Bar European Group.
Career: Called to the Bar 1999 Middle Temple.

NEWTON-PRICE, James
Pump Court Chambers, Winchester
01962 868 161
jnp@pumpcourtchambers.com
Featured in Crime (Western)
Practice Areas: James is an experienced and busy barrister in criminal and regulatory law. He prosecutes and defends in large, multi-defendant organised crime trials (drugs conspiracies, armed robberies, fraud and money laundering and murder) with large volumes of complex telephone and forensic evidence. He is regularly instructed in difficult cases of rape and child abuse, which require sensitive handling of vulnerable witnesses. He also defends in Court Martial hearings and in serious road traffic cases, including causing death by dangerous driving. He has particular expertise in Regulatory law and his practice encompasses health and safety matters, maritime law and medical disciplinary hearings.
Professional Memberships: Association of Regulatory and Disciplinary Lawyers, Criminal Bar Association, Western Circuit.
Career: Called Middle Temple 1992, James is a Level 4 Prosecutor and appears on the Attorney General's A list for regulatory work.
Personal: BA (Honours) University of Oxford, Diploma in Law City University, London.

NG, Jern-Fei
Essex Court Chambers, London
020 7813 8000
jfng@essexcourt.net
Featured in Energy & Natural Resources (London), Fraud (London), Tax (London)
Practice Areas: Barrister specialising in civil fraud, commercial litigation, energy and commodities, international arbitration, shipping and indirect tax, with offices in London and Singapore. Cases include: RBS Deutschland (sole counsel for RBS in the ECJ against the governments of the UK, Germany, Italy, Ireland and Denmark); Fiona Trust litigation (civil fraud, shipping, described by The Times as "the shipping trial of the century"); Thiess v Kaltim Prima Coal (commodities, energy); Ikos hedge fund litigation (civil fraud); Chambers Finance Ltd v Brent (promissory notes); BlackRock v HMRC (compound interest claim); Chubb Insurance Company v HMRC (insurance premium tax); American Express v HMRC (partial exemption). Also has extensive experience in a large number of arbitrations, both ad hoc and institutional (HKIAC, ICC, KLRCA, LCIA, LMAA, SIAC and UNCITRAL rules). Named by Legal Week as one of ten Stars at the Bar for 2012 and named by the Tax Journal as one of the 40 leading tax practitioners under the age of 40. Recommended by Legal 500 and Chambers UK for up to four categories: civil fraud, energy, shipping and VAT. Recommended also by Chambers Asia and Chambers Global for international arbitration for both the Asia Pacific-wide and Singapore categories (Band 1).
Career: Education: Trinity College, Cambridge (MA). Called 2002, Lincoln's Inn.

NICE, Amelia
5 St Andrew's Hill, London
020 7332 5400
amelianice@5sah.co.uk
Featured in Extradition (London)
Practice Areas: Amelia Nice is a barrister specialising in extradition. She has a busy appellate practice and has appeared in leading Article 8 cases involving children and vulnerable individuals, mental health, prison conditions and other human rights considerations, notably trafficking and the use of assurances and undertakings. Cases include Basionkina v Lithuania [2014] EWHC 1432 (Admin); Pamula v Poland [2014] EWHC 617 Admin); Wolkowicz and Ors v Poland [2013] 102 (Admin); Aleksynas v Lithuania [2014] EWHC 437 (Admin Amelia has particular experience in UK cases involving children law, including those with parallel international child abduction proceedings and those involving domestic Care Proceedings. She has also been involved in numerous cases involving technical areas of law (e.g. Pomiechowski v Poland [2012] UKSC 20). Amelia is also instructed by the National Crime Agency in extradition and related judicial review proceedings and regularly advises individuals and judicial authorities on issues concerning the preparation of extradition requests from this jurisdiction to other countries, particularly those concerning historic child abuse.
Professional Memberships: Extradition Lawyers Association.
Career: BA, MA, GDL, Called 2006 (Inner Temple).

NICHOLLS, John QC
Maitland Chambers, London
020 7406 1200
jnicholls@maitlandchambers.com
Featured in Chancery (London)
Practice Areas: Business and commercial chancery litigation, including contractual and shareholder disputes, fraud claims and banking and finance law. Has particular experience of large professional negligence claims and professional disciplinary proceedings. Also has considerable experience of aspects of sports law and telecommunications law. Notable cases include BCCI v Price Waterhouse, Barings v Coopers & Lybrand, Electra v KPMG, Money Markets International v London Stock Exchange, Cambridge Antibody Technology v Abbott Biotechnology, Scottish & Newcastle PLC v PricewaterhouseCoopers, GSK v Abbott Biotechnology and Royal Bank of Scotland v Highland.
Professional Memberships: Chancery Bar Association; COMBAR.
Career: Called to the Bar 1986, appointed QC 2006.
Personal: Born 1963; educated Winchester College and Trinity Hall, Cambridge (BA Law, 1st Class honours); married with two children; lives in Twickenham; particular interests are sport and travel; member Hawks Club, Aula Club, Lensbury Club, Bombay Gymkhana; speaks French and German.

NICHOLLS, Paul QC
11KBW, London
020 7632 8500
paul.nicholls@11kbw.com
Featured in Employment (London)
Practice Areas: Employment law, public law, procurement law and commercial law. Specialist in employment cases with a commercial element, in particular in the High Court. Recent cases include applications for and resisting restrictive covenant injunctions, garden leave cases and bonus and breach of contract claims. Public law claims include acting for the Bar Standards Board in judicial review challenges to disciplinary decisions (Mehey v Visitors to the Inns of Court and McCarthy v Visitors to the Inns of Court), acting for the legal aid authority in a leading case concerning payment of experts' fees in family law cases (R (JG) v Lord Chancellor) and acting for the Association of Personal Injury Lawyers in its claim against the Secretary of State for Justice. Procurement law claims have included a series of cases for the LSC in challenges to its tendering exercise. Commercial cases include shareholder disputes and commercial arbitrations.
Career: Called 1992, QC 2012.
Publications: Sometime contributor to Tolley's Employment Law Handbook and Halsbury's Laws.
Personal: LLB (Sheffield), BCL (Oxford) – Vinerian scholarship.

NICHOLSON, Jeremy QC
4 Pump Court, London
020 7842 5555
jnicholson@4pumpcourt.com
Featured in Construction (London), Professional Negligence (London)
Practice Areas: Construction and engineering, energy, professional negligence, insurance, and general commercial work. He has an outstanding track record in achieving successful conclusions to major and difficult cases. He is known for mastery of technical detail and legal argument, lateral thinking, strategic advice, and team leadership in large and complex cases. He acts for insurers, contractors, employers, engineers, architects, surveyors, and other professionals; in litigation, arbitration, and mediation. Very wide experience of different types of buildings, structures, plant, and sites. Involved as advo-

cate or arbitrator in international arbitrations in Dubai, Geneva, Paris, and London. Major TCC cases include Co-op v John Allen 2012 28 ConstLJ 27; Southwark v IBM 2011 135 ConLR 136; Skanska v Somerfield 2007 CILL 2449; AXA v Cunningham Lindsey 2007 EWHC 3023; SST v AMEC 2006 EWHC 2909; Alfred McAlpine v Panatown 2001 1 AC 518; Alstom v British Airways 2000; J Sainsbury v Broadway Malyan 1999 PNLR 286.
Professional Memberships: CIArb, HKIAC, LCIA, SCL, SCLHK, TECBAR, PNBA, BILA, COMBAR, LCLCBA. Registered with DIFC Courts, listed on the HKIAC List of Arbitrators.
Career: Call 1977; QC 2000; FCIArb 2011.
Personal: Educated Rugby School; Trinity Hall, Cambridge; College of Law (Harmsworth Scholar). Interests: sailing, travelling, walking.

NISSEN, Alexander QC
Keating Chambers, London
020 7544 2600
anissen@keatingchambers.com
Featured in Construction (London), Professional Negligence (London)
Practice Areas: Specialist in advisory work and in adjudication, arbitration, litigation and the mediation of construction, engineering, energy, shipping and professional negligence disputes. Practice covers a wide variety of cases ranging from client/ developer claims (extensions of time, loss and expense etc), defects, PFI disputes, professional negligence, contractors' and sub contractors' claims, adjudication enforcement, disputes relating to bonds (both domestic and international), rail disputes, power stations and oil and gas projects. Chartered Arbitrator, an accredited adjudicator and mediator. Arbitration work covers both domestic and international disputes, including appointments by the ICC in Paris. Recent cases include UK Highways A55 Ltd v Hyder Consulting UK Ltd [2013] BLR 95, and Accolade v Volker Fitzpatrick, One of the top 20 Cases 2014 in The Lawyer, regarding a£150m claim for defects arising out of piling and floor slab issues at a production centre for very substantial drinks distributor.
Professional Memberships: SCL; TECBAR; COMBAR; Law Society Panel of Arbitrators 2006; SCMA.
Career: Called 1985; FCI Arb (2000) and Chartered Arbitrator (2003); TECBAR adjudicator (2002); accredited mediator (2004); QC (2006); Recorder (2007); Public Access Training (2008); Deputy High Court Judge (2013).
Publications: Contributor - Keating on Construction Contracts Ninth Edition (2012).

NOLAN, Dominic QC
Ropewalk Chambers, Nottingham
01159 472 581
dominicnolanqc@ropewalk.co.uk
Featured in Clinical Negligence (Midlands), Personal Injury (Midlands)
Practice Areas: He practises principally in high value and catastrophic personal injury, complex clinical negligence, criminal regulatory and disease claims. He is particularly sought after for cases involving head or spinal injuries. He advises upon procedural issues including costs issues and has on many occasions acted for insurers where fraudulent or exaggerated claims have been challenged. He has an interest in all areas of professional discipline and regulation. He prides himself on being approachable and sensitive when dealing with all parties involved in cases that arise under tragic circumstances. Since taking silk, he has also acted in commercial cases, either alone or with a specialist junior. He is an Accredited Mediator and has acted as Leading Counsel in mediations in more complex cases.
Professional Memberships: Personal Injuries Bar Association; Professional Negligence Bar Association; Nottinghamshire-Medico Legal Society
Career: Called in 1985; Silk 2006; called to the Gibraltar Bar: 2007; LLB, University of Nottingham; Recorder on the Midland Circuit; Honorary Lecturer in Law - University of Nottingham 2003; Honorary Professor in Law - University of Nottingham 2009; President of Nottinghamshire Medico-Legal Society 2014; Head of Ropewalk Chambers: 2009 – 2012. He was awarded Barrister of the Year by Nottinghamshire Law Society in 2013.

NOLTEN, Sonia
2TG - 2 Temple Gardens, London
020 7822 1200
snolten@2tg.co.uk
Featured in Insurance (London), Property Damage (London)
Practice Areas: Insurance and reinsurance: coverage disputes, policy construction, fraudulent and exaggerated claims. Property damage, especially arising from floods, fires, explosions and subsidence. Commercial litigation: banking and finance, fraud, contractual claims. Professional negligence: particularly claims against brokers, solicitors and construction professionals including architects, engineers, surveyors. Recent cases include Bate v Aviva [2013] EWHC 1687 (Comm) (insurance: non-disclosure); Smyth v St Andrews [2012] EWHC 2511 (insurance: arson, coverage); Employers' Liability Trigger Litigation [2012] UKSC 14, [2010] EWCA Civ 1096 (insurance: principles of interpretation, scope of statutory cover); Dennard v PriceWaterhouse Coopers LLP [2010] EWHC 812 (Ch) (professional negligence: undervaluation of PHI project)
Professional Memberships: COMBAR, LCLCBA, PNBA, BILA, Health Claims Forum.
Career: Called 2002, Inner Temple. Major Scholar 2001, 2002. Tenant at 2 Temple Gardens since 2003. Treasury Panel of Counsel since 2009.

NORBURY, Hugh QC
Serle Court, London
020 7242 6105
HNorbury@serlecourt.co.uk
Featured in Chancery (London), Commercial Dispute Resolution (London), Fraud (London)
Practice Areas: Commercial and chancery litigation including fraud, domestic and international trust litigation, contractual disputes in many different business areas. Extensive experience of cross-examination in fraud and other commercial/chancery cases.
Professional Memberships: Chancery Bar Association, Commercial Bar Association.
Career: CPE at City University. LLM at King's College London. Called 1995. QC, 2012.
Personal: Married with two sons. Keen on playing and watching almost any sport.

NORMAN, John
1 Chancery Lane, London
020 7092 2900
jnorman@1chancerylane.com
Featured in Professional Negligence (London)
Practice Areas: John specialises in professional negligence, the liabilities of public authorities, in particular education claims, personal injury and product liability. He has considerable experience of dealing with claims for stress-related illness. On the professional negligence side he represents parties concerned primarily with the defaults of barristers, solicitors, surveyors, architects, engineers and accountants. He has also been involved with insurance and re-insurance disputes. Reported cases in which John has appeared include: Stevenson and others v Southwark London Borough Council [2011] (damages; planning); Ahmad v Brent London Borough Council & Others [2011] (human rights; detention); Jubilee Motor Policies Syndicate 1231 v Volvo Truck & Bus (Southern) Ltd [2010] (damages; insurance); Whiteside v Croydon London Borough Council [2010] (psychiatric injury); West Sussex County Council v Russell [2010] CA (highways); Nuttall v LB Sutton [2009]; Palmer v Palmer and PZ Products [2008] CA; Paterson v Surrey Police Authority [2008].
Professional Memberships: Professional Negligence Bar Association; London Common Law and Commercial Bar Association.
Career: Called to the Bar 1979.
Publications: Contributor 'Liabilities of Local Authorities', Morrell and Foster 2009; Specialist editor 'Pittaway & Hammerton: Professional Negligence Cases', Butterworth 1998.
Personal: Educated at Sherborne School and London School of Economics. Leisure pursuits include tennis and cricket.

NOSWORTHY, Jonathan
St Philips Chambers, Birmingham
01212 461 600
jnosworthy@st-philips.com
Featured in Family/Matrimonial (Midlands)
Practice Areas: Jonathan specialises in financial remedy proceedings (including high net worth cases), claims under the Trusts of Land and Appointment of Trustees Act 1996 and applications under Schedule One of the Children Act 1989. Jonathan has significant experience in dealing with claims for financial orders where interveners claim beneficial interests in matrimonial property, and where there are overseas assets (particularly in India). He also has experience in dealing with complex cases where there are issues of significant non-disclosure.
Professional Memberships: Family Law Bar Association.
Career: Birmingham University, Harmsworth Scholarship Middle Temple. Called to the Bar in 2000.

NOURSE, Edmund
One Essex Court, London
020 7583 2000
enourse@oeclaw.co.uk
Featured in Company (London)
Practice Areas: Edmund Nourse is a senior junior practising in civil fraud, commercial law and litigious company law. He has appeared in such high profile cases as Re Barlow Clowes [2006] 1 WLR 1476 and Digicel v Cable & Wireless [2010] EWHC 774 (Ch); [2010] EWHC 888 (Ch). In 2012-13, Edmund acted for Sir David and Sir Frederick Barclay and their interests in the unfair prejudice dispute over ownership of the Connaught, Berkeley and Claridge's hotels: Re Coroin plc:[2013] 2 BCLC 583-786 (Ch D and CA). He is currently acting for the defendants in the group litigation relating to alleged blacklisting of construction workers.
Professional Memberships: COMBAR; ChBA.
Career: Call 1994.

NURSE, Gordon
Radcliffe Chambers, London
020 7831 0081
gnurse@radcliffechambers.com
Featured in Chancery (London)
Practice Areas: All aspects of traditional and commercial chancery, including real property, landlord and tenant, trusts, wills and family provision, charities, partnership, company (in particular minority shareholders rights), and related professional negligence. Particular interest in the constitutions and regulations of sports clubs and governing bodies, including disciplinary regulations and procedures.
Professional Memberships: Chancery Bar Association; Professional Negligence Bar Association; Bar Sports Law Group; Charity Law Association.
Career: Deputy Master in the High Court Chancery Division; International Hockey Federation (FIH) Disciplinary Commissioner; Chairman of the England Hockey Appeal Panel.

NUVOLONI, Stefano
No5 Chambers, Birmingham
08452 105 555
sn@no5.com
Featured in Family/Matrimonial (Midlands)
Practice Areas: Experienced in all aspects of the law relating to children and acts predominately in public law children act cases. Regularly instructed in complex child care proceedings involving child death, fictitious and fabricated illness, serious physical injury, sexualised abuse, internet pornography, child exploitation and trafficking and care proceedings involving an international element. He is currently involved in advising and representing parties in claims arising from discharge of freeing order cases. Regularly provides training to child care professionals. Within the private law sphere he represents clients in residence and contact disputes and cases of internal and international relocations and child abduction.
Professional Memberships: Family Law Bar Association.
Career: Notable Cases A City Council v DC [2013] EWHC 8 (Fam) Re J (A Child) [2009] EWCA Civ 1210 Sandwell Metropolitan Borough Council v GC & HC & X & MMC [2008] EWHC 2555 (Fam) RE S (A child) [2008] EWCA Civ 1140 Re F (A child) [2008] EWCA Civ 218 Evans v Amicus [2003] EWHC 2161 (Fam) Re S & Ors; Re W & Ors Sub nom Re W & B [2002] UKHL 10.
Personal: LLB (Hons)University of London MA (Medical Law and Ethics)University of London Italian Speaker.

O'BRIEN, Paul
Axiom Advocates, Edinburgh
07739 638 967
paul.obrien@axiomadvocates.com
Featured in Restructuring/Insolvency (Scotland), Intellectual Property (Scotland), Commercial Dispute Resolution (Scotland)

Practice Areas: Commercial litigation, intellectual property, and insolvency; also acts in other areas of civil and public law. Appears regularly in Court of Session commercial court, and has First-Tier Tribunal, Inner House and Supreme Court experience. Cases include Farstad Supply AS v Enviroco Ltd [2010] UKSC 18, [2010] Bus LR 1087 (rights of contribution) and [2013] CSIH 9, 2013 SLT 421 (rate of interest); Verathon Medical (Canada) ULC v Aircraft Medical Ltd [2011] CSOH 19 (patents); Winding Up Board of Landsbanki Islands HF v Mills [2013] UKSC 13, [2013] 1 WLR 725 (recognition of foreign insolvencies); Joint Administrators of Rangers FC plc, Noters [2012] CSOH 55, 2012 SLT 599 (effect of administration on contracts); Regus (Maxim) Ltd v Bank of Scotland plc [2013] CSIH 12, 2013 SLT 477 (letters of comfort); David T Morrison & Co Ltd v ICL Plastics Ltd [2013] CSIH 19, 2013 SLT 413 (timebar; Supreme Court decision awaited); Clark v TripAdvisor LLC [2014] CSOH 20, 2014 SLT 418 (attempted recovery of internet user details); Ted Jacob Engineering Group Ltd v Robert Matthew, Johnson-Marshall & Partners [2014] CSIH 18 (pre-action disclosure and foreign law)
Career: Qualified 1999. Solicitor at Maclay Murray & Spens, Glasgow 1999-2003. Called 2004.

O'BRIEN, Susan QC
Compass Chambers, Edinburgh
01312 265 071
susan.obrien@compasschambers.com
Featured in Personal Injury (Scotland), Clinical Negligence (Scotland)
Practice Areas: Specialist in personal injury, clinical negligence, and disease cases; has a particular interest in psychiatric injury. Extensive experience of litigation in all Scottish courts. Regularly instructed in multi-million pound claims, such as catastrophic injury and cerebral palsy. Reported cases include: Holdich v Lothian Health Board 2014 SLT (OH) 495 (debate on the law relating to storage of sperm samples, including liability for psychiatric injury when they were destroyed); Eric Wallace, Curator to Ronald Pate v Stewart Homes (Scotland) Ltd - 2013 CSOH 30, (building site accident, high level of contributory negligence); Marjorie Campbell v Borders Health Board 2011 CSOH73 and 2012 CSIH49, (contested proof regarding obstetric negligence); John Aitchison v Glasgow City Council (correct interpretation of Carnegie case and time bar, 5 judges, 2010 SC 411); B v Murray 2008 SLT 561 HL (interpretation of time bar provisions in historic abuse cases); Cross v Highlands and Islands Enterprise 2001 IRLR 336 (pioneering stress at work claim, relying on EU legislation). Employment cases include Helen Percy v Church of Scotland Board of National Mission 2006 SC(HL)1, 2006 IRLR 195 HL (sex discrimination claim for lady minister, implementation of Directive, constitutional bar to suing church overturned); Archibald v Fife Council 2004 IRLR 197 (IH) (early case on interpretation of disability discrimination legislation); Cannop v Highland Council 2008 IRLR 634, 2008 SLT 625,(instructed by trades unions in equal value claims in case on interpretation of Dispute Resolution Regulations) Public law cases include: Petition of Rehab Abdel-Rahman for Judicial Review 2013 CSOH 201 (representing university sued by PHD student, in claim involving Human Rights); BJ v Pauline Proudfoot, Children's Reporter (2011 SC201), (Human Rights challenge to legislation detaining a child as being outside the legislative competence of the Scottish Parliament); Brian Black, Curator ad Litem v Mental Health Tribunal for Scotland and The Scottish Ministers 2011 CSIH 83 (competence of appeal by Curator); Potter v Scottish Ministers 2007 SLT 1019 (IH), (prisoner with ECHR claim); Sutherland-Fisher v Law Society of Scotland 2003 SC 562 (IH) (instructed by Law Society in disciplinary appeal); Tehrani v UK Central Council for Nursing 2001 SC 581, 2001 IRLR 208(OH)-(defending nursing body in test case on compliance of its disciplinary rules soon after introduction of Human Rights Act 1998).
Career: Chairman of Faculty Services Ltd 2005- 2007 (elected office bearer of Faculty of Advocates); Chaired Inquiry on death of Caleb Ness for Lothian and Borders Child Protection Committee 2003; Called to Bar 1987, silk 1998; Solicitor 1980-86. Current judicial posts - Member of Investigatory Powers Tribunal 2009 to date; Fee paid Employment Judge 2000 to date; Part time Chairman Pensions Appeal Tribunal (Scotland) 2012 to date.

O'DEMPSEY, Declan
Cloisters, London
020 7827 4000
dod@cloisters.com
Featured in Employment (London)
Practice Areas: Declan O' Dempsey specialises in sensitive and difficult employment, discrimination, public and regulatory law, directors' employment and employment injunctions. He has been recommended as a leading junior for many years, recently with the comment that he "knows employment law like the back of his hand.". His practice covers all areas of employment and trade union cases, data protection, confidentiality, and ECHR human rights law. His cases include Homer v Chief Constable of West Yorkshire[2012] UKSC 15); the Heyday retirement age judicial review; Seldon v Clarkson Wright and Jakes [2012] UKSC 16); Coleman v Attridge Law; X v Mid Sussex CAB [2012] UKSC 59; Azmi v Kirklees MBC (niqab); Gurkha Welfare Association pension rights case; Bent v Central Manchester University Hospital Trust (construction of the NHS Agenda for Change contracts) Manchester College v Hazel [2014] EWCA (TUPE, ETO reasons), Sobhi v Commissioner Of Police Of The Metropolis [2013] UKEAT (UNRCPD application in the UK), Lockwood v DWP EWCA (age discrimination, comparators), and Begraj v Heer Manak (2014 UKEAT, recusal). He accepts work under the Public Access Scheme. His practice includes goods and services and public functions cases. He is an author of the statutory code on Goods and Services and Public Functions for the EHRC under the Equality Act 2010, its Age Supplement (2013) and the EHRC Guidance on the Public Sector Equality Duty. He has an international reputation as an expert on European anti-discrimination law. In 2011 he co-authored a Thematic Report on Age Discrimination in the EU for the European Commission.
Professional Memberships: Bar Council's Equality and Diversity Committee; International Bar Association; Executive Committee of Human Rights Law Association. ELBA ELAAS, and the Bar Pro Bono Unit.
Career: Called in 1987, first employment worker for the FRU 1987-88. PLC's Employment Law Consultative committee; Halsbury's Law Exchange. Appointed Part time fee paid Employment Judge 2013.
Publications: Discrimination Law handbook (LAG, 2013). LCN Handbook on Goods Facilities and Services Discrimination (2014), Age Discrimination Law Handbook (Legal Action 2006), Employment Law and the Human Rights Act 1998 (Jordans, 2001), and Disability Discrimination: The Law and Practice. Guides for litigants in person to ET rules 2013 (open access, Youtube).

O'FARRELL, Finola QC
Keating Chambers, London
020 7544 2600
fofarrell@keatingchambers.com
Featured in Construction (London), Energy & Natural Resources (London)
Practice Areas: Specialist in construction and engineering disputes and domestic and international arbitration. Practice includes loss and expense claims; ship building disputes, information technology, insurance and energy disputes, professional negligence, bonds and guarantees, and health and safety matters. Recent work includes arbitration concerning an offshore wind farm project, litigation, arbitration and mediation concerning commercial contracts, adjudication concerning major rail infrastructure contracts, disputes concerning letters of credit and performance bonds in respect of infrastructure and technology projects in the Middle East, and adjudications and mediations on various construction and engineering developments.
Professional Memberships: TECBAR; COMBAR; SCL; SCMA; UK Energy Law Group.
Career: Called 1983; QC 2002; TECBAR Accredited Adjudicator & ADR Accredited Mediator 2004; Recorder 2008.
Publications: Bonds, Parent Company Guarantees and other Security - ICE Manual of Construction Law 2010; Litigation - Engineer's Dispute Resolution Handbook (1st and 2nd Editions); Consulting Editor, Construction Law Reports; Editorial team, Sweet & Maxwell electronic Construction Law Service; Editorial team, Keating on Building Contracts (5th, 6th and 7th editions).

O'HAGAN, Rachael
Thirty Nine Essex Street, London
020 7832 1111
rachael.ohagan@39essex.com
Featured in Construction (London)
Practice Areas: Rachael specialises in construction, engineering, technology, nuclear/energy and commercial disputes and also advises in relation to professional negligence claims associated with those sectors. In those sectors, she is experienced in seeking to resolve parties' disputes by various types of proceedings including: litigation, arbitration, adjudication and mediation. This experience includes international and domestic dispute resolution. Rachael is instructed (as a junior and in her own right) by a variety of clients, including: employers, contractors, professionals and governmental bodies/departments. Her case profile includes complex high-value claims and also in smaller domestic disputes.
Professional Memberships: SCL (Rachael is an active member of the Junior SCL Committee), TECBAR, COMBAR.
Career: Year of Call: 2006.
Publications: Wilmot-Smith on Construction Contracts (3rd Edn) (contributor), The Law of Waiver, Variation and Estoppel, Sean Wilken QC and Karim Ghaly, 3rd Edition OUP 2012 (assisted with research); RICS Case in Point: Rights to Light, by Sarah Hannaford Q.C., Jessica Stephens and Rachael O'Hagan (October 2008).

OHRENSTEIN, Dov
Radcliffe Chambers, London
020 7831 0081
dov@radcliffechambers.com
Featured in Chancery (London), Commercial Dispute Resolution (London)
Practice Areas: Litigation and dispute resolution relating to commercial chancery (eg banking, companies, guarantees, insolvency and mortgages), property and professional negligence. Significant cases include Blindley Heath Investments Ltd v Peter Bass [2014] EWHC 1366 (Ch) (Shareholder pre-emption agreement, estoppel, refusal of registration of share transfer), Norwood v Nabai, ChD, LTL 27/5/2014 (Contempt of Court for breach of freezing order, custodial sentence), Hawkes & Telerate Ltd v County Leasing Asset Management ChD, LTL 21/10/2011 (Company Restoration and Limitation Override), United Vending Ltd v Desai [2011] EWHC 919 QB (assignment, administration, bailment), Immingham Storage Co Ltd v Clear Plc [2011] EWCA Civ 89 (contract formation, offer and acceptance), Lui v Chong [2010] EWCA Civ 398 (assents, bare trusts, gifts, intention and beneficial interests), Basinghall Finance PLC v Butler [2009] EWCA Civ 1262 (mortgages, assignment, securitisation, privity).
Professional Memberships: Chancery Bar Association, Professional Negligence Bar Association.
Career: MA Cantab (Selwyn College). Called to the Bar in 1995.
Publications: The Civil Court Practice 2014 ("the Green Book"), co-author of 'Companies'. Butterworths Law of Limitation, co-author of "Equity". Halsbury's Laws of England (4th Ed, Reissue), co-author of "Money".

OLDHAM, Jane
11KBW, London
020 7632 8500
Jane.Oldham@11kbw.com
Featured in Education (London), Local Government (London)
Practice Areas: Administrative law including the following: vires, capital finance, charging for services, public procurement, freedom of information including environmental information (representing both the Information Commissioner and public authorities), local authority and health body disputes, education, community care, political balance and monitoring officer issues, challenges to budget cuts, public sector equality duty, defending claims against local authorities in restitution. Represented 14 local authorities in the Interest Rate Swap litigation between local authorities and banks. Advised on capital finance issues arising from several major millennium projects undertaken by local authorities. Complex District Auditor investigations and proceedings. Examples of cases: R (Lewisham London Borough Council) v AQA and Ofqual [2013] PTSR D13 (judicial review of 2012 award of English GCSEs); R (UNISON) v NHS Wiltshire and nine other PCTs [2012]

EWHC 624 (Admin) (trade union's judicial review challenge to PCTs' alleged breach of procurement rules; standing and delay issues); R (Hunt) v North Somerset Council [2013] EWCA Civ 1320 and 1483, SC forthcoming (public sector equality duty); R (Omotosho) v The Governing body of Harris Academy Crystal Palace [2011] EWHC 3350 (Admin) (judicial review of Academy school's admission arrangements and admissions appeals process);R v Richmond LBC ex parte McCarthy and Stone Developments Ltd [1992] 2 AC 48 (HL) (charging for services); Suppiah v Secretary of State for Home Department [2011] EWHC 2 Admin (disclosure of serious case review in challenge to government policy of detaining children of failed asylum seekers with their parents pending deportation); R(L) v Governors of J School [2003] 2 WLR 518 (HL) (teachers' industrial action and whether pupil entitled to be reinstated after appeal against school exclusion); R (Swords) v Secretary of State for Communities and Local Government [2008] HLR 17 (housing stock transfers); R (Daskaloulis) v University of Western England [2008] EWHC 2981 (Admin) (retaking university exams); R (Crouch) v Secretary of State for Health (2009) ICR 461 (terms of NHS dentists' contracts); Financial Services Authority v Information Commissioner [2009] EWHC 1548 and 1784 (Admin) (degree to which context of request for information to be taken into account in considering exemption under Freedom of Information Act 2000); North Western and North Wales Sea Fisheries Committee v Information Commissioner [2008] UKIT EA/2007/0133 (commercial confidentiality exception to disclosure of environmental information); McBride v Information Commissioner and Ministry of Justice [2008] UKIT EA/2007/0105; Craven v Information Commissioner [2008] EA/2008/0002; Boddy v Information Commissioner and North Norfolk District Council [2008] UKIT EA/2007/0074; Salmon v Information Commissioner and King's College Cambridge [2008] UKIT EA/2007/0135; Welsh v Information Commissioner [2008] UKIT EA/2007/0088; Tuckley v Information Commissioner [2008] UKIT EA/2006/0077; Financial Services Authority v Information Commissioner [2008] UKIT EA/2007 0093 and 0100; Financial Services Authority v Information Commissioner and Riverstone Management Agency Ltd [2008] UKIT EA/2008/0047; Financial Services Authority v Information Commissioner [2009] UKIT EA/2008/0061; East Riding of Yorkshire Council v Information Commissioner [2010] UKIT EA/2009/0069; Youth Justice Board v Information Commissioner EA/2010/0013; Dunn v Information Commissioner and National Audit Office EA/2010/0060; Davis v Information Commissioner and Tate Gallery EA/2010/0060.

Professional Memberships: ALBA, COMBAR, Procurement Lawyers' Association.

OLDHAM, Peter QC
11KBW, London
020 7632 8500
peter.oldham@11kbw.com
Featured in Education (London), Local Government (London)

Practice Areas: Public, local government, education, employment, procurement. Recent cases include: R ota BAPIO v Royal College of GPs [2014] EqLR 409 – equalities challenge to GPs' exam; R ota Nestwood Ltd v South Holland DC [2014] BLGR 354 – challenge to LA's refusal to follow Ombudsman's recommendation; Bugden v LB Bromley June 2014 – mass claim of inducement against collective bargaining under s 145B TULRCA; CIT v Kensal Rise School 2014/2015 – whether school's entry into photocopying contract was lawful; Compromise Agreements Ltd v BIS 2014 – whether unfair dismissal compensation cap lawful.

Career: 1990 call; silk 2010. Very wide experience as litigator and adviser.

Personal: Born 1963.

O'LEARY, Robert
Civitas Law, Cardiff
08450 713 007
clerks@civitaslaw.com
Featured in Personal Injury (Wales & Chester), Personal Injury (All Circuits)

Practice Areas: Robert is regularly instructed by trade unions, insurers, government departments and individuals. He has particular experience in industrial injuries and occupational disease work, including NIHL, HAVS, respiratory disorders, asbestos claims, stress, and work related upper limb disorders. Robert has been involved in some of the most complex and high profile work in the disease field, including the Nottinghamshire and Derbyshire Deafness Test Litigation heard by the Supreme Court (Baker v Quantum [2011] UKSC 17); the Phurnacite Workers' Group Litigation (cancer and respiratory disease); Thomas and others v Arriva Trains Wales Ltd (upper limb disorders), and the BT workers' deafness claims.

Professional Memberships: APIL, PIBA.

Publications: Robert is author of the chapters on Occupational Cancer and Assaults at Work in Munkman on Employer's Liability (16th Edition).

O'LEARY, Sam
One Essex Court, London
020 7583 2000
soleary@oeclaw.co.uk
Featured in Commercial Dispute Resolution (London), Company (London)

Practice Areas: Sam O'Leary has a broad commercial practice encompassing litigation, arbitration and advice. He has particular experience of complex financial matters; contentious corporate and shareholder litigation; energy and resources; jurisdictional disputes; and civil fraud. He has substantial trial experience, both alone and with a leader. Significant cases include: Re Charterhouse Capital Limited (six-week trial and forthcoming appeal relating to the management buy-out of a leading private equity business); Euroption Strategic Fund Ltd v Skandinaviska Enskilda Banken (two-week trial relating to the forced close out of a hedge fund's trading portfolio); Kleanthous v Paphitis (£100 million claim relating to the acquisition of the La Senza lingerie business); F&C Alternative Investments Holdings Ltd v Barthelemy (nine-month trial relating to the management of a fund of hedge fund business during the financial crisis and the exercise of put option rights by the fund managers); ITV v Scottish Television (£30 million contractual dispute relating to the management of the Channel 3 television network); and Re Kaupthing Singer & Friedlander Ltd; Brazzill v Willoughby (High Court and Court of Appeal dispute regarding the validity and operation of a £100 million trust account established by Kaupthing at the direction of the FSA following Kaupthing's collapse).

OLIVER, Crispin
Dere Street Barristers, York
08443 351 551
c.oliver@derestreet.co.uk
Featured in Family/Matrimonial (North Eastern)

Practice Areas: Crispin is once again recommended this year in Chambers UK as a leading family law specialist. He has an increasing emphasis on high value financial and property matters. He concentrates on complex care work in the High Court and particularly on difficult financial cases arising from divorce, separation of cohabiting partners and civil partners. He has a very strong background in dealing with intractable residence and contact disputes and acting for the children in public law cases. He also has a developing case load in the Court of Protection. He is heavily in demand as a lecturer at seminars and training events in which he has been described as "charismatic and a good teacher". In his capacity as Coroner he has handled serious Article 2 related Inquests.

Professional Memberships: North Eastern Circuit; Family Law Bar Association, Resolution, Collaborative Lawyer, Inquest Lawyers Group.

Career: Called 1990. Senior Assistant Coroner for North and South Durham and Darlington.

Personal: Born 1965. Married with 3 children. Interests are family, family holidays, competitive cycling and duathlon, charity fund raising, history and comparative religion.

OLIVER, Heather
3 Raymond Buildings Barristers, London
020 7400 6400
heather.oliver@3rblaw.com
Featured in Crime (London)

Practice Areas: Heather prosecutes and defends a full range of criminal matters, along with appearing in extradition, licensing and regulatory cases. She is currently instructed as led junior for the first defendants in Operation Cotton (land banking fraud) and Operation Kyrenia (NHS fraud), and for the second defendant in Operation Apple (making and accepting corrupt payments). She represents police officers from forces across the country in criminal trials and misconduct hearings. She appears for requested persons in extradition matters at first instance and on appeal; she successfully resisted extradition on appeal to the High Court in R v Majchrzak [2013] EWHC 3584 (Admin) on grounds of delay. She regularly appears in regulatory matters, particularly in connection with fire safety and breaches of environmental legislation. She represents applicants and appellants in a range of licensing work. She has successfully appeared in the Court of Appeal twice in the last year in criminal matters, appealing conviction and sentence.

Career: Oxford (Univ.) (1st class, BA Hons), City (GDL, Distinction), Call 2010.

O'MAHONY, David
7BR, London
020 7242 3555
clerks@7br.co.uk
Featured in Offshore (London)

Practice Areas: Offshore, Civil Fraud, Arbitration, Criminal Fraud, International Criminal Law, Corruption and Financial Regulation. David's particular areas of expertise are cases involving international issues (both conflicts of laws / jurisdiction in civil proceedings and jurisdiction / mutual legal assistance and international criminal law issues in criminal proceedings), offshore issues (including trusts and offshore structures) and cross-over issues between civil and criminal fraud. David's arbitration experience includes proceedings in ICSID and under the DIFC - LCIA rules and his civil fraud experience includes civil forfeiture actions by the USDOJ. David has worked on high profile cases in countries all over the world and has extensive knowledge of the institutional, legal and cultural issues that arise, particularly in politically sensitive cases and cases involving corruption issues.

Professional Memberships: David has been called to the Queensland and Australian Federal Bars, the bar of the Turks and Caicos Islands (for a particular case) and is admitted to practice in the Dubai International Financial Centre (DIFC) courts. He is a member of the ARDL, the Fraud Lawyers Association, the Commercial Fraud Lawyers Association, the International Bar Association and Chatham House.

Career: LLB Hons (first class) University of Queensland, Australia. LLM, Jesus College, Cambridge. Tutor in Public Law, LSE (1999-2000). European University Institute (Florence), Human Rights Law Summer School.

Publications: Butterworths Fraud Practice – co author of chapter on civil fraud and cross – over issues between civil and criminal fraud.

OMAMBALA, Ijeoma
Old Square Chambers, London
020 7269 0300
omambala@oldsquare.co.uk
Featured in Employment (London)

Practice Areas: Ijeoma specialises in trade union, employment, pensions and discrimination law including equal pay. As well as providing excellent advocacy services and strong relational skills Ijeoma provides high quality strategic advice in connection with all aspects of the management and litigation of complex trade union, employment and discrimination law cases. Ijeoma is instructed in difficult and/or factually complex, high profile and high value discrimination and whistle-blowing claims. Most recently she successfully resisted a challenge to paternity pay arrangements v additional maternity pay arrangements for a leading employer. Other recent cases involved local government, trade union, manufacturing, banking and financial sector clients. Her trade union law practice includes matters within the certification officer's jurisdiction, contractual disputes as well as injunction and other proceedings. Her employment law practice includes high court cases involving restrictive covenants, bonuses, search and seizure orders and executive severance. Ijeoma regularly undertakes work advising and representing healthcare professionals, their training providers and their employers on employment and discrimination law matters. Recent cases have involved judicial review proceedings and applications for injunctive relief. Ijeoma also practices as a mediator. She is a member of the Civil Mediation Council and CEDR exchange.

Professional Memberships: Justice, ELBA, ILS, DLA. CEDR Exchange, CMC.

Career: Called in 1989 Gray's Inn, Bencher 2014. CEDR Accredited mediator.

O'NEILL, Brian QC
2 Hare Court, London
020 7353 5324
briano'neilqc@2harecourt.com
Featured in Crime (London)

Practice Areas: "A very strong practice... he is very level headed and very cool" Chambers & Partners. "Recommended for heavy criminal cases requiring good strong advice and advocacy." Legal 500. For many years Brian O'Neill QC has been consistently recommended by industry guides, as one of the leaders at the Criminal Bar. Now in his fifth year in Silk, his practice spans serious crime, fraud and corporate crime and regulatory and professional disciplinary proceedings. Brian defends and prosecutes in equal measure, in cases of serious and organised crime particularly in cases of murder, terrorism, armed robbery, sexual offences, drugs and firearms. He is regularly instructed to represent high-profile individuals, professionals, and sportsmen (including a number of Premiership footballers) facing criminal allegations. Brian is particularly sought after in "paper heavy" and substantial multi-handed cases where his diligence, analytical skills and attention to detail, are highly valued. These skills, have led to him being instructed in a number of cases involving serious financial crime. He also advises corporate clients in this jurisdiction and abroad on fraud and business crime issues. Additionally, Brian advises and appears in cases concerning regulatory law and professional discipline. In particular he is instructed (to prosecute and defend) in cases involving accountants and auditors before the Conduct Committee of the Financial Reporting Council (formerly the Accountancy & Actuarial Disciplinary Tribunal). He also undertakes cases before the General Medical Council, the Solicitors' Disciplinary Tribunal, and the PhonepayPlus Tribunal.
Professional Memberships: Brian was a member of the Bar Council for a number of years and is a former Secretary of the Criminal Bar Association.
Career: Called 1987. Silk 2010. Brian was appointed as a Recorder of the Crown Court in 2000 and is authorised to sit at the Central Criminal Court.

O'NEILL, Sally QC
Furnival Chambers, London
07860 223 753
son@furnivallaw.co.uk
Featured in Crime (London)

Practice Areas: Specialises in very serious violent and sexual crime and murder including baby shaking murder allegations involving complex medical evidence. Has a particular interest in young and vulnerable defendants and witnesses. Past cases include the prosecution of the 'Baby "P" case' (in 2008), defending in R v. Whiting (the murder and abduction of Sarah Payne), defending in R v Farhi, (the Jimmy Mizzen case), prosecuting in R v B, the rape of a very young child. Defending in the murder of the defendant's female partner by stabbing her over 60 times. This was the first prosecution under the amended partial defences of loss of control and diminished responsibility. Defending in a double jeopardy prosecution for the murder 15 years earlier of a woman walking her dog, defendant then aged 20. Defending allegations of rape of a 10 year old, aiding and abetting prostitution. Defending allegations of assault and child cruelty on a young baby involving complex medical evidence. Defending in a multi-handed murder and attempted murder of two members of the defendants' family by shooting and running over with a Range Rover. Defending in the murder of a woman in her own home by attacking her with a golf club and a video recorder. Defending in a multi-handed murder with young defendants. Defending in the murder of a female jogger on Mitcham Common and burying the body. Defending in R v Wray, a high profile allegation of murder of a 4 month old baby who was found to be suffering from congenital rickets. Acquitted. Defending in a multi-handed allegation of fraud ("sham marriages"). Acquitted. Recent cases include S.18 on a baby who survived and Child cruelty and attempting to pervert the course of justice involving a 12 week old baby who died. Also defended a defendant currently serving 7 life sentences on a very serious allegation of rape. Defended 1st defendant in Oxford grooming case. Defended Ian Watkins (Lost Prophets) on very serious child sexual abuse.
Professional Memberships: Criminal Bar Association. Chairman of the CBA 2007-8. South-Eastern Circuit.
Career: Called 1976. Queen's Counsel 1997. Recorder 1997.Bencher of Grays Inn 2003. Member of CBA/NSPCC working group which produced "A Case For Special Measures" DVD as a training material. Member of ATC working group which recently published a report "Raising the Bar : Improving the handling of vulnerable witnesses and defendants in court." Member of current CBA/NSPCC working group which has produced a new DVD training material relating to above report.

ONSLOW, Robert
8 New Square, London
020 7405 4321
robert.onslow@8newsquare.co.uk
Featured in Information Technology (London), Intellectual Property (London)

Practice Areas: A Barrister whose principal areas of practice are information technology and intellectual property. Contractual IT disputes form a large part of Robert's practice with additional areas including all aspects of computer law, internet and domain names, e-commerce and data protection. IP areas include patents, trade marks, musical and literary copyright and industrial designs. Recent cases: SAS v World Programming [2014] R.P.C. 8, Shanley v Lloyds TSB [2014] EWCA Civ 40, Volkswagen v Garcia [2014] F.S.R. 12, HTC v Nokia [2013] EWHC 2917, IPCom v HTC [2013] EWHC 2880. For comprehensive CV visit www.8newsquare.co.uk.
Professional Memberships: Member of Bar Council IT Panel; Society for Computers and the Law (SCL) Intellectual Property Bar Association (IPBA); The Intellectual Property Lawyers Organisation (TIPLO).
Career: Called 1991. Director of software house with programming experience in Java, Python and Haskell and associated technologies such as SQL, MongoDB and XML
Publications: Laddie Prescott & Vitoria: Modern Law of Copyright
Personal: Born 1965. Educated at Eton College and Magdalen College, Oxford (1987 BA Physics). Hobbies include music and entertaining 4 children.

ORCHARD, Anthony QC
Carmelite Chambers, London
020 7936 6300
aorchard@carmelitechambers.co.uk
Featured in Crime (London)

Practice Areas: Significant experience defending and prosecuting in organised and very serious crime, particularly complex fraud, money-laundering, confiscation, computer related crime, drugs and murder. Has appeared in numerous high profile fraud and murder trials, notably the "the Derby fire case" and the "Lulzsex hacking case". Frequently advises client under investigation. Regularely defends and prosecutes cases brought by the Serious Fraud Office and the Financial Conduct Authority.Has appeared in over eighty homicide trials, many involving allegations of multiple shooting, gangland murder and revenge.Regularly advises on SOCPA contracts, PACE, PII matters, RIPA, Surveillance and Computer law. Recent cases: R v Michale Philpott. Accused with others of starting the fire that led to the death of six young children at this Derby home in May 2012. R v Al-Bassam. Worldwide denial of server attacks on UK and international law enforcement and commercial organisations over a period of several months in 2011. R v Islam. Murder of elderly lady customer by shopkeepers in Chatham. R v FB others and R v F. Allegations of importing commercial quantities of class A and B drugs via legitimate commercial businesses.

ORME, Emily
Arden Chambers, London
020 7242 4244
emily.orme@ardenchambers.com
Featured in Social Housing (London)

Practice Areas: All areas of housing, landlord and tenant and local government law.
Professional Memberships: Housing Law Practitioners Association, Social Housing Law Association.
Career: Called to the Bar in 2003, Emily advises both public and private sector clients (including local authorities, social landlords, tenants and the homeless) on a variety of matters including housing, landlord and tenant disputes, business tenancies, administrative and local government, mortgages, homelessness, housing benefit, anti-social behaviour, nuisance, disrepair and possession claims. Notable cases include: Birmingham CC v (1) VB (2) HC (3) F [2008] EWHC 1224 (QB); R (Hassan) v Croydon LBC [2009] JHL D56; Makisi v Birmingham CC [2011] HLR 27; Akhtar v Birmingham CC [2011] HLR 28; Willougby v Solihull MBC [2013] HLR 36; Mohamoud v Birmingham City Council [2014] HLR 22.
Publications: Co-author: Current Law Statutes, Annotations to Housing and Regeneration Act 2008; Homelessness and Allocations, (8th and 9th editions). Author: "Child tenants – a minor problem" New Law Journal, Vol 155, No. 7196, p1522, approved by the Court of Appeal in Alexander-David v Hammersmith & Fulham LBC [2009] HLR 39. Other articles published in Journal of Housing Law and Solicitors Journal.
Personal: Emily particupates in triathlons and marathons and uses the latter to raise money for charity.

ORNSBY, Suzanne QC
Francis Taylor Building, London
020 7353 8415
suzanne.ornsby@ftb.eu.com
Featured in Planning (London)

Practice Areas: Suzanne Ornsby is a highly proficient public, planning and environmental lawyer with wide experience of acting for utilities, multinationals, planning authorities, action groups and individuals. She is regularly involved in controversial judicial challenges as well as promoting or opposing major infrastructure proposals relating to water and electricity supply, minerals and waste, together with commercial and residential schemes including those affecting the built heritage. Her advice has been extensively sought from both the private and public sector on the interrelationship and legality of the new NPPF and the Localism Act 2011 in particular in the context of the five year housing supply, the duty to co-operate and neighbourhood planning. Suzanne acted for the successful respondent authority in a recent judicial review relating to neighbourhood planning. She successfully appeared for Thames Water at the major inquiries held into the UK's first desalination plant and into its Water Resources Management Plan. She advises on the implications of the Environmental Assessment of Plans and Programmes Regulations 2004, the Habitats Assessment Regulations 2010 and the Water Framework Directive. She has recently acted at a major inquiry into two urban extensions to Aylesbury and at four Core Strategy examinations for the Local Planning Authority. She acted for English Heritage concerning the site of the Battle of Tewkesbury and for developers on a highly controversial scheme in the Clifton Conservation Area, for two neoclassical town houses designed by Robert Adam, architectural adviser to Prince Charles. She has appeared at numerous inquiries for housing proposals, including proposals affecting a listed building previously owned by Agatha Christie. She also works for student accommodation providers advising on their responsibilities and liabilities under the Housing Act 2004 and has recently successfully acted in demonstrating that Bristol City Council's approach to licensing of HMOs is unlawful .
Professional Memberships: Member and previous secretary of the Planning and Environment Bar Association, UKELA, the Administrative Law Bar Association, the Criminal Bar Association, the Compulsory Purchase Association and Health and Safety Lawyers Association. She is a trained advocacy instructor for the Middle Temple.
Career: Called to Bar: 1986 Appointed Queen's Counsel : 2012.

ORR, Craig QC
One Essex Court, London
020 7583 2000
corr@oeclaw.co.uk
Featured in Banking & Finance (London), Commercial Dispute Resolution (London), Insurance (London)

Practice Areas: Barrister practising across the broad spectrum of commercial dispute resolution (both litigation and domestic and international arbitration). Expertise includes, but is not limited to, banking and finance, energy and natural resources, professional negligence (especially accountants' negligence), civil fraud, insurance and reinsurance, breach of confidence, breach of warranty and all forms of contractual disputes (including joint ventures). Recent work includes representing an AIM listed mineral resources company in proceedings to recover misappropriated mineral rights; representing a global risk consultancy in a US$800 million breach of confidence claim; representing a Luxembourg bankruptcy administrator in a hedge fund dispute; representing an international investment bank in a US$120 million derivatives claim; representing the administrators of Glitnir Bank hf in disputes arising out of the bank's collapse; representing an international betting and gaming group in claims arising out of its online gambling joint venture; representing telecommunications and defence contractors in UNCITRAL and LCIA arbitrations against an East African government; and representing an international oil company in disputes with a West African government. As well as appearing in the Senior Courts in England and Wales, he has wide experience of appearing before other tribunals, including the Supreme Court of Bermuda and LCIA and UNCITRAL arbitration tribunals. He also has extensive experience of giving evidence on English law in foreign proceedings (most recently in a major derivatives dispute in the High Court of Singapore).

Professional Memberships: COMBAR.

Career: Called to the Bar in 1986. Fox Scholar (at McCarthy Tetrault in Canada) from 1986-87. Joined Fountain Court in 1988. Took silk in 2006. Joined One Essex Court in 2011.

Publications: Contributor to Fountain Court on Carriage by Air and Professional Negligence & Liability.

Personal: Educated at Cambridge University 1981-84 (MA) and Oxford University (BCL, Vinerian Scholar). Born 8 January 1962.

OSBORNE, Richard
4 Pump Court, London
020 7842 5555
clerks@4pumpcourt.com
Featured in Information Technology (London)

Practice Areas: Commercial litigation and arbitration with particular experience in Information Technology disputes, where he has been instructed by some of the largest contractors, IT outsourcing providers and government departments in relation to a number of complex and substantial disputes. Also significant experience in the fields of insurance and professional negligence.

Professional Memberships: Society for Computers and Law (London Committee member), TECBAR, COMBAR, PNBA.

Career: MA (Oxon), called 2005.

OSEPCIU, Ligia
Monckton Chambers, London
020 7405 7211
lospciu@monckton.com
Featured in Public Procurement (London), Telecommunications (London)

Practice Areas: Ligia specialises in competition law, public procurement, telecommunications law and utilities regulation.

Career: Ligia has a broad advisory and litigation practice across her areas of specialism. In the competition sphere, she has been involved in a number of important private damages actions (e.g. National Grid v ABB et al – High Court; Albion Water v Dwr Cymru – CAT) and regulatory appeals (e.g. Groupe Eurotunnel v Competition Commission – CAT, merger decision; Merck KGaA v European Commission – General Court, pay for delay). Ligia's public procurement practice sees her regularly advising and representing contracting authorities, utilities and bidders in relation to High Court disputes (often unled) as well as providing strategic, risk-based advice to authorities and utilities on procurement design and compliance during the tendering phase. In the telecommunications field, Ligia was notably instructed as Junior Counsel to the successful Appellant in BT plc v Telefonica et al [2014] UKSC 42 concerning the scope of Ofcom's dispute resolution powers under section 185 of the Communications Act 2003. She also has experience of challenging the regulatory decision of PhonepayPlus (premium rate services) and ATVOD (on-demand audio-visual services).

Personal: BA (Cantab), LLM (Cornell) Languages: French (fluent), Romanian (native/fluent)

OSLER, Victoria
Five Paper, London
07810 560 949
victoriaosler@fivepaper.com
Featured in Social Housing (London)

Practice Areas: Recent housing cases include R. (on the application of IA) v Westminster LBC QBD, 20 May 2013 concerning Pt.7 Housing Act 1996, Camden v Stafford [2012] EWCA Civ 839, CA regarding introductory tenancies, Sharples v Places For People Homes Ltd: Godfrey v A2 Dominion Homes Ltd (2011) HLR 45, CA decision concerning debt relief orders, Abdullah v Westminster CC [2011] EWCA Civ 1171 and Hanton-Rhouila v Westminster CC, [2010] EWCA Civ 1334 concerning gate-keeping. Property cases include: Senpalit v Demirkiran, renewal of a business tenancy, and Andre v Robinson, Court of Appeal, 14th December 2007 concerning the surrender and re-grant of a protected tenancy. LVT cases include Cromwell Business Management Centre Company Ltd v Leaseholders of Cambray Court, Robertson v Red Kite Community Housing Ltd (1) HIgh Wycombe DC (2), Longmint v Rye, Unicourt Ltd v Bernhard Baron RTM Company, Lands Tribunal,Leaseholders of Spa Green Estate v London Borough of Islington, Leaseholders of Ingestre Road v London Borough of Camden, Evertitt v Budhram [2010] Ch. 170; Stealth Developments Ltd v Daejan Investments Ltd, Bland & Ors v Trustees of Calthorpe Estates Limited (1), Lambert Smith Hampton Group Limited, R (on the application of MT) by his litigation friend GT) v Oxford CC

Publications: Assistant editor of Encyclopedia of Housing Law from January 2003 to December 2011; co-author of Blackstone's Guide to the Anti-social Behaviour Act 2003; contributor to Jowitt's Dictionary on housing and local government definitions.

OSMAN, Osman
25 Bedford Row, London
Featured in Crime (London)

Practice Areas: Osman Osman is a specialist and highly sought after defence advocate practising in cases involving grave and complex crime, fraud and regulatory law. He is regularly instructed in both this jurisdiction and abroad in some of the largest and most complex cases. He is known for his attention to detail and ability to present complex evidence in understandable and digestible form. He is known for his calm and engaging jury style. He is an advocate of the use of technology in court and is familiar with case-map, live-note and the use of presentation software before juries. He is experienced in the management of high profile and heavy media related trials. Is used to representing high net-worth individuals. Osman is also specialist external counsel within the insurance industry advising on Bribery Act compliance in co-insurance agreements, third party and brokerage contracts. Osman advises both pre-and post charge in respect of FCA and SFO enquiries and investigations, with a specialisation in white-collar crime. He is regularly instructed on confiscation proceedings and resisting asset recovery both in the administrative courts and upon appeal. Osman advises upon the safety of convictions and regularly appears before the Court of Appeal, as well as, in the Administrative Court.

Professional Memberships: Financial Services Lawyers Association (FSLA) Fraud Lawyers Association (FLA) Criminal Bar Association (CBA) Proceeds of Crime Lawyers Association (POCLA) Association of Regulatory and Disciplinary Lawyers (ARDL) Member of the Gibraltar Bar.

Career: Notable Cases and work Fraud and financial regulation Re AXA insurance – in 2012 Osman was nominated sole external counsel to AXA Insurance PLC, advising on Bribery Act Compliance in respect of co-insurance agreements, commission contracts and third party brokerage arrangements. Operation Valley – Gibraltar based multi-million pound commercial fraud Operation Bangor – one of the largest investigations into banking fraud within the UK. Operation Rouble – complex money laundering investigation involving two other major investigations. Operation Krakatoa – complex money laundering conspiracy, largest investigation by the midlands police based on the illicit running of brothels in central London. Operation Intermediate – largest and most complicated counterfeiting operation to come before the UK courts, involving sterling and euro bank notes. Complex non-fraud cases Operation Montecarl 1 & 2, complex drug trafficking and money laundering conspiracy allegedly involving significant foreign syndicate, this case has been on going for 4 years. With an aspect of the case relating the seizure of a converted traveller by the Royal Marines off the Spanish Coast. Operation Nimjask, complex drugs conspiracy involving alleged foreign syndicate. R v S, M & Others – large scale Ebay trading standards fraud. R v P & Others – largest shame marriage conspiracy to come before a UK court. Eurovet – DEFRA investigation 2011, pan-European investigation into the multi-million pound in illicit trading of vetinary medicines through Europe into the UK. Operation Blue Sky – representing the principal in a Pan-European facilitation of illegal immigrants into the UK, the known facilitation case involvement the movement an estimated 100,000 individuals. The investigated spanned 3 EU countries to Turkey, with significant intercept evidence. Grave crime R v R – high profile cold case review murder from 1982 R v D – female accused of murdering her lover a case which, attracted significantly publicity in Turkey R v G – high profile triple murder by arson, which resulted in the accused being extradited from Europe Reported Cases: Osman regularly appears before the court of appeal, below is a sample few cases of significance R v Naseri [2014] EWCA authority following on from Avazi relating to the importation of opium and the sentencing guidelines council advisory notes re opium. R v Pimenta [2012] EWCA Crim 2998, female appellant following on from the case of R v Petherick [2012] EWCA Crim 2012 in relation to the imprisonment of sole carers. R v Abdulla Ali & Other [2011] EWCA Crim 260, leading authority in respect of autrefois convict, autrefois acquit, following a second re-trial abuse of process in the light media prejudice, as well as, conspiracies plots and sub-plots. In respect of the liquid bomb plot. R v Avazi & Others [2007] EWCA Crim 3443, leading authority on sentencing regarding large-scale opium importation. R v Bourgass & Others [2007] 2 Cr.App.R S40. Leading authority on sentence in respect of public nuisance connected to the Ricin terror plot. R v Valentine [2006] EWCA Crim 2717 leading authority on the ruling of hidden assets under PCA in confiscation proceedings. R v Matheos Dennis Michael [2005] EWCA, lead authority on cut-throat defences and ability to deploy cut-throat in a closing speech against first defendant when no challenge or case put during the calling of live evidence. Associated work Osman regularly lectures upon numerous topics of his specialisation Bribery & Corruption, regulatory and financial compliance, use and presentation of technological evidence in court, as well as, forensic evidence in homicide and sexual offences. He is a visiting lecturer to Barts & London School of Medicine & Dentistry, and has been invited to give talks at Middlesex and Wolverhampton Universities. He is an Advanced Advocacy Trainer and Assessor at Inner Temple and the School of Advanced Legal Studies.

Personal: Include walking and flamenco dancing.

O'SULLIVAN, Michael
5 Stone Buildings, London
020 7242 6201
clerks@5sblaw.com
Featured in Chancery (London), Court of Protection (All Circuits)

Practice Areas: A barrister with a wide Chancery practice, which incorporates trust litigation and advice, contentious and non-contentious probate applications, Inheritance Act applications, professional negligence in relation to negligent conveyancing and tax advice, Court of Protection applications, capital gains tax and inheritance tax planning. Notable recent cases include: Khan v Crossland [2012] WTLR Removal of Executor under S116 SCA 1982; EB v RC [2011] EWHC 3805 (CoP)Removal of Deputy under MCA 2005; Re P [2010] Ch 33 (the leading modern case on statutory wills in the Court of Protection); Carr v Thomas [2008] EWHC 2859 (contentious probate); PEER v EMC [2007] E.C.D.R 1[2006] EWHC 2883 (probate and copyright); Allardyce v Roebuck [2004] 3 All ER 754 (testamentary options).

Professional Memberships: STEP, ACTAPS, Chancery Bar Association, Property Bar Association.

Career: MA Cantab (Magdelene College) BCL Oxon (St Catherine's College). Called 1986 Lincoln's Inn. Accredited Mediator.

Publications: Author of 'Asset Protection' (Butterworths 2000). Co-author of 'A Practitioner's Guide to Trustee Investment' (Lexis Nexis Tolley, 2004). Contributor to Tottel's 'Trust Drafting and Precedents - purpose trusts and protective trusts'.

O'SULLIVAN, Sean QC
4 Pump Court, London
020 7842 5555
sosullivan@4pumpcourt.com
Featured in Commercial Dispute Resolution (London), Energy & Natural Resources (London), Insurance (London), International Arbitration (London), Shipping (London)
Practice Areas: Commercial Dispute Resolution: instructed in a wide range of contractual disputes, with a particular focus on shipping, shipbuilding and energy-related issues. He deals with shipping disputes of all shapes and sizes (whether involving dry bulk or liquid cargoes, containers, towing, support vessels, or the carriage of passengers or livestock) and the full range of shipbuilding and ship sale and purchase cases (covering everything from luxury yachts to semi-submersible drilling rigs). He also represents oil majors, petrochemicals traders and contractors in "energy" disputes (e.g. commodity sales, farm in/ farm out agreements, share purchase agreements, drilling contracts, distribution agreements, etc.). Other areas of expertise include insurance/ reinsurance (both marine and non-marine), professional negligence (esp. brokers, solicitors and accountants/auditors), and media and entertainment (esp. recording artists, music videos and advertising). He regularly appears before the Commercial Court in London and in arbitrations, both ad hoc and under the auspices of the various arbitral bodies around the world.
Professional Memberships: TECBAR, COMBAR. Called to the Bar of the Cayman Islands.
Career: MA (Oxon) Modern History. Called to the Bar in 1997. Silk in 2014.

OUDKERK, Daniel QC
Essex Court Chambers, London
020 7813 8000
doudkerk@essexcourt.net
Featured in Commercial Dispute Resolution (London), Employment (London)
Practice Areas: Daniel Oudkerk QC's practice spans commercial and employment law, with a particular emphasis on commercial disputes with an employment or partnership 'twist'. He acted for the successful claimants in the landmark conspiracy and team poaching litigation Tullett Prebon v BGC and for the Swiss IDB ContiCap in ContiCap v GFI in its Unfair Competition Act claim, one of The Lawyer's "top 20 cases for 2013". In 2014 he acted at trial for the successful claimant in a Commercial Court action against the oligarchs known as the Trio based on an oral contract. His clients range from investment banks, Lloyd's brokers, hedge funds, insurers and IDBs to private individuals, public bodies and regulators.
Professional Memberships: COMBAR, ELA, ELBA, LCIA.
Career: Called to the Bar 1992, QC 2010.

OVEY, Elizabeth
Radcliffe Chambers, London
eovey@radcliffechambers.com
Featured in Chancery (London), Consumer Law (London), Pensions (London)
Practice Areas: Principal specialist areas of work are pensions, mortgage lending and building society work, and other retail financial services. Also handles general chancery work, including professional negligence. Joint editor of 'Wurtzburg and Mills - Building Society Law' and 'Current Law Commentary on Building Societies Act 1986'. Joint author, 2nd edition of 'The Law of Investor Protection', including pensions chapter (1st ed. Fisher and Bewsey) and 'Retail Mortgages: Law, Regulation and Procedure' (2013), Member of working party responsible for the Standard Conditions of Sale (5th edition published April 2011) and the Standard Commercial Property Conditions (2nd edition published June 2004). Lectures and gives seminars occasionally. Contributes to pensions section of Lexis PSL.
Professional Memberships: Chancery Bar Association; Association of Pension Lawyers; Professional Negligence Bar Association; Charity Law Association.
Career: Called to the Bar 1978. Deputy Judge of the Upper Tribunal.
Publications: As above.
Personal: Educated at Southampton Grammar School for Girls 1966-73 and St. Anne's College, Oxford 1974-77. Lives in London. Born 1 December 1954.

OWER, Susan
Axiom Advocates, Edinburgh
07818 571 091
susan.ower@axiomadvocates.com
Featured in Restructuring/Insolvency (Scotland), Commercial Dispute Resolution (Scotland)
Practice Areas: Practices exclusively in commercial and company law; commercial litigation; commercial contracts; insolvency and restructuring; professional negligence. Recent cases include Ahmad -v- The Rangers Football Club Limited, Unreported (acting for football club in defence of action by former director); Alan Alexander Brown and John Bruce Cartwright, the Joint Administrators of Oceancrown Limited -v- Stonegale Limited [2013] CSOH 190 (acting for joint administrators in actions for recovery of property worth approximately £2.5million); Blair C Nimmo and Gary S Fraser, the Joint Administrators of Station Properties Limited [2013] CSOH 120 (acting for creditor in application by joint administrators for directions); Patricia Polley -v- West Lothian Council and Accountant in Bankruptcy [2014] CSOH 98 (acting for AIB in action for reduction of sequestration); Search Consultancy Limited -v- Gareth Biggerstaff & Others, Unreported (acting for recruitment consultancy in action for ex parte recovery of confidential information and associated action for interim orders and damages); Clydesdale Bank Plc -v- Allied Souter & Jaffrey, Unreported (acting for bank in respect of action against firm of surveyors, for professional negligence).
Career: Qualified as a solicitor 2003; called to Bar 2009; appointed standing junior counsel to the Scottish Government 2012 - date.

PACKMAN, Claire
4 Pump Court, London
020 7842 5555
cpackman@4pumpcourt.com
Featured in Construction (London)
Practice Areas: Primarily construction and engineering disputes, and associated professional negligence claims. Also fire and flood claims and related insurance issues, solicitor's negligence cases and general contractual disputes. Recent instructions include various high value arbitrations for the MOD and a number of engineer's negligence cases in the TCC relating to the construction of motorways, hospitals, commercial premises and large domestic building projects.
Professional Memberships: TECBAR, COMBAR, PNBA.
Career: Called to the Bar 1996, appointed Junior Counsel to the Crown 2010.
Publications: Contributing editor to LexisNexis online Adjudication KnowHow.
Personal: BA (Hons) Oxon in Modern Languages. Hobbies include Latin American travel and literature. Fluent in Spanish.

PADFIELD, Alison
Devereux, London
020 7353 7534
padfield@devchambers.co.uk
Featured in Insurance (London)
Practice Areas: Commercial barrister specialising in insurance and reinsurance, professional negligence and professional disciplinary proceedings. Substantial experience of insurance and reinsurance work for both underwriters and insureds across a wide range of types of insurance and reinsurance business. Recent cases include: Teal v Berkley [2013] Lloyd's Rep IR 56, Supreme Court (with Colin Edelman QC); Aspen Insurance UK Ltd v Adana Construction Ltd [2013] Lloyd's Rep IR 656 (with Colin Wynter QC); Synergy Health (UK) Ltd v CGU Insurance plc [2011] Lloyd's Rep IR 500 (with Colin Wynter QC) and Kamidan v Holt [2009] Lloyd's Rep IR 242.
Professional Memberships: COMBAR (Executive Committee member 2005-2008 and 2010-2013); BILA; PNBA; ARDL; Bar European Group.
Career: Called to the Bar in 1992. Case lawyer at the European Court of Human Rights (1999-2000). Judicial assistant at the Court of Appeal (part-time) (2007-08). Elected member of Bar Council 2012-14.
Publications: Author of 'Insurance Claims' (2012, 3rd edition, Bloomsbury Professional).
Personal: Education: BA (Oxon), Lic Sp Dr Eur (Brussels), BCL (Oxon).

PAGET, Michael
Cornerstone Barristers, London
020 7421 1826
michaelp@cornerstonebarristers.com
Featured in Social Housing (London)
Practice Areas: Property Litigation including Housing. Court of Protection and Mental Health
Career: Property practitioner with strengths in the public law elements of real estate litigation. Acts in claims for adverse possession, an equitable interest, rectification of the Register, forfeiture, planning enforcement, mortgage repossessions, under TOLATA, SWAP compensation, 1954 Act lease renewals, dilapidations, rent reviews, neighbour disputes including private law nuisance and boundary issues, service charge disputes, enfranchisement, unlawful evictions, and generally the use of land. In Housing litigation acts in possession actions, disrepair, homelessness disputes (including interim relief), allocation and general public authority duties. Also recognised as a costs expert and in enforcement actions. Acts in Court of Protection on financial deputy matters and welfare best interest declarations. Has expertise in mental health law including the role and responsibilities of the nearest relative.

PALEY, Ruth
23 Essex Street, London
020 7413 0353
ruthpaley@23es.com
Featured in Crime (London)
Practice Areas: Specialising in crime, fraud and financial regulation. Ruth is a sophisticated and confident advocate, known for her meticulous trial preparation and an ability quickly and efficiently to master the detail in large and complex cases. She has experience spanning the full range of criminal offences, from murder, rape and serious violence to organised crime and fraud. She enjoys particular expertise in matters involving fraud and financial regulation and is frequently engaged by high-profile clients requiring specialist advice in this field. In 2013 she was approached to lead the London project team of a highly confidential financial services regulatory investigation involving complex issues of corporate governance, risk management and AML, with an advisory role continuing into 2014. Other recent advisory work includes a sensitive sanctions investigation for an offshore regulator and an engagement with the FRC arising from the Equitable Life scandal. Ruth has also spent time at the RCPO as counsel to a specialist disclosure review team, at the SFO advising on disclosure in complex fraud cases, and with the National Crime Squad's FIU (now part of SOCA). She has government security clearance.
Career: Called to the Bar 2003, Appointed to CPS Advocate Panel Specialist lists for Serious Crime, Fraud and Proceeds of Crime. Grade III Prosecutor and CPS Rape List.

PALIN, Sarah
One Brick Court, London
020 7353 8845
sp@onebrickcourt.com
Featured in Defamation/Privacy (London)
Practice Areas: Media law; defamation; malicious falsehood; privacy and breach of confidence; data protection; freedom of information; contempt and reporting restrictions; pre-publication advice; injunctive relief; harassment; malicious falsehood/ trade libel; media related judicial review and regulatory work; media-related human rights law. Notable cases include: junior counsel for Associated Newspapers in The Leveson Inquiry; J. K. Rowling v Associated Newspapers [2014] EWHC 1170; Thour v Royal Free Hampstead NHS Trust [2012] EWHC 1473; Spiller v Joseph [2010] UKSC 53; Horlick v Associated Newspapers [2010] EWHC 1544; R(Dacre) v Westminster Magistrates Court [2009] 1 WLR 2241; Burstein v Associated Newspapers [2007] All ER 319; Neil & Christine Hamilton v Max Clifford [2004] EWHC 1542; The Hutton Inquiry; Grobbelaar v News Group Newspapers [2002] 1 WLR 3024 (HL).
Publications: Author of Atkin's Court Forms on Confidence, Privacy, Data Protection, Freedom of Information and Regulation of Investigatory Powers. Contributor to Arlidge, Eady and Smith on Contempt 4th Edition and supplement.
Personal: Brasenose College, Oxford.

PALMER, Norman E QC
3 Stone Buildings, London
020 7242 4937
npalmer@3sb.law.co.uk
Featured in Art and Cultural Property Law (London)
Practice Areas: All legal controversies and transactions related to art, antiquities and other forms of portable wealth, management of public and private art collections, museum governance, legislative drafting, investment and security in art, law and policy on cross-border art mobility, import and export of cultural objects, claims for restitution of unlawfully removed heritage material, repatriation claims by indigenous peoples and other dispossessed groups, architecture of art loans, joint acquisitions, repatriation arrangements and other agreements for sharing of cultural objects, co-operative transacting between different cultures and markets, authenticity and attribution, mediation of art-related disputes. Adviser and advocate on movable assets and personal property law, including bailment, carriage, chattel securities, finance leasing, sale of goods, claims in conversion and other title-related disputes, limitation periods, general commercial and contract law, arbitration and mediation in civil and commercial disputes. Clients include foreign governments, UK governmental departments and executive agencies, national and overseas museums, art dealers, archaeologists, private collectors, indigenous communities, banks, finance companies and other commercial corporations, insolvency practitioners, insurers, loss adjusters, transport companies, local authorities, ecclesiastical bodies, animal welfare groups.
Professional Memberships: Expert Adviser, Spoliation Advisory Panel, and formerly member (2000+); Chair, Treasure Valuation Committee (2001-11); Chair, Illicit Trade Advisory Panel (2000-05); Chair, Ministerial Working Group on Human Remains in Museum Collections (2000-2003); Standing International Counsel, National Gallery of Australia (2002+); Honorary Member, Seven Wentworth (Sydney) (2006+); Chair, ArtResolve (2014+).
Career: Called 1973. Professor of Commercial Law at UCL (1990-2002) and now Emeritus Professor of Law of Art and Cultural Property (2002+); Chairs in Law at many other English and Australian Universities (1981+); Doctor of Law Honoris Causa, University of Geneva (2005). Appointed CBE (2006) for services to art and to law.
Publications: Palmer on Bailment (3rd edn 2009); Museums and the Holocaust (2000); Cultural Heritage Statutes (2nd edn 2004); Art Loans (1997); Recovery of Stolen Art (1998); Interests in Goods (2nd edn 1998); Individual Liability of Museum Personnel (2011); Halsbury, Laws of England (titles: Bailment, Carriers, Confidentiality, Damages, Libraries and other Scientific and Cultural Institutions, Lien, Tort); Crossley Vaines on Personal Property (5th edn, 1973); Encyclopaedia Forms and Precedents; English Private Law (3rd edn, 2013) title Bailment; Laws of Australia; numerous others. Founded and co-edits Art Antiquity and Law (quarterly, Institute of Art and Law, 1996+). Publications by him have been cited by appellate courts of leading common law jurisdictions, eg House of Lords, Judicial Committee of the Privy Council, Court of Appeal, High Court of Australia, Supreme Court of Canada, Courts of Appeal of New Zealand, New South Wales, Victoria, British Columbia etc.
Personal: Married, two daughters.

PALMER, Robert
Monckton Chambers, London
020 7405 7211
rpalmer@monckton.com
Featured in Administrative & Public Law (London), Immigration (London), Telecommunications (London)
Practice Areas: Public, Regulatory, Telecommunications and EU law.
Professional Memberships: Administrative Law Bar Association (ALBA), Bar European Group (BEG).
Career: Robert has particular expertise in commercial judicial review proceedings in the Administrative Court and Competition Appeal Tribunal. He often appears unled in the Court of Appeal. Robert's EU law practice extends to frequent appearances in the Court of Justice of the European Union. Robert's wide experience includes work in the aviation, energy, financial services, pharmaceutical and telecommunications sectors. In addition, he has considerable judicial review experience in the areas of environmental, immigration, local government, and planning law. He is a member of the Attorney General's A Panel of counsel. He is also a member of the Equality and Human Rights Commission's Preferred Panel of Counsel. He is direct access qualified.
Personal: BA (Hons), Oxford (First Class), Diploma in Law (City University), Scarman Scholarship (ICSL), Prince of Wales Scholarship (Gray's Inn), President of the Oxford Union (1995).

PANESAR, Deshpal
Old Square Chambers, London
020 7269 0300
panesar@oldsquare.co.uk
Featured in Employment (London)
Practice Areas: An employment specialist, Deshpal regularly acts in complex, high value claims. He successfully represented BA cabin crew, NHS Trusts, Local Authorities, Trade Unions, Multi-national companies and government departments, with a heavy successful appellate practice. Recent Reported cases: Age discrimination Woodcock v Cumbria I.C.R. 1126; [2012] I.R.L.R. 491; Court v. Dennis Publishing (IDS Brief 840) Selden v Clarkson Wright and Jakes [2012] I.C.R. 716 where he provided the first advice. Games v University of Kent (Times Higher Education Supplement 2013). Collective agreements Gilgrove Ltd v Hay [2013] ICR 1139, George v MOJ [2013] EWCA Civ 324. Contracts of employment Qantas Cabin Crew v. Lopez and Hooper [2013] I.R.L.R. 4. Trade unions Kelly and Others v Unison [2012] I.R.L.R. 442. Unfair dismissal Bowater v Northwest [2011] I.R.L.R. 331. Race discrimination Nazir v Aslam [2010] I.C.R 1225 Described in Chambers and Partners as 'a cracking cross examiner', 'a fantastic team worker''Highly eloquent' and 'utterly reliable', and in Legal 500 as 'exceptionally well prepared', he has been at the forefront of age discrimination litigation. He has a growing High Court practice. PROFESSIONAL DISCIPLINE Particular articular experience in cases involving professionals in the healthcare industry, inculding Lakshmi v Mid Cheshire Hospitals NHS Trust [2008] IRLR 956 .
Professional Memberships: ELBA (Secretary) ELA, ILS, LSE Alumni Committee.

PARKER, Christopher R QC
Maitland Chambers, London
020 7406 1200
crparker@maitlandchambers.com
Featured in Offshore (London), Restructuring/Insolvency (London)
Practice Areas: Main areas of practice are company and insolvency law. Recently advised on and litigated in disputes in relation to the collapse of offshore hedge funds as well as other complex financial vehicles. Advised on aspects of the insolvency of Lehman Brothers. Recently appeared on a Bahamian insolvency matter in the Privy Council as well as appearing in shareholders' disputes before the Caribbean Court of Justice in Trinidad and in the LCIA. Appears regularly in the BVI. He has also advised on cases in Bermuda, Hong Kong, Guernsey and Jersey. He is registered with the Dubai International Financial Centre Courts (DIFC). Notable Cases: Ebbvale Ltd v Hosking [2013] UKPC 1 (winding up petition not an abuse of process); Bilta v Nazir [2013] EWCA Civ 968 (non-application of ex turpi causa claim by company against sole director/shareholder); Fanmail v Cooper (2011) (appropriation of business); Credit Suisse v Compass Global (BVI: 2010) (hedge fund); Raydens v Tchenguiz (2009) (share sale agreement, guarantee); Fanmail v Cooper (2009) (share ownership dispute); Re Neath Rugby Limited (2009) (unfair prejudice petition, acting for the Ospreys).
Professional Memberships: ILA, PNBA, ChBA, COMBAR, CLFA, ACTAPS.
Career: Called to the Bar 1984. Silk 2008. Called to the BVI bar 2006. Ad hoc admissions: Bahamas 2009 and Trinidad & Tobago 2010.
Personal: Educated at Keble College, Oxford BA Jurisprudence, 1st class, (1977-80) and BCL (1980-81), University of Illinois LLM (1981-82), Harvard Law School LLM (1982-83). Born 13 October 1958.

PARKER, Matthew
3 Verulam Buildings, London
020 7831 8441
mparker@3vb.com
Featured in Banking & Finance (London), Commercial Dispute Resolution (London), Energy & Natural Resources (London), Fraud (London), Offshore (London), Professional Negligence (London)
Practice Areas: Matthew's practice encompasses most aspects of general commercial litigation and arbitration, with particular expertise in banking and financial services, commercial fraud and professional negligence.
Professional Memberships: COMBAR, LCLCBA.
Career: Matthew is an experienced trial advocate, appearing in Alegro v Allproperty Media [2013] EWHC 3376 (QB), Lawlor v Sandvik [2012] EWHC 1188 (QB), Redmayne Bentley v Isaacs [2010] EWHC 1504 (Comm), Innovatis v Ejder Group [2010] EWHC 1850 (Ch), Fitzalan-Howard v Hibbert [2010] PNLR 11 and M&J Polymers v Imerys [2008] 1 All ER (Comm) 893. He has also appeared as sole advocate in the Court of Appeal, in Lawlor v Sandvik [2013] 2 Lloyd's Rep 98 and Morin v Bonhams & Brooks [2004] 1 Lloyd's Rep 702. Acting as a junior, he recently appeared in the Court of Appeal in NML v Chapman Freeborn [2013] 1 CLC 968 and regularly appears in heavy commercial litigation, such as Primary Group v RBS [2014] EWHC 1082 (Ch) and Porton v 3M Company [2011] EWHC 2895 (Comm). He has also acted in a number of high profile banking cases, particularly in the Bahamas and the Cayman Islands, in claims involving fraud and professional negligence arising out of the collapse of banks and investment funds. He has been called to the Bars of the British Virgin Islands and the Cayman Islands. Arbitration also forms a significant part of his practice, and he appeared in the series of reported decisions in Republic of Kazakhstan v Istil [2006] 2 Lloyd's Rep 307, [2007] 2 Lloyd's Rep 548, and [2008] 1 Lloyd's Rep 382.
Personal: Oundle School and Jesus College, Cambridge (foundation scholar).

PARKER, Paul
4 New Square, London
01608 641 827
p.parker@4newsquare.com
Featured in Professional Discipline (London)
Practice Areas: Principal areas are (i) professional liability claims and disciplinary proceedings involving lawyers (including wasted costs), accountants and auditors, financial services professionals, insolvency practitioners, insurance brokers, and construction professionals; (ii) general commercial and chancery commercial litigation, with particular emphasis on insurance law. Cases include: Roberts v Hook (2013) (QB Admin): SDT appeal from dismissal of private complaint; Nationwide BS v Davisons (2012) (QB and CA): solicitors' liability for breach of trust; Makar v Russell Jones and Walker (2012) (QB Comm): strike-out and CROs; Webb Resolutions v Waller Needham and Green (2012) (Ch): costs, effect of Protocol non-compliance on efficacy of Part 36 offer; Crabtree v Ng (2011) (CA): stage 1 wasted costs order quashed; Media CAT Ltd v Adams (2011) (PCC): wasted costs in P2P file sharing litigation; Dhamija v McBains Cooper (2010) (TCC): no duty on QS to report defects; Yechiel v Kerry London (2010) (QB Comm): insurance claim proved falsified; Angel Solicitors v Jenkins O'Dowd and Barth (2009) (Ch): conveyancing solicitors' undertakings; Rind v Theodore Goddard (2008) (Ch): duty of care and limitation in failed IHT avoidance scheme; Hooper v Biddle (2006) (Ch): incidence of costs on compromise of exaggerated claim; 1st Property Finance v Martin and Haigh (2006) (Ch): meaning of "completion"; Medisys plc v Arthur Andersen (2002) (QB): pre-action disclosure; R v PIA Ombudsman ex p Davies Walters (2001) (QB Admin): challenge to vires of ombudsman's award; Re A Firm of Solicitors (1999) (TCC): conflicts of interest and chinese walls; Nationwide BS v Lewis (1998) (CA): no liability of salaried partner without reliance.
Professional Memberships: PNBA, ChBA, COMBAR, LCLCBA.
Career: MA (Cantab). Called (Middle Temple) 1986. Joined Four New Square (formerly 2 Crown Office Row) 1987.
Publications: Editor of Jackson & Powell: Professional Liability Precedents; chapters on solicitors, IT professionals and appeals.
Personal: Educated at Mill Hill School and Christ's College, Cambridge. Leisure interests: family, singing and lawn tennis. Languages: French and Serbian.

PARKER, Timothy
9 Gough Square, London
020 7832 0500
tparker@9goughsquare.co.uk
Featured in Family/Matrimonial (London)
Practice Areas: Care proceedings featuring non-accidental injury, death and sexual abuse. Adoption and Special Guardianship. Judicial review of local authority decisions. Financial remedies upon divorce, cohabitee disputes, financial provision for children and family property disputes.
Professional Memberships: Family Law Bar Association, South Eastern Circuit, Association of Lawyers for Children.
Career: Called 1995.

PARRY, Clare
Cornerstone Barristers, London
020 7242 4986
clarep@cornerstonebarristers.com
Featured in Planning (London)
Practice Areas: Public law, planning, local government, social housing, property, licensing, regulatory.
Professional Memberships: PEBA, ALBA.
Publications: Contributor to Kolvin on 'Gambling for Local Authorities' and 'Licensed Premises: Law and Practice'.

PARTRIDGE, Richard
Serjeants' Inn Chambers, London
020 7427 5000
rpartridge@serjeantsinn.com
Featured in Clinical Negligence (London), Professional Discipline (London)
Practice Areas: Richard Partridge was called to the Bar in 1994. Richard specialises in clinical negligence, personal injury, professional discipline and regulation and inquests and inquiries. An earlier edition notes that "he is a bigger picture person and someone who always pursues what is right for the client. His background in medicine gives him an edge on medical issues." Please click on the link to the Serjeants' Inn Chambers website for his profile, which sets out full details of his practice including relevant work of note.
Career: Mb BCh, LLB Hons.
Publications: Co-author of Medical Treatment: Decisions and the Law.

PATERSON, Fiona
Serjeants' Inn Chambers, London
020 7427 5000
fpatterson@3serjeantsinn.com
Featured in Court of Protection (All Circuits)
Practice Areas: Fiona Paterson was called to the Bar in 2003. Fiona specialises in clinical negligence and healthcare, Court of Protection, inquests and inquiries, professional discipline and regulatory and public and administrative law. Before coming to the Bar, she practised for nine years as a solicitor in Scotland, advising on all aspects of medical and regulatory law. Since coming to the Bar, she has continued to develop her interest in these and related fields, representing both claimants and defendants. Please click on the link to the Serjeants' Inn Chambers website for her profile, which sets out full details of her practice including relevant work of note.
Professional Memberships: Justice, Human Rights Lawyers Association, Professional Negligence Bar Association.
Career: Attorney General's London C Panel of Junior Counsel, CEDR Accredited Mediator.
Publications: Co-author of Medical Treatment: Decisions and the Law.

PATTEN, Ben QC
4 New Square, London
020 7822 2000
b.patten@4newsquare.com
Featured in Construction (London), Professional Negligence (London)
Practice Areas: Principal areas of practice are professional negligence and construction, including claims against construction professionals. Frequently involved in cases involving solicitors, barristers, accountants, surveyors, financial advisers, insurance brokers, architects, engineers and project managers. Also, substantial experience in commercial and insurance disputes. Recent cases include Cheshire Building Society v Dunlop Haywards Limited [2008] PNLR 19, Biffa Waste Services Limited v Machinenfabrik Ernst Hese Gmbh [2009] BLR 1, Levicom International BV v Linklaters [2010] PNLR 29, Carillion v Phi Group Ltd [2010] EWHC 496, Asiansky Television Plc v Khanzada [2011] EWHC 2831, Guy v Mace and Jones [2012] EWHC 1022; Newcastle Airport Ltd v Eversheds [2013] PNLR 5.
Professional Memberships: Professional Negligence Bar Association, TECBAR, London Common Law and Commercial Bar Association.
Career: Called to the Bar in 1986 and joined 22 Old Buildings in 1988. Joined 1 Crown Office Row 1997. Joined 2 Crown Office Row (now 4 New Square) 1999. Queen's Counsel 2010.
Publications: Professional Negligence in Construction, Spon, [2005]. Co-editor of Jackson and Powell 'Professional Liability Precedents'.
Personal: Oxford University, City University, Middle Temple. Called to the Irish Bar.

PATTON, Conall
One Essex Court, London
020 7583 2000
cpatton@oeclaw.co.uk
Featured in Banking & Finance (London), Commercial Dispute Resolution (London), Competition/European Law (London), Energy & Natural Resources (London)
Practice Areas: Conall Patton has a broad commercial practice, including energy, competition, banking and finance, jurisdiction/choice of law, company and commercial judicial review. Recent cases include: acting (with Laurence Rabinowitz QC) for Mr Igor Kolomoisky in a large-scale Commercial Court dispute between three Ukrainian businessmen; acting (with Jon Turner QC) for British Airways in follow-on damages claims arising from an alleged cartel in the air cargo sector; appearing with Lord Grabiner QC in the Court of Appeal in a landmark decision on act of state and issue estoppel (Yukos Capital v Rosneft); appearing without a leader for private equity group Warburg Pincus in a two-week Commercial Court trial and in the Court of Appeal (Barbudev v Eurocom Cable); appearing with Lord Grabiner QC in the Supreme Court on a judicial review appeal (Gaines-Cooper v HMRC); appearing without a leader for a major investment bank in a one-week LCIA arbitration concerning claims for c. $100 million; arguing a novel point about the cost consequences of discontinuance in the Court of Appeal (Safeway Stores v Twigger); appearing with Thomas Sharpe QC in the Competition Appeal Tribunal in a construction penalty appeal; appearing with Lord Grabiner QC in the Eastern Caribbean Court of Appeal in the Yukos litigation. Conall is a member of the Bar of the British Virgin Islands.

PAXTON, Chris
Red Lion Chambers, London
01245 280 880
christopher.paxton@18rlc.co.uk
Featured in Crime (South Eastern)
Practice Areas: Chris Paxton defends and prosecutes both as a leading and led junior across a broad range of crime and related disciplines including Fraud, Road Transport and Regulatory work. His practice comprises the full range high-end crime, including murder, manslaughter, serious organised crime and serious sexual offences. Chris prosecutes for the CPS, VOSA and local authorities and defends both private individuals and companies. For the CPS Chris is a grade 4 prosecutor (the highest grade) and an accredited rape prosecutor. He has further developed particular expertise in Road Transport and Regulatory work, practising throughout the UK both in Court and in an advisory capacity. Recent work includes FRAUD: R v McMurray (2013), defence, fraud in a road haulage business involving income tax, national insurance and VAT fraud in excess of a million pounds; R v Jordan and others (2012), leading counsel (defence) in a multi-million pound mortgage fraud involving brokers, agents and solicitors; HOMICIDE: R v C (2014), leading for the Crown - Murder of young mother in presence of 4-year-old child. The case involved several expert witnesses on topics including DNA, footwear impressions, blood distribution and toxicology; R v McMurray (2013), defending in gross negligence manslaughter in road haulage industry; R v Jacobs (2012), defending a husband who killed his wife and left the body in a lake; complex legal/factual issues including psychiatric evidence; SEXUAL OFFENCES: R v X (2014), prosecuting rape of 3-year-old; R v C (2014), defending double rape allegation with complainant suffering unique communication condition; R v S (2014), defence, gang rape; R v M (2013), prosecuting multi-complainant rape/serious sexual offences.
Professional Memberships: Criminal Bar Association; Essex Bar Mess.

PAY, Adrian
New Square Chambers, London
020 7419 8000
adrian.pay@newsquarechambers.co.uk
Featured in Chancery (London)
Practice Areas: Adrian Pay's practice focuses on contentious chancery work, in particular, commercial chancery and property work. His commercial work includes commercial fraud, company and insolvency matters and contractual disputes (including matters with an information technology aspect). Recent cases include Caldero v Beppler & Jacobson Ltd [2013] EWHC 2191 (Ch); [2014] EWCA Civ 935, a high-profile dispute relating to two prestigious hotels in Montenegro. His property work includes, in particular, disputes arising out of property developments and deficient conveyancing. Recent cases include Angel Solicitors v Jenkins O'Dowd & Barth [2009] 1 WLR 1220; Clark v Lucas LLP [2010] 2 All ER 955; Kind v Northumberland County Council [2013] 1 WLR 743; R (Trail Riders Fellowship) v Dorset CC [2013] PTSR 987, CA.
Professional Memberships: Chancery Bar Association; COMBAR.
Career: Called to the Bar 1999.
Personal: Educated King's School, Canterbury; Balliol College, Oxford - MA (Oxon).

PAYNE, Alan
5 Essex Court, London
020 7410 2000
clerks@5essexcourt.co.uk
Featured in Immigration (London)
Practice Areas: Practice Areas: - Administrative and Public law, Immigration, Human Rights and Civil Liberties, Police law, Inquests, Inquiries, employment. Significant cases include: - EM (Eritrea) & Ors v Secretary of State for the Home Department [2014] UKSC 12; The Azelle Rodney Inquiry (representing the MPS and all officers save for the shooter); E7 v Sir Christopher Holland and the Commissioner of the Police of the Metropolis & Ors (Interested Parties) [2014] EWHC 452; Tabrizagh & 5 Ors v Secretary of State for the Home Department [2014] EWHC 1914; Bianca Durrant v Chief Constable of Avon & Somerset Nottinghamshire [2013] EWCA Civ 1624; John Yapp v Foreign & Commonwealth Office [2013] EWHC 1098; MPS v Chairman of the Inquiry into the death of Azelle Rodney and various interested parties [2012] EWHC 2783; Kent County Council v HM Coroner for Kent & Mr and Mrs Barry (Interested Parties) [2012] EWHC 2768; Desmond v Chief Constable of Nottinghamshire [2011] EWCA Civ 3.
Career: Called to the Bar 1996. Attorney General's 'A' Panel (2011) (previously 'B' panel 2007-10 and 'C' panel 2004-07). Develop Vetted.
Publications: Tolley's Employment Tribunals Handbook – first published October 2002 (fourth edition published by Bloomsbury Professional August 2014).

PAYNE, Geoffrey
25 Bedford Row, London
020 7067 1500
clerks@25bedfordrow.com
Featured in Financial Crime (London)
Practice Areas: Geoff Payne is a specialist in defending heavy fraud cases. He has acted in some of the longest, heaviest and highest value cases prosecuted, some involving allegations of fraud of up to £450 million. He is tenacious and proactive and has a strong track record in defending in some of the most complex cases dealt with by the criminal justice system. He appears in cases both alone and as junior counsel. This year, he has been instructed in a very large alleged sideways loss investment tax fraud arising out of the film industry. He also appeared in one of the earliest cases of Film Tax Credit Fraud. He also has a particular expertise in Missing Trader Intra-Community Fraud and acted for the defence in the largest 'Ponzi Fraud' ever prosecuted. He has also acted in cases of alleged advance fee frauds, long firm frauds and construction frauds, often acting for professionals such as accountants and liquidators. He regularly appears in cases involving allegations of misconduct in public office. He has successfully dealt with a number of confiscation proceedings and has appeared alone in the Court of Appeal. This year, he was in the case of Okedare [2014] EWCA Crim 228 which made new law on absconders in confiscation proceedings.

Professional Memberships: Criminal Bar Association, Proceeds of Crime Lawyers Association (POCLA), Association of Regulatory and Disciplinary Lawyers (ARDL).
Career: Called 2000; St Edmund Hall, Oxford, Modern History; City University, London, Common Professional Examination in Law; Inns of Court School of Law, London, Bar Vocational Course.

PAYNE, Tom
Red Lion Chambers, London
020 7520 6000
thomas.payne@18rlc.co.uk
Featured in Financial Crime (London)
Practice Areas: Tom Payne specialises in fraud and professional discipline, particularly cases involving complex issues of taxation, accountancy and anti-competitive behaviour. He has recently concluded the very first paperless criminal trials in England and Wales, using EPE and iPad jury bundles in a series of three highly complex construction industry VAT/PAYE frauds involving 20 defendants (Operation Savate). Other recent instructions include: Re A (investigation by the Financial Reporting Council), Operation X (criminal investigation by Competition and Markets Authority), Operation Y (complex money laundering investigation), Operation Z (criminal tax investigation into VHNWI), FRC v Corr and Miller (proceedings before FRC disciplinary tribunal concerning Cattles plc), Operation Rust (diversion fraud), Operation Inertia (MTIC), Operation Fastback (MTIC), Operation Victor (medicines), Operation Condor (British Airways price fixing case), R. v George [2010] EWCA Crim 1148 (cartel offence does not require reciprocal dishonesty), R. v IB [2009] WLR 357 (cartel offence is not a 'national competition law'), Operation Heron (the marine hose cartel) and R v. Briggs-Price [2009] UKHL 19 (proving benefit in confiscation proceedings).
Career: MA (Oxon), Trinity, 1996. LLM (Birmingham), 1998. Called Middle Temple, 1998. Appointed Recorder in 2012. Appointed to SFO A list in 2013. Grade 4 CPS prosecutor, 2012. Grade 4 CPS specialist panels for fraud, organised crime and proceeds of crime, 2013. Treasurer of the Criminal Bar Association, 2013-2014.

PEACOCK, Jonathan QC
11 New Square, London
020 7242 4017
jonathan.peacock@11newsquare.com
Featured in Tax (London)
Practice Areas: Jonathan advises financial institutions, multi-nationals and high net worth individuals on capital market, corporate finance, structured finance, venture capital, media financing and employee remuneration matters. He has a broad indirect tax practice, especially in relation to VAT and financial and insurance services and also has an extensive energy practice (predominantly oil and gas but also covering renewables and hydro-electric) which focuses on the North Sea but also extends to advising on interests and assets in the Barents Sea, Malaysia, West Africa, the Caribbean and offshore Brazil. He frequently appears in courts and tribunals in the UK and Europe (including the UK Supreme Court, the European Court of Justice and the European Court of Human Rights) on tax matters and has acted both for and against the UK Government in significant tax avoidance matters. He has been instructed in arbitrations and to provide expert opinions in overseas litigation and is the author of numerous articles and several books on aspects of revenue law.
Professional Memberships: Member of the VAT Practitioners Group, the Society of Trust & Estate Practitioners and the UK Offshore Industry Tax Committee. Chairman of the Revenue Bar Association.
Career: Corpus Christi College, Oxford, First Class (Jurisprudence).

PEACOCK, Nicholas
Hailsham Chambers, London
020 7583 0816
clerks@4pb.com
Featured in Clinical Negligence (London), Professional Discipline (London)
Practice Areas: Specialises in medical and dental law, including (i) clinical and dental negligence damages claims, in which he represents patients, individual doctors (whether in primary or secondary care), dentists and NHS Trusts/Health Authorities in all courts and in claims at all values; (ii) disciplinary and regulatory matters, including appearing at the MPTS (formerly GMC) (FTPPs considering conduct, performance, health; interim orders), GDC, GOC, internal PCT disciplinary hearings and the former FHSAA; also consequential High Court appeals and applications for JR; (iii) coroners' inquests; (iv) clinical confidentiality, consent to treatment and general healthcare advisory issues. Appointed Legal Adviser to the General Pharmaceutical Council (formerly RPSGB) in April 2006. See his website CV for further details.
Professional Memberships: PNBA; ARDL.
Career: Called 1992.

PEEL, Robert QC
29 Bedford Row Chambers, London
020 7404 1044
rpeel@29br.com
Featured in Family/Matrimonial (London)
Practice Areas: Principal area of practice is financial remedy.
Professional Memberships: FLBA.
Career: Oxford University (BA Hons). City University (DIP Law). Called to the Bar 1990. Appointed QC in 2010. Recorder on the Midland Circuit.
Personal: Fluent in French and Spanish.

PENNIFER, Kelly
Kings Chambers, Manchester
08450 343 444
clerks@kingschambers.com
Featured in Commercial Dispute Resolution (Northern), Construction (North Eastern)
Practice Areas: Commercial : agency and commercial agency; banking and finance; civil fraud; credit (including consumer credit); director/employee fiduciary duties, duties of confidence and restrictive covenants; guarantees and indemnities; injunctive relief (in particular freezing injunctions, search orders, springboard injunctions and injunctions to restrain the misuse of confidential/ private information, breach of fiduciary duty and restrictive covenants); insurance; sale and carriage of goods (domestic and international); share/asset purchase agreement disputes; general commercial litigation. Construction : construction litigation, arbitration and adjudication. Professional Negligence : construction professionals, solicitors, accountants, surveyors.
Professional Memberships: Middle Temple, Northern Circuit Commercial Bar Association.
Career: Called to the Bar 1994.

PERKINS, Joanna
South Square, London
020 7696 9900
joannaperkins@southsquare.com
Featured in Financial Services (London)
Practice Areas: Banking, Financial Services, Commercial Litigation.
Professional Memberships: COMBAR, The Chancery Bar Association.
Career: Joanna is regularly instructed in cases concerning the construction of the ISDA Master Agreement, in particular in relation to the valuation of a company's liability under the close-out provisions. She also acts for clients in commercial cases concerning structured products and insolvency cases, particularly those involving financial institutions. Joanna serves as Chief Executive of the Financial Markets Law Committee (established by the Bank of England), and as the Chair of the ICE LIBOR Oversight Committee. She has held lectureships at a number of prestigious universities. In 2011, Joanna was appointed Finance Expert to P.R.I.M.E Finance. In 2012, she was voted one of the 100 most influential women in the European Financial Markets by Financial News. Called to the Bar in 2001.
Publications: 'A Question of Priorities: Choice of Law and Proprietary Aspects of the Assignment of Debts' (2008) 02 Law and Financial Markets Review 238 (May); 'The Registration of Overseas Company Charges on Intangible Assets – Clarify or Abandon Says Author' (2009) 09 JIBFL 519 (September); 'Proprietary Issues Arising from the Assignment of Debts: A New Rule? Key Factors in the Development of a Proprietary Rule for Financial Assignments' (2010) 06 JIBFL 333 (June); 'Choice of Law and the Assignment of Debts' (2010) 3-4 Digest 20 May); 'Registration of Charges over Intangible Assets' (2010) 04 Law and Financial Markets Review (July); (as co-author) various FMLC Papers (2004 to present).

PERRINS, Gregory
One Paper Buildings, London
020 7353 3728
clerks@onepaper.co.uk
Featured in Crime (South Eastern)
Practice Areas: Criminal law, fraud, regulatory law.
Professional Memberships: South Eastern Circuit, CBA.
Career: Gregory Perrins practice covers all areas of serious crime with an emphasis on serious sexual offences, whilst retaining a significant white-collar crime, serious fraud and regulatory law practice. In 2012 Gregory was appointed Recorder, becoming one of the youngest members of the Bar ever to be appointed. Since 2003 he has prosecuted regulatory offences on behalf of OFCOM, gaining significant experience of both advisory work and litigation across a broad spectrum of English and European regulatory law. In 2012 Gregory played an active role in advising OFCOM on the regulatory framework to be adopted at the London 2012 Olympic Games. He has prosecuted and defended several multi-million pound frauds. He also has experience of large-scale confiscation work and was counsel in the leading authority on extending time for compliance with a confiscation order. Recently Gregory was instructed as leading counsel by the CPS Complex Case Unit in the successful prosecution of 8 defendants involved in 3 interlinked conspiracies to steal goods worth in excess of £400k as well as defence counsel in a multi-million pound "crash for cash" fraud on multiple insurance companies.
Publications: Westlaw UK Insight – Contributing author.

PESTER, Iain
11 Stone Buildings, London
020 7831 6381
pester@11sb.com
Featured in Chancery (London), Fraud (London), Restructuring/Insolvency (London)
Practice Areas: Iain is a commercial barrister, with particular experience in the areas of general contractual disputes (including claims to enforce guarantees and indemnities), arbitrations, conflict of laws and jurisdictions, civil fraud, insolvency/restructuring, shareholder and partnership litigation and professional negligence work. Chambers UK has recommended him for a number of years as a leading junior in commercial chancery, civil fraud and insolvency. For more information, please see the "Barristers" section at www.11sb.com.
Professional Memberships: Chancery Bar Association, Commercial Bar Association, Commercial Fraud Lawyers Association.
Career: Called to the Bar 1999 (Lincoln's Inn).
Publications: Two chapters in Goldrein, Commercial Litigation: Pre-Emptive Remedies (loose-leaf edition, updated annually), one on Provisional Liquidators and the other on Injunctions in Insolvency Proceedings. Contributor to Lexis PSL Insolvency & Restructuring Chapter.
Personal: BA (Oxon) First Class Honours. BCL First Class Honours. Languages: French, Russian, German.

PETERS, Edward
Falcon Chambers, London
020 7353 2484
peters@falcon-chambers.com
Featured in Real Estate Litigation (London)
Practice Areas: Specialist in all aspects of real property and landlord and tenant litigation, and related areas including professional negligence. Reported cases include: Fulham Broadway Trustees no 1 Ltd v Telefonica UK Ltd [2014] EWHC 1048 (ch) (rent review); Compton Beauchamp Estates Ltd v Spence [2013] 2 P&CR 15 (arbitration);George Wimpey Bristol Ltd v Gloucestershire Housing Association Ltd [2011] UKUT 91 (restrictive covenants); PGF II SA v Royal & Sun Alliance [2011] 1 P&CR 11 (dilapidations); Bocardo SA v Star Energy UK Onshore Ltd [2010] UKSC 35; Shaw v Doleman (CA) [2009] 2 BCLC 123; Brown's Operating System Services Ltd v Southwark RCDC (CA) [2007] L&TR 25 (service charges); Elmbirch Properties PLC v Schaefer-Tsoropatzadis [2007] 2 EGLR 167(rent review); Edlington Properties Ltd v JH Fenner & Co (CA) [2006] 1 WLR 1583 (equitable set-off); Kintyre Ltd v Romeomarch Property Management Ltd [2006] 1 EGLR 67 (enfranchisement); Stroude v Beazer Homes Ltd [2006] 2 EGLR 115 (s. 106 agreement); Malekshad v. Howard de Walden Estates (HL) [2003] 1 AC 1013 (enfranchisement); Ashworth Fraser v

Gloucester City Council (HL) [2001] 1 WLR 2180 (consent to assign).
Professional Memberships: LCLCBA, Chancery Bar Association, Property Bar Association, Agricultural law Association, Chartered Institute of Arbitrators.
Career: Caius College, Cambridge (BA, 1996); City University (1997); Called 1998 (MT).
Publications: Editor, Woodfall's Law of Landlord and Tenant; Contributor to Fisher & Lightwood's Law of Mortgage (11th (2002) 12th (2008) & 13th (2010) eds.); Co-author "Charging Orders" (2013); Co-author "Commonhold" (OUP) 2004. Blundell Lecturer (2012).

PHELPS, Rosalind
Fountain Court Chambers, London
020 7583 3335
rp@fountaincourt.co.uk
Featured in Aviation (London), Banking & Finance (London), Commercial Dispute Resolution (London), Fraud (London), Travel (London)
Practice Areas: Civil and commercial litigation including aviation, banking, civil fraud, conflicts of law and jurisdiction, financial services, professional negligence and public law/regulatory work in a commercial context. Cases include: Tchenguiz v SFO (2012 to date, including [2014] EWCA Civ 136), Alpstream AG v PK Airfinance [2013] EWHC 2370 (Comm), DAE Leasing v Kingfisher Airlines [2013] EWHC 3926, the Bitel litigation in the Isle of Man, Rawlinson and Hunter Trustees v Kaupthing Bank (2010-11), Kneale v Barclays Bank [2010] EWHC 1900 (Comm) (pre-action disclosure), the Tajik Aluminium litigation (2005-2008) including Tajik Aluminium Plant v Ermatov [2005] All ER (D) 467 (overturning freezing injunction) and [2006] All ER (D) 448 (jurisdiction), Ashton Investments v Russian Aluminium [2007] Lloyd's Rep 311 (jurisdiction in relation to computer hacking claim), Law Society v Sephton & Co [2006] 2 AC 543 (HL) (leading case on limitation in professional negligence claims).
Career: Called 1998. Member COMBAR.
Publications: Co-author 'The Law of Privilege' (OUP, 2nd edition 2011) and 'Carriage by Air' (Butterworths, 2001).
Personal: Pembroke College, Oxford: BCL, 1997 (1st Class Hons) and Law with French Law, 1996 (1st class Hons).

PHILIPPS, Guy QC
Fountain Court Chambers, London
020 7583 3335
gp@fountaincourt.co.uk
Featured in Commercial Dispute Resolution (London), Financial Services (London), Professional Negligence (London)
Practice Areas: A broadly based commercial litigation and arbitration practice, with particular specialisations in banking and financial services, insurance and reinsurance, and professional negligence. Notable reported cases include Williams v Central Bank of Nigeria (2014) (Sup. Ct); Young v Anglo American South Africa Ltd (CA) (2014); John Pottage v FSA (2012) (Financial Services Tribunal); Rainy Sky SA v Kookmin Bank (2011) (Sup. Ct); Fellowes International Holdings Ltd v Kyrgyz Mobil Tel Ltd (2011) (PC); Gard Marine v Glacier Reinsurance (2010) (CA); Brit Syndicates Ltd v Grant Thornton International (2008) (HL); 7E Communications Ltd v Vertex (2007) (CA); Royal Bank of Canada v Cooperatieve Centrale Raiffeisen Boerenleenbank (2004) (CA); Lloyds TSB General Insurance Holdings v Lloyds Bank Group Insurance Company (2003) (HL); Insured Financial Structures v Elektrocieplownia Tychy (2003) (CA).
Career: Called to the Bar 1986; QC 2002. Admitted to the Eastern Caribbean, Bahamas and Isle of Man Bars. Appointed as ICC, LCIA and LMAA arbitrator.
Personal: Born 1961. MA Oxford.

PHILLIPS, Jane
One Brick Court, London
020 7353 8845
jsp@onebrickcourt.com
Featured in Defamation/Privacy (London)
Practice Areas: All forms of media law including libel and slander, malicious falsehood, contempt, breach of confidence, privacy, reporting restrictions, data protection and pre-publication advice in particular for celebrity/ sport books. Independent Barrister for the Voicemail Interception Compensation Scheme. Advises on libel in Hong Kong, Singapore & Jamaica. Cases include: A v B (Privacy Injunction); Adams v Associated (CA); Allason v BBC; Ashby v Times; Blackstone v Mirror Group; Bonnick v Morris (Privy Council); Bunt v Tilley; C v Mirror Group (CA); Khalili v Associated (CA); Lloyd v Express (CA); Heather Mills McCartney v Associated & News Group; Mori v BBC; Rackham v Sandy; Sir Alex Ferguson v Associated; Strachan v Gleaner (Privy Council); Upjohn v BBC; Materazzi v Associated Newspapers; Bray v Deutsche Bank; Taranissi v BBC; Trafigura v BBC; W v M (re an adult patient)(Court of Protection); Citation v Ellis Whittam (CA); White v Southampton University Trust.
Career: Call July 1989, Inner Temple Scholar.
Publications: Co-author of the section on Libel and Slander, Malicious Falsehood in Bullen & Leake, 'Precedents & Pleadings'. Contributor to Arlidge, Eady and Smith on Contempt 4th Edition.
Personal: St. Paul's Girls' School and Worcester College, Oxford. Chair of Governors at The Henrietta Barnett School.

PHILLIPS, Jeremy
Francis Taylor Building, London
020 7353 8415
clerks@ftb.eu.com
Featured in Licensing (London)
Practice Areas: Highly regarded and active at the Bar, appreciated for the unusual breadth of his practice, which brings together his practical experience as a solicitor with his legal knowledge and application at the Bar. Expertise: "Singled out by several commentators for his "encyclopaedic knowledge" of liquor, gambling and entertainment licensing law. He's noted for his straightforward and extremely persuasive representation of both commercial and public body clients before all types of tribunal. "A calm, organised and measured advocate who has the benefit of many years' practical experience." "He's a polished and very persuasive opponent." " All aspects of leisure and entertainment, including licensing of alcohol, festivals, gambling, sex establishments and taxis. Busy practice includes planning, environment, judicial review and regulatory law. Represents operators, police, local authorities and residents' groups. Appeared in many leading cases. Acts from sub-committee level through to the Court of Appeal.
Professional Memberships: DCMS Advisory Group (since 2001). ALBA. PEBA. UKELA. Member of expert panel on Plying for Hire, The Law Commission Report: Taxi and Private Hire Services (2014).
Career: Solicitor (1980). Founder Holt Phillips (1984); equity partner Eversheds (1994), Osborne Clarke (2001). Leader of National teams both firms. Called to the Bar (2004). Accredited CEDR Mediator (2007). Elected member Bar Council (2014).
Publications: Paterson's Licensing Acts (1997), Editor in Chief (2014); Consultant editor – various volumes Halsbury's Laws of England; contributor - Gambling for Local Authorities; co-author The Law of Regulatory Enforcement and Sanctions, and numerous other publications
Personal: Family, motorcycling, history of England, long-distance travel.

PHILLIPS, Mark QC
South Square, London
020 7696 9900
markphillips@southsquare.com
Featured in Chancery (London), Restructuring/Insolvency (London), Sports Law (London)
Practice Areas: Insolvency – Administration, Liquidation, Restructuring, claims arising out of insolvencies. Banking. Commercial. Sports law. Mark has appeared in Courts at every level both in England and overseas. In the past year, Mark was brought in to appear for the Lehman's administrators in the Supreme Court, on the successful appeal against the ruling that sums due under the Pensions Act 2004 were expenses. He acted for the hedge funds who took over the Co Op Bank. He acted for the Liquidators of Rangers Football Club on the claim arising out of the takeover of the Club by Craig Whyte. He represented the Football League in establishing the validity of the "football creditors rule". He also acted on a dispute between investors in a large property project in London. He is acting for the liquidators of Chesterfield and Partridge, Kaupthing SPVs. Mark acted in numerous major administrations, including Maxwell (for the Administrators of the Private side), Olympia & York (Canary Wharf) (for the Banks), British & Commonwealth (for the Administrators) and Paramount Airways (for the Administrators), and the EMI pre-pack. Mark successfully defended the Bank of England at trial against the misfeasance claim brought by the liquidators of BCCI. Mark appeared for the shareholders of Northern Rock in the Court of Appeal on the appeal against the valuation of the Northern Rock shares.
Professional Memberships: International Insolvency Institute, Insolvency Lawyers Association (Past President), Association of Business Recovery Professionals (Fellow and Former Council Member), INSOL International, INSOL Europe, Commercial Bar Association, Chancery Bar Association.
Career: Called to the Bar (Inner Temple) 1984, Queen's Counsel 1999, Recorder 2000-08, Vice President Insolvency Lawyers' Association 2001-02, President Insolvency Lawyers' Association 2002-03, Council Member Insolvency Lawyers' Association to 2004, Fellow and Former Council Member of R3 – Association of Business Recovery Professionals.
Publications: Editor of Butterworth's Insolvency Law Handbook (Butterworths LexisNexis, 1986 to date); contributor to chapter on insolvency in Paget's Law of Banking (2007); contributor to Insolvency of Banks: Managing the Risks (1996).
Personal: Motorsport enthusiast, football fan. Enjoys theatre and family life.

PHILLIPS, Paul
Charter Chambers, London
07973 835 866
ginger.london@virgin.net
Featured in Crime (London), Financial Crime (London)
Practice Areas: Paul has over the last several years consistently been regarded by independent publications as a leader in his field. He is a specialist defence advocate instructed in many high profile criminal and regulatory cases. He has considerable experience as leading and junior counsel in all areas of serious crime. His main areas of practice are in serious and organised crime and fraud. In serious and organised crime he has a particular expertise in murder, large scale drug importations, money laundering and people smuggling. In fraud he often represents professional people being investigated or accused of crime, and has represented accountants, solicitors, barristers, company executives and other professionals charged with fraud. Paul is approachable and available outside of normal working hours to assist solicitors with any aspect of a case.
Professional Memberships: Criminal Bar Association.
Career: Called to the Bar 1991. A comprehensive list of his recent cases can be found at www.charterchambers.com.

PHILLIPS, Simon QC
New Park Court Chambers, Leeds
01132 433 277
simon.phillips@npc-l.co.uk
Featured in Professional Discipline (The Regions), Financial Crime (The Regions)
Practice Areas: Crime, professional discipline, health and safety, regulatory, environmental, sports law, licensing. Prosecutes and defends complex and serious crime, including multiple homicide and industrial and maritime fatalities, financial crime, serious sexual offences, multi-handed conspiracies. Instructed in Major Enquiry Team/Complex Case Unit casework, particularly involving medical/scientific issues. Major fisheries prosecutions, including EU law test cases. International drug-trafficking and computer-related casework. High-profile rape and historic sexual abuse. General Medical Council fitness to practise hearings (Medical Practitioners Tribunal Service). Professional disciplinary appeals (QBD/Administrative Court and CA). Inquests. Instructed by the Attorney-General, Departmental and Non-Departmental Government, Local Authorities, Chief Constables and Emergency Services, including cases requiring security clearance for national security issues before the Court of Appeal (Criminal Division) and Planning Inspectorate. Direct Access instructions accepted.
Career: In practice at New Park Court Chambers (Leeds/Newcastle), and Francis Taylor Building (London). Current appointments: Queen's Counsel; Serious Fraud Office QC Panels (Prosecutions, Proceeds of Crime); Attorney-General's leader-list of Special Advocates; Recorder (Crime/Civil/Serious Sexual Offence cases); First-tier Tribunal Judge (Immigration/Asylum); Rugby Football Union Disciplinary Appeal Panel-member; Sport Resolution UK National Child Safeguarding Panel-member; Bar Standards

Board Panel of Advocates; Healthcare Legal Assessor; Bar Council Member. Formerly (as a junior): Attorney-General's A-list Panel, and CPS Grade 4 prosecutor.

PHIPPS, Charles
4 New Square, London
020 7822 2000
c.phipps@4newsquare.com
Featured in Professional Negligence (London)
Practice Areas: Professional negligence (lawyers, accountants, financial advisors, surveyors, architects, engineers, insurance brokers); confidentiality disputes; insurance; more general chancery and common law litigation. Interesting cases include: Mallon v Halliwells LLP [2012] EWCA Civ 1212; Sharma v Hunters [2012] PNLR 6; CMCS Common Market Commercial Services AVV v Taylor [2011] PNLR 17; Jones v Kaney [2011] 2 AC 398; Mortgage Express v Sawali [2011] PNLR 11; Williams v Lishman Sidwell Campbell & Price Ltd [2010] Pens.L.R.227; Nayyar v Denton Wilde Sapte [2010] PNLR 15; National Westminster Bank plc v Lloyd (LTL 10/2/2009); the CLE and TAG multi-party litigation against panel solicitors; Terry v Tower Hamlets LBC (2005) NPC 144; Charles v Westminster City Council [2004] PNLR 25; Cranfield v Bridgegrove [2003] 1 WLR 2441; Mortgage Express Ltd v Newman [2000] Lloyd's Rep (PN) 745; Hanif v Middleweeks [2000] Lloyd's Rep (PN) 920; BCCI (Overseas) Ltd v Price Waterhouse [1998] Lloyd's Rep (Banking) 85.
Professional Memberships: COMBAR, PNBA.
Career: Called in 1992.
Publications: Co-author, with Lord Justice Toulson, of Toulson and Phipps on Confidentiality (Sweet & Maxwell, 3rd edition, 2012).
Personal: Educated at Merton College, Oxford (Literae Humaniores, 1st class); City University (Diploma in Law).

PHIPPS, Sarah
Queen Elizabeth Building, London
020 7797 7837
s.phipps@qeb.co.uk
Featured in Family/Matrimonial (London)
Practice Areas: Matrimonial finance and private law Children Act applications including leave to remove applications and financial claims on behalf of children under Schedule 1.
Professional Memberships: Family Law Bar Association.
Career: Educated at Brasenose, Oxford and College of Law. Called 1997. Pupil and tenant at Queen Elizabeth Building.

PICKUP, James QC
2 Hare Court, London
020 7353 5324
jamespickupqc@2harecourt.com
Featured in Financial Crime (London)
Practice Areas: James Pickup Q.C. has an excellent reputation both in Manchester and London for handling the most serious and complex fraud cases. Chambers 2014 ranked him as the star silk for criminal fraud in the regions, describing him as "phenomenal on his feet" and "tenacious, with a good courtroom delivery". He has been complimented as someone who is "excellent at case management" and "brilliantly focussed on getting the best out of the client", and described as "the top man for the big fraud cases", and "the first choice for any serious complex fraud" (Legal 500). He has a wealth of experience in commercial fraud and corporate crime, whether that be in the criminal courts (most recently HMRC v Allad and Others, 2010-2014 and HMRC v Arif Patel and Others, continuing), the civil and commercial courts (Abbey Forwarding (in Liquidation) v Hone and Others 2010, Rochdale Drinks v HMRC 2011/12) or in the VAT and Duties Tribunal (CCA Distribution 2012, Advent Worldwide Distribution 2013, BTS/NTS 2013/14). His practice now concerns all aspects of indirect tax (VAT) and excise duty fraud. In 2010 he represented the lead appellant in the conjoined appeals of Mobilx, Calltel Opto and Blue Sphere Global before the Court of Appeal. This is to date the only MTIC tax appeal to have been taken from the High Court (now the UT) to the Court of Appeal, and it remains the leading authority. In July 2010 he successfully defended the former directors of the bonded warehouse Abbey Forwarding against allegations of fraud brought in the Chancery Court by the liquidator. He has appeared for the Eastenders Group initially before the CCC and the Court of Appeal to discharge restraint and receivership orders obtained under POCA, and thereafter in the High Court to challenge by way of judicial review search warrants obtained by HMRC and most recently the CCC to resist HMRC's application to retain unlawfully seized property. In November 2013, he appeared before the Supreme Court on behalf of First Stop Wholesale in an appeal as to the interpretation of s139 of the Customs and Excise Management Act 1979, and the need for officers on detention of goods to give reasons.
Professional Memberships: Criminal Bar Association.
Career: Year of call: 1976 (Grays Inn). Assistant Recorder 1993, Recorder 1998, Silk 2000.

PICTON, Julian QC
Hailsham Chambers, London
020 7643 5000
julian.picton@hailshamchambers.com
Featured in Professional Negligence (London), Personal Injury (London)
Practice Areas: Professional negligence, personal injury and clinical negligence, with a particular emphasis on high value, complex, catastrophic and acquired brain injury cases and professional negligence actions arising out of the mismanagement or undersettlement of personal injury and clinical negligence claims. Regularly acts for and against members of all the main professions including solicitors, barristers, accountants, surveyors, architects and financial advisers. General insurance and coverage matters.
Professional Memberships: Professional Negligence Bar Association (PNBA).
Career: Called to the Bar, Middle Temple 1988; Everard Van Hayden Prize Bar Finals; QC 2010.
Publications: McGregor on Damages.
Personal: Education: Reigate Grammar School; Oriel College, Oxford (Exhibitioner) BA Oxon 1986. Lives in North Cambridgeshire. Interests: buildings, English furniture.

PIERCY, Catherine
Hardwicke, London
020 7242 2523
catherine.piercy@hardwicke.co.uk
Featured in Construction (London)
Practice Areas: Catherine Piercy has a broad commercial and insurance practice, specialising in construction and engineering disputes involving loss and expense claims, defective works, professional negligence (contractors, architects, engineers, surveyors) and delay and disruption. She acts for and against contractors in court proceedings and alternative forms of dispute resolution, providing both advisory work, drafting and advocacy services. Her experience includes acting for the main contractor in a multimillion pound adjudication regarding the defective construction of a new building, junior counsel in proceedings in the TCC concerning a defective road and acting for the fit out contractor in a series of adjudications with a major high street chain.
Professional Memberships: SCL, TECBAR, COMBAR, Adjudication Society.
Career: Call 2007.
Publications: Contributor to Construction All Risks Insurance by Paul Reed QC (2014).

PIGOTT, Frances
Atkin Chambers, London
020 7404 0102
fpigott@atkinchambers.com
Featured in Construction (London)
Practice Areas: Specialist in construction, engineering, infrastructure, energy, IT and related professional negligence. Cases include: Bluewater v Mercon [2014] EWHC 2132 (TCC) a claim under a sub-contract for a soft yoke mooring system for installation in the Caspian Sea; Wales & West Utilities Ltd v PPS Pipeline [2014 EWHC 54 (TCC) resisting enforcement of an adjudicator's decision; Interserve Industrial Services v ZRE Katowice [2012] EWHC 3205 (TCC) stay of proceedings to arbitration; Mears v Artel Scaffolding (2012) (unreported) claims under a subcontract for the provision of scaffolding for breach of various construction contracts on standard forms; LG Blower v Reeves [2010] 1 WLR 2081 (CA) part 36 offers; Traditional Structures v HW Construction [2010] EWHC 1530 (TCC) a claim of unilateral mistake in respect of a subcontractor's tender; Atwal v Rochester [2010] EWHC 2338 (TCC) a building contract discharged by frustration; Hurst Stores & Interiors Ltd v ML Europe [2004] EWCA Civ 490 a claim of unilateral mistake in respect of a final account agreement. Frances has also been involved as junior in a multi-million pound international arbitration concerning a mixed use development. Recently instructed to act on behalf of a major utility in respect of construction of a power station, works at a power station site and construction of a bulk handling unit; in relation to s.278 agreements; professional negligence claims against construction professionals and solicitors; drafting construction contracts and warranties. Adjudication experience includes drafting, advising, representation at substantive hearings and enforcement. Frances has represented national and international clients at arbitration. An experienced strategist in ADR. Appears regularly in the TCC. With considerable trial and court experience, Frances is gaining a reputation as a formidable advocate.
Professional Memberships: TECBAR; ACIArb; SCL.
Career: Called in 1994. Admitted to the roll as a Solicitor of the Supreme Court of England and Wales in 1996. Commenced practice as a Barrister in 2004.

PILGERSTORFER, Marcus
11KBW, London
020 7632 5800
Marcus.Pilgerstorfer@11kbw
Featured in Employment (London), Product Liability (London)
Practice Areas: Hainsworth v MOD [2014] EWCA Civ 763, Portnykh v Nomura [2014] IRLR 251, QCCA v Lopez [2013] IRLR 4, Edwards v Chesterfield [2012] 2 AC 22, the BA Cabin Crew Litigation, English v Thomas Sanderson [2009] ICR 543, the PIP Breast Implant Group Litigation, the Sabril Group Litigation, Keyu v SoS [2012] EWHC 2445 (Admin).
Professional Memberships: ILS, ELBA, ELA, EELA, DLA, BIICL Product Liability Forum, Common Core Product Liability group.
Career: MA English Law with German Law: St John's College, Oxford (first class honours); Called 2002 (Gray's Inn Scholar). AG's B Panel of Counsel to the Crown.
Publications: Numerous publications in specialist law journals as well as contributor to Tolley's Employment Law Handbook (2013-14); Cambridge Companion to EU Private Law (2010); Discrimination in Employment, Tucker & George (2006).
Personal: Languages: English (native) and German.

PILLAI, Rajesh
3 Verulam Buildings, London
020 7831 8441
rpillai@3vb.com
Featured in Commercial Dispute Resolution (London), Fraud (London), International Arbitration (London)
Practice Areas: Rajesh is one of the leading junior barristers at the London Bar. He specialises in commercial litigation and arbitration across a variety of business and financial sectors. In 2013 he was nominated for International Arbitration Junior of the Year. Rajesh has particular experience of disputes involving contract, fraud, breach of fiduciary duty and negligence – often arising out of shareholder disputes and failed joint ventures. Rajesh has a well-regarded international practice: in addition to regularly appearing in the English High Court he has recently acted in arbitrations seated in Singapore, India and Bahrain. Rajesh is usually instructed either as sole advocate or co-counsel and he has worked with lawyers from a variety of different jurisdictions including New York, India, Singapore, Dubai, Bahrain, Jordan, Kuwait, Australia and the Isle of Man. He also advises on the interpretation of finance documentation in relation to debt restructuring and bondholder disputes. Rajesh was appointed Junior Counsel to the Crown in 2008 (elevated to the B Panel 2013). He is currently instructed by HMRC in the ongoing Eclipse appeals involving film finance and tax avoidance schemes and has advised the OFT on regulation of the payday lending market. Rajesh has advised UK and foreign government departments on questions of private and public international law. Rajesh is also admitted to the New York Bar.
Professional Memberships: IBA; ICC UK; LCIA and YIAG; New York State Bar Association; COMBAR; Commercial Fraud Lawyers' Association; Middle Temple.
Career: English Bar (2002); New York Bar (2003.
Publications: "Suing insolvent banks: can parties preserve their choice of jurisdic-

tion?" - Journal of International Banking and Financial Law, Vol 27 No, April 2012.
Personal: BA Hons (Oxon); BA Hons (Cantab); LLM International Law (NYU).

PILLING, Benjamin
4 Pump Court, London
020 7842 5555
bpilling@4pumpcourt.com
Featured in Banking & Finance (London), Commercial Dispute Resolution (London), Construction (London), Information Technology (London), Professional Negligence (London)
Practice Areas: Commercial litigation with an emphasis on banking and finance including derivatives (interest rate swaps, total return swaps, FX swaps), distressed debt (including receivables financing), structured products and retail banking. Professional negligence cases including both financial services professionals and construction professionals. Awarded Professional Negligence Junior of the Year 2013. Construction cases arising from a range of onshore and offshore projects. IT cases (including computer games contracts). International arbitration.
Professional Memberships: COMBAR, Professional Negligence Bar Association, TECBAR, London Common Law and Commercial Bar Association, Society for Computers and Law.
Career: Called 1997.
Publications: 'Halsbury's Laws: Arbitration' (2003, with Professor Martin Hunter), 'The Arbitration Act 1996: A Guide for Consumers and Small Businesses' (HMSO 1997).
Personal: BA (Oxon) (First Class) 1994; Dip Law (City) 1996; BVC (Outstanding) 1997; MA Law of Arbitration (City) 1997.

PIMLOTT, Charles
Crown Office Chambers, London
020 7797 8116
pimlott@crownofficechambers.com
Featured in Construction (London), International Arbitration (London)
Practice Areas: Construction, engineering, energy, insurance, professional negligence and general commercial litigation, arbitration and dispute resolution both in the UK and internationally. Cases have involved technical issues in civil, structural, mechanical and electrical engineering under a wide variety of standard form (notably, JCT, NEC and FIDIC) and bespoke contracts, often with large amounts of paperwork and involving difficult expert evidence of a highly scientific nature, and contested oral evidence. His work has ranged from domestic conversions to major infrastructure projects and process plant design. He is frequently instructed in adjudications and related court proceedings (such as enforcement proceedings and Part 8 claims). He also acts as adjudicator and is a TECBAR accredited adjudicator and a member of the CEDR Panel of Adjudicators. He acts as counsel in domestic and international arbitrations, particularly in connection with construction, engineering, infrastructure and energy projects and related insurance disputes. Further details are available on www.crownofficechambers.com.
Professional Memberships: TECBAR, Society of Construction Law (UK and Dubai, UAE), Professional Negligence Bar Association, COMBAR, London Common Law and Commercial Bar Association LCIA Young International Arbitration Group.
Career: Called 2001, Middle Temple.
Publications: Contributor to Emden's Construction Law and a contributor to Construction Insurance and UK Construction Contracts.

PIPE, Adam
Number 8 Chambers, Birmingham
01212 365 514
adampipe@no8chambers.co.uk
Featured in Immigration (Midlands)
Practice Areas: He practices in immigration, asylum and human rights, undertaking cases in the First-tier Tribunal, Upper Tribunal, Administrative Court and Court of Appeal. In both 2013 and 2014 he was shortlisted for Barrister of the Year in the Birmingham Law Society Legal Awards. Regularly speaks at conferences and seminars around the country providing updates upon the latest developments in the law. Also regularly provides analysis of the latest case law for Lexis Nexis' UK Legal News Analysis.
Professional Memberships: Immigration Law Practitioners' Association and Justice. Fellow of the Institute of Continuing Professional Development.
Career: Called to the Bar in 1999 and has been a member of No8 Chambers throughout.
Publications: Contributing Editor to Butterworths Immigration Law Service and has worked on Lexis PSL. Regularly posts articles on LinkedIn http://uk.linkedin.com/pub/adam-pipe/60/b15/ab/ and 'tweets' on Immigration Law @adampipe.
Personal: In his spare time enjoys reading theology and cinema.

PITCHERS, Henry
No5 Chambers, Birmingham
01216 060 500
hp@no5.com
Featured in Clinical Negligence (Midlands), Personal Injury (Midlands)
Practice Areas: Principally in three areas: high value and/or complex personal injury work; clinical negligence and defending fraudulent compensation claims. Henry works for both claimants and defendants with an emphasis on more serious injuries, such as brain injury, spinal injury, amputation cases and fatal accidents. This work spans employer's liability (including disease work; asbestos, dermatitis, deafness, WRULD etc.), public liability (with particular experience of highways claims), road traffic (including claims involving the MIB), criminal injuries (with two recent pre-tariff cases being concluded with awards of around £4M), inquests and consumer protection. Henry has experience of group litigation, having been part of the lead claimants' team in the recent Linkwise 'sofa litigation', with several thousand successful claims having been concluded. A wide range of clinical negligence work is undertaken by Henry. Some of the more serious and interesting recent cases have included failures to diagnose cancer, a sub-dural haemorrage and infant hip dysplasia. Instructions have been received in relation to numerous injuries sustained shortly prior to or during birth (such as cerebral palsy, avoidable still birth causing 'nervous shock' to the parents and orthopaedic injuries sustained during caesarian section). Henry has been instructed in many cases involving allegedly negligent surgery: such as termination of pregnancy, removal of gall bladder, hip replacement, hernia repair and unnecessary removal of ovarian cyst. He has advised in relation to negligent private fertility treatment and the negligent prescription of diazepam. Henry often acts in inquests touching on hospital deaths on behalf of families, Trusts and healthcare professionals. Regular instructions are received from insurers in relation to fraudulent personal injury claims, often but not exclusively arising out of actual or alleged road traffic accidents. Henry has significant experience of defending claims involving allegations of staged accident, induced accident, bogus passenger and low velocity impact. He also acts in relation to large and complex fraud rings. Henry also has significant experience of solicitors' negligence litigation, particularly in relation to personal injury and clinical negligence work.
Career: Studied law at Worcester College, Oxford University, before taking the bar course in London. Following successful completion of pupillage, Henry took tenancy at 22 Old Buildings, Lincoln's Inn (now 42 Bedford Row), before moving to No5 Chambers in January 2003.
Publications: Henry is a contributing editor to Butterworths Personal Injury Litigation Service.

PITT-PAYNE, Timothy QC
11KBW, London
020 7632 8500
Timothy.Pitt-Payne@11kbw.com
Featured in Administrative & Public Law (London), Data Protection (London), Employment (London)
Practice Areas: Principal areas of practice are employment law, administrative and public law, data protection, freedom of information, and other information law areas. Has acted in over 50 cases before Information Rights Tribunal, and in numerous information law cases at all appellate levels from Upper Tribunal to Supreme Court. Contributor to 'Supperstone, Goudie & Walker on Judicial Review' (LexisNexis 2010, and earlier editions); 'Computer Law' (OUP 2011); 'Media Law' (OUP 2009). Visiting Professor of Information Law at Northumbria University 2007-13.
Professional Memberships: Employment Law Bar Association; Administrative Law Bar Association; Commercial Bar Association; Society for Computers and Law.
Career: Called to the Bar in 1989. Joined present chambers in 1990. Appointed QC 2010.
Personal: University education: Worcester College, Oxford 1982-86 (BA (Hons) Jurisprudence 1985, BCL 1986). Vinerian Scholar 1986.

PITTAWAY, David QC
Hailsham Chambers, London
020 7643 5000
david.pittaway@hailshamchambers.com
Featured in Clinical Negligence (London), Professional Discipline (London)
Practice Areas: QC specialising in medical law; clinical negligence; regulatory and disciplinary inquiries and inquests; product liability and insurance law. David is presently instructed in two major group actions, breast surgery cases in the West Midlands and obstetric claims in the South West, and in the Hillsborough Inquest, as well as a large number of clinical negligence actions. He has an enviable reputation for advocacy and is recognised in the legal directories for his ability to navigate complex medical cases in the QBD, Admin Court and CoA. He is recognised by both claimants and defendants for his tactical abilities at round table meetings. He is often instructed in high profile litigation e.g. Cervical Screening Litigation, Shipman Inquiry, and Northwick Park Clinical Trials cases. His practice regularly includes specialist advice in coronial law, regulatory and disciplinary cases. He advises regulators on their processes and procedures. He prosecutes for the SRA at the SDT.
Professional Memberships: Past Chairman of the PNBA, LCLCBA, PIBA, BEG.
Career: Called to the Bar, Inner Temple 1977; Northern Ireland 2011; FCIArb 1988; Bencher 1998; assistant recorder 1998; recorder; QC 2000; accredited mediator 2002; Member of MHRT 2002; GMC Legal Assessor 2002-04; RCVS Legal Assessor 2004; Chancellor of the Diocese of Peterborough 2006; Deputy High Court Judge 2008.
Publications: Contributor; 'Atkins Court Forms - Personal Injury (2014) Professional Negligence' (2012); 'National Health Service' (2014); 'Carriers' (2010); Advanced Civil Litigation (OUP) (2002); Co-general Editor 'Pittaway & Hammerton Professional Negligence Cases' (Butterworths) (1998).
Personal: Education: Uppingham School; Sidney Sussex College, Cambridge (Exhibitioner) BA (Cantab) 1976 MA (Cantab) 1979); married, two sons; interests include gardening, music, art, sailing.

PLATT, Heather
Pump Court Chambers, Winchester
020 7353 0711
h.platt@pumpcourtchambers.com
Featured in Employment (Western)
Practice Areas: Employment, discrimination, contract, commercial, personal injury, regulatory.
Career: During a decade at the Bar, Heather has built an impressive reputation in Employment Law, Discrimination Law and related areas. Client testimonials have praised Heather as a "highly competent and reliable counsel" who is valued for her "patient and professional conduct", her "ability to analyse and grasp detailed information" and her "excellent preparation". They add that she is a "tenacious advocate" who is "razor sharp both in cross-examination and her delivery". Heather represents a wide cross-section of businesses, from multinational corporations to SMEs, as well as public bodies and individuals. She has handled numerous cases before the employment tribunals, the Employment Appeal Tribunal, the High Court and the Court of Appeal; Heather is particularly in-demand for her expertise in disability, sex and race discrimination, sexual orientation, unfair dismissal, redundancy, stress at work, bullying and harassment, whistleblowing and TUPE. Acting for both claimants and respondents, Heather has substantial experience in discrimination law. She has acted in several high-value cases for and against large organisations and public bodies, including Primary Care Trusts, schools and colleges, local authorities, housing associations, police forces and major airlines. Her professional negligence practice largely relates to the conduct of tribunal proceedings. Heather has expertise in regulatory matters, in particular the regulation of professionals such as Doctors, nurses, social workers, teachers, police officers, accountants and within the provision of financial services. Heather regularly advises businesses, partnerships and companies on a range of matters including debt recovery, disputes about fees, breach of partnership agreements

and insolvency. Heather is in demand for advice and representation in relation to restrictive covenants and their enforceability, she drafts contracts and also acts and advises in relation to injunction proceedings in the High Court.
Personal: Heather is an extreme sports enthusiast and keen traveller.

PLATTS-MILLS, Mark QC
8 New Square, London
020 7405 4321
mark.platts-mills@8newsquare.co.uk
Featured in Intellectual Property (London)
Practice Areas: Barrister (QC) specialising in all aspects of intellectual property, including patents, trade marks, passing off, registered designs, copyright and design right; database rights, data protection and commercial work with a technical content. Recent cases; Vestergaard Frandsen AG v Bestnet Europe Ltd (Confidential Information); Fine & Country v Okotoks (Trade Mark Infringement and Passing off); Tsit Wing (Hong Kong) v TWG Pte Ltd (Hong Kong Trade Mark Infringement and Passing Off); Trek Technology (Singapore) Limited and M-Systems Flash Disk (Patents); British Horseracing Board v William Hill (Database rights), Tsit Wing v TWG Tea (Hong Kong, trademarks). For comprehensive CV visit chambers website at www.8newsquare.co.uk.
Professional Memberships: Intellectual Property Bar Association (IPBA); Chancery Bar Association.
Career: Called 1974; QC 1995. Head of Chambers 2001 to date.
Personal: Born 1951. Educated at Bryanston School; Balliol College, Oxford (1972 BA Engineering Science and Economics).

PLIENER, David
Hardwicke, London
020 7242 2523
david.pliener@hardwicke.co.uk
Featured in Construction (London), Insurance (London), Property Damage (London)
Practice Areas: David has developed a very successful construction, insurance and commercial based practice. He acts for various insurance, construction and other major companies in high value and complex pieces of litigation, domestic and international arbitration and adjudication and mediation. He enjoys strong working relationships with his solicitors and has a reputation for a common sense approach and effective advocacy.
Professional Memberships: COMBAR London Common Law and Commercial Bar Association, Tecbar, Society of Construction Lawyers, Professional Negligence Bar Association, British Insurance Law Association, Adjudication Society.
Career: Called to the Bar 1996. TECBAR accredited adjudicator 2011.
Publications: Contributor to Construction All Risks Insurance by Paul Reed QC (2014); 'Not so elementary, my dear Nulty', Insurance Day, 26 June 2013. 'Robinson Redux: be careful what you wish for', Construction Law Journal (2011) Vol 27 No.2 p117-132 (with Michael Wheater). 'Yeganeh' ruling adds fuel to fraudulent claims fire', Insurance Day, 23 July 2010 (with Jeffrey Thomson). 'Outflanking Murphy v Brentwood: Claiming in Tort for Pure Economic Loss', Construction Law Journal (2010) 26 Const.L.J. Issue 4, 270 – 277.

POCOCK, Christopher QC
1 King's Bench Walk, London
020 7936 1500
cpocockqc@1kbw.co.uk
Featured in Family/Matrimonial (London)
Practice Areas: Family (including divorce and dissolution of civil partnership), matrimonial finance and property. Pre-Nuptial Agreements. Financial disputes between unmarried couples, inheritance and family provision. IFLA accredited Arbitrator.
Professional Memberships: S E Circuit; Family Law Bar Association; Institute of Family Law Arbitrators
Career: Called in 1984 by Inner Temple. Silk 2009.
Personal: Born 1960. Educated at St Dunstan's College and Pembroke College, Oxford (BA Juris). Working knowledge of French.

POKU, Mary
9-12 Bell Yard, London
020 7400 1800
m.poku@912by.com
Featured in Crime (London)
Practice Areas: Mary Poku is an experienced defence advocate with an impressive track record. She is highly regarded for her client care with a high acquittal rate that has led to a loyal professional and lay client following. She is frequently instructed in murder cases, notably in the highly publicised case of R v Stuart Hazell, involving the murdered school girl Tia Sharpe. Mary Poku has also acted as leading counsel in a broad spectrum of cases of serious violence, including more recently in a multi defendent murder case, prosecuted and defended by Queen's Counsel. She has also conducted serious international fraud trials investigated by HM Revenue & Customs, Department of Work and Pensions and the Serious and Organised Crime Agency. In February 2014, Mary was appointed as legal advisor on the National Crime Agency and the Foreign and Commonwealth's cybercrime initiative in Ghana. Since this appointment she has been instructed by leading maritime and shipping firms to provide legal and strategic advice in ongoing cases in Ghana. She is on the list of approved counsel for the International Criminal Tribunal for the Former Yugoslavia.
Career: Called 1993. Pupil Supervisor.
Publications: Cyber crime: civil remedies (Westlaw Insight: Sweet and Maxwell)
Personal: French, Twi (Native Ghanaian language)

POLE, Tim
No5 Chambers, Birmingham
08452 105 555
tp@no5.com
Featured in Crime (Midlands)
Practice Areas: Tim Pole is a specialist regulatory and criminal barrister. He was appointed to the Attourney General's list of specialist regulatory barristers in 2012 (Health and Safety, Environmental, Office of Rail Regulation). He appeared on behalf of the Health and Safety Executive in the well publicised Copthorne Hotel legionnaires case and has appeared in a large number of the most serious Health and Safety cases involving death both for the defence and prosecution. He has a vast experience of coronial law and is often instructed by companies and individuals at this crucial stage in any investigation. He has a keen interest in Sports Law and is regularly instructed to appear before regulatory tribunals in sports such as Football and Boxing. He is an expert in the Proceeds of Crime and has advised and appeared in the Court of Appeal in many cases arising out of the "Chambers"review VAT duty cases, securing the return of 6 figure sums for appellants. He is regularly instructed in motoring cases by high profile figures in the worlds of sport and entertainment. He has worked for a range of leading insurers where he is considered the go to man for this specialist area particularly in cases involving death.
Career: Called 2001. No 5 Chambers 2006 - present.
Personal: Personal: A keen sportsman and fluent French Speaker

POLLEY, Alexander
One Essex Court, London
020 7583 2000
apolley@oeclaw.co.uk
Featured in Banking & Finance (London), Commercial Dispute Resolution (London), Fraud (London)
Practice Areas: Commercial dispute resolution; commercial arbitration; banking litigation; civil fraud.
Professional Memberships: COMBAR.
Career: Alex practises in commercial litigation and arbitration, including banking, civil fraud, professional negligence and general commercial disputes. Recent cases include: Nomihold v Mobile Telesystems (enforcement of arbitration award, anti-suit injunctions e.g. [2012] 1 Lloyd's Rep 442); HSBC v AHAB (recoverability of loans to Saudi partnership in context of alleged fraud on the partnership by its manager, and consequential actions e.g. [2011] 2 CLC 736); Assetco v Grant Thornton (audit negligence and pre-action disclosure - e.g. [2013] EWHC 1215 (Comm)); Network Rail v Conarken (recoverability of financial losses incurred following vehicle collisions with railway infrastructure - [2012] 1 All ER (Comm) 692); and CPC v Qatari Diar (the Chelsea Barracks litigation - [2010] EWHC 1535 (Ch)). Educated at King's College, Taunton; Merton College, Oxford (BA, Ancient and Modern History – first class, with proxime accessit to the Gibbs Prize in History; MPhil, Roman History – with the Ancient History Prize); Oxford Brookes University (Graduate Diploma in Law – distinction, with the Law Department CPE Prize). Called to the Bar in 2005, Inner Temple.

POLLI, Timothy
Tanfield Chambers, London
020 7421 5300
timpolli@tanfieldchambers.co.uk
Featured in Real Estate Litigation (London)
Practice Areas: Landlord and tenant including dilapidations claims, lease renewals, forfeiture and applications for relief, claims arising out of the insolvency of landlord or tenant, service charge disputes, RTM and enfranchisement; real property disputes concerning boundaries, adverse possession, easements and restrictive covenants (for example, Beech v Kennerley [2012] EWCA Civ 158); party walls; mortgages, mortgage fraud and subrogation (for example, UCB Home Loans Corporation v Grace & Co (2010) LTL 15/12/2010 (Ch) and [2011] EWHC 851; Menelaou v Bank of Cyprus v Boulter & Co [2014] 1 WLR 854; [2013] EWCA Civ 1960; Credit & Mercantile v Kaymuu Ltd [2014] EWHC 1746 (Ch)); Claims for equitable interests pursuant to constructive trusts or proprietary estoppel (for example, Credit & Mercantile v Kaymuu Ltd [2014] EWHC 1746 (Ch)); property-related professional liability, particularly that of valuers and solicitors (for example UCB Home Loans Corporation v Soni [2013] EWCA Civ 62); Chancery/commercial contract disputes including disputes concerning development agreements and joint-ventures. Regularly instructed to advise in relation to non-contentious property work, usually at very short notice.
Professional Memberships: Property Bar Association (Committee Member); Chancery Bar Association; Bar Pro Bono Unit.
Career: Worked at the Law Commission 1996-97 and was called to the Bar in 1997.
Publications: Contributor to 'The Law of Service Charges and Management' by Tanfield Chambers.
Personal: Born in 1973; educated at St Columba's College, St Albans and Hertford College, Oxford (MA, BCL); married with two children; interests include theatre and travel.

PONTER, Ian
Kings Chambers, Manchester
08450 343 444
clerks@kingschambers.com
Featured in Administrative & Public Law (Northern), Planning (Northern)
Practice Areas: Planning, administrative and public law.
Professional Memberships: PEBA.
Career: The focus of Ian's practice is planning and public law. His practice includes all aspects of planning law. He appears at planning inquiries in all disciplines including housing, retail, employment, energy and waste. He has appeared at many development plan examinations both for local planning authorities and developers. His Court practice encompasses statutory challenges (in respect of planning matters) and judicial review proceedings. His public and administrative law practice includes environmental law and other regulatory matters. He is membership secretary of PEBA.

POOLE, Anna QC
Axiom Advocates, Edinburgh
07739 639 239
anna.poole@axiomadvocates.com
Featured in Civil Liberties & Human Rights (Scotland)
Practice Areas: Public and administrative law, with a particular interest in judicial review, human rights and EU law.
Career: QC 2012; part time fee paid Judge (First Tier Tribunal, Social Entitlement Chamber) 2014; member of panel of preferred counsel for the Equality and Human Rights Commission 2013; Ad hoc Advocate Depute 2013; Standing Junior Counsel to the Scottish Government (latterly as Second then First Standing Junior Counsel) 2002-2012; called to Scots Bar 1998; solicitor, Scotland 1997 (Brodies); solicitor, England and Wales 1996 (Linklaters). Has acted in cases in European Court of Human Rights, Supreme Court, Court of Session (Inner and Outer House), Criminal Appeal Court, High Court of Justiciary, Sheriff Court, Scottish Land Court, and various Tribunals. Clients have included local authorities, NHS trusts, the Lord Advocate, the Scottish Ministers, the Scottish Information Commissioner, the Scottish Legal Complaints Commission, the EHRC and the Keeper of the Registers.

Publications: Court of Session Practice, ed Macfadyen (contributor); various articles published including in Judicial Review, SLT, SLPQ, Int ILR, IJPICL, Juridical Review, the Scotsman and JLSS.
Personal: Educated Madras College, St Andrews; Somerville and Magdalen Colleges, Oxford (BA Hons (1st Class), MA, MSt).

POOLE, Christopher
New Court Chambers, London
020 7583 5123
cpoole@newcourtchambers.com
Featured in Family/Matrimonial (London)
Practice Areas: All aspects of the law relating to children including in particular care and adoption proceedings. Representing often but not exclusively Local Authorities and Children's Guardians. Particular interest in cases involving serious factual disputes. Recent Cases: Re S (finding of fact; honour based violence) [2013] EWHC 15 (fam). Re T (Residential parenting assessment) [2012] 2 FLR 308. Kent CC v A mother, F and X, Y and Z [2011] 2 FLR 1088.
Professional Memberships: FLBA.
Career: Called 1996, Lincoln's Inn (Thomas More Bursary). Joined New Court Chambers upon completion of pupillage in 1997. Pupil supervisor and advocacy trainer (Lincoln's Inn). Delivers seminars and lectures to social work students, social workers and social work managers as well as Chambers' Instructing Solicitors.
Personal: LLB (Hons) English & European Law, Queen Mary College, University of London and Katholieke Universiteit Leuven, Belgium. Enjoys the gym and a day in the sun watching cricket.

POOLE, Nigel QC
Kings Chambers, Manchester
08450 343 444
clerks@kingschambers.com
Featured in Clinical Negligence (Northern), Personal Injury (Northern)
Practice Areas: All areas of clinical negligence including birth injury, delay in diagnosing cancer, surgical, A&E, mental health, primary healthcare and cosmetic surgery, Personal injury litigation for claimants and defendants in cases of the utmost severity, Healthcare law including human rights claims, Inquests and inquiries. Nigel's recent cases involve acting for a claimant with severe brain injury following failure to treat a rise in intracranial pressure following an assault, a monk who suffered a limb amputation following negligent surgery, several cases of suicide following negligent psychiatric care and an octogenarian who suffered paraplegia after negligent hospital treatment. He acted for the family at a three week Inquest at which a finding of neglect was made when a young woman died following routine surgery , and he successfully defended a £10m claim for catastrophic injury following a go-kart accident.
Professional Memberships: Personal Injury Bar Association Professional Negligence Bar Association.
Career: 2004 to present - Kings Chambers 1989 to 2004 - 18 St John Street Chambers 2000 to 2012: Attorney-General's Provincial Panel of Junior Counsel 2002 to 2009: Legal Assessor, General Medical Council 2009 to date: Recorder (Civil and Private Family matters) 2012 Queen's Counsel 2013 Bar Tribunals and Adjudication Service Panel Member.

POOLES, Michael QC
Hailsham Chambers, London
020 7643 5000
michael.pooles@hailshamchambers.com
Featured in Professional Negligence (London)
Practice Areas: Principal area of practice is professional negligence, particularly concerning lawyers. Also acts for and against members of other professions including accountants, surveyors, architects, engineers and veterinary surgeons. Other main areas of practice are personal injury and general insurance matters, on behalf of claimants as well a large number of insurance companies. He is experienced in costs and disciplinary proceedings.
Professional Memberships: PNBA; COMBAR.
Career: Called to the Bar 1978 and joined present Chambers in 1980. Silk 1999. Recorder 2000. Head of Hailsham Chambers 2004 -09. Bar Standards Board member 2006-09. Master of the Bench of Inner Temple.
Publications: 'Professional Negligence and Liability (LLP)' (Solicitors' chapter).
Personal: Educated at Perse School, Cambridge, 1967-74 and University of London 1974-77. Born 14 December 1955. Lives in Cambridge.

POOTS, Laura
Pump Court Tax Chambers, London
020 7414 8080
clerks@pumptax.com
Featured in Tax (London)
Practice Areas: All areas of taxation, direct and indirect, whether planning or in the course of disputes and litigation. Direct tax practice covers personal and corporate taxes. Particular expertise in private client advice and planning for individuals, trustees and family businesses (UK and international). Indirect tax practice includes VAT, SDLT and landfill tax. Also advises on commercial disputes involving tax issues. Recent cases include Brockenhurst College (Upper Tribunal, VAT Exemption) and Dean & Reddyhoff (Corporation tax relief).
Professional Memberships: Revenue Bar Association, London Chancery and Commercial Bar Association.
Career: Barrister since 2008. March 2013: Appointed to the Attorney General's C Panel.

POPAT, Prashant QC
Henderson Chambers, London
020 7583 9020
ppopatqc@hendersonchambers.co.uk
Featured in Health & Safety (London), Product Liability (London)
Practice Areas: Prashant was recognised as "Health and Safety Silk of the Year" by Chambers and Partners last year. Over 2 decades he has represented defendants in major manslaughter, corporate manslaughter and health and safety prosecutions (and associated inquiries, inquests and litigation) arising from significant incidents such as the railway crashes at Southall, Ladbroke Grove, Hatfield, Potters Bar and Lambrigg, the explosion at the Buncefield oil depot, the Atherstone upon Stour fire and the Glesion Mine flooding. He has also acted for private and public sector defendants in a variety of industries in similar prosecutions, inquests and litigation. In the field of product liability his substantial group action experience encompasses litigation concerning: Benzodiazepines; Norplant; MMR; Sabril; Seroxat; Hip replacements; gastric bands and PIP breast implants. He has also been instructed in unitary product liability cases as well as advising companies on compliance with their obligations under consumer protection legislation in a variety of industries (e.g. pharmaceutical; motoring; mobile telephones).
Professional Memberships: He is a founding and former committee member of the Health and Safety Lawyers' Association and a member of COMBAR.
Career: MA (Oxon) First Class Honours. University Scholar. Baker and McKenzie International Scholar. Gray's Inn Scholar. Judicial Assistant to the Court of Appeal. Judicial Assistant to Lord Woolf MR (as he then was).
Publications: He is the co-editor of the "International Product Law Manual" published by Kluwer.

POPE, Sarah
Fourteen, London
020 7242 0858
spope@fourteen.co.uk
Featured in Family/Matrimonial (London)
Practice Areas: Children law specialist - public and private law. Solicitor for twelve years prior to transfer to the Bar and Member of Law Society Children Panel for eight years. Frequently instructed on behalf of children and their Guardians as a result of Children Panel experience and enhanced knowledge of Guardian's role in public law proceedings; also instructed in complex and intractable private law disputes, the Court of Protection and international cases. Fluent French speaker. Conversational Italian.
Professional Memberships: Lincoln's Inn; Family Law Bar Association; Association of Lawyers for Children; British Agencies for Adoption and Fostering.
Career: Admitted as a solicitor 1994; training and post qualification experience at small and medium sized publicly funded social welfare practices in London; Member of Law Society Children Panel 1998 until transfer to the Bar; Founding Partner of Wilkinson Pope 2002 (specialist Family practice); Higher Rights of Audience (Civil) 2006; Called to the Bar 2006; Tenant Fourteen (formerly 14 Gray's Inn Square) 2006 to present. Trainer in adoption law and contributor to Legal Network Television Training Series. Legal Aid Agency Independent Costs Adjudicator.

POPLE, Alison
Cloth Fair Chambers, London
020 7710 6444
alisonpople@clothfairchambers.com
Featured in Crime (London), Financial Crime (London)
Practice Areas: Principal areas of practice are serious and complex fraud, corporate and business crime and high profile serious crime. Acts in cases involving allegations of banking fraud, insurance fraud, insider trading, 'ponzi' fraud, tax fraud, cartel offences, money laundering, bribery and corruption and VAT offences. Instructed by both the defence and the prosecution, including the Serious Fraud Office. Defended in a number of high profile cases including Mustafa & others (Operation Saturn, FSA prosecution); George & others (BA/VAA cartel allegation, OFT prosecution); Goldshield Group plc & others (Operation Holbein, 'pharmaceuticals', SFO prosecution); Bright & others (Independent Insurance, SFO prosecution); Rayment & others (Jubilee Line Fraud, CPS prosecution). Recent notable cases include, successfully representing Nigel Horn, former legal director of Torex Retail Plc, over conspiracy to defraud charges. Advised a leading nationwide market research company regarding bribery. Acted for William Lowther over corruption offences, acquitted (SFO charges); represented Richard Joseph for insider trading offences; advised the SFO regarding investigation into national sports retailer. Represented Andy Coulson, the former editor of News of the World, in phone hacking case. Retained for former Barclays Senior Executive in SFO/FCA investigation. Instructed to represent former director of Swift Group over corruption offences. For further information please visit www.clothfairchambers.com
Career: 1993 - Called to the Bar.

POPPLEWELL, Simon
Gough Square Chambers, London
020 7353 0924
simon.popplewell@goughsq.co.uk
Featured in Consumer Law (London)
Practice Areas: Simon specialises in all aspects of consumer and regulatory law, in particular in the areas of consumer credit and trading standards law. In relation to consumer credit Simon practises in both adversarial and non-adversarial work. He drafts and advises on consumer credit practice and procedure, including reviewing and drafting consumer credit agreement documentation. Simon also regularly appears in court on consumer credit matters and advises in respect of FCA authorisation. In the area of trading law Simon acts for both regulators and defendants in civil actions brought under Part 8 of the Enterprise Act 2002. He regularly advises and appears in respect of the civil aspects of consumer law, including unfair contract terms and the Consumer Protection from Unfair Trading Regulations 2008.
Career: Called to the Bar in 2000.
Publications: Annotated the Consumer Credit Act 2006 for Current Law Statutes, and is a contributor to Atkin's Court Forms Consumer Protection edition. Co-author of the Law of Consumer Credit and Hire.
Personal: Educated at Lincoln College, Oxford.

PORTER, Joanne
Stour Chambers, Canterbury
01227 764 899
joanne.porter@stourchambers.co.uk
Featured in Family/Matrimonial (South Eastern)
Practice Areas: Joanne has experience in all areas public and private law relating to children, with a particular interest in public law children cases and adoption involving complex issues. Joanne has been involved in a number of cases both in the County Court and the High Court involving Roma and Eastern European families which have required consideration of transferring the matter to other EU member states and various cultural and jurisdictional issues. Joanne has particular interest in cases involving minority cultures and the unique questions that these cases raise.
Professional Memberships: Joanne joined the Law Society Children Panel as a Local Authority member in 2004 and as a Children's representative in 2006. Joanne transferred to the Bar in 2010 and is a member of the ALC and FLBA.

Career: Before being called to the Bar in 2010 Joanne practised as a Solicitor from 2000, both for the Local Authority and in private practice.
Publications: Joanne has written an article for Family Law entitled "Families from eastern Europe and care proceedings" and has been involved in a number of reported cases.

PORTER, Martin QC
2TG - 2 Temple Gardens, London
020 7822 1200
MPorter@2tg.co.uk
Featured in Clinical Negligence (London), Personal Injury (London)
Practice Areas: Clinical negligence and other personal injury work particularly where there is a sporting, insurance, aviation, professional negligence or public law aspect or complication. Experienced in dealing with catastrophic injuries and fatal claims and all forms of employers' and occupiers' liability including industrial disease. Works for most major insurers, medical defence organisations and for claimants (particularly cyclists). An experienced appellate court advocate. Often praised for his calm and efficient manner and ability to get to the heart of a problem.
Professional Memberships: Inner Temple, Western Circuit, British Association of Sports Lawyers, LCCBA, Personal Injuries Bar Association (former Committee Member and contributor to PI Handbook). Often lecture to PIBA and to APIL.
Career: Born 1962. Call 1986. Silk 2006. Educated St John's College, Cambridge: MA (Law) LLM (Public Law).
Publications: Many articles in New Law Journal, The Times and others on personal injury and public law/constitutional matters. Also interviewed by BBC's 'Law in Action' and many radio stations on cycling. Writes extensively on cycle related matters.
Personal: Married, two daughters. Cycling (Chairman of a BC affiliated club); PPL (1989); skiing. Appointed Ambassador to CTC, the National Cycling Charity. Secondary school governor.

POST, Andrew QC
Hailsham Chambers, London
020 7643 5000
andrew.post@hailshamchambers.com
Featured in Clinical Negligence (London), Costs Litigation (London)
Practice Areas: Clinical negligence, professional discipline and the law of costs. Particular expertise in dealing with technically complex cases arising out of medical specialisms such as neurosurgery and cardiac surgery and in cerebral palsy cases. Regularly appears before the Court of Appeal and High Court Judges on costs appeals. Significant recent cases include R v Zinga CA 2014 (intervention in case in Court of Criminal Appeal as to costs recoverable by private prosecutors), MW and NW v (1) Dr Thomas (2) North West Strategic HA QBD 2014 (complex CP case arising out of birth and neonatal treatment of premature twins who suffered brain damage by two different mechanisms), K v Tunbridge Wells QBD 2012 (CP case – monitoring of maternal instead of fetal heart), Sherwood v Sherwood Forest [2011] EWHC 3104 (CP following failure to induce delivery), BSG v HMRC [2010] EWCA 1448 (Part 36 penalties in test cases), Aldous v East Kent (obstetric negligence), B v NW Strategic HA (CP following maternal stroke), McCarthy v Essex Rivers (success fees), GOC v Simmons (longest ever GOC case), Burgess v Tameside (CP case - damages recovered in relation to neonatal stroke), Roach v Home Office [2009] EWHC 312 QB (recoverability of costs of inquest), C v W [2008] EWCA 1459 (success fee where liability admitted), Beggs v Medway NHS Trust (brachial plexus injury).
Career: Educated at Trinity College, Cambridge and City University. Called 1988. QC 2012. Head of Hailsham Chambers Costs Group. Assessor for High Court Costs Appeals.

POTTS, James QC
Erskine Chambers, London
020 7242 5532
jpotts@erskinechambers.com
Featured in Commercial Dispute Resolution (London), Company (London), Restructuring/Insolvency (London)
Practice Areas: Company law, corporate insolvency, financial services, partnership and related commercial litigation. Currently, about 75% of cases are contentious matters, with the remainder being non-contentious advisory work. Notable recent cases include: Re Charterhouse Capital Ltd; Arbuthnott v Bonnyman [2014] EWHC 1410 (Ch) (acted for successful Respondents in resisting unfair prejudice petition in private equity firm); Global Energy Horizons Corp v Grey [2012] EWHC 3703 (Ch) (imposition of fiduciary duties in a non-traditional context); Broughton v Kop Football (Cayman) Ltd [2012] EWCA Civ 1743 (acting successfully for RBS on numerous hearings, applications and an appeal on the Liverpool FC litigation); in resisting application for permission to appeal against active case management directions in Liverpool FC litigation; MSL Group Holdings Ltd v Clearwell International Ltd [2012] EWCA Civ 1440 (test for disguised distributions); Halliwells v Austin [2012] EWHC 1194 (Ch) (construction of retirement deed, meaning of fraud, enforceability of releases); Belmont Park Investments PTY Limited v BNY Corporate Trustee Services Limited [2011] UKSC 38 (scope of anti-deprivation principle in Lehmans' insolvency); Fulham Football Club (1987) Ltd v Richards & Anor [2011] EWCA Civ 855 (arbitrability of shareholder disputes); various large commercial arbitrations. Company advisory work includes many reductions of capital and members' schemes of arrangement.
Professional Memberships: Chancery Bar Association, COMBAR.
Career: Called Gray's Inn 1994.

POWELL, Debra
Serjeants' Inn Chambers, London
020 7427 5000
dpowell@serjeantsinn.com
Featured in Clinical Negligence (London), Court of Protection (All Circuits)
Practice Areas: Debra Powell was called to the Bar in 1995. Debra specialises in clinical negligence and healthcare, Court of Protection, police, inquests and inquiries, public and administrative, mental health and professional discipline law. An earlier edition notes that "she is very knowledgeable and personable" and is known for being "a very courageous, clear and direct advocate who is able to cut through multiple issues and get to the key points." Please click on the link to the Serjeants' Inn Chambers website for her profile, which sets out full details of her practice including relevant work of note.
Professional Memberships: ALBA, PNBA, LCLCBA.
Publications: Medical Treatment: Decisions and The Law (co-author); Inquest Law Reports (joint editor 2000-12); The Mental Health Act Explained (co-author).

POWELL, Giles
Old Square Chambers, London
020 7269 0300
Powell@oldsquarechambers.co.uk
Featured in Professional Discipline (London)
Practice Areas: Giles practices in Administrative and Public Law, Employment, Partnership, Professional Discipline and Sports Law. He also undertakes Commercial and Company law cases where they are interrelated with Employment or Partnership issues. He has been involved in a number of high profile Employment and Professional Discipline cases including Chakrabarty v Ipswich Hospitals NHS Trust [2014] QB, Mattu v University Hospitals of Coventry and Warwickshire [2012] CA; A v HTX [2012] QB; Chief Constable of Hampshire v Bullahe [2012] QB; and R (Puri) v Bradford Teaching Hospitals NHS Foundation Trust [2011] Admin.
Professional Memberships: ALBA, Bar Pro Bono, ELA, ELLAS South Eastern Circuit Committee.
Career: Called 1990 Gray's Inn. Old Square Chambers May 2008.
Publications: Contributor to West Law Online Encyclopedia, Employment Topics; and to 'Equality and Discrimination Law', Oxford University Press, European Court of Justice Procedure (to be published).

POWELL, John L QC
4 New Square, London
020 7822 2000
j.powell@4newsquare.com
Featured in Financial Services (London), Professional Negligence (London)
Practice Areas: Commercial practice in UK and overseas, especially investment fraud, professional liability, financial services and securities regulation and insurance. Arbitration (advocate and arbitrator) in UK and overseas.
Professional Memberships: COMBAR, Chancery Bar Assoc, PNBA; Society of Construction Law (President 1991-3).
Career: Called 1974. Silk 1990. Deputy High Court Judge and Recorder. Bencher, Middle Temple. Head of Chambers 1997-99. Bar Council member 1999 - (Chairman Bar Law Reform Committee (1997-98).
Publications: 'Jackson and Powell on Professional Liability'; 'Encyclopaedia of Financial Services Law' (with Prof Eva Lomnicka). 'Palmer's Company Law' (specialist editor 24th ed); 'Issues and Offers of Company Securities'; various papers in national and international legal publications.
Personal: Trinity Hall, Cambridge (MA, LLB).

POWELL, Katie
4 New Square, London
020 7822 2000
k.powell@4newsquare.com
Featured in Construction (London), Product Liability (London), Professional Negligence (London)
Practice Areas: Commercial practice, particularly in the context of investment fraud and professional liability claims, encompassing disputes in the areas of (a) financial services, (b) insurance, and (c) construction and IT. Practice also includes more general commercial disputes, together with a strong product liability element. Experienced in all methods of dispute resolution (arbitration, litigation, adjudication, mediation and negotiation), both domestically and overseas.
Professional Memberships: CHBA, COMBAR, PNBA, TECBAR.
Career: Magdalen College, Oxford (PPE, 2003); City University (Diploma in Law, 2004); Called 2005.
Publications: Editor of financial services chapters of Jackson & Powell on Professional Liability.

POWER, Alexia
Furnival Chambers, London
020 7405 3232
apower@furnivallaw.co.uk
Featured in Crime (London)
Practice Areas: Leading junior with an exclusively criminal practice primarily for the defence. Regularly instructed in high profile and complex cases and appeals, recent examples - rape/child abuse (R v IW - Lostprophets singer), murder (R v YJ) -Tooting Mosque murder, baby-shaking manslaughter (R v S), (R v MF) -(9 handed gang murder), large scale drug importation (R v SA - supply two tons of cocaine cutting agent), fraud and money-laundering (particularly the representation of professional clients), racially aggravated assault (R v Terry). Particular experience and sensitivity in representing young and vulnerable clients. On the CPS list of Specialist Rape Prosecutors since its inception in 2007 and has extensive experience of prosecuting and defending sexual offences including serial rape, historical rape and cases involving child abuse, kidnapping and child abduction. Worked with NSPCC, CPS London and local authorities to establish disclosure protocols for third party material. Expertise in Appeals by way of Case Stated and Judicial Review before the Administrative Court. Reported cases include DPP v Wood and McGillicuddy - defence statements and third party disclosure and R (Hoar-Stevens) v Richmond Magistrates' Court - jurisdiction of the Administrative Court.
Professional Memberships: Criminal Bar Association, Surrey and South London Bar Mess Committee Member, Grays Inn Mentor, Association of Women Barristers. Granted licence to appear as an advocate on the Isle of Man in 2010.
Career: Called 1992 Grays Inn.

POWER, Eloise
Doughty Street Chambers, London
020 7404 1313
e.power@doughtystreet.co.uk
Featured in Product Liability (London)
Practice Areas: Clinical negligence; product liability; regulatory law; public law; inquests; human rights
Career: Eloise Power's current/ recent cases include the metal-on-metal hip prosthesis litigation, the PIP breast implant litigation, the Pandemrix litigation, Brown v HM Coroner for the County of Norfolk [2014] EWHC 187 (Admin), Professional Standards Agency v Health and Care Professions Council and Ghaffar (judgment awaited), and acting for a large group of claimants who were sexually abused by their General Practitioner. She is regularly instructed to act in a range of clinical and dental negligence work in areas such as obstetrics, spinal injury, delayed diagnosis of cancer and orthopaedics. She frequently

acts in professional disciplinary matters in the High Court and before regulators such as the General Medical Council and General Dental Council.
Publications: Munkman on Employer's Liability (contributing editor, "The Liability of Third Parties"); Professional Discipline and Healthcare Regulators, a Legal Handbook (author, "General Dental Council").
Personal: Eloise Power was educated at Clare College, Cambridge (starred double first class degree), City University and the Inns of Court School of Law (Prince of Wales Scholar, Gray's Inn). She has been appointed by the Bar Standards Board as an external examiner, and she is an advocacy trainer for Gray's Inn. She is accredited to undertake Public Access work.

POWER, Lewis QC
Lamb Building, London
020 7797 7788
lewis.power2@btopenworld.com
Featured in Crime (South Eastern), Crime (London)
Practice Areas: Specialist criminal defence practitioner, murder, fraud, regulatory, health and safety, disciplinary, coroners and inquests, serious sexual offences, white collar crime, sports law. Specialist Defence Counsel in International law and extradition.
Professional Memberships: Bar of England & Wales; Full Member N. Ireland Bar; International Bar Association; North American, War Crimes Forums of IBA; Business Crime Committee IBA; Criminal Bar Association ; Special Tribunal for Lebanon (Defence Lead Counsel); Full Member Association of Defence Counsel before ICTY (International Tribunal for Former Yugoslavia); Approved Foreign Lawyer and authorised to appear before Extraordinary Chamber in Courts of Cambodia; Approved English Football Association lawyer.
Career: A highly experienced and formidable criminal defence counsel with a dynamic and diverse practice who is recognised as a leading light in complex Jury trials where his market leading tactical genius is becoming legendary. Sources reveal he is an "unrivalled cross-examiner" where his style is said to be nothing short of brilliant. He is often the "silk of choice" for heavyweight criminal cases involving fraud, regulatory issues and cases with an International dimension. This was recognised by his appointment as Queens Counsel in 2011. has continued to successfully defend high profile, celebrity and sports persons and his practice has ranged from the infamous Grobelaar "football match fixing" case to the "London Terrorist Bombings" case and the "Missing Body" murder case. He has carved out a niche as an expert in murder cases involving mentally ill Defendants.He was appointed as Defence lead Counsel to the Special Tribunal for Lebanon, said to constitute in the effect the World's First International Terrorist Court. He has recently been instructed in the first 2 major cases in which the crime of Slavery has been charged - the first such cases in the last 200 years. He is a Specialist in Confiscation and Proceeds of Crime cases. he has recently been acknowledged as being in the Top Ten List of barristers in the UK.
Publications: "Call to Arms": A Paper for the International Bar Association on behalf of the North American Forum dealing with matters of International Criminal Justice: 2013; "Slavery & Trafficking - An International Criminal Epidemic" - IBA - December 2013 ; "21st Century Slavery: Hidden in Plain Sight" - Lead Article in "Counsel Magazine -England & Wales - February 2014.
Personal: Passionate football supporter; golf; Irish sports; architecture; travel; theatre: international law; currently studying to become an attorney at the Californian Bar.

POWER, Richard
Fountain Court Chambers, London
020 7583 3335
rjp@fountaincourt.co.uk
Featured in Commercial Dispute Resolution (London)
Practice Areas: Broad commercial litigation and arbitration practice, including: banking and financial services; insurance and reinsurance; professional negligence; civil fraud; and conflict of laws. Recent cases include: Haugesund Kommune v Depfa ACS Bank [2012] 2 W.L.R. 199 (Court of Appeal) and Depfa ACS Bank v Wikborg Rein & Co [2011] 3 All E.R. 655 (Court of Appeal), Excalibur Ventures LLC v Texas Keystone Inc. and Gulf Keystone Petroleum Limited, one of The Lawyer's Top 20 Cases of 2012 (57 day trial) [2013] EWHC 2767 (Comm), Dexia Crediop v Comune di Firenze, one of The Lawyer's Top 20 Cases of 2013, and UBS & Depfa v Kommunale Wasserwerke Leipzig, one of The Lawyer's Top 20 Cases of 2014.
Career: Called 2007 (Lincoln's Inn).
Publications: Co-author of 'Law of Bank Payments' (eds. Brindle & Cox, 4th edition).
Personal: Christ Church, Oxford (BA, First Class; BCL, Distinction), Crowther Shield for Advocacy, Lincoln's Inn (2006).

POWNALL, Orlando QC
2 Hare Court, London
020 7353 5324
clerks@2harecourt.com
Featured in Crime (London), Financial Crime (London)
Practice Areas: Orlando Pownall Q.C. is cited as a leader in Crime by The Legal 500 UK, and as a "Star" Silk by Chambers UK which describes him as "One of the most highly sought-after criminal silks, and as an extremely persuasive and impressive jury advocate. He is a supreme performer and an artist of the courtroom." He is widely regarded as one of the leading jury advocates of his generation. In 1999 he was appointed First Senior Treasury Counsel and since taking Silk in 2001 he has almost exclusively defended. Notable cases included the defence of Danny Preddie, the alleged Omagh Bomber and the man charged with the murder of two soldiers at the Masseerene Barracks. Recent instructions include acting for the defence in the alleged manslaughter of a deportee and the murder of gambler by means of a "honey-trap". Apart from being instructed for the defence in murder prosecutions he is instructed in Frauds including Operation Tabernula, the FCA's largest ever market abuse prosecution and a large scale fraud in the Cayman Islands. He has also been instructed in Medicine Act prosecutions. Over the last ten years he has dealt with numerous Appeals against sentence and conviction and CCRC applications.

PRAGER, Sarah
1 Chancery Lane, London
0207 092 2900
sprager@1chancerylane.com
Featured in Travel (London)
Practice Areas: Sarah Prager specialises in travel law claims, including claims under the Package Travel Regulations 1992, the Athens and Montreal Conventions, and at common law. She frequently advises on conflict of laws issues and off-package sales. She has considerable experience in travel claims, both in respect of drafting terms and conditions, advisory work, and representing consumers and tour operators to trial. Cases she has appeared in include: Japp v Virgin Holidays Ltd [2013] EWCA Civ 1371 (high-profile case involving claim for damages for personal injury); Harrison v Jagged Globe [2012] EWCA Civ 835 (liability for off-package services), Milner v Carnival Plc [2010] 3 All ER 701 (measure of damages in holiday claims); Moore v Hotelplan Ltd [2010] EWHC 276 (liability for excursion sold in resort); and Bonsall v Cattolica Assicurazioni [2010] 13th January, unreported (entry into force of Rome II). She is a regular contributor to the International Travel Law Journal, Personal Injury Brief Update Law Journal and Travel and Tourism Lawyers' Association newsletter.
Professional Memberships: Personal Injury Bar Association; Travel & Tourism Lawyers' Association (Chair).
Career: Called to the Bar in 1997, Inner Temple.
Personal: Educated at Ipswich High School and Nottingham University.

PRATLEY, Michelle
Thirty Nine Essex Street, London
020 7832 1111
michelle.pratley@39essex.com
Featured in Court of Protection (All Circuits), Education (London)
Practice Areas: Administrative and public law; human rights; regulatory and commercial law. Areas of public law expertise include community care and mental capacity. Frequently instructed in complex proceedings in the Court of Protection concerning health and welfare (including forced marriage, capacity to consent to sexual relations and deprivation of liberty) and serious medical treatment (including DNAR orders). Acts for and advises local authorities, academies, universities and students on all aspects of education law, including admissions and exclusions, special educational needs and discrimination claims. Experience in international regulatory compliance disputes in banking and financial services, as well as offshore fraud and money laundering. Notable cases include ACCG v MN [2013] EWCOP 3859 (jurisdiction of the Court of Protection); SMBC v RG [2013] EWCOP 2373 (capacity to marry); BCC v ED (Upper Tribunal, assessing unreasonable public expenditure); DPP v IPOC (British Virgin Islands, confiscating US$40 million as the proceeds of crime).
Career: Solicitor, King & Wood Mallesons, Sydney (2002-2003); Legal Officer, Australian Human Rights Commission, Sydney (2003-2004); called to the Bar, Lincoln's Inn (2006); admitted as a barrister in the British Virgin Islands (2007).
Publications: Contributing author, McManus, 'Education and the Courts' (Jordans, 2012).
Personal: BA/LLB, University of New South Wales, Sydney (1997-2002), LLM, University of Cambridge (2004-05).

PRENTIS, Sebastian
New Square Chambers, London
020 7419 8000
sebastian.prentis
@newsquarechambers.co.uk
Featured in Company (London), Restructuring/ Insolvency (London)
Practice Areas: Company law, especially shareholder disputes. Insolvency and Restructuring, including cross-border.
Professional Memberships: Chancery Bar Association; Licencing Committee, British Horseracing Authority.
Career: New Square Chambers.
Personal: Born 20 May 1969. Educated Winchester College; Peterhouse, Cambridge; City University. Lives Oxfordshire. Other interests painting, modern jazz, inter-war literature, cider-making.

PRESSDEE, Piers QC
29 Bedford Row Chambers, London
020 7404 1044
PPresddee@29br
Featured in Family/Matrimonial (London)
Practice Areas: Piers practises exclusively in children law, undertaking complex and important cases at first instance and on appeal, and has appeared in numerous reported cases. His private children law work comprises relocation, residence, contact and LGBT parenting disputes, surrogacy and parental order proceedings (he appeared in Re K (children) (private law proceedings: direction to investigate child's circumstances) [2013] 1 FCR 87; MA v RS (Contact: Parenting Roles) [2012] 1 FLR 1056; and Re F and H (children: relocation) [2008] 2 FLR 1667). His public children law work mainly involves cases with allegations of very serious physical or sexual abuse (he recently appeared in the high profile case of Sutton v Gray and others (No.s 1 and 2) [2013] 1 FLR 833 and 914).
Professional Memberships: Co-Chair, Association of Lawyers for Children, 2008-10; FLBA.
Career: Called, 1991. Silk 2010.
Publications: Co-author, 'Contact: The New Deal' (Family Law, 2060; Co-author, 'The Public Law Outline: The Court Companion' (Family Law, 2008); Updater of the Children Volumes of Halsbury's Laws of England.
Personal: Born, 1968. Educated, St John's College, Cambridge (President, Cambridge Union). Married, four daughters.

PRESTON, Hugh QC
7BR, London
020 7242 3555
hpreston@plilegal.com
Featured in Clinical Negligence (London), Product Liability (London)
Practice Areas: Product liability, clinical negligence, personal injury. Recent product liability cases include PIP breast implants group litigation (ongoing), DePuy ASR hips group litigation (ongoing), O'Byrne v Aventis Pasteur (2010) - ECJ / Supreme Court ruling on time limits under EC Product Liability Directive, ABG1 hips group litigation (2008). Also instructed in numerous individual hip cases including metal-on-metal devices from a range of manufacturers, vaccine damage cases, and a range of general product liability cases incl. heart valves, defibrillators, and non-medical / home appliance products. In his clinical negligence practice he acts for claimants throughout the jurisdiction in a wide range of claims including birth injuries and maximum severity claims, internal

injuries, orthopaedic injuries, consent issues, cosmetic surgery etc.. Presently instructed in a large number of high value birth injury / CP cases and has extensive experience in maximum severity litigation. Recent personal injury cases include Smith v Northamptonshire CC (2009) – landmark House of Lords ruling on PUWER and several high value claims against private security companies operating in Iraq including Newton-Sealey v Armorgroup (2009) and Cardy v Erinys (ongoing). Extensive experience in employers liability litigation / six pack regulations etc.
Professional Memberships: PIBA, AVMA.
Career: Called in 1994 (Middle Temple). Silk (2012).
Personal: He is married with four children and lives in Somerset. Age 44. Educated at Eton College and Durham University.

PRICE, Clare
Hailsham Chambers, London
020 7643 5000
Clare.Price@hailshamchambers.com
Featured in Clinical Negligence (London), Professional Discipline (London)
Practice Areas: Clinical negligence, professional discipline, professional negligence, personal injury.
Professional Memberships: Member of Professional Negligence Bar Association (PNBA).
Career: Called 1988. Specialises in medical law including clinical negligence claims, consent to treatment issues, inquests and disciplinary and regulatory matters (CCCs considering both conduct and competence issues, interim orders hearings and Health, Education and Social Care Tribunals). Chair of 5 Independent Inquiries commissioned by NHS into the care and treatment of patients following homicides. Also specialises in professional indemnity claims involving solicitors and barristers and high value personal injury work. Please see website CV for further information.

PRICE, Richard
9 St John Street, Manchester
01619 559 000
richard.price@9sjs.com
Featured in Chancery (Northern)
Practice Areas: Real property including land registration, boundaries and adverse possession, co-ownership; rights of way and easements and restrictive covenants; Business landlord and tenant and social housing; Wills, trusts and probate; Professional negligence.
Professional Memberships: Chancery Bar Association; Professional Negligence Bar Association; Northern Circuit Commercial Bar Association.
Career: Magdalene College, Cambridge (MA); Admitted as a solicitor in 1992 (Partner in Pannone LLP 1996 - 2009); CEDR accredited Mediator (2008); Called to the Bar in 2010 (Lincoln's Inn); Member of the Law & Polity Committee of the Methodist Church of Great Britain from 2010.

PRICE, Roderick
187 Fleet Street, London
020 7430 7430
chambers@187fleetstreet.com
Featured in Crime (London)
Practice Areas: Specialises in criminal defence work with particular emphasis on fraud, terrorism, drug trafficking and murder cases. Defends in cases which concern racialist issues. Regularly instructed in cases referred to the Court of Appeal by the Criminal Cases Review Commission. Recent trials in which instructed as a leading junior include R v Phillips [2007] (Bournemouth: Conspiracy to Steal/Remove Criminal Property) R v Gallagher [2006] (Manchester: Murder) R v Close [2005] (Bolton: Fraud) R v Santharatnam [2004] (CCC: Murder) R v Siraj-Eldin [2004] (Kings Lynn: Attempted Murder) and R v Yilmaz [2003-2004] (Woolwich: Class A Drugs Supply). Some noted reported cases in the Court of Appeal include R v Alleyne [2003] (foreseeability/intent in murder cases) R v Harding [1998] (mandatory life sentences) R v Avis [1997] (sentencing guidelines in firearms cases) R v Jones and Barham [1997] (conditional admissibility rule/joint enterprise cases) R v Gray and Liggins [1995] (insider dealing) R v Preston [1994] (interception of communications).
Professional Memberships: Criminal Bar Association.
Career: Called to the Bar 1971, Inner Temple.
Personal: Interests include sailing, badminton, tennis and cricket.

PRICE OBE, Richard QC
Littleton Chambers, London
020 7797 8652
rprice@littletonchambers.co.uk
Featured in Mediators (All Circuits), Professional Discipline (London)
Practice Areas: Commercial and business law, entertainment and media law (including defamation), intellectual property, professional negligence, tort and professional regulation. Mediator in all these areas, and employment, property law, construction and all other types of civil law disputes, including disputes involving local authorities and government departments. Also specialises in election law.
Professional Memberships: COMBAR, London Common Law and Commercial Bar Association, Professional Negligence Bar Association, Association of Disciplinary and Regulatory Lawyers, Member of the Association of Northern Mediators, Member of the Chartered Institute of Arbitrators, Member of the LCIA.
Career: Called to Bar 1969; QC 1996; CEDR accredited mediator 1997; Bencher of Gray's Inn 2002; recorder (civil work) 2004; Chairman/Vice-Chairman of the Professional Conduct Committee of the Bar 2002-05; Chairman of the Complaints Committee and Member of the Bar Standards Board 2006-07; legal assessor to the Disciplinary Committee of the Royal College of Veterinary Surgeons 2007, and to the Fitness to Practice Panels of the General Medical Council 2009; lecturer in mediation, civil procedure, commercial and election law.
Publications: Editor of Parker's 'Law and Conduct of Elections', Consulting editor of Halsbury's 'Laws of England', 4th Edition 2007 Re-issue, on Elections and Referendums, contributor to 'Burton on Civil Appeals', and Bowers on 'Whistleblowing Law and Practice'.
Personal: Educated King Edward VII School, Sheffield; King's College London (LLB Hons).

PRINCE, Laura
Matrix Chambers, London
020 7404 3447
lauraprince@matrixlaw.co.uk
Featured in Employment (London)
Practice Areas: Laura specialises in employment and discrimination law. Laura has a substantial appellate practice having appeared in the Court of Justice of the European Union (Parkwood Leisure Ltd v Alemo-Herron and Others [2011] ICR 920; TUPE transfers and collective agreements), twice in the Supreme Court (Alemo-Herron and Hounga v Allen [2014] All ER (D) 289 (Jul); illegality) and on numerous occasions in the Court of Appeal and the EAT. Recent Court of Appeal cases include Hounga (above), Gallop v Newport City Council [2013] IRLR 23 (the concept of knowledge in disability discrimination claims) and Burke v College of Law [2012] EqLR 279). Recent EAT cases include; Atkinson v Community Gateway Association UKEAT/0457/12/BA (Whistle-blowing, constructive dismissal and Article 8 rights), Bradley v RHUL UKEAT/0459/13/SM (professorial equal pay claim), Iqbal v MPC [2012] NLJR 1536 (postponements) and Bozeat-Manzi v Telephonica UK UKEATPA/1799/11 (just and equitable extensions and the need to hear evidence at PHRs). Laura also has experience of all types of Employment Tribunal claim. She has particular expertise in sex discrimination and equal pay claims where she has been instructed in test cases (Schafer v Royal Holloway and Bedford New College [2011] EqLR 429; the first professorial equal pay claim; Bradley v Royal Holloway (see above), large multiple claims (involving over 1000 Claimants) and Tan v SOAS [2013] EqLR 924.
Professional Memberships: BPBU, ELA, ELBA and ELAAS.
Career: LLB Law (First Class) UCL; called to the Bar 2003. Nominated for the Bar Pro Bono Award 2012.

PRINGLE, Watson
New Square Chambers, London
020 7419 8000
watson.pringle
@newsquarechambers.co.uk
Featured in Chancery (London)
Practice Areas: Commercial civil fraud litigation, Commercial dispute resolution, Offshore, Company and Insolvency
Professional Memberships: Chancery Bar Association; COMBAR; Fraud Lawyers Association; Young Fraud Lawyers Association
Career: Watson specialises in commercial and civil fraud litigation, with a particular emphasis on cases involving asset tracing, forensic accounting analysis, jurisdictional issues and conflict of laws. He has since 2011 acted as junior Counsel for the family of the late Georgian billionaire Arkadi Patarkatsishvili. This has involved him in many different pieces of litigation in both England and the BVI, including the trial of Berezovsky v Abramovich [2012] EWHC 2463 (Comm) and the related litigation in Gudavadze & ors v Anisimov. He also regularly represents and advises creditors, debtors and office-holders in both personal and corporate insolvency matters where there is a cross-border and/or fraud element. He has experience in cases involving phoenix companies, transactions defrauding creditors, preferences and jurisdiction issues including litigation surrounding a debtor's centre of main interests (COMI) for the purposes of the EC Regulation.
Personal: Educated Edinburgh Academy, Brasenose College, Oxford, BA (Hons) Oxon. Languages: French, German. Watson is a keen footballer, golfer and follower of Scottish rugby.

PRITCHARD, Sarah
Kings Chambers, Manchester
08450 343 444
sloxton@kingschambers.com
Featured in Clinical Negligence (Northern)
Practice Areas: Specialises in clinical negligence with particular emphasis on surgical negligence, birth damage claims and orthopaedic cases. She also has a substantial personal injury practice dealing with cases of the utmost severity.
Professional Memberships: Personal Injuries Bar Association.
Career: University of Manchester (LLB), Called to the bar in 1993 (Gray's Inn) Junior Scholarship.

PROCHASKA, Elizabeth
Matrix Chambers, London
020 7404 3447
elizabethprochaska@matrixlaw.co.uk
Featured in Civil Liberties & Human Rights (London)
Practice Areas: Public, human rights and equality law, including education, health, inquests, community care, commercial and EU. Recent cases include R (Catt) v The Commissioner of Police of the Metropolis & Ors and another case [2013] EWCA Civ 192, Kiobel v Royal Dutch Petroleum (2012, US Supreme Court), Ladele v UK (2012) (European Court of Human Rights), AM v Secretary of State for the Home Department (High Court/CA, 2012), R(RMC) v Metropolitan Police Commissioner (High Court, 2012), R (JM and NT) v Isle of Wight Council (High Court, 2012), Milner v South Central SHA (High Court/CA, 2011), Hillingdon LBC v Neary (Court of Protection, 2011), WL (Congo) (UKSC, 2010).
Career: Educated at St John's College, Cambridge (BA Hons, 2002), City University (GDL, 2004), Somerville College, Oxford (BCL, 2006). Called to the Bar 2007. Judicial Assistant to Lady Hale and Lord Brown (2008-09).
Publications: Co-author, Blackstone Guide to the Human Rights Act 1998 (OUP, 7th edition, forthcoming 2014). Contributor, Clayton and Tomlinson, Law of Human Rights (2nd edition, 2009). Contributor, Livingstone, Owen and Macdonald, Prison Law (OUP, 5th edition, forthcoming 2014).

PROOPS, Anya
11KBW, London
020 7632 8500
Anya.Proops@11kbw.com
Featured in Administrative & Public Law (London), Data Protection (London), Employment (London)
Practice Areas: Information, public and employment law. Member of Information Commissioner's panel of counsel. Notable cases include: Dhoorihaka v Director of Public Prosecutions (Privy Council, contempt of court proceedings brought against Mauritian journalist/freedom of expression); Steinmetz v Global Witness (first ever case to deal with the substantive application of the journalistic exemption in the Data Protection Act 1998 (DPA)); Fish Legal v Information Commissioner & Ors (CJEU, whether privatised

water companies public authorities under the EIR), Central London Community Healthcare NHS Trust v Information Commissioner (first ever appeal against a monetary penalty notice issued under the DPA); R(Plantagenet Alliance) v Secretary of State for Justice and University of Leicester (judicial review of decision as to the burial of King Richard III's remains); Southampton City Council v Information Commissioner (first ever case under the DPA concerning the application of surveillance technology); Grant v Land Registry [2011] EWCA Civ 769 (application of the Sexual Orientation Regulations to the alleged 'outing' of a gay employee); Corbette v National Bank of Dominica [2009] UKPC 32 (Privy Council, wrongful dismissal); Lawson v Serco [2006] 1 All ER 823 (House of Lords, rights of overseas workers).
Professional Memberships: ELA, ELBA, ALBA.
Career: Called in 1998.
Publications: Contributor to Tolley's 'Employment Handbook'. Co-editor of Justis/11KBW Information Law Reports. Co-founder of the information law blog Panopticonblog.com.
Personal: Cambridge (BA); London School of Economics (PhD); City University (CPE).

PROSSER, Kevin QC
Pump Court Tax Chambers, London
020 7414 8080
clerks@pumptax.com
Featured in Tax (London)
Practice Areas: Widely recognised and consulted in all types of revenue work with a particularly strong litigation practice. Recent cases include: HMRC v Tower MCashback (Supreme Court), Lookers plc v HMRC (Court of Appeal), UBS v HMRC (Court of Appeal), Aberdeen Asset Management v HMRC (Upper Tribunal), Bristol & West v HMRC (Upper Tribunal) Vaccine Research LP v HMRC (Upper Tribunal), Mercedes Benz v HMRC (Upper Tribunal).
Professional Memberships: Chairman, Revenue Bar Association (2009-2013); London Common Law & Commercial Bar Association.
Career: Called 1982, QC 1996; Recorder 2000, Lincolns Inn Bencher 2005; Deputy High Court Judge (2008).
Publications: Tax Appeals (Potter & Prosser).

PRYOR, Michael
Maitland Chambers, London
020 7406 1200
mpryor@maitlandchambers.com
Featured in Real Estate Litigation (London)
Practice Areas: Barrister specialising primarily in litigation and advisory work related to real estate. In particular, all aspects of commercial and residential landlord and tenant (including leasehold enfranchisement), real property, insolvency law (personal and corporate) in a property context, and property-related professional negligence (solicitors and property/finance related professionals). Also, probate, partnership, unincorporated associations, and finance matters arising in a real estate context. Hauser v. Howard de Walden Estates Ltd [2013] UKUT 597 (LC) (leasehold enfranchisement, relativity, flying freeholds), Deutsche Bank Suisse SA v Khan & Ors [2013] EWCA Civ 1149, [2013] EWHC 1020, [2013] EWHC 482 (mortgage possession, misrepresentation, consumer law, loan agreement, costs liability, re-entry after enforcement of a warrant, full and frank disclosure), Hortense Littlewood v David Radford [2010] 1 P& CR 18 (CA) (professional negligence, leasehold enfranchisement, time-limit), Risegold Ltd v Escala Ltd [2009] 2 P&CR 1 (CA) (development, nature of easement), Cadogan v. Sportelli [2008] 1 WLR 2142 (CA) (leasehold enfranchisement, deferment rates), Ultimate Leisure v. Tindle [2008] 1 P&CR DG11 (CA) (option, business tenancies, security of tenure), Meretz Investments NV v. ACP Ltd [2007] Ch. 197 (CA) (conspiracy, abuse of process, estoppel, mortgagee's powers), Re Edwards [2007] WTLR 1387 (setting aside will for fraud)
Professional Memberships: Chancery Bar Association, Property Bar Association.
Career: Qualified 1992.
Personal: University of Newcastle upon Tyne (LLB). Born 1969.

PRZYBYLSKA, Sarah
2 Hare Court, London
020 7353 5324
clerks@2harecourt.com
Featured in Professional Discipline (London), Crime (London)
Practice Areas: Sarah prosecutes (Grade 3; rape list; security cleared) and defends in criminal cases of the utmost seriousness, and has an extensive profession regulation practice. Recent criminal cases include murder; people trafficking; conspiracy to rape; fraud on Ryanair; gang-related firearms matters; and importation of Class A drugs. Sarah has particular expertise in PII and complex disclosure. In her professional disciplinary work she has appeared (both at first instance and appeal) at the GMC, GDC, NMC and other healthcare regulators, including on a public access basis. Sarah has a particular interest in equestrian law and has recently appeared at the British Horseracing Authority. She also has experience in coronial proceedings acting on behalf of healthcare professionals. Sarah has a developing practice in public law, particularly judicial review and appeal by way of case stated. She was instructed as junior counsel in the 'Twitter Joke Trial', representing Paul Chambers, who was prosecuted for Tweeting a joke about blowing up an airport. The conviction of Mr Chambers was finally overturned in July 2012 by the Divisional Court in a judgment delivered by the Lord Chief Justice. She has a strong advisory practice, including advice on private prosecutions, and has recently advised private clients on their potential exposure in areas including Advertising Standards Authority investigations, overseas surrogacy arrangements and mercenary activities.

PUGH, Richard
Compass Chambers, Edinburgh
07968 531 360
richard.pugh@compasschambers.com
Featured in Personal Injury (Scotland), Clinical Negligence (Scotland)
Practice Areas: Richard has a varied practice but his principle areas of expertise are professional and clinical negligence, personal injury, property damage and fatal accident inquiries. He also acts in a number of ongoing commercial causes and judicial reviews. Richard has dealt with a number of leading cases in the area of personal injury law. He is experienced in dealing with high value and complex matters. In addition, Richard has a particular interest in cases arising in the course of sporting and other outdoor activities, and has dealt with a number of such actions. Recent cases include: Leonard v Loch Lomond and the Trossachs (2014) - concerning an accident on the West Highland Way; ICL v Johnson Oils - test case concerning duties of suppliers of gas; Campbell v Gordon (2014) - debate concerning civil actionability of employer's obligation to provide insurance; Thomson v Dennis Thomson Builders (2012) - Case resulted in a change in practice for the conduct of civil jury trials in Scotland; Munro v Sturrock t/a Scotmaps (2010) and (2012) - Proof, and subsequent appeal, concerning an accident during the Scottish Rally Championships; Smith v The Scottish Legal Aid Board (2011) and (2012) – the right to payment under the Late Payment of Commercial Debts (Interest) Act 1998, and corresponding European Directives.
Career: 1996-2000: LLB (HONS) (Strathclyde); 2000-01: Dip LP (GGSL); 2008 Called to the Bar.

PURCHAS, Christopher QC
Crown Office Chambers, London
020 7797 8100
purchas@crownofficechambers.com
Featured in Personal Injury (London)
Practice Areas: Principle areas of practice are personal injury, clinical negligence, health and safety, professional negligence, insurance and product liability. He is highly regarded for the depth of his experience in high-value catastrophic injury work. Sources note his ability when handling complex technical points, his excellent client manner, and his fine performances in court. Involved in several leading cases including Wells v Wells, Page v Sheerness Steel, Heil v Rankin, Baker v Quantum Clothing and Gray v Thames Trains. Appears before the Court of Appeal and the Supreme Court and acts for both claimants and defendants. Involved in many different kinds of personal injury litigation including industrial deafness NDDL; fatal accidents Williams v Welsh Ambulance and Arnup v White; fibromyalgia and chronic pain syndrome Bennet v Smith; work stress Jimenez v London Borough of Southwark; PTSD White v London Fire Brigade; refusal to mediate Halsey v Milton Keynes; striking out for failure to serve in time Aktas v Adepta, Cranfield v Bridgegrove and Hashtroodi v Hancock; valuation of loss of a chance Doyle v Wallace; and assessment of gratuitous care Evans v Pontypridd Roofing.
Career: Called to the Bar in 1966 and joined Chambers at 2 Crown Office Row in 1967. Appointed a Recorder of the Crown Court in 1986 and made Queens Counsel in 1990. Deputy High Court Judge from 1999 and Accredited Mediator since 2004.

PURCHAS, James
4 Pump Court, London
020 7842 5555
jpurchas@4pumpcourt.com
Featured in Financial Services (London), Insurance (London)
Practice Areas: Commercial litigation with an emphasis on financial services, banking (wholesale and retail) and insurance and reinsurance disputes. Other work includes civil fraud, conflict of laws issues, trade disputes (particularly between manufacturers and distributors) and professional negligence work (accountants, financial intermediaries, lawyers and surveyors) and fire cases. Regularly instructed in respect of related urgent injunctive relief and other interim applications. Appears in all civil courts, tribunals and domestic and international arbitrations.
Professional Memberships: Commercial Bar Association, Financial Services Lawyers Association, Professional Negligence Bar Association and TECBAR.
Career: MA (Hon) (Cantab.) Classics. Dip. Law (City) 1996. Dip. European Law (Kings) 1997. Call 1997. Inner Temple Major Scholarship. Bar European Commission Scholarship 1998. Foreign Associate Shearman & Sterling, New York 1999. Tenant at 4 Pump Court 2000. FSA Secondment 2007.
Publications: Co-author of 'Civil Appeals'– Sweet & Maxwell 2010. Law Brief Update: Financial Services, Insurance and Professional Negligence. Lloyds Financial Crime Reports, Editorial Panel.

PURCHAS, Robin QC
Francis Taylor Building, London
020 7353 8415
robin.purchas@ftb.eu.com
Featured in Planning (London)
Practice Areas: Robin Purchas QC's main areas of work are in the fields of administrative, environmental, local government and planning law, the High Court and tribunals and inquiries, including questions of human rights and European law. He deals with cases in Hong Kong and elsewhere in the world. He is a leading specialist in compulsory purchase, valuation and compensation matters. He has wide experience in connection with the promotion of and opposition to major government and public schemes, including the 2012 Olympics (advising the ODA), Thames Tunnel, the Channel Tunnel, the Channel Tunnel Rail Link and Crossrail and the Victoria Station Upgrade, West Coast Main Line, East Midlands Parkway, Thameslink 2000, the Cambridge and the Bristol Guided Bus orders. He is regularly involved in infrastructure schemes in the water, aviation, energy, transport and other related fields as well as major retail, residential, institutional, waste, minerals, highway, leisure and commercial schemes. He is regularly consulted on and appears in cases concerning heritage and listed building matters. He has an extensive environmental law practice.
Professional Memberships: Member of the Bar Council: 2000-02 - (Chairman of the Education and Training Committee 2001-02); Member of the South Eastern and the European Circuits, Administrative Law Bar Association, Bar European Group, the National Infrastructure Planning Association, the Planning and Environment Bar Association (Chairman 2004-08) and Leader of the Parliamentary Bar (2002-12) and Fellow of Society for Advanced Legal Studies.
Career: Called to Bar: 1968, QC: 1987. Master of the Bench of the Inner Temple: (1996 -). MA(Cantab) Senior Exhibitioner. Attorney-General's Panel (1979-87). Recorder: (1989 -). Deputy High Court Judge: (1994 -).Deputy Chairman - Information Tribunal (national security cases) (2001-). Assistant Parliamentary Boundary Commissioner (1999-2011). Accredited Mediator (CEDR 2004). Head of Chambers Francis Taylor Building (2001-11).

PURCHASE, Mathew
Matrix Chambers, London
020 7404 3447
mathewpurchase@matrixlaw.co.uk
Featured in Education (London), Employment (London)
Practice Areas: Public and administrative law, employment and discrimination, education, human rights. Notable recent cases include: Kemeh v Ministry of Defence [2014] ICR 625, CA; McKinnon v London Borough of Redbridge [2014] EWCA Civ 178, CA; R (UNISON) v Lord Chancellor [2014] ICR 498, DC; R (Care North East Northumberland) v Northumberland CC [2014] PTSR 658, CA; R (Davis) v West Sussex County Council [2013] PTSR 494, QBD; R (Green) v Gloucestershire County Council [2012] EqLR 225, QBD.
Professional Memberships: Adminstrative Law Bar Association; Employment Law Bar Association; Employment Lawyers Association; Human Rights Lawyers Association; Industrial Law Society.
Career: Called 2002. Appointed to B Panel of junior counsel to the Crown. Member of Bar Pro Bono Unit and ELAAS.
Publications: Contributing editor of Clayton and Tomlinson's The Law on Human Rights (2nd edition, OUP); contributor to Simor's 'Human Rights Practice'; Judicial Review practice guides for LexisNexis; articles on disability discrimination, legitimate expectations, and misfeasance in public office for Practical Law.

PURNELL, James
Henderson Chambers, London
020 7583 9020
jpurnell@hendersonchambers.co.uk
Featured in Health & Safety (London), Product Liability (London)
Practice Areas: Product Liability, Health & Safety and Environmental, Personal Injury, Employment, Regulatory Law, Public & Administrative Law.
Professional Memberships: HSLA, COMBAR, ELBA, PIBA.
Career: Middle Temple Queen Mother Scholar 2001, Called to Bar 2002, Attorney General's Panel of Counsel 2009, Specialist Regulatory List Advocate in Health & Safety and Environmental Law 2012.
Personal: In his spare time devoted to bringing the glory days back to Clapham Rovers FC.

PURNELL, Nicholas QC
Cloth Fair Chambers, London
020 7710 6444
nicholaspurnell@clothfairchambers.com
Featured in Crime (London), Financial Crime (London)
Practice Areas: Practises predominantly in Commercial & Business Crime and in regulatory and professional disciplinary matters. Member of the Lord Chancellor's Advisory Committee on Legal Education and Conduct 1991-97. Member of the Criminal Committee Judicial Studies Board 1991-96. Has twice been appointed an Inspector by the DTI inspecting insider share dealing and has extensive experience of defending in such cases including McCormack (Atlantic Computers), Townsend (Hoare Govett), Steele (Knox D'Arcy), and Crosswell (Selborne Brick). Trials include Guiness, Brinks Mat, Blue Arrow, McNicolas, Morgan Grenfell (anti-dumping prosecution), Mabey (international sanctions violations), Bowbelle Marchioness Disaster, Lord Archer and Jonathan Aitken's perjury trials. Led the team on behalf of Balfour Beatty in the settlement of the SFO investigation, the first civil recovery order entered into by the prosecution authority. Advised British Airways executives in the first contested prosecution under the Enterprise Act. Innospec; represented company in global plea agreement between SFO, DoJ and SEC. Successfully represented a major travel operator in the first prosecution by the Civil Aviation Authority under the Air Travel Organisers License regulation at trial and again at Appeal; advised renowned airline in respect of licensing with the civil aviation authority. Advised regarding a shipping inquest; continues to represent a leading travel business in cross border investigations into deaths outside the jurisdiction. Advised two global companies in separate cases re. Competition and Cartel investigations. Appeared at the Competition Appeals Tribunal. Advised Icelandic banking executives. Advised Police forces on the implications of the Hookway ruling. Recent notable cases; Represented a defendant in the 'Vantis' tax fraud trial; represented a former governor of the Delta State in a multi-million pound corruption case; advised a former editor of a national newspaper in relation to the Leveson Enquiry; advised the director of a global events company in relation to criminal proceedings revolving around the sale of corporate tickets for the Olympic games. Advised a national broadcaster re corruption, successfully represented Victor Dahdaleh over international corruption charges. Advised a multinational defence technology company; Advising global security company amid fraud allegations, SFO investigation. Advising a national pharmaceutical company. Advising individual in SFO investigation regarding Rolls Royce; Acting for former Senior Executive of Barclays in SFO/FCA investigation. For further information please visit www.clothfairchambers.com.
Career: Called to the Bar 1968. Silk 1985

PUZEY, James
St Philips Chambers, Birmingham
01212 467 000
jpuzey@st-philips.com
Featured in Health & Safety (Midlands)
Practice Areas: James has been a member of the Attorney-General's Panel of Prosecution Advocates since 1996. He was recently appointed to Panel 'A' of the newly created Unified Regulatory List of Crown Counsel. He is instructed regularly to appear in the most challenging and serious health and safety prosecutions. These include recently: R v McHale Engineering Ltd, engineering company charged with designing unsafe agricultural machinery; R v Clegg Food Projects and Others, concerning a construction fatality in Leicestershire; R v Eaton and Aegis Ltd, trial of water treatment contractor for failures in legionella control in West Midlands factory; and R v Woods, prosecution for breach of duty by a lifeguard at a public pool where a drowning occurred. James writes and lectures on health and safety law. He has been a member of the Treasury Solicitor's Panel of Counsel since 1998 and thus has considerable experience of other high level regulatory advocacy, having appeared regularly in the Higher Courts including judicial review cases and appeals by way of case stated.
Career: Called 1990.

PYMONT, Christopher QC
Maitland Chambers, London
020 7406 1200
clerks@maitlandchambers.com
Featured in Chancery (London), Real Estate Litigation (London)
Practice Areas: Commercial chancery, property (especially landlord and tenant), professional negligence, company and insolvency. Cases include: Gencor ACP Ltd v Dalby (2000 breach of directors' duties); Half-Moon Bay v Crown Eagle (PC 2001 restrictive covenants, land registration in Jamaica); Ashworth Frazer v Gloucester City Council (HL 2001 tenant's covenants against alienation without consent); China National v Fenwick Elliott (VC 2002 solicitors' duties and confidentiality); Chadwick v McGowan (CA 2002 Receiver's duties); Robinson v Bank of Bermuda (Bermuda CA 2002 bankers' duties and limitation); Evans v Virgin Radio (Ch Div 2003 breach of contract and effect on share options); Westminster CC v Dame Shirley Porter (2003 sham trusts); John Laing v Amber Pass (2004 break clause in lease); Chahal v Mahal (CA 2005 partnership); Shirayama v Danovo (Ch Div 2005 forfeiture of lease); Littman v Aspen Oil (CA 2005 rectification); Peekay v ANZ (CA 2006 misrepresentation); Carphone Warehouse v Malekout (CA 2006 issue estoppel); Berkeley v Pullen (Ch Div 2007 construction of planning consultancy agreement); St Ivel v Wincanton (CA 2008 construction of warehousing agreements); Choudhary v Bhatter (CA 2009 jurisdiction); Akzo Nobel v Arista Tubes (CA 2010 interpretation of lease agreement); Payne v Strand (Bahamas CA 2010, procedure); Howard v Howard-Lawson (Ch Div 2010 and CA 2011 construction of will); Bellway v Beazer (CA 2011 construction of shareholders' agreement); Woodford v Persimmon (Ch Div 2011 and CA 2012 rectification); FHR European Ventures v Mankarious (Ch Div 2011, CA 2012 and Supreme Court 2014 fiduciary duties and constructive trusts); Sharab v HRH Al Waleed (CA 2009 and Ch Div 2012 jurisdiction); Ridgewood v Valero (Ch Div 2012 and 2013 breach of option agreement); Sheffield v Sheffield (Ch Div 2013 breach of trust); Krys v New World Value Fund (E Caribbean CA 2014 construction of limited partnership articles).
Professional Memberships: Chancery Bar Association, Property Bar Association, COMBAR.
Career: Called to the Bar 1979; QC 1996; recorder 2004; Deputy High Court Judge.
Personal: Born 1956; educated at Christ Church, Oxford, MA (scholar).

QUINEY, Ben QC
Crown Office Chambers, London
020 7797 8100
quiney@crownofficechambers.com
Featured in Construction (London), Insurance (London), Professional Negligence (London), Property Damage (London)
Practice Areas: Ben practises in all areas of commercial litigation and arbitration; he specialises in commercial and insurance disputes, construction, professional negligence, private international law, and restitution and tracing remedies. Reported cases include: Item Software v Fassihi [2003] 2 BCLC 1 and [2005] 2 BCLC 91 (CA); Re Cooling Equipment Wholesale Ltd [2002] 2 BCLC 74; Mirant Asia-Pacific v Ove Arup [2005] PNLR 10; Margate Theatre Trust v White & ors [2006] Lloyds Rep IR 93; Catlin Estates Ltd v Carter Jonas [2006] PNLR 273; ALE v MSD [2006] EWHC 2080 (TCC); Hart v Larchpark & Fidler [2007] BLR 30 & 160; Bennett (Electrical) Services v Inviron [2007] EWHC 49 (QB); Schmid v Fortmann [2007] All ER (D) 107 (Oct); Crowson Ltd v Concept Ltd [2008] IRLR 288; RBS Invoice Finance Ltd v Karia [2008] All ER (D) 131 (May); Buncefield [2008] EWHC 2218 (Comm); Markel & QBE v SGC & ors [2009] Lloyd's Rep IR 77 and [2008] EWHC 3087 (Comm) and [2009] EWCA Civ 790; Berryland Books v BK Books & ors [2009] 2 BCLC 709 and in CA [2010] All ER (D) 209 (Dec); Premier Waste Management Ltd v Towers [2010] EWHC 2440 (Ch) & [2012] BCC 72 (CA); Liberty v Campagna 27 Con LJ 275; Cadbury v ADT [2011] BLR 661, [2012] BLR 441(CA), & 145 Con. L.R. 14, Templeton Insurance Ltd v Motorcare Warranties Ltd [2012] All ER (D) 75 (Apr), [2012] EWHC 2309 (QB), & [2013] All ER (D) 32 (Feb) (CA), Bembridge Marine v Allen & ors [2012] EWHC 2213 (TCC), Rivercove v Euro Rubberlines [2012] EWHC 2593 (TCC), Daniel v Mode [2013] EWHC 3614 (TCC), and Bank of Ireland v Phillip Pank Partnership [2014] EWHC 284 (TCC).
Professional Memberships: TECBAR; PNBA; COMBAR; London Commercial and Common Law Association.
Career: Appointed Qc 2014. Called 1998, Gray's Inn. University College, Oxford (1994 Law, First Class; 1996 BCL 2(1)); ICSL (1997 BVC). Birkdale School, Sheffield.

QUINN, Chris
Littleton Chambers, London
020 7797 8600
cquinn@littletonchambers.co.uk
Featured in Employment (London)
Practice Areas: High Court litigation (mainly Employment- related and commercial) including fraud (civil). Also general common law including Partnership/ LLPs, Professional Negligence, Professional Discipline, regulatory work including FCA matters, Sports/ Entertainment and IP. Injunction specialist. Full-range of Employment Tribunal practice.
Professional Memberships: ELBA, COMBAR, LCLCBA, ELAAS
Career: Recent appellate appearances include: Bates van Winkelhof v Clyde and Co (Supreme Court); PHS Limited v Rentokil (CA). Recent High Court trials include: Holliday v J M Finn (garden leave restrictions); Towry EJ v Bennett and others (successful defence of £6 million solicitation claim), the Rubcon hedgefund dispute, Yousefi v SJ Solicitors (successful claim of solicitor's negligence), Lonmar v West and others (successful defence of £2 miillion team move claim). Other noteworthy recent High Court work includes the successful application for summary judgment in Thomson Ecology v Hall and Others (team moves). Ongoing/ recent arbitration instructions including the alleged £2 billion dispute over Marathon Asset Management (as well as the related High Court claim) and the successfully concluded claim in Kellow Health Limited v London Orthopaedic Clinic Other recent High Court/ ET work includes: Allen v Investec; Bou Simon v BGC; McCarthy v BSB; Gimson v The Telegraph (age discrimination). Other recent instructions include: Nayyar v Credit Suisse (dual discrimination claim), Pedropillai v PwC (victimisation claim following Tribunal) Chris' older cases include the "Gay Banker" case (Lewis v HSBC), the CA case

that established that unions could be liable to their members for discrimination (Allen v GMB), a management claim brought against the celebrity chef Gary Rhodes, the successful CA claim against the BNP in Redfearn v Serco as well as numerous reported cases.
Personal: Skiing, cinema, theatre, (watching) football.

QURESHI, Khawar QC
Serle Court, London
020 7242 6105
kmqureshi@aol.com
Featured in International Arbitration (London), Public International Law (London)
Practice Areas: Commercial litigation, international arbitration, public international law, administrative and constitutional law.
Professional Memberships: COMBAR, ALBA, ILA, Bar Council (Vice-Chairman International Relations Committee).
Career: LLB, LLM (First Class Cantab). Called to the Bar 1990 (Middle Temple, Queen Mother's Scholar). 'A' Panel Treasury Counsel (2003-06). Taught commercial law at Cambridge University (1989-93), Public International law at King's College London (1993-2002) and was appointed a Visiting Professor in Commercial Law at the University of London (SOAS) in 2004. Extensive appearances in Court at all levels and in Commercial/arbitration matters for and against the UK government and foreign governments. Youngest advocate to have appeared in the ICJ (1993 - Counsel for Bosnia in the 'Genocide' case). Chairman of TheCityUK Legal Services Group (2010-). Vice Chair International Committee Bar Council (1998-2010).

RADCLIFFE, Andrew QC
2 Hare Court, London
020 7353 5324
andrewradcliffeqc@2harecourt.com
Featured in Financial Crime (London)
Practice Areas: A white collar crime fraud specialist, most of his recent work in this country has been defending in serious fraud and fraud related cases although, in the past, he has, in addition, regularly been instructed by the SFO (including MLA cases) and the CPS. Since taking silk in 2000, his cases have included most aspects of fraud and allied offences, including allegations of price fixing, money laundering, MTIC fraud, duty evasion, tax evasion and advance fee fraud as well as confiscation. He has defended successfully in the Kent Pharmaceuticals case and the OFT prosecution of British Airways executives accused of price fixing in collusion with Virgin Atlantic Airlines. He was subsequently instructed for the lead defendant in the "Blue Index" case, the first cross-jurisdictional insider dealing prosecution brought by the FSA, involving proceedings and evidence on both sides of the Atlantic. He also acts in murder and other cases of serious crime and is instructed in regulatory matters, for example on behalf of the Football Association. He frequently works in the Cayman Islands, both in an advisory capacity and in Court there. Recent examples of work in that jurisdiction include various allegations of corruption, misconduct in a public office and fraud as well as murder and firearms cases. He is a member of the Turks & Caicos Islands Bar and is currently instructed in relation to allegations concerning the Revenue there. He was a contributor to the CBA's responses to the Law Commission in respect of the law relating to fraud and dishonesty and, later, the review of the laws of conspiracy and attempt. He is the author of two chapters (on insider dealing and regulatory offences, respectively) in 'Fraud: Law, Practice and Procedure' (published by LexisNexis in 2012).
Career: Called 1975; Assistant Recorder 1998; Recorder 2000; Queen's Counsel 2000.

RADEVSKY, Anthony
Falcon Chambers, London
020 7353 2484
clerks@falcon-chambers.co.com
Featured in Real Estate Litigation (London)
Practice Areas: Landlord and tenant law relating to commercial and residential property, including leasehold enfranchisement; real property disputes and professional negligence claims against solicitors and surveyors. Recently reported cases include: Hosebay Ltd v Day [2012] 1 WCR 2884 (SC); Prospect Estates v Grosvenor Estates [2009] 1 WLR 1313 (CA); Howard de Walden v Aggio [2009] 1 AC 39 (HL); Boss Holdings v Grosvenor West End Properties [2008] 1 WLR 289 (HL); 9 Cornwall Crescent v Royal Borough of Kensington and Chelsea [2006] 1 WLR 1163.
Professional Memberships: Chancery Bar Association; Property Bar Association.
Career: Educated at Alleyn's School, Dulwich; Southampton University (LLB Hons 1977); Called 1978 (Inner Temple).
Publications: Hague on Leasehold Enfranchisement (Sweet & Maxwell 2014); Tenants' Right of First Refusal (Jordans 2008); Drafting Pleadings (Tolley 1995); Service of Documents (Longman 1989).
Personal: Married with 2 daughters.

RADFORD, Nadine QC
187 Fleet Street, London
020 7430 7430
nadineradford@187fleetstreet.com
Featured in Crime (London)
Practice Areas: Nadine Radford has specialised solely in criminal practice all her professional life. She has extensive experience in defending serious criminal offences with particular expertise in terrorism, commercial fraud, money laundering and murder. She has undertaken many high profile cases including the Kurdish Terrorist trial, the Louise Sullivan Shaken Baby case also known as the Australian nanny case, the "Mardi Gra" Bomber and the Afghan Hijacking at Stansted Airport. She has frequently been instructed in complex fraud cases including a gold VAT fraud, diversion frauds including various bonded warehouses and fraudulent trading.
Career: Nadine Radford was made Queen's Counsel in 1995 and was made a Bencher of Lincolns Inn in 1999.

RAFFERTY, Angela
One Paper Buildings, London
020 7353 3728
angelarafferty@onepaper.co.uk
Featured in Crime (South Eastern)
Practice Areas: Criminal law.
Professional Memberships: South Eastern Circuit, CBA, Cambridge & Peterborough Bar Mess.
Career: Angela Rafferty has defended or prosecuted in many of the most high profile, sensitive and complex cases in East Anglia from an early stage in her career. She is recognised as a leading junior in her areas of practice and has been described as 'one of the most formidable advocates seen in recent times' by those who instruct her regularly. She combines meticulous preparation, thorough knowledge of the law and procedure with an ability to deal with people at every level and stage of criminal litigation. She was called to the Bar in 1995 after studying at and working within the University of Cambridge and Clifford Chance. She was made a Recorder aged 39 and regularly sits across the South Eastern Circuit. Her caseload includes matters involving paedophile abuse, child abuse imagery, group and serial sex offending, rape in a domestic setting, human trafficking for the sex trade, complex multi jurisdictional prosecutions of multiple offenders and historic abuse cases. She also acts regularly in cases involving serious violence, drug importation and supply, firearms offences, robbery, fraud and theft, death by careless and dangerous driving and arson.

RAINEY, Philip QC
Tanfield Chambers, London
020 7421 5300
philiprainey@tanfieldchambers.co.uk
Featured in Real Estate Litigation (London)
Practice Areas: All aspects of commercial and residential property litigation (including social housing); also ADR and some mainstream commercial work. Particular expertise in leasehold enfranchisement, RTM and service charge disputes. Representative cases include: R(Best) v Land Registry [2014] EWHC 1370 (Admin) (adverse possession); Daejan v Benson [2013] 1 WLR 854 (SC) (service charges); Bolton v Godwin-Austen [2014] HLR 15 (CA) (enfranchisement); Stannard v Gore [2014] QB 1 (CA) (escape of fire); Wilky v LSI [2011] Arb LR 38 (expert determination); Stablewood Properties v Virdi [2011] WTLR 723 (CA) (trusts); Cadogan v Sportelli [2010] 1 AC 226 (enfranchisement); Howard de Walden v Aggio [2009] 1 AC 39 (enfranchisement).
Professional Memberships: Chartered Institute of Arbitrators, Chancery Bar Association, Property Bar Association, Association of Leasehold Enfranchisement Practitioners.
Career: LLB, MCIArb. Silk 2010. Called to the Bar 1990, joined Tanfield Chambers in 2001. Head of Chambers 2013- date. Member of the Civil Procedure Rule Committee 2001-08.
Publications: (With other members of Tanfield Chambers) 'Service Charges and Management' (Sweet & Maxwell, 3rd ed 2013); Co-author: "Megarry's Manual of the Law of Real Property" (9th ed 2014); Co-author 'Rent Review: A Surveyor's Handbook' (RICS, 2008).
Personal: Born 1968, married with three children.

RAINSFORD, Mark QC
The Chambers of Andrew Mitchell QC, London
020 7440 9950
clerks@33cllaw.com
Featured in POCA Work & Asset Forfeiture (All Circuits)
Practice Areas: An internationally renowned silk specialising in international asset recovery, civil and criminal fraud, proceeds of crime and corporate crime. Relevant experience includes fraud cases concerning carbon credit awards, rare earth metals, boiler room investor schemes, "Ponzi" schemes, cyber hacking and corporate blackmail. He represents corporates, organisations and individuals facing investigation and asset recovery by UK and overseas law enforcement authorities. Notable cases include: Representing the Ministry of Environment of a European sovereign state after their stock exchange was compromised by cyber-hackers; shares were switched to the London Stock Exchange and spot trading commenced; obtaining emergency freezing injunctions and Norwich Pharmacal orders. Representing the Lithuanian State in obtaining restraint orders over the UK assets of a well known Russian oligarch, after he allegedly misappropriated €1 billion of securities from a high street bank of which he was the Chairman. Obtaining management receivership and restraint orders over the assets of a group of companies with an annual turnover of £140m. Representing the former Chairman and CEO of RBG Metals plc and Allied Deals Inc in £1.2 billion hidden assets proceedings. Representing the CEO of a chain of Money Service Bureaus, dubbed "Britain's biggest money launderer".
Professional Memberships: Called to the Bar in the British Virgin Islands (2012), Grand Cayman (2007, pro hac) and the Turks and Caicos Islands (2011, pro hac).
Publications: Contributing author: Fraud: Law, Practice and Procedure, Butterworths LexisNexis.

RAJAH, Eason QC
Ten Old Square, London
020 7405 0758
easonrajah@10oldsquare.com
Featured in Chancery (London), Court of Protection (All Circuits), Offshore (London), Trusts (London)
Practice Areas: Chancery litigation and advisory work in the UK and offshore, including domestic, off shore and cross-border trusts and will disputes, related tax and professional negligence issues, the drafting, structuring and advising in relations to trusts, succession planning and tax and related areas.
Professional Memberships: Eason is an officer of the Chancery Bar Association and a member of the committee of STEP Central London. He is a member of ACTAPs and the Charity Law Association. He is a former Chair of the Education and Training Committee for the Chancery Bar Association, a former member of the Bar Council Professional Standards Committee, the Bar Standards Board Rules Committee and a former Vice Chairman of one of the Bar Council Pupillage Monitoring Panels. He is a member of the Bar Pro Bono Unit.
Career: Called to the Bar 1989; Silk 2011. Called to the Malaysian Bar 1991. Recent cases include Crociani v Crociani and others [2013] (contentious breach of trust claim; Al Sadi v Al Sadi [2013] (Claim by certain children of deceased that under Sharia, Liechtenstein and Monagasque law, assets held in a Liechtenstein Foundation and a Panamanian company form part of the estate); High Commissioner of Pakistan v Nat West Bank [2013] (involves issues of sovereign immunity and trust law, and Indian and Shari'a succession law); Rodman v Rodman [2013] Claims for intermeddling and misappropriation from $125m estate– value £millions; Scarfe v Matthews [2012] WTLR 1579 (doctrine of election – estate of Bernard Matthews); Re the Valetta Trust [2011] JRC 227(the validity of third party litigation funding arrangements for trust litigation in

Jersey); Re MN [2010] WTLR 1355 (the first decision on the ambit of the international jurisdiction of the Court of Protection); Re IMK Family Trust [2008] JLR 430 (the landmark decision on the enforcement of foreign matrimonial judgments in Jersey) C v C (Privilege) [2008] 1 FLR 115 – applicability of legal professional privilege to disclosure by anstalt where wife claimed anstalt attempting to defeat her ancillary relief claim.
Publications: He is an Editor of Mellows Taxation of Executors and Trustees, an Editor of the Court of Protection Law Reports and is the Consultant Editor of Ranking Spicer Pegler, Executorship Law, Trusts and Accounts.

RAJGOPAUL, Craig
Littleton Chambers, London
020 7797 8600
cr@littletonchambers.co.uk
Featured in Employment (London)
Practice Areas: Employment; Commercial; Education.
Professional Memberships: ELA; ELBA; COMBAR.
Career: Craig Rajgopaul has been a lawyer since 2005, and was a Solicitor-Advocate (with Higher Rights of Audience in all English Courts) from 2007-11. He worked as a Solicitor-Advocate specialising in Tribunal and High Court work in the highly rated employment departments of Ashurst and McDermott Will & Emery. Craig joined Littleton Chambers as a Barrister in 2011. Since moving to the Bar in March 2011, he has developed a practice commensurate with his years of experience as a lawyer. He has been instructed on a variety of different commercial matters, numerous multi-day claims in the Employment Tribunal, including complex discrimination claims, in High Court team move, restrictive covenant and confidential information cases, including cases seeking urgent injunctive relief, and in education matters across different courts and Tribunals. Craig also has good experience of litigation in the Employment Appeals Tribunal, and the Court of Appeal, and frequently acts on high profile (and high value) claims.

RALPH, Craig
Kings Chambers, Manchester
08450 343 444
clerks@kingschambers.com
Featured in Costs Litigation (Northern)
Practice Areas: Craig has a national practice exclusively in the Law of Costs. His expertise is in demand in contentious and non-contentious costs issues arising in both civil and criminal matters. He regularly appears before all levels of judiciary from the County Courts and the Supreme Court Cost Office as well as appearing before the Court of Appeal on important points of principle. His expertise on influential cost questions is regularly sought after in appeals and test cases. Craig has a particular expertise in the incidence of costs, managing broken retainers and is particularly praised for his ability in matters concerning issues of conduct, especially in solicitor and own client matters. Craig is registered for Public Access work; receiving instructions directly from members of the Bar and costs professionals in relation to fee recovery in both Civil and Criminal matters. In addition to his advisory work, Craig is highly sought after for his engaging bespoke lectures and seminars.
Career: LLB Honours, University of Central Lancashire. Year of Call: 2002 Joined Middle Temple: 1998.
Publications: Craig has had numerous articles published in the New Law Journal.

RAMASAMY, Selva
QEB Hollis Whiteman, London
020 7933 8855
barristers@qebhw.co.uk
Featured in Professional Discipline (London), Financial Crime (London)
Practice Areas: Selva Ramasamy is a specialist in cases involving professionals charged in criminal, regulatory and disciplinary proceedings. His principal focus is financial crime, and cases involving doctors and other healthcare professionals, particularly those involving complex technical issues. He has substantial experience in cases of fraud involving banks, companies, financial advisers and share dealing, as well as in the healthcare sector. His General Medical Council, General Dental Council, General Chiropractic Council and Health Professions Council experience includes conduct, conviction, performance, health and restoration cases, including cases on appeal in the High Court. He also specialises in health and safety cases, and those involving general crime. He has substantial experience in presenting cases on behalf of the Security Industry Authority, including conducting the first prosecutions of companies under the Private Security Industry Act 2001. Recent cases include SRA private prosecutions under the Solicitors Act and the Legal Services Act; defending an actress/ producer in the first prosecution for fraudulent claims for film tax credit; acting in an inquest for the family of a Royal Navy officer who died in a fall from a warship; defending a sub-postmaster accused of trading in counterfeit stamps; defending a CEO in a prosecution for making misleading statements to the market in the largest fraud on the Alternative Investment Market; conducting the first prosecutions of non-GDC registered companies and individuals for commercial tooth whitening; defending in a substantial "boiler room" fraud case; defending a tractor manufacturer in relation to the escape of hazardous gas at a test facility; defending a lighting expert in the Millennium Dome corruption case; defending a HSBC employee against allegations of a £12m computer banking theft; defending a doctor against allegations of prescription fraud; defending a businessman against FBI-led allegations of arms trafficking and funding Colombian terrorists; defending a financial director against allegations of fraud and corruption; and representing a businessman in connection with contempt of court proceedings in the High Court. Recent disciplinary cases include defending an osteopath against allegations of sexual assault during the course of examinations; an inquiry into a series of exposure prone procedures leading to the largest "look back" exercise in NHS history; a fatality arising from conflicting opinions about the use of alternative remedies; a fatality arising from neglect in a hospital in Gibraltar (in which the majority of proceedings were conducted via a live TV link); and a case involving allegations of incompetent analysis by a genetics expert.
Professional Memberships: Elected member of the Bar Council (1997-2000); Criminal Bar Association committee (1997-2000 and 2008-09); British Association of Sport and Law; Association of Regulatory & Disciplinary Lawyers; Health and Safety Lawyers Association; registered with the Bar Council Public Access Directory; Public Access Bar Association.
Career: Called Inner Temple 1992. Recorder 2009. Member of the Bar Standards Board Prosecuting Counsel Panel for Disciplinary Hearings.

RAMPTON, Richard QC
One Brick Court, London
020 7353 8845
rr@onebrickcourt.com
Featured in Defamation/Privacy (London)
Practice Areas: Defamation, privacy, confidence, contempt of court and media related law generally. Cases include: Lucas-Box v Associated Newspapers; Atkinson v Fitzwalter; Control Risks v New English Library; Telnikoff v Matusevich; Shah v Standard Chartered Bank; Aldington v Tolstoy; McDonald's Corp v Steel and Morris; Irving v Lipstadt and Penguin Books; Sugar v News Group; Sugar v Associated Newspapers; Holden & Dennis v Express Newspapers; Kearns v General Council of the Bar; Carlton v News Group; Oryx v BBC; King v Telegraph; McArdle v Newcastle Chronicle; Galloway v Telegraph; Henry v BBC; Campbell v Safra; Heather Mills McCartney v Associated Newspapers and News Group Newspapers; Condoco Grand Cayman v KYC News; Materazzi v Associated Newspapers; Bray v Deutsche Bank; Taranissi v BBC; Flood v Times Newspapers; Bento v Ch Cons Bedfordshire Police; Waterson v Lloyd; Citation v Ellis Whittam Ltd; Cruddas v Times Newspapers.
Career: Educated at Bryanston and The Queen's College, Oxford. Called to the Bar in 1965, took Silk in 1987.
Publications: 'Duncan & Neill on Defamation' 3rd Edition co-author; Report on Death on the Rock, with Lord Windlesham, Faber & Faber (1989).
Personal: Speaks French, some Italian and German.

RAMSAHOYE, Indira
29 Bedford Row Chambers, London
020 7404 1044
iramsahoye@29br.co.uk
Featured in Family/Matrimonial (London)
Practice Areas: International law relating to children in particular child abduction, jurisdictional disputes, relocation cases and all other areas of family work with respect to children. Particular interest - experience in work concerning the Sub-Continent and Middle East, and the representation of children in abduction proceedings. Reported cases include: MK v CK (Relocation) (2012) C/A; R and another v A [2011] All ER (D) 136 (May), FD; P v G (Family Law Act 1986: Jurisdiction); [2010] 2 FLR 1888, FD; Re S (Foreign Contact Order) [2010] 1 FLR 982, FD; RS v KS (Abduction: Wrongful Retention [2009] 2 FLR 1231, FD; Re W (Leave to Remove)[2008] EWCA Civ 1181; Re L (Abduction: Future Consent) [2008] 1 FLR 914, FD; Re C (Costs: Enforcement of Foreign Contact Order [2008] 1 FLR 619, FD; JPC v SLW and SMW [2007] 2 FLR 900, FD; Re S (Financial Provision)[2005] 2 FLR 94, CA.
Professional Memberships: FLBA.
Career: Called in 1980. Lincolns Inn.
Personal: Lives in London. One daughter.

RAÑALES-COTOS, Tina
Kings Chambers, Manchester
08450 343 444
clerks@kingschambers.com
Featured in Commercial Dispute Resolution (Northern)
Practice Areas: Tina Rañales-Cotos practises in chancery and commercial litigation and advisory work, mainly in the specialist courts in Manchester, Liverpool and Leeds (Merchantile, Chancery and TCC). Her work frequently involves interim injunctive relief hearings in the High Court in the business restraint field, including freezing, springboard, misuse of confidential information and restrictive covenant injunctions and search orders. Her specialist practice includes the following areas: Agency (including commercial agency) Banking and finance (including guarantees and indemnities) Civil/commercial fraud (including VAT/MTIC fraud) Confidential Information Commercial contracts (including share sale/purchase and warranties) Company (especially shareholder disputes and breach of directors' duties) Competition – UK and EU Director disqualification Employment (contractual and statutory) Insolvency (corporate and individual) Intellectual Property (trademark infringement and passing off) Mediation Partnership Professional negligence Restraint of trade including restrictive covenants (commercial and employment) Sale and carriage of goods (domestic and international).
Professional Memberships: Chancery Bar Association Northern Chancery Bar Association Northern Circuit Commercial Bar Association Employment Law Association Northern and North Eastern Circuits Lincoln's Inn.
Career: University of Oxford (Brasenose College) BCL 1997-1998 Lecturer in Competition Law Universities of Oxford and Leicester 1998-1999 Called to the Bar '99 Hardwicke Scholar & Sir Thomas More Bursar Lincoln's Inn Pupillage at Monckton Chambers, Gray's Inn, London 1999-2000 Lincoln's Inn Stage Scholar - DGIV Competition, Brussels 2000-01 Joined current Chambers in 2001 AGs Provincial Panel – Junior Counsel 2008-12.
Publications: Financial Times - regular contributor to reader dilemmas on employment law issues.

RANATUNGA, Asitha
Cornerstone Barristers, London
020 7242 4986
ar@cornerstonebarristers.com
Featured in Licensing (London), Planning (London)
Practice Areas: Asitha is a specialist in the fields of Planning and Licensing law. Within those fields, he has a broad practice, incorporating all aspects of Planning, Licensing, and related Administrative & Public Law work. He is regularly instructed by Local Authorities and third parties to advise and appear at all stages of the planning process. He has a particular interest in renewable energy and has a busy practice appearing at wind farm inquiries. He is familiar with all aspects of the enforcement process and has considerable experience in statutory appeals and the judicial review of Local Authority and Secretary of State decisions. Asitha's expertise in the field of Licensing takes him across the country acting both for the trade and Local Authorities. He is regularly instructed

to defend licensing authority decisions on appeal, and appears regularly for the trade both before licensing sub-committees and on appeal for all types of premises (pubs, bars, clubs, old off-licences, academic institutions). He has a particular interest in stress area and cumulative impact policy.
Professional Memberships: PEBA, IOL, ALBA, UKELA.
Publications: Contributor to 'Licensed Premises: Law and Practice' (Kolvin, 2nd edition).
Personal: Called in 2001 (Inner-Temple). Pembroke College, Cambridge (MA, MPhil in Classics). Bristol Grammar School. Interests: Cricket and Travel.

RANDALL, John QC
St Philips Chambers, Birmingham
01212 467 000
jrandall@st-philips.com
Featured in Chancery (Midlands), Commercial Dispute Resolution (Midlands), Partnership (Midlands), Professional Negligence (Midlands), Real Estate Litigation (Midlands)
Practice Areas: Principal areas of practice are chancery and commercial law, companies, corporate insolvency, judicial review, partnerships, professional negligence and real property.
Professional Memberships: Midland Circuit; International Bar Association; Chancery Bar Association; COMBAR; Midland Chancery and Commercial Bar Association.
Career: Called Lincoln's Inn 1978; Bar of New South Wales 1979; Silk 1995; Assistant Recorder 1995-99; Deputy Head of Chambers 1998-2001; Recorder 1999; Deputy High Court Judge 2000; Member, Legal Services Consultative Panel 2000-09; Head of Chambers 2001-04; Barrister and Solicitor of Western Australia 2001; Bencher of Lincoln's Inn 2003; Adjunct Professor, University of New South Wales 2013 (Visiting Fellow 2004-13).
Publications: Rethinking the Economic Torts (with Simon Deakin) Modern Law Review, 2009; 'The Tort of Conversion' (with Sarah Green), 2009 (Finalist, Inner Temple Book Prize 2011); Caparo v Dickman: Legal Celebrity or Jurisprudential Substance? in 'Cases that Changed our Lives', 2010; Proprietary Estoppel and the Common Intention Constructive Trust - Strange Bedfellows or a Match in the Making? Journal of Equity, 2010; Detinue, Trover and Conversion (with Brendan Edgeworth) in 'Historical Foundations of Australian Law, Vol.II - Commercial Common Law', 2013; Express Termination Clauses in Contracts, Cambridge Law Journal 2014; When Louisa Carlill Caught the Flu (Carlill v Carbolic Smoke Company) in 'Cases that Changed our Lives 2', 2014.
Personal: Educated at Rugby School; Loomis Institute, Conn USA; Jesus College, Cambridge (MA).

RANDALL, Nicholas QC
Devereux, London
020 7353 7534
RandallQC@devchambers.co.uk
Featured in Employment (London), Sports Law (London)
Practice Areas: Practices in the fields of Sport, Employment and Pensions. Clients include high profile individuals, City institutions, trade unions and regulatory bodies. Regularly sits as an arbitrator in sports related matters and is a member of the FA Premier League Arbitration Panel and the Sports Disputes Resolution Panel.
Professional Memberships: ELBA; ELA.
Career: Has been a member of Devereux Chambers since 1990.
Publications: Co-Author of 'Contract Actions in Employment Law' with Professor Ian Smith (2010). Former Contributing Editor to 'Harvey on Industrial Relations and Employment Law'.
Personal: Educated at St Andrews Comprehensive School, Worthing and the LSE. Interests include: football; QPR; cricket; rugby league; Marshall amplifiers; Gibson Les Pauls; classic rock; punk rock; new wave and NWOBHM.

RANKIN, James
Francis Taylor Building, London
020 7353 8415
clerks@fbt.eu.com
Featured in Licensing (London)
Practice Areas: With almost thirty years of experience in licensing and regulatory work, James Rankin is widely regarded as one of the leading licensing juniors in the country. He has been ranked as a star junior since 2006. He appears up and down the country on behalf of applicants and objectors. He also represents the police and local authorities on reviews of licences and on appeals from local authority decisions. James has extensive Betting and Gaming experience. He appeared on behalf of The Hippodrome in their successful appeal to license their London casino premises. He advises on internet gaming, together with lotteries and competitions and firearms regulation. He advises The Marine Management Organisation on licensing matters. He has been involved in many of the leading licensing cases involving judicial review of decisions by local authorities and magistrates. His clients are high profile and varied. They include the major operators such as Wetherspoons, Whitbreds and Greene King, together with the smaller operators such as The Mean Fiddler Group. He has represented Aspinall's Casino, Ladbrokes, Corals, Peter Stringfellow, The Mayor of London, The Commissioner of the Metropolitan Police, The Chief Constables of Northamptonshire, Dorset, Devon and Cornwall, Kenwood House, and Garsington House.
Career: Year of Call: 1983; Buckingham University LLB (hons).
Publications: He has lectured for Paterson's, IBC and CLT for over ten years on a wide range of topics relating to licensing and regulation. Examples include enforcement, cumulative impact policies, case law update, test purchases, firearms licensing and the relationship between the licensing and planning regimes.

RAUDNITZ, Paul
QEB Hollis Whiteman, London
020 7933 8855
paul.raudnitz@qebhw.co.uk
Featured in Financial Crime (London)
Practice Areas: A leading junior practising in fraud, crime and regulatory law. His reputation in white-collar and financial crime is particularly strong. He is currently instructed by the SFO in a significant international bribery investigation, and by the FCA in Operation Cotton (the first FCA land-banking prosecution, and the largest criminal matter that it has yet brought; the case recently made headlines over Very High Cost Case funding). Other recent high-profile cases include leading for the defence of the operations manager in the Highway driver-training fraud (Rahman & Others); the successful defence of the finance director charged in the Cawston Park Psychiatric Hospital alleged "extra care" fraud (Wilson & Breeze); the defence of the company secretary in the Tempaid revenue fraud (Sidhu); leading for the Financial Services Authority in its first successful criminal prosecution for boiler room fraud (Mason); leading for Trading Standards in its largest counterfeit goods case (Grover & Arura); the successful prosecution of City Police's most substantial identity theft case (Peters) and leading a multi-agency operation uniting UKBA, DWP and HMRC in the successful phased prosecutions of 15+ defendants for a multi-million pound benefits and immigration fraud conspiracy stretching back almost 20 years (Op Spenser). In mainstream crime, the last few years have also seen him instructed in a number of very high-profile cases, including representing defendants in both the first Victoria Station murder trial (Akra) and the Camberwell arson murder trial (John-Lewis). In addition, he has a thriving regulatory and professional discipline practice, appearing regularly before the General Medical Council and other regulatory bodies.
Professional Memberships: Criminal Bar Association; Association of Regulatory and Disciplinary Lawyers; Financial Services Lawyers' Association; Proceeds of Crime Lawyers' Association; Health and Safety Lawyers' Association; BASL; Public Access Bar Association; Registered with the Bar Council Public Access Directory.
Career: St John's College, Oxford. Called 1994. Appointed to the CPS external list of advocates at Grade 4 from 2007 (also appointed to the Rape List and Fraud Panel). Appointed to the "A" Panel of the Serious Fraud Office list of counsel from 2009. Chambers Treasurer.

RAWLEY, Dominique QC
Atkin Chambers, London
020 7404 0102
drawley@atkinchambers.com
Featured in Construction (London), Professional Negligence (London)
Practice Areas: Dominique Rawley specialises in large scale disputes arising from engineering and construction and other technical projects, located within the UK or in foreign jurisdictions. Typically that involves contract and tort disputes arising in the context of technical projects. Dominique has a particular specialism in disputes concerning large infrastructure and PFI projects, particularly in relation to railways, telecomms, energy projects (including renewables), natural resources and utilities. She regularly deals with issues regarding bonds and guarantees used in projects. She also specialises in professional negligence for and against construction professionals and their professional indemnity insurers. She has wide experience of representing clients in the UK high court and appellate courts as well as in arbitration both domestic and international. She often deals with conflict of laws and jurisdiction issues. She has recently acted in a number of international arbitrations including disputes concerning a Russian oil and gas project (ICC arbitration) and a Dubai skyscraper (ADCCAC arbitration), a Middle Eastern processing plant with power co-generation (UNCITRAL arbitration). She is a qualified TECBAR adjudicator and is co-author of the Construction Adjudication & Payments Handbook published by Oxford University Press.
Professional Memberships: TECBAR and Combar.
Career: BA (Cantab) in Law. Called to bar 1991. Silk 2012.

RAWLINSON, Michael QC
Kings Chambers, Manchester
08450 343 444
clerks@kingschambers.com
Featured in Personal Injury (Northern), Personal Injury (All Circuits)
Practice Areas: Personal Injury, Disease Litigation and Clinical Negligence. Significant reported cases include the "Nimrod" and "Snatch Land Rover" inquests; Fairchild v Glenhaven; Sowden v Lodge; Grieves v Everard ('The Pleural Plaques 'test litigation"; Thompson & Rice v Secretary of State for the Department of Trade & Industry; Howe v Houlton & Marshall [2009] EWHC 3344.
Professional Memberships: Northern Circuit Medical Law Association. PIBA.
Career: University: Manchester LLB (Harry Street Tort Prize, Lawson Prize and Dauntsey Scholarship). Inner Temple (Major scholarship).

RAYNER, Catherine
7BR, London
020 7242 3555
clerks@7br.co.uk
Featured in Employment (London)
Practice Areas: Employment ; Equalities and Discrimination ;professional regulation.
Professional Memberships: Employment law Association; Discrimination Law association; Industrial law Society.
Career: Catherine represents claimants, employers, small and large businesses, individuals and large and small trade unions. She has represented in many reported cases, spanning matters from whistle blowing (Babula v Waltham Forest College [2007] IRLR 346 CA); equal pay in the context of male bonus payments (Coventry City Council v Nicholls & ors [2009] IRLR 345 EAT); disability and race discrimination(Rihal v London Borough of Ealing [2004] IRLR 642 CA ; Collins v Royal National Theatre Board Ltd [2004] EWCA Civ 144.); employment status (Quashie V Stringfellows Restaurants Ltd [2012] EWCA civ 1735 [2013] IRLR 99) and service provisions under TUPE (Pannu and Others v Geo W King Ltd (In Liquidation) and Others [2012] IRLR 190 EAT) . Catherine appears regularly in the ET ; the EAT and the Court of Appeal, She has broad experience of negotiation and mediation in discrimination and whistle blowing cases and in contractual and termination disputes at all levels. She contributes to a variety of professional journals and is a regular speaker and trainer at conferences and seminars for lawyers , claimant representatives and advisers and human resources personnel.
Publications: Employment law Journal August 2014 – The 'ban' on exclusivity contracts, Legal Action group – updates on Discrimination - from 2004.

READ, Graham QC
Devereux, London
020 7353 7534
read@devchambers.co.uk
Featured in Telecommunications (London)
Practice Areas: Specialist in all types of commercial law (including contract law, computer and construction disputes, ADR and arbitration), telecommunications and

environmental law. Extensive experience in commercial litigation and all ancillary matters, for example conflict of laws (Connelly v RTZ, [and Africa v Cape) and international freezing orders (Banco Nacional de Commercio v Empressa de Telecommunicaciones [2007] 2 All ER(Comm) 1093). Wide experience of virtually all types of contract dispute including TCC Work (see e.g. JDM v DEFRA) and information technology (see e.g. Ardentia v BT (2008) 119 Con LR 50). Very extensive knowledge of all aspects of telecoms law, including Interconnect agreements - see e.g. Tonylogo v Totem and BT (2005) LTL 9/2/05; regulatory disputes - see e.g. Orange v Ofcom [2007] CAT 36, BT v Ofcom (MNO charges) [2008] CAT 12, BT v Ofcom (cost orientation) [2010] CAT 15, and BT v Ofcom (080 numbers) [2011] CAT 24 and [2012] EWCA Civ 1002.; tariff charging; telecoms misuse and wayleaves. Thorough knowledge of the Competition Appeal Tribunal's powers – see e.g. BT v Ofcom [2011] 4 All ER 372. Has been involved in some of the largest environmental law disputes e.g. Reay v British Nuclear Fuels, R v Secretary of State for Trade and Industry v ex p Duddridge, Ngcombo v Thor Chemical Holdings.
Professional Memberships: Combar; Professional Negligence Bar Association.
Career: MA Trinity Hall, Cambridge; Arden Scholar Gray's Inn; called 1981.

READE, David QC
Littleton Chambers, London
020 7797 8600
dr@littletonchambers.co.uk
Featured in Employment (London)
Practice Areas: Commercial, Employment and Sport. Employment: all areas of both contentious and non-contentious employment law (including EU Law). David has appeared in numerous leading decisions in the field, including Barton v Investec, Hounga v Allen, NUM v UK Coal, Brennan v Sunderland, Rhys-Harper v Relaxion, Rutherford v Harvest Town Circle and Foley v Post Office. David has appeared as an advocate at all levels from Tribunal to the House of Lords and the Supreme Court. He is presently conducting a reference to the CJEU. He has particular experience of urgent injunctive relief, including search orders, freezing orders and anti suit injunctions. He has appeared in a number of leading cases in the field including Ashcroft v National Theatre (interim specific performance) QBE v Dymoke (springboard injunctions), TFS Derivatives v Morgan (restrictive covenants), Pennwell v Ornstein (confidential data and database misuse) and Standard Life v Gorman (garden leave injunctions). David has extensive experience of TUPE and collective redundancy claims; his cases include Kavanagh v Crystal Palace, Solectron v Roper and CWU v Royal Mail. His practice includes collective labour law issues, acting for both Trade Unions and employers. He acted for British Airways before the Court of Appeal in the industrial action by its' cabin crew. His collective work has included advising and acting on recognition issues and in cases involving the restraint of industrial action. He successfully judicially reviewed the CAC on its recognition decision against Boots PLC. He has experience of pension and share option claims and has advised various companies on the pension and employment issues arising out of changes to final salary pension schemes. Commercial litigation: (including banking, financial services, insolvency and consumer credit). His work in this field includes extensive experience of partnership disputes, including LLP disputes. He has advised and acted in shareholder and joint venture disputes including issues arising from breach of fiduciary and director's duties and the misuse of intellectual property or confidential information. In the field of Sport he has wide experience of sports related litigation, including manager, agent and players disputes. These have included claims under the FA dispute resolution scheme. He is an accredited mediator and has experience of both mediating and acting as a representative in mediations.
Professional Memberships: COMBAR, Employment Law Association. Employment Bar Association. Industrial Law Society. Professional Negligence Bar Association. British Association for Sport and the Law. Associate American Bar Association and International Bar Association.
Career: LLB Birmingham. Called to Bar, Middle Temple, 1983. Appointed Queen's Counsel 2006 Bencher of Middle Temple 2008 Mediator 2006, Lectured law before entering practice.
Publications: Former editor of 'Employment Law and Litigation'. Frequent writer and lecturer on employment issues. Co-author of OUP's 'The Law of Industrial Action and Trade Union Recognition' (2011). Contributor to Sweet and Maxwell's 'The Transfer of Undertakings'. Co-author of "The Guide to the Equality Act". Co Editor of Blackstone's Employment Law.
Personal: Interests: Anything competitive and music. Trustee of the London on Library.

READHEAD, Simon QC
1 Chancery Lane, London
020 7092 2900
clerks@1chancerylane.com
Featured in Clinical Negligence (London), Personal Injury (London)
Practice Areas: Principal areas of practice: clinical negligence (including dental negligence); professional negligence work (especially solicitors' and barristers' negligence in the areas of clinical negligence and personal injury); a wide range of personal injury work including industrial accidents and occupational diseases; health and safety work; public and administrative law including judicial review and human rights. Expertise of and special interest in catastrophic injury claims including birth trauma, cerebral palsy, head injuries and spinal injuries: psychiatric injuries including PTSD and abnormal grief reactions especially in children.
Professional Memberships: Professional Negligence Bar Association; Personal Injury Bar Association; London Common Law and Commercial Bar Association; Association of Regulatory and Disciplinary Lawyers; Commonwealth Lawyers Association; Medico-Legal Society.
Career: Called to the Bar - 1979. Junior of the Midland Circuit - 1989. Recorder - 1995. Queen's Counsel - 2006. Bencher of the Middle Temple - 2012.
Personal: Educated Lincoln College, Oxford. BCL, MA.

READY, Hannah
One Brick Court, London
020 7353 8845
HR@onebrickcourt.com
Featured in Defamation/Privacy (London)
Practice Areas: Defamation, privacy and confidence, harassment, data protection, freedom of information, reporting restrictions, contempt of court, malicious falsehood, media-related human rights law. Notable recent cases include: PNM v Times Newspapers Ltd & Ors [2014] EWCA Civ 1132; Melvyn Cartwright v Dai Havard MP; PNM v Times Newspapers Ltd & Ors [2013] EWHC 3177; Higgins v Totaljobs Group Ltd; Hank Roberts v Times Newspapers Ltd; Lashkariani v The Mayor of the London Borough of Camden; Skylet Andrew v Laurence Bassini; Ofoborey v Authorhouse UK Ltd; Bento v The Chief Constable of Bedfordshire Police [2012] EWHC 1525
Professional Memberships: Human Rights Lawyers Association; The Media Society
Career: Graduate Scheme in public relations, Fishburn Hedges (2008-2009); Called (2010, Lincoln's Inn); Secondment as a Pegasus Scholar to Levine Sullivan Koch & Schulz LLP, New York (2012)
Publications: Contributor to Arlidge Eady & Smith on Contempt (4th Edition, 1st Supplement); Co-author of Atkin's Court Forms on Defamation (forthcoming reissue)
Personal: Churchill College, University of Cambridge (MA Hons, First Class, Law); Silverman Sherliker Award for Legal Excellence; Churchill College Scholarship; Lord Denning Scholarship; Hardwicke Entrance Award; Bar Vocational Course, BPP Law School (Outstanding); Buchanan Prize; Hubert Greenland Scholarship; Interests include the theatre, cinema and travel.

REARDON, Madeleine
1 King's Bench Walk, London
020 7936 1500
mreardon@1kbw.co.uk
Featured in Family/Matrimonial (London)
Practice Areas: All areas of family law, with a particular interest in children work (public and private.)
Professional Memberships: FLBA; Bar Pro Bono Unit.
Career: Call 2001. Trained as mediator 2006. Deputy District Judge (Civil) 2010.
Publications: Update editor, Hershman and McFarlane, Children Law and Practice (Family Law). Co-author, McFarlane and Reardon, Child Care and Adoption Law: A Practical Guide, (Family Law, 2010).
Personal: Educated Wimbledon High School, London; Magdalen College, Oxford (BA, Classics, 1st class.).

REED, Lucy
St John's Chambers, Bristol
01179 213 456
lucy.reed@stjohnschambers.co.uk
Featured in Family/Matrimonial (Western)
Practice Areas: Lucy is a family law specialist and has practiced in family law throughout her professional career. Her practice now spans all areas of family law with a particular emphasis on children work. She often acts in complex, multi-party or high conflict intractable private law disputes. In public law children cases she acts for parents, children, local authorities and extended family. Lucy has experience of handling cases cases involving suspected FGM or non-accidental injury, sexual abuse, neglect and domestic violence, where there are parental mental health, learning disability or capacity issues, concerns around substance abuse and addiction, and involving children with special educational needs and / or complex medical needs. Lucy also has experience of child abduction work including Hague Convention, and international adoption matters. Her practice also encompasses Pt IV Family Law Act injunctive work, including forced marriage. In appropriate cases Lucy accept instructions via public access.
Professional Memberships: Family Law Bar Association, Association of Lawyers for Children, Human Rights Lawyers Association.
Career: Call 2002.
Publications: The Family Court without a Lawyer - A Handbook for Litigants in Person (2014, Bath Publishing), Pink Tape blog.

REED, Paul QC
Hardwicke, London
020 7691 0040
paul.reed@hardwicke.co.uk
Featured in Construction (London), Insurance (London), Property Damage (London)
Practice Areas: Paul Reed QC is a leader in the areas of construction and insurance. He has been involved in a number of major disputes both in the UK and overseas, including the Caribbean, Saudi Arabia and Dubai. Practising primarily as an advocate, he is also highly regarded for his advisory work. Regularly instructed in complex and high-profile construction, insurance and commercial disputes, often raising multijurisdictional issues. Acts for leading insurance companies, e.g. AIG, Zurich, RSA and Generali, Lloyds syndicates, banks and construction companies, e.g. Carillion, Morgan Est, Balfour Beatty, utility companies, including EDF and Veolia. Approachable, client-focused and a team player, he is regularly instructed in domestic and international arbitration (Dispute Resolution Boards, ICC and ad hoc), adjudication and in Courts in the UK and overseas. Also a postgraduate tutor and occasional lecturer in construction law and arbitration at Kings College. Experienced mediation advocate, arbitrator and mediator.
Professional Memberships: COMBAR; Institute of Arbitrators; London Common Law and Commercial Bar Association; Professional Negligence Bar Association; Technology and Construction Bar Association.
Career: Qualified 1988; Inner Temple; QC 2010, Head of Chambers 2011.
Publications: Construction All Risks Insurance, Sweet & Maxwell, 2014.

REED, Penelope QC
5 Stone Buildings, London
020 7242 6201
clerks@5sblaw.com
Featured in Chancery (London), Court of Protection (All Circuits), Mediators (All Circuits), Trusts (London)
Practice Areas: Principal area of practice is general chancery work both in the UK and offshore, comprising trust litigation: applications to the Court relating to trusts and drafting of trusts and tax related to these areas; wills, contentious probate, Inheritance Act claims, equitable relief of all kinds and a particular specialism in proprietary estoppel cases. Reported cases include: Simon v Byford [2014] W.T.L.R. 1097; Burgess v Hawes [2013] WTLR 453 (probate); Ilott v Mitson [2014] Fam. Law 789 (Family Provision); Loring v Woodland Trust [2014] 2 All E.R. 836 (will construction: now on appeal); Berger v Berger [2013] W.T.L.R. 1489 (extension of time in family

provision claims) Re M [2013] WTLR 681 (Court of Protection) Suggitt v Suggitt [2012] [2012] W.T.L.R. 1607 (proprietary estoppel); Brudenell-Bruce v Moore& Cotton [2012] WTLR 931; Perrins v Holland [2011] 2WLR 1086 (testamentary capacity); RSPCA v Sharp [2010] WTLR 855, (construction of will); Alkin v Raymond [2010] WTLR 1117 (removal of trustees); Jiggens v Low [2010] BTC 631; Servoz-Gavin [2010] 1 All ER 410 (privileged wills); Thorner v Majors [2009] 1 WLR 776; Man v Blackman[2008] WTLR 389 (contentious probate); Goodchild v Bradbury [2007] WTLR 463 (CA) (presumed undue influence); Re Harding [2007] EWHC 3 (Ch) (Construction of will); Re Cuncliffe [2006] Ch 361 (CA) (family provision claim); Jones v Jones [2006] WTLR 1847; Price v Williams-Wynn[2006] WTLR 1633; Drew v Daniel [2005] WTLR 807 (CA) (actual undue influence).
Professional Memberships: Chancery Bar Association (Chair 2014); ACTAPS; STEP.
Career: Called to the Bar 1983. Silk 2009. Accredited Mediator. Recorder 2010 Deputy High Court Judge 2013. Lectures widely.
Publications: Co-author of 'Risk and Negligence in Wills, Estates and Trusts', 2nd edition pub. OUP, " Practical Guide to the Trustee Act 2000" (Jordans), "With the best will in the world" (Legalease), "Annotated Trusts and Estates Law Handbook"(Bloomsbury Professional), "Inheritance Act Claims: A Practitioners Guide"(Law Society). Contributor to Butterworths Forms and Precedents (Wills and Trusts) and to "Practical Approach to Joint Property" (pub Bloomsbury Professional).

REED, Steven
No5 Chambers, Birmingham
08452 105 555
sr@no5.com
Featured in Commercial Dispute Resolution (Midlands)
Practice Areas: Steven advises, drafts pleadings and appears in all types of commercial litigation including contractual, tortious and restitutionary disputes from procedural and interim applications (such as strike out/summary judgment, security for costs and disclosure applications as well as interim remedies including injunctions and freezing injunctions) to trials. Steven has particular experience in utility disputes and regularly advises and appears on behalf of the leading utility providers, in breach of warranty disputes following a share sale and in commercial disputes that involve aspects of intellectual property law such as contract disputes in relation to music/software agreements. Steven also has experience in disputes involving jurisdiction/international issues, the Sale of Goods Act (including hire purchase, return of goods and conversion disputes), the Consumer Credit Act and the forfeiture/return of deposits.
Professional Memberships: MCCBA.
Career: Steven graduated with First Class Honours in LLB English and German Law from the University of Kent and the Philipps-Universität, Marburg, Germany before completing an LLM at the University of London. Called to the Bar in 2005, in October 2010 he was named by Legal Week as one of the top ten stars at the commercial and chancery Bar under ten years call.

REES, David
5 Stone Buildings, London
020 7242 6201
clerks@5sblaw.com
Featured in Chancery (London), Court of Protection (All Circuits)
Practice Areas: General chancery practice including trusts, wills, administration of estates, family provision, and capital taxation with particular specialisation in Court of Protection work. Reported cases include: Parry v HMRC [2014] UKFTT 419 (Inheritance Tax); Baker Tilly v Makar [2013] COPLR 245 (capacity to conduct legal proceedings); NT v FS (statutory will) [2013] COPLR 313; Re HM [2012] WTLR 281 (appointment of deputy preferable to personal injury trust); Re G (TJ) [2011] WTLR 231 (best interests principle in relation to statutory gifts); Re MN [2010] WTLR 1355 (leading authority on Court of Protection's international jurisdiction); Baker v H [2009] WTLR 1719 (setting of security bonds for deputies); Re J [2009] 2 All ER 1051 (registration of enduring power of attorney); Re P [2009] WTLR 651(statutory wills); Re Harrison [2006] 1 All ER 858 (construction of will).
Professional Memberships: Chancery Bar Association; ACTAPS; STEP; Honorary member of Solicitors for the Elderly.
Career: Called to the Bar 1994. Recorder 2012. Member of the Rules Group advising on drafting of the Court of Protection Rules (2006-7; 2010; 2014).
Publications: General Editor Heywood & Massey's Court of Protection Practice. Writes regularly for various professional journals.
Personal: BA Oxford.

REID, J Gordon QC
Terra Firma Chambers, Edinburgh
01312 605 071
Featured in Agriculture & Rural Affairs (Scotland), Construction (Scotland), Real Estate Litigation (Scotland), Commercial Dispute Resolution (Scotland)
Practice Areas: Commercial dispute resolution; land law including commercial leases; agricultural law; commercial law; civil engineering and building disputes.
Professional Memberships: Member of the Faculty of Advocates, Member of the Inner Temple, Fellow of the Chartered Institute of Arbiters in Scotland. He is Chairman of the Faculty of Advocates Dispute Resolution Service (FDRS) [2012-] and a director the Scottish Arbitration Centre [2011-]
Career: 1976-80 solicitor, 1980 admitted to the Faculty of Advocates, 1986-93 Standing Junior to Scottish Office Environment Department, 1991 Called to the Bar of England and Wales, Door Tenancy Atkin Chambers. Gray's Inn. 1993 Silk, 1994 Fellow of the Chartered Institute of Arbitrators, Part-time Chairman VAT and Duties Tribunals 1997-2009, Deputy Special Commissioner for Income Tax etc 1997-2009; 2009- Judge of the First-tier Tribunal and Deputy Judge of the Upper Tribunal (Tax Chamber). 2002, Temporary Judge of the Court of Session and High Court of Justiciary; 2004- Arbitrator under MIB Scheme.
Publications: Contributed to the Stair Memorial Encyclopaedia of the Laws of Scotland. Numerous reported Judicial Opinions and Tax Tribunal Decisions.
Personal: Married. Lives near St Andrews. Apartment at Quartermile, Edinburgh. Three children.

REINDORF, Akua
Cloisters, London
020 7827 4000
ar@cloisters.com
Featured in Employment (London)
Practice Areas: Akua Reindorf is an employment and equality law specialist. She appears for both Claimants and Respondents in tribunals and the Court of Appeal and has significant expertise in managing long-running discrimination trials in the Employment Tribunal. Her practice focuses on complex and often highly sensitive cases. She is valued for her incisive cross-examination, her measured and effective advocacy, her flexibility and ability to think on her feet, and her sensitivity and communication skills with clients. Akua is instructed by unions and individual Claimants across all sectors of employment. She has acted in pro bono cases representing migrant domestic workers who have been subjected to degrading and abusive treatment. In her Respondent practice Akua frequently receives repeat instructions from national and multinational companies, local authorities, trade unions, voluntary sector organisations and NHS Trusts. She is instructed by the University of Oxford in internal disciplinary and dismissal proceedings. Akua also is also instructed in civil claims brought under the Protection from Harassment Act, having appeared in one of the only two cases to reach Supreme Court level in this area of law (Hayes v Willoughby). In suitable cases Akua accepts direct instructions from members of the public under the Public Access scheme.
Professional Memberships: Discrimination Law Association, Employment Lawyers Association, Employment Law Bar Association, Institute of Employment Rights.

REIZ, Stan
Carmelite Chambers, London
020 7936 6300
sreiz@carmelitechambers.co.uk
Featured in Crime (London)
Practice Areas: Stan Reiz has substantial experience in all areas of serious crime and complex fraud. He advises companies on financial crime and is regularly instructed as leading counsel or alone, to defend in high profile caes attracting national interest.
Career: He has successfully defended in cases of the highest gravity, including the Graffs £40 million jewellery robbery, as leading counsel in the M1 arson case, and the prosecution of a solicitor accused of complicity in a £19 million mortgage fraud. Over the past year, he was instructed as leading counsel for a defendant accused of conspiring to import 100kgs of cocaine. He successfully argued that the indictment should be stayed as a result of an abuse of process following a 5 month trial. He acted for a defendant in a multi-million pound wine investment fraud, represented a company director indicted with breaches of the Money Laundering Regulations, advised a client under investigation for unlawfully negotiating an arms deal between countries and defended a professional footballer accused of making a homophobic gesture in a Championship match. He is presently instructed to defend a company director accused of conspiring to launder £35 million in a conspiracy to import automatic weapons.

REYNOLDS, Kirk QC
Falcon Chambers, London
020 7353 2484
reynolds@falcon-chambers.com
Featured in Real Estate Litigation (London)
Practice Areas: All aspects of property law including landlord and tenant and real property, associated arbitration and professional negligence. Advisor to Royal Institution of Chartered Surveyors on arbitration practice and course tutor on official RICS training courses for arbitrators. Appointed on a number of occasions by President of RICS and/or Law Society as an arbitrator, and by arbitrators as a Legal Assessor.
Professional Memberships: Elected an Honorary Member of RICS in 1997; Honorary Member of ARBRIX; Chancery Bar Association; LCLCBA; Property Bar Association.
Career: Educated at Campbell College, Belfast; Peterhouse, Cambridge (MA 1972); called 1974 (Middle Temple); Silk 1993; Blundell Memorial Lecturer 2002/2010; Honorary Doctor of Laws, University of Bedfordshire; Bencher of the Middle Temple.
Publications: Co-Author, Handbook of Rent Review, The Renewal of Business Tenancies and Dilapidations: the Modern Law and Practice.

RHEE, Deok Joo
11KBW, London
020 7632 8500
Deokjoo.Rhee@11kbw.com
Featured in Competition/European Law (London), Public Procurement (London)
Practice Areas: EU, administrative and public, human rights and local government law. In particular, immigration and asylum (including free movement within the EU), social security (free movement), public procurement and state aid law. Recent cases include Case C-121/14 UK v Parliament and Council (Court of Justice) (Trans-European Rail Network measure, validity), R (Cornwall Council) v Secretary of State for Health [2014] EWCA Civ 12 (Court of Appeal) ("ordinary residence" of person lacking capacity), United Kingdom of Fish Producer Organisations v Secretary of State for Communities and Local Government [2013] EWHC 1959 (Admin) (allocation of EU fishing quotas and Article 1, Protocol 1 ECHR), Gallastegui v Westminster City Council) [2013] EWCA Civ 28 (Court of Appeal) (Parliament Square, right to protest), R (Bailey) v. Brent London Borough Council [2011] EWCA Civ 1586 (Court of Appeal) (library closures and the equality duty), Risk Management Partners v London Borough of Harrow and London Authorities Mutual Limited [2009] EWCA Civ 490 (Court of Appeal) (local government vires, EU procurement), M and A v London Borough of Lambeth and Secretary of State for the Home Department [2009] UKSC 8 (Supreme Court) (asylum, Article 6), Case C-325/08 Olympique Lyonnais [2010] ECR I-2177 (Court of Justice) (transfer of "youth" football players).
Professional Memberships: Bar European Group, Administrative Law Bar Association (Treasurer), Bar Council European Committee (2006-08), Liberty Council Member (2007-11), Liberty's Conference and Appeals Committee (2013-16).
Career: Tutor EC Law, Lady Margaret Hall, Oxford University 1997, Called to the Bar 1998, Judicial assistant to the Law Lords

2000-01, Référendaire - European Court of Justice 2002-04, Attorney-General's A Panel.
Personal: Education at Westminster School and Hertford College, Oxford University, University of Paris II (BA, BCL).

RHODES, Nicholas QC
Charter Chambers, London
07973 162 481
nprhodes@btinternet.com
Featured in Crime (London)
Practice Areas: A highly regarded defence advocate with a particular interest and experience in corporate crime specialising in serious commercial fraud, including bribery and corruption, revenue offences, MTIC, money laundering offences and confiscation. His practice includes advising and representing commercial organisations, company directors, legal and other professionals, on compliance issues from the earliest pre-litigation stage through investigation, referral to regulator and in the event the Courts. Considered approachable and client-friendly with a hard-hitting court style, his extensive trial experience in Silk includes defending in cases alleging murder, manslaughter and offences involving serious organised crime, drugs trafficking and illegal arms- trading, in courts in the UK, Northern Ireland and the Cayman Islands. His practice includes appearances before the Courts of Appeal (England and Wales) and (Caribbean) and the Privy Council (ex Jamaica). He has also appeared in Courts Martial. He is registered to receive work by direct access.
Professional Memberships: CBA, SE Circuit.
Career: Joint Head of Chambers.
Publications: Nick Rhodes has written published articles on Beating Bribery and Corruption (with Calvin Jackson) and on the Criminal Liabilities of Incorporated and Unincorporated Entities (with Alex Jamieson and Peter Melleney).

RICH, Barbara
5 Stone Buildings, London
020 7242 6201
clerks@5sblaw.com
Featured in Chancery (London), Court of Protection (All Circuits)
Practice Areas: Specialises in contentious succession and trusts litigation, and in the property and affairs jurisdiction of the Court of Protection under the Mental Capacity Act 2005. Has dealt with a number of cases of substantial value and/or legal complexity and importance in these fields. She is also an experienced mediator with a rapidly-growing mediation practice, and is regularly in demand for prestigious speaking engagements within her field of expertise. Recent cases: NT v FS [2013]EWHC 684 (COP) ; Re JC, D v JC[2012] MHLO 35 (CoP); Public Trustee v Butler [2012] EWHC 858(Ch); Webster v Ashcroft [2012] 1 WLR 1309.
Professional Memberships: Chancery Bar Association, ACTAPS, STEP.
Career: Called 1990 Gray's and Lincoln's Inn. Accredited mediator ADR Chambers UK.
Publications: Consultant editor of Jordan's 'Elder Law Journal', Assistant Editor 'Heywood & Massey: Court of Protection Practice'.
Personal: Education: St Paul's Girls' School, London; Emmanuel College Cambridge (BA, MA); Polytechnic of Central London (Dip Law). Languages: French.

RICH, Jonathan
Five Paper, London
020 7815 3200
clerks@fivepaper.com
Featured in Consumer Law (London)
Practice Areas: Leading consumer lawyer - conducts commercial, regulatory (esp Trading Standards), property work. Jonathan ("Joe") Rich is best known for High Court/ appellate work involving sale of goods and/or supply of services - works in both a commercial and regulatory context - defended many businesses in criminal proceedings, usually where a substantial civil claim lies in the background - acts for both consumers and businesses alike - member of widely-respected Property Team at Five Paper and its strong Commercial Team, which he led for several years - Bar Conference Organising Committee 2009-10, ex-Chairman of Middle Temple's barristers ("Hall Committee"), and ex-Middle Temple Executive Committee - District Councillor for Stansted North & Ugley (Conservative).
Professional Memberships: COMBAR, CBA, Bar European Group, TECBAR, AWSELVA, LCCLBA, South Eastern Circuit, Society of Conservative Lawyers.
Career: 5 Paper Buildings ("Five Paper") from 1989 to date.
Publications: Regular contributor to legal publications - recently wrote "The Browne Report - A Verdict" for The Times.
Personal: Family, music, the countryside, cooking and politics.

RICHARDS, Ian
Pump Court Tax Chambers, London
020 7414 8080
clerks@pumptax.com
Featured in Tax (London)
Practice Areas: Ian Richards advises in all areas of tax, especially in respect of offshore trusts and non domiciled UK residents, personal tax planning for high net worth individuals (including many household names in the entertainment sector and other industries) and providing tax strategies for sheltering future profits and gains. He has substantial experience in negotiating with the Inland Revenue.
Professional Memberships: Revenue Bar Association; London Common Law & Commercial Bar Association.
Career: Called 1971, Lincoln's Inn.
Publications: Tax Editor, Revenue Volume, Halsbury's Laws; Butterworths Encyclopaedia Forms and Precedents; Akins Court Forms; Co-author Tax Advisers Guide to Trusts (Tolley); Hong Kong Stamp Duty (Longmans).

RICHARDSON, Giles
Serle Court, London
020 7242 6105
grichardson@serlecourt.co.uk
Featured in Chancery (London), Offshore (London)
Practice Areas: Trust disputes; civil fraud and asset tracing; commercial and banking; company; insolvency; partnership. Recent cases include: A v B [2013] JRC075 on Jersey foundations; FGH Inc v Gecamines [2012] UKPC 27; Lloyds v Crowborough [2013] EWCA Civ 107; Lehman Brothers International (Europe) v Lehman Brothers Finance SA & Others, Alhamrani v Alhamrani, and Barclays Wealth Trustees (Jersey) Ltd v Equity Trust (Jersey) Ltd.

Professional Memberships: Chancery Bar Association, COMBAR, STEP.
Publications: Co-author of Minority Shareholders: Law, Practice and Procedure.
Personal: born: 1973; Merton College, Oxford 1992-96 (BCL; MA); called to the Bar 1997.

RICHARDSON, James
Trinity Chambers, Newcastle upon Tyne
01912 321 927
j.richardson@trinitychambers.co.uk
Featured in Family/Matrimonial (North Eastern)
Practice Areas: James is a specialist in family finance cases, dealing both with ancillary relief and cohabitation claims. He has represented a wide variety of clients from all walks of life, including high profile sports personalities, business persons, high net worth individuals, professionals and farmers. He is well known for his careful forensic preparation, pragmatic advice and robust approach to litigation.
Professional Memberships: North Eastern Circuit; Family Law Bar Association.
Career: Called 1982. Appointed Deputy District Judge 2001. Long-standing Member of the North East Area Public Funding Appeals Committee.
Personal: Born in 1958. Married with one child. Lives in Woolsington, Newcastle upon Tyne.

RICHES, Philip
Stone Chambers, London
020 7440 6900
philip.riches@stonechambers.com
Featured in Commercial Dispute Resolution (London), International Arbitration (London), Shipping (London)
Practice Areas: Commercial litigation and arbitration: Energy, joint ventures, commodities and trade, telecoms, mining and oil exploration disputes. Emerging market expertise, particularly Russia and CIS, Brazil and China. Frequently appear in English courts and international arbitrations - LCIA, ICC, SIAC, HKIAC, SCC, CIETAC and ad hoc. Applications to High Court in support of arbitration, particularly freezing injunctions and anti-suit injunctions; jurisdiction disputes; enforcement of foreign judgments and arbitral awards in England; actions against sovereign states. Shipping and international trade: Regularly instructed in disputes arising out of charterparties and bills of lading; shipbuilding, principally in China; marine insurance. Commercial Court and LMAA and LCIA arbitrations. Civil Fraud: particular expertise in high value fraud disputes from Russia and CIS in LCIA arbitrations and in High Court litigation. Philip also accepts appointments as an arbitrator, with experience as an ICC arbitrator.
Professional Memberships: COMBAR, London Common Law and Commercial Bar Association, RCAN, LCIA.
Personal: Education: Trinity College, Cambridge (History). Languages: Advanced Spanish and French; good spoken Mandarin. Frequent speaker at arbitration events in China.

RICKARD, Susanna
Serjeants' Inn Chambers, London
020 7427 5000
srickard@serjeantsinn.com
Featured in Court of Protection (All Circuits)
Practice Areas: Susanna Rickard was called to the Bar in 2009. Susanna specialises in judicial review, police, human rights, inquests and healthcare law. An earlier edition notes that "she is a strong public lawyer who is admirable on her feet and has real poise." Please click on the link to the Serjeants' Inn Chambers website for her profile, which sets out full details of her practice including relevant work of note.
Professional Memberships: ALBA, Statute Law Society.
Publications: Contributor to the Medical Law Reports and co-author of "Public Order: Law and Practice" Blackstone's Practical Policing, with John Beggs QC and George Thomas, OUP, 2012.

RIDGWAY, Philip
Temple Tax Chambers, London
020 7353 7884
clerks@templetax.com
Featured in Tax (London)
Practice Areas: Philip specialises in all areas of revenue law both corporate and personal, direct and indirect with special emphasis on mergers and acquisitions, demergers and reconstructions, financing, share transactions and loan relationships. He also specialises in the taxation of insolvencies including administrations, liquidations and receiverships. Clients include solicitors, accountants, insolvency practitioners and corporates.
Professional Memberships: Revenue Bar Association; Fellow Chartered Institute of Taxation; Member of the Association of Business Recovery Professionals (R3); Stamp Tax Practitioners Group.
Career: Called to the Bar 1986; Pupillage 1986-87; Paisner & Co 1987-89; Allen & Overy 1989-93; Coopers & Lybrand 1993-96; Deloitte 1996-2007 (Tax Partner 1999); Temple Tax Chambers 2007- present; Visiting Lecturer in Law City University London (LLM International Tax and EU Tax) 2007- present.
Publications: Co-author with Tim Sanders "Tax Indemnities and Warranties" 3rd ed; Contributor to Lightman & Moss: The Law of Administrators and Receivers of Companies" 5th ed.; Contributor to Totty & Moss; "Insolvency"; Contributor to "Whiteman and Sherry on Capital Gains Tax"; Member of the editorial board of "Insolvency Intelligence".
Personal: Born 14th September 1962 Sheffield; Educated City of London Polytechnic (BA Business Law) 1981-84; Cambridge University (LLM) 1984-85; supports Sheffield United.

RIGNEY, Andrew QC
Crown Office Chambers, London
020 7797 8100
rigney@crownofficechambers.com
Featured in Construction (London), Insurance (London), International Arbitration (London), Professional Negligence (London), Property Damage (London)
Practice Areas: Andrew has an extensive domestic and international practice which encompasses a wide range of civil and commercial work, in particular large-scale disputes involving complex factual and technical evidence, leading large multi-disciplinary (and often multi-national) teams of lawyers and experts. His areas of expertise include (i) construction and engineering disputes (both in the TCC and in domestic and international arbitration) (ii) insurance and reinsurance (iii) commercial litigation including sale of goods, financial instruments, aviation, product liability, commercial leasing agreements, Brussels Convention/Judgments Regulation

and other jurisdictional disputes and (iv) professional indemnity work (in particular engineers, architects, surveyors, solicitors and accountants). He is recognised as a leading Silk in the fields of Construction, Energy, Insurance & Reinsurance, Property Damage, International Arbitration and Professional Negligence.
Professional Memberships: He is one of the editors of Emden's Construction Law and a contributor to Construction Insurance and UK Construction Contracts (Marshall Levine and Roger ter Haar QC). Commercial Bar Association Technology and Construction Bar Association (Committee member) Society of Construction Law Society of Construction Law (Gulf) London Common Law and Commercial Bar Association Professional Negligence Bar Association LCIA

RILEY, Jamie
11 Stone Buildings, London
020 7831 6381
riley@11sb.com
Featured in Chancery (London), Restructuring/Insolvency (London)
Practice Areas: Jamie Riley is a commercial litigator dealing with all types of business litigation and advisory work in commercial, commercial chancery, company and insolvency matters. He has an established practice in banking, fraud, asset-tracing and has developed a strong reputation in the commercial fields of media, broadcasting and sport. He has built up substantial trial experience, often appearing on his own against leading silks, as well as regularly appearing in the Interim Applications and Companies Courts. He has represented major firms and organisations such as NatWest/RBS, the BBC, IPs from the Big Four accountancy firms, the All England Lawn Tennis Club and the RFU. Jamie has been a member of the FA Premier League Disciplinary Committee and was also one of the 19 individual advocates appointed to the London 2012 Pro Bono Legal Advice and Representation Service during the Olympics and Paralympics. For more information, please visit the 'Barristers' section on www.11sb.com.
Professional Memberships: Chancery Bar Association. Commercial Bar Association.
Career: Call: 1995.
Personal: MA (Cantab).

RILEY-SMITH, Toby
Henderson Chambers, London
020 7583 9020
trileysmith@hendersonchambers.co.uk
Featured in Consumer Law (London), Environment (London), Health & Safety (London), Product Liability (London)
Practice Areas: He has a broad commercial and common law practice with particular emphasis on product liability, health and safety, environmental law, consumer law and banking and finance. He regularly appears in cases involving consumer products, pharmaceutical / medical devices, financial products, environmental pollution or disasters, health and safety litigation, international mass tort claims, sales of goods, cross-border disputes and commercial recovery actions. He has great experience of group litigation in all of his fields – having acted in some of the most high-profile group actions of recent years (including the Tobacco Litigation, the MMR/MR Vaccine Litigation and the PIP Breast Implant Litigation). He has appeared in civil and criminal courts at every level. He has particular experience in inquests.
Professional Memberships: Member of the Personal Injury Bar Association, COMBAR and Health and Safety Lawyers' Association; CEDR Accredited Mediator (2000).
Career: Jules Thorne Scholar, Middle Temple (1994), called 1995. Junior Counsel to the Crown, Attorney General's A Panel (2012).
Publications: Contributor to 'Product Liability Law and Insurance'(2000). Contributor to Volume 9(1) of Halsbury's Laws - Consumer Credit (1998). Contributor to Volume 37 of Halsbury's Laws - 'Practice and Procedure' (2001). Contributing editor of 'Goode: Consumer Credit Law and Practice (Looseleaf). Co-Editor of Butterworths 'Encyclopedia of Forms and Precedents - Consumer Credit' and Blackstone's 'Guide to Consumer Credit Act 2006'; Butterworths' Commercial and Consumer Law Handbook.
Personal: Born 1969; educated Eton College and Trinity College, Cambridge. Married with three children.

RISOLI, Andreá
Old Square Chambers, Bristol
020 7269 0300
risoli@oldsquare.co.uk
Featured in Personal Injury (Western)
Practice Areas: Andreá is a specialist personal injury barrister of 9 years call, prior to being called to the bar Andrea practiced as a Solicitor for 7 years and he has in excess of 16 years experience of personal injury litigation. His practice is exclusively in the field of personal injury inclusive of clinical negligence and product liability. Amongst his client base, Andreá is regularly instructed by the panel solicitors of well known Legal Expenses Insurers and Trade Unions. He specialises in serious and catastrophic injury litigation arising out of accidents on the road and at work; these actions can involve life changing injuries inclusive of traumatic brain damage, spinal injury, amputee and brachial plexus injuries. Andreá is used to dealing with complex, high value actions involving multiple specialist experts and he continues to help his clients obtain superb results. Most of his opponents in litigation are high ranking personal injury Counsel. In addition, Andreá is known for his expertise in high-value CICA applications, reviews and Appeals; the applications typically centre upon serious sexual assault, psychiatric injury and traumatic brain injury.

RITCHIE, Andrew QC
9 Gough Square, London
020 7832 0500
aritchie@9goughsquare.co.uk
Featured in Clinical Negligence (London), Personal Injury (London)
Practice Areas: Andrew acts for claimants who have suffered injuries due to clinical negligence or other torts. Many of his clients have suffered brain, spinal or psychiatric injuries. Andrew has extensive experience of cerebral palsy claims and is also a leader in MIB work. Sample cases: Andrews v MIB [2013] Stuart-Smith QC in Arbitration (Lawtel), paraplegia; W v South Yorkshire HA [2012] Sheffield, child who suffered athetoid cerebral palsy due to negligent intubation, Approved award: £2 million plus PPOS of £112,400 pa for life; Phillips v Rafiq [2007] CA, fatal accident/Uninsured Drivers Agreement; Corr v IBC [2008] HL, suicide after industrial accident; Clough v First Choice [2005] CA, paraplegia in swimming pool fall; the X v NHS [1998], phobia of needles after needlestick injury.
Professional Memberships: Personal Injuries Bar Association (chairman); Member PNBA; Fellow of APIL (Executive Committee 1996-99); Legal Services Commission Appeal Board member 1999-2001.
Career: MA Cambridge in Law 1981, Qualified solicitor 1984, Called 1985, QC 2009.
Publications: General Editor (04-09) "Kemp & Kemp; Kemp" Personal Injury Law, Practice and Procedure'; Deputy Editor of Vols 3 & 4 of 'Kemp & Kemp on Quantum'; co-author: 'Asbestos Claims', 9GS Publishing; author "Manual Handling Claims", 9GS publishing; General editor: 'The Journal of Personal Injury Law' 2000-03; author: 'MIB Claims' 3rd ed Jordans; co-editor: 'The Professional Negligence and Liability Reports' 1996-99; author: 'Medical Evidence in Whiplash Cases' 1998.

RITCHIE, Shauna
2 Bedford Row, London
020 7440 8888
sritchie@2bedfordrow.co.uk
Featured in Health & Safety (London), Crime (London)
Practice Areas: Specialist in criminal and regulatory law with particular expertise in serious crime and health and safety. Health and Safety: Wide-ranging experience in cases of gross negligence manslaughter, corporate criminal liability, and inquests. B List Specialist Regulatory Advocate in Health and Safety and Environmental Law for prosecutions on behalf of the Health and Safety Executive, Environment Agency, and Office of Rail Regulation. Advisory and defence work on behalf of companies: from small firms to national chains, individuals, and directors. Notable Cases: Pyranha Mouldings Ltd (Court of Appeal), Claxton Engineering Inquest (quadruple construction fatality), Balfour Beatty Rail Track Systems Ltd (serious industrial injury), Parcol Developments Ltd (gross negligence manslaughter of a three-year-old), Marks & Spencer PLC (asbestos management), Metropolitan Police Commissioner and Others (double drowning). Acts for interested parties at inquests ranging from deaths on the railway to carbon monoxide poisoning, suspected suicide, agricultural and construction industry deaths. High profile inquests have included a crane collapse, a multi-fatality gas explosion, and the death of a teenager falling from a tower block window. Represents medical professionals at inquests in relation to patient deaths. Crime: Defence and prosecution – Instructed in serious and complex cases including murder, serious violence, fraud, excise offences, drugs, and serious sexual offences, including those relating to children. Particular experience in dealing with young or vulnerable defendants and witnesses. Special interest in cases concerning challenges to DNA evidence. Cases in the last year include: Defence junior counsel representing a fourteen-year-old defendant with ADHD in a six handed murder (Liverpool launderette sword stabbing) and in a case involving three-year-old complainants alleging sexual offences; prosecuting a high value fraud on the NHS; junior alone in several historical rape cases.
Professional Memberships: Criminal Bar Association, Health and Safety Lawyers Association
Career: King's College London LLB (Hons), Called 2000 (Lincolns Inn).
Personal: Born 24th January 1978 in Belfast, Northern Ireland.

RIVETT, James
Pump Court Tax Chambers, London
020 7414 8080
clerks@pumptax.com
Featured in Tax (London)
Practice Areas: James practises in all areas of revenue law, including advice and litigation in respect of personal tax, corporate tax and VAT. He also advises on issues of tax law arising in the context of wider transactions, and regularly appears before the Courts and Tribunals in non-tax litigation which raises questions relating to tax, including public law proceedings, trust disputes, non-contentious trust applications and divorce proceedings. Recent cases include Forde & McHugh (Court of Appeal); the Class IV GLO (Court of Appeal); Shiner & Sheinman (Court of Appeal); the Trustees of the BP Pension Scheme (Upper Tribunal); Wyndham v Egremont (Chancery Division); GR Solutions (Upper Tribunal); AC v DC (Family Division); Bristol & West (First-tier Tribunal).
Professional Memberships: Revenue Bar Association. VAT Practitioner's Group. International Fiscal Association.
Career: Called 2004 (Lincoln's Inn); 2014 appointed to the Attorney's General's Panel (B Panel).
Publications: Contributor to Potter and Monroe's Tax Planning with Precedents and Atkins Court Forms (Revenue); author of the statutory construction and anti-avoidance chapters of Simon's Direct Tax Service.

ROBERTS, Allan
Guildhall Chambers, Bristol
01179 309 000
allan.roberts@guildhallchambers.co.uk
Featured in Employment (Western)
Practice Areas: A specialist employment barrister, noted as having a particular expertise in discrimination and whistleblowing claims. He is frequently instructed in high value and media sensitive cases including actions involving the Ministry of Defence, Crown Prosecution Service and several Police Forces. His reputation in complex matters led to him acting in a whistleblowing claim connected with the shooting of Jean-Charles De Menezes. He regularly appears in the Employment Appeal Tribunal, where in a judgment of Underhill J his arguments were described as "vigorous" and "effective". He has also successfully appeared in the Court of Appeal and is presently instructed in a case in the Court of Justice of the European Union. As an employment barrister, he also specialises in related civil court actions such as restraint of trade and acts for professionals at hearings for internal and regulatory discipline; including doctors, nurses and social workers.
Professional Memberships: Employment Lawyers Association, Employment Law Bar Association, Industrial Law Society and Discrimination Lawyers Association.
Career: Called to the Bar 2004 after receiving the Lord Diplock Scholarship he is now part of the dedicated employment law specialist team of Guildhall Chambers.

Publications: He is currently co-writing a book on Employment Disputes and contributing to a book on Limitation, with responsibility for Employment Appeals. He also writes articles for the ELA Briefing and Jordon's Employment Law Portal.
Personal: A longstanding competitive practitioner of Judo, Allan has recently taken up Kendo (the art of Japanese fencing).

ROBERTS, Catherine
Erskine Chambers, London
020 7242 5532
croberts@erskinechambers.com
Featured in Company (London)
Practice Areas: Specialist in company law and in commercial litigation involving issues of company law, corporate insolvency, shareholder disputes, professional negligence and partnership disputes; strong advisory practice in the same areas. Much in demand for both her forensic advocacy and cross-examination skills. Author of Financial Assistance for the Acquisition of Shares (OUP 2005) and co-author of Company Meetings and Resolutions- Law, Practice and Procedure (OUP 2013).
Professional Memberships: COMBAR. Chancery Bar Association.
Career: Churchill College Cambridge MA LLM. Called to Lincoln's Inn 1986.
Publications: Financial Assistance for the Acquisition of Shares (OUP 2005); Company Meetings and Resolutions- Law, Practice and Procedure (OUP 2013).

ROBERTS, Gemma
No5 Chambers, Birmingham
01216 060 500
gr@no5.com
Featured in Employment (Midlands)
Practice Areas: A combative and committed advocate who specialises in all areas of employment law, with particular expertise advising and representing in discrimination, TUPE, whistleblowing, breach of contract and dismissal claims in the ET and EAT. She acts for both claimants and respondents and her clients include multi-national and FTSE 100 companies, NHS Trusts, local authorities, trade unions, employment agencies, educational establishments and charities. Notable cases include Wilcox v Birmingham CAB Services Ltd [2011] EqLR810 and Hibbins v Hestors Way Neighbourhood Project [2009] IRLR 198 EAT.
Professional Memberships: ELBA, ELA, Gray's Inn.
Career: MA, Oxford University; Philosophy Politics and Economics; Gray's Inn (Lord Uthwatt Scholar 2005).
Personal: Gemma enjoys running ultra marathons and sailing across oceans.

ROBERTS, James
1 King's Bench Walk, London
020 7936 1500
jroberts@1kbw.co.uk
Featured in Family/Matrimonial (London)
Practice Areas: Practice is divided between the areas of Financial Remedy proceedings, Schedule 1 Children Act 1989 disputes, international child abduction, leave to remove permanently from the Jurisdiction and private law child arrangement / contact disputes. Many of his cases have an international element. Experienced in finance cases involving offshore trusts and complex corporate structures and the tracing of assets. Recommended for both financial remedy and children work he often deals with both the finance and children's side of cases. Sits as a Recorder (part time Judge) in the Financial Remedies Unit of the Central Family Court and is a qualified mediator and undertakes private FDRs / Early Neutral Evaluations.
Professional Memberships: Treasurer Family Law Bar Association (FLBA) 2005 to date. FLBA (Elected National Committee Member since 1997). Bar Council Quality Advisory Panel. Family Mediators Association. Director, Institute of Family Law Arbitrators Ltd. Fellow of International Academy of Matrimonial Lawyers.
Career: Called in 1993. Appointed Recorder in 2009 (Family Private and Public Law and Crime). Authorised to hear Financial Remedy cases at the Central Family Court. Soon to qualify as an IFLA Arbitrator.
Publications: Wildblood & Eaton (Enforcement Chapter).
Personal: Born 21 September 1969. Oriel College, MA Oxon. (Jurisprudence).

ROBERTSON, Eric W
Arnot Manderson, Edinburgh
07590 298 380
ericrobertson@amadvocates.co.uk
Featured in Commercial Dispute Resolution (Scotland)
Practice Areas: Eric Robertson is a highly experienced litigator with a diverse civil practice - specialising in commercial and property issues - in both Court of Session and Sheriff Courts. He has also dealt with property arbitrations and appeared in the First Tier Tax Tribunal, and as junior counsel in the House of Lords and the Supreme Court. His expertise spans contract (including construction) and professional negligence cases, judicial review, intellectual property and data protection, judicial review company law (including unfair prejudice petitions) and commercial lease disputes. Notable recent cases include Gyle Shopping Centre General Partners Ltd v Marks and Spencer plc [2014] CSOH 59 and 122 and Soccer Savings (Scotland) Ltd v Scottish Building Society [2013] CSOH 51 and 90.
Professional Memberships: Member of Arnot Manderson Advocates (Stable Director from April 2011 to October 2013)
Career: Called to the Scottish Bar in 1994. Previously an Associate Litigation Partner at Dundas & Wilson CS.

ROBERTSON, Patricia QC
Fountain Court Chambers, London
020 7583 3335
pr@fountaincourt.co.uk
Featured in Banking & Finance (London), Commercial Dispute Resolution (London), Financial Services (London), Professional Discipline (London), Professional Negligence (London)
Practice Areas: Civil and commercial: in particular, professional negligence (especially financial and legal services), banking (especially internet banking and plastic money), financial services (in particular, disputes relating to investment management or misselling), legal services, professional discipline and judicial review of regulatory bodies. Advisory work relating to electronic commerce, electronic money, regulation of financial services and regulation of legal services. Contributor to 'The Law of Bank Payments', editors Brindle and Cox, Sweet and Maxwell 2004, on plastic money and on internet payments, 'Professional Negligence and Liability', editor Simpson, on liability of expert witnesses and liability of fund managers, "Legal Services Act 2007" ed Miller & Thorne and Cordery on Legal Services. Extensive experience of mediation of very large commercial and professional negligence claims as advocate and now also an accredited CEDR mediator.
Professional Memberships: COMBAR, London Common Law and Commercial Bar Association, Bar European Group. Past member ICC United Kingdom Electronic Commerce Group.
Career: Called to the Bar in 1988. Joined Fountain Court 1989. Stage in Brussels 1991. Took Silk in 2006. Board of Bar Standards Board from January 2010. Vice Chair of Bar Standards Board from January 2013.
Publications: Chapters on the liability of Expert Witnesses and on the liability of Fund Managers in Professional Negligence and Liability (ed. Simpson, Informa, Looseleaf). Chapters on Plastic Money and on Internet payments in The Law of bank Payments (eds. Brindle & Cox, 3rd Ed. Sweet and Maxwell). Chapters on the new regulatory regime and on the Legal Services Board in The Guide to the Legal Services Act 2007 (eds. Miller & Thorne, Butterworths Lexis-Nexis, 2009) and in Cordery on Legal Services.
Personal: Educated at St. George's, Edinburgh and Balliol College, Oxford (Brackenbury Scholar; BA 1986). Duke of Edinburgh Scholarship, Inner Temple, 1988. Born 1964. Languages: French and Italian.

ROBINS, Stephen
South Square, London
020 7696 9900
stephenrobins@southsquare.com
Featured in Banking & Finance (London), Restructuring/Insolvency (London)
Practice Areas: Restructuring and insolvency; banking and finance; company; commercial; civil fraud; financial services. Recent insolvency cases include Saad in the Privy Council (for the Cayman liquidators), the Lehman/Nortel pensions appeals in the Supreme Court (for the administrators of LBIE), Rubin v Eurofinance in the Supreme Court (for the intervener, the SIPA trustee of Bernard L Madoff Investment Securities LLC), Landsbanki v Heritable in the Supreme Court (for the winding-up board of Landsbanki) and Tambrook in the Court of Appeal (for the successful appellant). Other insolvency cases include Peacocks (for the administrators), IBRC (for the Irish liquidators), Pan Ocean (for the Korean administrator), Comet (for the administrators), MF Global (for the U.S. trustee), Sanko (for the Japanese trustee) and Kaupthing Singer & Friedlander (for the administrators). Banking and finance cases include Lomas v Firth Rixson in the Court of Appeal, as well as Anthracite and Britannia Bulk. Other cases include Rangers FC v Collyer Bristow (for the liquidators of Rangers FC) and the EL policy 'trigger' issue litigation in the Court of Appeal and the Supreme Court.
Professional Memberships: Commercial Bar Association; Chancery Bar Association; Insolvency Lawyers' Association.
Career: Called to the Bar November 2001 (Lincoln's Inn).
Publications: Contributor to Simon Mortimore QC (ed.), Company Directors: Duties, Liabilities & Remedies (Oxford University Press); contributor to Boxell (ed.), A Practitioner's Guide to Directors' Duties and Responsibilities (City & Financial).
Personal: Educated at Christ Church, Oxford; BA (Hons) Modern History (First Class).

ROBOTTOM, James
7BR, London
020 7242 3555
clerks@7br.co.uk
Featured in Inquests & Public Inquiries (London)
Practice Areas: Inquests and public inquiries, employment and equality law, clinical negligence, criminal law, fraud and business crime, human rights law.
Professional Memberships: INQUEST, Discrimination Law Association, Liberty, ELA.
Career: James has extensive experience representing bereaved families at high profile inquests and in subsequent civil claims, including for clinical negligence and claims under the Human Rights Act 1998. His inquest experience covers Article 2 inquests in relation to prisoners and patients detained under the Mental Health Act 1983; deaths in care homes, and suicide amongst young persons. His recent work includes representing the family of Tallulah Wilson, who took her own life in October 2012, having become involved with self-harm and suicide related blogs and websites. James has a multi-disciplinary practice which also encompasses equality law (he recently appeared in the Court of Appeal in Taiwo v Olaigbe [2014] ICR 571, a case concerning domestic servitude and the mistreatment of migrant workers), clinical negligence, criminal law, and public and human rights law as it impacts upon his areas of expertise.

ROCHFORD, Thomas
St Philips Chambers, Birmingham
01212 467 000
trochford@st-philips.com
Featured in Clinical Negligence (Midlands), Personal Injury (Midlands)
Practice Areas: Tom practises principally in the fields of clinical negligence and personal injury, mostly representing claimants. His PI work arises from both trauma and disease and includes claims under the FAA. His workload tends to be in complex and high value cases, usually requiring detailed schedules of loss. Several recent cases have involved issues of co-morbidity, for example, a victim of childhood polio who suffered a hip fracture (caused by first defendant) that was negligently treated by second defendant with very disabling consequences. He has been instructed in professional negligence cases arising from the negligent conduct of personal injury claims. Tom also has a thriving employment practice which is mainly tribunal based. Tom's recent cases include Nicholls v Ladbrokes Betting and Gaming Ltd [2013] EWCA Civ 1963 (CA); Woods v Pasab Ltd [2013] IRLR 305 (CA); and Andrews v Kings College NHS Foundation Trust [2012] EqLR 1032 (EAT).
Professional Memberships: APIL, PIBA, ELA, ELBA, DLA.
Career: Called 1984. Recorder (Crown and County Court) since 2005.
Personal: Cambridge University (MA) (Law).

ROGERS, Amy
11KBW, London
020 7632 8500
amy.rogers@11kbw.com
Featured in Administrative & Public Law (London), Employment (London)

Practice Areas: Amy Rogers practises in employment, commercial and public law. Her recent work includes acting for Société Générale in the Supreme Court in Geys v Société Générale, for Tullett Prebon in its long-running high profile team poaching and conspiracy claim against rival BGC Brokers LP, and for the Iranian commercial bank Bank Mellat in sanctions litigation culminating in a successful Supreme Court challenge to the Financial Restrictions (Iran) Order 2009. She is frequently instructed in conspiracy, team poaching and restrictive covenant disputes, in claims involving breaches of directors' duties, fiduciary duties, duties of confidence and database rights, and in broader commercial litigation, including litigation with a substantial cross-border element. In the public law field, Amy has a particular interest in the use of public law litigation to protect commercial interests.
Professional Memberships: COMBAR, ELA, ELBA, ALBA.
Career: Called to the Bar 2007. Member of the Attorney General's C Panel of Counsel.
Publications: Contributor to Halsbury's Laws on Judicial Review, Supperstone, Goudie and Walker on Judicial Review and Tolley's Employment Law Handbook.

ROGERS, Beverly-Ann
Serle Court, London
020 7242 6105
brogers@serlecourt.co.uk
Featured in Mediators (All Circuits)
Practice Areas: Mediation across a wide range of chancery and commercial disputes. Recent examples include claims under Inheritance (Provision for Family and Dependants) Act 1975; breach of trust claims involving substantial international trusts; shareholder disputes; landlord and tenant disputes; professional negligence claims against solicitors and accountants; employment disputes with allegations of sex-discrimination and whistle-blowing; breakdown in professional partnerships. Experienced in multi-party and cross-cultural disputes.
Professional Memberships: Chancery Bar Association. Association of Contentious Trust and Probate Specialists. Property Bar Association. PIM: Senior Mediators. Distinguished Fellow of International Academy of Mediators.

ROLFE, Patrick
5 Stone Buildings, London
020 7242 6201
clerks@5sblaw.com
Featured in Real Estate Litigation (London)
Practice Areas: A contentious Chancery practice, specialising in real property. He deals with all aspects of the acquisition, ownership and use of land, and has particular experience in the areas of landlord and tenant and mortgages and easements. He also acts in professional negligence disputes associated with these areas of work, for both claimants and defendants. Reported cases include John D Wood & Co v Craze [2007] 50 EG 108; Macepark v Sargeant [2003] 1 WLR 2284 (use of right of way to access non-dominant land), Paragon Finance plc v Banks [2003] 1WLR 284, CA, (limitation periods in respect of mortgage debts).
Professional Memberships: Chancery Bar Association, Property Bar Association.
Career: LLB, King's College, London. Called to the Bar in 1987.

ROLLIN, Aron
Carmelite Chambers, London
020 7936 6300
arollin@carmelitechambers.co.uk
Featured in Crime (London)
Practice Areas: Aron Rollin works predominantly as criminal defence counsel. He is regularly instructed in the most high-profile and complicated cases. His areas of expertise include serious fraud and complex financial crime, serious violence, terrorism, money laundering, civil restraint and POCA. He was instructed to represent one of the News of the World journalists standing trial as part of the principal 'phone hacking' case. Other high profile cases include Operation Bullfinch, thte Oxford grooming and child prostitution case, and representing the main defendant in Operation Beigy, the country's largest ever DWP prosecution. He has recently been instructed to represent one of those charged as part of the Operation Pallhill murder trial. He is frequently instructed in large scale frauds, MTIC and money-laundering cases. He regularly advises on POCA, asset restraint and forfeiture and civil recovery. He has a specialist practice in appellate work and has advised on a full range of matters including homicide and terrorism. He has a background in Human Rights work and has advised NGOs, governments and individuals on cases throughout Africa and the Caribbean and at the International Criminal Court. More information and recent instructions are available at www.carmelitechambers.co.uk
Professional Memberships: Criminal Bar Association, Young Fraud Lawyers, Human Rights Lawyers Association.

ROMNEY, Daphne QC
Cloisters, London
020 7827 4000
dr@cloisters.com
Featured in Employment (London)
Practice Areas: Daphne is an expert in high-value, very complex litigation with a fearsome reputation as an advocate, specialising in all forms of employment law and, in particular, discrimination, equal pay and victimisation claims. She has a broad range of clients, from multi-national companies, banks and universities to high profile individuals to thousands of local authority employees bringing mass equal pay claims against their employers. She regularly appears in the employment Tribunal and the EAT and had conduct of 2 landmark appeals in the Court of Appeal, Manchester NHS v Fecitt [2012] ICR 372; [2014] IRLR 64 and Kemeh v Ministry of Defence [2014] ICR 625 [2014] IRLR 377. She secured the largest ever equal pay settlement for her clients against Birmingham City Council, appeared in Fox Cross Claimants v Glasgow CC [2013] ICR 954 in the EAT and is involved in a substantial equal pay claim against North Lanarkshire CC. Daphne also appears in the High Court, including restrictive covenant, disciplinary and contract claims (she acts for former Super-Head Jo Shuter), as well as appearing in disciplinary tribunals and hearings for sportsmen, doctors, teachers and councillors.
Professional Memberships: ELBA (and Chair 2007-09). ELA (and Current Committee Member). ILS.
Career: Called 1979. Silk 2009. In addition to her practice, she has lectured extensively for Michael Rubinstein, ILS, ELA and others and comments on legal matters in the media.
Personal: Devoted Arsenal season ticket holder. Trustee of Save A Child, a charity paying for education for children living in orphanages in Bengal and Delhi.

ROOTS, Guy QC
Francis Taylor Building, London
020 7353 8415
clerks@ftb.eu.com
Featured in Local Government (London), Planning (London)
Practice Areas: Guy Roots QC specialises in town and country planning, environment, compulsory purchase and compensation, rating and valuation, and other local government and administrative law subjects. He advises a wide spectrum of clients including companies, local authorities, government and other agencies and individuals. Examples of major schemes in which he acted for the promoter include: London Olympic Games 2012; regeneration of Greenwich Peninsula; decommissioning of Trawsfynydd Nuclear Power station; Terminal 5 at Heathrow; new electricity transmission lines for National Grid and EDF. He is one of the leading experts on compulsory purchase, compensation for compulsory purchase and other categories of statutory compensation, rating and land valuation. He has appeared in many compensation cases in the Lands Tribunal including several arising out of the Channel Tunnel Rail Link and he is advising in relation to claims for compensation for Crossrail. He has also appeared in the Lands Tribunal and Court of Appeal in Hong Kong and in the Grand Court of the Cayman Islands.
Professional Memberships: Past chairman of the Planning and Environment Bar Association (PEBA) (2000-04). Member of Compulsory Purchase Association and the National Infrastructure Planning Association. Member of the DETR's Compulsory Purchase Policy Review Advisory Group. Assistant Boundary Commissioner.
Career: Called to Bar: 1969; QC: 1989. MA in Jurisprudence from Oxford University. Harmsworth Scholar (Middle Temple). Bencher of Middle Temple. Fellow of the Society of Advanced Legal Studies.
Publications: 'The Law of Compulsory Purchase' (2nd Ed 2011) published by Bloomsbury Professional ; 'Compulsory Purchase and Compensation Service' (looseleaf) published by Bloomsbury Professional. 'Ryde on Rating and the Council Tax' published by Butterworths/LexisNexis.

ROSE, Paul QC
Old Square Chambers, London
020 7269 0300
roseqc@oldsquare.co.uk
Featured in Personal Injury (London)
Practice Areas: Personal injury and employment law. In employment law has acted in leading cases in discrimination, unfair dismissal and Transfer of Undertakings Regulations. In personal injury acted on behalf of the plaintiffs in Opren litigation, Benzodiazepine litigation, British Midland air crash, Camelford Water Pollution, Mull of Kyntyre helicopter crash. Acted in a substantial number of catastrophic injury claims particularly involving servicemen in claims against Ministry of Defence, including the recent case of Tomlinson v MOD where the claimant was awarded £4.6m for a frontal lobe brain injury. He has also been instructed in many spinal injury and traumatic brain injury cases which have resolved at round table meetings rather than at trial. Recent reported cases include: Lightfoot v Go Ahead Group PLC [2011] RTR 11 (RTA contributory negligence); Johnson Controls Ltd v Campbell [UKEAT 0042/12] (Service Provision Change); Caston v Chief Constable Lincolnshire Police [2010] IRLR 327 (Time limits, Discrimination); IB v CB [2010] EWHC 3815(QB) (Content of periodical payments offer); Okunu v G4S Security [2008] ICR 598 (meaning of 'on racial grounds' 1976 Race Realtions Act); James v Redcats (Brands) Ltd [2007] IRLR 296 (meaning of 'worker' ; Sowerby v Charlton [2006] 1 WLR 568 (Court of Appeal - pre action admissions); Kerry Foods v Lynch [2005] IRLR 680 'some other substantial reason' in unfair dismissal); Scott v Commissioners of Inland Revenue [2004] IRLR 713 (Court of Appeal: compensation under Sex Discrimination Act 1975); Mattis v Pollock [2003] IRLR 603 (Court of Appeal: scope of vicarious liability); Franks v Reuters [2003] IRLR 423 (meaning of 'employee' in Employment Rights Act 1996); Croft v Royal Mail [2003] IRLR 592 (Court of Appeal discrimination, transsexual) Liversidge v Chief Constable of Bedfordshire Police [2002] IRLR 15 (vicarious liability under Race Relations Act 1976); Kerry Foods v Creber [2000] IRLR 10 (Transfer of Undertakings: meaning of transfer, consultation); Bici v Ministry of Defence Times [2004] EWCH 786 (QB). (Scope of combat immunity). Paul Rose speaks regularly at professional conferences on topical issues in the areas he specilaises in.
Professional Memberships: ELA, ELBA, PIBA, APIL.
Career: Called to Bar 1981, Silk 2002, Fee Paid Employment Judge since 2003.

ROSENTHAL, Adam
Falcon Chambers, London
020 7353 2484
rosenthal@falcon-chambers.com
Featured in Real Estate Litigation (London)
Practice Areas: All aspects of commercial and residential real property, landlord and tenant and related professional negligence and insolvency.
Professional Memberships: Chancery Bar Association; LCLCBA; Property Bar Association.
Career: Educated at King David High School, Liverpool; St Catherine's College, Oxford (BA Law/French Law 1998); called 1999 (Gray's Inn).
Publications: Co-Author, Commercial and Residential Service Charges (2013); Contributor, Fisher & Lightwood's 'Law of Mortgage' (2010); joint editor, Barnsley's Land Options 5th Edn (2009).

ROSENTHAL, Dennis
Henderson Chambers, London
020 7583 9020
drosenthal@hendersonchambers.co.uk
Featured in Consumer Law (London)
Practice Areas: Consumer; consumer credit; retail banking; retail financial services; asset finance and leasing; commercial contracts; commercial and consumer law; data protection; money laundering and fraud prevention. Advises on and drafts all kinds of regulated, unregulated and exempt credit and hire agreements; consumer credit issues; funding agreements; security issues and documentation; pre- and post-contract documents; promotional materials. Advises

on financial services issues including on CONC, MCOB and FCA Handbook generally; Payment Services Regulations; FCA authorisation. Advises on interest rate swops; unfair contract terms; retail products; systems and procedures; anti money laundering and data protection issues and procedures; due diligence.
Professional Memberships: COMBAR.
Career: Attorney of the Supreme Court of S Africa (1969); Solicitor, England (1977);formerly partner Berwin Leighton Paisner LLP; called to Gray's Inn and joined Henderson Chambers in 2009.
Publications: Editor of Goode: Consumer Credit Law and Practice; Goode: Consumer Credit Reports; Encyclopaedia of Forms and Precedents (Consumer Credit); Contributor to Halsbury's Laws of England on Consumer Credit (4th Ed.); Author of 'Consumer Credit Law and Practice - a Guide' (4th Ed., Bloomsbury Professional) and 'Financial Advertising and Marketing Law'.
Personal: BA LLB (Witwatersrand); BA (Hons) University of S Africa; born 1944.

ROSS, James
Gough Square Chambers, London
020 7353 0924
james.ross@goughsq.co.uk
Featured in Consumer Law (London)
Practice Areas: All aspects of consumer and regulatory law, especially banking and finance (including consumer credit), commercial litigation, mortgages, insolvency and regulatory crime.
Professional Memberships: Association of Regulatory and Disciplinary Lawyers; Consumer Credit Forum; Finance Litigation Forum; London Common Law and Commercial Bar Association.
Career: Called Inner Temple (2006). Regularly appears in court and advises on issues relating to financial services, consumer credit, payment services, electronic money, mortgages and commercial disputes. Acted as a sole advocate in the Court of Appeal on behalf of a finance company in Kulkarni v Manor Credit (Davenham) Limited [2010] 2 Lloyd's Rep 431. Successfully appeared in Barnes v Black Horse Limited [2011] 2 All ER (Comm) 1130, leading authority on transitional provisions in the Consumer Credit Act 2006 relating to unfair relationships and extortionate credit bargains. Successfully represented the bank in Santander UK plc v Harrison [2013] Bus LR 501, leading authority on the meaning of "credit in the form of a cash loan" and the interaction between securitisation and unfair relationships under the Consumer Credit Act 1974.
Publications: General editor of the textbook 'Modern Financial Regulation'.
Personal: LLB (First Class) King's College London (2005). Duke of Edinburgh and Major Exhibition scholarships awarded by the Inner Temple.

ROSS, John QC
1 Chancery Lane, London
020 7092 2900
jross@1chancerylane.com
Featured in Professional Negligence (London), Personal Injury (London), Travel (London)
Practice Areas: Specialises in professional liability and insurance-related claims, contract and commercial, public and regulatory law and product liability as well as catastrophic injury claims. His professional liability cases include claims involving solicitors and barristers, insurance brokers, accountants, architects, engineers and valuers. Has considerable experience in cases involving local authorities and other public bodies, including judicial reviews. Appearances also include commercial and NGO arbitrations and construction adjudication hearings. Has a significant first instance and appellate practice, having appeared before the House of Lords and Court of Appeal in a series of test cases concerning the application of the CPR, the Limitation Act and public body liability, with many cases reported in the Official Law Reports. His practice additionally encompasses claims originating abroad involving private international law issues and he has acted and appeared in actions brought in the courts of The Cayman Islands and in Jersey, as well as in arbitrations brought against UK multinational corporations in Southern Africa.
Professional Memberships: Professional Negligence Bar Association (Committee 2006-09, Vice-Chair 2010 and 2011, Chair 2012 and 2013); London Common Law and Commercial Bar Association (Committee 2006-11), Association of Regulatory and Disciplinary Lawyers, Technology and Construction Bar Association, Personal Injuries Bar Association.
Career: Called to the Bar 1971; appointed Recorder 1994; QC 2001; Bencher Inner Temple 2006; Legal Assessor to the Royal College of Veterinary Surgeons 2006; Head of Chambers 2007 to present.
Publications: Specialist editor, Professional Negligence Cases, Butterworths
Personal: LLB (1969), LLM (1970) - University College London. Leisure interests: golf, cricket, racing, bridge and music.

ROUSSAK, Jeremy
Kings Chambers, Manchester
08450 343 444
clerks@kingschambers.com
Featured in Clinical Negligence (Northern)
Practice Areas: Clinical negligence, personal injury, regulatory (General Medical Council Fitness to Practise panels).
Professional Memberships: Professional Negligence Bar Association Personal Injuries Bar Association Northern Circuit Medical Law Association (Treasurer).
Career: Jeremy qualified as a doctor in 1983. He trained in surgery, passing the examinations for fellowship of the Royal College of Surgeons of Edinburgh (FRCSEd) in 1988. He then specialised in surgery of the heart and chest. He has extensive experience of clinical negligence litigation, acting mainly but not exclusively on behalf of claimants, and of mid- and high-value personal injury claims, instructed by both claimants and defendants. He has both prosecuted and defended doctors before the Fitness to Practice panels of the GMC (now the MPTS). Jeremy has been a member of the Attorney-General's Provincial Panel of Counsel since 2002. From January 2008 to April 2010 he was Counsel to the Redfern Inquiry into Human Tissue Analysis in UK Nuclear Facilities.

ROWELL, David
9 Stone Buildings, London
020 7404 5055
clerks@9stonebuildings.com
Featured in Chancery (London)
Practice Areas: Chancery and personal taxation, especially capital taxes, wills, trusts, land law, charities and landlord and tenant. Cases include Re Erskine's Settlement Trusts, Gregg v Pigott (effect of the Human Rights Act on the interpretation of wills and trusts); Hambro v Duke of Marlborough (the management of Blenheim Palace); Judge v IRC (inheritance tax); Challock Parish Council v Shirley (land valuation); Rabin v Gerson Berger (trusts); Re Box Hill Common (common land); Re Evans deceased (claims against estates).
Professional Memberships: Chancery Bar Association.
Career: Called 1972. Practised at 3 New Square, Lincoln's Inn 1973-2001. Joined 9 Stone Buildings in October 2001.
Publications: Law Pack's 'Last Will and Testament', chapters in Jordans Chancery Litigation Handbook, articles in 'Trusts and Estates Law Journal' and 'Trust Quarterly Review' and CPDcast on 'Human Rights - The Construction of Wills and Trusts'.
Personal: New College Oxford BA (First Class Honours).

ROWLANDS, Marc QC
Keating Chambers, London
020 7544 2600
mrowlands@keatingchambers.com
Featured in Construction (London)
Practice Areas: Specialises in all forms of dispute avoidance and resolution and advisory work in all aspects of construction, engineering, technology and energy disputes both in the UK and internationally. Appears regularly in the High Court and domestic arbitrations, adjudications and mediations (both as advocate and adjudicator and mediator). Extensive experience of substantial international arbitrations and litigation, in particular in the Middle East, Far East and Caribbean (called to the Bar of the Bahamas). In depth knowledge of all major construction (JCT, NEC), engineering (FIDIC, ICE) and UK rail related forms of agreement. Particular expertise in railway related disputes, covering vehicles, infrastructure, derailment and the UK regulatory environment (Railways Acts, Network Rail Standards) and including PFI. Rail related litigation in arbitration and Court includes the following: Channel Tunnel, le Shuttle, Dubai Metro, Taiwan Shinkansen, Singapore Metro, Amtrak North East Corridor, New York Port Authority, West Coast Mainline upgrade, Heathrow Tunnel collapse, Crossrail, East London Line, Ely derailment. Rail related advisory work includes TOC financial modelling, vehicle leasing arrangements and the PWRA. Other recent work includes energy (4 week trial relating to offshore compressors), technology (2 week trial relating to satellite tracking systems) and shipping (Commercial Court ship arrest) and Court of Appeal (estoppel, insolvency). Has appeared in the Crown Court in proceedings brought by the HSE, judicial review proceedings in the Admin Court, High Court libel proceedings relating to the British Museum and has advised on appeals to the Privy Council from the Turks and Caicos.
Professional Memberships: TECBAR; COMBAR; Society of Construction Law.
Career: Call 1990, Queen's Counsel 2012, CEDR accredited Mediator 2007, Bahamian Bar 2008.

ROWLEY, James QC
Byrom Street Chambers, Manchester
01618 292 100
james.rowley@byromstreet.com
Featured in Clinical Negligence (Northern), Personal Injury (Northern)
Practice Areas: Personal injuries: Dunhill v Burgin [2014] UKSC 18 affirming [2012] EWCA Civ 397 and [2012] EWHC 3163 (QB); Scott and Evans v Griffiths QBD Lawtel 29/01/14; Dixie v. British Polythene Industries PLC [2010] EWCA Civ 1170; Threlfall v. Hull City Council [2010] EWCA Civ 1147; Stanley v Bryn Close t/a Armthorpe Moto Parc [2009] EWHC 2849 (QB); The Kajaki Dam Disaster v MoD (2008); Samantha Roberts v MoD (2006); In the PTSD Group Actions - Multiple Claimants v MOD (In the PTSD Group Actions) [2003] EWHC/1134 (QB); Craven v John Riches et al and Knockhill Racing Circuit [2001] EWCA CIV 375; Jebson v MOD [2000] 1 W.L.R. 2055, I.C.R. 1220 CA) Clinical Negligence: Beech v Timney [2013] EWHC 2345 (QB); Spencer v NHS North West [2012] EWHC 2142 (QB); Parkes v Mann [2011] EWHC 1724 (QB); Inquiries: Report of the Royal Liverpool Children's Inquiry - HMSO (2001) - Counsel to the Alder Hey Inquiry
Professional Memberships: Personal Injuries Bar Association (Chairman 2010-12); Professional Negligence Bar Association
Career: MA (Classics) Cantab; Dip Law; Stonyhurst and Emmanuel. Hardwicke Scholar of Lincoln's Inn. Called 1987. Regional Treasury Counsel (2000). Counsel to the Royal Liverpool Children's Inquiry (2000-01). Recorder (Crown Court 2002, County Court 2007). Silk 2006. Lectured widely in PI.
Publications: Author of chapter on claims for care and assistance in Facts & Figures since 2012. Serious Personal Injury Litigation - a Quantum Update [2008] JPIL 109, still updated at www.byromstreet.com. Periodical Payments Orders - Useful or Useless? - Kemp Quantum Update 1/2007. Combat Immunity and the Duty of Care [2004] JPIL 280.
Personal: Married with three children. High Legh CC, armchair sportsman, gardener and cook.

ROWNTREE, Edward
Hardwicke, London
020 7242 2523
edward.rowntree@hardwicke.co.uk
Featured in Real Estate Litigation (London)
Practice Areas: Edward Rowntree's is a wide-ranging commercial Chancery practice. He acts as advisor and advocate covering all aspects of real property; commercial landlord and tenant; company, insolvency and commercial litigation often with an international aspect relating to jurisdiction and applicable law; and inheritance and probate. His probate practice encompasses contested wills, domicile, disputes in relation to the administration of estates and applications under the Inheritance (Provision for Family and Dependants Act) 1975 has seen numerous High Court trials, including the most recent anti-suit injunction obtained in support of probate proceedings in this country. Edward combines academic excellence with an acute sensitivity to the commercial needs of his clients. His practice encompasses a wide range of commercial and property work before all levels of tribunal. He enjoys working as part of a team, whether with solicitors or other counsel and is known for is pragmatic and

well-informed advice. He aims to ensure that his clients are always aware of the options available to them enabling them to appreciate the merits and risks of contemplated courses of action. In addition, Edward was called to the Bar of the Cayman Islands in 2002.
Professional Memberships: Chancery Bar Association, Property Bar Association, Commercial Bar Association.
Publications: Contributor to "The Law of Mortgages" by Cousins (2nd and 3rd editions)

ROY, Andrew
12 King's Bench Walk, London
020 7583 0811
roy@12kbw.co.uk
Featured in Personal Injury (London)
Practice Areas: Personal injury, clinical negligence, costs, professional negligence, property damage, common law. Andrew covers all aspects of personal injury including road traffic accidents, employers' liability, public liability, product liability, fatal accidents, industrial disease (asbestos, RSI, WRULD) and psychiatric injury (in particular stress at work). Andrew's clinical negligence practice encompasses all aspects of medical and dental negligence (especially surgical and A&E negligence), as well as claims involving other healthcare professionals. Andrew has a special interest and extensive experience and expertise in contentious costs litigation, in particular with respect to CFAs and fixed costs of all types. Andrew also has particular expertise in limitation. His other areas of practice include professional negligence (especially arising out of personal injury litigation), insurance, fire, flood and contract claims.
Professional Memberships: PIBA, APIL, PNBA.
Career: Attended RBAI then Newcastle University (LLB (Fist Class Honours), MA in English Literature). Called 2002. Previously worked as a caseworker for the LSC, and as an insurance claims handler.
Publications: Co-author, Personal Injury Limitation Law 3rd Edition. Frequent contributor to JPIL, PILJ and PIBULJ.
Personal: Born Belfast. Outside interests include running, rugby, cricket, wildlife and literature.

RUBIN, Stephen QC
Fountain Court Chambers, London
020 7583 3335
sr@fountaincourt.co.uk
Featured in Commercial Dispute Resolution (London), Fraud (London), Telecommunications (London)
Practice Areas: General commercial litigation particularly civil fraud, commercial disputes. Major cases: Primary Group v RBS & Direct Line LTL 11/4/14 (Banker-customer relationship; Bankers' duties; Breach of confidence; Breach of contract; Confidentiality); Deutsche Bank v Sebastian Holdings & Vik (Non-party costs; Service by alternative permitted method; Service out of jurisdiction) LTL 30/1/14; VTB Capital plc v Nutritek [2013] 2 WLR 398 SC and also Bannister J in BVI (commercial fraud, Russia, worldwide freezing orders, jurisdiction); A-G of TCI v Coxco 2013 Supreme Court of TCI (Norwich Pharmacal, alleged bribes); Palmer & Harvey v Garrad 2013 - 3 week trial before Blackburne J June 2013; A-G of TCI v Salt Cay Ltd 2010-2012 TCI Supreme Court and COA (commercial fraud, bribery, rescission); Digicel v Cable & Wireless [2010] EWHC 774 (Ch) Ch D (Morgan J) 15/4/2010 LTL 21/4/2010 - 5 month trial (conspiracy to injure, telecoms); BNP Paribas v TH Global LTL 19/1/09 (Norwich Parmacals, fraud); The Wahr-Hansen/Jahre litigation: Cayman Islands, 2004-2008 (fraud, trusts); EUNetworks Fiber Ltd v Abovenet Communications UK Ltd [2007] EWHC 3099 Ch D (Briggs J) LTL 9/1/2008 (telecoms, commercial contracts, rectification; Miller & Moody v Condor Insurance [2006] 1 All ER 934 (Guarantees by deed poll); As a Junior: First American v Sheikh Zayad Al Nahayan [1999] 1 WLR 1154 (fraud, letters of request); Den Norske Bank v Antonatos [1999] QB 271, (fraud, freezing orders); Pharaon v BCCI [1998] 4 All ER 455 (fraud, foreign subpoena); BOC plc v Centeon Inc [1999] 1 All ER (Comm) 970 (contractual construction).
Professional Memberships: COMBAR; London Common Law and Commercial Bar Association;
Career: QC 2000; Bencher of the Middle Temple; Recorder 2004 (crime and civil). Professional Conduct and Complaints Committee of Bar 1995-99; Hon Board of UKLSA; Panel chairman Bar Disciplinary Tribunals - appointed 2013
Personal: Merchant Taylor's School, Northwood; Brasenose College, Oxford, entrance exhibition - MA Jurisprudence; married with four children.

RUCK, Mary
Byrom Street Chambers, Manchester
01618 292 100
mary.ruck@byromstreet.com
Featured in Clinical Negligence (Northern)
Practice Areas: Specialises in clinical negligence, medical law and medical regulatory cases (GMC); practice also involves human rights, fatal accident claims and personal injury (catastrophic injury). Particular interest in neurological injury including birth injury claims, subarachnoid haemorrhage and acquired brain injury. Regularly instructed in high value cases resulting in significant capital awards with PPOs. Also wrongful birth, obstetric injury, mistakes in organ transplantation; negligent surgery, delayed diagnosis/ treatment of cauda equina syndrome. Notable litigation includes cases in the Strasbourg jurisdiction resulting in successful judgment by the Grand Chamber and friendly settlements; currently instructed on behalf of Kenyan nationals in claims connected to the 1952 State of Emergency (Mau Mau insurgency). Recent concluded cases include: 90% liability settlement achieved in birth brain injury case (2014); £850,000 settlement in case involving loss of sight (2013); £600,000 settlement arising failure to identify family member as appropriate organ donor; £215,000 settlement for negligent surgery (Defendant's first offer was £10,000); chronic regional pain settlement: £400,000 (2013); £500,000 settlement in cauda equina case with difficult causation argument (2012); birth injury from prolonged partial hypoxic ischaemia: £1m plus PPO of £90,000 per annum (with Chris Melton QC, 2012); birth injury with liability previously concluded at 66%, settlement achieved of £1.65m with PPO of £125,000 to age 19 and £160,000 post - 19 (with Geoffrey Tattarsall QC, 2012) Ongoing cases include birth injuries arising out of prolonged partial hypoxic ischaemia (syntocinon administration) and acute profound hypoxia ischaemia (cord compression); unnecessary insertion of pacemaker resulting in somatisation disorder.
Professional Memberships: AVMA; PNBA; founder member of Northern Circuit Medical Law Association.
Career: Called to the Bar 1993 (Gray's Inn); practised in London until moving to the Northern Circuit in 1999; appointed First Tier Tribunal Judge to the Health and Social Care Chamber (Mental Health) in 2007.
Publications: Former Editor, now Assistant Editor, Fatal Accidents Chapter, Butterworths 'Personal Injury Litigation Service'.
Personal: Originally from the South West. Now lives in Cheshire.

RUCK KEENE, Alexander
Thirty Nine Essex Street, London
020 7832 1111
alex.ruckkeene@39essexstreet.com
Featured in Administrative & Public Law (London), Court of Protection (All Circuits)
Practice Areas: Court of Protection: eg James v Aintree University NHS Hospitals Foundation Trust [2013] 3 WLR 1299 (first Supreme Court decision relating to MCA 2005); X & Ors (Deprivation of Liberty) [2014] EWCOP 25 ('streamlined' applications to CoP regarding deprivation of liberty); JO v GO [2014] 3 WLR 453 (definition of habitual residence in CoP context); Mental health: eg Munjaz v UK [2012] MHLR 351 (status of MHA Code of Practice); HSE Ireland v SF [2012] 2 FLR 1131 (cross-border placement of child in psychiatric institution); Sessay v SLAM & Anor [2012] QB 760 (power to detain pending admission under MHA 1983).
Professional Memberships: STEP, ALBA, ARDL, ELF, LAPG
Career: Attorney General's Junior Counsel to the Crown (B Panel); EHRC Panel Counsel; Honorary Research Lecturer at University of Manchester
Publications: The International Protection of Adults (forthcoming, OUP, co-author); Court of Protection Handbook: A Users Guide (LAG, 2014, editor and co-author); Court of Protection Practice 2015 (co-author); Mental Capacity: Law and Practice (2nd edition, 2012, co-author); Assessment of Mental Capacity, 2010 (co-author); Clayton & Tomlinson, The Law of Human Rights, 2nd edition, 2009 (contributor). Editorial Board of Court of Protection Law Reports. Creator of www.mentalcapacitylawandpolicy.org.uk.

RUDOLF, Nathaniel
25 Bedford Row, London
07803 927 218
nrudolf@25bedfordrow.com
Featured in Financial Crime (London)
Practice Areas: White collar crime almost exlusively defending in serious fraud matters, high value confiscation and asset forfeiture. Additionally he undertakes crime and asset forfeiture-related work in the High Court including judicial review and cases stated. In 2014 Nathaniel was scheduled to defend an accountant in 'Operation Valgus' - one of the country's largest ever mortgage frauds. A further highlight is a seven day 'Certificate of Inadequacy' hearing in the High Court. In 2015 he is looking forward to defending the second defendant - an accountant - in 'Operation Lift' in Birmingham - an allegation of international money laundering of £34m; an investment banker charged with tax fraud and one of the defendants who worked for ICAP charged by the SFO as part of the LIBOR prosecutions.
Professional Memberships: Criminal Bar Association (Secretary 2011-12), South East Circuit, American Bar Association.
Career: University of Warwick 2:1 (Hons) in Law, Diplock Scholar of the Middle Temple, LAA High Cost Crime Independent Funding Adjudicator (2012 - present) Member, Criminal Procedure Rules Committee (2011 - present).
Publications: International Money Laundering and Terrorist Financing: A UK Perspective, Sweet & Maxwell (2009); Contributer, LexisPSL Bribery Toolkit (2011 - present); 'Fraud: A Practitioner's Handbook', Bloomsbury (2014).

RUSSELL, Paul QC
12 King's Bench Walk, London
020 7583 0811
russell@12kbw.co.uk
Featured in Personal Injury (London)
Practice Areas: Paul has a strong reputation in the specialist fields of personal injury, clinical negligence and professional negligence and is regularly instructed to act in high value claims. He is particularly experienced in dealing with both the bringing and defending of claims involving catastrophic injury, industrial disease, RSI, stress at work and employers' liability generally.
Professional Memberships: He is an ex-serving Member of the Bar Council Professional Conduct Committee, but remains a member of the Barristers' Complaints Advisory Panel. He is presently a Member of the PIBA Executive Committee.
Career: Called 1984.
Personal: Paul is a graduate of Durham University and away from the Bar, he is a Youth Offending Team panel member at the London Borough of Wandsworth.

RUSSEN, Jonathan QC
Maitland Chambers, London
020 7406 1200
jrussen@maitlandchambers.com
Featured in Chancery (London), Commercial Dispute Resolution (London), Financial Services (London)
Practice Areas: Commercial litigation (domestic and offshore); trusts; insolvency (corporate and personal); financial services; shareholders' disputes; partnership and property.
Professional Memberships: Chancery Bar Association. COMBAR.
Career: University of Wales LLB (1st Class Hons.) 1984. University of Cambridge LLM 1985. Called to Bar (Lincoln's Inn) 1986. QC 2010.
Publications: Financial Services: Authorisation, Supervision and Enforcement: A Litigator's Guide (OUP).
Personal: Married, two children.

RUTHERFORD, Emma
Number 8 Chambers, Birmingham
01212 365 514
emmarutherford@No8chambers.co.uk
Featured in Immigration (Midlands)
Practice Areas: Immigration and asylum, crime, general civil litigation
Professional Memberships: Immigration Law Practitioners Association
Career: Having been called to the bar in 2002, Emma has specialised in asylum and immigration law. She appears frequently before the First Tier Tribunal and the Upper Tribunal in all types of cases that are heard in

the Immigration and Asylum Chamber. She is also experienced in judicial review work and is instructed in Court of Appeal matters. As an experienced criminal practitioner she has a particular insight into issues surrounding deportation cases. She also has an interest in immigration cases with an EEA element. Her recent reported cases include SS (Zimbabwe) and Others v SSHD [2013] EWCA Civ 237, AK (15(c)) Afghanistan CG [2012] UKUT 163 (IAC), R v (on the application of Ahmed) v SSHD [2014] EWHC 300 (Admin) and R v (on the application of Reid) [2014] EWHC 1772 (Admin).

SABBEN-CLARE, Rebecca QC
7 King's Bench Walk, London
020 7910 8300
rsabbenclare@7kbw.co.uk
Featured in Commercial Dispute Resolution (London), Insurance (London), Professional Negligence (London)
Practice Areas: Commercial Law, including professional negligence, shipping, insurance and international arbitration. Current cases include Cattles v PwC (audit negligence), ICC arbitrations concerning oil exploration rights, Teal v. Berkley (reinsurance; preliminary issues were determined by the Supreme Court in 2013) and a number of LCIA and LMAA arbitrations. Reported cases include: ICSOP v. Equitas (2013 - reinsurance; conflict of laws); Quadra v. Ergo (2012 – cargo insurance claim); Atlasnavios v. Navigators (2012 – war risks insurance); Rok Plc v. S Harrison Group (2011 – share sale agreement); Orient Express v. Generali (2009 – hurricane Katrina); Curtis v. Lockheed Martin (2008 - share sale agreement), Calvert v. William Hill Credit Limited (2008 - bookmakers' duties of care), BBC Worldwide v Bee Load (2008 - recording archive agreement); Hollywood 4 and 5 (2002 – film finance insurance).
Professional Memberships: COMBAR (former executive committee member).
Career: Called 1993, QC 2012.

SACHDEVA, Vikram
Thirty Nine Essex Street, London
020 7832 1111
vicram.sachdeva@39essexstreet.com
Featured in Costs Litigation (London), Court of Protection (All Circuits), Professional Discipline (London)
Practice Areas: Administrative and Public Law, Commercial, Financial Services, Regulatory and Disciplinary, European Law, Procurement, Professional Negligence, Direct and Indirect Tax, and Costs Law.
Professional Memberships: Administrative Law Bar Association (Executive Committee Member), Financial Services Lawyers Association, Association of Regulatory and Disciplinary Lawyers (Executive Committee Member).
Career: MA (Cantab), BCL (Oxon), BM, BCh (Oxon). Formerly Tutor in Administrative and Public Law, Tort, and Crime, at various colleges in Oxford and Cambridge. Attorney General's A Panel. Appeared in James v Aintree University Hospitals [2014] AC 591; Denton v White [2014] EWCA Civ 906; R (Kebede) v SSBIS [2014] PTSR 92; Heron v TNT [2014] IWLR 1277; R (Kadri) v Birmingham CC and SSHD [2013] 1 WLR 1755; NHS Trust v Baby X [2013] 1 FLR 225; R (Tracey) v Cambridge University Hospital and SSH [2014] EWCA Civ 822; R (MD Afghanistan) v SSHD [2012] 1 WLR 2422; Re M (Adult Patient) (Minimally Conscious State: Withdrawal of Treatment) [2012] 1 WLR 1653 and [2012] 1 WLR 287; Lower Mill Estate Ltd v HMRC [2011] STC 636; DEFRA v Downs [2009] ACD 71

SADIQ, Tariq
St Philips Chambers, Birmingham
01212 467 000
tsadiq@st-philips.com
Featured in Employment (Midlands), Sports Law (The Regions)
Practice Areas: Tariq Sadiq practises from Birmingham and London and specialises in commercial employment, sports law and professional discipline disputes, and is recognised by Chambers & Partners as a leading practitioner in employment and sports law. In 2013, Tariq won the award for 'Barrister of the Year' at the Birmingham Law Society Legal Awards, the national award for 'Professional of the Year' at the premier diversity GG2 Leadership Awards, as well as being nominated for 'Human Rights Lawyer of the Year' in Liberty's Human Rights Awards. In 2014 he was shortlisted for the third consecutive year for the 'Barrister of the Year' award in the Birmingham Law Society Legal Awards. Tariq is regularly instructed in all aspects of employment litigation, including large-scale commercial employment litigation (restrictive covenants, confidentiality, fiduciary duties and TUPE) and individual employment proceedings (including discrimination, equal pay, whistleblowing). He is the leading Special Advocate in the UK for employment cases involving national security and has Developed Vetting, the highest level of security clearance to work in this area. Tariq's sports law practice sees him represent a number of leading sportsmen and women in disciplinary hearings as well as leading sports organisations including the FA and the Premier League. In 2014 he was appointed as an Arbitrator on the Football Association (FA) Arbitration Panel and Chair of the new FA Anti-Discrimination Panel which was created following the high profile cases involving John Terry and Luis Suarez. He is also a member of the Sport Resolutions Panel of Legal Arbitrators, hearing high-profile discipline, anti-doping and employment disputes involving leading sportswomen and men. Tariq's professional discipline practice encompasses healthcare, sports and financial sectors (including applications of injunctive relief to prevent misconduct and/or capability proceedings).
Professional Memberships: ELA (Elected Midlands Representative), ELBA, ILS and ADL (Association of Disciplinary Lawyers).
Career: Called to Bar 1993. Appointments: 2014: Chair, FA Anti-Discrimination Panel; Arbitrator, FA Arbitration Panel; ELA Midlands Representative. 2012: Welsh Government A Panel of Counsel; Treasury Solicitors Freedom of Information Panel; Member of ELA Briefing Editorial Board; Arbitrator, Sport Resolutions Panel. 2011: Equality and Human Rights Commission's Panel of Preferred Counsel. 2009: Attorney General's Panel of Special Advocates. 2000: Junior Counsel to the Crown, Provincial Panel (Reappointed 2003, 2007 & 2010).
Publications: Member of the Editorial Board that publishes the ELA newsletter ELA Briefing; Co-Editor of Bloomsbury's Discrimination Law.

SADLER, Rhiannon
9 Bedford Row, London
020 7489 2727
rhiannon.sadler@9bedfordrow.co.uk
Featured in Crime (South Eastern)
Practice Areas: Rhiannon is a dynamic prosecution and defence advocate with broad experience at all levels of criminal law. She has an outstanding reputation, "a strong work ethic and excellent organisational skills". She is a highly regarded junior and has been led in a multitude of cases including a 3-month long conspiracy to steal, a conspiracy to defraud the Secretary of State involving international visa fraud, as well as murder, both prosecuting and defending. She is a persuasive negotiator with exceptional communication skills and experience in handling highly sensitive cases. She has a keen interest in honour based crimes and successfully secured an acquittal for a father accused of honour based kidnap and false imprisonment. Rhiannon is lauded for a her "willingness to go the extra mile" and delivery at the highest of standards. She is a Grade 3 prosecutor and routinely briefed in both London and the Provinces. She has a proven ability to adapt quickly to new and complex environments and thrives under pressure.

SAHONTE, Rajinder
Guildhall Chambers, Bristol
01179 309 000
rajinder.sahonte
@guildhallchambers.co.uk
Featured in Real Estate Litigation (Western)
Practice Areas: Raj has a traditional chancery practice which regularly includes contentious and non-contentious real estate work in the commercial and residential field. In addition he undertakes a significant amount of contentious and non-contentious probate work including cases in the Court of Protection. Raj also has specialist expertise in common rights and village greens and has successfully conducted a number of public inquiries for developer clients in the context of adverse registrations. Further, he has successfully acted for a number of telecommunication companies in relation to installations over private land.
Professional Memberships: Chancery Bar Association
Personal: Married with two children. Enjoys running, cooking and fencing. Languages - speaks Punjabi, Hindi and Urdu.

SALMON, Sarah
Arden Chambers, London
020 7242 4244
sarah.salmon@ardenchambers.co.uk
Featured in Social Housing (London)
Practice Areas: Housing and landlord and tenant, with a particular emphasis on anti-social behaviour, local government (including information rights and education) and the public law aspects of housing law.
Professional Memberships: Administrative Law Bar Association, Social Housing Law Association, Housing Law Practitioners Association and Education Law Association.
Career: After graduating from university Sarah obtained an LLM in Public Law at University College London. She was called to the Bar, and joined Arden Chambers as a pupil, in 2007. Sarah's noteworthy cases include James v Birmingham City Council [2013] EWCA Civ 552 and Morrison Facilities Services Limited v Norwich City Council [2010] EWHC 487 (Ch).
Publications: Assistant editor (2012-) of the Encyclopedia of Housing Law (Sweet & Maxwell) and co-author of Judicial Review Proceedings - A Practitioner's Guide (2013, LAG). She has had articles on housing and local government law published in the New Law Journal, Solicitors Journal, Journal of Housing Law and Local Government Lawyer.

SAMEK, Charles QC
11 Stone Buildings, London
020 7831 6381
samek@11sb.com
Featured in Commercial Dispute Resolution (London), Fraud (London)
Practice Areas: Charles Samek QC is a recognised commercial litigator and trial advocate specialising in commercial and contract disputes, civil fraud and asset tracing, private international law jurisdiction disputes, financial and investment disputes, intellectual property, both contentious and non-contentious, domestic and worldwide freezing orders and proprietary injunctions, search orders and other interim remedies. Charles acted throughout in the landmark Dadourian litigation which gave rise to 3 leading Court of Appeal authorities in the field of worldwide freezing injunctions, contempt, committal and the remedies for deceit. He is currently acting in the VAB v Maksimov litigation concerned with Court-ordered relief in support of arbitration proceedings. Almost all of Charles' work is in the Commercial Court and Chancery Division. Charles is also experienced in employment law claims of a commercial hue, such as in relation to misuse of confidential information; covenants in restraint of trade and team move cases. He is a member of the LCIA European Users Council and acts as advocate and arbitrator in arbitrations. For more information and for a selection of Charles' recent cases please visit the 'Barristers' section on www.11sb.com.
Professional Memberships: COMBAR; London Common Law and Commercial Bar Association; Chancery Bar Association; British-Italian Law Association; Commercial Fraud Lawyers Association; the International Bar Association.
Career: Call: 1989 – Silk: 2009.
Personal: Oriel College, Oxford University; City University. Charles speaks Italian and conversational French.

SAMSON, John
Ely Place Chambers, London
020 7400 9600
jsamson@elyplace.com
Featured in Defamation/Privacy (London)
Practice Areas: Advocate and former Guardian lawyer specialising in Confidential Information, Data Protection, Defamation, Freedom of Information, Harassment, Human Rights, Injunctive Relief, Malicious Falsehood, Media Law and Privacy with an active caseload for claimants and defendants including phone hacking (defendant) and blacklisting (claims include misuse of private information and conspiracy for secret vetting of claimants' political and trade union activities). John is instructed by university colleges, foreign embassies, actors, CEOs, academics, politicians, town clerks, doctors, dentists, brokers, high net worth individuals, publishers, film and TV production companies, local authorities, law firms, food manufacturers, public authorities, charities, trade unions, private companies and public

corporations. A media production and arts background including senior editorial stints in broadcast journalism adds a unique perspective to John's media related cases. Appearances include High Court, Information Tribunal, Court of Appeal and Privy Council. John also acts in employment cases including reputation management, bonus claims, sham contracts, discrimination, equality, redundancy, restrictive covenants, TUPE, unfair dismissals and whistle-blowing and acts as an adviser to the pro bono legal surgery for London's Latin American community at St Georges Cathedral, Southwark.
Career: LLB (London) First Class; called 2001, Inner Temple; counsel, media practice (2002); Ely Place Chambers (2005); Accredited Mediator (2009).

SAMUELS, Leslie QC
Pump Court Chambers, London
020 7353 0711
l.samuels@pumpcourtchambers.com
Featured in Family/Matrimonial (Western)
Practice Areas: All aspects of family law including care proceedings, representing parents, local authorities and children's guardians in cases involving complex issues including alleged non-accidental injury (death, brain injury, subdural and retinal bleeding, fractures, FII, bruising), alleged sexual abuse and difficult welfare issues. High value ancillary relief claims with expertise and experience in cases involving, farms, companies, trusts and pensions. Equitable co-ownership claims. Private law children matters (residence, contact, leave to remove, child abduction). Judicial Review claims particularly those involving local authority duties to children and vulnerable adults. Probate claims (wills, capacity and claims under the Inheritance Act). Employment related claims including discrimination allegations. Highly experienced at County Court, High Court and appellate levels.
Professional Memberships: Family Law Bar Association (Chair of the Money and Property Sub Committee), Western Circuit.
Career: Called Gray's Inn 1989, 2003 Deputy District Judge Principal Registry of the Family Division, 2005 ADR accredited mediator, 2011 appointed QC, 2012 Recorder (South Eastern Circuit) Family.
Personal: MA (Law) Cambridge, MA (Criminology) University of Toronto, married with two children. Lives in London.

SANDBACH, Carly
Exchange Chambers, Manchester
01618 332 722
sandbach@exchangechambers.co.uk
Featured in Commercial Dispute Resolution (Northern), Restructuring/Insolvency (Northern)
Practice Areas: Practices in all areas of commercial and chancery litigation, with an emphasis on insolvency (corporate and personal), company and professional negligence matters. Notable cases include the recent winding up in the public interest of Solar Energy Savings Limited.
Professional Memberships: Chancery Bar Association, Insolvency Lawyers Association, Association of Business Recovery Professionals (R3), Northern Circuit Commercial Bar Association, Northern Circuit Bar Association, Northern Administrative Law Association.
Career: First Class BA (Hons) Law, Cambridge 2005. Called to the Bar 27th July 2006 (Inner Temple). Junior Counsel to the Crown (Provincial Panel).
Personal: Interests - walking, dining, theatre and travel.

SANDERSON, David
12 King's Bench Walk, London
020 7583 0811
sanderson@12kbw.co.uk
Featured in Personal Injury (London)
Practice Areas: David acts for both claimants and defendants dealing with high value claims across the spectrum of personal injury, clinical negligence and fatal accident claims.
Professional Memberships: Professional Negligence Bar Association, Personal Injury Bar Association, London Common Law and Commercial Bar Association, Western Circuit.
Career: Called 1985 Inner Temple. Pupil Master. Recent cases include: Simmons v Castle [2012] PIQR P22; Tavares v Hudson-Rotin [2012] Globe J 13/2/13; Smithurst v Sealant Construction [2012] Med LR 258; Rust-Andrews v First Tier Tribunal (Social Entitlement Chamber) [2012] PIQR P7; Micklewright v Surrey County Council [2011] EWCA Civ 922; Richardson v Butcher [2010] EWHC 214; R v Lane [2009] EWCA Crim 1630; Wade v Turffrey [2007] LS Law Medical 352; Denton Hall v Fifield [2006] Lloyd's Rep Med 251; Ellis v Royal Surrey County Hospital [2004] EWHC 3510; Morris v Richards [2004] PIQR Q3; Simonds v Isle of Wight Council (2004) ELR 59; Pearce v Lindfield [2003] EWCA Civ 647.
Personal: Stowe School. Sussex University (BA). Married with one daughter. Away from the Bar his interests include cycling, sea swimming, opera and India.

SANDERSON, Eleanor
2 Bedford Row, London
07780 660 836
esanderson@2bedfordrow.co.uk
Featured in Health & Safety (London), Professional Discipline (London)
Practice Areas: Predominantly defence barrister with a record of acting in complex and high profile cases in the fields of criminal, regulatory and disciplinary law. She is regularly instructed by both individuals and companies in cases where allegations attract public or political interest. She also acts for professionals facing disciplinary proceedings before their regulatory bodies. In the regulatory criminal field, she has acted for both prosecution and defence in relation to allegations of gross negligence manslaughter, corporate manslaughter, and breaches of section 2 and 3 HSAW, for companies facing prosecution by the Environment Agency, and in proceedings under the Fire Safety Order. She is an experienced advocate in inquests having acted for a range of properly interested persons. Eleanor's financial criminal practice incorporates the full range of fraud and money laundering offences, also confiscation and cash forfeiture proceedings, and she frequently acts in the most high value cases where investigations span multiple jurisdictions. In the field of professional disciplinary law she has appeared before a wide range of regulatory bodies and specialises particularly in acting for medical and healthcare professionals. Recent cases include R v X: instructed for the defence in relation to allegations of corporate manslaughter, R v RB and others: Instructed for defendant D in relation to allegations of perverting the course of justice arising from the investigation into phone hacking, R v S: Instructed by defendant company prosecuted by the EA and HSE for breaches of an environmental permit and transport regulations at their nuclear installation, R v X: Instructed for the defence in relation to a multimillion pound money laundering allegation, Lakanal House Inquest: Instructed for the landlord, Southwark Borough Council, in the "Super Inquest" into the deaths of 6 people whose deaths resulted from a fire in a high-rise block in Peckham. More details of Eleanor's work can be found at www.2bedfordrow.co.uk.
Professional Memberships: Criminal Bar Association, South Eastern Circuit,
Career: Called to the Bar 2005 (Inner Temple).
Publications: Consultant Editor, Lloyds Law Reports Financial Crime.
Personal: Educated Bramcote Hills Comprehensive, Nottingham; New College, Oxford (MA Oxon); City University, London (Dip. Law). Lives London.

SANGSTER, Nigel QC
25 Bedford Row, London
020 7067 1500
nsangster@25bedfordrow.com
Featured in Financial Crime (London)
Practice Areas: Nigel Sangster QC took Silk in 1998 and practices exclusively as a defence specialist. He regularly defends solicitors, accountants, financial advisers and others accused of white-collar crime. In recent years he has been involved in series of lengthy MTIC Vat fraud trials and any subsequent money laundering and confiscation proceedings.
Professional Memberships: He has sat as a Recorder in the Crown Court for the past 17 years, was a Head of Chambers for 11 years, is an elected member of the Bar Council, a member of the Criminal Bar Association and a Bencher of the Middle Temple.
Career: After twenty five years in practice from St Pauls Chambers on the North Eastern circuit, he moved full time to London 10 years ago and practices from 25 Bedford Row. He now defends in many of the major fraud and money laundering trials throughout the country.

SAOUL, Daniel
4 New Square, London
020 7822 2000
d.saoul@4newsquare.com
Featured in Costs Litigation (London), Sports Law (London)
Practice Areas: Domestic and cross-border commercial litigation and arbitration of all types, including contract and trade disputes, civil fraud, financial services, insolvency, professional liability and insurance/reinsurance. Sports law. Costs litigation.
Professional Memberships: COMBAR, British Association for Sport and the Law.
Career: Joined 4 New Square in 2008 after training and practising as a solicitor-advocate at City firm Herbert Smith LLP (now Herbert Smith Freehills). Has also practised as a litigator in the British Virgin Islands for leading offshore firm Conyers Dill & Pearman. His commercial case-load is broad and reflects his training in the City (including stints in two investment banks) as well as his international background – he is a fluent French speaker and has studied and worked in a number of different countries. Dan's sports law practice benefits from his experience as a former international standard rowing cox and past member of both the Council of British Rowing and the Committee of Leander Club. He has acted for governing bodies, athletes, clubs and other entities on contentious and non-contentious matters, including in landmark or high-profile disciplinary, governance, selection and doping cases. He is a member of Sport Resolutions' Panel of Arbitrators and the Glasgow 2014 Commonwealth Games Sports Advocacy Service. Where costs litigation is concerned, he has expertise in all aspects of the field both at first instance and at appellate level, including several appearances in the Court of Appeal.
Publications: Many articles on commercial litigation, sports law and costs law, including recent publications in the Journal of International Banking and Financial Law, the New York State Bar Association's International Journal, the Journal of the British Association for Sport and Law and various costs law publications.
Personal: Education – Lycee Français Charles de Gaulle, London; University of Edinburgh; University of California, Berkeley; University of Oxford.

SARTIN, Leon
5 Stone Buildings, London
020 7242 6201
clerks@5sblaw.com
Featured in Chancery (London), Court of Protection (All Circuits), Tax (London)
Practice Areas: Specialises in both the advisory and litigation aspects of private client taxation, trusts, estates, wills, inheritance and family provision, Court of Protection, pensions, property disputes and related professional negligence. Notable cases include: Hughes & ors v Bourne & ors [2012] EWHC 2232 (Ch); Lilleyman v Lilleyman [2012] 3 WLR 754; In the matter of the Wedgwood Museum Trust Ltd (in administration), Young & ors v Attorney-General & ors [2011] [2012] Pens LR 175; Fine v Fine [2012] EWHC 1811(Ch); Maskell v Denham & UBS Pensions Trustees [2012] LTL AC9200991; Franks v Sinclair [2007] WTLR 439.
Professional Memberships: STEP, ACTAPS, Chancery Bar Association. Lectures regularly on tax, trusts, wills and probate.
Career: Called 1997.
Publications: Co-author with James Kessler QC of ' Drafting Wills and Trusts', 11th edition.

SAUNDERS, Kevin
St Ives Chambers, Birmingham
01212 360 863
kevin.saunders@stiveschambers.co.uk
Featured in Crime (Midlands)
Practice Areas: Crime, Regulatory
Professional Memberships: Criminal Bar Association, British German Jurists' Association
Career: Mr Saunders is a specialist criminal practitioner with particular expertise and experience of defending. His extensive practice includes offences of homicide and complex conspiracies concerning multi-million pounds of criminal property. Mr Saunders utilises skills and experience gained from his strong Crown Court Criminal practice to prosecute and defend regulatory matters with confidence. His practice in this

area incorporates advisory work for and representation of private clients, companies, government agencies and local authorities. He possesses considerable experience of prosecuting and defending matters concerning consumer protection, waste, health and safety, food hygiene, planning and licensing. Representation of both the defence and the Crown in contested confiscation proceedings concerning considerable sums of money. Mr Saunders has also developed a reputation for establishing a good rapport with clients.
Personal: Kevin is fluent in German

SAUNDERS, Neil
3 Raymond Buildings Barristers, London
020 7400 6400
Neil.saunders@3rblaw.com
Featured in Inquests & Public Inquiries (London), Professional Discipline (London), Crime (London), Financial Crime (London)
Practice Areas: The legal directories regard Neil as one of the best leading juniors in Crime and Fraud. He has recently defended Charlie Brooks in the "hacking case" acting as sole counsel unlike every other team. Neil has for some years been instructed in high profile cases, both alone and as part of a team. He specialises as a criminal and serious fraud advocate, representing professional people and companies. He is regularly instructed by large City and specialist white-collar fraud firms providing strategic advice to corporate clients during all stages of investigation pre-charge. Neil has experience prosecuting and defending and is currently instructed by the FCA to prosecute an insider trading case. He covers leading and junior work including violence, sex and drugs cases as well as confiscation hearings. Neil attends Police disciplinary proceedings both before Metropolitan and provincial forces. He was significantly involved throughout the 7/7 inquest and in other inquests he has represented interested parties such as police or families. Also appears on behalf of respondents to special procedure hearings and appearing in sports disciplinary hearings.
Career: BA (Hons) Law 1982; called to the Bar 1983. Past committee member South Eastern Circuit(2014 co opted), CBA and Bar Council; also various committees on specific issues. Interests: Rugby Union qualified referee: Golfer with stable handicap. Appeal steward British Boxing Board of Control.

SAUNDERS, Zoë
St John's Chambers, Bristol
01179 234 700
Zoe.Saunders@stjohnschambers.co.uk
Featured in Family/Matrimonial (Western)
Practice Areas: Zoë has extensive experience of cohabitation disputes involving ToLATA and Applications under Schedule 1 of the Children Act, and is often asked to advise both in writing and in conference as well as acting in disputed cases in the High Court, County Court and before the land registry adjudicator. She has expertise in financial remedy cases involving multiple properties, trusts of land, complex pensions and insolvency as well as both big and small money cases including in relation to professional negligence issues and cases involving Proceeds of Crime Act confiscation orders and international elements. Zoë is usually instructed in relation to professional negligence claims involving solicitors arising from cohabitant disputes including ToLATA, trusts and estates, divorce, financial remedies and general matrimonial work. Zoë's practice includes both advisory and contentious work relating to trusts, wills and the administration of estates, including claims based on proprietary estoppel and under the Inheritance (Provision for Family and Dependants) Act 1975.
Professional Memberships: Family Law Bar Association, Professional Negligence Bar Association, Western Circuit, South Eastern Circuit
Career: Zoë was called to the bar in 2003, completed her pupillage with Falcon Chambers, before moving to Bristol to practice family law in October 2004. This background gives her particular insight into cases involving Chancery law issues.
Publications: Zoë is a contributor to Horse Law' 3rd ed. (2012) J.A. Allen & Financial Provision in Family Matters (2013) Thomson.
Personal: Zoë is a keen freediver, skier and will occasionally be seen scubadiving.

SAUVAIN, Stephen QC
Kings Chambers, Manchester
08450 343 444
clerks@kingschambers.com
Featured in Environment (Northern), Local Government (Northern), Planning (Northern)
Practice Areas: Planning (retail, housing, waste, major infrastructure), highways and public rights of way, compulsory purchase, judicial review, local government, parking law and environmental law.
Professional Memberships: PEBA, Northern and North Eastern Circuits.
Career: MA (Cantab); LLB (1971). Lecturer in Law at Manchester University (1971-78). Call: 1977; Silk 1995; Assistant Boundary Commissioner (2000).
Publications: Highway Law (Sweet & Maxwell) (5th Ed. 2013); Encyclopedia of Highway Law and Practice (General Editor); Law Relating to Local Government (DETR Research Report - with Colin Crawford, Andrew Coulson and Michael Clarke); Joint Working Arrangements revisited after the Local Government Act 2000 (Journal of Local Government Law, 2002); Bridges: responsibility to repair them (1997 ROWLR -with Ross Crail).

SAVAGE, Amanda
4 New Square, London
020 7822 2000
a.savage@4newsquare.com
Featured in Professional Negligence (London)
Practice Areas: All aspects of commercial and civil litigation with an emphasis on: (i) professional liability (particularly those involving lawyers, financial professionals and insurance brokers), (ii) insurance disputes and (iii) commercial litigation. Cases include: Milton Furniture Ltd v Brit Insurance Ltd [2014] EWHC 965 (QB) (insurance) , Richard Craven v BSB (30.1.2104) (sitting as Visitor to the Inns of Court), Greene Wood McLean v Templeton [2010] EWHC 2679 (Comm) (claim against barristers, GLO); Patel v Air India [2010] EWCA Civ 443 (CA) (wasted costs); Williams v Thompson Leatherdale [2008] EWHC 2574 (QB) (claim against barrister, family law); Daniels v Thompson (2004) PNLR 33 (CA) (claim against solicitor, limitation and duty of care); London Fire and Emergency Planning Authority v Meritor Light Vehicle Systems (UK) and others (TCC) [2003] ALL ER (D) 76, LTL 12/9/2003 (product liability, indemnity costs) and Brown v Bennett (No. 2) [2001] 1 WLR 713 and (No. 3) [2001] 1 WLR 713 (barristers, wasted costs).
Professional Memberships: PNBA, COMBAR, TECBAR.
Career: LLB (King's College London), BCL (Worcester College, Oxford). Research assistant, Law Commission 1998-99. Part-time Judicial assistant to the Court of Appeal 2000. Tenant 4 New Square 2000 to date.
Publications: Editor, Jackson and Powell on Professional Liability. Former contributor to Sweet and Maxwell CPR reports.
Personal: Family, music and travel.

SCHERBEL-BALL, Jonathan
One Brick Court, London
020 7353 8845
jsb@onebrickcourt.com
Featured in Data Protection (London), Defamation/Privacy (London)
Practice Areas: Defamation, privacy and breach of confidence, media-related public law and judicial review, freedom of information, malicious falsehood, harassment, data protection, contempt of court, protection of journalists' sources, reporting restrictions, media regulation, media-related intellectual property law (copyright, trade mark, passing off and format disputes). Notable reported cases include: Loughran v Century Newspapers (2014); Morrice v BBC (2013); Hunt v Obregan (2012); R v Premier News Ltd (2012); Newbery v ICO (2012); Montford v ICO (2012); Tilbrook v Parr (2012); King v Grundon (2012), Morrissey v Associated Newspapers Ltd (2011); Haddock v MGN and others (2008-09) (solicitor); Taranissi v BBC (2007-09) (solicitor); R (Craig) v BBC (2008) (solicitor).
Career: MA (Hons) Modern History and Politics, Lincoln College, Oxford. MPhil, Modern European History, Fitzwilliam College, Cambridge. Qualified as solicitor in 2007, having trained at Dechert LLP. Solicitor, BBC Litigation and IP Department (2007-09). Called to the Bar in 2010. Tenant at One Brick Court since July 2011.
Publications: Contributing Editor of 'Survey of English Libel Law', Media Law Resource Center, 2011, 2012. Contributor, Arlidge, Eady & Smith on Contempt, 4th Ed Supplement
Personal: Enjoys sport especially football, squash, cricket, and skiing. Interested in contemporary European and American politics; enjoys cooking.

SCHWARZ, Jonathan S
Temple Tax Chambers, London
020 7936 3988
jonathan.schwarz@taxbarristers.com
Featured in Tax (London)
Practice Areas: International aspects of taxation: double tax relief, tax treaties, e-commerce, transfer pricing, cross-border mergers, acqusitions and reorganisations; cross- border employment; entertainers and sportsmen; licensing, joint ventures and private equity; group structures, finance; shipping and tonnage tax; residence and domicile, EU law. Tax and tax related disputes and appeals.
Professional Memberships: Visiting Professor - Faculty of Law, Kings College, London University; International Tax Committees - CIOT and ICAEW Tax Faculty, International Fiscal Association, International Bar Association, Tax Committee.
Publications: Author: 'Schwarz on Tax Treaties' 3rd Edition (Wolters Kluwer); 'Booth and Schwarz: Residence, Domicile and UK Taxation' 17th Edition (Bloomsbury Professional). Contributor: 'Transfer Pricing and Business Restructuring' (IBFD).
Personal: BA, LLB (Witwatersrand); LLM (Berkeley, California); FTII; Advocate: South Africa; Barrister and solicitor: Alberta, Canada.

SCOLDING, Fiona
Outer Temple Chambers, London
Featured in Court of Protection (All Circuits), Education (London)
Practice Areas: Fiona has a wide ranging public law practice with an emphasis upon social welfare, human rights, discrimination and public procurement, and has experience of all aspects of public law and local government cases. She has a particular interest in and knowledge of cases concerning children, young people and vulnerable adults, particularly those with disabilities. She has expertise in cases before the Court of Protection. She has expertise in all Courts and Tribunals from First Tier/County Court to the Court of Appeal. Fiona was appointed a Deputy District Judge in 2010. Fiona has been appointed as Panel Counsel to the Equality and Human Rights Commission with effect from 1st February 2011. Fiona was appointed to the B Panel of the Attorney General's Panel of Counsel from 1st March 2013. Fiona undertakes training both for national training organisations on issues relating to both education and community care, as well as public law and regularly provides bespoke training to charities, individuals and local authorities in these areas.
Publications: Fiona was editor of the Education Law Monitor (Informa) from November 2003 until February 2005. She is the co-author of the Law Society "Health and Social Care Handbook" (published July 2006).

SCOTT, Ian
Old Square Chambers, London
020 7269 0329
scott@oldsquare.co.uk
Featured in Employment (London)
Practice Areas: Discrimination, in particular disability, race and whistleblowing. Also specialising in labour law including recognition. Specialist knowledge of employment issues in the national health service and local government. Recent Cases: Chief Constable of West Midlands Police v. Gardner [2012] EqLR 21; Wincanton Plc v. Mr S.L.Atkinson UKEAT/0040/11; Publicis Consultants Ltd v Ms S. O'Farrell UKEAT/0430/10; Dr S.Salem v. Humber Mental Health Teaching Trust UKEAT/0619/10; Mr P. Raithatha v. Leicester City Council UKEAT/0303/10; Tapere v. South London and Maudsley NHS Trust [2009] IRLR 972.
Professional Memberships: ELA, ELBA, ILS, IER.
Career: Prior to being called to the Bar in October 1991, had been employed by a major trade union as a research and press officer and negotiator. Also held position of elected councillor in a London Borough.
Personal: BA Hons Economics, Newcastle-upon-Tyne University; MSC Inductrial Relations, London School of Economics. Enjoys sport.

SCOTT, Janys M QC
Westwater Advocates, Edinburgh
01312 262 881
janys.scott@westwateradvocates.com
Featured in Family/Matrimonial (Scotland)
Practice Areas: Civil practice with particular expertise in family law and education law. Numerous reported cases, including two successful appeals to the Supreme Court in Principal Reporter v K [2010] UKSC 56 (unmarried father's right to be heard, challenge to legislation on human rights grounds) and Gow v Grant [2012] UKSC 29 (financial provision for cohabitants). Other recent cases include M v M and W Trustees Limited, [2011] CSOH 33 (setting aside transfer of funds to trust, financial provision on divorce); S v S, [2012] CSIH 17, 2012 Fam LR 32 (appeal, relocation of child); W v Aberdeenshire Council, [2012] CSIH 37, 2012 Fam LR 91 (appeal, permanence order, authority to adopt); Simpson v Downie,[2012] CSIH 74, 2012 Fam LR 121 (appeal, statutory interpretation, time-limit for cohabitant's financial provision claim); S v Authority Reporter, 2012 SLT (Sh Ct) 89 (appeal, referral to children's hearing, alleged assault by parent); W v W [2013] CSOH (financial provision on divorce, transfer of shares, capital gains tax); Midlothian Council v CMP, [2013] CSIH 71, 2014 SC 168 (appeal, permanence order, authority to adopt).
Professional Memberships: Chairman Advocates' Family Law Association; Patron Scottish Child Law Centre; UK delegate to Family and Succession Working Group of CCBE.
Career: Solicitor in England 1978-86. Solicitor in Scotland 1987-91. Called to the Bar in 1992. Appointed part-time sheriff in 2005. Took silk in 2007.
Publications: Include: Education Law in Scotland, Thomson/W Green (2003); The Laws of Scotland, Stair Memorial Encyclopaedia (Education Section), Lexis Nexis (2010); Scottish Human Rights Service (Family and Education sections), Thomson/W Green; Court of Session Practice (Family Section), Tottel; Editor of Family Law Reports, Thomson/W Green.
Personal: MA (Hons) (History and Law), University of Cambridge; Lecturer Sulaimaniyah University, Iraq 1976-78; Visiting Bye-Fellow Newnham College, Cambridge 2002; member of Scottish Executive Adoption Policy Review Group 2005.

SCOTT, Rachel
3 Raymond Buildings Barristers, London
020 7400 6400
rachel.scott@3rblaw.com
Featured in Extradition (London)
Practice Areas: Crime (particularly fraud), extradition and international law, and public law including inquests. Rachel has notable expertise in financial and corporate crime and is a member of the SFO's B Panel. She regularly acts in complex fraud, corruption and cartel cases. When defending, she also appears in linked civil fraud proceedings in the Commercial Court. In extradition, Rachel represents foreign governments and judicial authorities as well as requested persons, both at first instance and on appeal. Notable cases include Bucnys (Supreme Court), Fuller (Privy Council), Khelifa (first Algerian extradition request to the UK; complex fraud concerning the high-profile collapse of an Algerian bank) and Ganic (Serbian extradition request for war crimes allegations against the former Bosnian vice-president). Rachel also offers specialist advice to prosecution agencies concerning 'import' extradition requests and matters of mutual legal assistance. In inquests she appears on behalf of a range of interested persons, including families of the deceased and police officers. Rachel has expertise in judicial review applications and is currently acting for the IPCC in judicial review proceedings arising out of the so-called 'Plebgate' investigation.
Professional Memberships:
Career: MusB (Hons) Manchester (Music) 2001, Call 2004, SFO C-Panel 2009, SFO B-Panel 2013.

SCOTT, Timothy QC
29 Bedford Row Chambers, London
020 7404 1044
tscott@29br.co.uk
Featured in Family/Matrimonial (London)
Practice Areas: Legal 500 Children and Family Silk of the Year 2013 – 14. Chambers & Partners Family Silk of the Year 2011 – 12. Leading specialist in international family law including EU Regulations, jurisdiction and forum disputes, Part III MFPA, recognition of foreign marriages and divorces, offshore trusts, family relocation and child abduction. Instructed regularly by leading family law firms. Recent cases include Ray v Sekhri [2014] EWCA Civ 119 (Divorce jurisdiction, domicile); CC v NC [2014] EWHC 703 (Fam) (MPS, jurisdiction); M-T v T [2013] EWHC 2061 (Fam); EA v AP [2013] EWHC 2344 (Fam) (EU Maintenance Regulation, recognition of foreign order); Z v Z (No 2) (Financial Remedy: Marriage Contract) [2012] 1 FLR 1100 (French premarital separation of goods agreement); MK v CK [2011] EWCA Civ 793 (family relocation); M v M (Financial Provision) [2011] 1 FLR 1773 (interim order under Part III MFPA); JKN v JCN (Divorce: Forum) 2011] 1 FLR 826; Agbaje v Akkinoye-Agbaje [2010] 1 FLR 1813 (Supreme Court – Part III MFPA)
Professional Memberships: Lady Justice Black's International Family Law Committee; Bar Council EU Law Committee; International Academy of Matrimonial Lawyers; International Bar Association; Chartered Institute of Arbitrators.
Career: Called to the Bar 1975. Appointed QC 1995. Appointed Recorder 1999. Family arbitrator, mediator and collaborative lawyer.
Publications: Contributor of articles to Family Law magazine and other specialist publications. Regular speaker at seminars on a wide range of family law topics.
Personal: Queen's Scholar Westminster School, Exhibitioner New College Oxford. Lives in London.

SCOTT HOLLAND, Gideon
Keating Chambers, London
020 7544 2600
gscottholland@keatingchambers.com
Featured in Construction (London)
Practice Areas: Specialist in construction, engineering, process engineering, waste water treatment, energy and all aspects of related professional negligence disputes. Experienced in advising on many forms of standard and bespoke contracts including the JCT, ICE and NEC as well as PFI contracts. Experienced advocate in the TCC and Court of Appeal and in ICC arbitrations. Has acted for clients in mediations and at all stages of the adjudication process, including enforcement in the TCC. Accepts appointments as adjudicator and mediator.
Professional Memberships: TECBAR, COMBAR, SCL, South Eastern Circuit and Standing Conference of Mediation Advocates.
Career: Called to Bar 1999, trained mediator 2006, public access training 2008, TECBAR adjudication panel 2013.
Publications: Contributor to Halsbury's Laws of England, Volume 4(3) Building Contracts (2002), Volumes 42-44 Energy and Climate Change (2011), and Volume 23 Income Taxation of Sub-contractors (2014); Contract Administration RICS Case in Point Series (2007); contributor to Keating on Construction Contracts, 8th to 9th Editions and first supplement to the 9th edition (2013).

SEAMAN, Jennifer
3 Stone Buildings, London
020 7242 4937
jseaman@3sb.law.co.uk
Featured in Pensions (London)
Practice Areas: Commercial, Chancery and Pensions litigation. Amongst other cases, Jennifer has recently been instructed in: two high-profile Supreme Court cases - Futter v. HMRC [2013] UKSC 26 (concerning the application of the so-called rule in Re Hastings-Bass) and Benedetti v. Sawiris [2013] UKSC 50 (concerning the restitutionary principles applicable to a quantum meruit claim); Ballinger v. Mercer Ltd [2014] EWHC 372 (Ch) and [2014] EWCA Civ 996 (a professional negligence claim against the defendant companies who provided actuarial services to a pension scheme); GE v. KE [2013] EWHC 1938 (Fam) (a dispute as to whether a widow was legally married to the deceased at the date of his death).
Professional Memberships: ChBA; COMBAR; APL.
Career: Called 2007; Joined Chambers 2009.
Publications: Contributor to Tolley's Pension Law chapter: "Dispute Resolution and Pension Scheme Litigation"; Co-Author of "An Exercise in Good Citizenship?" on the Pitt v. HMRC and Futter v. HMRC decisions in TQR Oct 2013; Author of various Lexis-Nexis Practice Notes on pensions litigation.
Personal: Education: New College, Oxford University (2005 BA (Jurisprudence); 2006 BCL).

SEGAL, Oliver QC
Old Square Chambers, London
020 7269 0300
segal@oldsquare.co.uk
Featured in Employment (London)
Practice Areas: Oliver is regarded as a leading Silk in employment law and acts regularly for major commercial clients and for most of the major trade unions. Within employment law he has particular specialist experience in: industrial action and collective disputes (appearing for the successful trade unions in the recent Court of Appeal cases of RMT v Serco Ltd; Anderson & ors v London Fire and Emergency Planning Authority); breach of contract claims (including claims involving restrictive covenants, PHI and negligent references) (appearing for the successful claimant in the Court of Appeal case of Gibb v Madistone and Tunbridge Wells NHS Trust); Working Time and TUPE claims. Oliver is also probably the leading barrister within the field of Commercial Agency claims; he acts for both agents and principals and has appeared in several of the most important reported cases, including the House of Lords case of Lonsdale v Howard and Hallam Ltd.
Professional Memberships: ELBA.
Career: Corpus Christi College, Oxford (1981-85). School Oriental and African Studies, University. London (1985-86). Called 1992, Middle Temple; QC 2011.
Personal: Expert bridge player and writer.

SEGAL, Sharon
1 Garden Court Family Law Chambers, London
020 7427 5578
Segal@1gc.com
Featured in Family/Matrimonial (London)
Practice Areas: All aspects of family law relating to children whether in the private law field or in public law proceedings. Within the public law arena, she is instructed in complex cases, whether acting for the local authority, parents or guardian and has undertaken a range of cases involving vulnerable clients, serious allegations of abuse and non accidental injury with complex medical issues; and exceptional cases involving honour killing and wardship. Within the private law field, she has extensive experience of contact and residence disputes, and is regularly instructed in intractable contact cases, leave to remove applications as well as having significant experience being instructed on behalf of the child in rule 16 cases.
Professional Memberships: Family Law Bar Association, The Association of Lawyers for Children.
Career: LLB Law (Hons) Queen Mary and Westfield College, University of London. Called to the Bar, Inner Temple (2000).
Publications: Contributor to "Key Authorities" in Family Law. Various reported cases, including the Supreme Court.
Personal: Enjoys travelling, listening to music and going to the theatre.

SELBY, Jonathan
Keating Chambers, London
020 7544 2600
jselby@keatingchambers.com
Featured in Construction (London)
Practice Areas: Specialist in construction and engineering, energy, oil rig and pipeline disputes including related professional negligence claims (architects, engineers, surveyors and valuers). Extensive knowledge of all forms of contract including the JCT, ICE and NEC standard forms. Regularly acts in high value litigation, in particular in the Technology and Construction Court, and has represented clients in the Privy Council and Court of Appeal. Often instructed to act for clients through the adjudication process and to represent clients at mediation. An accredited adjudicator, Jonathan accepts both party and nominating body appointments.
Professional Memberships: Technology and Construction Bar Association (TECBAR); Society of Construction Law; Commercial Bar Association (COMBAR); London Common Law and Commercial Bar Association.
Career: Called to the Bar 1999; TECBAR accredited adjudicator 2007.
Publications: Researcher, Keating on Construction Contracts - 7th to 9th Editions.

SELBY, Lawrence
9 Bedford Row, London
lawrence.selby@9bedfordrow.co.uk
Featured in Crime (London)

Practice Areas: Crime; fraud and disciplinary/ regulatory.
Professional Memberships: Member of the South Eastern Circuit; the Criminal Bar Association, the British Association for Sport and Law and the Chartered Institute of Arbitrators. Vice Chair of the Japan Karate-Do Ryobu-Kai International Mediation and Arbitration Committee.
Career: Specialises in defending high profile and complex cases of homicide, fraud and significant drugs' offences: R v Patino & Others –'The King of Viagra' case: "the biggest worldwide conspiracy involving medicines ever brought to trial"; R v Marshall and Bush –'The Jigsaw Man' murder; R v Bellchambers & Others - 'Operation Augusta': "the largest counterfeiting operation ever uncovered on Ebay"; R v Kent & Others - SFO prosecution of Corruption, Fraud and Money Laundering within Shropshire Learning Skills Council; R v Craven and Others - 'Operation Posh': Leading Junior in a multi-million pound "en primeur" wine fraud; R v Divan & Others - 'Operation Arcadia': Leading Junior in a case involving the "UK's biggest counterfeit DVD gang". Currently instructed in: R v M & Others - 'Operation Curlew/Oak': Leading Junior in a 32 handed Conspiracy to Supply Heroin; R v P & Others - 'Operation Razorback': a 22 handed "Sham Marriage" conspiracy; R v H & Others - 'Operation Veerde': Leading Junior in a 9 handed "Sham Marriage" and "Sex Trafficking" conspiracy.
Personal: Fluent in French, Italian and Spanish. Educated at Millfield School, Reading University (BA Hons), Sussex University (CPE), Birkbeck, University of London (Postgraduate Certificate in Sports Governance).

SELF, Gary
Pump Court Chambers, London
01962 868 161
g.self@pumpcourtchambers.com
Featured in Employment (Western)
Practice Areas: Employment: Gary Self has been serving the needs of employment solicitors both locally and nationally for many years. He provides clear and pragmatic advice to both claimants and respondents. He is an accomplished litigator who uses his trial acumen to excellent effect. He has substantial experience across the full range of the Employment Tribunal disputes as well as High Court and County Court litigation. He has acted for a range of private and public sector employers and has enormous experience of police matters having acted for a number of Police Authorities for many years. In addition he has often been successful for a range of claimants providing easily understandable, down to earth advice. He has appeared in the EAT and court of appeal to great effect and is highly regarded for this appellant work. He undertakes Direct Professional Access work for individuals, Businesses and Human Resources Consultancies.
Professional Memberships: Employment Lawyers Association
Career: Called Lincoln's Inn 1991, Employment Tribunal Judge
Personal: BA (Hons)(Manc) Dip Law

SELMAN, Elizabeth
1 King's Bench Walk, London
020 7936 1500
eselman@1kbw.co.uk
Featured in Family/Matrimonial (London)
Practice Areas: Private Law Children and Matrimonial Finance.
Professional Memberships: FLBA and South Eastern Circuit.
Career: Elizabeth Selman's practice covers both matrimonial finance and private law children work. This breadth can provide clients with the very significant advantage of retaining her for both potential areas of dispute following marital or relationhsip breakdown. She undertakes complex child arrangement disputes, international and internal relocation cases as well as discrete specific issue and prohibited steps order applications. Elizabeth's finance practice covers both matrimonial finance and Schedule 1 work, concentrating on mid to high net worth clients.
Personal: Elizabeth has three sons and spends much of her free time supporting them on rugby and hockey touch lines, swapping that for the cricket pitch in the summer, when the weather allows.

SELVARATNAM, Vasanti QC
Stone Chambers, London
020 7440 6900
vasanti.selvaratnam
@stonechambers.com
Featured in Shipping (London)
Practice Areas: All aspects of international commercial litigation and arbitration, including shipping, commodities, banking and finance, conflict of law and jurisdiction disputes, all forms of interim urgent relief including freezing orders and anti-suit injunctions, and civil fraud. She is particularly noted for her user friendly 'hands on' approach to cases and for her ability quickly to get to grips with disputes raising complex factual and technical issues which require a sound grasp of expert evidence and mastery of detail. Reported leading cases include: The Starsin [2003] UKHL 12; Arkin v Borchard Lines and ors [2004] EWCA Civ 1873 and [2005] EWCA Civ 655; Noga v Abacha Defendants [2002] EWCA Civ 1142; [2003] EWCA Civ 1100, 1101; [2004] EWHC 2601 (Comm); [2005] EWHC 225 (Comm); Front Ace c/w Vicky 1 [2008] EWCA Civ 101; The Wadi Sudr [2009] EWCA Civ 1397 (jurisdiction post Front Comor); Rimpacific v Daehan Shipbuilding [2009] EWHC 2941 (Comm) and [2011] EWHC 2618 (Comm); Madoff Securities International Ltd (in liquidation) v Yacht Bull Corporation [2010] EWHC 133 (Ch); BNP Paribas SA v (1) Open Joint Stock Co Russian Machines (2) Joint Stock Asset Management Co Ingosstrakh-Investments [2012] EWCA Civ 644 (non contractual anti suit injunction and jurisdiction); Nakanishi Marine v Gora Shipping and Attica Finance [2012] EWHC 3383 (Comm) (liabilities under suite of financing documents); RBS v FAl Oil Co Ltd and ors [2012] EWHC 3628 (Comm) (section 25 CJJA 1982); Stolt Kestrel [2014] EWHC 1731 (Adm) (section 190 MSA 1995); Emirates Trading Agency v PMEPL [2014] EWHC 2014 (Comm) (friendly discussions clause a condition precedent to right to commence ICC arbitration).
Professional Memberships: COMBAR, Chancery Bar Association, LCLBA, BMLA, LMAA, London Shipping Law Centre (Head of education sub-committee), Bar European Group, ICC's Banking and Finance committee.
Career: Called to the Bar 1983: LLM 1984; practising barrister at the Commercial Bar 1985 to date; Recorder 2000 to date; Queen's Counsel 2001; Bencher of Middle Temple 2011. Also accepts appointments as arbitrator in a wide range of commercial disputes.

SELWAY, Kate
Radcliffe Chambers, London
020 7831 0081
kselway@radcliffechambers.com
Featured in Chancery (London), Real Estate Litigation (London)
Practice Areas: Real property, landlord and tenant (agricultural, business and residential), trusts, estates and probate, revenue, charities, personal insolvency, and other areas of general chancery practice. Reported cases include: Nicholls v Highways Agency; Secretary of State for the Environment Transport & the Regions v Baylis (Gloucester) Limited; King v Walden (HMIT); IRC v Hashmi; McAdam Homes Limited v Robinson; Sevenoaks District Council v First Secretary of State & Anr; Lonsdale v Braisby (HMIT); IRC v Arkwright; Coombes v HMRC; Elizabeth Court (Bournemouth) Ltd v HMRC; Solicitor for the Affairs of HM Treasury v Doveton; The Serious Organised Crime Agency v Szepietowski; Taff v Highways Agency; Siaw v Lock; Holden-Hindley v Holden-Hindley.
Professional Memberships: Chancery Bar Association, Charity Law Association.
Career: Called 1995. Member of Attorney General's B Panel (2003-08); C Panel (1999-2003).
Personal: Educated at Newlands School, Maidenhead, Bristol University (BA, History, Class I), New College, Oxford (DPhil in Medieval History), City University (CPE). Leisure interests: hockey, photography.

SHAH, Akhil QC
Fountain Court Chambers, London
020 7583 3335
axs@fountaincourt.co.uk
Featured in Aviation (London), Product Liability (London), Travel (London)
Practice Areas: General commercial disputes including aviation, re/ insurance, and arbitration. Expertise in aviation disputes including aircraft finance, aircraft leasing, product design, aviation insurance and reinsurance, regulatory work and carriage by air. Notable cases include: Alpstream v PK and GECAS (aircraft finance); Blue Sky v Chartis & Others (insurance dispute re: theft of Boeing 747 aircraft to Iran); PK v Mahan (arrest of aircraft and enforcement of judgment); Pindell v Air Asia (Aircraft lease dispute); DTVA v bmibaby (low cost airline dispute with airport); Kibris v SoS and Republic of Cyprus (review of right to fly from UK); HSH Nordbank v Air Astra (recovery of distressed aircraft); Hill & others v CAA (Review of airspace design); IHRC v CAA (Review of Carriage of Weapons); Amiri Flight Authority v BAE System Plc (Aircraft design); Airbus Industrie G.I.E v Patel (Jurisdiction; anti-suit injunction; product liability); Western Digital v British Airways (Warsaw Convention: title to sue); acting in Bermuda Form and other international arbitration disputes (parties confidential).
Professional Memberships: COMBAR.
Career: Called 1990; QC 2010; British Virgin Islands Bar 1999.
Publications: Contributor to Bullen & Leak & Jacobs 'Precedents of Pleading' (17th ed) and 'Carriage by Air'.

SHAND, Lesley QC
Compass Chambers, Edinburgh
07739 639 273
lesley.shand@compasschambers.com
Featured in Personal Injury (Scotland)
Practice Areas: Specialist Areas:- Personal injury and clinical negligence; professional negligence; property damage. Lesley's personal injury practice embraces all aspects of personal injury including psychiatric injury, occupational stress, bullying and harassment, catastrophic injury including spinal injuries and brain injuries, fatal claims, disease cases, and product liability. She acts for both pursuers and defenders. She has a particular interest in brain injury claims. Her work takes her most often to the Court of Session (Inner and Outer House) but she has appeared regularly in the Sheriff Court and before a variety of tribunals. Lesley is experienced in representing parties at Fatal Accident Inquiries. She has given talks at seminars and conferences on personal injury topics. Lesley served as a full-time Advocate Depute in Crown Office from 2010 to 2013 undertaking both trial work and appeals. She was appointed as a Fee Paid Judge of the First Tier Tribunal (Social Entitlement Chamber) in 2014.
Professional Memberships: Convener of the Reparation sub-committee of the Faculty of Advocates Law Reform Committee (2013 – present): Advocacy skills trainer, Faculty of Advocates Training and Education Unit (2014 -); Advocates Personal Injury Law Group; Advocates Professional Negligence Law Group; Member of the Court of Session Rules Council (2000 to 2011).
Career: LLB (Hons) Edinburgh University (1978-82); Diploma in Legal Practice, Edinburgh University (1982 -83); Solicitor in private practice until 1989; Called to the Bar in July 1990: Standing Junior to the Department of Transport 1995-2005; Year of silk – 2005; Advocate Depute (2010-13); Fee Paid Judge of the First Tier Tribunal (Social Entitlement Chamber) (2014 -).

SHANE, Michael
Atkin Chambers, London
020 7404 0102
mbshane@atkinchambers.com
Featured in Mediators (All Circuits)
Practice Areas: Over 25 years' experience as a mediator and arbitrator and has successfully mediated in excess of 1500 disputes and served as arbitrator in excess of 100 cases involving a variety of subjects. Brings experience as an arbitrator, former litigator and public company director to disputes involving construction, insurance, intellectual property and licensing, professional negligence, infrastructure, power generation and oil and gas. Has a busy practice in the UK, the US and in Asia, Africa and South America. He brings a commercial approach to mediation including cross cultural and multi-party disputes arising from a variety of complex commercial, intellectual property, insurance and financial transactions. Further information is available at his website www.mbshane.com.
Career: Juris Doctor, University of California, Berkeley School of Law; Master of Laws, University College London.

SHAPIRO, Daniel
Crown Office Chambers, London
020 7797 8100
shapiro@crownofficechambers.com
Featured in Energy & Natural Resources (London), Insurance (London), Professional Negligence (London), Property Damage (London)
Practice Areas: Daniel is regularly instructed in legally and technically complex claims in his practice areas of insurance and reinsurance, professional negligence, energy, construction, property damage, and product liability. He has been instructed in a number of cutting-edge claims following his success in Jones v Kaney, the decision of the Supreme Court which established that expert witnesses can be sued for negligence. He was instructed on much of the litigation arising out of the explosions at the Buncefield Oil Terminal. Daniel is regularly instructed on substantial insurance policy disputes and in insurance broker's negligence cases. Daniel's commerciality, commitment and court room skills gain him instructions for and against a wide range of commercial parties and professionals. They appreciate his clear advice, tactical awareness and commitment to delivering a first rate service. Daniel is instructed in Court, arbitration and adjudication proceedings, but always seeks the effective commercial solution to disputes as quickly as possible. He regularly acts for clients in successful mediations and other forms of ADR. Further details are available on www.crownofficechambers.com.
Professional Memberships: COMBAR, TECBAR, Professional Negligence Bar Association.
Publications: Daniel writes the chapter in Emden: "Formation of contract and vitiating factors"

SHARLAND, Andrew
11KBW, London
020 7632 8500
andrew.sharland@11kbw.com
Featured in Administrative & Public Law (London), Community Care (London), Data Protection (London), Education (London), Local Government (London)
Practice Areas: Specialises in all aspects of public law (commercial, regulatory, education, community care, mental health, local government, coroners, and planning and environmental law) human rights, employment, public procurement and information law. He practises in English and European courts acting for private individuals, public authorities, commercial organisations and NGOs. Junior Counsel for the Crown (A Panel) and member of the Equality and Human Rights Commission panel. Notable cases include: MacDonald v UK (Private life and community care in ECHR), Washington First v UK (freedom of expression in ECHR), Campbell v MGN Ltd (Article 10 ECHR and costs, HL), Kennedy v Charity Commission (freedom of information and Article 10 ECHR in the Supreme Court), R (Plantagenet Alliance) v Secretary of State for Justice and Leicester City Council (challenge to the decision to bury Richard III's remains in Leicester) and DWF v Insolvency Service (public procurement and time limits in the Court of Appeal).
Professional Memberships: ALBA, PEBA, ADRL, Procurement Lawyer's Association.
Career: Called to the Bar in 1996. Appointed to Attorney-General's 'A' Panel of Counsel to the Crown.
Publications: Co-author of Judicial Review: Principles and Procedure (OUP, 2013); Co-author of Media Law and Human Rights' (OUP) (2nd Edn, 2009). Co-author of the Human Rights section in Atkins Court Forms, Contributor to 'Information Rights' and 'Education and the Courts'.
Personal: Educated at Queen Mary and Westfield College, University of London (LLB), College of William and Mary, Virginia, USA (LLM) and Worcester College, Oxford (BCL).

SHARP, Christopher QC
St John's Chambers, Bristol
01179 234 700
clerks@stjohnschambers.co.uk
Featured in Family/Matrimonial (Western), Personal Injury (Western)
Practice Areas: Family law - high value ancillary relief with corporate and trust elements, often resolved outside court process (eg private FDRs). Recent reported decisions: RP v RP [2008] 2 FCR 613 (Application of Miller/McFarlane); Van Laethem v Brooker [2006] 2 FLR 495 (TLATA); Ram v Ram [2005] 2 FLR 75 (bankruptcy). Public law Children Act - particularly cases involving complex medical issues in fact finding hearings. Re Q (Children) [2014] EWCA Civ 918, Re JS (A Child) sub nom A County Council v (1) RH (2) KS (3) JS (by his children's guardian) [2012] EWHC 1370 (Fam) – child abuse, expert evidence, causation; Bath & North East Somerset Council v A Mother & Ors. [2009] EWHC B10 (Fam),publication of judgment in family proceedings; H (A Child) [2009] EWCA Civ 334, sexual abuse, appropriate approach to judicial analysis of evidence. Private Law (children): Re A (Suspended Residence Order) [2010] 1 FLR 1679 (Fam Div), intractable opposition to contact, residence order suspended pending compliance; Re D (Children) [2009] CA (Civ Div) child sexual abuse, contact orders, expert reports; Personal Injury - catastrophic injury with extensive expertise in brain injury cases. Clinical negligence, particularly cases involving medical causation issues. Procedural appeals. Historic abuse/care cases. Recent reported cases: Hide v Steeplechase Company (Cheltenham) Ltd [2013] EWCA Civ 545 (reg 4 PUWER in jump racing); Devon CC v TR [2013] EWCA Civ 418; AC & DC v TR v Devon County Council [2012] EWHC 796 (QB)[2012] All ER (D) 26 (Apr) - Highways Act Part 20 claim; 'A' v Hoare [2008] UKHL 6; [2006] EWCA Civ 395 - sexual assault, limitation and Human Rights; Poppleton v Peter Ashley Activity Centre [2008] EWCA Civ 646 (tetraplegia, sporting injury); Leeson v Marsden [2006] 1 WLR 1945 service and extension of time (clinical negligence); B v B [2005] EWCA 237: lifting stay in sexual abuse claim; Stimpson v Excel Logistics [2004] EWCA Civ 1249: causation in product liability; Nineham v Glynwed International Ltd [2004] QBD (Brain damage: bottom up structured settlement); Mirvahedy v Henley [2003] 2 AC 491; [2002] CA (Animals Act 1971). Professional negligence - in these fields.
Professional Memberships: FLBA, PIBA, PNBA.
Career: Call 1975, Silk 1999, Recorder 2004, Deputy High Court Judge 2011, Visiting Fellow UWE.
Publications: Legal Journals in UK and abroad.

SHARPE, Tim
Temple Garden Chambers, London
020 7583 1315
timsharpe@tgchambers.com
Featured in Fraud (All Circuits)
Practice Areas: Tim was described by Chambers & Partners 2012 as being "bright, hard-working and dependable". The 2010 edition said he is "as tenacious a young man as you'll find at the Bar". Previous editions of Chambers & Partners described him as "the rising star of the set". Tim's practice in relation to motor insurance fraud encompasses Low Velocity Impact claims, bogus passenger claims, staged and contrived accidents, and "fraud rings". He provides advice and advocacy at all stages of such claims, including prior to proceedings being issued, at the pleadings stage, at trial and, when appropriate, in relation to Contempt of Court proceedings. Recent cases have included representing an insurance company in successfully defending a "slam-on" case where the trial judge made findings of fraud and referred the transcript to the Attorney General, and representing a respondent to contempt of court proceedings.

SHAW, Andrew
One Paper Buildings, London
020 7353 3728
clerks@onepaper.co.uk
Featured in Crime (South Eastern)
Practice Areas: Criminal law, local authority/regulatory law.
Professional Memberships: South Eastern Circuit, CBA, East Anglian Bar Mess, Bar Pro Bono Unit.
Career: Andrew Shaw both prosecutes and defends across the South Eastern Circuit. He has been instructed in cases involving homicide and other serious violence, firearms, armed robbery, rape and other sexual offences, significant drug trafficking and all aspects of fraud and dishonesty. He is regularly instructed in cases involving fraud and the proceeds of crime, has particular expertise in cases involving the historic physical and sexual abuse of children and is frequently instructed in cases where there are young or otherwise vulnerable witnesses. He is noted for his preparation and handling of document heavy cases and his capacity quickly to come to terms with complicated legal and factual issues. In addition, Andrew also has considerable experience of appellate work and Courts-Martial. He is regularly instructed as both a leading junior and junior counsel, and is an approved pupil supervisor.

SHAW, Annabel
4 New Square, London
020 7822 2000
a.shaw@4newsquare.com
Featured in Construction (London)
Practice Areas: Acting for and against contractors, architects, engineers and quantity surveyors. Part of Counsel team acting on behalf of joint venture in relation to nuclear installations in the UK. Part of Counsel team acting for a European government in relation to a large IT dispute. Was one of team acting for Multiplex in a series of adjudications and also part of team preparing for a quantum trial in respect of the Wembley Stadium dispute. Was also part of team acting for a major Saudi Arabian group in relation to an ICC Arbitration, subject to Saudi Arabian law, with hearings in Paris.
Professional Memberships: TECBAR, SCL, PNBA, COMBAR.
Career: BA (Oxon) 1st Class. Called to Bar (Gray's Inn) 2002. David Karmel Entrance Award. Prince of Wales Scholar.
Publications: Contributor to Jackson & Powell on Professional Liability.
Personal: Educated New College, Oxford, 1996-99.

SHAW, Antony QC
Red Lion Chambers, London
020 7520 6600
tonyshaw@blueyonder.co.uk
Featured in POCA Work & Asset Forfeiture (All Circuits), Crime (London), Financial Crime (London)
Practice Areas: Serious fraud including SFO, VAT, corporate, mortgage, ECGC, tax, charity, insider trading; money laundering; corruption; confiscation; conspiracy and drugs. Major SFO cases include Guinness, Polly Peck, Eagle Trust, BCCI, Butte Mining, Alpine, Alliance, VWS, Operation Holbein (pharmaceutical cartel), VHP (high yield investment); Operation Aloof (insider trading); Innospec 2.
Professional Memberships: Criminal Bar Association; Fraud Advisory Panel.
Career: Major History Scholar, Trinity College, Oxford, 1967-70; Astbury Scholar, Middle Temple, 1976; Queen's Counsel, 1994; Assistant Recorder, 1998; Recorder, 2000-07; Bencher, Middle Temple 2003.
Publications: Various journals; Co-editor: Archbold, 'Criminal Pleadings and Practice' (1991 to date). Contributor and Deputy Editor: Fraud: Criminal Practice and Procedure (OUP, 2008 to date).

SHAW, Benjamin
Erskine Chambers, London
020 7242 5532
bshaw@erskinechambers.com
Featured in Company (London)
Practice Areas: Ben specialises in company, insolvency and general commercial law. His practice is divided equally between litigation and advisory work. In the past year, Ben has been heavily involved in litigation concerning MF Global. He has also advised on schemes of arrangement and other substantial corporate matters.
Professional Memberships: COMBAR, Chancery Bar Association.
Career: Called Lincoln's Inn 2002.

SHAW, Nicola
Trinity Chambers, Newcastle upon Tyne
01912 321 927
n.shaw@trinitychambers.co.uk
Featured in Family/Matrimonial (North Eastern)
Practice Areas: Matrimonial Finance & Trusts of Land- special interest in matrimonial finance/ancillary relief cases and proceedings relating to co-ownership of property under the Trusts of Land and Appointment of Trustees Act 1996 (ToLATA). Delivers continuing professional development lectures in the field of matrimonial finance and Trusts of Land law. She appears in the local County Court, and also in the High Court, and has been involved in cases in the Court of Appeal, both led and appearing as junior counsel. Alternative Dispute Resolution -one of only two barristers in the North East trained in collaborative law. She has a longstanding interest in mediation and alternative dispute resolution. Member of the

Institute of Family Law Arbitrators (IFLA) Panel and is qualified to conduct family law arbitrations and make orders under the IFLA rules, including in ancillary relief and Trusts of Land and Appointment of Trustees Act proceedings.
Professional Memberships: FLBA Member CIArb Institute of Family Law Arbitrators (IFLA) Panel
Career: Delivers CPD lectures in the field of financial remedies and Trusts of Land law. Deputy District Judge in 2010. Taught on the Bar Vocational Course and the LlB Family Law module at Northumbria University, 2000-02.

SHAW, Nicola QC
Gray's Inn Tax Chambers, London
020 7242 2642
ns@taxbar.com
Featured in Tax (London)
Practice Areas: A litigation focused practice concerning all aspects of tax law, including tax related judicial reviews, with particular emphasis on VAT and corporate/commercial taxes. Appears regularly in courts and tribunals at all levels on behalf of HMRC and taxpayers. Cases of note in the last 12 months include: M&S (cross-border group relief), Hutchison 3G (cross-border consortium claim), Davies and James and Gaines-Cooper (status and meaning of IR20), Deutsche Bank Group Services (efficacy of employment-related security plan), TNT Post (exemption from VAT on postal services), Secret Hotels 2 (agency status of online hotel database), Volkswagen Financial Services (partial exemption method on hire purchase transactions), Greenbank Holidays (meaning of internally generated goodwill).
Professional Memberships: Member of the Revenue Bar Association, the Chancery Bar Association and the Administrative Law Bar Association.
Career: Called to the Bar in 1995. Member of the Attorney General's Panel of Junior Counsel to the Crown from 2002 to 2012. Appointed QC 2012.
Personal: Educated at Pembroke College, Oxford (BA, BCL).

SHEEHAN, James
Maitland Chambers, London
Featured in Chancery (London)
Practice Areas: Commercial and chancery disputes, including civil fraud, contract and other business disputes, company and partnership, insolvency, fund and banking litigation, claims against directors and other fiduciaries, property litigation. Particular experience of international disputes involving issues of jurisdiction and choice of law. Notable recent cases include: Dar Al Arkan v Al-Refai (Comm Ct and CA: conspiracy, breach of confidence, jurisdiction for contempt proceedings); BTA v Ablyazov (Comm Ct and CA: US$5bn fraud claim against Kazakh banker); Erste v Red October (Comm Ct and CA: conspiracy, jurisdiction, choice of law); a dispute in the Ch Div and CA involving multi-million dollar fraud claims relating to an offshore fund; Med Mining v Nusantara Plc (Comm Ct; directors' duties); Berezovsky v Hine (Ch Div; joint venture claim against Patarkatsishvili estate); Re Tobian Properties Ltd; Re Annacott Holdings Ltd (Ch Div and CA: unfair prejudice); Nomad International Shipping Corp v DST Shipping Inc (Comm Ct: joint venture dispute).
Professional Memberships: COMBAR, Chancery Bar Association, Financial Services Lawyers' Association.
Career: Called 2008.
Personal: St. Catharine's College, Cambridge (French and German, starred first, top of year); BPP (CPE); Inns of Court School of Law (Outstanding, second in year). Queen Mother scholar; Baron Dr Ver Heyden de Lancey prize (Middle Temple).

SHEEHAN, Malcolm
Henderson Chambers, London
020 7583 9020
clerks@hendersonchambers.co.uk
Featured in Product Liability (London), Real Estate Litigation (London)
Practice Areas: Commercial and common law practice concentrating on product liability, group actions, property, arbitration and insurance, personal injury and health and safety. Product liability experience includes acting for defendants in leading multi-party and individual claims relating to pharmaceutical products, medical devices and motor vehicles. Malcolm's Property expertise includes commercial and residential landlord and tenant, covenants, dilapidations and public law property claims. His personal injury practice includes international tort claims,employer liability claims and sporting accidents. Malcolm's reported cases include Young v Home Office(leading House of Lords limitation decision), Motto v Trafigura and Rogers v Hoyle. He is experienced in health and safety and environmental criminal and civil litigation.
Professional Memberships: Commercial Bar Association; Professional Negligence Bar Association; Health and Safety Lawyers Association; Personal Injury Bar Association.
Career: Oriel College, Oxford (First Class Honours). Mansfield Scholarship; Denning Scholarship; Inns of Court Studentship; Judicial assistant to Lord Woolf while Master of the Rolls. Junior Counsel to the Crown ('A' Panel). Judge of First Tier Tribunal.
Publications: Contributor to 'The Civil Practitioner's Guide to the Human Rights Act 1998', 'Halsbury's Laws' (Vol 37), Butterworths Civil Court Precedents, and Kluwer International Product Law Manual.

SHER, Adam
Fountain Court Chambers, London
020 7583 3335
ads@fountaincourt.co.uk
Featured in Banking & Finance (London)
Practice Areas: Civil and commercial litigation including banking, financial services, insurance, civil fraud and professional negligence. Much of recent work has been related to derivatives (interest rate, currency and credit), including mis-selling claims, LIBOR litigation (including the lead case of Deutsche Bank v Unitech, one of The Lawyer's Top 20 Cases of 2014) and disputes with Italian local authorities (including Merrill Lynch v Verona and Merrill Lynch v Florence, one of The Lawyer's Top 20 Cases of 2013). Various international arbitrations, including $1.4 billion dispute between GMR and the Government of the Maldives over Malé international airport.
Professional Memberships: Member COMBAR, London Common Law and Commercial Bar Association.
Career: Called 2007.
Publications: 'Consensus, separability and Article 23 of the Brussels Regulation' [2009] LMCLQ 275.
Personal: Oriel College, Oxford, BA (First Class), BCL (Distinction), Harvard Law School, LLM.

SHERATT, Matthew
Carmelite Chambers, London
020 7936 6300
clerks@carmelitechambers.co.uk
Featured in Crime (London)
Practice Areas: A specialist defence advocate with a wealth of experience as junior and leading junior in cases involving serious and complex crime. Junior counsel in a number of high profile cases including acting on behalf of: the millionaire businessman Nicholas Van Hoogstraten in the criminal hearings which resulted in his acquittal; Christopher Edward Buckingham "The Lord of Fraud; one of the Defendants in the Johnson Matthey Gold bullion robbery and in R v. Maxwell (Appellant) [2010] UKSC 48. He has also appeared in a number of important reported decisions including: Darmalingum v Secretary of State for Mauritius (PC) [2000] WLR 2303; R (Mudie) v Dover Magistrates [2003] 2 WLR 1344 (CA); R v Van Hoogstraten [2004] Crim LR 498; Att-Gen's Ref (No.3 of 2004) [2006] Crim.L.R 63,CA; R v. Maxwell [2010] UKSC 48. Now a busy leading junior appearing predominantly in cases of serious organised crime, fraud and money laundering. Recent instructions include the acquittal of the principal in a £10 million money laundering conspiracy allegedly derived from advanced fee fraud; acquittal of Second Defendant in an alleged £24 million Eastern European money laundering conspiracy; instruction by the Registrar in an appeal against conviction in a boiler room fraud on grounds of incompetence of counsel and currently acting for Defendant alleged to be head of an OCG which imported 24 million cigarettes; a tonne of cannabis and 121 kgs of class A drugs. With a strong civil background regularly instructed to advise in respect of civil fraud and POCA claims.
Professional Memberships: Panel member of French Consulate official panel of recommended lawyers and member of CBA.
Career: Called: 1994.

SHERBORN, Natalie
25 Bedford Row, London
020 7067 1500
nsherborn@25bedfordrow.com
Featured in Crime (London)
Practice Areas: Specialises in criminal defence work across a broad spectrum. Experience in the conduct of the most serious and complex cases including regular instructions in high-profile trials ranging from murder, terrorism, fraud, drugs importation, distribution and supply, people trafficking, money laundering and organised crime. Practices in proceeds of crime and asset forfeiture as both leading junior and junior alone. Recent cases include representing a defendant alleged to be involved in the funding of terrorist activities in Syria (R v El-Wahabi, 2014). Instructed to represent a defendant engaged in the large-scale importation, supply and distribution of non-duty paid cigarettes and tobacco into the UK via the UAE and Bangladesh (R v K & others 2014). Conspiracy to money launder £32 million pound from the Ukraine into the UK (R v S & others 2012). Instructed to represent an international businessman facing allegations of laundering the proceeds of a "boiler room" fraud involving complex layering of companies and financial transactions in order to disguise the proceeds of crime (R v L 2012). Instructed in a sophisticated conspiracy to make counterfeit bank notes, to date £17 million of counterfeit notes produced as a result of this operation have been recovered from the UK economy (R v Altifincan & others 2011). Led junior defending Dano Sonnex in the high profile case of the torture and murder of two French students (R v Sonnex & Famer, 2009). Led junior in a highly-publicised manslaughter trial involving young children 'stoning' to death a father in the presence of his son. Conviction quashed on appeal following complex legal submissions on the issue of causation (R v D & others, 2008).

SHERIDAN, Amber
29 Bedford Row Chambers, London
020 7404 1044
asheridan@29br.co.uk
Featured in Family/Matrimonial (London)
Practice Areas: Matrimonial Finance; Financial Provision for Children; Pre and post-nuptial agreements; Civil Partnerships; Cohabitation; Inheritance Act. Reported cases include: Shield v Shield [2014] EWHC 23 (Fam); Shield v Shield [2013] EWHC 3525 (Fam); Golubovich v Golubovich [2011] EWCA Civ 528; Golubovich v Golubovich [2011] 2 FLR 1193; Golubovich v Golubovich [2010] 2 FLR 1614; Agbaje v Agbaje [2010] 1 FLR 1813.
Professional Memberships: FLBA; Resolution.
Career: Called to the Bar in 2008; Middle Temple.
Personal: Educated at Sevenoaks School, Edinburgh University and BPP. Middle Temple Certificate of Honour and Benefactors' Scholar. Resides in London.

SHERIDAN, Matthew
Littleton Chambers, London
020 7797 8600
msheridan@littletonchambers.co.uk
Featured in Employment (London)
Practice Areas: All areas of employment law. Appears regularly in the High Court, Employment Tribunals, EAT and Court of Appeal. Principal areas of Tribunal practice include complex discrimination law, whistleblowing, TUPE and employee/worker status. Principal area of High Court practice is employee competition focusing on confidential information, restrictive covenants and springboard relief. Private sector clients include investment banks, publishers, law firms and the Church of England. Public sector clients include various local authorities, the health sector and professional regulatory bodies. Recent appellate cases include and Revd Mark Sharpe v The Bishop of Worcester (EAT, 2013) and Law Society of England & Wales v Secretary of State for Justice [2010] IRLR 407 (High Court).
Professional Memberships: ELBA, COMBAR.
Career: Called 2000.
Personal: Educated at King's College School and Queens' College, Cambridge (Law).

SHERRARD, Charles QC
Furnival Chambers, London
07590 530 243
CSherrard@furnivallaw.co.uk
Featured in Financial Crime (London)

Practice Areas: Criminal practitioner with extensive experience in all areas of heavyweight criminal work. Specialist advocacy and advice, pre and post charge, in serious fraud and restraint (FSA, SFO, professional clients, MTIC, Revenue and Customs and corruption), 'quasi-criminal', confiscation and money laundering proceedings. Engaged in numerous high profile and gangland murder trials. Developing significant sports law practise. Regularly appears in all courts including Coroners. Please see Furnival Chambers website for extensive profile including references to representing UBS Rogue Trader and defendant in conspiracy to pervert course of justice relating to phone hacking.
Professional Memberships: South East Circuit; Criminal Bar Association.
Career: Queens Counsel since 2012 Called to the bar 1986 Member of chambers since 1988 Director of Furnival Chambers Ltd since 2007 Chairman of Pupillage since 2003 Middle Temple Advocacy Trainer.
Personal: Married with three gorgeous children. Educated at University College School, Hampstead LLB Hons from U.E.A Active and keen cricketer, golfer and tennis player in Hertfordshire leagues, as well as being a 'Gooner'.

SHERRY, Michael
Temple Tax Chambers, London
020 7353 7884
michael.sherry@templetax.com
Featured in Tax (London)
Practice Areas: Revenue law, covering all aspects of direct and indirect taxation for commercial and substantial private clients, including advice, tax planning, estate planning and litigation in all courts to the Supreme Court, with particular emphasis on owner managed businesses (including hedge fund managers) and anti-avoidance and abuse.
Professional Memberships: Institute of Chartered Accountants (Faculty of Taxation; Chairman 1999-2001, also Institute Treasurer 2007-09), Institute of Taxation, STEP, Gray's Inn Barrister's Committee, formerly Bar Council (2007-11); President, Institute of Indirect Taxation (1995-98)
Career: Called to the Bar in 1978. Temple Tax Chambers (since 1984) (Ernst & Young 1978-83). Cases of note include Forde McHugh v HMRC, Blackpool Football Property Holdings Ltd v HMRC, Gray's Timber v HMRC, Monro v HMRC, Mansworth v Jelley, Langham v Veltema and College of Estate Management v C&E. Tax Lawyer of the Year 2004, Tax Junior (Chambers & Partners) 2013.
Publications: 'Whiteman and Sherry on Capital Gains Tax', 'Whiteman & Sherry on Income Tax', 'Tax Planning for Family Company Shareholders'.
Personal: Scholar of Lincoln College, Oxford 1974-77.

SHIU, Ming-Yee
Littleton Chambers, London
020 7797 8600
myshiu@littletonchambers.co.uk
Featured in Employment (London)
Practice Areas: Specialises in employment law and commercial litigation, with particular expertise in relation to applications for injunctive relief in the High Court, including interim injunctions, freezing injunctions and search orders. Extensive experience of race, sex, disability and age discrimination, unfair dismissal,wrongful dismissal, redundancy, TUPE and employment status; contract disputes and intellectual property claims involving directors, employees and workers, including restrictive covenants, breach of confidence, breach of copyright and passing off; and company law and insolvency issues,in particular the fiduciary duties of directors and senior employees. Particular expertise in shareholder disputes and all aspects of commercial fraud. Clients include UK and multinational corporations, public sector bodies, charities and individuals.
Professional Memberships: ELBA, ELA, COMBAR, PNBA.
Career: Called 2001 (Middle Temple); Called New York Bar 2005; Pegasus Scholar 2005 (Bermuda). Joined Littleton Chambers in 2012.
Publications: A Position of Trust – Employees as Fiduciaries (2011) NLJ 1503-04.
Personal: BA (Cantab) (Class I), LLM (University of Pennsylvania).

SHUMAN, Karen
1 Chancery Lane, London
020 7092 2900
kshuman@1chancerylane.com
Featured in Professional Negligence (London), Real Estate Litigation (London)
Practice Areas: Karen is a specialist in real property and conveyancing, mortgages and contentious probate claims. She is instructed by solicitors and insurers on all aspects of professional negligence in her specialist areas and property litigation generally . She has a particular interest in professional negligence claims arising out of probate claims both will preparation and administration; conveyancing transactions with financial remedy and trust of land issues; and lender claims with restitutionary issues. Reported cases include: King v Executors of Estate of James King [2014] EWHC 2827 (Ch) summary judgment on probate claim upheld on appeal; Jackson v Thompson Solicitors & Ors HC QB 22.7.14 successfully resisted application for production of documents on the grounds of litigation privilege; Sahota v Executor of Estate or Pritam Nahal HC Ch 11.10.13 successfully resisted application to strike out for abuse on the basis that the estate was primarily situated in India; Nahal Kingerlee Holdings Ltd v Dunelm (Soft Furnishings) Ltd [2013] EWHC 47 (Ch) specific performance of an agreement for a lease ; D R Sheridan v Higgins & another [2012] EWHC 547 (ChD) dispute between solicitor and two executors; Padden v Bevan Ashford (a firm) [2011] EWCA Civ 1616 and [2013] EWCA Civ 824 solicitor's failure to advise per Etridge; Kang v Eau [2010] EWHC 1837 (QB) dispute over share purchase agreement and lease of Soho bar; Anastasia v Papakyricou HC Fam 22.4.09 trusts and illegality; Chief Constable of Wiltshire v McDonagh [2008] EWHC 654 delivery up of a caravan and home; Blackwood v Saunders (A Firm) TLQ/07/0476 (QB) 8.11.07 solicitor negligence during right to buy process; White v White [2003] EWCA Civ 924 joinder of trusts of land and children act applications; Dharamshi v Dharamshi [2000] EWCA Civ 305 financial remedy claim with substantial assets and offshore trusts.
Professional Memberships: Chancery Bar Association, Professional Negligence Bar Association, Property Bar Association, LCLCBA.
Career: Called in 1991.
Publications: Karen regularly provides lectures and seminars on professional negligence and Chancery related topics.

SIBSON, Clare
Cloth Fair Chambers, London
020 7710 6444
claresibson@clothfairchambers.com
Featured in Crime (London), Financial Crime (London)
Practice Areas: Considerable experience in fraud and business/corporate crime, cartel and competition offences. Experienced in mutual assistance, international investigations and enforcement. Also financial services regulation, professional services regulation and professional discipline. Past cases include; Represented a leading pharmaceutical company in the high profile failed SFO prosecution regarding alleged cartel offences. Advised and represented West Ham Football Club following the Carlos Tevez affair. Successfully represented K, a Solicitor accused of tax fraud; privilege against self-incrimination in ancillary relief proceedings, without prejudice privilege and abuse of process. Successfully represented an individual in FSA insider dealing prosecution. Advised a high profile Oligarch. Represented a director of a company charged with corruption and international sanctions busting. Advised one of the world's largest law firms on implications of UK Bribery Act for their clients, particularly in relation to private equity structures; advised a leading hedge fund on potential Market Abuse; advised real estate Company Walshaw Moor regarding a dispute with Natural England. Advised renowned airline in respect of licencing with the civil aviation authority. Instructed by Aivars Lembergs, a Latvian politician, over $135 million commercial court worldwide freezing order. Innospec; advised company in global plea agreement between SFO, DoJ and SEC. Advised the director of a global events company in relation to criminal proceedings revolving around the sale of corporate tickets for the Olympic Games. Represented a defendant in the 'Vantis' tax re-trial. Advised a leading travel business in cross border investigations into deaths outside the jurisdiction. Advised Robert Tchenguiz in judicial review of the search used by the SFO. Represented defendant in multi-million pound land banking fraud. More recently, advised the FCA; advising Olympus Corporation during SFO investigation and subsequent charges. Represented Rebekah Brooks, former chief executive of News International, in phone hacking trial. Retained for former Barclays Senior Executive in SFO/FCA investigation. Regulatory/ disciplinary practice includes instructions to advise and appear before the Financial Services and Markets Tribunal for the defence. For further information please visit www.clothfairchambers.com
Career: 1997 - Called to the Bar
Personal: Cambridge University, 1993-96 (Law 1st Class Double Honours). Foundation Scholar of Corpus Christi College 1996.

SIDDALL, Nicholas
Littleton Chambers, London
08450 343 444
clerks@kingschambers.com
Featured in Employment (Northern)
Practice Areas: Nicholas specialises in employment and industrial relations law. He practises in all facets of employment law including unfair dismissal, collective redundancy, TUPE and Working Time claims. He undertakes significant and complicated discrimination and equal pay work on behalf of individuals, unions and employers of all sizes. He further undertakes significant employment related high court litigation encompassing injunctive relief, wrongful dismissal and high value contractual claims.
Professional Memberships: ELA, ELBA and North Eastern Circuits
Career: Significant reported decisions include: Roberts v Skelmersdale College [2004] IRLR 69 (dismissal provisions of 2001 rules), GMB v Holis and Newell [2008] IRLR 187 (territorial jurisdiction of TUPE), Cokayne v BASC [2008] ICR 185 (issue estoppel), Matuszowicz-v-Hull City Council [2009] IRLR 292 (when a failure to make reasonable adjustments is deemed to occur), Fenton & UNISON-v-SYPS [2010] IRLR 930 (validity of a claim under the 2004 rules), Pinewood-v-Page [2011] ICR 508 (fairness of redundancy), Bridgeman-v-ABP [2012] IRLR 639, [2012] ICR D26 (CJEU reference as to proper approach to the Working Time Regulations derogation) and Bray-v-Monarch Personnel [2013] IDS Brief 972 (addressing the scope of the Swedish derogation in the Agency Workers Regulations).

SILVERTON, Catherine
Sovereign Chambers, Leeds
01132 451 841
catherine.silverton@sovereignchambers.co.uk
Featured in Crime (North Eastern)
Practice Areas: Catherine Silverton's practice is exclusively criminal. She defends and prosecutes serious crime across the board. She has vast experience of defending serious sexual and violent offences, including rape and homicide, and offences involving child victims. She regularly defends people under the age of 16 charged with serious criminal offences. She has specialist accountancy training and has undertaken significant high value (multi million pound) fraud and money laundering cases. She has a particular interest in cases involving unusual or complex medical or scientific issues, and has considerable experience of cross examining expert witnesses and running difficult legal arguments. She regularly instructs experts and analyses DNA, financial and cell site evidence. She has experience of being led and acting as leading junior. Her recent cases include arson with intent to endanger life, a nationwide conspiracy to supply class A drugs into prison, joint enterprise homicide, historic child sex, child abduction and conspiracy to commit armed robbery.
Professional Memberships: Lincoln's Inn, North Eastern Circuit, Criminal Bar Association, Crimeline, Amnesty UK.
Career: CPE scholarship, Hardwick entrance scholarship, Sir Thomas Moore scholarship, Pupillage award (all Lincoln's Inn). Called 2001. Pupillage (2001) and tenancy (2002) at Sovereign Chambers. Rape panel prosecutor.

SILVESTER, Bruce
Devereux, London
020 7353 7534
silvester@devchambers.co.uk
Featured in Personal Injury (London), Travel (London)
Practice Areas: Over 20 years of experience of all aspects of personal injury, health and safety, and clinical negligence litigation.

All levels of work including catastrophic inquiry, particularly brain injury, spinal injury and multiple injuries. Practice also includes registration and consumer protection. Also, since 2001 increasing specialisation in travel litigation, particularly large group actions involving injury abroad, gastro-intestinal illness and loss of enjoyment due to poor quality accommodation. Recent cases include Stych v. Dibble & Tradex Insurance Co Ltd [2012] EWHC 1606.
Professional Memberships: PIBA, PNBA.
Career: Called to the Bar 1983.
Personal: University of London, Queen Mary College London LLB (1982).

SIMCOCK, Sarah
Serjeants' Inn Chambers, London
020 7427 5000
ssimcock@serjeantsinn.com
Featured in Police Law (All Circuits)
Practice Areas: Sarah Simcock was called to the Bar in 2001. Sarah specialises in public and administrative, police, Court of Protection, inquests and inquiries, clinical negligence and healthcare and professional discipline law. An earlier edition notes that "she is measured, calm and impressive." Please click on the link to the Serjeants' Inn Chambers website for her profile, which sets out full details of her practice and relevant work of note.
Professional Memberships: HRLA, LCLCBA, PNBA, Treasury C Panel (2006-11).
Publications: Medical Treatment: Decisions and the Law (co-author).

SIMMONDS, Andrew QC
5 Stone Buildings, London
020 7242 6201
clerks@5sblaw.com
Featured in Pensions (London)
Practice Areas: Specialises in pensions and professional negligence work but also undertakes litigation in the trust, probate and financial services fields. Pension experience covers advice and litigation relating to all manner of problems and disputes arising between trustees, employers and members, complaints to the Pensions Ombudsman, the powers and duties of the Pensions Regulator and the Pension Protection Fund and claims against pensions professionals. In the professional negligence field, has particular experience of claims against solicitors, barristers, actuaries and accountants but has also acted in claims against insurance brokers, fund managers, stockbrokers and others. Recent notable cases include: Honda Motor Europe Ltd v Powell [2014] PLR 255; IBM UK Holdings Ltd v Dalgleish [2014] EWHC 980; Serjeant v Rigid Group Ltd [2014] PLR 143; LB Re Financing No.1 Ltd v Trustees of the Lehman Bros Pension Scheme [2013] EWCA Civ 751; IBM UK Pension Trust v IBM UK Holdings Ltd [2012] PLR 469, [2013] PLR 33; Premier Foods v RHM Pension Trust [2012] PLR 151; Bridge Trustees v Yates [2011] PLR 313; Prudential Staff Pensions Ltd v Prudential Assurance [2011] PLR 239; BT Pension Scheme Trustees v BT/Secretary of State for Business, Innovation & Skills [2010] PLR 487 ; Independent Trustee Services v Hope [2009] PLR 379; Thorner v Majors [2009] 1 WLR 776; Foster Wheeler v Hanley [2009] PLR 39: Eastearly Ltd v Headway plc [2009] PLR 279; Re Kostic [2008] WTLR 655; Allied Domecq (Holdings) Ltd v Allied Domecq Pension Trustees [2008] PLR 425: L v M Ltd [2007] PLR 11: Hodgson v Toray Textiles Europe [2006] PLR 253; Capital Cranfield Trustees v Walsh [2005] PLR 251; MNOPF Trustees v Everard [2005] PLR 225 ; Re T&N: Alexander Forbes v Jackson [2005] PLR 33.
Professional Memberships: Association of Pension Lawyers (former member of the Legislative and Parliamentary sub-committee); the Professional Negligence Bar Association; the Pension Litigation Court Users' Committee (1998-2014); Trustee of the Bar Council Pension Scheme (2000-2006). Chancery Bar Association.
Career: Called 1980. Silk 1999. Has sat as a Deputy High Court Judge in the Chancery Division since 2006.

SIMPSON, Philip J D
Terra Firma Chambers, Edinburgh
01312 605 830
philip.simpson@terrafirmachambers.com
Featured in Tax (Scotland)
Practice Areas: All aspects of UK tax planning and litigation, including corporation tax, VAT, income tax, CGT, IHT, SDLT and stamp duty, and customs and excise duties. Philip Simpson is instructed by all the leading firms of accountants and solicitors. Recent cases include successfully representing Tunnocks in classifying their snowball product as a cake; advising on the demerger of a corporate group; VAT in the context of a shooting estate; inheritance tax / CGT issues in relation to an information memorandum for potential investors in a limited partnership; SDLT in the context of a restructuring of a property development group including companies and limited liability partnerships; incorporation of a professional LLP; and principal private residence relief for CGT.
Professional Memberships: Faculty of Advocates; Bar of England and Wales (Inner Temple); Chartered Institute of Taxation.
Career: Advocate (called 2001); Barrister (called 2001); CTA (2006).
Publications: Reduced rate VAT on renewables 2010 S.L.T. (News). Share and Share Alike (2009) TELTJ, part 12, p. 14. Chapter entitled Accounting for VAT in VAT law textbook Value Added Tax: Commentary and Analysis (2009; Paul Lasok, General Editor). Tax relief for gifts to European charities 2009 S.L.T. (News) 119. Inland Revenue certificates: Section 70, HMRC and the Scottish courts [2007] Tax Adviser (February) Cadbury Schweppes plc v. Commissioners of Inland Revenue: the ECJ sets a strict test for CFC legislation [2006] BTR 677 Loss, Tax, Tax Losses and Lost Tax [2001] BTR 173 Planning for Tax Results 2011 S.L.T. (News) 86.

SIMS, Alice
Keating Chambers, London
020 7544 2600
asims@keatingchambers.com
Featured in Construction (London)
Practice Areas: Recognised specialist in construction, engineering, and utilities disputes along with professional negligence, regulatory and insurance claims related to these sectors. Alice has particular expertise in energy-related construction and commercial disputes (both onshore and offshore) and has acted for clients in a wide range of litigation concerning renewables, nuclear, oil and gas projects. She also regularly acts in cases relating to the sale and supply of chemicals and the construction of chemical processing plants. She appears in domestic and international arbitrations as well as the High Court. Alice also undertakes all aspects of alternative dispute resolution including representations to adjudicators and enforcement proceedings. She accepts appointments as a mediator (she is TECBAR accredited) and also accepts instructions on a public access, licensed access and pro bono basis. Recent work includes a multi-million pound international arbitration about the construction of an offshore wind-farm, litigation concerning defects at the Olympic Village, a multi-million dollar international arbitration concerning the construction of a gas fired power plant in Trinidad, a multi-million pound international arbitration about the construction of commercial buildings in down-town Moscow and a number of TCC disputes about architects' negligence.
Professional Memberships: Society of Construction Law, Technology & Construction Bar Association; Commercial Bar Association; Professional Negligence Bar Association.
Career: Called 2004.
Publications: Researcher for Keating on Construction Contracts. Former editor of the construction section of Law Brief.

SINCLAIR, Duncan
Thirty Nine Essex Street, London
020 7832 1111
duncan.sinclair@39essex.com
Featured in Energy & Natural Resources (London)
Practice Areas: Administrative/public law, Energy, EU/Competition, Commercial
Professional Memberships: Regulatory Policy Institute, BIICL; JUSTICE
Career: Called to the Bar 1996. After pupillage worked in London and Brussels focussing on EU, co0mpetition and the regulated sectors, leaving private practice for 5 years to take the post of Legal Director, Ofgem (a Senior Civil Service post in the Government Legal Service) before returning to the Bar in 2010.
Publications: Co-Author, Butterworths Competition Law Encyclopedia(looseleaf); Original (now co-) author, PLC manual on competition law, chapter on Intellectual Property Transactions. Numerous journal articles, in particular in the ECLR. Jean Monnet lectures on regulatory law, Malta 2011; speaker at Butterworths and Sweet and Maxwell conferences on Judicial Review.

SINCLAIR, Fiona QC
4 New Square, London
020 7822 2000
f.sinclair@4newsquare.com
Featured in Construction (London), Professional Negligence (London)
Practice Areas: Queen's Counsel specialising in all methods of dispute resolution (international and domestic arbitration, litigation, adjudication, mediation, negotiation) in the areas of (1) professional and product liability (2) construction and engineering, including transport, (3) insurance/reinsurance and (4) financial services. An acknowledged expert in professional liability, particularly in cases concerning construction, technology and finance. Typically instructed in high-profile and high-value disputes arising from major construction and engineering projects, fire/flood/collapse recovery actions, investment management and financial product misselling claims, product liability; and all related insurance issues. Particular expertise in managing multi-party litigation.
Professional Memberships: TECBAR (Committee Member), SCL, COMBAR, PNBA, ChBA.
Career: Called 1989. QC 2013. Chambers & Partners UK Construction Junior of the Year 2012.
Publications: Editor of 'Jackson and Powell on Professional Liability' since 1993 (responsible for Chapter 10, 'Construction Professionals').
Personal: Jesus College, Cambridge (MA, LLM). Interests: mountaineering, skiing, Italy. Speaks Italian.

SINGER, Andrew
Kings Chambers, Manchester
08450 343 444
clerks@kingschambers.com
Featured in Construction (North Eastern)
Practice Areas: Andrew practises from both Manchester and Leeds Chambers. Construction Litigation, Arbitration, Adjudication; Claims for and against construction professionals; General Commercial Litigation. Andrew is authorised to sit as a Recorder in the TCC.
Professional Memberships: TECBAR ,including membership of Adjudicators and Arbitrators panel; Member of Northern Ireland Bar; Member of Chartered Institute of Arbitrators ADR Group Accredited Mediator for Civil and Commercial Disputes.
Career: Practiced since 1990 now exclusively in Construction Law and related Professional Negligence claims, appearing regularly in TCC in England and Wales , has appeared in large number of reported decisions on adjudication and generally in Appellate Courts at all levels, including House of Lords case of Reinwood v Brown. Acted as Counsel in mediations and as Mediator, he is an Accredited Mediator. Appears in Commercial Court and Court of Appeal in Northern Ireland . Also has been appointed as Arbitrator and Adjudicator of several disputes. Authorised to sit as a Recorder in the TCC.
Publications: Contributed articles to Construction Law Journal on various topics.

SINGER, Samantha
Queen Elizabeth Building, London
020 7797 7837
ssinger@qeb.co.uk
Featured in Family/Matrimonial (London)
Practice Areas: All areas of family law with a particular emphasis on matrimonial finance and private child law; regularly appears in complex and high value matrimonial finance cases as a junior to QEB's Silks and to Silks of other Chambers. Has also appeared successfully against Silks on her own in both children and finance cases.
Professional Memberships: Family Law Bar Association.
Career: First Class Honours in Law, Bristol; Gray's Inn Prince of Wales Scholar 2003; called 2004; pupillage and tenancy at QEB; winner of the Bracewell Essay Prize 2008 ([2009] 39 Fam Law 234); Pegasus Scholarship to Washington DC in September - October 2010.
Publications: (Of Note) "Financial Provision: a second bite at the cherry" Family Law Journal No.62 December 2006/January 2007 p.14; "Integrating Diversity" The Collected Papers of the Dartington Hall Conference, edited by the Rt. Hon. Lord Justice Thorpe and Samantha Singer published by Jordans in 2008.

SINGH, Kuldip QC
Serle Court, London
020 7242 6105
ksingh@serlecourt.co.uk
Featured in Chancery (London), Fraud (London)
Practice Areas: Main areas of practice include commercial litigation, chancery commercial, contentious trusts, civil fraud, criminal fraud, arbitration, financial services, banking, professional discipline, professional negligence, human rights, sports law, defamation, contempt, health and safety, and business crime.
Professional Memberships: Commercial Bar Association; Chancery Bar Association; London Common Law and Commercial Bar Association; Commercial Fraud Lawyers Association; Financial Services Lawyers Association; Association of Regulatory and Disciplinary Lawyers; and Human Rights Lawyers Association.
Career: Called to the Bar in 1975 (Middle Temple). Appointed Queen's Counsel in 1993. Bencher of Middle Temple. Secretary of COMBAR (2007-10). Former co-opted member of Bar Council.

SINGH, Sarabjit
1 Crown Office Row, London
020 7797 7500
sarabjit.singh@1cor.com
Featured in Tax (London)
Practice Areas: Has a diverse civil practice, which includes public law/ immigration, tax/ rating, personal injury, clinical negligence, disciplinary and education cases and inquests. As a member of the Attorney General's A Panel of counsel, regularly appears in the High Court and Court of Appeal and has developed substantial expertise acting for Government departments in most of his practice areas. Has used this expertise to develop his work acting for others.
Career: Called 2001; appointed to Attorney General's C Panel of Junior Counsel to the Crown in March 2006; appointed to Attorney General's B Panel in February 2009; appointed to Attorney General's A Panel in March 2014.
Publications: Article 2 and Investigating Deaths [2004] JR 147; Immigration and Article 8 Family Life [2010] JR 377; contributor to 'Value Added Tax: Commentary and Analysis' by Sweet and Maxwell.
Personal: MA (Jurisprudence) from Corpus Christi College, Oxford.

SINGLETON, Michael
St Ives Chambers, Birmingham
0121 236 0863
michael.singleton@stiveschambers.co.uk
Featured in Social Housing (Midlands)
Practice Areas: Michael specialises in all aspects of housing work with particular emphasis on Human Rights, anti-social behaviour and regulatory matters. Experienced in claims under the Environmental Protection Act 1990 and claims arising following stock transfers. Regularly instructed on behalf of local authorities, Housing Associations and by specialist tenant advisers including not for profit bodies. Recent cases include Birmingham City Council v Ashton [2012] EWCA Civ 1557; Corby BC v Scott [2012] EWCA Civ 276; Birmingham City Council v Frisby [2011] UKSC 8 & Knowsley HT v White [2008] UKHL 70.
Professional Memberships: Social Housing Law Association (Founder Member); Midland Circuit; Fellow of the Royal Society for Public Health &amp Safety; Birmingham Medico-Legal Society.
Career: LLB (Hons) University of Leicester 1985. Called to the Bar 1987. Head of St Ives Chambers Housing & Property Group.
Publications: Advised the Chartered Institute of Housing on the Guidance Notes for the Community Harm Statement.
Personal: Lectures on most aspects of housing law to solicitors and other housing professionals.

SINNATT, Simon
Crown Office Row, Brighton
01273 625 625
clerks@1cor.com
Featured in Real Estate Litigation (South Eastern)
Practice Areas: Landlord and tenant (commercial, non-residential and residential); boundary disputes, easements, trusts of land; building contracts; planning; traveller's rights. Reported and notable cases: Sinclair Gardens (Kensington) Investments Ltd v 2 Medina Villas [2012] PLSCS 132: (Collective enfranchisement case concerning the valuation of car parking spaces and what amounts to a substantive interference of a right of way) Clarke v Meadus [2012] EWHC 3729 (Ch) (An application for a third party costs order prior to trial was held to be premature where assessment of the costs would require a hearing on many contentious issues that would have to be explored at the trial on the merits anyway) Henley v Bloom [2010] EWCA Civ 202; [2010] 1 W.L.R. 1770; [2010] H.L.R. 29; [2010] N.P.C. 29; [2010] 2 P. & C.R. DG13 (Case concerning whether a dilapidations claim should be struck out for abuse of process) Bluestorm v Portvale Holdings [2004] 22 EG 142 (case casting doubt on Yorkbrook); Brighton & Hove City Council v Collinson [2004] 28 EG 178 (security of tenure under the 1954 act). R (Boyejo, Towler, Rush, Sanders and Kemp) v Barnet London Borough Council and R (Ronald Smith) v Portsmouth City Council [2009] EWHC 3261 (Admin) (Case dealing with the level of consultation and involvement of the Disabled and compliance with Section 49A(1) of the DDA); Clarke v Meadus [2010] EWHC 3117 (Ch) (Case dealing with Proprietary Estoppel where there was a Deed of Trust setting out the interests of the parties).
Professional Memberships: Property Bar Association.
Career: Called 1993, Lincoln's Inn.
Personal: University of York (1991 BA Hons History); University of Sussex (1992 CPE); Inns of Court School of Law (1993). Interests: Hill walking, cinema, swimming, tennis.

SIRIKANDA, Morgan
Queen Elizabeth Building, London
020 7797 7837
m.sirikanda@queb.co.uk
Featured in Family/Matrimonial (London)
Practice Areas: All aspects of family law with a particular emphasis on matrimonial financial cases. Morgan has appeared before every level of tribunal from the Family Proceedings Court to the Court of Appeal. In recent years he has been instructed as junior counsel in a number of High Court matrimonial finance cases with very large asset bases. He is also regularly instructed on his own in family finance cases where leading counsel have been retained on the other side. In addition to this financial work Morgan also has a particular interest in international child cases raising issues of jurisdiction.
Professional Memberships: Middle Temple, Family Law Bar Association.
Career: Called to the Bar 2002. Pupillage at QEB.
Personal: Morgan read English at Liverpool University (1st class honours). He then obtained a Diploma in Law from the City University (commendation). He was awarded a Diplock scholarship by the Middle Temple. In 2006 Morgan was awarded a Pegasus scholarship to work as a judicial assistant to the Chief Justice of the Family Court of Australia.

SLATER, Matthew
3 Stone Buildings, London
020 7242 4937
mslater@3sb.law.co.uk
Featured in Administrative & Public Law (London)
Practice Areas: Matthew's practice covers a broad range of Chancery, commercial and public law matters, together with an increasing amount of offshore and appellate litigation. His client base includes a wide spectrum of commercial operators: property companies, investment funds, banks, technology and telecoms companies, offshore trusts, investors; and, as one of the Treasury Counsel, Government departments, including the Business Department, HM Treasury, the MoJ, HMRC and the Home Office.
Professional Memberships: Chancery Bar Association.
Career: Junior Counsel to the Crown/Treasury Counsel, 'B' Panel. Lecturer in Law, Oriel College, Oxford. Visiting Professor in Trusts, Institute of Law Jersey. Formerly, Judicial Assistant to Lord Bingham of Cornhill.

SLOBODA, Nicholas
One Essex Court, London
020 7583 2000
nsloboda@oeclaw.co.uk
Featured in Commercial Dispute Resolution (London)
Practice Areas: Nick has a broad commercial practice, divided equally between Court litigation and international arbitration. Alongside general commercial disputes and advice, he has particular experience of disputes involving civil fraud, energy, banking & finance and jurisdiction disputes/ interim injunctions. Recent cases include a multi-billion dollar ICC Geneva arbitration between national oil&gas and power companies; Dar Al Arkan v Al Refai (US$1 billion conspiracy/financial regulatory dispute); Alliance Bank v Aquanta (US$1 billion banking fraud claim/jurisdiction challenge); acting for a major bank in a US$600m+ LCIA arbitration against a broker; acting for SABMiller plc subsidiaries in litigation against Diageo plc subsidiaries in the English courts and in two consecutive major ICC arbitrations; MWP v Sinclair (inter-relationship between arbitration/court for abuse of process).
Professional Memberships: COMBAR, YIAG.
Career: Called 2007 (Lincoln's Inn). History at St Anne's Oxford (first class), CPE at City University and BVC at Inns of Court School of Law.

SLOW, Camille
Atkin Chambers, London
020 7404 0102
clerks@atkinchambers.com
Featured in Construction (London), Professional Negligence (London)
Practice Areas: Her practice covers a broad range of commercial disputes with a particular focus on construction and professional negligence disputes. She is experienced in all forms of dispute resolution, domestic and international arbitration, DAB's, mediation, adjudication and obviously the High Court. She undertakes work in numerous industry sectors but with particular experience of social housing, transport, infrastructure and energy projects. Her professional negligence experience is considerable in particular in a construction context having often acted for and against, architects, engineers, surveyors, project managers, planning professionals and multi-disciplinary firms, amongst many others. She is frequently instructed by insurers, professionals, governments, local governments and government departments, small and large developers and construction companies as well as private individuals both domestically and internationally. She has a particular interest in and experience of fraud and dishonesty, construction related insolvency, public procurement and multiparty disputes. She undertakes a large amount of oral advocacy in various forums and is often instructed as sole counsel in high value disputes.
Professional Memberships: LCLCBA (Committee); TECBAR; Combar; SCL.
Career: Bristol University, LLB, 2001. Called to the Bar in 2002.

SMALL, Jonathan QC
Falcon Chambers, London
020 7353 2484
small@falcon-chambers.com
Featured in Real Estate Litigation (London)
Practice Areas: Property litigation specialist. Recently reported cases include: Cooper v Albion [2013] EWHC 2993 (Ch) (adverse possession of riparian rights); Re 89 Holland Park [2013] EWHC 391 (Ch) (restrictive covenants); Canonical v Millbank [2012] EWHC 3710 (Ch) (break clauses); Lancashire v MS Frontier [2012] UKPC 42 (rescission of agreement for sale); Samarenko v Dawn Hill [2011] EWCA Civ 1445 (purchase deposits); Extra v Accor [2011] EWHC 775 (Ch) (recission of agreement for sale); Geo Networks v Bridgwater Canal [2010] EWHC 548 (telecoms); PGF II v Royal & Sun Alliance [2010] EWHC 1459 (dilapidations).
Professional Memberships: Chancery Bar Association; LCLCBA (Committee Member 2001-06); elected Member of The Bar Council (1994-97).
Career: Nottingham University (BA Hons History); City University (Dip Law); Inns of Court Studentship; Wolfson & Kennedy Scholarships; called 1990 (Lincoln's Inn); joined Falcon Chambers 1992; Silk 2006.

SMALLER, Elizabeth
9-12 Bell Yard, London
020 7400 1800
e.smaller@912by.com
Featured in Crime (London)
Practice Areas: Efficient, sensitive and thorough. Elizabeth Smaller is highly experienced in the prosecution and defence of serious crime. Either as leading Junior counsel or instructed alone. Specialises in sexual

offences including: Multiple complainant historical familial rape cases; stranger rapes; cases involving defendants and witnesses with significant learning or physical disabilities or other very limited functioning; very young complainants and defendants. Also appellate advocacy including Attorney-General's references re: unduly lenient sentences. She has dealt with allegations of baby shaking and other infant injuries and serious violent offences, including attempted murder and armed robbery. She is also familiar with dealing with intermediaries, psychiatrists, consultant neurologists, paediatricians and DNA evidence. Recent reported cases: R v SK Court of Appeal [2011] EWCA Crim 1691.A 'slavery' case.
Professional Memberships: Criminal Bar Association Recorder of the Crown Court.
Career: Called to the Bar 1995. Specialist trained Rape Prosecutor. Grade 4 Prosecution Panel advocate.
Publications: 'Giving the Vulnerable a Voice' Counsel Magazine, January, 2012.

SMITH, Alan
Old Square Chambers, London
020 7269 0367
asmith@oldsquare.co.uk
Featured in Personal Injury (London)
Practice Areas: Practising in personal injury and clinical negligence. Workload is an even balance between claimant and defendant. Majority of work involves maximum severity injuries, eg. brain/spinal, arising out of road traffic, employment and public liability accidents. Maintains an interest in criminal jurisdiction relating to health and safety law and appearing at inquests.
Professional Memberships: Personal Injury Bar Association, AvMA
Career: Called to the Bar in 1981. Combined common law and criminal practice until specialised in personal injuries and clinical negligence 20 years ago. Advocacy biased background means that he relishes court work.
Personal: Motor racing and boating enthusiast. Homes in Buckinghamshire and the South of France.

SMITH, Andrew
Matrix Chambers, London
020 7404 3447
andrewsmith@matrixlaw.co.uk
Featured in Employment (London)
Practice Areas: Andrew is an employment and discrimination law specialist, who also undertakes work in the fields of commercial and sports law. His work was recognised in an article published by Legalweek.com, entitled 'First among equals: Stars at the Bar 2012'. Andrew regularly appears in Employment Tribunals on behalf of claimants and respondents, and advises on all aspects of employment law. He is often instructed on high value and complex disputes involving allegations of discrimination and whistleblowing. With regard to appellate work, Andrew's EAT practice includes the following cases: Begum v Pedagogy Auras UK; McCarthy v Jaguar Cars; SPS Technologies v Chughtai; Senator Hotels v Ratkowksi; Montracon Ltd v Hardcastle; Gill v AWE Plc; Boanu v Group 4 Securicor; Olayemi v Athena Medical Centre; and Thomson v London Borough of Haringey.
Professional Memberships: ELA; ELBA.
Publications: Andrew is the author of the discrimination law section of Jordan's Employment Law and a contributor to the ELA Briefing. He produces articles on a range of topics for the LawinSport.com website and is an author of the forthcoming book, 'Football and the Law' (Bloomsbury Professional).
Personal: University of Sheffield (LLB – 1st class); Manchester Metropolitan University (BVC – Outstanding).

SMITH, Andrew QC
St Philips Chambers, Birmingham
01212 467 000
asmith@st-philips.com
Featured in Crime (Midlands)
Practice Areas: Andrew prosecutes and defends in cases of gravity and complexity and is regularly instructed in cases involving allegations of homicide, organised crime and serious fraud. He has significant experience of homicide cases ranging from the deaths of babies and young children through to gang related murders. Andrew has been instructed in many cases involving organised criminal activity at both national and regional level. Andrew's cases frequently involve international aspects. In fraud cases, Andrew has represented company directors and professionals. He also has substantial experience of money laundering investigations and has often advised parties pre-charge.
Professional Memberships: Criminal Bar Association; Midland Circuit.
Career: MA (Hons) Oxford; Queen Mother's Scholarship, Middle Temple; Called to the Bar in 1997; Recorder (Midland Circuit); Queen's Counsel 2012; Joint Head of Advocacy Training for the Midland Circuit.

SMITH, Barry
Compass Chambers, Edinburgh
01312 605 648
barry.smith@compasschambers.com
Featured in Health & Safety (Scotland)
Practice Areas: Member of the regulatory crime team at Compass Chambers. Experienced in the defence of charges under the Health and Safety at Work etc Act 1974 and related Regulations. Acts for major clients in the engineering, oil / off-shore, rail, construction, transport and retail industries. He is also experienced in fatal road traffic accident prosecutions and in the conduct of fatal accident inquiries. He regularly speaks at seminars and conferences on regulatory crime.
Professional Memberships: Health & Safety Lawyers' Association; Association of Regulatory and Disciplinary Lawyers.
Career: Graduate of Strathclyde University (LLB (1st Class Hons)) and Harvard Law School (LLM) (Kennedy Scholar); Trained at Crown Office 2000-02; Qualified (solicitor) in 2002; Procurator Fiscal Depute 2002 -04; Faculty of Advocates Lord Reid Scholar 2004; Called to the Bar 2005; Session Cases Reporter.

SMITH, Ian
11 Stone Buildings, London
020 7831 6381
smith@11sb.com
Featured in Fraud (London), POCA Work & Asset Forfeiture (All Circuits)
Practice Areas: Ian practiced as a solicitor from 1995 and was a solicitor advocate until he came to the Bar in 2003. He is a commercial litigator specialised in civil court fraud litigation, private international law, asset recovery and anti-money laundering law. His practice frequently involves complex and high value cases often with an international dimension. He deals with obtaining and discharging/responding to freezing injunctions; other urgent interim relief; fraud cases arising out of business sales, bribery, theft, embezzlement and undisclosed profits as well as conflicts of interests involving fiduciaries and banking/mortgage fraud. He also works with law firms on their own professional conduct and liability issues. For more info, please visit the 'Barristers' section on www.11sb.com.
Career: Call - 2003; Solicitor from 1995; Solicitor Advocate (all courts).
Publications: Lead editor and co-author of the practitioners' loose-leaf text Smith, Owen & Bodnar on Asset Recovery: Criminal Confiscation and Civil Recovery (Oxford University Press). Co-author of The Illicit Trade in Art and Antiquities: International Recovery and Criminal and Civil Liability by Ulph and Smith (Hart, 2012).
Personal: LLB (Birmingham). College of Law. Working knowledge - Italian.

SMITH, Jamie
4 New Square, London
020 7822 2040
j.smith@4newsquare.com
Featured in Professional Negligence (London)
Practice Areas: Principal areas of practice are professional negligence (with particular emphasis on auditors and accountants, lawyers and insurance brokers), insurance and commercial dispute resolution. Notable cases include: Moy v Pettman Smith [2005] 1 WLR 581 (HL) (barrister's role as to advice on settlement); Sugar Hut v Great Lakes Insurance [2011] Lloyd's Rep IR 198 (successful declinature by insurers following nightclub fire); IEGL v. Zurich [2013] PIQR P10 (CA) (EL insurer's liability for mesothelioma claims under Fairchild doctrine); Schumann v. Veale Wasbrough [2014] PNLR 14 (barrister's role in advising on merits); Clydesdale Bank plc v. Workman [2014] PNLR 18 (dishonest assistance claim against solicitors) and Gladman Commercial Properties v. FHP [2014] PNLR 11 (fraud claim against property agents).
Professional Memberships: PPNBA, COMBAR, Chancery Bar Association, LCLCBA, BILA.
Career: MA (Cantab). Called to Bar 1995. Joined Four New Square 1996.
Personal: Enjoys cycling.

SMITH, Joan
Trinity Chambers, Newcastle upon Tyne
01912 321 927
EJ.Smith@trinitychambers.co.uk
Featured in Licensing (North Eastern)
Practice Areas: Joan is well known nationally as a specialist licensing advocate and has extensive experience in a variety of licensing areas. She regularly appears in taxi licensing, firearms licensing, alcohol and gambling cases before Licensing Committees, Magistrates' Court and Crown Courts. Joan's practice involves significant work in the Administrative Court largely concerning Local Authorities and Police Authorities and she regularly advisers on enforcement, appeals, judicial review and policy. Joan represents the trade, public bodies and local communities. Joan's practice covers complimentary areas such as health and safety, trading standards, environmental protection and animal welfare. Joan has a wide ranging regulatory and disciplinary practice and has a particular interest in disciplinary and misconduct proceedings including fitness to practise. Joan is regularly instructed in complex Inquests. Joan has an interest in Zoo licensing, Street Trading and Sexual Entertainment Venue licensing.
Professional Memberships: North Eastern Circuit, Institute of Licensing, Association of Regulatory and Disciplinary Lawyers, Association of Prison Lawyers, The Honourable Society of the Middle Temple.
Career: Grade 2 Prosecutor CPS, List C Specialist Regulatory Advocate in Health and Safety and Environmental Law, Appointed by the Department of Energy and Climate Change to hear Carbon Reduction Commitment Energy Efficiency Scheme (CRC) Appeals.

SMITH, Joel
Furnival Chambers, London
020 7405 3232
jsmith@furnivallaw.co.uk
Featured in Extradition (London)
Practice Areas: Crime and extradition, including matters in the High Court, Court of Appeal and judicial review, representing both requested individuals and foreign authorities. Cases include allegations of murder, terrorism, rape and large scale fraud. Recent extradition cases include: Brazil v. W [2014] (prison conditions and article 3), Croatia v. A [2014] (Successful representation of individual accused of war crimes in Croatia), Bucnys and ors v Lithuania [2014] (Supreme Court, meaning of 'judicial authority' for purposes of s2 of the Extradition Act 2003), Biskup and ors v Poland [2013] (suicide risk in extradition cases), and Redya and Zaporozhchenko v Ukraine [2013] (extradition, large scale investment fraud).
Professional Memberships: Criminal Bar Association, Extradition Lawyers' Association.

SMITH, Julia
Henderson Chambers, London
020 7583 9020
JSmith@hendersonchambers.co.uk
Featured in Consumer Law (London), Financial Services (London)
Practice Areas: Consumer law, banking and finance, including consumer credit, mortgages, sale and supply of goods, unfair contract terms and unfair commercial practices. Cases include OFT v Ashbourne Management Services Ltd [2011] All E R (D) 276 (May) (unfair terms, unfair commercial practices, and whether credit provided under minimum term contracts with monthly payments); Adris v Royal Bank of Scotland plc (2010) 160 NLJ (non-party costs orders); Carey v HSBC Bank plc, Times 25 January 2010 (unfair relationships and burden of proving improper execution); McGuffick v Royal Bank of Scotland plc [2010] 1 All E R 634 (whether reporting to credit reference agencies enforcement); and Royal Bank of Scotland plc v Etridge (No.2) [2001] UKHL 44, [2002] 2 AC 773 (undue influence and extent of solicitor's duty when advising third party provider of security). Clients include banks, regulators, leasing companies and retailers.
Professional Memberships: London Common Law and Commercial Bar Association.
Career: Called 1988.
Publications: Atkin's Court Forms on Consumer Credit (Lexis Nexis 2012); The Law of Consumer Credit and Hire (OUP 2009);

Consumer Credit Act 2006, A Guide to the New Law (Law Society Publishing 2006).
Personal: Educated at Cheltenham Ladies' College and the University of Liverpool.

SMITH, Leonard QC
Carmelite Chambers, London
020 7936 6300
clerks@carmelitechambers.co.uk
Featured in Financial Crime (London)
Practice Areas: A specialist criminal defence advocate with particular expertise in serious fraud and complex financial crime. Extensive experience in several jurisdictions, defending in all forms of complex and grave cases. Throughout 2013 and 2014, has continued to represent and advise professionals and high ranking officers of large Corporations and private practices concerning a wide range of corporate and institutional, regulatory and international and domestic corporate compliance problems. In 2013, Mr Smith has defended the notorious self-styled "Devil's Advocate", Giovanni Di Stefano in a long running fraud trial at Southwark Crown Court. He is also briefed for the main defendant in the gigantic mortgage fraud trial, the North East Property Buyers Case, to be tried in late 2015 at Teesside and for the property tycoon Paul Cummins in his prosecution in Manchester arising out of Spanish Property developments. At Southwark Crown Court in 2014, he represented the FIA, Joseph Silva who was charged with corporate offences over a 20 year period. In 2012, he achieved an acquittal of his logistics accountant client in the five month –Jan-June 2012 MTIC trial at Kingston Crown Court of the FCIB defendants in Operation Vex. This long awaited prosecution had Mr Smith's client as the second defendant and after a grueling battle, the jury acquitted his client (who had been extradited from Dubai) on all charges. The previous November, his female client was acquitted in Operation Fastback at Newcastle Crown Court. In 2011, Mr Smith was briefed in the largest Insider Trading prosection by the FSA for one of three defendants charges with Insider trading over a 4 year period. He is briefed for the main defendant in Operation Bamburg, the gigantic mortgage fraud prosecution in Newcastle involving the collapse of Newcastle Home Loans and the North east Property Buyers Groups. In June 2011, achieved the acquittal, after a five month trial, of a senior solicitor in trial which (as the jury was told by the SFO) concerned "...the largest mortgage fraud ever prosecuted in this Country". (R v Ferrigan - Southwark Crown Court). The case involved the fraudulent acquistion of approximately £63m from banks and building socities between 2004 and 2006. The case required details cross examination of various experts as to the duties of and rules regulating, the performance and conduct of bankers, introducers, mortgage brokers and solictiors. In July 2010 achieved the acquittal, after a 160 day trial, of his CEO client in The Imperial Consolidated Group case, the largest investment fraud trials yet prosecuted by the SFO. Has defended accountants, solicitors, portfolio providers and company directors and has regularly advises senior executive officers under investigation. Other major cases include- R v Olivier – Operation Gnawed - Massive Customs MTIC fraud – acquittal following abuse of process submissions. R v Routledge – Large VAT fraud- appeared for chartered accountant. R v Haughton – Chester- Large MTIC fraud-acquittal following abuse of process submissions concerning disclosure.;R v Murden – large VAT evasion fraud involving imported motor vehicles; R v Anderson- Bristol- Intellectual Property Fraud on Investors.-Has appeared in numerous murder trials and appellate proceedings including the Privy Council (3 Appeals) and in the House of Lords. Libel- Marshall v Express Newspapers -- The Brixton Prison Breakout. R v H & C (House of Lords, Court of Appeal and trial) -the seminal case on disclosure and PII.
Career: Called 1986 - QC 2008.

SMITH, Matthew
Kings Chambers, Leeds
08450 343 444
clerks@kingschambers.com
Featured in Costs Litigation (Northern)
Practice Areas: Costs, mediation and employment
Professional Memberships: ACL
Career: Barrister, Costs Draftsman & Mediator (MA Cantab – law 2.1).
Publications: Various costs articles together with other members of the Kings Chambers costs team.

SMITH, Matthew
Maitland Chambers, London
01483 741 397
msmith@maitlandchambers.com
Featured in Charities (London)
Practice Areas: Commercial chancery litigation, including company and insolvency questions, contractual and trust-related disputes. Particular interest in charity law. Matthew acted for the Independent Schools Council in their successful judicial review of the Commission's public benefit guidance; he appeared in the poverty trusts references brought by the Attorney General; he now acts for the Plymouth Brethren Christian Church in their appeal against the Commission's refusal to register. Other notable cases have included acting for the Catholic adoption agencies in their appeals concerning the scope of the charitable exemption in the Equality Act 2010 and appearing for the Attorney-General in the litigation over the assets of the Wedgwood Museum. He has advised and acted for and against the Commission on a number of other matters. He has appeared in the Tribunal and in Court for charities, the Commission and the Attorney.
Professional Memberships: COMBAR, Chancery Bar Association and Charity Law Association.
Career: Called in 2001. Junior Counsel to the Crown (B Panel).
Personal: MA (Cantab) First Class, LLM (rules concerning charities and politics; the relationship in charity law between purposes and activities and the comparative state of the law in England, Australia, New Zealand and Canada).

SMITH, Stephanie
Arden Chambers, London
020 7421 9489
Stephanie.smith@ardenchambers.com
Featured in Social Housing (London)
Practice Areas: Housing, Landlord and Tenant, Local Government, Property.
Professional Memberships: HLPA, PBA.
Career: Stephanie read for a BA in Jurisprudence at Oxford University before joining the Bar. Her practice encompasses all areas of chambers work with particular emphasis on possession, anti-social behaviour, disrepair and homelessness. She represents and advises on all aspects of housing and property law and has provided training on proportionality and possession proceedings, homelessness, disrepair, anti-social behaviour and succession. Reported cases include: Yosief v Birmingham CC [2011] HLR 27,CA; Maswaku v Westminster CC [2012] HLR 37, CA; El Goure v Kensington & Chelsea RBC [2012] HLR 36,CA and AT v Islington LBC [2013] EWHC 4142 (Admin).
Publications: Former Assistant Editor of the Encyclopaedia of Housing Law (2007-14).

SMITH, Stephen QC
Erskine Chambers, London
020 7242 5532
ssmith@erskinechambers.com
Featured in Chancery (London), Commercial Dispute Resolution (London), Fraud (London), Offshore (London)
Practice Areas: Stephen Smith is a leading Silk who specialises in litigating high-value, complex commercial disputes. He is particularly sought-after for cases involving jurisdictional issues and restraints on the disposals of assets (including freezing orders and interim relief). Notable cases include Derby v Weldon, the BCCI liquidation, proceedings arising out of the collapse of the Maxwell empire,Trustor v Smallbone, Alfa Telecom v Cukurova and the Rastogi litigation. Since 2009 Stephen has been the lead advocate in the complex fraud and asset recovery proceedings known as JSC BTA Bank v Ablyazov, in which over 60 leading decisions have been given so far (including 12 in the Court of Appeal), and judgment has been obtained for over $3.7bn. Stephen also has a successful offshore practice and regularly appears in the courts in the Eastern Caribbean, the Bahamas, the Isle of Man and the Cayman Islands; and he has advised in connection with cases proceeding in Bermuda and Hong Kong. Stephen has appeared before the Privy Council on ten occasions.
Professional Memberships: Middle Temple, Chancery Bar Association.
Career: Scholar, University College Oxford 1979-82. First Class Degree in Jurisprudence, Oxford University 1982 (Wronker and Jurisprudence Prizes winner). Called to the Bar in England and Wales, 1983; Eastern Caribbean (BVI) 1994; QC 2000; Bahamas 2004; Recorder 2004; Deputy High Court Judge (Chancery Division and Commercial Court) 2006; licensed advocate Isle of Man (ad hoc) 2007; Cayman Islands 2010.
Personal: Married to Lorraine, five children. Principal leisure interests: family, deer, alpaca farming.

SMITH, Tom QC
South Square, London
020 7696 9900
tomsmith@southsquare.com
Featured in Banking & Finance (London), Chancery (London), Commercial Dispute Resolution (London), Company (London), Restructuring/Insolvency (London)
Practice Areas: Banking/finance, corporate insolvency, commercial litigation, and company law. Recent banking cases include Saltri III v MD Mezzanine, Assenagon v Anglo Irish Bank, Morgan Stanley v Tael, Carey Value Added v Grupo Urvasco and Lehman Brothers RASCALS. Recent insolvency cases include Nortel v Pensions Regulator, Rubin v Eurofinance SA and Mills v HSBC Trustee all in the Supreme Court, and many of the recent out of court restructurings involving both schemes and CVAs such as Fitness First, Travelodge, Vietnam Shipbuilding, Stemcor, hibu, Café Rouge. Commercial litigation matters include the recent Formula One/Ecclestone litigation, Madoff litigation and Smithton v Naggar relating to the collapse of Dawnay Day.
Professional Memberships: COMBAR, Chancery Bar Association.
Career: Called to the Bar (Middle Temple, 1999). Temporary admission to the Bar of Northern Ireland (2012). Admitted to the Bar of the Cayman Islands (2014). Queen's Counsel (2014).
Publications: Contributor to Cross-Border Insolvency, The EC Regulation on Insolvency Proceedings, EU Banking and Insurance Insolvency, Halsbury's Laws of England, Company Directors.
Personal: Educated at Clare College, Cambridge, MA (1st Class), LLM (1st Class).

SNOWDEN, Steven
Crown Office Chambers, London
020 7797 8100
snowden@crownofficechambers.com
Featured in Personal Injury (London), Personal Injury (All Circuits)
Practice Areas: Steven's main areas of practice are personal injuries and industrial disease, within which he regularly deals with aspects of procedure and costs and appears at inquests. His practice extends to associated insurance, professional negligence and clinical negligence work. He is highly regarded for his advocacy skills in combination with his experience and his calm manner, and he regularly appears in court and in settlement meetings against silks. He deals with cases of the highest severity on all aspects of liability and quantum and he acts for claimants and defendants with equal enthusiasm. His regular work is in the High Court and County Courts and he has experience of the House of Lords and the Court of Appeal. Reported cases include Dowdall v William Kenyon (limitation/ abuse of process), Kotula v EDF (paraplegic claim/ periodical payments/ provisional damages), Dixie v British Polythene (abuse of process), Gray v Thames Trains (illegality/ ex turpi causa), Glaister v Appleby (duty of care), Carver v BAA (Part 36), Drake v Provident (contribution between insurers).
Career: Called to the Bar in 1989. Secretary of the Personal Injuries Bar Association. Editor of the Judicial College Guidelines for the Assessment of General Damages in Personal Injury cases.

SOARES, Patrick
Field Court Tax Chambers, London
020 3693 3700
ps@fieldtax.com
Featured in Tax (London)
Practice Areas: Taxation of land transactions, overseas structures and companies and double tax treaties and EU law.
Professional Memberships: Fellow of the Chartered Institute of Taxation.
Career: Formerly a tax partner in a leading firm of solicitors.
Publications: Tax Editor of the Property Law Bulletin.
Personal: Plays the clarinet and piano. Enjoys reading and cycling.

SOLLEY, Stephen QC
Charter Chambers, London
020 7618 4400
stephensolley@charterchambers.com
Featured in Crime (London)
Practice Areas: Defended successfully (through two exceedingly long trials from 2008 to July 2010) of the lead defendant Jared Brook, in the SFO prosecution of the owners of Imperial Consolidated for an alleged £250 million fraud. Plus Health and Safety advice for corporate clients. Practice has historically encompassed the gravest cases over a wide spectrum of specialisms, including, political or alleged terrorist crime, from the IRA Brighton Bombers, to Iranian alleged bomber Merdad Kokabi, to Red Mercury Dirty bomb plots. Corporate manslaughter/ health and safety, from the captain of the Herald of Free Enterprise to railway manslaughter. Environmental offences, from the Petrus Oil Company case (R v Interline) to the Landfill Tax fraud. Complex fraud from BCCI (R v Baqi), The Savings and Investment Bank, Isle of Man fraud, to the Hungarian National Bank fraud. Insider trading, ramping etc, from the City Slickers to Security printers, to DTI enquiries. Murder and drugs, from the Reading torture murder (Mary-Ann Lineghan) to Mr Nice, (R v Howard Marks). Criminal Cases Review Commission cases, R v Twitchell, tortured confession. House of Lords leading cases, ASBO's R v Clingham; trial absent defendant, DPP v Jones. High profile defendants include Howard Marks, Richard Madeley and Craig Charles.
Professional Memberships: Former Chair of Bar Human Rights Committee 1999-02. Board director of Reprieve, the organisation that uses the law to enforce the human rights of prisoners, from death row to Guantánamo Bay.
Career: Inspector, Insider Dealing (DTI) 1987-90. Appointed Recorder 1988. Silk 1989. Bencher, Inner Temple 1999.
Publications: Chapter on 'the Role of the Advocate' in Oxford University Press 'Criminal Justice Process', a book designed for the understanding of the English criminal justice system around the world, and translated into, amongst other languages, Chinese.
Personal: Member of Board of Directors of Hackney Empire Theatre since 1995.

SOOLE, Michael QC
4 New Square, London
020 7822 2000
m.soole@4newsquare.com
Featured in Construction (London), Professional Negligence (London)
Practice Areas: Professional negligence; construction/commercial contracts; insurance. Notable cases include: Co-operative Group v. Birse [2014] EWHC 530 (TCC) (limitation period in tort); WSP v. Dalkia [2012] EWHC 2428 (TCC) (NEC3 adjudication/jurisdiction); SG v Hewitt [2012] EWCA Civ 1053 (CPR Pt 36); How Engineering v Southern Insulation [2010] EWCA Civ 999; [2010] EWHC 1878 (TCC) (subcontractors duty of care); Griffin v Hacker Young [2010] PNLR 20 (insolvency advice); Shore v Sedgwick [2008] EWCA Civ 863 (pension mis-selling); Rind v Theodore Goddard [2008] PNLR 598 (solicitors; tax advice); Dalkia v Celtech [2006] 1 Lloyds Rep 599 (energy contract); Norwich Union v Meisels [2006] Lloyds Rep IR 69 (insurance); Mandrake v Balanus [2006] EWCA Civ 1716 (pensions indemnity); R (Bramall) v Law Society [2006] PNLR 4 (judicial review); Actionstrength v International Glass [2003] 2 AC 541 guarantee/estoppel); Speshal Investments v Corby Kane [2003] EWHC 390 (valuers negligence); Consarc Design v Hutch Investments [2002] PNLR 310 (architects negligence); Munckenbeck v Kensington Hotel [2001] 78 Con LR (architects negligence); Arab Bank v Zurich Insurance [1999] 1 Lloyds Reps 262 (insurance: fraudulent agent); Esso Petroleum v Milton [1997] 1 WLR 938 (direct debits); First National Bank v Thompson [1996] Ch 231 (land registration/estoppel); Gale v Superdrug [1996] 1 WLR 1089 (withdrawing admissions); Barclays Bank of Swaziland v Hahn [1989] 1 WLR 506 (service of writ).
Professional Memberships: TECBAR (Chairman); PNBA; COMBAR; LCLBA.
Career: Called 1977; recorder 2000; Silk 2002.
Personal: Educated Berkhamsted School and University College Oxford (MA; President Oxford Union).

SOUTHERN, David QC
Temple Tax Chambers, London
020 7353 7884
david.southernqc@templetax.com
Featured in Tax (London)
Practice Areas: Tax. David Southern QC has an extensive advocacy practice and advises across all areas of tax, with a particular speciality in corporate debt and VAT.
Professional Memberships: Revenue Bar Association; Chartered Insitute of Taxation (Fellow).
Career: David Southern is a highly experienced tax barrister. He is an "enormously personable" and "brave advocate who offers inventive analysis of a case" (Chambers & Partners 2011). He was leading counsel in the House of Lords in Fleming (t/a Bodycraft) v R & C Comrs [2008] STC 325, described by the Financial Times as 'the VAT case of the decade', which has generated tax repayments of £13.1 billion. He is lead counsel in BAA v R & C Comrs [2010] SFTD 587, the lead case on recovery of VAT on mergers and takeovers. Before going to the Bar he worked both for the Inland Revenue and in the tax department of LLoyds Bank, giving him unusual breadth and depth of tax experience. He was a member of the Attorney General's panel of Counsel.
Publications: Taxxation of Loan Relationships and Derivative Contracts (Bloomsbury Professional); 9th edition 2012. This is the standard work in this area. Contributor: Gore-Browne on Companies; Law Society Company Law Handbook (3rd edition, 2013), VAT and the City (7th edition, 2012).
Personal: Bencher of Lincoln's Inn.

SOUTHEY, Hugh QC
Matrix Chambers, London
020 7404 3447
HughSouthey@matrixlaw.co.uk
Featured in Administrative & Public Law (London), Civil Liberties & Human Rights (London), Immigration (London), Police Law (All Circuits)
Practice Areas: Human rights, international law, terrorism, prisoners' rights, police law, immigration and asylum, mental health, crime and extradition, contempt, election, privacy, community care and other public law. Five Supreme Court cases in 2013 and the same in 2014. Recent significant cases include: R(T) v Secretary of State [2014] UKSC 35, R(Nunn) v Chief Constable of Suffolk [2014] UKSC 37, Richardson v DPP [2014] 2 All ER 20, R(Roberts) v Commissioner of Police of the Metropolis [2014] 2 Cr App R 80, ZZ v Secretary of State [2014] 2 WLR 791, R(Haney) v Secretary of State [2014] 1 WLR 1208 and Sarjantson v Chief Constable of Humberside Police [2014] 1 All ER 960.
Professional Memberships: Administrative Law Bar Association, Association of Prison Lawyers, Immigration Law Practitioners Association, Mental Health Lawyers Association, Human Rights Lawyers Association, Legal Action, Liberty, Justice, Amnesty International.
Career: Admitted as a solicitor in 1991. Headed the Immigration and Crime Departments at Glazer Delmar. Recorder of the Crown Court. Called in Northern Ireland.
Publications: Joint author of Judicial Review: A Practical Guide. Joint editor of United Kingdom Human Rights Reports.

SOUTHGATE, Jonathan QC
29 Bedford Row Chambers, London
020 7404 1044
jsouthgate@29br.co.uk
Featured in Family/Matrimonial (London)
Practice Areas: Financial remedy; cohabitation; civil partnerships; inheritance and family provision; Children Act (private law) including financial provision for children. Recent cases include: Ahmend and Mehmet v Mustafa [2014] EWCA Civ 27; JM v CZ [2014] EWHC 1125 (Fam); DR v GR and Others (Financial Remedy: Variation of Overseas Trust) [2013] EWHC 1196 (Fam); BJ v MJ (Financial Remedy: Overseas Trusts) [2012] 1 FLR 667; Riding v Riding [2011] EWHC 3093; Golubovich v Golubovich [2010] EWCA Civ 810; H v H [2009] EWHC 3739 (Fam); McFarlane v McFarlane [2009] EWHC 891 (Fam); P v P [2010] 1 FLR 1126; P v P (Financial Relief: Procedure) [2009] 1 FLR 696; Kimber v Kimber (Writ Ne Exeat Regno) [2006] EWCA Civ 706; Kimber v Brookman Solicitors [2004] 2 FLR 221; Reid v Reid [2004] 1 FLR 736.
Professional Memberships: Middle Temple; FLBA.
Career: Called 1992; pupil and tenant at 29 Bedford Row. QC 2013.
Publications: 'Judgment Summons: Still Scope for a Comeback?', Family Law June 2003. 'Costs in Ancillary Relief Proceedings', Family Law February 2005; 'Orders in relation to surplus income' The Review March 2008. "Privilege" a chapter in the Resolution Family Disputes Handbook 2010.
Personal: Clifton College and MMU (LLB). Married with three children; tennis.

SPAIN, Timothy
Trinity Chambers, Newcastle upon Tyne
01912 321 927
t.spain@trinitychambers.co.uk
Featured in Family/Matrimonial (North Eastern)
Practice Areas: Timothy is a recognised expert in high value ancillary and financial relief cases, especially those involving companies, partnerships, farms, "hidden wealth" and insolvency. He is a member of the Institute of Family Law Arbitrators (IFLA) Panel and is qualified to conduct family law arbitrations and make orders under the IFLA rules, including in matrimonial finance and Trusts of Land and Appointment of Trustees Act 1996 proceedings. Timothy has extensive experience of dealing with Local Authority Public law Children cases. He is regularly instructed in relation to Court of Protection matters relating to vulnerable adults. He also deals with issues relating to care home fees. Timothy is frequently instructed by Local Authorities in relation to safeguarding issues. He has also Chaired Independent Services Case Reviews.
Professional Memberships: FLBA. Chartered Institute of Arbitrators. Bar Pro Bono Unit. Resolution (Affiliate)
Career: Deputy District Judge 2000 Appointed by the Department of Energy and Climate Change to hear Carbon Reduction Commitment Energy Efficiency Scheme (CRC) Appeals 2012 Institute of Family Law Arbitrators (IFLA) Panel 2013 Delivers seminars and in-house events to local solicitors, local Law Societies and Local Authorities, relating to ancillary relief, public law children proceedings, PII disclosure and the Vetting and Barring Scheme.

SPALTON, George
4 New Square, London
020 7822 2000
barristers@4newsquare.com
Featured in Commercial Dispute Resolution (London), International Arbitration (London), Professional Discipline (London), Professional Negligence (London)
Practice Areas: George's practice falls into five principal areas: Commercial litigation, international commercial arbitration, financial services, professional liability claims and disciplinary work. His experience of commercial work encompasses a wide variety of disputes – ranging from construction claims, insurance and reinsurance matters, banking claims to civil fraud. He has significant experience of international work and is currently instructed in an on-going, high value arbitration in Dubai as well as acting in a number of arbitrations in Europe, South-East Asia, and elsewhere. George's expertise in the context of professional liability work focusses on accountants and auditors' negligence and solicitors' negligence – especially in the context of financial services and commercial transactions.
Professional Memberships: George is on the Executive Committee of the Commercial Bar Association. He is also a member of the LCIA; TECBAR; ChBA; and the PNBA.
Career: MA Oxon; LLM Columbia University (New York); Called 2004.
Publications: Co-Editor: 'Jackson & Powell on Professional Liability' (Sweet & Maxwell) Co-Editor: 'Encyclopaedia of Financial Services Law' (Sweet & Maxwell).

SPEAIGHT, Anthony QC
4 Pump Court, London
020 7842 5555
aspeaight@4pumpcourt.com
Featured in Construction (London)
Practice Areas: Barrister with a practice in construction and technology, professional negligence, financial services, other public law and disciplinary work, and other property-related and commercial cases. Cases include : K/S Victoria Street v House of Fraser [2012] 2 WLR 470, Court of Appeal; Shoreline Housing Partnership v Mears (2013) Court of Appeal (construction contract); R (ABS) v Financial Services Compensation Scheme (2011) judicial review; Mon Tresor v Mauritius (2008) Privy Council; Sumukan v Commonwealth Secretariat [2008] 1 Lloyd's Rep, international arbitration appeal; Malmesbury v Strutt & Parker (2007) £100 million professional negligence claim.
Professional Memberships: TECBAR, COMBAR, PNBA, ALBA, LCIA Users'

Council, Kuala Lumpur Regional Arbitration Centre's Panel.
Career: Barrister in practice in the Temple since 1973. Silk 1995.
Publications: 'Butterworths Professional Negligence Service' (co-editor); 'Architect's Legal Handbook' (editor); 'Law of Defective Premises' (co-author).
Personal: Chairman of Bar Council's Access to the Bar Committee 2004-6; Vice Chairman, Bar Council IT Panel 2000-3, Member of the government Commission on a UK Bill of Rights (2011-12). Trained Mediator; Accredited Adjudicator.

SPEARMAN, Richard QC
Thirty Nine Essex Street, London
020 7242 7803
rspearman@4-5.co.uk
Featured in Data Protection (London), Defamation/Privacy (London), Media & Entertainment (London)
Practice Areas: Practice Areas: Chancery, Commercial, Common Law, including: civil fraud, media and entertainment, copyright, privacy, confidence, data protection, defamation, sports law, insurance and reinsurance, sale of goods, restraint of trade, professional negligence. Reported cases include: Warren v Mendy (boxing); Istel v Tully (self-incrimination); R v Jockey Club ex p Aga Khan, Law Society v DCA (judicial review); Brinks v Abu Saleh, Independent Trustee Services v GP Noble (tracing); Kazakstan Wool Producers v NCM (insurance/construction of contract); Papamichael v National Westminster Bank, National Westminster Bank v Malhan (banking); AIRC v PPL, Hyde Park v Yelland, Ashdown v Telegraph, Nottinghamshire v NGN; Sony v Easyinternet, Sawkins v Hyperion, Independiente v Music Trading Online, Twentieth-Century Fox v BT; Twentieth-Century Fox v Harris (copyright); Grobbelaar v NGN, Loutchansky v Times, Chase v NGN, Collins Stewart v FT, Polanski v Conde Nast, Greene v Associated, Armstrong v Times; ZAM v CFW (defamation); A v B (Flitcroft), Jockey Club v Buffham, Campbell v MGN, A-G v Parry, Cream Holdings v Banerjee, Johnson v MDU, Lord Browne of Madingley v Associated, Murray v Big Pictures; Re X (A Child); Terry v Persons Unknown, BBC v Harper Collins, Goodwin v NGN, Giggs v NGN ; McLaren v NGN; Fairstar v Adkins (confidence/privacy/data protection); Athletic Union of Constantinople v NBA (basketball/arbitration/award/jurisdiction); Napoleons Leisure v Singh (cheques/gaming); Adidas v USTA (tennis/competition law); Scopelight v FACT and Northumbria Police (police powers).
Professional Memberships: COMBAR, ChBA, Bar Sports Law Group
Career: Career: Called 1977; QC 1996; assistant recorder 1998; Recorder 2000; bencher Middle Temple 2006; Deputy High Court Judge 2013.

SPECK, Adrian QC
8 New Square, London
020 7405 4321
adrian.speck@8newsquare.co.uk
Featured in Information Technology (London), Intellectual Property (London), Media & Entertainment (London)
Practice Areas: Barrister (QC) specialising in all aspects of intellectual property, media and entertainment, and information technology. IP areas include patents, trade marks, copyright, passing off, confidential information, registered and unregistered designs, M&E areas include broadcasting (terrestrial and satellite), publishing, performers' rights, moral rights. IT specialisms include internet law, database rights, telecommunications. Also specialises in jurisdiction disputes under the CJJA 1982 Brussels Convention. Recent cases include Hospira (AG) v Novartis Uk Ltd (patents), Specsavers v Asda (trademarks), virgin Atlantic Airways v Air Canada (patents). For comprehensive CV visit chambers website at www.8newsquare.co.uk
Professional Memberships: Patent Bar Association (PBA); Chancery Bar Association.
Career: Called 1993.
Publications: 'Modern Law of Copyright', 3rd edn.
Personal: Born 1969. Educated at Seaford Head Comprehensive; Kings College, Cambridge (1991 BA Physics and Theoretical Physics - 1st Class); College of Law 1992 (Common Professional Exam with distinction); ICSL 1993 (Bar Vocational Course). Appointed QC 2012.

SPEIR, John
Westwater Advocates, Edinburgh
07739 639 286
john.speir@westwateradvocates.com
Featured in Family/Matrimonial (Scotland)
Practice Areas: John Speir has extensive experience appearing at all levels of civil courts and tribunals. He is recognised as one of the notable family law practitioners in Scotland, in particular financial provision on divorce and termination of cohabitation and also in cases involving international relocation of children. He is also regularly instructed in other areas in particular professional and medical negligence cases and has been an ad hoc Advocate Depute for several years. In addition he is both an accredited mediator and arbitrator and is a member of the Faculty of Advocates Alternative Dispute Resolution Service. Recent significant cases include: C v M 2012 GWD 9-170 (international relocation of children); B v B 2012 Fam LR 65 (financial provision on divorce - valuation of property and special circumstances); MC v Borders Health Board 2012 CSIH 49 (medical negligence); Whigham v Owen 2013 SLT 483 (financial claims by former cohabitants); W v W 2013 Fam LR 85 (financial provision on divorce, valuation of shares and claims of economic advantage/disadvantage); Yazdanparast v Yazdanparast 2013 Fam LR 44 (Divorce; decree by default).

SPENCE, Simon QC
Red Lion Chambers, Chelmsford
01245 280 880
chelmsford@18rlc.co.uk
Featured in Crime (South Eastern)
Practice Areas: Even mix of prosecuting and defending work across East Anglia and London. In 2008 Simon was the Prosecution Junior in the successful prosecution of Steven Wright for murdering five Ipswich prostitutes. His practice covers a wide variety of serious crime but since taking silk has specialised in cases of homicide and serious violence. Recent high-profile examples include: the successful defence of one defendant in a multi-handed murder trial arising from a combined stabbing and assault with a vehicle; a successful prosecution for murder (and dismembering) despite the absence of a body; a successful response to a CCRC-referred appeal against a murder conviction from 2003. The CCRC appeal turned on disputed fibre evidence and was described by the Court of Appeal as "uniquely complex in terms of forensic evidence". Simon has extensive experience of recent and historic sexual offences cases, particularly concerning very young and vulnerable victims and witnesses. He has also prosecuted illegal entry cases in Suffolk for many years, and defended matters prosecuted by HSE, VOSA and Trading Standards. He is also a door tenant at Dere Street Chambers based in York and Newcastle.
Professional Memberships: Criminal Bar Association; South Eastern Circuit; Chairman of the East Anglian Bar Mess (2011).

SPENCE, Stephen
One Paper Buildings, London
020 7353 3728
clerks@onepaper.co.uk
Featured in Crime (South Eastern)
Practice Areas: Criminal law, sports law, aviation law, courts martial.
Professional Memberships: CBA, South Eastern Circuit, The Guild of Air Pilots and Air Navigators (GAPAN).
Career: Stephen Spence deals with all aspects of serious crime - murder, drug offences, sexual offences and offences involving child abuse. He has been extensively briefed in cases involving Internet crime and Internet child pornography. He has acted as leading counsel in a number of high profile cases, including the recent Yarlswood detention centre case. An RAF trained pilot with wide experience of flying from gliders to fast jets, Stephen Spence has been briefed in aviation cases involving CAA prosecutions, aircraft accidents and parachuting cases. He has also advised a number of sports governing bodies on disciplinary procedures and drug testing, appearing in numerous disciplinary tribunals involving a variety of sports and chairing both disciplinary proceedings and Olympic selection appeals. Stephen has experience of successfully defending fitness to practice cases before the General Medical Council. Stephen Spence is currently a Board member of the British Bobsleigh Association, a member of the Special Advisory Committee of the FIBT (Federation International de Bobsleigh et de Tobogganing) and an advisor to the British Parachute Association.

SPENCER, Andrew
1 Chancery Lane, London
020 7092 2900
ASpencer@1chancerylane.com
Featured in Professional Negligence (London)
Practice Areas: Andrew has a busy professional negligence practice, focusing on claims against solicitors and surveyors. He has also developed a growing practice in personal injury and travel cases as well as acting in property cases, contract and commercial claims and public and regulatory work. Andrew is regularly instructed by Chambers & Partners ranked firms and acts for both claimants and defendants. Andrew leads the Junior Practitioners Group in Chambers, regularly provides training for clients and contributes to the quarterly Briefings issued by Chambers.
Professional Memberships: Personal Injuries Bar Association, Professional Negligence Bar Association, Travel and Tourism Lawyers' Association, London Common Law and Commercial Bar Association and Association of Regulatory and Disciplinary Lawyers.
Career: Called to the Bar in 2004, Gray's Inn.

SPENCER, Martin QC
Hailsham Chambers, London
020 7643 5000
martin.spencer@hailshamchambers.com
Featured in Clinical Negligence (London)

SPENCER, Paul
Serjeants' Inn Chambers, London
020 7427 5000
pspencer@serjeantsinn.com
Featured in Professional Discipline (London)
Practice Areas: Paul Spencer was called to the Bar in 1988. Paul practises in civil law with a specialism in social and healthcare advice and litigation. He is noted in an earlier edition "for being highly knowledgeable and a great team player" and being "very easy to contact... and a fabulous advocate." Please click on the link to the Serjeants' Inn Chambers website for his profile, which sets out full details of his practice including relevant work of note.
Professional Memberships: ALBA, ARDL, CBA and ELBA.
Publications: Co-author of Blackstone's Guide to the Care Standards Act (2000), Contributor to Bullen & Leake; Jacob's Precedents and Pleadings (Sweet and Maxwell), Contributor to Commercial Judicial Review (Sweet and Maxwell).
Personal: Bencher of the Middle Temple, Legal Member of the Inns of Court Conduct Committee, Middle Temple advocacy trainer.

SPRINZ, Lucy
1 Garden Court Family Law Chambers, London
020 7797 7900
sprinz@1gc.com
Featured in Family/Matrimonial (London)
Practice Areas: Lucy specialises exclusively in children law, in the public, private and international law fields. In the public law arena she is regularly instructed on behalf of local authorities, parents and children and frequently appears in cases involving serious allegations of domestic violence, sexual abuse, illegal substance or alcohol abuse and cases involving complex medical issues. In the private law field she has considerable experience of residence and contact disputes. Lucy also undertakes children work involving an international element, particularly intercountry adoption.
Professional Memberships: FLBA, Bar Pro Bono Unit.
Career: BA (Hons) History and Politics, University of Nottingham. GDL Nottingham Law School. Inner BA (Hons) History and Politics, University of Nottingham. GDL Nottingham Law School. Inner Temple Major Scholarship. BVC College of Law. Inner Temple Outstanding BVC Award. Called to the Bar 2008. Pupil and then tenant at 1 Garden Court.
Publications: Special guardianship orders versus adoption orders - Re BS and ED (Children): (Placement Order or Special Guardianship Order) [2013] EWHC 2607, Kinship carers and looked after child status - KS v Bradford Metropolitan District Council [2014] EWHC 11 (Admin), Adoption in 2014 [2014] Fam Law 335. Re A (A Child) [2012] UKSC 60, Re E (A Child) (Application to withdraw Proceedings, Grounds for Emergency Removal of a Child) [2013]

EWHC 2400 (Fam), A Father v SBC & Ors [2014] EWFC 6.

ST VILLE, James
8 New Square, London
020 7405 4321
St.Ville@8newsquare.co.uk
Featured in Information Technology (London), Intellectual Property (London)

Practice Areas: James specialises in intellectual property law and appears in disputes relating to patents, confidential information, trade marks, passing off, trade libel, registered designs, unregistered design rights, copyright, database right, and IT and computer contracts many of which deal with complex engineering, electronics and software. He also has expertise in areas of practice such as search orders, Norwich Pharmacal orders, disk imaging orders, delivery up of source code, ex-parte injunctions to identify and deal with computer hackers and other interim injunctions which need to be kept confidential, jurisdiction disputes, pre-action disclosure, third party disclosure, UK Border Agency seizures and disputes over letters of request and the examination of witnesses for the purpose of foreign proceedings. He is a chartered engineer with substantial experience of commercial electronics, optical communications and engineering research. Please see his website entry at www.8newsquare.co.uk/jsv for recent cases such as Alfa Laval Tumba v Separator Spares [2013] 1 WLR 1110 (CA), Ecge AG v OHIM ('KMIX' Community Trade Mark, Case T 444/10) and First Subsea v Balltec [2014] EWHC 866.

Professional Memberships: Intellectual Property Bar Association (IPBA); The Intellectual Property Lawyers Organisation (TIPLO); Society of Computers and Law (SCL); Chartered Engineer (CEng); Institution of Engineering and Technology (IET); Chancery Bar Association (ChBA).

Career: Called 1995, Gray's Inn.

Personal: Resides London.

STACEY, Dan
Hailsham Chambers, London
020 7643 5000
dan.stacey@hailshamchambers.com
Featured in Costs Litigation (London)

Practice Areas: Specialises in professional indemnity (solicitors, surveyors, accountants, financial advisors etc.), commercial and banking litigation and costs. He has appeared in various claims in the High Court and Court of Appeal (with a leader and on his own) with numerous cases reported on Lawtel and BAILII. As a former litigator at Allen & Overy, he is familiar with large-scale, document heavy cases. With significant trial experience, he has particular expertise in limitation, equitable relief, claims against fiduciaries and contractual and statutory interpretation. He has also been involved in several recent lenders' claims against well-known valuers/surveyors and solicitors (both for claimant and defendant)

Personal: Education: Magdalen College, Oxford (Modern History, First Class); City University (Diploma in Law);ICSL School of Law (Gray's Inn Prince of Wales Scholar)

STAGG, Paul
1 Chancery Lane, London
020 7092 2900
Pstagg@1chancerylane.com
Featured in Police Law (All Circuits), Personal Injury (London)

Practice Areas: Paul specialises in police law (mainly for defendants), personal injury, clinical negligence and claims against public authorities, particularly in the education and social services fields. He also has extensive experience of public law disputes, especially in social security and community care law, and has significant experience of judicial review and inquests. Recent reported cases include: Symes v St George's Healthcare NHS Trust (2014) HC; R (McGrath) v Secretary of State for Work and Pensions (2012) HC; Ryan v Shropshire Council (2012) HC; R (Cooper) v Secretary of State for Work and Pensions (2011) SC; Hufton v Somerset County Council (2011) CA; OOO v Commissioner of Police of the Metropolis (2011) HC; Murdoch v Department for Work & Pensions (2010) HC; Mason v Richard Freeman & Co (2010) CA; Peters v East Midlands SHA (2009) CA, Adorian v Commissioner of Police of the Metropolis (2009) CA, Ashley v Chief Constable of Sussex (2008) HL.

Professional Memberships: Personal Injuries Bar Association; Professional Negligence Bar Association; Administrative Law Bar Association.

Career: Called to the Bar in 1994, Gray's Inn. LLB (Hons) First Class, University of Warwick.

Publications: Co-editor Kemp & Kemp, 'The Quantum of Damages'.

STANSFIELD, Piers QC
Keating Chambers, London
020 7544 2600
pstansfield@keatingchambers.com
Featured in Construction (London)

Practice Areas: Specialist with wide experience of construction, engineering and energy disputes, and professional negligence within these areas of expertise, known for his ability to master technical detail including engineering, delay analysis and forensic accountancy. He has been involved in complex and high value claims arising out of hospitals, tunnels, port facilities, shipbuilding, aircraft manufacturing, chemical plants, and power stations. He has a wide range of advocacy experience, in domestic and international arbitrations, in the High Court, and in alternative dispute resolution. He also has considerable experience of adjudication, including making written and oral submissions to adjudicators, advising and appearing in enforcement proceedings, and acting as adjudicator himself.

Professional Memberships: Technology and Construction Bar Association (TECBAR); Commercial Bar Association (COMBAR); Society of Construction Law; Society for Computers and Law.

Career: Called to Bar 1993, Queen's Counsel 2012, TECBAR accredited adjudicator.

Publications: Contributor - Keating on Construction Contracts Ninth Edition and Keating on NEC 3.

STARKS, Nicholas
St Ives Chambers, Birmingham
01212 360 863
nicholas.starks@stiveschambers.co.uk
Featured in Family/Matrimonial (Midlands)

Practice Areas: Family Finance.

Professional Memberships: Family Law Bar Association.

Career: Nicholas is a senior junior counsel of over 20 years' experience. He specialises in family financial provision, principally financial orders upon divorce but also claims under TLATA, IPFDA, sch 1 Children Act and Civil Partnership Act 2004. Nicholas frequently deals with high net worth claims, involving business, farming and overseas assets. In 'Chambers and Partners Directory 2011' he is praised for his detailed approach to ancillary relief" and was commended by the Court of Appeal for his 'lucid argument' in the recent case of Kaur v Matharu [2010] EWCA Civ 930.

STARTE, Harvey
One Brick Court, London
020 7353 8845
hs@onebrickcourt.com
Featured in Defamation/Privacy (London)

Practice Areas: Defamation, malicious falsehood, privacy and breach of confidence, contempt, reporting restrictions, data protection, freedom of information and publication-related media and information law generally, including pre-publication/ broadcast advice. Cases include: S v Newham LBC; Reid Minty v Taylor; Rahamin v Channel Four; Al-Fagih v HH Saudi Research Publishing; The Rt Hon Lester Bird v BBC; Musa King v Telegraph Group; Pritchard Engelfield v Steinberg; Robbie Williams v MGN Ltd; Koronky and anr v Time Life Entertainment Group; David Moyes v Wayne Rooney and Harper Collins; Dizaei v News Group Newspapers Ltd; SA v Sec of State for Home Dept; Henry v News Group Newspapers Ltd; Morrissey v Associated Newspapers Ltd; Maisto v Kyrgiannakis; Serrano v Associated Newspapers Ltd.

Career: Call to the bar 1985, Gray's Inn. Legal Manager of Independent and Independent on Sunday Newspapers 1995-96. Practising from One Brick Court 1987-95 and from 1996 onwards.

Publications: Carter-Ruck on Libel and Slander, 4th & 5th editions, editor; Carter-Ruck on Libel & Privacy, 6th Edition (2010), contributing editor.

Personal: Millfield School; Fitzwilliam College, Cambridge (1977 BA Hons English; MA (Cantab)); City University (1984 Diploma in law).

STEEL, John QC
Thirty Nine Essex Street, London
020 7832 1111
john.steel@39essex.com
Featured in Aviation (London), Planning (London)

Practice Areas: John's practice is for national and international clients at the highest level in planning, aviation and aerospace, infrastructure, real-estate, regulatory and environmental law; advocay and advisory work in UK and abroad. Recent cases: Airport and airspace (London and Regional Airports and airlines), Olympic CPOs, retail, infrastructure, energy, housing and village green inquiries; local plans; minerals and waste cases; planning and environmental public inquiries and High Court cases in England and Wales.

Professional Memberships: Planning and Environment Bar Association; Administrative Law Bar Association; Fellowships: Chartered Institute of Arbitrators, Royal Geographical Society, Royal Aeronautical Society, Royal Society of Arts; Hon. Legal Adviser Air League, BBGA.

Career: Called to the Bar 1978; Silk 1993; Recorder 2000; CEDR Mediator; International arbitrator.

Personal: Durham University (BSc Hons Chemistry); Hon. Fellow Durham University (Law); Gray's Inn Prizewinner 1978; Bencher Gray's Inn, Chairman of Management Committee 2013; Recorder Civil and Crime.

STEELE, Gordon QC
Terra Firma Chambers, Edinburgh
gordon.steele@terrafirmachambers.com
Featured in Planning (Scotland)

Practice Areas: Planning.

Professional Memberships: Chairman of the Scottish Planning Local Government and Environmental Bar Group 2002 to 2012.

STEINBERG, Harry
12 King's Bench Walk, London
020 7583 0811
steinberg@12kbw.co.uk
Featured in Personal Injury (London), Personal Injury (All Circuits)

Practice Areas: Harry Steinberg is a specialist in serious personal injury (particularly cases involving catastrophic or brain injury), industrial disease and product liability. He acted as junior counsel for the claimants in the pleural plaque test cases from trial up to the appeal in the House of Lords. He is often instructed in group actions (he is currently instructed in the PIP breast implant cases) and claims of high value. He was Chambers & Partners' Personal injury/Clinical negligence junior barrister of the year 2011. He represents claimants and defendants and is known for his handling of difficult cases, complicated schedules of loss and tricky legal issues. Chambers & Partners 2011 described him as a junior with a "fantastic brain" and a formidable reputation for his handling of industrial disease cases.

Professional Memberships: PIBA and TECBAR.

Career: Called in 1997. Former judicial assistant to Lord Woolf and Lord Justice Brooke.

Publications: Contributor to Butterworths' Professional Negligence Service.

STEINERT, Jonathan
Henderson Chambers, London
020 7583 9020
clerks@hendersonchambers.co.uk
Featured in Real Estate Litigation (London)

Practice Areas: Jonathan Steinert's practice focusses on all aspects of contentious and non-contentious property and landlord and tenant and associated areas including competition, commercial, business, telecoms, planning, insolvency, professional negligence, product liability and IT. His work has a particular emphasis on the leisure industry. His commercial practice centres on product liability, franchising, partnership, joint venture, development agreements and shareholder disputes. His clients include the UK's largest companies in the sector. Recent cases include: JP Tupper Associates -v- Pearson-Chisman (2011, Kitchin J,LTL 23/5/11); Lambe v Saunders (2009 Blake J LTL 14/12/09); Rouf v Cafe Rouge (2009) All ER (D) 29; Clarkson v Credit Agricole [2008] EWHC 41 (QB); Anderson Antiques (UK) Ltd v Anderson Wharf (Hull) Ltd and Another [2007] All ER (D)409; Carnegie v Glessen and Others [2005] All ER (D) 22(CA); Re a debtor (No 503 SD 2001) [2002] All ER (D)500; Aylesbond Estates Ltd v McMillan and Garg [2000] 32 HLR 1(CA).

Professional Memberships: COMBAR, Chancery Bar Association, PNBA, ACI Arb.

Career: B.A. Hons PPE Balliol College Oxford 1983; Dip Law 1984; called 1986.
Publications: Competiton Law, Butterworths 2004.

STEPHENS, Jessica
Keating Chambers, London
020 7544 2600
jstephens@keatingchambers.com
Featured in Construction (London)
Practice Areas: Specialist in construction, engineering, shipbuilding and energy disputes, including advising on high value residential and commercial premises. Adjudication including advising, drafting submissions and appearing at hearings before adjudicators. Appeared on applications for the enforcement of adjudicators' decisions and in disputes concerning professional negligence of construction professionals. International arbitration experience includes disputes relating to the construction of ultra harsh environment rigs, alleged defects in design and construction of a container port in the Caribbean, additional costs and delays in relation to one of the largest mega-yachts ever constructed, and a project relating to the conversion of a bulk carrier into a pipe laying vessel. Advises and appears in procurement disputes (including Alstom v Eurostar) and general commercial disputes. Advised in disputes relating to of party walls, rights to light and nuisance.
Professional Memberships: TECBAR; SCL; COMBAR.
Career: Called 2001; Public Access Training 2008.
Publications: Contributor, Keating on Construction Contracts – Ninth Edition 2012; Contributor; Keating on JCT Contracts, 2011; Co-Author: RICS Case in Point: Rights to Light (co-authored with Sarah Hannaford QC) 2008; Contributor, Keating on Construction Contracts - Eighth Edition 2006; Co-Author: RICS Case in Point: Party Walls, 2004.

STEPHENSON, Christopher
9 Gough Square, London
020 7832 0500
cstephenson@9goughsquare.co.uk
Featured in Clinical Negligence (London), Personal Injury (London)
Practice Areas: Personal injury and clinical negligence, predominantly for Claimants. Wide experience of the whole range of personal injury claims, from the very small to the catastrophic including employer's liability (accident and disease). Now focused on high value claims, with particular expertise in quantifying high value complex claims. Well established clinical negligence practice, used to dealing with complicated and high value claims, usually in the High Court.
Professional Memberships: PIBA, APIL, PNBA.
Career: Pupillage at 9 Gough Square under Nicolas Hillier and Grahame Aldous QC, called in 1994. Broad common law practice for 7 years, including extensive criminal work, before concentrating on personal injury and clinical negligence. Now a well established senior junior used to cases of high value and complexity, usually in the High Court. Regularly instructed alone against Silks and led by Silks in Chambers. Pragmatic and commercial approach to litigation with a particular ability to get on with clients and opponents alike.
Publications: Contributing editor to 9 Gough Square Publication: Guide to Clinical Negligence Claims, chapter author of APIL Guides to RTA Claims and Evidence. Author of numerous articles for range of publications including JPIL.
Personal: Interests include passion for cooking, eating and drinking, followed by vigorous repentance.

STERN, David
5 St Andrew's Hill, London
020 7332 5400
DavidStern@5sah.co.uk
Featured in Financial Crime (London)
Practice Areas: Financial regulatory, business crime and serious fraud with a particular emphasis on financial services and insurance, proceeds of crime and asset forfeiture.
Professional Memberships: Fraud Lawyers Association and Association of Regulatory and Disciplinary Lawyers
Career: Head of Financial Regulation and Business Crime Practice Groups. Acted as leading junior and junior counsel in many high profile proceedings, especially cases brought by the Serious Fraud Office and the FCA and those with international agency involvement. Currently instructed in the SFO's first prosecutions of alleged manipulation of US$ (Contogoulas) and Yen (Wilkinson) Libor benchmarks. Recent cases include Katcharian (prime bank guarantee high yield investment fraud), GFX Capital Markets (FX Ponzi scheme), Hughes (£100 million Spanish boiler room), Carney (commercial mortgage fraud) and Sandison (stock exchange listing fraud). Historical expertise includes Guinness II (Lord Spens), Wallace Duncan Smith and Dr Clewes (Butte Mining). Technical expertise in appellate and divisional court work, including leading case law on the right to silence. Particular expertise in advisory, regulatory and tribunal work arising out of financial transactions. Instructed to represent corporates and individuals in FCA regulatory investigations. Commercial negotiator and accredited mediator, handling commercial disputes involving financial services and high value insurance claims.

STERNBERG, Daniel
9-12 Bell Yard, London
020 7400 1800
d.sternberg@912by.com
Featured in Extradition (London)
Practice Areas: Daniel is a specialist extradition and public law practitioner. He represents both requesting authorities and defendants, and advise pre-arrest and in import extradition cases, involving the full range of criminal offences. Daniel is adept as arguing points of law on appeal in the Administrative Court and on applications for permission to appeal to the Supreme Court. He is experienced in Judicial Review and Habeas Corpus proceedings concerning judicial discretion, time limits and failure to remove. Recent instructions: representing the USA in requests to prosecute complex frauds (Jethwa & Others 2011-2014); Ghana in a death penalty case (Gambrah, 2014); and Brazil and Albania in the Magistrates' and High Court. Daniel advised CPS Kent on the extradition of Jeremy Forrest. Defence work includes advising on the UK's extradition relations with Japan, and securing the discharge of a mentally ill person in the High Court (Arshad v Malta, 2013-2014).
Professional Memberships: CBA, Extradition Lawyers Association, Young Barristers Committee, YFLA, Three Faiths Forum Legal Group.
Career: MA (Cantab), Called 2006 (Gray's Inn), Appointed to SFO prosecution and POCA C Panels, CPS prosecution and extradition specialist panels.
Publications: Backstone's Criminal Practice 2013 Chapter on Extradition, Westlaw Insight articles on Extradition (with Katherine Tyler).

STEVENS, Andrew
4 Pump Court, London
020 7842 5555
clerks@4pumpcourt.com
Featured in Shipping (London)
Practice Areas: The bulk of Andrew's work is in heavyweight international commercial arbitration (incl. LMAA, ICC, UNCITRAL, LCIA, HKIAC and SIAC seated in e.g. London, HK, Singapore and Geneva) as well as Commercial & Admiralty Court and TCC litigation. The majority of his cases involves Asian parties including Chinese state owned enterprises. Specific areas of expertise include: Energy, oil & gas and nuclear; Offshore (including wind farms, oil and gas platforms and FPSOs); Shipbuilding; Construction; Banking/Finance (e.g. refund guarantee disputes) and commercial fraud; and Shipping and commodities (full range of charterparty disputes, cargo claims, ship management claims, and Admiralty matters such as ship mortgage claims).
Professional Memberships: COMBAR, LMAA Supporting Member, LSLC Young Maritime Professionals, Bar Council China Special Interest Group
Career: Call, Lincoln's Inn (2007). Pupillage, Essex Court Chambers (2007-2008); 2 Temple Gardens (2008-2011) including 6 months at Gide Loyrette Nouel, Paris; 4 Pump Court (2011 to date).
Personal: MA (Cantab). Frequent traveller. Speaks fluent French, German and basic Mandarin.

STEWARD, Claire
Kings Chambers, Manchester
08450 343 444
clerks@kingschambers.com
Featured in Clinical Negligence (Northern)
Practice Areas: Specialises in clinical negligence with extensive experience in all areas including: surgical negligence, delay in diagnosing cancer, orthopaedics, obstetrics and gynaecology, A&E, primary healthcare, cosmetic surgery and dentistry. She also has a substantial personal injury practice in cases involving serious injury.
Professional Memberships: Personal Injury Bar Association.
Career: University of Manchester BA (Hons) Modern History with Economics CPE (Manchester Metropolitan University) BVC (Manchester Metropolitan University) Called to the Bar 2002 (Lincolns Inn – Lord Denning Scholarship).

STEWART, Roger QC
4 New Square, London
020 7822 2000
r.stewart@4newsquare.com
Featured in Construction (London), Insurance (London), International Arbitration (London), Professional Negligence (London)
Practice Areas: Construction, international arbiration, commercial and insurance.
Professional Memberships: LCIA, Combar, LCLCBA, TecBar, PNBA.
Career: Called 1986, Silk 2001, Deputy High Court Judge (TCC), recorder.
Publications: General Editor: Jackson & Powell on Professional Negligence.
Personal: Married, 4 children, 4 step-children; Senior Bar Auditor Inner Temple; Skiing, Sailing and Switzerland.

STEWART SMITH, Rodney
New Square Chambers, London
020 7419 8000
rodney.stewartsmith@newsquarechambers.co.uk
Featured in Chancery (London)
Practice Areas: Traditional chancery (with a special knowledge and practical experience of esoteric and ancient law from Magna Carta onwards), including in particular wills, trusts and estates, inheritance tax and capital gains tax, land registration matters, easements, restrictive covenants, landlord and tenant (commercial and residential) and other real property matters, partnership and professional negligence.
Professional Memberships: Society of Trust and Estate Practitioners, Chancery Bar Association.
Career: Called to the Bar 1964. Practised since then at 1 New Square and New Square Chambers, Lincoln's Inn. Assistant Recorder 1990-94. Recorder 1994-2004. Member of Land Registration Rule Committee 1991 to date. General Tax Commissioner 1991-2009. Master of the Bench of the Middle Temple since 1998 and Autumn Reader 2011. Deputy Commissary of the Court of Faculties 2000 to date.
Publications: 'Butterworths Land Development Encyclopaedia' (1976).
Personal: Winchester College and Trinity Hall, Cambridge (BA 1963, LLB 1964). Leisure interests: watching cricket, theatre and music and hill walking.

STEYN, Karen QC
11KBW, London
020 7632 8500
karen.steyn@11kbw.com
Featured in Administrative & Public Law (London), Civil Liberties & Human Rights (London), Data Protection (London), Local Government (London)
Practice Areas: All aspects of public law and human rights. Specialisms include public international law, environmental and information law, education, immigration and asylum, equality and local government. Recent Supreme Court cases: Kennedy [2014] UKSC 20 (A10 ECHR; FOIA); Smith v MOD [2014] 1 AC 52 (combat immunity; A2 ECHR); SG [2014] UKSC (benefit cap case); Evans v AG [2014] UKSC (FOIA/EIR veto) and Al Rawi [2012] 1 AC 531 (Guantanamo; closed hearings). Other recent cases include: R (Noor Khan) v SSFCA [2014] 1 WLR 872 (drone strikes challenge; justiciability); Belhaj v Straw [2014] CA (State immunity; Act of State); R (PMI) v MCO [2014] HC (Royal Charter JR; bias; Wednesbury); Serdar Mohammed v SSD [2014] HC (power to detain in armed conflict; Crown Act of State); Jaloud v Netherlands (2014) ECtHR GC (A1 jurisdiction); R (Al Saadoon & ors) v SSD (Iraq JRs; A3 and A5 ECHR; UNCAT); Recyclate [2013] Env LR – transposition of Waste Framework Directive.
Career: Called: 1995. QC: 2014.

STILITZ, Daniel QC
11KBW, London
020 7632 8500
Daniel.Stilitz@11kbw.com
Featured in Administrative & Public Law (London), Employment (London)
Practice Areas: Employment law, public law, commercial law. Recent cases include: LMR v Dover (anti-harassment injunction), R (Islington BC) v Mayor of London (closure of fire stations), Gregg v Troy (maternity and sex discrimination), R (Green Transport Company) v West Midlands ITA (travel reimbursements), Unison v IBM & Accenture (TUPE), GNC Ltd v Palletways (QBD, road distribution), Turner v Merrill Lynch (QBD, bonus claim), A v B (whistleblowing), Skipper v BP plc (age discrimination), Stone v Merrill Lynch International (whistleblowing), R (K & AC Jackson & Sons) v DEFRA (bovine tuberculosis, abuse of power), BTIG v Reiss (Comm Ct, unauthorized trading), Nescar v Middlesbrough FC (transfer of professional footballer), Powell v Hounslow LBC (SC, homelessness, introductory tenancies and human rights), Tenner v PwC (disability discrimination), Manchester City Council v Pinnock (SC, demoted tenancies and Article 8), Gascoyne v Force India (Formula One, wrongful dismissal), R (Servier) v NICE (commercial JR, procedural fairness), CIBC v Beck (age and race discrimination, disclosure), R (A) v Croydon LBC (Social services), R (Eisai Ltd) v NICE (commercial judicial review), City Index Ltd v Gawler (Knowing receipt). Also sits as a Mediator.
Professional Memberships: ELBA; ALBA; ELA; COMBAR; CEDR Solve Mediator.
Career: Called to the Bar in 1992. QC 2010.
Personal: New College Oxford, BA (1st class hons). City University CPE (distinction), MA. Born 1 August 1968.

STOCKLEY, Ruth
Kings Chambers, Manchester
08450 343 444
clerks@kingschambers.com
Featured in Environment (Northern), Planning (Northern)
Practice Areas: Town and country planning; highways and rights of way; compulsory purchase; environment; village greens; taxi licensing; local government and judicial review. Recent significant reported cases include: R (on application of Barkas) v North Yorkshire County Council [2014] UKSC 31 (village greens); R (on application of Barrow Borough Council) v Cumbria County Council [2011] EWHC 2051 (consultation on development plan documents); R (on application of Peat) v Hyndburn Borough Council [2011] EWHC 1739 (Housing Act selective licensing); Thompson v Pendle Borough Council [2011] EWHC 1751 (tree preservation orders); Chauffeur Bikes Limited v Leeds City Council [2005] All ER 106 (private hire vehicle licensing); R (on application of Hampson) v Wigan Metropolitan Borough Council [2005] All ER 383 (planning).
Professional Memberships: Planning and Environment Bar Association; Administrative Law Bar Association.
Career: University: Nottingham; degree: Law (LLB); called: 1988 (Lincoln's Inn).
Publications: Assistant editor of Sweet and Maxwell's Encyclopaedia of Highway Law and Practice.

STOKES, Mary
Erskine Chambers, London
020 7242 5532
mstokes@erskinechambers.com
Featured in Company (London)
Practice Areas: Principal area of practice is company law, including corporate insolvency. Also LLPs and partnership; financial services.
Professional Memberships: Chancery Bar Association; COMBAR.
Career: Called to the Bar in 1989 and joined Erskine Chambers in 1990.
Publications: Consulting Editor of Butterworths Company Cases; Contributor to Buckley on the Companies Acts.
Personal: Educated at the Cambridgeshire High School for Girls; Brasenose College, Oxford and Harvard Law School. Former Fellow and Tutor of Brasenose College, Oxford.

STONE, Christopher
Devereux, London
020 7353 7534
stone@devchambers.co.uk
Featured in Employment (London), Tax (London)
Practice Areas: Employment – Chris has a broad practice covering all areas of employment and discrimination law. He often appears in multi-day discrimination and whistleblowing hearings in the Tribunals and advises on and acts in restrictive covenant cases in the High Court. Cases include: Jose v Julio [2012] IRLR 180; Andorful v LBHF UKEAT/0410/11; and Keegan v Newcastle United [2010] IRLR 94. Tax – Chris acts for HMRC and taxpayers in a broad range of direct tax disputes. Specialisms include: residence and domicile; deductibility of expenses; and taxation of employment (including employment status and intermediaries). Cases include: Gaines-Cooper (Supreme Court); Daniel and Mertrux (CoA); Samadian, Duckmanton, McLaren and Ramsay (UT). Chris is also instructed in general commercial matters including professional negligence and insurance; and sports disputes.
Professional Memberships: ELA, RBA, LCLCBA, Combar, PNBA
Career: Appointed to Treasury Panel of Counsel (C Panel) in March 2012. Called 2007; Droop Scholar at Lincoln's Inn. Started practice in 2009. Educated St. Anne's College, Oxford and Australian National University. Before coming to the Bar, Chris was a strategy consultant at Accenture and then Mergers and Acquisitions Manager at News International. This background supports his commercial and practical approach to legal issues.
Publications: Contributing author to Bloomsbury Professional's Discrimination Law.
Personal: Chairman Kew Occasionals RFC.

STONE, Judy
11KBW, London
020 7632 8500
Judy.Stone@11kbw.com
Featured in Employment (London)
Practice Areas: Employment and business law specialist. Judy is regularly instructed in claims involving breaches of directors' duties, fiduciary duties, duties of confidence and restrictive covenants, as well as in pension, bonus and other contractual disputes, including those with an international element. In the employment tribunal, Judy has considerable experience of high value whistleblowing and discrimination litigation. Judy appears regularly in the High Court (both Chancery and QBD), employment tribunals, the EAT, and the Court of Appeal. She represents both claimants and respondents/defendants. Judy often acts as sole counsel and as a junior in multi-day and high value litigation. Key cases include: Mindimaxnox LLP v Gover, EAT (lead case on tribunal stays pending the outcome of High Court proceedings); Johal v Equality and Human Rights Commission (no discrimination when employer mistakenly neglects to advise employee on maternity leave of promotion opportunity), RMG v CWU (TUPE consultation – employer's genuine belief); MacCulloch v ICI (Age discrimination in enhanced redundancy schemes).
Professional Memberships: ELBA; ALBA.
Career: Called in 2003.
Publications: Tolley's Employment Handbook (Retirement, Directors).
Personal: Educated at Balliol College, Oxford (first class degree in PPE, Jenkins Scholar), Harvard University (Frank Knox Memorial Fellow) and City University (CPE, Princess Royal Scholarship).

STONE, Lucy QC
Queen Elizabeth Building, London
020 7797 7837
l.stone@qeb-personal.co.uk
Featured in Family/Matrimonial (London)
Practice Areas: All aspects of family law, particularly matters of financial complexity involving substanial assets; prenuptial and postnuptial agreements;complex private law applications relating to children including relocation; and substantial Inheritance Act claims. Has acted for a plethora of celebrities, particularly in the music industry. Consistently lauded for her meticulous attention to detail, absolutely thorough preparation, realistic advice, approachability to professional and lay clients and discretion. Known amongst her peers for her no-nonsense approach.
Professional Memberships: Fellow of the International Academy of Matrimonial Lawyers; has served on the Bar Council and FLBA Committee.
Career: MA Cantab; Called to the Bar in 1983; Silk 2001; Head of Chambers 2007-10. Bencher Middle Temple 2010.
Personal: Married with one child. Blessed with an ability to survive on little sleep, combines a prestigious pratice with a full family life.

STONE, Sally
1 Garden Court Family Law Chambers, London
020 7797 7900
stone@1gc.com
Featured in Family/Matrimonial (London)
Practice Areas: All aspects of children law. Acts in private law proceedings on behalf of parents and on behalf of the child in Rule 16 cases but the main focus of her work is care proceedings and adoption, often acting for Local Authorities but also parents, children and other interested parties. Frequently instructed in cases where there is conflicting and/or complex medical evidence involving non-accidental injury to or death of a child and/or multiple potential perpetrators. Also instructed in cases where there are complex allegations of sexual harm and mental health issues. Often brought into cases as a junior at the request of leading Counsel. Involved in training days for social workers, Guardians and solicitors representing parties in care proceedings.
Professional Memberships: Family Law Bar Association, The Association of Lawyers for Children.
Career: BA (Hons) University of Kent. Called 1994 (Inner Temple). Tenant at Francis Taylor Building 1995-1999, then 1 Garden Court to date.
Personal: Enjoys travelling, skiing and watching rugby.

STONER, Christopher QC
Serle Court, London
020 7242 6105
clerks@serlecourt.co.uk
Featured in Real Estate Litigation (London), Sports Law (London)
Practice Areas: All aspects of property litigation and sports law (with a particular emphasis on litigation drafting and enforcement of rules and regulations). Recent sports law cases include Wilander & Anor v Tobin & Anor; Korda v ITF Limited; Bingham v British Boxing Board of Control; premier league disciplinary proceedings against Liverpool FC and Christian Ziege; Leeds Rugby Limited v Iestyn Harris and Bradford Bulls Holdings Ltd; Various selection appeals. Recent property litigation cases include McDonalds Property Co Limited v HSBC plc; Ipswich Borough Council v Duke & Moore; Barclays Bank plc v Savile Estates Limited; Pound v Ashford Borough Council; Hawksbrook Leisure Limited v Reece-Jones Partnership; Kilmartin v Safeway; Scottish & Newcastle v Raguz; Greatorex v Newman; Geronimo (1) British Waterways (2) v Brentford Yacht & Boat; Moore v British Waterways; EDF Energy v BOH Limited; and Phillips v Francis.
Professional Memberships: ChBA, PBA, Bar Sports Law Group (committee member) BASL.
Career: Called to the Bar in 1991.
Personal: Educated at Shoreham College and the University of East Anglia.

STONOR, Nicholas
Trinity Chambers, Newcastle upon Tyne
0191 232 1927
n.stonor@trinitychambers.co.uk
Featured in Family/Matrimonial (North Eastern)
Practice Areas: Family Law Public law children - has acted as leading junior in a number of complex care cases. He receives regular instructions from local authorities and acts on behalf of family members and children's guardians. He has a particular interest in cases involving complex medical evidence and cultural/religious issues. Private law children - acts for adult family members and children (by their "rule 16.4 guardian") across the spectrum of private law disputes including residence, contact and removal from the jurisdiction. Forced Marriage - provides advice and representation, often at short notice, for local authorities and family members involved in proceedings under the Forced Marriage (Civil Protection) Act 2007. Ancillary - provides robust, realistic and constructive advice and representation. Mental Health /court of Protection: represents vulnerable adults (by litigation friends including the Official Solicitor) and local authorities and family members.

Professional Memberships: FLBA. Appointed Junior Counsel to the Crown (Regional Panel) in 2012.
Career: University College London. Inns of Court School of Law. Delivers seminars to solicitors (recent topics including 'Re B-S and Re W', 'Part 25 Experts', 'The Perils of Social Media in Family Cases' and 'Concurrent Care and Court of Protection Proceedings') also court skills training to social workers.

STOREY, Jeremy QC
4 Pump Court, London
020 7842 5555
jstorey@4pumpcourt.com
Featured in Information Technology (London)
Practice Areas: Information technology, construction, professional negligence and commercial work.
Professional Memberships: Chartered Institute of Arbitrators, Society for Computers and Law, TECBAR, Society of Construction Law, LCIA Users' Council
Career: Called to the Bar 1974, assistant recorder 1990, QC 1994, recorder and Deputy Judge of TCC 1995, Deemster (Judge) of the Isle of Man Courts 1999, Deputy High Court Judge (QBD) 2008, qualified mediator and arbitrator, Civil Mediation Council, World Intellectual Property Organization of Arbitration and Mediation Center (Geneva) Panel of Neutrals (IT), Mediator with Kuala Lumpur Regional Centre for Arbitration
Personal: Cambridge University (Scholar, BA Law 1st Class) 1970-73. Born 1952.

STOREY, Paul QC
29 Bedford Row Chambers, London
020 7404 1044
clerks@29br.co.uk
Featured in Family/Matrimonial (London)
Practice Areas: Family law: Public Law, all areas including appeals CoA and Supreme Court. Representation of vulnerable adults. Private Law and Adoption.
Professional Memberships: FLBA.
Career: Called Lincoln's Inn 1982. Articles in Family Law (12/95, 4/96, 10/96, 3/97). Regular speaker at national and local conferences/training days and JSB. Recorder. Deputy High Court Judge.
Personal: Married, six children.

STOUT, Holly
11KBW, London
020 7632 8500
Holly.Stout@11kbw.com
Featured in Data Protection (London), Education (London), Employment (London)
Practice Areas: Practice Areas: Employment law, education law, public law (local government, community care, immigration and human rights), information and data protection law. Recent cases include: Essex County Council v Secretary of State for Education (equalities duties and funding cuts); Dowsett v SSJ, HC (searching of male prisoners discriminatory); Anderson v LFEPA (collective agreement, interpretation); Pannu v Geo W King, EAT (supply of goods exception to TUPE); O'Brien v Ministry of Justice, SC (part-time judicial pensions); Bury MBC v SU, UT (mainstream education for child with SEN); Domb v Hammersmith and Fulham, CA (community care charges and equality duties); Chandler v Camden (re proposed UCL Academy).
Career: Called 2003. Attorney General's B Panel for civil litigation.
Publications: Contributor to Tolley's Employment Law Handbook, Butterworths Employment Law, Halsbury's Laws (Administrative Law section), Tottel's Local Government Law.
Personal: Cambridge University (MA); City University CPE Dip. Law (Distinction).

STRAKER, Timothy QC
4-5 Gray's Inn Square, London
020 7404 5252
clerks@4-5.co.uk
Featured in Environment (London), Local Government (London), Planning (London)
Practice Areas: Principal areas of practice: local government, public law and planning. Major infrastructure cases (e.g. bridge over the Mersey, Felixstowe, Crossrail, Oxford-Marylebone Railway and HS2). Has acted in many leading public law cases concerning inter alia, environmental assessments, compulsory purchase, planning, housing and housing benefits, Sunday trading, caravan sites and 'new age travellers', free speech, professional advertising, discrimination and professional conduct. Appeared in many cases at the higher levels. Represented returning officers in the first challenge to a European election result and in the only challenges to parliamentary results for 80 years. Acts for many local authorities and regulatory bodies. Consultant editor of the Registration of Political Parties Act 1998, contributor to the 'Rights of Way Law Review' and to 'Judicial Review'. Editor Public Health and Environmental Protection (Halsbury's Laws of England) and Local Government (Halsbury's Laws of England). Editor 'Civil Court Practice', also author, 'Markets' (Halsbury's Laws of England) and 'Judicial Review: Case Studies in Context'.
Professional Memberships: Administrative Law Bar Association, Planning Bar Association, Administrative Court Users' Committee, Parliamentary Bar Mess.
Career: Called to the Bar 1977. Silk 1996. Assistant recorder 1998, recorder 2000, Planning and Environmental Bar Silk of the Year 2009, Deputy High Court Judge 2010, Times Lawyer of the week 2013, Justice of Appeal (Falklands Court of Appeal), Election Commissioner. Joint Head of Chambers.
Personal: Educated at Malvern College and Downing College, Cambridge (1st Class Hons). Senior Harris Scholar, Downing College Prize for Law, Holt Scholar of Gray's Inn, Lord Justice Holker Senior Award. Admitted to the Bars of Northern Ireland and Trinidad and Tobago.

STREET, Amy
Serjeants' Inn Chambers, London
020 7427 5000
astreet@serjeantsinn.com
Featured in Administrative & Public Law (London), Court of Protection (All Circuits)
Practice Areas: Amy Street was called to the Bar in 2002. Amy specialises in clinical negligence and healthcare, Court of Protection, employment, police, professional discipline and regulatory and public and administrative law. An earlier edition notes that "she is an exceptionally bright barrister who is able to cut through complex issues." Please click on the link to the Serjeants' Inn Chambers website for her profile, which sets out full details of her practice including relevant work of note.
Professional Memberships: ALBA.
Publications: Co-author: Select Committees and Coercive Powers – Clarity or Confusion?, contributor: Medical Treatment: Decisions and the Law; Medical Law Reports, Legal consultant: BBC Radio 4's 'Unreliable Evidence'.

STRONG, Benjamin QC
One Essex Court, London
020 7583 2000
bstrong@oeclaw.co.uk
Featured in Banking & Finance (London), Commercial Dispute Resolution (London), Financial Services (London)
Practice Areas: All types of domestic and international commercial and regulatory disputes, including asset tracing, banking, financial services, insurance, professional negligence, jurisdiction disputes, mergers and acquisitions, company law and commercial aspects of Revenue litigation. Recent cases include Hannam v FCA (market abuse); Credit Suisse v Vestia (swaps and capacity of Dutch housing association); BVI arbitration (breach of contract and loss of profits); RBS v Highland (claim following failure of proposed CDO; trial of anti-suit injunction; setting aside judgment for fraud); Isis v Kaupthing (claim alleging shadow directorship and breach of duty to insolvent company); various derivatives arbitrations; claim on undertaking in damages in interim injunction; Hall v Cable & Wireless (liability of company to shareholders for market announcements); multi-jurisdiction investment fund litigation and arbitration (alleging misconduct by fund manager); Post Office v Tele2 (effect of no waiver clause).
Professional Memberships: COMBAR, Financial Services Lawyers Association.
Career: QC 2014. Called 2001. Solicitor 1994-2001 (Slaughter and May).
Personal: Educated at Jesus College, Cambridge (Philosophy Part I; Law Part II, 1st Class in both).

STRUDWICK, Linda
QEB Hollis Whiteman, London
020 7933 8855
barristers@qebhw.co.uk
Featured in Crime (London)
Practice Areas: Linda Strudwick specialises in serious crime as an experienced leading junior, prosecuting and defending murder, manslaughter, serious fraud, VAT fraud, large-scale drugs importation, human trafficking and confiscation. She is known for her hard work, team work and for getting on with her clients. She has particular expertise in sexual offences and is a specialist rape prosecutor and Category 4 CPS prosecutor. She is frequently called upon by the CPS to advise in difficult cases involving sexual allegations. She is also notably experienced in cases where women are charged with the murder of their children. She has wide-ranging expertise working with witnesses appearing via video links, vulnerable adult and child witnesses and those with learning disabilities. She is a trained intermediary, able to help learning disabled adults and children to understand legal questions and communicate their answers. She has also appeared in cases involving investment frauds, mortgage frauds, and diversion frauds. She has for many years undertaken disciplinary work in the General Medical Council, Courts Martial appeals and advisory work for the Ministry of Defence.
Professional Memberships: Criminal Bar Association, Justice, Association of Regulatory & Disciplinary Lawyers, Public Access Bar Association, registered with the Bar Council – Public Access Directory
Career: Call 1973.
Personal: LLB (Hons), Manchester University.

STUART, Damian
Fourteen, London
020 7583 5123
dstuart@newcourtchambers.com
Featured in Family/Matrimonial (London)
Practice Areas: All areas of family law, particularly public law children's matters. Represents local authorities, parents, extended family members and children on a variety of matters with a particular interest in serious non-accidental injury and child sexual abuse cases, especially where there is a serious factual dispute. Recent Cases: Re K (Children) [2008] 2FCR 599, 101 BMLR 99 Re T (A Child) [2009] EWCA Civ 1208 Re G and E (Children)(Vulnerable Witness) [2011] EWHC 4063 (Fam) SB v A Local Authority and Others [2012] EWCA Civ 1269.
Professional Memberships: FLBA.
Career: Called to the Bar in 2009, Inner Temple. Admitted as a Solicitor in 1998. Formerly a member of the Law Society's Children Panel and a Higher Court advocate from 2004. Direct Access Barrister from 2012. Delivers seminars to social workers and solicitors.
Publications: The Slaying of Re M [2004] Fam Law (August); The Care Lawyer's Number 22 Bus [2004] Fam Law (November).
Personal: Enjoys horse riding, the theatre, good food and good wine.

STUBBS, Rebecca QC
Maitland Chambers, London
020 7406 1200
rstubbs@maitlandchambers.com
Featured in Company (London), Restructuring/Insolvency (London)
Practice Areas: Company and chancery commercial litigation with particular emphasis on company, insolvency, financial services, civil fraud and conflicts of law. Recent cases include advising and acting for the joint administrators of Lehman Brothers International (Europe) on client money and currency issues, advising and acting for the administrators and liquidators of Global Trader (Europe) Limited in connection with issues arising out of MiFID, the FSA's CASS Rules, the insolvency regime, contractual deduction and set-off, and the proper interpretation and effect of ISDA Master Agreements with prime brokers, advising in relation to the meaning and effect of the Landsbanki Freezing order, the Banking Consolidation Directive, Directive 94/19 on Deposit Guarantee Schemes, and the operation of the FSCS, advising counterparties of Kaupthing, Singer & Friedlander in relation to the TBMA/ISMA Global Master Repurchase Agreement, advising a major UK bank in relation to a negative basis trade, and advising the Law Society in connection with the interplay between the regulatory provisions and the granting of security and the onset of insolvency.
Professional Memberships: Chancery Bar Association, COMBAR, Insolvency Court Users' Committee.
Career: Called to the Bar 1994. Junior Counsel to the Crown (1999-2007). Called to the Bar of Grenada and the West Indies Associated States 2005. Registered with the Dubai International Finance Centre courts. Queen's Counsel 2012.
Publications: Contributor to Butterworths 'Practical Insolvency', Butterworth' s Guide

to the Legal Services Act 2007, Mithani on Directors' Disqualification; consultant editor, French's Applications to Wind Up Companies.
Personal: Educated at Darton High School and Downing College Cambridge (1st class hons 1993). Former Queen Mother Scholar of the Middle Temple.

STUBBS, Richard
Trinity Chambers, Newcastle upon Tyne
01912 321 927
r.stubbs@trinitychambers.co.uk
Featured in Employment (North Eastern)
Practice Areas: Richard's employment practice includes multi-day hearings in dismissals, discrimination, TUPE, equal pay, restrictive covenants and contractual disputes. He represents individuals, trade unions, companies, NHS Trusts and local authorities. Richard acted in the mass equal pay litigation involving local authorities and NHS Trusts, including in several GMF hearings. He appears in the EAT and the CA and is also regularly instructed to draft pleadings and to advise on cases. Richard is also a member of Chambers' Business and Chancery groups and practices regularly in those areas, accepting instructions in all areas of insolvency, landlord and tenant, probate, commercial contracts, professional negligence, commercial fraud and company law including director and shareholder disputes.
Professional Memberships: Industrial Law Society, Employment Lawyers Association, R3 - The Association of Business Recovery Professionals.
Career: Called 2005 by Lincoln's Inn (Wolfson Scholar). Practiced at Trinity Chambers since 2006. Appointed to the Attorney General's Panel of Regional Counsel and the Equality and Human Rights Commission Preferred Panel of Counsel. ADR Group Accredited Civil and Commercial Mediator.
Personal: Richard was born in Sheffield in 1981. He is married to Emma and they live in Newcastle upon Tyne with their son Patrick.

STUDD, Anne QC
5 Essex Court, London
020 7410 2000
studd@5essexcourt.co.uk
Featured in Police Law (All Circuits)
Practice Areas: Public & Administrative, Police, Inquests and Inquiries, Professional Discipline.The Hillsborough Inquests; R (on the application of Revenue & Customs Commissioners) (Claimant) v HM Coroner For The City Of Liverpool (Defendant) & (1) Estate Of Roderick Carmichael, deceased (Interested Party) (2) Association Of Personal Injury Lawyers (Interveners) (2014) EWHC 1586;The Azelle Rodney Inquiry – represented the MPS and all officers save for shooter; ZH (by his father & litigation friend GH) v Commissioner of Police of the Metropolis [2013] EWCA Civ 69 [2013] 1 WLR 3021 - The impact of MCA 2005 on policing those with disability; R (on the application of Metropolitan Police Service) (Claimant) v Chairman Of The Inquiry into the death of Azelle Rodney and others [2012] EWHC 2783 - Guidance on disclosure within the meaning of the Inquiry Rules 2006 r.12(4)(a); R (on the application of B) v Chief Constable of Derbyshire (2011) [2011] EWHC 2362 (Admin) - R (on the application of Alandi Salimi) v (1) Secretary of State for the Home Department (2) Independent Police Complaints Commission (2011) EWHC 1714 (Admin) - UKBA and IPCC remit; Re Naomi Bryant (Hampshire) – failures in MAPP provision; Re Mark Nunes and Andrew Markland
Professional Memberships: ARDL, PIBA.
Career: Called to the Bar 1988; Silk 2012

STUDER, Mark
Wilberforce Chambers, London
020 7306 0102
chambers@wilberforce.co.uk
Featured in Chancery (London), Charities (London)
Practice Areas: Trusts and estates, charities, real property and conveyancing and related professional negligence matters.
Professional Memberships: Chancery Bar Association, Society of Trusts & Estates Practitioners, Association of Contentious Trust & Probate Specialists, Charity Law Association, Property Bar Association and Professional Negligence Bar Association.
Career: Mark's trust work embraces equity drafting and advice (both for UK and overseas clients) and the full range of private client litigation. In addition to his English court work, Mark has recently been involved in proceedings in the Bahamas, Bermuda, Guernsey and Scotland, and has been working with local advisers in Hong Kong in various substantial asset recovery, probate, estate administration and family provision matters. Professional directories recommend Mark as a leading junior in chancery, private client, trusts and probate and charity matters. He has personal experience of charity administration as a trustee of a number of charities. Professional directories recommend him as a leading junior in chancery, private client, trusts and probate and charity matters. Chambers UK 2014 described Mark as "well versed in property, trusts and professional negligence matters" and stated that he has "an encyclopaedic knowledge of trusts and estates" and is "a very good analyst, who cuts to the real issues of a case quickly and without any fuss". Other recent editions of the professional directories have stated that "He is excellent at reassuring difficult or anxious clients", "commentators respect Mark Studer for his intelligence" and have described him as "popular with leading solicitors", "a good team player and also considered very clear, quick and an excellent draftsman", "solid and long established" and one who "impresses with his aptitude for the ultra complex". Mark is said to be "meticulous and approachable", and his drafting skills are noted as being "clear and to the point".
Personal: Bencher of Lincoln's Inn, Director of Lincoln's Inn Trust Companies, Trustee of Lincoln's Inn Heritage Fund, Director and Joint Honorary Treasurer of Barristers' Benevolent Association, Trustee of Westminster Amalgamated Charity, Trustee of the Nicholas John Trust (promoting opera), Secretary of The Institute.

STURMAN, Jim QC
2 Bedford Row, London
020 7440 8888
JSturman@2bedfordrow.co.uk
Featured in Health & Safety (London), Sports Law (London), Crime (London), Financial Crime (London)
Practice Areas: Specialist defence advocate instructed in many high profile fraud, criminal, regulatory and sports law cases as well as advising in civil cases where criminal allegations arise. Frequently acts and advises abroad. Particular expertise in corruption, sanctions offences, data protection, homicide, regulatory work (frequently representing professionals from all professions before disciplinary tribunals) and advisory work to banks and corporate clients as well as individuals on criminal matters and mutual assistance requests and in 'quasi criminal' tribunals. Advises in SFO cases in early stages of enquiries on warrants as well as section 2 requests and also frequently advises solicitors and city institutions in money laundering cases. Extensive experience of health and safety work, advising before charge and acting at trial in cases involving industry (for example the trial arising from the Buncefield explosion), railways and farming. Acts in public inquiries and inquests, for example The Turks and Caicos Commission of Inquiry and representing Primrose Shipman before The Shipman Inquiry and at the inquest into the death of Dr Harold Shipman. Extensive experience of asset confiscation and restraint proceedings under POCA, CJA and DTA. Considerable experience in The Court of Appeal Criminal Division, particularly in cases where he did not act in the lower court. Examples include, R v Lummes, conviction for murder quashed and no evidence offered at the re-trial, R v Dallagher ('ear print' identification case) and R v Dixon (Customs and Excise non-disclosure in a large drugs case known as 'Operation Cinema'. Notable cases in general crime include R v Stagg (Wimbledon common murder). R v Gould and Charles Kray. R v M 'sex on an aeroplane case'. R v Kelly, first appeal on 'two strikes' life sentence. Acted in 2 'Operation Care' cases in Liverpool. R v C and others (Serbian sanctions busting case), R v Hardstaff (co-defendant in the Bowyer and Woodgate trial). Enormously experienced in drugs cases, R v A White, R v Doherty (Part of the Michael Michaels series of cases). Acted for Joey Barton on assault charge incident at Manchester City training ground. Extradition cases include USA v Sukharno, USA v Newton (part of the Howard Marks case) and USA v Kleasen - the 'Texas chainsaw' case. Fraud cases include the appeal of Michael Villiers in the LCB diversion case (the first of the chain of LCB appeals), and the subsequent abuse of process hearing based on non-disclosure that was heard at Liverpool Crown Court. R v Goldstone (largest ever cigarette diversion fraud), R v F (SFO prosecution arising out of the theft of the Cheney Pension Fund), R v Eardley (International Internet piracy first investigated in the USA as 'Operation Buccaneer'), acted for three of the British MP's charged with "expenses fraud" and has extensive experience of all types of financial fraud, including mortgage, ponzi, advance fee, insider dealing and derivatives 'ramping', revenue, VAT and diversion frauds. Frequently advises in international and domestic corruption investigators. Regularly appears before FA, FAPL, UEFA and FIFA disciplinary tribunals in relation to on field and off the field matters, (including 'doping offences', betting irregularities and allegations of misconduct by fans), acting for the defence and on behalf of the FA. Has acted for Chelsea FC, Tottenham Hotspur FC, Newcastle United FC, Jose Mourinho, Frank Lampard, John Terry, Didier Drogba, Jens Lehman, Millwall FC, Wimbledon AFC, Tottenham Hotspur FC, Robbie Keane, Michael Dawson, Dennis Wise, Gustavo Poyet, Emre of Newcastle on a 'racism' allegation that was dismissed, Peter Cech, Frank Lampard, Ashley Cole, Jermaine Defoe and Kieran Dyer. Acted for Newcastle United in Premier League Tribunal hearing brought by Kevin Keegan. Instructed by the FA to prosecute Roy Keane in relation to the autobiography by that player. Has represented Chelsea FC, Didier Drogba, Jose Bosingwa, Marcel Desailly, Jose Mourinho and Steve Clarke before UEFA, and John Terry before FIFA and UEFA. Acted for Chelsea FC in the 'Ashley Cole tapping up case'. Acted for CSKA Moscow in Parma's protest against the result of the 2005 UEFA semi final. Acted for Tottenham Hotspur FC v Sergei Rebrov in relation to FAPL dispute. Acted for West Ham in the Carlos Tevez affair. Has acted for UEFA, national FAs and for individual players in relation to doping allegations. Acted for Wigan FC in the 'Webster' case on Article 17 of the FIFA statutes. Acted for Mohammed Bin Hammam in his successful appeal to CAS from FIFA findings arising out of his campaign to run for the FIFA Presidency against Sepp Blatter. Successfully has represented agents suing players who attempted to "cut out" the agent from transfer deals. Has advised national associations in South America and the Far East in relation to disputes under FIFA regulations. Frequently appears in The Court of Arbitration for Sport. Sits as an RFU appeals Chairman.
Professional Memberships: Member of Gibraltar Bar, CBA, IBA, EBA and BAFS.
Career: Called 1982, joined chambers 1983, Silk 2002.
Publications: Contributor (with Professor David Ormerod) to 'The Forensic Psychologists casebook' published in 2005.

SULLIVAN, James
12 King's Bench Walk, London
Featured in Personal Injury (London)
Practice Areas: James has extensive experience in cases concerning credit hire (ranging from fast track level cases through to cases involving claims in excess of £100,000). He appeared as junior counsel in the cases of Copley v Lawn and Maden v Haller [2009] EWCA Civ 580 (concerning the issue of 'intervention' by defendant insurers in the credit hire process) and he regularly provides lectures and presentations on the subject of credit hire. James also has considerable experience of cases concerning allegations of fraud (both from the perspective of defendants and claimants) - including cases concerning alleged phantom passengers, allegedly staged accidents, allegedly induced collisions, and suspected paper accidents.

SULLIVAN, Lisa
Cloisters, London
020 7827 4000
ls@cloisters.com
Featured in Clinical Negligence (London)
Practice Areas: Lisa principally specialises in clinical negligence and personal injury law including inquests and CICA claims. Lisa has wide experience in high value cases including birth injury, brain and spinal injury cases on both liability and quantum. She also undertakes regulatory tribunal work, in particular care standards. Notable cases include Crofton v NHSLA [2007] EWCA Civ 71, Collins v Plymouth City Council [2009] EWHC 3279 (Admin) (whether damages can be taken into account in charging for

local authority care) and Pringle v Nestor Primecare [2014] EWHC 1308 (QB).
Professional Memberships: PIBA, AvMA.
Career: Called to the Bar in 1997. Advocacy trainer for PIBA, Inner Temple and South Eastern Circuit.
Publications: Butterworth's Personal Injury Litigation Service Limitation Chapter (co-author with Patricia Hitchcock QC) and contributor to Lewis and Buchan on Clinical Negligence.

SUMMERS, Alan A.
Terra Firma Chambers, Edinburgh
01312 605 830
alan.summers@terrafirmachambers.com
Featured in Restructuring/Insolvency (Scotland)
Practice Areas: An experienced litigator who has appeared at all levels in the Scottish courts in a variety of high profile cases. He is presently instructed on behalf of Rangers FC in their dispute with a former director Mr Ahmad over an unpaid bonus (due for proof in November 2014). He is also senior counsel for the Pursuer in Massie v McCaig a defamation action due for proof in October 2014. He has appeared in a number of cases arising out of company administrations. He appeared in the Commercial Court in 2013 in Station Properties Ltd (in admin.) v Dunedin Property Services. In recent years Alan has been senior counsel for the appellants in the Supreme Court in Royal Bank of Scotland v Wilson, a ground breaking case on commercial securities. He was senior counsel for the UK Government in Cadder v HMA in the Supreme Court. Alan appeared for Deutsche Bank in their insolvency dispute with Globespan, the economy airline, in the Commercial Court in 2012. Recently he advised the Foreign Office in connection with the publication of sensitive information arising from the Lockerbie case. His practice is extremely varied and covers public, commercial, insolvency and property law.
Career: Called to bar 1994; silk 2008. Alan is the Treasurer of the Faculty of Advocates. At present he is also acting Chairman of Faculty Services Ltd, the service company that supports the bar in Scotland. He was a standing junior to the Scottish Government 2000-07 and was appointed as Special Counsel in 2007 for security sensitive work.
Personal: Educated Oxford University, Edinburgh University and Dundee University. Lecturer in Scots Law, Edinburgh University 1986-88.

SUMMERS, Ben
3 Raymond Buildings Barristers, London
020 7400 6400
Ben.Summers@3rblaw.com
Featured in Financial Crime (London)
Practice Areas: Ben was called to the Bar in 1994 and following a civil pupillage, he joined QEB Hollis Whiteman where he was in independent practice for eight years. He joined leading white collar firm Peters & Peters in March 2003 as an employed Barrister and transferred to the Solicitors' profession in 2004; he was appointed as a partner in 2007. In May 2009 Ben resumed independent practice at the Bar and joined Three Raymond Buildings. Ben has a practice in business crime, professional discipline, public inquiries and regulatory matters, with specialist experience in compliance issues, including corruption & bribery, fraud and anti-trust, financial services, professional discipline, public inquiries and DPA/FOIAct matters. He has acted in some of the largest fraud and corruption matters over recent years including LIBOR, Innospec, Oil for Food, Johnson & Johnson, Torex Retail, Vantis Tax and Imperial Consolidated. He also advises upon, and acts for, the Information Commissioner's Office and individuals / corporate in data protection matters.
Professional Memberships: Criminal Bar Association, Fraud Lawyers Association, Association of Regulatory & Disciplinary Lawyers, South Eastern Circuit.
Career: University of Sussex: LLB (Hons) (1990-93) Inns of Court School of Law (1993-94).

SUMMERS, Mark QC
Matrix Chambers, London
020 7404 3447
marksummers@matrixlaw.co.uk
Featured in Extradition (London), Crime (London)
Practice Areas: Specialist in extradition and MLA, EU and terrorism law. Recent EXTRADITION cases include: Bucnys v Lithuania [2014] AC 480 SC; HH & PH v Italy [2013] 1 AC 338 SC; Woolley v UK (2013) 56 EHHR 15 ECtHR; Assange v Sweden [2012] 2 AC 471 SC; Harkins & Edwards v UK (2012) 55 EHRR 19 ECtHR; Gomes & Goodyer v Trinidad [2009] 1 WLR 1038 HL; McKinnon v US [2008] 1 WLR 1739 HL; Caldarelli v Italy [2008] 1 WLR 1724 HL; Dabas v Spain [2007] 2 AC 31 HL; the Madrid train bombings; the 9/11 attacks; Enron/ the 'Natwest three'; 2001 US anthrax bioterrorism attacks. Recent CRIMINAL cases include: R v John Downey (Hyde Park bombing); Hicks v Metropolitan Police [2014] 1 WLR 1532 CA (article 5 ECHR and breach of peace); R v Amir [2012] 2 Cr App R 68 CA (international cricket match fixing); Brown v Trinidad [2012] 1 WLR 1577 PC (death penalty fresh evidence). Recent TERRORISM cases include: R v Ali [2011] 3 All ER 1071 CA (liquid-bomb conspiracy to explode US-bound transatlantic flights); R v Sherif [2009] 2 Cr App R 235 CA (assisting the 21/7 bombing attempts); R v Tsouli [2008] 2 Cr App R 247 CA (cyber-Jihadist 'terrorist007'); the ricin conspiracy; the Stansted Afghan Airlines hijacking.
Professional Memberships: Extradition Lawyers' Association (former Chair).
Publications: Co-author of "Abuse of Process in Criminal Proceedings" (Bloomsbury, 4th. ed., 2014); "The Law of Extradition and Mutual Assistance" (OUP, 3rd ed., 2013), "Human Rights and Criminal Justice" (Sweet & Maxwell, 3rd ed., 2012). Contributing editor to "Fraud: Criminal Law and Procedure" (OUP).

SUMNALL, Charlene
5 Paper Buildings, London
020 7583 6117
CS@5pb.co.uk
Featured in Consumer Law (London)
Practice Areas: Charlene provides advisory and specialist advocacy services and has appeared in all levels of tribunals including those at appellate level. She has built up a wealth of experience by appearing for both the prosecution and defence in areas such as trademark and copyright infringement, food, toy and general product safety, licensing and offences concerning the Consumer Protection from Unfair Trading Regulations and the Business Protection from Misleading Marketing Regulations. Charlene has lectured at the annual Trading Standards Conference for the last 9 years and has provided training to local authorities and private prosecutors on a range of topics including the Fraud Act, Proceeds of Crime Act (confiscation, restraint and forfeiture provisions) and investigatory procedures. She regularly provides advice to business on due diligence compliance. Please see chambers website for fuller details of all areas of her practice including relevant cases in this area.

SUSMAN, Peter QC
Henderson Chambers, London
020 7583 9020
psusmanqc@hendersonchambers.co.uk
Featured in Information Technology (London)
Practice Areas: Complex commercial and contract litigation and international and domestic arbitration, with particular experience of commercial contract disputes; information technology, telecoms, broadcasting and other high tech areas; financial transactions, including consumer credit; construction and engineering; insurance; professional negligence, and professional regulatory and disciplinary law; company law; employment, property and other issues arising in relation to commercial transactions and disputes; especially involving complicated issues or facts, more than one area of law, or other difficulties. He acts for and against government departments, local authorities, companies and individuals, in court in England and in foreign and domestic arbitrations.
Career: Called 1966, took Silk 1997.

SUTERWALLA, Azeem
Monckton Chambers, London
020 7405 7211
asuterwalla@monckton.com
Featured in Administrative & Public Law (London), Civil Liberties & Human Rights (London), Community Care (London)
Practice Areas: Administrative law, Civil Liberties and Human Rights and Community Care
Professional Memberships: Administrative Law Bar Association, Human Rights Lawyers Association
Career: Azeem specialises in public and human rights law across a range of subject areas, notably: community care, children related, education, immigration, asylum support, procurement and regulatory judicial reviews. In addition to his High Court practice, Azeem is regularly instructed in appeals in the Court of Appeal and has worked on litigation at all levels up to the House of Lords/ Supreme Court and the European Court of Human Rights. Before coming to the bar Azeem worked for the United Nations in the Middle East and was a Judicial Assistant to the former Master of the Rolls, now Supreme Court Justice, Lord Clarke.
Publications: Co-author of Children in Need: Local Authority Support for Children and Families (Legal Action Group, 2013). Azeem is the author of "Collection and Retention of Person Data" in "Human Rights in the Investigation and Prosecution of Crime" (2009), OUP, ed. Madeleine Colvin and Jonathan Cooper.
Personal: BA (Oxon) Modern History 1st Class, MA (Harvard) Arabic and Middle Eastern Studies, Thesis with Distinction.

SUTHERLAND, Robert
Terra Firma Chambers, Edinburgh
01312 605 830
Rdsadvocate@aol.com
Featured in Agriculture & Rural Affairs (Scotland)
Practice Areas: Specialist in rural; residential; commercial property and public law - agricultural and crofting tenancies; commercial leases; conveyancing; environmental law; judicial review; landlord and tenant; local government; planning; private and social housing; regulatory offences. Also has considerable arbitration experience.
Professional Memberships: Chartered Institute of Arbitrators (Associate); Chartered Institute of Housing (Associate); Agricultural Law Association; Crofting Law Group; Scottish Planning, Local Government and Environmental Bar Group; United Kingdom Environmental Law Association.
Career: MA; LLB; called 1992. Legal Adviser to Lothian Association of Youth Clubs; Director (since 1999) and Convenor (since 2004) of Scottish Legal Action Group; Director, Scottish Legal News Ltd.
Publications: Stair Memorial Encyclopaedia "Housing" (Reissue); Scottish Planning Fact Book (Conservation & Other Controls); Contributor to 'SCOLAG' journal; 'Scots Law Times' and Bulletin of the Agricultural Law Association; Contributor to 'Green's Litigation Styles', 'Claiming Criminal Injuries Compensation', 'Scottish Human Rights Service' (Scocial Security).

SWAIN, Jon
Furnival Chambers, London
020 7405 3232
clerks@furnivallaw.co.uk
Featured in Crime (London)
Practice Areas: Crime, inquests, regulatory work. Direct access qualified.
Professional Memberships: Lincoln's Inn, South Eastern Circuit, CBA.
Career: Called to Bar 1983. Member of Furnival Chambers since 1986. Instructed in number of high profile cases since then in various regions of England and Wales. Recent cases: R. v. R, Lewes Crown Court, historic rapes (acquitted), R. v. Bass, Reading Crown Court, murder/manslaughter with mental health and causation issues (convicted manslaughter & hospital order). R. v. H, stranger rape (convicted & hospital order) & historic rape of ex-partner (acquitted). R. v. Frew, Leeds Crown Court (manslaughter). R. v. O'Brien, Manchester Crown Court (importation of 10 lorry loads of cannabis; (acquitted). R. v. Dell, Oxford Crown Court (attempt handling stolen scrap metal; acquitted). R. v. T, Aylesbury Crown Court multiple rapes of partner (acquitted), R. v. Carroll, Norwich Crown Court (att murder, att GBH, rape of prostitute (historic DNA case). Forthcoming trials: R. v. Mughal Birmingham Crown Court, (complex fraud), R. v. Zare Manchester Crown Court (money laundering.
Personal: Born 1959. Leisure interests include cricket, tennis and country life.

SWEET, Louise
Carmelite Chambers, London
Featured in Crime (London)
Practice Areas: For more than 20 years Louise has been trusted to defend in legally complex, emotive and a number of high profile cases. Her practice is wide ranging

and includes financial crime, murder, serious drugs cases and sexual violence
Professional Memberships: CBA, Fraud Lawyers Association, Howard League for Penal Reform. Organiser of Carmelite Chambers lecture programme, Pupil Supervisor.
Career: Career highlights include representing the now infamous Mick Philpott whose 6 children died in a Derby house fire and representing stars of the small screen and football pitch cleared of rape allegations. Recent cases include representation of a mother cleared of killing her child involving complex medical evidence and a nasty cut-throat (Gacek and Ors) defending one of 18 men accused in a charge back fraud (Iqbal and Ors) and defending a university student accused of manufacturing and supplying illegal steroids with links across Europe, USA and China ("Veyron Pharma") Instructions for 2015-16 include a multi million pound class A importation and money laundering allegation (Operation Meclenberger) a Hungarian people trafficking ring for sexual exploitation (Operation Peltier) and child rape allegations spanning three generations in one family.

SWIFT, Jonathan QC
11KBW, London
020 7632 8500
Jonathan.Swift@11kbw.com
Featured in Administrative & Public Law (London), Civil Liberties & Human Rights (London), Data Protection (London), Competition/European Law (London)
Practice Areas: Has in-depth experience across the whole range of public law, including human rights, civil liberties; constitutional law and devolution; data protection and freedom of information; regulatory law (in particular energy regulation, and financial regulation); and strategic planning and environmental issues. From 2006 to 2014 he was First Treasury Counsel, leading for the Government on major cases covering all aspects of public administration. He has particular experience on the application of international sanctions schemes to individuals and corporations. He has led for HM Revenue and Customs on major litigation concerning rights under EU law to recover interest on overpayments of tax; the nature of restitution rights, and the quantification of restitutionary damages in claims for recovery of money paid by mistake. He regularly appears in the Court of Appeal and in the Supreme Court (over 30 cases during the last 2 years). Recent cases include; Littlewoods v HMRC [2014] EWHC 868 (Ch); R (Evans) v Attorney General [2014] EWCA Civ; R (Youssef) v Foreign Secretary [2013] EWCA Civ 1302; R (New London College) v Home Secretary [2013] UKSC 51; Al Jedda v Home Secretary [2013] UKSC 62; Bank Mellat v HM Treasury [2013] UKSC 38 and 39; Gallestegui v Westminster City Council, and Home Secretary [2013] EWCA Civ 28; Irfan v Home Secretary [2012] EWCA Civ 1471; Alvi v Home Secretary [2012] UKSC 33; Attorney General v Counsel General for Wales [2012] UKSC 53; Investment Trust Company v HMRC [2012] EWHC 458 (Ch).
Career: Called 1989; First Treasury Counsel 2006-14; Master of the Bench Inner Temple 2007; QC 2010. Education: Southend-on-Sea High School; New College Oxford; Emmanuel College, Cambridge.
Personal: Born 1964; resides London.

SWIFT, Malcolm QC
2 Hare Court, London
020 7353 5324
malcolmswiftqc@2harecourt.com
Featured in Crime (London)
Practice Areas: Malcolm Swift QC first appeared in the Court of Appeal in the guideline sentencing case of R v Guilfoyle (causing death by dangerous driving) in 1973. As a junior, he had a multi-disciplinary practice dealing with crime, personal injury, medical negligence, contract, building disputes and defamation. Since taking Silk in 1988, he has practised exclusively in crime and in quasi-criminal cases establishing a reputation as a fine tactician, a skilful and highly effective cross-examiner (particularly of expert witnesses) and a formidable speech-maker. He is described in recent times by Chambers as "a strong opponent known for his brilliant handling of cases", "a force to be reckoned with", as having a "long and distinguished history" at the Criminal Bar and as "the best on Circuit from a defence point of view". Amongst the many highlights of his career was the ground-breaking appeal of R v Davis [2008] 3 WLR 196 (witness anonymity), in which the House of Lords upheld the fundamental common law right of confrontation and forced the Government to enact primary legislation. In recent years he has appeared in many notable murder, fraud, drug importation and terrorism trials. He is a former Leader of the North Eastern Circuit and sits from time to time as an Acting Grand Court Judge of the Cayman Islands.
Career: LLB; AKC (Kings College London). Called to the Bar Trinity 1970 - Grays Inn. Recorder of the Crown Court (1987-2008). Queens Counsel (1988). Master of the Bench - Gray's Inn 2000.

TAGER, Romie QC
Selborne Chambers, London
020 7420 9500
romie.tager@selbornechambers.co.uk
Featured in Chancery (London), Commercial Dispute Resolution (London), Real Estate Litigation (London)
Practice Areas: Romie is a specialist in commercial and property law. His experience covers a vast range of work in these fields, and the breadth and specialisation of his practice and career give him a commanding position. He is frequently instructed in cases involving complex issues and commercial sensitivity, often calling for original presentation and the identification of novel solutions. His practice includes considerable advisory work, and he has extensive experience of international commercial arbitration. Described by his peers as a 'fiercely aggressive' advocate, the 2009 edition of Chambers UK describes him as being a 'terrier of a litigator' who is 'quick to grasp the technical details and deploy them to devastating effect in cross-examination'. And again another client said, 'If you have a problem case and need to rip the other side limb from limb, go to Tager.' Chambers UK 2010 Edition describes Romie as a 'very big name' and notes that he has made a name for himself as 'a highly forceful silk who fights doggedly for client interests."
Professional Memberships: Chancery Bar Assoc. Professional Negligence Bar Assoc. Property Bar Assoc. London Common Law & Commercial Bar Assoc.

Career: Called 1970; QC 1995. Recent cases include: Group Seven Ltd v Allied Investments Corporation Ltd and others [2013] EWHC 1423 (Ch),(the court considered whether the fraud exception to legal professional privilege applied to all of the documents held or generated by solicitors under a joint retainer); Crossco No4 Unlimited v Jolan Piccadilly Ltd [2011] EWHC 803 (Ch) (a 35 day 1954 Act trial in which he was successful); Baturina v Times Newspapers Ltd [2011] EWCA Civ 308 (the case clarified the law relating to innuendo); Innovatis Inestment Fund v Ejder Group Ltd [2010] EWHC 1851 (the legal nature of a securities repurchaser agreement); Baturina v Times Newspapers Ltd [2010] EWHC 696 (QB) (innuendo and liability for re-publication in context of overseas sales of English newspaper); Good Harvest Partnership v Centaur Services Ltd [2010] NPL 22 (whether original guarantor's guarantee of assignee is enforceable under 1995 Covenants Act); Transview Properties Ltd v City Site Properties Ltd [2009] EWCA Civ 1255 (admissibility of fresh evidence on appeal; rectification of override liabilities under a sale contract); Pocket Kings Ltd v Safenames Ltd & Kentucky [2009] EWHC 2529 (Ch) (US state of Kentucky not a state for the purposes of the State Immunity Act 1978); Invertec Ltd v de Mol Holdings BV [2009] EWHC 2471 (Ch) (liability for fraudulent warranties in share sale agreement, and extent of liability for post-completion losses).

TAHIR, Perican
1 King's Bench Walk, London
020 7936 1500
Ptahir@1kbw.co.uk
Featured in Family/Matrimonial (South Eastern)
Practice Areas: Perican Tahir has specific expertise in advising and acting in all areas of Family Law. She has particular expertise in Financial Remedy and Private Law Children matters. In the field of Financial Remedy, she has experience in matters involving foreign or complex assets; trust and intervenors; business and partnership assets; issues of non-disclosure of assets and pre-post nuptial agreements; as well as advising and appearing in disputes between cohabitants under the Trusts of Land and Appointment of Trustees Act 1996 and Schedule 1 of the Children Act 1989. In the field of Private Law Children, she has experience in matters involving complex intractable disputes, leave to remove and international relocation cases as well as internal relocation applications and abduction matters. Perican is Direct Access qualified.
Professional Memberships: Family Law Bar Association, South Eastern Circuit, Kent Bar Mess, Association of Lawyers for Children.
Career: Call: 2004.
Personal: Education: Haberdashers Aske's Hatcham Girls School, University of Sussex - Law LLB, Inns of Court School of Law.

TAM, Robin QC
Temple Garden Chambers, London
020 7583 1315
robintam@tgchambers.com
Featured in Administrative & Public Law (London), Inquests & Public Inquiries (London), Immigration (London)
Practice Areas: Administrative/public law, immigration/asylum, nationality, human rights. Inquests. Personal injuries. General common law. Major reported cases (year reported): Bugg (1993); M (1996); Percy v Hall (1997); Flood (1998); Harris v Evans (1998); Defence Secretary v Percy (1999); Jeyeanthan (2000); Horvath (2001); Montana (2001); SSHD v IAT (2001); Balbo (2001); Svazas (2002); Gardi (2002); Rehman (2003); Kariharan (2003); M (2003); Wainwright (2004); Akrich (2004); Scotcher (2005); Refugee Legal Centre (2005); Khadir (2006); A (No.2) (2006); K (2007); O'Brien (2007); McCoubrey (2007); E (2008); SSHD v Information Tribunal (2008); RB (2010); AP (No.2) (2010); ZO (2010); AP (2011); Cart (2011); ZA (2011); Kambadzi (2011); Adams (2012); Lumba (2012); W (2012); BB (2012); IR (2012); CB (2012); XX (2013); B (2013); BB (No.2) (2013); AA (2013); Bank Mellat (No.1) and (No.2) (2013); George (2014).
Professional Memberships: Administrative Law Bar Association. Personal Injuries Bar Association. South Eastern Circuit. Hong Kong Bar. New South Wales Bar.
Career: Called 1986. Prosecuting counsel to Inland Revenue 1993. Junior counsel to Crown 1994-2006 (A Panel 1999-2006). Queen's Counsel 2006.
Publications: Asylum and Human Rights Appeals Handbook (2008) (with Anna Kotzeva, Lucy Murray and Ian Burnett QC).

TAMBLING, Richard
29 Bedford Row Chambers, London
020 7404 1044
rtambling@29br.co.uk
Featured in Family/Matrimonial (London)
Practice Areas: Handles all aspects of financial remedies including matrimonial finance and Schedule 1 cases. Regularly instructed on TOLATA claims in a domestic context including those brought by cohabitees and concurrent Schedule 1 applications. Court of Protection cases dealing with property and affairs. Private law children specialising in leave to remove cases.
Professional Memberships: FLBA, HRLA
Career: Recently moved to 29 Bedford Row from 1 Garden Court. BA (Hons), LLB (Hons), Blackstone Entrance Exhibition Scholarship - Middle Temple. Called to the Bar in 2005. Regularly asked to speak on his practice areas for Young Resolution, TVFLS, CLT and at Jordans Family Law seminars.
Publications: Contributor to Applications Under Schedule 1 Children Act 1989, Jordans. Regular contributor of articles to publications including Family Law Week and recently wrote for the Trusts and Estates Law & Tax Journal on one of the judgments in Tchenguiz-Imerman v Imerman (2013) highlighting the tensions between courts of different jurisdiction despite the principle of comity between states.
Personal: A keen traveller of foreign lands, enthusiastic cook, enjoys listening to music and sampling cultural London.

TAMPAKOPOULOS, Alex
2 Hare Court, London
020 7353 5324
Alexandratampakopoulos
@2harecourt.com
Featured in Inquests & Public Inquiries (London)
Practice Areas: A criminal, fraud and regulatory practitioner with a particular expertise in Coroner's Inquests. Crime: Defends and prosecutes in all serious and complex criminal cases. Fraud (Criminal and Civil): Acts in white collar fraud and financial crime matters particularly related to Russia and the CIS. She also acts in the High Court in civil recovery proceedings and before the First

Tier Tax Tribunal in respect of high value MTIC frauds. Regulatory: Extensive practice advising and defending in health and safety prosecutions on behalf of companies and individual directors. Inquests: Expertise in coronial proceedings. She is instructed as junior counsel to the inquest into the death of Alexander Litvinenko, the former Russian FSB agent poisoned by Polonium 210. She regularly acts in inquests representing the full range of interested persons including families, schools, care homes and companies. Alexandra speaks fluent Russian and is regularly instructed in matters requiring both her language skills and specialist knowledge of Russia and the CIS.

Professional Memberships: Criminal Bar Association, Health and Safety Lawyers' Association, Young Fraud Lawyers' Association, British Russian Law Association.

TANCHEL, Vivienne
2 Hare Court, London
020 7353 5324
VivienneTanchel@2harecourt.com
Featured in Crime (London), Financial Crime (London)

Practice Areas: Vivienne Tanchel is a defence advocate who has a reputation for thorough preparation and is commended for her intellectual rigour. Her practice includes a range of financial criminal, regulatory and civil proceedings. Drawing on her many years of experience as a trader in London and other financial market (prior to her call to the Bar), her special expertise is a detailed understanding of complex financial wrongdoing, including criminal and civil fraud, insider trading, MTIC fraud, money laundering and cases involving several jurisdictions. A large part of her work involves advice and representation in concurrent criminal, civil and regulatory proceedings and is called upon to advise on the tactical and legal considerations unique to such circumstances. Vivienne has expertise in advising both corporate and individual clients during the course of an investigation and prior to any charges being brought.

Career: Called 2005 (Middle Temple)

TANNEY, Anthony
Falcon Chambers, London
020 7353 2484
tanney@falcon-chambers.com
Featured in Real Estate Litigation (London)

Practice Areas: All aspects of the law of real property both commercial and residential, including litigation and advisory work, with an emphasis on landlord and tenant.

Professional Memberships: Chancery Bar Association; LCLCBA; Property Bar Association.

Career: Educated at Whitley Bay High School; Durham University (BA 1989, MJur 1992); called 1994 (Lincoln's Inn).

Publications: Co-author, 'Distress for Rent' (Jordans 2000); co-editor, Fisher and Lightwood's 'Law of Mortgage' 11th edn (Butterworths 2002).

TAPPIN, Michael QC
8 New Square, London
020 7405 4321
michael.tappin@8newsquare.co.uk
Featured in Intellectual Property (London)

Practice Areas: Barrister specialising in all aspects of intellectual property law but with a particular interest in chemical, pharmaceutical and biotechnological work. Recent cases include: Eli Lilly v HGS (SC/CA), Generics v Lundbeck (HL), Conor v Angiotech (HL), Hospira & Mylan v Novartis (CA), Resolution v Lundbeck (CA), Regeneron / Bayer v Genentech (CA), Fresenius v Carefusion (CA), Mylan v Yeda / Teva (CA), KCI v Smith & Nephew (CA), Napp v ratiopharm (CA), Nokia v HTC (HC), HTC v Apple (HC), HTC v Gemalto (HC), Ivax v Glaxo (HC of Ireland). For comprehensive CV and list of recent cases, visit website at www.8newsquare.co.uk

Professional Memberships: Intellectual Property Bar Association.

Career: Called 1991. Appointed QC 2009. Standing Counsel to the Comptroller-General of Patents, Designs and Trade Marks 2003-08.

Publications: Co-author of Laddie, Prescott & Vitoria's Modern Law of Copyright and Designs (4th edn, 2011).

Personal: Born 1964. Educated at Cheltenham Grammar School; St John's College, Oxford (1986 BA Chemistry); Merton College, Oxford (1989 DPhil Biochemistry).

TAPSELL, Paul
Becket Chambers, Canterbury
01227 786 331
clerks@becket-chambers.co.uk
Featured in Local Government (South Eastern)

Practice Areas: Paul undertakes: local Authority work, both civil and criminal, including benefit fraud, planning enforcement, licensing, environmental protection and food safety matters; customs-related proceedings especially "POCA" confiscation and/or forfeiture, cash seizure and condemnation proceedings; recovery of care charges and disputes arising from residential and nursing care costs; planning – Paul is regularly instructed by Local Authorities and others in matters involving planning appeals, listed building consent and development control and in connection with injunction proceedings in respect of unauthorised activities in breach of planning control; employment - extensive experience, acting for employers and employees, dealing with claims involving unfair and/or wrongful dismissal, discrimination, redundancy, TUPE and restraint of trade; housing and land law – especially landlord and tenant matters and boundary/ property disputes.

Professional Memberships: Planning and Environmental Bar Association (PEBA), Employment Law Bar Association (ELBA), South Eastern Circuit, Kent Bar Mess (Junior 2010-13).

Career: CPS panel of Prosecuting Advocates (Grade 3). Accepts work under the Direct Public Access scheme. Qualified Pupil Supervisor.

Publications: R v Czyzewski [2003] EWCA Crim 2319 (sentencing guidelines for excise evasion). Barratt v Ashford Borough Council [2011] EWCA Civ 27 (requirements as to the description of Listed Building).

TASKIS, Catherine
Falcon Chambers, London
020 7353 2484
clerks@falcon-chambers.com
Featured in Agriculture & Rural Affairs (London), Real Estate Litigation (London)

See under Leaders at the Bar for profile.

TAUBE, Simon QC
Ten Old Square, London
020 7242 5002
simontaube@tenoldsquare.com
Featured in Chancery (London), Charities (London), Offshore (London), Trusts (London)

Practice Areas: Simon Taube's practice covers the broad range of Chancery activities in both litigation and advisory work. He also conducts cases abroad in other common law jurisdictions.His special expertise includes the fields of UK and foreign trusts and estates, tax planning and trust and personal taxation. He also has wide experience in charity, property, securities, partnership, professional negligence and family provision matters.

Professional Memberships: Simon Taube is a member of the Chancery Bar Association, the Revenue Bar Association and the Society of Trust and Estate Practitioners.

Career: Called 1980, Silk 2000. Notable cases include Re Nina Wang (2014) HKCA: charitable trust and company law; Buzzoni v HMRC (2013) CA: IHT and unjust enrichment; Labrouche v Frey (2012) CA: breach of trust, abuse of process; In the Matter of the A Trust (2012) Bermuda: trust jurisdiction clauses; A-G's Poverty Reference (2011) public benefit in charity; Fattal v Walbrook (2010) trustee exoneration clause; Helmsman v BNY (2009) Cayman: trust jurisdiction clauses; AB v Barclays Private Bank (2006) Cayman: no contest clause;Sieff v Fox (2005) trustees' mistake; Ingram v IRC (2000) HL: IHT and leases; X v A (2000) trustees' rights of indemnity; Public Trustee v Cooper (1999) court's trust jurisdiction, conflicts of interest; IRC v Berrill (income tax); Re: Trafford (CTT); Sinclair v Lee (ICI demerger); Keene v Martin (CA) company law

TAVERNER, Marcus QC
Keating Chambers, London
020 7544 2600
mtaverner@keatingchambers.com
Featured in Construction (London), Energy & Natural Resources (London), International Arbitration (London), Professional Negligence (London)

Practice Areas: Leading commercial Silk in the fields of construction, energy, engineering and professional negligence within those and related fields. Has an extensive advisory practice and a formidable reputation as an advocate and in particular for his cross-examination. Well known not only for his considerable strategic acumen and understanding of the commercial aspects of litigation but, in particular, for his mastering of the technical detail of the many complex and high value cases he undertakes. Acts on behalf of clients engaged in adjudications, mediations and other forms of alternative dispute resolution. Has an extensive practice acting as advisor and advocate, on major arbitrations both in the in UK and abroad. Sits as arbitrator on domestic and international claims for bodies such as the ICC and also acts as an adjudicator in the United Kingdom.

Professional Memberships: Technology & Construction Bar Association (TECBAR); Commercial Bar Association (COMBAR); Society of Construction Law (SCL).

Career: Call 1981, QC 2000; Bencher Gray's Inn 2007; Construction Silk of the Year Chambers and Partners Bar Awards 2009; a Deputy Head of Chambers 2013.

TAYLOR, Christopher
Queen Square Chambers, Bristol
01179 211 966
cht@qs-c.co.uk
Featured in Personal Injury (Western)

Practice Areas: He practises exclusively in personal injury and clinical negligence. Since 1993 he has undertaken a large number of high value cases especially fatal accident, head injury and catastrophic spinal injury in addition to industrial accident and diseases claims. He was appointed Deputy District Judge (civil) in 2004 and Head of Chambers in 2010. He appears in Court of Appeal, High Court, County Court plus Inquests. Recent cases: Christopher Mowatt v Claire McNabb [2012]; Karl Bauld v Stephen Williams [2011]; Rees and others v County Heating and others [2012]; Christopher Payne v Scott- Baumann [2012]. Reported cases: Poppleton v Trustees of Portsmouth Youth Activities Committee [2008] EWCA Civ 646 [liability for indoor climbing centre]; Carlson v Townsend [2001] 3 All ER 663 [disclosure of expert reports].

Professional Memberships: PIBA, APIL, AvMA.

Career: Called 1982.

Publications: Basic Principles in Courts and Tribunals, N. Fridd – contributed to chapter on civil costs Article in New Law Journal 'Interpretation of PI Protocol' 2001 151 NLJ 1035 Article in New Law Journal 'Expert evidence: a review of the proposed Code' 2001 151 NLJ 1052 Article in New Law Journal 'Expert evidence: the code unscrambled' 2002 February p255 Book reviewer for NLJ on expert issues and general civil procedure

TAYLOR, John QC
Fountain Court Chambers, London
020 7583 3335
jt@fountaincourt.co.uk
Featured in Aviation (London), Banking & Finance (London), Commercial Dispute Resolution (London)

Practice Areas: Commercial litigation including banking, financial services, aviation, commercial fraud, insurance/reinsurance and professional negligence. Current and recent banking cases include the PPI litigation, the AIG Bond litigation and the swaps mis-selling litigation. Recent aviation cases include Virgin Atlantic v Mitsubishi (sale of goods/ incorporation of contractual terms/ warranties and indemnities) and Shaker v VistaJet [2012] 2 Lloyd's Rep. 93 (contractual formation/ certainty/estoppel). Recent commercial fraud cases include Corinth Pipeworks v Barclays (banking/trade finance/ DIFC Court), and Hemsley & RBC Trustee Ltd v Graham and Ors (fraudulent prospectus inducing investment/Ponzi scheme). Recent professional negligence claims include an LCIA arbitration hearing concerning the collapse of a hedge fund involving allegations of negligence against the manager, investment manager and valuation agent.

Professional Memberships: Commercial Bar Association; Professional Negligence Bar Association; British Association for Sport and Law.

Career: Called to the Bar 1993. Silk 2013.

Publications: Contributor to 'The Law of Bank Payments' (4th ed, Sweet & Maxwell 2010); contributor to 'Carriage by Air' (1st ed, Butterworths 2001).

Personal: Born 1968. Cambridge University MA 1st class.

TAYLOR, Martin
Carmelite Chambers, London
020 7936 6300
mtaylor@carmelitechambers.co.uk
Featured in Crime (London)
Practice Areas: Criminal defence advocate, with leading junior practice in serious crime especially fraud, including VAT, charity, banks, the DWP, the FSA, Buckingham Palace and other complex Financial frauds. Practice also includes drug cases, homicides, firearms and serious violence. Within the last two years, R v Aheer [million pound fraud on Amazon and iTunes], R v A [£2 million fraud on Olympic Funds], R v Whittaker [£20 million MTIC VAT Fraud], R v Salter [£8 million MTIC VAT Fraud - 5 month trial], R v Matthew Ekuku [£1 million benefits fraud], R v Stirling [Conspiracy to supply cannabis], R v Noon [Fraud of building suppliers of £1 million], R v Agar [Fraud from bank of £209 million], R v T [£3 million fraud on gambling investments], R v Fuller [£3.1 million fraud on Land Registry], R v Goble [£1.8 million fraud on major bookselling company], R v Wells [death by dangerous driving trial], R v Shah [£1 million fraud on banks], R v Symes [large scale confidence fraud of £1 million on the elderly].

TAYLOR, Michael
4 Pump Court, London
020 7842 5555
mtaylor@4pumpcourt.com
Featured in Information Technology (London)
Practice Areas: Information Technology, Construction, Professional Negligence, Commercial Dispute Resolution.
Professional Memberships: Society for Computers & Law (London Committee), Society of Construction Law, COMBAR.
Career: Tenant at 4 Pump Court since 2001. Former Judicial Assistant to Lord Woolf MR.
Publications: Contributor to Computers & Law magazine.
Personal: Educated at Oxford university (BA Hons First Class).

TAYLOR, Simon
Keating Chambers, London
020 7544 2600
staylor@keatingchambers.com
Featured in Public Procurement (London)
Practice Areas: Practices in EU, public procurement and competition law. Contentious and non-contentious. Procurement work includes disputes and strategic advice on the preparation and conduct of tenders. Advises on competition, state aid and regulatory issues arising from mergers and commercial conduct, cases before competition authorities and follow on damages actions. Specific expertise in healthcare, communications and rail. Advises widely on NHS competition, procurement and commercial disputes. Acted on Covanta v MWDA, MSL v NW London Hospital Trust and several other procurement cases. Mediations and hearings before the TCC. Advised on CMA approval submission for Basildon/Southend/iPP pathology JV.
Professional Memberships: Procurement Lawyers Association; Society of Labour Lawyers; Association of London Welsh Lawyers; Competition Lawyers Association.
Career: Called to Bar 1987; Pupillage 2 Temple Gardens 1987-88; Squire Sanders & Dempsey (Brussels)- 1990-92; Norton Rose (Brussels)- 1992-96; Cable & Wireless Communications–Regulatory counsel 1996-2000; Enrolled as a solicitor 1999; Allen & Overy-Associate 2000-04; Wragge & Co - Antitrust Partner-2004-2011; Keating Chambers 2012.
Publications: Frequent contributor to Plc on procurement and competition law.
Personal: Lives in Putney. Speaks French and Spanish. Likes travel, food, wine, theatre and rugby.

TAYLOR, Simon W QC
Cloisters, London
020 7827 4000
st@cloisters.com
Featured in Clinical Negligence (London)
Practice Areas: Specialises in medical law and personal injuries, including clinical negligence, medical disciplinary, mental health, and health service administrative law, and inquests. Simon Taylor QC is a medical doctor as well as a barrister. His caseload includes a very substantial proportion of cases of maximum or near-maximum severity, including birth injury, cerebral palsy and other brain injuries; cases involving multiple amputations following delay in diagnosis of meningococcal septicaemia; severe psychiatric injury cases; and many other cases in which exceptional expertise in dealing with complex medical evidence is critical.
Professional Memberships: PNBA, PIBA.
Career: Qualified doctor. Barrister 1984. Recorder 2002. Silk 2003.
Personal: BA Hons Cantab 1983. MB BChir 1987. Born 4 July 1962.

TEACHER, Petra
29 Bedford Row Chambers, London
020 7404 1044
Clerks@29br.co.uk
Featured in Family/Matrimonial (London)
Practice Areas: All areas of Family Law with a particular emphasis on matrimonial finance, cohabitees' disputes, and private law Children Act cases.
Professional Memberships: Family Law Bar Association.
Career: Called 2006, Inner Temple.
Personal: Lady Margaret Hall, Oxford University (MA (Oxon) (Modern Languages)) City University (CPE) Inns of Court School of Law (BVC).

TEMPLE, Eleanor
Kings Chambers, Leeds
08450 343 444
clerks@kingschambers.com
Featured in Banking & Finance (Northern), Chancery (Northern), Commercial Dispute Resolution (North Eastern), Restructuring/Insolvency (North Eastern)
Practice Areas: Eleanor Temple practises in commercial and insolvency litigation and advisory work, specialising in company and partnership law, corporate and personal insolvency, director disqualification, banking and finance - including recoveries, guarantees and investment trusts, restitution, fiduciaries, contract, commercial fraud, asset tracing, professional negligence and sports law. Eleanor is instructed on international work and has recently acted on cases in Jersey C.I., New York and Turks and Caicos. Eleanor was featured in The Times "Future Stars of the Regions" Report and was selected to speak to the New York City Bar Association on Cross Border Insolvency as a representative of the Bar Council. Her recent reported cases include: Jones v The Financial Conduct Authority [2013] EWHC 2731 (Ch) [2013] BPIR 1033, Jones v Financial Services Authority [2013] BPIR 589, Gately (Manchester) LLP v Rose and others [2013] All ER (D) 29 (Mar); Department of Business, Innovation and Skills v Compton [2012] BPIR 1108; People's Phone Limited v Theophilos Nicolaou [2011] EWHC 1129 (Ch); Rawnsley and another v Weatherall Green & Smith North Ltd and another [2010] 1 BCLC 658, [2010] BPIR 449; Parveen v Manchester City Council and Hellard [2010] BPIR 152.
Professional Memberships: R3 Committee Member (Yorkshire), Insolvency Lawyers Association, Chancery Bar Association, Northern Circuit Commercial Bar Association, Northern Chancery Bar Association, EQLA, British Association for Sports and Law.
Career: Called to the Bar 2000. Junior Counsel to the Crown 2008-11.
Publications: Misfeasance: Shadow Director Versus De Facto Director, Insolvency Intelligence 11/02/2011, 44, (2011) 24 Ins. Int. 4 Family Law and Bankruptcy Update, Insolvency Intelligence 11/02/2011, 39, (2011) 24 Ins. Int. 1 Equine Law: Taking the reins (2008) LS Gaz, 7 Aug, 14.

TERRY, Jeffrey
Kings Chambers, Manchester
08450 343 444
clerks@kingschambers.com
Featured in Chancery (Northern), Commercial Dispute Resolution (Northern)
Practice Areas: Commercial, especially insurance, chancery, professional negligence and construction. Recent cases at Court of Appeal level include: Brinks v Igrox [2011] IRLR 343 (Carriage of Goods, Torts, Bailment): Lambert v Barratt Homes & Rochdale MBC [2010] BLR 527, (Nuisance, Flooding by Construction Works); City & General v RSA (2010) BLR 639 (Construction, Insurance), Baynes v Hedger [2009] 2 FLR 183, CA (Succession, Inheritance Act); Ansari v New India Assurance [2009] Lloyds Rep IR 562 (Commercial Property, Fire Insurance).
Professional Memberships: Northern Circuit Commercial Bar Association; Northern Circuit Chancery Bar Association; Professional Negligence Bar Association; Bar European Group.
Career: LLB (Lond) 1975. Called 1976. MA (Business Law) with Distinction 1981, Fellow of the Chartered Institute of Arbitrators 1996. CEDR accredited mediator 1999.
Publications: Various papers and publications in England, USA and Canada.

TETHER, Melanie
Old Square Chambers, London
020 7269 0300
tether@oldsquare.co.uk
Featured in Employment (London), Employment (Western)
Practice Areas: All aspects of employment law, both individual and collective. Melanie is a tenacious advocate and is known for her ability to master challenging briefs. She is regularly instructed in heavyweight equal pay and discrimination claims and has appeared in a number of landmark cases, including several references to the Court of Justice of the European Union. She is a leading expert on the Transfer of Undertaking Regulations. Melanie has appeared in many reported cases. Examples include; Griffiths v. Secretary of State for Work and Pensions UKEAT/0372/13: whether the duty to make reasonable adjustments for an employee's disability applies to the employer's attendance management policy; Preston & Ors v. Wolverhampton Healthcare NHS Trust & Ors, Fletcher & Ors v. Midland Bank (HoL No.1): Sex discrimination alleged by part-time workers in an appeal against dismissal of their claim to a right to participate in the employer's occupational pension schemes; British Airways plc v Mak and others [2011] ICR 735 CA and Kelly v The Hesley Group Ltd [2013] IRLR 514 EAT.
Professional Memberships: ELA, ELBA, former Chair and current Vice President of ILS.
Career: Called to the Bar 1995. Previously a partner in Norton Rose.

THACKER, James
9 Gough Square, London
020 7832 0500
jthacker@9goughsquare.co.uk
Featured in Financial Crime (London)
Practice Areas: Criminal law with specialisms in Financial Crime and Regulatory offences. James has prosecuted and defended in several high profile, multi-handed, high value complex frauds as leading counsel, sole counsel and junior to Queen's Counsel. He has also prosecuted cases as sole counsel against Queen's Counsel. James is adept in dealing with cases involving large volumes of evidence and expert evidence. Prosecution cases include: Operation Crystal (multi handed fraud involving 12 deaf defendants), Operation Dec (£2million multi handed bank fraud), Operation Glider (multi handed Gift Aid fraud). Defence cases include: Operation Exempt (multi handed confidence fraud). James is also experienced with restraint and confiscation proceedings. He appeared in the Court of Appeal case of R v R [2013] EWCA 1105 (restraint variations).
Professional Memberships: Criminal Bar Association and South Eastern Circuit (committee member 2009-2012).
Career: Called to the Bar in 2001 (Gray's Inn). Grade 3 CPS prosecutor. Grade 3 specialist Fraud prosecutor. Appointed to prosecute rape and serious sexual offences. Appointed to Regulatory list (Health and Safety and Environmental Law). Approved for Direct Access.

THANKI, Bankim QC
Fountain Court Chambers, London
020 7583 3335
bt@fountaincourt.co.uk
Featured in Aviation (London), Banking & Finance (London), Commercial Dispute Resolution (London), Financial Services (London), Fraud (London), Insurance (London), International Arbitration (London), Offshore (London), Professional Negligence (London), Travel (London)
Practice Areas: Commercial dispute resolution (litigation and arbitration) in all its guises. A considerable amount of work is now offshore. Notable cases since taking Silk include acting for GMR in its dispute with the Maldives government over the international airport at Malé, for Vincent Tchenguiz in his claim against the SFO, for Deloitte LLP over the Phoenix Four/MG Rover investigation, for the Central Bank of Trinidad & Tobago in the Colonial Life Enquiry, for the Bar Council in R (Prudential) v HMRC, for Lloyds Banking Group in the OFT test case on bank charges, for the son of the King of Bahrain in his claim against Michael Jackson, for the Bank of England in Three Rivers and for Qantas in the DVT litigation.
Professional Memberships: Commercial Bar Association.
Career: Called to the Bar 1988. Silk 2003. Bencher, Middle Temple 2008.

Personal: Educated at Balliol College, Oxford (BA, 1st Class Hons 1986; MA 1989). Harmsworth Scholar, Middle Temple, 1988.

THOM, James QC
New Square Chambers, London
020 7419 8000
james.thom@newsquarechambers.co.uk
Featured in Offshore (London)

Practice Areas: James has an extensive practice in property and corporate law with a strong emphasis on offshore work. His practice includes insolvency and corporate reconstruction, including shareholders' disputes, company liquidation and restructuring, usually with an offshore connection, and often involving hedge funds. He also undertakes property litigation, mainly development contract disputes, mortgage and subrogation claims, claims in nuisance or negligence for damages to land and buildings by flood, pollution and the like, disputes over site boundaries and easements, claims involving proprietary estoppel and constructive trust and landlord and tenant disputes. In the last 12 months James has appeared in court in shareholders' disputes in England and Wales and the BVI, in a claim against the former auditors of a collapsed hedge fund in the Cayman Islands and in a property dispute between a mortgage fund and the government in the Turks and Caicos Islands.
Professional Memberships: Chancery Bar Association, Professional Negligence Bar Association, Property Bar Association.
Career: Called to the Bar 1974. Called to the Bar of St Vincent and the Grenadines 1997. Queen's Counsel 2003. Called to the Bar of the British Virgin Islands 2005.
Publications: Joint author of 'Handbook of Dilapidations' (Sweet & Maxwell, 1992, looseleaf).
Personal: Educated at Felsted School 1965-68 and Corpus Christi College, Oxford 1969-73 (BA 1972, BCL 1973). Born 19th October 1951. Lives in Highgate, London.

THOMAS, Bryan
Civitas Law, Cardiff
08450 713 007
bryan.thomas@civitaslaw.com
Featured in Clinical Negligence (Wales & Chester), Personal Injury (Wales & Chester)

Practice Areas: Bryan has a wide-ranging and high volume PI practice; highly experienced in catastrophic injury claims arising out of head or spinal injuries. He also has a significant clinical negligence practice covering high value claims, particularly brain injury at birth cases. Bryan is regularly instructed to prosecute and defend in the most serious industrial accidents and acts for many local authorities and PLCs. He is also an experienced mediator, arbitrator and adjudicator for a wide spectrum of civil disputes, including construction, professional negligence, personal injury and general commercial.
Professional Memberships: Memberships: APIL, PIBA, HSLA and is a Fellow of the Chartered Institute of Arbitrators.
Career: Called to the Bar in 1978

THOMAS, David QC
Keating Chambers, London
020 7544 2600
dthomas@keatingchambers.com
Featured in Construction (London), International Arbitration (London)

Practice Areas: Specialist in construction, engineering, energy, technology, related professional Negligence, Insurance and general commercial work. Known for his forceful advocacy, cross-examination skills, commercial awareness and the incisiveness and practicality of his advice. Enjoys leading the team in litigation and arbitration and working with clients and experts on strategy and detailed presentation. Regularly appears before the Technology and Construction Court, but a large part of his practice relates to international and domestic arbitration, adjudication, expert determination and mediation as well as all related advisory work. Accepts appointments as arbitrator, expert, mediator and adjudicator.
Professional Memberships: TECBAR; UK Energy Law Group; PNBA; SCL; Treasurer of the Omani-British Lawyers Association.
Career: Called to Bar 1982; Called to Bar of Gibraltar 1996; Queens Counsel 2002; CEDR Accredited Mediator 2003; Trained in Dispute Adjudication Board Hearings and Procedure 2005.
Publications: Contributor – Construction Law International. Editor Keating on NEC3, 2012. Contributor – Keating on Construction Contracts Eight Edition (2006) and First Supplement (2008).
Personal: David is a keen gardener, cricket player and spectator, and is a member of the MCC.

THOMAS, George
Serjeants' Inn Chambers, London
020 7427 5000
gthomas@serjeantsinn.com
Featured in Police Law (All Circuits)

Practice Areas: George Thomas was called to the Bar in 1995. George specialises in public and administrative, police, Court of Protection, employment, inquests and inquiries, clinical negligence and healthcare and professional discipline law. An earlier edition notes that "he is very knowledgeable and very efficient" and "strong on public order and very aware of police law...he can answer any question you ask him." Please click on the link above to the Serjeants' Inn Chambers website for his profile, which sets out full details of his practice including relevant work of note.
Professional Memberships: PNBA, ARDL, ELBA, ALBA.
Publications: "Public Order: Law and Practice" Blackstone's Practical Policing, with John Beggs QC and Susanna Rickard, OUP, 2012.

THOMAS, Nigel
Maitland Chambers, London
020 7406 1200
nthomas@maitlandchambers.com
Featured in Agriculture & Rural Affairs (London), Chancery (London)

Practice Areas: Chancery law: Oatley v Oatley [2014] EWHC 1956 (rectification of voluntary settlement); Perdoni v Curati [2012] WTLR 505 : 14 ITELR 725 (establishing domicile); Taylor v Saunders & ors LTL 19/7/2012 (setting aside will for lack of testamentary capacity due to Alzheimer's disease); Dunbar v Plant [1998] Ch 412 (Forfeiture Act 1982). Agricultural law: Davies v H & R Eckroyd Ltd (1996) EGCS 77 (Law of Commons and Village Greens); R v Suffolk CC ex Parte Steed (1995) 2EGLR 232, Lord Dynevor v Richardson [1995] ChD 173. Property: Parshall v Hackney [2013] 1 Ch D 568; Dwr Cymru Cyf v Edgar 2004 All ER(D) 05 (Nov); Carmen Johnson v WR Shaw [2003] EWCA (Civ) 894 and National Car Parks Ltd v Trinity Developments (Banbury) Ltd [2002] 1P+CR P37.
Professional Memberships: Chancery Bar Association, Wales and Chester Circuit.
Career: Called to the Bar 1976 (Gray's Inn). Chairman Agricultural Land Tribunal (Midland Area), Recorder.

THOMAS, Roger QC
Pump Court Tax Chambers, London
020 7414 8080
clerks@pumptax.com
Featured in Tax (London)

Practice Areas: Practice covers all areas of corporate and personal taxation and has developed a particular profile in SDLT and VAT. Cases include Yarburgh Children's Trust v CCE (High Court); Public & Commercial Services Union v CCE (High Court); St Paul's Community Development Trust v CCE (High Court); Messenger Leisure Developments Ltd v CCE (Court of Appeal); Marshall Motor Group v HMRC, (VAT Tribunal); St Helen's School v HMRC (High Court); Telent plc v HMRC (VAT Tribunal); Northampton Theatres Trust v HMRC (VAT Tribunal); HSBC v HMRC (ECJ); Atrium Club Ltd v HMRC (VAT Tribunal); Garsington Opera v HMRC (First-Tier Tribunal); Future Health v HMRC (ECJ); Longridge on the Thames v HMRC (First-tier Tribunal); Project Blue v HMRC (Upper Tribunal); DV3 v HMRC (Court of Appeal); Zipvit v HMRC (First-tier Tribunal)
Professional Memberships: Revenue Bar Association; London Common Law & Commercial Bar Association; VAT Practitioners Group; Stamp Taxes Practitioners Group.
Career: Called 1979, Lincoln's Inn. QC 2014.
Publications: VAT (Halsbury's Laws of England); Customs & Excise Duties (Halsbury's Laws of England); Customs Duty De Voil vol 6.
Personal: Born 1955; Resides in London.

THOMAS-SYMONDS, Nicklaus
Civitas Law, Cardiff
08450 713 007
nick.thomas-symonds@civitaslaw.com
Featured in Chancery (Wales & Chester), Commercial Dispute Resolution (Wales & Chester)

Practice Areas: Nick receives instructions in a wide range of high value chancery and commercial matters, including challenges to wills, and claims under the Inheritance (Provision for Family and Dependants) Act 1975. He deals with a wide range of property law, including disputes of title and boundaries. Nick regularly acts in contractual claims; he appears in commercial mediations and arbitrations, and construction cases. He also deals with landlord and tenant disputes, and cases of professional negligence.
Professional Memberships: Chancery Bar Association.
Career: Fellow of the Royal Historical Society. Lecturer in Politics at St. Edmund Hall, Oxford University, and an ADR-Group Accredited Mediator. Nick is a registered Pupil-Supervisor. He appears regularly as a newspaper reviewer on BBC Radio Wales.
Publications: "The Hard Sell: When does a new car actually belong to the purchaser?" Solicitors' Journal, Volume 154, Number 35, 21 September 2010. "Attlee: A Life in Politics," London: I.B. Tauris, published 2010 (ISBN-10: 1845117794; ISBN-13: 978-1845117795). "Nye: The Political Life of Aneurin Bevan," London: I.B.Tauris, published 2014 (ISBN-10: 1780762097; ISBN-13: 978-1780762098).
Personal: Nick is married to Rebecca, and has two daughters, Matilda and Florence. He is also a Labour Party activist.

THOMPSON, Andrew
Red Lion Chambers, Chelmsford
01245 280 880
andrew.thompson@18rlc.co.uk
Featured in Crime (South Eastern)

Practice Areas: Andrew defends and prosecutes in East Anglia, London and the South East. He specialises in serious sexual offences, particularly those involving historical allegations or with child witnesses. Andrew's recent cases include alleged sexual offences in schools, care and foster homes, by medical practitioners and within youth organisations. Andrew is regularly chosen for trials involving mentally disadvantaged defendants or witnesses and those with other special requirements. He has extensive experience in cases of murder/manslaughter, serious assault and where 'non-accidental' injuries to children or vulnerable adults are alleged. Other cases include large-scale public disorder, serious drug offences (recently a £11.5 million drug importation), money laundering and fraud. He is also instructed in appeals which were not pursued by the accused's original legal team. Andrew has defended and prosecuted in many rape, murder and high profile historical sexual abuse allegations, including the largest ever historical child sexual abuse investigation in the East of England which featured in a BBC1 documentary. He is known for his highly effective cross-examinations, his tactical skills and his meticulous eye for detail.
Professional Memberships: CBA, South Eastern Circuit, JUSTICE.

THOMPSON, Andrew QC
Erskine Chambers, London
020 7242 5532
athompson@erskinechambers.com
Featured in Company (London)

Practice Areas: Andrew Thompson is a sought-after, specialist commercial litigator, with particular expertise in: corporate litigation (including shareholders' disputes, claims against directors and constructive trust claims); LLP and partnership disputes; corporate insolvency; commercial litigation (including large-scale contractual disputes, fraud and breach of warranty claims); professional negligence claims (including lawyers, accountants, valuers and management consultants); and disputes within unincorporated associations. Andrew has been involved in leading cases in all of these areas, with specific expertise in litigation in the fund management industry. Andrew also undertakes advisory work in the same fields. A list of reported and recent cases is available at www.erskinechambers.com.
Professional Memberships: COMBAR, Chancery Bar Association.
Career: Merchant Taylors' School; St Catharine's College, Cambridge (1989 BA; 1990 LLM; 1992 MA); Called to Inner Temple 1991.
Personal: Leisure: family, cricket, gardening, hill-walking, birding.

THOMPSON, James
Keating Chambers, London
020 7544 2604
jthompson@keatingchambers.com
Featured in Construction (London)
Practice Areas: Recognised specialist in construction and engineering, energy, infrastructure and related commercial disputes involving claims relating to delay and disruption, defects, payment and termination. Has extensive advocacy experience in the High Court (particularly the TCC) and arbitration (both domestic and international). Regularly instructed in adjudication proceedings involving drafting referral and response documents, written and oral submissions and subsequent enforcement hearings. Recent work includes: acting for the main contractor in ICC arbitration arising out of the construction of a power plant in the Caribbean; sole counsel in TCC proceedings relating to subsidence of properties forming part of a large UK development; junior counsel on behalf of the contractor in high-profile proceedings in the TCC concerning the construction of a busway; junior counsel in ICC arbitration concerning chemical cleaning works to a power station. Has particular experience of disputes in the Middle East having recently acted for clients in Dubai, Qatar, Oman and Saudi Arabia and is a committee member of the Omani British Lawyers Association.
Professional Memberships: Technology and Construction Bar Association (TECBAR); Society of Construction Law; Commercial Bar Association (COMBAR); Omani British Lawyers Association (committee member).
Career: MA Law (Cantab) Selwyn College, Cambridge (2004); Called 2005 (Middle Temple) (Astbury Scholar); Pupillage Keating Chambers (2005-06); Keating Chambers (2006).
Publications: Researcher for Keating on Construction Contracts, 8th and 9th Editions; Contributory Author for the Practical Law Company.

THOMPSON, Rhodri QC
Matrix Chambers, London
020 7404 3447
rhodrithompson@matrixlaw.co.uk
Featured in Competition/European Law (London), Telecommunications (London)
Practice Areas: Competition law, EU law, public law, telecoms law. Current cases include: MasterCard (appeal pending CJEU); BT v Ofcom (Ethernet dispute, appeal CAT/CA); R(Sky Blue) v. Coventry CC (JR, Admin Ct/CA); Lafarge Tarmac v. CMA (CAT). Major historic cases include: Tetra Pak II (abuse of dominance, CFI); Net Books (Article 101, ECJ); Chagos Islanders Group Litigation (misfeasance, CA); Hoverspeed v HMCE (restrictions on imports of alcohol and tobacco, DCt); Three Rivers DC v Bank of England (misfeasance in public office, HL); R (GNER) v ORR (access pricing, Admin Ct); Adidas (sporting rules; arts 81 and 82, Ch); food supplements directive (challenge to legality, ECJ); Attheraces (collective selling of sports rights, CAT); Genzyme (pricing abuse, CAT); pre-insulated pipes cartel (Commission fining policy, ECJ); The Number v. OFCOM/BT (EU telecoms regulation, directory information); Stagecoach v. Competition Commission (merger review, CAT); Albion Water (pricing abuses, CAT, CA); Co-op v OFT (Chapter 1 pricing decision "Tobacco", CAT); Somerfield v. OFT ("Tobacco" late appeal, CAT, CA).
Professional Memberships: Middle Temple; CLA; UKAEL; BEG.
Career: Call, 1989; Brussels, 1990-92; Monckton Chambers, 1990-2000; Treasury B Panel 1997-2002; Founder member, Matrix, 2000-; QC 2002; Chair of Matrix Management Committee, 2004-06, 2014-; Civil Recorder 2010-; Joint Chair JWP of UK Bars and Law Socs. on competition law; Hon, Treasurer, UKAEL.
Publications: Bellamy and Child, 'EC Law of Competition' (7th edition, contributor, abuse of dominance); 'The Single Market for Pharmaceuticals' (author). Regular speaker at conferences, in-house seminars.

THOMSON, David
1 Chancery Lane, London
020 7 092 2900
DThomson@1chancerylane.com
Featured in Clinical Negligence (London)
Practice Areas: David is a specialist in personal injury, clinical negligence, sports law, safeguarding and disciplinary matters. He has considerable experience in clinical negligence and personal injury with particular expertise in catastrophic and neurological damage. He also undertakes health regulatory matters including Tier 1 panels. He is a leading sports lawyer appointed an Independent Commissioner on the Football Regulatory Authority, and an appointed member of National Safeguarding in Sport panel and several other disciplinary appeal bodies. David is an arbitrator (previous Fellow of the Chartered Institute of Arbitrators) and mediator.
Professional Memberships: PIBA, PNBA, ARDL.
Career: David was called in 1994 (Inner Temple) and was previously a medical practitioner. Qualified in law and medicine: MB ChB (Sheffield University Medical School 1985); worked as a surgeon 1986-89 and as a GP 1989-96; LLB (London Univ 1992); LLM (Cambridge Univ - Peterhouse 1993); medico-legal consultant 1990-96; Army reserve medical officer 1995. Appointed Chairman of various sports disciplinary bodies for disciplinary and safeguarding cases. FA Commissioner (independent) 2007 to date. Bar Standards Board – Chairman of Panel 2 Qualifications Committee – from 2009 to date. Specialist legal member Sports Resolutions Panel 2005 to date. National Safeguarding in Sport Panel, June 2012.
Personal: Horse riding cross country, motor cycling, cricket and skiing. Rugby coach. Army (Reserve Forces RARO). Trustee of two charities – Spinal Research and LawCare. Watching any theatre, especially musicals.

THOMSON, David
Axiom Advocates, Edinburgh
07500 813 598
david.thomson@axiomadvocates.com
Featured in Company (Scotland), Restructuring/Insolvency (Scotland), Real Estate Litigation (Scotland), Commercial Dispute Resolution (Scotland)
Practice Areas: Practises exclusively in commercial disputes, with a particular emphasis on company law, property/real estate litigation and insolvency law.
Career: 1995-97: Trainee Solicitor, Steedman Ramage WS; 1997-2003: solicitor at various commercial law firms; 2004: called to the Bar; 2005-09: Standing Junior Counsel to the Scottish Ministers; 2009-date: Standing Junior Counsel to the Advocate General for Scotland.

THORNHILL, Andrew QC
Pump Court Tax Chambers, London
020 7414 8080
clerks@pumptax.com
Featured in Tax (London)
Practice Areas: Head of Chambers specialising in all areas of tax but with special emphasis on employee remuneration, share schemes, inheritance tax, capital gains tax, planning and litigation. Cases include: Laird v CIR (House of Lords); Eversden v CIR (Court of Appeal); Dextra Accessories v MacDonald (House of Lords), Optos Plc v CIR (Special Commissioners), Sempra Metals v HMRC (Special Commissioners), Murray Group v HMRC (First-tier and Upper Tribunal)(Rangers FC litigation case), Scotts Atlantic Ltd v HMRC (First-tier Tribunal).
Professional Memberships: Revenue Bar Association; STEP, London Common Law and Commercial Bar Association.
Career: Called 1969, Middle Temple; Pump Court Tax Chambers 1969 to date; QC 1985; formerly Recorder Western Circuit. Head of Pump Court Tax Chambers 1991 to present.
Publications: Potter & Monroe's 'Tax Planning with Precedents' 4th-7th editions; 'Passing Down the Family Business/the Family Farm'; Contributor to 'Gore-Brown on Companies' and 'Kerr on Receivers'.
Personal: Clifton College; Corpus Christi College, Oxford.

THORNLEY, Hannah
South Square, London
020 7696 9900
hannahthornley@southsquare.com
Featured in Restructuring/Insolvency (London)
Practice Areas: International and Domestic Company and Insolvency law, with particular interest and experience in the Duties of Directors, Shareholder Disputes and Fraud situations; General Commercial and International Litigation; Insurance; Trusts; Property; Banking; Finance; Professional Negligence and Disciplinary Proceedings.
Career: Hannah is an experienced advocate and litigator. She appears regularly in the High Court and advises on domestic and international cases which are often of a complex or urgent nature. Hannah has advised, represented or appeared in Court for numerous high profile banks, companies and private individuals. Her clients include: Bank of Ireland; Standard Chartered Bank; Abbey National; Anglo-Irish Bank; Volksbank, Commerzbank (the Company that previously owned Manchester City Football Club); Landlords in Games Station; Landlords in Woolworths; Connaught; Barratts; Birthdays; Thomson Directories, Dawnay Day; East London Bus Group; Oilexco; Lemma Insurance; Independent Insurance; UIC Insurance; Brit Insurance; National House Building Council. Hannah is recommended as an "up and coming" junior in Chambers & Partners 2014. Appointed to sit on the Bar Disciplinary Panel 2013; elected onto the Chambers Executive Committee 2012; appointed as a Chambers Equality and Diversity Officer 2012; pupillage at South Square 2003-2004; called to the Bar (Middle Temple) 2003; Bar Vocational Course, ICSL 2002-2003; Brasenose College, Oxford University, BCL 2001-2002; Downing College, Cambridge University, MA Law 1998–2001.

THORNTON, Andrew
Erskine Chambers, London
020 7242 5532
clerks@erskinechambers.com
Featured in Company (London)
Practice Areas: Company law, with a particular emphasis on mergers and acquisitions both domestic and cross-border and associated advisory matters. He has advised on a number of substantial schemes of arrangement in the past year including those for Xstrata Plc, Vodafone Plc and Dixons Plc.
Professional Memberships: COMBAR, Chancery Bar Association.
Career: Called Lincolns Inn 1994.
Publications: Contributor to Buckley on the Companies Acts. Consultant editor Scheme of Arrangement: Law and Practice.

THOROGOOD, Bernard
No5 Chambers, Birmingham
01216 060 500
regulatory@no5.com
Featured in Consumer Law (Midlands), Health & Safety (Midlands)
Practice Areas: The most serious categories of health and safety and other regulatory cases of gravity and complexity, including gross negligence and corporate manslaughter. Advises large organisations, including major businesses and public bodies, in regulatory matters concerning their present and future practice. Has specialised in regulatory work for many years - always involved in a very substantial number of fatal cases usually instructed from well before the Inquest. Cases include: construction; leisure; transport; manufacturing; farming; quarries and mining; distribution; asbestos; fires; deaths in hospitals and care homes; domestic and commercial gassing; nuclear industry; deaths in water; military deaths and a fire in the Atomic Weapons Establishment. Also the prosecution and defence of local authorities; tree preservation orders; Sites of Specific Scientific Interest; environmental (water and land); trading standards; food standards. His time spent in manufacturing helps to maintain focus on the reality of the workplace. His trademarks include thorough attention to detail and getting to grips with complex and technical evidence. Works throughout the country. Travels to client's workplace to study processes/technicalities etc. and to confer.
Professional Memberships: Health and Safety Lawyers Association; Forensic Science Society; Agricultural Law Association; Criminal Bar Association.
Career: Gap year in industrial production 1976-77, 1981-85 Short Service Commission (Infantry), Called to the Bar 1986.
Personal: Married, three children.

THORPE, Alexander
Queen Elizabeth Building, London
020 7797 7837
A.Thorpe@qeb.co.uk
Featured in Family/Matrimonial (London)
Practice Areas: Alexander specialises in all aspects of private family law with particular emphasis on complex financial work, encompassing jurisdiction disputes, trusts and other off-shore structures. Much of his work has an international element.
Professional Memberships: A member of the FLBA and the Western Circuit.

THWAITES, Ronald QC
Ely Place Chambers, London
020 7400 9600
rthwaites@elyplace.com
Featured in Defamation/Privacy (London), Inquests & Public Inquiries (London)
Practice Areas: Ronald Thwaites is universally acknowledged as an adviser, strategist and advocate who is versatile and effective before all courts, (with juries or without) and who is capable of producing results that others can only dream of. He acts for both claimants and defendants. He continues to operate in the areas of defamation and privacy, health and safety and other regulatory regimes, pensions mis-selling, general commercial work as well as occasionally returning to criminal work in which he is steeped and from which he originally developed his noted court room skills. It is testimony to his fluency, tenacity and powers of cross-examination that his opponents fear him and judges appreciate both his clarity and his direct approach to litigation. He acts for corporate as well as private clients, newspaper groups and Police Forces, and has appeared in many major fiercely contested trials as well as public inquiries. He has acted in a long and complex rail crash trial where technical subjects had to be mastered and detailed daily cross-examination had to be carried out by him on expert witnesses. He prefers to be asked to advise early in any litigation so that he can put his stamp on it. Many solicitors consider that instructing Ronald Thwaites encourages the other side to settle the action.
Career: Call 1970; QC 1987.
Personal: Born 1946.

TIDMARSH, Christopher QC
5 Stone Buildings, London
020 7242 6201
clerks@5sblaw.com
Featured in Chancery (London), Pensions (London)
Practice Areas: Practice Areas: Chancery practitioner, particular emphasis on trusts and probate, tax, pensions, professional negligence, (solicitors and accountants). Experienced in both contentious and non-contentious aspects of the administration of trusts (UK and offshore), estates and pension schemes. Before taking Silk, Christopher was a standing Junior Counsel to the Inland Revenue (1995-2002) and brings that experience to bear in his private practice. Extensive experience in tax cases before the special and general commissioners and in the High Court and the Court of Appeal. Reported cases include: Boyer Allan Investment Services Ltd v Revenue & Customs [2012] UKFTT 558 (TC); Greenbank v HMRC [2011]STC 1582; Re Nelson Dance Settlement [2009] EWHC (Ch) 71; Johnston Publishing North v HMRC [2008] EWCA Civ 858; Underwood v HMRC [2008] EWCA Civ 1423; Random House (UK) Ltd v Allason & Ors [2008] EWHC (Ch) 2854; Hearn v Dobson [2008] EWHC (Ch) 1620; Re Rogers [2006] 1 WLR 1577; Re T&N [2005] PLR 33; Hearn v Younger [2005] PLR 49; Property Co v Inland Revenue [2005] STC (SCD) 59; Aon v KPMG [2004].
Professional Memberships: Chancery Bar Association, STEP.
Career: Called 1985; Silk 2002.

TINDAL, Jim
St Philips Chambers, Birmingham
01212 467 000
jtindal@st-philips.com
Featured in Civil Liberties & Human Rights (Midlands), Employment (Midlands)
Practice Areas: In Employment, Jim is a Part-Time Employment Judge in Bristol. He has appeared in the Court of Appeal in the first case to define a 'teacher' and also the new leading case on the power of the EAT to decide cases or remit. In the EAT he has appeared in cases concerning discrimination and the burden of proof, victimisation, unfair dismissal, strike-out and TUPE. Jim specialises in appeals, test cases and complex employment and injunction cases in the civil courts. In Civil Liberties and Human Rights, Jim is a Recorder of the Crown Court, a Deputy District Judge in the Magistrates' Courts, and a Treasury Counsel for Public Law. He has appeared in the Court of Appeal on a test case on restricted leave for foreign-born criminals, and a complex judicial review on immigration, prison law and local authorities involving human rights and EU law. He is regularly instructed by local authorities and individuals in social welfare cases and in the Court of Protection.
Professional Memberships: Midland Circuit; Employment Lawyers' Association.
Career: Solicitor 2000-02; Barrister from 2002; EJ and DDJ from 2009; Recorder from 2012.
Publications: Encyclopedia of Employment Law; Tucker and George Discrimination in Employment.

TIPPLES, Amanda QC
Maitland Chambers, London
020 7406 1200
atipples@maitlandchambers.com
Featured in Chancery (London), Charities (London), Partnership (London), Real Estate Litigation (London)
Practice Areas: Amanda is experienced in general chancery and commercial litigation, in particular traditional chancery, partnership, real property and landlord and tenant, insolvency/corporate recovery, professional negligence, civil fraud, charities, VAT and Duties, confiscation proceedings. Recent cases include: University of London v Professor Prag (trusts/charities); Pollen Estate v HMRC (stamp duty/charities); A-G v Charity Commission (charities); Silkstone v Tatnall (real property); Franks v Bedward (real property); Herbert v Doyle (constructive trusts/proprietary estoppel); Tann v Herrington (partnership); Reichmann v Gauntlett (landlord and tenant).
Professional Memberships: Chancery Bar Association, COMBAR, ACTAPS, Charity Law Association.
Career: Called to the Bar in 1991; Junior Counsel to the Crown (A Panel) 2006-11; Recorder (Crown Court) 2009; Queen's Counsel 2011; Deputy High Court Judge (Chancery Division) 2013.
Personal: Gonville and Caius College, Cambridge (MA).

TOD, Jonathan
29 Bedford Row Chambers, London
020 7404 1044
jtod@29br.co.uk
Featured in Family/Matrimonial (London)
Practice Areas: Matrimonial finance and Schedule 1 Children Act Proceedings. Re P (A Child: Financial Provision) (2003) 2 FLR 865 CA; B v B (Mesher Order) (2003) 2 FLR 285; Hill v Morgan (Child: Financial Provision) [2007] 1 FLR 1480; N v D (Child: Financial Provision) (2008) 1 FLR 1629; G v G (Child Maintenance: Interim Costs Provision) [2010] 2 FLR 1264; PK v BC [2012] 2 FLR 1426; Z v Z No2 [2012] 1 FLR 1100; PG v TW (No 1)(Child: Financial Provision: Legal Funding) [2014] 1FLR 508; PG v TW (no 2) (Child: Financial Provision) [2014] 1FLR 923; Y v Z [2014] FLR forthcoming.
Professional Memberships: Family Law Bar Association.
Career: Qualified 1990, Inner Temple. Currently involved in a number of big money and high profile matrimonial finance cases including those with jurisdictional issues. He also specialises in advising on and drafting nuptial agreements. Continues to be instructed in many Schedule 1 Children Act disputes.
Publications: He has written with others six articles relating to Schedule 1 Children Act. 'Consider the Mother's Furture' (2007) Family Law 140; 'Tax Implications: Schedule 1 Trusts (2007) Family Law 708; 'Schedule 1 To The Children Act 1989: N v D 'And The Need for Reform' [2008 Family Law 751]and 'Jurisdiction and Forum Issues in Schedule 1 Children Act Procedures' (2008) Family Law 880. Schedule 1 Children Act 1989: Update on Jurisdiction, Law & Procedure (2012) Fam Law 543, Schedule 1 Important Development PG v TW (2013) Fam Law 1286. He regularly lectures on Schedule 1 issues and Pre-nuptial Agreements.
Personal: Educated at Wellington College, Berkshire and Southampton University. Married with two children.

TODD, Michael QC
Erskine Chambers, London
020 7242 5532
mtodd@erskinechambers.com
Featured in Company (London), Offshore (London)
Practice Areas: Michael is head of Erskine Chambers. He specialises in litigation and transactional advice on company law, corporate finance, capital markets and corporate insolvency, in the UK and internationally. Described as one of the first people to call for legal advice on complex restructurings and contested takeovers and schemes. Significant cases and transactions include: Pfizer / AstraZeneca; Xstrata / Glencore; Coroin plc; Bumi plc; Nortel and Tyco (expert evidence); Rangers plc v Ticketus; BAT v Winward (asset protection); Re PCCW Ltd (CA Hong Kong; scheme of arrangement), Validus v IPC (Bermuda; hostile scheme); Belmont Asset Based Lending (Cayman) and Culross Global v Strategic Turnaround Master Partnership Ltd (PC) (redemption of interests in funds); Chaston v SWP; Anglo Petroleum Ltd v TFB Mortgages (CA; financial assistance); Re Prudential Enterprise Ltd (CFA Hong Kong; shareholder dispute); American Patriot Agency (PC Bermuda; commercial fraud); Tenaga (Malaysia; piercing the corporate veil); Waddington v Chan (Hong Kong/BVI; derivative actions). Michael has advised various regulatory bodies including the Financial Conduct Authority, Channel Islands Stock Exchange, Hong Kong Stock Exchange and Hong Kong Securities and Futures Commission.
Professional Memberships: Chairman of the Bar of England & Wales (2012, VC 2011); Chairman of Chancery Bar Association (2008-11); COMBAR, Chairman of BarCo; Director of the Global Law Summit; Executive Committee of the Commonwealth Lawyers Association; Trustee of the Bar Pro Bono Unit; Trustee of Bar Pro Bono Community.
Career: Called: 1977. Silk 1997. Michael has appeared in the courts of Hong Kong, British Virgin Islands, Bermuda, Cayman Islands, Isle of Man, Turks & Caicos Islands and Northern Ireland as well as in the Privy Council.

TOLLEY, Adam QC
Fountain Court Chambers, London
020 7583 3335
art@fountaincourt.co.uk
Featured in Employment (London)
Practice Areas: All aspects of employment litigation, including large-scale commercial employment litigation (restrictive covenants, confidentiality, fiduciary duties, TUPE) and individual employment proceedings (including discrimination, equal pay, whistleblowing). Recent cases include: Reed Employment v HMRC [2014] BTC 511 (over-arching employment contracts); Ashcourt Rowan v Hall [2013] IRLR 637 (garden leave and enforceability of non-competition clause); Towry EJ v Bennett [2012] EHWC 224 (QB) (non-solicitation and confidentiality); Brandeaux v Chadwick [2011] IRLR 224 (confidentiality, fiduciary duties); Weightwatchers v HMRC [2010] STI 1620 (employment status of Weightwatchers' Leaders); HMRC v Ainsworth [2009] ICR 985 (holiday pay and sick leave); Day v HRH The Prince of Wales, London South ET, 2005 (successful defence of claim of race discrimination).
Professional Memberships: ELBA; ELA; ILS; COMBAR; PNBA.
Career: Called to Bar 1994. Educated at Hutchesons' Grammar School (Glasgow), St Anne's College, Oxford (BA Juris, 1st, 1992; BCL, 1st, 1993). Member of Fountain Court Chambers since 1995. Attorney General's A Panel 2007-14. Silk: 2014.
Publications: Co-author, Financial Services chapter in Professional Negligence and Liability (Informa, looseleaf). Co-author (with Professor McKendrick) of Halsbury's Laws volume on Restitution, published December 2000.

TONEY, Rachel
Stone Chambers, London
020 7440 6900
rachel.toney@stonechambers.com
Featured in Shipping (London)
Practice Areas: Rachel Toney's shipping and commercial practice includes all aspects of international trade and maritime work including bills of lading/charterparty disputes, shipbuilding disputes, indemnity claims, Agency Agreement disputes, contamination and cargo claims; Admiralty claims, primarily collisions/allisions, unsafe port, including jurisdictional and procedural issues; contracts for the sale and carriage of goods together with insurance and reinsurance. Rachel has acted in a number of complex, high profile "megayacht" disputes, including acting for the Purchaser of one of the world's largest superyachts in a lengthy shipbuilding dispute. Employment law practice encompasses all aspects of unfair dismissal, discrimination (particularly age and disability), breaches of contract and PI. As part of her Treasury Counsel (Panel B) practice she represents Government entities and agencies on particularly sensitive and often highly confidential matters.

Professional Memberships: COMBAR, Admiralty Bar, London Common Law and Commercial Bar Association, British German Jurists Association; BMLA.
Career: Called to the Bar 1998; Junior Counsel to the Crown - Panel C 2004, promoted to Panel B March 2008; Member of Attorney General's Panel of Special Advocates, 2010.
Personal: Educated Oxford University Law with Legal Studies in Europe BA Hons (1st) 1997; Konstanz University, Germany, LLM (finalised 1999).

TOOGOOD, Claire
Crown Office Chambers, London
020 7797 8100
toogood@crownofficechambers.com
Featured in Clinical Negligence (London)
Practice Areas: Claire specialises in clinical negligence, industrial disease and medical product liability. Claire is predominantly instructed by the NHSLA and the defence unions but also acts for Claimants. Her wide experience includes claims involving obstetrics, orthopaedics, oncology, gynaecology, paediatrics, neurology, urology, diabetes and general surgery. Claire is frequently instructed to attend joint settlement meetings and has a reputation for negotiating satisfactory outcomes, but she is unafraid to pursue a case to trial where Claire's strong advocacy skills can be utilised. She is known as an effective cross-examiner with a detailed knowledge of her cases.
Professional Memberships: Personal Injury Bar Association; Professional Negligence Bar Association; London Common Law and Commercial Bar Association
Career: Claire read Jurisprudence at Oxford, where she was awarded an Exhibition and was twice the winner of the Oxford University Mooting Competition. She was called to the Bar in 1995 and won the Middle Temple Mooting Competition the following year, having been awarded a Queen Mother's Scholarship by the Inn. She was offered tenancy after completion of her pupillage at 1 Paper Buildings and has remained with the set following the merger with 2 Crown Office Row to form Crown Office Chambers.

TOUBE, Felicity QC
South Square, London
020 7696 9900
felicitytoube@southsquare.com
Featured in Chancery (London), Company (London), Restructuring/Insolvency (London)
Practice Areas: Barrister whose recent work in England, the EU, the US, and the Caribbean (and in particular the Cayman Islands) includes: RBG; Saad; MF Global; Nortel; Lehman; Madoff; Stanford; Icelandic banks; Sigma; ARM; Global Trader; BCCI; Re Hawk Insurance Co; Re Toshoku Finance; Enron; Allders; Barlow Clowes; Queen's Moat Houses; TXU; Versailles; Eurotunnel; and Sphinx.
Professional Memberships: Insolvency service/ILA committees on the EU regulation and UNCITRAL; International Association for Asset Recovery; COMBAR; Chancery Bar Association; INSOL.
Career: Called 1995; QC 2011; Inner Temple.
Publications: Editor of 'Toube on International Asset Tracing in Insolvency'. Case editor for 'Totty & Moss on Insolvency'. Recent articles for various publications including: 'Insolvency Intelligence' and 'Eurofenix'. Contributor to Halsbury, Moss, Fletcher & Isaacs on the 'EC Regulation on Insolvency Proceedings', 'Lightman & Moss on The Law of Receivers of Companies', and 'Rowlatt on Principal and Surety'. Member of Editorial Board of 'Insolvency Intelligence'.
Personal: Born 1972.

TOWNEND, Samuel
Keating Chambers, London
020 7544 2600
stownend@keatingchambers.com
Featured in Construction (London)
Practice Areas: Specialist in construction and engineering disputes, professional liability (especially architects engineers and surveyors), adjudication (as advisor and advocate), domestic and international arbitration and mediation (as advocate). Energy, water, technology, waste, dredging, rail and infrastructure are also specialities. Samuel is regularly in the High Court and Court of Appeal. He is also the Standing Counsel to the National House Building Council (NHBC).
Professional Memberships: Sometime elected Member of the Executive Committee of the LCLCBA. Former Treasurer of the FRU; Vice-Chair, Society of Labour Lawyers; COMBAR; TECBAR; SCL.
Career: Called 1999; Member of the Bar Council 2006-08; Trained Mediator 2011; London Mediation Board and TECBAR Accredited Mediator; TECBAR Accredited Adjudicator.
Publications: Co-author with Mr Justice Coulson and Jane Lemon of "Architects, Engineers and Quantity Surveyors" in "Professional Negligence and Liability" pub. LLP (2014); Has also contributed chapters of "Construction Dispute Resolution Handbook" ed. Dr Gaitskell QC pub. ICE (2011).

TOWNSEND, Harriet
Cornerstone Barristers, London
020 7242 4986
htownsend@cornerstonebarristers.com
Featured in Planning (London)
Practice Areas: Planning, Environment, Compulsory Purchase and Compensation, Highways and Rights of Way, Town and Village Greens, Local Government, Public Law and Judicial Review.
Professional Memberships: Planning and Environment Bar Association (PEBA), UK Environmental Law Association (UKELA), Compulsory Purchase Association (CPA), National Infrastructure Planning Association (NIPA).
Career: Barrister specialising in planning and environment law and related areas since 1994. Recent experience includes environmental impact assessment, housing land supply, major development in the green belt, heritage assets, species and habitats protection, renewable energy proposals, complex enforcement issues, highways impact and development, and planning policies for sustainable development within city centres. Advocate acting for private individuals, businesses, and public authorities, and advising on law, procedure, and strategy. Since 2009: Mediator. Since 2010: Direct (Public) Access.
Publications: Contributing author to Westlaw's Insight web-based service on the Local Government Ombudsman and on Local Authority Byelaws. Specialist contributing editor on Local Government Law and Planning Law for Jowitt's Dictionary of English Law (3rd edition, 2010). Journal of Planning and Environment Law, 2009, "The Climate Change Act 2008: Something to be Proud of After All?" [2009] JPL 842. Environmental Law Review, The climate change act 2008 — will it do the trick?, 2009 Enviro LR 11 2 (116).
Personal: BSc Mathematics and Economics 1st Class. Loves walking and music of all kinds.

TOZER, Stephanie
Falcon Chambers, London
020 7353 2484
clerks@falcon-chambers.com
Featured in Real Estate Litigation (London)
Practice Areas: All aspects of real property, landlord and tenant and property-related professional neligence, with a particular emphasis on mortgage-related work. Recently reported cases include: Parshall v Bryans [2013] EWCA Civ 240 (land registration; adverse possession), Bower Terrace Student Accomodation Ltd v Space Student Living [2012] EWHC 2206 (receivers; interim injunctions; student housing) and Unique Pub Properties v Fitzpatrick [2012] (committal for breach of undertaking).
Professional Memberships: Chancery Bar Association, LCLCBA; Professional Negligence Bar Association; Property Bar Association; CEDR accredited mediator; First Tier Tribunal Judge; MCIArb.
Career: Educated at St Swithun's, Winchester; Keble College, Oxford (BA Jurisprudence 1st 1995, MA 1997); Called 1996 (Lincoln's Inn - top Student in Bar Finals); formerly Maitland Chambers, joined Falcon 2008.
Personal: Diploma in Advanced Business French.

TOZZI, Nigel QC
4 Pump Court, London
020 7842 5555
ntozzi@4pumpcourt.com
Featured in Commercial Dispute Resolution (London), Energy & Natural Resources (London), Information Technology (London), Insurance (London), International Arbitration (London), Professional Negligence (London), Shipping (London)
Practice Areas: Commercial litigation and arbitration for clients operating in various sectors including commodities, energy, manufacturing, IT, pharmaceutical, insurance and reinsurance, ship construction and conversion, media and financial services. Commercial fraud and asset recovery. Misuse of confidential information. Professional negligence (solicitors, accountants, financial advisers, surveyors, valuers, brokers). Fire claims.
Professional Memberships: COMBAR, Professional Negligence Bar Association, London Common Law and Commercial Bar Association, British Insurance Law Association, Society for Computers & Law, LCIA, LMAA.
Career: Called to the Bar 1980, took Silk 2001.
Personal: Educated at Exeter University (LLB Hons first class) 1976-79. Bar Finals 1980 (first class). Leisure pursuits include sport (especially hockey), theatre and cinema.

TRACE, Anthony QC
Maitland Chambers, London
020 7406 1200
atrace@maitlandchambers.com
Featured in Chancery (London), Commercial Dispute Resolution (London), Company (London), Fraud (London), Offshore (London), Professional Negligence (London), Real Estate Litigation (London), Restructuring/Insolvency (London)
Practice Areas: Principal area of practice encompasses fraud, insolvency, property, trusts, company, chancery and general commercial work, including a number of cases outside the UK. Recent cases include: Re Jeffrey S. Levitt Ltd [1992] (privilege against self-incrimination); Re Mirror Group (Holdings) Ltd [1993] (liability of assignees on liquidation); Gomba Holdings (UK) Ltd v Minories Finance Ltd (No.2) [1993] (mortgagee's costs); Lotteryking Ltd v AMEC Properties Ltd [1995] (set - off against assignees); Re BCCI SA (No.10) [1996] (insolvency set - off); Slough Estates Plc v Welwyn Hatfield DC [1996] (measure of damages for fraudulent misrepresentation); Grand Metropolitan plc v The William Hill Group Ltd [1997] (rectification); Bogg v Raper [1998] (will drafting and exclusion clauses); Plant v Plant [1998] (individual voluntary arrangements); Jordan Grand Prix Ltd v Baltic Insurance Group [1999] (Brussels Convention); Landare Investments Ltd v Welsh Development Agency [2000] (misfeasance in public office); Shalson v Russo [2001] (committal); Shalson v Russo (No 2) [2002] (purging contempt); SMAY Investments v Sachdev [2003] (submission to jurisdiction); JSC Zestafoni v Ronly Holdings Ltd [2004] (arbitration agreements); Might SA v Redbus [2004] (fiduciary duties); Newgate Stud v Penfold (No1) [2004] (directors' duties); Watford Petroleum Ltd v Interoil [2005] (cross-examination in interlocutory proceedings); Newgate Stud v Penfold (No2) [2005] (accounts of profits and limitation); Harley Street Capital v Tchigirinsky [2005] (fortification of cross-undertaking in damages); Shalson v Russo (No3) [2005] (constructive trusts and tracing); Walker International Holdings Ltd v Congo [2005] (transactions defrauding creditors); Kyrie-Royle v Burger King [2005] (conspiracy); Farepak [2006] (unconscionability and constructive trusts); Donegal v Government of Zambia [2007] (illegality); London Allied Holdings v Lee [2007] (fraud); Prudential Assurance v Ayres [2008] (construction of documents); Menolly v Cerep [2009] (estoppel); Zahoor v Masood [2009] (striking out for abuse of process); NML Capital v Republic of Argentina [2009] (sovereign immunity); Wirecard Bank AG v Scott [2010] (conspiracy and fraudulent misrepresentation); BTA Bank v Ablyasov [2011] (receivership); Yukos Capital v Rosneft [2011] (act of state); Westwood Shipping v Universal [2012] (insolvency proceedings and Regulation 1346/2000); Energy Venture Partners v Malabu Oil [2012] (evidence required for fortification of cross-undertaking in damages); Gorbunova v Boris Berezovsky [2013] (setting aside freezing order); Aeroflot v Berezovsky [2014] (enforcement of foreign judjment). Has sat as an Arbitrator. Hon Secretary, Chancery Bar Association (1997-2001). Vice-Chairman, Chancery Bar Association (2001-04).
Professional Memberships: Chancery Bar Association; COMBAR; ACTAPS (As-

sociation of Contentious Trust and Probate Specialists); Insolvency Lawyers Association; CFLA (Commerical Fraud Lawyers Association); R3 (The Association of Business Recovery Professionals).
Career: Called to the Bar 1981.
Publications: Contributor to 'Butterworths European Law Service' (company law) and 'Butterworths Practical Insolvency'. Deputy managing editor: 'Receivers, Administrators and Liquidators Quarterly' (1993-2002).
Personal: Educated at Magdalene College, Cambridge (MA, 1st Class Honours).

TRACY FORSTER, Jane
Hailsham Chambers, London
020 7643 5000
jane.tracyforster@hailshamchambers.com
Featured in Clinical Negligence (London)
Practice Areas: Clinical negligence, particularly birth-related neurological injury, gynaecological injury, cancer diagnosis, psychiatric injury. A growing best interests in healthcare Court of Protection practice. Also employment and regulatory issues relating to the medical and allied healthcare professions. Reported cases: Miles v West Kent Health Authority 1997 Med LR 191; Smith v Leicester Health Authority 1998 Lloyds Rep. (Med) 77; Thurman v Bath and Wiltshire Health Authority 1997 P.I.Q.R. Q115; Carmon v Page [2000] Clinical Risk v6 no1; Subramanian v GMC [2002] UKPC 64; Purver v Winchester and Eastleigh Healthcare NHS Trust [2007] LS Law Medical 193. Garth v Grant and MIB [2007] All ER (D) 45; St George v The Home Office [2009] 1 WLR 1670; DH NHS FoundationTrust v PS [2010] EWHC 1217 (Fam). Head of the Medical Law Group at Hailsham Chambers 2004–10, now Head of the Marketing Committee.
Professional Memberships: Professional Negligence Bar Association; Personal Injury Bar Association; Employment Law Bar Association; Associate Member, Royal Society of Medicine.
Career: LLB (Hons) Liverpool University; Called July 1975 (Inner Temple).
Personal: Married. Lives in London.

TRAVERS, David QC
6 Pump Court, London
020 7797 8400
davidtravers@6pumpcourt.co.uk
Featured in Consumer Law (London), Environment (London), Health & Safety (London)
Practice Areas: Regulatory crime, public law and associated areas including corporate governance and professional standards. Advises, negotiates and appears as an advocate for companies, organisations and individuals, as well as for Local Authorities and various Regulatory Bodies. In Regulatory Crime he practices predominantly in Health and Safety (including Fire Safety), Food Law, Environmental Protection and Trading Standards. In Public Law he practices predominantly in Environment, Planning and Local Government matters, particularly related to the management of waste. David Travers QC also acts in disputes involving the governance of corporations and the administration of Local Authorities and professional conduct and disciplinary matters. He also acts for decision-makers susceptible of Judicial Review and those who are challenging the lawfulness of the exercise of discretion. He has particular experience in cases involving scientific or technical evidence.
Professional Memberships: Food Law Group, Planning and Environment Bar Association, Midland Circuit.
Career: Called to the Bar by the Honourable Society of the Middle Temple 1981 (Harmsworth Scholar 1982). Member of the Bar Council 1995-2000. Visiting Professor at Business Accountability and Responsibility Centre, University of South Wales; Honorary Fellow of the Society of Food Hygiene and Technology; Accredited Mediator; Legal Advisor to the Medical Practitioner Tribunal Service (formerly Legal Advisor to the General Medical Council); legal advisor to the General Dental Council Fitness to Practice Panel.
Publications: Include (with Giles Atkinson and Noemi Byrd) Planning Law and Practice published in April 2013 by Wildy, Simmons and Hill and Planning Enforcement (with Emmaline Lambert and Ed Grant) to be published in Summer 2014. Article, Towards Professional-Model Regulation of Directors' Conduct in the International Journal of Law and Management; Int. JL.M. (2013) 55 (2) 123-140.

TREMBATH, Graham QC
5 Paper Buildings, London
020 7583 6117
clerks@5pb.co.uk
Featured in Crime (London)
Practice Areas: A specialist jury advocate, noted for his abilities in cross examination and jury speeches. He has been described as "a class act". Substantial experience over a very broad range of serious crime, including murder, firearms cases, complex fraud, substantial drug cases, money laundering and complex confiscation proceedings. Recent cases include representing a solicitor in a multi million pound substantial and complex international fraud case prosecuted by the SFO, representing defendants in the "Matalan" and "Facebook" murder cases, and representing one of the members of the "London Fields Boys" involved in a gang murder, and representing a former director of Crawley Town FC indicted for multi million pound tax evasion and money laundering allegations. Represented one of the accused in the "Securitas Robbery", the largest cash robbery in UK criminal history, and represented one of the accused in the "Bling Bling" drugs case, said to be one of the largest international drug smuggling cases to appear before a British court. Appeared in a 'landmark ruling' case involving poker ("Texas-Hold-Em"), a prosecution brought on behalf of the Gaming Commission. Has appeared in numerous murder cases, single defendant and multi handed, involving close analysis of a wide range of forensic and expert evidence.
Professional Memberships: Member of the Criminal Bar Association.
Career: Called to the Bar 1978. Queen's Counsel 2003.
Personal: Educated at Cambusdoon School, Alloway, Ayrshire. Fettes College, Edinburgh. Southampton University, Faculty of Law. LLB (Hons). Lifelong Chelsea FC supporter.

TRIGGER, Simon
1 Chancery Lane, London
020 7092 2900
STrigger@1chancerylane.com
Featured in Professional Negligence (London)
Practice Areas: Specialises in professional negligence (particularly solicitors and valuers in the context of mortgage fraud as well as surveyors and engineers); clinical negligence (particularly claims involving sexual abuse) and personal injury. Simon has particular experience of fraud cases in the personal injury context, including road traffic accident and employers liability claims. Simon also has extensive experience in low velocity impact litigation on behalf of Insurers. He has been involved in several high value cases concerning claims of mortgage fraud and sexual abuse claims. Reported cases include: Di Matteo v Marcus Lee [2010] (solicitors negligence action); Godden v Kent & Medway Strategic Health Authority [2004] (sexual abuse group action); A v Archbishop of Birmingham [2005](sexual abuse claim).
Professional Memberships: PIBA; PNBA.
Career: Called to the Bar 2000; Cambridge University MA (Cantab); Astbury Scholar of Middle Temple; Harmsworth Entrance Exhibitioner of Middle Temple.
Personal: Loyal supporter of Wrexham Football Club.

TROLLOPE, Andrew QC
187 Fleet Street, London
020 7430 7430
andrewtrollope@187fleetstreet.com
Featured in Crime (London), Financial Crime (London)
Practice Areas: Wide experience of fraud and serious or organised crime cases. Long established practice in City, commercial and tax cases in courts and tribunals. Specialisations include money laundering, asset forfeiture/confiscation,VAT and Duty cases [tax tribunal], sports law. Cases include R v Relton [Brinks Mat], R v Viccei [Knightsbridge Safe Deposit], R v Stainforth [Blue Arrow], R v T Ward [Guinness], R v Masterson [Caird plc], R v M Ward [European Leisure plc], R v James [Harrovian Properties/Leisure], R v Keyes [McNicholas], R v Myles [Richmond Oil and Gas plc]. R v McKeown [Powerscreen plc], R v Sykes [Cheney Pension Scheme], R v Golechha /Op Venison, R v Lindsay/Op Vitric [MTIC Carousel Frauds], R v Hoult [Ikea], R v Matthews [Peakviewing plc,VAT/film financing], R v Auchi [Goldshield-pharmaceuticals cartel], Megantic Services Ltd v HMRC [FTTT], R v Ibori [money laundering], R v Storrie and Mandaric[Portsmouth FC], R v Perrin [Vantis Tax Ltd].
Professional Memberships: Committee Member of Criminal Bar Association 1990-2001, Bar Council International Relations Committee 2001-08, Advisory Council British Institute of International and Comparative Law, fellow of the Institute of Advanced Legal Studies 1998-99. Bencher of Inner Temple.
Career: Head of Chambers specialising in criminal law. Appointed assistant recorder 1984, recorder 1989.
Publications: Contributor [with others from 187 Fleet Street] to 'Fraud; Law, Practice and Procedure' [Lexis Nexis, Butterworths].

TROMAN, Carl
4 New Square, London
020 7822 2000
c.troman@4newsquare.com
Featured in Professional Negligence (London)
Practice Areas: Commercial litigation with particular emphasis on claims against professionals including solicitors, accountants, barristers, surveyors, engineers, insurance brokers, architects and financial advisers. Insurance particularly in relation to policy construction, coverage, the minimum terms of professional bodies, aggregation, fraud, misrepresentation and non-disclosure. Other areas include: chancery litigation (especially concerning mortgages), construction, automotive law (including motor sports), costs and agriculture. Formally accredited mediator and accepts instructions as an arbitrator. A recent case was Green v Eadie [2012] Ch 363.
Professional Memberships: COMBAR and PNBA.
Career: LLB (first class honours) 2000, Diploma in Law 2001, Called to the Bar 2001, Taught at Reading University 2001-02, 4 New Square Chambers 2002 to date.
Personal: Photography, chess and tropical fish.

TROMPETER, Nicholas
Selborne Chambers, London
020 7420 9500
nicholas.trompeter@selbornechambers.co.uk
Featured in Chancery (London), Real Estate Litigation (London)
Practice Areas: Commercial Chancery practitioner with experience in civil fraud, asset recovery, company law, directors disqualification, professional negligence, commercial/residential landlord and tenant matters, corporate/personal insolvency, real property, trusts, contract and restitution. He regularly appears in the High Court and has been involved in a number of mediations and arbitrations.
Professional Memberships: Property Bar Association; Chancery Bar Association.
Career: Called in 2006. Nick has significant trial and appellate experience, as well as applying for (and resisting) freezing and other injunctions. Nick has acted as a judicial assistant in the Supreme Court of Israel. He is the recipient of the Wilfred Watson Award from Gray's Inn.
Publications: Nick regularly provides seminars on Commercial Chancery related topics. He is a co-author of Break Clauses, the only book dealing exclusively with break clauses in leases.
Personal: New College, Oxford (MA classics; New College scholar); City University (CPE, distinction); Inns of Court School of Law (BVC, outstanding; Barstow Law Scholarship for coming third in the year overall; Du Cann Memorial Prize for the highest overall marks in the advocacy assessments).

TROTTER, Helen
Kings Chambers, Manchester
08450 343 444
clerks@kingschambers.com
Featured in Employment (Northern)
Practice Areas: Helen has a built a thriving practice in employment law, and commercial matters with employment law principles. She has particular experience in complex discrimination and equality act cases, both in the Tribunal and the County Court, and is first choice counsel for a wide variety of Government departments and clients from the aviation, education and healthcare industries. Helen also specialises in unfair/wrongful dismissal, TUPE and commercial matters including injunctions, the enforceability of employee guarantees and restrictive covenants. Helen is known for her ability to put clients at their ease during

proceedings, whilst approaching the litigation with tenacity and vigour.
Professional Memberships: Employment Lawyers Association, Employment Law Bar Association.
Career: David Karmel Scholar (2003) , Gerard Moody Scholar (2004), Called October 2004 (Grays Inn). Appointed to the Attorney General's Regional Panel of Junior Counsel to the Crown (November 2010).
Personal: BA Hons: Anglo-Saxon, Norse and Celtic (Cantab, 2000), CPE (City University, London, 2003), BVC (Inns of Court School of Law, London, 2004).

TROWLER, Rebecca QC
Doughty Street Chambers, London
020 7404 1313
r.trowler@doughtystreet.co.uk
Featured in Crime (London)
Practice Areas: Beccy Trowler QC has extensive experience in the most serious and complex criminal cases. She has appeared in many legally significant and/or high profile trials and appeals, including: Anxiang Du, a doctor of chinese medicine who killed 4 members of the same family following an acrimonious business dispute; Al-Khawaja and Tahery v UK, Grand Chamber of the European Court of Human Rights (whether sole or decisive hearsay evidence is in breach of Article 6); Chaytor and Ors, Supreme Court, (ambit of parliamentary privilege); Jim Devine (former MP charged with false claims in relation to parliamentary expenses); Hamza (soliciting the murder of four members of the Egyptian Government); the 'Dragons Den' fraud. In 2014 she has already appeared in a number of high profile murder trials and appeals. In 2014 and into 2015 she is due to represent a member of the European Bank for Reconstruction and Development at the Central Criminal Court charged with corruption in the oil and gas sector.
Career: Beccy also regularly provides advice to corporate clients and others on criminal related matters. She is also instructed in extradition appeals and in criminal related civil cases and inquiries.
Publications: She is a contributing author to the 2nd Edition of 'Taylor on Criminal Appeals' OUP.
Personal: Beccy is Deputy Head of Doughty Street Chambers and Chair of the Chambers Management Board.

TUCK, Rebecca
Old Square Chambers, London
020 7269 0300
tuck@oldsquare.co.uk
Featured in Employment (London)
Practice Areas: Rebecca practices all areas of employment law, including unfair dismissal, discrimination, equal pay, TUPE, redundancy and collective disputes. She is in the ET & EAT regularly and also carries out non-litigation work including conducting investigations and advising disciplinary panels. She has appeared before the Certification Officer, as well advising on, and appearing in, claims in the County and High Courts, most often involving non-employment discrimination, breach of contract claims and restrictive covenants. Rebecca is a qualified mediator and sits as a fee paid employment judge.
Professional Memberships: Industrial Law Society, Employment Lawyers Association, Employment Law Bar Association, Council of Employment Judges.
Career: City of Stoke-On-Trent Sixth Form College; Lady Margaret Hall; MA (Oxon) (1997). Called to the Bar 1998. Joined Old Square Chambers 1999.
Publications: Co-author 'Employment Tribunal Procedure' 2nd and 3rd editions. LAG; Annual Labour Law Review 2000-2013. Institute of Employment Rights. Editor of Harvey on Industrial Relations and Employment Law.
Personal: Mother of two and when she gets time – a rugby fan.

TUCKER, Lynton
New Square Chambers, London
020 7419 8000
lynton.tucker@newsquarechambers.co.uk
Featured in Chancery (London), Offshore (London), Trusts (London)
Practice Areas: Lynton Tucker specialises in trust law and related private client work. Kinds of trusts covered are family trusts, charitable trusts, pension and commercial trusts, employee trusts, and constructive trusts. The specialisation ranges from non-contentious drafting and advisory work to contentious trust litigation. Particular aspects of trust law covered are construction and effect of trusts, effect of UK taxation on UK and non-UK trusts, attacks by creditors and others on trusts and trustees, breach of trusts and trust litigation, conflict of interest and self dealing, the effect of divorce ancillary relief claims on trusts, Beddoe applications and other applications by trustees to the court for directions and variation of trusts. The offshore jurisdictions primarily involved are the Channel Islands, Hong Kong, Cayman Islands, The Bahamas and the British Virgin Islands. He also advises and litigates in company law matters, particularly in the field of unfair prejudice claims, duties of directors and protection of minority shareholders..He is called to the Bar of the Eastern Caribbean Court in the territories of the British Virgin Islands and Anguilla. He won the Chambers Chancery Junior of the Year award in 2011.
Professional Memberships: Member of STEP and ACTAPS.
Publications: Editor of Lewin on Trusts.

TUCKER, Paul QC
Kings Chambers, Manchester
0845 034 3444
clerks@kingschambers.com
Featured in Planning (Northern)
Practice Areas: Town and country planning; environmental law; local government law; highway law compulsory purchase; retail proposals; minerals; landfill proposals;
Professional Memberships: Planning and Environment Bar Association; Administrative Law Bar; National Infrastructure Planning Association;
Career: University: Cambridge (Selwyn College); degree: Law (MA); Called: 1990 (Gray's Inn); Silk: 2010.
Publications: Each year, Paul undertakes various speaking commitments at Planning Conferences and In-House Events as well as engaging in Mock Inquiries. In addition he has written for Estates Gazette, Planning and the Lawyer.
Personal: Paul practises in the areas of town and country planning, environmental law, local government law, highway law, and the law of compulsory purchase. He acts for both the public and the private sectors throughout England and Wales. He has acted for a local authorities, Government Agencies and a wide range of private sector developers, in cases involving diverse areas including major retail proposals, mineral and landfill proposals, large housing sites and other environmentally sensitive proposals. He is regularly engaged to act on behalf of major retailers and housing developers. He has been involved in a number of nationally important planning cases both before the Courts and at inquiry. His recent work has involved a diverse range of interests from the nuclear industry to Premiership Football Clubs, as well as national house builders, developers and retailers.

TURNER, James M QC
Quadrant Chambers, London
020 7583 4444
james.turner@quadrantchambers.com
Featured in Shipping (London)
Practice Areas: Highly experienced advocate across wide range of shipping (wet and dry), shipbuilding, commodities, commercial and related private international law. For detailed CV, see bit.ly/jamesmt.
Professional Memberships: COMBAR; TECBAR; LCLCBA; British-German Jurists; Chartered Institute of Linguists.
Career: BA (Dunelm), LLM (Tuebingen). Call 1990. CEDR accredited mediator 2001. Silk 2013.
Publications: Derrington & Turner on Admiralty Matters, OUP, 2007.
Personal: Married, four children. Fluent German and Dutch.

TURNER, Jon QC
Monckton Chambers, London
020 7405 7211
jturner@monckton.com
Featured in Administrative & Public Law (London), Competition/European Law (London), Environment (London), Competition/European Law (London), Telecommunications (London)
Practice Areas: Jon Turner QC is one of the Bar's foremost litigators in Competition law, EU law, and Telecommunications and Utilities Regulation, and is recognised by peers and alike clients as a pre-eminent practitioner in the field. He combines mastery in the trial and appellate settlings up to Supreme Court level, and in the European courts and has been involved in many of the leading cases in these areas in recent years. He is equally a highly regarded and sought after litigator in the fields of Commercial, Public & Administrative, and Environmental law.
Career: Called 1988; Standing Counsel to the Office of Fair Trading from 1997 to 2006; Junior Counsel to the Crown (A Panel) from 2002 until taking silk; Attorney-at-law at the New York Bar; Silk 2006.
Publications: Jon Turner QC is Consulting Editor for the supplement of Bellamy and Child's European Union Law of Competition, 6th edition (edited by the now Mr Justice Roth and Mrs Justice Rose, supplement edited by Laura Elizabeth John) and he has contributed regularly to previous editions.
Personal: MA(Cantab), LLM(Harvard). Good French, working German.

TURNER, Jonathan QC
6KBW College Hill, London
020 3301 0910
jonathan.turner@6kbw.com
Featured in Crime (London)
Practice Areas: Jonathan has been in practice at the Criminal Bar for 40 years, the last 11 of them as Queen's Counsel. He has prosecuted and defended in equal measure in many homicide cases and prefers it that way. He has appeared in many of the highest-profile criminal matters tried in recent years, not only in London but also in the west and north of England, where he is a door tenant at Exchange Chambers in Liverpool. Jonathan also welcomes white collar crime, multi-handed defences and cases involving 'difficult' Defendants. His wide experience in such matters may be gleaned from his website profile.
Professional Memberships: Bar Council; Criminal Bar Association; SFO Counsel List; Direct Access List.
Career: UCL (Hons) 1969-72; Chambers of Jeffrey Thomas QC (pupil and junior tenant) 1974-92; Tenant at 6KBW (Temple and then College Hill) 1992 - present; Recorder 1997-2004 (retd.) Full profile and CV appears on 6KBW College Hill website (www.6kbw.com).

TURNER, Justin QC
Three New Square, London
020 7405 1111
turner@3newsquare.co.uk
Featured in Intellectual Property (London)
Practice Areas: Justin Turner's practice extends to all areas of IP and to commercial disputes of a technical character. In addition to appearing in the UK courts he also represents clients at the EPO and the CJEU. He has been involved in a number of leading patent cases particularly within the fields of pharmacology and biotechnology.

TURTON, Philip
Ropewalk Chambers, Nottingham
01159 472 581
philipturton@ropewalk.co.uk
Featured in Personal Injury (Midlands)
Practice Areas: He has over 20 years' experience of personal injury cases and specialises in high value personal injury actions, clinical negligence claims and industrial disease cases, including Group Actions. He has been cited as a Leader at the Bar in the field of Personal Injury work for many years.
Professional Memberships: Personal Injuries Bar Association; Professional Negligence Bar Association; Health and Safety Lawyers Association; Nottinghamshire-Medico Legal Society (Committee member)
Career: Called in 1989; LLB (Hons), University College of Wales, Aberystwyth. He was a Bar Standards Board appointed External Moderator for the Bar Professional Training Course (Civil Litigation) from 2010 – 2012 and, with Marc Howe, was appointed to reformulate the syllabus for the Civil Litigation module on the BPTC course in 2014. He has delivered annual lectures on Drafting to the Bar Professional Training Course at Nottingham Trent University and the Kaplan Law School in London. He has also delivered a Guest Lecture to the students of the University of Darwin, Northern Territories, Australia, on the subject of Tort law. He has been a voluntary adviser at the Hyson Green Law Centre since 1990.

TWEEDY, Laura
Hardwicke, London
020 7242 2523
laura.tweedy@hardwicke.co.uk
Featured in Social Housing (London)
Practice Areas: All aspects of property litigation, landlord and tenant and social housing. Laura has a particular interest and expertise in real property, first tier tribunal

property chamber work, anti-social behaviour, welfare reform, mental capacity and TOLATA cases. In addition to her strong real estate and social housing practice Laura has developed a niche where real estate matters merge with public law such as government issues, equality issues and human rights. She is regarded as the go-to barrister for cases in that field. She provides regular seminars to solicitors and lay clients and is often called upon for her tactical advice. Laura was led in the Supreme Court and Court of Appeal in Mexfield v Berrisford, a case which changed the landscape of leasehold tenure. She was awarded a prestigious Pegasus scholarship to New Zealand where she undertook judicial marshalling in the District, High and Supreme Courts which provided her with the unparalleled insight into judicial decision making which is invaluable to advocacy.
Career: LLB (hons) 2005, MJur 2006, Lincolns Inn Call 2007, Barrister at Hardwicke 2008, led in Court of Appeal 2010, led in Supreme Court 2011, Pegasus Scholar 2013, PBA Committee Member 2014.

TWIGGER, Andrew M QC
3 Stone Buildings, London
020 7242 4937
atwigger@3sb.law.co.uk
Featured in Banking & Finance (London), Chancery (London), Commercial Dispute Resolution (London)
Practice Areas: Andrew Twigger QC has appeared extensively in both the Chancery Division and the Commercial Court. He has a particular interest in cases related to banking and finance, but undertakes a wide variety of other corporate and commercial cases relating to contractual disputes, commercial fraud, shareholders' rights, auditors' (and other professional) negligence and company insolvency. During 2013-14 he represented, amongst others, Edmond de Rothschild Securities in a dispute concerning a financial advisory contract; Reliance Security Group in a dispute arising out of its sale of a prisoner escorting business; the claimant in a dispute concerning the sale of a motor insurance broker business; beneficiaries of the estate of the late composer, Sir Malcolm Arnold, in the Court of Appeal in a dispute concerning ownership of various manuscripts of his works ([2013] W.T.L.R. 591) and Mr Benedetti in his appeal to the Supreme Court, now the leading authority on the valuation of benefit in unjust enrichment claims ([2013] 3 WLR 351).
Professional Memberships: Chancery Bar Association; Combar.
Career: Called 1994; joined chambers 1995; QC 2011; Head of Chambers 2012.
Personal: Educated at Aylesbury Grammar School and St. John's College, Oxford.

TYACK, David
No5 Chambers, Birmingham
08452 105 555
dgt@no5.com
Featured in Clinical Negligence (Midlands)
Practice Areas: Specialist in high value and complex clinical negligence and personal injury cases. A selection of cases worked on in the last year includes: four claims against GPs involving failures to refer for investigations into cancer, resulting in terminal prognosis - claim in relation to failure to undertake endartectomy procedure resulting in above knee amputation - cerebral palsy birth injury claim - cauda equina syndrome claim - claim involving failure to diagnose and treat arachnoiditis in the spine - obstetrics claim involving failure to spot and act upon signs of post Caesarean complications leading to severe multiple conditions including the need for a colostomy - gynaecological claim involving unnecessary hysterectomy and salpingo oophorectomy - Fatal Accidents Act claim against hospital involving failure to treat post operative infection and subsequent death - claim in relation to unnecessary cardio ablation leading to defunctioning of heart's pace making ability and life long dependence on permanent pacemaker - claim for unnecessary removal of larynx - claim in relation to inappropriate surgery in young man resulting in bowel incontinence - RTA claim involving catastrophic brain injury - RTA claim involving severe degloving injury - RTA claim involving severe multiple life changing injuries
Professional Memberships: AVMA.
Career: MA Law, Christ Church, Oxford. Call: 1994 (Middle Temple). Regularly presents and chairs seminars. Invited AVMA speaker.
Personal: Lives Shropshire. Interests: Running and rugby. Languages: Conversational Japanese.

TYLER, William QC
36 Bedford Row, London
020 7421 8000
wtyler@36bedfordrow.co.uk
Featured in Family/Matrimonial (London)
Practice Areas: William is a specialist children law Silk, appearing in the most serious, complicated or sensitive private and public law cases. His extensive public law Children Act practice sees him litigating high profile cases around the country, principally in the High Court. He has particular expertise in cases involving life-threatening injury and death, sexual abuse or international and jurisdictional difficulties. In private law his practice comprises the most complex or the most sensitive cases, and very often those involving difficult international issues (abduction, relocation etc.) or questions relating to parenthood and child arrangements after surrogacy, gamete donation or the breakdown of same-sex relationships. He has very considerable experience of appellate advocacy, often appearing in the Court of Appeal. Notable cases in the last couple of years include: Sutton v Gray and Others (No 1) [2013] FLR 833; Sutton v Gray and Others (No 2) [2013] FLR 914; Re TG (A Child) [2013] 1 FLR 1250; Re M (Children) [2013] EWCA Civ 388; Re W (A Child) [2013] EWCA Civ 662; Re DF and GF (Children) (Placement Order or Special Guardianship Order) [2013] EWHC 2607 (Fam); Re D–R (Children) [2013] EWCC 5 (Fam) (10 October 2013); Re E [2014] 2 FLR 151; Re X (A Child) [2014] EWHC 1871
Professional Memberships: Family Law Bar Association (FLBA), Association of Lawyers for Children (ALC), Resolution.
Career: Call: 1996. Recorder: 2012. Silk: 2014.
Personal: Educated at Worcester College, Oxford University. William is married with three children.

TYZACK, William
Queen Elizabeth Building, London
020 7797 7837
w.tyzack@qeb.co.uk
Featured in Family/Matrimonial (London)
Practice Areas: (1) All areas of family law relating to finance and children, particularly EU and international cases – child abduction, relocation, jurisdiction disputes and international maintenance issues. Advised on English/EU law in European jurisdictions and in the USA and has provided expert evidence to the Supreme Court of New York, USA. (2) growing practice in Court of Protection cases, involving both welfare and financial issues. Recent cases: C v B [2014] EWHC 2069 (abduction); EY v RZ [2013] EWHC 4403 (abduction); Re B [2012] EWCA Civ 1082 (EU Maintenance Regulation).
Professional Memberships: FLBA, Western Circuit, Reunite (child abduction) Legal Working Group.
Career: Pupillage at QEB 2007-8; Oxford University (First Class hons), City University and BPP. Middle Temple (Diplock scholarship, Harmsworth exhibition).
Publications: Joint author of article on the EU Maintenance Regulation in International Family Law [2012] IFL 277; joint editor with Thorpe LJ of the collected papers of the 2011 Dartington Interdisciplinary Conference.

UFF, John QC
Keating Chambers, London
020 7544 2600
juff@keatingchambers.com
Featured in International Arbitration (London)
Practice Areas: Over 30 years experience of specialising in construction and engineering domestic and international arbitration. Appointed on many substantial arbitrations, throughout the world from Australasia and the Far East to the Middle East, Europe and North America. Appointed to Chair Public Inquiries in the water and railway industries. Closely involved in developments in the construction industry over the past two decades, most recently spearheaded the engineering professions drive to establish a code of ethical principles. Appointed Tribunal Chairman for the inquiry into the Trinidad & Tobago Construction Industry. Formerly Vice President of the LCIA and President of the Society of Construction Arbitrators.
Career: Assistant engineer 1966-70; Called 1970; QC 1983; Recorder and Deputy Judge TCC 1998; Emeritus Professor of Engineering Law, King's College, London 2003; FICE, FCI Arb, Fellow Royal Academy of Engineering 2005. Treasurer of Gray's Inn 2011.
Publications: Joint author, Institution of Civil Engineers Arbitration Practice, Thomas Telford (1983); Contributor, Keating on Construction Contracts - 4th to 9th Edition (2011); Joint author, Chapter on Construction Contracts in 28th to 30th Edition of Chitty on Contracts (2008); Construction Law, 11th Edition (2011); principal author CIMAR and JCT Arbitration Rules.
Personal: Awarded CBE for services to rail safety 2002.

UNDERWOOD, Dean
Cornerstone Barristers, London
020 7421 1835
deanu@cornerstonebarristers.com
Featured in Social Housing (London)
Practice Areas: Public and administrative law; Local government; Social housing; Property;
Professional Memberships: Administrative Law Bar Association; Chartered Institute of Housing; Property Bar Association; Social Housing Law Association
Career: Dean specialises in administrative, housing, property and public law. He has particular expertise in housing and related administrative law, having built his practice representing local authorities and housing providers in the county court, High Court and Court of Appeal. He has since developed a broad public law practice, covering: community care; council tax; the Court of Protection; homelessness; housing allocation, management and regulation; human rights; welfare benefits; and welfare reform. Dean appeared in the Supreme Court in 2014 in Sims v Dacorum Borough Council [2014] UKSC (tbc). His work received judicial commendation in both R (George) v Hammersmith & Fulham LBC [2012] EWHC 2369 (Admin); [2012] All ER (D) 124 (Apr) and Howard v Stanton [2011] EWCA Civ 1481; [2012] All ER (D) 201 (May) and he has acted in the following notable cases: Sims v Dacorum Borough Council [2013] EWCA Civ 12; [2013] HLR 14 Fernandes v Kenny [2012] EWCA Civ 910; [2012] All ER (D) 242 (Oct) Oxford City Council v Basey [2012] EWCA Civ 115; [2012] 3 All ER 71 Brough v Law and CMEC [2011] EWCA Civ 1932; [2012] 1 WLR 1021

URELL, Kate
Gough Square Chambers, London
020 7353 0924
kate.urell@goughsq.co.uk
Featured in Consumer Law (London)
Practice Areas: Consumer law, including consumer credit and retail banking, consumer contracts, trading law and food law.
Professional Memberships: Food Law Group.
Career: Called in 2002. Kate acts in a range of credit and non-credit related regulatory matters. In particular, she is experienced in consumer finance litigation and advisory work and regularly acts for banks and financial institutions on matters relating to compliance with the Consumer Credit Act and other consumer issues, including unfair terms, harassment, credit referencing errors and payment protection insurance misselling. Kate has advised on the implementation of the Consumer Credit Directive, the Consumer Rights Directive and the Green Deal. She is also experienced in drafting and reviewing consumer credit documentation on behalf of lenders and for securitisations. Her non-credit practice includes advising on trading laws, product compliance, advertising issues and enforcement action under the Enterprise Act. Kate has also been instructed by a number of multinational organisations in the area of food labelling. Recent reported cases: Brandon v American Express Services Europe Ltd [2011] EWCA Civ 1187.
Publications: Atkins Court Forms on Consumer Protection, Advertising Law and Regulation, 2nd edn, ed. Bloomsbury Professional.
Personal: Languages: French. Education: LLB (Europe) Hons with French; LLM (Cantab). Middle Temple (Harmsworth Scholar).

VALENTIN, Ben
Fountain Court Chambers, London
020 7583 3335
bv@fountaincourt.co.uk
Featured in Banking & Finance (London), Commercial Dispute Resolution (London), Fraud (London), International Arbitration (London)
Practice Areas: Broad practice in general commercial litigation and arbitration, with particular expertise in disputes involving

banking and financial services, oil and gas, corporate law and civil fraud, and issues as to privilege, jurisdiction and the conflict of laws. Also has a significant offshore practice.
Professional Memberships: Commercial Bar Association, Chancery Bar Association, New York State Bar Association, LCIA, CEDR Accredited Mediator.
Career: Called 1995 (England and Wales); New York (1998); British Virgin Islands (2007).
Personal: Born January 1971. Educated at Worcester College, Oxford (BA, BCL) and Cornell (LLM).

VALLAT, Richard
Pump Court Tax Chambers, London
020 7414 8080
clerks@pumptax.com
Featured in Tax (London)
Practice Areas: Practises in all areas of revenue law,including advice and planning in the following areas: personal tax, corporate taxes, VAT and other indirect taxes, stamp duty land tax and tax-related litigation including professional negligence; as well as undertaking litigation, he also advises on a range of matters both in contemplation of and seeking to avoid litigation, including contractual disputes with a tax element. Recent cases include Royal Borough of Kensington & Chelsea (First-tier Tribunal); DB Group Services (Court of Appeal); Aspect Capital Ltd (Upper Tribunal); Coulter Trust (Chancery Division); Greene King Plc (Upper Tribunal); Perrin (First-tier Tribunal); Standfast Corporate Underwriters Ltd (First-tier Tribunal); Ardmore Construction (First-tier Tribunal); Hancock & Hancock(First-tier Tribunal); Morgan & Donaldson (Upper Tribunal).
Professional Memberships: Secretary Revenue Bar Association; London Common Law and Commercial Bar Association; Chancery Bar Association; Stamp Taxes Practitioners Group; Moderator of the Trusts Discussion Forum; Society of Trust & Estates Practicioners.
Career: Called 1997, Gray's Inn; March 2011 Appointed to the Attorney General's B Panel.

VAUGHAN JONES, Sarah QC
2TG - 2 Temple Gardens, London
020 7822 1200
svaughanjones@2tg.co.uk
Featured in Clinical Negligence (London)
Practice Areas: Clinical negligence, conducting civil proceedings for claimants and defendants. Recent High Court cases include representing the successful defendants in Reeve v Heart of England NHS Foundation Trust [24.5.2011] (fetal bradycardia while regisgtrar in theatre on another case: no prior failure to call in consultant); Mungai v Chelsea & Westminster Healthcare NHS Trust [2006] (no liability for not diagnosing rare intestinal perforation in A&E), Smithers v Taunton & Somerset NHS Trust [2004] EWHC 1179 (no liability for failure to attend obstetric emergency where clinicians inextricably occupied with alternative procedure) and Rashid v Essex Rivers Healthcare NHS Trust [2004] EWHC 1338 (Erbs palsy in posterior shoulder: no liability). Professional discipline: conduct of cases before Panels of the General Medical Council and General Dental Council, and related appeals. Major cases include Williams v GMC [2007] EWHC 2603 Admin (appeal from PCC inquiry into conduct of Dr. Alan Williams, forensic pathologist instructed in R v Sally Clarke), Silver v General Medical Council [2003] UKPC 33 (Privy Council: test for serious professional misconduct) Crabbie v General Medical Council [2002] UKPC 45 (Privy Council: correct approach to applications to refer to Health Committee): Dad v General Dental Council [2000] 1 WLR 1538: (Privy Council: principles applicable to conviction cases).
Professional Memberships: PNBA, PIBA.
Career: Called 1983. Recorder 2004. QC 2008.

VAVRECKA, David
Coram Chambers, London
020 7092 37003
David.Vavrecka@coramchambers.co.uk
Featured in Family/Matrimonial (London)
Practice Areas: Children Human Rights International Adult and Social Care
Professional Memberships: Professional Memberships: Family Law Bar Association, BAAF, Association of Lawyers for Children South Eastern Circuit Middle Temple
Career: Career: Called 1992, Recorder South Easter Circuit 2012 David is an experienced barrister and has always practiced in the area of family law, with expertise across all areas of both domestic and international proceedings involving children and in adult social care matters. David has built up expertise in public law proceedings, acting regularly for all parties. He is regularly instructed in lengthy and complex care proceedings, including those involving parallel criminal proceedings. He has acted a number of times for parents accused of killing their partner or child. David has also been asked to appear in a number of appeals in which the focus has been on human rights as they relate to children. His High Court work has included representing CAFCASS legal and NYAS (National Youth Advocacy Service). In adult social care matters, David's work includes being instructed by the Official Solicitor in the Court of Protection. As well as providing advice to foreign jurisdictions on English law, (see Coventry City Council -v- S., [2010] IEHC 303) David is a regular speaker at public conferences, a contributor to the College of Law's Legal Network Television training programmes and involved in the training of expert witnesses.

VENTHAM, Charlotte
5 Essex Court, London
020 7410 2000
ventham@5essexcourt.co.uk
Featured in Police Law (All Circuits)
Practice Areas: Police Law; Inquests; Public and Administrative; Professional Discipline ; Personal Injury; Employment. Notable cases: Daniel Morgan Independent Panel Review and related civil actions (representing the Commissioner of Police of the Metropolis); 7/7 London Bombings Inquest; R (Simpson & ors) v Chief Constable of Greater Manchester Police [2013] EWHC 1858 (Admin) (legitimate expectation in light of promotion freeze); R (Stratton) v Chief Constable of Thames Valley Police [2013] EWHC 1561 (Admin) (police cautions – informed consent); R (L) v Chief Constable of Cumbria Police [2013] EWHC 869 (Admin) (ECRC disclosure); R (Monger) v Chief Constable of Cumbria Police [2013] EWHC 455 (Admin) (Special Constables Regulations 1965); Nunes and Markland Inquest (fatal interception of armed robbery by police); R (Montgomery) v 1) Police Appeals Tribunal, 2) Commissioner of Police of the Metropolis [2012] EWHC 936 (Admin) (PAT grounds of appeal); R (Boyle) v Haverhill Pub Watch [2009] EWHC 2441 (Admin) (reviewability of a ban issued by a pub watch scheme).
Professional Memberships: ALBA; ELBA.
Career: Called to the Bar 2001; Appointed to Attorney General's B Panel of Counsel 2014.

VERDUYN, Anthony
St Philips Chambers, Birmingham
01212 467 010
averduyn@st-philips.com
Featured in Real Estate Litigation (Midlands)
Practice Areas: Real estate litigation; landlord and tenant; land registration; professional negligence in property matters (including conveyancers, surveyors and brokers); and, social housing.
Professional Memberships: Property Bar Association; Midland Chancery and Commercial Bar Association.
Career: Called 1993 (Lincoln's Inn); Head of St Philips Chambers Property Team; Recorder (Civil, 2009; Private Family, 2013); Judge, First Tier Tribunal Property Chamber (formerly, Deputy Adjudicator to HM Land Registry (2008) and Lawyer Chairman of the Residential Property Tribunal (2006)); and ADR Group Accredited Mediator. Now also working from St Philips Chambers in London and Leeds. Recent cases of interest: Balevents v Sartori [2014] EWHC 1164 (Ch) [2012] EWCA Civ 1508 (retrial following new evidence in adverse possession); Durden v Aston [2012] EWCA Civ 636 (extrinsic evidence in boundary dispute); and Unique Pub Properties Ltd v Broad Green Tavern Ltd [2012] 2 P. & C.R. 17 (construction of lease).
Personal: Attended University of Durham, Collingwood College, BA (Hons) first, University of Oxford, Wolfson College, D.Phil., and City University. Contributor to Oxford Dictionary of National Biography and academic journals. Leisure interests include history, fine wine and foreign travel.

VERNON, Robert
9 Park Place, Cardiff
02920 382 731
clerks@9parkplace.co.uk
Featured in Employment (Wales & Chester)
Practice Areas: Robert specialises in employment law and has an evenly split claimant/respondent practice. He has acted for all levels of employees including company directors and senior teachers. His respondent clients include local authorities, solicitors, dental practices and numerous SMEs. He has extensive experience of all aspects of employment work including unfair dismissal, wrongful dismissal, redundancy, all forms of discrimination, breach of contract, wages claims and TUPE. An accomplished tribunal advocate, he is also regularly instructed to provide tactical advice to claimants and respondents in relation to a wide range of employment-related issues. He is also familiar with claims for breach of contract and restraint of trade in the county court. In 2013, Robert was appointed as a Fee-Paid Judge of the Employment Tribunal in the East Midlands Region.
Professional Memberships: Employment Law Bar Association.
Career: Called to the Bar in 2000, Lincoln's Inn. Appointed Fee-Paid Employment Judge (East Midlands Region) (2013)
Personal: Educated at the University of Wales, Cardiff. Married with two children. Interests include music, particularly playing drums.

VINCENT, Patrick
12 King's Bench Walk, London
020 7583 0811
vincent@12kbw.co.uk
Featured in Personal Injury (London)
Practice Areas: High value and catastrophic personal injury claims and insured losses. Transport and aviation accidents. Insurance policy construction. Insurance related EC Directives and legislation.
Professional Memberships: PIBA, PNBA.
Career: Call 1992. Special interest in claims involving a technical or scientific element. Many appearances in the Court of Appeal. Regularly instructed to appear against silks.
Personal: Patrick enjoy time with my family and playing the guitar and bass.

VINDIS, Tara
9 Gough Square, London
02078 320 500
tvindis@9goughsquare.co.uk
Featured in Family/Matrimonial (London)
Practice Areas: Specialist in child law, both public and private law. Care proceedings including those involving allegations of serious injuries to children. Adoption and special guardianship. Frequently instructed by local authorities. Represents all parties. Disclosure applications where Public Interest Immunity arguments apply. Tara also practises in all aspects of personal injury and clinical negligence.
Professional Memberships: Family Law Bar Association, The Association of Lawyers for Children, Personal Injuries Bar Association, Assocation of Personal Injury Lawyers.
Career: Called 1996.
Publications: MIB claims Practice and Pro cedure under the 1999 Agreement, (1st and 2nd editions) contributing editor to Jordans APIL guide to Road Traffic Accident Liability (1st and 2nd editions).
Personal: Educated at the Perse School for Girls, Cambridge and Exeter Univeristy. Two young sons.

VINEALL, Nicholas QC
4 Pump Court, London
020 7842 5555
nvineall@4pumpcourt.com
Featured in Energy & Natural Resources (London), Financial Services (London), Fraud (London), Shipping (London)
Practice Areas: Commercial and construction litigation and arbitration. Nick has a broadly based commercial practice. He has appeared in a wide range of arbitral tribunals (including LMAA, LCIA and ICC) and at all levels in the UK courts. In financial services Nick is a recognised expert in FSMA regulation. For the FCA he has obtained injunctions to stop unauthorised investment schemes, ponzi frauds insider dealing and collective investments schemes, and has acted in many recovery actions. He has appeared in RDC hearings and FSMA tribunals for and against the FCA, and has acted for the FSCS. He is acting for a group of investors following the collapse of a multimillion pound investment vehicle. In the energy, shipbuilding and offshore area Nick acts regularly for both yards and owners on new-

build and conversion disputes, and has built a strong relationship with Chinese yards. Offshore work includes loss and expense and delay claims on exploration and drill contracts. More general commercial work includes insurance (especially fire insurance and related claims), joint venture and SPA disputes, and the usual range of international debt collection.
Professional Memberships: COMBAR, LCLCBA, PNBA.
Career: Christ's College Cambridge (MA Natural Sciences), MA Pittsburgh University (Harkness Fellow), Diploma in Law City University, Called to the Bar 1988, Silk 2006.
Publications: Editor, Lloyds Law Reports (Financial Crime).

VINES, Anthony
Civitas Law, Cardiff
08450 713 007
anthony.vines@civitaslaw.com
Featured in Commercial Dispute Resolution (Wales & Chester), Employment (Wales & Chester)
Practice Areas: Commercial dispute resolution (contract performance and lending disputes, consumer law, consumer credit, licensing), employment (claimants, respondents and unions), regulatory crime and enforcement (health and safety, food, noise, trading standards, intellectual property, care standards, animal welfare, planning etc), fraud (civil and criminal) and public law. Mediation of all manner of disputes.
Professional Memberships: Employment Lawyers' Association, London Commercial and Common Law Bar Association, Administrative Law Bar Association, Health and Safety Lawyers' Association, Association of Regulatory and Disciplinary Lawyers.
Career: Called to the Bar (1993), Gough Square Chambers, London (1993-2002), CEDR mediator (1995), ADR Group mediator (2002), Attorney General's Panel of Prosecuting Advocates (2001-12), junior counsel to Welsh Assembly Government in employment law and criminal law (Panel A) (2010-), panel of junior counsel to Equality and Human Rights Commission (2010-), List of Specialist Advocates in Health & Safety and Environmental Law (List A) (2012-), Called to Bar of Northern Ireland (2014).
Personal: Married. 3 children. Lives Monmouth. Music.

VOKES, Stephen
Number 8 Chambers, Birmingham
01212 365 514
stephenvokes@no8chambers.co.uk
Featured in Immigration (Midlands)
Practice Areas: Head of the Chambers immigration, asylum, and human rights team. Area of practice is now, and has been for a considerable period, solely immigration, asylum and public law, including refugee, marriage, family reunion, work permit and student cases. Also specialises in cases involving the ECHR, and EEA National law. Extensive experience and has specialised in this area since his call to the Bar; 2014 has seen 25 years experience in this field of law. Frequently lectures in this field on behalf of Chambers. He has regularly appeared in the Administrative Court, and Court of Appeal. Numerous Country Guidance cases relating to asylum matters, and recent leading cases include the lead Country Guidance cases on Afghanistan (AK (Article 15 (c)) Afghanistan CG [2012] UKUT 163 (IAC)) and Uzbekistan (LM (returnees-expired exit permit) Uzbekistan CG [2012] 390 (IAC).
Professional Memberships: Immigration Law Practitioners Association
Personal: Cardiff High School for Boys, University of Wales (Lampeter) BA Hons. Worked in a wide variety of manual occupations before call to the Bar in 1989.

VON WACHTER, Victoria
5 Essex Court, London
020 7410 2000
wachter@5essexcourt.co.uk
Featured in Employment (London)
Practice Areas: Victoria's specialises solely in employment law and encompasses all areas in particular discrimination(including sexual orientation and transsexualism cases),whistleblowing and TUPE. She is also frequently involved in restrictive covenant, breach of contract and constructive dismissal claims. She appears for both Claimants and Respondents and is Direct Access licensed. She has a wealth of experience at appellate level and normally has at least one appeal on the go at any one time. She is particularly involved in representing police forces on the whole range of employment and discrimination matters as well as being retained employment Counsel for Total Oil Marine, the world's third largest oil company. Notable cases include: Costello v Gloucestershire CC EAT 2014 Appeal on judgment that intention of the manager was determining factor in whether or not a fundamental breach had occurred. Tudor & Ors v Civil Nuclear Constabulary EAT 2014 Appeal on whether Employment Tribunal had sufficiently specified 'information' in a PID to constitute a qualifying disclosure and therefore whether any detriment flowed from it. Chandler v Civil Nuclear Constabulary 2013 EAT appeal against substantive judgment and further appeal against Employment Judge's refusal to recuse himself from costs hearing. Peters & Anor v Chief Constable of Gloucestershire Constabulary EAT 2012 Appeal on refusal of Employment Judge to postpone proceedings pending outcome of criminal investigation into Claimants. Blackburn & Anor v Chief Constable of West Midlands Police [2009] ICR 505 – sex discrimination and equal pay
Professional Memberships: ELBA, ELA, Fellow Chartered Institute of Personnel and Development, Member British Psychological Society.
Career: Career: 20 years in industry working in Industrial relations and HR up to Director level prior to coming to the Bar. This vast experience allows her to give a uniquely practical and pragmatic approach to all her cases.
Publications: Author of Collective Bargaining chapter of – British Personnel Management (Croner). Frequent contributor to NLJ and Police Law Journal on employment related issues.

WAGSTAFFE, Christopher QC
29 Bedford Row Chambers, London
020 7404 1044
cwagstaffe@29br.co.uk
Featured in Family/Matrimonial (London)
Practice Areas: Family Law especially matrimonial finance, with a particular emphasis on cases featuring trust and international elements. Has been involved in litigation in Gibraltar, Hong Kong, the Isle of Man and the Channel Islands. Cases include: Hamilton v Hamilton [2013] EWCA Civ 13; Masa v Holliday [2012] EWCA Civ 1268; Prest v Prest [2011] EWHC 2956 (Fam); Vaughan v Vaughan [2010] EWCA Civ 349; B v R [2010] 1 FLR 563; Hashem v Shayif & Anor [2008] EWHC 2380 (Fam); A v A & St. George Trustees Limited (No 2) [2007] EWHC 1810 (Fam); A v A & St George Trustees Limited [2007] 2 FLR 467, FD; Prazic v Prazic [2006] 2 FLR 1128, CA; Charalambous v Charalambous [2004] 2 FLR 1093, CA; Oxley v Hiscock [2004] 2 FLR 669, CA; C v C (Variation of Post-nuptial Settlement: Company Shares) [2003] 2 FLR 493, FD; Rampal v Rampal (No 2)[2001] 2 FLR 1179, CA; Rampal v Rampal [2000] 2 FLR 763, FD; Purba v Purba [2000] 1 FLR 444, CA.
Professional Memberships: Member of the IAML; FLBA International Committee with particular responsibility for trust issues. FLBA & South East Circuit.
Career: Called 1992, Inner Temple. Silk 2011.
Publications: Co-author, Cohabitation and Trusts of Land (Sweet & Maxwell, 2006, second edition 2009). Also published various articles in Family Law and Family Affairs. Has lectured both nationally and internationally on various aspects of matrimonial finance.

WALFORD, Philip
11 New Square, London
020 7242 4017
philip.walford@11newsquare.com
Featured in Tax (London)
Practice Areas: All major taxes including corporation tax, income tax, capital gains and VAT, as well as some more specialist taxes such as petroleum revenue tax. Particular areas have included structured finance and repo transactions, double taxation, life assurance taxation, tax arbitrage, oil and gas, and inheritance tax. Philip's work ranges from high-value cases involving hundreds of millions of pounds to small matters where some principle is at stake. Among some notable cases are: P&O v HMRC (First-tier); HMRC v First Nationwide (Court of Appeal); Land Securities plc v HMRC (Upper Tribunal); Scottish Widows plc v HMRC (Supreme Court); HMRC v DCC Holdings (Supreme Court); Talisman Energy v HMRC (First-tier); Johnston Publishing v HMRC (Court of Appeal); Ford Motor Company v HMRC (Court of Appeal); HMRC v Bank of Ireland Britain Holdings (Court of Appeal).
Professional Memberships: Member of the Revenue Bar Association and the Honourable Society of Lincoln's Inn.
Career: Called to the Bar 2003. Corporate finance analyst at UBS Warburg, London 2000-01.
Publications: Administration of Estates: Post-death Tax Planning - Deeds of Variation and Disclaimers.
Personal: Educated at Westminster School, London; Merton College, Oxford (Master of Mathematics); and City University, London (Dip Law).

WALKER, Adam
7BR, London
020 7242 3555
clerks@7br.co.uk
Featured in Clinical Negligence (London)
Practice Areas: Clinical negligence, personal injury, inquests, employment, com mercial and sports law.
Professional Memberships: AvMA, APIL, PIBA, LCLCBA, Guild of Professional Teachers of Dance
Career: Adam has a broad civil practice with an emphasis on clinical negligence, personal injury and inquests. He acts for both Claimants and Defendants and is regularly instructed to advise, draft documents and to appear in court and before tribunals. He regularly appears at Coroners' inquests in respect of instances of alleged negligence leading to death, which may involve issues arising from Article 2 ECHR and which may require a jury. Adam's personal injury practice includes claims involving occupiers' liability, employers' liability, product liability, Highways Act claims and road traffic collisions. He is regularly instructed in cases involving industrial disease and disputes in respect of limitation. He is frequently involved in cases of maximum severity resulting from brain injury and in cases arising from fatal accidents. Adam also has extensive experience of acting in a wide variety of military claims, including disputes in respect of the provision of appropriate equipment. Adam also undertakes a wide variety of employment work, including unfair dismissal and discrimination claims and a broad range of commercial work, including the sale and supply of goods, insolvency and consumer credit.

WALKER, Amelia
Hardwicke, London
020 7242 2523
Amelia.walker@hardwicke.co.uk
Featured in Education (London)
Practice Areas: Amelia Walker's practice focuses on Education, Local Government, Community Care, Court of Protection, Public Inquiries, Mental Health, Regulatory Law and Housing. She is a member of the Treasury Solicitor's C Panel. She appears as an advocate in all levels of Court, predominantly in appeals and judicial reviews in the Upper Tribunal and Administrative Court. Also appears in the First-tier Tribunal and County Courts (special educational needs cases, discrimination claims and breach of contract claims arising from education contracts). She was junior counsel in the Court of Appeal for the Respondent family foster carer in R (on the application of X) v Tower Hamlets LBC [2013] 4 All E.R. 237. Amelia acted for one of the core participants to the Mid-Staffordshire NHS Foundation Trust Public Inquiry and recently acted in a Traffic Commissioner's Public Inquiry.
Professional Memberships: Member of the Bar Council's (Civil) Public Panel, Constitutional and Administrative Law Bar Association.
Career: MA Hons. (Ist class) 2002, Joseph Hodges Choate Memorial Fellow (Harvard University) 2003, MPhil in Historical Studies 2004, CPE (Distinction) 2005, Called to the Bar (Inner Temple) 2007, Barrister at Hardwicke 2008 to date.

WALKER, Andrew QC
Maitland Chambers, London
020 7406 1200
awalker@maitlandchambers.com
Featured in Real Estate Litigation (London)
Practice Areas: Litigation, arbitration, ADR and expert advice, particularly in the following areas: property and property-related disputes of all kinds (including contractual and development disputes, leases, rights over land, mortgages, disputed property disposals, and leasehold enfranchisement claims); professional negligence

in the fields of property, finance, investment, commerce, tax, and valuation; company law and director/shareholder/investor disputes; securities, investment and financial disputes; other commercial/equity disputes (including civil fraud and asset tracing); valuation disputes and challenges of all kinds; insolvency; partnerships.
Professional Memberships: Chancery Bar Association, Professional Negligence Bar Association, Property Bar Association, Commercial Bar Association, Financial Services Lawyers Association.
Career: Called Lincoln's Inn (1991); QC (2011). Elected member of the Bar Council (2005- ; currently Chairman, Professional Practice [Ethics] Committee and Vice-Chairman, Law Reform Committee). Winner of the Bar Pro Bono Award 2009.
Personal: Haberdashers' Aske's School, Elstree; Trinity College, Cambridge (MA).

WALKER, Elizabeth
St Philips Chambers, Birmingham
01212 461 600
ewalker@st-philips.com
Featured in Family/Matrimonial (Midlands)
Practice Areas: Elizabeth specialises in public law children matters, in particular complex High Court proceedings concerning serious non-accidental injury and death acting for local authorities, guardians and parents. She also has a particular focus on cases involving parents with significant learning disabilities or communication difficulties and challenging local authority decision making. She has appeared in a number of high pressure applications for permission to leave the jurisdiction, as well as contentious private law matters. Reported decisions: Re G [1999] 1 FLR 771; Re E (Wardship Order: Child in Voluntary Accommodation) [2012] EWCA Civ 1773; Coventry City Council v SB, SA, SS, RY, KK [2012] EWHC 4014 (Fam); Re N (Death of a Child in the DRC: Order for Return: Contempt) [2014] EWHC 337 (Fam).
Professional Memberships: Family Law Bar Association; British Association of Adoption and Fostering.
Career: Called to the Bar in October 1994. Appointed as recorder on the North East Circuit in June 2012.
Personal: Attended Durham University. Leisure interests include keeping fit, a thriving book group and travel.

WALKER, Ronald QC
12 King's Bench Walk, London
020 7583 0811
walker@12kbw.co.uk
Featured in Personal Injury (London), Personal Injury (All Circuits)
Practice Areas: Professional negligence; insurance; personal injury; building and engineering contracts; HSWA prosecutions; environmental law. Recent cases include: Jones v Department of Energy & Climate Change (the Phurnacite litigation)[2012]; Shaw v Fuller & Kingsley School [2012]; United Marine Aggregates Ltd v GM Welding Ltd [2012]; Divia v Toyo Tire Co [2011]; Dalling v RJ Heale Ltd [2011]; Greene Wood & McLean v Templeton Insurance Ltd [2010]; Shulman v Simon Ltd [2010].
Professional Memberships: PNBA. LCLCBA, TECBAR, PIBA.
Career: Called 1962, Silk 1983, Deputy High Court Judge 1993. Mental Health Tribunal Judge 1999-2012. Acts as arbitrator and is an accredited mediator and adjudicator. Listed as a leading silk (Personal Injury) in Legal 500 and Chambers Directory.
Publications: Walker & Walker: The English Legal System; Butterworths Professional Negligence Service; Butterworths Personal Injury Litigation Service: Asbestos Disease Claims.

WALKER, Steven
Stone Chambers, London
07970 533 305
steven.walker@stonechambers.com
Featured in International Arbitration (London)
Practice Areas: A leading advocate, barrister and attorney, Steven is an international commercial lawyer with a specialisation in international arbitration, energy, construction and engineering and commercial disputes. In the United Kingdom, he regularly appears in the courts and before various arbitration tribunals. Steven has an extensive international arbitration practice with an emphasis on commercial, energy and construction arbitration. He regularly acts as counsel in multiple ad hoc and institutional international arbitrations conducted in many countries around the world and subject to a wide variety of governing substantive and procedural laws. He has built a formidable reputation acting in international cases involving exploration and production disputes, engineering, procurement and construction disputes, power purchase disputes as well as a whole range of commercial/corporate disputes concerning joint venture agreements, shareholders agreements and other financial and commercial agreements. Steven is an accredited public access barrister and can be instructed directly. He is also an accredited arbitrator and sits on numerous arbitrator panels both in the UK and abroad.
Career: LLB (Hons); admitted Member of the Scottish Bar 1999; admitted as Attorney-at-Law (Cayman Islands) 2007; called to the Bar of England and Wales 2008; appointed Honorary Fellow of the University of Edinburgh 2011; appointed Seminar Director & Lecturer at The Energy Studies Institute, National University of Singapore 2014.
Publications: Co-author of leading book 'Pleadings in Arbitration – A Practitioner's Guide', Sweet & Maxwell/Thompson Reuters, 2012. Numerous articles and papers on commercial law.

WALKER, Steven QC
Atkin Chambers, London
020 7404 0102
clerks@atkinchambers.com
Featured in Construction (London), Energy & Natural Resources (London)
Practice Areas: Steven specialises in disputes arising in connection with construction and engineering projects both in the UK and internationally. His practice involves a diverse range of subject matter including buildings, offshore structures, ships and IT systems. Recent cases include: Seele Middle East v Drake & Scull International (2014) CILL 3147, Doosan Babcock v Commercializadora De Equipos Y Materiales Mabe [2014] BLR 33, SABIC UK Petrochemicals v Punj Lloyd [2014] BLR 43, Parkwood Leisure v Laing O'Rourke [2013] BLR 589 and Mi Space Construction v Lend Lease [2013] BLR 600.
Professional Memberships: TECBAR, Combar.
Career: Called to the Bar of England and Wales 1993. Silk 2012.
Publications: Formerly joint editor of 'Building Law Reports' and Sweet and Maxwell's 'Technology and Construction Law Reports.'

WALLACE, Sam
New Court Chambers, London
020 7583 5123
swallace@newcourtchambers.com
Featured in Family/Matrimonial (London)
Practice Areas: Specialist family practitioner with an emphasis on public law child care work. Represents local authorities, parents and children with substantial experience in undertaking lengthy and complex litigation in cases involving non-accidental injury and sexual abuse (including cases where there is disputed or conflicting expert evidence), and cases with an international element including cases involving the placement of children permanently outside of the jurisdiction and cases where issues arise under Brussels II Revised.
Professional Memberships: FLBA.
Career: LLB Hons, London School of Economics (2003), Called to the Bar, Gray's Inn (2004). Regularly delivers seminars and training to solicitors and social work professionals in relation to developing areas of law and practice. Registered as a pupil supervisor.

WALMISLEY, Lisa
Kings Chambers, Manchester
08450 343 444
clerks@kingschambers.com
Featured in Restructuring/Insolvency (Northern)
Practice Areas: Asset recovery (for and against office-holders, banks, asset-based lenders and other institutions); banking (guarantees and mortgages); commercial litigation (including commercial fraud and injunctions); company (directors' duties, shareholder disputes and remedies); insolvency (personal and corporate, including directors disqualification and defending public interest winding-up), partnership.
Professional Memberships: Chancery Bar Association, Northern Chancery Bar Association, Northern Circuit Commercial Bar Association (committee member).
Career: Called by Middle Temple 2000.

WALSH, Stephen QC
3 Raymond Buildings Barristers, London
020 7400 6400
stephen.walsh@3rblaw.com
Featured in Health & Safety (London), Licensing (London)
Practice Areas: A specialist in regulatory and licensing law with broad experience in criminal enforcement and coronial proceedings. Regulatory practice is focused on health and safety (primarily fatal accidents in the workplace), food safety and trading standards. Prosecuting and defending in a broad range of cases and representing interested parties at inquests. Advising regulatory authorities generally on matters of enforcement; advising corporate and individual clients on compliance including the preparation of health and safety policies and risk assessments. Licensing expertise encompasses all forms of licensable activities including liquor and entertainment, late night refreshment, sports stadium safety, gambling, lotteries, television, firearms, street trading and charities. Providing advice to licensing authorities and all sectors of the leisure industry on licensing issues. Appearing on behalf of applicants, responsible authorities and interested parties before local authorities and courts throughout England and Wales including applications for judicial review.

WALSH, Timothy
Guildhall Chambers, Bristol
01179 309 000
tim.walsh@guildhallchambers.co.uk
Featured in Real Estate Litigation (Western)
Practice Areas: Tim Walsh is the head of Guildhall Chambers' Property and Estates Team and specialises exclusively in property, probate and trusts law. He has particular experience in disputes over co-owned land, Inheritance Act claims and general disputes concerning contested wills and estates. Tim is also an expert on residential property disputes between landlord and tenant.
Career: Tenant at Guildhall Chambers since 2001. Appointed Junior Counsel to the Crown from 2007 to 2012 (Attorney General's Regional Panel). Appointed as a Lawyer Chairman of the Residential Property Tribunal in Wales in 2013. Head of Guildhall Chambers' Property and Estates team since 2014.
Personal: Born 1976. Educated at Hertford College, Oxford. Married with two sons. Enjoys running and cycling.

WALTERS, Graham
Civitas Law, Cardiff
08450 713 007
graham.walters@civitaslaw.com
Featured in Administrative & Public Law (Wales & Chester), Chancery (Wales & Chester), Commercial Dispute Resolution (Wales & Chester)
Practice Areas: Graham's practice concentrates on property, planning and public and administrative law. Instructions include work for the Welsh Government and many local authorities. Subject areas include planning, highways, compulsory purchase, housing, environment, grant entitlement, education, disclosure and judicial review generally. In addition he has a significant Chancery practice including probate, inheritance and landlord and tenant work.
Professional Memberships: PEBA.
Career: Graham is instructed by a large number of public bodies and by individuals and organisations. He undertakes a very significant amount of advisory work. He has been appointed to make recommendations on appeals under the Greenhouse Gas Emissions Trading Scheme, appeared before a committee of the National Assembly for Wales under Special Assembly procedure and represented Welsh Ministers at Highway Inquiries. Appointed to the Welsh Assembly Panel of Counsel (Public and Regulatory) and to the Attorney General's Regional Panel, Wales. Assistant Boundary Commissioner, Wales.

WALTON, Alastair
Maitland Chambers, London
020 7406 1200
awalton@maitlandchambers.com
Featured in Chancery (London)
Practice Areas: General chancery practice including company, insolvency, property, professional negligence, trusts, and contract and commercial disputes and in particular fiduciary duties, economic torts, beneficial co-ownership and estate agents' commission disputes. Cases include Premier Waste v Towers, Henry Boot v Alstom, Templeton v Penningtons, Attorney General v Parry; Raja v Hoogstraten; Standard Life v Egan Lawson; Alstom v British Airways; Prince Jefri v

Manoukian and others; TBV Power v Elm Energy; Re H and others; McDonald v Horn; Re Little Olympian Each Ways Limited; Re BSB Holdings Limited; Lonrho v Fayed; Lloyds Bank v Rosset.
Professional Memberships: Chancery Bar Association; COMBAR.
Career: Called 1977.
Publications: Author of the chapter on Interest and co-author of the chapter on Damages in Lender Claims.
Personal: Born 26 August 1954. Educated at Winchester and Balliol College, Oxford (BA 1976). Married with four children. Lives in London.

WARD, Alexandra
9-12 Bell Yard, London
020 7400 1800
a.ward@912by.com
Featured in Crime (London)
Practice Areas: Crime, fraud: civil and criminal, corporate crime and investigations, POCA and asset forfeiture, local authority prosecutions. Recent cases: Junior counsel to the FCA in its largest insider dealing investigation R v Dodgson & Others (Operation Tabernula)(FCA), junior counsel (HMRC) £151m fraud before the First Tier Tax Tribunal, junior counsel in the defence of a British Embassy official charged with misconduct in public office. Regularly acts for local authorities in respect of EU regulations and nuisance cases. Regularly prosecutes and defends those charged with sexual offences. Regularly defends those charged with road traffic offences. Accepts direct access instructions in appropriate cases.
Professional Memberships: Bar Council (Law Reform Committee; Chair of the working party considering the Confiscation of Sentencing Provision) recent responses on behalf of the LRC include: Deferred Prosecution Agreements, Legal Professional Privilege and RIPA, "Plea Negotiation in Fraud Cases" and "Powers to Prevent Fraud and Compensate Victims" Criminal Bar Association, Member of the Rook Committee considering "Advocacy Training for Cases Involving Vulnerable Witnesses and Defendants".
Career: Appointed to the following CPS lists as a Grade 3 prosecutor: Serious Crime, Fraud & Serious Sexual Offences. Appointed to the SFO's list of approved advocates - B Panel. Instructed by Dept BIS, Royal Mail Group plc. Secondments: Irwin Mitchell LLP (Regulatory Investigations & Enforcement Group) 2009, Financial Services Authority (Wholesale Markets: Enforcements) 2005
Publications: Co-Editor: Lloyd's Law Reports: Financial Crime. Editor: The Encyclopaedia of Road Traffic Law & Practice, Sweet & Maxwell. Contributing Author: Rook and Ward on Sexual Offences, Sweet & Maxwell, Fourth & Third Editions. Researcher: "Legal Professional Privilege: Let the Fight-Back Begin" Counsel Magazine. May 2012.
Personal: Lives in London, enjoys theatre and music.

WARD, Henry
8 New Square, London
020 7405 4321
henry.ward@8newsquare.co.uk
Featured in Intellectual Property (London)
Practice Areas: Barrister specialising in intellectual property law. Notable reported cases include: Rovi v Virgin (patent - set-top boxes and broadcasting systems), Doosan v Babcock (trade mark - nuclear power industry); Virgin v Premium etc (HC, CA and SC) (patent - aircraft seating); ACS v GBS (confidential information - concrete formulations); Novartis v Mylan (pharmaceutical patent - resolution of enantiomers); Hospira v Novartis (pharmaceutical patent - interim relief pending appeal); Sudarshan v Clariant (patent - crystal form of pigments); Sealed Air v Sharpak (design right - fruit punnets); Clinisupplies v Richardson (confidential information and UDR - medical supplies); Mainetti v Hangarlogic (registered design - coathangers); Westwood v Knight (trade mark, passing off and copyright - fashion designs); MMI v CellXion (patent -mobile phone interception); Hasbro v Nahrmittel (trade mark - play dough); KCI v Smith & Nephew (patent - medical devices); Research in Motion v Vista (patent - BlackBerry synchronisation); Queensland v Siemens (patent - MRI); and Wobben v Vestas (patent - wind turbines).
Personal: Educated at Ellesmere College, and Emmanuel College, Cambridge 1998, Master of Engineering. Bachelor of Arts (Honours) Engineering.

WARD, Tim QC
Monckton Chambers, London
020 7405 7211
tward@monckton.com
Featured in Administrative & Public Law (London), Competition/European Law (London), Telecommunications (London)
Practice Areas: European law; public and administrative law; telecommunications. Tim has appeared in over 50 cases before the CJEU and has particular expertise in commercial regulation. Tim has also acted in many competition damages claims. Cases include: EFTA Surveillance Authority v Iceland: collapse of Icelandic banks; Tesco v Mastercard and VISA (interchange fees), Sony v Toshiba & Ors (LCD); Akzo Nobel v Competition Commission (merger control jurisdiction); Drax Power v Secretary of State, renewable energy generation; R(Shoesmith) v Ofsted & Ors: inspection of Children's Services; BT v OFCOM, TalkTalk and Sky: wholesale broadband.
Career: Called 1994; Prior to taking silk, was a member of the Attorney General's A Panel; Silk 2011; The Lawyer Awards"Barrister of the Year' 2013. Chairman of the Bar European Group 2013-15.
Publications: Competition Litigation in the UK (with Kassie Smith, Sweet & Maxwell 2005), Judicial Review and the Human Rights Act (2000) and The Strasbourg Case Law - Leading Cases from the European Human Rights Reports (2001). Editor in Chief of the Human Rights Law Reports - UK Cases (Sweet & Maxwell) and Contributor to Bellamy & Child, The European Community Law of Competition.
Personal: BA, MA.

WARNER, David
New Square Chambers, London
020 7419 8000
david.warner@newsquarechambers.co.uk
Featured in Real Estate Litigation (Midlands)
Practice Areas: David has a substantial property practice which embraces the entire range of property and landlord and tenant related work. He has particular experience in actions concerning claims of adverse possession and trusts of land. David has considerable expertise in property cases with a public law element. He appeared in R(Morris) v Westminster City Council [2006] 1 WLR 505 (CA) and more recently in R(Grimsby Institute of Further and Higher Education) v Chief Executive of Skills Funding [2010] 3 EGLR 125. David also has experience of rights of way law, including appearing at public inquiries. He has a particular interest in property disputes with a trusts element, acting for the defendant in Olszanecki v Hillocks [2004] WTLR 975. David's landlord and tenant practice covers contested lease renewals, rent review and dilapidations claims. He represented the successful landlord in Picture Warehouse Ltd v Cornhill Investments Ltd [2008] 12 EG 98 and appeared for the appellant in Kullar v Kingsoak Homes Ltd [2013] UKUT 15 (LC). David also has a commercial litigation practice and is an experienced commercial litigator. He represented the defendant in Murray Vernon Holdings Ltd v Hassall [2010] EWHC 7 (Ch) and appeared in Azure East Midlands Ltd v Manchester Airport Group Property Developments Ltd [2014] EWHC 1644 (TCC).
Professional Memberships: Chancery Bar Association; Property Bar Association.
Career: LLB, London, 1995; Called 1996.
Publications: Contributor to the Law of Freedom of Information, OUP, 2002.
Personal: Married with 2 children. Chairman of Droitwich RFC.

WARNOCK, Andrew QC
1 Chancery Lane, London
020 7092 2900
awarnock@1chancerylane.com
Featured in Education (London), Local Government (London), Police Law (All Circuits), Professional Negligence (London), Personal Injury (London)
Practice Areas: Specialises in professional negligence (particularly solicitors, surveyors and accountants negligence); claims against public bodies, in particular education negligence, social services negligence and highways as well as sexual abuse (Andrew has acted in the Jimmy Saville case); claims involving the police; personal injury with particular experience of claims involving psychiatric injury, head injury and duty of care issues. He has been involved in several high profile cases concerning the liabilities in tort of local authorities. He has also developed a particular expertise in solicitors' negligence actions, usually on behalf of the professional indemnity insurer. He has appeared in a number of high profile inquests, including an inquest following a police shooting where the jury returned a verdict of suicide. Reported cases include: Flaherty v Tanbridge D.C [2013] (duty of regulators); Hanningfield v Essex Police [2013] (necessity of arrest) Furmedge v Chester-le-Street District Council and Others [2011] (personal injury; liability); Dermott v Harrow LBC [2011] (harassment); VL v Oxfordshire County Council [2010] (criminal injuries; local authority); Connor v Surrey County Council [2010] CA (psychiatric injury; education); A v Chief Constable of Sussex Police [2010] CA (police protection powers); A v Essex County Council [2010] SC (human rights); X&Y v Hounslow LBC [2009] CA (local authority duties); A v Essex County Council [2008] CA (human rights).
Professional Memberships: Professional Negligence Bar Association; Personal Injury Bar Association; London Common Law and Commercial Bar Association.
Career: Called to the Bar 1993.
Publications: Contributor, 'Local Authority Liability' (Morrell and Foster, 4th edition, 2009); Co author 'Advanced Civil Litigation in Practice', (3rd ed OUP 2005); Contributor, Atkin's Court Forms: Professional Negligence, Vol. 29(2) 2003; Contributor, 'Pittaway and Hammerton: Professional Negligence Cases', Butterworths, 1998.

WARNOCK-SMITH, Shân QC
5 Stone Buildings, London
020 7242 6201
clerks@5sblaw.com
Featured in Chancery (London), Charities (London), Offshore (London), Trusts (London)
Practice Areas: Advice and litigation in connection with all aspects of trusts, succession, charities and related professional negligence claims in the UK and internationally, particularly the Cayman Islands, the British Virgin Islands, Bermuda, Hong Kong, Singapore, Jersey, Guernsey and the Isle of Man. Has a particular interest in wealth structuring (including charity and philanthropy) for international families from both the advisory and the litigation standpoints. Accredited mediator specialising in trust and estate disputes.
Professional Memberships: Society of Trust and Estate Practitioners, Chancery Bar Association, Association of Contentious Trust and Probate Specialists and The International Academy of Estate and Trust Law.
Career: Called to the Bar 1971. Silk 2002. Admitted to practise in the Cayman Islands, the Eastern Caribbean Supreme Court and England and Wales. Established International Chancery and Trusts Chambers in the Cayman Islands in 2010 and practises from there and from 5 Stone Buildings in London
Publications: Lecturer, writer and broadcaster on trust and estate matters. Sits on the Editorial Board of The Wills and Trusts Law Reports.

WARRINGTON, John
5 St Andrew's Hill, London
020 7332 5400
JohnWarrington@5sah.co.uk
Featured in Crime (London)
Practice Areas: John is an experienced criminal practitioner who is regularly instructed in complex and document heavy, multi-handed cases of the utmost gravity for both the defence and prosecution, often involving multi-million pound criminal revenues. His practice encompasses a wide spectrum of offending, including homicide, serious violence, human trafficking, drug importation and distribution, public order, robbery, firearms, sexual offences and serious dishonesty. John has defended members of some of the most prolific organised crime groups in the country. In particular, he has extensive experience in white-collar crime, including serious fraud, money laundering, bribery, corruption and all aspects of related restraint and proceeds of crime proceedings. In this regard, John has been retained to advise pre-charge in the course of a number of high-profile investigations and has acted in complex applications for production orders. He has been appointed to the CPS serious crime, fraud and proceeds of crime panels, the Bar Standards Board prosecution panel and the list of Specialist Regulatory Advocates in health and safety and environmental law. John has a busy regulatory and professional disciplinary practice, with an emphasis on health and safety, the environ-

ment, public utilities, legal services and medical/healthcare professionals. He is direct access qualified and an advocacy tutor with Lincoln's Inn.
Professional Memberships: Association of Regulatory and Disciplinary Lawyers, Fraud Lawyers Association, Proceeds of Crime Lawyers Association, Criminal Bar Association, South Eastern Circuit.
Career: Called to the Bar in 2000 (Lincoln's Inn); Law/LLB Honours (Queen Mary & Westfield College, University of London).

WARWICK, Mark QC
Selborne Chambers, London
020 7420 9500
mark.warwick@selbornechambers.co.uk
Featured in Real Estate Litigation (London)
Practice Areas: Mark is a leading practitioner in property litigation.
Professional Memberships: Chancery Bar Association; Property Bar Association; Professional Negligence Bar Association.
Career: Mark is a leading practitioner in property litigation. He also acts in cases involving contracts relating to construction and enforcement of commercial agreements. He advises on property related professional negligence and is recognised for his expertise in contentious chancery work including partnership and trusts of land. He is often instructed in cases that call for original ways of presenting or defending a claim. He has appeared in more than 100 reported cases. Recent cases include: Bank of Scotland v Joseph [2014] 1 P&CR 18 (Land Registration Act 2002); Menelaou v Bank of Cyprus [2014]1WLR 854(Bank's claim to subrogation); Barrett v Bem [2012]Ch 573 CA (Death bed will invalid); BOH v Eastern Power [2011]CA (Merger of Freeehold and Leasehold interests); Milebush Properties v Tameside Council [2011]CA (Availability of declaratory relief); Bindra v Chopra, CA, Lawtel 20.3.09 (construction of trust deed, dealing with interests on death). Leonora Investment Co v Mott Macdonald; CA, Lawtel 23.7.08 (a landlord's failure to follow the prescribed machinery for the collection of service charges means that its claim fails).
Publications: Mark is the joint author of a book on break clauses and writes regularly for legal periodicals.

WATERS, Julian
1 Chancery Lane, London
020 7092 2900
clerks@1chancerylane.com
Featured in Personal Injury (London)
Practice Areas: Specialises in personal injury with particular experience in catastrophic injury, brain damage and psychiatric cases; clinical negligence and the misdiagnosing of cancer; claims against public authorities; claims involving the police, including unlawful arrest, malicious prosecution and challenges to warrants; libel and slander. He has been involved in several high profile inquests. He has also developed a particular expertise in Human Rights Act law. Reported cases include: Painting v University of Oxford (costs in personal injury action where Claimant exaggerated claim); Van Colle v. Hertfordshire Police (Article 2, Osman duty); W v Westminster City Council (Libel/Article 8); Armsden v Kent Police (road traffic accident, police on emergency call); Clarke v Essex Police (bullying within the police force); Arnott v Sprake (road traffic accident in country lane); R. v Associated Octel (liability of employers for failures of independent contractors); Cooper v Royal United Hospital Bath NHS Trust (failure to diagnose cancer); Gates v McKenna (stage hypnotism); Booth v White (liability of claimant in contributory negligence for not asking whether driver was drunk).
Professional Memberships: PNBA; PIBA.

WATERS, Malcolm QC
Radcliffe Chambers, London
020 7692 2059
mwaters@radcliffechambers.com
Featured in Banking & Finance (London), Consumer Law (London)
Practice Areas: Principal specialist areas are retail banking, mortgages and consumer credit; regulation of retail financial services; and the law relating to building societies and other mutuals. Extensive experience in the law on unfair terms and in the drafting of standard form mortgage, current account, savings and consumer credit documentation. Reported cases include Director General of Fair Trading v First National Bank (unfair terms); OFT v Abbey National (unfair terms); Southern Pacific Mortgage v Heath (consumer credit); JP Morgan Chase v NRAM (consumer credit); C&G v Norgan (mortgages); Woolwich v Gomm (mortgages); Bristol & West v Bartlett (mortgages); C&G v BSC (building society conversion) and BSC v Halifax (building society conversion). Member of the working parties responsible for drafting the Standard Conditions of Sale and the Standard Commercial Property Conditions.
Professional Memberships: Chancery Bar Association; Professional Negligence Bar Association.
Career: Called to Bar 1977. Took Silk 1997.
Publications: Joint author of 'Retail Mortgages: Law Regulation and Procedure' and 'Current Law Commentary on the Building Societies Act 1986'. Joint editor of 'Wurtburg & Mills – Building Society Law' and 'The Law of Investor Protection'. Consultant editor of 'Halsbury's Laws of England' 4th edition, Friendly Societies title and 5th edition Mutual Societies and Industrial and Provident Societies title.
Personal: Educated at Whitgift School 1963-71 and St. Catherine's College Oxford 1972-76 (BA and BCL).

WATSON, Ben
3 Raymond Buildings Barristers, London
020 7400 6400
ben.watson@3rblaw.com
Featured in Administrative & Public Law (London), Civil Liberties & Human Rights (London), Extradition (London)
Practice Areas: Particular expertise in crime, extradition, public law, international mutual legal assistance, and asset recovery. Regularly instructed in heavyweight crime (particularly fraud) and the leading extradition cases, see recently: for South Africa in Dewani (accused of murdering wife on honeymoon), and for the Secretary of State in Gary McKinnon (computer hacker). Also instructed for UK Government in six US terrorism cases before ECtHR (Abu Hamza et al.) As member of Attorney General's B Panel regularly acts in a judicial review proceedings for a wide-range of Government departments – including for MoD and FCO in claims following the conflicts in Iraq and Afghanistan. As a 'Special Advocate', acted for Ms Zatuliveter (Lib-Dem MP's researcher accused of spying for Russia), and is instructed in the first Closed Material Procedures before the Court of Appeal. Has 'Developed Vetted' security clearance.
Professional Memberships: Criminal Bar Association, Young Fraud Lawyers Assocation.
Career: Call 2002; Attorney General's 'C' Panel 2006; Attorney General's Special Advocate Panel 2010; Attorney General's 'B' Panel 2011.
Publications: Asset Recovery (OUP, 2007-13).
Personal: MA Hons (Cantab); Diploma in law.

WATSON, Claire
Serjeants' Inn Chambers, London
020 7427 5000
cwatson@serjeantsinn.com
Featured in Professional Discipline (London)
Practice Areas: Claire Watson was called to the Bar in 2011. Claire specialises in clinical negligence and healthcare, Court of Protection, inquests and inquiries, police, professional discipline and public and administrative law. An earlier edition notes that "she is an outstanding advocate who is exceedingly well prepared" and that "she thinks of everything and has all the makings of a star." Please click on the link to the Serjeants' Inn Chambers website for her profile, which sets out full details of her practice including relevant work of note.
Professional Memberships: PNBA, ARDL, LCLCBA.
Publications: Co-author of Medical Treatment: Decisions and the Law.

WATSON, Duncan
1 Garden Court Family Law Chambers, London
020 7797 7900
watson@1gc.com
Featured in Family/Matrimonial (South Eastern)
Practice Areas: Duncan is a specialist in family finances, including financial remedies on divorce, financial applications relating to children pursuant to Schedule 1 Children Act 1989 and civil actions between former co-habitants. Undertakes private law Children Act work.
Professional Memberships: Family Law Bar Association
Career: Duncan is a specialist in family finances, including financial remedies on divorce, financial applications relating to children pursuant to Schedule 1 Children Act 1989 and civil actions between former co-habitants.

WATSON, James QC
Serjeants' Inn Chambers, London
020 7427 5000
jwatson@serjeantsinn.com
Featured in Clinical Negligence (London), Police Law (All Circuits)
Practice Areas: James Watson QC was called to the Bar in 1979 and took silk in 2000. James specialises in clinical negligence, police law, inquests and inquiries, professional discipline and mediation. An earlier edition notes that "he is great to work with and is also a brilliant negotiator, who is full of useful, practical ideas...his tactical brilliance enables him to handle the most complex of claims with sensitivity." Please click on the link above to the Serjeants' Inn Chambers website for his profile, which sets out full details of his practice including relevant work of note.
Professional Memberships: PNBA, LCLCBA.

WATT-PRINGLE, Jonathan QC
Temple Garden Chambers, London
020 7583 1315
jwpringle@tgchambers.com
Featured in Health & Safety (London), Personal Injury (London)
Practice Areas: Barrister specialising in personal injury, insurance, clinical negligence, professional negligence, health and safety and inquests. Cases include: Griffiths v Brown (The Times, 23 October 1998); Griffin v Kingsmill [1998] PNLR 157, [1998] PIQR P 24; Kirby v Cross (The Times, 5 April 2000); Sam v Atkins [2006] RTR 14; Newman v Laver [2006] EWCA Civ 1135; BRB (Residuary) Ltd v Connex South Eastern Ltd [2008] 1 WLR 2867; Monk v P C Harrington Ltd [2009] PIQR P32; Ansari v New India Assurance Limited [2009] EWCA Civ 93, [2009] Lloyd's Rep. I.R. 562; Goad v Butcher [2011] EWCA Civ 158; Bowen v National Trust [2011] EWHC 1992 (QB); Eden v Rubin [2011] EWHC 3090 (QB), [2011] All ER (D) 189; Whiteford v Kubus UAB [2012] EWCA Civ 1017, [2012] All ER (D) 66; Williams v Williams [2013] EWCA Civ 455, [2013] PIQR P17; Maclennan v Morgan Sindall (Infrastucture) PLC [2013] EWHC 4044 (QB), [2013] WLR (D) 509; Raleys v Barnaby [2014] EWCA Civ 686.
Professional Memberships: PNBA; PIBA.
Career: Called 1987, Middle Temple; QC 2008; Chair of the Appeal Committee of the Human Fertilization and Embryology Authority.
Personal: University of Stellenbosch (1978 BA; 1980 LLB); Rhodes Scholar, Keble College, Oxford (1983 BA; 1984 BCL; 1987 MA).

WATTHEY, James
4 Pump Court, London
020 7842 5555
jwatthey@4pumpcourt.com
Featured in Shipping (London)
Practice Areas: Shipping, insurance, international trade, banking and commercial.
Professional Memberships: Combar, LCLCBA, Worshipful Company of Shipwrights, BILA, LMAA, Young Maritime Professionals, London Shipping Law Centre, Bar Pro Bono Unit.
Career: MA (Cantab) 1998 (Squire and Christ's College Scholarships; de Hart Prize). BCL (Oxon) 1999. Called Gray's Inn, 2000 (Prince of Wales Scholar; Barristers Committee). Worked at Lovells 2001-02, in insurance/reinsurance. Arbitrator. Direct access accredited. Consistently recommended by the leading directories as "great counsel" who deals with matters "swiftly and effectively" and for his "impressively commercial" approach and "sensible and strategic advice".
Personal: Lives in London with wife and young daughter. Likes cycling, sailing, food and family.

WAUGH, Andrew QC
Three New Square, London
020 7405 1111
clerks@3newsquare.co.uk
Featured in Intellectual Property (London)
Professional Memberships: Intellectual Propery Lawyers Association, Chancery Bar Association, AIPPLA
Career: Graduated in 1980 from the City University, London with a first class honours degree in Chemical and Administrative Studies which included subjects on vitamin

chemistry, structure and reactivity correlations and materials science and a thesis on Pharmaceutical Research and Development. Post-graduate Diploma in law in 1981. Called to the Bar 1982. Pupillage with Martin Moore-Bick 1982, 3 Essex Court (The Chambers of Kenneth Rokison QC). Pupillage with Simon Thorley 1983, 6 Pump Court (The Chambers of William Aldous QC). Queen's Counsel 1998 Admitted to the Irish Bar 2010.

WAY, Patrick QC
Field Court Tax Chambers, London
020 3693 3700
pw@fieldtax.com
Featured in Tax (London)

Practice Areas: One of the founders of Field Court Tax Chambers, he has strong advocacy and advisory practices. He has successfully represented clients at all levels of the UK system from top to bottom and he acts for both taxpayer and HMRC alike in cases where the tax at stake may run into many hundreds of millions of pounds. He has also advised on some of the biggest UK takeovers and property developments involving multinationals. His clients include major corporates, as well as famous celebrities, charities, wealthy individuals and businesses of all types whom he has advised in relation to virtually every form of UK tax and on many aspects of double taxation and the impact of EU law. He has also appeared in the Privy Council. Throughout his career he has only ever appeared as lead or sole counsel.
Professional Memberships: Revenue Bar Association; Chancery Bar Association
Career: Called to the Bar 1994 (Lincoln's Inn). Member of Attorney General's B Panel as Junior Counsel to the Crown 2010-2013; QC 2013. Previously a solicitor and a partner in two leading London law firms, first becoming an equity partner at the age of 31.
Publications: Death and Taxes (1985), Maximising Opportunities under the BES (1986), the BES and Assured Tenancies – The New Rules (1988), Tax Advice for Company Transactions (1992), The Enterprise Investment Scheme (1994), Transactions: Taxation of Joint Ventures (1994), Tolley's Tax Planning (contributor from 1984-5 to 2012-13); founding editor of Trusts and Estates (1985) and tax editor of the BES Magazine (1986)
Personal: Director of Richmond (Rugby) Football Club

WEALE, James
3 Stone Buildings, London
020 7242 4937
jweale@3sb.law.co.uk
Featured in Chancery (London)

Practice Areas: James Weale has a chancery commercial litigation practice and regularly appears in both the Chancery Division and the Commercial Court. He undertakes a wide variety of commercial cases relating to contractual disputes, insurance litigation as well chancery litigation including trustee disputes. Recent cases include: Earl of Cardigan v Cotton & Moore (3 week trial in the Chancery Division for the removal of trustees and compensation); Lord Northampton v Northampton County Council (claim for the recovery of a valuable Egyptian artefact); Cherney v Deripaska (a multi-billion dollar damages claim and a claim to a proprietary interest in United Company Rusal).
Professional Memberships: Chancery Bar Association; ComBar.
Career: Called: 2007.

Publications: Contributor to Palmer on Bailment (3rd ed); "A Good Arguable Case for Restricting the Canada Trust Gloss" [2010] JBL 36; Probate Litigation: the incidence of costs, Trusts and Trustees (2014).
Personal: Educated at Latymer Upper School, Bristol University (LLB) and Lincoln College, Oxford (BCL).

WEAVER, Matthew
St Philips Chambers, Birmingham
01212 467 000
mweaver@st-philips.com
Featured in Restructuring/Insolvency (Midlands)

Practice Areas: Chancery/commercial litigation including all aspects of corporate and personal insolvency, company law including shareholders' disputes, general commercial litigation and directors' disqualification proceedings. Recent notable cases include Re Hotel Company 42 The Calls Ltd [2013] EWHC 3925 (Ch) (nature, extent, registration and enforceability of paragraph 99 charge), Re Parmeko Holdings Ltd [2014] B.C.C. 159 (administrator's powers when proposals are not approved), Sun Legend Investments Ltd v Ho [2013] B.P.I.R. 533 (creditor's ability to petition for bankruptcy based upon an unrecognised foreign judgment), Harris v Secretary of State for Business Innovation and Skills [2013] EWHC 2514 (Ch) (section 17 permission to act), and Appleyard v Reflex Recordings Ltd [2013] EWHC 4514 (Ch) (freezing injunctions and payment of proper and reasonable solicitor's costs prior to an administration order being made).
Professional Memberships: Chancery Bar Association, COMBAR, Midland Chancery and Commercial Bar Association, Birmingham Law Society.
Career: Called in 2002. Buchanan Prize Winner (Lincoln's Inn). Junior Counsel to the Crown (Regional Panel).
Publications: Regular contributor to Corporate Rescue and Insolvency (LexisNexis).
Personal: A keen sportsman, particularly cricket, golf and rugby. Married with two young children.

WEBB, Geraint QC
Henderson Chambers, London
020 7842 9613
gwebb@hendersonchambers.co.uk
Featured in Insurance (London), International Arbitration (London), Local Government (London), Product Liability (London), Property Damage (London)

Practice Areas: Commercial, product liability, insurance and arbitration. Particular emphasis on group actions/mass tort claims, product liability (including product safety/recalls), major property damage, contamination claims, sale of goods and services, cross-border disputes, international arbitration and insurance/reinsurance coverage disputes. Other areas of practice include professional indemnity (including clinical negligence), public procurement, local government, information technology, environmental, and health and safety. Pharmaceutical actions include vaccine damage claims, birth defect claims, psychiatric injury claims. Medical device/products claims include Hep C/HIV contaminated blood factors claims, CJD contaminated medical product claims, PIP breast implant litigation. Food contamination claims include Benzene Litigation, Para Red, Sudan 1. Property damage claims include major explosions/fires/failures in factories, power stations, oil depots, ships etc. International arbitrations under ICA, UNICITRAL, LCIA etc. Further details on Henderson Chambers' website: http://www.hendersonchambers.co.uk
Professional Memberships: COMBAR, LCLCBA, PIBA, ARDL.
Career: Christ Church, Oxford (BA - 1st Class), Exhibitioner, Princess Royal Scholar. Called to the Bar 1995, CEDR accredited mediator (2000). Appointed QC 2013.

WEBB, William
Keating Chambers, London
020 7544 2600
wwebb@keatingchambers.com
Featured in Construction (London)

Practice Areas: Specialist in construction, engineering, energy and technology disputes including claims relating to payment, defects, delay and disruption and professional negligence in the High Court, domestic and international arbitration (particular experience in the Middle East) and adjudication. Experience includes road projects, power stations, PFI contracts, solar projects, waste disposal and incineration contracts as well as a wide variety of commercial and residential building projects. Regularly appears in the TCC for trials and interlocutory hearings with particular experience of adjudication enforcement.
Professional Memberships: Society of Construction Law; Technology and Construction Bar Association (TECBAR); Commercial Bar Association (COMBAR).
Publications: Contributor, Keating on Construction Contracts Ninth Edition (2012). Consultant editor of the Construction Law Reports.

WEDDELL, Geoffrey
1 Chancery Lane, London
020 7092 2900
gweddell@1chancerylane.com
Featured in Police Law (All Circuits)

Practice Areas: Geoffrey specialises in personal injury work, claims against the police, professional negligence, regulatory and property work and contract and tort. He is Chair of the 1 Chancery Lane Regulatory practice group and has substantial experience of representing defendants at disciplinary proceedings and of advising disciplinary panels. Geoffrey undertakes a variety of cases for local authorities in both contract and tort, including claims for personal injuries and flood damage. He has substantial experience of acting for both claimants and defendants in these areas. He has a sub-specialism in industrial disease claims. He handles a wide variety of police law cases including claims of false imprisonment, assault and malicious prosecution. Reported cases include: Chief Constable of Hampshire v Taylor [2013] PIQR P20; Wilson v Haden and Clyne Farms [2013] EWHC 1211 (QB); Chief Constable of Wiltshire v McDonagh [2008] EWHC 654 (QB).
Professional Memberships: Professional Negligence Bar Association, Personal Injuries Bar Association, London Common Law and Commercial Bar Association, Western Circuit.
Career: Called to the Bar in 1989.

WEEKS, Janet
5 Paper Buildings, London
020 7583 6117
JW@5pb.co.uk
Featured in Financial Crime (London)

Practice Areas: A leading fraud junior. Janet has been involved in many of the highest profile or most complex fraud cases. She has a specialism in fiscal offences. She was junior counsel in the Harry Redknapp, Peter Storrie and Milan Mandaric prosecution for tax evasion. She has prosecuted a number of senior solicitors and accountants for money-laundering offences, VAT fraud and fraud on the Legal Services Commission. She is Secretary to Accountancy and Actuarial Disciplinary Board. She is 'B' list advocate for the HSE and 'A' list advocate for the SFO. She is regularly instructed by BIS, CPS Special Casework and Fraud. She has defended this year in large-scale mortgage frauds, and complex fraudulent trading trials.
Personal: LLB (Hons) Exeter.

WEETMAN, Gareth
7BR, London
020 7242 3555
clerks@7br.co.uk
Featured in Crime (Midlands)

Practice Areas: He specialises in crime and personal injury. His criminal work encompasses murder, terrorism, serious sexual offences, drugs trafficking, organised crime and fraud. He is a grade 4 prosecutor and has been appointed to the Attorney General's panel of Special Advocates. He regularly deals with cases involving issues of very high sensitivity. His personal injury work includes long-term disability cases, fatal accidents, brain injury and stress-related claims. His practice has developed across England and his instructions are evenly divided between prosecution and defence in crime and claimant and defendant in personal injury. He is a member of the Gray's Inn "A" panel of advocacy trainers.
Professional Memberships: Criminal Bar Association, Personal Injury Bar Association.
Career: Gareth has been a member of 7 Bedford Row since his call in 1999. He studied law at Christ's College, Cambridge.

WEIR, Robert QC
Devereux, London
020 7353 7534
Weir@devchambers.co.uk
Featured in Clinical Negligence (London), Personal Injury (London), Travel (London)

Practice Areas: Specialises in all aspects of personal injury and clinical negligence and the impact of the Human Rights Act on those areas. Particular emphasis on brain and spinal injury cases and on personal injury claims with a foreign element. Recent cases include:Smith v MoD (SC), Wall v Mutuelle de Poitiers (CA), Cox v MOJ (CA), Haxton v Philips (CA) and Akhtar v Boland (CA)
Professional Memberships: Vice Chairman of Personal Injury Bar Association; Founder and past Chairman of Oxford Medico-Legal Society.
Career: Called in 1992, took silk in 2010.
Publications: Editor of Kemp & Kemp, author of chapter in Butterworths Personal Injury Litigation Service.
Personal: Born in 1969. Married with 3 children. Enjoys outdoor activities with friends and family.

WELFARE, Damien
Cornerstone Barristers, London
020 7242 4986
damienw@cornerstonebarristers.com
Featured in Data Protection (London)

Practice Areas: Specialises in Information Law, and in local authority powers

and governance. Advocacy in First-Tier Tribunal, Information Rights (LB Southwark v ICO and ors, EA/2013/0162). Advice on all aspects of Data Protection, Freedom of Information, and Environmental Information Regulations (EIR), including: handling of complex subject access and information requests; complaints to Information Commissioner and Tribunal appeals; data sharing powers and agreements; and, data security. Regularly gives seminars and presentations on Information Law issues, including: definition of personal data; information requests that include third party personal data; and, the law on data sharing. Recent advisory work on local government includes: innovative uses of local authority general powers; state aids rules; trading by local authorities; council tax reduction schemes; constitutional advice and drafting; and, councillors' rights to information.
Professional Memberships: ALBA. HRLA. FRSA. Head of Examination Board, Practitioner Certificate in Freedom of Information (run by PDP).
Career: Called July 2001. Previously a local government officer.
Publications: Recent articles on definition of personal data ("Privacy and Data Protection" Journal), and on vexatious FOI requests and scope of Environmental Information Regulations (both in "Freedom of Information" Journal). Member, Editorial Board, "Freedom of Information" journal.
Personal: Married with two children.

WELLS, Colin
25 Bedford Row, London
020 7067 1500
cwells@25bedfordrow.com
Featured in Financial Crime (London)
Practice Areas: Fraud and regulatory defence work, advising and representing individuals and companies in Fraud, Money Laundering, Restraint and Confiscation. Criminal procedure judicial review. Claimant civil actions against state agencies including the Police. Representation provided at VAT First and Second Tier Tribunal hearings. Instructed as a specialist in criminal abuse of process. Costs appeals in criminal cases.
Professional Memberships: Criminal Bar Association, European Criminal Bar Association, Proceeds of Crime Lawyers Association, Association of Regulatory and Disciplinary Lawyers, Financial Services Lawyers Associations.
Publications: 'Abuse of Process - a practical approach', 2nd edition published by Jordan Publishing, (2010). Articles on Criminal Procedure published in Solicitors Journal, New Law Journal, Legal Executive, Criminal Bar Quarterly, Legalhub, Crimeline, The Barrister, Counsel, Criminal Law & Justice Weekly. Forthcoming publication : Fraud handbook (Bloomsbury).

WELLS, Jason
18 St John Street, Manchester
01612 781 800
civil@18sjs.com
Featured in Clinical Negligence (Northern)
Practice Areas: Clinical Negligence, Personal Injury.
Professional Memberships: PNBA, PIBA.
Career: MBChB Sheffield 1993. FRCS 1998. LLB Nottingham Law School 2007. Called 2007. Jason practised as a surgeon in the NHS for 12 years before retraining as a barrister. He specialises in medical law and personal injury. His medical law practice includes both clinical negligence and disciplinary work. Jason regularly appears in Coroner's court.

WELLS, Nathan
Radcliffe Chambers, London
020 7831 0031
nwells@radcliffechambers.com
Featured in Chancery (London)
Practice Areas: General Chancery practice, with a particular emphasis on wills, probate and administration of estates; trusts and trustees; real property; landlord and tenant and related professional negligence. He is also regularly involved in general commercial litigation and has considerable experience of litigation involving local authorities. Notable cases include Green v Eadie [2012] Ch 363, Ferneley v Napier [2011] WTLR 1303, Shaw v Lighthouseexpress Ltd [2010] EWCA Civ 161, Creque v Penn (2007) 70 WIR 150 (PC), Owers v Bailey [2007] P&CR DG17 and London Diocesan Fund v Phithwa (Avonridge Property Co Ltd, Part 20 defendant) [2005] 1 WLR 3956 (HL).
Professional Memberships: Chancery Bar Association, ACTAPS, Northern Ireland Bar.
Career: Called 2000. Judicial Assistant to the President of the Family Division (Michaelmas 2001) and the Vice-Chancellor (Hilary 2002).
Publications: Contributor to Tolley's Practitioners' Guide to Powers and Duties of Trustees; Editor of the Trusts and Estates section of Butterworths' Civil Court Precedents.
Personal: Educated at the Royal School Dungannon, Pembroke College Oxford (BA) and St Catharine's College Cambridge (LLM).

WEST, Mark
Radcliffe Chambers, London
020 7831 0081
mwest@radcliffechambers.com
Featured in Chancery (London), Real Estate Litigation (London)
Practice Areas: Bankruptcy and insolvency, charities, general commercial and contract, company law, equity and trusts, landlord and tenant (agricultural, business and residential), partnership, probate, professional negligence (especially solicitors' negligence), real property/conveyancing/mortgages, restitution. Reported cases: Kleinwort Benson v Sandwell BC [1994] 4 All ER 890; Morgan Grenfell v Welwyn Hatfield DC [1995] 1 All ER 1; Kleinwort Benson v Birmingham CC [1997] QB 380; Kleinwort Benson v Lincoln CC [1999] 2 AC 349 (restitution of monies paid under ultra vires interest rate swap contracts); Chong Kai Tai Ringo v Lee Gee Kee [1997] HKLRD 491 (Privy Council) (sale and purchase of property in Hong Kong); Portman Building Society v Hamlyn Taylor Neck [1998] 4 All ER 202; Portman Building Society v Bevan Ashford [2000] Lloyd's Rep PN 354 (solicitors' negligence); Batchelor v Marlow [2001] 1 EGLR 119, (2001) 82 P & CR 459 (whether parking of cars an easement); Barclays Bank v Bee [2002] 1 WLR 332 (business tenancy: s.25 notices). Weir v. Secretary of State for Transport (No.1) [2005] EWHC 812 (Ch) (costs capping orders); Weir v. Secretary of State for Transport (No.2) [2005] EWHC 2192 (Ch) (misfeasance in public office); Banfield v. Leeds Building Society [2007] EWCA Civ 1369 (effect of failure to surrender insurance policy on existence of possession action); McLean Estates Ltd v. Earl of Aylesford [2009] EWHC 697 (Ch) (mines and minerals; whether Mercia Mudstone within a 1922 exception and reservation of mines and minerals; powers of working minerals).
Professional Memberships: Chancery Bar Association; Professional Negligence Bar Association; Property Bar Association.
Publications: 'Swaps & Local Authorities: A Mistake?' (with Catherine Newman QC) in Swaps & Off-Exchange Derivatives Trading: Law & Regulation (FT Law & Tax, 1996). 'Know Your Limits: Trustees' Mistakes under the Limitation Act' (2007) 86 Trusts & Estates Law Journal 12 'Breach of Warranty of Authority in Solicitors' Liability Claims' (with Professor Francis Reynolds) (2009) 25 Journal of Professional Negligence 131; The Ownership of Surface Voids Created by Mineral Extraction (2011) Conveyancer 30; Section 5 of the Limitation Act 1980 and Restitutionary Claims for Money Had and Received (2011) 30 Civil Justice Quarterly 366.
Personal: Part of DTI Team under Hilary Heilbron QC and Michael Boohan FCA to inquire into affairs of Blue Arrow Plc (Blue Arrow II) (report published September 1992). Member of joint Bar Council/Law Society working party to review civil justice system: Report 'Civil Justice on Trial, The Case for Change', published June 1993. Contributing editor Lloyd's Law Reports (Professional Negligence) 1999-2003. Junior counsel to shareholders in Weir v Secretary of State for Transport (the Railtrack litigation) 2005. Member of Committee of Chancery Bar Association 2005 to date; Deputy Judge of the Upper Tribunal (Administrative Appeals Chamber) 2012.

WESTON, Jeremy QC
St Ives Chambers, Birmingham
01212 360 863
jeremy.weston@stiveschambers.co.uk
Featured in Family/Matrimonial (Midlands)
Practice Areas: Family.
Professional Memberships: Chair of the West Midlands FLBA Member of the Association of Lawyers for Children Member of BAAF.
Career: Jeremy is Queen's Counsel specialising in family law. He has vast expertise in the most complex of care cases involving the death or serious injury of children (with a particular interest in head injuries), sexual abuse, poisoning cases, fabricated or induced illness. His practice also includes Judicial Review. Jeremy has extensive experience in protracted and complicated private law proceedings involving Residence (including internal relocation, Contact (including parental alienation and intractable contact disputes, allegations of physical, emotional and sexual abuse, disputes over education, religion, medical procedures and changes of name, child abduction, international relocation, surrogacy and Parental Order applications and parenting disputes arising from same-sex relationships. Jeremy is well attuned to the needs of the client and is highly regarded for his approachable and personable manner. Jeremy is regularly instructed by local authorities, parents and on behalf of the Children's Guardian. He has also acted for adults acting under a disability. Notable cases: Birmingham City Council v S, R & A [2006] EWHC 3065 Fam Re R sub nom Birmingham City Council v LR, PNG, AK, AW & MRR [2006] EWCA Civ 1748 Staffordshire County Council v A, B, C, D, E & F [2009] EWHC 1982 Fam Birmingham City Council v AG, IA & JA [2009] EWHC 3720 Fam R (on the application of Johns) v Derby City Council [2011] EWHC 375.
Publications: Co-Author of 'Challenging and Defending Local Authority Child Care Decisions: A Practical Guide' (2013) Jordans Publishing.
Personal: Jeremy is regularly involved in giving lectures on all aspects of family law to other professionals, both locally and nationally, including the Bar and solicitors.

WESTWOOD, Andrew
Maitland Chambers, London
020 7406 1200
awestwood@maitlandchambers.com
Featured in Charities (London)
Practice Areas: Chancery practice including charities, insolvency, directors' disqualification, company law and property. Reported cases include: Attorney General v Charity Commission [2012] UKUT 420 (TCC), HMRC v Begum [2011] BPIR 59, Grogan v HMRC [2011] STC 1, Re Metrocab Ltd [2010] 2 BCLC 603, Re Aaron Ltd [2009] 1 BCLC 55, Vintage Hallmark plc [2007] 1 BCLC 788, Mea Corporation Ltd [2007] 1 BCLC 618, Crystal Palace FC (1986) Ltd [2004] 2 BCLC 63, Egleton v IRC [2004] BPIR 476, Promwalk Services [2003] 2 BCLC 305, J A Chapman & Co [2003] 2 BCLC 206, Phoneer Ltd [2002] 2 BCLC 241, Ashworth Frazer v Gloucester C.C. [2001] 1 WLR 2180, Britannia Home Centres [2001] 2 BCLC 63, Khazanchi v Faircharm [1998] 1 WLR 1603.
Professional Memberships: Chancery Bar Association, COMBAR, Charity Law Association.
Career: Called to Bar 1994. Admitted to the Bar of the Eastern Caribbean Supreme Court (BVI).
Publications: Consultant Editor of 'Mithani: Directors' Disqualification'.
Personal: Educated at St Catherine's College, Oxford (MA).

WHALE, Stephen
Landmark Chambers, London
020 7430 1221
swhale@landmarkchambers.co.uk
Featured in Licensing (London), Planning (London)
Practice Areas: Specialises in planning and environmental law; administrative and public law; licensing law (especially Licensing Act 2003); highway law; local government law. Regularly represents developers, local authorities, interest groups and the Secretary of State. Experienced inquiry/examination advocate. Notable cases include: A160/A180 DCO examination (2014); Leith Hill Action Group v Europa Oil & Gas Ltd [2014] EWCA Civ 825; SSCLG v Ahmed [2014] EWCA Civ 566; Redhill Aerodrome inquiry (2014); A556 DCO examination (2013); A21 inquiries (2013); Delaney v SSCLG [2013] EWCA Civ 585; SSCLG v Proudfoot Properties [2013] JPL 1356; R (Manchester Ship Canal Co. Ltd) v EA [2013] JPL 515; R (Barnsley MBC) v SSCLG [2013] PTSR 23; Dunsfold Aerodrome inquiry (2012); Doran v SSCLG [2011] EWCA Civ 1798; Lee v SSCLG [2011] JPL 814; Rencher-Paine v SSCLG [2011] JPL 813; Farnborough Airport inquiry (2010); Kent International Gateway inquiry (2009);

Daventry housing appeals inquiry (2009); Woodhouse School v Webster [2009] ICR 818; R (Carroll) v South Somerset DC [2008] JPL 991; Uttlesford DC v English Heritage [2007] LLR 273; Coventry Airport inquiry (2006); Hammersmatch Properties Ltd v First Secretary of State [2006] JPL 843, CA; South Downs National Park inquiry (2003-2005); R (Mount Cook Land Ltd) v Westminster City Council [2004] JPL 470, CA; R (Medway Council and ors) v Secretary of State for Transport [2003] JPL 583.
Professional Memberships: Planning and Environment Bar Association; Administrative Law Bar Association.
Career: Called to the Bar in 1999. Gray's Inn Karmel Award 1997; Gray's Inn Junior Award 1998; Bar European Group Scholarship 2001; Junior Counsel to the Crown (C Panel) 2007-2012; (B Panel) 2012-date.
Publications: Specialist contributor: Encyclopedia of Planning Law; Journal of Planning and Environment Law; Bulletin of the Encyclopedia of Local Government Law; Phipson on Evidence.

WHEATER, Michael
Hardwicke, London
020 7242 2523
michael.wheater@hardwicke.co.uk
Featured in Construction (London)
Practice Areas: Construction and engineering disputes together with related insurance, professional negligence, procurement, insolvency and commercial matters. Acts in all manner of disputes from residential developments to commercial and industrial buildings, process plants, pharmaceutical and scientific facilities, public sector buildings (schools, hospitals), onshore and off-shore energy, renewables and infrastructure projects. Appears as an advocate in all levels of Court, predominantly the TCC, arbitrations (both domestic and international), adjudications, mediations and other forms of ADR (ENE, DABs, DRBs).
Professional Memberships: Society of Construction Law; TECBAR; Adjudication Society; COMBAR; London Common Law and Commercial Law Bar Association.
Career: LLB (Hons) 2001, LLM (Distinction) 2002, Called to the Bar (Lincoln's Inn) 2003, Barrister at Hardwicke 2003 to date, MSc (Distinction) 2011, MCIArb 2011, TECBAR Adjudicator 2011.
Publications: Contributor to Construction All Risks Insurance by Paul Reed QC (2014) and to academic publications such as Construction Law Journal and Lexis PSL Construction.

WHEATLEY, Geraint
Kings Chambers, Manchester
08450 343 444
clerks@kingschambers.com
Featured in Real Estate Litigation (Northern)
Practice Areas: Established chancery and commercial practitioner with expertise in all aspects of commercial and residential property work, banking and commercial litigation. Professional negligence within these practice areas. Experience before courts of all levels up to and including the Court of Appeal, as well as proceedings before the Property Chamber: Land Registration (formerly the Adjudicator to HM Land Registry).
Professional Memberships: Chancery Bar Association, Northern Circuit Commercial Bar Association, Northern Chancery Bar Association.
Career: 1st Class Law Degree: Oxford University (St. Edmund Hall), 1st in year on the BVC: MMU, 2001 call (Gray's Inn, Edmund-Davies Award holder).

WHITE, Andrew QC
Atkin Chambers, London
020 7404 0102
clerks@atkinchambers.com
Featured in Construction (London), Energy & Natural Resources (London), International Arbitration (London), Professional Negligence (London)
Practice Areas: Principal areas of expertise are domestic and international civil engineering, building, shipbuilding and ship repair disputes, and energy law. Also covers professional negligence and general commercial law. Has extensive experience of arbitration conducted under the ICC, LCIA, LMAA and UNCITRAL rules. Significant cases include: Harman CFM Facades v Corporate Officer of the House of Commons (UK procurement law); ABB Lummus Global Ltd v Keppel Fels Ltd (arbitration, curial law), BICC v Parkman (jurisdiction under Civil Liability Contribution Act), Channel Tunnel Group Ltd v Balfour Beatty Construction (jurisdiction of English Court to grant injunctions in foreign arbitration), Murphy v Brentwood (negligence), Simon Carves Ltd v Ensus UK Ltd (on demand performance bonds)
Professional Memberships: TECBAR, Combar, Western Circuit.
Career: Called to the Bar 1980, QC (1997), Bencher of Lincoln's Inn 2003.
Publications: Contributor: 'Atkins Forms and Precedents: Building Contracts'.
Personal: Educated University College Cardiff, LLB (Hons), 1975-79. Megarry Scholar and Hardwicke Scholar of Lincoln's Inn. Born 25 January 1958. Lives London and Dorset. Interests include music, horses, farming and gardening.

WHITE, Antony QC
Matrix Chambers, London
020 7404 3447
antonywhite@matrixlaw.co.uk
Featured in Commercial Dispute Resolution (London), Data Protection (London), Defamation/Privacy (London), Employment (London)
Practice Areas: Practises in commercial law and arbitration, employment law, media and information law and public law. Commercial work focuses on fraud, bribery, constructive trusts, asset tracing, conflicts and new technology disputes. Notable commercial cases include AG for Hong Kong v Reid (1994) (constructive trusts and dishonest fiduciaries); Jyske Bank v Spjeldnaes (1999) (equitable remedies in commercial fraud); Fyffes Group v Templeman (2000) (remedies against briber in commercial fraud); Chellaram v Chellaram (No. 2) (2002) (conflicts of laws - overseas trusts); Marubeni v Government of Mongolia (2002) and (2005) (conflicts of laws - foreign government guarantee/performance bond); Tigana v Decoro (2003) (commercial agency). Pakistan v Zardari (2006) (conflicts of law and constructive trusts); Film Finance Inc v Royal Bank of Scotland (2007) (arbitration clauses). Internet Broadcasting v Mar LLC (2009) (construction of exemption clauses); AES Ust-Kamenogorsk HPP v Ust-Kamenogorsk HPJSC (2011) (arbitration, anti-suit injunctions); Twentieth Century Fox v BT (2011) (web blocking injunction); Dowans Holdings v TANESCO (2011) (enforcement of NY convention awards). Also a number of high value international arbitrations in energy, film and hospitality industries etc, mainly in India, Africa and the Middle East. Employment practice focuses on public sector collective disputes, trade union work and discrimination. Notable cases include Midland Mainline v RMT (2001) (industrial action/balloting); R (Arthurworry) v LB Haringey (2002) (duty of trust and confidence); Crossley v Faithfull and Gould (2004) (duty of employer to safeguard economic well-being of employee); Dunnachie v Kingston Upon Hull (2004) (compensation for unfair dismissal); Igen Ltd v Wong (2005) (discrimination - burden of proof); Murphy v Slough BC (2005) (disability discrimination - reasonable adjustments); HM Prison Service v Beart (2005) (disability discrimination - causation of loss); Birmingham City Council v Wetherill (2007) (unilateral variation of employment contracts); Cooper v Isle of Wight College (2008) (strike deductions); Crowson Fabrics Ltd v Rider (2008) (employee competition); UNISON v Brennan (2008) (discrimination in collective agreements); Bewley v Walton etc NHS Trust (2008) (equal pay hypothetical comparator); R (Marrion) v LFCDA (2009) (Firefighters' Pension Scheme); Brennan v Sunderland City Council (2009) (legal privilege in collective bargaining); Coventry City Council v Nicholls (2009) (equal pay); Armstrong v Newcastle etc NHS Trust (2010) (equal pay, market forces defence); Buckland v Bournemouth University (2010) (constructive dismissal); Gibb v Maidstone & Tunbridge wells NHS Trust (2010) (ultra vires compromise, restitution); Enterprise Management Services v Connect-Up (2012) (TUPE service provision change); Brennan v Sunderland CC (2012) (discrimination, damages, contribution) also major NHS and local government collective disputes. Recent Media work has focused on privacy and data protection with cases including Sara Cox v MGN (2003); the leading case of Naomi Campbell v MGN (2004); Harrods Ltd v Times Newspapers (2006) (public interest defence in breach of confidence); Author of a Blog v Times Newspapers (2009) (privacy); Metropolitan International Schools v Google (2009) (search engine liability); A v Independent (2010) (media access to Court of Protection proceedings); Imerman v Tchenguiz (2011) (confidential information/ privacy, relevance of "Hildebrand Rules"); Davison v Habeeb (2012) (online defamation); R (BT) v Sec. of State (2012) (online copyright piracy); Trimingham v Associated Newspapers (2012) (privacy/harassment by media); Tamiz v Google Inc (2013) (online defamation liability of blog platform); Karpov v Browder (2013) (libel tourism); Vidal-Hall v Google Inc (2014) (cookies, privacy); Hannon & Dufour v NGN (2014) (misuse of private information, injury to reputation); FOI Tribunal cases Leveson Inquiry. Recent public law work includes judicial review in areas such as local government, telecoms and financial services.
Professional Memberships: Administrative Law Bar Association Commercial Fraud Lawyers Association.
Career: Called 1983 (Middle Temple). Silk 2001.
Publications: Privacy and Trade Union sections of Bullen & Leake & Jacobs 'Precedents of Pleadings' (17th Ed. 2012); Administrative Law chapter of 'Civil Appeals' (edited by Sir Michael Burton 2002); co-author of 'Privacy and the Media - The Developing Law' (2002); Data protection/Freedom of information chapter in The Freedom of Information Handbook (ed. Carey and Turle) 3rd ed. 2012.

WHITE, Jeremy
Pump Court Tax Chambers, London
020 7414 8080
jeremy@whites.idps.co.uk
Featured in Tax (London)
Practice Areas: Jeremy White's practice covers advice and litigation in both civil and criminal matters regarding international trade and Customs & Excise law. He specializes in trade barriers and trade preference, especially when involving classification, origin, customs valuation and other technical issues. He has been instructed to represent clients in disputes with the Customs Authorities of Belgium, Cameroon, Ireland, India, Kenya, Korea, Thailand, Turkey and the UK. Landmark cases have included Terex C-430/08, Pace C-288/09 and Carlsberg.
Professional Memberships: CIOT Indirect Tax Committee, Revenue Bar Association, Customs Practitioners Group, London Common Law & Commercial Bar Association, VAT in Industry Group.
Career: Called 1976 (Gray's Inn); 1977-83: Barrister, 7 Fountain Court, Birmingham; 1983-96: Solicitors Office, HM Customs & Excise; 1996-2000: Senior lawyer, KPMG (led team specialising in indirect tax investigations, litigation disclosure and risk management): 2000-01: Senior lawyer, KLegal solicitors (responsible for firm's trade and customs practice in the UK); 2001-present: Barrister, Pump Court Tax Chambers.
Publications: Consultant editor of Butterworth's Customs Duties Handbook since 1995; Consultant editor of Tolley's Excise Duties Handbook since 2001; Consultant editor of Halsbury's Laws sice 2007; Regular contributor to De Voil Indirect Tax Intelligence; Contributor to LexisNexis Finance Act Handbook since 2008.

WHITE, Robin
Old Square Chambers, London
020 7269 0300
clerks@oldsquare.co.uk
Featured in Employment (London)
Practice Areas: Barrister specialising in employment law (all aspects). Appears in Tribunals and Higher Courts in whole of UK including Scotland and Northern Ireland. Cases include Post Office v Foley; Beedell v West Ferry Printers (both test for unfair dismissal); Martyres v Connex (collective agreements); W v HMG (national security - MI6 employee); Bentwood v Shepherd (Calculation of Quantum), G v H (Disability Discrimination - Quantum over £1m), Symes v Eaton-Williams (Discrimination - lifetime loss), Rule v University of Arts (technicalities of uplift for failure to follow procedures), Short v Land Rover (interaction of DDA responsibilities and union collective agreements), Beavan v Cabinet Office (whether pay progression in Civil Service contractual), Pietzka v Price Waterhouse (sex, flexible and part-time working request discrimination).
Professional Memberships: ELBA, ELA, MCIT, ARCS.
Career: Called 1995, Gray's Inn.
Publications: Regular CPD lectures on discrimination and other employment topics.

Personal: Sexey's School Bruton; Imperial College, London (1986 BSc Hons Chemistry); Manager in transport industry 1986-91; Exeter (1994 LLB Hons). Lives in Somerset. Hobbies: house renovation, long-distance walking and classic car restoration.

WHITEHEAD, Thomas

Stone Chambers, London
020 7440 6900
tom.whitehead@stonechambers.com

Featured in Shipping (London)

Practice Areas: Tom Whitehead is recommended as a leading junior barrister in Chambers & Partners UK Bar and the Legal 500. He specialises in all areas of shipping and commercial law including the carriage and sale of goods, international trade, and arbitration. Tom has considerable experience of jurisdiction disputes and anti-suit injunctions. Recent cases include: The Alexandros T [2013] UKSC 70 - leading case in England on Article 27 of EU Regulation 44/2001; The Alexandros T [2014] EWCA Civ 1010 - leading case on compatibility of declarations and damages with EU law post-Front Comor. Application of Fiona Trust to settlement agreements; The Wadi Sudr [2009] EWCA Civ 1397 - leading case on recognition and enforcement in England and Wales of a foreign judgment obtained from a court in another EU Member State in breach of a London arbitration clause under Regulation 44/2001; The Channel Ranger [2013] EWHC 3081 (Comm) - incorporation of charterparty dispute resolution clauses into bills of lading; The Barito [2013] EWHC 1240 (Comm) - anti-arbitration injunction and s.9 Arbitration Act 1996.

Professional Memberships: COMBAR, LCLCBA, Supporting Member LMAA, ACIArb.

Career: Called to the Bar, Inner Temple, 2002. Major Scholar, Duke of Edinburgh Entrance Award.

Personal: Worcester College, Oxford BA (1st Class) Jurisprudence (2000), BCL (2001).

WHITEHOUSE, Christopher

5 Stone Buildings, London
020 7242 6201
clerks@5sblaw.com

Featured in Chancery (London), Tax (London)

Practice Areas: Advises on all aspects of private client taxation, trusts, estates and wills.

Professional Memberships: Fellow of CIOT, member of STEP and the Chancery Bar Association.

Career: Called 1971. Lectures extensively on the subjects of tax, trusts and will drafting. STEP Barrister of the Year 2006 and awarded a Founder's Award for Outstanding Achievement from STEP in November 2009.

Publications: Co-author of 'Trust Taxation' (pub. 2014, 4th edition, Sweet and Maxwell); 'A Modern Approach to Wills, Administration and Estate Planning' (pub 2013, 2nd edition); 'A Modern Approach to Lifetime Tax Planning for Private Clients (pub 2014); 'Pre-owned Assets and Tax Planning Strategies' (3rd edition, pub. Dec 2009);'Trusts of Land, Trustee Delegation and The Trustee Act 2000'; 'Dymonds Capital Taxes'. Principal contributor to 'Encyclopaedia of Forms and Precedents' dealing with gifts, trusts and settlements. Consulting Editor of 'Private Client Business'.

WHITEHOUSE, Sarah QC

6KBW College Hill, London
020 3301 0910
sarah.whitehouse@6kbw.com

Featured in Crime (London)

Practice Areas: Sarah Whitehouse QC was listed in the top 100 barristers in the UK in 2013 and as Crime Junior of the Year in 2011. She was appointed Queen's Counsel and Senior Treasury Counsel in 2014. She practises in crime as well as undertaking advisory work for public agencies, corporates and individuals on a wide range of topics. She has an extensive appellate court practice. She is a grade A advocacy trainer and tutors on the international advanced advocacy training course at Keble College, Oxford University. She has recently joined delegations to provide training in St. Lucia and Singapore. For a more detailed profile, please refer to the 6KBW College Hill website (www.6kbw.com).

Career: Domestic and investment banking ending as Assistant Director Barclays de Zoete Wedd Ltd 1992. Called to the Bar 1993. Junior Treasury Counsel 2006. Senior Treasury Counsel 2014. Queen's Counsel 2014.

Publications: Contributor to: 'Fraud' (Oxford University Press); 'Millington and Sutherland Williams on the Proceeds of Crime' (Oxford University Press); 'EU Law and Criminal Practice' (Oxford University Press).

Personal: Educated at Felixstowe College, Suffolk and St. Andrews University (MA (Hons.) English Literature and Language). Westminster University (PGDL).

WHITELAW, Francesca

5 Essex Court, London
020 7410 2000
whitelaw@5essexcourt.co.uk

Featured in Professional Discipline (London)

Practice Areas: Police Law, Public/Administrative Law, Inquests and Inquiries, Professional Discipline, Human Rights. Recent cases: Inquest touching the death of Frances Andrade deceased (who died during the course of the trial of her music teacher who had abused her while she was a pupil at Chetham's Music School); Chief Constable of Devon and Cornwall v HM Coroner for Plymouth & Ors [2013] EWHC 3729 (Admin) (judicial review which arose out the inquest into the death of a child and suicidal driver in circumstances where police had attempted to stop the suicidal driver's vehicle); Inquest touching the death of Barry deceased (who died after drinking methadone – see R (on the application of Kent County Council v HM Coroner for Kent (North-West District) [2012] EWHC 2768 (Admin); Cummings & Ors v Ministry of Justice [2013] EWHC 33 (claim by prisoners at HMP Frankland for assault and misfeasance in public office by prison officers)

Professional Memberships: Administrative Law Bar Association.

Career: Called to the Bar in 2003. Appointed to the Attorney-General's C Panel of Junior Counsel to the Crown in 2012. Recognised in Chambers and Partners UK 2013 in the field of Professional Discipline.

Personal: MA(Hons) Cantab (English), MA (Law) City.

WHITTAKER, David

2 Hare Court, London
020 7353 5324
davidwhittaker@2harecourt.com

Featured in Crime (London), Financial Crime (London)

Practice Areas: David Whittaker is highly regarded by the industry as a leading barrister who advises and appears in cases of serious fraud, complex crime and, more recently, regulatory matters. Significant and complex fraud cases form a substantial part of his practice. He has extensive experience of most forms of white-collar work. He also has experience of ancillary proceedings, including restraint and confiscation. He regularly advises pre-charge. Serious crime has always formed part of his practice and continues to do so. He is also instructed by high-profile individuals and professionals in motoring and other cases. Forthcoming cases in 2014 and 2015 include: fraud on the NHS; land banking fraud; insider trading.

Professional Memberships: Criminal Bar Association; SE Circuit; Health and Safety Lawyers' Association.

Personal: University College, London, BA (Hons). City University, Dip Law.

WHITTING, John QC

1 Crown Office Row, London
020 7797 7500
john.whitting@1cor.com

Featured in Clinical Negligence (London)

Practice Areas: Clinical negligence, professional negligence, professional discipline and construction.

Professional Memberships: PNBA, TECBAR.

Career: Called to Bar 1991, appointed Q.C. in 2011. appointed Welsh Government Panel of Queens Counsel in 2012.

Publications: Contributor, Clinical Negligence 4th edition Powers & Harris.

Personal: BA (Hons) in Jurisprudence Oxford University (Oriel College), 1989. LLM in Commercial Law Kings College, London, 1990.

WHYTE, James

8 New Square, London
020 7405 4321
james.whyte@8newsquare.co.uk

Featured in Intellectual Property (London)

Practice Areas: Barrister specialising in intellectual property law, with a particular emphasis on technically complex cases in biotechnology, pharmaceuticals, telecoms and electronics. James' practice is focused on patents but he also practises in the fields of copyright, confidential information, database rights and registered and unregistered design rights. Cases include Vestergaard Frandsen v Bestnet, Rovi v Virgin, Novartis v Hospira (injunction pending appeal), Medinol v Abbott (Ireland), Medimmune v Novartis, Siemens v Seagate (N.Ireland), Dr Reddy's v Eli Lilly, ITV v TV Catchup, Football Association Premier League v QC Leisure. For a comprehensive CV visit chambers' website at www.8newsquare.co.uk.

Professional Memberships: Intellectual Property Bar Association (IPBA) and Chancery Bar Association.

Career: Called 2005, Lincoln's Inn.

Publications: Co-author of Laddie Prescott and Vitoria on the Modern Law of Copyright and Designs (4th Ed).

Personal: Educated at Trinity College, Cambridge (top 1st in genetics; PhD in molecular biology); City University (distinction in postgraduate diploma in law); BPP (outstanding in bar vocational course).

WILD, Alison

Westwater Advocates, Edinburgh
01312 262 881
alison.wild@westwateradvocates.com

Featured in Family/Matrimonial (Scotland)

Practice Areas: Family law, in particular, divorce, financial provision, cohabitation, child related issues including international child abduction, relocation and adoption. Reported cases include A Petitioner, 2012 SLT 370 (child abduction), M v M 2011 Fam LR 124 (relocation), B v B [2011] CSOH 127 (contact), Aberdeenshire Council, Petitioners 2011 Fam LR 16 (freeing orders), Lindsay v Murphy 2010 Fam LR 156 (cohabitation), Z Petitioner 2010 SLT 285 (child abduction).

Professional Memberships: Scottish Family Law Association – member 1992 to 2007; Treasurer 2005 to 2007. Advocates Family Law Association – member 2008 to date.

Career: Solicitor in private practice for 16 years. Admitted to the Cayman Islands Bar in March 2001. Called to the Scottish Bar in July 2008.

Publications: Co-editor of the Family Law Reports. Editor of "Miscellaneous consequences of marriage" and "International aspects of the law relating to parental rights and responsibilities" sections in Butterworths Scottish Family Law Service.

Personal: LLB, Edinburgh University 1988. CALM mediator 1998-2007. Tutor in Family Law at Edinburgh University 1998-2001. Accredited Family Law Specialist 1999-2007. Peer Reviewer 2004-2009. Faculty Scholarship 2007/08. Director of Birthlink 2011 to date.

WILDING, Lisa QC

Furnival Chambers, London
020 7405 3232
lwqc@furnivallaw.co.uk

Featured in Crime (London)

Practice Areas: Lisa Wilding QC is a specialist criminal advocate who prosecutes and defends, primarily in cases of homicide, fraud or serious sexual offences. Since being appointed to Queen's Counsel in 2014 Lisa has been instructed (for both the Crown and defence) in complex joint enterprise murders. Having been involved in murder cases at the Old Bailey for over 10 years, her experience in this area includes baby-shaking cases, contract killings, gang related killings, and cases involving complex telephone and forensic evidence. Lisa has a noted specialisation in complex fraud and financial crime. These cases cover a wide range of offences including offences under the Companies Act, fraud against the Revenue and Customs, diversion fraud, mortgage fraud, corruption, money laundering, and advance fee (or Ponzi) frauds. Her recent cases include the successful defence of a multi-million pound allegation of fraudulent trading involving the running of a property company. Further recent instructions of note include Operation Inertia (largest MTIC ever prosecuted), Operation MFB (£25m MTIC fraud), Operation Savate (£5m Construction Industry Scheme Fraud in the Midlands and North West). Lisa is also regularly instructed in the most serious sexual cases and those involving vulnerable witnesses or defendants or where capacity is in issue. In addition,

she has considerable experience of appellate and advisory work. Lisa is known for her meticulous preparation, clear advice, excellent client-handling and collaborative team approach.
Career: Called 1993. Queen's Counsel 2014. Inner Temple.

WILKINSON, Kate
6KBW College Hill, London
020 3301 0910
kate.wilkinson@6kbw.com
Featured in Crime (London)
Practice Areas: Kate Wilkinson is an extremely able and personable advocate described by those who instruct her as "excellent and lovely". Known for her strong intellect and ability to handle sensitive and complex cases, Kate has a wealth of experience in difficult criminal appeals, both in relation to prosecution and defence, including providing advice to the Attorney General. Kate has been instructed in several high profile cases, including murder, rape and fraud. She was recently instructed as a leading junior in a multi-handed drugs exportation case with terrorist funding connections. Kate's vast practice also covers cybercrime and international criminal law, regularly advising in criminal cases where jurisdictional issues arise from evidence gathered abroad. She is also strongly grounded in financial crime including ancillary proceedings such as confiscation, restraint, cash seizures.
Professional Memberships: Criminal Bar Association; South Eastern Circuit.
Career: Called in October 1998; pupillage at 2 Hare Court then 6KBW. Tenancy at 6KBW (Temple and now College Hill) since 2000. Appointed by the Attorney General as a Treasury Counsel Monitoree and as Junior Counsel to the Attorney General's Panel of Prosecuting Advocates. Appointed as a Serious Crime Group Grade 4 Prosecutor.
Personal: University of Sheffield, LLB, Law. Kate enjoys cycling.

WILKINSON, Richard
Temple Garden Chambers, London
020 7583 1315
RichardWilkinson@TGchambers.com
Featured in Costs Litigation (London), Personal Injury (London)
Practice Areas: Richard's two main practice areas are personal injury and costs. In the personal injury field Richard regularly handles high value / complex cases on behalf of both Claimants and insurers. He has dealt with many seven figure claims, particularly arising from serious head injuries. He has experience of group litigation from both sides: Porton Down (Claimants) and Scania (Defendants) as well involvement in other large-scale litigation (Southall Rail & Victoria Climbie public inquiries). He is a current editor of the Judicial College (formerly JSB) Guidelines on General Damages in Personal Injury Cases. Richard has long-standing expertise in the costs arena and appears regularly in the SCCO and on cost budgeting issues in large value claims. In 2013 he was instructed as junior counsel in Mitchell v NGN in the Court of Appeal. He has particular experience of funding and CFA issues following involvement in cases including Atack v Lea/Ellerton v Harris, Holmes v Alfred McAlpine, Sidhu v Sandhu and Stephens v Tesco.
Professional Memberships: Personal Injury Bar Association.
Career: Called to the Bar in 1992.
Publications: Editor of the JC (formerly JSB) Guidelines on General Damages in Personal Injury Cases.
Personal: Educated at RGS High Wycombe and Bristol University. Avid sports fan.

WILLIAMS, A John
Crown Office Chambers, London
020 7797 8100
williams@crownofficechambers.com
Featured in Personal Injury (London)
Practice Areas: A. John Williams is an experienced Junior who is recognised as one of the leading practitioners in occupational disease litigation and personal injury work. In the last 3 years he has appeared in the Supreme Court in both Baker v Quantum Clothing Group plc [2011] 1 WLR 1003 and the EL Trigger Litigation [2012] 1 WLR 867. His practice covers a wide range of industrial disease litigation including complex occupational cancer and high value mesothelioma claims. He also undertakes high value claims for chronic pain; workplace bullying and stress and traumatic physical injuries. Over the years John has had regular successes (both at trial and in ADR) against leading silks in his field: see e.g Garner v Salford City Council [2013] EWHC 1573 (QB). John works closely with others in the litigation team to secure the right outcome. Clear and pragmatic advice outside the Court room and focussed, persuasive advocacy in the Court room ensure that cases are handled both efficiently and effectively. John undertakes work for both Claimants and Defendants.
Career: Called to the Bar in 1983 John is an accredited Advocacy Tutor for Lincoln's Inn and is a Trustee and Vice Chair of SOSSEN! – a charity that provides helpline advice and workshops for parents of children with special educational needs.

WILLIAMS, Ben
Kings Chambers, Manchester
08450 343 444
clerks@kingschambers.com
Featured in Licensing (Midlands)
Practice Areas: A specialist in Employment, Regulatory and Licensing law. Regularly appears in taxi licensing cases both for local authorities and appellants involving both hackney carriage and private hire vehicles. He has advised extensively on the formulation and implementation of local authority taxi licensing policy. Vastly experienced in all aspects of liquor licensing. Acts for the industry, Local Authorities, interested parties and the police both in terms of representation at hearings and in an advisory capacity. Regularly conducts in-house training and seminars. Has appeared in a number of high profile licensing matters and reported cases including Leeds CC v Shell UK (2013); Blackpool Council v Blacktax (2009); Blackpool Council v Howitt (2008); Luminar Leisure v Wakefield Magistrates Court (2008).
Professional Memberships: Road Transport Lawyers Association; Association of Regulatory and Disciplinary Lawyers; Institute of Licensing; Employment Lawyers' Association; Employment Law Bar Association.
Career: Called to the Bar in 2001, joined Kings Chambers in 2006.
Publications: Contributing Author to 'Judicial Review : Law and Practice'– Licensing chapter.

WILLIAMS, Ed
Cloisters, London
020 7827 4000
ew@cloisters.com
Featured in Employment (London)
Practice Areas: Ed practices in all areas of employment, discrimination, trade union, ECHR human rights law and commercial law. Cases include: Camurat v Thurrock Borough Council [2014] EWHC 2482, QB (whether ex employers owe any duty of care in negligence and contract when making safeguarding disclosures); Moran v Ideal Cleaning and Celanese [2014] ICR 442, EAT; (the meaning of the word "temporary" in the AWD and the AWR); Henderson v GMB [2013] EqLR 1137; (whether left wing democratic socialism is a protected belief). X v Mid Sussex CAB, [2011] ICR 460, CA whether volunteers are protected under the EU Framework Directive from discrimination), Bournemouth University v Buckland [2010] ICR 908, CA (whether an employer can rectify a fundamental breach of contract)
Professional Memberships: ELA, ILS and ELBA.
Career: Called to the Bar in 2000. Ed is a Member of the College of Law's Higher Rights Teaching Panel and has been a visiting Human Rights Lecturer at Nottingham Law School.
Publications: Co-author of the Practice and Procedure Chapter in Sweet and Maxwell's Discrimination Law for Employment Lawyers. Contributor to Guardian Legal.
Personal: Ed is co-founder and a trustee of Cricket Without Boundaries, a charity dedicated to using cricket to raise awareness of HIV/AIDS and bridging ethnic division in Africa. www.cricketwithouboundaries.com. Ed is also a director of witness familiarisation company Assurety: www.assuretytraining.com

WILLIAMS, Geoffrey QC
Farrar's Building, London
02920 227 608
law@gwcg.globalnet.co.uk
Featured in Professional Discipline (London)
Practice Areas: Specialises in representing regulatory bodies and regulated professionals in proceedings before disciplinary tribunals and on appeals to the higher Courts. Has appeared in many leading cases in relation to the conduct of Solicitors including Salsbury v The Law Society (Court of Appeal).
Professional Memberships: London Common Law & Commercial Bar Association.
Career: Solicitor 1978-2013. Took Silk 2003. Transferred to the Bar 2014 becoming a Tenant at Farrar's Building.
Publications: The Guide to the Professional Conduct of Chartered Surveyors.
Personal: West Monmouth Grammar School Pontypool. Trent Polytechnic, Nottingham, BA Law (Upper Second Class Honours). College of Law (Solicitors' Final Examinations - Second Class Honours with 3 Distinctions). Called to the Bar at Gray's Inn Michaelmas Term 2013.

WILLIAMS, Joanne
Civitas Law, Cardiff
08450 713 007
joanne.williams@civitaslaw.com
Featured in Personal Injury (Wales & Chester)
Practice Areas: Joanne has a substantial personal injury practice acting for both Claimants and Defendants in employers liability, public liability, occupiers liability, product liability and road traffic accidents. A significant part of her practice involves acting for Local Health Boards across Wales in defending personal injury and contractual claims. Joanne is also a specialist in employment law.
Professional Memberships: PIBA.
Career: Joanne was called to the Bar in 1999 and completed her pupillage in 2001.She was appointed to the Regional Panel of Treasury Counsel in 2007 and receives regular instructions in that capacity in personal injury, employment and public law work.
Personal: Joanne was educated in Porth County Comprehensive School and the University of Bristol. She is married with two daughters. Her interests include yoga and skiing.

WILLIAMS, Rhodri QC
Henderson Chambers, London
020 7583 9020
clerks@hendersonchambers.co.uk
Featured in Data Protection (London), Local Government (London), Public Procurement (London)
Practice Areas: European Community law, local government and administrative law. Significant cases include: R(Wiltshire Council) v Hertfordshire County Council [2014] EWCA Civ 71, Montpellier Estates Ltd-v-Leeds City Council [2013] EWHC 166 (QB); Local Government Byelaws (Wales) Bill 2012 – Reference by the Attorney General for England and Wales [2012] UKSC 53; R (Governors of Brynmawr Foundation School) v Welsh Ministers & Blaenau Gwent CBC [2011] EWHC 519 (Admin); Brent LBC v Risk Management Partners Ltd & London Authorities Mutual Ltd & Harrow LBC [2011] UKSC 7; [2011] LGR 169; Lancashire County Council v EWC Ltd [2010] EWCA Civ 1381; [2011] LGR 350; Henry Brothers (Magherafelt) Ltd v Department of Education for Northern Ireland [2011] NICA 59; Case C-406/08 Uniplex (UK) Ltd v NHS Business Services Authority [2010] ECR I-817.
Professional Memberships: Bar European Group; Administrative Law Bar Association; Procurement Lawyers Association; Public Law Wales.
Career: Qualified 1987 Gray's Inn; Thirty Park Place Chambers since 1997; Henderson Chambers since 1999. Attorney General's list of approved Counsel from 2000; list of Counsel General to the Welsh Government since 2000. Took Silk in 2010.
Publications: Public Procurement Law Review.
Personal: Also member of Thirty Park Place Chambers, Cardiff (02920 398421).

WILLIAMS, Simon
Radcliffe Chambers, London
020 7831 0081
swilliams@radcliffechambers.com
Featured in Real Estate Litigation (London)
Practice Areas: Property and commercial litigation and related professional negligence. Cases include: Good v Onsette Ltd [2013] EWHC 3447 (Ch) (beneficial ownership of shares/ dishonest assistance; Smart v Lambeth [2013] EWCA Civ 1375 (adverse possession/implied or actual consent. Scott v Kennedys Law & Vertex Law [2011] EWHC 3808 (Ch) (method of calculating

loss on no transaction basis) Islam v Al Sami [2011] EWCA Civ 32 (validity of equitable charge) Joyce v Bowman Law [2010] PNLR 22 (measure of lost chance to develop land); Ofulue v Bossert [2009] 1 AC 990 HL (acknowledgement of title, without prejudice rule) [2009] Ch 1 CA (adverse possession, human rights) LSC v Banks [2008] 20 EG 137 (statutory charge) Mortgage Credit v Kalli [2007] EWCA Civ 1156 (adverse possession, misconduct by trial judge) Filobake v Rondo & Frampton [2005] EWCA Civ 563 (construction of contract) Pena v Coyne & Sunmoor [2004] BCLC 703 & 730 (transaction at undervalue).
Professional Memberships: Chancery Bar Association, Property Bar Association, Professional Negligence Bar Association.
Career: Called 1984, Accredited Mediator (ADR Group) 2006.
Personal: Born 1961, married, 3 children, resides Hampshire.

WILLIAMSON, Adrian QC
Keating Chambers, London
020 7544 2600
awilliamson@keatingchambers.com
Featured in Construction (London), Professional Negligence (London)
Practice Areas: Specialist in construction, engineering, energy, technology disputes. Highly regarded for expertise in professional negligence and insurance actions within these specialist areas. Practice covers advisory work (including work relating to standard and bespoke contracts), drafting and advocacy, for which he is widely seen as a formidable opponent. Regularly appears in the TCC, and the Court of Appeal, and in domestic and international arbitration. Has represented clients in adjudication and mediation and is an adjudicator and arbitrator.
Professional Memberships: TECBAR; COMBAR; SCL.
Career: Called to the Bar 1983; QC 2002; Recorder (Civil) 2004, (Crime) 2009; TECBAR accredited adjudicator, Deputy High Court Judge (2010); Completed PhD in economic history at Cambridge 2014 on "The Birth of Thatcherism".
Publications: Keating on JCT Contracts - General Editor; Contributor - Keating on Construction Contracts Ninth Edition (2011); Halsbury's Laws of England on Building Contracts.

WILLIAMSON, Alisdair
3 Raymond Buildings Barristers, London
020 7400 6400
alisdair.williamson@3rblaw.com
Featured in Crime (London)
Practice Areas: Alisdair has a varied serious crime, fraud and tribunal practice with an emphasis on defence. Often appearing as leading junior high profile work in the last year has included murder, fraud and the defence of celebrities accused of sexual offences. He has extensive experience of defending police officers; he also undertakes Inquests and disciplinary tribunals.
Professional Memberships: Criminal Bar Association.
Career: Call 1994.
Personal: MA (Oxon), Dip. LL (City).

WILLIAMSON, Oliver
Serjeants' Inn Chambers, London
020 7427 5000
owilliamson@serjeantsinn.com
Featured in Police Law (All Circuits)
Practice Areas: Oliver Williamson was called to the Bar in 2008. Oliver specialises in public and administrative, police, healthcare, inquests and inquiries, employment, civil liberties and human rights, professional discipline and product liability law. An earlier edition notes that "he is impressive on the advocacy side, he has intellectual weight" and "he is an excellent junior with a good eye for detail, he has great technical know how." Please click on the link to the Serjeants' Inn Chambers website for his profile, which sets out full details of his practice including relevant work of note.
Publications: Co-author of Medical Treatment: Decisions and the Law (2nd ed).
Personal: LLB, College of Law (First Class) Bar Vocational Course, College of Law (Outstanding). Queen Mother Scholarship, Middle Temple. Graduate Diploma in Law, College of Law (Distinction). MSci (Chemistry) University College, London (First Class).

WILLSON, William
South Square, London
020 7696 9900
williamwillson@southsquare.com
Featured in Restructuring/Insolvency (London)
Practice Areas: Insolvency/restructuring, commercial litigation, company law, banking/finance, fraud/asset recovery, insurance, professional negligence. Has a particular interest in cases with a Russian/CIS element. Recent cases include the Lehman Brothers "RASCALS" litigation (beneficial ownership of securities); McKillen v Sir Frederick Barclay (unfair prejudice/conspiracy). Currently instructed in a number of ongoing proceedings as both junior and sole Counsel in the Commercial Court and the Chancery Division, as well as significant pieces of litigation in the Cayman Islands, the British Virgin Islands, Jersey and Guernsey.
Professional Memberships: COMBAR, Chancery Bar Association, Insolvency Lawyers Association, INSOL.
Career: Called to the Bar of England & Wales (2006); Member of South Square (2007); called to the Bar of Gibraltar (2013); called to the Bar of the Cayman Islands (2014). Previously worked as journalist/documentary producer, specialising in the former Soviet Union, terrorism and the intelligence services.
Publications: Contributor to Lexis Nexis PSL Notes (Insolvency/Restructuring) (2012); Rowlatt on Principal and Surety (OUP, 2011); Company Directors: Duties, Liabilities and Remedies (OUP, 2009; second ed, 2013); Totty & Moss on Insolvency; International Corporate Rescue; Insolvency Intelligence.
Personal: Educated at Oxford University (Classics, First Class) and City University (GDL, Distinction). Interests include travel, cricket, film/theatre production.

WILSON, Elizabeth
Pump Court Tax Chambers, London
020 7414 8080
ewilson@pumptax.com
Featured in Tax (London)
Practice Areas: Barrister practising in revenue law. She was appointed as Junior Counsel to the Crown B panel in 2010. Her advisory work covers private client (including trusts) and corporate tax. Notable cases include: Shop Direct Group v HMRC (CA); Aspinalls v HMRC (CA); TMF Trustees Singapore Ltd (formerly Equity Trust (Singapore) Ltd) v HMRC (QROPS) (CA); Land Securities PLC v HMRC (UT); HMRC v O'Rorke (UT); Pertemps Recruitment Partnership Ltd v HMRC (UT); HMRC v The Late fourth Earl of Balfour (UT); Parry & ors v HMRC (FTT); Wintershall (A&P) Ltd v HMRC (FTT); Farnell Electronics Ltd v HMRC (FTT); Newey t/a Ocean Finance v HMRC (CJEU). She also represented Her Majesty's Attorney General in Re Longman Deceased (Exors of the estate of Elizabeth Longman v IBS-STL (UK) Ltd & anor LTL 12.3.12) (construction of section 75F Charities Act 1993).
Professional Memberships: Revenue Bar Association; London Common Law and Commercial Bar Association; Chancery Bar Association.
Career: Qualified 1995; Middle Temple; Junior Counsel to the Crown, B panel 2010.
Publications: Contributor to 'Taxation of Corporate Debt and Derivatives' (LexisNexis UK).

WILSON, Julian
11KBW, London
020 7632 8000
Julian.Wilson@11kbw.com
Featured in Employment (London)
Practice Areas: Business litigation particularly disputes concerning the breakdown of shareholder, director, partnership, LLP, joint venture and employment relationships, fraud and injunctions, unlawful competition, restraint of trade, confidential information, team moves and springboard relief. Regularly acts in disputes concerning shareholder agreements, minority shareholder unfair prejudice, share schemes, bonus, carried interest and profit share arrangements. He has a lot of experience of the City, its markets, banks, financial services, and regulation. Also experienced in offshore structures, cross-border litigation, and commercial arbitration. Recently appeared in the BVI and in Gibraltar. Cases include: Sanders v Trigor One Limited [2014] EWHC 1646 (Comm); In the matter of Cloudbluff Properties Limited [2011] EWHC 649 (Ch); Goldstone v Goldstone & Ors [2011] EWCA Civ 39; Broome & Wellington LP v Greenstein [2009] EWCA Civ. 589; Hays v Ions [2008] EWHC 745; Duarte v Black & Decker [2008] 1 All ER (Comm) 401; Takacs v Barclays [2006] IRLR 877; Foote Cone v Theron [2006] EWHC 1585; Cantor Fitzgerald International v Horkulak [2005] ICR 402.
Career: BA, Oxon, Jurisprudence, 1981. Solicitor: 1984-97; Litigation Partner, Herbert Smith 1990-97; Higher Court Advocacy Rights (Civil) 1994; Called to the Bar: 1997, Inner Temple.

WILSON, Richard
3 Stone Buildings, London
020 7242 4937
rwilson@3sb.law.co.uk
Featured in Chancery (London), Offshore (London), Trusts (London)
Practice Areas: General chancery, with a strong emphasis on litigation (both onshore and offshore) in the fields of trusts, estates, probate, 1975 Act claims, tax and related professional negligence. Recent notable cases include Futter v. Futter [2013] UKSC 26 (leading case of the application of the Rule in Re Hastings-Bass) and Slutsker v. Haron Investments [2013] EWCA Civ 430 (application of Russian matrimonial property rules to UK property settled on Cayman trust). Richard is currently involved in cases in most of the principal offshore jurisdictions and was called to the Bar of the Eastern Caribbean Supreme Court (BVI) in 2012.
Professional Memberships: Chancery Bar Association, STEP, ACTAPS, Revenue Bar Association, Professional Negligence Bar Association.
Career: LLB (Sheffield) LLM (London), Called to the Bar 1996 (Middle Temple). Formerly worked as a Tax Consultant with Price Waterhouse.
Publications: Co-author of 'The Trustee Act 2000: A Practical Guide' (Jordans). Author of numerous articles.
Personal: Married with four children. Lives in Wiltshire.

WILSON-SMITH, Christopher QC
Outer Temple Chambers, London
020 7353 6381
christopher.wilson-smithqc
@outtemple.com
Featured in Clinical Negligence (London), Personal Injury (London)
Practice Areas: For more information visit http://www.outertemple.com/barristers/christopher-wilson-smith-qc.asp TESTIMONIAL: Muiris Lyons, Partner, Head of Clinical Negligence, Stewarts Law LLP: "Christopher Wilson-Smith QC is the sort of silk you want on your side in a tough fight. His "larger than life" character and bluff amiability disguise his sharp forensic skills honed over many years in both criminal and civil cases of the highest order giving him an ability to see through to the real issues and address them quickly and effectively. His ability to turn around a set of papers in short order is testament to his considerable work ethic and yet his eye for detail often catches out the unwary or ill-prepared. He is a superb trial advocate noted for his cross-examination. He is excellent in consultation. He puts clients at their ease with his undoubted mischievous sense of humour whilst ensuring they fully understand what is happening. He is very skillful in his dealings with experts, exploring their evidence and ensuring there is clarity and consistency. He has for over 15 years been my first choice of silk." PROFILE: Christopher Wilson-Smith QC (CWS) was called to the Bar in 1965 and took Silk in 1986. In 1977 he became a Civil and Crime Recorder, in 1996 a Bencher of Gray's Inn and in 2000 he became a Member of the New South Wales Bar. His practice covers Personal Injury, often compounded by breaches of duty in healthcare following the initial trauma; Clinical Negligence and serious Crime, primarily involving Corporate Manslaughter and Health & Safety cases. In Clinical Negligence CWS acts for claimants and defendants (NHSLA), often involving babies with birth injuries and often compounded by breaches of duty in healthcare following the initial trauma. He both prosecutes and defends in major crimes, primarily on Circuit, particularly relating to Corporate Manslaughter and Health & Safety offences. CWS also defends Police Officers. Across the major legal directories he is listed as a leader in Personal Injury, Clinical Negligence, Crime and Health & Safety. He is often called to Chair and speak at major conferences, including those run by the AvMA and SIA. Legal Directory Quotes: In Chambers UK and Legal 500, they say he is, "He is really good at focusing on the key issues in a case. He is also excellent in conference and always

takes control when there are a large number of experts." 'a brilliant lawyer', with a 'sharp mind and refreshing candour', leading teams with a 'combination of exacting demands, reassuring foresight and warm support'. 'He's an absolutely outstanding advocate and in terms of being able to consider tactically where the other side will go, he's always spot-on." "He's an excellent advocate when it comes to cross-examination." 'Commentators highlight his "great attention to detail and tactical advice," and his willingness to put himself out for his clients.' A defence stalwart applauded as a "commanding presence who comes over very well in court.' And "a firm advocate who is excellent when confronted with novel issues and situations that might unman a lesser barrister. Although charming, he shows "real steel and determination in court." One source said of him, "I trust his judgment implicitly, find him excellent at analysing detailed evidence, and am in awe of his cross-examination skills." Another said, "If you're in a real scrap, it's Christopher Wilson-Smith you want." He's described as a "robust performer" who is "guaranteed to deliver great results", whilst also being "superb in settlement negotiations. Cases include: Clinical Negligence - Simon Szatmari -v- Oxford Radcliffe Hospital NHS Trust; Maureen Spencer -v- Guy's & St Thomas' NHS Foundation Trust; Beaumont-v-MoD; Ian Roy Newman -v- E. Kent Hospitals University NHS Trust; Piccolo-v-Larkstock & Others; David Hocking -v- St Georges Healthcare NHS Trust. Personal Injury - Candice Smith -v-Mathew Aylward & Motor Insurers Bureau; Bethany Davis v Mark Smith & Coventry Blaze Junior Ice Hockey Academy; Anderson-v-Snowbizz; Christopher March -v- Paul Taylor & Vital Group; Romain Simon -v- Patrick Selby ; Gawler-v-Raettig; Lurens-v-Ling; Jamie Yates -v- The National Trust & Joe Jackman; Cela-v-Official Solicitor. Crime & Health & SAFETY - Buncefield Oil Refinery Fire; R v. Imco Plastics; R v. Southwest Water Authority; R v. Rudkin; R v. Williams; R v. Gloyne; R v. British Gas; R v. Bayley; R v. DeVey & Others; R v. Whittington; R-v-Challacombe. For more information visit http://www.outertemple.com/barristers/christopher-wilson-smith-qc.asp.

Professional Memberships: Western Circuit, CBA, CLBA, COMBAR, APIL, PNBA, PIBA, AvMA.

Career: Called 1965. Silk 1986. Recorder of Crown Court [civil & crime] 1977. Master of Bench, Gray's Inn 1996. Admitted as QC to Bar of New South Wales. Head of Chambers 2001-04.

Personal: DoB 18-02-44. Rudolph Steiner schools in England and Switzerland. Keen golfer and Bridge player.

WILTON, Simon

Hailsham Chambers, London
020 7643 5000
simon.wilton@hailshamchambers.com

Featured in Professional Negligence (London)

Practice Areas: Professional negligence, insurance and commercial litigation. Cases include: EMW v RSA (2014) - acting for excess layer insurers in £3m Commercial Court action led by Justin Fenwick QC; Johnson v Hibberts (2014) solicitor's negligence trial turning on rule marriage revokes a will; Tinseltime v Roberts [2013] PNLR 4, wasted costs/non-party costs order; defending City firm in arbitrated claim (2011); acting for an IFA in the Innovator litigation (2011); Coomber v Alan Bloom (& Ors) (2010) – claim against receivers sued by developers struck-out after 3-day hearing; Nationwide v BKW v Hiscox (2010) - led by Christopher Symons QC in defence of insurer's declinature of £2.5m valuer's claim; Bonham v (1) Fishwick, (2) Fenner (2008) EWCA Civ 373 - dismissal of claims against accountant trustee; Leonard v Byrt (2008) EWCA Civ 20 - dismissal of appeal in "loss of a chance" case; Jessup v Wetherell [2007] PNLR 10 – solicitors' claim defeated on limitation grounds; Sinclair v Woods of Winchester Ltd (2005) 102 Con LR 127- successful defence of application to remove arbitrator; Sangster v Biddulphs [2005] PNLR 33 - whether solicitor held out as partner; Kesslar v Moore & Tibbits [2005] PNLR 17 - CA - whether solicitor could be substituted as defendant; Aldi, B&Q, Grantchester v Holmes and Others (2004) - acting for specialist subcontractor in multi-party claim arising out of subsiding supermarkets; Griffiths v Last Cawthra Feather [2002] PNLR 27 - solicitors' negligence - assessment of loss issues.

Professional Memberships: Professional Negligence Bar Association; London Common Law and Commercial Bar Association.

Career: Called in 1993. Karmel Scholar, Gray's Inn.

Publications: Contributor to Professional Negligence and Liability, contributing editor (1999-2003) and editor (2007-10) of the Lloyds Law Reports: Professional Negligence.

Personal: Educated at Sussex and Montpellier Universities. Married with three children.

WINSER, Crispin

Crown Office Chambers, London
020 7797 8100
winser@crownofficechambers.com

Featured in Construction (London)

Practice Areas: Construction, engineering, energy, insurance, IT, telecommunications, professional indemnity and general commercial litigation, arbitration and dispute resolution both in the UK and internationally.

Professional Memberships: Fellow of the Chartered Institute of Arbitrators (FCIArb); Registered practitioner in the DIFC; British Japanese Law Association; COMBAR; LCLCBA; LCIA European Users Council and Young International Arbitration Group; Society of Construction Law (UK and Gulf); TECBAR (committee member)

Publications: Contributor to Emden's Construction Law (chapters on Insurance and Responsibilities of Local Authorities) and European International Arbitration Review. Published articles include: "Set-Off in Adjudication" (2014) 30 Const LJ 103; "Adjudicators' entitlement to their fees" (2012) 28 Const LJ 369 and "Shutting Pandora's Box: The Prevention Principle after Multiplex v Honeywell" (2007) 23 Const LJ 511.

WINSTON, Naomi

Ten Old Square, London
020 7405 0758
naomiwinston@tenoldsquare.com

Featured in Partnership (London)

Practice Areas: Practice areas: Naomi's practice covers litigation, drafting and advisory work across the full range of commercial chancery and chancery matters, but with particular focus on partnership and LLPs. Her practice also covers property and probate and trust matters. In her partnership work, Naomi represents clients in litigation (both at hearings and at the settlement stage), advises on internal issues within partnerships/LLPs and undertakes non-contentious advisory and drafting work, both for firms and individuals.

Professional Memberships: Professional memberships: Naomi is a member of the Chancery Bar Association and the Association of Partnership Practitioners.

Career: Career: Naomi was called to the bar in 2006 after graduating with a first class degree. She spent the following year working as a research assistant in the Law Commission's Family, Property and Trust Team. Recent cases include: Reinhard v Ondra (awaiting judgment,HC) (nature of member's interest in an LLP), Malik v Fassenfelt [2013] EWCA Civ 798 (CA) (property; possession; trespassers; Art 8), Mehta v Steinbeck-Reeves (2012) (CC) (partnership; account; partnership property; application of s 24 PA 1890), Castledine v Bentley Jennison (a firm) [2011] EWHC 2363 (Ch) (HC) (partnership; retention of share of goodwill after retirement): Kahlon v Isherwood [2011] EWCA Civ 602 (CA) (landlord & tenant; whether a Tomlin order a HA 1988 prescribed form), TWM Trust Corporation Ltd v AG [2010] All ER (D) 139 (May) (HC) (wills; charities; gift to an unincorporated association).

Publications: Publications: Naomi is a contributor to the APP Newsletter and Mellows: Taxation for Executors and Trustees.

WINSTONE, Hilary

Old Square Chambers, London
020 7269 0300
winstone@oldsquare.co.uk

Featured in Employment (London), Employment (Western)

Practice Areas: Hilary is an employment specialist with excellent advocacy skills and a sensible commercial approach. She has an impressive client base, ranging from public sector employers, local authorities, commercial organisations, private individuals, trade unions and their members. Hilary's experience in a broad range of employment matters, and her 'robust', 'hands on' and 'approachable' style, ensures that she continues to be a leader in her areas of expertise.

Professional Memberships: Justice, Human Rights Lawyers Association. Employment Lawyers Association. Employment Lawyers Bar Association. Personal Injury Bar Association. Health & Safety Lawyers Association. Western Circuit. European Employment Lawyers Association.

WINTER, Alexander

Maitland Chambers, London
020 7406 1200
awinter@maitlandchambers.com

Featured in Chancery (London), Fraud (London)

Practice Areas: Commercial and chancery litigation, with emphasis on civil fraud, insolvency and heavy contractual disputes (often in the banking context). Also has substantial experience in professional negligence actions, real property, company, partnership and trust litigation. Contributor to Lender Claims (Sweet & Maxwell, 2010). Frequently instructed on cases with an international element, involving conflicts of law/jurisdictional issues. Notable cases include: Re Pan Ocean Co Ltd (effect of Art. 21 of UNCITRAL Model Law on cross border insolvency); Joint Stock Co Aeroflot – Russian Airlines v Berezovsky (enforcement of foreign judgments/confidentiality issues); Isis Investments Ltd v Oscatello Investments Ltd (allegations of fraud in the wake of the collapse of Kaupthing Bank); JSC BTA Bank v Ablyazov (fraud/freezing orders/receivership); Westwood Shipping Lines Inc v Universal Schifffahrtsgesellschaft Mbh (EC Regulation on Insolvency); Rok plc v S Harrison Group Ltd (contractual notice provisions); Platform Funding Ltd v Bank of Scotland plc (duties of valuer/identity fraud); Bank of Tokyo Mitsubishi UFJ Ltd v Baskan Gida Sanayi ve Pazarlama AS (banking fraud).

Professional Memberships: COMBAR, Chancery Bar Association, ILA, FSLA

Career: Called 2003.

Personal: Educated at St Catherine's College, Oxford (English Literature, First Class Honours), the Courtauld Institute (Architectural History, MA) and City University (CPE); Queen Mother Scholar and Harmsworth Exhibitioner of Middle Temple.

WINTER, Ian QC

Cloth Fair Chambers, London
020 7710 6444
IanWinter@clothfairchambers.com

Featured in Professional Discipline (London), Crime (London), Financial Crime (London)

Practice Areas: Specialist in criminal law with a particular emphasis on fraud, corporate and business crime. Practice also covers police powers and civil liberties law, regulatory tribunals, judicial review, international mutual assistance, inquests and extradition. Acted for the defence in the Lady Aberdour and Swindon Town FC frauds. Represented Langaker, a defendant in the Morgan Grenfell Management Fraud. Represented Bossino in a multi-million pound money laundering, entrapment, 'Bennett' abuse of process. Represented Dr Harold Shipman. Represented Professor Sir Roy Meadow at Appeal and the Crown at the Appeal Court. R -v- Dougall, leading authority on sentencing executive level whistle blowers entering plea agreements in corruption cases. Represented K, a solicitor accused of tax fraud; privilege against self-incrimination in ancillary relief proceedings, without prejudice privilege and abuse of process. HKSAR -v- Lai, secured the quashing of a solicitor's $2bn takeover fraud conviction in the Hong Kong Court of Final Appeal. Continues to advise internationally renowned Surgeon during proceedings at the Singapore Medical Council, complaint arising from the Brunei Royal Family. Represented a solicitor in two substantial money laundering and takeover fraud cases. Advised News International re. phone hacking. Acted in BTA Bank v Mukhtar Ablyazov, civil contempt of court proceedings regarding the failure to disclose multi-million pound assets in complex off shore trust structures. Lead the team for Aivars Lembergs, a Latvian politician, over $135 million commercial court worldwide freezing order. Advising international company in relation to the bribery act. Successfully defendant Kirsty Milczarek in front of the British Horseracing Authority on corruption charges. Advised one of the world's largest, privately owned, independent insurance brokers; Successfully represented Reg Traviss over rape charges. Acquittal secured after trial in Gibraltar re murder charges. Acting for principle defendant in large FSA investigation re. insider dealing. Advising former Senior Executive of Barclays in SFO/FCA investigation. Advised a city trader charged with Libor fixing. Advising global security company amid fraud

allegations, SFO investigation. Representing Thomas Chan over corruption charges in Hong Kong. Has advised in a number of Libel matters including Captain Shah -v- Associated Newspapers (successful trial on behalf of the claimant with substantial damages), represented Richard Desmond in his action against Tom Bower, McKeown v NGN (for the Claimant), and represented a premiership footballer For further information please visit www.clothfairchambers.com.
Career: Called to the Bar 1988. Joined Hollis Whiteman Chambers in 1990. Silk & Founder member of Cloth Fair Chambers 2006.
Personal: Educated at Bristol UWE 1984-87.

WINTER, Stephen
Terra Firma Chambers, Edinburgh
07962 207 712
stephen.winter@advocates.org.uk
Featured in Immigration (Scotland)
Practice Areas: advocate practising across a wide range of areas including public law, EU law and international law. The practice also focuses on commercial disputes and encompasses disputes of a general civil nature. The practice has involved appearing at all court levels in a variety of procedural, first instance, judicial review and appeal hearings both within the tribunal structure (First Tier Tribunal, Upper Tribunal, Mental Health Tribunal, Employment Tribunal, Employment Appeal Tribunal and Scottish Solicitors Disciplinary Tribunal) and court structure (Sheriff Court, Court of Session, UK Supreme Court and the European Court of Human Rights).
Professional Memberships: curator to the Mental Health Tribunal; Special Counsel; tutor on the Diploma in Legal Practice at Glasgow University; ad hoc lecturer on the Diploma in Legal Practice at Glasgow University; Faculty of Advocates trainer; sits on the Law Society's Law Reform Committee; pending application for membership with Chartered Institute of Arbitrators.
Career: LLB (Hons), Glasgow University; DipLP (with distinction), Glasgow University; exchange scheme to the Law School at the University of North Carolina at Chapel Hill, USA; LLM (Human Rights), Glasgow Graduate School of Law; litigation solicitor for 11 years before calling at the Bar; qualified to practice as a solicitor in England and Wales (2006-10); solicitor advocate (civil) (2007-10); Diploma in International Commercial Arbitration, Dundee University, 2014.
Publications: see profile on Terra Firma Chambers website.

WISEMAN, Naomi
Queen Elizabeth Building, London
020 7797 7837
n.wiseman@qeb.co.uk
Featured in Family/Matrimonial (London)
Practice Areas: Naomi Wiseman is a junior tenant at QEB, a chambers specialising in family law. Naomi advises and represents clients on a range of domestic and international family matters, including complex matrimonial finance, children, jurisdictional disputes and leave to remove. She has acted as junior to several leading silks representing high net worth individuals as well as developing her own individual practice.
Professional Memberships: Family Law Bar Association, Resolution, Bar Human Rights Committee and Society of Labour Lawyers.
Career: Member of chambers since 2012 following successful completion of pupillage. Previously worked as senior parliamentary researcher in Westminster (2006-2010) and policy advisor at the National Children's Bureau (2010-11). Residential Volunteer at Toynbee Hall (2009-10).
Publications: Co-author of 'Maintenance' for Practical Law Company
Personal: Naomi read History at Trinity College Cambridge (2004) before undertaking an MA in International Relations and Law at University of Sussex (2006). Naomi has lived and worked in Tanzania and Malawi, including 5 months at the Legal Aid Department in Blantyre. Provides parliamentary briefings to peers and MPs in relation to relevant legislation and regularly lectures on family law topics.

WOLFE, David QC
Matrix Chambers, London
020 7404 3447
davidwolf@matrixlaw.co.uk
Featured in Administrative & Public Law (London), Civil Liberties & Human Rights (London), Community Care (London), Education (London), Environment (London)
Practice Areas: Public law, including challenges to central government, local authorities, NHS and other bodies and regulators in the fields of environmental law (JRs of complex planning and environmental decisions particularly including EU/ECHR law), education law (statutory appeals and JRs including relating to special educational needs, discrimination/equality, exclusions, admissions and school reorganisations), community care/disability/health law (JRs relating to discrimination/equality including withdrawal of care decisions, care planning, rationing, mental health, charging, complaints procedures, health care, hospital closures/re-organisations, consultation). Is happy to discuss matters ahead of formal instruction where appropriate. Enjoys working as part of a relatively informal team with clients and those instructing him.
Professional Memberships: Administrative Law Bar Association, Discrimination Law Association, Planning and Environmental Bar Association, UK Environmental Law Association, Education Law Association.
Career: BSc MEng (Manchester) 1987, PhD (Engineering, Cambridge) 1991, Barrister since 1992. Former part time Special Educational Needs and Disability Tribunal chair, former Board Member of the Legal Services Board and former Legal Services Commission Commissioner. Currently (part time) Chair of the Press Recognition Panel created by Royal Charter following the Leveson Inquiry.
Publications: Author of blog www.acanofworms.org.uk on academies and the law.

WOLFE, Georgina
5 Essex Court, London
020 7410 2000
wolfe@5essexcourt.co.uk
Featured in Police Law (All Circuits)
Practice Areas: Police Law; Inquests; Public and Administrative; Professional Discipline; Personal Injury; Employment. Notable cases: Catt and T v Commissioner of Police of the Metropolis and ACPO [2013] EWCA Civ 192 and in the forthcoming Supreme Court appeal (police retention of data); R (E7) v Chairman of the Azelle Rodney Inquiry [2014] EWHC 452 (Admin) (challenging the findings of a public inquiry); R (Roberts) v Commissioner of Police of the Metropolis [2014] EWCA Civ 69 (stop and search) and in R (TD) v Commissioner of Police of the Metropolis [2013] EWHC 2231 (Admin) (police retention of CRIS reports); R (Ramsden) v IPCC [2013] EWHC 3969 (Admin) (defending a challenge to the police and IPCC's decision not to take witness statements from witnesses to an alleged assault); Inquests into the deaths of Roger and Mathilde Lamb, David Askew, Richard Need, Charlotte Shaw, Colette Lynch and Sabrina Akhtar.
Professional Memberships: ALBA; ELBA
Career: Called to the Bar 2006 (Queen Mother scholarship; Harold G. Fox scholarship and Blackstone Entrance Exhibition). Appointed to the Attorney General's C Panel of Counsel 2012
Publications: The Path to Pupillage (Sweet & Maxwell, 2008; Third Edition 2013) with Alexander Robson.

WOLFFE, James QC
Axiom Advocates, Edinburgh
01312 262 881
james.wolffe@axiomadvocates.com
Featured in Administrative & Public Law (Scotland), Construction (Scotland), Commercial Dispute Resolution (Scotland)
Practice Areas: Public and administrative law; constitutional law; human rights; commercial dispute resolution; construction law
Professional Memberships: Advocate (Scotland) 1992; QC (Scotland) 2007; barrister (England and Wales) 2013. James Wolffe is a member of Axiom Advocates, Edinburgh, and a door tenant of Brick Court Chambers, London.
Career: First Standing Junior Counsel to the Scottish Government 2002-7; Senior Advocate Depute 2007-10; Vice-dean of Faculty 2013-14; Head of the UK Delegation of the CCBE (current); Dean of Faculty (current)
Personal: James Wolffe has been instructed in the Scottish civil and criminal courts at all levels, as well as the UK Supreme Court, the Judicial Committee of the Privy Council, the Court of Justice of the European Union and the European Court of Human Rights.

WONG, Natasha
187 Fleet Street, London
020 7430 7430
natashawong@187fleetstreet.com
Featured in Financial Crime (London)
Practice Areas: Specialist defence counsel with considerable expertise over the full range of investigations into civil fraud, financial crime, confiscation, regulatory and disciplinary hearings. Her practice is focused particularly on defending those charged with or being investigated in respect of serious and complex fraud cases, allegations of cheating the revenue, and regulatory proceedings. The majority of these cases have been prosecuted by the Serious Fraud Office (SFO), Crown Prosecution Service (CPS) or Her Majesty's Revenue and Customs (HMRC) and many have involved multi-jurisdictional aspects as well as detailed legal arguments, including the admissibility of evidence, joinder and severance, challenging expert evidence, legal professional and litigation privilege, applications to stay the proceedings on the grounds of abuse of process and or fitness to stand trial, public interest immunity and disclosure issues, and submissions of no case to answer. Very experienced at managing large quantities of documents, disclosure databases and expert forensic evidence. Natasha is a Registered Lawyer under the Football Association (FA) Football Agents Regulations.

WOOD, Benjamin
4 New Square, London
020 7822 2000
b.wood@4newsquare.com
Featured in Professional Negligence (London)
Practice Areas: Professional liability claims involving financial, legal, construction and valuation professionals, as well as general commercial and Chancery litigation (both onshore and offshore), particularly financial services, civil fraud and property-related litigation. Reported cases include Newcastle International Airport v Eversheds [2014] 2 All ER 728 and Thompson v Foy [2010] 1 P&CR 16.
Professional Memberships: Professional Negligence Bar Association, COMBAR, Chancery Bar Association.
Career: Called to the Bar in 2005. Formerly corporate financier at NM Rothschild & Sons. Appointed Deputy District Judge in 2013. Ben is also an advocacy trainer for Lincoln's Inn and a member of the Bar Standards Board's Education & Training Committee.
Personal: BA Hons (Oxon). Leisure interests: travel, skiing and diving.

WOODHAM, Samantha
4 Paper Buildings, London
020 7583 0816
sw@4pb.com
Featured in Family/Matrimonial (London)
Practice Areas: Samantha's practice covers all areas of financial provision (including high value Schedule One), cohabitation claims and complex private law children disputes, including leave to remove. She has successfully appeared against Silks on her own as well as being led.
Professional Memberships: Family Law Bar Association (FLBA), South Eastern Circuit, Qualified Collaborative Lawyer.
Career: Samantha was called to the Bar in 2006, having previously qualified as a solicitor at a magic circle law firm. Her experience at a corporate law firm developed her skills as an efficient and thorough practitioner which she combines with a friendly and approachable style.
Publications: Samantha regularly speaks at seminars and conferences on financial provision and private law children, including at the Family Law Conference.
Personal: Samantha read Law at St Catharine's College, Cambridge. She is married with a family. Her interests include travel, shopping and long family walks with her golden retriever Teddy.

WOODHOUSE, Charles
Old Square Chambers, London
020 7269 0300
woodhouse@oldsquare.co.uk
Featured in Personal Injury (Western), Personal Injury (London)
Practice Areas: Charlie is instructed by Claimants and Defendants predominantly in high value, catastrophic and fatal injury claims in civil proceedings and inquests. His caseload includes accidents resulting in brain injury, amputation, chronic pain disorders resulting in severe disability and cases involving contested mental capacity but he is also regularly instructed in matters in which liability is contested including complex and multi-party road traffic accident claims and

accidents involving the use or malfunction of industrial machinery. Charlie has considerable experience of acting for members of the armed forces in claims against the Ministry of Defence and other Defendants. He is regularly instructed by insurers in respect of fraudulent claims or claims in which policy cover is avoided by virtue of the insured's conduct. Recent examples of such cases include claims involving racing by multiple drivers resulting in multi vehicle fatal accidents and a claim involving the reckless use of a car to injure several of a group of pedestrians by an unidentified driver Charlie also acts for Claimants in clinical negligence claims and at Inquests into deaths in hospital or during the course of medical treatment.

WOOLF, Eliot
Outer Temple Chambers, London
020 7353 6381
eliot.woolf@outertemple.com
Featured in Clinical Negligence (London), Personal Injury (London), Personal Injury (All Circuits), Travel (London)
Practice Areas: Nationwide practice in clinical negligence, personal injury and professional negligence acting for claimants and defendants. Clinical negligence work covers a wide variety of fields with an emphasis on obstetric injuries and spinal surgery. His personal injury practice is also wide ranging but has a particular focus on accidents abroad, military claims, disease work and catastrophic brain and spinal injury claims. He appears in the CICA and at inquests.
Professional Memberships: PNBA, PIBA, AVMA, APIL, TATLA.
Career: Called to the Bar 1993.
Publications: Joint author of ' Personal Injury Practice, The Guide to Litigation in the County Courts and High Court'.
Personal: Born 1967. Robinson College, Cambridge (MA 2(1)), City University Dip.

WOOLF, Jeremy
Pump Court Tax Chambers, London
020 7414 8080
clerks@pumptax.com
Featured in Tax (London)
Practice Areas: Barrister specialising in all areas of tax work, including VAT, Customs & Excise duties, negligence and judicial review litigation connected with tax issues; recent cases include CCE v Pegasus Birds (Court of Appeal); CCE v Madgett & Baldwin (ECJ); Holly v HMIT (Special Commissioners); King v United Kingdom (ECHR); IRC v Eversden (Court of Appeal); My Travel plc v CCE (ECJ); Abbey National Fund Management (ECJ); Household Estate Agents Ltd v HMRC (High Court); HMRC v Talentcore (Upper Tribunal).
Professional Memberships: Revenue Bar Association; Administrative Law Association; European Bar Association; London Common Law and Commercial Bar Association; VAT Practitioners Group; He is a Chartered Institute of Taxation representative on the fiscal committee of the Confederation Fiscale Europeenne; He is chair of CIOT's European Union and Human Rights sub-committee, CFE's alternate representative on the European Commission's VAT Exports group and the CIOT's alternate representative on the European Commission's Expert Group on removing tax problems facing individuals who are active across borders within the EU.
Career: Called 1986; Inner Temple.
Publications: Zamir and Woolf, 'The Declaratory Judgment'; DeSmith, Woolf and Jowell, 'Judicial Review of Administrative Action' (6th Edition), Halsbury's Laws of England, Customs & Excise; 'De Voil: Indirect Tax Service'; 'Simon's Direct Tax Service' (contributor and editorial board) 'Civil Appeals'; 'Potter & Monroe's Tax Planning'.
Personal: University of Sussex (BA); University of Cambridge (LLM).

WOOLFE, Philip
Monckton Chambers, London
020 7405 7211
pwoolfe@monckton.com
Featured in Competition/European Law (London), Telecommunications (London)
Practice Areas: Competition Law and State Aid, Commercial, European Union Law, Public & Administrative Law, Public Procurement, Telecommunications Regulation and VAT.
Professional Memberships: He is a committee member of COMBAR and a member of the Competition Law Association, Bar European Group and Procurement Lawyers' Association.
Career: BA (Hons) in History (Cambridge University 1998-2001), BA (Hons) in Law (Oxford University) (2001-03), BCL (Oxford University) (2004-05), Fellow of All Souls College, Oxford (2003-10), Call (2004), Pupillage at Monckton Chambers (2005-06), Tenant at Monckton Chambers (2006-present).
Publications: Contributor to Bellamy & Child: European Community Law of Competition (7th edition) (OUP, 2013), Contributor to Value Added Tax: Commentary & Analysis (Sweet & Maxwell, 2009).
Personal: Philip speaks fluent French and German and has conversational Italian. He has a strong interest in mathematics, science and technology.

WORTHINGTON, Stephen QC
12 King's Bench Walk, London
020 7583 0811
worthington@12kbw.co.uk
Featured in Personal Injury (London)
Practice Areas: Personal injury, clinical negligence, professional negligence, insurance, environmental, construction. Blue Circle v Ministry of Defence, Nuclear Pollution, [1998] 3 All ER 385. Heil v Rankin (2001) QB 272. Martin v Lancashire County Council (2000) 3 All ER 54 (TUPE). Watson v British Boxing Board of Control (2001) QB 1134. Hall v Gwent NHS Trust (2004) EWHC 2748, Browning v Brachers (a firm) (2005) EWCA Civ 753.
Professional Memberships: PIBA, LCLCBA, TECBAR, PNBA.
Career: Trinity College, Cambridge. Called to Bar 1976, recorder 2002, Silk 2006.
Publications: Contributor to Butterworths 'Professional Negligence' and 'Structured Settlements: A Practical Guide'.

WRAIGHT, William
2TG - 2 Temple Gardens, London
020 7822 1260
wwraight@2tg.co.uk
Featured in Clinical Negligence (London)
Practice Areas: Clinical negligence and personal injury, acting for claimants and defendants. Notable cases: M v N NHS (QBD, 26-30 November 2012), mismanagement of prolapsed lumbar spinal disc in A&E; T v N-T (Central London CC, 17-20 June 2013), successful defence of allegedly negligent hysteroscopy and polypectomy procedure during in-vitro fertilisation; E v G NHS (Central London CC, 28-29 January 2014), successful defence of a claim concerning a fall in a physiotherapy falls-prevention class. Also S v U NHS (QBD, June 2014, settled), leg amputation following negligent vascular surgery, led by Martin Porter QC. Multi-million-pound catastrophic PI and clinical negligence cases led by Benjamin Browne QC and Sarah Vaughan-Jones QC.
Professional Memberships: PNBA, PIBA, Member of the Royal College of Surgeons
Career: Graduated from Oxford University in medicine in 2001; also with first class honours degree in Physiological Sciences in 1998. Taught anatomy at Cambridge University. Research in intensive care, anatomy and plastic surgery. General surgical training in A&E, colorectal surgery, trauma and orthopaedics and cardiothoracic surgery. Attained Membership of the Royal College of Surgeons in 2004. Specialised in plastic surgery including hand surgery, trauma and cancer reconstruction, burns and cosmetic surgery. Called to the Bar in 2009.

WRAY, Laura
Westwater Advocates, Edinburgh
07739 639 189
mrslaurawray@btinternet.com
Featured in Personal Injury (Scotland)
Practice Areas: Laura has specialised for over 25 years in personal injury, medical and dental negligence and industrial disease claims. She also has considerable experience in product liability cases including organophosphate exposure, silicone implants, steroids and CJD. Laura was junior counsel in the settled case of Cooper v Merck (the first publicly funded Vioxx action in the world) initially acting on her own, and thereafter with Andrew Hajducki QC. She is instructed in complex and high value cases, including catastrophic injuries such as tetraplegia and brain injury. She acts for pursuers and defenders in the Court of Session and Sheriff Courts. Laura is happy to work on a speculative or legally aided basis.
Career: 1985-87 - trainee solicitor; thereafter Litigation Partner then Senior Partner of trade union and personal injury firm, L & L Lawrence, Glasgow and Edinburgh. Acted as Scottish agent to several English, Irish and American law firms. Qualified in English law in 1992. Elected to the Executive Board of the Association of Personal Injury Lawyers (APIL) and appointed Vice Chair of the International Section of the Association of Trial Lawyers of America (ATLA). Consultant to Drummond Miller 1998-2002. Called to the Bar in 2003.

WRIGHT, Alexander
4 Pump Court, London
020 7842 5555
awright@4pumpcourt.com
Featured in Shipping (London)
Practice Areas: Shipping and commodities matters including disputes arising out of charterparties, contracts of affreightment and bills of lading, ship sale MOAs, forward freight agreements (FFAs), the international sale and carriage of goods, commodity sale and purchase agreements, and shipping-related guarantee claims. Shipbuilding disputes across a range of types of vessels, including bulk carriers, oil/chemical tankers, ro-ro passenger ferries, and superyachts. Wet shipping matters including arrests, collision and towage. Claims against ship managers. General commercial dispute resolution including insurance (marine and non-marine) and reinsurance, construction and engineering, banking, derivatives, guarantees, purchase options, agency disputes, commercial fraud, joint venture agreements, shareholders' agreements and other general contractual matters.
Professional Memberships: COMBAR, London Shipping Law Centre, Young Maritime Professionals Association (Committee Member), TECBAR, SCL.
Career: Called 2007 (Middle Temple). Pupil at 4 Pump Court 2007-08. Tenant at 4 Pump Court 2008 to date.
Personal: MA (Cantab) (Peterhouse).

WRIGHT, Peter QC
2 Hare Court, London
020 7353 5324
clerks@2harecourt.com
Featured in Crime (London)
Practice Areas: Peter Wright QC has been continually rated by Chambers UK in both London and Northern Sections for many years. Described as "the complete package" possessing "astounding attention to detail and is a really good tactician who is very good with clients." He is "A QC of the highest calibre- simply outstanding" with "advocacy skills second to none". He has prosecuted and defended in a number of high profile cases recently including M.P's expenses and the alleged rape and indecent assault by the Deputy Speaker of the House of Commons. His practice is now predominantly in fraud and business crime, in defending directors and companies both here and in the Isle of Man. He continues to prosecute cases of the utmost gravity, including the 'Libor' scandal and Cartel price-fixing arrangements.

WYGAS, Luke
4 Pump Court, London
020 7842 5555
LWygas@4pumpcourt.com
Featured in Commercial Dispute Resolution (London), Professional Negligence (London)
Practice Areas: Commercial litigation focusing on construction, IT, insurance, energy and professional negligence (with a particular emphasis on construction professionals). He is a qualified engineer who worked in the industry, mainly in the Far East, before coming to the Bar. Recent cases include representing a building contractor in a multi-party contractual dispute with a related insurance dispute; fire loss claims, particularly when they include issues of technical complexity; fraud cases (particularly in relation to mortgage fraud) and IT disputes, particularly in relation to delay and defects cases. He is frequently instructed in relation to construction adjudications and has experience of domestic and international arbitrations.
Professional Memberships: COMBAR, Professional Negligence Bar Association, Society of Construction Law, Society for Computers and Law.
Career: Called 2004.
Publications: Atkins Court Forms: Professional Negligence Aktins, Court Forms: Mortgages, Lexis Nexis: Adjudication Know-how, Lexis Nexis: Construction Module.

WYNNE, James
Littleton Chambers, London
020 7797 8676
jwy@littletonchambers.co.uk
Featured in Employment (London)

Practice Areas: Employment law practice covers the High Court, Employment Tribunals, EAT and CA including high value and high profile disputes. Statutory employment claims involving complex discrimination, TUPE, whistleblowing, WTR and employment status. On the collective side, experience in national industrial actions. Regularly instructed at the EAT. High Court practice of restrictive covenant/confidential information/garden leave disputes and injunctions and general commercial disputes. Regulatory and disciplinary matters including representation at professional disciplinary panels. Professional liability including that of barristers, solicitors and trade unions. Rights of audience before the DIFC Courts in Dubai with appearances in two full trials. Clients from public sector, charities, retail, engineering, financial institutions, media technology and communications, outsourcing and logistics, professional services. Recent reported decisions: Seawell v Ceva Freight (UK) Ltd [2012] IRLR 802 and Kerr v Ernst & Young Services Ltd [2011] ICR D13.
Professional Memberships: ELA, ELBA, ILS, Combar, PNBA.
Career: Called 2002. Educated at Cambridge University (Engineering, MA), UCL (LLB), LSE (LLM). Before studying law worked in engineering for the MoD and in the private sector.
Publications: 'Transfer of Undertakings' (loose-leaf) Thomson Sweet and Maxwell; 'The Law of Industrial Action and Trade Union Recognition', 2nd Edition 2011, Oxford University Press; 'The Equality Act', The Law Society.

YANG, Zizhen
Pump Court Tax Chambers, London
020 7414 8080
clerks@pumptax.com
Featured in Tax (London)
Practice Areas: Zizhen advises and litigates on all aspects of revenue law, as well as in other areas of law where tax-related issues feature. Her litigation practice extends to the First-tier Tribunal, the Upper Tribunal, the High Court and the Court of Appeal. Recent cases include Bookit Ltd v HMRC (VAT); British Film Institute v HMRC (VAT); King's College London v HMRC (SDLT); Patersons of Greenoakhill Ltd v HMRC (Landfill Tax); Trinity Mirror Plc v HMRC (VAT); DM-WSHNZ Ltd v HMRC (Corporation Tax); Euroceanica (UK) Ltd v HMRC (Tonnage Tax); Flanagan & ors v HMRC (Income Tax); Leeds City Council v HMRC (VAT); Price & ors v HMRC (Income Tax); Vaccine Research Limited Partnership & anor v HMRC (Capital Allowances, income tax); Purolite International Ltd v HMRC (Corporation Tax); Chadderton Total Care Group Ltd v HMRC (PAYE/NIC penalty); Albermarle 4 LLP v HMRC (Income Tax).
Professional Memberships: Revenue Bar Association; London Common Law and Commercial Bar Association.
Career: Called 2009 (Lincoln's Inn); PhD (Cambridge University, molecular biology) 2007.

YATES, David
Pump Court Tax Chambers, London
020 7414 8080
clerks@pumptax.com
Featured in Professional Negligence (London), Tax (London)
Practice Areas: David frequently advises on or acts in litigation relating to private client, corporation tax, VAT and customs and duties. He is also very experienced in advising on and appearing in professional negligence and discipline cases arising in a tax context. David was appointed to the Attorney General's C panel in February 2009 and B panel in February 2013 and undertakes work for both taxpayers and HMRC. Recent tax cases include States of Guernsey and Jersey v HMRC (judicial review of removal of VAT exemption for Channel Island imports), R (Bampton Property Group Ltd) v HMRC (judicial review on refusal of late claims for group relief), Sanderson (discovery assessments), Proteus & Samarkand (film schemes) and Mayes (Chargeable events regime & Ramsay); Birmingham Hippodrome (Set-off time limits) & Giles v RNIB (Rectification).
Professional Memberships: Professional Negligence Bar Association, Revenue Bar Association.
Career: Called 2004. March 2009: Appointed Junior Counsel to the Crown - "C" Panel. March 2013: Appointed Junior Counsel to the Crown - "B" Panel.
Personal: Educated at Cambridge University (1998-2001, MA) and City University (2002-03, PgDL). Lord Denning Scholar of Lincoln's Inn. Born 1979.

YATES, Nicholas
1 Hare Court, London
020 7797 7070
yates@1hc.com
Featured in Family/Matrimonial (London)
Practice Areas: Nicholas specialises in financial remedy cases (including Civil Partnership and Schedule 1 claims) often involving substantial assets, complex company valuations, trusts, tax issues and international dimensions. He also frequently drafts nuptial agreements and advises on their enforceability, as well as representing clients on jurisdiction matters, marriage/non-marriage cases, Inheritance Act claims and complex private law children disputes. He is one of the few members of the family bar to have won a second tier appeal to the Court of Appeal in a financial case within the first three years of practice. Nicholas is highly regarded by the professionals with whom he works. He is well-known to establish quickly a solid rapport with his clients. Recent reported cases include: Chai v Peng [2014] EWHC 1519 (Fam); B v B [2013] EWHC 1232 (Fam); F v F (Financial Remedies: Premarital Wealth) [2012] EWHC 438 (Fam); Bokor-Ingram v Bokor-Ingram [2009] EWCA Civ 412 and I v I (Ancillary Relief: Disclosure) [2009] 1 FLR 2011.
Professional Memberships: A member of the committee of The Family Law Bar Association.
Career: Trinity College, Cambridge. Called to the Bar in 1996, Inner Temple.
Publications: Articles for Family Law.
Personal: Classical music, singing (tenor) and cycling.

YEGINSU, Can
4 New Square, London
020 7822 2047
c.yeginsu@4newsquare.com
Featured in Administrative & Public Law (London)
Practice Areas: Can Yeginsu practises in all areas of Chambers' work, with a particular emphasis on commercial dispute resolution (including international arbitration), investment treaty claims, professional liability, sports law, and public law, constitutional law and human rights law. Aside from regular commercial disputes instructions (often with an international element), Can's recent work includes: The David Miranda Judicial Review before the Divisional Court and the Court of Appeal (the lawfulness of Schedule 7 to the Terrorism Act 2000); UKIP v the Electoral Commission in the Supreme Court (law on party political donations); Emptage v FSCS in the Court of Appeal (lawfulness of FSCS discretion on compensation awards); Araci v Fallon in the Court of Appeal (prohibitory injunctions in the sports context); Sik and Sener v Turkey before the ECtHR (freedom of speech for journalists in Turkey).
Professional Memberships: LCIA, ASA, IBA, ALBA, COMBAR, PNBA, Lawyers for Liberty.
Career: Called to the Bar 2007; 4 New Square Chambers since 2010.
Publications: Jackson & Powell on Professional Liability (Sweet & Maxwell, 2012), The Protections for Religious Rights: Law and Practice (OUP, 2013).
Personal: University College Oxford, BA (Double First Class Hons); Princeton University (Jane Eliza Procter Fellow); City University, LLB (First Class Hons); Harvard Law School, LLM (Cravath Scholar). Languages: Turkish (native); French (working knowledge).

YEO, Colin
Garden Court Chambers, London
020 7993 7600
coliny@gclaw.co.uk
Featured in Immigration (London)
Practice Areas: Well known in the immigration sector for his very widely read Free Movement immigration law website Colin Yeo's practice covers the full range of immigration law. He regularly trains other immigration lawyers, has contributed to a number of publications and practitioner texts and is often approached for immigration law commentary in the media. Strategic in his approach, he switches easily between campaigning work and quiet, sensitive handling of difficult cases.

YEO, Nik
Fountain Court Chambers, London
020 7583 3335
ny@fountaincourt.co.uk
Featured in Banking & Finance (London), International Arbitration (London), Professional Negligence (London)
Practice Areas: Commercial litigation and arbitration, with an emphasis on cross border disputes and matters concerning (i) derivatives, securitisations and other structured finance, (ii) financial regulation; (iii) energy and natural resources, (iv) information technology, (v) insurance and re-insurance; and (vi) professional negligence, particularly arising out of the foregoing areas. Accustomed both to working as part of a team as well as acting as lead advocate. For example, involved in what has been described in the press as the "valuation trial of the century", arising out of a commercial mortgage-backed securitisation; represented Lehman Brothers Inc (the US broker dealer) in various matters before the English courts; representing various leading phone manufacturers in arbitrations in relation to mobile phone technology. Comfortable with technological-intensive disputes of all kinds.
Professional Memberships: Commercial Bar Association, LCIA.
Career: Called 2000. Former solicitor at London magic circle firm practising in structured finance.
Personal: Educated Melbourne University (BA (Hons), LLB (Hons)) and Wadham College, Oxford (BCL - 1st class).

YOUNG, Andrew R W QC
Arnot Manderson, Edinburgh
07739 639 336
andrewyoung@amadvocates.co.uk
Featured in Personal Injury (Scotland), Professional Negligence (Scotland), Tax (Scotland), Clinical Negligence (Scotland), Commercial Dispute Resolution (Scotland)
Practice Areas: Andrew has a wide ranging civil law practice ranging from professional and clinical negligence through to commercial disputes. He also acts in many high value catastrophic personal injury claims. On account of his previous experience as a standing junior counsel to HMRC for many years, he is also instructed in tax related matters up to and including the Supreme Court.
Career: Andrew was called to the Bar in 1992 and took silk in 2007. He was the standing junior counsel for the Foreign and Commonwealth Office and subsequently for HM Customs & Excise and HMRC. He is a Chairman of the Police Appeals Tribunal.
Publications: "Commission & Diligence", co-author with Archibald MacSporran. Contributor to Gloag & Henderson, "The Law of Scotland" 10th and 11th editions.

YOUNG, David
9 Bedford Row, London
020 7489 2727
david.young@9bedfordrow.co.uk
Featured in Crime (London)
Practice Areas: An International Criminal Law Defence Counsel, who has been instructed as Lead Defence Counsel before The Special Tribunal for Lebanon in the Hague since 2011. He defends the accused Assad Sabra, who is alleged to have been complicit in the assassination of the former Prime Minister of Lebanon, Rafic Hariri, who was killed in a Beirut explosion. He is also an ICC list Defence Counsel, and can advise private individuals, corporate entities, foreign lawyers and NGO's on international criminal law and human rights matters. He is currently advising as a consultant an accused alleged to have carried out terrorist activity involving Ethiopia, Kenya and Yemen. Previously, in the UK, he defended in the following international cases: R v. Lambert (first Tamil Tiger prosecution in the UK); R v Janus Khan (Operation Pathway SIAC case); R v Abdul Ghayur & others [the 'Afghan Hi-Jacking case', R v Sidali Feddag [The Ricin Poison case-a 9 month CCC trial- re an alleged Algerian terrorist group], R v Aabid Khan re Al Qaida in Pakistan; Germany v Iqtidar Dara [exporting nuclear weapon parts to Pakistan- extradition].
Professional Memberships: Criminal Bar Association [former Committee Member], Former Bar Council International Committee member, SE Circuit, ICTY, ICC and Special Tribunal for Lebanon lists of approved Defence Counsel at The Hague.
Career: BA [Hons]. LLM from Queen Mary College, London University
Publications: Author of Young, Corker and Summers on 'Abuse of Process in Criminal Proceedings', 4th edition in 2014 [with first

published chapter on Abuse of Process in the International Courts].
Personal: Married with four children.

ZELLICK, Adam
Fountain Court Chambers, London
020 7583 3335
az@fountaincourt.co.uk
Featured in Aviation (London), Banking & Finance (London), Commercial Dispute Resolution (London), Fraud (London)
Practice Areas: Strong, broad-based, commercial practice with extensive experience in arbitration and arbitration appeals, aviation, banking, civil fraud, commercial litigation, conflict of laws, and insurance/reinsurance. Acts in a wide range of commercial cases and appeals including the very heavy, multi-party, expert-intensive, high value, publicity-sensitive; and at home whether in arbitration or commencing in the Commercial Court, Chancery or Queen's Bench Division. Regularly instructed in mediations and to assist litigation outside England. Aims to bring a client-focused, pragmatic, thorough and good-humoured approach to every case. Recent cases include: Deutsche Bank v Unitech, Pakistan v NatWest, Access Bank v Akingbola, Re Air France – AF447, Re Dewey LeBoeuf, Re Antonio Gramsci, Societe General v Saad, ICD v Tuwairqi Steel Mills, Merchant International v Naftogaz, Arbuthnot Latham v Amundi, Spliethoff's v Bank of China, Commerzbank v Credit Agricole.
Professional Memberships: COMBAR, LCLCBA, BILA, SE Circuit, ICC YAF, Burma Justice Committee.
Career: MA, University of Cambridge (Squire Scholar); Called 2000 (Middle Temple, Queen Mother Scholar); Research Assistant, Law Commission, 2000; Supervisor in Law, Gonville and Caius College, 2001.
Publications: Author, Civil Aviation, Atkin's Court Forms, 2006 and 2010; contributor, Bullen and Leake and Jacob's Precedents of Pleadings, 2000. Member, Editorial Board, Counsel Magazine, 2012-.

ZWART, Christiaan
Thirty Nine Essex Street, London
020 7832 1111
christiaan.zwart@39essex.com
Featured in Planning (London)
Practice Areas: Christiaan has an extensive practice in Planning, Environmental, Public and Local Government Law. He regularly represents developers, local authorities, government agencies including the Environment Agency, DEFRA, DECC, Highways Agency and the Secretary of State, HMRC, and the Cabinet Office. He has a great deal of experience at planning inquiries and hearings; at DCO, CPO and TWA hearings; at High Court challenges, the Court of Appeal and the House of Lords (Supreme Court). He also has experience in other jurisdictions including Hong Kong and Jersey. As a planning barrister, Christiaan's significant DCO experience includes: promoting at Milford Haven a new 500MwE CHP plant for ExxonMobil in a national park (the most environmentally complex); acting for the Government at TTT (most number of objections) and for EA at Hinkley Point 2 (the most technically challenging); and objecting to Rookery South (the first). Other infrastructure experience includes HS2 partitioning for key land interests at Euston Station and Birmingham for multi-national corporation. Christiaan's also has considerable experience in residential housing development of all scales and complexities, from single homes, to inner city housing-led cpo regeneration, and urban extensions into AONBs near SAMs and into green wedges. Having developed extensive property-related tax expertise with HMRC, as a planning/tax barrister, he has a particular specialism in CIL and planning viability, and planning related VAT.
Professional Memberships: NIPA, PEBA, CPA, UKELA.
Career: Appointed 2010 to Attorney General's B Panel against "unprecedented competition"; C Panel 2004. Called 1997 Inner Temple. Duke of Edinburgh Scholar. City University 1996-97 (CPE). RIBA Part III 1995. Newcastle University 1986-92 (BA, 1st class; & B.Arch, 1st class).
Personal: Born 1967. Lives West London. Interests include ancient history, art & architecture.

THE BAR A-Z LONDON

ARDEN CHAMBERS Christopher Baker

Arden Chambers, 20 Bloomsbury Square, London, WC1A 2NS
Tel (020) 7242 4244 **Fax** (020) 7242 3224 **DX** 29 Chancery Lane
Email clerks@ardenchambers.com **Website** www.ardenchambers.com

Head of Chambers	Christopher Baker
Clerk to Chambers	Mike Alexander
Junior Clerks	Neil Goodwright
	Sam Windle
Fees Clerk	Martin Cornwell
Tenants	30

MEMBERS

Andrew Arden QC (1974) (QC-1991)
John Robson (1974) ^
Christopher Baker (1984) ^
Clare Roberts (1988)
Jonathan Manning (1989) ^
Iain Colville (1989) ^
William Okoya (1989) ^
Andrew Dymond (1991)
Timothy Leader (1994) ^
Annette Cafferkey (1994) ^
Stuart Armstrong (1995) ^
Toby Vanhegan (1996) ^
Sarah McKeown (1998)
Tobias Eaton (2001) ^
John McCafferty (2000)
Ian Loveland (2001)
Gillian Ackland-Vincent (2001)
James Sandham (2002) ^
Justin Bates (2003) ^
Emily Orme (2003) ^
Stephanie Smith (2004) ^
Laura West (2006)
David Cowan (2006)
Rebecca Chan (2006)
Sarah Salmon (2007)
Sam Madge-Wyld (2008)
Robert Brown (2008)
Clare Cullen (2009)
Amy Knight (2011)
Senay Nihat (2012)
Linda Hayton (1975) *
Siobhan McGrath (1982) *
Martin Partington QC (Hon) (1984) * (QC-2008)
Caroline Hunter (1985) *
Ceilidh Halloran (1992) *
Emma Saunders (1994) *
Sarah Pengelly (1996) *

* Door Tenant ^ Public/Direct Access

THE CHAMBERS Arden Chambers provides specialist expertise in its chosen fields. The changing needs of clients are met by a forward-thinking, imaginative and adaptable approach which extends beyond the comprehensive service for legal advocacy, advice and drafting which barristers might ordinarily provide. Clients can obtain free current legal information by email, and also take advantage of tailor-made training and an active seminar programme, the expertise for which is supported by the large volume of publications for which the set is responsible (see below). Alongside a national network of solicitor and local authority clients, the set is in the forefront of licensed access work through individual housing organisations and others with these access rights, and through its own dedicated online advisory service, HousingLawDirect (see website: www.housinglawdirect.com), for the 7,500 corporate members and fellows of the Chartered Institute of Housing. Clients include individuals (tenants, owners, homeless persons, applicants, service users) as well as public authorities, commercial and social bodies, Ombudsmen and regulatory authorities. The set operates its own pro bono scheme, and work is undertaken for the Bar Pro Bono Unit. Current news and information are available on the website.

WORK UNDERTAKEN Specialism and expertise are provided in all aspects of housing, local government, property and planning work, embracing both public and private law. Particular areas include: landlord and tenant (residential and commercial), home ownership, enfranchisement, right to buy, mortgages, homelessness and housing allocation, public and administrative law, human rights, local government powers and finance, procurement, local government prosecutions and enforcement proceedings, regulation and administration of registered social landlords, housing administration and intervention, anti-social behaviour, environmental health, food safety, health and safety, community care, development and planning, compulsory purchase, highways, licensing, trading standards, housing grants, benefits and social security.

PUBLICATIONS Members of chambers and those collectively writing under the umbrella of 'barristers at Arden Chambers', are involved in a very wide range of leading publications, closely linked with the areas of practice. Members are frequently invited to address in-house and professional conferences around the country. The set supplies weekly online housing and local government update services available to a wide audience through Sweet & Maxwell's HousingView. Full details of publications, including copies of recent articles, are available on the website.

RECRUITMENT The set has an active recruitment policy. Current information about pupillage applications, awards and recruitment is available on the website.

arden
chambers

ATKIN CHAMBERS Andrew White QC

Head of Chambers	Andrew White QC
Principal contacts for counsel appointment	Justin Wilson
Principal contact for arbitrator, adjudicator & mediator appointments	Daniel Jones
Tenants	43

1 Atkin Building, Gray's Inn, London, WC1R 5AT
Tel (020) 7404 0102 **Fax** (020) 7405 7456 **DX** 1033
Email clerks@atkinchambers.com **Website** www.atkinchambers.com

MEMBERS

Andrew White QC (1980) (QC-1997)
Nicholas Dennys QC (1975) (QC-1991)
Jonathan Acton Davis QC (1977) (QC-1996)
Nicholas Baatz QC (1978) (QC-1998)
Martin Bowdery QC (1980) (QC-2000)
Stephen Dennison QC (1985) (QC-2001)
David Streatfeild-James QC (1986) (QC-2001)
Andrew Goddard QC (1985) (QC-2003)
Stephanie Barwise QC (1988) (QC-2006)
Simon Lofthouse QC (1988) (QC-2006)
Chantal-Aimée Doerries QC (1992) (QC-2008)
Peter D Fraser QC (1989) (QC-2009)
Manus McMullan QC (1994) (QC-2010)
Fiona Parkin QC (1993) (QC-2011)
Dominique Rawley QC (1991) (QC-2012)
Steven Walker QC (1993) (QC-2012)
James Howells QC (1995) (QC-2014)
Darryl Royce (1976)
Andrew Burr (1981)
Robert Clay (1989)
Nicholas Collings (1997)
Patrick Clarke (1997)
Christopher Lewis (1998)
Rupert Choat (1998)
Serena Cheng (2000)
Riaz Hussain (2001)
Camille Slow (2002)
Mark Chennells (2002)
Jennifer Jones (2003)
Lucie Briggs (2004)
Frances Pigott (1994-Practicing since 2004)
Simon Crawshaw (2005)
Marc Lixenberg (2005)
Ronan Hanna (2006)
Andrew Fenn (2007)
Zulfikar Khayum (2006)
Peter Land (2007)
Edmund Neuberger (2008)
Omar Eljadi (2009)
David Johnson (2010)
Felicity Dynes (2010)
Mischa Balen (2011)
Lauren Adams (2013)
John Blackburn QC (1969) (QC-1984) *
A J Butcher QC *
Delia Dumaresq *
Sir Thayne Forbes *
Professor Doug Jones (Australia) *
Frances Kirkham (1978)*
Humphrey Lloyd QC (1963) (QC-1979) *
Colin Reese QC (1973) (QC-1987)*
Gordon Reid QC (Scotland) *
Michael Shane (USA) *

* Door Tenant

THE CHAMBERS Atkin Chambers is a leading set of chambers particularly well known for its advocacy and advice on cases concerning domestic and international construction and engineering contracts and projects. Along with this wide area of practice it has extensive expertise and experience in areas such as information technology, energy, professional negligence, shipping and general commercial law. Since 1959 the leading construction standard textbook, Hudson's Building and Engineering Contracts, has been edited in chambers. The 12th edition was published in 2011 with supplements published annually thereafter. The editors of the Building Law Reports, the Construction Law Journal and the consultant editor to Emden's Construction Law are also members.

WORK UNDERTAKEN

Construction & Engineering: Members provide representation and advice on a wide range of legal issues in a domestic and international context in relation to road building, power plants, tunnels, bridges, office construction, airports, telecommunication projects, railway construction and rolling stock disputes, hydrocarbon and chemical pipelines, offshore and submarine structures, shipbuilding and ship repair projects. These services range from advice in connection with the drafting of contracts for their procurement, advice on claims and representation in court or in domestic or international arbitrations and representation in mediations and adjudications. Clients seek advice and representation on matters such as PFI, PPP and public procurement.

Energy: Members act on large-scale national and international projects for the exploration and exploitation of oil and gas, often involving joint ventures. Advice is given on many aspects of the oil and gas world including long-term natural gas contracts, joint operating agreements, tariff agreements, oil and gas transportation, pipeline installation and the design and construction of offshore structures. Members also act in connection with contracts and disputes concerning the design, construction and commissioning of power stations.

Information Technology: Members advise on and represent clients in disputes concerning hardware and software development, procurement and maintenance, systems integration, distribution, licensing and outsourcing agreements. Members also act in more general technical litigation including smart cards, robotics, micro-electronics and network infrastructures. There is a particular expertise in all aspects of telecoms including specification and performance, as well as its regulation.

Professional Negligence: Members often provide advice and representation to professionals covering such aspects as negligence, breach of contract, breach of fiduciary duty and fraud. Such professionals include architects, engineers, surveyors, project managers, valuers, solicitors and those who provide information technology services.

Shipbuilding, Repair & Conversion: Members have acted in some of the largest shipbuilding disputes in the world. Instructions have covered a wide range of vessels including pipe laying vessels, yachts, FSPO's, pontoons, drilling platforms and deepwater drill ships.

Commercial Law: Services are provided in connection with banking, performance bonds and guarantees, insurance, PFI matters and the financing and structuring of large multi-party commercial projects.

AtkinChambersBarristers

BAR MARK

2 BEDFORD ROW William Clegg QC

Head of Chambers	William Clegg QC
Senior Clerk	John Grimmer
Tenants	73

2 Bedford Row, London, WC1R 4BU
Tel (020) 7440 8888 **Fax** (020) 7242 1738 **DX** LDE 17
Email (initialsurname)@2bedfordrow.co.uk **Website** www.2bedfordrow.co.uk

MEMBERS

William Clegg QC (1972) (QC-1991) +
Jim Sturman QC (1982) (QC-2002)
Howard Godfrey QC (1970) (QC-1991)
Peter Griffiths QC (1970) (QC-1995) +
Andrew Munday QC (1973) (QC-1996) +
Nigel Lithman QC (1976) (QC-1997) +
Michael Wolkind QC (1976) (QC-1999)
Maura McGowan QC (1980) (QC-2001) + Deputy HC Judge
Peter Lodder QC (1981) (QC-2001) +
Richard Kovalevsky QC (1983) (QC-2003)
Tracy Ayling QC (1983) (QC-2006)
Ian Stern QC (1983) (QC-2006) +
Mark Milliken-Smith QC (1986) (QC-2006) +
Brian Altman QC (1981) (QC-2008) +
Richard Whittam QC (1983) (QC-2008) + **
Richard Matthews QC (1989) (QC 2010) °
Dean Armstrong QC (1985) (QC-2014)
Stephen Vullo QC (1996) (QC-2014)
Charles Conway (1969)
Deborah Champion (1970) +
Nigel Ingram (1972)
Mark Halsey (1974)
John Caudle (1976) +
Anthony Abell (1977)
Barry Gilbert (1978)
Michael Haynes (1979)
Margaret Dodd (1979) ±
Michael Levy (1979)
John Livingston (1980)
John Donnelly (1983)
Gelaga King (1985) +
Timothy Kendal (1985)
Ian McMeekin (1987) ±
Craig Rush (1989)
Sean Hammond (1991)
Stephen Ferguson (1991)
Valerie Charbit (1992)
Adam Budworth (1992)
Christine Agnew (1992)
Michael Epstein (1992)
John Hurlock (1993)
Richard Ferry-Swainson (1994)
Allan Compton (1994)
Maria Dineen (1997)
Jamas Hodivala (1998)
Ashraf Khan (1999)
Robert Garson (1999) ±
Andrew McGee (1999)
Jacqueline Carey (1999)
Garry Green (1999)
Charles Langley (1999)
Emma King (1999)
Quentin Hunt (2000)
Shauna Ritchie (2000)
Hanna Llewellyn-Waters (2000)
Louise Oakley (2001)
Archangelo Power (2001)
Dean George (2002)
James Harrison (2002)
Samuel Magee (2003)
Rebecca Dix (2004)
Kevin Toomey (2004)
Sandesh Singh (2004)
Eleanor Sanderson (2005)
Austin Stoton (2007)
Christopher Martin (2008)
Jonas Milner (2008)
Vedrana Pehar (2008)
Michael Williams (2008) ±
Thomas Daniel (2009)
David Patience (2009)
Christopher Saad (2009)
Alice Bricogne (2011)

+ Recorder ± Associate Tenant ** Senior Treasury Counsel at CCC ° Standing Counsel to the Health and Safety Executive

THE CHAMBERS Clients of 2 Bedford Row benefit from the knowledge, expertise and support of one of the country's leading criminal and regulatory sets. Committed to all aspects of criminal and regulatory law, chambers advises and represents clients in a wide variety of proceedings and investigations, from high profile fraud and murder cases, to health and safety and professional disciplinary proceedings. Members of 2 Bedford Row have appeared in the ICTY in The Hague, the ECHR, Privy Council, Supreme Court, Court of Appeal, Administrative Court and all courts and tribunals of first instance, as well as public inquiries and inquests. An increasing volume of work is international and members attend hearings around the globe. Chambers serves a variety of clients, spanning national governments, international companies, local authorities and other public bodies, regulators, trade unions, corporations and directors and professional and sporting authorities, as well as individuals. It can call upon the combined expertise of 18 Queen's Counsel and 55 juniors, including a Deputy High Court Judge, both the former and current First Senior Treasury Counsel, standing counsel to the Health and Safety Executive, and a number of recorders as well as 2 former Chairs of the Bar Council and both a former and current Chair of the CBA. Supporting them is a clerking team recognised as one of the best in the country.

WORK UNDERTAKEN

Crime: As one of the acknowledged 'magic circle' criminal sets, it has an outstanding track record in high profile trials, including corporate crimes and war crimes. Examples include the News International Phone Hacking; the Hillsborough Football Stadium disaster; the Hatfield and Potters Bar rail disasters; the Buncefield prosecution; Michael Stone; Colin Stagg; Tony Martin; Levi Bellfield (Milly Dowler murder); Stephen Lawrence; Kenneth Noye (M25 murder); Barry George; Vincent Tabak, Sgt Danny Nightingale; murder of Corporal Lee Rigby; and Corporal Lee Clegg.

Fraud: Criminal fraud is an important part of the chambers workload. Its members have appeared in complex, high profile cases, such as JJB Sports, Torex Retail, Asil Nadir, Imperial Consolidated Pharmaceuticals, BAE, Op. Condor, Jubilee line, Torex, Brent Walker to Levitt, WSTC, Cheney Pensions, Izodia pic, Robinsons.

Health & Safety & Environmental Enforcement: Chambers has a commanding presence in health and safety, including corporate and gross negligence manslaughter. Members include Standing Counsel to the

2 BEDFORD ROW

2 BEDFORD ROW (continued)

HSE and ORR, the co-author of the leading practitioners' textbook and the author of Blackstone's Guide to the Corporate Manslaughter Act. Members have been instructed in all of the most significant appellate cases including Chargot [2009] 2 All ER 645 HL. Chambers also has an enviable reputation in environmental work with particular experience of alleged pollution offences, environmental permit breaches and Transfontier Shipment Regulations breaches.

Professional & Disciplinary Tribunals: Over the years members have developed an intuitive understanding of how professional bodies think, which allows them to tailor their advocacy for the greatest effect. 2 Bedford Row represents professionals before the GMC, GDC, GOC, NMC and SDT among others, as well as acting for professional bodies themselves.

Financial Services Regulation: The team has considerable experience in SFO, FCA, and Revenue & Customs investigations, prosecutions and appeals.

Inquests & Public Inquiries: The regulatory group assists clients before coroners' inquests and public inquiries, providing high quality advice and representation. Examples include Duggan, De Menezes, Lakanal fire, Shipman, Climbié, Lawrence and the Ashwood Hospital Inquiries.

Sports Law: Members also frequently appear before professional sporting tribunals, particularly football, rugby and cricket, and represent many premiership clubs and individual players.

INTERNATIONAL: Members have undertaken work in the US, West Indies, Middle East, Gibraltar, Hong Kong, Turks and Caicos and most of mainland Europe. It can work in Arabic, Dutch, French, German, Hebrew, Italian, Krio (Sierra Leone), Russian and Serbo-Croat. For more details please see the website.

9 BEDFORD ROW Anthony Berry QC

9 Bedford Row, London, WC1R 4AZ
Tel (020) 7489 2727 **Fax** (020) 7489 2828 DX LDE 453
Email clerks@9bedfordrow.co.uk **Website** www.9bedfordrow.co.uk

Head of Chambers	Anthony Berry QC
Chambers Director	Martin Secrett
Senior Clerk	Paul Outen
24-hour Duty Clerk	07971 153 192
Tenants	59

MEMBERS

Anthony Berry QC (1976) (QC-1994)
Steven Kay QC (1977) (QC-1997) ^
Elizabeth Marsh QC (1979) (QC-1999) ^
Richard J Carey-Hughes QC (1977) (QC-2000) ^
Antony Chinn QC (1972) (QC-2003) ^
Abbas Lakha QC (1984) (QC-2003)^
Lee Karu QC (1985) (QC-2010) ^
Jane Bickerstaff QC (1989) ^ (QC-2012) ^
Patricia May (1965)
Richard Germain (1968) ^
Roger Carne (1969) ^
Jane Mirwitch (1974)
Derek Zeitlin (1974) ^
David Burgess (1975)
John Traversi (1977) ^
Louis French (1979)
David Hughes (1980) ^
Justin Rouse (1982) ^
John King (1983) ^
Adrian Amer (1984) ^
David Young (1986) ^
Wayne Cleaver (1986)
John Cammegh (1987) ^
Jonathan Carroll (1987)
Simon Stirling (1989)
Peter Glenser (1993) ^
Jonathan Akinsanya (1993) ^
Anita Arora (1994)
Samantha Cohen (1995)
Anne Faul (1996)
Lawrence Selby (1997) ^
Yogain Chandarana (1997) ^
Gillian Higgins (1997) ^
Matthew Banham (1998) ^
Camilla De Silva (1999) ^
Will Noble (2000)
Mustapha Hakme (2000)
Polly Darling (2000)
Toby Cadman (2001) ^
Daniel Higgins (2003) ^
Lucinda Dannatt (2003)
Sean Sullivan (2004) ^
Max Hardy (2004) ^
Ruth Jones (2004) ^
Rhiannon Sadler (2004)
Richard Paton-Philip (2005)
Corinne Bramwell (2005) ^
David Hammond (2006) ^
Lennart Poulsen (2006)
Jessica Clarke (2006)
Eeva Heikkila (2007)
Aneurin Brewer (2008) ^
Kathryn Hovington (2008)
Tessa Shroff (2009)
Sarah Bafadhel (2009)
Benjamin Joyes (2010)
Marija Bračković (2010)
Kirsty Sutherland (2010)
Kabir Sondhi (2010)
Caroline Macpherson (2011) ^
Gregor Guy-Smith
Colleen Rohan
Prof William Schabas *
Ignatius Hughes QC *
Gaon Hart *
Nicholas Worsley *
James Welsh

* Door Tenant ^ Public/Direct Access

THE CHAMBERS 9 Bedford Row has a strong reputation as one of the finest specialist criminal chambers both nationally and internationally, with an enviable reputation for client service. The set's aims are achieved by its progressive approach to developing new work in a rapidly changing market in a professional, flexible, approachable and efficient way. Member's strength in advocacy, diversity, depth and range of skills allows them to compete in this challenging world and most are public access accredited.

WORK UNDERTAKEN Chambers have a dedicated group of practitioners who specialise in serious sexual offences, experienced in both the defence and prosecution of sexual offences. It has defended in many of the most high profile murder and terrorism cases tried in this country. Financial crime is an important part of Chambers work, as it has the experience and knowledge to assist businesses and individuals in identifying and addressing risks before they escalate. Chambers have a dedicated group of practitioners who specialise in serious sexual offences, experienced in both the defence and prosecution of sexual offences. It has defended in many of the most high profile murder and terrorism cases tried in this country. Chambers prides itself on providing high quality representation and advice on all aspects of the military justice system. Chambers prides itself on providing high quality representation and advice on all aspects of the military justice system. Chambers barristers have a reputation for active, involved case management and team leadership, operating closely with those who instruct. Prosecuting, members provide a comprehensive case preparation which delivers a robust, efficient and effective trial. Defending, members advise on case management at an early stage and throughout the proceedings. The set will always give clients frank and professional solutions when addressing legal issues, without losing track of their commercial interests.

INTERNATIONAL 9 Bedford Row has an outstanding team of international criminal lawyers. Members have a global reputation having been involved in many high profile trials at the international courts and tribunals, including the ICC, ICTY, ICTR, ECCC, SCSL, STL, the ICT in Bangladesh and Bosnian War Crimes Chamber. The team has now developed a very strong human rights focus, taking on important issues in conflict zones and States in revolutionary flux for international institutions seeking to promote national stability and establish the rule of law (Syria, Libya, Iraq). Recent projects under the Business and Human Rights heading have also been developed for institutions needing to satisfy compliance procedures of which the Human Rights at Sea initiative launched by David Hammond received international attention that followed hard on the heels of his 100 Series Rules for the Use of Force at Sea to combat piracy for the maritime States and security industry. Expertise is sought after to challenge States that abuse Interpol Red Notices with faux arrest warrants and persecute individuals and minorities by the theft of their assets. The extensive skills available at all levels allows chambers to provide full top to bottom teams to tackle all forms of international criminal litigation and to deal with legal and political issues on the international stage. The ARC project run by Gill Higgins which is a vehicle for claimants to instruct counsel to take cases to the Africa Court of Human and People Rights has been recognised as a unique and valuable international litigation asset.

BAR MARK

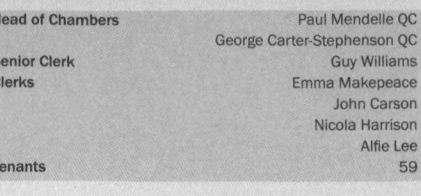

25 BEDFORD ROW Paul Mendelle QC & George Carter-Stephenson QC

25 Bedford Row, London, WC1R 4HD
Tel (020) 7067 1500 **Fax** (020) 7067 1507 **DX** 1043 (Ch.Ln)
Email clerks@25bedfordrow.com **Website** www.25bedfordrow.com

Head of Chambers	Paul Mendelle QC George Carter-Stephenson QC
Senior Clerk	Guy Williams
Clerks	Emma Makepeace John Carson Nicola Harrison Alfie Lee
Tenants	59

MEMBERS

George Carter-Stephenson QC (1975) (QC-1998)
Paul Mendelle QC (1981) (QC-2006)
Charles Salmon QC (1972) (QC-1996)
Nigel Sangster QC (1976) (QC-1998)
Courtenay Griffiths QC (1980) (QC-1998)
Diana Ellis QC (1978) (QC-2001)
Peter Doyle QC (1975) (QC-2002)
Kim Hollis QC (1979) (QC-2002)
Jeremy Dein QC (1982) (QC-2003)
Paul Keleher QC (1980) (QC-2009)
David Hooper QC (1971) (QC-2010)
Rudi Fortson QC (1976) (QC-2010)
John Cooper QC (1983) (QC-2010)
Tom Price QC (1985) (QC-2010)
Paul Hynes QC (1987) (QC-2010)
Jo Sidhu QC (1993) (QC-2012)
Chris Daw QC (1993) (QC-2013)
Tyrone Smith QC (1994) (QC-2014)
Ronald Jaffa (1974)
Jonathan Mitchell (1974)
Chester Beyts (1978)
Roger Offenbach (1978)
Simon Pentol (1982)
Bill Maley (1982)
Leroy Redhead (1982)
Colin Wells (1987)
Adrian Eissa (1988)
Helen Valley (1990)
Arlette Piercy (1990)
Emma Akuwudike (1992)
Harry Potter (1993)
Richard Furlong (1994)
Aisling Byrnes (1994)
Nicola Howard (1995)
Osman Osman (1995)
Carolina Guiloff (1996)
Samantha Riggs (1996)
Nathaniel Rudolf (1996)
Sebastian Gardiner (1997)
Dermot Keating (1997)
Melanie Simpson (1998)
Michael Neofytou (1999)
Ben Smitten (1999)
Laurie-Anne Power (2000)
Geoffrey Payne (2000)
Natalie Sherborn (2000)
Yasin Patel (2002)
Monica Stevenson (2004)
Rebecca Randall (2005)
Matt Radstone (2005)
Roy Ledgister (2005)
Daniel Chadwick (2006)
Sam Blom-Cooper (2006)
Priya Malhotra (2007)
Kathryn Arnot Drummond (2008)
Emma Stuart-Smith (2009)
Sushil Kumar (2009)
Abimbola Johnson (2011)
Duncan Jones (2012)

THE CHAMBERS This innovative set specialise in every aspect of modern defence advocacy, acting in the very highest profile cases. Having achieved and maintained the quality standard for the Bar (BarMark) since 1999, chambers is consistently assessed as a centre of excellence. Widely recognised as the leading chambers in its core practice areas, due to its client focused, high quality service. Their reputation for excellence is best demonstrated by involvement in almost every recent major criminal trial, whether in fraud, organised crime or murder. Expansion of its fraud and financial litigation practice is testament to its reputation for providing advocacy and advisory services of the highest quality. Practitioners are experienced in the conduct of civil cases, including defamation and privacy, professional disciplinary and environmental law. Its excellence extends to the high quality of its staff who have a justified reputation for expertise and integrity.

WORK UNDERTAKEN

Criminal: Unrivalled defence experience and expertise across the entire spectrum of criminal law. Covering all aspects of serious crime including murder, organised crime, drug trafficking, money laundering and crimes of extreme and sexual violence. Members also act for UK nationals charged with serious criminal offences in other national jurisdictions. Private client specialists accept instructions on all criminal matters, including minor matters, in order to reduce the impact on individuals' reputations, careers and personal lives.

Fraud & Financial Litigation: Specialising in defending individuals and corporations against allegations of international, corporate and financial crime. Providing a full range of advice and representation in both the criminal and civil aspects of this discipline from preliminary stages, including restraint, right through to appeal , confiscation and civil recovery. Experienced in dealing with all of the various types of fraud before the courts. Assistance is also provided in relation to risk management and compliance, training and advisory work.

Professional Disciplinary & Regulatory: Acting on behalf of individuals appearing before their professional bodies, disciplinary tribunals and regulatory authorities. Including accountants, solicitors, police officers of all ranks, healthcare professionals, sports people or sports organisations amongst others. Advice is available from an early stage in these often complicated cases, which frequently run parallel with criminal or quasi-criminal proceedings.

Civil Liberties & Human Rights: Acting for persons whose human rights are infringed in a wide range of areas of law including actions against the police and public authorities, extradition, international law, inquests, mental health, prisoners' rights and public and administrative law. Chambers' public and administrative law experts are involved in judicial review and appellate cases and challenges to decisions of a wide range of public authorities.

INTERNATIONAL WORK Experts in defending those accused of offences perpetrated by States, including war crime and other human rights abuses and offences against states, including espionage and terrorism. Advice and representation in international human rights law and trans-national justice issues, for individuals, governmental organisations and major NGOs in a wide range of jurisdictions. Members act for and advise clients who face action from foreign governments including for the freezing or forfeiture of their assets.

29 BEDFORD ROW CHAMBERS Nicholas Francis QC

29 Bedford Row Chambers, London, WC1R 4HE
Tel (020) 7404 1044 **Fax** (020) 7831 0626 **DX** 1044
Email clerks@29br.co.uk **Website** www.29br.co.uk

Head of Chambers	Nicholas Francis QC
Senior Clerk	James Shortall
Clerks	Julie Holcombe
	Hudson Brewer
	Ben Cross
	Sean Gentleman
Fees Clerks	Steve Pickin
	Nicola Applebee
Chambers Administrator	Nicola Kessell
Tenants	55

MEMBERS

Nicholas Francis QC (1981) (QC-2002)
Timothy Scott QC (1975) (QC-1995)
Paul Storey QC (1982) (QC-2001)
Philip Cayford QC (1975) (QC-2002)
Robert Peel QC (1990) (QC-2010)
Patrick Chamberlayne QC (1992) (QC-2010)
Piers Pressdee QC (1991) (QC-2010)
Howard Shaw QC (1973) (QC-2011)
Christopher Wagstafffe QC (1992) (QC-2011)
Jonathan Southgate QC (1992) (QC-2013)
Peter Duckworth (1971)
The Hon Clare Renton (1972)
Jonathan Swift (1977)
Indira Ramsahoye (1980)
Jacqueline Wehrle (1984)
David Walden-Smith (1985)
Mark Emanuel (1985)
Stephen Reynolds (1987)
Alexa Storey-Rea (1990)
Nicholas Chapman (1990)
Lee Arnot (1990)
Alexis Campbell (1990)
Annabel Wentworth (1990)
Jonathan Tod (1990)
Sally Max (1991)
Richard Bates (1992)
Victoria Domenge (1993)
Judith Butler (1993)
Roshi Amiraftabi (1993)
Brent Molyneux (1994)
Nicholas Allen (1995)
Peter Mitchell (1996)
Ken Collins (1996)
Sassa-Ann Amaouche (1996)
Dafydd Griffiths (1997)
Lucy Owens (1997)
Laura Heaton (1998)
Georgina Black (1999)
Simon Calhaem (1999)
Anne Hudd (2000)
Anthony Geadah (2000)
Victoria Francis (2001)
Ben Fearnley (2001)
Max Lewis (2002)
Christopher Butterfield (2004)
Lynsey Cade Davies (2005)
Richard Tambling (2005)
Petra Teacher (2006)
Conor Fee (2006)
Helen Williams (2007)
Amber Sheridan (2008)
Anton Eriera (2010)
James Finch (2011)
Matthew Long (2011)
Miriam Foster (2011)

THE CHAMBERS 29 Bedford Row Chambers is committed to providing its clients with an effective and efficient legal service. It operates from three magnificent grade II listed buildings in the heart of legal London, completely modernised for the latest technology.

WORK UNDERTAKEN Chambers offers specialist expertise at all levels of seniority in every aspect of family law including matrimonial finance, children (both public and private law), child abduction, co-habitation law, domestic violence and under the Civil Partnership and Inheritance Acts. Chambers has a strong team of top flight financial remedy practitioners. Seventeen members of chambers are trained as collaborative lawyers. Several members practise as mediators and several are qualified as family law arbitrators. A number of senior members of chambers chair private FDRs and Early Neutral Evaluation hearings, and, with large boardroom and conference room facilities, chambers is well suited to these processes. Some members of chambers accept Public Access instructions. Several former members of chambers have been given judicial appointments, and many current members sit as Deputy High Court or Circuit Judges, or as Deputy District Judges.
Chambers organises a comprehensive seminar programme which is highly regarded by solicitors and trainees. The seminars are accredited for CPD points. Members of chambers appear in courts around the country and abroad. Chambers has dedicated conference rooms, but members will travel to see clients wherever necessary.

Administration: Chambers is served by nine full time clerks and also has two dedicated fees clerks, allowing work to be processed quickly and efficiently. The clerks' room is staffed between 8.30 am and 7.00 pm, but emergency contact is always available outside that time. The clerking is praised for its efficient, friendly and commercial approach.
For information about the work of chambers generally, or the practice of individual members of chambers in particular, please contact the Senior Clerk, James Shortall, or visit the website.

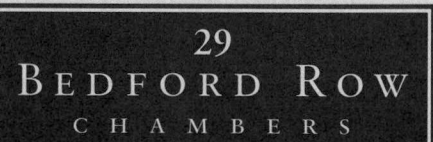

29
BEDFORD ROW
CHAMBERS

36 BEDFORD ROW

36 Bedford Row, London, WC1R 4JH
Tel (020) 7421 8000 **Fax** (020) 7421 8035 **DX** 360 LDE
Email chambers@36bedfordrow.co.uk **Website** www.36bedfordrow.co.uk

Joint Heads of Chambers	Richard Wilson QC William Harbage QC
Chief Executive	Malcolm Taylor
Tenants	88

MEMBERS

Richard Wilson QC (1981) (QC-2003)
William Harbage QC (1983) (QC-2003)
Frances Mary Oldham QC (1977) (QC-1994)
Christopher Donnellan QC (1981) (QC-2008)
Amjad Malik QC (1987) (QC-2010)
Jonathan Kirk QC (1995) (QC-2010)
David Herbert QC (1992) (QC-2013)
John Lloyd-Jones QC (1993) (QC-2013)
Adrienne Lucking QC (1989) (QC-2014)
Felicity Gerry QC (1994) (QC-2014)
William Tyler QC (1996) (QC-2014)
David Altaras (1969)
David Lee (1973)
Jamie De Burgos (1973)
Sam Mainds (1977)
Gillian Temple-Bone (1978)
Paul Infield (1980)
Mercy Akman (1982)
Jacqueline Matthews-Stroud (1984)
Joanne Ecob (1985)
Robert Underwood (1986)
Peter Dean (1987)
Richard O'Dair (1987)
Gregory Pryce (1988)
Andrew Howarth (1988)
Patricia Cave (1989)
Mary Prior (1990)
Amanda Johnson (1990)
Matthew Lowe (1991)
Sarah Gaunt (1992)
Andrew Copeland (1992)
Rebecca Herbert (1993)
Andrzej Bojarski (1995)
Philippa Daniels (1995)
Mary Loram (1995)
Jonathan Spicer (1995)
Rhys Taylor (1996)
James Collins (1997)
Steven Evans (1997)
Jonathan Rushton (1997)
Kevin Barry (1997)
Stephen Goodfellow (1997)
Hannah Markham (1998)
Simon Harding (1998)
Simon Ash (1999)
Jane Bacon (1999)
Martin Kingerley (1999)
Katya Savdek (1999)
Mark Roscoe (1999)
Caroline Bray (2000)
Clare Meredith (2000)
Adam Pearson (2000)
Jessica Franses (2000)
Allison Summers (2000)
Georgina Gibbs (2000)
Miriam Carrion Benitez (2001)
Geoffrey Sullivan (2001)
Daniel McDowell (2001)
Nadia Silver (2001)
Christopher Carr (2002)
Michael Rudd (2002)
Cameron Crowe (2002)
John Small (2002)
Kate Tompkins (2003)
Joanna O'Connell (2003)
Claire Howell (2003)
Kathryn Howarth (2005)
Paul Prior (2005)
Victoria Lorne (2005)
Kakoly Pandé (2005)
Kate Makepeace Grieve (2006)
Sïnead King (2006)
Gavin Lyon (2006)
Richard Roberts (2006)
Stephen Roberts (2006)
Stephen Bishop (2006)
James McLennon
David Ball (2008)
Emilie Pottle (2008)
Piers von Berg (2009)
Saoirse Townshend (2010)
Malcolm Macdonald (2010)
Florence Iveson (2010)
Rosa Abulafia (2011)
Rebecca Rothwell (2011)
Pranjal Shrotri (2012)
Sarah Parkes (2012)
Hannah Jones (2012)

THE CHAMBERS 36 Bedford Row has 88 tenants including 11 QCs, all of whom are committed to excellent service and are recognised for operating with real pride and strength in depth. Barristers from Chambers regularly appear in high profile Crown Court cases and in the High Court, Court of Appeal (Criminal and Civil Divisions) and in the Supreme Court of the United Kingdom – across all the set's specialist areas. Members have also built an international profile with work arising from jurisdictions in Europe, The Hague, the Middle East, Asia and Africa – particularly in international criminal and human rights cases.

WORK UNDERTAKEN

Criminal: Chambers has an outstanding track record conducting high profile and complex cases across the criminal and regulatory tribunals both for the defence and for prosecuting authorities. Members regularly undertake cases ranging from terrorism, murder, rape and sexual offences against children, internet crime, drug offences including importation and distribution, fraud, money laundering, corruption, civil and criminal seizure of assets, proceeds of crime and extradition.

Family: Members of the family team are organised into practice sub-groups specialising in all aspects of family law, including matrimonial finances, TOLATA, divorce, public and private children law, forced marriages, pre-nuptial and cohabitation agreements, child abduction and Court of Protection. The team enjoys its reputation as an up and coming family law specialist team.

Consumer: Members of the team are experts in all areas of consumer law, trading standards and brand protection, providing advice and representation to local authorities, private companies and individuals. They write the leading text book, Consumer and Trading Standards: Law and Practice (Jordans 2013) and regularly lecture at the annual Trading Standards Institute Conference.

Public & Human Rights: The public law and human rights team at 36 Bedford Row is dynamic and growing in strength and reputation. Its members undertake a wide variety of public law work at all levels including immigration, human rights, education, housing, planning and extradition.

Employment: The team offers expertise in all areas of employment law in the Employment Tribunal, the EAT, the Court of Appeal and Supreme Court. Members represent respondents, claimants and Local Authorities in the full range of discrimination claims, TUPE claims and unfair dismissal claims.

Commercial & Civil: The civil practice group provides specialist advisory, drafting and advocacy services in six fields: commercial and business, property and trusts, landlord and tenant, personal injury and clinical negligence, professional negligence and regulatory/disciplinary matters, and art law. Members represent clients nationwide in courts and tribunals (litigation), acting for clients in mediations and arbitrations (ADR) and non-contentious business (including drafting contracts and advising on specific terms in contractual or other documents).

42 BEDFORD ROW Frank Feehan QC

42 Bedford Row, London, WC1R 4LL
Tel (020) 7831 0222 **Fax** (020) 7831 2239 **DX** 201 London Chancery Lane
Email clerks@42BR.com **Website** www.42BR.com

Head of Chambers	Frank Feehan QC
Senior Clerk	Alan Brewer
Clerks	Steve Sheridan
	James Tidnam
Commercial Manager	Tony Charlick
Tenants	106

MEMBERS

Frank Feehan QC (1988) (QC-2010)
Tina Cook QC (1988) (QC-2011)
Patrick Hamlin (1970)
Mark Batchelor (1971)
Michael Daiches (1977)
Philip Newman (1977)
Anthony Higgins (1978)
Charles Utley (1979)
Charles Scott (1980)
Francis Treasure (1980)
Howard Lederman (1982)
Andrew Pote (1983)
Rehna Azim (1984)
David Dabbs (1984)
Jonathan Bennett (1985)
Jeremy Rosenblatt (1985)
Neil Vickery (1985)
Fawzia King (1985)
Mark Maitland Jones (1986)
Garfield Braithwaite (1987)
Jeremy Hall (1988)
Gemma Taylor (1988)
Sinclair Cramsie (1988)
Sheila Phil-Ebosie (1988)
Ronald Coster (1989)
Anthony Jerman (1989)
Martin Haukeland (1989)
Desmond Kilcoyne (1990)
Adrian Higgins (1990)
Richard Furniss (1991)
Mary Lazarus (1991)
Deborah Todman (1991)
Deborah Shield (1991)
Stephen Murch (1991)
Mukhtiar Otwal (1991)
Edmund Walters (1991)
Benjamin Uduje (1992)
Gabriel Buttimore (1993)
Susan Chan (1994)
Naomi Hawkes (1994)
Anna McKenna (1994)
Philip McCormack (1994)
Stuart Nicol (1994)
Damian Woodward-Carlton (1995)
Fareha Choudhury (1995)
Matthew Feldman (1995)
Scott Matthewson (1996)
Jude Shepherd (1996)
Aysha Ahmad (1996)
Eilidh Gardner (1997)
Nigel Woodhouse (1997)
Christopher Mann (1998)
Rebecca Thomas (1999)
Sebastian Naughton (1999)
Richard Gregory (2000)
Richard Little (2000)
Francis Cassidy (2000)
Jessica Lee (2000)
Andrew Holmes (2000)
Julie Stather (2000)
Natalie Ganteaume (2001)
Angela Piears (2001)
Thomas Wood (2002)
Katie Phillips (2002)
Mark Chaloner (2002)
Robert Cameron (2003)
Anne Dillon (2003)
Murray Grant (2003)
Maria-Amália Walker (2003)
Sian Gough (2004)
Paul Gurnham (2004)
Safia Tharoo (2004)
Orlando Holloway (2004)
Timothy Adkin (2004)
Mark Bradley (2004)
Edward Bennion-Pedley (2004)
Tim Brown (2005)
Mary Robertson (2005)
Iris Ferber (2005)
Matthew Corrie (2006)
Ruth Webber (2006)
Nicholas Singer (2006)
Janet Oganah (2007)
Neil Clark (2007)
Delia Minoprio (2007)
Celeste Irvine (2007)
Christopher Barnes (2008)
Zimran Samuel (2008)
Philippa Tcstar (2009)
Jonathan Newman (2009)
Ben Stimmler (2009)
Richard Williams (2009)
Helen Nettleship (2009)
Samson Spanier (2009)
Francesca Conn (2010)
Anushka Chakravarty (2010)
Hamed Zovidavi (2010)
Pauline Troy (2011)
Jennifer Kotilaine (2011)
Patrick Maxwell (2011)
Stephen Hackett (2011)
Justin Leslie (2011)
Shiv Haria-Shah (2012)
Martha Gray (2012)

42 BEDFORD ROW

Community Legal Service

THE CHAMBERS Areas of specialisation: clinical negligence and personal injury, contract and commercial, employment, family, professional negligence, property, public and environmental law.

48 BEDFORD ROW (PARTNERSHIP COUNSEL) Roderick I'Anson Banks

Head of Chambers	Roderick I'Anson Banks
Practice Manager	Tyroon Win
Tenants	2

48 Bedford Row, London, WC1R 4LR
Tel (020) 7430 2005 **Fax** (020) 7831 4885 **DX** 284 LDE
Email tyroon@partnershipcounsel.co.uk **Website** www.partnershipcounsel.co.uk

MEMBERS

Roderick I'Anson Banks (1974) LLB (London)
Simon Jelf (1996) LLB (Eur)

THE CHAMBERS Specialise exclusively in partnership and limited liability partnership law and provide solicitors and other professional and trading partnerships and LLPs with a full range of legal services, from the drafting of new agreements and the review of existing agreements to advice and representation in partnership disputes, arbitrations and mediations. Chambers' aim, where possible, is to assist clients with the process of resolving disputes, without recourse to litigation and provide ongoing advice and support from the embryonic stages of a developing dispute, right through to the conclusion of any litigation or until a negotiated settlement is reached. Chambers also carries out a significant amount of drafting and advisory work relating to limited and corporate partnerships. Licensed and Public Access work is undertaken in appropriate cases.

PUBLICATIONS Roderick I'Anson Banks is the editor of *Lindley & Banks on Partnership* , the authoritative guide to partnership law (19th ed. published December 2010), and the author of the *Encyclopedia of Professional Partnerships*. Simon Jelf is a contributor to the *Encyclopedia of Professional Partnerships*.

PARTNERSHIP • COUNSEL •

BLACKSTONE CHAMBERS Monica Carss-Frisk QC & Anthony Peto QC

Blackstone House, Temple, London, EC4Y 9BW
Tel (020) 7583 1770 **Fax** (020) 7822 7350 **DX** 281
Email clerks@blackstonechambers.com **Website** www.blackstonechambers.com

Head of Chambers	Monica Carss-Frisk QC Anthony Peto QC
Senior Clerk	Gary Oliver
Chambers Director	Julia Hornor
Tenants	95

MEMBERS

Monica Carss-Frisk QC (1985) (QC-2001)
Anthony Peto QC (1985) (QC-2009)
Sir David Edward QC (1962) (QC-1974)
Stanley Brodie QC (1954) (QC-1975)
Lord Woolf of Barnes (1955)
Lord Lester of Herne Hill QC (1963) (QC-1975)
Michael Beloff QC (1967) (QC-1981)
David Donaldson QC (1968) (QC-1984)
Robert Englehart QC (1969) (QC-1986)
David Hunt QC (1969) (QC-1987)
Barbara Dohmann QC (1971) (QC-1987)
Maurice Mendelson QC (1965) (QC-1992)
Jonathan Harvie QC (1973) (QC-1992)
Lord Pannick QC (1979) (QC-1992)
Sir Jeffrey Jowell QC (1965) (QC-1993)
Stephen Nathan QC (1969) (QC-1993)
John Howell QC (1979) (QC-1993)
Richard Keen QC (1980) (QC-1993) Scotland
Charles Flint QC (1975) (QC-1995)
Michael Bloch QC (1979) (QC-1998)
Ian Mill QC (1981) (QC-1999)
Harish Salve SC (2013)
Paul Goulding QC (1984) (QC-2000)
Hugo Page QC (1977) (QC-2002)
Mark Shaw QC (1987) (QC-2002)
Robert Anderson QC (1986) (QC-2006)
Dinah Rose QC (1989) (QC-2006)
Michael Fordham QC (1990) (QC-2006)
Timothy Otty QC (1990) (QC-2006)
James Eadie QC (1984) (QC-2008)
Robert Howe QC (1988) (QC-2008)
Pushpinder Saini QC (1991) (QC-2008)
Adam Lewis QC (1985) (QC-2009)
Alan Maclean QC (1993) (QC-2009)
Andrew Green QC (1988) (QC-2010)
Javan Herberg QC (1992) (QC 2011)
Sam Grodzinski QC (1996) (QC-2011)
Andrew Hunter QC (1993) (QC-2012)
Thomas de la Mare QC (1995) (QC-2012)
Kieron Beal QC (1995) (QC-2012)
Tom Weisselberg QC (1995) (QC-2014)
Jane Mulcahy QC (1995) (QC-2014)
Kate Gallafent QC (1997) (QC-2014)
Guy Goodwin-Gill (1971)
Gerard Clarke (1986)
Adrian Briggs (1989)
Thomas Croxford (1992)
Andreas Gledhill (1992)
Joanna Pollard (1993)
Gemma White (1994)
Jane Collier (1994)
Emma Dixon (1994)
Andrew George (1997)
Claire Weir (1998)
Ben Jaffey (1999)
Brian Kennelly (1999)
Catherine Callaghan (1999)
Stephanie Palmer (2000)
Diya Sen Gupta (2000)
Leona Powell (2000)
Nick De Marco (2001)
David Pievsky (2001)
Shaheed Fatima (2001)
Victoria Windle (2001)
Ivan Hare (1991)
Mark Vinall (2002)
Sarah Wilkinson (2003)
Robert Weekes (2003)
Tom Hickman (2003)
Catherine Donnelly (2003)
James Segan (2004)
Iain Steele (2005)
Naina Patel (2005)
Tom Richards (2006)
Tristan Jones (2006)
Hanif Mussa (2007)
Simon Pritchard (2007)
Jessica Boyd (2007)
Christopher McCrudden (1996) (NIRE 2006)
David Lowe (2008)
Emily Neill (2008)
Paul Luckhurst (2009)
Tom Cleaver (2009)
Tom Mountford (2009)
Andrew Scott (2010)
Shane Sibbel (2010)
Fraser Campbell (2010)
Ravi Mehta (2010)
Daniel Burgess (2011)
Harry Adamson (2012)
Jason Pobjoy (2012)
Jana Sadler-Forster (2012)
Kerenza Davis (2012)
Tom Coates (2013)
Eesvan Krishnan (2013)

THE CHAMBERS Blackstone Chambers is a long established set, combining formidable strengths in commercial litigation, EU and competition, public international law, human rights, administrative and public law, and employment, with state of the art facilities and a friendly and open approach to client service.

LANGUAGES include Finnish, French, German, Hindi, Italian, Punjabi, Spanish, Swedish and Urdu.

RECRUITMENT Blackstone Chambers is a member of Pupillage Gateway. A first or upper second class degree is usually required, although not necessarily in law. Pupillage awards of up to £60,000 are available. Mini-pupillages for a week in the year preceding pupillage are required for potential pupils of chambers.

For further details of an individual barrister's work and for a full breakdown of Chambers' areas of practice, please visit the website: www.blackstonechambers.com.

Blackstone
CHAMBERS

7 BR Simeon Maskrey QC

Head of Chambers	Simeon Maskrey QC
Chief Executive	Fay Gillott
Senior Clerks	Paul Eeles (Civil)
	Rod McGurk (Crime & Family)
Tenants	87

7 Bedford Row, London, WC1R 4BU
Tel (020) 7242 3555 **Fax** (020) 7242 2511 **DX** 347 (Ch.Ln.)
Email clerks@7br.co.uk **Website** www.7br.co.uk

MEMBERS

Simeon Maskrey QC (1977) (QC-1995) +
David Farrer QC (1967) (QC-1986) + ^
Timothy Barnes QC (1968) (QC-1986) +
Alan Newman QC (1968) (QC-1989)
Richard Latham QC (1971) (QC-1991) +
Nigel Rumfitt QC (1974) (QC-1994) +
Philip P Shears QC (1972) (QC-1996) +
Collingwood Thompson QC (1975) (QC-1998) +
Yvonne A Coen QC (1982) (QC-2000) +
Timothy Spencer QC (1982) (QC-2001) + ^
Derek Sweeting QC (1983) (QC-2001) + ^
Maureen Baker QC (1984) (QC-2009) + ^
Rachel Langdale QC (1990) (QC-2009)
Steven Ford QC (1992) (QC-2010)
Barabara Connolly QC (1986) (QC-2011)
Hugh Preston QC (1994) (QC-2012) ^
Deirdre Goodwin (1974)
Julian D Matthews (1979) +
Simon Wheatley (1979)
Jeremy Pendlebury (1980)
Farooq Ahmed (1983)
Susan C Reed (1984)
Timothy Walker (1984) ^
Adam Clemens (1985)
Jacqueline Julyan (2009) S.A. 1986
Simon King (1987) +
David Matthew (1987) ^
Andrew Wheeler (1988)
Gordon Aspden (1988)
Smair Soor (1988)
Catherine Rayner (1989)
Tim Meakin (1989) ^
Brendan Roche (1989) +
Susan Belgrave (1989)
Leslie Keegan (1989)
Graham Huston (1991) +
Jason Mansell (1991) ^
Adam Korn (1992)
Maryam Syed (1993)
Adam Weitzman (1993)
Luke Blackburn (1993) ^
Vanessa Marshall (1994) ^
Jeffry Jupp (1994) ^
Bilal Rawat (1995)
James House (1995)
Anwar Nashashibi (1995)
Andrea Chute (1995)
Hari Kaur (1995)
Sarah Wood (1996) ^
Elaine Banton (1996) ^
Susannah Johnson (1996) ^
Adrian Langdale (1996)
Anita Guha (1997)
Peter Ellis (1997) ^
Nigel Povoas (1998) ^
Justin Slater (1999) ^
Jenny Carter-Manning (1999) ^
Nick Cropp (1999)
Kate Lumbers (1999)
Gareth Weetman (1999)
Adam Walker (2000)
Steven Gray (2000) ^
Richard Baker (2000)
David O'Mahony (2000) ^
Gemma Lindfield (2002)
Hanisha Patel (2002)
Gina Allwood (2002) ^
William Chapman (2003) ^
Tim Bowden (2003)
Jonathan Bertram (2003) ^
Conor Dufficy (2004)
Christina Lyons (2004)
Craig Carr (2005)
Rob Harland (2006)
James Weston (2007)
Patricia Leonard (2007)
Daniel Bishop (2007)
Alex Young (2008)
Ben Isaacs (2009)
Kathryn Duff (2009)
James Robottom (2009)
Caroline Lody (2009)
James Macdonald (2010)
Saara Idelbi (2008)
Madelaine Power (2010)
Helen Compton (2011)
Dr Gregory Burke (2012)

\+ Recorder ^ Public/Direct Access

THE CHAMBERS 7 Bedford Row is a leading national and international set of chambers, established over 50 years ago and recognised today as one of the leading sets with a reputation for excellence.

Chambers has deliberately avoided evolving into a specialist set; appreciating that legal problems are not easily pigeonholed and that there is a real advantage to offering expertise across a wide range of criminal and civil disciplines.

With a membership of 87 barristers, 16 of whom are Queen's Counsel, the set is able to field large teams of experienced practitioners, each capable of providing exceptional experience and speciality, enabling chambers to deliver a team tailor-made to suit the requirements of a particluar case.

WORK UNDERTAKEN Chambers offers strength and depth in areas of:

- Clinical and professional negligence
- Personal injury
- Product liability
- Complex fraud
- Financial and regulatory crime
- Child and family law
- Employment
- Civil commercial
- Contract and tort
- Insurance disputes
- Sports law

7BR SEVEN BEDFORD ROW

ONE BRICK COURT Andrew Caldecott QC

1 Brick Court, Temple, London, EC4Y 9BY
Tel (020) 7353 8845 **Fax** (020) 7583 9144 **DX** 468 LDE
Email clerks@onebrickcourt.com **Website** www.onebrickcourt.com

Head of Chambers	Andrew Caldecott QC
Senior Clerk	David Mace
Tenants	18

MEMBERS

Andrew Caldecott QC (1975) (QC-1994)
Richard Rampton QC (1965) (QC-1987)
Sir Edward Garnier QC (1976) (QC-1995)
Manuel Barca QC (1986) (QC-2011)
Dr Matt Collins QC (1999) (QC-2011) (Aus) *
Harvey Starte (1985)
Timothy Atkinson (1988)
Jane Phillips (1989)
Caroline Addy (1991)
Catrin Evans (1994)
Sarah Palin (1999)
David Glen (2002)
Aidan Eardley (2002)
Ian Helme (2005)
Kate Wilson (2005)
Clare Kissin (2009)
Jonathan Scherbel-Ball (2010)
Hannah Ready (2010)
Clara Hamer (2013)

* Door Tenant

THE CHAMBERS One Brick Court is a leading set specialising in media law and information-related law. Members of chambers appear regularly in the High Court and chambers can offer expertise and considerable experience in the House of Lords/Supreme Court, the Privy Council and the Court of Appeal. Members also appear before professional, disciplinary and regulatory tribunals, including the First Tier and Upper Tribunals, Ofcom and sports disciplinary tribunals, as well as arbitrations and mediations. Included in their number are two members appointed to the prestigious Attorney General's Panel of Counsel. In addition to contentious work, members advise on a pre-publication basis to the entire spectrum of publishers and broadcasters, in both traditional and new media. Within chambers, there is experience of advising on media claims in other jurisdictions, most recently in Northern Ireland, Hong Kong, Singapore, Malaysia and the Cayman Islands.

WORK UNDERTAKEN

Defamation & Malicious Falsehood: Libel, slander, slander of goods, trade libel.
Privacy & Confidence: All matters arising from the tensions between the right to free speech and the right to privacy, under the Humans Rights Act; obtaining and resisting applications for injunctions, including emergency out-of-hours injunctions; image rights and reputation management; the regulation of the state's investigatory powers; commercial confidentiality; confidentiality and employment contracts.
Contempt & Reporting Restrictions: Including urgent advice and representation in the civil, criminal and family courts and employment tribunals on the reporting of proceedings; anonymity orders; judicial review; protection of journalists' sources.
Information Law: Advice and representation on all matters arising out of the Freedom of Information Act and Data Protection Act.
Other: Harassment; negligent misstatement; passing-off; malicious prosecution; obscenity; media related intellectual property law.

PUBLICATIONS Members of chambers have written and contributed to many of the leading works on media law, including *Duncan & Neill on Defamation, Arlidge, Eady and Smith on Contempt, Carter-Ruck on Libel and Privacy, Halsbury's Laws of England, Bullen & Leake Precedents of Pleadings* and *Atkin's Court Forms* titles on libel and slander, confidence, privacy, data protection, freedom of information and regulation of investigatory powers, and contempt.

BRICK COURT CHAMBERS Jonathan Hirst QC & Helen Davies QC

Head of Chambers	Jonathan Hirst QC Helen Davies QC
Senior Clerks	Julian Hawes Ian Moyler
Tenants	81

7-8 Essex Street, London, WC2R 3LD
Tel (020) 7379 3550 **Fax** (020) 7379 3558 **DX** 302 Chancery Lane
Email clerks@brickcourt.co.uk **Website** www.brickcourt.co.uk

MEMBERS

Jonathan Hirst QC (1975) (QC-1990)
Helen Davies QC (1991) (QC-2008)
David Vaughan QC (1963) (QC-1981)
Hilary Heilbron QC (1971) (QC-1987)
Timothy Charlton QC (1974) (QC-1993)
Richard Gordon QC (1972) (QC-1994)
Mark Hapgood QC (1979) (QC-1994)
Mark Howard QC (1980) (QC-1996)
William Wood QC (1980) (QC-1998)
Stephen Ruttle QC (1976) (QC-1997)
Charles Hollander QC (1978) (QC-1999)
David Anderson QC (1985) (QC-1999)
Catharine Otton-Goulder QC (1983) (QC-2000)
Richard Lord QC (1981)(QC-2002)
Mark Brealey QC (1984) (QC-2002)
Michael Swainston QC (1985) (QC-2002)
James Flynn QC (1978) (QC-2003)
Andrew Lydiard QC (1980) (QC-2003)
Neil Calver QC (1987) (QC-2006)
Tom Adam QC (1991) (QC-2008)
Tim Lord QC (1992) (QC-2008)
Fergus Randolph QC (1985) (QC-2009)
Mark Hoskins QC (1991) (QC-2009)
Aidan Robertson QC (1995) (QC-2009)
Richard Slade QC (1987) (QC-2010)
Harry Matovu QC (1988) (QC-2010)
Jemima Stratford QC (1993) (QC-2010)
Daniel Jowell QC (1995) (QC-2011)
Simon Salzedo QC (1995) (QC-2011)
Michael Bools QC (1991) (QC-2012)
Marie Demetriou QC (1995) (QC 2012)
Andrew Henshaw QC (2000) (QC-2013)
Roger Masefield QC (1994) (QC-2013)
Jasbir Dhillon QC (1996) (QC-2013)
Martin Chamberlain QC (1997) (QC-2013)
Kelyn Bacon QC (1998) (QC-2014)
Peter Irvin (1972) ^
Peter Brunner (1971) ^
Sarah Lee (1990)
Paul Wright (1990)
Alan Roxburgh (1992)
Alec Haydon (1993)
Jeremy Gauntlett SC (1993) (SC-1989 SA)
Andrew Thomas (1996)
Robert O'Donoghue (1996)
Klaus Reichert SC (1996 E&W) (1992 IRL) (SC-2010 IRL)
Margaret Gray (1998)
Simon Birt (1998)
Colin West (1999)
Maya Lester (2000)
Nicholas Saunders (2001)
Fionn Pilbrow (2001)
Stephen Midwinter (2002)
Sarah Ford (2002)
Tony Willis (2004)
Victoria Wakefield (2003)
David Scannell (2003)
Gerard Rothschild (2005)
Jonathan Dawid (2005)
Fred Hobson (2005)
Sarah Abram (2006)
Sarah Love (2006)
Tony Singla (2007)
Richard Blakeley (2007)
Richard Eschwege (2008)
Edward Harrison (2008)
Thomas Plewman (2009)
Oliver Jones (2009)
Craig Morrison (2008)
Max Schaefer (2010)
Daniel Piccinin (2010)
Michael Bolding (2010)
Tim Johnston (2011)
Malcolm Birdling (2011)
Andrew McIntyre (2011)
David Bailey (2012)
Geoffrey Kuehne (2012)
Emily MacKenzie (2012)
Joanne Box (2012)
Kyle Lawson (2012)
Zahra Al-Rikabi (2012)
Lord Phillips (1962) (QC-1978) *
HH Nicholas Chambers QC (1966) (QC-1985) *
Derrick Wyatt QC (1972) (QC-1993) *
Mark Cran QC (1973) (QC-1988) *
Richard Macrory (1974) *
Sir Sydney Kentridge QC (1977) (QC-1984) *
Andrew Le Sueur (1987) *
Mads Andenas (1997) *
Sir Roger Buckley (1962) *
Peter Muchlinski (1981) *
Sir Oliver Popplewell (1951) *
Jan Woloniecki (1983) *
Lord Hoffmann (1964) (QC-1977) *
Alastair Sutton (1972) *
Johnny Mok SC (1986) Hong Kong *
Prof. Robert McCorquodale (2011)*
Judge Fidelma Macken SC (1987) *
Lord Hope (1965 Scotland) (QC-1989 Scotland) *
John Sturrock QC (1986 Scotland) (QC-1999 Scotland) *
James Wolffe QC (1992 Scotland) (QC-2007 Scotland)*
Geoff Sharp (1992 NZ)*

* Door Tenant ^ Public/Direct Access

THE CHAMBERS There are 81 members who practise full-time, including 36 QCs. Chambers specialises in commercial, EU/competition and public law, maintaining a strong reputation in all areas.

WORK UNDERTAKEN Commercial work includes international trade, finance and commerce, with particular emphasis on banking, insurance, reinsurance, shipping and 'city' work, and private international law, as well as fields as diverse as professional negligence, media and entertainment law, takeovers and mergers, sports law and public international law. Chambers have an outstanding team of EU and competition litigation specialists. Practitioners appear in the full range of English courts and tribunals, before the OFT, Competition Commission and CAT, as well as in the Court of Justice and General Court and other international courts and arbitral tribunals.
Considerable expertise in human rights and in commercial and regulatory judicial review enables chambers to combine its strengths in public, commercial and EU law. Recent key cases include: Constantin Medien v Bernie Ecclestone & Bambino Holdings, Noor Khan v FCO (Drones Litigation), Excalibur v Gulf Keystone, Unitech v UBS, Benedetti v Sawaris (Supreme Court), VTB v Nutritek (Supreme Court), FIFA & UEFA v European Commission ("crown jewels" broadcasting case), WM Morrison Supermarkets v Mastercard Inc, (Leyton Orient & Tottenham Hotspur) v OLPC & The Mayor of London (Olympic Stadium JR); FIA –v- Mercedes McLaren (Tyregate dispute).

BRICK COURT CHAMBERS
BARRISTERS

CARMELITE CHAMBERS Charles Bott

9 Carmelite Street, London, EC4Y 0DR
Tel (020) 7936 6300 **Fax** (020) 7936 6301 **DX** 226
Email clerks@carmelitechambers.co.uk **Website** www.carmelitechambers.co.uk

Head of Chambers	Charles Bott QC
Senior Clerk	Marc King
Deputy Senior Clerk	Matthew Butchard
Chambers Administrator	Orla O'Sullivan
Clerks	Dean Allen
	Thomas Barnes
	Zach May
	Stephanie Langmead
	Robert Lindsell
Fees Clerks	Sian Marshall & Emlyn Meheux
Receptionist	Hannah Jones

MEMBERS

Charles Bott QC (1979) (QC-2008)
Nigel Lambert QC (1974) (QC-1999) + ^
Robert Marshall-Andrews QC (1967) (QC-1987)
John Richard Jones QC (1981) (QC-2002) +
Leonard Smith QC (1986) (QC-2008)
Anthony Orchard QC (1991) (QC 2011) ^
Simon Csoka QC (1991) (QC-2011) ^
Pavlos Panayi QC (1995) (QC-2014)
Peter Corrigan (1973)
Michael Cousens (1973) ^
Barry Kogan (1973) +
Sonja Shields (1977)
Andrew Turton (1977)
Isabelle Gillard (1980)
Simon Molyneux (1986)
Martin Taylor (1988)
Adrian Kayne (1989) ^
Grahame James (1989)
Christopher Henley (1989)
Colin Aylott (1989) ^
Ben Hargreaves (1989) ^
Sangita Modgil (1990) ^
Tony Ventham (1991)
William England (1991)
Simon Gruchy (1993)
Adam Kane (1993)
Richard Button (1993)
Ayaz Qazi (1993)
Louise Sweet (1994)
James Walker (1994)
Matthew Sherratt (1994) ^
Matthew Lawson (1995)
Alphege Bell (1995)
Mark Harries (1995) ^
Jacqueline Zoest (1995) ^
Jonathan Page (1996) ^
James Tilbury (1996)
Roxanne Morrell (1996)
Elaine Stapleton (1997)
Gregory Johnson (1998)
Matthew Buckland (1998)
Lee Halliday-Davis (1999) ^
Soraya Lawrence (1999)
Gerard Hillman (1999) ^
Graeme Knight (1999)
Marie Spenwyn (1999) ^
Louise Muir Wilson (1999)
Edward Boateng-Addo (2000)
Stan Reiz (2001) ^
Houzla Rawat (2001) ^
Andrew Hallworth (2002)
Stephen Leake (2002) ^
Darryl Cherrett (2004) ^
Hugh O'Donoghue (2004) ^
Aron Rollin (2004)
Ashley Hendron (2005)
Laura Hocknell (2005)
Victoria Sheppard-Jones (2005) ^
Joe Hingston (2007) ^
Alice Jarratt (2007) ^
Jennifer Oborne (2007) ^
Sabha MacManus (2008) ^
Paul Duester (2008)
Rebecca Saillet (2009)
Simon Ralph (2009)
Alexandra Scott (2011)

+ Recorder ^ Public/Direct Access

THE CHAMBERS Carmelite Chambers is one of the largest and longest established criminal sets in the UK. The set's advocates are at the forefront of UK and international practice and are regularly instructed in high profile cases.

WORK UNDERTAKEN As leaders within the field, members of chambers undertake work in all criminal and related investigations and proceedings, with specific expertise in serious fraud, terrorism, murder, money laundering, miscarriages of justice, courts martial and health and safety. Chambers offers a highly skilled and experienced team of advocates in all of its specialist areas with a particular emphasis to fraud and regulatory matters.
Fraud: Carmelite Chambers has represented both individuals and companies in some of the most notable fraud cases in recent years, counsel are instructed in both private and publicly funded fraud matters in both the civil and criminal courts which include complaints related to corruption, cartels, boiler room fraud, diversion fraud, carousel fraud, NHS fraud and mortgage fraud.
Prominent cases involving members of chambers include cases such as the ongoing investigation into the alleged Libor rate fixing, the current FCA Investigation described as the largest insider dealing case to be prosecuted in the UK, the iSoft PLC trial which concerns alleged fraud of multi-million pound contracts for the provision of software to National Health Authorities in the UK and Ireland, the North East England Property Fraud "Operation Bamburgh" Parts 1 & 2, Operation Savate an alleged large scale manipulation of the Construction Industry Scheme ("CIS"), Operation Cactus at Birmingham Crown Court the alleged conspiracy to defraud HMRC involving a multi million pound "SIPP" [Self Invested Personal Pension] scheme and hundreds of investors throughout the UK and "Operation Tulipbox" the first prosecution of a Carbon Trading Fraud in the UK held at Southwark Crown Court.
Members of chambers are also instructed in large scale MTIC operations throughout the country such as "Chert" "Vaulter", "Vex", "Forbear", "Euripus", "Immersed", "Duma", "Erasure" and "Ghast".
Crime: Chambers enjoys a reputation that is second to none in the defence of allegations of serious and organised crime, recognised nationally and internationally for providing advice and representation of the highest quality in the most serious high-profile criminal trials.
Recent instructions include representing defendants charged as part of Operation Weeting and Operation Elvenden involving phone hacking by News of the World journalists and subsequent associated prosecutions, R –v- Cregan & others the Preston Crown Court Trial concerning the shooting of two female Manchester police officers and other linked matters, R –v- Philpott & others the much publicised case in Nottingham Crown court where the defendant was accused of starting a fire that led to the death of his six children, a six month immigration fraud at Manchester Crown Court involving an alleged successful and lucrative enterprise to assist illegal migrants to deceive the UK Borders Agency, Operation Bullfinch the child sex ring/grooming case at CCC where Asian men living in the Oxford area who were said to be exploiting vulnerable local girls, the Manchester

carmelite chambers

CARMELITE CHAMBERS (continued)

"Honour Killing" murder case, where the defendants were the mother and father of the teenage victim, and the "Victoria Station Murder" case where one group of armed school children charged across the concourse of Victoria Station and attacked a rival gang, stabbing to death one schoolboy.

Civil Fraud Asset Recovery: Carmelite Chambers has an unparalleled reputation in defending allegations of serious fraud and our specialist Asset Recovery & Civil fraud team has been formed from the set's leading experts in criminal fraud. Their experience and judgment is increasingly sought after by those involved in civil fraud litigation who recognise the significant crossover between commercial, civil, criminal and regulatory.

Carmelite Chambers' Civil Fraud and Asset Recovery team is regularly instructed in cases involving:

- A wide range of fraud related matters including corruption, investment fraud, bribery and money laundering
- Multi-party claims across international jurisdictions
- Civil injunctive relief including freezing orders, civil search & seizure orders and "Norwich Pharmacal" third party disclosure orders
- Significant overlap between civil and criminal proceedings
- Restraint and confiscation proceedings under Part 5 of the Proceeds of Crime Act 2002
- Companies affected by restraint proceedings brought in the criminal courts

In addition, with prosecuting authorities placing an ever-increasing burden upon companies to investigate internal wrongdoing and to self-report, Carmelite Chambers can advise corporate clients where criminal activity by directors, employees or advisors is suspected within a business as to the proper approach and strategies to be adopted in investigating such activity and where necessary the appropriate co-operation strategies with regulators and prosecuting authorities.

Regulatory & Disciplinary Proceedings: Chambers' members are regularly instructed amongst others on behalf of doctors, dentists, nurses, lawyers, police officers and accountants before the Bar Standards Board Disciplinary Tribunal, the Solicitors Disciplinary Tribunal, the Police Disciplinary Tribunal, the General Dental Council, the General Medical Council, the NMWC, Accountancy and Actuarial disciplinary panels as well as at Disciplinary Tribunals on behalf of professional sportsmen and women. With their extensive fraud experience members frequently appear before the FSA, VAT and HMRC tribunals.

THE CHAMBERS OF ANDREW MITCHELL QC

33 Chancery Lane, London, WC2A 1EN
Tel (020) 7440 9950 **Fax** (020) 7430 2818 **DX** 33 London
Email clerks@33cllaw.com **Website** www.33cllaw.com

Head of Chambers	Andrew Mitchell QC
Practice Director	Martin Adams
Tenants	20

33 CHANCERY LANE

THE CHAMBERS Formed in November 2008 by a group of practitioners to provide specialist advice to commercial organisations, individual clients and the public sector in all areas of suspected commercial wrongdoing including bribery, corruption, civil fraud, asset recovery and financial crime.

WORK UNDERTAKEN Recent cases include acting nationally and internationally in major bribery and corruption cases; acting in the Supreme Court in Proceeds of Crime Act cases; acting in the Caribbean for a client in a Commission of Inquiry into the collapse of financial institutions; acting for a former Yen derivatives trader for UBS and Citigroup for alleged manipulation of the international LIBOR index; acting nationally and internationally in major money laundering, MTIC and fraud cases; and acting for applicants, respondents, foreign governments, third parties and receivers in all aspects of restraint and receivership.

CHARTER CHAMBERS Nicholas Rhodes QC & Neil Hawes QC

33 John Street, London, WC1N 2AT
Tel (020) 7618 4400 **Fax** (020) 7618 4401 **DX** 429 Ch.Ln
Email clerks@charterchambers.com **Website** www.charterchambers.com

Head of Chambers	Nicholas Rhodes QC & Neil Hawes QC
Senior Clerk	Patrick Duane
Chambers Director	Ian Payn
Clerks	Ian Sheridan
	James Hall
	Sam Kennett
	Sophie Kent
Fees	Chris Blake
Billing	Sandeep Bhandal
Administration	Holly Muhit
Tenants	53

MEMBERS

Nicholas Rhodes QC (1981) (QC-2008) + ^
Neil Hawes QC (1989) (QC-2010) ^
Stephen Solley QC (1969) (QC-1989) + ^
Joanna Greenberg QC (1972) (QC-1994) ^
Henry Grunwald OBE QC (1972) (QC-1999) ^
Jerome Lynch QC (1983) (QC-2000) ^
Ian Bourne QC (1977) (QC-2006) + ^
David Batcup (1974) + ^
David Martin-Sperry (1971)
Peter Higginson (1975) ^
Calvin Jackson (1975) ^
Mark Tomassi (1981) ^
Thomas Buxton (1983) ^
David Taylor (1986) ^
Neil Guest (1990) ^
Michael Lavers (1990)
Paul Phillips (1991) ^
Dr Mary-Teresa Deignan (1991) ^
Claire Robinson (1991) ^
Jonathan Simpson (1993) ^
Robert Benzynie (1992) ^
Sean Kivdeh (1992) ^
Tana Adkin (1992) ^
Julia Flanagan (1993) ^
Ragveer Chand (1994)
Martin Goudie (1996) ^
Rachel Darby (1997) ^
Jason Cross (1998) ^
Roderick James (1999) ^
Alexander Dos Santos (1999) ^
Leila Gaskin (2000) ^
Darren Snow (2001) ^
Rajinder Gill (2001) ^
Lara Maroof (2001) ^
Kathrine Mansfield (2001)
Nicholas Dixey (2002)
William Davis (2003) ^
Tyrone Silcott (2004) ^
Rishy Panesar (2004)
Chloe Barton (2006) ^
Marie Lewiecki (2006)
Alex Jamieson (2007)
David Wood (2007)
Grace Pelly (2007)
Craig Weston (2007)
Elizabeth Wheeler (2007)
Kathryn Pitters (2008)
Oliver Renton (2008) ^
David Ewings (2009)
Briony Molyneux (2009)
Peter Melleney (2010)
Laura Bayley (2010)
Gareth Thomas (2011)

+ Recorder ^ Public/Direct Access

THE CHAMBERS Charter Chambers is a busy criminal and common law set offering expertise in a variety of fields at all levels of seniority.

WORK UNDERTAKEN
Criminal Law: (Both defence and prosecution). Notable high-profile cases in fraud, money-laundering, business crime, murder, sexual offences etc.
Family Law: All aspects from divorce to domestic violence.

Also practitioners specialising in civil law; regulatory work; commercial law; mental health; extradition; immigration; employment law; licensing. Public Access certified.

INTERNATIONAL International practice includes strong ties with Bermuda, Turks and Caicos and the Cayman Islands. Languages spoken include French, German, Spanish; Malay and Indonesian.

CLOISTERS

Cloisters, 1 Pump Court, Temple, London, EC4Y 7AA
Tel (020) 7827 4000 **Fax** (020) 7827 4100 **DX** LDE 452
Email clerks@cloisters.com **Website** www.cloisters.com

Head of Chambers	Robin Allen QC
Senior Clerk	Glenn Hudson
Clerks	Mark Skipp
	Andy Hunter
	Ben Fitzgerald
	Tayla Burkey
Tenants	52

MEMBERS

Robin Allen QC (1974) (QC-1995)
Brian Napier QC (1986) + (QC-2002) Scotland
Simon W Taylor QC (1984) (QC-2003)
Paul Epstein QC (1988) (QC-2006)
Daphne Romney QC (1979) (QC-2009)
Patricia Hitchcock QC (1988) (QC-2011)
Joel Donovan QC (1991) (QC-2011)
Jacques Algazy QC (1980) (QC-2012)
Caspar Glyn QC (1992) (QC-2012)
Jason Galbraith-Marten (1991) (QC-2014)
Martin Seaward (1978)
Philip Engelman (1979)
Andrew Buchan (1981)
Simon Dyer (1987)
Declan O'Dempsey (1987)
Michael Potter (2013) (1988 Northern Ireland) +
Catherine Casserley (1991)
Yvette Genn (1991)
Paul Michell (1991)
John Horan (1993)
Rachel Crasnow (1994)
Daniel Lawson (1994)
Sally Robertson (1995)
William Latimer-Sayer (1995)
Sally Cowen (1995)
Lisa Sullivan (1997)
Martyn McLeish (1997)
Thomas Coghlin (1998)
Schona Jolly (1999)
David Massarella (1999)
Akua Reindorf (1999)
Claire McCann (2000)
Thomas Brown (2000)
Linda Jacobs (2000)
Ed Williams (2000)
Anna Beale (2001)
Adam Ohringer (2001)
Hannah Godfrey (2002)
Dee Masters (2004)
Sarah Fraser Butlin (2005)
Daniel Dyal (2006)
Chris Milsom (2006)
Olivia-Faith Dobbie (2007)
Will Dobson (2008)
Caroline Musgrave (2008)
Catriona Stirling (2008)
Nathaniel Caiden (2009)
Siân McKinley (2009)
Sheryn Omeri (2010)
Chesca Lord (2011)
Catherine Richmond (2011)
Rachel Barrett (2012)
Tamar Burton (2012)
Jennifer Danvers (2012)
Sir Stephen Sedley (1964) +
Prof Alan Neal (1972) +
Delroy Duncan (1984) +
Prof Anthony Bradley QC (1989) +
Rachel Chambers (2002) +

+ Associate member

THE CHAMBERS Cloisters is a leading set advising on employment, discrimination and equality, personal injury, clinical negligence, human rights and sport and commercial law, with a reputation for delivering exceptional results. Its barristers appear in courts at all levels here and in Europe.

TYPES OF WORK UNDERTAKEN

Employment; Discrimination & Equality: Cloisters won Employment Set of the Year at the Chambers & Partners awards ceremony in October 2013 and was shortlisted for the same award in 2014. Its barristers include current and former Chairs of the Industrial Law Society and the Employment Law Bar Association as well as Executive Committee members of the Employment Lawyers Association. This reflects the legal services industry's view of Cloisters as a leading set for its mix of cutting edge, law-making work, its high quality, dedicated barristers and its facility to work equally successfully for employers and employees alike across diverse industries and sectors. No other chambers is so well respected for its barristers' ability to understand the concerns of both business and employees and to work hard for wise, pragmatic solutions to their client's problems. This makes Cloisters the "go to" destination for the best employment and equality law service at the Bar, with its clerks' team regularly praised as being extremely accessible and practical.

Clinical Negligence: Cloisters has an outstanding reputation as the pre-eminent claimant clinical negligence chambers. It has a particularly outstanding reputation for dealing with complex brain injury cases, quantum issues in cases of the highest value, and in cases involving psychiatric injury. A team of three silks and outstanding juniors has achieved some of the most high value clinical negligence claims of recent years, including A v Powys Local Health Board (£10.7m), the highest ever PI/CN award at trial and the first to break through the £10m barrier; and Iqbal v Whipps Cross University Hospitals, the leading case on "lost years"; and Castle v Simmons (10% increase in general damages). In 2013 Cloisters barristers and their solicitors recovered in excess of £60 million for their clients. Andrew Buchan edits Buchan and Lewis on Clinical Negligence to which many other members of chambers contribute.

Personal Injury: Cloisters is a pre-eminent claimant set and has achieved some of the highest settlements ever in personal injury cases including Sarwar v Ali, one of the leading cases on care cost indexation (£7.158m); and in 2014 Farrugia v Burtenshaw. Cloisters has also been involved in many of the landmark personal injury cases over recent years including the leading House of Lords stress claim, Barber v Somerset CC; Majrowksi v Guys and St Thomas' (the leading House of Lords case on harassment); Hartman v South Essex Mental Heal and Community Care NHS Trust (one of the leading Court of Appeal level stress cases); A v Hoare (the House of Lords case extending limitation for rape victims); and Gravil v Redruth Rugby Football Club (vicarious liability for pitch violence by employed players). William Latimer-Sayer's, Personal Injury Schedule has established itself as a leading practitioner text. Members of chambers also contribute to Butterworth's Personal Injury Service and Bullen & Leake's Precedents of Pleadings.

Human Rights: Cloisters was founded as set with a strong commitment to civil liberties. Its barristers write and publish extensively on the subject and are at the forefront of legal developments such as the Equality Act 2010 and the abolition of the default retirement age. Members are involved in both litigation and advisory work. They have appeared at the highest level in cases such as Preddy and Hall v Bull and Bull and Jivraj v Hashwani.

Sport & Entertainment: Cloisters' sport practitioners act for football clubs and players up to premier league, as well as a diverse range of sports bodies and personalities. They handle disciplinary regulations, consultative work, litigation, non-professional sporting activity cases and matters arising from sports and entertainment cases such as employment or contractual issues.

CLOISTERS

CORAM CHAMBERS

Coram Chambers, 9-11 Fulwood Place, London, WC1V 6HG
Tel (020) 7092 3700 **Fax** (020) 7092 3777
Email mail@coramchambers.co.uk **Website** www.coramchambers.co.uk

Head of Chambers	Martha Cover
Senior Clerk	Paul Sampson
Business Manager	Catherine Culley
Tenants	65

MEMBERS

Roger McCarthy QC (1975) (QC-1996)
Iain Goldrein QC (1975) (QC-1997)
Jane Drew (1976) [A]
David Boyd (1977)
Cathy Nicholes (1977) [A]
Aditya Kumar Sen (1977) [A]
Christine Sheldrake (1977)
Martha Cover (1979)
Anne Spratling (1980) [A]
Kate Hudson (1981)
Meena Gill (1982)
Fiona Gibb (1983)
Christina Morris (1983)
Jacqueline Marks (1984) [A]
Pamela Warner (1985)
Nick OíBrien (1985) [A]
Divya Bhatia (1986)
Elpha LeCointe (1988) [A]
Gill Honeyman (2011)
Georgia Mitropoulos (1989) [A]
Neil Bullock (1989)
Susan George (1990)
Mark Twomey (1990)
John Paul Cregan (1990)
Shiva Ancliffe (1991)
Neil Fry (1992) [A]
David Vavrecka (1992) [A]
Sima Kothari (1992) [A]
Marcia Hyde (1992)
Sharon Sawyerr (1992)
Sabuhi Chaudhry (1993) [A]
Michael Horton (1993) [A]
Niki Langridge (1993)
Alison Easton (1994)
Dermot Casey(1994)
Sarah Marley (1995) [A]
Siobhan Kelly (1995) [A]
William Metaxa (1995)
Danielle Lewis (1995)
Jerry Fitzpatrick (1996)
Caitlin Ferris (1996) [A]
Katy Rensten (2010)
Lynn Freeston (1996) [A]
Christopher Archer (1996)
Susan Stamford (1997)
Nicholas Horsley (1998)
Richard Beddoe (1999) [A]
Anne-Marie Glover (2000)
Sarah Branson (2001) [A]
Tosin Oguntayo (2001)
Mary-Jane Taylor (2003) [A]
Laura McMullan (2004)
James Schofield (2004)
Rosina Aman (2005)
Richard Yorke (2006) [A]
Katherine Andrews (2006)
Lucinda Wicks (2006)
Georgina Rushworth (2007)
Radhika Handa (2008)
Neil Shah (2008)
Tracy Chapman (2009)
Jeremy Brown (2009)
Sarah Tyler (2009)
Melissa Harrison (2009)
Ariel Ricci (2012)

[A] Direct/Public Access

THE CHAMBERS Coram Chambers is a leading family law set with a national reputation for excellence in advocacy and client care across all areas of family law and mental health law. Chambers prides itself on delivering excellent standards of client care to both lay and professional clients.
Coram Chambers has a particularly strong commitment to equality and diversity, and to the representation of minorities including alternative family structures. Members of chambers are at the forefront of developments in family law, and appear regularly in leading and landmark cases.
Chambers has strong dedicated teams specialising in children, family finance, human rights, international/abduction, Court of Protection, adult social care, and mediation fielding both experienced senior practitioners and more junior members.
Chambers has no fewer than 13 current members who hold part-time judicial appointments.
In the past seven years chambers has produced seven female Circuit Judges and one female Queens Bench Master.
Members of chambers appear regularly at all levels of court including the Court of Appeal and Supreme Court and have a strong track record in the Court of Protection and the Administrative Courts.
Members of chambers are frequently asked to deliver seminars, write articles and provide commentary and training in both legal and related areas. It also contributes to the wider debate on family law policy and actively participates in a number of family law associations and committees.
Coram's dynamic and innovative approach to family law enables its members to adapt and embrace non-traditional ways of working including mediation, direct access and collaborative law, all of which are growing areas of practice. Coram Chambers fields accredited family arbitrators.
Chambers retained its top ranking in the Diversity League tables with an overall ranking position of second. In 2013 Michael Horton was nominated for the Bar Pro Bono Award and Radhika Handa for the family law young barrister of the year award at the Jordan's Family Law awards.

TYPES OF WORK UNDERTAKEN

Adult & Social Care: Coram provides representation and advice for children and young people in care proceedings or leaving care, where they are affected by both the Mental Capacity Act 2005 and the Children Act 1989, 'best interest' disputes about residential arrangements, contact and moving overseas for protected persons, and in deprivation of liberty cases, including applications under s21A MCA 2005 and damages claims.
Children: Coram is renowned for its expertise in public law children cases. Members of chambers provide a wide knowledge base, and determined and thoughtful representation at all levels of tribunal. It regularly represents both public bodies and private individuals, and is committed to providing excellence in representation whether involved in high-profile, landmark cases or appearing in more straightforward matters.
Family Finance: The set is experienced in advising and representing clients from both traditional and alternative family structures. It offers representation at all levels of matrimonial finance and cohabitation disputes.
Human Rights: The team has leading expertise in all aspects of human rights work, including cases involving

coram
chambers

CORAM CHAMBERS (continued)

fundamental rights and freedoms protected by the Human Rights Act 1998 and the European Convention on Human Rights (ECHR).

Dispute Resolution: Chambers offers the full range of dispute resolution services including: mediation in family, divorce and children disputes; arbitration and neutral evaluation in family and financial disputes.

INTERNATIONAL Coram recognises that both solicitors and lay clients need a prompt and comprehensive service. As applications are frequently made on an emergency basis, members of chambers are ready to advise by phone on an emergency basis and are available to make without notice applications at very short notice. In addition to advising on immediate practical steps, members of the team will assist in the preparation of documentation, case management and procedure; taking the case through court from the first application to the final hearing.

CORNERSTONE BARRISTERS

2-3 Gray's Inn Square, Gray's Inn, London, WC1R 5JH
Tel (020) 7242 4986 **Fax** (020) 7405 1166 **DX** 316 (Ch.Ln.)
Email clerks@cornerstonebarristers.com **Website** www.cornerstonebarristers.com

Joint Head of Chambers	Mary Cook and James Findlay QC
Chief Executive	Warren Foot
Tenants	48

MEMBERS

Mary Cook (1982)
James Findlay QC (1984) (QC-2008)
Anthony Dinkin QC (1968) (QC-1991)
Mark Lowe QC (1972) (QC-1996)
Ashley Underwood QC (1976) (QC-2001)
Vincent Fraser QC (1981) (QC-2001)
Philip Kolvin QC (1985) (QC-2009)
Steven Gasztowicz QC (1981) (QC-2009)
Bryan McGuire QC (1983) (QC-2010)
Gerard Forlin QC (1984) (QC-2010)
Ranjit Bhose QC (1989) (QC-2012)
Kelvin Rutledge QC (1989) (QC- 2013)
David Lamming (1972)
Adrian Trevelyan Thomas (1974)
Alun Alesbury (1974)
Graham Stoker (1977)
Ian Albutt (1981)
Paul Shadarevian (1984)
Michael Bedford (1985)
Michael Druce (1988)
Jonathan Clay (1990)
Jon Holbrook (1991)
Robin Green (1992)
Harriet Townsend (1992)
Catherine Rowlands (1992)
Matthew Hutchings (1993)
Thomas Cosgrove (1994)
Richard Ground (1994)
Wayne Beglan (1996)
Michael Paget (1995)
David Lintott (1996)
Rory Clarke (1996)
Kuljit Bhogal (1998)
Sian Davies (1999)
Shomik Datta (2000)
Asitha Ranatunga (2001)
Peggy Etiebet (2001)
Damien Welfare (2001)
Josef Cannon (2002)
Clare Parry (2005)
Estelle Dehon (2006)
Ryan Kohli (2006)
Jennifer Oschoft (2006)
Hugh Flanagan (2008)
Rob Williams (2008)
Emma Dring (2009)
Zoe Whittington (2009)
Jack Parker (2011)

Offering exceptional ability at all levels, Cornerstone Barristers has a market-leading reputation for advice and representation in planning, public law, housing, property, licensing and regulatory law.
Clients include companies, central and local government, private developers, public development agencies, third party objectors and individuals.

THE CHAMBERS Members act as Treasury Counsel, hold part-time judicial appointments and sit as arbitrators and legal assessors on disciplinary boards and tribunals
Members appear on a regular basis at the Supreme Court, Court of Appeal, High Court, County Court and before the various specialist tribunals including the Upper Tribunal (Lands Chamber), the Leasehold Valuation Tribunal and the Adjudicator to HM Land Registry. With offices in London and Cardiff Bay, the set's scope extends to Hong Kong, Malaysia, Singapore, and the West Indies, and includes European law and the European Convention on Human Rights.
Friendly, approachable and professional, the set delivers a streamlined, cost-effective service while cherishing the connection with inescapable former member Sir Edward Marshall Hall.

WORK UNDERTAKEN The set's expertise takes in the most lengthy, complex and high profile cases as well as more routine matters.
Planning: as one of the leading planning sets, Cornerstone Barristers handles the full range of issues including high-profile infrastructure and other nationally important projects involving property, public and environmental law, compulsory purchase and compensation, minerals and waste, rights of way, highways, village greens and commons. Members handle major inquiries and advise on prominent developments, statutory challenges and judicial review.
Social Housing: the set is well known for landlord and tenant law, homelessness, asylum, housing benefit fraud, possession claims, contested succession, unlawful subletting, anti-social behaviour and disrepair.
Property: as well as advising and representing private and public-sector clients in relation to commercial and residential property, members act as mediators and arbitrators.
Public Law & Judicial Review: the set defends and challenges public law decisions in many areas including planning, housing, highways, community care, court of protection, immigration, human rights, education and employment. Members take part in the most prominent public inquiries and inquests.
Licensing: the set drives professional development in this area by advising, training and educating across the whole field, including alcohol, entertainment, gambling and taxis, on behalf of licensing authorities, police, leading industry operators, trade associations and campaign and community groups.
Regulatory Law: in conjunction with a leading reputation in corporate manslaughter, the set provides a comprehensive service in consumer protection, trading standards, health and safety and environmental regulation.

RECRUITMENT Pupils are received each year; pupillage funds are available.

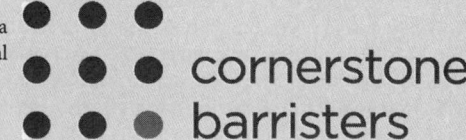

cornerstone barristers

CROWN OFFICE CHAMBERS Richard Lynagh QC

2 Crown Office Row, Temple, London, EC4Y 7HJ
Tel (020) 7797 8100 **Fax** (020) 7797 8101 **DX** 80 LONDON/CHANCERY LANE
Email clerks@crownofficechambers.com **Website** www.crownofficechambers.com

Head of Chambers	Richard Lynagh QC
Senior Managing Clerk	Andy Flanagan
Senior Team Clerks	Steve Purse
	Paul Hurst
	Simon Wigley
Arbitrator, Mediator Adjudicator's Clerk	Nick Hamilton
Tenants	91

MEMBERS

Richard Lynagh QC (1975) (QC-1996)
Michael Harvey QC (1966) (QC-1982)
Michael Spencer QC (1970) (QC-1989)
Christopher Purchas QC (1966) (QC-1990)
Roger ter Haar QC (1974) (QC-1992)
Andrew Bartlett QC (1974) (QC-1993)
Michael Kent QC (1975) (QC-1996)
Jonathan Waite QC (1978) (QC-2002)
Margaret Bickford-Smith QC (1973) (QC-2003)
Michael Curtis QC (1982) (QC-2008)
Christopher Kennedy QC (1989) (QC-2010)
Andrew Rigney QC (1992) (QC-2010)
David Platt QC (1987) (QC 2011)
John Cooper QC (1985) (QC-2014)
Alexander Antelme QC (1993) (QC-2014)
Ben Quiney QC (1998) (QC-2014)
Martyn Berkin (1966)
Cyril Chern (1972)
Colin Nixon (1973)
John Stevenson (1975)
Nicholas Davies (1975)
Andrew Phillips (1978)
John Greenbourne (1978)
Gordon Catford (1980)
Julian Field (1980)
Paul Dean (1982)
Charlotte Jones (1982)
A John Williams (1983)
Steven Coles (1983)
Kim Franklin (1984)
James Medd (1985)
Shaun Ferris (1985)
Catherine Foster (1986)
Andrew Smith (1988)
William Vandyck (1988)
Peter Morton (1988)
Dermot Woolgar (1988)
Simon J Brown (1988)
Steven Snowden (1989)
Ian Wright (1989)
Erica Power (1990)
Jason Evans-Tovey (1990)
James Ageros (1990)
Toby Gee (1992)
Isabel Hitching (1992)
Patrick Blakesley (1993)
Richard Tyrrell (1993)
Claire Toogood (1995)
James Maxwell-Scott (1995)
Robert Stokell (1995)
Suzanne Chalmers (1995)
Simon Antrobus (1995)
Mark A Balysz (1995)
Jamie Clarke (1995)
Andrew Davis (1996)
Edward Broome (1996)
Muhammed Haque (1997)
Dominic Kay (1997)
Susan Lindsey (1997)
Victoria Woodbridge (1998)
Jack Ferro (1998)
Anna Laney (1998)
Daniel Shapiro (1999)
Farah Mauladad (1999)
Mark Armitage (1999)
Matthew Boyle (2000)
Alexander MacPherson (2000)
Rebecca Taylor (2001)
Charles Pimlott (2001)
Jane Davies Evans (2001)
Anna Symington (2002)
Crispin Winser (2003)
Michele De Gregorio (2003)
Rosanna Hellebronth (2004)
Justin Davis (2003)
Peter Houghton (2005)
Julia Kendrick (2005)
Elizabeth Boon (2006)
Richard Sage (2006)
David Myhill (2006)
Mike Atkins (2006)
Siobhan Lambertsen (2007)
Nadia Whittaker (2007)
Helen Pagett (2008)
Jack Macauley (2009)
Rory Holmes (2009)
James Sharpe (2009)
Carolyn McColgan (2010)
Carlo Taczalski (2010)
Athena Markidas (2011)
Lara Knight (2012)

THE CHAMBERS Crown Office Chambers is a leading civil and commercial set widely recognised as a market leader with a reputation for combining high-quality advice and advocacy with a modern, flexible and commercially-minded approach.
Specialist, focused and knowledgeable clerking teams assist highly-rated Silks and juniors in providing an efficient, high-quality service for professional and lay clients alike. Chambers has a wide range of experienced arbitrators, adjudicators and mediators and offer a fully administered ADR service.

WORK UNDERTAKEN

Professional Negligence: Members have been instructed in some of the leading cases in professional negligence, including Jones v Kaney and Kidsons v Lloyds Underwriters. Chambers undertakes all forms of professional negligence work, with particular focus on: construction professionals, lawyers (barristers and solicitors), accountants, insurance brokers, insolvency practitioners and financial services advisors.
Health Care: Chambers has a broad expertise in healthcare-related litigation work including, but not limited to, acting in clinical negligence claims for claimants, the NHS, private providers, insurers and defence organisations. The expertise of a number of barristers in several areas of law ensures that clients can obtain balanced and specialist advice even when a case touches on different practice areas.
Product liability: Members have been instructed in most of the major pharmaceutical multiparty claims which have so far been brought. These have included: breast implant litigation, Depuy ASR and Hylamer hip prostheses litigation. Chambers also has considerable involvement in non-pharmaceutical product liability litigation and members also advise in relation to cover under product liability insurance policies.
Criminal Regulatory & Environmental: Chambers is widely regarded as the leading set in criminal regulatory and environmental law.
Members have been involved in the leading cases that have shaped this niche area of corporate criminal law including Lion Steel, M5 Fireworks Disaster and continue to be instructed in the highest profile cases, such as the Hillsborough inquest, Lakanal Fire Inquest, Lion Steel and the Inquest into the Amenas Incident.

CROWN OFFICE CHAMBERS

CROWN OFFICE CHAMBERS Richard Lynagh QC (continued)

Personal Injury & Disease: Chambers is one of the leading personal injury and industrial disease sets in the country. In the last 12 months, members have been involved in a number of high profile cases including: Joyce v O'Brien and Tradex Insurance; Uren v Corporate Leisure & MOD; Saunderson v Sonae Inustria. Personal injury work is undertaken at all levels with Silks and juniors regularly undertaking the most serious of cases – brain and spinal injuries; group litigation; fatal injuries and complex psychiatric and chronic pain cases.
Insurance & Reinsurance: Chambers is highly rated for its work in this specialist field and has strong links with the insurance market, and are regularly instructed by many of the major insurers, underwriting syndicates and brokers. All forms of contentious and advisory work are undertaken, including work in the Commercial Court and in arbitration.
Property Damage: Chambers has particular expertise in property damage claims arising out of fires, floods, explosions, storms (including hurricanes), subsidence (including tree roots) etc. Its expertise in construction, insurance and professional negligence means that its members are ideally suited to handling such claims.
International Arbitration: Chambers has a dedicated and increasingly popular practice group of high-calibre Silks and juniors that undertake a range complex, high-value international arbitration work acting as both counsel and arbitrators.
Commercial & Chancery: Members receive regular instructions in a variety of commercial cases, in particular franchising disputes acting for franchisees and franchisors, plus a range of contractual claims such as, banking, company law, financial services, insolvency, fraud and asset tracing, and many more.
Construction & Engineering: This forms a significant part of the chambers' workload. Members have substantial expertise acting for employers, contractors, construction professionals, insurers and developers in an advisory capacity and as advocates in all forms of dispute resolution. Chambers continue to edit and contribute to the Emden publication, which has been rebranded as Emden's Construction Law by Crown Office Chambers. Recent cases include: Harrison v Shepherd Homes; Cadbury v ADT; Milton Keynes BC v Nulty; Liberty Syndicates v Campagna; Greenwich Millennium Village v Essex Services.

1 CROWN OFFICE ROW Philip Havers QC

Head of Chambers	Philip Havers QC
Chambers Director	Bob Wilson
Senior Clerk	Matthew Phipps
Tenants	69

Temple, London, EC4Y 7HH
Tel (020) 7797 7500 **Fax** (020) 7797 7550 **DX** LDE1020
Email mail@1cor.com **Website** www.1cor.com Blog ukhumanrightsblog.com

MEMBERS

Philip Havers QC (1974) (QC-1995)
Robert Seabrook QC (1964) (QC-1983)
James Badenoch QC (1968) (QC-1989)
Stephen Miller QC (1971) (QC-1990)
Kieran Coonan QC (1971) (QC-1990)
Terence Coghlan QC (1968) (QC-1993)
Guy Mansfield QC (1972) (QC-1994)
Sally Smith QC (1977) (QC-1997)
Elizabeth-Anne Gumbel QC (1974) (QC-1999)
Paul Rees QC (1980) (QC-2000)
Margaret Bowron QC (1978) (QC-2001)
Neil Garnham QC (1982) (QC-2001)
David Balcombe QC (1980) (QC-2002)
Joanna Glynn QC (1983) (QC-2002)
David Hart QC (1982) (QC-2003)
Martin Forde QC (1984) (QC-2006)
William Edis QC (1985) (QC-2008)
Christina Lambert QC (1988) (QC-2009)
Angus McCullough QC (1990) (QC-2010)
Philippa Whipple QC (1994) (QC-2010)
John Whitting QC (1991) (QC-2011)
David Evans QC (1988) (QC-2012)
Richard Booth QC (1993) (QC-2013)
James King-Smith (1980) ++
John Gimlette (1986)
Marina Wheeler (1987)
Henry Witcomb (1989)
Andrew Kennedy (1989)
Martin Downs (1990)
Jeremy Cave (1992) ++
Giles Colin (1994)
Sydney Chawatama (1994)
Sarah Lambert (1994)
Justin Levinson (1994)
Owain Thomas (1995)
Jeremy Hyam (1995)
Oliver Sanders (1995)
Shaheen Rahman (1996)
Clodagh Bradley (1996)
Peter Skelton (1997)
Zoe Taylor (1998)
Neil Sheldon (1998)
Richard Smith (1999)
Christopher Mellor (1999)
Robert Kellar (1999)
Matthew Barnes (2000)
Iain O'Donnell (2000)
Sarabjit Singh (2001)
David Manknell (2001)
Suzanne Lambert (2002)
Judith Rogerson (2003)
Andrea Lindsay Strugo (2003)
Amy Mannion (2003)
Robert Wastell (2004)
Richard Mumford (2004)
John Jolliffe (2005)
Rachel Marcus (2005)
Pritesh Rathod (2006)
Caroline Cross (2006)
Matthew Donmall (2006)
Kate Beattie (2007)
Adam Wagner (2007)
Isabel McArdle (2008)
Matthew Hill (2009)
Alasdair Henderson (2009)
Claire McGregor (2009)
Matthew Flinn (2010)
Paul Reynolds (2010)
Lois Williams (2012)
Jim Duffy (2012)
Dominic Ruck-Keene (2012)
Rosalind English (1993) **
Duncan Fairgrieve (2002) **
Martin Matthews (1970) **

++ Mainly practise from Brighton ** Academic Consultants

THE CHAMBERS One Crown Office Row is a long-established civil set providing advisory and advocacy services with a pre-eminent reputation for its clinical negligence and healthcare practise, its expertise in public law and human rights and its professional disciplinary work. 44 Members practice from an Annexe at Crown Office Row, Brighton. Established over 60 years ago, this is a leading civil set whose reputation for quality is reflected in the fact that it counts among its Members and former Members the former Lord Chief Justice, Lord Woolf, four Lords Justices of Appeal, and three former Chairmen of the Bar. Clients receive high order advocacy and professional skills from barristers and a friendly, client-oriented and efficient service from its staff. The set occupies a prominent building in Temple with modern IT, conference and video-conference facilities. It runs the widely-acclaimed UK Human Rights Blog at ukhumanrightsblog.com and the unique free Human Rights Update website at www.humanrights.org.uk.

WORK UNDERTAKEN Members have been recognised as leading practitioners in all aspects of healthcare law, clinical negligence, personal injury and inquests, professional disciplinary proceedings, public and administrative law, public inquiries, human rights, immigration and asylum, employment, professional negligence, costs, tax, matrimonial finance and environmental law. They also have successful practices in multi-party actions, technology and construction and sports law. Chambers has a team of 13 accredited mediators, 11 of whom are silks.

PUBLICATIONS The Regulation of Healthcare Professionals, Principle and Process (published by Sweet and Maxwell) was co-authored by Joanna Glynn QC. Several Members contributed to the 2nd and 3rd editions of Burnett Hall on Environmental Law. Clinical Negligence – A Practitioners Handbook was co-authored by Lizanne Gumbel QC. Four members contribute to Clinical Negligence (editors Powers & Harris). Five contribute to Personal Injury Handbook (editors Brennan & Curran) and four to Professional Negligence and Liability (published by Informa Law).

RECRUITMENT Up to two pupils are taken annually for 12 months. An award of £45,000 is offered, split between the first six months (£22,250) and a guaranteed £22,250 of earnings for the second six. A first or upper second class degree is required. The set is a member of Pupillage Gateway. Applications for a third six month pupillage are usually invited in June.

1COR
ONE CROWN OFFICE ROW

DEVEREUX Timothy Brennan QC

Head of Chambers	Timothy Brennan QC
Chambers Director	Vince Plant
Tenants	50

Devereux Chambers, Devereux Court, London, WC2R 3JH
Tel (020) 7353 7534 **Fax** (020) 7583 5150 **DX** 349 London Chancery Lane
Email clerks@devchambers.co.uk **Website** www.devereuxchambers.co.uk

MEMBERS

Timothy Brennan QC (1981) (QC-2001)
Colin Edelman QC (1977) (QC-1995)
Robert Glancy QC (1972) (QC-1997)
Jonathan Fisher QC (1980) (QC-2003)
Graham Read QC (1981) (QC-2003)
Stephen Killalea QC (1981) (QC-2006)
Colin Wynter QC (1984) (QC-2006)
Bruce Carr QC (1986) (QC-2009)
Robert Weir QC (1992) (QC-2010)
Nicholas Randall QC (1990) (QC-2013)
Nicholas Bard (1979)
Bruce Silvester (1983)
Colin Mendoza (1983)
Thomas Keith (1983)
Richard Royle (1983)
Oliver Hyams (1989)
Richard Harrison (1991)
Peter Edwards (1992)
Alison Padfield (1992)
Andrew Burns (1993)
Richard Cartwright (1994)
Timothy Frith (1996)
Jolyon Maugham (1997)
Stephen Cottrell (1998)
Akash Nawbatt (1999)
Shaen Catherwood (2000)
Robert Hunter (2000)
Sophie Belgrove (2001)
Alice Mayhew (2001)
Ben Lynch (2001)
Rachel Avery (2003)
Jonathan Butters (2003)
Lucinda Harris (2004)
Laura Bell (2004)
Thomas Vonberg (2004)
Talia Barsam (2006)
Thomas Cordrey (2006)
Adam Baradon (2006)
John Townsend (2006)
Sam Nicholls (2006)
Christopher Stone (2007)
Alice Carse (2008)
Ryan Hawthorne (2008)
Kate Balmer (2009)
Georgina Hirsch (2009)
Jesse Crozier (2009)
Sebastian Purnell (2010)
David Peter (2012)
Georgia Hicks (2012)
Rory Cochrane (2013)

THE CHAMBERS Devereux is proud of its reputation in all its fields of work, with 10 established specialist silks and a large team of talented juniors. Chambers covers the professional markets in insurance and reinsurance, employment law, tax, finance, sport, energy, telecommunications and education. It has a large and successful team advising and representing those engaged in cases involving personal injury, clinical negligence and health and safety. Chambers offers arbitration and mediation services.
Devereux offers in-depth expertise at all levels and takes pride in providing a tailored approach to all its clients. Well known for its professional yet client friendly approach, chambers is supported by an excellent team of staff. Clients of chambers include employers and unions, underwriters and brokers, victims and insurers, airlines and passengers, taxpayers and governments, patients and doctors, parents and schools, students and universities, regulators and utilities, clients and their professional advisers, sports personalities and clubs. The key to Devereux's client service is the seamless integration of market knowledge with first-class advocacy and a tailored approach to each client.

WORK UNDERTAKEN Chambers' work is continually developing as UK and European legislation changes and new legal avenues open. The website at www.devereuxchambers.co.uk is constantly updated with news of what members of chambers are doing.
Insurance & Reinsurance Law: Construction of policy and treaty wording, warranties, non-disclosure and misrepresentation, affirmation, aggregation, notification, ICOB, claims with a foreign dimension.
Professional Negligence & Regulation: Doctors, solicitors, barristers, accountants, IFAs, auditors, agents, brokers, construction professionals.
Telecommunications: Regulation, competition, tariffs, technical issues, artificial inflation of traffic, fraud, wayleaves.
Employment: Collective and individual employment law, domestic and European. Trade disputes, restrictive covenants and confidential information. Data protection. Whistle-blowers, unfair and wrongful dismissal, discrimination, redundancy, TUPE, equal pay. Working time, minimum wage. Share schemes, remuneration, pensions and other benefits.
Injunctions: Devereux are experts in business protection cases and in particular injunctive work. Barristers have unrivalled expertise in search and seizure, freezing orders, fiduciary orders and industrial relations.
Tax & Finance: Direct and indirect taxes, duties and national insurance contributions. Advice and litigation in all the statutory tribunals, on appeal, and on judicial review. Tax avoidance, statutory investigation powers, assessment procedures, taxation of employees. Investigations, disclosures. Confiscation, money laundering and fraud.
Personal Injury: Accidental injury, health and safety and clinical negligence work at the highest level. Multi-million pound catastrophic injury claims, industrial and traffic accidents, explosions, disease, the armed forces. A strong team of juniors provide a complete service in multi-track and fast-track trials in courts up and down the country.

RECRUITMENT Devereux is hugely popular and it is difficult to obtain a pupillage. Those who are successful in doing so are likely to have excellent academic qualifications and to offer something extra. Ambition for a successful career at the Bar, capacity for work and a sense of humour are the basic equipment.

devereux

DOUGHTY STREET CHAMBERS

Doughty Street Chambers, 54 Doughty Street, London, WC1N 2LS
Tel (020) 7404 1313 **Fax** (020) 7404 2283 **DX** 223 Chancery Lane
Email enquiries@doughtystreet.co.uk **Website** www.doughtystreet.co.uk

Heads of Chambers	Geoffrey Robertson QC
	Edward Fitzgerald CBE QC
Chambers Director	Robin Jackson
Senior Criminal Clerk	Graham Briggs
Senior Civil Clerk	Paul Friend
Criminal Clerks	Richard Goodman
	Emily Martin
	Chole Gibbs
Civil Clerks	Richard Bayliss
	Paul Read
	Sian Wilkins
	Eresha Reid
	Anthony Ward
	Elliott Gardner
	Callum Stebbing
Junior Clerks	Louis Wilkins
	Daniel Moore
Tenants	119

MEMBERS

Geoffrey Robertson QC (1973) (QC-1988)
Edward Fitzgerald QC (1978) (QC-1995)
James Wood QC (1975) (QC-1999) ^
Gavin Millar QC (1981) (QC-2000)
Helena Kennedy QC (1972) (QC-1991)
Patrick O'Connor QC (1970) (QC-1993) ^
Christopher Sallon QC (1973) (QC-1993) ^
Edward Rees QC (1973) (QC-1998)
Andrew Hall QC (1991) (QC-2002)
Heather Rogers QC (1983) (QC-2006)
Jon Whitfield QC (1985) (QC-2010)
Heather Williams QC (1985) (QC-2006)
Joel Bennathan QC (1985) (QC-2006)
Robin Oppenheim QC (1988) (QC-2006)
Nicholas Bowen QC (1984) (QC-2009) ^
Isabella Forshall QC (1982) (QC-2010)
Martin Westgate QC (1985) (QC-2010)
Francis FitzGibbon QC (1986) (QC-2010) ^
David Hislop QC (1979) (NZ bar 1979) (QC-2010) ^
Ian Wise QC (1992) (QC-2010) ^
Kirsty Brimelow QC (1991) (QC-2010)
Tim Moloney QC (1993) (QC-2011) ^
Judith Farbey QC (1992) (QC-2011) ^
Paul Bowen QC (1993) (QC-2012)
Rebecca Trowler QC (1995) (QC-2012) ^
David Bentley QC (1984) (QC-2013) ^
Stephen Cragg QC (1996) (QC-2013)
John RWD Jones QC (1992) ^ (QC-2013)
Kate Markus QC (1981) (QC-2014)^
Wayne Jordash QC (1995) (QC-2014)
Sarah Elliot QC (1996) (QC-2014)
David Carter (1971)
Nick Paul (1980)
Christopher Hough (1981)
Jeannie Mackie (1995) (Solicitor 1982)
Aswini Weereratne (1986) ^
Gerwyn Samuel (1986)
Lauren Soertsz (1987)
Paul Taylor (1989)
Joe Stone (1989) ^
Nicholas Brown (1990)
Quincy Whitaker (1991)
Stephen Reeder (1991)
Jonathan Cooper OBE (1992)
John Walsh (1993)
Mark Henderson (1994)
Paula Sparks (1994)
Richard Fisher (1994) ^
Paul Draycott (1994)
Siobhan Grey (1994)
Katy Thorne (1994)
Althea Brown (1995)
Dominic Preston (1995)
Rupert Bowers (1995)
Anthony Hudson (1996)
Nick Toms (1996)
Tublu Mukherjee (1996)
Joseph Middleton (1997) ^
Ulele Burnham (1997)
Henrietta Hill (1997) ^
Steven Powles (1997)
Nick Stanage (1997) ^
Lindsay Johnson (1997) ^
Jim Shepherd (1998)
Farrhat Arshad (1998) ^
Jamie Burton (1999)
Benjamin Narain (1999)
Ben Cooper (1999) ^
Charlotte Kilroy (1999)
John Hobson (1999)
Guy Vassall-Adams (2000) ^
Daniel Bennett (2000)
Erimnaz Mushtaq (2000) ^
David Lemer (2000) ^
Philip Haywood (2001) ^
Ruth Brander (2001) ^
Caoilfhionn Gallagher (2001) ^
Amanda Hart (2001)
Susan Sleeman (2001)
Piers Marquis (2001)
Amos Waldman (2001)
Liam Walker (2001) ^
Laura Dubinsky (2002)
David Rhodes (2002)
Richard Thomas (2002)
Eloise Power (2002)
Adam Straw (2004)
Alison Gerry (2003)
Alasdair Mackenzie (2004)
Azeem Suterwalla (2004)
Benjamin Newton (2004)
David Haines (2005)
Nichola Higgins (2005)
Gemma Hobcraft (2006)
Jude Bunting (2006)
Louise Price (2006) ^
Malcolm Hawkes (2006)
Kate Annand (2007)
Tunde Okewale (2007)
Alison Pickup (2007)
Annabel Timan (2007) ^
Tanya Eatwell (2007)
Harry Lambert (2008)
Steve Broach (2008)
Alex Gask (2008)
Catherine Meredith (2008)
Tom Stevens (2008)
Michelle Knorr (2008)
Sarah Steinhardt (2008)
Ben Silverstone (2009)
Amal Alamuddin (2010)
Nikolaus Grubeck (2010)
Abigail Bright (2010)
Maria Roche (2010)
Kate O'Raghallaigh (2011)
Sam Jacobs (2011)
Martha Spurrier (2010)
Graham L Hall (2011)
Fiona Murphy (2013)
Paul Harris SC (1976) ++
Sadakat Kadri (1989) ++
Dr Guénaël Mettraux ++

++ Associate Tenant ^ Public/Direct Access

THE CHAMBERS Doughty Street Chambers is a buoyant and cutting-edge set, renowned for and committed to defending freedom and civil liberties, and has a truly national and international profile across its wide range of practice in criminal law, civil law, administrative and public law, international law and human rights. Since their foundation in 1990, their aim has been and will always be to improve access to justice and to promote human rights and civil liberties through the law. Founded by fewer than 30 barristers, Doughty Street Chambers has grown to become one of the largest sets in the country with over 119 members, of whom 30 are Queen's Counsel, and they have established chambers in Manchester and Bristol as well as London.

doughty street chambers

ELY PLACE CHAMBERS William McCormick QC

Head of Chambers	William McCormick QC
Senior Clerk	Christopher Drury 07885 469845
First Junior	Richard Sheehan 07870128617
Second Junior	Kevin Morrow 07736288055
Third Junior	Dave Lovitt 07795 233444
Administrator	Carol Belford
Tenants	35

30 Ely Place, London, EC1N 6TD
Tel (020) 7400 9600 **DX** 291 Chancery Lane
Email admin@elyplace.com **Website** www.elyplace.com

MEMBERS

William McCormick QC (1985) (QC-2010) ^
Ronald Thwaites QC (1970) (QC-1987)
Nicholas Stewart QC (1971) (QC-1987) ^ ± Fellow of the Institute of Chartered Arbitrators
Malcolm Bishop QC (1968) (QC-1993) +
Robert Willer (1970) ^ ±
William Evans (1977) + ^ ±
Clifford Darton (1988) ^
Leslie Millin (1988) ^
Jeffrey Bacon (1989)
Russell Stone (1992) ^ ±
Iain Daniels (1992)
Craig Barlow (1992)
Angus Gloag (1992) ^
Mark Friston (1997) ++
Simon Perhar (1997) ^ ±
Ali Reza Sinai (1997)
Gillian Crew (1998) ^ ±
Michael Salter (1999) ^
James Newman (2000) ^
Faisel Sadiq (2000) ^
Bushra Ahmed (2001) ^
Paul Hughes (2001) ++
John Samson (2001) ^ ±
Sally Blackmore (2003)
David Mitchell (2004) ^ **
Amy Stroud (2004) ^
Thomas Kirk (2007) ^ **
Liam Ryan (2007) ^
Aidan Briggs (2009) ^
Paul Powlesland (2009) ^
George Woodhead (2009)
Anna Lintner (2009) ^
Naveeta Sawh (2009) ^
Catherine Urquhart (2010)
Max Cole (2011) ^

\+ Recorder ^ Public Access Approved ** Junior Treasury Counsel ± CEDR Accredited ++ Door tenant

Ely Place Chambers

RANKED IN CHAMBERS UK 2013 LEADING SET

THE CHAMBERS Friendly, progressive and dynamic, the set provides clear pragmatic advice and a tradition of robust polished advocacy to public and private sector clients, while the long-serving clerking team offers its expertise to clients regarding suitability of counsel and provides strong administrative support thereafter. The ethos is that providing the best result for the client depends upon a team effort.

WORK UNDERTAKEN Ely Place's workload covers the following areas: commercial litigation; employment law; defamation, media and sports law; personal injury, clinical negligence and healthcare; property and housing litigation; police and prison law; regulatory law and business offences; local government, public and administrative law. Allied to the set's continued involvement in many of the highest profile defamation cases, there has been a programme of development within its other areas of work. The commercial team has been in demand in disputes over the ownership and management of businesses (including the misuse of assets by directors); contractual issues and the misconduct of banks. Chambers receives instructions from the Caribbean, Europe and the DIFC. The employment team has benefitted from forging links with major firms and employers and the property and housing team has also made substantial progress with both having secured individual recommendations as a result. Chambers continues to represent and advise parties to actions involving the police or prison law and to provide assistance to persons and organisations concerned in accident liability, from representation at inquests through to trial, both in actions for civil liability and prosecutions under health and safety legislation.

ENTERPRISE CHAMBERS Zia Bhaloo QC

9 Old Square, Lincoln's Inn, London WC2A 3SR
Tel (020) 7405 9471 **Fax** (020) 7242 1447 **DX** LDE 301
Email london@enterprisechambers.com **Website** www.enterprisechambers.com

Head of Chambers	Zia Bhaloo QC
Senior Clerk	Antony Armstrong
Clerks	Mark Belford
	Michael Ireland
	Luke Daws
	Jake Hubbard
Tenants	37

MEMBERS

Zia Bhaloo QC (1990) (QC-2010)
Bernard Weatherill QC (1974) (QC-1996)
Hugh Jory QC (1992) (QC-2014)
Charles Morgan (1978)
Caroline Hutton (1979)
Linden Ife (1982)
Geoffrey Zelin (1984)
James Barker (1984)
Hugo Groves (1980)
Stephanie Jarron (1990)
James Pickering (1991)
Robert Duddridge (1992)
Bridget Williamson (1993)
Jonathan Klein (1992)
Edward Francis (1995)
Shanti Mauger (1996)
Shaiba Ilyas (1998)
Timothy Calland (1999)
Jonathan Rodger (1999)
Niall McCulloch (2000)
Simon Johnson (2000)
Rebecca Page (2001)
Matthew West (2000)
Olivier Kalfon (2003)
Kavan Gunaratna (2004)
Cristín Toman (2004)
Margaret Griffin (2004)
Susannah Markandya (2005)
Kelly Bond (2007)
Duncan Heath (2007)
Jennifer Meech (2008)
Phillip Gale (2008)
James Davies (2009)
Matthew Maddison (2010)
Christopher Buckingham (2009)
Louise Bowmaker (2011)
Rowena Page (2012)
HH Peter Langan QC (1967) (QC-1983) *
Jeremy Child (BVI) *

* Door tenant

THE CHAMBERS Enterprise Chambers is a leading commercial chancery set, with experts who are consistently recommended in their field by Chambers and Partners (for details of individual recommendations, please see the chambers website). The set is in a position to offer specialists across the range of commercial chancery work, including commercial, company, insolvency and restructuring, landlord and tenant, and property; so for example, the expertise within the set in insolvency and property uniquely places it to deal with disputes which involve both. Clients comment on both the outstanding quality of the work done by the set and its flexible and unstuffy approach, in particular the excellence of its clerking. The set also has northern branches in Leeds and Newcastle.

TYPES OF WORK UNDERTAKEN Enterprise is able to provide specialist barristers in the following areas (for details of recent cases in each area, please see the chambers website):
Commercial Disputes: Including contracts, banking, guarantees, securities, financial services regulation, insurance, sale and carriage of goods, consumer credit, competition, restraint of trade, breach of confidence, civil fraud and private international law.
Company: Including unfair prejudice, derivative and other shareholders' claims, directors' disqualification, solvent and insolvent schemes, capital reductions, business transfers, companies' securities, and claims against directors.
Equitable Remedies: Including constructive and resulting trusts, tracing, injunctions, freezing injunctions, and search orders.
Insolvency & Restructuring: Relating to companies, partnerships and individuals, including receiverships, administrations, voluntary arrangements, liquidations, bankruptcy, wrongful and fraudulent trading, preferences, transactions at an undervalue, other antecedent transactions, and cross-border insolvency.
Intellectual Property: Including copyright, trademarks, and passing off.
Landlord & Tenant: Relating to business, residential and agricultural tenancies including security of tenure, possession claims, forfeiture, unlawful eviction, dilapidations, leasehold enfranchisement, rent control and review, service charges, and business tenancy renewals under Part II of the 1954 Act, together with all aspects of social housing law.
Pensions: Relating to occupational and personal pension schemes.
Professional Liability: Relating to accountants, actuaries, auditors, barristers, solicitors, insolvency practitioners, surveyors and construction professionals, and trustees.
Real Property: concerning the legal and beneficial ownership of real property, including conveyancing and the sale of land, easements, restrictive covenants, adverse possession, boundary disputes, land registration, mortgages, LPA receivers, defective buildings, construction and engineering contracts and planning.
Regulatory & Licensing: Affecting commercial activity, including environmental, water and waste licensing, building regulation and remediation, as well as liquor, gaming, and sex establishments.
Traditional Chancery: including associations (partnerships, clubs and societies), charities, trusts, settlements, family provision, wills and probate, and Court of Protection.

PUBLICATIONS Publications include the Enterprise Chambers Annotated Guide to Insolvency Legislation and Practice; Bailey and Groves on Corporate Insolvency – Law and Practice; The Landlord and Tenant Factbook; Estates Gazette Questions and Answers series.

INTERNATIONAL Several members have previously practised in fused professions overseas for extended periods of time and are admitted to practise there, including the Cayman Islands and the British Virgin Islands. The set can provide barristers who are used to working abroad (often at very short notice) and who have material insight as to the workings of particular jurisdictions.

Enterprise Chambers
London Leeds Newcastle

ERSKINE CHAMBERS

Senior Clerk	Mike Hannibal
Tenants	31

33 Chancery Lane, London, WC2A 1EN
Tel (020) 7242 5532 **Fax** (020) 7831 0125
Email clerks@erskinechambers.com **Website** www.erskinechambers.com

MEMBERS

Michael Todd QC (1977) (QC-1997)
John Cone (1975)
David Mabb QC (1979) (QC-2001)
Martin Moore QC (1982) (QC-2002)
David Chivers QC (1983) (QC-2002)
Peter Arden QC (1983) (QC-2006)
Stephen Smith QC (1983) (QC 2000)
Ceri Bryant QC (1984) (QC-2012)
Richard Snowden QC (1986) (QC-2003)
Raquel Agnello QC (1986) (QC-2009)
Andrew Thompson QC (1991) (QC 2014)
James Potts QC (1994) (QC-2013)
Catherine Roberts (1986)
Philip Gillyon (1988)
Mary Stokes (1989)
Dan Prentice (1982)
Nigel Dougherty (1993)
Andrew Thornton (1994)
Edward Davies (1998)
Stephen Horan (2002)
Benjamin Shaw (2002)
Ben Griffiths (2004)
Tim Akkouh (2004)
Matthew Parfitt (2005)
Alex Barden (2005)
Emily Gillett (2005)
Patrick Harty (2008)
Jack Rivett (2010)
Anna Scharnetzky (2011)
Chantelle Staynings (2012)
Richard Nolan (1999)*

* Door Tenant

THE CHAMBERS Erskine Chambers is recognised as being pre-eminent in company law and a leading set in associated fields including insolvency, financial services, commercial litigation and asset recovery.
Chambers' size (31 barristers including 11 QCs) allows it to maintain expertise in its core practice areas while fielding effective teams in Commercial Court and Chancery Division litigation. Prominent former members include Arden LJ and David Richards J, while present members sit on various law reform committees and are editors and contributors to the leading texts on company law.

WORK UNDERTAKEN In pure company law, Erskine is a major destination for shareholder disputes such as Kleanthous v Paphitis and Bumi, as well as technical company litigation such as Enviroco v Farstad (Supreme Court on the definition of "subsidiary") and Eclairs v JKX (notice of beneficial interest in shareholdings). On the non-contentious side, members have advised on most of the largest UK corporate transactions of recent years, including Glencore-Xstrata, Vodafone-Verizon and Aegis Plc. Erskine provides counsel for the majority of schemes, cross-border mergers (including for Honda Europe and Itau BBA), Part 7 transfers of insurance business, and reductions of capital.
A large proportion of Erskine's work is at the intersection between company, commercial and insolvency law, including breach of fiduciary duty and commercial fraud. Chambers has provided the lead counsel teams for BTA Bank in Ablyazov (over 60 reported judgments), Kaupthing Bank's UK litigation and Lehman Brothers US' UK litigation. Members also acted in the recent Liverpool FC and Barclay Brothers litigation (Re Coroin Ltd).
Recent cases involving LLPs and investment funds include Charterhouse Capital, and F&C Investments v Barthelemy, while Chambers also has a substantial involvement in financial services litigation, including the Supreme Court's Bank Charges decision, and interest rate swap claims against banks.
In the insolvency field, members regularly appear in the major cases, including Nortel & Lehman Bros v Pensions Regulator, the Lehman Client Money case and Belmont Park v BNY (all in the Supreme Court) and MF Global. Members regularly advise on restructurings including insolvency schemes of arrangement, administrations and CVAs – high profile cases include Halliwells, Baugur and Miss Sixty.

INTERNATIONAL Erskine's work is highly international, and includes many of the large international insolvencies of recent years, such as Akai and Grande (Hong Kong), Sphinx (Cayman Islands), Bell Group (Australia) and Carlyle Capital (Guernsey and the USA).

ONE ESSEX COURT Lord Anthony Grabiner QC

One Essex Court, Temple, London, EC4Y 9AR
Tel (020) 7583 2000 **Fax** (020) 7583 0118 **DX** 430 (Ch.Ln.)
Email clerks@oeclaw.co.uk **Website** www.oeclaw.co.uk

Head of Chambers	Lord Grabiner QC
Tenants	85
Senior Clerk	Darren Burrows

MEMBERS

Lord Grabiner QC (1968) (QC-1981)
Nicholas Strauss QC (1965) (QC-1984)
Peter Leaver QC (1967) (QC-1987)
Ian Glick QC (1970) (QC-1987)
Geoffrey Hobbs QC (1977) (QC-1991)
Thomas Sharpe QC (1976) (QC-1994)
Jeffery Onions QC (1981) (QC-1998)
Susanna FitzGerald QC (1973) (QC-1999)
Rhodri Davies QC (1979) (QC-1999)
Stephen Auld QC (1979) (QC-1999)
Kenneth MacLean QC (1985) (QC-2002)
Laurence Rabinowitz QC (1987) (QC-2002)
Malcolm Gammie QC (1997) (QC-2002)
John McCaughran QC (1982) (QC-2003)
Charles Graham QC (1986) (QC-2003)
Christopher Style QC (2012) (QC-2006)
Richard Gillis QC (1982) (QC-2006)
Andrew Lenon QC (1982) (QC-2006)
Craig Orr QC (1986) (QC-2006)
Anthony de Garr Robinson QC (1987) (QC-2006)
Michael Sullivan QC (1983) (QC-2008)
Neil Kitchener QC (1991) (QC-2008)
Alain Choo Choy QC (1991) (QC-2009)
David Wolfson QC (1992) (QC-2009)
Daniel Toledano QC (1993) (QC-2009)
David Cavender QC (1993) (QC-2010)
Richard Boulton QC (2003) (QC-2011)
Emma Himsworth QC (1993) (QC-2012)
Sa'ad Hossain QC (1995) (QC-2013)
Camilla Bingham QC (1996) (QC-2013)
Michael Fealy QC (1997) (QC-2014)
Benjamin Strong QC (2001) (QC-2014)
Michael Malone (1975)
Alan Griffiths (1981)
Clare Reffin (1981)
Hannah Brown (1992)
Zoe O'Sullivan (1993)
Edmund Nourse (1994)
Alan Redfern (1995)
Philip Roberts (1996)
Orlando Gledhill (1998)
Simon Colton (1999)
Matthew Cook (1999)
Steven Elliott (2001)
Guy Hollingworth (2001)
Derek Spitz (2001)
Anna Boase (2002)
James Goldsmith (2002)
James Nadin (2002)
Daniel Hubbard (2003)
Michelle Menashy (2003)
Conall Patton (2004)
Laurence Emmett (2004)
Henry Forbes Smith (2004)
Alexander Polley (2005)
Sebastian Isaac (2005)
Marcos Dracos (2005)
Eleanor Campbell (2005)
Michael Clark (2005)
Andrew Foyle (2006)
Richard Mott (2006)
David Caplan (2006)
Rachel Oakeshott (2006)
Saul Lemer (2007)
Nicholas Sloboda (2007)
Sam O'Leary (2007)
Abra Bompas (2008)
Michael d'Arcy (2008)
Nehali Shah (2008)
Owain Draper (2008)
Alexander Brown (2009)
Mehdi Baiou (2009)
Douglas Paine (2009)
Michael Watkins (2009)
James Petkovic (2009)
Emma Jones (2010)
Oliver Butler (2010)
Adam Rushworth (2010)
Gideon Cohen (2010)
Sophie Weber (2011)
Tamara Kagan (2011)
Andrew Lodder (2012)
Patricia Burns (2011)
Alaina Newne (2012)
Maximillian Schlote (2013)

THE CHAMBERS One Essex Court is a pre-eminent set of barristers' chambers, providing specialist legal advice, support and advocacy services worldwide, and their expertise covers all areas of arbitration, litigation, regulation and dispute resolution. Work at the chambers embraces all aspects of domestic and international trade, business, commerce and finance, with members regularly accepting nominations as arbitrators, mediators and experts. Principal areas of practice are commercial litigation, arbitration, banking and financial services, civil fraud, company and insolvency, competition and EU law, energy and natural resources, insurance and reinsurance, intellectual property, licensing, professional negligence and revenue law. The pre-eminent team of energy lawyers is consistently ranked as the leading group at the Bar. Barristers regularly appear before the domestic courts and tribunals, dealing with short County Court applications to major trials in the High Court and appeals before the Court of Appeal, the Privy Council and the Supreme Court, as well as hearings at the CJEU and EGC. Their counsel also appear in a wide range of foreign jurisdictions, particularly in the Caribbean and the Far East and their international arbitrators are regularly appointed to panels with both domestic and overseas arbitral seats. In addition to the arbitration administration in London, they are able to provide real-time, high quality support through their Singapore office at Maxwell Chambers. Situated within the Singapore dispute resolution complex, the One Essex Court office is able to deal with enquiries through a full-time member of the adminstrative staff.

WORK UNDERTAKEN Accounting and auditing, administrative and public law, agency, arbitration, aviation finance, banking, breach of warranty, civil jurisdiction and judgements/conflict of laws, commercial, commodities, company, competition, derivatives, directors' disqualification, economic torts, employment and industrial relations law, energy and natural resources, EU law, financial services regulation, fraud and asset tracing, guarantees, information technology, insolvency, insurance and reinsurance, intellectual property, joint ventures agreements, licensing and gambling, media and entertainment, mergers and acquisitions, partnership, professional negligence, restitution, restraint of trade restructuring, share sale agreements, shareholder's agreements, sports law, tax/revenue.

ONE ESSEX COURT

5 ESSEX COURT Fiona Barton QC

Head of Chambers	Fiona Barton QC
Senior Clerk	Mark Waller
Tenants	38

5 Essex Court, Temple, London, EC4Y 9AH
Tel (020) 7410 2000 **Fax** (020) 7129 8606 **DX** 1048
Email clerks@5essexcourt.co.uk **Website** www.5essexcourt.co.uk

MEMBERS

Fiona Barton QC (1986) (QC 2011)
Geoffrey Tattersall QC (1970) (QC-1992)
Jason Beer QC (1992) (QC 2011)
Jeremy Johnson QC (1994) (QC 2011)
Anne Studd QC (1988) (QC-2012)
Samantha Leek QC (1993) (QC-2012)
John Bassett (1975)
Nicholas Wilcox (1977)
Charles Apthorp (1983) ^
Alison Hewitt (1984)
Andrew Waters (1987)
Simon Walsh (1987)
Dijen Basu (1994)
Richard Oulton (1995) ^
John-Paul Waite (1995)
Alan Payne (1996)
Victoria von Wachter (1997) ^
Melvyn Harris (1997) ^
Alastair Hodge (1997)
Matthew Holdcroft (1998)
Barnabas Branston (1999)
Russell Fortt (1999)
Charlotte Ventham (2001)
Elliot Gold (2001)
Francesca Whitelaw (2003)
Kate Cornell (2004)
Beatrice Collier (2004) ^
Mark Thomas (2006) ^
Georgina Wolfe (2006)
Jonathan Dixey (2007)
Peter Taheri (2007)
Cicely Harward (2008)
Alex Ustych (2010) ^
Robert Talalay (2010)
Robert Cohen (2009)
Amy Clarke (2009)
Catriona Hodge (2012)

* Door Tenant ^ Direct/Public Access

The Chambers 5 Essex Court is a specialist civil set and is acknowledged to be one of the leading chambers practising in the field of police law. Members of chambers appear in the great majority of significant cases and public inquires concerning police forces. In addition, chambers has a highly successful Public Law Team, a thriving Employment Team, a well-established Personal Injury Team and a strong Licensing Team. Individual members have successful practices in a variety of other areas including immigration, equine law, insolvency, commercial disputes, contractual disputes, professional negligence, and landlord and tenant. Chambers' unique expertise and depth of experience, combined with its commitment to excellence, ensures that it is able to handle any case within its fields. Members of chambers provide advocacy and advice of the highest standard in an efficient, effective, helpful and sensitive manner. These attributes, combined with a friendly, accessible and open approach to clerking, allow chambers to offer its clients a comprehensive service in an utterly reliable, highly effective and straightforward manner.

WORK UNDERTAKEN

Police Law: Chambers is instructed by virtually every police force in the country and has an unrivalled record in police law. Chambers has the highest number of counsel specialising in police law of any set in the country. It has more members identified by the reputable legal practice directories as leaders in the fields of police law than any other set. Members of chambers have appeared in significantly more reported cases concerning police than members on any other set of chambers.

Public Law: Chambers acts for government departments, government agencies, police authorities and other public bodies. It has extensive experience in public inquiries, judicial review, the Human Rights Act, the Data Protection Act and the Freedom Of Information Act. Members of chambers appear in a wide spectrum of cases concerning equality, discrimination, civil liberties, disciplinary tribunals and immigration. Nine members of Chambers are appointed Junior Council to the Crown (Common Law); 2 A Panel 2 B Panel - 5 C Panel.

Employment: Members of chambers are at the forefront of employment jurisprudence, appearing in related jurisdictions from the Employment Tribunal to the Court of Appeal. The team comprises dedicated specialist practitioners, each with extensive personal experience of industry and commerce, who offer advice and advocacy on all aspects of contentious and non-contentious work. Members of chambers have strength and depth in all areas of employment law relating to commercial organisations and a collective understanding to deal with the most complex issues. In addition to police forces, clients include global energy suppliers, international construction companies and investment banks, as well as employees at all levels.

Personal Injury: Members of chambers appear for both claimants and defendants, and instructions are received from insurers, local authorities and the police, as well as from privately paying clients. A substantial amount of work is also carried out under conditional fee agreements.

Due to the strength in depth of the team at all levels of experience, chambers are able to cover the whole range of personal injury cases, from the most serious and complex multi-track claims to the simplest small track claims. Chambers has extensive experience of advising on and appearing in personal injury claims arising out of accidents at work, product liability, defective premises, highway claims, holiday claims and road traffic accidents.

Licensing: In response to the introduction of the Licensing Act 2003, chambers has brought together its licensing practitioners to establish a dedicated Licensing Team able to provide expertise in licensing work. Instructions have expanded to include liquor, entertainment, gaming and taxi licensing.

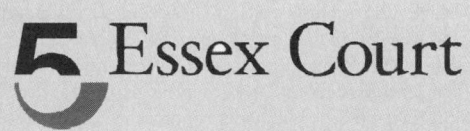

5 Essex Court

ESSEX COURT CHAMBERS

24 Lincoln's Inn Fields, London, WC2A 3EG
Tel (020) 7813 8000 **Fax** (020) 7813 8080 **DX** 320 LONDON CHANCERY LANE
Email clerksroom@essexcourt.net **Website** www.essexcourt.net

Senior Clerk & Head of Administration	David Grief
Deputy Senior Clerk	Joe Ferrigno
Clerks	Ben Perry
	Jack Wood
Office Manager	Lisa Nwachukwu
Tenants	83

MEMBERS

Richard Jacobs QC (1979) (QC-1998)
Graham Dunning QC (1982) (QC-2001)
Gordon Pollock QC (1968) (QC-1979)
Ian Hunter QC (1967) (QC-1980)
Stewart Boyd QC (1967) (QC-1981)
V V Veeder QC (1971) (QC-1986)
Richard Siberry QC (1974) (QC-1989)
Jonathan Gilman QC (1965) (QC-1990)
Franklin Berman QC (1966) (QC-1992)
Roderick Cordara QC (1975) (QC-1994)
Simon Crookenden QC (1975) (QC-1996)
Jeffrey Gruder QC (1977) (QC-1997)
Andrew Hochhauser QC (1977) (QC-1997)
David Mildon QC (1980) (QC-2000)
Steven Berry QC (1984) (QC-2002)
Malcolm Shaw QC (1988) (QC-2002)
Mark Templeman QC (1981) (QC-2003)
David Joseph QC (1984) (QC-2003)
Richard Millett QC (1985) (QC-2003)
Joe Smouha QC (1986) (QC-2003)
Huw Davies QC (1985) (QC-2006)
Martin Griffiths QC (1986) (QC-2006)
John Lockey QC (1987) (QC-2006)
Simon Bryan QC (1988) (QC-2006)
David Foxton QC (1989) (QC-2006)
Hugh Mercer QC (1985) (QC-2008)
Vernon Flynn QC (1991) (QC-2008)
Vaughan Lowe QC (1993) (QC-2008)
Toby Landau, QC (1993) (QC-2008)
Christopher Smith QC (1989) (QC-2009)
Claire Blanchard QC (1992) (QC-2010)
Paul Stanley QC (1993) (QC-2010)
Daniel Oudkerk QC (1992) (QC-2010)
Sara Cockerill QC (1990) (QC-2011)
Tim Eicke QC (1993) (QC-2011)
Paul McGrath QC (1994) (QC-2011)
James Collins QC (1995) (QC-2012)
Nigel Eaton QC (1991) (QC-2013)
Stephen Houseman QC (1995) (QC-2013)
Paul Key QC (1997) (QC-2013)
Sam Wordsworth QC (1997) (QC-2013)
Charles Ciumei QC (1991) (QC-2014)
Anthony Dicks QC (1961) (QC-1994) Hong Kong
Shane Doyle QC (2001) (QC - 1995) Australia
Alan Boyle (1977)
Philippa Watson (1988)
John Snider (1982)
Brian Dye (1991)
Martin Hunter (1994)
Philippa Hopkins (1994)
Martin Lau (1996)
David Scorey (1997)
Nathan Pillow (1997)
David Craig (1997)
Salim Moollan (1998)
Ricky Diwan (1998)
Neil Hart (1998)
Edmund King (1999)
Iain Quirk (2002)
Jern-Fei Ng (2004)
David Davies (2004)
Edward Brown (2002)
Jeremy Brier (2004)
Jessica Wells (2004)
Jane Russell (2004)
Dan Sarooshi (2005)
Damien Walker (2006)
David Peters (2005)
Siddharth Dhar (2005)
James Willan (2006)
Emily Wood (2006)
Amy Sander (2006)
Tom Ford (2008)
Anton Dudnikov (2008)
Anna Dilnot (2008)
Catherine Jung (2010)
Adam Board (2010)
Andrew Legg (2010)
John Robb (2011)
Claudia Renton (2011)
Rebecca Stripe (2012)
Adam Woolnough (2012)
Peter Webster (2012)

THE CHAMBERS Essex Court Chambers is a leading set of barristers' chambers specialising in commercial, international and European law. Its members advise and act in a broad range of litigation, arbitration and dispute resolution worldwide.

Chambers is not a firm, nor are its members partners or employees. Rather, chambers contains the separate, self-contained offices of individual barristers, each self-employed and working separately. Indeed, (as in all specialist sets) individual barristers within chambers are commonly retained by opposing sides in the same dispute, both in litigation and arbitration.

Recent cases in the public domain include: Deutsche Bank Ag v Sebastian Holdings Inc; JP Morgan Chase Bank plc and JP Morgan Securities Ltd. v BVG v Clifford Chance; Robert Tchenguiz and others v The Director of the SFO; Astro v Lippo and Otkritie.

Founded in 1961, the then five members of chambers included the future judges Lord Mustill, Lord Justice Evans and Lord Justice Kerr. Other distinguished alumni include Lords Saville and Steyn, Lord Justices Thomas and Beatson, Sir Anthony Colman, Mr Justice Eder, Mrs Justice Andrews, Dame Rosalyn Higgins (former president of the International Court of Justice) and Sir Christopher Greenwood (the current British judge at the ICJ). The set is managed by David Grief and his team of clerks who have acquired a reputation for responsiveness and integrity and there is a modern approach to client care and commercial requirements.

WORK UNDERTAKEN Annual market research and award ceremonies confirm that members are consistently recognised as leading individuals by clients and peers in a number of key areas but most notably: international

ESSEX COURT CHAMBERS (continued)

commercial arbitration; commercial dispute resolution; public international law; energy and natural resources; civil fraud; insurance; shipping and commodities; indirect tax; banking and finance; media, entertainment and sport; employment; professional negligence; civil liberties and human rights; administrative and public law; agriculture, fisheries and farming; information technology; immigration; aviation; EU and competition; offshore litigation; commercial chancery; insolvency and corporate recovery.
The strong international nature of chambers differentiates it from other practices. It has barristers qualified to practise in non-UK jurisdictions and with a wide range of commercial language skills.

PUPILLAGE Chambers typically offers up to four funded 12 month tenancy seeking pupillages per year. Applications should be made via the Pupillage Gateway. Applicants for pupillage are encouraged to undertake a mini-pupillage (of 1-2 days). Information about mini-pupillage, including deadlines for mini-pupillage applications and an online application form, is available at www. essexcourt.net.

20 ESSEX STREET Iain Milligan QC

20 Essex Street, London, WC2R 3AL
Tel (020) 7842 1200 **Fax** (020) 7842 1270 **DX** 0009 (Ch.Ln.)
Email clerks@20essexst.com **Website** www.20essexst.com

Head of Chambers	Iain Milligan QC
Senior Clerks	Neil Palmer Home (020) 7842 1201
	Mobile (0777) 5713 925
	Brian Lee Home (020) 8642 5865
	Mobile (0797) 7590 220
Chambers Manager	Daniel Clark
Tenants	58

MEMBERS

Iain Milligan QC (1973) (QC-1991)
Prof Sir Elihu Lauterpacht CBE QC (1950) (QC-1970)
Alexander Layton QC (1976) (QC-1995)
Timothy Young QC (1977) (QC-1996)
Michael Tselentis QC (1995) (QC-2003)
Stephen Morris QC (1981) (QC-2002)
Christopher Hancock QC (1983) (QC-2000) *
Duncan Matthews QC (1986) (QC-2002)
Andrew Baker QC (1988) (QC-2006)
Sir Daniel Bethlehem QC (1988) (QC-2003)
Stephen Atherton QC (1989) (QC-2006)
Philip Edey QC (1994) (QC-2009)
Michael Coburn QC (1990) (QC-2010)
Charles Kimmins QC (1994) (QC-2010)
Michael Collett QC (1995) (QC-2013)
Michael Ashcroft QC (1997) (QC-2011)
+ Arbitrator
Lawrence Akka QC (1991) (QC-2012)
Sara Masters QC (1993) (QC-2-12)*
David Lewis QC (1999) (QC-2014)*
Sir Michael Wood (1968)
Edmund Broadbent (1980)
Anthony Thompson SC (1988)
David D Caron (1984)
Clare Ambrose (1992)
Julie Anderson (1993)
Sudhanshu Swaroop (1997)
Julian Kenny (1997)
Malcolm Jarvis (1998)
Susannah Jones (1999)
Thomas Raphael (1999)
Andrew Fulton (1999)
Zannis Mavrogordato (1999)
Sean Snook (2000)
Henry Byam-Cook (2000)
Socrates Papadopoulos (2001)
Blair Leahy (2001)
Angharad Parry (2002)
Colleen Hanley (2003)
Ben Olbourne (2003)
Christopher Newman (2003)
Tony Beswetherick (2003)
Simon Milnes (2005)
Guglielmo Verdirame (2006)
Daniel Bovensiepen (2004)
Josephine Davies (2006)
Patricia Edwards (2006)
Stefan Talmon (2007)
Charlotte Tan (2008)
Sarah Tresman (2008)
Luke Pearce (2007)
Edward Ho (2009)
Penelope Nevill (2010)
Rupert Hamilton (2010)
Thomas Corby (2011)
Mahnaz Malik (2012)
Oliver Caplin (2012)
Alex Carless (2012)
Leonora Sagan (2012)
Sir Brian Neill +
Sir Philip Otton +
Lord Neill QC +
The Honorable Charles Brower +
Michael Lee +
David St John Sutton +
J William Rowley QC +
Malcolm Holmes QC +
Dr Michael Pryles +
Gil Carlos Rodriguez Iglesias +
Anthony Hallgarten QC +
Francisco Orrego Vicuña +
Dr Julian Lew QC +
Sir Simon Tuckey +
Dr Michael Moser +
Murray Pickering QC +
Yves Fortier QC +
Sir Bernard Rix +
David Owen QC +

THE CHAMBERS This long-established, progressive set of chambers is one of the leading sets in commercial law. Members advise on all aspects of international trade, commerce and finance with specialist expertise in banking, competition, shipping, arbitration, insurance, energy, insolvency, public international law, and European Community law. In light of the increasingly international practices of its members, the set opened an office in Maxwell Chambers in January 2010 (tel: +65 62257230). Simon Milnes and Ben Olbourne are currently practising from the office in Singapore and other members travel there regularly.

WORK UNDERTAKEN

Commercial Dispute Resolution: Members both advise and act as advocates in relation to all types of commercial disputes and have particular expertise in disputes with an international dimension. These may be resolved in the English and Welsh Courts, by institutional or ad hoc international arbitration, or by London maritime and commodity trade arbitrations. Members are experienced in representing overseas and large corporate clients and advising in complex, high value and multi-forum litigation.

EU & Competition: A number of members specialise in the substantive law of the EU and in UK and EU Competition law and virtually all members deal with aspects of EU law regularly in their practice. Members appear before the Competition Appeal Tribunal, Competition Commission, European Commission, European Court of First Instance, and European Court of Justice, in addition to domestic courts and tribunals.

International Arbitration: 20 Essex Street has a strong reputation as a leading arbitration set. It has an exclusive team of 18 leading international arbitrators and 58 barrister members who act as advocates and arbitrators under all of the world's major institutions' auspices, dealing with all manner of international commercial disputes.

Insolvency & Company Law: Members are well known for their expertise in contentious and non-contentious restructurings, insolvency law and company law, spanning all business and industry sectors. They regularly advise and represent insolvency office-holders, companies, creditors, shareholders and company directors and have been heavily involved in many of the recent major restructurings and insolvencies.

Public International Law: 20 Essex Street is well represented in public international law. Members specialising in this area regularly provide legal and strategic advice to States and other parties and appear before English courts (at all levels) in cases in which issues of public international law arise, as well as before international courts and tribunals. Members also have a wealth of experience in investor state disputes.

20 ESSEX STREET BARRISTERS

23 ESSEX STREET Simon Russell Flint QC

Head of Chambers	Simon Russell Flint QC
Chambers Director	Richard Fowler
Senior Clerk	Sean Hulston (Manchester/Nottingham)
Tenants	99

23 Essex Street, London, WC2R 3AA
Tel (020) 7413 0353 **Fax** (020) 7413 0374 **DX** 148 LDE

Manchester annexe 14 St Mary's Parsonage, Manchester, M3 2DF
Tel (0161) 870 9969 **DX** 303434

Nottingham annexe: 21 – 23 Castle Gate, Nottingham, NG1 7AQ
Tel (0115) 824 0128

MEMBERS

Simon Russell Flint QC (1980) (QC-2003) †
Charles Miskin QC (1975) (QC-1998) † ^A^
Anesta Weekes QC (1981) (QC-1999) † ^A^
Daniel Janner QC (1980) (QC-2002) ^A^
Nirmal Shant QC (1984) (QC-2006)†
Dafydd Enoch QC (1985) (QC-2008) † ^A^
John Price QC (1982) (QC-2009) † ^A^
Alan Kent QC (1986) (QC-2009) ^A^
Iain Morley QC (1988) (QC-2009)
Cairns Nelson QC (1987) (QC-2010)
Paul Bogan QC (1983) (QC-2011)
Zafar Ali QC (1994) (QC-2012) ^A^
Mark Fenhalls QC (1992) (QC-2014) ^A^
John Causer (1979) ^A^
Michael Harrison (1979)
Walton Hornsby (1980)
Oscar Del Fabbro (1982) † ^A^
Ian Jobling (1982) ^A^
Roy Brown (1983) ^A^
John Riley (1983)
Hugh McKee (1983) ^A^
Rupert Pardoe (1984) ^A^
Shay Stephen (1984)
Gary Summers (1985) ^A^
Wayne Cranston-Morris (1986)
Allison Hunter (1986) ^A^
Neil Moore (1986)
Paul Ozin(1987) ^A^
Hugh Forgan (1989) ^A^
Andrew Easteal (1990) †
Patrick Thompson (1990) ^A^
Christopher Amis (1991)
Cameron Scott (1991)*
Isobel Ascherson (1991) ^A^
Giles Curtis-Raleigh (1992) †
Richard Milne (1992) ^A^
Mark Trafford (1992)
Tim Clark (1993) †
Kate Lumsdon (1993) ^A^
Gerard O'Connor (1993)
Eloise Marshall (1994)
Rufus Stilgoe (1994)
Adam Watkins (2004) ^A^
Bart Casella (1995) ^A^
Alexia Durran (1995) †
Francis McGrath (1995) ^A^
Keith Raynor (1995)
Laurence Aiolfi (1996)
Ian Hope (1996)
Ahmed Hossain (1996)
Bob Sastry (1996) ^A^
Sarah Campbell (1997)
Alan Gardner (1997)
Katherine Hunter (1997)
Toyin Salako (1998)
Neil Sandys (1998) ^A^
Rossano Scamardella (1998)
Tetteh Turkson (1998)
Jane Greenhalgh (1998) *
Flora Page (1998) *
Lesley Bates (1999) ^A^
Oliver Dunkin (1999)
Daniel Fugallo (1999)
Tim Grey (1999)
Graham Smith (1999)
Zoe Van Den Bosch (1999)
Abigail Husbands (2000) ^A^
David Povall (2000)
Dapinder Singh (2000)
Christopher Hamlet (2000) *
William Eaglestone (2001)
Adrian Harris (2001) ^A^
Christopher Badger (2002) ^A^
Sonya Saul (2002)
Aisha Khan (2002)
John Dye(2002)
Hamish Common (2003)
Tom Godfrey (2003) ^A^
Ruth Paley (2003)
Rashad Mohammed (2004)
Nicholas Rimmer (2004) ^A^
Alexander Upton (2004) ^A^
Louise Culleton (2005)
Hannah Kinch (2006)
Joseph Templeton (2006)
Rebecca Vanstone (2006)
Holly Webb (2006)
Patrick Duffy (2007) ^A^
Roshani Pulle (2007)
Nathan Rasiah (2007) ^A^
Carolina Cabral (2009) ^A^
Daniel Lister (2009) ^A^
Richard Saynor (2009) ^A^
Elisabeth Acker (2010) ^A^
Helena Duong (2010)
Yousif Elagab (2010)
Victoria Gainza (2010) ^A^
Hannah Evans (2011) ^A^
Alex Mills (2012)
James Richardson QC (1975) (QC-2010) *
Michael Austin-Smith QC (1969) (QC-1990) *
Simon Davis (1990) *
Stephen Platt (1999)*
James Austin-Smith (1999) *
Samantha Hatt (2000) *
Elisabeth Lees (2002) *
Sarah Harris (2007) *
Tom Devlin (2009) *
Elena Elia (2009) *

† Recorder * Door Tenant ^A^ Direct/Public Access

THE CHAMBERS 23 Essex Street is a modern, innovative, approachable set of barristers, with a leading reputation in the fields of crime, fraud and a range of regulatory and disciplinary matters. Chambers has a genuine commitment to teamwork, supported by both its formal training programme and its inherent culture, which ensures important recent experience is shared across chambers. This experience is broad, with members of chambers undertaking the entire range of mainstream criminal law, as well as associated regulatory and civil work. Within this, chambers has set up a number of specialist teams, offering a strong portfolio of barristers who are effective at all levels, to harness and develop expertise in certain niche practice areas. Members regularly appear in high-profile cases in all levels of court in England and Wales as well as other jurisdictions, including the International Criminal Court and the European Court of Human Rights.

Chambers are supported by a motivated clerking team that are committed to delivering a first-class service to clients and members alike. Chambers has continued to grow nationally, with members working (prosecuting and defending) across the country; consequently the annexes in Manchester and Nottingham are flourishing. Highlighting this is the fact that the set has undergone significant redevelopment and expansion of its Manchester base with a dedicated Senior Clerk for the Manchester and Nottingham annexes now recruited.

23es
23 essex street
Criminal Defence Service
Community Legal Service
Quality Mark - Legal Services Accredited Chambers

23 ESSEX STREET (Continued)

WORK UNDERTAKEN Chambers deals with crime, fraud and financial crime, and regulatory and professional discipline work. Specialist teams include corporate and financial regulatory, police civil actions, healthcare discipline, police discipline, environmental crime, IP crime and trading standards. Chambers also undertakes court martial, inquests and tribunals, prison law, public inquiries and direct access work. Chambers also has a strong track record in international work with members appearing in human rights cases involving genocide, war crimes, and international terrorism and civil and criminal work in Cambodia, Kenya and the Carribean.

RECRUITMENT

Tenancy: Applications to Simon Russell Flint QC.

Pupillage: Applications to Kate Lumsdon. Chambers offer one funded 12-month pupillage of £25,000. Travel allowances are available. Full details are published in the Pupillages Handbook on the website.

Mini-pupillages: A limited number are available. Applications to Rebecca Vanstone and Holly Webb.

THIRTY NINE ESSEX STREET Stephen Tromans QC & Neil Block QC

39 Essex Street, London, WC2R 3AT
Tel (020) 7832 1111 **Fax** (020) 7353 3978 **DX** 298 London/Chancery Lane
Email clerks@39essex.com **Website** www.39essex.com

82 King Street, Manchester, M2 4WQ

Maxwell Chambers, 32 Maxwell Road, #02-16 Singapore, 069115

Head of Chambers	Stephen Tromans QC Neil Block QC
Chief Executive & Director of Clerking	David Barnes
Senior Clerks	Alastair Davidson Michael Kaplan
Tenants	122

MEMBERS

Stephen Tromans QC (1999) (QC-2009)
Neil Block QC (1980) (QC-2002)
Simon Goldblatt QC (1953) (QC-1972)
John Tackaberry QC (1967) (QC-1982)
Edwin Glasgow QC (1969) (QC-1987)
Matthew Horton QC (1969) (QC-1989)
Brian Ash QC (1975) (QC-1990)
Nigel Pleming QC (1971) (QC-1992)
Augustus Ullstein QC (1970) (QC-1992) +
John Steel QC (1978) (QC-1993) +
Richard Wilmot-Smith QC (1978) (QC-1994) +
Richard Spearman QC (1977) (QC-1996) +
William Norris QC (1974) (QC-1997)
Matthias Kelly QC (1979) (QC-1999) +
Hodge Malek QC (1983) (QC-1999) +
Vincent Nelson QC (1980) (QC-2001)
David Melville QC (1975) (QC-2002)
Gregory Treverton-Jones QC (1977) (QC-2002) +
Susan Rodway QC (1981) (QC-2002)
Alison Foster QC (1984) (QC-2002)
Stuart Catchpole QC (1987) (QC-2002) +
Peter Village QC (1983) (QC-2002)
Colin McCaul QC (1978) (QC-2003)
Timothy Lyons QC (1980) (QC-2003)
Charles Cory-Wright QC (1984) (QC-2006)
Adrian Hughes QC (1984) (QC-2006)
Charles Manzoni QC (1988) (QC-2009)
Thomas Hill QC (1988) (QC-2009)
Peter Rees QC (2014) (QC-2009)
Gordon Nardell QC (1995) (QC-2010)
Steven Kovats QC (1989) (QC-2010) +
Sean Wilken QC (1991) (QC-2010)
Jenni Richards QC (1991) (QC-2011)
Eleanor Grey QC (1990) (QC-2011)
Lisa Giovannetti QC (1990) (QC-2011)
Paul Stinchcombe QC (1985) (QC-2011)
Fenella Morris QC (1990) (QC-2012)
Hefin Rees QC (1992) (QC-2013) +
Richard Harwood OBE QC (1993) (QC-2013)
James Strachan QC (1996) (QC-2013)
John Tonna (1974)
John Pugh-Smith (1977)
John Judge (1977) (Ontario)
Simon Edwards (1978)
Geoffrey Brown (1981)
Marion Smith (1981)
Martin Edwards (1995)
Christian Du Cann (1982)
Karen Gough (1983)
David Mayhew (2011)
Jonathan Bellamy (1986) +
David Bradly (1987)
James Ramsden (1987)
Derek O'Sullivan (1990)
Bernard Doherty (1990)
James Todd (1990)
Rashda Rana (1990)
Andrew Tabachnik (1991)
Emily Formby (1993) +
David Brynmor Thomas (2011)
Damian Falkowski (1994)
Justine Thornton (1994)
Adam Robb (1995)
Parishil Patel (1996)
Duncan Sinclair (1996)
Christiaan Zwart (1997)
Richard Wald (1997)
John Denis-Smith (1998)
Judith Ayling (1998)
Kate Grange (1998)
Caroline Truscott (1998)
Vikram Sachdeva (1998)
Camilla Church (1998)
Nicola Greaney (1999)
Colin Thomann (1999)
Neil Allen (1999)
Jonathan Auburn (1999)
Katharine Scott (2000)
Jess Connors (2000)
Karim Ghaly (2001)
James Burton (2001)
Alexander Ruck Keene (2002)
Rory Dunlop (2002)
Saima Hanif (2002)
Christopher Staker (2003)
Alexandra Bodnar (2004)
Sadie Crapper (2004)
Robert Lazarus (2004)
Anna Bicarregui (2004)
Mungo Wenban-Smith (2004)
Caroline Allen (2005)
Victoria Butler-Cole (2005)
Alexis Hearnden (2005)
Andrew Deakin (2006)
Peter Mant (2006)
Rachael O'Hagan (2006)
Quintin Fraser (2006)
Ned Helme (2006)
Michelle Pratley (2006)
Jack Anderson (2006)
Rebecca Drake (2007)
Ellen Wiles (2007)
Thomas Amraoui (2007)
Jennifer Thelen (2007)
Jack Holborn (2008)
Philippa Jackson (2008)
Catherine Dobson (2009)
Benjamin Tankel (2009)
Patrick Hennessey (2010)
Rose Grogan (2010)
Angela Rainey (2010)
Hannah McCarthy (2010)
Annabel Lee (2011)
Stephen Kosmin (2011)
Daniel Stedman Jones (2011)
James Potts (2011)
Yash Bheeroo (2011)
Cleon Catsambis (2011)
Samar Abbas (2011)
Tom Tabori (2011)
Jon Darby (2012)
Nicola Kohn (2012)
Sir David Keene (1964) (QC-1980) *
Patrick Lane SC (South Africa) (1977) *
Mansoor Jamal Malik (1983) *
Kristina Stern SC (1996) *
Archibald Findlay SC (South Africa) (1999) *
Paul Hayes (2005) *
Professor Dr Nael G Bunni (Non Lawyer) *
Thierry Marembert (Paris) (1994)

+ Recorder * Door Tenant

THE CHAMBERS Thirty Nine Essex Street is a long established barristers' set of 40 Queen's Counsel and 82 juniors. With offices in London, Manchester and Singapore, the set offers substantial expertise in almost every

THIRTY NINE ESSEX STREET Stephen Tromans QC & Neil Block QC (continued)

aspect of civil liability, commercial, construction and engineering, commercial fraud, financial services, costs and litigation funding, aviaton, energy, planning, environmental and property, personal injury and clinical negligence, public, regulatory and disciplinary law and alternative dispute resolution, both in the UK and worldwide. Members of chambers have wide experience of all courts and tribunals including the Supreme Court, Privy Council, Court of Appeal, the European Court of Human Rights and the European Court of Justice, specialist courts, tribunals and planning and other public inquiries, as well as of domestic and international arbitrations. Members have participated in many significant investigations before Parlimentary Select Committees and 17 members are on the Attorney General's Panel of Counsel instructed on behalf of the Crown. Members also undertake pro bono work for public interest organisations.

WORK UNDERTAKEN

Administrative & Public: Judicial review and public law, including civil liberties and human rights, education, local authorities, health trusts, mental health, community care, court of protection, housing and housing associations, immigration, VAT and customs and excise.

Commercial: Insurance and reinsurance, commodities and derivatives, funding disputes, banking, mergers and acquisitions, sale and carriage of goods, insolvency, company law, financial services law, professional negligence and professional indemnity work for auditors and legal advisors and international commercial arbitration.

Construction & Engineering: Litigation and related claims, including professional negligence and indemnity work, from major international ventures to smaller domestic contracts, acting for employers, contractors, subcontractors and professional advisors. Members act as advocates, mediators and arbitrators in the United Kingdom, the EU and worldwide.

Costs: Members of chambers appear in every court and tribunal where costs issues arise. Members also carry out advisory work on potential funding arrangements and in drafting cost documentation including CFAs, CCFA and legal expenses insurance policies.

Employment: Work for employers and employees, local authorities and central government. Particular emphasis is on public law-related work, discrimination, restrictive covenants, wrongful dismissal and breach of fiduciary duties.

Energy: A unique capability to cover corporate/commercial, construction, engineering, projects, environmental, planning, public and regulatory work in the electricity, nuclear, oil and gas and renewable sectors.

Entertainment & Sports: Entertainment and media-related work including performers' contracts, passing-off, breach of confidence, film and management agreements and broadcasting regulation. Sports-related work includes public liability of sports clubs for acts of their players, employer's liability, disciplinary tribunals, disputes concerning control of clubs, transfer fee disputes, EU free movement and other employment issues.

European: EU law before domestic and EU courts, including competition, discrimination and equality law, public procurement, free movement, state aids and milk quotas.

Human Rights: Members of chambers regularly appear in domestic Human Rights Act cases and also have extensive experience as advocates before the European Court of Human Rights and in courts overseas. Members have appeared in leading cases with a human rights dimension in diverse fields including civil liberties, commercial law, healthcare, housing, immigration, local government, mental health and community care, planning, police and prisoners.

Personal Injury & Clinical Negligence: Sea, air and crowd disasters, group actions, industrial disease, sports injuries, injuries of maximum severity, pharmaceuticals, product liability and high profile and complex matters, ranging from sensitive consent-to-treatment cases to those involving serious disability and death.

Planning & Environmental: Compulsory purchase, contaminated land, environmental civil liability, environmental regulation, European law and human rights, health and safety and product liability, insurance, international environmental law, licensing, marine environment, parliamentary and public affairs, planning law, nuisance and rating.

Public Inquiries: Members of chambers have been instructed in most of the major public inquiries over the past 10 years, including Hillsborough, BSE, the King's Cross fire and more recently, the Bristol Royal Infirmary, Victoria Climbié, the Saville Inquiry, the Hutton Inquiry and the Leveson Inquiry.

Regulatory & Disciplinary: Appearing in tribunals and hearings, and carrying out advisory work across the entire medical sphere, appearing before the Solicitors Disciplinary Tribunal and in challenges to interventions by the Law Society, social care, education, financial services, broadcasting, communications and the media, sport, transport and health and safety, buildings and housing, local government standards, licensing.

PUBLICATIONS *Wilmot-Smith on Construction Contracts (Third Edition) (2014); Phipson on Evidence, 17th Edition (2012) (Hodge M. Malek QC); Environmental Impact Assessment, Second Edition (2012) (Stephen Tromans QC); The Law of Entertainment and Broadcasting (Nelson); Waiver, Variation and Estoppel (Wilken); Judicial Renew-Principle and Procedure 2013 (Auburn); Encyclopaedia of Environmental Law (Tromans); Planning Enforcement, Second Edition (Harwood) 2013; Mental Capacity (Morris and Greaney); A Guide to the New Law: Shackleton on the Law and Practice of Meetings (Pugh-Smith, Ruck Keene, Burton); Accidents Abroad: International Personal Injury Claims (Doherty); The Solicitors Handbook 2009 (Treverton-Jones and Hopper).*

INTERNATIONAL Thirty Nine Essex Street has a number of members who have been called to the Bars of various international and offshore jurisdictions including California, France, Hong Kong, New South Wales, South Africa, Trinidad and Tobago and the British Virgin Islands. Chambers also has experience of acting in disputes in various foreign jurisdictions including Western and Central Europe, Africa, the USA, India, China and Hong Kong SAR, Malaysia, Singapore, the Middle East and the Caribbean.

RECRUITMENT The set is a member of Pupillage Gateway and also advertises recruitment via its website.

FALCON CHAMBERS Jonathan Gaunt QC & Guy Fetherstonhaugh QC

Falcon Court, London, EC4Y 1AA
Tel (020) 7353 2484 **Fax** (020) 7353 1261 **DX** 408
Email clerks@falcon-chambers.com **Website** www.falcon-chambers.com

Head of Chambers	Jonathan Gaunt QC Guy Fetherstonhaugh QC
Chambers Director	Edith A Robertson
Senior Clerk	Steven Francis
Tenants	37

MEMBERS

Jonathan Gaunt QC (1972) (QC-1991) BA
Guy Fetherstonhaugh QC (1983) (QC-2003) BSc
Derek Wood QC (1964) (QC-1978) MA BCL
Kirk Reynolds QC (1974) (QC-1993) MA
Nicholas Dowding QC (1979) (QC-1997) MA
Timothy Fancourt QC (1987) (QC-2003) MA
Jonathan Karas QC (1986) (QC-2006) MA
Jonathan Small QC (1990) (QC-2006) BA
Stephen Jourdan QC (1989) (QC-2009) MA
Joanne Moss (1976) MA LLM (EC Law)
Anthony Radevsky (1978) LLB
Edward Cole (1980) MA
Wayne Clark (1982) LLB BCL
Barry Denyer-Green (1972) LLM PhD
Gary Cowen (1990) LLB
Janet Bignell (1992) MA, BCL
Martin Dray (1992) LLB
Anthony Tanney (1994) BA MJur
Caroline Shea (1994) MA
Catherine Taskis (1995) BA BCL
Emily Windsor (1995) BA DSU (EC Law)
Mark Sefton (1996) MA
Stephanie Tozer (1996) MA
Edward Peters (1998) BA
Adam Rosenthal (1999) BA
Charles Harpum (1976) MA LLD
Elizabeth Fitzgerald (2001) LLB
Greville Healey (2002) MA D Phil
Nathaniel Duckworth (2002) BA
Oliver Radley-Gardner (2003) BA
Tamsin Cox (2005) BA
Philip Sissons (2005) BA BCL
Joseph Ollech (2006) BSc
Daniel Robinson (2008) BA
Jamie Sutherland (2010) MA
Kester Lees (2010) BA LLB BCL
Ciara Fairley (2011) BA MPhil PhD

THE CHAMBERS Chambers specialises in litigation and advice on all aspects of the law of property and matters relating to it. Falcon Chambers is regarded as one of the leading sets for property litigation and commercial property, as well as landlord and tenant and agricultural law.
A number of members are authors of leading textbooks in their specialist fields, including *Woodfall on Landlord and Tenant, Megarry on The Rent Acts, Muir Watt and Moss on Agricultural Holdings, Megarry & Wade's Law of Real Property, Gale on Easements, Fisher and Lightwood's Law of Mortgage, Hague on Leasehold Enfranchisement, Registered Land, and Commonhold.*

WORK UNDERTAKEN All members are expert in landlord and tenant law, including commercial property, rent review, residential landlord and tenant, and agricultural holdings, tenancies and production controls. They also provide expertise in the more general areas of property law, including easements, restrictive covenants, mortgages, conveyancing, co-ownership and trusts of land, options, rights of pre-emption, the Telecommunications Code, mining and mineral rights.
Members are frequently instructed in cases where property rights and principles of insolvency law meet, and where claims for negligence arise against solicitors and surveyors. Some members specialise in the fields of town and country planning, compulsory purchase, EU competition law and building and engineering disputes. Chambers is frequently involved in advisory and litigious work in other jurisdictions, particularly in other common law countries in the Commonwealth. Members of chambers appear in appeals to the Privy Council. Even in members' specialist fields, a good deal of their work is concerned with contract law and statutory interpretation. Their activities in commercial property matters have given them considerable expertise in arbitration law and practice, and in work involving valuers and the principles of valuation.
Chambers accepts work through the Bar Council's Licensed Access scheme in appropriate cases. Members also accept appointments as arbitrators, legal assessors or experts.

Falcon Chambers

FARRAR'S BUILDING Patrick Harrington QC

Farrar's Building, Temple, London, EC4Y 7BD
Tel (020) 7583 9241 **Fax** (020) 7583 0090 **DX** 406
Email chambers@farrarsbuilding.co.uk **Website** www.farrarsbuilding.co.uk

Head of Chambers	Patrick Harrington QC
Senior Clerk/Practice Manager	Alan Kilbey MBE
Chambers Manager	Janet Eades
Tenants	44

MEMBERS

Patrick Harrington QC (1973) (QC-1993) +
John Leighton Williams QC (1964) (QC-1986) +
Douglas Day QC (1967) (QC-1989) +
Ian Murphy QC (1972) (QC-1992) +
Alan Jeffreys QC (1970) (QC-1996)
Paul Lewis QC (1981) (QC-2001) +
Geoffrey Williams QC (2013) (QC-2003)
Ian Unsworth QC (1992) (QC-2010)
Christopher Quinlan QC (1992) (QC-2011)
Michael Mather-Lees QC (1981) (QC-2012)
Richard Nussey (1971)
Ian Ridd (1975)
Nigel Spencer Ley (1985)
Andrew Peebles (1987)
John Meredith-Hardy (1989)
Shabbir Lakha (1989)
Leighton Hughes (1989)
Helen Hobhouse (1990)
Peter Freeman (1992)
Rhiannon Jones (1993)
Lee Evans (1996)
Nick Blake (1997)
Huw Davies (1998)
James Pretsell (1998)
Sarah Tozzi (1998)
Andrew Wille (1998)
Howard Cohen (1999)
Guy Watkins (1999)
Carwyn Cox (2002)
Matthew Kerruish-Jones (2003)
James Plant (2004)
Matthew Hodson (2004)
Clive Thomas (2005)
Tom Bourne-Arton (2005)
Emma Sole (2005)
Grant Goodlad (2006)
Tim Found (2006)
David Roderick (2005)
Daniel Read (2006)
Edmund Townssend (2006)
Georgina Crawford (2006)
Changez Khan (2008)
Bonike Erinle (2008)
Hannah Saxena (2010)
Joshua Hedgman(2011)
Arden O'Brien (2011)
Robert Colin (2011)

+ Recorder

THE CHAMBERS Farrar's Building is a long established specialist set of chambers with particular expertise in the following five main areas of practice: personal injury; employment; serious and white-collar crime; health and safety; inquiries; and professional liability and disciplinary tribunals. Members of chambers also specialise in clinical negligence, professional negligence, insurance, product liability and commercial (see individual biographies). Chambers has an established reputation for excellence, with members acting for a variety of corporate bodies, insurance companies, prosecuting authorities, the Treasury, sporting bodies and players, disciplinary, regulatory and professional bodies, as well as individuals. It is a friendly and reliable set of chambers, which prides itself on the way it is efficiently clerked and administered, by an experienced team.

WORK UNDERTAKEN Personal injury is the largest field of practice for chambers. The PI Team is involved in the whole spectrum of cases from very serious catastrophic injury claims to straightforward small track claims. It covers all aspects of work, from road traffic accidents, including mechanical defect and causation issues, to accidents at work, 'slips and trips', injuries caused by defective products, disaster and disease litigation. The Health and Safety Team works closely with, and benefits from, Farrar's Building's strong PI Team. Chambers has been involved in a number of high profile cases in this area. Employment law is a major area of practice for chambers, which has a growing reputation in this field. It specialises in all aspects of employment law, dealing with a wide range of employment issues, from advocacy in Employment Tribunals, the Employment Appeal Tribunal, and higher courts to advisory work. Chambers has a specialist criminal team, involved in major fraud and serious crime cases, and has close links with Wales where it remains a dominant force on the Welsh Circuit. Chambers is and has been involved in many of the major cases on the circuit and members of the Criminal team are highly sought-after. Chambers has a long history of involvement in Public Inquiries and of chairing/appearing before a range of Regulatory and Disciplinary Tribunals. Members carry out a great variety of administrative and public law matters, including judicial review, local government, education, health, housing and pharmaceuticals. Members of chambers also offer expertise in: contract and commercial litigation, covering such areas as sale of goods and consumer credit and commercial fraud, insurance matters and product liability; clinical negligence and all areas of professional negligence and surveyors; costs and taxation matters include solicitors' bills of costs, counsels' fees and legal aid costs; sports and competition cases include contracts, advertising and sponsorship and restraint of trade.

FARRAR'S BUILDING

FIELD COURT TAX CHAMBERS

Field Court Tax Chambers, 3 Field Court, Gray's Inn, London WC1R 5EP
Tel (020) 3693 3700 **DX** 374 LDE
Email chambers@fieldtax.com **Website** www.fieldtax.com

Head of Chambers	Patrick C Soares
Practice Manager	Marie Burke
Assistant Practice Manager	Stephanie Talbot
Tenants	4

MEMBERS

Patrick C Soares (1983)
Patrick Way QC (1994)
Philip Baker QC (1979)
Imran S Afzal (2008)

THE CHAMBERS Chambers was created on 1st August 2014 to provide dedicated taxation services of the highest quality. The four founding members each bring a track record of established excellence both as tax advisers and advocates.

WORK UNDERTAKEN

National & International: The set focuses on all aspects of taxation and is led by highly experienced and respected leaders in the sector. Specialist advice and representation includes international and European tax, property matters, value added tax, corporate taxation, trusts and estate planning, including acting for high-profile individuals and multinational companies. All members of chambers appear at all levels of the UK court system including the Privy Council and in the European Court of Justice. Patrick C Soares advises on all aspects of taxation, providing notable expertise on the taxation and structuring of property transactions, as well as value added tax, trusts and offshore tax planning and tax advocacy. Patrick Way QC has appeared in leading tax cases at all levels of the UK court system and also advised on some of the largest corporate transactions in the UK, where the tax at stake has been in the multi-millions. Philip Baker QC is one of the most renowned tax advisers on international tax matters in the world, handling cases in jurisdictions, including India and Mauritius and at the European Court of Justice. He advises the UK government and other governments on tax matters. He also was one of the founders of the Advanced Diploma in International Taxation offered by the Chartered Institute of Taxation. Imran S Afzal has been involved in a range of domestic and international matters, acting for taxpayers and revenue authorities. He has been instructed in various high-profile and high-value matters, e.g. he assisted a foreign company in a matter involving over £1bn.

PUBLICATIONS Patrick Soares is the Tax Editor of the Property Law Bulletin. Patrick Soares, Patrick Way QC and Philip Baker QC have between them written books on a wide range of tax related subjects including those concerning real estate, trusts, corporates, individuals, incentives, international tax and double taxation.

FIELD COURT TAX CHAMBERS

187 FLEET STREET Andrew Trollope QC and Richard Christie QC

187 Fleet Street, Temple, London, EC4A 2AT
Tel (020) 7430 7430 **Fax** (020) 7430 7431 **DX** 464
Email chambers@187fleetstreet.com **Website** www.187fleetstreet.com

Heads of Chambers	Andrew Trollope QC Richard Christie QC
Senior Clerk	John Pyne
Tenants	78

MEMBERS

Andrew Trollope QC (1971) (QC 1991)
Richard Christie QC (1986) (QC 2006)
Nadine Radford QC (1974) (QC1995)
Philip King QC (1974) (QC 2002)
Jonathan Fuller QC (1977) (QC 2002)
Simon Mayo QC (1985) (QC 2008)
Roderick Price (1971)
Brian Argyle (1972)
Brian Reece (1974)
Peter Guest (1975)
Gerard Renouf (1977)
Diana Pigot (1978)
Anthony Rimmer (1983)
Stella Reynolds (1983)
Gareth Hughes (1985)
James Lachkovic (1987)
David Lyons (1987)
Christopher Kerr (1988)
Grant Vanstone (1988)
Kate Davey (1988)
Andrew Newton (1989)
Terence Woods (1989)
Neil FitzGibbon (1989)
Avirup Chaudhuri (1990)
Nicholas Barraclough (1990)
Mark Graffius (1990)
Rachel Bright (1991)
Richard Potts (1991)
Natasha Wong (1993)
Richard Burrington (1993)
Karl Volz (1993)
Matthew Bagnall (1993)
Warwick Aleeson (1994)
Mark Roochove (1994)
Jason Bartfeld (1995)
Andrew Frymann (1995)
Gideon Cammerman (1996)
Gregory Fishwick (1996)
Laureen Husain (1997)
Sarah Vine (1997)
Adam Butler (1997)
Catherine Bradshaw (1998)
Leon Kazakos (1999)
Emma Kurzner (1999)
Margia Mostafa (1999)
Peter Clark (2000)
Neelam Sharma (2000)
Yasmin Punjani (2000)
Mozammel Hossain (2001)
Emma Nash (2001)
Frances Coles-Harrington (2001)
Marc Brown (2001)
Alex Price-Marmion (2002)
Sasha Bailey (2002)
Nneka Akudolu (2002)
David Baird (2003)
Charlotte Eadie (2003)
Henry Hughes (2003)
Rebecca Lee (2004)
Ben Hayhurst (2004)
Matt Morgan (2004)
James Onalaja (2004)
Steven Fitzpatrick (2004)
Joseph Abadoo (2004)
Alison Lambert (2005)
Jamie Sharma (2005)
Jack Walsh (2006)
Scott Wainwright (2006)
James Bewley (2007)
Anna Keighley (2006)
Greg Unwin (2008)
Donal Lawler (2008)
Satya Chotalia (2008)
Laura Fearnfield (2009)
Ali Dewji (2010)
Gerwyn Wise (2010)
Harry Warner (2011)
Susannah Brooke (2012)

THE CHAMBERS 187 Fleet Street and 2 Pump Court, two leading criminal sets in their own right, have recently merged to form one large and dynamic set of chambers with over 75 members.
Chambers is a leading set specialising in criminal and regulatory work, providing representation at every level for the Prosecution and the Defence, in both publicly and privately funded instructions. Many members of chambers can also be instructed directly through the Public Access Scheme.
A key strength of chambers lies in the breadth and depth of experience of its members who are regularly instructed in high profile and leading cases. The set has gained a reputation for excellence in its advocacy and advisory work, offering a first class service to professional and lay clients alike.
Chambers has particular expertise in serious fraud and white collar crime, as well as homicide, terrorism, sex offences, revenue cases, money laundering and all forms of serious organised crime. A wealth of experience is also offered in many areas related to the criminal law, and specialist representation is offered in respect of VAT tribunals, police discipline, professional regulation, Courts-Martial, judicial review, parole board hearings, mental health reviews, prison law, health and safety, sports law, inquests, extradition, human rights, licensing, DVSA (formerly VOSA) and all road traffic related matters.
Members of chambers prosecute at all levels for the Crown Prosecution Service, HM Revenue & Customs, the Serious Fraud Office, Local Authorities and Government Departments. Chambers has a number of Counsel who have been appointed to the Attorney General's List and conducts cases on behalf of the Department of Business, Innovation and Skills, the Department of Work and Pensions and the Health and Safety Executive.
There are 8 clerks, an administrator and a fees administrator. Please refer to chambers' website for more information.

WORK UNDERTAKEN

Corporate Crime & Serious Fraud: Cases include those involving market rigging in share issues and takeovers, cartels and price fixing, advance fee, high yield investment/ponzi and 'boiler room' frauds, fraudulent trading/Phoenix, money laundering/confiscation, MTIC cases involving a wide web of contra trading companies, off shore finance institutions and offshore banking evidence, VAT/excise evasion and revenue cases. MTIC/ diversion cases include: Operations Vitric, Venison, Vex, Carina, Campaign, Domic, Tulipbox (carbon credits) and Devout. Other fraud cases include: the Cheney pension fraud, the Dome fraud, Ikea fraud/corruption case, SFO prosecution of 'Lord' Edward Davenport, SFO Pharmaceutical cartel case, R v Peter Storrie (Harry Redknapp case) and Operation Amazon (HMRC's largest ever case).
Members of Chambers also have specialist knowledge and experience of acting both for the Revenue and the taxpayer before the VAT Tribunal and the High Court.

No 187 Fleet Street

Criminal Defence Service

Community Legal Service

Quality Mark - Legal Services Accredited Chambers

187 FLEET STREET (Continued)

Serious Crime: Murder, serious sexual offences, large scale drugs conspiracies, offences against the person, terrorism offences, bribery and corruption. Cases have included the Joss Stone murder plot; R v Ian Watkins and others (involving lead singer of the Lostprophets); R v Davis (Conspiracy to hack SOCA and News International); R v Donovan ('Good Samaritan' case during the London riots); R v Connors (first ever 'slave' trial); terrorist conspiracies to murder (Heathrow and transatlantic flights); the fertiliser bomb plot (Operation Crevice); the Tonbridge Securitas robbery; murder of Damilola Taylor; the murder of the private eye, Daniel Morgan, which is linked to the News of the World phone-hacking case, the Stephen Lawrence case and alleged police corruption, R v Abrams (attempted murder of George Harrison), R v Tovey (Oxford bomber).

Members of chambers have been appointed to review 'Rough Justice'/historic appeal cases and have particular expertise in this area. They have been engaged to act on behalf of both prosecution and defence in such cases, including receipt of instructions on a Direct Access basis. They have also regularly been instructed by the the Criminal Cases Review Commission in judicial reviews of the Commission's refusal to refer cases to the Court of Appeal, including in the cases of Jeremy Bamber and Kenneth Noye.

Professional Regulation: A number of members of Chambers have been instructed by, or have represented regulated persons before, various regulatory bodies including ACCA, NMC, GDC and GMC. Members are also experienced at representing professionals and military personnel accused of serious offences.

Sports Law: Members of Chambers have represented individuals before the British Horseracing Authority, the British Judo Association, the Rugby Union Disciplinary Tribunal and represented Peter Storrie in the Portsmouth Football Club fraud.

INTERNATIONAL Bengali, Hindi, French and German are spoken. Counsel have also appeared in other jurisdictions such as the Cayman Islands and been admitted to the Bar there.

FOUNTAIN COURT CHAMBERS Stephen Moriarty QC

Head of Chambers	Stephen Moriarty QC
Senior Clerk	Alex Taylor
Head of Administration	Julie Parker
Tenants	68

Fountain Court, Temple, London, EC4Y 9DH
Tel (020) 7583 3335 **Fax** (020) 7353 0329 **DX** 5LDE
Email chambers@fountaincourt.co.uk **Website** www.fountaincourt.co.uk

MEMBERS

Michael Brindle QC (1975) (QC-1992)
Michael Crane QC (1975) (QC-1994)
David Railton QC (1979) (QC-1996)
Timothy Dutton QC (1979) (QC-1998)
Brian Doctor QC (1991) (QC-1999)
Stephen Moriarty QC (1986) (QC-1999)
Stephen Rubin QC (1977) (QC-2000)
Michael McLaren QC (1981) (QC-2002)
Simon Browne-Wilkinson QC (1981) (QC-1998)
Philip Brook Smith QC (1982) (QC-2002)
Raymond Cox QC (1982) (QC-2002)
Guy Philipps QC (1986) (QC-2002)
Bankim Thanki QC (1988) (QC-2003)
Charles Béar QC (1986) (QC-2003)
Patricia Robertson QC (1988) (QC-2006)
Timothy Howe QC (1987) (QC-2008)
Mark Simpson QC (1992) (QC-2008)
Michael Green QC (1987) (QC-2009)
Richard Handyside QC (1993) (QC-2009)
Jeffrey Chapman QC (1989) (QC-2010)
Derrick Dale QC (1990) (QC-2010)
Akhil Shah QC (1990) (QC-2010)
Marcus Smith QC (1991) (QC-2010)
Andrew Mitchell QC (1992) (QC-2011)
Paul Gott QC (1991) (QC-2012)
Richard Coleman QC (1994) (QC-2012)
John Taylor QC (1993) (QC-2013)
Adam Tolley QC (1994) (QC-2014)
Patrick Goodall QC (1998) (QC-2014)
Bridget Lucas (1989)
Ben Valentin (1995)
Paul Sinclair (1997)
Deepak Nambisan (1998)
Giles Wheeler (1998)
Henry King (1998)
Rosalind Phelps (1998)
Edward Levey (1999)
James Cutress (2000)
Nik Yeo (2000)
Adam Zellick (2000)
Chloe Carpenter (2001)
Paul Casey (2002)
Katherine Watt (2002)
Tamara Oppenheimer (2002)
Marianne Butler (2003)
David Murray (2004)
James McClelland (2004)
Simon Atrill (2004)
James Duffy (2005)
Rupert Allen (2005)
Alexander Milner (2006)
Adam Sher (2007)
Richard Power (2007)
Craig Ulyatt (2008)
Natasha Bennett (2009)
Nico Leslie (2010)
Daniel Edmonds (2010)
Deborah Horowitz (2010)
Christopher Langley (2011)
Tetyana Nesterchuk (2011)
Rebecca Loveridge (2011)
Christopher Knowles (2011)
Philip Ahlquist (2012)
Niamh Cleary (2012)
Giles Robertson (2012)
Samuel Ritchie (2012)
James Hart (2012)
Joseph Farmer (2013)

THE CHAMBERS Door Tenants/Academics/Arbitrators and Mediators/Judges: Sir Mark Potter (1963) (QC-1981); Sir Henry Brooke (1963) (QC-1981); Sir Gordon Langley (1966) (QC-1983); Sir Francis Jacobs (1964) (QC-1984); Andrew Burrows QC (1985) (QC-2003); Timothy Wormington (1977); Philippa Hamilton (1996); David R Wingfield (Toronto, Canada); Professor Lawrence Boo (Singapore); Professor Peter Watts (Auckland, New Zealand); Louise MErrett (1995), Anthony Boswood QC (1979) (QC-1986), Kanaga Dharmananda SC, Sebastian Said (2004) and Luca G Di Radicati Brozolo.
Fountain Court is a long established and leading set of commercial barristers' chambers. Based in the Temple, London and moments away from the Royal Courts of Justice, Fountain Court is at the forefront of civil and commercial litigation. Commonly described as a magic circle set, chambers comprises of 68 barristers, 29 of whom are silks. Members' knowledge ranges in relation to practice areas, experience and spoken languages, enabling the clerks at Fountain Court to match an individual members' expertise to a given case.

WORK UNDERTAKEN Leaders in: commercial litigation; banking and finance; insurance and reinsurance; professional negligence; energy and natural resources; civil fraud; international arbitration; aviation; financial regulation; professional discipline; public law; judicial review; and employment.
Other prominent areas include: media and entertainment; intellectual property; company; insolvency; product liability; human rights; administrative; sport; international trade; shipping; offshore; competition; and telecommunications.
Members sit as arbitrators, mediators and counsel in alternative dispute resolution matters. Members also sit as recorders and deputy high court judges.

INTERNATIONAL Members have been admitted to the Bar and have experience of law in the following jurisdictions: Australia; Azerbaijan; Bahamas; Bermuda; Brazil; British Virgin Islands; California; Canada; Cayman Islands; Channel Islands; Chile; China; Cyprus; Delaware; Dubai; France; Germany; Gibraltar; Hong Kong; India; Isle of Man; Italy; Kazakhstan; Kenya; Liechtenstein; Luxembourg; Malaysia; Mauritius; New York; Nigeria; Norway; Northern Ireland; Russia; Singapore; South Africa; Spain; St. Kitts & Nevis; Sweden; Switzerland; Tajikistan; Trinidad and Tobago; and USA.
Languages spoken: Fluent: Afrikaans; French; German; Italian; Russian; and Modern Hebrew. Working knowledge: Spanish and Greek.

Fountain Court CHAMBERS

FOURTEEN

14 Gray's Inn Square, London, WC1R 5JP
Tel (020) 7242 0858 **Fax** (020) 7242 5434 **DX** 399 (Ch.Ln.)
Email clerks@fourteen.co.uk **Website** www.fourteen.co.uk

Head of Chambers	Sarah Forster
Senior Clerk	Geoffrey Carr
Tenants	48

MEMBERS

Sarah Forster (1976)
Barbara Slomnicka (1976)
Andrew Bainham (2009) (sol. 1977)
Richard Kingsley (1977)
Edward Lloyd-Jones (2012) (sol. 1978)
Gillian Marks (1981)
Geraldine More O'Ferrall (1983)
Monica Ford (1984)
Joan Connell (1985)
David Sharp (1986)
Camille Habboo (1987)
Judith Spooner (1987)
Patricia Roberts (1988)
Dylan Evans (1989)
Jean-Paul Sinclair (1989)
Helen Soffa (1990)
Rhys Jones (1990)
Carolyn Pearson (1990)
Richard Alomo (1990)
Rachael James (1992)
Martin Ward (1992)
Jane De Zonie (1993)
Robin Powell (1993)
Ronan O'Donovan (1995)
Samantha Whittam (1995)
Sara Hammond (2009) (sol. 1996)
Richard Balchin (1997)
Christopher Miller (1998)
Mai-Ling Savage (1998)
Damian Stuart (2009) (sol. 1998)
Michael Glaser (1998)
Gillon Cameron (2001)
Jay Banerji (2001)
Laura Scott (2001)
Mandy Short (2003)
Anna Spencer (2004)
Henry Lamb (2004)
Ben Boucher-Giles (2004)
Anne-Marie Lucey (2004)
Byron James (2006)
Ella Calnan (2007)
Ranjit Singh (2007)
Phillip Blatchly (2008)
Ewan Murray (2008)
Jenna Shaw (2009)
Chris Stevenson (2009)
Victoria Miler (2010)
Roseanna Peck (2011)
Mhairi McNab (1974) *
Jonathan Wilkinson (2006) (sol. 1988) *
Sarah Pope (2006) (sol. 1994) *
Sally Gore (2006) *

* Associate member

THE CHAMBERS Fourteen is a leading specialist family law set with a national reputation for excellence. Chambers provides first-rate representation and advice across all areas of family law, including children, family finance, international family law and the Court of Protection. Members of chambers frequently appear in complex and high-profile cases. Fourteen is a dynamic and forward-thinking set of chambers and is praised for its professional, efficient and personal service.

FOURTEEN

FRANCIS TAYLOR BUILDING Andrew Tait QC

Francis Taylor Building, Inner Temple, London, EC4Y 7BY
Tel (020) 7353 8415 **Fax** (020) 7353 7622 **DX** 402 LDE
Email clerks@ftb.eu.com **Website** www.ftb.eu.com

Head of Chambers	Andrew Tait QC
Senior Clerk	Paul Coveney
Principal Clerks	Andrew Briton
	James Kemp
	Tom Rook
Tenants	53

MEMBERS

Andrew Tait QC (1981) (QC-2003)
Robin Purchas QC (1968) ^ (QC-1987)
Guy Roots QC (1969) (QC-1989)
Charles George QC (1974) (QC-1992)
Clive Newberry QC (1978) (QC-1993)
Stephen Sauvain QC (1977) (QC-1995)
Kevin de Haan QC (1976) ^ (QC-2000)
Robert McCracken QC (1973) ^ (QC-2003)
Michael Humphries QC (1982) ^ (QC-2003)
Gerald Gouriet QC (1974) ^ (QC-2006)
David Matthias QC (1980) ^ (QC-2006)
Morag Ellis QC (1984) (QC-2006)
Craig Howell Williams QC (1983) (QC-2009) ^
Richard Glover QC (1984) (QC-2009)
Mark Hill QC (1987) (QC-2009) ^
Simon Bird QC (1987) (QC-2009)
Simon Phillips QC (1985) ^ (QC-2010)
Andrew Newcombe QC (1987) (QC-2010)
Douglas Edwards QC (1992) (QC-2010)
Gregory Jones QC (1991) (QC-2011)
Suzanne Ornsby QC (1986) ^ (QC-2012)
James Pereira QC (1996) (QC-2014) ^
Saira Kabir Sheikh QC (2000) (QC-2014) ^
Robert Fookes (1975)
Philip Petchey (1976) ^
Timothy Comyn (1980) ^
James Rankin (1983) ^
Meyric Lewis (1986) ^
Charles Mynors (1988) ^
Andrew Fraser-Urquhart (1993) ^
Gary Grant (1994) ^
Hereward Phillpot (1997)
Leo Charalambides (1998) ^
Alexander Booth (2000) ^
Prof Andrea Biondi (2004) ++
Jeremy Pike (2001) ^
Melissa Murphy (2001)
Juan Lopez (2002) ^
Denis Edwards (2002) ^
Richard Honey (2003) ^
Jeremy Phillips (2004) ^
Mark Westmoreland Smith (2006)
Pavlos Eleftheriadis (2006) ++
Cain Ormondroyd (2007) ^
Annabel Graham Paul (2008)
Stephanie Knowles (2008) ^
Sarah Sackman (2008) ^
Rebecca Clutten (2008)
Ned Westaway (2009)
Isabella Tafur (2009)
David Graham (2010)
George MacKenzie (2011)
Jack Connah (2012)

++ Academic Member ^ Public/Direct Access

THE CHAMBERS Francis Taylor Building (FTB) has a long-standing reputation for excellence in providing advocacy and advisory services. FTB is consistently featured as a leading set in the independent legal directories for its expertise and leading role in planning, land valuation, infrastructure, environmental, public law, regulatory law and licensing. Its position at the forefront of these areas of law is evidenced by members consistently appearing in many of the leading cases.

Members of chambers appear in courts at all levels in this country and abroad, including specialist tribunals and public inquiries and undertake specialist advisory work. The set owes its long-standing reputation for excellence to its wide range of clients, the major projects it handles and the number and quality of its practitioners. They are also supported by a highly motivated and professional team of clerks, led by Paul Coveney as Senior Clerk.

WORK UNDERTAKEN As part of its specialist practice, FTB undertakes works connected with planning, environment, licensing, National Infrastructure Planning projects, transport and works schemes, utilities, highways, rating, heritage and conservation, Parliamentary Bills, common land and village greens, minerals, statutory nuisance and regulation, health and safety, environmental crime, compulsory purchase and compensation, land valuation, property law including easements and covenants, religious liberty and ecclesiastical, education and energy.

FTB maintains a panel of qualified and specialist CEDR and ADR accredited mediators.

FTB offers a wide range of client facilities including a dedicated seminar suite to support its established programme of events and an arbitration and mediation suite which complements Chambers' mediation and ADR expertise. The premises are fully DDA compliant.

FULCRUM CHAMBERS LLP

11 Old Square, Lincoln's Inn, London WC2A 3TS
Tel (020) 7186 0420 **Fax** (020) 7831 6944
Email enquiries@fulcrumchambers.com **Website** www.fulcrumchambers.com

Practice Manager	Warren Foot
Non-lawyer Member	Russ Corn

MEMBERS

David Huw Williams QC (1988) (QC-2008)
Ivan Pearce (1994)
Helen Garlick (1974)
Simon Taylor (1993)
Lydia Jonson (2000)
Wayne Barnes (2002)
Quinton Newcomb (2005)
Anthony Wheatley (1998)

THE CHAMBERS Fulcrum Chambers is an innovative partnership of barristers, solicitors and other professionals. It has established itself as an award winning law firm providing advice and representation for public, private and commercial clients in cases involving bribery and corruption, commercial fraud, corporate governance, money laundering, asset tracing, and all regulatory and compliance matters.

WORK UNDERTAKEN Fulcrum specialises in the conduct of internal investigations for corporates and has wide experience in conducting such investigations in many parts of the world. The sensitive and privileged collection of information has enabled companies to efficiently resolve issues themselves and where appropriate or necessary, engage with authorities both in the UK and abroad. Members frequently resolve complex corporate issues on behalf of commercial clients and chambers experience of dealing with international issues of corruption and money laundering enables it to efficiently represent, advise and resolve. Members are renowned experts in their fields, and having been involved in a number of the leading cases and investigations in the UK and abroad, provide clients with proven expertise. Fulcrum provides commercial, public and private clients with direct access to specialist counsel with real experience and a support team to provide advice from the very beginning of an investigation through to any resolution. Chambers intention is to provide its clients with a solution based approach. Fulcrum has received the following awards: 2011 Acquisition International Legal Award Winner for UK Anti-Money Laundering Chambers of the Year, 2012, Corporate LiveWire Global Awards for UK Anti- Money Laundering Chambers of the Year, 2012 ACQ Global Awards for UK Anti-Corruption Law Chambers of the Year, 2012 Finance Monthly Global Awards Winner for Anti-Corruption Law Firm of the Year, 2013 M&A International Global Award for Anti-Corruption Chambers of the Year, 2013 ACQ Global Award Winner for UK Bribery & Corruption Chambers of the Year, UK Commercial Fraud Chambers of the Year and UK Anti- Money Laundering Chambers of the Year, 2014 Corporate Bribery & Corruption Law Firm of the Year.

fulcrum
CHAMBERS

GARDEN COURT CHAMBERS

57-60 Lincoln's Inn Fields, London, WC2A 3LJ
Tel (020) 7993 7600 **Fax** (020) 7993 7700 **DX** 34 Chancery Lane
Email info@gclaw.co.uk **Website** www.gardencourtchambers.co.uk

Senior Clerk	Colin Cook
Clerks	Christina Allen
	Phil Bamfylde
	Lauren Barber
	Carol Basulwa
	Alex Bennett
	Stephen Bush
	Helen Louise D'Agostino
	Donna Denton
	Sheila Doyle
	Luke Harvey
	Sarah Laurie
	Emma Manning
	Robert Minns
	Matt O'Dowd
	Lisa O'Leary
	Lesley Perrott
	Keith Poynter
	Holly Proctor
	Charlie Tennent
Tenants	193

MEMBERS

Ian Macdonald QC (1963)
(QC 1988)
Ian Peddie QC (1971)
(QC 1992)
Mark George QC (1976)
(QC 2009)
Henry Blaxland QC (1978)
(QC 2002)
Icah Peart QC (1978)
(QC 2002)
Laurie Fransman QC (1979)
(QC 2000)
Stephen Kamlish QC (1979)
(QC 2003)
Jan Luba QC (1980)
(QC 2000)
Michael Turner QC (1981)
(QC 2002)
James Scobie QC (1984)
(QC 2010)
Bernard Tetlow QC (1984)
(QC 2011)
Marc Willers QC (1987)
(QC 2014)
Dexter Dias QC (1988)
(QC 2009)
Leslie Thomas QC (1988)
(QC 2014)
Peter Wilcock QC (1988)
(QC 2012)
Judy Khan QC (1989)
(QC 2010)
Stephanie Harrison QC (1991)
(QC 2013)
Peter Weatherby QC (1992)
(QC 2012)
Ali Naseem Bajwa QC (1993)
(QC 2011)
Stephen Knafler QC (1993)
(QC 2010)
Rajiv Menon QC (1993)
(QC 2011)
Kieran Vaughan QC (1993)
(QC 2012)
Richard Harvey (1971)
Michael House (1972)
Terry Munyard (1972)
Marguerite Russell (1972)
Patrick Roche (1977)
Lalith de Kauwe (1978)
James Bowen (1979)
Kathryn Cronin (1980)
Elizabeth Woodcraft (1980)
Celia Graves (1981)
Michael Hall (1983)
Ravinder Rahal (1983)
Stephen Cottle (1984)
Nerida Harford-Bell (1984)
Beatrice Prevatt (1985)
Peter Jorro (1986)
Mary McKeone (1986)
Amanda Meusz (1986)
Elizabeth Veats (1986)
Sorrel Dixon (1987)
Martin Huseyin (1988)
Christopher Williams (1988)
Piers Mostyn (1989)
Alistair Polson (1989)
Alex Taylor-Camara (1989)
Rebecca Chapman (1990)
Edward Fitzpatrick (1990)
Bethan Harris (1990)
Carol Hawley (1990)
Colin Hutchinson (1990)
Maggie Jones (1990)
Peter Rowlands (1990)
Clare Wade (1990)
Nadine Finch (1991)
Michael Ivers (1991)
Catrin Lewis (1991)
Sonali Naik (1991)
Stephen Simblet (1991)
Malek Wan Daud (1991)
Nicola Braganza (1992)
Helen Curtis (1992)
Valerie Easty (1992)
Alastair Edie (1992)
Julia Krish (1992)
Allison Munroe (1992)
Henry Drayton (1993)
Sandra Fisher (1993)
Rajeev Thacker (1993)
Kelly Webb (1993)
Navita Atreya (1994)
Liz Davies (1994)
David Jones (1994)
Keir Monteith (1994)
Duran Seddon (1994)
Dafna Spiro (1994)
Amina Ahmed (1995)
Grace Brown (1995)
Edward Grieves (1995)
Amanda Weston (1995)
David Emanuel (1996)
Sean Horstead (1996)
Birinder Kang (1996)
Judith Trustman (1996)
Shiraz Aziz (1997)
Louise Hooper (1997)
Anya Lewis (1997)
Patrick Lewis (1997)
Sharon Love (1997)
Di Middleton (1997)
Roger Pezzani (1997)
Maya Sikand (1997)
Jacqueline Vallejo (1997)
Nick Wrack (1997)
Adrian Berry (1998)
Adrian Marshall Williams (1998)
Rachael Rowley-Fox (1998)
Paul Troop (1998)
Rebekah Wilson (1998)
Michelle Brewer (1999)
Emma Favata (1999)
Femi Omere (1999)
Beth O'Reilly (1999)
Hannah Rought-Brooks (1999)
Ronan Toal (1999)
Minka Braun (2000)
Ed Elliott (2000)
Catherine O'Donnell (2000)
Sam Parham (2000)
Marina Sergides (2000)
Christian Wasunna (2000)
Felicity Williams (2000)
Navtej Singh Ahluwalia (2001)
Kate Aubrey-Johnson (2001)
Allison Bailey (2001)
Tim Baldwin (2001)
Desmond Rutledge (2001)
Sadat Sayeed (2001)
Paramjit Ahluwalia (2002)
Sareta Ashraph (2002)
Brenda Campbell (2002)
Stella Harris (2002)
Victoria Meads (2002)
Maya Naidoo (2002)
Sam Robinson (2002)
Irena Sabic (2002)
Smita Shah (2002)
Colin Yeo (2002)
John Beckley (2003)
Alex Rose (2003)
Abigail Smith (2003)
Bansi Soni (2003)
Tom Wainwright (2003)
Abigail Bache (2004)
Andrew Eaton (2004)
Anthony Harrison (2004)
Davina Krishnan (2004)
Christopher McWatters (2004)
Mark Symes (2004)
William Tautz (2004)
Matt Brooks (2005)
Joanne Cecil (2005)
Vikki Kerly (2005)
Stephen Marsh (2005)
Stephanie Ward (2005)
Hossein Zahir (2005)
Sarah Hemingway (2006)
Leonie Hirst (2006)
Artis Kakonge (2006)
Stephen Lue (2006)
Shu Shin Luh (2006)
Anna Morris (2006)
Greg Ó Ceallaigh (2006)
Omar Shibli (2006)
Anthony Vaughan (2006)
Alex Grigg (2007)
Kirsten Heaven (2007)
Srikantharajah Nereshraaj (2007)
Giles Newell (2007)
Marie Philippou (2007)
Richard Reynolds (2007)
Jo Wilding (2007)
Shahida Begum (2008)
Helen Foot (2008)
James Mehigan (2008)
David Renton (2008)

GARDEN COURT CHAMBERS
BAR MARK
bsi. ISO 9001 Quality Management
FS 58838

GARDEN COURT CHAMBERS (Continued)

MEMBERS

Ali Bandegani (2009)
Raza Halim (2009)
Terry McGuinness (2009)
Bryony Poynor (2009)
Jacob Bindman (2010)
Paul Clark (2010)
Emma Fenn (2010)
Michael Goold (2010)
Owen Greenhall (2010)
Connor Johnston (2010)
Grainne Mellon (2010)
Jesse Nicholls (2010)
Bijan Hoshi (2011)
Taimour Lay (2011)
Maria Moodie (2011)
Catherine Oborne (2011)
Ifeanyi Odogwu (2011)
Tom Stoate (2011)
Tessa Buchanan (2012)
Tony Cross QC * (1982)
(QC 2006)
Nicos Trimikliniotis * (1993)
Shereener Browne * (1996)
Alex Offer * (1998)
Rahim Shamji * (2000)
Gul Hussain * (2000)
Karman Chodhury * (2001)

* Working Door Tenant

THE CHAMBERS Garden Court Chambers' inter-disciplinary approach brings together a wealth of expertise across criminal defence, family law, housing, immigration and public law. Their passion for human rights and social justice has shaped the development of the law over the last 40 years in these areas and continues to do so today. All of this is reflected in their ground-breaking cases, ways of working and client care. The largest set in London, its barristers are driven by fundamentally strong ethics and a commitment to progressive values. Quality of advocacy and advice are matched by professional practice management and clerking.

WORK UNDERTAKEN Administrative and public law, civil law, commercial law, community care, Court of Protection, crime, education, employment and discrimination, environmental law, extradition, family law (children law, financial remedies and international family law), fraud, housing, immigration (asylum, human rights, business and private), inquests, mental health, planning law, police law, prison law, property law, regulatory law, Romani Gypsy and Traveller rights and welfare benefits.

Garden Court International provides advice, representation and training to clients worldwide.

Garden Court Mediation provides an alternative dispute resolution service in all types of civil disputes.

1 GARDEN COURT FAMILY LAW CHAMBERS Janet Bazley QC & Charles Geekie QC

1 Garden Court, Temple, London, EC4Y 9BJ
Tel (020) 7797 7900 **Fax** (020) 7797 7929 **DX** 1034 (Ch.Ln.)
Email clerks@1gc.com **Website** www.1gc.com

Head of Chambers	Janet Bazley QC Charles Geekie QC
Chief Executive	Joe Turner
Senior Clerk	Howard Rayner
First Junior Clerk	Paul Harris
Tenants	66

MEMBERS

Janet Bazley QC (1980) (QC-2006)
Charles Geekie QC (1985) (QC-2006)
Eleanor F Platt QC (1960) (QC-1982)
Alison Ball QC (1972) (QC-1995)
Jane Crowley QC (1976) (QC-1998)
Susan Jacklin QC (1980) (QC-2006)
Sarah Morgan QC (1988) (QC-2011)
Caroline Willbourne (1970)
Suzanne Shenton (1973)
Elizabeth Szwed (1974)
Peter Horrocks (1977)
Kay Halkyard (1980)
David Burles (1984)
Sylvester McIlwain (1985)
John Stocker (1985)
Susan Pyle (1985)
Gary Crawley (1988)
Nicholas Daniels (1988)
Rachel Gillman 1988)
Alev Giz (1988)
Frances Orchover (1989)
Andrew Bagchi (1989)
Michael Liebrecht (1989)
Malcolm Chisholm (1989)
Kate Mather (1990)
Catherine Jenkins (1990)
Claire Heppenstall (1990)
Simon Sugar (1990)
Doushka Krish (1991)
Andrew Norton (1992)
Ian Bugg (1992)
Darren Howe (1992)
Denise Gilling (1992)
Rohan Auld (1992)
Jillian Hurworth (1993)
Gillian Downham (1993)
Jennifer Kavanagh (1993)
Alison Moore (1994)
Sally Stone (1994)
Emma Hudson (1995)
Sam Momtaz (1995)
Julien Foster (1995)
Francesca Wiley (1996)
Daisy Hughes (1999)
Sharon Segal (2000)
Rebecca Mitchell (2000)
Deirdre Fottrell (2001)
Gillian Stanley (2001)
Caroline Middleton (2002)
Edward Flood (2002)
Philip Perrins (2002)
Richard Jones (2003)
Matthew Fletcher (2003)
Alfred Procter (2005)
Ajmal Azam (2006)
Elena MacLeod (2007)
Georgina Cole (2007)
Penelope Clapham (2007)
Nasstassia Hylton (2007)
Gemma Kelly (2007)
Lucy Sprinz (2008)
Thomas Dudley (2008)
Eleri Jones (2009)
Joseph Moore (2009)
Jessica Bernstein (2011)
Marlene Cayoun (2012)
Christopher Sharp QC (1975) (QC-1999)*
Elizabeth Darlington (1998)*
Peter McEleavy (1999)*

* Door Tenant

THE CHAMBERS 1 Garden Court specialises in all areas of family law and the number and seniority of its barristers ensures expertise at all levels in the major disciplines and increasingly, in closely related areas of law. In particular, the set is renowned in family finance, care and adoption, child abduction, international and private child law, local authority matters, Court of Protection cases, mediation and human rights. Established in 1989, chambers is one of the largest sets in which all members specialise in family law. The set is acknowledged as a leader in family law issues and in 1997 was the first set to create a family mediation service.

WORK UNDERTAKEN The dedicated practice teams at 1 Garden Court cover the full spectrum of family law and its related fields. Members of chambers deal with all levels of cases including regular appearances in the Supreme Court and Court of Appeal. The family finance team undertakes matters ranging from high value cases to modest value claims. Areas of specialism include preventing dissipation of assets, foreign and offshore assets, complex trust arrangements or company structures and representing interveners. The team also deals with issues of enforcement as well as other associated areas such as Child Support Act work, Schedule 1 applications, Inheritance Act claims and cohabitation disputes as well as preparation of pre-nuptial agreements. The expertise of chambers in relation to private child proceedings is extensive, ranging from applications for child arrangement orders between parents to complex considerations of domestic abuse, intractable contact disputes, specific issue orders for schooling and cases requiring separate representation of children. A major area of the work in chambers is in the field of public child law, covering all aspects of care and adoption proceedings including emergency applications and injunctions, applications under the inherent jurisdiction, secure accommodation cases, public interest immunity and restraint of publicity cases. Members of chambers are also highly proficient in Court of Protection cases including applications for serious or urgent medical treatment. Chambers' work also includes domestic abuse cases, judicial review and professional negligence in family law. 1 Garden Court offers mediation and collaborative law services. A number of members also sit as part-time judges.

INTERNATIONAL Members of chambers provide specialist advice in relation to international considerations across all areas of family law. In particular, chambers offers expertise in cases about:

- Foreign or off-shore assets and international maintenance obligations
- The international movement of children, including applications for leave to remove from the jurisdiction
- International child abduction to both Hague and non-Hague Convention countries
- Applications incorporating the 1996 Hague Convention
- International care proceedings including transfer of cases across borders and placement of children abroad
- International adoption and surrogacy arrangements

Members have acted and advised in cases involving a number of foreign jurisdictions worldwide. Several members have gained experience working in foreign jurisdictions, particularly in North America and the Caribbean.

1 Garden Court
FAMILY LAW CHAMBERS

GOUGH SQUARE CHAMBERS Claire Andrews

6-7 Gough Square, London, EC4A 3DE
Tel (020) 7353 0924 **Fax** (020) 7353 2221 DX 476
Out of hours 07860219162
Email gsc@goughsq.co.uk **Website** www.goughsq.co.uk

Head of Chambers	Claire Andrews
Senior Clerk	Bob Weekes
Tenants	19

MEMBERS

Fred Philpott (1974)
Peter Sayer (1975) *
Claire Andrews (1979)
Josephine Hayes (1980)
Jeremy Barnett (1980)
Jonathan Goulding (1984)
Stephen Neville (1986)
Julian Gun Cuninghame (1989)
Bradley Say (1993)
Jonathan Kirk QC (1995) (QC 2010)
Iain MacDonald (1996)
Simon Popplewell (2000)
Kate Urell (2002)
Geraint Howells (2002) *
James Ross (2006)
Ruth Bala (2006)
Anna Medvinskaia (2008)
Thomas Samuels (2009)
Lee Finch (2010)

* Door tenant

THE CHAMBERS Gough Square Chambers deals primarily with the civil and criminal aspects of consumer and regulatory law, including consumer credit and financial services.

WORK UNDERTAKEN Chambers' work is broadly divided into civil, criminal and regulatory aspects, each coming within the umbrella of "Consumer Law".
Chambers' civil work includes consumer credit (e.g. agreements, FCA authorisation and advertising), banking and financial services, secured lending/mortgages, asset finance and general commercial matters. Members have appeared in some of the most important and high profile cases of recent years.
The criminal aspects of chambers' work include prosecutions under the Consumer Protection from Unfair Trading Regulations 2008, food law, weights and measures, product safety, pharmaceuticals and cosmetics and copyright. In addition, several members of chambers are active members of the Food Law Group.
In relation to regulatory matters, members of chambers have advised and acted for and against an array of industry regulators. For example – the Office of Fair Trading, the Financial Conduct Authority, the Civil Aviation Authority, OFWAT and OFCOM. Members of Chambers also sit on the Bar Council's Law Reform Committee and are therefore well placed to understand the wider import of current and proposed regulation.

9 GOUGH SQUARE Andrew Ritchie QC

9 Gough Square, London, EC4A 3DG
Tel (020) 7832 0500 **Fax** (020) 7353 1344 DX 439
Email clerks@9goughsquare.co.uk **Website** www.9goughsquare.co.uk

Head of Chambers	Andrew Ritchie QC
Chief Executive	Fiona Robb
Tenants	69

MEMBERS

Andrew Ritchie QC (1985) (QC-2009)
John Foy QC (1969) (QC-1998) +
Andrew Baillie QC (1970) (QC-2001) +
Grahame Aldous QC (1979) (QC-2008) +
Jacob Levy QC (1986) (QC-2014)
Giles Eyre (1974) +
Trevor Davies (1978)
Christopher Wilson (1980) +
Martin Pinfold (1981)
Nicolas Hillier (1982)
Roger Hiorns (1983)
Gaurang Naik (1985)
Vincent Williams (1985)
Jonathan Loades (1986)
Edwin Buckett (1988)
Mark Whalan (1988)
James Holmes-Milner (1989)
Stephen Glynn (1990)
Philip Jones (1990)
Jeremy Crowther (1991)
Aileen Downey (1991) +
Laura Begley (1993)
Christopher Stephenson (1994)
Timothy Parker (1995)
Rajeev Shetty (1996) +
Laura Elfield (1996)
Jeremy Ford (1996)
Tara Vindis (1996)
Tom Little (1997) +
Timothy Godfrey (1997)
Stuart McKechnie (1997)
Simon Brindle (1998)
Perrin Gibbons (1998)
Giles Mooney (1998)
Tabitha Barran (1998)
Joanna Cobb (1999)
Shahram Sharghy (2000)
Linda Nelson (2000)
Adam Dawson (2000)
Claire Harden (2000)
Gareth Munday (2000)
Gurion Taussig (2001)
Eleanor Mawrey (2001)
Laura Briggs (2001)
James Thacker (2001)
Robert McAllister (2002)
Oliver Millington (2003)
Esther Pounder (2003)
Emily Verity (2003)
Esther Maclachlan (2005)
Alastair Hogarth (2005)
Jennifer Newcomb (2006)
Edward Lamb (2006)
Catherine Atkinson (2006)
James Dove (2006)
Kate Lamont (2007)
Tom Restall (2007)
Benedict Rogers (2007)
Laura Bumpus (2008)
Holly Tibbitts (2010)
Ben Zurawel (2010)
Tom Rainsbury (2010)
William Dean (2011)
Sarah Hunwick (2011)
Helen Pooley (2012)

+ Recorder

THE CHAMBERS This is a leading common law set based in London but appearing in courts throughout England and Wales and abroad. Key practice areas are personal injury/clinical negligence, professional negligence, fraud and serious crime, family, police law, employment and property. More than 50 members, including 4 of the QCs, are clinical negligence/personal injury specialists. They take active involvement in the Personal Injuries Bar Association and APIL and appear in very high profile cases: for instance Corr v IBC; Simmons v Castle. They edit the leading text books in personal injuries including Kemp & Kemp on Quantum and publish their own clinical negligence and PI books. Solicitor clients include high profile specialist PI and clinical negligence firms, local authorities, the Treasury Solicitor, the Serious Fraud Office, HMRC, police solicitors and the Crown Prosecution Service. Their barristers deliver advice and advocacy in a professional and approachable way and provide in-house and external CPD training to solicitors around England and Wales. There is a highly respected serious fraud practice with success in high profile cases such as R v Bright and others (Independent Insurance Group Ltd).

WORK UNDERTAKEN The largest group specialises in PI and clinical negligence. Leaders and senior juniors appear regularly in ground-breaking cases. Members mainly represent injured claimants but some do defendant work. Nine special interest sub-groups cover occupational health; clinical negligence; road traffic insurance; MIB; building site claims etc. They publish PI books: asbestos claims, clinical negligence claims, manual handling claims, workplace accident claims and work accidents at sea. They have expertise in costs assessment and Court of Protection work.
Complex fraud work is undertaken by the Crime Team for the SFO, the FCA BERR, and the CPS Fraud Unit. Criminal work also covers terrorism, murder, violent and sexual offences with an emphasis on prosecution work for most London Crown Prosecution Offices including the recent prosecution in R v Max Clifford. Members appear in High Court in public law hearings regarding prosecutorial decisions and in the Court of Appeal on matters of public importance such as R v Caley and others, and R v Bennett and others.
The Family Team has 23 members and is popular with local government solicitors, having preferred set status with most Greater London authorities. Members are instructed in high profile non-accidental injury and sexual abuse cases but also public law children's cases including applications for judicial review. There is a flourishing private client practice in financial remedies, trust for land claims, contact and residence disputes and removals from the jurisdiction.
The police law practitioners are involved in civil actions against the police, inquests (such as the Diana Princess of Wales's inquest), police led application, disciplinary proceedings, firearms and liquor licensing. The Commercial and Property Group has expertise in general commercial contract litigation and arbitration, sale of goods, consumer credit and leasing agreements, property work and insurance law. The Professional Negligence Group focuses on solicitors', surveyors' and accountants' negligence.
The Employment Team represents employees and employers in tribunals in England and Wales. A team of CEDR-accredited mediators provide ADR services and several practices include regulatory and disciplinary expertise.

9 GOUGH SQUARE

GRAY'S INN TAX CHAMBERS Milton Grundy

Third Floor, Gray's Inn Chambers, Gray's Inn, London, WC1R 5JA
Tel (020) 7242 2642 **Fax** (020) 7831 9017 **DX** 352 London Chancery Lane
Email clerks@taxbar.com **Website** www.taxbar.com

Head of Chambers	Milton Grundy
Senior Clerk	Chris Broom
Tenants	13

MEMBERS

Milton Grundy (1954)
Michael Flesch QC (1963) (QC-1983)
David Goldberg QC (1971) (QC-1987)
David Goy QC (1973) (QC-1991)
John Walters QC (1977) (QC-1997)
Nicola Shaw QC (1995) (QC-2012)
Nikhil Mehta (1976)
Conrad McDonnell (1994)
Michael Thomas (2000)
Hui Ling McCarthy (2005)
Michael Jones (2006)
Laurent Sykes (2007)
Michael Firth (2011)
Graham Wilson (1975) *
Brian Cleave QC (1999) (QC-1999) *

* Door Tenant

THE CHAMBERS Gray's Inn Tax Chambers is a leading set of specialist tax practitioners. Its members advise on all aspects of UK revenue law and have a long-established expertise in tax litigation before the Tribunals, the Supreme Court, the Privy Council, the European Court of Justice and certain Commonwealth and foreign jurisdictions. The chambers has a friendly approachable atmosphere and is known for its problem-solving approach to tax matters, seeking to find the optimum way to deal with the tax aspect of transactions ranging from structuring large land development projects and commercial deals to estate planning for farmers and businessmen. Chambers maintains a popular website, which offers a rapid reporting of tax cases. The address is www.taxbar.com.
Appointments & Memberships: All members of chambers belong to the Revenue Bar Association, of which David Goy QC and Michael Flesch QC are former Chairmen. Milton Grundy is President of the International Tax Planning Association and a Fellow of the Chartered Institute of Taxation. He is the draftsman of the Trusts Law of the Cayman Islands and of the IBC Act and the Trusts Act of Belize. John Walters QC is a Judge of the First-tier Tax Tribunal and a Deputy Judge of the Upper Tribunal. He, and Laurent Sykes are chartered accountants. Nikhil Mehta was formerly a partner in a leading firm of London solicitors. Hui Ling McCarthy is a member of the Attorney General's C Panel of Counsel and a CEDR Accredited Mediator. Michael Jones is a member of the Attorney General's C Panel of Counsel. Nicola Shaw QC was formerly a panel member before taking Silk in 2012. Michael Flesch QC, is a member of the Addington Society.

WORK UNDERTAKEN Members give advice to taxpayers who are in dispute with HMRC, and where litigation is inevitable, appear for them before the Tribunals and the Court. Members advise private clients on the planning of their business and personal affairs. They advise on corporate tax planning, including acquisitions, mergers, takeovers and methods of financing, property transactions, international business, cross-border transactions, offshore and domestic trusts, estate planning and all matters involving direct and indirect taxes, including VAT. Members also advise non-profit organisations, local authorities and charities. Direct Professional Access is accepted from members of the appropriate professional bodies.

PUBLICATIONS Members have written, contributed to or edited: *Norfolk and Montagu on the Taxation of Interest and Debt Finance; McCutcheon on Inheritance Tax; Whiteman and Sherry on Capital Gains Tax; Whiteman and Sherry on Income Tax; VAT and Property; British Tax Review; Asset Protection Trusts; Double Taxation Conventions and International Tax Law; Value Added Tax Encyclopaedia; Offshore Business Centres; The Law of Partnership Taxation; Copinger and Skone James on Copyright; the Laws of the Internet; The International Trust and Estate Law Reports and International Law Reports; Stamp Duty Land Tax; Essays in International Tax Planning; Six Fiscal Fables* and various articles on domestic and international tax developments. Some of the members are well known-lecturers in their fields.

INTERNATIONAL Languages spoken include French, German, Gujarati, Hebrew, Hindi, Italian, Marathi, Punjabi, Tamil, and Urdu. Members of chambers advise clients from Australia, Bermuda, Canada, the Caribbean, the Channel Islands, Europe, India, the Isle of Man, Hong Kong, Mauritius, Singapore and the USA. Members also advise the revenue departments of Commonwealth and other countries on the interpretation of their statutes, and advise and appear for HMRC in the United Kingdom and the Inland Revenue in Hong Kong.

HAILSHAM CHAMBERS

Head of Chambers	Martin Spencer QC
Senior Clerk	Stephen Smith
Tenants	48

4 Paper Buildings (Ground Floor), Temple, London, EC4Y 7EX
Tel (020) 7643 5000 **Fax** (020) 7353 5778 **DX** 1036 London/Chancery Lane
Email clerks@hailshamchambers.com **Website** www.hailshamchambers.com

MEMBERS

Martin Spencer QC (1979) (QC-2003)
Harvey McGregor QC (1955) (QC-1978)
Bernard Livesey QC (1969) (QC-1990)
Michael Pooles QC (1978) (QC-1999)
Laurie West-Knights QC (1977) (QC-2000)
David Pittaway QC (1977) (QC-2000)
Julian Picton QC (1988) (QC-2010)
William Flenley QC (1988) (QC-2010)
Andrew Post QC (1988) (QC-2012)
Alexander Hutton QC (1992) (QC-2012)
Anthony de Freitas (1971)
Jane Tracy Forster (1975)
Jane Mishcon (1979)
Fiona Neale (1981)
Derek Holwill (1982)
Glenn Campbell (1985)
Matthew Jackson (1986)
Francis Bacon (1988)
Clare Price (1988)
Dr Tejina Mangat (1990)
Simon Howarth (1991)
Dr Evelyn Pollock (1991)
Nicholas Peacock (1992)
Simon Wilton (1993)
Nicola Rushton (1993)
Sarah Christie-Brown (1994)
Spike Charlwood (1994)
Catherine Ewins (1995)
Dan Stacey (1996)
Eva Ferguson (1999)
Paul Mitchell (1999)
Jamie Carpenter (2000)
Joshua Munro (2001)
James Gilberthorpe (2002)
Lucy MacKinnon (2003)
Imran Benson (2005)
David Bennett (2005)
Jacqueline Simpson (2006)
Alice Nash (2006)
Henry Bankes-Jones (2004)
Niamh O'Reilly (2007)
Heather McMahon (1999)
Stephen Bailey (2006)
David Juckes (2008)
Justin Meiland (2010)
Nicholas Pilsbury (2008)
Nicola Campbell-Clause (2010)
Richard Anderton (2010)

THE CHAMBERS Hailsham Chambers strives to provide clients with excellent service. The multi-award winning set is frequently praised for its friendly and helpful clerking, the quality of its members' work and for its reliability. Established more than 100 years ago and today offering 48 barristers, 10 of whom are silks, Hailsham Chambers contains many of the most sought-after barristers at the London Bar. The set's progressive thinking and use of modern technologies help chambers to run efficiently and to offer clients choice and flexibility.

TYPES OF WORK UNDERTAKEN Chambers acts for claimants and defendants, providing advice and representation before all levels of courts and tribunals throughout the world, in the specialist areas of:
Professional Negligence: In cases involving lawyers, accountants, auditors, surveyors, valuers, financial professionals and trustees, as well as advising about professional indemnity insurance coverage points.
Clinical Negligence: Acting for patients, trusts, healthcare professionals, health authorities, private clinics and appearing at inquests and in the Court of Protection.
Costs Litigation: Involving points of principle and advising in disputes between solicitor and client, retainers, funding arrangements, DBAs, CFAs and costs budgets.
Professional Discipline: Advice and advocacy before tribunals and regulatory bodies, both medical and non-medical.
Personal Injury: Dealing with claims arising from injuries at work, road traffic accidents, traumatic brain and catastrophic spinal injuries.
Commercial Dispute Resolution: Acting in general commercial matters such as insurance claims, fraud and partnership disputes.

To find out about the availability of counsel, please contact Hailsham's clerking team by tel: (020) 7643 5000 or email: clerks@hailshamchambers.com.

hailshamchambers

CHAMBERS BAR AWARDS 2013 WINNER

HARCOURT CHAMBERS Frances Judd QC

2 Harcourt Buildings, Temple, London, EC4Y 9DB
Tel (0844) 561 7135 **Fax** (020) 7353 6968 **DX** 373 LOND/CHANCERY LN
Email clerks@harcourtchambers.co.uk **Website** www.harcourtchambers.co.uk

Head of Chambers	Frances Judd QC
Chambers Director	Simon Boutwood
Practice Manager	Judith Partington
Tenants	45

MEMBERS

Frances Judd QC (1984) (QC-2006)
John Vater QC (1995) (QC-2012) ^
Nicholas Goodwin QC (1995) (QC-2014)
Roger Evans (1970) ^
June Rodgers (1971) ^
Benedict Sefi (1972) ^
Alicia Collinson (1982)
Matthew Brett (1987) ^
Sarah Gibbons (1987)
Fiona Hay (1989) ^
Sara Granshaw (1991)
Damian Garrido (1993) ^
Louise Potter (1993) ^
Aidan Vine (1995)
Douglas Allen (1995) ^
Simon Miller (1996)
Jonathan Sampson (1997)
Matthew Brookes-Baker (1998) ^
Cecilia Barrett (1998) ^
Oliver Wraight (1998)
Andrew Leong (1998) ^
Edward Kirkwood (1999)
Helen Little (1999)
Margaret Styles (2000) ^
Craig Jeakings (2000)
James Turner (2001)
Edward Devereux (2001)
Jason Green (2001) ^
Alex Forbes (2003) ^
Alison Williams (2004)
Elizabeth Tomlinson (2004)
Frances Harris (2005) ^
Kit Firbank (2005)
Mark Higgins (2005) *
Chloe Wilkins (2006)
Helen Wilkinson (2007)
Alex Perry (2007)
Sian Cox (2008) ^
Stephen Crispin (2008)
Mehvish Chaudhry (2008)
Emily Rayner (2009) ^
Gemma Bowes (2009)
David Marusza (2009) ^
Annie Sayers (2009)
Justine Ramsden (2010) ^
Maria Scott-Wittenborn (2012)
Anna Yarde (2012)

* Door Tenant ^ Public/Direct Access

THE CHAMBERS Harcourt Chambers is one of the leading family law sets in the country. It is recommended for both children law and family finance, and combines its expertise in family law with a strong reputation in civil litigation. Based in the Temple and in Oxford, it is home to well-known family silks Frances Judd QC, John Vater QC, Nick Goodwin QC and 42 junior barristers, many of whom are acknowledged as leading practitioners in their fields. Over the past decade, Harcourt Chambers has established itself as one of the very top 'across the range' family law sets. It has grown significantly in size and prominence and its members are regularly to be found in high- profile and leading cases at first instance and on appeal. Harcourt Chambers is particularly known for the high quality of its advocacy, advice and client care, for its genuine strength in depth and for its modern and approachable style.

HARCOURT CHAMBERS
LONDON OXFORD

HARDWICKE Nigel Jones QC & Paul Reed QC

Hardwicke Building, New Square, Lincoln's Inn, London, WC2A 3SB
Tel (020) 7242 2523 **Fax** (020) 7691 1234 **DX** LDE 393
Email enquiries@hardwicke.co.uk **Website** www.hardwicke.co.uk

Heads of Chambers	Nigel Jones QC & Paul Reed QC
Chief Executive	Amanda Illing
Tenants	70

MEMBERS

George F Pulman QC (1971) (QC-1989) +
Nigel Jones QC (1976) (QC-1999) +
Lesley Anderson QC (1989) (QC-2006)
Paul Reed QC (1988) (QC-2010) ^
Brie Stevens-Hoare QC (1986) (QC-2013)
P J Kirby QC (1989) (QC-2013) ^
John de Waal QC (1992) (QC-2013)
John Friel (1974) ^
John Gallagher (1974) +
Stephen Lennard (1976) + ^
Robert Leonard (1976) ^
Graham Cunningham (1976) ^
Wendy Parker (1978) ^
Karl King (1985) + ^
Richard Buswell (1985) ^
Monty Palfrey (1985)
Mark Engelman (1987) ^
Steven Woolf (1989) ^
Sara Benbow (1990) ^
Daniel Gatty (1990) ^
Rupert Higgins (1991) ^
Arthur Moore (1992)
Colm Nugent (1992)
Andrew Skelly (1994) ^
Margaret Bloom (1994)
Clive Rawlings (1994) ^
Alexander Bastin (1995) ^
David Pliener (1996) ^
Edward Rowntree (1996) ^
David Lewis (1997) ^
Ian Silcock (1997) ^
Charles Bagot (1997) ^
Romilly Cummerson (1998)
Alison Meacher (1998) ^
Alastair Redpath-Stevens (1998)
Peter Petts (1998)
Mark Stephens (1998)
Henry Slack (1999)
David Lawson (2000)
Shazia Akhtar (2001) ^
Sarah McCann (2001) ^
Jonathan Titmuss (2001)
Sarah Venn (2002)
Jasmine Murphy (2002)
Michael Wheater (2003)
Rebecca Richardson (2003)
Morayo Fagborun Bennett (2004) ^
Andy Creer (2005)
Charles Raffin (2005)
Simon Allison (2005) ^
Paul Strelitz (2005) ^
Thomas Bell (2006)
Laura Tweedy (2007) ^
Helena White (2007)
Catherine Piercy (2007)
Gemma Witherington (2008)
Anna Tkaczynska (2008)
Emily Betts (2009)
Ebony Alleyne (2009)
Alexander Campbell (2010)
Lina Mattsson (2010)
Brenna Conroy (2010)
Laurence Page (2010)
Aileen McErlean (2011)
Leon Glenister (2011)
Rupert Cohen (2011)
Sri Carmichael (2012)
Caoimhe McKearney (2012)
Charlie Thompson (2012)
Jack Dillon (2012)

+ Recorder ^ Public/Direct Access

THE CHAMBERS Hardwicke specialises in commercial, insurance, property and private client, and public law. It is one of the most innovative and modern sets at the Bar, run as a commercial business with a strong focus on excellent client service. Hardwicke is an Investor in People (silver accreditation) and has won the UK Diversity Legal Award in 2012 and 2011.
Hardwicke has 70 barristers across its four specialist divisions, servicing UK and international clients, including professional services firms, businesses, banks, lenders, insurance companies, charities, government bodies and individuals. Barristers are supported by a strong team of practice managers, who are friendly and approachable.

WORK UNDERTAKEN Hardwicke works across the range of civil and commercial law, from administrative law to trade disputes, and can handle everything from informal advice over the telephone to representation in the most complex international disputes.
The set is organised into four specialist divisions:
Commercial: Arbitration, banking and finance, civil fraud, commercial litigation, companies and partnership, construction and engineering, costs, employment, franchising, insolvency and restructuring, intellectual property, shipping and trade, TMT.
Insurance: Clinical negligence, insurance and reinsurance, personal injury, professional liability, professional negligence, medical malpractice.
Public: Administrative law, community care, court of protection, education, healthcare, homelessness, human rights, inquests, judicial review, mental health, social housing, social welfare and benefits.
Property & Private Client: Commercial landlord and tenant, family, probate, procurement, real property, residential leases and tenancies, trusts.
Costs & ADR: In addition to the above specialist areas of law, members offer advice and representation in all aspects of costs and funding. Members have extensive experience of CFAs and are at the forefront of alternative dispute resolution and have a panel of qualified arbitrators and mediators. Many members accept public access instructions.

Hardwicke

1 HARE COURT Nicholas Cusworth QC

1 Hare Court, Temple, London, EC4Y 7BE
Tel (020) 7797 7070 **Fax** (020) 7797 7435 **DX** LDE 342 Chancery Lane
Email clerks@1hc.com **Website** www.1hc.com

Head of Chambers	Nicholas Cusworth QC
Senior Clerk	Steve McCrone
Tenants	42

MEMBERS

Nicholas Cusworth QC (1986) (QC-2009)
Bruce Blair QC (1969) (QC-1989)
Martin Pointer QC (1976) (QC-1996)
Valentine Le Grice QC (1977) (QC-2002)
Michael Nicholls QC (1975) (QC-2006)
Deborah Bangay QC (1981) (QC-2006)
Nigel Dyer QC (1982) (QC-2006)
Ann Hussey QC (1981) (QC-2009)
Richard Todd QC (1988) (QC-2009)
John Wilson QC (1981) (QC-2011)
Katharine Davidson (1987) (QC-2011)
Timothy Bishop QC (1991) (QC-2011)
Heather Pope (1977)
Nicholas Carden (1981)
Gavin Smith (1981)
Christopher Wood (1986)
Rachel Platts (1989)
Elisabeth Todd (1990)
Nichola Gray (1991)
Geoffrey Kingscote (1993)
Stephen Trowell (1995)
Justin Warshaw (1995)
Nicholas Yates (1996)
Simon Webster (1997)
Michael Bradley (1999)
Rebecca Carew Pole (1999)
Emma Sumner (1999)
Rebecca Bailey-Harris (2000)
Eleanor Harris (2001)
Tom Carter (2001)
Rachel Spicer (2002)
Christian Kenny (2003)
Jude Allen (2004)
Richard Sear (2005)
Amelia Harris (2006)
Nicholas Wilkinson (2006)
Katherine Cook (2007)
Matthew Brunsdon Tully (2007)
Madhavi Kabra (2008)
Amy Perkins (2010)
Kyra Cornwall (2011)
Lily Mottahedan (2012)
Sir Matthew Thorpe +
Sir Peter Singer +
Michael Horowitz QC +

+ Associate Member

THE CHAMBERS Chambers prides itself on having been the family law market leader in every legal guide for every year since those guides were first published. It is a position earned and retained by an unrivalled expertise in relationship generated disputes. More than half of all the specialist matrimonial money silks in England and Wales are at 1 Hare Court. The set's vibrancy is maintained by a rigorous policy of in-house training and by continued representation in the vast majority of leading cases.
Chambers traces its history back more than 200 years. Its illustrious former members include Law Lords and Lords Justice of Appeal. Very recent past members include Baroness Butler-Sloss, Lord Simon, Lord Cumming-Bruce, the former president of the family division Sir Nicholas Wall, The Rt Hon. Sir Mathew Thorpe and High Court Judges Nicholas Mostyn and Philip Moor.
Members write or contribute to the leading text books and leading periodicals. The 1 Hare Court annual seminar is an important fixture in the family law year for all of chambers' instructing solicitors, providing up to date analysis of the law from its expert barristers and a much-celebrated party afterwards. Chambers now numbers 12 silks, 30 juniors, 3 distinguished former judges as associate members and an 11 strong clerks team.

TYPES OF WORK UNDERTAKEN: Chambers provides cutting edge expertise at every level. The Supreme Court's three most important private family law cases were dominated by members of chambers; whether in international divorce (where Nigel Dyer QC and Eleanor Harris were for the successful Mrs Agbaje), the nine Justice Supreme Court decision in Radmacher v Granatino (where Richard Todd QC and Geoffrey Kingscote were pitted against fellow member of chambers, Nicholas Mostyn QC) or recently before seven Justices in the case of Petrodel v Prest (Richard Todd QC and Stephen Trowell acted for Mrs Prest). The most important private family law case in the Privy Council (Macleod v Macleod) involved Martin Pointer QC and Valentine Le Grice QC. Members of chambers have had an active part as advocates in all the most celebrated divorce cases of recent years: White, Cowan, Lambert, Miller, McFarlane, Charman and McCartney. 85% of the hundreds of reported cases referred to in At A Glance have had involvement by members of chambers. Obviously the higher court cases attract greater publicity but chambers maintains a strong representation at every level of litigation; the unsung every bit as valued as the celebrated. The majority of chambers' work takes the form of resolving disputes on divorce, both financial and regarding arrangements for children. The breakdown of civil partnerships or property disputes arising from unmarried parties' cohabitation (TOLATA, MWPA, Schedule 1 Children Act and Inheritance Act) also represents an important part of Chambers' work. Chambers has an excellent reputation in drafting nuptial agreements.
In addition to traditional court work, chambers has a strong offering in private dispute resolution services. 1 Hare Court offers private mediation services through a large and expert team of specialist barrister-mediators. Chambers has been at the forefront of the new family arbitration movement and has the largest number of family law arbitrators under one roof. Senior and associate members of chambers regularly act as evaluators in "private FDR" hearings, and some members are also associates of collaborative law pods.
Chambers also has an impressive international presence with its members providing representation or expert evidence in many other jurisdictions. In the last ten years members of chambers have acted in 30 foreign jurisdictions. In recent years members of chambers have been found advocating in cases as geographically far apart as the Cayman Islands and Hong Kong.
Members are supported by a highly efficient clerks' room run under the careful eye of Steve McCrone. 'I see the work of barrister and solicitor as being very much that of a team', says Steve. 'We in the clerks' room are proud to do what we can to help that team effort'.

1 HARE COURT

2 HARE COURT Jonathan Laidlaw QC

2 Hare Court, Temple, London, EC4Y 7BH
Tel (020) 7353 5324 **Fax** (020) 7353 0667 **DX** 444 (Ch.Ln.)
Email clerks@2harecourt.com **Website** www.2harecourt.com

Head of Chambers	Jonathan Laidlaw QC
Director of Clerking	Julian Campbell
Director of Business Development	Maurice MacSweeney
Tenants	57

MEMBERS

Jonathan Laidlaw QC (1982) (QC-2008) *
Orlando Pownall QC (1975) (QC-2002) ^
Malcolm Swift QC (1970) (QC-1988)
Martin Heslop QC (1972) (QC-1995) ^*
David Waters QC (1973) (QC-1999) ^
Andrew Edis QC (1980) (QC-1997) + •
Peter Wright QC (1981) (QC – 1999) *
Andrew Radcliffe QC (1975) (QC-2000) ^
James Pickup QC (1976) (QC-2000) ^*
David Howker QC (1982) (QC-2002)
Martin Hicks QC (1977) (QC-2003)
Sallie Bennett-Jenkins QC (1984) (QC-2006) ^*
Brendan Kelly QC (1988) (QC-2008) ^*
Jonathan Rees QC (1987) (QC-2010) ^ •
Brian O'Neill QC (1987) (QC-2010) ^*
Parmjit-Kaur (Bobbie) Cheema QC (1989) (QC-2013) ^ + •
Christopher Coltart QC (1998) (QC-2014)^
Jacqueline Samuel (1971)
W. John Jones (1972) ^*
Andrew Colman (1980) ^
Tyrone Belger (1984)
James Dawson (1984) ^*
David Whittaker (1986) *
Michael Logsdon (1988)
Kenneth Millett (1988) ^
Marios Lambis (1989) ^*
Alex Lewis (1990) ^
Christopher Gillespie (1991) ^
Craig Ferguson (1992) ^*
Kate Bex (1992) ^
Andrew Hurst (1992) ^
James Buchanan (1993) ^
Christopher Foulkes (1994) ^
Stephen Brassington (1994) ^
Zubair Ahmad (1995) ^
Oliver Glasgow (1995) ^++
Scott Ivill (1997) ^
Narita Bahra (1997) ^
Peter Lownds (1998)
Quinn Hawkins (1999)
Angus Bunyan (1999) ^
Gudrun Young (2001)
Robert Rinder (2001) ^
Rebekah Hummerstone (2002) ^
Naeem Mian (2002) ^
Julia Faure Walker (2004) ^
Vivienne Tanchel (2005) ^
Sarah Przybylska (2006) ^
Emily Dummett (2006) ^
Harry Bentley (2007)
Alexandra Tampakopoulos (2007)
Christopher Ware (2007)
Thomas Day (2008) ^
Fiona Robertson (2008)
Christopher Geering (2009) ^
Ben Rich (2010)
Nikita McNeill (2010)

* Recorder of the Crown Court +Deputy High Court Judge • Senior Treasury Counsel ++ Junior Treasury Counsel ^ Public/Direct Access

THE CHAMBERS 2 Hare Court is consistently recognised as one of the UK's leading sets of expert barristers specialising in crime, fraud, professional discipline, health and safety and other areas of regulatory law. Their individual and corporate clients instruct them via solicitors, other professional advisers, or on a direct access basis. The set's barristers provide early and strategic analysis and advice, as well as advocacy of the highest quality where cases cannot be resolved at an early stage and need to progress to court or other tribunal. According to the leading industry directories, 2 Hare Court "provides a blue-chip service to professional and lay clients alike", whilst sources "are keen to highlight the set's commitment to providing exemplary client care." More information on their barristers and work can be found at www.2harecourt.com

WORK UNDERTAKEN

Crime: The strength and depth of experience amongst 2 Hare Court's specialist advocates sees them advising, defending and prosecuting in all forms of criminal work, particularly in serious and complex cases of terrorism (including Special Advocate work), murder, honour killings, international drug and human trafficking, serious organised crime and sexual offences (especially historic). Recent cases include Brooks (phone hacking), Huhne & Pryce, Stock Exchange terrorist bombing plot, Bridger (murder of Welsh girl April Jones), Gnango (Supreme Court decision on law of murder), McCormick (fake bomb detectors sold in Iraq), Ali Dizaei (corrupt Met Police commissioner), PC Blakelock/Broadwater Farm riots, the Derby Hate Crime case, Lee Rigby murder, Victoria Station stabbing case, and Nigel Evans, MP amongst others.

Fraud & Financial Services Regulation: Members of Chambers are routinely instructed the largest and most complex financial crime cases. Their experience includes all forms of fraud, MTIC/VAT tribunal hearings, market abuse (insider dealing, LIBOR and other benchmark rates), asset recovery and forfeiture, and restraint/confiscation proceedings. Recent cases include BA price fixing, "Blue Index", SFO v Tchenguiz, Innospec, Operation Tabernula, Turks and Caicos corruption cases, MOBILX, Torex Retail, and MP/Lords Expenses. Members also defend financial services professionals in regulatory proceedings, and advise on potential liability under the criminal law in parallel with regulatory breaches (FSMA/Financial Services Act).

Professional Discipline: Members have extensive expertise in this field, appearing in particular before all healthcare regulators primarily defending members of all the major MDOs as well as other professionals. Members of the set also appear in proceedings involving the police, accountants and actuaries, tax advisers, solicitors, sports professionals, telecommunications, and other industry sectors.

Regulatory Crime: 2 Hare Court is now one of the leading sets in this field, and its members are regularly instructed in a wide variety of cases brought under the HSWA 1974 and related regulations and legislation, including advising companies and directors on corporate and gross negligence manslaughter, deaths at

2 HARE COURT

2 HARE COURT Jonathan Laidlaw QC (continued)

work, falls from height, mechanical injuries, poisoning, inhalation of gases, and so on. Recent and current instructions include the Hillsborough disaster, Lion Steel, the Armenas gas project terrorist attack, and several cases arising from major incidents on gas and oil platforms.

The set also advises on environmental cases (e.g. spillages, high toxicity gas releases). Members are also regularly instructed on behalf of claimants and defendants in civil litigation following workplace accidents and HSE prosecutions.

Dovetailing their healthcare, regulatory and health and safety experience, the set's barristers also specialises in cases involving care homes (inquests, HSE prosecutions, CQC proceedings or other regulatory breaches, professional discipline proceedings, etc).

Inquests: 2 Hare Court has a team of specialists with extensive experience of advocacy before the Coroner's Court, particularly in cases involving health and safety, healthcare and military service issues.

3 HARE COURT Peter Knox QC

Head of Chambers	Peter Knox QC
Senior Clerk	James Donovan
Tenants	36

3 Hare Court, Temple, London, EC4Y 7BJ
Tel (020) 7415 7800 **Fax** (020) 7415 7811 **DX** 212 London
Email clerks@3harecourt.com **Website** www.3harecourt.com **Twitter** @3harecourt

MEMBERS

Peter Knox QC (1983) (QC-2006)
Mark Strachan QC (1969) (QC-1987)
James Guthrie QC (1975) (QC-1993)
Simon Davenport QC (1987) (QC-2009)
Howard Stevens QC (1990) (QC-2012)
Thomas Roe QC (1995) (QC-2014)
Iain McLeod (1969)
Sebastian Neville-Clarke (1973)
Andrew Young (1977)
Pierre Janusz (1979)
William Godwin (1986)
Paul Letman (1987)
Rupert Butler (1988) ^
Professor Satvinder Juss (1989) ^
Aidan Casey (1992)
Richard Samuel (1996) ^
Katherine Deal (1997)
Sarah Crowther (1999)
Dan Saxby (2000)
Tom Poole (2001)
Navjot Atwal (2002)
Daniel Lewis (2003)
Robert Strang (2003)
James Hawkins (2003)
Daniel Clarke (2005)
Clara Johnson (2005)
Daniel Tivadar (2005) ^
Sara Ibrahim (2006)
Helen Pugh (2008)
Asela Wijeyaratne (2008)
Hafsah Masood (2006) *
Cosimo Ajmone-Marsan (2009)
Rowan Pennington-Benton (2008)
Alexander Halban (2009)
Richard Campbell (2007)
Sarah Ramsey (2012)
Hugh Small QC (1963) (QC-1985) *
Anthony Astaphan (1983) (SC-1999) * ++
David McMillen QC(1985) (QC-2011) * ±
Bertha Cooper-Rousseau *
Prof. Matthew Happold (1995) *
Sir George Newman (1965) °

* Door Tenant ++ Dominica ± Northern Ireland ° Arbitrator ^ Public/Direct Access

THE CHAMBERS Described as a 'leading civil and commercial set', Chambers has established a first-class reputation in its fields of practice, providing a wide range of advisory and advocacy services both domestically and internationally in an environment that meets modern business needs.

WORK UNDERTAKEN Civil fraud; Commercial; Employment; Insolvency; International work; Personal Injury and Travel/Accidents Abroad; Professional negligence; Property litigation; Public, Administrative and Constitutional law. Privy Council work is a notable area of expertise. Insolvency and restructuring is a growing area for Chambers and the set often acts for the main insolvency practitioners.

Chambers are strong on languages, with members fluent in Dutch, French, German, Hindi, Hungarian, Italian, Malay, Punjabi, Russian, Spanish, Swahili and Urdu.

3 HARE COURT

HENDERSON CHAMBERS Charles Gibson QC

2 Harcourt Buildings (Ground Floor), Temple, London, EC4Y 9DB
Tel (020) 7583 9020 **Fax** (020) 7583 2686 **DX** LDE 1039
Email clerks@hendersonchambers.co.uk **Website** www.hendersonchambers.co.uk

Head of Chambers	Charles Gibson QC
Chief Clerk	John White
Senior Practice Manager	Daniel Kemp
Tenants	47

MEMBERS

Charles Gibson QC (1984) (QC-2001) + ^
Richard Mawrey QC (1964) (QC-1986) + ^
Peter Susman QC (1966) (QC-1997) + ^
Lawrence West QC (1979) (QC-2003) + ^
Prashant Popat QC (1992) (QC-2008) ^
Sir Alan Dashwood QC (1969) (QC-2010) ^
Rhodri Williams QC (1987) (QC-2010) ^
Patrick Green QC (1990) (QC-2012) ^
Geraint Webb QC (1995) (QC-2013) ^
Oliver Campbell QC (1992) (QC-2014) ^
Bernard O'Sullivan (1971) ^
Jonathan Harvey (1974) ^
Kenneth Hamer (1975) + ^
William Hibbert (1979)
James Palmer (1983) ^
Jonathan Steinert (1986) ^
David Brook (1988) ^
Andrew Davies (1988) ^
Julia Smith (1988)
Linda Goldman (1990) ^
Malcolm Sheehan (1993) ^
Toby Riley-Smith (1995) ^
Angus Withington (1995) ^
Andrew Kinnier (1996) ^
Adam Heppinstall (1999) ^
Noel Dilworth (2001) ^
Anna Burne (2001) ^
James Purnell (2002) ^
Nazeer A Chowdhury (2002) ^
Matthew Bradley (2004) ^
Kathleen Donnelly (2005) ^
Hannah Wilson (2005) ^
Abigail Cohen (2005) ^
Matthew Richardson (2006)
Henry Warwick (2007)
Jonathan Lewis (2007) ^
Thomas Evans (2008)
Lucy McCormick (2008)
Dennis Rosenthal (2009)
Elizabeth Tremayne (2009)
Paul Skinner (2010)
Hannah Curtain (2010)
James Williams (2010)
Rachel Tandy (2010)
Ognjen Miletic (2010)
Chloe Campbell (2011)
Paris Aboro (2012)
Roger Henderson QC (1964) (QC-1980) + *
Adrian Garner (1985) *
John Ratliff (1990) *
Felicia Fenston (1994) *
Prof John Miller (1974) *
Tamara Trefusis (1999) *
Clive Stanbrook OBE QC (1972) (QC-1989) *
Philip Bentley QC (1970) (QC-1991) *
Frank Schoneveld (1992) *
Jeremy Scudamore (1982) *
Mark Piercy (1976) *
Natasha Newell (2001) ^

+ Recorder * Door Tenant ^ Public/Direct Access

THE CHAMBERS Henderson Chambers, since its foundation in 1954, has developed a solid reputation for excellence in both advocacy and advisory work over a wide range of practice areas and market sectors. Chambers' main focus is on civil and commercial contract and tort actions, public, regulatory and disciplinary law. Members act for multinational organisations, foreign and domestic corporations, financial services organisations, government departments and agencies, local authorities, NGOs, professional bodies, SME's and individuals in contentious and non-contentious matters. One of the first Chambers to obtain accreditation under the BarDirect scheme it remains pre-eminent in meeting the needs of lay and professional clients. Chambers draws the majority of its tenants from its pupils all of whom undertake part of their pupillage in Brussels. Chambers remains dedicated to providing a high standard of client care and received Bar Mark accreditation in 2011. Members of chambers are appointed to the Attorney General's Panel of Junior Counsel to the Crown.

WORK UNDERTAKEN

Product Liability & Group Actions: Chambers has an unrivalled position in product liability, having maintained its top ranking in the legal directories for over a decade. For more than 25 years, members of chambers have been instructed in many of the most significant unitary cases, group actions and commercial claims in respect of allegedly defective products.

Health & Safety & Environment: Widely recognised for its expertise in health and safety law, the set covers all aspects of environmental law and health and safety litigation, including prosecutions for corporate manslaughter, infringements of health and safety legislation and environmental and waste prosecutions. Consistently ranked as one of the leading sets in the field as well as being awarded Health & Safety Chambers of the Year 2010, members also provide advice on health and safety and environmental policy, regulatory issues, management and training.

Banking, Finance & Consumer Credit: One of the leading sets in consumer credit fielding a large team with great expertise in financial services, consumer credit, asset finance, debt recovery, mortgage lending, sale and carriage of goods, issues of title and consumer protection.

Employment: Chambers has a long and established practice in the field of employment law. It has particular expertise in restraint of trade and breach of confidence; wrongful dismissal and related contractual claims; unfair dismissal claims; sex, race and disability discrimination claims; redundancy; TUPE; re-structuring and EC employment law.

Commercial, Insurance & Arbitration: Work in this area has a significant international dimension, advising in cross border disputes.

Local Government & Public: Members have an established reputation for excellence in the field of public and administrative law, especially when working with local authorities and other statutory bodies on matters such as property, planning, highways, compulsory purchase, transport, finance/audit, environmental, education, social services, public procurement, employment and pensions.

Property: Chambers has a dynamic and innovative property team with particular strengths in commercial property and development, commercial and residential landlord and tenant, social housing, stock transfers, insol-

HENDERSON CHAMBERS

HENDERSON CHAMBERS Charles Gibson QC (continued)

vency, public law, property damage law and professional negligence.
Regulatory & Disciplinary: Chambers has a long tradition of practice in the field of regulation and professional discipline. Members act as advisers, legal assessors, representatives, advocates, or as tribunal members.
Technology & Construction: For many years Chambers has actively developed innovative remedies in IT and closely related fields, using modern technology (including social networking and up to the minute search techniques) to solve the legal problems that arise from it.
Commercial, Insurance & International Arbitration: Members have considerable experience of large scale disputes, often involving group actions or multiple parties, including those claims arising out of property damage, contamination or sale of goods and cross border disputes. Members regularly act for both insurers and insured in coverage disputes and many draw upon considerable experience in arbitrations under wide ranging procedural rules.
ADR: Committed to offering a full service for dispute management and resolution, members of chambers act as arbitrators and adjudicators and are accredited by CEDR as commercial mediators.

INTERNATIONAL Members advise on all aspects of European law, contentious and non-contentious, including constitutional matters and the law relating to the internal market.

HOGARTH CHAMBERS Alastair Wilson QC & Roger Wyand QC

5 New Square, Lincoln's Inn, London, WC2A 3RJ
Tel (020) 7404 0404 **Fax** (020) 7404 0505 **DX** 16 London
Email barristers@hogarthchambers.com **Website** www.hogarthchambers.com

Head of Chambers	Alastair Wilson QC Roger Wyand QC
Chambers' Director	Briget Harrison
Senior Clerk	Clive Nicholls
Assistant Clerks	Andy Clayton John Davies
Consultant	Ian Bowie
Chambers Administrator	Catherine Hanley
Tenants	21

MEMBERS

Alastair Wilson QC (1968) (QC-1987)
Roger Wyand QC (1973) (QC-1997)
Antony Watson QC (1968) (QC-1986)
Christopher Morcom QC (1963) (QC-1991)
Jonathan Rayner James QC (1971) (QC-1988)
Nicholas Caddick QC (1986) (QC-2011)
Gillian Davies (1961)
Alexander Stewart (1975)
Michael Hicks (1976)
Edward Bragiel (1977)
Amanda Michaels (1981)
Julia Clark (1984)
Guy Tritton (1987)
Gwilym Harbottle (1987)
Richard Davis (1992)
Andrew Norris (1995)
Jeremy Reed (1997)
Tom St Quintin (2006)
Benjamin Longstaff (2009)
Jonathan Moss (2009)
Charlotte Scott (2012)

THE CHAMBERS Hogarth Chambers is recognised as one of the leading sets of barristers' chambers for intellectual property and chancery, based in the UK. Chambers specialises in IT, media and entertainment, FOI, data protection, privacy and commercial disputes with a technical or non-technical IP element. Chambers also has a longstanding reputation for chancery and commercial law, as well as expertise in ADR, mediation and arbitration.
With 21 barristers, Hogarth Chambers is one of the largest intellectual property sets in the UK. Members have experience of appearing as advocates at all levels within the UK court system, including the High Court, Court of Appeal and Supreme Court, and in tribunals such as the UK Intellectual Property Office, Copyright Tribunal, VAT Tribunal and Lands Tribunal.
In recent years, members have developed an in depth experience of European aspects of IP; regularly appearing before the Court of Justice of the European Union, the General Court in Luxembourg, as well as before the European Patent Office in Munich.
Hogarth is dedicated to providing a high quality, cost-effective service. Chambers offers clients a wide range of counsel at all levels of seniority, from Queen's Counsel to recently called junior members. Chambers accepts instructions from solicitors, in-house lawyers, patent and trade mark attorneys, direct access and other approved bodies.

WORK UNDERTAKEN
Intellectual Property: All aspects of IP, including patents, copyright, designs, trade marks and passing off, threats/trade libel, confidential information, and entertainment and media contracts. Chambers also specialises in related areas such as computer contracts litigation, domain name disputes and internet-related infringements, IP insurance, personality and character merchandising, privacy rights, trade secrets, franchising, counterfeiting, customs and criminal proceedings connected with IP rights, data protection issues, FOI, privacy law, EU and UK competition law, and any commercial matter requiring technical competence or a detailed knowledge of the entertainment and media industries.
Information Technology: Contractual IT litigation and numerous confidential arbitrations.
Media & Entertainment: Including moral rights; performers' rights; comparative advertising; trade libel; malicious falsehood; entertainment industry contracts; confidential information; personality and character merchandising; privacy rights; criminal remedies; related EC aspects.
Chancery/Commercial: Insolvency (corporate and personal); company; partnership; banking and securities; e-commerce; commercial contracts; professional negligence; land law and conveyancing; landlord and tenant; charities; trusts and fiduciaries; wills and the administration of estates; and applications under the Inheritance Act.
Privacy: Since the advent of the phone hacking litigation, Chambers' members have established a reputed presence in this sector.

Leading practitioners' books edited in chambers include: *Copinger and Skone James on Copyright; Intellectual Property in Europe; Moral Rights, The Modern Law of Patents; The Modern Law of Trade Marks; A Practical Guide to Trade Mark Law; A User's Guide to Trade Marks and Passing Off; Williams, Mortimer and Sunnucks on Executors, Administrators and Probate.*

HOGARTH | CHAMBERS

11KBW James Goudie QC & John Cavanagh QC

11 King's Bench Walk, Temple, London EC4Y 7EQ
Tel (020) 7632 8500 **Fax** (020) 7583 9123/3690 **DX** 368 (Ch.Ln.)
Email clerksteam@11kbw.com **Website** www.11kbw.com

Head of Chambers	James Goudie QC John Cavanagh QC
Senior Clerks	Lucy Barbet Mark Dann
Operations Manager	Claire Halas
Business Development Director	Andrea Kennedy
Tenants	58

MEMBERS

James Goudie QC (1970) (QC-1984)
John Cavanagh QC (1985) (QC-2001)
Christopher Jeans QC (1980) (QC-1997)
Adrian Lynch QC (1983) (QC-2000)
Tim Kerr QC (1983) (QC-2001)
Nigel Giffin QC (1986) (QC-2003)
Elisabeth Laing QC (1980) (QC-2008)
Simon Devonshire QC (1988) (QC-2009)
Jonathan Swift QC (1989) (QC-2010)
Timothy Pitt-Payne QC (1989) (QC-2010)
Peter Oldham QC (1990) (QC-2010)
Daniel Stilitz QC (1992) (QC-2010)
Clive Sheldon QC (1991) (QC-2011)
Seán Jones QC (1991) (QC-2012)
Paul Nicholls QC (1992) (QC-2012)
Jason Coppel QC (1994) (QC-2013)
Charles Bourne QC (1991) (QC-2014)
Karen Steyn QC (1995) (QC-2014)
Jane Oldham (1985)
Sarah Moore (1990)
Akhlaq Choudhury (1992)
Julian Wilson (1997)
Nigel Porter (1994)
Cecilia Ivimy (1995)
Richard Leiper (1996)
Jonathan Moffett (1996)
Andrew Sharland (1996)
Anya Proops (1998)
Deok Joo Rhee (1998)
Jane McCafferty (1998)
Harini Iyengar (1999)
Paul Greatorex (1999)
Julian Milford (2000)
Andrew Blake (2000)
Ben Hooper (2000)
James Cornwell (2002)
Joanne Clement (2002)
Holly Stout (2003)
Andrew Edge (2003)
Judy Stone (2003)
Simon Forshaw (2004)
Patrick Halliday (2005)
Rachel Kamm (2006)
Tara Shahbahrami (2006)
Amy Rogers (2007)
Tom Cross (2007)
Robin Hopkins (2008)
Christopher Knight (2008)
Michael Lee (2009)
Katherine Eddy (2009)
Edward Capewell (2009)
Joseph Barrett (2009)
Heather Emmerson (2009)
Sean Aughey (2010)
Ronnie Dennis (2010)
Hannah Slarks (2011)
Tom Ogg (2012)
Rupert Paines (2012)

THE CHAMBERS 11KBW has an outstanding reputation in its specialist fields of commercial, employment and public law. The set is made up of 58 barristers including 18 QCs. 11KBW prides itself on the calibre of its advocates and its superior service to its clients. Chambers has some of the leading lawyers in the areas in which it practices. Members regularly appear in complex and high profile cases often for both defendant and claimant.

WORK UNDERTAKEN

Commercial: In-depth litigation experience of heavyweight commercial cases involving business protection, rewards, regulation, fraud and governance.

Education: Leader in the field covering all areas including exclusions and admissions, SENDIST matters, school governance and educational negligence.

Employment: The pre-eminent employment law set, 11KBW acts on behalf of employers, employees and trade unions often in the most complex, high value and important cases.

EU: Chambers' leading profile in this area flows from its pre-eminence in the fields of public and administrative law, employment law and procurement law. Work covered includes free movement of persons and goods, competition and state aid, environment and discrimination.

Health & Community Care: Regularly instructed in seminal cases involving the disputed boundaries between healthcare, community care, housing and children's services. Frequent appearances in the Court of Protection.

Human Rights: Unmatched breadth of experience in civil liberties and human rights, acting for both claimants and defendants in cases which are at the forefront of human rights law.

Information & Data Protection: 11KBW is unrivalled in this complex and quickly-evolving area, regularly acting in the top cases involving the application of FOIA, the EIR, the DPA and Article 8.

Mediation: 11KBW has several trained and accredited mediators acting as facilitators or evaluators in disputes.

Procurement: Acknowledged experts in this field, members act for tenderers and other claimants and public authorities of all types in leading High Court claims and significant judicial reviews.

Professional Discipline & Regulatory Law: Advising and acting for a wide range of individuals, firms and regulators in leading judicial review claims across a wide range of regulated activities.

Partnerships & LLPs: Acting for and advising general partnerships, limited partnerships and LLPs, across the whole range of business sectors

Public: Representing public and private sector organisations in almost every aspect of public law including judicial review, regulation, community care, health, education, FOI and public procurement.

Sport: Includes anti-doping tribunals, disciplinary, player restraints, free movement and competition rules.

RECRUITMENT A member of Pupillage Portal, 11KBW offers awards for 2015 of £55,000.

KEATING CHAMBERS Paul Darling QC

Head of Chambers	Paul Darling QC
Tenants	57

15 Essex Street, London, WC2R 3AA
Tel (020) 7544 2600 **Fax** (020) 7544 2700 **DX** 1045
Email clerks@keatingchambers.com **Website** www.keatingchambers.com

MEMBERS

Paul Darling QC (1983) (QC-1999) ^
Prof John Uff QC (1970) (QC-1983)
Richard Fernyhough QC (1970) (QC-1986)
Dr Christopher Thomas QC (1973) (QC-1989) ^
John Marrin QC (1974) (QC-1990)
Stephen Furst QC (1975) (QC-1991) ^
Timothy Elliott QC (1975) (QC-1992) ^
Dr Robert Gaitskell QC (1978) (QC-1994)
Philip Boulding QC (1979) (QC-1996) ^
Marcus Taverner QC (1981) (QC-2000)
Finola O'Farrell QC (1983) (QC-2002)
Adrian Williamson QC (1983) (QC-2002) ^
David Thomas QC (1982) (QC-2002)
Rosemary Jackson QC (1981) (QC-2006) ^
Alexander Nissen QC (1985) (QC-2006) ^
Nerys Jefford QC (1986) (QC-2008)
Sarah Hannaford QC (1989) (QC-2008) ^
Simon Hargreaves QC (1991) (QC-2009)
Richard Harding QC (1992) (QC-2009)
Veronique Buehrlen QC (1991) (QC-2010)
Vincent Moran QC (1991) (QC-2011) ^
Adam Constable QC (1995) (QC-2011) ^
Simon Hughes QC (1995) (QC-2011)
Marc Rowlands QC (1990) (QC-2012)
Piers Stansfield QC (1993) (QC-2012) ^
Fionnuala McCredie QC (1992) (QC-2013)
Justin Mort QC (1994) (QC-2014) ^
Alan Steynor (1975) ^
Louise Randall (1988)
Robert Evans (1989) ^
Jane Lemon (1993) ^
Jonathan Lee (1993)
Abdul Jinadu (1995) ^
Paul Buckingham (1995) ^
Krista Lee (1996) ^
Richard Coplin (1997) ^
Gaynor Chambers (1998) ^
Samuel Townend (1999) ^
Gideon Scott Holland (1999) ^
Jonathan Selby (1999) ^
Jessica Stephens (2001) ^
Lucy Garrett (2001)
Elizabeth Repper (2002)
Calum Lamont (2004) ^
Alice Sims (2004) ^
William Webb (2005) ^
Thomas Lazur (2005) ^
James Thompson (2005) ^
Peter Brogden (2006) ^
Ben Sareen (2008)
Sarah Williams (2008)
Paul Bury (2008)
David Sheard (2010)
David Gollancz (2010)
Tom Owen (2011)
Simon Taylor (2012)
Matthew Finn (2011)
Ian Pennicott QC (1982) (QC-2003) ++ ^
HH Peter Bowsher QC (1959) ++
Prof Michael Furmston (1960) ++
Michael Stimpson (1969) ++
Professor Chin Leng Lim (2011) ++

++ Door Tenant/Practising Associate Members ^ Public/Direct Access

THE CHAMBERS Keating Chambers is renowned as one of the leading barristers' chambers in all aspects of the law relating to the construction, engineering, energy, real estate and the technology sectors including professional negligence and EU procurement. The Chambers has received a number of awards for its expertise including Construction Chambers of the Year, Client Care Chambers of the Year, and both Construction Queens Counsel and Junior of the Year.

Currently 57 barristers strong, (including 27 Queen's Counsel) the Chambers has a thriving domestic and international practice. Members of the Chambers are active in UK courts and tribunals including the Technology and Construction Court, the Court of Appeal, the Supreme Court and the Privy Council. Their expertise in alternative dispute resolution covers UK and international arbitration, adjudication (statutory and contractual), mediation, dispute review boards and expert determination. The Chambers' excellent reputation for advocacy, is matched equally by their reputation for drafting, advisory and non-contentious services, at all levels. The barristers provide advisory services on all the internationally recognised forms of contract including FIDIC, NEC, IChemE and JCT. They also have extensive experience with PPP, PFI, and partnering and alliancing contracts.

Barristers are frequently appointed as arbitrators, adjudicators, expert determinators, mediators and legal assessors and an impressive number of the senior barristers also sit in the UK Courts as Deputy High Court Judges in divisions such as the Technology and Construction Court, Crown and County Courts.

The Chambers has a long history of acting for clients internationally. The barristers undertake advisory and advocacy services on behalf of clients in international arbitrations and other forms of international dispute resolution. Some members of the Chambers also have rights of audience in other jurisdictions (such as Hong Kong SAR, New Zealand, Northern Ireland and the Republic of Ireland) where they represent clients in litigation through the local Courts.

Senior members of the Chambers are often appointed as arbitrators by many of the world's leading appointing bodies such as the International Chamber of Commerce (ICC), the London Court of International Arbitration (LCIA) and other overseas centres including Dubai (DIAC), Hong Kong (HKIAC), Malaysia (KLRAC) and Singapore (SIAC).They are also appointed directly by parties to arbitrations under ICSID and UNCITRAL rules.

KEATING CHAMBERS
BARRISTERS

WORK UNDERTAKEN

Construction & Engineering: The Chamber's expertise covers the full range of contractual claims relating to

KEATING CHAMBERS Paul Darling QC (continued)

the construction industry, including development contracts, building defects claims and construction delays. Claims expertise includes civil, mechanical and electrical engineering works relating to major infrastructure projects such as airports, bridges, railways, roads and tunnelling.

Energy: Considerable expertise in claims relating to the construction of assets for the oil and gas industry including drilling platforms, FPSO's, oil tankers, pipe laying ships, support vessels, undersea pipelines and on shore process and storage facilities. Keating Chambers is also well known for its long history of expertise in claims relating to the construction of power stations in many parts of the world.

Shipbuilding & Marine Engineering: Many members of Keating Chambers have considerable expertise in technical marine engineering matters, and have advised and acted in many international shipbuilding disputes. This experience extends not only to vessels destined for the oil and gas industries, such as FPSOs and jack-ups, but also to ferries and to cable laying, naval and general cargo vessels.

Procurement: A team of barristers act for a variety of Government Departments and private clients in disputes relating to EU procurement law. Whilst this is predominately in relation to Chambers' core sectors of construction, engineering, energy and IT projects, it is also often acting for contracting authorities or unsuccessful tenderers for services such as provision of medical equipment and human resources.

Professional Negligence: Representing a range of clients in negligence actions including claims for and against architects, surveyors, valuers, engineers and other consultants concerned with buildings and engineering projects.

Technology: A substantial track record in dealing with IT contracts includes disputes concerning alleged failure to meet performance specifications and issues of alleged mismanagement in the development of new software. These claims have related to projects including railways, metro systems, marketing companies, utility companies, and government departments.

Commercial Litigation & Arbitration: The barristers at Keating Chambers regularly appear in the Commercial Court, the Chancery Division and all other domestic and overseas Courts handling commercial and business law disputes. They appear individually or as part of a counsel team and take a focused and innovative approach to litigation and arbitration problemts.

Real Estate: Expertise in party wall disputes, rights of light and subsidence claims including coal mining subsidence claims. Acting for clients in nuisance claims (noise, vibration, dust and odours) whether arising out of construction operations or otherwise. Tower crane trespass claims, property damage, fire and flood claims and dilapidations claims.

CLIENTS Architects, construction contractors, building and quantity surveyors, engineers, energy companies, accountants, banks, joint ventures, government departments, professional indemnity insurers, property developers, shipyards, software developers and specialist building sub contractors.

PUBLICATIONS Keating on Construction Contracts; Keating on NEC3, Keating on JCT Contracts; Chitty on Contracts (Contributor); Construction Law Reports; Engineers' Dispute Resolution Handbook; Halsbury's Law of England: Volume 6: Building and Building Contracts; Halsbury's Law of England: Energy and Climate Change; RICS Case in Point Series – Six Titles; Construction Law (10th edition); Understanding the FIDIC Red Book: a clause-by clause commentary; Understanding the New FIDIC Red Book: A clause by clause commentary; Building Magazine (Contributor); New Law Journal (Contributor); Construction Journal (Contributor).

1 KING'S BENCH WALK Deborah Eaton QC and Philip Marshall QC

1 King's Bench Walk, Temple, London, EC4Y 7DB
Tel (020) 7936 1500 **Fax** (020) 7936 1590 **DX** LDE 20
Email clerks@1kbw.co.uk **Website** www.1kbw.co.uk

Heads of Chambers	Deborah Eaton QC Philip Marshall QC
Senior Clerk	David Dear
Tenants	52

MEMBERS

Deborah Eaton QC (1985) (QC-2008)
Philip Marshall (1989) (QC-2012) +
Barry Singleton QC (1968) (QC-1989)
Pamela Scriven QC (1970) (QC-1992)
Richard Anelay QC (1970) (QC-1993) +
James Turner QC (1976) (QC-1998)
Charles Howard QC (1975) (QC-1999)
Anthony Kirk QC (1981) (QC-2001) +
Clive Newton QC (1968) (QC-2002)
Christopher Pocock QC (1984) (QC-2009)
Richard Harrison QC (1993) (QC-2012)
Caroline Budden (1977) +
Cherry Harding (1978) +
Caroline Lister (1980) +
Julian Woodbridge (1981)
Markanza Cudby (1983)
Elizabeth Selman (1989)
Marcus Fletcher (1990)
James Roberts (1993) +
Christopher McCourt (1993)
Ian Cook (1994)
Andrew Baughan (1994)
Victoria Green (1994) +
Alexander Chandler (1995)
Graham Crosthwaite (1995)
Dominic Brazil (1995)
Nicola Fox (1996)
Ashley Thain (1996) +
Nicholas Anderson (1995) +
Richard Castle (1998)
Shona Rogers (1998)
Harry Oliver (1999)
Madeleine Reardon (2001) +
Deepak Nagpal (2002)
Katherine Kelsey (2003) +
Martha Holmes (2003) +
Susan Wilkins (2004)
Caroline Harris (2004)
Jennifer Perrins (2004)
Peter Newman (2005)
Andrea Watts (2006) +
Alex Tatton-Bennett (2007)
Kate Ozwell (2007)
Kelan McHugh (2007)
Katy Chokowry (2008)
Laura Moys (2008)
Samantha Ridley (2009)
Charlotte Hartley (2009)
George Gordon (2010)
Jennifer Malicka (2011)
Louisa Peacock (2012)
Thomas Dance (2012)
Alistair MacDonald (QC) (1995) (QC-2011) *
Elizabeth Isaacs QC (1998) (QC-2013)*
Joanna Grice (1991) *
Carolyn Hamilton (1996)*

+ Accredited Mediator * Door Tenant

THE CHAMBERS 1KBW is a leading set specialising in family law, with a pre-eminent national and international reputation. The set is consistently top-ranked for both matrimonial finance and children work, and it remains at the cutting edge across the full spectrum of family law. Of all the specialist family sets, 1KBW has the highest number of practitioners who are ranked in the directories.

THE SET 1KBW comprises 52 barristers, including 11 QCs. The set is widely acknowledged to have an unrivalled breadth of talent, with leading practitioners at every level of seniority and juniors who consistently receive the highest praise.
The set adopts a highly professional , supportive and responsive service to clients. There is a tremendous sense of commitment at this set, both to the development of the law and to the needs of their clients.
For over a decade chambers has been awarded the 'Bar Mark' and 'Quality Mark' in recognition of the levels of service provided. The clerking at this set is second to none, with highly experienced and dedicated clerks with a wealth of industry knowledge and expertise, all of which is applied when assisting clients with cases honestly, openly and rigorously.
The chambers provides a comprehensive programme of CPD accredited conferences for solicitors, which remain extremely popular and are always highly recommended .

TYPES OF WORK UNDERTAKEN 1KBW is perhaps the only specialist family law set which has a stellar reputation in both matrimonial finance and also in children law.
In matrimonial finance, members of 1KBW have appeared in many of the leading and landmark cases of the last two decades, such as White, Moore, Macfarlane, Miller, Radmacher, Imerman, Charman and many more. Its members continue to act in some of the most high profile cases in the field of matrimonial finance.
In children law, the set boasts many of the current 'stars' in this field, both silks and juniors. Members of 1KBW regularly appear in the leading cases across every aspect of children law: private law children, Hague and wardship abduction and care and adoption proceedings.
Many members of the set also undertake work in the Court of Protection, and the experience in dealing with sensitive public and private children cases and also in finance cases means that its members have a unique set of skills to deal with Court of Protection work. The set's history of advocacy in the criminal courts is often said to give it the edge over its rivals within the family courts.
1KBW has one of the most innovative and experienced dispute resolution teams in the country, comprising 11 members of whom 5 are QCs, and led by nationally acclaimed mediator Anthony Kirk QC.

1kbw

Community Legal Service

7 KING'S BENCH WALK Gavin Kealey QC

7 King's Bench Walk, Temple, London, EC4Y 7DS
Tel (020) 7910 8300 **Fax** (020) 7910 8400 **DX** LDE 239
Email clerks@7kbw.co.uk **Website** www.7kbw.co.uk

Head of Chambers	Gavin Kealey QC
Senior Clerks	Bernie Hyatt
	Greg Leyden
Clerks	Eddie Johns
	Gary Rose
Administration Director	Lawrence Willliams
Tenants	54

MEMBERS

Gavin Kealey QC (1977) (QC-1994)
Timothy Saloman QC (1975) (QC-1993)
Francis Reynolds (Hon) QC (1960) (QC-1993)
Jonathan Gaisman QC (1979) (QC-1995)
Clive Freedman QC (1978) (QC-1997)
Dominic Kendrick QC (1981) (QC-1997)
Timothy Brenton QC (1981) (QC-1998)
Alistair Schaff QC (1983) (QC-1999)
Stephen Hofmeyr QC (1982) (QC-2000)
Christopher Butcher QC (1986) (QC-2001)
Adam Fenton QC (1984) (QC-2003)
Stephen Kenny QC (1987) (QC-2006)
Richard Southern QC (1987) (QC-2006)
Robert Bright QC (1987) (QC-2006)
David Bailey QC (1989) (QC-2006)
David Edwards QC (1989) (QC-2006) ^
Simon Picken QC (1989) (QC-2006)
Julia Dias QC (1982) (QC-2008)
David Allen QC (1990) (QC-2008)
S J Phillips QC (1993) (QC-2009)
Siobán Healy QC (1993) (QC-2010)
James Drake QC (1998) (QC-2011)
Peter MacDonald Eggers QC (1999) (QC-2011)
Andrew Wales QC (1992) (QC-2012)
Rebecca Sabben-Clare QC (1993) (QC-2012)
Richard Waller QC (1994) (QC-2012)
Charles Priday (1982)
Gavin Geary (1989)
Jawdat Khurshid (1994)
Timothy Kenefick (1996)
John Bignall (1996)
Charles Holroyd (1997)
Simon Kerr (1997)
James Brocklebank (1999)
Michael Holmes (1999)
Benjamin Parker (2000)
Anna Gotts (2002)
Alex MacDonald (2002)
Josephine Higgs (2000)
Jessica Sutherland (2003)
Marcus Mander (2005)
N G Casey (2005)
Richard Sarll (2005)
Emma Hilliard (2006)
Sarah Cowey (2006)
Sushma Ananda (2007)
Sarah Martin (2008)
Sandra Healy (2007)
Adam Turner (2008)
Elizabeth Lindesay (2009)
Tim Jenns (2009)
Jocelin Gale (2009)
Keir Howie (2010) ^
Stephen Du (2012)
Clara Benn (2013)
Andrew Pearson (2013)
Harry Wright (2012)
Stephen Du (2012)
Clara Benn (2012)
Andrew Pearson (2013)

^ Public/Direct Access

THE CHAMBERS 7 King's Bench Walk (7KBW) has a pre-eminent reputation for excellence and intellectual rigour in all areas of commercial law. The members of 7KBW pride themselves on adapting matters of intellect to practical and commercial priorities, producing a hand-crafted and modern approach to advocacy and advice. As advocates, members of 7KBW accept instructions to appear in any court, tribunal or board of enquiry in England and Wales. 7KBW specialises in cases before the Commercial Court and in commercial arbitrations in London. With their commercial expertise, members also appear in other jurisdictions, including Hong Kong, Singapore, Bermuda, Cayman Islands, the Bahamas, the British Virgin Islands and Gibraltar, and before international arbitration tribunals in numerous jurisdictions.
Members undertake advisory work and the creation of written submissions and legal documents for litigation and non-contentious matters. Members regularly sit as arbitrators and/or mediators and also as court appointed examiners for the purpose of conducting deposition hearings. Several members have written or contributed to leading legal textbooks, articles in the press and journals, and contributed to academic research.

TYPES OF WORK UNDERTAKEN 7KBW's practice areas are exclusively commercial. Members have a respected expertise in the full breadth of commercial law: 7KBW has maintained an enviable reputation and experience in all aspects of insurance and reinsurance; shipping and transport; professional negligence; international trade and commodities; energy, oil and gas; civil fraud; international arbitration; injunctions and arrests; shipbuilding; banking and financial services; futures and derivatives; aviation; media and communications; construction; conflicts of law; state immunity; and international investment.
A large proportion of 7KBW's practice is of an international flavour and members regularly work with overseas clients and foreign lawyers. In appropriate circumstances members are able to accept instructions directly from overseas clients and foreign lawyers.

RECRUITMENT 7KBW attracts pupils of only the highest quality, and pursues a policy of only taking tenants of such quality either from those starting their careers in law or from those in mid-career who have elected to change from another part of the profession. The emphasis on quality has meant a steady but selective growth in the overall number of tenants over the past years.
7KBW is the insurance set of the year, an accolade awarded by Chambers UK in 2006, 2007, 2008, 2009, 2010, 2011 and 2013
For further information about 7 King's Bench Walk and the range of work carried out by our members please visit the chambers website at www.7kbw.co.uk

7KBW BARRISTERS

12 KING'S BENCH WALK Andrew Hogarth QC

12 King's Bench Walk, Temple, London, EC4Y 7EL
Tel (020) 7583 0811 **Fax** (020) 7583 7228 **DX** 1037 (Ch.Ln.)
Email chambers@12kbw.co.uk **Website** www.12kbw.co.uk

Head of Chambers	Andrew Hogarth QC
CEO	Andrew Meyler
Senior Clerks	Graham Johnson
	John Cooper
Tenants	81

MEMBERS

Andrew Hogarth QC (1974) (QC-2003)
Ronald Walker QC (1962) (QC-1983)
Richard Methuen QC (1972) (QC-1997)
Frank Burton QC (1982) (QC-1998)
Gerard Martin QC (1978) (QC-2000)
Stephen Worthington QC (1976) (QC-2006)
William Featherby QC (1978) (QC-2008)
Paul Russell QC (1984) (QC-2010)
Michael Rawlinson QC (1991) (QC-2009)
John King (1973)
Brian Gallagher (1975)
Quintin Tudor-Evans (1977)
Simon Levene (1977)
Richard Davison (1982)
David Sanderson (1985)
Nigel Lewers (1986)
Henry Charles (1987)
Andrew Pickering (1987)
Hugh Hamill (1988)
Adam Chambers (1989)
Catherine Brown (1990)
Gary Thornett (1990)
Kate Chandler (1990)
James Candlin (1991)
Patrick Vincent (1992)
William Audland (1992)
Stephanie Jackson (1992)
Joel Kendall (1993)
Arun Katyar (1993)
Richard Viney (1994)
Carolyn D'Souza (1994)
Daniel Tobin (1994)
Marcus Dignum (1994)
Catherine Peck (1995)
Lucy Murray (1995)
Timothy Petts (1996)
Louise Thomson (1996)
Portia Spears (1996)
Simon John (1996)
Harry Steinberg (1997)
Benedict Leech (1997)
Pankaj Madan (1997)
Kweku Aggrey-Orleans (1998)
Katherine Awadalla (1998)
David Callow (1998)
David White (1999)
Lisa Stephenson (1999)
David Sharpe (1999)
Charlotte Reynolds (2001)
Angela Frost (2001)
Andrew Roy (2002)
Ruth Greenwood (2003)
Mary Newnham (2003)
James Sullivan (2005)
Gemma Scott (2005)
Patrick Kerr (2006)
Sarah Beslee (2006)
Henrietta Consolo (2006)
Alex Carington (2006)
John-Paul Swoboda (2006)
Roisin Kennedy (2006)
Emily Gordon Walker (2007)
Emily Read (2007)
Charles Robertshaw (2007)
Abha Pandya (2007)
Niall Maclean (2008)
Thomas Pacey (2008)
Lois Aldred (2008)
Thea Wilson (2009)
Oliver Rudd (2009)
Lucy Boyle (2009)
Vanessa Cashman (2009)
Ghazaleh Rezaie (2009)
Rory Badenoch (2010)
Thomas Banks(2010)
Nina Ross (2010)
Rachit Buch (2011)
Daniel Sokol (2011)
Isaac Hogarth (2011)
Aliyah Akram (2012)
Edward Ramsey (2012)

THE CHAMBERS 12 King's Bench Walk continues to grow rapidly and now has 81 barristers, including 9 silks. It provides a modern and professional service to its clients.
Chambers is best known for its expertise in the bringing and defending of personal injury claims, industrial disease claims and employment law. That said its expertise is actually much wider. When the ability to understand difficult areas in the law of tort is required you will find that 12KBW barristers have appeared in many of the leading cases. When issues of quantum of damages arise you will find that 12KBW barristers have appeared in many of the leading cases. When an understanding of employment law and personal injury work are both required you will find that 12KBW barristers have appeared in many of the leading cases. When fraud or professional negligence arises in the context of a personal injury or employment law claim you will find that 12KBW barristers have appeared in many of the leading cases. Chambers brings its expertise in its core areas of practice to clinical and professional negligence claims, to regulatory and disciplinary work, to travel litigation, to fraud and credit hire work and all aspects of work for public authorities.

WORK UNDERTAKEN

Covering the whole of England and Wales (and further afield).
From offices in London and Bristol 12KBW covers the whole of England and Wales. Three members of 12KBW are also members of the Irish and Northern Irish Bars and one is a member of the Ghanian Bar. Members of chambers also appear in Employment Tribunals and the EAT in Scotland and Northern Ireland on a regular basis.
From the smallest case to the largest: Whether the case is before a District Judge or the Supreme Court, chambers is able to offer a range of suitable barristers to handle the case.
Lectures and seminars: Chambers hold a series of evening seminars each year and two major half day programmes, one on personal injury litigation and the other on employment and discrimination law. In addition it provides lectures at its client's premises on request. Details of its current seminar programme is available on the website.

12
12 King's Bench Walk

LANDMARK CHAMBERS

180 Fleet Street, London, EC4A 2HG
Tel (020) 7430 1221 **Fax** (020) 7421 6060 **DX** 1042 LDE
Email clerks@landmarkchambers.co.uk **Website** www.landmarkchambers.co.uk

Heads of Chambers	David Holgate QC and Timothy Mould QC
Chambers Director	Holly Gavaghan
Senior Clerk	Jay Fullilove
Tenants	81

MEMBERS

David Holgate QC (1978) (QC-1997)
Timothy Mould QC (1987) (QC-2006)
David Woolley QC (1962) (QC-1980)
Christopher Lockhart-Mummery QC (1971) (QC-1986)
Patrick Clarkson QC (1972) (QC-1991)
Richard Drabble QC (1975) (QC-1995)
William Hicks QC (1975) (QC-1995)
Christopher Katkowski QC (1982) (QC-1999)
David Elvin QC (1983) (QC-2000)
John Male QC (1976) (QC-2000)
Neil King QC (1980) (QC-2000)
John Hobson QC (1980) (QC-2000)
Rhodri Price Lewis QC (1975) (QC-2001)
Timothy Corner QC (1981) (QC-2002)
Russell Harris QC (1986) (QC-2003)
Nathalie Lieven QC (1989) (QC-2006)
Neil Cameron QC (1982) (QC-2009)
Paul Brown QC (1991) (QC-2009)
Philip Coppel QC (1994) (QC-2009)
John Litton QC (1989) (QC-2010)
Katharine Holland QC (1989) (QC-2010)
David Lock QC (1985) (QC-2011)
David Holland QC (1986) (QC-2011)
Timothy Morshead QC (1995) (QC-2011)
Rupert Warren QC (1994) (QC-2012)
Sasha White QC (1991) (QC-2013)
Christopher Boyle QC (1994) (QC-2013)
James Maurici QC (1996) (QC-2013)
Reuben Taylor QC (1990) (QC-2014)
David Forsdick QC (1993) (QC-2014)
Stephen Bickford-Smith (1972)
Eian Caws (1974)
Christopher Lewsley (1976)
Simon Pickles (1978)
David Smith (1980)
Thomas Jefferies (1981)
Stephen Morgan (1983)
Richard Langham (1986)
Nicholas Taggart (1991)
Christopher Jacobs (1994)
Camilla Lamont (1995)
Declan O'Callaghan (1995)
Graeme Keen (1995)
Matthew Reed (1995)
Tom Weekes (1995)
Philip Nathan (1996)
Scott Lyness (1996)
Toby Watkin (1996)
Samantha Broadfoot (1997)
Daniel Kolinsky (1998)
Myriam Stacey (1998)
Carine Patry (1999)
Stephen Whale (1999)
Katherine Olley (1999)
Robert Walton (1999)
Lisa Busch (2000)
Galina Ward (2000)
Guy Williams (2000)
Tim Buley (2000)
David Blundell (2001)
Aaron Walder (2002)
Zoe Leventhal (2002)
Alex Goodman (2003)
Charles Banner (2004)
Gwion Lewis (2005)
Richard Moules (2005)
Sasha Blackmore (2005)
Jonathan Wills (2006)
Katrina Yates (2006)
Jacqueline Lean (2007)
Louisa Nye (2007)
Richard Turney (2007)
Richard Clarke (2009)
Zack Simons (2009)
Katie Helmore (2009)
Andrew Parkinson (2010)
Andrew Byass (2010)
Sonal Barot (2010)
Thomas Davis (2011)
Heather Sargent (2011)
Alistair Mills (2011)

THE CHAMBERS Landmark Chambers' 81 barristers offer advice and advocacy across the spectrum of planning, property, public, commercial and environmental law. Their work includes ratings and valuation, infrastructure and compulsory purchase, regulation, leasehold enfranchisement, mediation and arbitration in the UK, Europe and internationally. Members have significant experience of litigation in the Supreme Court, Court of Appeal, High Court, the European Court of Justice, the European General Court, the European Court of Human Rights, the UN Aarhus Compliance Committee, the Northern Ireland courts and the courts of a number of other jurisdictions, including Hong Kong.

WORK UNDERTAKEN

Planning: Landmark remains at the forefront of the UK planning world with members selected to advise on high-profile national and international issues regarding the built environment. Climate change, nuclear power, new coal-fired power stations with carbon capture storage, wind farms and other renewable energy schemes, airport expansion, iconic bridges and buildings, rail and road infrastructure, retail and leisure, housing and mixed-use schemes are dealt with on a daily basis.

Property: Landmark offers particular expertise in commercial and residential landlord and tenant, leasehold enfranchisement, boundary disputes, easements, restrictive covenants, mortgages, land registration, adverse possession and proprietary estoppel. Members of the property team continue to be the first choice for solicitors instructed by clients wishing to injunct or remove squatters and protestors from their premises.

Public: Landmark's barristers appear frequently in applications for judicial review and before a range of statutory tribunals and inquiries, as well as appeals, in the UK and beyond. Members cover the full range of public law cases, including education, local government, social security, human rights, immigration, mental health, housing, prisons, and planning and environmental.

Environmental: Landmark's barristers are experts in the environmental aspects of town and country planning and with their strength in public law they are the natural choice for environmental challenges in the higher courts. Their property barristers complete the package, with experience at all levels of advising on environmental issues in this area.

Landmark
CHAMBERS

LITTLETON CHAMBERS John Bowers QC & Naomi Ellenbogen QC

Head of Chambers	John Bowers QC Naomi Ellenbogen QC
Commercial Director	Nigel McEwen
Clerks	Alistair Coyne Tim Tarring Jason Drakeford
A/Cs Receivable Manager	Joanne Ashby
Tenants	51

3 King's Bench Walk North, Temple, London, EC4Y 7HR
Tel (020) 7797 8600 **Fax** (020) 7797 8699/8697 **DX** 1047
Email clerks@littletonchambers.co.uk **Website** www.littletonchambers.com

MEMBERS

Andrew Clarke QC (1980) (QC-1997)
Clive Freedman QC (1978) (QC-1997)
Ian Mayes QC (1974) (QC-1993)
Richard Price OBE QC (1969) (QC-1996)
John Bowers QC (1979) (QC-1998)
Selwyn Bloch QC (1982) (QC-2000)
David Reade QC (1983) (QC-2006)
Naomi Ellenbogen QC (1992) (QC-2010)
Damian Brown QC (1989) (QC-2012)
Stuart Ritchie QC (1995) (QC-2012)
Suzanne McKie QC (1991) (QC-2012)
Gavin Mansfield QC (1992) (QC-2013)
Richard Perkoff (1971)
Timothy Higginson (1977)
Shirley Bothroyd (1982)
Martin Fodder (1983)
Antony Sendall (1984)
Michael Duggan (1984)
Peter Trepte (1987)
Raoul Downey (1988)
Sam Neaman (1988)
Jeffrey Bacon (1989)
Rupert D'Cruz (1989)
Jeremy Lewis (1992)
Chris Quinn (1992)
Daniel Tatton-Brown (1994)
Carol Davis (1996)
Dale Martin (1997)
Niran de Silva (1997)
Adam Solomon (1998)
Jonathan Cohen (1999)
Lucy Bone (1999)
Matthew Sheridan (2000)
Ming-Yee Shiu (2000)
Eleena Misra (2001)
James Wynne (2002)
Martin Palmer (2003)
David Lascelles (2003)
Edward Kemp (2005)
John Mehrzad (2005)
Brian Lacy (2006)
Katherine Apps (2006)
Alexander Robson (2006)
Charlotte Davies (2006)
Lydia Banerjee (2007)
James Bickford Smith (2008)
Charlene Hawkins (2008)
Nicolas Goodfellow (2009)
Craig Rajgopaul (2010)
Benjamin Gray (2011)
Marc Delehanty (2011)
Mauro Rubino-Sammartano (1961) ++
The Lord Hacking (1963) ++
Pierre A Karrer (1969) ++
Colin Manning (1970) ++
Mark H Lomas QC (1977) (QC-2003) ++
Matthieu de Boisséson (1978) ++
Wolfgang Peter (1979) ++
Paul Kirtley (1982) ++
Kelly Pennifer (1994) ++
Erika Szyszczak (2004) ++
Samuel Haubold ++

++ Associate Tenant

WORK UNDERTAKEN A set specialising in employment law and commercial litigation with additional expertise in civil fraud, disciplinary and regulatory and sports law. Chambers are members of COMBAR. Chambers also provide mediation services and arbitration through Littleton International Arbitration Group.

Main Areas: There are six main specialities in chambers: employment law; commercial law incorporating banking, commercial fraud, financial services and insurance; disciplinary and regulatory; sports law; injunctions; mediation and arbitration.

Additional Areas: Carriage of goods; company law; consumer credit law; corporate finance; insolvency; international trade; letters of request; competition law; computer law; EU; environment; family; pharmaceuticals; telecommunications; transport; sale of goods; administrative law; construction commercial fraud, civil liberties; charities; discrimination; education; election law; housing; judicial review; landlord and tenant; local government; mental health; parliamentary; planning; construction; sports and entertainment law; and pensions. Members of chambers provide lectures on a wide range of subjects and chambers are accredited by the Law Society and Bar Council.

INTERNATIONAL Languages spoken include French, German, Italian and Spanish plus numerous others by the International Arbitration Group.

RECRUITMENT Members of chambers fund two pupils per year. Chambers are members of Pupillage Gateway.

LITTLETON

ISO 9001 Quality Assured Firm SGS Q55364 — UKAS Quality Management 005

MAITLAND CHAMBERS Christopher Pymont QC

7 Stone Buildings, Lincoln's Inn, London, WC2A 3SZ
Tel (020) 7406 1200 **Fax** (020) 7406 1300 **DX** LDE 326
Email clerks@maitlandchambers.com **Website** www.maitlandchambers.com

Head of Chambers	Christopher Pymont QC
Chambers Director	Stewart Thompson
Senior Clerk	John Wiggs
Deputy Senior Clerks	Rob Penson
	Harry Gilson
Clerks	Colin Dawson
	Danny Wilkinson
	Danielle Williams
	Sam Dempsey
	Amber Downey
Administrator	Valerie Piper
Tenants	67

MEMBERS

Christopher Pymont QC (1979) (QC-1996)
Christopher McCall QC (1966) (QC-1987)
Michael Driscoll QC (1970) (QC-1992)
Judith Jackson QC (1975) (QC-1994)
Catherine Newman QC (1979) (QC-1995)
Anthony Trace QC (1981) (QC-1998)
Mark Cunningham QC (1980) (QC-2001)
Paul Girolami QC (1983) (QC-2002)
John McGhee QC (1984) (QC-2003)
Matthew Collings QC (1985) (QC-2006)
John Nicholls QC (1986) (QC-2006)
Edwin Johnson QC (1987) (QC-2006)
Christopher Parker QC (1984) (QC-2008)
Nicholas Peacock QC (1989) (QC-2009)
Jonathan Russen QC (1986) (QC-2010)
Richard Morgan QC (1988) (QC-2011)
Amanda Tipples QC (1991) (QC-2011)
Andrew Walker QC (1991) (QC-2011)
Michael Gibbon QC (1993) (QC-2011)
Edmund Cullen QC (1991) (QC-2012)
Rebecca Stubbs QC (1994) (QC-2012)
Timothy Dutton QC (1985) (QC-2013)
Mark Wonnacott QC (1989) (QC-2013)
Thomas Grant QC (1993) (QC-2013)
James Aldridge QC (1994) (QC-2014)
Nigel Thomas (1976)
Alastair Walton (1977)
Timothy Evans (1979)
John Dagnall (1983)
Timothy Harry (1983)
James Clifford (1984)
Philomena Harrison (1985)
Gregory Banner (1989)
Michael Pryor (1992)
Andrew Westwood (1994)
Alan Johns (1994)
Siward Atkins (1995)
Daniel Margolin (1995)
Andrew Ayres (1996)
James Hanham (1996)
Paul Clarke (1997)
Catherine Addy (1998)
Louise Hutton (1998)
George Hayman (1998)
David Mumford (2000)
Matthew Smith (2001)
Adam Smith (2001)
Gabrielle Higgins (2002)
Benjamin John (2002)
Richard Fowler (2003)
Alexander Winter (2003)
Ciaran Keller (2004)
Alec McCluskey (2005)
Fiona Dewar (2005)
Thomas Munby (2006)
Jonathan Allcock (2007)
Rosanna Foskett (2008)
Laurie Scher (2008)
James Sheehan (2008)
Oliver Phillips (2009)
James Ballance (2009)
Narinder Jhittay (2010)
Hannah Ilett (2011)
Duncan McCombe (2012)
Maxim Cardew (2012)
Laurie Brock (2013)
James Kinman (2013)

THE CHAMBERS Maitland Chambers is widely recognised as one of the top sets at the English Bar practising primarily in the field of Commercial Chancery litigation. Its multi-disciplinary expertise across a broad range of both Chancery and Commercial disciplines has proved crucial to clients where cases span a number of areas, and provides an advantage in terms of the service offered when traditional specialisms overlap. Maitland Chambers is one of the largest Commercial Chancery sets, with over 65 members, including 25 silks.

WORK UNDERTAKEN Maitland Chambers have the breadth and depth to provide advocacy and advisory services in every area that can arise in a business dispute. It handles a very wide range of cases, from major litigation involving multi-national companies to county court disputes. Much of its work is done in London, although it frequently advises and appears for clients in other parts of the United Kingdom. Many of its members also practise in other jurisdictions including Hong Kong, Singapore, the Cayman Islands, the British Virgin Islands, Brunei, Cyprus, the Channel Islands and the USA.
Modern cases often do not fit neatly into traditional categories. Maitland's size and breadth of expertise ensures that it can provide teams of barristers to deal rapidly and thoroughly with complex cases that raise a wide range of issues. As such, it has an advantage over those who specialise in narrower fields of business law.

INTERNATIONAL Although based in London, Maitland Chambers regularly acts in non-UK cases where members' expertise in English law (and familiarity with overseas law and jurisdictions), oral and written advocacy skills, and litigation experience provide genuine added value. Members advise; appear as advocates before foreign courts and tribunals; otherwise assist in the conduct or resolution of disputes (including all forms of ADR); and provide expert evidence of law in foreign proceedings.

maitland
CHAMBERS

MATRIX CHAMBERS

Griffin Building, Gray's Inn, London, WC1R 5LN
Tel (020) 7404 3447 **Fax** (020) 7404 3448 **DX** 400 Chancery Lane
Email matrix@matrixlaw.co.uk **Website** www.matrixlaw.co.uk / www.matrixlawinternational.com

Chair of the Management Committee	Rhodri Thompson QC
Chief Executive	Lindsay Scott
Tenants	77

MEMBERS

Mark Afeeva (1997)
Nicholas Armstrong (2001)
Alex Bailin QC (1995) (QC-2010)
Andrew Bodnar (1995)
Cherie Booth QC (1976) (QC-1995) ++
Lord Daniel Brennan QC (1967) (QC-1985) ++
Christopher Brown (2002)
Chris Buttler (2004)
Michelle Butler (2007)
Joanna Buckley (2011)
Prof. Christine Chinkin (2003)
Prof. Andrew Choo (2002)
Prof. Andrew Clapham (1985) ++
Kate Cook (1990)
Edward Craven (2007)
Prof. James Crawford SC AC (1999) (NSW-1987) (SC-1997)
Claire Darwin (2005)
Raj Desai (2010) (Solicitor 2007)
Prof. Zachary Douglas (2006)
Ben Emmerson QC (1986) (QC-2000)
Danny Friedman QC (1996) (QC-2013)
Prof. Conor Gearty (1995)
Nicholas Gibson (2009) (Solicitor 2004)
Jonathan Glasson (1996) (Solicitor (Hons) 1995) (QC-2013)
Luis Gonzalez Garcia ++
Sarah Hannett (2003)
Richard Hermer QC (1993) (QC-2009)
Sir Anthony Hooper (1965) ++
Anthony Hudson (1996)
Raza Husain QC (1993) (QC-2010)
Phillippa Kaufmann QC (1991) (QC-2011)
Janet Kentridge (1999)
Thomas Kibling (1990)
Samantha Knights (1996)
Julian Knowles QC (1994) (QC-2011)
James Laddie QC (1995) (QC-2012)
Helen Law (2005)
Eloise Le Santo (2011)
Thomas Linden QC (1989) (QC-2006)
Rachel Logan (2008) ++
Alison Macdonald (2000)
Lord Ken Macdonald QC (1978) (QC-1997) ++
Sara Mansoori (1997)
Jonathan Marks (1992)
Prof. Aileen McColgan (2001)
Laura McNair-Wilson (2007)
Eleni Mitrophanous (1999)
Karon Monaghan QC (1989) (QC-2008)
Clare Montgomery QC (1980) (QC-1996)
Prof. Gillian Morris (1997)
Helen Mountfield QC (1991) (QC-2010)
Blinne Ní Ghrálaigh (2005)
Aidan O'Neill QC (1987 Scot) (1996 England) (QC-1999)
Tim Owen QC (1983) (QC-2000)
Laura Prince (2003)
Elizabeth Prochaska (2007)
Mathew Purchase (2002)
Matthew Ryder QC (1992) (QC-2010)
Adam Sandell (2008)
Philippe Sands QC (1985) (QC-2003)
Maurice Sheridan (1984)
Ben Silverstone (2009)
Jessica Simor QC (1992) (QC-2013)
Kirsten Sjøvoll (2012)
Lorna Skinner (1997)
Andrew Smith (2008)
Hugh Southey QC (1996) (QC-2010)
Daniel Squires (1998)
Mark Summers QC (1996) (QC-2014)
Booan Temple (2001)
Rhodri Thompson QC (1989) (QC-2002)
Hugh Tomlinson QC (1983) (QC-2002)
Prof. Takis Tridimas (1987)
Guy Vassall-Adams (2000)
Aaron Watkins (2006)
Antony White QC (1983) (QC-2001)
David Wolfe QC (1992) (QC-2012)

++ Associate

THE CHAMBERS Matrix is an organisation committed to excellence in all areas of service delivery, to innovation in responding to change, and to working in new ways to meet the needs of clients.

Matrix uses paralegals and legal researchers to provide case and research support to members and clients. It has associates worldwide and an office in Geneva. Matrix acts on the most complex and confidential cases providing advice, representation and advocacy at the highest level. Matrix prides itself on its extensive experience, unique knowledge and professional approach.

Matrix is founded on 'core values' including the independence of its practitioners, and a commitment to quality services, innovation, equality of opportunity and the provision of training opportunities.

matrix chambers
matrix international

MONCKTON CHAMBERS Paul Lasok QC

Head of Chambers	Paul Lasok QC
Senior Clerk	David Hockney
Tenants	51

1 & 2 Raymond Buildings, Gray's Inn, London, WC1R 5NR
Tel (020) 7405 7211 **Fax** (020) 7405 2084 **DX** 257 LDE
Email chambers@monckton.com **Website** www.monckton.com

MEMBERS

Paul Lasok QC (1977) (QC-1994) ^
Heriot Currie QC (1979) (QC-1992)
Michael Collins SC(1978) (SC-1994)
David Unterhalter SC (2009) (SC-2001)
Melanie Hall QC (1982) (QC-2002)
Michael Bowsher QC (1985) ^ (QC-2006)
Jon Turner QC (1988) (QC-2006)
Paul Harris QC (1994) (QC-2011)
Tim Ward QC (1994) (QC-2011) ^
Daniel Beard QC (1996) (QC-2011)
Philip Moser QC (1992) (QC-2012) ^
Kassie Smith QC (1995) (QC-2013)
Michael Fitzgerald (1979) ^
Ian Rogers QC (1995) (QC-2014) ^
Andrew Macnab (1986) ^
Peter Mantle (1989) ^
George Peretz (1990) ^
Raymond Hill (1992)
Alistair Lindsay (1993) ^
Rebecca Haynes (1994)
Ben Rayment (1996) ^
Josh Holmes (1997)
Robert Palmer (1998) ^
Meredith Pickford (1999) ^
Ronit Kreisberger (1999)
Eric Metcalfe (1999)
Piers Gardner (2000) ^
Valentina Sloane (2000) ^
Julian Gregory (2000)
Rob Williams (2000)
Gerry Facenna (2001) ^
Anneli Howard (2002) ^
Ben Lask (2003) ^
Alan Bates (2003) ^
Elisa Holmes (2003)
Philip Woolfe (2004)
Jeremy McBride (2004) ^
Brendan McGurk (2004)
Drew Holiner (2005) ^
Fiona Banks (2006) ^
Ewan West (2006) ^
Anneliese Blackwood (2007)
Laura Elizabeth John (2007) ^
Ligia Osepciu (2008)
Frank Mitchell (2010) ^
Tarlochan Lall (2010) ^
Julianne Stevenson (2010)
Elizabeth Kelsey (2010)
Alison Berridge (2011)
Michael Armitage (2011)
Thomas Sebastian (2012)

* Door Tenant ^ Public/Direct Access

THE CHAMBERS Monckton Chambers is a leading set with expertise across a wide range of commercial and civil law, with a particular focus on EU, competition, VAT, other indirect taxes and public and administrative law.
The interrelationship between domestic law, EU law and international human rights law is central to much of Chambers' work, and members have unrivalled expertise in these areas.
Monckton Chambers is recognised as a market leader in specialist advocacy, advisory and dispute-resolution services, and is renowned for members' intellectual rigour, commercial focus and ability to get results.
Members of Chambers act for private sector clients (from multinationals to SMEs and private individuals), the UK Government, regulators, local authorities, NGOs and non-UK bodies, including foreign states and the EU institutions. This breadth of experience means that members are sensitive to the commercial objectives of private clients and also have a good understanding of governmental and regulatory decision-making processes.
For the latest update on practice areas, barristers' CVs, cases, events, news and publications, please visit www.monckton.com.

INTERNATIONAL A number of members of Monckton Chambers have in-depth knowledge of foreign domestic laws, including a number of EU Member States. Several members are also qualified and have rights of audience in foreign jurisdictions, including the CIS republics, the Russian Federation, South Africa and Australia. Services are available to all foreign lawyers, businesses and individuals who are located outside the UK.

RECRUITMENT Monckton Chambers is a member of the Bar Council Pupillage Gateway. Chambers offers pupillage for twelve months. Typically, two pupillages have been offered each year, with pupillage awards of £60,000. In the past 10 years, 16 out of 17 Monckton pupils were offered tenancy.

MONCKTON CHAMBERS

NEW COURT CHAMBERS

New Court Chambers, New Court, Temple, London EC4Y 9BE **DX** 0018 LDE
Tel (020) 7583 5123 **Email** clerks@newcourtchambers.com **Website** www.newcourtchambers.com

Head of Chambers	Dr Giuseppe Cala
Senior Clerk	Paul Bloomfield
First Junior Clerk	James Stammers
Tenants	24

MEMBERS

Dr Giuseppe Cala (1971)
Ann Courtney (1987)
Elissa Da Costa-Waldman (1990)
Judith Charlton (1990)
Giles Bain (1993)
Angela Burstow (sol 1994) (2012)
Christopher Poole (1996)
Stephen Coyle (1998)
Jane Hayford (1997)
Dinali Nanayakkara (2000)
Sarah McMeechan (2000)
Andrew Shaw (2001)
Tali Michaels (2001)
Wing Chan (2002)
Stephanie Hine (2003)
Anna Hefford (2004)
Sam Wallace (2004)
Sally Jackson (2006)
Kyriacos Lefteri (2006)
Sally Homer (sol 2006) (2012)
Robert Wilkinson (2007)
Raisa Saley (2008)
Philippa Jenkins (2008)
Matthew Richardson (2009)

THE CHAMBERS New Court Chambers is a specialist family set offering expert advice and representation in Public and private Law Children, Court of Protection, Matrimonial Finance and TLATA.

NEW COURT CHAMBERS

THREE NEW SQUARE

3 New Square, Lincoln's Inn, London, WC2A 3RS
Tel (020) 7405 1111 **Fax** (020) 7405 7800 **DX** 454 Chancery Lane
Email clerks@3newsquare.co.uk **Website** www.3newsquare.co.uk

Head of Chambers	Richard Miller QC
Senior Clerk	Nicholas Hill
Tenants	17

MEMBERS

Richard Miller QC (1976) (QC-1995)
Guy Burkill QC (1981) (QC-2002)
Andrew Waugh QC (1982) (QC-1998)
Justin Turner QC (1992) (QC-2009)
Thomas Mitcheson QC (1996) (QC-2014)
Denise McFarland (1987)
Douglas Campbell (1993)
Thomas Hinchliffe (1997)
Simon Malynicz (1997)
Geoffrey Pritchard (1998)
Dominic Hughes (2001)
Miles Copeland (2004)
Joe Delaney (2006)
Jeremy Heald (2010)
Stuart Baran (2011)
Tim Austen (2012)
Katherine Moggridge (2012)

THE CHAMBERS Chambers has focused on intellectual property litigation for more than 60 years and its 17 tenants, including five QCs, are all leading practitioners in this area. The set was located at 6 Pump Court, Temple, until April 1995. Former members of chambers include Birss J, Aldous LJ and Falconer J.
All members appear frequently in the High Court, Intellectual Property Enterprise Court and Appellate Courts. They also engage regularly in arbitration work, both as advocates and arbitrators, and in hearings before the UK Intellectual Property Office, the European Patent Office in Munich, the Community Trade Mark and Designs Office (OHIM) in Alicante and the Court of Justice of the European Union in Luxembourg.
Members of chambers receive instructions from solicitors, patent and trade mark attorneys, in-house lawyers and lawyers practising overseas.
The majority of members are scientifically trained at least to graduate level.
Senior members also edit Terrell on the Law of Patents, the leading textbook in this area.

WORK UNDERTAKEN Patents, trade marks, passing off, copyright, design (registered and unregistered), breach of confidence, trade secrets malicious falsehood, entertainment and media, restrictive covenants, franchising and the licensing of all intellectual property rights, as well as all aspects of EU law relating to intellectual property.

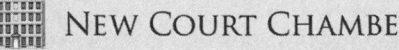

THREE NEW SQUARE
INTELLECTUAL PROPERTY

4 NEW SQUARE

4 New Square, Lincoln's Inn, London, WC2A 3RJ
Tel (020) 7822 2000 **Fax** (020) 7822 2001 **DX** 1041 L.D.E.
Email clerks@4newsquare.com **Website** www.4newsquare.com

Senior Clerk	Lizzy Stewart
Tenants	76

MEMBERS

Ben Hubble QC (1992) (QC-2009)
John L Powell QC (1974) (QC-1990)
Nicholas Davidson QC (1974) (QC-1993)
Justin Fenwick QC (1980) (QC-1993)
Roger Stewart QC (1986) (QC-2001)
Michael Soole QC (1977) (QC-2002)
Graham Eklund QC (1984) (QC-2002)
Patrick Lawrence QC (1985) (QC-2002)
Simon Monty QC (1982) (QC-2003)
David Halpern QC (1978) (QC-2006)
Mark Cannon QC (1985) (QC-2008)
Graeme McPherson QC (1993) (QC-2008)
David Turner QC (1992) (QC-2009)
Leigh-Ann Mulcahy QC (1993) (QC-2009)
Ben Patten QC (1986) (QC-2010)
Nicholas Bacon QC (1992) (QC-2010)
Anneliese Day QC (1996) (QC-2012)
Ben Elkington QC (1996) (QC-2012)
+ Door Tenant
Fiona Sinclair QC (1989) (QC-2013)
Jonathan Hough (1997) (QC-2014)
Graham Chapman (1998) (QC-2014)
Professor Eva Lomnicka (1974)
Charles Douthwaite (1977)
Glen Tyrell (1977)
Paul Parker (1986)
Hugh Evans (1987)
Nigel Burroughs (1991)
Andrew R Nicol (1991)
Charles Phipps (1992)
Paul Sutherland (1992)
Nicola Shaldon (1994)
Nicole Sandells (1994)
Benjamin Williams (1994)
Robert Marven (1994)
Jamie Smith (1995)
Neil Hext (1995)
Seánin Gilmore (1996)
Alex Hall Taylor (1996)
Paul Cowan (1996)
Siân Mirchandani (1997)
Michael Bowmer (1997)
Roger Mallalieu (1998)
Richard Liddell (1999)
Amanda Savage (1999)
Stephen Innes (2000)
Scott Allen (2000)
Dr Peter Feldschreiber (2000)
Helen Evans (2001)
Carl Troman (2001)
Annabel Shaw (2002)
Clare Dixon (2002)
Miles Harris (2003)
Timothy Chelmick (2004)
George Spalton (2004)
Benjamin Wood (2005)
Richard O'Brien (2005)
Katie Powell (2005)
Shail Patel (2006)
Simon Hale (2006)
George McDonald (2007)
Tom Asquith (2007)
Can Yeginsu (2007)
Daniel Saoul (2008)
Lucy Colter (2008)
Josephine Martin (2008)
Thomas Ogden (2008)
Ben Smiley (2009)
Nicholas Tolley (2009)
Christopher Greenwood (2009)
Philippa Manby (2010)
Nicholas Broomfield (2010)
Michael Ryan (2011)
Anthony Jones (2011)
Hamid Khanbhai (2011)
Benjamin Fowler (2011)
Paul Fisher (2012)
Dr Josh Wilson SC (1987) (SC-2008) +
Jalil Asif QC (1988) (QC-2010)
Dr Julie Maxton (1978) +
Jeffrey Benz (1994) +
Garry Borland (2000 – Scottish Bar, 2014 – English Bar) +
Claire Robey (2006) +

THE CHAMBERS: 4 New Square is a leading commercial set of barristers comprising 76 practitioners, 21 of whom are Queen's Counsel. Barristers at 4 New Square act as specialist advocates and advisers in a wide range of commercial disputes worldwide. They also act as advisers in non contentious disputes. The size of chambers and the range of experience of its members enable 4 New Square to put together balanced teams of counsel to suit the requirements of each individual case. The set has numerous international as well as academic connections.

WORK UNDERTAKEN: Members of chambers are consistently recommended for all types of commercial disputes, often with an international element. The reputation of chambers is particularly strong in relation to claims involving professionals and insurance work as well as in respect of construction disputes, costs, financial services and banking, international arbitration, product liability, sports law as well as regulatory public law and human rights law. Chambers expertise in professional liability covers the full range of claims against professionals, not just for negligence but for fraud, breach of fiduciary duty and breach of trust, and disciplinary and regulatory proceedings. All main professions are covered by chambers. Chambers has considerable experience in multi-party litigation in the context of civil fraud, product liability, professional negligence and disaster claims. In all those areas members of chambers appear as advocates in the courts and arbitrations at home and in overseas jurisdictions.

PUBLICATIONS: Many members of Chambers have written or contributed to legal textbooks and other published works. Highlights include the following. Jackson & Powell on Professional Liability (2013), written by members of the professional liability team, is in its 7th edition and remains a leading authority. The 5-volume Encyclopaedia of Financial Services Law (2013) is edited by John Powell QC and Professor Eva Lomnicka while Mark Cannon QC is the co-author of Cannon & McGurk on Professional Indemnity Insurance (2010). Charles Phipps is author, with Lord Toulson SCJ, of Confidentiality (2013) while Nicholas Bacon QC is a contributing editor of Cook on Costs (2013) as well as Halsbury's Laws of England. Leigh-Ann Mulcahy QC is the general editor of Human Rights and Civil Practice, to which Scott Allen, Anneliese Day QC and Alex Hall Taylor are contributors while Can Yeginsu is co-author of The Protections for Religious Rights: Law and Practice (2013).

8 NEW SQUARE Mark Platts-Mills QC

8 New Square, Lincoln's Inn, London, WC2A 3QP
Tel (020) 7405 4321 **Fax** (020) 7405 9955 **DX** 379 (Ch.Ln)
Email clerks@8newsquare.co.uk **Website** www.8newsquare.co.uk

Head of Chambers	Mark Platts-Mills QC
Senior Clerk	John Call
Deputy Senior Clerk	Tony Liddon
Practice Managers	Nicholas Wise
	Martin Williams
	Ben Newham
Assistant Practice Manager	Paul Worrall
Clerks	Jack Joselyn
	Phil Taylor
Business Development Manager	Harri Gibson
Tenants	27

MEMBERS

Mark Platts-Mills QC (1974) (QC 1995)
John Baldwin QC (1977) (QC 1991)
Martin Howe QC (1978) (QC 1996)
James Mellor QC (1986) (QC-2006)
Daniel Alexander (1988) (QC-2003)
Richard Meade QC (1991) (QC-2008)
Michael Tappin QC (1991) (QC-2009)
Adrian Speck QC (1993) (QC-2012)
Andrew Lykiardopoulos QC (2004) (QC-2014)
Charlotte May QC (1995) (QC-2014)
George Hamer (1974)
Fiona Clark (1982)
Robert Onslow (1991)
James St Ville (1995)
Thomas Moody – Stuart (1995)
Lindsay Lane (1996)
James Abrahams (1997)
Iona Berkeley (1999)
Mark Chacksfield (1999)
Henry Ward (2000)
Jonathan Hill (2000)
Jessie Bowhill (2004)
James Whyte (2006)
Isabel Jamal (2008)
Ashton Chantrielle (2011)
William Duncan (2012)
Jaani Riordan (2012)
Rt Hon Professor Sir Robin Jacob *
His Honour Michael Fysh QC SC *
Professor (Practice) David Llewelyn *

* Door Tenants

THE CHAMBERS 8 New Square is the largest set in the UK specialising entirely in intellectual property and related fields of law. All members of chambers are at the forefront of intellectual property litigation, advising on and presenting cases with considerable technical detail. Most have at least an undergraduate science qualification and some have advanced science degrees. Chambers handle litigation for leading commercial organisations around the world, high profile individuals as well as small companies and individuals. Members appear in the major English courts and tribunals including the High Court, Court of Appeal, Supreme Court, Privy Council, The Intellectual Property Office including Trade Marks and Design Registries, as well as in cases before the Copyright Tribunal and the Patents County Court. Several members have written leading textbooks on aspects of intellectual property. The Reports of Patent Cases and The Fleet Street Reports – the two main specialist intellectual property law reports, have been edited from these chambers for many years, as well as the most recent editions of Kerly on Trademarks and Trade Names and The Modern Law of Copyright and Designs.

WORK UNDERTAKEN Patents expertise covers every field of technology. A team from chambers acted in the first ever biotechnology patent appeal to reach the House of Lords, Biogen v Medeva and the subsequent cases of HGS v Lilly and Kirin v Amgen. Members act in cases concerning the validity, infringement and licencing of patents and know-how, including competition aspects. All members of chambers have wide experience in trademark infringement, validity and passing-off litigation as well as disputes concerning ownership of trademarks. Ground breaking cases, such as Jif Lemon in the House of Lords and the long running Budweiser trademark dispute have all been handled by members of 8 New Square. Copyright litigation and advice includes disputes over industrial design and artistic works, including fashion, as well as music and literary copyright. Breach of confidence is also an area of expertise including employer/employee disputes. Entertainment and media related disputes form a large part of chambers' work. Cases have involved leading companies and prominent individuals. Work in this area covers film, music, and other related media contracts, publishing and broadcasting disputes and performers rights. Information technology is another major area of chambers' practice. This includes contractual disputes before the Technology and Construction Court, advice on internet and domain names database rights and data protection. Further information and news is available on the chambers website www.8newsquare.co.uk

INTERNATIONAL Not only do members act in the major European courts, they also act in domestic and international arbitrations and mediations. Some are qualified to practise and appear in various courts overseas, including the Far East and the West Indies.

RECRUITMENT Chambers offers two pupillages per year via Pupillage Gateway (Online Pupillage Application Scheme). Pupils with a scientific or technical background are strongly encouraged. Two day mini pupillages are available during term time.

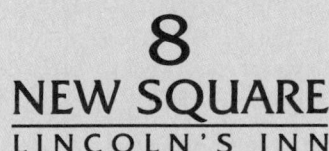

8
NEW SQUARE
LINCOLN'S INN

NEW SQUARE CHAMBERS Robin Hollington QC

12 New Square, Lincoln's Inn, London, WC2A 3SW
Tel (020) 7419 8000 **Fax** (020) 7419 8050 **DX** 1056 London/Chancery Lane
Email clerks@newsquarechambers.co.uk **Website** www.newsquarechambers.co.uk

Head of Chambers	Robin Hollington QC
Chief Executive	Simon Pizzey
Senior Practice Managers	Neil Garrett
	Phil Reeves
Marketing Manager	Paula Fox
Tenants	42

MEMBERS

John Macdonald QC (1955) (QC-1976)
George Laurence QC (1972) (QC-1991)
Robin Hollington QC (1979) (QC-1999)
James Thom QC (1974) (QC-2003)
Nicholas Le Poidevin QC (1975) (QC-2010)
Rodney Stewart Smith (1964)
Lynton Tucker (1971)
Malcolm Chapple (1975)
Christopher Semken (1977)
Alexander Hill-Smith (1978)
Leigh Sagar (1983)
David Eaton Turner (1984)
Claire Staddon (1985)
Thomas Graham (1985)
David Fisher (1985)
Ross Crail (1986)
Charles Holbech (1988)
Stephen Schaw Miller (1988)
Ian Peacock (1990)
Gerard van Tonder (1990)
Edwin Simpson (1990)
Simon Adamyk (1991)
Mark Hubbard (1991)
John Eidinow (1992)
Jane Evans-Gordon (1992)
Nigel Hood (1993)
Sebastian Prentis (1996)
Madeleine Heal (1996)
Gary Pryce (1997)
Adrian Pay (1999)
James Bailey (1999)
James Brightwell (2000)
Alexander Learmonth (2000)
Nicola Allsop (2002)
Watson Pringle (2005)
Charlotte Ford (2007)
Caley Wright (2008)
Anna Littler (2008)
Thomas Fletcher (2009)
Christopher Lloyd (2011)
Kira King (2011)
Francesca Perselli (2011)

THE CHAMBERS New Square Chambers is a leading commercial chancery set. It has 42 members, including five QCs. In addition to its extensive experience of advocacy before all levels of court and tribunal in England and Wales, the set has extensive experience in other jurisdictions, especially those offshore.

WORK UNDERTAKEN New Square Chambers' main fields of work are commercial litigation (including freezing injunctions, search and other interim orders and civil fraud), company and insolvency (including individual and corporate insolvency, voluntary arrangements, receiverships and administrations, claims relating to shareholders, directors and partnerships), trusts, estates and taxation (including contentious matters, offshore trusts, probate claims, commercial and pension trusts, revenue and capital taxation) and property law (including landlord and tenant, mortgages, enfranchisement, construction, conveyancing and real property rights). Members also practice in public and administrative law, particularly where relating to property rights and housing (including public enquiries, local government and planning law, judicial review and constitutional law) and in the fields of intellectual property and telecommunications. The set also deals with professional negligence and regulatory matters. Licensed Access work (formerly Bar Direct and Direct Professional Access) is accepted and a number of members accept Public Access instructions. New Square Chambers acts in mediations and before arbitrators.

INTERNATIONAL The set offers its clients the benefit of the wide experience it has built up over many years in other common law jurisdictions and in appeals to the Privy Council from those jurisdictions including: Antigua, the Bahamas, Bermuda, Botswana, the British Virgin Islands, the Cayman Islands, Gibraltar, Guernsey, Hong Kong, the Isle of Man, Jersey, Nevis and Singapore.

RECRUITMENT Applications for pupillage to be made directly to chambers via its website.

NEW SQUARE CHAMBERS

NO5 CHAMBERS Paul Bleasdale QC

Greenwood House, 4-7 Salisbury Court, London, EC4Y 8AA
Tel (0845) 210 5555 **Fax** (020) 7900 1582 **DX** 499 London Chancery Lane
Email info@no5.com **Website** www.No5.com

Head of Chambers	Paul Bleasdale QC
Deputy Heads	Rex Tedd QC
	Ian Dove QC
Practice Director	Tony McDaid
Tenants	246

THE CHAMBERS No5 Chambers is a national set offering a comprehensive across the board service. Throughout its 100-year history, No5 Chambers has developed a reputation for breaking new ground and continues to be regarded as a progressive and forward-thinking set, maintaining its success in traditional sectors of law whilst offering specialist advice and representation at the cutting edge of newly evolving areas. Having grown to over 240 barristers including 26 silks, No5 Chambers provides a truly nationwide service from its offices in Birmingham, London, Bristol and the East Midlands.
In recent years chambers has made significant inroads into the South West and Wales from its office in Bristol whilst its London office continues to go from strength to strength, housing more than 50 tenants. Chambers continues to attract high quality work in all disciplines, combining excellent service standards with a progressive, modern and flexible approach to clients' needs. For further information and a full list of tenants please see the Birmingham entry or visit www.No5.com.

No5 CHAMBERS

XXIV OLD BUILDINGS Martin Mann QC & Alan Steinfeld QC

Head of Chambers	Martin Mann QC Alan Steinfeld QC
Chambers Director	Sue Medder
Tenants	42

24 Old Buildings, Lincoln's Inn, London, WC2A 3UP
Tel (020) 7691 2424 **Fax** (0870) 460 2178 **DX** 307 Chancery Lane
Email clerks@xxiv.co.uk **Website** www.xxiv.co.uk

MEMBERS

Martin Mann QC (1968) (QC-1983)
Alan Steinfeld QC (1968) (QC-1987)
Bruce Collins QC (1974) (Austr) (QC-1989)
Michael Black QC (1978) (QC-1995)
Stephen Moverley Smith QC (1985) (QC-2002)
Philip Shepherd QC (1975) (QC-2003)
Francis Tregear QC (1980) (QC-2003)
Malcolm Davis-White QC (1984) (QC-2003)
David Brownbill QC (1989) (QC-2008)
Elspeth Talbot Rice QC (1990) (QC-2008)
Robert Levy QC (1988) (QC-2010)
Michael King (1971)
John Stephens (1975)
Richard Ritchie (1978)
Michael Gadd (1981)
Elizabeth Weaver (1982)
Helen Galley (1987)
Amanda Harington (1989)
Ian Meakin (1991) (Geneva)
Arshad Ghaffar (1991)
Marcus Staff (1994)
Stuart Adair (1995)
Alexander Pelling (1995)
Bajul Shah (1996)
Steven Thompson (1996)
Jessica Hughes (1997)
Nicole Langlois (2008)
Lyndsey de Mestre (1999)
Edward Knight (1999)
Tom Montagu-Smith (2001)
Sarah Bayliss (2002)
Neil McLarnon (2004)
Adam Cloherty (2005)
Edward Cumming (2006)
Erin Hitchens (2006)
Andrew Holden (2007)
Owen Curry (2009)
Daniel Warents (2009)
Heather Murphy (2009)
Harry Sharpe (2010)
Rebecca Lloyd (2011)
Matthew Watson (2012)
Graham Virgo (1989) *
Dr Matthew Conaglen (1995) * (New Zealand)

* Door Tenant

THE CHAMBERS XXIV Old Buildings is a specialist commercial and chancery chambers. Based in London, and with a permanent office in Geneva, the members of XXIV Old Buildings have an unrivalled reputation for their international, offshore and cross-border work. Members frequently advise and appear in the courts of other jurisdictions, with individual members called to the bars of Jersey, the BVI, the Cayman Islands, Dubai (DIFC), and many other leading offshore financial centres. XXIV Old Buildings is also regarded as a prime set for international arbitration, with individual members acting as arbitrators or appearing as counsel in large-scale disputes - often with a cross-border or multi-jurisdictional element - in all of the major arbitral centres. Recognised as one of the most forward-thinking and innovative sets at the London Bar, and with very highly ranked members across all of its fields of expertise (Chambers & Partners 2014 recognised the set as the leading commercial chancery chambers in London by proportion of barrister rankings), XXIV Old Buildings provides a full suite of legal advice and advocacy services for individuals and companies in the UK and globally.

WORK UNDERTAKEN The members of XXIV Old Buildings undertake litigation, arbitration and the provision of advice across the full gamut of commercial and chancery work, from 'traditional' chancery matters such as private family trust and succession disputes, through UK commercial litigation and insolvency work, to truly international litigation and arbitration involving large-scale business disputes, fraud and asset tracing, and cross-border insolvency and restructuring. This broad base of expertise is supplemented by members' specialist experience in fields such as hedge funds/SIVs; financial derivatives (including spread betting / CFDs); and aviation. Members are also highly experienced arbitrators (arbitrators.xxiv.co.uk) and mediators (mediators.xxiv.co.uk).

The calibre of XXIV Old Buildings' practice is demonstrated by the cases in which members are routinely instructed. In cross-border insolvency and fraud this includes the major matters arising out of the financial crisis: Kaupthing, Lehman Brothers, Bear Stearns and Madoff; in trusts, it includes defining decisions such as Schmidt v Rosewood and Re Esteem Settlement, as well as key recent decisions such as TMSF v Merrill Lynch; and in arbitration, leading reported cases such as B v A and Michael Wilson & Partners v Emmott. Members of chambers edit the loose-leaf International Trust Laws, and are responsible for a range of leading practitioners' works, including Kerr and Hunter on Receivers and Administrators and Trust Protectors.

XXIV Old Buildings adopts a commercial approach to instructions, and members have a great deal of experience working in close-knit teams with firms in London and elsewhere in the UK; with offshore advocates; with attorneys in other jurisdictions; and with liquidators, trustees and other professional service providers. More detail on members' expertise and profiles is available from the Practice Management Team (clerks@xxiv.co.uk, 020 7691 2424 - out of hours - 07774 240 112) and on the website: www.xxiv.co.uk.

XXIV
BARRISTERS' CHAMBERS

TEN OLD SQUARE

10 Old Square, Lincoln's Inn, London, WC2A 3SU
Tel (020) 7405 0758 **Fax** (020) 7831 8237 **DX** 306 LDE
Email clerks@tenoldsquare.com **Website** www.tenoldsquare.com

Head of Chambers	Francis Barlow QC
Senior Clerk	Keith Plowman
Deputy Senior Clerk	Marc Schofield
First Junior Clerk	Fay Bennett
Accounts & Administration	Debbie Thomas
Marketing & Business Development Manager	Carine Campbell

MEMBERS

Francis Barlow QC (1965) (QC-2006)
Simon Taube QC (1980) (QC-2000)
Michael Mello QC (1972) (QC-1990) Bermuda *
Eason Rajah QC (1989) (QC-2011)
Anthony Molloy QC (1969) * (QC-1984) New Zealand
Ken Handley QC (1959) * (QC-1973) Australia
Frances Burton (1972) *
Gregory Hill (1972)
Richard Wallington (1972)
Rt Hon James Arbuthnot MP (1975) *
David Schmitz (1976)
Paul Stafford (1987)
Julian Roberts (1987)
Susannah Meadway (1988)
Jeremy Callman (1991)
Jonathan Gavaghan (1992)
Samuel Laughton (1993)
Kevin Farrelly (1993)
Robert Arnfield (1996)
Evan Price (1997)
Caroline Bolton (1998)
Anthony Dearing (1998)
Richard Dew (1999)
Georgia Bedworth (2001)
Julia Beer (2003)
Philip Jenkins (2003)
Naomi Winston (2006)
Gideon Roseman (2007)
Caroline Waterworth (2008)
Leon Pickering (2010)
Kevin Shannon (2010)
James MacDougald (2011)

* Door Tenant

THE CHAMBERS Acknowledged as one of the finest, full-service Chancery sets, containing many outstanding barristers, Ten Old Square has an excellent reputation for traditional and commercial Chancery work and was recognised as "Chambers of the Year" at the STEP 2013/14 Private Client Awards.

THE SET Three QCs and 22 juniors form the wealth of specialist talent available at this set. The head of Chambers is Francis Barlow QC, and all three silks in chambers are distinguished experts in the private client Chancery disciplines.

The set boasts many highly-regarded juniors with busy, niche Chancery practices. Many are authors or editors of some of the foremost textbooks on Chancery law including the authoritative 'Williams on Wills'. All members belong to the Chancery Bar Association and many also belong to STEP, ACTAPS, APP, FLBA, PBA and COMBAR. Ten Old Square is LawNet's approved chambers for private client matters and is accredited by the SRA to provide CPD training to solicitors.

Ten Old Square is a pleasingly traditional Chancery set that employs the latest technology and know-how to deliver a modern and efficient client service. Keith Plowman is the Senior Clerk and, along with his colleague Marc Schofield, he manages Chambers and co-ordinates the practices of each barrister. Keith has been the Senior Clerk at Ten Old Square for over 22 years and Marc is similarly qualified. Together they have a built up an enviable reputation for their professional yet candid approach to their work.

WORK UNDERTAKEN The balance of traditional and commercial Chancery work at Ten Old Square is evenly distributed and compliments the demand from clients within the sector. Along with private client work the commercial Chancery disciplines are well catered for, along with property litigation, planning and land law. Additionally, Ten Old Square is now the foremost set for partnership/LLP disputes and advice.

The set handles a wide range of diverse cases, including major litigation in the Chancery and commercial divisions of the High Court and the Appellate courts. It has a significant presence in many offshore jurisdictions, as well as in the County Court and at planning inquiries and appeals, the Administrative Court, and other tribunals.

A substantial amount of ADR (arbitration and mediation) is also undertaken. As a general guide, the principal areas of work undertaken are:

Private Client: Ten Old Square is one of the leading sets for contentious and non-contentious trust work in the UK and in offshore jurisdictions. Capital taxes, wills, probate and the administration of estates, along with Court of Protection, family provision, matrimonial property and finance are also comprehensively covered.

Commercial Chancery: Partnership (including dissolution, expulsions, compulsory retirement, LLPs, MDPs restrictive covenants and partnership accounts), banking and financial services, insurance and reinsurance, commercial litigation, financial regulation, company, insolvency, professional negligence, and public procurement.

Property, Land & Real Estate: Planning inquiries and appeals, landlord and tenant, rent review, 1954 Act renewals, conveyancing, commercial property, leasehold enfranchisement, easements, intervener and third party property claims, cohabitation claims, mortgages, manorial rights including mineral rights, construction and fracking matters.

INTERNATIONAL The set has a number of barristers who have substantial private client practices overseas in Bermuda, Munich and New Zealand.

Other languages spoken: French, German

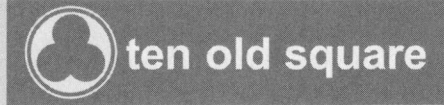

ten old square

OLD SQUARE CHAMBERS Nigel Cooksley QC & Jane McNeill QC

10-11 Bedford Row, London WC1R 4BU
Tel (020) 7269 0300 **Fax** (020) 7405 1387 **DX** 1046 Chancery Lane/London
Email clerks@oldsquare.co.uk **Website** www.oldsquare.co.uk **Twitter** @oldsquarechambers

Head of Chambers	Nigel Cooksley QC Jane McNeill QC
Senior Clerk	William Meade
Tenants	75

MEMBERS

Nigel Cooksley QC (1975) (QC-2002)
Jane McNeill QC (1982) (QC-2002) +
Frederic Reynold QC (1960) (QC-1982)
John Hendy QC (1972) (QC-1987)
Ian D Truscott QC (1996) (QC-1997)
David Wilby QC (1974) (QC-1998) +
Paul Rose QC (1981) (QC-2002)
Paul Gilroy QC (1985) (QC-2006)
Mary O'Rourke QC (1981) (QC-2009)
Oliver Segal QC (1992)(QC-2011)
Mark Sutton QC (1982) (QC-2011)
Simon Gorton QC (1988) (QC-2011)
Prof Sandra Fredman QC (2002) (QC-2012)
Michael Ford QC (1992) (QC-2013)
John H Bates (1973)
Prof Robert Upex (1973)
Charles Pugh (1975)
Christopher Makey (1975) +
Toby Kempster (1980)
Alan Smith (1981)
Louise Chudleigh (1987)
Ijeoma Omambala (1989)
Philip Mead (1989)
Jonathan Clarke (1990)
Christopher Walker (1990)
Giles Powell (1990)
Ian Scott (1991)
Simon Cheetham (1991)
Helen Gower (1992)
Brian Cummins (1992)
Malcolm Galloway (1992)
Prof Roy Lewis (1992)
Deshpal Panesar (1993)
Michael Nicholson (1993)
Elizabeth Melville (1994)
Katherine Howells (1994)
Mark Whitcombe (1994)
Stephen Garner (1994)
Melanie Tether (1995)
Emma Smith (1995)
Robin White (1995)
Ben Collins (1996)
Charles Woodhouse (1997)
Rebecca Tuck (1998)
Hilary Winstone (1998)
Spencer Keen (1998)
Stuart Brittenden (1999)
Anya Palmer (1999)
Katharine Newton (1999)
Ben Cooper (2000)
Bella Morris (2000)
Brent McDonald (2000)
Robert Moretto (2000)
Andrew Midgley (2000)
Betsan Criddle (2002)
David Rivers (2002)
Jonathan Davies (2003)
Adam Samuel (2003)
Nadia Motraghi (2004)
Hannah Freeman (2004)
Andreá Risoli (2005)
David Cunnington (2005)
Christopher Edwards (2006)
Charlie Sparling (2006)
Claire Bowsher-Murray (2007)
Kara Loraine (2006)
Nicola Newbegin (2008)
Katherine Fudakowski (2008)
Victoria Webb (2009)
Hannah Bennett (2010)
Lance Harris (2010)
Simon O'Dwyer (2010)
Rosalie Snocken (2010)
Laith Dilaimi (2011)
Francesca Lewis (2012)

+ Recorder

THE CHAMBERS Old Square Chambers is widely respected as one of the leading employment and personal injury sets, both in London and Bristol, and known for its unstuffy approach, pro-activity and responsiveness to client needs.

WORK UNDERTAKEN

Employment: Old Square is acknowledged as one of the leading sets in employment law. Awarded Employment Set of the Year by Chambers Bar Awards 2012.

Personal Injury: Members are regularly instructed in high value head, brain and spinal injury cases, including many involving ex service personnel, disaster litigation, multi-party actions and injuries abroad.

Clinical Negligence: Members have extensive experience in cerebral palsy, acquired brain damage claims and catastrophic injuries as well as dental negligence and obstetric and orthopaedic claims.

Professional Discipline: Members have been at the forefront of developing the law relating to injunctive relief and disciplinary procedures affecting the medical and other professions.

Environment: Members have comprehensive experience, particularly in cases involving nuisance, water law, contaminated land, statutory nuisance, waste management law and the application of EU law.

Health & Safety: Members are involved in both regulatory prosecutions/defence and public inquiries, and also edit leading texts such as Redgrave and Munkman.

Product Liability: Members undertake Consumer Protection Act prosecutions, product recall and product labelling work and are highly experienced in multi-claimant litigation, especially involving pharmaceuticals.

Public Inquiries: Members have been instructed in most of the significant or high-profile inquiries of the last decade, including Leveson, Potters Bar, Shipman, Climbie, Ladbroke Grove, Marchioness and Southall.

Human Rights: Members have been particularly innovative in their use of Article 6 in disciplinary cases and Article 11 in industrial action cases.

Mediation: Members are experienced CEDR trained and accredited mediators in employment, discrimination, personal injury and clinical negligence cases.

Pupillage: Old Square offers an excellent training, interesting work, a collegiate environment and an excellent chance of tenancy (9 out of 10 pupils in the last 5 years).

Visit Old Square Chambers' website at www.oldsquare.co.uk

OLD SQUARE CHAMBERS

ONE PAPER BUILDINGS Karim Khalil QC

1 Paper Buildings, Temple, London, EC4Y 7EP
Tel (020) 7353 3728 **Fax** (020) 7353 2911 **DX** 332 London/Chancery Lane
Email clerks@onepaper.co.uk **Website** www.onepaper.co.uk

Head of Chambers	Karim Khalil QC
Senior Clerk	Mark Cornell
Tenants	45

MEMBERS

Alastair R Malcolm QC (1971) (QC-1996)
Karim S Khalil QC (1984) (QC-2003)
Roger Harrison (1970)
John Farmer (1970)
Charles Kellett (1971)
Stephen Spence (1983)
Hugh Vass (1983)
Lindsay Cox (1984)
Maria Lamb (1984)
Christopher Wing (1985)
Christopher Morgan (1987)
Jonathan Seely (1987)
William Buckley (1987)
William Carter (1989)
Matthew Jewell (1989)
Sally Hobson (1991)
Robert Bryan (1992)
Duncan O'Donnell (1992)
Charles Myatt (1993)
Nick Tucker (1993)
Charlie Falk (1994)
Angela Rafferty (1995)
Barnaby Shaw (1996)
Joanne Eley (1997)
Gregory Perrins (1997)
Claire Matthews (1998)
Andrew Shaw (1998)
Louisa Bagley (2000)
Azza Brown (2000)
Rebecca Fairbairn (2000)
Phillip Farr (2001)
Nicola Devas (2003)
Louise Howard (2004)
Edward Renvoize (2004)
Unyime Davies (2006)
Jehad Mustafa (2007)
Jacob Edwards (2007)
Barnaby Hone (2006)
Lydia Waine (2007)
Charlotte Compton (2008)
Julian Norman (2012)
Nawraz Karbani (2007)
Simon Walters (2010)
Alice Carver (2012)
Edward Cole (2008)

THE CHAMBERS One Paper Buildings is a prominent set of Barristers Chambers offering a unique, efficient and friendly service in London and the regions, specifically East Anglia and the South West with a growing influence nationally. This provides One Paper Buildings with unique opportunities to develop a broad range of work over a substantial area of the country, helping it to stand apart from other sets.
Members have acted at every level of the criminal justice system in: General crime, corporate crime, VAT and tax fraud, proceeds of crime, regulatory/disciplinary work, prison law, courts martial, matrimonial and family, aviation, sports law.
The focus of Chambers' ethos is to provide outstanding advice and advocacy at every level of seniority, whilst understanding and respecting the need for clear communication to professional and lay clients alike. One Paper Buildings was one of the first sets to be awarded the 'Quality Mark' by the Legal Services Commission in recognition of the outstanding management and professional systems that were already in place.

WORK UNDERTAKEN
Crime: Prosecuting and defending in cases ranging from murder, fraud (including cases involving money laundering and confiscation complications), corporate crimes (often including an international element, such as in the Cayman Islands), drugs and sexual offences to motoring matters; courts martial; licensing law; regulatory work; acting for companies and Regulators; VAT tribunals; FSA hearings; inland revenue work; disciplinary tribunals; health and safety law; acting for local authorities, defendant companies and the University of Cambridge. Chambers has recently been working closely with corporate clients on a direct access basis and has provided regulatory and government bodies with secondees which enables our practitioners to gain invaluable experience and contacts. The Criminal team has an outstanding record in defending and prosecuting cases of notoriety or importance. Examples include the Soham murders, the Huntingdon Life Science Campaigners, Fallon racing fraud and Operation Mellor.
Sports: Members have advised upon Athlete's agreements, selection policies and procedures, sponsorship agreements, media and marketing agreements (including television/film contracts), anti-doping, R & D and intellectual property agreements, image rights and disciplinary procedures. One member was legal affairs director for the British Bobsleigh Association for ten years and remains a legal adviser to the association. Members have acted for Sportsmen and women in both Judicial Review and disciplinary proceedings.
Aviation: The team has defended a number of cases involving CAA prosecutions, with clients ranging from private pilots to ATPL holders. Chambers has successfully defended allegations following aircraft accidents, (including manslaughter) arising out of alleged negligent maintenance. It has advised many aviation bodies including (but not limited to) BALPA, the British Parachute Association, GAPAN, the BMAA and the LAA. Other experience includes advising upon aircraft ownership and leasing agreements and aircraft operating agreements on light aircraft through to multi-million pound business jets.
Family: Chambers barristers deal with Ancillary Relief and other financial applications, covering all aspects of matrimonial finance. This includes dealing with foreign assets and jurisdictional issues, financial provision for children and the financial rights of unmarried couples.

ADMINISTRATION A dedicated and progressive team of Clerks are at the heart of the administration, assisting in the development of each barristers practice and implementing Chambers growth and development plans. They are also praised in legal directories for their professionalism and efficiency as well as their accommodating service ethic. The presence of a Marketing Director, working closely with the Senior Clerk, enables them to focus upon the retention and servicing of existing clients coupled with the timely pursuit of broader categories of work through business development and recruitment.

ONE
PAPER BUILDINGS

Criminal Defence Service
Community Legal Service
Quality Mark - Legal Services Accredited Chambers

OUTER TEMPLE CHAMBERS Michael Bowes QC, David Westcott QC, Andrew Spink QC

The Outer Temple, 222 Strand, London, WC2R 1BA
Tel (020) 7353 6381 **Fax** (020) 7583 1786 **DX** 351 London
Email clerks@outertemple.com **Website** www.outertemple.com

Heads of Chambers	Michael Bowes QC David Westcott QC Andrew Spink QC
Commercial Director	Christine Kings
Business Development Directors	Steve Graham Graham Woods David Smith Dave Scothern
Tenants	76

MEMBERS

Alan Rawley QC (1958) (QC-1977)
Christopher Wilson-Smith QC (1965) (QC-1986)
Robert Rhodes QC (1968) (QC-1989)
Philip Mott QC (1970) (QC-1991)
Gordon Bebb QC (1975) (QC-2002)
Brendan Finucane QC (1976) (QC-2003)
Richard Lissack QC (1978) (QC-1994)
Christopher Gibson QC (1976) (QC-1995)
Michael Bowes QC (1980) (QC-2001)
David Westcott QC (1982) (QC-2003)
Andrew Spink QC (1985) (QC-2003)
Gerard McDermott QC (1978) (QC-1999)
Andrew Short QC (1990) (QC-2010)
Ben Compton QC (1979) (QC-2011)
Nicolas Stallworthy QC (1993) (QC-2011)
Keith Bryant QC (1991) (QC-2013)
Richard Hitchcock QC (1990) (QC-2014)
Hywel Jenkins (1974)
Richard Mawhinney (1977)
Michael Patchett-Joyce (1981)
Stephen Climie (1982)
James Counsell (1984)
Christopher Kemp (1984)
Patrick Sadd (1984)
Harry Trusted (1985)
James Aldridge (1987)
Alison McCormick (1988)
Mark Mullins (1988)
James Leonard (1989)
Jonathan Hand (1990)
Timothy Nesbitt (1991)
Fiona Horlick (1992)
Natasha Joffe (1992)
Nathan Tavares (1992)
Rachel Vickers (1992)
Matthew Phillips (1993)
Eliot Woolf (1993)
Daniel Barnett (1993)
Naomi Cunningham (1994)
Matthew McDonagh (1994)
Abhijeet Mukherjee (1995)
Andrew Allen (1995)
Benjimin Burgher (1995)
Lydia Seymour (1997)
Harriet Jerram (1998)
David E Grant (1999)
Robin Barclay (1999)
John McKendrick (1999)
Cara Guthrie (2000)
James Arnold (2000)
Samantha Presland (2001)
Naomi Ling (2001)
James Rickards (2002)
Oliver Assersohn (2003)
Eleanor Davison (2003)
Ali Almihdar (2003)
Michael Uberoi (2004)
Saul Margo (2005)
Farhaz Khan (2005)
Ben Bradley (2007)
Clare Baker (2007)
Robert Dickason (2007)
Samantha Cooper (2007)
Miranda de Savorgnani (2007)
Nicholas Hill (2008)
Will Young (2008)
Keira Gore (2008)
Jonathan Moffatt (2009)
Simon Oakes (2010)
Thomas Gibson (2010)
Katarina Sydow (2012)
Saaman Pourghadiri (2012)
David Russell QC (1977) (QC-1986)
Nicholas Haggan QC (1977) (QC-2003) *
Robin Tolson QC(1980) (QC-2001) *
Tim Horlock QC (1981) (QC-1997) *
Thomas Leeper (1991) *
Janet Walker*

* Door Tenant

THE CHAMBERS Outer Temple Chambers is noted for its health and its business expertise. In personal injury and clinical negligence the set has one of the most experienced catastrophic teams in the country and undertakes group litigation, cases involving complex medical issues, industrial disease, and spinal and brain injuries. In 2013 Outer Temple won the Legal 500 Award and the Chambers & Partners Award for Personal Injury and Clinical Negligence Set of The Year. Chambers is justifiably highly ranked as a leading pensions set and combines this with an established practice in professional negligence and an increasing practice in arbitration. Outer Temple has an enviable presence in the financial services and banking sector with demonstrable expertise in litigation, regulation and enforcement. The employment team has an outstanding reputation in equal pay and discrimination claims, and are frequently instructed for their knowledge of financial services particularly in contractual matters. Members have an unparalleled profile in corporate manslaughter and health and safety investigations. Practitioners provide representation in all types of disciplinary and regulatory tribunals, with particular emphasis on medical, solicitor, police and financial disciplinary hearings. In public law, Outer Temple is recognised for its expertise in major public inquiries, the Court of Protection and education matters. It is also known for its work in sports law and transport law. Chambers provides a range of international services and has a presence in Manchester, Dubai, Abu Dhabi and New York.

OuterTemple Chambers

4 PAPER BUILDINGS Alex Verdan QC

4 Paper Buildings, Temple, London, EC4Y 7EX
Tel (020) 7427 5200 **Fax** (020) 7353 4979 **DX** 1035
Email clerks@4pb.com **Website** www.4pb.com

Head of Chambers	Alex Verdan QC
Senior Clerk	Michael Reeves
Chambers Manager	Clare Bello
Tenants	73

MEMBERS

Alexander Verdan QC (1987) (QC-2006) + ± ^
Jonathan Cohen QC (1974) (QC-1997) + ± ^
Baroness Scotland QC (1977) (QC-1991)
Henry Setright QC (1979) (QC-2001) + ±
Marcus Scott-Manderson QC (1980) (QC-2006)
Kate Branigan QC (1985) (QC-2006) ^
Jo Delahunty QC (1986) (QC-2006) +
Michael Sternberg QC (1975) (QC-2008) ^
Catherine Wood QC (1985) + (QC- 2011)
Rex Howling QC (1991) (QC-2011) ^
Teertha Gupta QC (1990) (QC-2012) +
David Williams QC (1990) (QC-2013) ^
Charles Hale QC (1992) (QC-2014) ^
Brian Jubb (1971) ^
Amanda Barrington-Smyth (1972)
Robin Barda (1975)
Dermot Main Thompson (1977)
Jane Rayson (1982)
Mark Johnstone (1984)
Elizabeth Coleman (1985)
Alistair Perkins (1986)
Christopher Hames (1987) ^
Stephen Lyon (1987) ^
James Shaw (1988)
Mark Jarman (1989) ^
Sally Bradley (1989) ^
Barbara Mills (1990) + ^
Alison Grief (1990) + ^
Samantha King (1990) ^
Joanne Brown (1990)
Joy Brereton (1990) ^
David Bedingfield (1991) +
John Tughan (1991) ^
Cyrus Larizadeh (1992) ^
Michael Simon (1992)
Justin Ageros (1993) ^
Rob Littlewood (1993) ^
Paul Hepher (1994) ^
Ruth Kirby (1994) ^
Judith Murray (1994) ^
Cliona Papazian (1994) ^
Sarah Lewis (1995)
Nicholas Fairbank (1996) ^
James Copley (1997)
Justine Johnston (1997) ^
Oliver Jones (1998)
Lucy Cheetham (1999) ^
Hassan Khan (1999) ^
Cleo Perry (2000)
Harry Gates (2001) ^
Rebecca Foulkes (2001)
Katie Wood (2001) ^
Rhiannon Lloyd (2002) ^
Katherine Van Rol (2002) ^
Ceri White (2002) ^
Matthew Persson (2003) ^
Dorothea Gartland (2004) ^
Francesca Dowes (2004)
Greg Davies (2005)
Samantha Woodham (2006) ^
Laura Morley (2006) ^
Nicola Wallace (2006)
Jacqueline Renton (2007)
Michael Gration (2007)
Andrew Powell (2008) ^
Henry Clayton (2007) ^
Sophie Connors (2009)
Michael Edwards (2010)
Harry Nosworthy (2010)
Rachel Chisholm (2010)
Jonathan Evans (2010)
Julia Townend (2011)
Zoe Taylor (2011)

+ Recorder ± Deputy High Court Judge ** DDJ ° DDJ (Family Division) ^ Public/Direct Access

THE CHAMBERS 4 Paper Buildings ('4PB') has a long history as a friendly team of specialist barristers providing excellent expert yet common sense and practical advice and advocacy in all areas of family law. Many of the most serious, sensitive and significant family cases are undertaken by members of 4PB and instructions are received from a diverse array of clients including media organisations, the rich and/or famous, government departments, parents seeking to prevent children from being removed into care and guardians. Chambers also provides a wide spread of services by way of dispute resolution (ADR) and has 41 barristers available for direct public access.

WORK UNDERTAKEN

Family Law: Divorce and civil partnership dissolution, jurisdiction disputes, financial remedies on matrimonial and civil partnership breakdown, disputes between former cohabitants, marital, civil partnership and cohabitation agreements, financial arrangements for children, protection from domestic abuse, international family relocation disputes, child abduction, forced marriage, public children law, public inquiries, private children's arrangements, surrogacy (national and international), assisted conception, medical cases, court of protection work and professional negligence arising from family proceedings.

4pb Four Paper Buildings

5 PAPER BUILDINGS Miranda Moore QC & Julian Christopher QC

Heads of Chambers	Miranda Moore QC Julian Christopher QC
Senior Clerk	Dale Jones
Chambers Business Manager	Andrew Ross
Tenants	45

5 Paper Buildings, Temple, London, EC4Y 7HB
Tel (020) 7583 6117 **Fax** (020) 7353 0075 **DX** 365 Chancery Lane
Email clerks@5pb.co.uk **Website** www.5pb.co.uk

MEMBERS

Godfrey Carey QC (1969) (QC-1991)
Jonathan Caplan QC (1973) (QC-1991) + ^
Oliver Sells QC (1972) (QC-1995)
Edward Jenkins QC (1977) (QC-2000) + ^
Michael Brompton QC (1973) (QC-2003) +
Graham Trembath QC (1978) (QC-2003)
Miranda Moore QC (1983) (QC-2003)
Mark Wyeth QC (1983) (QC-2009)
Ian Wade QC (1977) (QC-2010)
Julian Christopher QC (1988) (QC-2010) ^
Robert O'Sullivan QC (1988) (QC-2012) ^
Nicholas Griffin QC (1992) (QC-2012) ^
Laura Brickman (1976) ^
Nicholas Fooks (1978) ^
Charles Judge (1981)
Maurice Aston (1982)
Miles Bennett (1986) ^
Kevin McCartney (1991)
Emma Deacon (1993)
Janet Weeks (1993)
Tom Allen (1994)
Deanna Heer (1994) + ^
Michael Hick (1995) ^
Denis Barry (1996) ^
Ben Douglas-Jones (1998) ^
Catherine Purnell (1999)
James Norman (2000)
Jonathan Rees (2000) ^
Dominic Lewis (2000) ^
Teresa Hay (2001) ^
Stephen Hopper (2001)
Rory Keene (2001) ^
Catherine Rabaiotti (2002)
Charlene Sumnall (2003) ^
Archie Mackay (2003)
Alan Richards (2004)
Michael Attenborough (2008) ^
Andrew Johnson (2008) ^
James Marsland (2008)
Anthony Hucklesby (2008)
Jennifer Dannhauser (2010)
Julianna Tolan (2010)
Olivia Potts (2011) ^
Carolina Bracken (2012) ^
Joshua Normanton (2012) ^

+ Recorder ^ Public/Direct Access

THE CHAMBERS 5pb has long been recognised as one of the leading criminal sets. Chambers draws on some of the best talent at the criminal bar and at present has 45 members, 12 of whom are QCs.
Members take a results-focused approach to criminal advocacy, working closely alongside clients to find practical solutions. Clients also benefit from the outstanding quality of chambers' case management and clerking, resulting in cost effective use of court time and resources. Members bring an exceptional quality of representation and case management to all cases, regardless of level, size or scale of complexity.

WORK UNDERTAKEN

Crime: Members prosecute and defend across the full range of criminal practice at every level, including large-scale drug importation, serious sexual offences, human trafficking, corruption of public servants, firearms offences and serious violence. With particular experience in cases involving PII and sensitive disclosure issues and vulnerable witnesses. Recent cases include defending in News of the World phone hacking trial. Prosecution in Op Yewtree, defending in "AG Ref: life sentences".

Financial Crime: Members of chambers are regularly instructed in the largest and most complex financial crime cases. Its experience includes all forms of fraud, MTIC/VAT frauds, market abuse, asset recovery and confiscation proceedings. Recent cases include £80 million VAT carousel fraud. Factoring fraud with £111million confiscation proceedings. A mortgage fraud involving over 1,000 mortgages.

Consumer Law: 5PB is one of the leading sets in consumer law and trading standards. Its expertise includes trade descriptions, pricing offences, consumer credit, property misdescriptions, trade mark and copyright theft, product safety, environmental law, health and safety, food and food safety, ticket touting and underage sales. Recent cases include prosecution of a major retailer over multi million pound allegations of misleading commercial practices in the promotion and sale of strawberries. £60 million money laundering case involving 30 different consumer scams, 9 countries, targeting the elderly.

Professional Discipline & Regulatory: 5PB are regularly instructed in healthcare regulation and professional discipline. Acting for the regulators, individuals and corporate clients and frequently appear in parallel proceedings involving criminal prosecutions, inquests and disciplinary inquiries. Members are also instructed in MHRA and FRC work. Regularly appear before the GMC, GPC and GOC and when necessary, on appeal. Members frequently represent doctors, pharmacists and NHS trusts at inquests. In addition matters involving accountants, architects, barristers, police officers among others.

Health & Safety: Members have extensive expertise dealing with HSE prosecutions and defending companies and individuals following workplace accidents. Recent cases include defending in the first ever acquittal at trial of a company charged with corporate manslaughter. Securing the conviction of one of the UK's largest engineering companies following the death of a construction worker.

Public Law & Inquiries: Chambers has considerable experience having been instructed in some of the most important recent inquiries including Leveson, The Rosemary Nelson Inquiry, The Bloody Sunday Inquiry and the Guantánamo Bay litigation.

PUBLICATIONS Jonathan Caplan QC (contributing editors of 'Fraud: Law, Practice and Procedure'), Julian Christopher QC (contributing editor of Archbold). Edward Jenkins QC, Dennis Barry, Ben Douglas-Jones, Charlene Sumnall have been commissioned to write Blackstone's Guide to the Consumer Protection Act (2015).

INTERNATIONAL Members have experience of work in Hong Kong, Singapore and the Caribbean.

Stonewall
DIVERSITY CHAMPION

FIVE PAPER Nicholas Grundy

5 Paper Buildings, Temple, London, EC4Y 7HB
Tel (020) 7815 3200 **Fax** (020) 7815 3201 **DX** 415 LDE
Email clerks@fivepaper.com **Website** www.fivepaper.com

Head of Chambers	Nicholas Grundy
Commercial Team Leader	Simon Mills
Property Team Leader	Stephen Evans
Employment Team Leader	Cyril Adjei
Family Team Leader	Mark Lyne
Senior Clerk	Alan Stammers
Pupillage co-ordinators	Lewis Preston
	Mary Glass
Tenants	45

MEMBERS

Nicholas Grundy (1993)
Paul Norris (1963) ^
Graham Platford (1970) ^
Donald Broatch (1971) ^
Robert Percival (1971) ^
Roger Bull (1974)
Mark Lyne (1981)
Terry Gallivan (1981) ^
Ian Wright (1983) ^
Lawrence Jacobson (1985) ^
Jonathan Rich (1989)
Peter John (1989)
Josephine Henderson (1990) ^
Satinder Gill (1991) ^
Stephen Evans (1992)
Simon Mills (1994) ^
Cyril Adjei (1995) ^
Rachel Sleeman (1996)
Jake Davies (1997) ^
Joanna Brownhill (1997)
Sean Pettit (1997) ^
Ben Maltz (1998) ^
Sonia Rai (1998)
Sara Beecham (1999)
Angela Jack (1999)
Angela Hall (2000)
Julie Leivesley (2000)
Jane Hodgson (2000) ^
Guy Holland (2001) ^
Mary Glass (2001)
Victoria Osler (2001)
Morwenna Macro (2002) ^
Tina Conlan (2002)
Gillian Christopher-Chambers JP (2003)
Christopher Rogers (2004) ^
Camilla Ter Haar (2005)
Jennifer Moate (2006)
Lewis Preston (2007)
Millie Polimac (2007)
Brynmor Adams (2008)
Gita Chakravarty (2010) ^
Sam Phillips (2011)
Jessica Powers (2012)
Steven Walsh (1965) ++ ^
Richard King (1978) ++

++ Associate ^ Public/Direct Access

THE CHAMBERS Five Paper specialises in commercial, property, employment and family law. Chambers works with clients from many sectors and believes accessibility, communication and strong relationships are key to delivering excellent results. Senior members are among the most experienced and innovative within their areas of expertise and the chambers' juniors deal with practical legal matters on a daily basis. This range of experience enables Five Paper to provide clients with a service that is both expert and cost-effective.
Professional development: Five Paper is accredited by the Law Society and Bar Council for continuing professional development. The set also runs seminars and bespoke training for professional clients. Please contact clerks for details.

WORK UNDERTAKEN Five Paper has four thriving practice teams:
Commercial: The Commercial Team works with clients involved in commercial finance, insolvency and asset recovery. The team specialises in factoring and invoice discounting, corporate insolvency, trade finance and the sale of goods, credit and securities, breach of directors' and fiduciary duties, personal bankruptcy, civil fraud and tracing and enforcement against land.
Property: The Property Team specialises in acting for local authorities, registered providers of social housing, and private landlords and tenants in the areas of housing, residential landlord and tenant law and public law. The team is also experienced in all property-related fields, including real property/general chancery work, commercial landlord and tenant law, and probate.
Employment: The Employment Team provides a full-service for all types of employment matters. The team also has specialists in regulatory matters, such as health and safety at work, with barristers on the List of Specialist Regulatory Advocates in Health and Safety and Environmental Law who are certified for this type of work and also business immigration.
Family: The Family Team specialises in all types of financial order cases, Schedule 1 cases, Children Act cases, financial provision and matrimonial jurisdiction law. The team has recently expanded its areas of expertise and members are now regularly instructed in matrimonial finance and children cases which touch upon issues of bankruptcy, housing and inheritance.

PUBLICATIONS Five Paper's senior members edit some of the leading specialist law publications. These include: Gutteridge and Megrah's Law of Bankers' Commercial Credits, 8th edition by Richard King; Sir Roy Goode's Proprietary Rights and Insolvency in Sales Transactions, 2nd edition by Simon Mills; Salinger on Factoring, 4th edition by Simon Mills and others.

RECRUITMENT Pupils spend time with different practice teams to experience a wide variety of work. Pupils receive an award of £25,000 each plus guaranteed earnings in the second six of £5,000. Five Paper also encourages applications from barristers with ten or more years' experience within one of their specialist areas. Please contact the clerks for details. Five Paper is committed to equal opportunities for all. Five Paper values diversity.

five paper
combar
The Commercial Bar Association
BAR MARK

3 PB BARRISTERS Ian Lawrie QC

Head of Chambers	Ian Lawrie QC
Head Chambers Director	Stephen Clark
Chief Executive	Joanna Poulton
Tenants	175

3 Paper Buildings, Temple, London, EC4Y 7EU
Tel (020) 7583 8055 **Fax** (020) 7353 6271 **DX** 1024 LDE
Email london@3pb.co.uk **Website** www.3pb.co.uk

MEMBERS

Michael Parroy QC (1969) (QC-1991)
Roger Farley QC (1974) (QC-1993)
Michael Vere-Hodge QC (1970) (QC-1993) ^
Stewart Jones QC (1972) (QC-1994)
Nicholas Braslavsky QC (1983) (QC-1999)
John Bromley-Davenport QC (1972) (QC-2002)
Nigel Lickley QC (1983) (QC-2006)
Ian Lawrie QC (1985) (QC-2011) ^
Paul Storey QC (1982) (QC-2010) *
Frank Freehan QC (1988) (QC-2010) *
Samuel Parrish (1962) ^
Stephen Parrish (1966)
Susan Solomon (1967)
David Swinstead (1970)
Christopher Aylwin (1970)
Michael Norman (1971) ^
Anthony Ward (1971) ^
Leo Curran (1972)
Peter Jennings (1972) ^
Anthony Coleman (1973)
Ben Stephenson (1973)
David Bartlett (1975)
Richard Tyson (1975)
Nigel Mitchell (1978)
Peter Kent (1978)
Nicholas Leviseur (1979)
Ian Partridge (1979)
Robin Leach (1979)
Robert Grey (1979) ^
Gavin Hamilton (1979) ^
Timothy Coombes (1980) ^
Ian Edge (1981)
David Marshall (1981)
Graeme Sampson (1981) ^
Martin Strutt (1981)
Nicola Martin (1982)
Richard Onslow (1982)
Paul Newman (1982) ^
Mark Lomas (1983)
Sarah O'Hara (1984)
Lucia Whittle-Martin (1985)
Tonia Clark (1986) ^
Elisabeth Hudson (1987) ^
Nicholas Rowland (1988)
Lucy Hendry (1988)
Tanya Zabihi (1988)
Timothy Bradbury (1989)
Paul Hester (1989) ^
David Richards (1989) ^
Guy Opperman (1989) *
Sophie Knapp (1990)
Omar Malik (1990)
Hayley Griffiths (1990)
Adam Hiddleston (1990) ^
Peter Aeberli (1990) ^
Amanda Buckley-Clarke (1991)
Cyrus Katrak (1991)
Imogen Robins (1991) ^
Hamish Dunlop (1991) ^
Iain Ross (1991) ^
Christian Sweeney (1992)
Tony Bingham (1992) ^
Kerry Musgrave (1992)
William Hansen (1992)
Jane Fousler McFarlane (1994)
Adam Feest (1994) ^
John Clargo (1994)
Judy Earle (1994)
Jack Mitchell (1994)
Megan Topliss (1994)
James Dawson (1994) ^
David Reid (1994)
Louis Weston (1994) ^
Colin McDevitt (1995) ^
Melanie De Freitas (1995) ^
David McIlroy (1995)
Elaine Strachan (1995)
Lachlan Wilson (1996)
Cheryl Jones (1996) ^
Andrew Lorie (1996)
Tom Tyler (1996) ^
James Davison (1996)
Martin Kenny (1997) ^
Catherine Purdy (1997)
Mark Sullivan (1997)
Nancy Dooher (1997)
Eleanor Davies (1998) *
Emma Griffiths (1998)
Kalsoom Maqsood (1998) *
Rufus Taylor (1998) ^
Martin Hirst (1998)
Melanie Churchill (1999)
Robert Horner (1999)
Stuart Kennedy (1999) ^
Charlotte Hadfield (1999) ^
Antonia Jameson (1999)
Nicholas Cotter (1999) ^
Rachel Goodall (2000) ^
Hala Helmi (2000) ^
Kenneth McGuire (2000) *
Oliver Isaacs (2000)
Rupert Jones (2000) ^
Louise Worton (2000)
Richard Owen-Thomas (2000) ^
Paul O'Doherty (2000) ^
Andrew Sheriff (2000)
Garvin Nicholas (2001) *
Sheena Cassidy (2001)
Christopher Whelan (2001)
Craig Ludlow (2002) ^
Gillian Campbell (2002) *
Karen Moss (2002)
Adam Norris (2002)
Julia Shillingford (2002)
Nicola Pearce (2002)
Michael Tomlinson (2002) ^
Robert Courts (2003) ^
Matthew Gullick (2003) ^
Victoria Jones (2003) ^
Emma Harman (2003)
Hugh Rimmer (2003)
Elizabeth Hepworth (2004)
Tom Horder (2004)
Richard Wheeler (2004) ^
Audrey Archer (2004)
James Davies (2004) ^
Jamal Demachkie (2004) ^
Caroline Sykes (2004) *
Sarah Langford (2005)
Katherine Anderson (2005)
Sarah Clarke (2005)
Anarkali Musgrave (2005) ^
Caroline Stone (2005)
Matthew Cannings (2006)
Oliver Powell (2006) ^
Naomi Rees (2006) ^
Hugh Saunders (2006)
Nicholas Robinson (2006)
Sunyana Sharma (2006) ^
Mark Green (2006)
Francisca Da Costa (2006)
Sarah Bowen (2006)
Carl Brewin (2006) ^
Nick Davies (2006)
Andrew MacPhail (2007) ^
Andrew Perfect (2007)
Mark Ellliott (2007) ^
Thomas O'Donohoe (2007) ^
Michael Paulin (2007) ^
Harriet Fear Davies (2007) ^
Sebastian Oram (2007)
Ximena Jones (2007)
Derek Pye (2008)
Christopher Edwards (2008) ^
Katherine Dunseath (2008)
Alex Hodge (2009)
Philip Currie (2009)
Richard Borrett (2009)
Nicola Frost (2009)
Alexander Line (2009)
Steven Howard (2009) ^
Sharan Sanghera (2009) ^
Edward Ross (2010)
Thomas Webb (2010)
Lloyd Maynard (2010)
Stephen Wyeth (2010)
Tom Evans (2010)
Nikolai Lazarev (2010)
Emma Waldron (2011)
Joe England (2011)
Susan Jones (2011)
Thomas Talbot-Ponsonby (2011)
Graham Kean (2012)
Darragh Connell (2012)

* Door Tenant ^ Public/Direct Access

3PB
BARRISTERS

3 PB BARRISTERS Ian Lawrie QC (continued)

THE CHAMBERS 3PB (previously known as 3 Paper Buildings) is one of the longest established sets in England with 175 members and ten silks and operates as a single set from its five well-equipped locations. The set is fully accredited by the Bar Council to provide CPD courses and is IiP and BarMark accredited. Each centre is staffed by friendly and experienced clerking teams who can advise clients on the most suitable counsel for a particular case, as well as discuss fees and provide estimates for anticipated work.

WORK UNDERTAKEN Chambers expertise covers 14 specialist work groups.
The Business and Commercial Group advises on general contract and commercial law. The Banking and Finance team offers specialist advice across the whole range of financial services.
The Criminal Law Group includes 6 leading QCs and its members advise and act in a broad spectrum of criminal law matters. Counsel also undertake publicly funded work.
The Employment Group provides expertise across all areas of contentious and non-contentious work, including all forms of discrimination. Jack Mitchell, Head of the Group, is co-author of the leading textbook 'Whistleblowing – Law and Practice' O.U.P (2012).
The Family Law Group provides expertise in every aspect of public/private childcare law and all forms of financial proceedings.
The Personal Injury and Clinical Negligence Group conducts cases at every level and clients include both claimants and defendants.
The Professional Negilgence Team provide advice in all aspects of the law.
The Property and Chancery Group undertake work in all areas of law concerning the ownership, occupation and use of land, as well as traditional Chancery law advice.
Public and regulatory law crosses the boundary between civil and criminal law and members of the group provide expertise across a range of legal fields, including consumer protection, health and safety and education law.
The Asset and Tax Team has been instructed in a number of high profile cases, and nearly all of the leading panel receivers and government agencies instruct 3PB, together with well known specialist defence firms.
Chambers Mediation Group has particular strength in the fields of adjudication, arbitration and mediation advocacy. Members are regularly appointed as adjudicators or arbitrators in both domestic and international disputes.
3PB's TCC Group provides expertise in all aspects of construction disputes and dispute resolution services, both domestic and international.
The Sports Law Group has an exceptional reputation for its expertise in sports regulation and discipline, doping issues, contractual disputes, IP, negligence and ancillary sporting issues including firearms licensing.

Other offices: Bournemouth, Bristol, Oxford and Winchester.

1 PUMP COURT

Senior Clerk	Ian Burrow
Tenants	92

1 Pump Court, Elm Court, Temple, London, EC4Y 7AH
Tel (020) 7842 7070 **Fax** (020) 7842 7088 **DX** LDE 109
Email clerks@1pumpcourt.co.uk **Website** www.1pumpcourt.co.uk

MEMBERS

Simon Bickler QC (1988) (QC-2011) ^
Lindsay Adams (1987) ^
Yinka Adedeji (1997) ^
Jonathan Adler (1999) ^
Lorna Archer (1986) ^
Jennifer Barker (2000)
Stephen Bartlet-Jones (2004) ^
James Bloomer (2000) ^
Doron Blum (1998)
Delphine Breese-Laughran (1991)
Helen Butcher (1999)
Sylvester Carrot (1980) ^
Parosha Chandran (1997) ^
David Chirico (2002)
Marisa Cohen (2010)
Justine Compton (2005) ^
Greville Davis (1976)
Christine Dean (2007) ^
Graham Denholm (2001)
Sally Dent (1989)
Zani Dingiswayo (2001)
Annie Dixon (1991)
Christopher Dowd (2012)
Edmund Eldergill (1991) ^
Amean Elgadhy (2008) ^
Robert English (1996) ^
Stephen Field (1993) ^
Russell Fraser (2010)
Kevin Gannon (1993) ^
Joshua Garwood (1992) ^
Julia Gasparro (1999) ^
Andrew Gilbert (2009)
Matthew Groves (1998)
Toby Hall (2008) ^
Michelle Harris (2000) ^
Philippa Hemery (2009) ^
Paul Higham (1982)
Rina Marie Hill (2002)
Martin Hodgson (1980) ^
Jane Hoyal (1976)
Abida Huda (1989) ^
Mary Hughes (1994) ^
Timur Hussein (1993) ^
Eleanor Hutchison (2007) ^
Michael Hyde (2006) ^
Samuel Jarman (1989) ^
Melanie Johnson (1996) ^
Manjeet Kaler (1993)
Ajanta Kaza (1998)
Ranjiv Khubber (1994)
Gilda Kiai (2004)
James Kirk (2011)
Raggi Kotak (2000)
Tahera Ladak (1986)
John Lamb (1990) ^
Victoria Laughton (1988)
Rebecca Littlewood (1988) ^
Gemma Loughran (2008) ^
Paul Mason (2011)
James McCrindell (1993)
Rebecca Martin (2002) ^
Alan Masters (1979) (Irish Bar 1993) ^
Helen Monah (1996)
Zia Nabi (1991) ^
Nicholas Nicol (1986)
Michele O'Leary (1983) ^
Charlie Peat (2003) ^
Terry Pedro (1996) ^
James Presland (1985) ^
Althea Radford (2009)
Rohan Ramdas-Harsia (1999) ^
Catherine Robinson (2011)
Anthony Ross (1991) ^
Jacqueline Rubens (1989) ^
Natasha Sammy (2006) ^
Ruby Sayed (1999) ^
Stuart Scott (1998) ^
Harriet Short (2007)
Daniel Sills (2011) ^
Caroline Sinclair (2005) ^
Priya Solanki (2008)
Simon Stafford-Michael (1982) ^
Bruce Stuart (19977) ^
Emma Stuart King (2005) ^
Lucy Taylor-Gee (2006)
Usha Teji (1981) ^
Timothy Thomas (2002) ^
Patricia Tueje (1999) ^
Nicola Wacey (2004)
Lorraine Waldron (2004) ^
Rupert Wheeler (2010)
Lucie Wibberley (2005)
Tamara Muhammad (1998) *
Helen Tracey (2001) *
Catriona Vine (2002) *
Adrienne Barnett (1981) *
Alice Hilken (1994) *
HHJ Sarah Singleton QC (1983) (QC- 2006) ++
Margaret Brazier ++
Asma Jahangir * ++
Dianna Kempe * ++
Beatrice Mtetwa * ++
Simon Roberts (1975) * ++
Mark Rowlands (1975) * ++

* Door Tenant ++ Honorary Door Tenant ^ Public/Direct Access

THE CHAMBERS 1 Pump Court is a dynamic and progressive set of Chambers. Established in 1978 Chambers has a firm commitment to removing inequality and providing access to justice, particularly in relation to publicly funded clients and those to whom funding is no longer available. Chambers has established a solid and growing reputation in its traditional areas of work while developing its client base through expansion of its direct access, private (domestic and international) and regulatory work and mediation.
Members sit as part-time Judges in County Courts and Tribunals (immigration, social security, property and employment). Former members have been appointed to the judiciary including to the High Court. Chambers is a democratic collective.
Members of Chambers regularly conduct seminars for practitioners and provide individualised training for advisors and external organisations such as ILPA, HLPA, JCWI, LAG, ATLeP, HJT and Shelter.
Chambers has been nominated for various professional awards e.g. Legal Aid Lawyer of the Year in 2012 and the LAPG Legal Aid Barrister of the Year Award in 2013, with Jane Hoyal – a founding member of Chambers - winning the award.

WORK UNDERTAKEN Chambers specialises in publicly funded work and has been involved in many high profile cases. Areas include administrative and public law, crime (including white collar), immigration, family, housing and community care, property, general civil litigation, social welfare and prison law. A large percentage of members are Direct Access accredited.

PUBLICATIONS Members have written and contributed to legal textbooks and other publications including but not limited to Butterworth's Immigration Law Service, the Journal of Housing Law, Legal Action Blackstone's Guide to the Domestic Violence Act, Family Law Week, Education Law and Practice, The Prisons Handbook, Human Trafficking Handbook, The Fuel Rights Handbook, The English/Japanese Legal Dictionary and Handbook and Butterworth's Money Laundering Law.

4 PUMP COURT Jeremy Storey QC & Nigel Tozzi QC

4 Pump Court, Temple, London, EC4Y 7AN
Tel (020) 7842 5555 **Fax** (020) 7583 2036 **DX** 303 LDE
Email chambers@4pumpcourt.com **Website** www.4pumpcourt.com

Head of Chambers	Jeremy Storey QC Nigel Tozzi QC
Chief Executive	Carolyn McCombe
Head Clerks	Carl Wall Stewart Gibbs
Clerk	Jon Robinson
Tenants	63

MEMBERS

Jeremy Storey QC (1974) (QC-1994)
Nigel Tozzi QC (1980) (QC-2001)
Anthony Temple QC (1968) (QC-1986)
David Friedman QC (1968) (QC-1990)
David Blunt QC (1967) (QC-1991)
Christopher Moger QC (1972) (QC-1992)
Jonathan Marks QC (1975) (QC-1995)
Anthony Speaight QC (1973) (QC-1995)
Michael Douglas QC (1974) (QC-1997)
Jeremy Nicholson QC (1977) (QC-2000)
James Cross QC (1985) (QC-2006)
Nicholas Vineall QC (1988) (QC-2006)
Alex Charlton QC (1983) (QC-2008)
Duncan McCall QC (1988) (QC-2008)
Aidan Christie QC (1988) (QC-2008)
Andrew Neish QC (1988) (QC-2009)
Sean Brannigan QC (1994) (QC-2009)
Michael Davie QC (1993) (QC-2010)
Alexander Gunning QC (1994) (QC-2012)
Allen Dyer (1976)
Oliver Ticciati (1979)
Peter Hamilton (1968)
Terence Bergin (1985)
Simon Henderson (1993)
Kate Vaughan-Neil (1994)
Rachel Ansell (1995)
Alexander Hickey (1995)
Claire Packman (1996)
Jonathan Lewis (1996)
Sean O'Sullivan (1997)
Benjamin Pilling (1997)
Lynne McCafferty (1997)
Michael Taylor (1996)
James Purchas (1997)
Alison Potter (1987)
James Leabeater (1999)
James Bowling (1999)
Jennie Gillies (2000)
James Watthey (2000)
Kate Livesey (2001)
Peter Oliver (2002)
Thomas Crangle (2002)
George Woods (2003)
James Hatt (2003)
Rangan Chatterjee (2004)
Matthew Lavy (2004)
Simon Goldstone (2004)
Luke Wygas (2004)
Neil Henderson (2004)
Laura Crowley (2005)
Richard Osborne (2005)
Alexander Wright (2007)
Andrew Stevens (2007)
Daniel Goodkin (2008)
Adam Temple (2008)
Iain Munro (2009)
Martyn Naylor (2009)
Sanjay Patel (2010)
Matthew Thorne (2011)
Gideon Shirazi (2012)
Ed Jones (2012)
Daniel Churcher (2012)
Robert Scrivener (2013)

THE CHAMBERS 4 Pump Court is one of the leading full-service commercial sets of barristers' chambers, with high rankings in international arbitration, commercial dispute resolution, professional negligence, IT and telecoms, energy, shipping, construction and engineering and insurance and reinsurance. The set's wide-ranging commercial work also includes banking, sale of goods, pensions and financial regulation, dry shipping, oil and gas.

4 Pump Court is a modern and progressive set, with an imaginative, client-friendly and efficient team of clerks. The set prides itself on anticipating, understanding and responding to clients' business and commercial needs and on providing a high-quality, efficient and effective service.

WORK UNDERTAKEN 4 Pump Court undertakes general commercial and contractual work, with a particular focus on the following areas:

International Arbitration: Members of chambers represent clients in major arbitrations in a wide range of disputes across their areas of expertise, appearing before tribunals throughout the world, as well as dealing with ancillary domestic applications for relief in relation to arbitration proceedings in the UK. Senior members of chambers also sit as arbitrators in the UK and abroad.

Construction: 4 Pump Court is one of the three leading chambers practising in construction law. The set's hugely experienced construction group has expertise in all aspects of construction, engineering and infrastructure disputes in relation to global and domestic projects. 4 Pump Court's construction specialists are regularly instructed as advisors and advocates in all forums for dispute resolution, including adjudication, expert determination, ADR, arbitration and litigation.

IT & Telecoms: 4 Pump Court's top-ranked technology and telecoms group has enormous experience in IT, e-commerce and telecommunications law. It primarily focuses on disputes of a contractual nature, which require industry and detailed technical knowledge, understanding of software, project implementation and the underlying commercial issues. The set has been involved in the majority of the leading cases in this area, with a quickly developing interest in intellectual property matters.

Energy: 4 Pump Court's energy practice group reflects its experience in the commercial and construction fields, experience which makes it uniquely qualified to advise and represent clients in relation to offshore construction and energy-related projects. Members of chambers have broad experience of the complex issues arising from contracts for the exploitation of natural resources and particular expertise in offshore construction and shipbuilding.

Shipping: The set has an outstanding reputation in marine-related disputes work, including dry shipping, shipbuilding, ship sale and purchase, international trade and commodities and yachting. The shipping group act for international law firms, charterers, ship owners, shipyards and P&I clubs.

Pump Court

4 PUMP COURT Jeremy Storey QC & Nigel Tozzi QC (continued)

Professional Negligence: 4 Pump Court is one of the leading chambers in this field, with experience in claims for and against professionals across the whole spectrum of professional liability work, including breach of fiduciary duty and fraud and in all forums. The set has particular expertise in disputes concerning architects and engineers; IT consultants; solicitors and barristers; accountants and auditors; financial advisers; insurance brokers and underwriting agents; and surveyors and valuers.
Insurance: 4 Pump Court's highly recommended insurance and reinsurance group continues to be instructed in connection with many significant events affecting the London insurance market. Members act on behalf of UK and international insurance companies and Lloyd's syndicates, as well as insurers and brokers, both domestically and abroad.
Financial Services & Banking: 4 Pump Court's financial services work straddles both financial regulation and banking litigation. Members of the group frequently act for the regulator and have in-depth knowledge of a variety of financial products and experience in perimeter policing, enforcement and FSMA. In addition to their historic involvement with bank charges and PPI, members of chambers regularly receive instructions involving swaps mis-selling, ISDA, forex trading and other complex financial instruments, as well as retail banking litigation.

6 PUMP COURT Stephen Hockman QC

Head of Chambers	Stephen Hockman QC
Senior Clerk	Richard Constable
Tenants	57

6 Pump Court, Temple, London, EC4Y 7AR
Tel (020) 7797 8400 **Fax** (020) 7797 8401 **DX** 293 Chancery Lane, London
Email clerks@6pumpcourt.co.uk **Website** www.6pumpcourt.co.uk

MEMBERS

Stephen Hockman QC (1970) (QC-1990) [A]
Richard Barraclough QC (1980) (QC-2003) [A]
David Travers QC (1981) (QC-2010)
Roy Martin QC (1990) (QC-2008)
Eleanor Laws QC (1990) (QC-2011) [A]
Oliver Saxby QC (1992) (QC 2013) [A]
Grant Armstrong (1978) [A]
Mark Harris (1980)
Anne Williams (1980)
Nicholas Baldock (1983) [A]
Caroline Topping (1984) [A]
Paul Taylor (1985)
Megan Thomas (1987)
Peter Forbes (1990) [A]
Jane Campbell (1990) [A]
John O'Higgins (1990) [A]
William Upton (1990)
Andrew Espley (1993) [A]
Ian Thomas (1993)
Mark Watson (1994)
Edward Grant (1994)
Nina Ellin (1994)
Danny Moore (1994) [A]
Pascal Bates (1994) [A]
Ian Whitehurst (1994)
Peter Alcock (1995) [A]
Thomas Stern (1995)
Mark Beard (1996) [A]
Deborah Charles (1996) [A]
Catherine Donnelly (1997) [A]
Tanya Robinson (1997) [A]
Simon Taylor (1997) [A]
Simon Wickens (1998)
Richard Banwell (1998)
Gordon Menzies (1998)
John FitzGerald (1998)
Lee Bennett (1998) [A]
Tom Dunn (1998)
Adaku Parker (2001) [A]
Lucy Luttman (2001)
David Hercock (2001)
Giles Atkinson (2002) [A]
Stuart Jessop (2002)
Christopher Badger (2002)
Emmaline Lambert (2003)
Grace Cullen (2005) [A]
Thaiza Khan (2006)
Isabella Crowdy (2008) [A]
Kieran Brand (2007)
Ian Rees Phillips (2009) [A]
Nicholas Ostrowski (2009) [A]
Laura Phillips (2009) [A]
William Hotham (2009)
Craig Evans (2010)
John Dowlman (2011)
Mukhtiar Singh (2011)

[A] Public/Direct Access

THE CHAMBERS Founded in the 1920s as a specialist criminal, civil and family set; now evolved into one of the strongest sets in environmental/planning, health and safety and all other forms of regulatory law as well.

WORK UNDERTAKEN

Civil & Commercial: Commercial disputes, professional negligence and landlord and tenant work.
Criminal: Proven track record both prosecuting (including private prosecutions) and defending (individuals and corporations). Particularly noted for expertise in cases of homicide and serious sexual offences.
Employment: Unfair dismissal claims, discrimination cases (including disability discrimination), pension rights, redundancy, part-time working, TUPE transfers and rights of employees employed abroad.
Family: Matrimonial finance including corporate, agricultural, overseas trusts and high-value matters. Private child care applications. Care proceedings, alleged child abuse adoption and other public cases.
Financial Conduct: All financial litigation and advice, including civil commercial fraud, criminal serious fraud, confiscation, revenue/BIS investigations/prosecutions, bribery, financial professional discipline/corporate governance, Financial Conduct Authority regulation, utility regulation and consumer credit.
Inquests & Inquiries: Including Article 2 inquests and Coroners' reports to prevent future deaths.
Personal Injury: Including employers' liability, road traffic accidents and clinical negligence.
Planning & Environmental: Public inquiries and regulatory criminal proceedings for and against regulators/authorities. Particular expertise at the interface of environmental, planning and human rights law.
Public: Judicial review and advice, often with a planning/environmental or regulatory subject matter.
Regulatory: Prosecuting and defending regulatory criminal offences including health and safety (e.g. construction, energy, transport), food and consumer protection/trading standards. Licensing. Professional discipline.

PUMP COURT CHAMBERS Oba Nsugbe QC

3 Pump Court, Temple, London, EC4Y 7AJ
Tel (020) 7353 0711 **Fax** (0845) 259 3241 DX 362
Email clerks@pumpcourtchambers.com **Website** www.pumpcourtchambers.com

Head of Chambers	Oba Nsugbe QC
Chief Clerk	David Barber
Deputy Chief & Senior Family Clerk	Tony Atkins
Senior Criminal Clerk	Tony George
Senior Civil Clerk	Jonathan Cue
Tenants	92

MEMBERS

Oba Nsugbe QC (1985) (QC-2002)
Nigel Pascoe QC (1966)(QC-1988)
Anthony Donne QC (1973) (QC-1988)
Jonathan Cohen QC (1974) (QC-1997) *
Susan Campbell QC (1986) (QC-2009)
Leslie Samuels QC (1989) (QC-2011) +
Stewart Patterson (1967) +
Giles Harrap (1971) +
Frank Abbott (1972) +
Charles Parry (1973) +
John Ker-Reid (1974)
Michael Butt (1974)
Charles Gabb (1975)
Julie MacKenzie (1978) +
Stephen Jones (1978)
Martin Blount (1982)
Kevin Haven (1982)
Matthew Scott (1985)
Hugh Travers (1988)
Justin Gau (1989)
David Wicks (1989) +
Edward Boydell (1989)
Andrew Houston (1989)
Anthony Akiwumi (1989)
Catherine Breslin (1990)
Helen Khan (1990)
Claudia Lorenzo (1991)
Penny Howe (1991)
Peter Binder (1991)
Gary Self (1991)
Colin Banham (1991)
Geoffrey Kelly (1992)
James Newton-Price (1992)
Mark Ruffell (1992)
Marcus Tregilgas-Davey (1993)
Leonorah Smith (1993)
Mark Ashley (1993)
Oliver Peirson (1993)
Gary Morton (1993) +
Elizabeth Gunther (1993)
Robert Pawson (1994)
Richard Hall (1995)
Mark Dubbery (1996) +
Peter Asteris (1996)
Sarah Jones (1996)
Michael Hall (1996)
Andrew Grime (1997) +
Ruth Arlow (1997)
Maria Gallagher (1997)
Anne Ward (1997)
Amy Ephgrave (1997)
Timothy Dracass (1998)
Andrew Bond (1999)
Louise De Rozarieux (1999)
Rachel Spearing (1999)
Richard Tutt (2000)
Lubeya Ramadhan (2000)
Anne Brown (2000)
Naznin Islam (2000)
Stuart McGhee (2000)
Jason Nickless (2001)
Alison Burge (2002)
Caroline Hartley (2002)
Heather Platt (2002) +
Neelo Shravat (2002)
David Josty (2002)
John Chapman (2003)
Charlotte Street (2003)
Zoe Rudd (2003)
Lucy Davis (2003)
Conor Mullan (2003)
Amy Berry (2003)
Claire Fox (2003)
Helen Trotter (2004)
Adam Gadd (2004)
Tara Lyons (2005)
Corinne Iten (2006)
Patricia O'Driscoll (2006)
Sally Davidson (2006)
Jennifer Lee (2007)
Daniella Gilbert (2007)
Eleanor Bruce (2008)
Simon Purkis (2008)
Guy Draper (2008)
Jennifer Swan (2009)
Nicholas Williamson (2009)
Monika Sobiecki (2010)
Paul Mertens (2010)
Victoria Ellis (2010)
Naomi Gyane (2010)
Jack Rundall (2010)
Stephen Fielding +

* Associate Member + Mediator/Arbitrator

THE CHAMBERS Pump Court Chambers is a large and well established common law set specialising in civil, criminal and family law. The set has 92 barristers including six silks based across three offices in London, Winchester and Swindon. Each centre is staffed by an experienced clerking team which is known for providing a consistently high service. Although based in London and on the Western Circuit, the work done by members extends throughout the UK and abroad.

WORK UNDERTAKEN

Criminal: Pump Court Chambers' criminal advocates enjoy an outstanding reputation. Over the last 20 years more than 15 of the group have become Circuit Judges. In the same period 15 members of chambers have been appointed as Queen's Counsel. Members have particular expertise in the fields: sexual offences, courts martial, regulatory and disciplinary, dishonesty, drugs, fraud, money laundering, violence, corporate manslaughter and other health and safety prosecutions. The team is made up of 3 Silks and 29 juniors tenants.

Civil: The team has gone from strength to strength with a number of established practitioners recently joining, it is made up of 46 practising members of varying calls including two Silks. Chambers has particular expertise in all areas of business and commercial, employment, inheritance, property, personal injury and clinical negligence, professional negligence and transport law.

Family: With 49 members including three QCs, Pump Court Chambers has one of the largest specialist family law teams at the Bar. The team practices in three main areas: family finance and children public and private law. The family finance team undertakes a wide spectrum of work from complex high net worth "Big Money" cases to actions with more modest assets and incomes. The private children law team specialises in residence and contact disputes and applications for permission to remove children from the jurisdiction. In public law they advise and represent local authorities, parents and guardians in all areas of children work.

PUMP COURT
CHAMBERS

INTERNATIONAL Oba Nsugbe QC is a barrister and solicitor of the Supreme Court of Nigeria. Anthony Akiwumi is admitted as an Attorney of the Cayman Islands and has practised in this jurisdiction since 1997.

PUMP COURT TAX CHAMBERS Kevin Prosser QC

Head of Chambers	Kevin Prosser QC
Senior Clerk	Nigel Jones
Tenants	34

16 Bedford Row, London, WC1R 4EF
Tel (020) 7414 8080 **Fax** (020) 7414 8099 DX London 312
Email clerks@pumptax.com **Website** www.pumptax.com

MEMBERS

Andrew Thornhill QC (1969) (QC-1985)
David Milne QC (1970) (QC-1987)
William Massey QC (1977) (QC-1996) [A]
Kevin Prosser QC (1982) (QC-1996)
John Tallon QC (1975) (QC-2000) [A]
Giles W J Goodfellow QC (1983) (QC-2003) [A] [ADR]
David Ewart QC (1987) (QC-2006)
Julian Ghosh QC (1993) (QC-2006)
Rupert Baldry QC (1987) [A] (QC-2010)
Andrew Hitchmough QC (1991) (QC-2013)
Roger Thomas (1979) (QC-2014)
Ian Richards (1971)
Janek Matthews (1972) [A]
Penny Hamilton (1972) [A] [ADR]
Jeremy White (1976) [A]
Jeremy Woolf (1986) [A]
Emma Chamberlain (1998) [A]
Elizabeth Wilson (1995)
Richard Vallat (1997) [A]
James Henderson (1997) [A]
Sarah Dunn (1998)
Sadiya Choudhury (2002) [A]
Oliver Conolly (2003) [A]
James Rivett (2004)
Jonathan Bremner (2005)
David Yates (2004) [A]
Laura Poots (2007) [A]
Thomas Chacko (2007) [A]
Zizhen Yang (2009) [A]
Charles Bradley (2010)
Edward Waldegrave (2011)
Barbara Belgrano (2011)
Ben Elliot (2012)
Peter Nias (2012) [ADR]
Sir Stephen Oliver QC [ADR]
Dr John Avery Jones CBE [ADR]

[A] Public/Direct Access [ADR] ADR Member

THE CHAMBERS Pump Court Tax Chambers is the largest specialist set of barristers practising exclusively in tax law. Its work extends from large-scale corporate litigation in the higher courts to advisory work on complex personal tax planning. Members of chambers regularly receive instructions from solicitors and accountancy firms of all sizes (from the 'Magic Circle' solicitors and the 'Big Four' accountants to high street advisors), trust companies and directly from in-house professionals from a wide variety of industries. Members also represent the UK government (including HM Revenue & Customs) and foreign governments, including those of Bermuda, Mauritius, New Zealand, Australia, Singapore and Hong Kong. In addition to a popular annual programme of tax seminars, members are frequent speakers at industry events, and contribute to many specialist textbooks and journals: among other works, the set houses the authors of the pioneering tax planning work Potter and Monroe's Tax Planning with Precedents, together with many of the contributing authors of Simon's Direct Tax Service, and the Consulting Editor of Simon's Tax Cases. All members of chambers accept instructions under licensed access and some can accept instructions under Public Access. Full information about how to instruct members of chambers can be found on chambers' website.

WORK UNDERTAKEN Pump Court Tax Chambers fields experts in a full range of corporate and business tax issues, from group reorganisations and mergers to structured finance. Its members advise on a daily basis with regards to international and EU aspects of tax law both for the purposes of tax planning and in a litigious context. Almost all of the leading cases concerning the application of EU law to the direct tax code have featured members of Pump Court Tax Chambers. In addition to appellate work (before the tax tribunals and higher courts) and judicial review proceedings, members of chambers also appear before the courts in other types of litigation which raise tax issues, such as professional negligence claims, trust litigation and matrimonial disputes. Chambers has a strong private client following, with a long history of advising individuals, family companies, trusts and estates. It is able to provide advice on all relevant taxes, including inheritance tax, capital gains tax, income tax and stamp duty land tax issues. Typical examples of such work include the sale and reorganisation of family companies, advice on family trusts and tax planning for landed estates. Its members regularly advise on business property relief, agricultural property relief and specialist heritage property reliefs and, for international clients, expert advice is offered on issues surrounding residence and domicile. Chambers has a number of experts in the niche field of employee remuneration, who advise regularly on share options, pension schemes, employee share ownership plans, profit sharing schemes and national insurance contributions. A considerable proportion of chambers' work concerns VAT advice and litigation. All VAT topics are covered, including partial exemption, business/non-business activity, the Single Market, European law and alternative remedies such as judicial review and actions for Francovich damages. Chambers also provides advice on other indirect taxes, including insurance premium tax, customs duties, landfill tax, climate change levy and aggregates levy. Members of chambers have specialist expertise in all stamp taxes and, in particular, issues with regard to corporate acquisitions and restructuring, property transactions, developments and refinancing. In addition to their daily work as advocates, chambers' Barristers are often instructed to appear as expert witnesses. They also have a particular interest in the use and development of ADR in a tax context, and can offer accredited tax mediators, arbitrators and facilitators.

PUMP COURT
TAX CHAMBERS

QEB HOLLIS WHITEMAN Mark Ellison QC

1-2 Laurence Pountney Hill, London, EC4R OEU
Tel (020) 7933 8855 **Fax** (020) 7929 3732 DX 858 London City
Email barristers@qebhw.co.uk **Website** www.qebholliswhiteman.co.uk

Head of Chambers	Mark Ellison QC
Senior Clerk	Chris Emmings
Chambers Director	Alastair Rhodes
Tenants	64

MEMBERS

Mark Ellison QC (1979) (QC-2008)
Peter Whiteman QC (1967) (QC-1977)
Robin Grey QC (1957) (QC-1979)
John Hilton QC (1964) (QC-1990)
Sir David Calvert-Smith (1969) *
Peter Kyte QC (1970) (QC-1996)
David Spens QC (1973) (QC-1995)
William Boyce QC (1976) (QC-2001)
Tim Roberts QC (1978) (QC-2003) *
David Jeremy QC (1977) (QC-2006)
Edward Brown QC (1983) (QC-2008)
Crispin Aylett QC (1985) (QC-2008)
Peter Finnigan QC (1979) (QC-2009)
Tom Kark QC (1982) (QC-2010)
Sean Larkin QC (1987) (QC-2010)
Sarah Plaschkes QC (1988) (QC-2011)
Zoe Johnson QC (1990) (QC-2012)
Adrian Darbishire QC (1993) (QC-2012)
Anthony Wilcken (1966)
Linda Strudwick (1973)
Ian Paton (1975)
James Bagge (1979) *
Caroline Carney SC (1980) (SC-2001) *
David Groome (1987)
Edward Henry (1988)
Roger Smart (1989)
Paul Wakerley (1990)
Lydia Barnfather (1992)
Selva Ramasamy (1992)
Nicholas Corsellis (1993)
Benn Maguire (1994)
Paul Raudnitz (1994)
Robin Sellers (1994)
Philip Evans (1995)
Mark Aldred (1996)
Susannah Stevens (1997)
Julian Evans (1997)
Rebecca Harris (1997)
Natasha Tahta (1998)
Jocelyn Ledward (1999)
Alexandra Felix (1999)
Ben FitzGerald (2000)
Karen Robinson (2000)
Kerry Broome (2003)
Ari Alibhai (2003)
Philip McGhee (2003)
Philip Stott (2004)
Joanna Warwick (2004)
Tom Baker (2004)
Fraser Coxhill (2004)
Adam King (2005)
Caoimhe Daly (2005)
Rachna Gokani (2006)
Jim Wormington (2007) *
Tom Broomfield (2007)
John Lynch (2008)
Fallon Alexis (2008)
Rhys Meggy (2009)
Katherine Buckle (2009)
Tim Naylor (2010)
Polly Dyer (2010)
Tom Doble (2011)
Isobel Coates (2011)
Thomas Coke-Smyth (2011)

* Associate member

THE CHAMBERS QEB Hollis Whiteman is regarded both nationally and internationally as a leading set within the fields of business crime, general crime, professional regulation and discipline, and intellectual property. Excellence is at the core of the business strategy which is reflected in the approach that is taken to work, across the board. Members and clerks are flexible and innovative, professional, approachable and highly efficient to ensure that chambers continues to develop in a rapidly changing and competitive market place. Public access is accepted by many members of these chambers.

THE SET Chambers is renowned for its wide ranging skills and experience; most often for its strength in advocacy and advisory work. Clients are consistently reassured that chambers remains the number one choice in its respective fields.

WORK UNDERTAKEN

Business Crime & Fraud: Chambers brings high levels of expertise and experience of UK and international jurisdictions to its provision of advice and representation in all areas of fraud and financial crime; bribery/corruption; corporate manslaughter; sanctions; cartels/price fixing; asset forfeiture and recovery; money laundering; insider dealing; market rigging; search warrants and other orders; intellectual property; consumer liability. Members continue to appear in ground breaking trials and as a result of experience of both the 'criminal' and 'corporate' fraud worlds are adept at managing complex investigations.
Professional Regulation: Chambers has an enviable reputation in the regulation of a whole host of professions both in prosecuting and defending. Members regularly appear before disciplinary tribunals (including healthcare, accountants, police, solicitors, courts martial) and regulatory authorities, including the General Medical Council, the General Dental Council, the FCA and sports governing bodies. The knowledge and skill that chambers has gleaned from the directly relevant general and corporate crime practice areas, particularly fraud, significantly sets QEB Hollis Whiteman aside from its competitors.
Crime: Chambers is very proud of its long-standing reputation as one of the finest criminal chambers in the country in both general and corporate crime. Members of chambers continue to prosecute and defend in many of the most significant and high profile criminal trials. Experience is vast and expertise is offered at all levels.
The breadth and depth of experience in criminal and regulatory law has ensured chambers' development in the following areas: public inquiries; inquests; health and safety; consumer law and trading standards.
Tax: Peter Whiteman QC continues to specialise in corporation tax, capital tax and income tax.

QEB
HOLLIS
WHITEMAN

QUADRANT CHAMBERS Luke Parsons QC

Quadrant House, 10 Fleet Street, London, EC4Y 1AU
Tel (020) 7583 4444 **Fax** (020) 7583 4455 **DX** 292 London (Chancery Lane)
Email info@quadrantchambers.com **Website** www.quadrantchambers.com

Head of Chambers	Luke Parsons QC
Chief Executive	Tim Gerrard
Senior Clerks	Gary Ventura
	Simon Slattery
Tenants	61

MEMBERS

Luke Parsons QC (1985) (QC-2003)
Michael N Howard QC (1971) (QC-1986)
Jeremy Russell QC (1975) (QC-1994)
Lionel Persey QC (1981) (QC-1997)
Simon Rainey QC (1982) (QC-2000)
Simon Kverndal QC (1982) (QC-2002)
Nigel Jacobs QC (1983) (QC-2006)
David Goldstone QC (1986) (QC-2006)
Simon Croall QC (1986) (QC-2008)
Robert Lawson QC (1989) (QC-2009)
Nigel Cooper QC (1987) (QC-2010)
Stephen Cogley QC (1984) (QC-2011)
Poonam Melwani QC (1989) (QC-2011)
Robert Thomas QC (1992) (QC-2011)
Chirag Karia QC (1988) (QC-2012)
James M Turner QC (1990) (QC-2013)
Michael Davey QC (1990) (QC-2014)
John Russell QC (1993) (QC-2014)
Guy Blackwood QC (1997) (QC-2014)
Michael Nolan (1981)
Michael McParland (1983)
Matthew Reeve (1987)
John Passmore (1992)
Nevil Phillips (1992)
Thomas Macey-Dare (1994)
John Kimbell (1995)
Nichola Warrender (1995)
Jonathan Chambers (1996)
Stewart Buckingham (1996)
Robert-Jan Temmink (1996)
Peter Ferrer (1998)
Yash Kulkarni (1998)
Christopher M Smith (1999)
Jeremy Richmond (2000)
Timothy Marland (2002)
David Semark (2002)
Ruth Hosking (2002)
Caroline Pounds (2003)
Paul Toms (2003)
Emmet Coldrick (2004)
Paul Henton (2004)
Saira Paruk (2004)
Turlough Stone (2004)
Gemma Morgan (2006)
David Walsh (2007)
Natalie Moore (2007)
Stephanie Barrett (2008)
Benjamin Coffer (2008)
Claudia Wilmot-Smith (2008)
Lucas Bastin (2009)
Christopher Jay (2009)
Liisa Lahti (2009)
Ben Gardner (2010)
Andrew Leung (2010)
Mark Stiggelbout (2011)
Tom Bird (2011)
Emily McCrea-Theaker (2011)
Max Davidson (2013)
Michael Proctor (2013)
Andrew Carruth (2013)
George Economou (1965)

THE CHAMBERS Quadrant Chambers is widely recognised as being one of the leading commercial sets. Members of chambers provide outstanding advocacy in court, arbitration and inquiries, and expert advice across the whole spectrum of commercial law, both nationally and internationally. The set also offers highly experienced arbitrators, mediators and expert witnesses.
Quadrant members pride themselves on being approachable and responsive and are renowned for being attuned to the concerns and business priorities of their clients, combining expertise as advocates with their thorough knowledge of the sectors served. The chambers has a highly motivated support team of clerking and administrative staff, noted for their commitment to providing the highest level of service to all for whom they work. The set also has a modern and flexible attitude to structuring fees. Quadrant House is equipped with conference and arbitration facilities.

WORK UNDERTAKEN Quadrant Chambers holds a pre-eminent international position in the shipping, aviation and travel law sectors. In addition to continuing to strengthen its leading market presence in these areas, the set has reorganised internally to bring a renewed focus on other practice areas in which it already operates, such as energy (offshore), commodities and cross border insolvency.
Quadrant's specialist areas include: arbitration; aviation and travel; banking and finance; commercial litigation; commodities and transport; dry shipping; energy; fraud; insolvency; insurance and reinsurance; international arbitration; mediation; oil and gas; salvage collision and admiralty; shipbuilding and construction.

INTERNATIONAL A large proportion of Quadrant's work is for international clients or involves international commercial law. Members have appeared as advocates and expert witnesses before courts and tribunals worldwide, and several have been called to the bars of other jurisdictions, including those of Hong Kong, Singapore, Korea, Gibraltar, New South Wales, California, Germany, Greece and South Africa.
Members of chambers and arbitrator members also accept appointments as inquiry chairmen, arbitrators and mediators.
For further details please visit the Quadrant website at www.quadrantchambers.com.

quadrant chambers

QUEEN ELIZABETH BUILDING (QEB) Lewis Marks QC

Queen Elizabeth Building, Temple, London, EC4Y 9BS
Tel (020) 7797 7837 **Fax** (020) 7353 5422 **DX** 339 London/Chancery Lane
Email clerks@qeb.co.uk **Website** www.qeb.co.uk

Head of Chambers	Lewis Marks QC
Senior Clerk	Ivor Treherne
Tenants	33

MEMBERS

Lewis Marks QC (1984) (QC-2002)
Lucy Stone QC (1983) (QC-2001)
Charles Hyde QC (1988) (QC-2006)
Tim Amos QC (1987) (QC-2008)
Jennifer Roberts QC (1988) (QC-2009)
Stewart Leech QC (1992) (QC-2011)
Michael Hosford-Tanner (1974)
Andrew Tidbury (1976)
Thomas Brudenell (1977)
Oliver Wise (1981)
Sarah Edwards (1990)
Matthew Firth (1991)
Elizabeth Clarke (1991)
Alexander Thorpe (1995)
Catherine Cowton (1995)
James Ewins (1996)
Sarah Phipps (1997)
Marcus Lazarides (1999)
Duncan Brooks (2000)
Daniel Bentham (2000)
Tristan Harvey (2002)
Morgan Sirikanda (2002)
Rosemary Budden (2003)
Charanjit Batt (2003)
Samantha Singer (2004)
Marina Faggionato (2006)
William Tyzack (2007)
Saima Younis (2008)
Amy Kisser (2009)
Fitzrene Headley (2011)
Sophie Wellings (2011)
Naomi Wiseman (2011)
Robert Cornick (2012)

Dr Jens M Scherpe (Cambridge)+
Hannah Baker (Hague Conference)*
Sir Alan Ward **
Sir Hugh Bennett **
Sir Paul Coleridge **

* Door Tenant + Academic Door Tenant ** Associate Members

THE CHAMBERS QEB specialises in family law, particularly in matrimonial finance and international family law, but also in child law including child abduction and forced marriage. The set has been established for well over 100 years and is consistently rated as one of the best sets for family law. It is also very forward-looking and client-focussed. Chambers has expanded premises to provide more conference rooms and enhanced facilities for private FDRs and other forms of dispute resolution including arbitration, mediation and collaborative law. Many members of chambers are listed as leaders in their field in 'Chambers & Partners', 'The Legal 500' and 'Legal Experts'. The legal directories' praise for QEB includes the following published reviews: "heavyweight family law chambers"; "impressive family set [that] excels in complex financial work"; "long held reputation for excellence"; "hotbed of talent"; "good commercial sense"; "fine tradition of producing the very best financial barristers"; "phenomenally bright barristers abound"; and "jam-packed with trouble shooters capable of tackling the thorniest money cases" (Chambers & Partners); while 'The Legal 500' praises it as having "few peers for expertise in complex ancillary relief" and "almost without exception the barristers are exceptional."
QEB's success and distinction are not a recent phenomenon. QEB has always had an excellent reputation for the quality of the advocates it produces and has been involved in many high profile and historic decisions. Many members of chambers have continued into high judicial office and Lord Wilson sits in the Supreme Court. In addition Sir Alan Ward, following his retirement from the Court of Appeal, and Sir Hugh Bennett and Sir Paul Coleridge, former High Court Judges, have joined chambers as associate members. Sir Alan Ward is the chair of the Civil Mediaton Council and acts as an arbitrator, private FDR-Judge and mediator. Sir Hugh Bennett and Sir Paul Coleridge act as arbitrators and private-FDR Judges.

WORK UNDERTAKEN QEB is particularly well known for dealing with the financial consequences of relationship breakdown but there is immense experience in all aspects of family law including: jurisdictional disputes, foreign divorces, pre-marital agreements, civil partnerships, injunctions both financial and domestic, public and private law child work, child abduction and forced marriage, Inheritance Act claims and disputes between former cohabitees. In addition some members practise in general common law with particular emphasis on personal injury and professional negligence work.
As a complement to its international work QEB offers a range of languages including members of chambers professionally fluent in French, German, Hindi, Punjabi and Urdu.
Members of QEB appear in courts throughout the country and abroad, ranging from magistrates' courts to the Supreme Court and the European Court of Human Rights. The confidentiality of chambers' work is strictly respected but recent public decisions in which members of QEB were briefed include Miller, Charman, Spencer, Marano, Weiner, Robson, Schofield, Jones, Z v Z (No.2.) and Petrodel v Prest. QEB has always been at the forefront of the development of matrimonial law and members have appeared in many of the leading authorities including such seminal decisions as Wachtel, F v F, Duxbury, Preston and White.
The current clerks' room of five is headed by Ivor Treherne who has been senior clerk since 1979. He is assisted by Stephen Morley and the rest of the team. They are happy to recommend particular members for particular cases and provide charging rates on request as well as practical assistance in the management of cases. The QEB clerks are regularly singled out for special praise by external commentators who have hailed the "superlative clerking" at QEB, which is rightly described as "seamless, professional and courteous."

QEB

RADCLIFFE CHAMBERS Keith Rowley QC

11 New Square, Lincoln's Inn, London, WC2A 3QB
Tel (020) 7831 0081 **Fax** (020) 7405 2560 DX LDE 319
Website www.radcliffechambers.com

Head of Chambers	Keith Rowley QC
Senior Clerks	Keith Nagle
	John Clark
Chief Executive	Fiona Fitzgerald
Tenants	44

MEMBERS

Peter Crampin QC (1976) (QC-1993)
Malcolm Waters QC (1977) (QC-1997)
Keith Rowley QC (1979) (QC-2001)
Robert Pearce QC (1977) (QC-2006)
Francesca Quint (1970)
David di Mambro (1973)
Gordon Nurse (1973)
Grant Crawford (1974)
Michael Heywood (1975)
Stephen Acton (1977)
Elizabeth Ovey (1978)
Thomas Dumont (1979)
Ulick Staunton (1984)
Simon Williams (1984)
Piers Feltham (1985)
Howard Smith (1986)
Mark West (1987)
Roger Mullis (1987)
Clive Moys (1998) Admitted as a solicitor (1988)
Katherine McQuail (1989)
Peter Dodge (1992)
Shantanu Majumdar (1992)
Marie-Claire Bleasdale (1993)
Justin Holmes (1994)
Dov Ohrenstein (1995)
Kate Selway (1995)
William Moffett (2000)
Nathan Wells (2000)
Mark Mullen (2001)
Joshua Winfield (2001)
Marcus Flavin (2001)
Frances Ratcliffe (2002)
Tom Beasley (2003)
Steven Barrett (2003)
Christopher Buckley (2004)
Mark Fell (2004)
Edward Hicks (2004)
Josh Lewison (2005)
Wendy Mathers (2005)
Catherine Doran (2008)
Natalie Brown (2009)
Daniel Burton (2009)
Henry Day (2011)
Chris Jeffs (2012)
Nicholas Macklam (2013)

THE CHAMBERS Radcliffe Chambers is one of the largest commercial Chancery chambers in the country. It has 44 barristers, with many recommendations in the current editions of The Legal 500 and Chambers and Partners directories, covering the principal areas of commercial and Chancery law. The achievements of individual members have been recognised in recent years in The Lawyer's Hot 100, the STEP Private Client Awards and The Lawyer Awards. Radcliffe Chambers was a recent winner of the Client Service Set of the Year at the Chambers and Partners Bar Awards. Chambers has a dedicated and experienced staff led by two senior clerks and a Chief Executive; they all help to provide the very best service for its clients, whether they are law firms in the UK or offshore; in-house lawyers; government departments; financial and other institutions; local authorities; or professional or public direct access clients.

WORK UNDERTAKEN Members of Radcliffe Chambers practise in the fields of banking and financial services; charities and associations; company and commercial law; consumer credit and mortgages; insolvency; pensions; planning, environment and local government; professional negligence; property law; tax; and trusts and private client work. Members of chambers have also acquired notable expertise in other areas such as agriculture, bloodstock law, court of protection cases, ecclesiastical law, employment, mines and minerals and telecommunications. For full details please see the chambers website at www.radcliffechambers.com or contact chambers directly for further assistance.

Radcliffe Chambers

THREE RAYMOND BUILDINGS Alexander Cameron QC

3 Raymond Buildings, Gray's Inn, London, WC1R 5BH
Tel (020) 7400 6400 **Fax** (020) 7400 6464 **DX** 237 London
Email clerks@3rblaw.com **Website** www.3rblaw.com

Head of Chambers	Alexander Cameron QC
Senior Clerk	Eddie Holland
Tenants	49

MEMBERS

Alexander Cameron QC (1986) (QC-2003) ^
Clive Nicholls QC (1957) (QC-1982) ^
Colin Nicholls QC (1957) (QC-1981) ^
Richard Horwell QC (1976) (QC-2006)
Michael Borrelli QC (1977) (QC-2000)
Trevor Burke QC (1981) (QC-2001) ^
Michael Bromley-Martin QC (1979) (QC-2002) ^
James Lewis QC (1987) (QC-2002)^
Jane Humphryes QC (1983) (QC-2003)
Simon Farrell QC (1983) (QC-2003) ^
Patrick Gibbs QC (1986) (QC-2006) ^
Helen Malcolm QC (1986) (QC-2006) ^
John Hardy QC (1988) (QC-2008)
Stephen Walsh QC (1983) (QC-2009) ^
Hugo Keith QC (1989) (QC-2009)
Hugh Davies OBE QC (1990) (QC-2013) ^
Richard Atchley (1977)
James Hines (1982) ^
Neil Saunders (1983) ^
Jonathan Ashley-Norman (1989)^
Campaspe Lloyd-Jacob (1990)
Ben Brandon (1991)
Richard Wormald (1993) ^
Alisdair Williamson (1994) ^
Siza Agha (1994) ^
Ben Summers (1994) ^
Saba Naqshbandi (1996) ^
William Emlyn Jones (1996)
Edmund Gritt (1997)
Ailsa Williamson (1997)
Kevin Baumber (1998)
Clair Dobbin (1999)
Guy Ladenburg (2000) ^
Nicholas Yeo (1999) ^
Sarah Le Fevre (2001)^
Matthew Butt (2002) ^
Ben Watson (2002) ^
Luke Ponte (2003)
Rachel Scott (2004)
Rachel Barnes (2004) ^
Rachel Kapila (2006) ^
Bo-Eun Jung (2005) ^
Robert Morris (2008)
Emma Collins (2008)
Heather Oliver (2010)
Patrick Hill (2010)
Kitty St Aubyn (2010)
John Greany (2012)
Daniel Mansell (2012)

^ Public/Direct Access

THE CHAMBERS A multi-disciplined set with a national and international reputation in criminal and quasi-criminal matters.

WORK UNDERTAKEN

Crime: The practice encompasses advocacy and advisory work in every aspect of criminal law, including serious violent and sexual crime, terrorism, drug and human trafficking, bribery and corruption, organised crime, child exploitation, cybercrime, breaches of the Official Secrets Act. They also have expertise across all levels of call in restraint, civil recovery and confiscation.

Recent cases include PC Simon Harwood (manslaughter); advice and representation in respect of charges levelled against Rebekah Brooks and Charles Brooks; charges arising from Operations Elvedon, Sasha and Weeting; Michael Turner, Max Clifford.

Fraud & Financial Regulation: Chambers has a long-established reputation in fraud, money laundering, insider-dealing, and anti-competitive conduct. Expertise extends to civil and commercial fraud claims initiated in the UK and abroad. They are also experienced in Financial Services law and are instructed by both the FCA and individuals and corporations in the financial services industry. Members advise in relation to the full range of FSMA matters including authorisation, compliance and enforcement. Recent matters include Silvio Berlusconi; the LIBOR investigation; the iSoft Fraud.

Extradition & Mutual Legal Assistance: Members have acted in many of the landmark cases of the last 50 years and have helped shape the development of extradition law. They are experts in mutual legal assistance and are instructed regularly by the UK authorities to advise upon and draft letters of request to foreign jurisdictions. They also provide advice and representation to individuals and companies affected by mutual legal assistance requests. Recent cases include Gary McKinnon; Shrien Dewani; Vladimir Antonov.

Public Law: Members appear frequently in judicial review proceedings for both claimants and defendants. They have particular expertise in dealing with applications arising out of extradition proceedings, inquests, decisions relating to the investigation and prosecution of criminal matters, and prison welfare. Members are regularly instructed by the government in public law matters. Hugo Keith QC was a member of the 'A' Panel of civil Treasury Counsel for 8 years and continues to be instructed by the government in matters of public law, and as members of the 'A' and 'B' panels respectively, Clair Dobbin and Ben Watson are instructed in a wide variety of judicial review claims and advise government departments on a range of public law issues.

Inquests & Inquiries: Members are regularly instructed in inquests of the highest importance, most recently the '7/7' Inquests, Raoul Moat; Alexander Litvinenko and Mark Duggan. They also have considerable experience in representing core participants and witnesses before Public Inquiries and have been instructed for various parties in some of the most important Inquiries of recent times, including Leveson and Baha Mousa. Members are also instructed in relation to Hillsborough.

Regulatory Enforcement: The set provides expert advice and representation on a wide range of statutory regimes that regulate the conduct of public bodies, corporations, and individuals. Members regularly appear for prosecuting authorities and defendants in cases concerning health and safety, fire safety, environmental law, consumer protection, and trading standards. They are also active in the areas of financial regulation and regularly appear before VAT and duties tribunals.

THREE RAYMOND BUILDINGS Alexander Cameron QC (continued)

Recent cases include advising the London Fire Authority in the latter stages of the 7/7 Inquests and in the inquest into the deaths resulting from the Lakanal House tower block fire, and acting for the Office of the Rail Regulator in the prosecution of Network Rail following the death of 2 girls on a level crossing at Elsenham railway station.
Licensing: Members have been involved in most of the major licensing and gaming cases in the last 45 years. They advise and represent all those engaged with licensing authorities and the Gambling Commission, including the licensing authorities themselves, individual and corporate applicants and other interested parties, such as the police and residents. Clients include many of the major operators of pubs, clubs, hotels, casinos and betting offices in the United Kingdom.
Professional Discipline: Members are regularly instructed by a wide range of disciplinary authorities and respondents in professional misconduct proceedings. The set has also developed a strong reputation in sports law. Members have acted in proceedings before the International Cricket Council, the British Boxing Board of Control, the Lawn Tennis Association, UK Athletics and others.
International: Members are highly experienced in dealing with matters involving international criminal and humanitarian law before domestic courts as well as international tribunals. They also advise governments, companies and individuals involved in international business transactions about jurisdictional issues and applicable international and regional laws. They have particular expertise in the applicability of international and domestic trade and financial sanctions and the extra-territorial reach of some US laws.

5RB Desmond Browne QC & Matthew Nicklin QC

5 Gray's Inn Square, Gray's Inn, London WC1R 5AH
Tel (020) 7242 2902 **Fax** (020) 7831 2686 **DX** LDE 1054
Email clerks@5RB.com **Website** www.5RB.com

Head of Chambers	Desmond Browne QC and Mark Warby QC
Senior Clerk	Kim Janes
Clerks	Andrew Love
	Jamie Clack
	Antony Braeger
	Alexandra King
	Sam Pringle
	Jack Button

MEMBERS

Desmond Browne QC (1969) (QC 1990) [A]
Matthew Nicklin QC (1993) (QC 2013) [A]
Patrick Milmo QC (1962) (QC 1985) *
Adrienne Page QC (1974) (QC 1999) [A]
James Price QC (1974) (QC 1995) [A]
Justin Rushbrooke QC (1992) (QC 2013) [A]
Stephen Bate (1981) * [A]
Andrew Monson (1983) *
Iain Christie** (1989) [A]
Alexandra Marzec (1990) [A]
Professor Tony Smith (1992)**
David Sherborne (1992)
Jonathan Barnes (1999) [A]
Godwin Busuttil (1994) [A]
Adam Wolanski (1994)
William Bennett (1994) [A]
Christina Michalos (1994) [A]
Jacob Dean (1995) [A]
Nigel Abbas* (1995) [A]
Anna Coppola (1996)** [A]
Adam Speker (1999) [A]
Richard Munden (2003) [A]
David Hirst (2003) [A]
Victoria Shore (2005) [A]
Victoria Jolliffe (2005) [A]
Yuli Takatsuki (2007) [A]
Patrick McCafferty (2008)**
Felicity McMahon (2008)
Chloe Strong (2010)
Gervase de Wilde (2012)

* Non-resident practising member ** Associate member [A] Direct/Public Access

THE CHAMBERS There are presently 30 members, including six Silks. Members represent clients in all courts and before professional, regulatory and disciplinary tribunals, such as OFCOM, the British Horseracing Authority and the Football Association. Junior tenants provide pre-publication advice to newspapers, magazines, book and online publishers, as well as to public authorities. There are four accredited mediators in chambers and one practitioner on the Attorney-General's A Panel. Most members of 5RB undertake direct access work in their specialised fields.
Members are available to advise from the very beginning of a matter through to conducting advocacy at trial and on appeal. In the early stages of a pre-publication matter, this may involve urgent advice followed by an application for or resistance of a High Court injunction. There are out-of-hours contact arrangements and an on-call barristers' rota for advice over weekends and public holidays. Most members are licensed to undertake direct access work. 5RB is sensitive to the fact that, as a leading specialist set, different members are often instructed on opposing sides of the same dispute. There are robust arrangements in place to preserve client confidentiality, including split clerking teams and systems for the separate receipt of oncoming correspondence.

WORK UNDERTAKEN 5RB enjoys a pre-eminent reputation for defamation, malicious falsehood, privacy, breach of confidence, contempt of court and reporting restrictions work but specialises across the broader spectrum of media, entertainment, IP and sports law, including: data protection, freedom of information, harassment, internet law, passing off, copyright, judicial review, particularly of regulatory decisions and professional negligence involving media cases. Members of chambers are often instructed in ongoing litigation in all courts where article 8 (privacy) or article 10 (freedom of expression) issues arise and specialist advice or advocacy is required. For a list of members' cases see www.5rb.com.

PUBLICATIONS Members of the set write or contribute to the principal textbooks in their field: Gatley on Libel and Slander; Blackstone's Guide to The Defamation Act 2013; The Law of Privacy and the Media; Arlidge, Eady & Smith on Contempt; Borrie & Lowe: The Law of Contempt; The Law of Photography and Digital Images; Clerk & Lindsell on Torts and the Entertainment and Media Law Reports. They have written and spoken extensively about the new Defamation Act 2013 and the Operators of Websites Regulations.

5RB
Media and entertainment law

SELBORNE CHAMBERS Romic Tager QC

10 Essex Street, London, WC2R 3AA
Tel (020) 7420 9500 **Fax** (020) 7420 9555 **DX** DX 185 London Chancery Lane
Email clerks@selbornechambers.co.uk **Website** www.selbornechambers.co.uk

Head of Chambers	Romic Tager QC
Senior Clerk	Greg Piner
Deputy Senior Clerk	Paul Bunting
Deputy Director of Chambers	Darren Madle
Administrator	Angela Wiggett
Tenants	29

MEMBERS

Romic Tager QC (1970) (QC-1995)
Ajmalul Hossain QC (1976) (QC-1998) ^
Mark Warwick (1974) QC
Philip Kremen (1975)
Stephen Boyd (1977) ^
Stuart Cakebread (1978) ^
Hugh Jackson (1981) ^
David Uff (1981) ^
Neil Mendoza (1982) ^
William Bojczuk (1983)
Ian Clarke (1990)
Stuart Hornett (1992) ^
Juliette Levy (1992) ^
Gary Blaker (1993) ^
Duncan Kynoch (1994) ^
Alexander Goold (1994) ^
Richard Clegg (1999) ^
Steven Walker (1999) ^
Justin Kitson (2000)
Jonathan McNae (2001) ^
Zoe Barton (2003)
Henry Webb (2005) ^
Nicholas Trompeter (2006) ^
Paul De La Piquerie (2006)
Camilla Chorfi (2008)
Simon McLoughlin (2009)
Justina Stewart (2010)
Joseph England (2011)
David Welford (2010) *

^ Public/Direct Access * Door tenant

THE CHAMBERS Selborne Chambers is a leading commercial-chancery set. It is noted for the clear and practical advice it provides, which can be innovative, and is always mindful of clients' commercial considerations. Chambers recognises the benefits of working closely with those instructing and lay clients, and Members with expertise in complimentary areas can work together in teams to clients' best advantage. Chambers is frequently praised in legal directories for the quality of its service, communicability and helpful and reliable clerking.

WORK UNDERTAKEN Members are instructed in a wide variety of Commercial and Chancery areas, with an emphasis on business, corporate and commercial matters (at both litigious and transactional stages); company and financial services; corporate and personal insolvency; all areas of property related matters; trusts and estates work; international/offshore work; civil fraud and asset recovery; energy and natural resources (including oil, gas and onshore and offshore renewable energy); construction, engineering and mining; telecommunications; sports law; gambling and spread betting. Professional negligence is covered in all these fields, solicitors, valuers, accountants, professional trustees and financial managers and advisors. Much of the work is done in London, though members frequently advise and appear throughout the United Kingdom and in other foreign jurisdictions.

selborne
CHAMBERS

SERLE COURT Alan Boyle QC

6 New Square, Lincoln's Inn, London, WC2A 3QS
Tel (020) 7242 6105 **Fax** (020) 7405 4004 **DX** LDE 1025
Email clerks@serlecourt.co.uk **Website** www.serlecourt.co.uk

Head of Chambers	Alan Boyle QC
Chief Executive	Nicola Sawford
Head Clerk	Steven Whitaker
Senior Clerk	Nick Hockney
Tenants	56

MEMBERS

Alan Boyle QC (1972) (QC-1991)
Patrick Talbot QC (1969) (QC-1990)
Kuldip Singh QC (1975) (QC-1993)
Frank Hinks QC (1973) (QC-2000)
Elizabeth Jones QC (1984) (QC-2000)
Paul Chaisty QC (1982) (QC-2001)
Dominic Dowley QC (1983) (QC-2002)
Conor Quigley QC (1985) (QC-2003)
Philip Marshall QC (1987) (QC-2003)
Philip Jones QC (1985) (QC-2006)
Lance Ashworth QC (1987) (QC-2006)
Khawar Qureshi QC (1990) (QC-2006)
Nicholas Lavender QC (1989) (QC-2008)
David Casement QC (1992) (QC-2008)
Christopher Stoner QC (1991) (QC-2010)
Michael Edenborough QC (1992) (QC-2010)
John Machell QC(1993) (QC-2012)
Hugh Norbury QC (1995) (QC-2012)
David Blayney QC (1992) (QC-2013)
Jonathan Adkin QC (1997) (QC-2013)
Nicholas Asprey (1969)
Julian Burling (1976)
Andrew Francis (1977)
William Henderson (1978)
James Behrens (1979)
Richard Walford (1984)
Nicholas Harrison (1988)
Geraldine Clark (1988)
Andrew Moran (1989)
Andrew Bruce (1992)
David Drake (1994)
Justin Higgo (1995)
Daniel Lightman (1995)
Timothy Collingwood (1996)
Giles Richardson (1997)
Thomas Braithwaite (1998)
Simon Hattan (1999)
Jennifer Haywood (2001)
Ruth Jordan (2001)
Ruth den Besten (2001)
Dakis Hagen (2002)
Jonathan Fowles (2004)
Matthew Morrison (2004)
Professor Jonathan Harris (2006)
James Mather (2006)
Robin Rathmell (2006)
Dan McCourt Fritz (2007)
Gareth Tilley (2007)
Paul Adams (2008)
Thomas Elias (2008)
Sophie Holcombe (2009)
Adil Mohamedbhai (2010)
Jonathan McDonagh (2011)
Emma Hargreaves (2012)
Zahler Bryan (2012)
Suzanne Rab (2013)

THE CHAMBERS *"Serle Court provides top-level expertise across the full range of business law, and its 56 members possess the requisite expertise to handle any business dispute that may arise". "Its members are valued by instructing solicitors for their 'outstanding brainpower and focus,' and are noted for being amongst the most modern of practitioners at the Bar today". "This modern and commercial approach is followed wholesale by Serle Court's barristers, who 'have no airs or graces, roll up their sleeves and work as part of a team'... 'this is a chambers that your client will like, and one they will believe shares their values'". - Chambers & Partners.* Widely recognised as one of the top sets at the English Bar, Serle Court is also one of the largest commercial chancery sets, with 56 members, including 20 silks. Serle Court's members offer genuine expertise across a broad range of chancery and commercial disciplines. Serle Court covers the whole range of 'business' law, from offshore litigation about the world's largest companies to domestic advice on probate matters, servicing a similarly disparate lay and professional client base at home and abroad.

WORK UNDERTAKEN Serle Court's core practice is litigation: Serle Court can provide barristers at all levels to conduct all types of business litigation, and are experienced at putting together streamlined and powerful teams for some of the largest cases in the world. In the past few years these have included Weissfisch (in the Bahamas), Alhamrani (in Jersey) and, closer to home, JSC BTA Bank v Ablyazov, Fiona Trust & Holding Corporation & Ors v Privalov, Re Lexi Holdings plc, the NHS drugs cartel litigation, and the RBS rights issue litigation amongst many others. Members also undertake a significant amount of advisory work. Serle Court was in the vanguard of the ADR revolution, and has established itself as one of the leading ADR sets, with a large number of highly regarded mediators and arbitrators as well as many members with extensive experience of appearing in 'alternative' dispute resolution forums. Please see Serle Court's website for comprehensive details of the wide-ranging areas of practice of its members.

INTERNATIONAL A significant proportion of Serle Court's work originates overseas: Serle Court has particularly close relationships with professional clients in the Channel Islands and the Caribbean, but members have advised and appeared in proceedings all over the world, from Russia to the USA, and from Europe to the Middle East.

serle court

SOUTH SQUARE

3-4 South Square, Gray's Inn, London, WC1R 5HP
Tel (020) 7696 9900 **Fax** (020) 7696 9911 **DX** 338 (Ch.Ln.)
Email practicemanagers@southsquare.com **Website** www.southsquare.com

Chambers Director	Ron Barclay-Smith
Practice Managers	Michael Killick
	Dylan Playfoot
	Jim Costa
	Marco Malatesta
Tenants	41

MEMBERS

Michael Crystal QC (1970) (QC-1984) LLB (Lond), BCL (Oxon)
Christopher Brougham QC (1969) (QC-1988) BA (Oxon)
Gabriel Moss QC (1974) (QC-1989) MA, BCL (Oxon)
Simon Mortimore QC (1972) (QC-1991) LLB (Exon)
Richard Adkins QC (1982) (QC-1995) MA (Oxon)
Richard Sheldon QC (1979) (QC-1996) MA (Cantab)
Richard Hacker QC (1977) (QC-1998) MA (Cantab) Lic sp Dr Eur (Bruxelles)
Robin Knowles CBE QC (1982) (QC-1999) MA (Cantab)
Mark Phillips QC (1984) (QC-1999) LLB, LLM (Bristol)
Robin Dicker QC (1986) (QC-2000) BA, BCL (Oxon)
William Trower QC (1983) (QC 2001) MA (Oxon)
Martin Pascoe QC (1977) (QC-2002) BA, BCL (Oxon)
Fidelis Oditah QC (1992) (QC-2003) MA, BCL, D Phil (Oxon)
David Alexander QC (1987) (QC-2006) MA (Cantab)
Antony Zacaroli QC (1987) (QC-2006) BA, BCL (Oxon)
Glen Davis QC (1992) (QC-2011) MA (Oxon)
Barry Isaacs QC (1994) (QC-2011) BA (Oxon)
Felicity Toube QC (1995) (QC-2011) BA, BCL (Oxon)
Mark Arnold QC (1988) (QC-2013) MA (Cantab)
Jeremy Goldring QC (1996) (QC-2013) BA (Oxon) MA (Yale)
Lucy Frazer QC (1996) (QC-2013) MA (Cantab)
David Allison QC (1998) (QC-2014) MA (Cantab)
Tom Smith QC (1999) (QC-2014) BA, LLM (Cantab)
John Briggs (1973) LLB (Lond) Ex, Du D d'U (Nancy)
Adam Goodison (1990) BA (Dunelm)
Hilary Stonefrost (1991) MSC (Lond)
Lloyd Tamlyn (1991) BA (Cantab) MA (HARV) ASA
Daniel Bayfield (1998) MA (Cantab)
Richard Fisher (2000) LLB (Lond) BCL (Oxon)
Stephen Robins (2001) BA (Oxon)
Joanna Perkins (2001) BA, LLM (Cantab) D Phil (Oxon)
Marcus Haywood (2002) BA (Oxon)
Hannah Thornley (2003) MA (Cantab), BCL (Oxon)
William Willson (2006) MA (Oxon)
Georgina Peters (2005) MA (Cantab)
Adam Al-Attar (2007) BA BCL (Oxon)
Henry Phillips (2008) BA BCL (Oxon)
Charlotte Cooke (2008) MA MPhil (Cantab) BCL (Oxon)
Alexander Riddiford (2011) BA (Oxon)
Matthew Abraham (2012) LLB (Lond) BCL (Oxon)
Toby Brown (2005) BSc (Nottingham)
Prof Ian Fletcher QC (Hon) (1971) (QC-2013) MA, LLM, Phd, LLD (Cantab), MCL (Tulane) ++
Prof Sarah Worthington (2005) BSc LLB LLM PhD (Cantab) ++
Prof Riz Mokal (1997) PhD BCL LLB BSc ++
Barry Mortimer QC (1956) (QC-1971) MA (Cantab) **
Seenath Jairam SC (1998) LLM **
John Sheahan SC (1997) BA LLB (Hons) (UQ) **
Ronald DeKoven (2009) BA (Stanford), JD (Chicago) **
Sandy Shandro (2008) BA (Alberta) MA (McGill) BCL MA (Oxon) **
Sandra Bristoll (1989) MA (Cantab) **
Roxanne Ismail SC (1993) LLB (Lond) **
Colin Bamford (2002) MA (Cantab) **
Volker Heinz (1989) DipLaw (City) **
Simon Fuller (2003) BA (Cantab) LLM (Cornell) **

++ Academic Member ** Associate Member

THE CHAMBERS South Square is one of the leading commercial law sets of barristers. It specialises in restructuring/insolvency, banking, commercial, company, financial services and fraud related disputes. Members regularly appear in the courts and tribunals of various international jurisdictions in addition to those of England and Wales.

WORK UNDERTAKEN

Insolvency & Restructuring: South Square is recognised as being the leading set of chambers for restructuring/insolvency work.

Members have appeared in recent significant Supreme Court cases such as BNY v Eurosail [2013] UKSC 28 (test for inability to pay debts), Nortel/Lehman [2013] UKSC 52 (status of liabilities under the Pensions Act 2004 in insolvencies), Rubin v Eurofinance [2012] UKSC 46 (recognition of judgments delivered in foreign insolvency proceedings), Belmont v BNY [2012] AC 383 (anti-deprivation principle) and HSBC v Mills [2012] AC 804 (non-competition clauses and the rule against double proof).

Banking & Finance: South Square has a strong presence in all aspects of banking and finance work, with a particular specialisation in large scale financial disputes, derivatives and structured finance products. Due to its leading restructuring practice, South Square is uniquely positioned to deal with credit crunch litigation and advisory work.

Members have appeared in recent significant cases, including Lehman client money [2012] UKSC 6 (FSA client money rules), Lomas v Firth Rixson [2013] 1 BCLC 27 (interpretation of ISDA Master Agreement), HHY Luxembourg v Barclays [2011] 1 BCLC 336 (release provisions in intercreditor agreement), Assenagon v Anglo Irish Bank [2013] 1 All ER 495 (resolutions to amend terms of subordinated bonds) and Azevedo v Imcopa Importacao [2013] EWCA Civ 364 (validity of consent payments in a bond restructuring).

Commercial Dispute Resolution: South Square has a strong presence in the field of commercial dispute resolution. Members have appeared in recent significant cases, including Northern Rock [2013] EWCA Civ 492 (compensation payable to shareholders following the nationalisation of Northern Rock), Henderson PFI Secondary Fund II LLP

SOUTH SQUARE (continued)

[2012] 2 CLC 905 (private equity fund manager's liability for breach of investment mandate) and Standard Chartered Bank v Ceylon Petroleum [2012] EWCA Civ 1049 (corporate capacity to enter into derivatives trades).

Company: South Square plays a major role in company law cases. Representative matters include schemes of arrangement, directors' duties, shareholders' agreements, joint venture agreements and technical issues of statutory interpretation arising under the Companies Act 2006.

Recent significant matters include Re Rodenstock [2012] BCC 459 and Re PrimaCom [2013] BCC 201.

Civil Fraud & Asset Recovery: South Square regularly takes a leading role in large scale civil fraud and asset recovery litigation.

Members have appeared in litigation arising from the Madoff fraud, the Saad Group fraud, the Stanford fraud and the Snoras Bank fraud.

International & Offshore: Members of Chambers are at the forefront of insolvency, banking, company and fraud matters before the courts of all the major offshore jurisdictions.

Recent matters include Madoff, Saad Group and Sphinx.

Chambers also specialises in claims in relation to offshore trusts, such as the Thyssen litigation in Bermuda and the Tchenguiz litigation in Guernsey.

11 SOUTH SQUARE Michael Silverleaf QC

11 South Square, Gray's Inn, London, WC1R 5EY
Tel (020) 7405 1222 **Fax** (020) 7242 4282 **DX** 433
Email clerks@11southsquare.com **Website** www.11southsquare.com

Head of Chambers	Michael Silverleaf QC
Senior Clerk	Ashley Carr
Tenants	16

MEMBERS

Michael Silverleaf QC (1980) (QC-1996)
Henry Carr QC (1982) (QC-1998)
Iain Purvis QC (1986) (QC-2006)
Mark Vanhegan QC (1990) (QC-2009)
Piers Acland QC (1993) (QC-2010)
Heather Lawrence (1990)
Jacqueline Reid (1992)
Hugo Cuddigan (1995)
Benet Brandreth (1999)
Brian Nicholson (2000)
Anna Edwards-Stuart (2002)
Kathryn Pickard (2001)
Tom Alkin (2006)
Chris Aikens (2005)
Chris Hall (2010)
Professor Lionel Bently (2009) *

* Door Tenant

THE CHAMBERS 11 South Square is a leading set of barristers' chambers specialising in intellectual property law. The set is additionally respected for its information technology and entertainment work. Former member, Richard Hacon, joined the list of members who have been called to the bench in his recent appointment as the presiding Judge of the Intellectual Property Enterprise Court. Current Court of Appeal Judge Lord Justice Floyd and current Patents Court Judge Mr Justice Arnold are also previous members, as was the late Lord Justice Pumfrey.

WORK UNDERTAKEN Patents; copyright and designs; trademarks and passing off; confidential information and privacy; computer law and other technical litigation; data protection and freedom of information; entertainment and media law and performers rights; and European Community law.

Additional work: Members of chambers are often involved in arbitrations and mediations, as advocates, mediators and members of the panel.

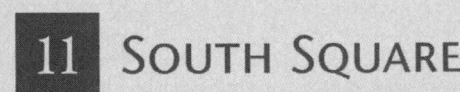

11 SOUTH SQUARE

5 ST ANDREW'S HILL Simon Draycott QC

5 St Andrew's Hill, London, EC4V 5BZ
Tel (020) 7332 5400 **Fax** (020) 7489 7847 **DX** 417 London/Chancery Lane
Email clerks@5sah.co.uk **Website** www.5sah.co.uk

Head of Chambers	Simon Draycott QC
Chambers Director	Wayne King
Clerks	Gary Norton (First Junior)
	Dean Cook (Second Junior)
	Theresa Burke (Fees Clerk)
	Adam Murray
	Micky Pullinger
Tenants	57

MEMBERS

Simon Draycott QC (1977) (QC 2002) + ^
David Nathan QC (1971) (QC-2002)
David Josse QC (1985) (QC 2009)
Edward Munir (1956) ^
Roger Bartlett (1968) ++
Charles Bennett (1972) **
James Harris (1975) ^
James Vine (1977) ^
Roger A Birch (1979) ^
Bernard Devlin (1980) ^
Christopher May (1983) ^
Jonathan Ingram (1984) ^
Anthony Prosser (1985)
Ian Foinette (1986) ^
Andrew Bird (1987) *
Dominic Connolly (1989) ^
David Stern (1989)
Allister Walker (1990)
David Hewitt (1991) *** ^
Vivian Walters (1991) ^
Kevin Dent (1991)
Jenny Goldring (1993) ^
Philip Galway-Cooper (1993) ^
Mark Cotter (1994) ^
Paul Valder (1994) ^
Mark Mullins (1995) ^
Gary Pons (1995) ^
Edward Connell (1996) + ^
Bridget Todd (1996)
Edmund Burge (1997) ***
Richard Scott (1997)
Francesca Levett (1997) ^
Don Ramble (1998) ^
Wendy Hewitt (1999)
John Warrington (2000) ^
James Fletcher (2000) ^
Abigail White (2000)
Alex Rooke (2001)
Serena Gates (2002) ^
Claire Cooper (2002)
Ini Udom (2002)
David McNeill (2003) ^
Dennis Kavanagh (2003)
John Keal (2004)
Benjamin Keith (2004) ^
Rebecca Hill (2004)
Louisa Collins (2004)
Natasha Draycott (2005)
Amelia Nice (2006)
Mary Westcott (2007)
Christopher Williams (2008)
Krystal Whyment (2008)
David Williams (2009)
Hannah Adams (2010)
Richard Reid (2010)
Ben Burge (2010)
Karl Masi (2011)

^ Public/Direct Access + Recorder ++ Deputy Chancery Master * Treasury Solicitor Panel A counsel
** Immigration Appeals Adjudicator *** Special Advocate

THE CHAMBERS 5 St Andrew's Hill consists of 57 members, including 3 Queen's Counsel. Chambers is a leading specialist multi-practice set, with specific expertise in asset recovery and confiscation, business crime, civil fraud, crime, extradition, regulatory and professional disciplinary work.

WORK UNDERTAKEN

Asset Recovery, Civil Fraud & Confiscation: 5 St Andrew's Hill is a set of leading London asset forfeiture and confiscation barristers, and has been involved in this area of work for many years. Barristers act for both applicants and respondents, and have appeared in many of the leading cases in this fast developing and increasingly important area.

Business Crime: Barristers of 5 St Andrew's Hill regularly accept instructions to act in complex and serious fraud litigation on behalf of both the prosecution, including the SFO, and the defence. The team expertise include Libor, FCA investigations, Excise duty fraud, VAT fraud, Missing Trader Intra-Community (MTIC) fraud, tax credit fraud, insurance fraud, mortgage fraud, charities fraud, corruption, bribery and other high level financial crime. Members of the team also frequently appear at the VAT tribunal. Barristers advise and appear for clients both in the UK and overseas.

Civil Litigation: Barristers of 5 St Andrew's Hill cover all the principal areas of chancery litigation. The team act in cases involving wills and probate, Inheritance Act claims, trusts, co-ownership, boundary and neighbour disputes, easements and restrictive covenants. The team also deal with and specialise in areas of modern commercial Chancery and company law with a particular emphasis on insolvency and restructuring, banking law and civil fraud. 5 St Andrew's Hill's barristers advise and appear for clients both in the UK and overseas.

Crime: Barristers of 5 St Andrew's Hill have expertise in defending and prosecuting in cases covering the full spectrum of criminal offences, including the most serious and complex cases. The team are supported by 3 leading Queens Counsel and 50 juniors appear at all levels from the Supreme Court to Magistrates Court.

Disciplinary & Regulatory: Barristers at 5 St Andrew's Hill are known for their breadth of experience in the field of regulatory law. The regulatory team are highly experienced in environmental, housing, planning, street works, health and safety, food hygiene, public utility, infringement of trademarks and copyright, trading standards and licensing matters.

The healthcare team regularly appear on behalf of the medical professions/professionals before the General Dentist Council, Nursing and Midwifery Council and the Health and Care Professions Council. .

Extradition: Barristers at 5 St Andrew's Hill are experts in defending and prosecuting extradition cases. Chambers is a leading set for extradition work and represents requested persons in proceedings both inside and outside the European Arrest Warrant (EAW) system including Westminster Magistrates' Court, and appeals to the Divisional and Administrative Courts, Supreme Court and the European Court of Human Rights. The barristers represent clients both in the UK and overseas.

3 STONE BUILDINGS Andrew M Twigger QC

Head of Chambers	Andrew Twigger QC
Senior Clerk	Andrew Palmer
Tenants	30

3 Stone Buildings, Lincoln's Inn, London, WC2A 3XL
Tel (020) 7242 4937 **Fax** (020) 7405 3896 **DX** 317
Email clerks@3sb.law.co.uk **Website** www.3stonebuildings.com

MEMBERS

Andrew M Twigger QC (1994) (QC-2011) BA (Oxon)
Peter Crampin QC (1976) (QC-1993) MA (Oxon)
Gilead Cooper QC (1983) (QC-2006) MA (Oxon) Dip Law
David W Lord QC (1987) (QC-2009) LLB (Bristol)
Prof. Norman E Palmer QC (1973) (QC-2010) MA, BCL (Oxon)
Fenner Moeran QC (1996) (QC-2014) BSc Bristol
Andrew J Cosedge (1972) LLB (Exon)
James Gibbons (1974)
Alan M Tunkel (1976) BA (Oxon)
Robert A Hantusch (1982) MA (Cantab)
Teresa Rosen Peacock (1982) MA, BA (Mich)
Francis Collaco Moraes (1985) BA (Law)
Adrian Francis (1988) LLB (Wales)
Ian Watson (2005) BA (Brown) JD (Columbia)
David Pope (1995) LLB (Hons) (Edin) LLM (Harvard)
Joseph Carney (2004) LLB, BEC (Adelaide)
Richard Wilson (1996) LLB (Sheffield) LLM (London)
Andrew J Child (1997) BA (Cantab)
Paul Burton (1998) LLB, LLM (Lond)
Kerry Bornman (1999) LLB (Reading)
Constance McDonnell (2000) MA (Oxon)
Luke Harris (2001) LLB (Lond)
Oliver Hilton (2002) LLB (Lond)
Matthew Slater (2005) BA (Oxon)
James Weale (2007) LLB (Bristol) BCL (Oxon)
Jennifer Seaman (2007) BA, BCL (Oxon)
Edward Hewitt (2007) LLB (Lond) BCL (Oxon)
Seth Cumming (2010) BSc (Rhodes) MSc (Lond) BPP
Daisy Boulter (2010) LLB (Kent)
Harry Martin (2012) BA, BCL (Oxon)

THE CHAMBERS 3 Stone Buildings is a leading set of chancery and commercial chambers. Its main practice areas are commercial and chancery litigation, pensions, property, trusts and tax, company and insolvency, insurance and reinsurance. In addition, 3 Stone Buildings offers specialists in media entertainment and sports, partnership, professional negligence, banking and financial services, and cultural property. Members of chambers undertake litigation drafting and advice in all these areas. Direct instructions are accepted from accountants, actuaries, surveyors and others under the Licensed Access Scheme.

INTERNATIONAL Chambers also has an annexe in New York - 10 Rockefeller Plaza, 16th Floor, New York, NY 10020-1903. Tel: (1) 212 713 7680 Fax: (1) 212 713 7679.

3 Stone Building

4 STONE BUILDINGS George Bompas QC

Head of Chambers	George Bompas QC
Senior Clerk	David Goddard
Tenants	31

4 Stone Buildings, Lincoln's Inn, London, WC2A 3XT
Tel (020) 7242 5524 **Fax** (020) 7831 7907 DX 385
Email clerks@4stonebuildings.com **Website** www.4stonebuildings.com

MEMBERS

George Bompas QC (1975) (QC-1994)
John Brisby QC (1978) (QC-1996)
Robert Miles QC (1987) (QC-2002)
Jonathan Crow QC (1981) (QC-2006)
Richard Hill QC (1993) (QC-2012)
Andrew Clutterbuck QC (1992) (QC-2014)
Orlando Fraser QC (1994) (QC-2014)
Stephen Hunt (1968)
Peter Griffiths (1977)
Sarah Harman (1987)
Christopher Harrison (1988)
Jonathan Brettler (1988)
Paul Greenwood (1991)
Nicholas Cox (1992)
Charles Marquand (1987)
Anna Markham (1996)
Hermann Boeddinghaus (1996)
Andrew de Mestre (1998)
Gregory Denton-Cox (2000)
Sharif Shivji (2001)
Tiran Nersessian (2002)
Alastair Tomson (2004)
Adam Holliman (2005)
Tom Gentleman (2005)
Donald Lilly (2006)
Alexander Cook (2008)
Nicola Timmins (2008)
James Knott (2008)
Eleanor Holland (2010)
Joseph Wigley (2010)
Nienke van den Berg (2012)

THE CHAMBERS Chambers currently consist of 31 members, including seven silks. Four members are currently on the Treasury panels. Four members are appointed to sit as Deputy Judges of the High Court. One of the silks is Attorney General to the Duchy of Lancaster and another is Attorney General to the Prince of Wales. One member is on the board of the Charity Commission. Chambers belong to the Commercial Bar Association and the Chancery Bar Association.

WORK UNDERTAKEN Work covers all aspects of company and commercial litigation, including share holders disputes, corporate fraud and asset recovery as well as commercial arbitration, banking, financial services and regulatory work, international trusts and public law. The clerks' room is staffed during term from 8am to 8pm Monday to Friday and chambers can be contacted out of hours on the number given on the chambers' answering machine and on the website. Further information about chambers and the work undertaken is available on the website www.4stonebuildings.com.

PUBLICATIONS Members of chambers have contributed to numerous publications in their specialist fields including Annotated Companies Acts (Oxford University Press), Tolley's Company Law, Atkin Court Forms 2nd ed., (volumes on companies, winding up and equitable remedies), Halsbury's Laws of England 4th ed. (volumes on corporations and money); A Practitioner's Guide to Directors' Duties and Responsibilities (City & Financial Publishing).

INTERNATIONAL Chambers undertake a substantial amount of work for overseas clients and members regularly receive instructions from the Caribbean, the United States, Europe, Central Asia and the Far East. In recent years, members have appeared in court in Bermuda, the Cayman Islands, Bahamas, Gibraltar, Anguilla, the British Virgin Islands, the Turks and Caicos Islands, Malaysia, Singapore, Nevis, Dominica, Seychelles and Trinidad. In addition certain members are full members of the Northern Ireland Bar, the Cayman Islands Bar and the Bar of the British Virgin Islands.

RECRUITMENT 4 Stone Buildings' policy is to seek to recruit one new member each year from among its pupils. Prospective applicants for pupillage will find further information including details of chambers' awards in the Pupillage Pack which is available on request. Mini-pupillages are encouraged.

5 STONE BUILDINGS Henry Harrod

Head of Chambers	Henry Harrod
Senior Clerk	Paul Jennings
Tenants	28

5 Stone Buildings, Lincoln's Inn, London, WC2A 3XT
Tel (020) 7242 6201 **Fax** (020) 7831 8102 **DX** 304 London/Chancery Lane
Email clerks@5sblaw.com **Website** www.5sblaw.com

MEMBERS

Henry Harrod (1963)
Shân Warnock-Smith QC (1971) (QC-2002)
Christopher Whitehouse (1971)
Mark Herbert QC (1974) (QC-1995) ++
Mark Blackett-Ord (1974)
Andrew Simmonds QC (1980) (QC-1999) ++
Miranda Allardice (1982)
Penelope Reed QC (1983) (QC-2009) ++
Christopher Tidmarsh QC (1985) (QC-2002)
Tracey Angus QC (1991) (QC-2012)
Henry Legge QC (1993) (QC-2012)
Michael O'Sullivan (1986)
Patrick Rolfe (1987)
Barbara Rich (1990)
David Rees (1994) +
Anna Clarke (1994)
Leon Sartin (1997)
Sarah Haren (1999)
Thomas Entwistle (2001)
Joseph Goldsmith (2003)
Caroline Kenny (2006)
Mark Baxter (2006)
Charlotte Edge (2006)
Ruth Hughes (2007) **
William East (2008)
Jordan Holland (2009)
Mathew Roper (2011)
Alexander Drapkin (2012)

++ Deputy High Court Judge + Recorder ** Member of Attorney General's (C Panel)

THE CHAMBERS 5 Stone Buildings is one of the outstanding sets of chancery chambers. With expertise at all levels in the fields of private client, estate planning, tax, probate disputes, partnership, property litigation, art and cultural property, professional negligence, pensions and all chancery related commercial matters. Chambers has an extensive team experienced in the field of advice, drafting and litigation relating to trusts, wills and associated taxation both in the UK and overseas; and a specialist team experienced in Court of Protection work. Chambers aims to provide a fast, efficient modern service of the highest standard.

FIVE STONE BUILDINGS

9 STONE BUILDINGS Edward Denehan

9 Stone Buildings, Lincoln's Inn, London, WC2A 3NN
Tel (020) 7404 5055 **Fax** (020) 7405 1551 **DX** 314 Chancery Lane
Email clerks@9stonebuildings.com **Website** www.9stonebuildings.com

Head of Chambers	Edward Denehan
Senior Clerk	Alan Austin
Clerks	David Clayton
	Jake Price
	Harry Feldman
Tenants	27

MEMBERS

Edward Denehan (1981)
Vivian R Chapman QC (1970) (QC-2006)
Michael Ashe QC (1971) (QC-1994) (QC N I 1998) (SC Ireland 2000)
Isaac E Jacob (1963)
David Rowell (1972)
Christopher Cant (1973)
Martin Young (1984)
Lynne M Counsell (1986)
Christopher Spratt (1986)
Timothy Sisley (1989)
Philip Flower (1979)
Philip Brown (1991)
Helene Pines Richman (1992)
Andrew Noble (1992)
Alana Graham (1993)
Peter Shaw (1995)
Daniel Bromilow (1996)
Elaine Palser (2002)
JonathanO'Mahony(2000)
Joseph Curl (2007)
Conn MacEvilly (1997)
Rory Brown (2009)
Shuvra Deb (2007)
Raj Arumugam (2008)
Paul Wilmshurst (2007)
Graham Callard (2001)
Giselle McGowan (2011)

THE CHAMBERS The strength of chambers lies in its long history and proven experience in the areas of traditional and commercial chancery. Many members of chambers are recognised as leading practitioners in their fields. Chambers are one of the oldest established sets of barristers' chambers in Lincoln's Inn. Chamber's history is easily traceable since 1893.

WORK UNDERTAKEN The chambers main practice areas are:
Land & Property Law: Land easements and covenants, mortgages, charges, guarantees and credit arrangements, landlord and tenant including business, agricultural and residential tenancies, housing associations and leasehold enfranchisement, the law of commons, village greens and open spaces, stamp duty land tax.
Private Client Law: Charities, Court of Protection, revenue including income tax, capital gains tax, corporation tax, value added tax, inheritance tax and SDLT, also trusts, settlements and wills, probate, administration of estates and family provision.
Insolvency & Company Law: Personal and corporate insolvency, companies and partnerships including share holders and partners' actions, minority rights, directors' duties, internal disputes and company acquisitions, confiscation and asset recovery.
Business, Financial & Commercial Law: Injunctions and other equitable remedies, fraud, conspiracy, mistake, misrepresentation, constructive trusts, tracing and restitution, securities regulation including share and other investment transactions, investor protection, regulation of financial services, market abuse and insider dealing, contract and commercial, banking, professional negligence, conflict of laws, judicial review, employment law, confidential information, covenants restraining business activity or employment, intellectual property and passing off.

PUBLICATIONS Members of chambers produce a wealth of articles and publications in the core practice areas. Details may be found on the website.

INTERNATIONAL 9 Stone Buildings has an abundance of expertise and experience in foreign jurisdictions and international law. Chambers has members who regularly act as advocates or advisers in SE Asia (particularly Singapore and Malaysia), the Caribbean (particularly the Cayman Islands, Turks and Caicos Islands and the British Virgin Islands), North America and Europe (particularly Eire, Gibraltar, the Bahamas and Switzerland). Some members are regularly instructed in the UK offshore jurisdictions of the Channel Islands and the Isle of Man. 9 Stone Buildings is considerably strengthened in this area by its overseas members who, as well as being members of the English Bar, are leading practitioners in their jurisdictions: Nicholas Critelli, a trial attorney in the states of Iowa and New York, a member of the Bar of the Supreme Court and former Chair of the Iowa Bar Association (2004); James Levy QC and Anthony Provasoli are partners in the internationally known law firm of Hasans in Gibraltar. Dr Raymond Ashton is a member of the English and Irish Bar and a Guernsey Advocate. He is also a chartered accountant. Gabrielle Culmer is a member of the English Bar and of the New York and Bahamas Bar.

RECRUITMENT The chambers has a committed policy to recruit excellent barristers both at the established and junior levels.

9 STONE BUILDINGS
Barristers' Chambers

11 STONE BUILDINGS Edward Cohen

Head of Chambers	Edward Cohen
Chambers Director	Michael Couling
Clerks	Matthew Curness
	Richard Powell
	Gary Collins
	Harrison Killick
	Lee Wright
	Charlotte Temple
	Sue Harding
	Justin Yoong
	Giovanna Scozzaro
	Frank Fenton
Tenants	42

11 Stone Buildings, Lincoln's Inn, London, WC2A 3TG
Tel (020) 7831 6381 **Fax** (020) 7831 2575 **DX** 1022 London
Email clerks@11sb.com **Website** www.11sb.com

THE CHAMBERS 11 Stone Buildings is a leading set of 42 commercial and chancery barristers based in London, with a recognised expertise in commercial litigation, insolvency, company, banking/finance, civil fraud, professional negligence and real estate matters.
Chambers acts as advocates, advisers, arbitrators and mediators for law firms across the country and internationally, for in-house legal departments and for direct and public access clients. The set has fully equipped ADR/arbitration facilities available.
Chambers' instructing solicitors appreciate that the set offers a multi-disciplinary advantage as a large number of our barristers possess expertise across several disciplines. It is the depth and strength of the interplay between general commercial litigation and areas such as banking, fraud, IP, insolvency, real estate and pensions, which is at the heart of their expertise. It is also the reason why people go to them with complex matters.
Besides offering excellent expert advice, clients appreciate that a number of its members are multi-lingual and are commercially minded through their experience gained outside the Bar, such as in investment banking, in management consultancy, as solicitors or running their own business. Barristers speak French, German, Italian, Russian, Romanian and Spanish.

WORK UNDERTAKEN Chambers' expertise is grouped around four pillars of law: commercial, company/insolvency, real estate and private client work. In each area they have specialist teams which can assist you with the following:
Commercial: Banking and finance, employment, fraud, IP, professional negligence, media and entertainment, sports, technology.
Company/Insolvency: Company, insolvency (personal and corporate), partnership and LLPs.
Real Estate: Real property, landlord and tenant.
Private Clients: Succession and trusts and related tax issues.

For more information please visit www.11sb.com or contact the clerks on 020 7831 6381 or clerks@11sb.com.

11|SB

STONE CHAMBERS Steven Gee QC

4 Field Court, Gray's Inn, London, WC1R 5EF
Tel (020) 7440 6900 **Fax** (020) 7242 0197 **DX** 483 London/Chancery Lane
Email clerks@stonechambers.com **Website** www.stonechambers.com

Head of Chambers	Steven Gee QC
Senior Clerks	Jean-Pierre Schulz
	Luke Irons
Barristers	29

MEMBERS

Steven Gee QC (1975) (QC-1993)
Andrew Moran QC (1977) (QC-1993)
Elizabeth Blackburn QC (1978) (QC-1998)
Vasanti Selvaratnam QC (1983) (QC-2001)
Timothy Hill QC (1990) (QC-2009)
Sarah Miller (1971)
Colin Wright (1987)
Charles Debattista (1978)
Dominic Happé (1993)
Rachel Toney (1998)
Ishfaq Ahmed (1999)
Mary Gibbons (1999)
Mark Jones (2000)
Ravi Aswani (2000)
Philip Riches (2002)
Thomas Whitehead (2002)
James Shirley (2002)
Jeremy Lightfoot (2006)
Henry Ellis (2008)
Peter Stevenson (2008)
Rani Noakes (2010)
Thomas Steward (2011)
Jason Robinson (2012)
James Smithdale (2012)
John Reeder QC (1971) (QC-1989) ++
Allan Myers (1988) (QC Aus.) ++
David Martin-Clark (1961) ++
Jonathan Lux (2013) ++
Mary Thomson (1983) (2013 Hong Kong) ++

++ Associate member

THE CHAMBERS A specialist commercial and shipping set, practising in international commercial litigation and arbitration, established under the direction of leading Silk Steven Gee QC.
Stone Chambers is a leading set of commercial and shipping barristers based in London and Singapore, specialising in international commercial litigation and arbitration. They provide advocacy, advisory, arbitral and mediation services, representing clients in a wide range of courts and tribunals in England and Wales, European and international jurisdictions. They act as arbitrators, mediators and expert witnesses.
Combining a dynamic, friendly and innovative approach with a comprehensive and client-focused service, Stone Chambers' barristers provide leading expertise in matters ranging from urgent applications for relief, freezing and search orders, and other interim relief, through to trial and beyond.
Stone Chambers has a strong international client base, with barristers appearing in jurisdictions such as Antigu, Argentina, Dubai, Gibraltar, HongKong, New York and Singapore. Languages spoken include: French, German, Italian, Spanish, Urdu, Hindi, Gujarati, Finnish, Swedish and Mandarin. Barristers write or contribute to numerous publications, including *Gee on Commercial Injunctions, The Maritime Law of Salvage, Law of the European Union, Halsbury's Laws The Rotterdam Rules: A Practical Annotation, Bills of Lading in Export Trade, Bankers' Law, PLC, Butterworths Journal of International Banking and Financial Law, Commercial Litigation Journal, Law Quarterly Review* and *Lloyd's List.*

WORK UNDERTAKEN Stone Chambers offers expertise in the following key areas:
Commercial: All aspects of international trade and commerce, contractual disputes, joint venture disputes; jurisdiction and conflict of laws.
Shipping: Charterparty and bill of lading disputes; contracts of affreightment and containerisation contracts (including connecting carrier and slot chartering agreements); ship sale purchase; shipbuilding contracts; super yachts; offshore and shipping activities, including oil and gas, environmental, fisheries and conservation matters; Admiralty work, including arrests, collisions, salvage and general average.
Arbitration: Arbitration law and practice, including ICC, GAFTA, LMAA, LCIA, SCMA, SIAC, LOF, UNCITRAL and CIETAC.
Injunctive Relief: Urgent interim relief, including freezing and search orders and anti-suit injunctions.
Commodities & Sale of Goods: International and domestic contracts, as well as related transactions (letters of credit, bills of exchange, insurance, FFAs, guarantees and performance bonds).
Insurance & Reinsurance: All aspects of marine and non-marine insurance and reinsurance law.
International Trade & Commodities: All types of international sales contracts, including CIF, FOB, EXW, CIP, FAS. All disputes relating to sale and/or transport of goods, as well as related matters such as letters of credit, bills of exchange and insurance.
Road, Rail & Air Transport: Carriage of goods and passengers, including terms of carriage, arrangements with freight forwarders/other transport intermediaries, regulatory/ competition issues, environmental matters and safety.
Energy & Natural Resources: Oil and gas trading disputes, mining and utilities disputes, related offshore construction disputes.
Banking & Finance: Freezing orders, asset tracing, leases, loans, securitisation, bills of exchange, promissory notes, documentary credits, insolvency, mortgage enforcement and consumer credit.
Competition: Advisory work and advocacy in all aspects of domestic and EU competition law – prohibited behaviour, market share, abuse of dominant position, damages claims in the context of the competition rules.
Civil Fraud: Injunctive relief (in particular freezing and search orders) in the context of civil fraud disputes; deceit actions, claims for knowing receipt and dishonest assistance; proprietary claims and equitable relief.
Employment: All aspects of employment law, acting in both an advisory capacity and as advocates before the ET and EAT.
Professional Negligence: Provide advocacy and advice in relation to professional negligence claims.

TANFIELD CHAMBERS Philip Rainey QC

Head of Chambers	Philip Rainey QC
Senior Clerk	Kevin Moore
Chambers Administrator	Eamonn Kelly
Tenants	61

2-5 Warwick Court, London, WC1R 5DJ
Tel (020) 7421 5300 **Fax** (020) 7421 5333 **DX** 46 London Chancery Lane
Email clerks@tanfieldchambers.co.uk **Website** www.tanfieldchambers.co.uk

MEMBERS

Philip Rainey (1990) MCI Arb (QC-2010) ^
Iain Mitchell QC (Scotland) (1976 Scotland) (2012 England) (QC Scotland 1992) ^
Edward Raw (1963) ^
Gavin Merrylees (1964)
David Guy (1972) FCI Arb ^
Philip Conrath (1972) ^
Stephen Monkcom (1974) ^
DA Pears (1975) ^
Paul Staddon (1976) ^
Mark Dencer (1978) ^
Kerstin Boyd (1979) ^
Christopher Coney (1979) ^
Simon Cheves (1980) ^
Charles Joseph (1980) FCI Arb ^
Sebastian Reid (1982) ^
Mark Loveday (1986) MCI Arb
Michael Bailey (1986) ^
Christopher Bamford (1987) ^
John Buck (1987) ^
Michael Buckpitt (1988) ^
Gerald Wilson (1989) ^
Phillip Aliker (1990) FCI Arb ^
Stephen Heath (1992) ^
Kerry Bretherton (1992) ^
Catriona MacLaren (1993) ^
Nicholas Isaac (1993) ^
Andrew Butler (1993) ^
Robin Powell (1993) ^
Stan Gallagher (1994) ^
Peter Linstead (1994) ^
Michelle Marnham (1994)
Christopher Heather (1995)
Karen Jones (1995) ^
Rob Bowker (1995) ^
Timothy Polli (1997) ^
James Fieldsend (1997) ^
Piers Harrison (1997) ^
Daniel Dover (1997) ^
Martina Murphy (1998) ^
Chris Maynard (1998) ^
Nicola Muir (1998) ^
Marc Glover (1999) ^
Ellodie Gibbons (1999) ^
Adrian Carr (1999) ^
Sarah Stanzel (1999) ^
Rebecca Cattermole (1999)
Carl Fain (2001) ^
Olivia Murphy (2001) ^
Laura Robinson (2001) ^
Tom Carpenter-Leitch (2002) ^
Tim Hammond (2003) ^
Amanda Gourlay (2004) ^
Jonathan Upton (2004) ^
Paul Stevenson (2006) ^
Estelle Lear (2006) ^
Gemma de Cordova (2006)
Michael Walsh (2006) ^
Gwyn Evans (2007) ^
Cecily Crampin (2008) ^
Niraj Modha (2010) ^
Harriet Holmes (2011) ^
Richard Alford (2011) ^

^ Public/Direct Access

THE CHAMBERS Tanfield Chambers continues to make its mark in its core areas of property, commercial disputes, employment and private client. It is recognised by The Legal 500 and Chambers & Partners as a 'Leading Set' for property litigation.

WORK UNDERTAKEN Tanfield continues to focus on the following core areas of work:
Property: This area of expertise has emerged as its strongest core area in recent years, with chambers being particulars well regarded for the high-profile contributions made by its members to the law of leasehold enfranchisement. Service charges and right to manage are also key areas, having been the subject of a book Service Charges and Management, which his now in its third edition. Tanfield's library has expanded further this year by the addition of the highly respected Megarry's Manual of the Law of Real Property (co-edited by Philip Rainey QC, Michael Walsh, Piers Harrison and Daniel Dovar). Nicholas Issac has published The Law and Practice of Party Walls, which draws on his widely acknowledged expertise in this field. Piers Harrison has also published the first edition of his work, Leasehold Enfranchisement: Law and Practice.
Commercial Disputes: Tanfield offers the broad-range of commercial expertise that one would expect, but also has pockets of particular specialism that mark it out as a shrewd alternative to its competitors.
Employment: Chambers has an energetic, junior-driven and increasingly well-regarded employment expertise with experience of all types of employment disputes. Members of chambers have particular experience of undertaking tribunal work for local authority respondents.
Private Client: Members undertake work across the broad spectrum of trusts, wills, tax and ancillary relief. There is also significant experience of work in the Court of Protection.

TANFIELD CHAMBERS

TAX CHAMBERS 15 OLD SQUARE Stephen Brandon QC

15 Old Square, Lincoln's Inn, London, WC2A 3UE
Tel (020) 7242 2744 **Fax** (020) 7831 8095 **DX** 386 LDE
Email taxchambers@15oldsquare.co.uk **Website** www.taxchambers.com

Head of Chambers	Stephen Brandon QC
Senior Clerk	Anthony Hall
Tenants	10

MEMBERS

Robert Venables QC (1973) (QC-1990)
Stephen Brandon QC (1978) (QC-1996)
James Kessler QC (1984) (QC-2003)
Amanda Hardy (1993)
Rory Mullan (2000)
Patrick Cannon (2003)
Setu Kamal (2004)
Harriet Brown (2005)
Oliver Marre (2011)
Etienne Wong (2014)

THE CHAMBERS Tax Chambers has established a reputation for excellence in all areas of tax law. Members cut through the complexities of tax legislation to give clients clear, commercial advice. Tax Chambers offers some of the most experienced tax counsel available at the UK bar today. Year after year this team receives strong ranking in Chambers UK. Clients can instruct Chambers through solicitors, accountants/ other licensed practitioners and under the Public Access scheme.

WORK UNDERTAKEN

Corporate Taxation: With a pure tax focus, members cover all aspects of corporate taxation, both in and out of court. The team has particular strengths in advising on corporate reconstructions, entrepreneurs, multinational corporate structuring and international tax disputes. This experience sets this group apart from its competitors in the UK. The tax treatment of intangible financial assets is another area of specialist expertise as are employee remuneration strategies.

Personal Taxation: Members counsel an elite group of clients and tend to be called to advise at the high end for both UK and foreign domiciliaries. The team has played a lead role on a number of major matters of first importance over the past year. Members advise private clients in plain English in all aspects of their tax affairs, both in the UK and across borders. The ability to combine trust, land and charity law expertise with private client tax advice makes this a unique resource in the UK market.

International: Chambers cross-border tax offering is a key factor which sets members apart from the majority of tax advisers at the UK Bar. Members appear in front of foreign tribunals and bring years of experience to the table. In addition, Tax Chambers is one of the leading teams in the UK when it comes to advising private clients based in the UK or elsewhere on all of their cross-border tax affairs.

Specialist Expertise: Members cover all areas of tax law, however each experienced practitioner has particular strengths:

- Head of Chambers, Stephen Brandon QC is consulted widely on corporate restructuring, entrepreneurs, international tax disputes, employee remuneration, foreign domiciliaries, non-resident companies and tax litigation, including appearing before foreign tax tribunals
- Robert Venables QC focuses on litigation, trusts, EC, offshore and international, VAT and remedying botched planning
- James Kessler QC was a founder of STEP with particular strengths in foreign domiciliaries, trust and charities
- Patrick Cannon is an expert on SDLT issues
- Amanda Hardy is a noted expert on both trusts and pensions taxation and is a highly experienced litigator
- Rory Mullan, advises at the intersection of EU law and tax
- Harriet Brown is also a qualified Jersey advocate and has appeared before foreign courts and tribunals

PUBLICATIONS Members are sought out as thought leaders and have written a significant number of major works including the following:
Drafting Trusts & Will Trusts, Taxation of Trusts, Taxation of Foundations, Taxation of Charities, Taxation of Non-Residents and Foreign Domiciliaries, Taxation of Non-UK Resident Companies and their Shareholders, The Interaction of EU Treaty Freedoms and the UK Tax Code, The Jersey Law of Trusts, Tolley's Stamp Taxes and The GAAR: A Practical Approach.

TAX CHAMBERS
15 OLD SQUARE

TEMPLE GARDEN CHAMBERS Robin Tam QC

Head of Chambers	Robin Tam QC
Senior Clerk	Dean Norton
Tenants	63

1 Harcourt Buildings, London, EC4Y 9DA
Tel (020) 7583 1315 **Fax** (020) 7353 3969 **DX** 382 London
Email clerks@tgchambers.com **Website** www.tgchambers.com

MEMBERS

Robin Tam QC (1986) (QC-2006)
Nigel Wilkinson QC (1972) (QC-1990)
Andrew Prynne QC (1975) (QC-1995)
Simon Jackson QC (1982) (QC-2003)
Dominic Grieve QC (1980) (QC-2008)
Jonathan Watt-Pringle QC (1987) (QC 2008)
Murdo MacLeod QC (Scotland) (1994) (QC-2008)
Simon Browne QC (1982) (QC-2010)
Keith Morton QC (1990) (QC-2010)
Karim A. A. Khan QC (1992) (QC-2010)
Andrew Cayley QC (2007) (QC-2012)
David Barr QC (1993) (QC-2014)
Rodney Dixon QC (2000) (QC-2014)
John Bate-Williams (1976)
James Holdsworth (1977)
Ian Ashford-Thom (1977)
Angus Macpherson (1977)
Kevin McLoughlin (2007)
William Hoskins (1980)
George Alliott (1981)
Paul Kilcoyne (1985)
James Bell (1987)
Mark James (1987)
Philip Astor (1989)
Cathryn McGahey (1990)
James Laughland (1991)
Charles Curtis (1992)
Richard Wilkinson (1992)
James Arney (1992)
Marcus Grant (1993)
Alexander Glassbrook (1995)
Nicholas Moss (1995)
Melissa Pack (1995)
Andrew O'Connor (1996)
Emma-Jane Hobbs (1996)
Edward Hutchin (1996)
Julia Smyth (1996)
Paul McGrath (1997)
Dominic Adamson (1997)
Sacha Ackland (1998)
George Davies (1998)
Shaman Kapoor (1999)
Benjamin Casey (2000)
Heather Dardis (2000)
Fiona Canby (2001)
Michael Rapp (2002)
Tim Sharpe (2002)
Lydia Sweeney (2002)
Louise Jones (2004)
Rhys Davies (2004)
Aidan Ellis (2005)
Lionel Stride (2005)
Anthony Johnson (2006)
Joanna Hughes (2007)
Emma Price (2007)
Sian Reeves (2006)
David R. White (2009)
William Irwin (2010)
Emma Northey (2009)
James Henry (2010)
Emily Wilsdon (2011)
Anthony Lenanton (2011)
Richard Boyle (2012)

THE CHAMBERS Temple Garden Chambers is one of the leading civil sets in the country and is repeatedly recognised as such by Chambers UK and the Legal 500. With 13 QCs and 50 practising barristers, it provides a formidable breadth of talent at all levels in a broad range of domestic and international work. It has an outstanding clerking team which prides itself on providing a strong administration with an approachable and friendly ethos. Temple Garden Chambers provides market-leading facilities to accommodate the needs of its clients.

WORK UNDERTAKEN Temple Garden Chambers has a strong reputation for legal excellence, which ensures that its counsel are repeatedly at the vanguard of new and developing areas of law. Members of chambers specialise in clinical negligence, credit hire, coronial law and inquests, costs, employment, fraud, health and safety, insurance, international public law, personal injury and fatal accidents, product liability, professional negligence, professional discipline and public law.

tgc temple garden chambers

2TG - 2 TEMPLE GARDENS Benjamin Browne QC

2 Temple Gardens, London, EC4Y 9AY
Tel (020) 7822 1200 **Fax** (020) 7822 1300 **DX** 134 (Ch.Ln.)
Email clerks@2tg.co.uk **Website** www.2tg.co.uk

Head of Chambers	Benjamin Browne QC
Senior Clerk	Lee Tyler
Chambers Manager	Sarah Webbe
Tenants	52

MEMBERS

Benjamin Browne QC (1976) (QC-1996)
Dermod O'Brien QC (1962) (QC-1983) *
Michael de Navarro QC (1968) (QC-1990)
Robert Moxon Browne QC (1969) (QC-1990)
Howard Palmer QC (1977) (QC-1999)
Martin Porter QC (1986) (QC-2006)
Jacqueline Perry QC (1975) (QC-2006)
Monya Anyadike-Danes (1980) (QC NI 2007) *
Sarah Vaughan Jones QC (1983) (QC-2008)
Neil Moody QC (1989) (QC-2010)
Paul Downes QC (1991) (QC-2010)
Caroline Harrison QC (1986) (QC-2013)
Charles Dougherty QC (1997) (QC-2013)
Andrew Miller QC (1989) (QC-2014)
Rosalind Foster (1969)
Alison Green (1974)
Stephen Archer (1979)
John McDonald (1981)
Christopher Russell (1982)
Daniel Matovu (1985)
Jennifer Gray (1988)
Jonathan de Rohan (1989)
Bradley Martin (1990)
Daniel Crowley (1990)
John Snell (1991) *
Christopher Lundie (1991)
Marie-Louise Kinsler (1992)
Rupert Reece (1993) *
Clare Brown (1993)
Dore Green (1994)
Lucy Wyles (1994)
Bruce Gardiner (1994)
Nina Goolamali (1995)
Roger Harris (1996)
Niazi Fetto (1999)
Darren Eales (2000) *
Anastasia Karseras (2000)
Nina Unthank (2001)
Helen Bell (2002)
Sonia Nolten (2002)
Helen Wolstenholme (2002)
Stuart Benzie (2002)
Rehana Azib (2003)
Elizabeth Wale (2004) *
Meghann McTague (2004)
Emily Saunderson (2005)
Stewart Chirnside (2005)
Jack Harris (2006)
Joseph Sullivan (2006)
Hayley McLorinan (2008)
Anna Hughes (2008)
David Thomas (2009)
Henry Morton Jack (2009)
William Wraight MRCS (Eng) (2009)
Isabel Barter (2010)
Timothy Killen (2010)
Robert Cumming (2010)
Andrew Bershadski (2010)
William Clerk (2012)

* Door Tenant

THE CHAMBERS Established civil and commercial set, known for its advocacy and client-centred approach.

WORK UNDERTAKEN

Personal Injury: Catastrophic injury, fatal accidents, animal, sport, H&S and work injuries, UK and overseas.
Clinical Negligence: Claimants, NHSLA, Defence Organisations, insurers, GMC, GDC, Hospital Trusts.
Insurance & Reinsurance: Commercial claims, mesothelioma, high value insurance fraud, Lloyds Syndicates.
Travel & Jurisdiction: Large foreign claims in PI, insurance, product liability and professional negligence.
Product Liability: Wide range of high cost product fault and failure claims in multiple jurisdictions.
Professional Negligence: Mainly defence of high value claims in all professions. Specialists in professional indemnity.
Employment: Contracts, equal pay claims, workplace stress, racial, sexual and religious discrimination.
Commercial Dispute Resolution: High value commercial litigation, civil fraud and arbitration in multiple jurisdictions.
Property Damage: High value fire, flood, explosions and subsidence claims on commercial, public and private premises.
Banking & Finance: Retail banking, securities, swaps, derivatives, hedge funds, asset finance.
Commercial Fraud: Complex commercial fraud claims in the UK and overseas.
Sport: All major sports: rules, regulations, contractual breaches, technical issues, players, officials, regulators.

TEMPLE TAX CHAMBERS Michael Sherry

Head of Chambers	Michael Sherry
Senior Clerk	Claire James
Tenants	15

3 Temple Gardens, Temple, London, EC4Y 9AU
Tel (020) 7353 7884 **Fax** (020) 7583 2044
Email clerks@templetax.com **Website** www.templetax.com

MEMBERS

Michael Sherry (1978) ^
Richard Bramwell QC (1967) (QC-1989)
Christopher Sokol QC (1975) ^ (QC-2006)
David Southern QC (1982) (QC-2014)
Alun James (1986)
Jonathan S Schwarz (1998) (SA 1977, Can 1981)
Tim Brown (2001)
Scott Redpath (1996)
Michael Collins (2003)
Philip Ridgway (1986)
Rebecca Murray (2001)
Anne Redston (2010)
Stephen Arthur (2002) ^
Michael Quinlan (1984) ^
Derek Francis (1985)

^ Direct/Public Access

THE CHAMBERS Long established leading set of tax chambers, strongly represented at all levels of experience in both direct and indirect tax. Chambers seeks to combine the highest standards of expertise and technical excellence with a commercial approach and genuine accessibility. Members collaborate closely with professional clients to provide them with a dynamic service that fits their commercial requirements, ably assisted by the team of clerks. Members lecture widely and publish regularly.

WORK UNDERTAKEN

Direct Tax: Advice and litigation in all aspects of corporate and personal tax, corporate/business tax advisory and planning issues for large corporates and groups including transaction and IPO work, corporate finance, break-up bids, MBOs and corporate rescues, and for owner-managed businesses/SMEs including reconstruction and clearance work (in particular transactions in securities issues), employment-related securities/share scheme and other remuneration issues, and planning work with LLPs and partnerships, including structuring for hedge fund managers/venture capitalists. Personal tax expertise ranges from IHT planning, onshore and offshore trust issues and drafting, and maximising BPR, to offshore income tax/CGT/IHT issues including transfers of assets abroad and advising non-domiciled individuals in matters such as remittances, excluded property settlements and UK homes structures. SDLT planning and transactional work as well as SDLT/stamp duty advice in relation to reorganisations.

VAT & Customs & Excise Duties: Several members specialise in VAT and customs and excise duties matters in both advisory work and litigation. VAT expertise covers land and buildings, charities, partial exemption, financial services, grouping, fraud/investigations, single/multiple supplies and three-year capping. Customs and excise duties matters include Mtic classification, licensing, preferences, quotas, reliefs, warehousing, duty suspended movements and seizures.

International Tax: International work includes permanent establishment issues, double tax relief, the effect of EU law on UK legislation, international employments, supply chain structuring, internationally mobile executives.

Recent Cases: Chambers has developed a real tax litigation presence at all levels and has featured in many recent significant cases:

Supreme Court: Forde & McHugh v HMRC (Richard Bramwell QC, Michael Sherry & Anne Redston); R & C Comrs v Cotter (Scott Redpath); R & C Comrs v Tower MCashback (Rebecca Murray).

Court of Appeal: Mertrux Ltd v R & C Comrs (Richard Bramwell QC & Alun James); BAA Ltd v R & C Comrs (David Southern & Rebecca Murray); Nicholas Pike v HMRC (Scott Redpath).

Upper Tribunal: McLaren Racing v R & Comrs (Alun James); Eclipse Film Partners (No 35) LLP v R & C Comrs (Rebecca Murray); R & C Comrs v The Honourable Society of Middle Temple (Richard Bramwell QC & Michael Collins); HMRC v Marco Trading Ltd (David Southern); HMRC v SHS International Ltd (Tim Brown); Julian Martin v R & C Comrs (Philip Ridgway); TNT (UK) v HMRC (Tim Brown); Aberdeen Asset Management Ltd v R & C Comrs (Rebecca Murray); R (on the application of De Silva) v R & C Comrs (David Southern).

First tier tax Tribunal: Edward Bears & Minerals v HMRC (Tim Brown); Peel Investments UK v HMRC (Alun James); Bishop and Others v R & C Comrs (Anne Redston); Armajaro v HMRC (Alun James); Roden v R & C Comrs (Tim Brown); Metso Paper Bender (Forrest) Ltd v HMRC (Alun James); Lady Margaret Hall, Oxford v R & C Comrs (Tim Brown); Finmeccanica v HMRC (Tim Brown); European Tour Operators Association Limited v HMRC (Tim Brown).

PUBLICATIONS Many members of chambers write or contribute to some of the major practitioners' works on tax. Richard Bramwell QC, Alun James and Michael Collins are co-editors of *Bramwell* on *"Taxation of Companies and Company Reconstructions"*, one of the most highly regarded tax books on the market. Michael Sherry is general editor and co-author of *Whiteman and Sherry on Income Tax; Whiteman and Sherry on Capital Gains Tax* (the leading tax text books). Jonathan Schwarz, who specialises in cross-border work, is author of Schwarz on *Tax Treaties, Annotated UK Double Tax Treaties, Booth & Schwarz: Residence, Domicile and UK Taxation 15th Edition and Transfer Pricing and Business Restructurings: Streamlining all the way.* Philip Ridgway is co-author of *Bloomsbury Professional's Tax Indemnities and Warranties.* David Southern has written *Taxation of Loan Relationships and Derivative Contracts* and is contributor to *Gore-Browne on Companies and Law Society Company Law Handbook.* Rebecca Murray is author of *"Tax Avoidance".*

TEMPLE TAX CHAMBERS
3 TEMPLE GARDENS LONDON EC4Y 9AU

3 VERULAM BUILDINGS Ali Malek QC

3 Verulam Buildings, Gray's Inn, London, WC1R 5NT
Tel (020) 7831 8441 **Fax** (020) 7831 8479 **DX** LDE 331
Email chambers@3vb.com **Website** www.3vb.com

Head of Chambers	Ali Malek QC
Senior Practice Manager	Paul Cooklin
Tenants	67

MEMBERS

Ali Malek QC (1980) (QC-1996)
John Jarvis QC (1970) (QC-1989)
Christopher Symons QC (1972) (QC-1989)
Nicholas Elliott QC (1972) (QC-1995)
Richard Salter QC (1975) (QC-1995)
Michael Blair QC (1965) (QC-1996) (Hon Causa)
Gregory Mitchell QC (1979) (QC-1997)
Andrew Sutcliffe QC (1983) (QC-2001)
Andrew Onslow QC (1982) (QC-2002)
Rory Phillips QC (1984) (QC-2002)
Tom Weitzman QC (1984) (QC-2003)
Ewan McQuater QC (1985) (QC-2003)
Andrew Fletcher QC (1980) (QC-2006)
Jonathan Nash QC (1986) (QC-2006)
Adrian Beltrami QC (1989) (QC-2008)
Paul Lowenstein QC (1988) (QC-2009)
Cyril Kinsky QC (1988) (QC-2010)
Sonia Tolaney QC (1995) (QC-2011)
John Odgers QC (1990) (QC-2012)
David Quest QC (1993) (QC-2013)
Jonathan Davies-Jones QC (1994) (QC-2013)
Catherine Gibaud QC (1996) (QC-2014)
Matthew Hardwick QC (1994) (QC-2014)
Clive Freedman (1975)
Elizabeth Birch (1978)
Peter Cranfield (1982)
Michael Lazarus (1987)
Angharad Start (1988)
Jonathan Mark Phillips (1991)
James Evans (1991)
Richard Edwards (1993)
Richard Brent (1995)
Ian Wilson (1995)
Matthew Parker (1997)
David Head (1997)
Ewan McKendrick (1998)
Peter Ratcliffe (1998)
Nicholas Craig (1998)
Peter de Verneuil Smith (1998)
Sophie Mallinckrodt (1999)
Laura John (2001)
Tariq Baloch (2001)
William Edwards (2002)
Christopher Harris (2002)
Rajesh Pillai (2002)
George McPherson (2003)
David Simpson (2003)
Lisa Lacob (2004)
Charlotte Eborall (2004)
Adam Kramer (2004)
James MacDonald (2005)
Richard Hanke (2006)
Robert Purves (2007)
Alexia Knight (2007)
Christopher Bond (2008)
Anne Jeavons (2008)
Sandy Phipps (2008)
Kate Holderness (2008)
Tom De Vecchi (2009)
Theodor van Sante (2009)
Christopher Burdin (2010)
Teniola Onabanjo (2010)
Paul Choon Kiat Wee (2010)
Miriam Schmelzer (2010)
Ian Higgins (2011)
Scott Ralston (2012)
Anthony Pavlovich (2012)

++ Associate Member

THE CHAMBERS 3 Verulam Buildings is a leading set of chambers specialising in commercial work. Members accept instructions and briefs to advise and represent clients in court, arbitration and other tribunals in England, Wales and internationally.

WORK UNDERTAKEN All members of chambers are specialist advocates in various aspects of commercial work. Among them are acknowledged experts in the fields of banking; insurance and reinsurance; professional negligence; insolvency; entertainment and media; commercial fraud regulation; public international and environmental law. The set also has an established reputation in international and domestic arbitration. Chambers include a number of individuals who have been involved in EU cases in the national courts and the European Court of Justice. Expertise is also offered in an extremely wide range of other matters, including agency, agriculture, building and construction, commodities trading, all aspects of company law, competition law, IT, telecoms and computer legislation, employment, financial services and financial regulation, gaming, intellectual property, judicial review, landlord and tenant matters, pensions, restraint of trade and sale of goods. The diversity of experience available enables 3 Verulam Buildings to offer advice and representation to clients in the huge variety of business contexts in which legal issues arise. Barristers work individually or in teams to carry out all the preparatory and interlocutory work necessary to bring a case to trial or to settle a case by way of ADR. They also undertake non-contentious legal work, for example, drafting standard terms and conditions in contracts both for financial institutions and commercial clients. Additionally, members advise clients on the effects of new law. Chambers are managed by a friendly and efficient team of practice managers and support staff. In appropriate circumstances, chambers will carry out work on a conditional fee basis. The practice managers would be pleased to discuss this further and a draft agreement is available on request.

RECRUITMENT Chambers offer up to three pupillages of 12 months each. The pupillage award for 2015/16 will be not less than £60,000, up to £20,000 of which may be drawn down in the BVC year. Candidates should have a first class or 2:1 degree (not necessarily in law). Applications must be made through OLPAS.

3VB
THREE VERULAM BUILDINGS

WILBERFORCE CHAMBERS John Martin QC

8 New Square, Lincoln's Inn, London, WC2A 3QP
Tel (020) 7306 0102 **Fax** (020) 7306 0095 **DX** 311 London Chancery Lane
Email chambers@wilberforce.co.uk **Website** www.wilberforce.co.uk

Head of Chambers	John Martin QC
Practice Director	Nick Luckman
Executive Director	John Treacy
Head Clerk	Mark Rushton
Clerks	Danny Smillie
	Fraser Geddes
	Colin Everson
	Robert Johnstone
	Stewart Cameron
	Andrew Barnes
Tenants	56

MEMBERS

John Martin QC (1972) (QC-1991)
Edward Nugee QC (1955) (QC-1977)
Michael Barnes QC (1965) (QC-1981)
Jules Sher QC (1968) (QC-1981) ° ARB
Lawrence Cohen QC (1974) (QC-1993)
Ian Croxford QC (1976) (QC-1993)
Robert Ham QC (1973) (QC-1994)
John Furber QC (1973) (QC-1995)
Terence Mowschenson QC (1977) (QC-1995)
David Phillips QC (1976) (QC-1997)
Brian Green QC (1980) (QC-1997)
Michael Furness QC (1982) (QC-2000)
John Wardell QC (1979) (QC-2002)
Jonathan Seitler QC (1985) (QC-2003)
Michael Tennet QC (1985) (QC-2006)
Thomas Lowe QC (1985) (QC-2008)
James Ayliffe QC (1987) (QC-2008)
Joanna Smith QC (1990) (QC-2009)
Paul Newman QC (1991) (QC-2009)
Stephen Davies QC (1983) (QC-2000) °
Joanne Wicks QC (1990) (QC-2010)
Martin Hutchings QC (1986) (QC-2011)
John Child (1966)
Thomas Seymour (1975)
Mark Studer (1976)
Gabriel Hughes (1978)
Daniel Hochberg (1982)
Judith Bryant (1987)
Gabriel Fadipe (1991)
Caroline Furze (1992) °
Jonathan Evans (1994)
Graeme Halkerston (1994)
Clare Stanley (1994)
Emily Campbell (1995)
Rupert Reed (1996)
Julian Greenhill (1997)
Tiffany Scott (1998)
Nicholas Medcroft (1998)
Nikki Singla (2000)
Edward Sawyer (2001)
Harris Bor (2006) ++
Jonathan Davey (2003)
Jonathan Hilliard (2003)
Andrew Mold (2003)
Emily McKechnie (2005)
Charlotte Black (2006)
Sebastian Allen (2006)
James Walmsley (2007)
Benjamin Faulkner (2008)
James McCreath (2009)
Emer Murphy (2009)
Tom Roscoe (2010)
Jonathan Chew (2010)
Simon Atkinson (2011)
Bobby Friedman (2011)
Jack Watson (2012)
James Goodwin (2013)
Michael Ashdown (2013)

++ former solicitor (2002) ** former solicitor (1988) ° Door Tenant ARB Arbitrator

THE CHAMBERS The set is widely recognised as one of the leading chambers in its core specialist areas of commercial and financial services, pensions, private client and trusts, property and professional negligence. With 56 barristers (23 QCs) (including 2 door tenants), the set is able to offer specialist barristers at all levels of seniority and across the spectrum of commercial and chancery work. It has individuals who possess excellent reputations for their specialist capabilities in the additional fields of arbitration and dispute resolution, company, banking, insolvency, oil and gas law, intellectual property, sports and media law, planning, employment and charities. With its strength and depth of expertise, members of chambers undertake many of the most complex and important cases. They work hard to build and maintain strong long-term relationships with their clients, who include the leading UK and international law firms, multinational corporations, major organisations, private companies and individuals. Clients value the modern quality of chambers' clerking and organisational management and the approachable service provided by barristers and clerks. Details of each individual member's practice, including selected report cases, can be found on the set's website listed above.

WORK UNDERTAKEN The set's aim is always to provide practical and effective advice and to settle disputes in its clients' favour by the most effective means available.
Commercial & Other Contracts: Commercial contracts, banking, insurance loans and security, guarantees, Lloyds' drafting and litigation, economic torts, breach of confidence, oil and gas law.
Financial Services & Regulatory Work: Pensions, unit trusts, property enterprise trusts and collective investment schemes; regulatory work including investigations and disciplinary proceedings under the Financial Services Act 1986, Financial Services and Markets Act 2000, subordinate legislation and rules of conduct.
Property: All matters relating to land, commercial property transactions, landlord and tenant, property finance negligence and fraud, mortgages and other securities.
Professional Liability: Accountants, actuaries, auditors, barristers, solicitors, surveyors and trustees and construction related professional negligence.
Pensions: Occupational and personal pension schemes.
Trusts: Drafting, advice on administration and construction and contentious and non-contentious litigation.
Tax & Estate Planning: Including offshore tax planning and a wide range of tax litigation.
Company Law & Insolvency: Including shareholder disputes, directors' disqualification proceedings, mergers and acquisitions, partnerships and joint ventures, corporate and personal insolvency.
Arbitration & Dispute Resolution: Advice and representation at arbitrations, or acting as Arbitrator, in a wide range of commercial disputes in the UK and internationally.
Intellectual Property & Information Technology: Advice and advocacy across the full range of IP and IT, including representation in specialist tribunals and European courts.

Wilberforce CHAMBERS

WILBERFORCE CHAMBERS John Martin QC (continued)

Sports & Media Law: Representing sports personalities, sports clubs, sports associations, publishers and artists in a range of contract negotiations and disputes in UK courts, domestic and international tribunals, including a variety of non-contentious work.
Equitable Remedies: Injunctions, search orders, freezing injunctions, tracing, constructive trusts and proprietary estoppel.
Wills & Probate: Contentious and non-contentious, administration of estates, intestacy and family provision.
Charities, Partnerships & Associations: Housing associations, clubs, societies and the law as it relates to other associations.

INTERNATIONAL Members of chambers frequently advise and appear in jurisdictions outside the UK including Bahamas, Bermuda, USA, British Virgin Islands, the Caymans, Jersey, Guernsey, Isle of Man, Gibraltar, Hong Kong, Singapore, The Republic of Ireland and Russia, and the European Court of Justice.

THE BAR A-Z REGIONS

KINGS CHAMBERS Nicholas Braslavsky QC

Embassy House, 60 Church Street, Birmingham, B3 2DJ **DX** 13023 (Birmingham)

36 Young Street, Manchester, M3 3FT **DX** 718188 (MCH3)

5 Park Square East, Leeds, LS1 2NE **DX** 713113 (Leeds PK SQ)

Tel 0845 034 3444 **Fax** 0845 034 3445
Email: clerks@kingschambers.com **Website:** www.kingschambers.com

Chambers Director	Debra Andrés
Senior Clerks	William Brown
	Colin Griffin
	Stephen Loxton
Clerks	Gary Smith
	Jake Brooke
	Gary Young
	Paul Clarke
	Harry Young
	Mark Ronson
	Scott Leach
	Aaron Smith
	Andrew Reeves
	Rory Davis

MEMBERS

Dr Nicholas Braslavsky QC (1983) (QC-1999)
Mr Stephen J Sauvain QC (1997) (QC-1995)
Mr Vincent Fraser QC (1981) (QC-2001)
Mr Paul Chaisty QC (1982) (QC-2001)
Mr Richard Clayton QC (1977) (QC-2002)
Mr David Manley QC (1981) (QC-2003)
Ms Lesley Anderson QC (1989) (QC-2006)
Mr Anthony Crean QC (1987) (QC-2006)
Mr David Casement QC (1992) (QC-2008)
Mr Michael Rawlinson QC (1991) (QC-2009)
Mr Paul Tucker QC (1990) (QC-2010)
Mr Nigel Poole QC (1989) (QC-2012)
Reverend Eric Owen (1969)
Mr Jeffrey Terry (1976)
Mr Roger Lancaster (2002)
Mr Alan Evans (1978)
Mr Shokat Khan (1979)
Mr John Barrett (1982)
Mr Neil Berragan (1982)
Mr Mark Halliwell (1985)
Mr Gary Grant (1985)
Mr Simon Hilton (1987)
Mr Nigel Clayton (1987)
Miss Ruth Stockley (1988)
Miss Fiona Ashworth (1998)
Mr Andrew Singer (1990)
Mr Paul Johnson (2006)
Mr Simon Burrows (1990)
Mr Matthew Smith (1991)
Mr Andrew Grantham (1991)
Mr Martin Carter (1992)
Mr Wilson Horne (1992)
Miss Lucy Powis (1992)
Mr Mark Harper (1993)
Miss Sarah Pritchard (1993)
Mr Richard Lander (1993)
Mr Ian Ponter (1993)
Mr Michael Ditchfield (1993)
Miss Sarah Clover (1993)
Mr James Boyd (1994)
Miss Kelly Pennifer (1994)
Mr Andrew Latimer (1995)
Mr Gavin McBride (1996)
Mr Jeremy Roussak (1996)
Mr Louis Doyle (1996)
Mr Jonathan Easton (1996)
Mr Adam Fullwood (1996)
Mr Simon Plaut (1997)
Mr Colin Bourne (1997)
Dr Mark Friston (1997)
Mr Simon Young (1998)
Mr Stephen Maguire (2007)
Mr Giles Cannock (1998)
Professor Andrew McGee (1998)
Mr Matthew Hall (1999)
Miss Helen Mulholland (1999)
Mr Martin Budworth (1999)
Miss Tina Ranales-Cotos (1999)
Mr Brian Griffiths (1999)
Miss Eleanor Temple (2000)
Mrs Lisa Walmisley (2000)
Mr Paul Lakin (2000)
Miss Claire Jackson (2002)
Mr Paul Hughes (2001)
Mr Ben Williams (2001)
Mr Geraint Wheatley (2001)
Miss Claire Steward (2002)
Mr Craig Ralph (2002)
Mr Michael Rudd (2002)
Mr John Hunter (2002)
Mr Sam Karim (2002)
Miss Emily Duckworth (2003)
Miss Michelle Mayoh (2003)
Miss Sarah Lawrenson (2003)
Miss Sarah Reid (2004)
Miss Francesca Gardner (2004)
Miss Rachel Galloway (2004)
Miss Sophie Allan (2004)
Mr Paras Gorasia (2005)
Miss Charlotte Law (2005)
Mr Ben Harding (2005)
Miss Cheryl Dainty (2006)
Mr Richard Livingston (2006)
Mr Johnny Ward (2007)
Dr Nathan Smith (2007)
Miss Gemma Lieberman (2007)
Mr Kevin Latham (2007)
Mr Stephen McNamara (2008)
Mr Anthony Gill (2008)
Miss Eleanor d'Arcy (2008)
Miss Anna Macey (2008)
Mrs Laura Daniels (2009)
Miss Ruth Taylor (2010)
Mr Jonathan Wright (2010)
Mr Aidan Reay (2011)
Mr Freddie Humphries (2011)
Miss Erica Bedford (2012)
Mr Clive Freedman QC (1978) (QC-1997) *
Mr Marcus F Daly SC (1987) (SC-1999) *
Mr Colm Ó hOisin SC (1998) (SC-2005) *
Mr Colin Crawford (1997) *
Mr James Henderson (1997) *
Mr Leo Charalambides (1998) *
Professor Andrew Keay (2010) *
David Gilliland QC (1964) (QC-1984) +

* Associates + Arbitrator

THE CHAMBERS Kings Chambers is ranked one of the country's leading sets. It provides barristers with the highest reputation for advocacy, knowledge and standards to service.
This is a large specialist set with a national reputation practising from Manchester, Leeds and Birmingham in several practice areas: predominantly chancery and commercial law; planning and environmental law, personal injury and clinical negligence, costs, employment, sports law, mediation, arbitration and public law.

WORK UNDERTAKEN
Planning: Kings Chambers is one of the largest planning and environmental chambers, with members appearing before a wide range of dedicated tribunals and inquiries. Chambers acts in all aspects of town and country planning and environmental law (including waste disposal and management), compulsory purchase compensation and highways.
Public Law: The public law group practises extensively in the Administrative Court, sitting in London and the regions. The group encompasses the range of public law work in community care, education, housing,

KINGS CHAMBERS Nicholas Braslavsky QC (continued)

mental health, immigration, licensing, local government and social security matters. Members advise and appear before courts at all levels.

Chancery & Commercial: The chancery and commercial group has extensive experience in litigation (including agency, contracts, sale of goods, restraint of trade and restrictive covenants, corporate law); corporate and personal insolvency (including winding up, administration, administrative receivership and tracing assets), banking and professional negligence. Residential and commercial landlord and tenant work (including renewals, rent review, possession claims, arbitrations), partnership and all aspects of property and conveyancing. Chambers also undertakes trusts and probate work and has members specialising in construction disputes, intellectual property and taxation.

Personal Injury: All aspects of personal injury, including work-related diseases and injuries, sporting injuries, clinical negligence and all aspects of civil liability, contracts, negligence, nuisance, breach of statutory duty, health and safety are undertaken.

Employment: The employment team covers the entire spectrum of employment law and has particular strengths in race, sex, equal pay and disability discrimination.

Sports Law: The sports law team have been involved in some of the most substantial and high profile sports cases nationally in recent years involving, commercial dispute resolution, disciplinary and regulatory proceedings, anti-doping rules, employment issues, sports-related personal injury, breach of confidentiality and privacy, wealth management issues, intellectual property including image rights, trademark infringement and breach of copyright.

Costs: There is a specialist and dedicated costs team, practising exclusively in costs law, disputes and litigation funding.

Mediation: Mediation is an important part of the litigation process. The team comprises accredited mediators at various levels and with expertise in differing areas of law.

Arbitration: Kings Arbitration provides a panel of arbitrators and a panel of arbitration counsel based in the UK and Ireland operating in both domestic and international arbitrations.

NO5 CHAMBERS Paul Bleasdale QC

Fountain Court, Steelhouse Lane, Birmingham, B4 6DR
Tel 0845 210 5555 **Fax** (0121) 606 1501 DX 16075 Birmingham Fountain Court
Email info@no5.com **Website** www.No5.com

Head of Chambers	Paul Bleasdale QC
Deputy Heads	Rex Tedd QC
	Ian Dove QC
Practice Director	Tony McDaid
Tenants	246

MEMBERS

Paul Bleasdale QC (1978) (QC-2001) + ^
Rex Tedd QC (1970) (QC-1993) + Deputy High Court Judge
Ian Dove QC (1986) (QC-2003) ^ Deputy High Court Judge +
Sir Richard Tucker QC (1954) (QC-1972) °
Anthony Smith QC (1958) (QC-1977) ^
Martin Kingston QC (1972) (QC-1992)
Christopher Hotten QC (1972) (QC-1994) + ^
Gareth Evans QC (1973) (QC-1994) +
Richard Jones QC (1972) (QC-1996) + ^
Manjit Gill QC (1982) (QC-2000) ^
Jeremy Cahill QC (1975) (QC-2002) ^
Satinder Hunjan QC (1984) (QC-2002) Deputy High Court Judge + ^
David Howker QC (1982) (QC-2002) ^
Douglas Armstrong QC (1990) (QC-2005) Scotland °
Lorna Meyer QC (1986) (QC-2006)
Richard Humphreys QC (1986) (QC-2006) ° ^
Michael Burrows QC (1979) (QC-2008) +
Christopher Bright QC (1985) (QC-2009) +
Mark Anderson QC (1983) (QC-2010) + ^
David Mason QC (1986) (QC-2010) + ^
Michael Duck QC (1988) (QC-2011) ^
Adrian Keeling QC (1990) (QC-2011) ^
Mark Heywood QC (1986) (QC-2012) ^
Gary Bell QC (1989) (QC-2012) ^
Jonathan Jones QC (1994) (QC-2013)
John Butterfield QC (1995) (QC-2014)+ ^
John West (1965)
Gerald Bermingham (1967) ^
Roger Smith (1968) ^
John Harvey (1973) + ^
Stephen Whitaker (1970)
Allan Dooley (1991) + ^
Peter Arnold (1972) ^
Graham Cliff (1973) +
Timothy Jones (1975) ^
Simon Worlock (1975) ^
Roger S Giles (1976) ^
Walter Bealby (1976)
Graham Henson (1976)
Anne E Smallwood (1977) ^
David Iles (1977)
Christopher James (1977) ^
Robin Rowland (1977) + ^
William Pusey (1977)
Kevin O'Donovan (1978) ^
Simon Michael (1978)
Anthony Korn (1978) ^
Andrew Keogh (1978) ^
Paul Cairnes (1980) ^
Roger Dyer (1980)
Timothy Newman (1981) ^
Stephanie Brown (1982) ^
Neil Thompson (1982) ^
Stephen Campbell (1982) + ^
Professor Christopher Newdick (1982) °
Andrew McGrath (1983) ^
Irvine Maccabe (1983) ^
Ramby de Mello (1983) ^
Nadia Sharif (1985)
Richard Moat (1985)
Mark Kelly (1985) ^
Anthony Bell (1985)
Russell Bailey (1985) ^
Kevin Barrett (1985) ^
James Doyle (1985) ^
Bernard Thorogood (1986) +
Kevin Leigh (1986) ^
Gordon Wignall (1987) ^
Michael O'Brien (1987)
Caroline Baker (1988) Deputy DJ
Joanna Chadwick (1988) ^
Ekwall Singh Tiwana (1988) ^
Ian Bridge (1988) ^
Andrew Wallace (1988) ^
Dewinder Birk (1988)
Samantha Forsyth (1988) ^
Malcolm Duthie (1989)
Becket Bedford (1989) ^
Moira Phillips (1989) °
Martin Liddiard (1989) ^
Carole Murray (1989) °
Timothy Hanson (1989) °
Jasvir Mann (1990) ^
Michael Anning (1990)
Ashley Wynne (1990) ^
Andrew Baker (1990) ^
Celina Colquhoun (1990) ^
Mark Radburn (1991)
Michele Friel (1991)
Sarah Buckingham (1991) ^
Edward Grant (1991) °
Mahmud Al-Rashid (1991) ^
Paul Marshall (1991) ^
Peter Goatley (1992) ^
Nicholas Xydias (1992)
Marc Wilkinson (1992) ^
Nicola Preston (1992) ^
Hugh Richards (1992) ^
Nigel Brockley (1992) ^
Adam Farrer (1992) ^
Steven Bailey (1992) ^
Paul Joseph (1992) ^
Abid Mahmood (1992) + ^
Nazmun Ismail (1992) ° ^
Nabila Mallick (1992) ^
Danny Bazini (1992) ^
David Taylor (1993) ^
Caroline Sumeray (1993)
Phillip Bradley (1993)
Param K Bains (1993)
Nandini Dutta (1993)
Joanne Rothwell (1993) ^
Edward Nicholson (1993) ^
Emma Edhem (1993) ^
Robert Smallwood (1994)
Anthony Potter (1994) + ^
Satnam Choongh (1994) ^
Dr Simon Fox (1994)
Nageena Khalique (1994) ^
David Tyack (1994)
Mark Renouf (1994) °
Brian Dean (1994) ^
James Stoll (1994)
Stefano Nuvoloni (1994) ^
Anna Diamond (1995)
David Mitchell (1995) ^
Tim Sheppard (1995) ^
Richard Hignett (1995) ^
Dean Kershaw (1995) + ^
Susan Monaghan (1995) ^
Jeremy Wright MP (1996) °
Sally Hancox (1996) +
Henry Pitchers (1996)
Elizabeth Power (1996)
Richard Case (1996) ^
David Holloway (1996) °
Laura Davidson (1996) ^
Ravinder Bagral (1996) ^
Mugni Islam-Choudhury (1996) ^
Carol Knotts (1996) ^
Karl Hirst (1997) ^
Christopher Young (1997) ^
Richard Hadley (1997)
Harbinder Singh Lally (1997) ^
Matthew Brunning (1997) ^
Adreeja Chatterjee (1997) ^
Gareth Compton (1997)
Talbir Singh (1997) ^
Vinesh Mandalia (1997) ^
Alexander Stein (1998) ^
Richard Kimblin (1998) ^
Jonathan Derrington (1998) ^
Kristina Brown (1998)
Susanne Muth (1998) ^
Jamie Gamble (1999)
Louisa Denning (1999) ^
Teresa Hargreaves (1999)
Charles Crow (1999) ^
Jonathan Barclay (1999) °

FS71518

NO5 CHAMBERS Paul Bleasdale QC (continued)

MEMBERS

John Coughlan (1999) ^
Charles Price (1999) ^
Helen Barney (1999) ^
Nassera Butt (1999) ^
Dr Fayyaz Afzal OBE (1999) ^
S Chelvan (1999) ^
Matthew Brook (1999)
Saleema Mahmood (2009) ^
Raza Mithani (2000) °
Glenn Willetts (2000)
Neil Chawla (2000) ^
Jenny Wigley (2000) ^
Omar Ensaff (2000) ^
Sharon Bahia (2000) ^
Paul Evans (2001) ^
Michelle Heeley (2001) ^
Rupert Beloff (2001) ^
Bridget Forster (2001) ^
Emma Brown (2001) ^
Michael Wingrave (2001) °
Tim Pole (2001) ^
Tom Schofield (2001) ^
Olivia Chaffin-Laird (2001) ^
Richard Adkinson (2001) ^
James Dixon (2001) ^
Esther Gamble (2001) ^
Philip Mantle (2002) ^
Victoria Clifford (2002) ^
Mark Bradshaw (2002) ^
Lynette McClement (2002)
Fatim Kurji (2003) ^
Helen Arthur (2003) ^
Daniel Oscroft (2003) ^
Earl Pinnock (2003) ^
Claire van Overdijk (2003) ^
Nicholas Cobill (2003) ^
Denise Owen (2003) °
Heather Popley (2003) ^
Jennifer Fox (2004) °
Mamta Gupta (2004)
James Leslie (2004) ^
Philip Williams (2005) ^
Sarah Allen (2005) ^
Dr Jonathan Punt (2005)
Richard Cooke (2005)
Orla Grant (2005) ^
Harpreet Singh Sandhu (2005) ^
Steven Reed (2005) ^
Suella Fernandes (2005) ^
Kathryn Taylor (2005) °
Katie Feeney (2005)
Yasmin Yasseri (2005) ^
Peter Tyers-Smith (2005) °
Jack Feeny (2005) ^
Gemma Roberts (2006) ^
Professor Nelson Enonchong (2006) ^
Victoria Yates (2006) ^
Kirsty Gallacher (2006) ^
Claire Howell (2006) ^
Simon Hunka (2007) ^
Jack Smyth (2007) ^
Richard Oakes (2007)
Rowena Meager (2007) ^
Matthew Boyden (2007)
Laura Vickers (2007) ^
Louise Corfield (2008)
Hermione Williams (2008) ^
Jonathan Shaw (2008) ° ^
Russell Holland (2008) ^
Naomi Owen (2008) ^
Charlotte Robinson-Jones (2008)
Jessica Smeaton (2008)
James Burke (2009)
Sara McCarthy (2009) ^
Ian Brownhill (2009)
Richard Grimshaw (2010)
Thea Osmund-Smith (2010)
Caroline Jennings (2010)
Catherine Jones (2010)
Hashi Mohamed (2010)
Emma Corkill (2010)
Katie Miller (2010)
James Corbet Burcher (2011)
Victoria Hutton (2011)
Nina Pindham (2012)
Philip Dayle (2012)
Richard Gibb (2012)

+ Recorder ° Associate ^ Public/Direct Access

THE CHAMBERS No5 Chambers is a national set offering a comprehensive across the board service. Throughout its 100-year history, No5 Chambers has developed a reputation for breaking new ground and continues to be regarded as a progressive and forward-thinking set, maintaining its success in traditional sectors of law whilst offering specialist advice and representation at the cutting edge of newly evolving areas. Having grown to over 240 barristers, including 26 silks, No5 Chambers provides a truly nationwide service from its offices in Birmingham, London, Bristol and the East Midlands.

In recent years chambers has made significant inroads into the South West and Wales from its office in Bristol whilst its London office continues to go from strength to strength, housing more than 50 tenants. Chambers continues to attract high quality work in all disciplines, combining excellent service standards with a progressive, modern and flexible approach to clients' needs.

No5 prides itself on forming partnerships with solicitor clients and other professionals. In 2011 it joined the Turkish British Chamber of Commerce and Industry, cementing its growing links with Turkey, and has recently forged a direct link with a Jersey law firm (the first such arrangement on the island). Chambers has associate tenants in Dubai, Spain, Cayman, Hong Kong, Singapore and India and is keen to develop further links particularly in the fields of construction, international arbitration, commercial work and environmental.

Dedicated specialist clerking teams based throughout the country have detailed knowledge of the individuals and groups they manage and support and are available to advise clients on the most suitable Counsel for a particular case. Chambers organises a structured training and induction program for clerks and members alike. A highly respected set, No5 Chambers remains a well-reputed provider of informative and topical seminars, allowing the latest issues and developments to be discussed with highly qualified speakers and sector experts. Many members of chambers write or contribute to legal textbooks and specialist journals.

No5 Chambers has a wide-ranging practice and has for many years modelled itself as a top-end one-stop shopping service whilst maintaining the quality, service and experience it offers clients. Further details on No5 and its members can be found on its website www.No5.com.

ST IVES CHAMBERS Nicholas Cole

1-3 Whittall Street, Birmingham, B4 6DH
Tel (0121) 236 0863 **Fax** (0121) 236 6961
Email clerks@stiveschambers.co.uk **Website** www.stiveschambers.co.uk

Chambers Director:	Jackie Maskew
Practice Managers:	Philip Hidson (Crime)
	Clare Radburn (Civil, Family Finance & Regulatory)
	Sarah Robinson (Family & Court of Protection)
Tenants:	62
Door Tenants	6

THE CHAMBERS St Ives Chambers is proud of its reputation for outstanding service, excellence in all areas of advocacy and advisory work; this continues to grow locally and nationally. Chambers is a multi-disciplinary set with particular expertise in family, housing and property, chancery and commercial, regulatory and criminal law and is regarded for boasting some of the most renowned and experienced practitioners in the Midlands past and present.

Chambers has 62 tenants including three highly regarded QCs, in addition to six door tenants. Chambers is routinely listed in national legal directories and many of the barristers are regular contributors to legal publications and published authors of seminal legal texts.

Members of chambers hold various Judicial appointments including Deputy High Court Judge, Recorder(s) of the Crown Court, County Court and Mercantile and Construction Court, Deputy District Judge and Tribunal Judge. Former members include a Lady Justice of Appeal, High Court Judge and two Circuit Judges.

ST PHILIPS CHAMBERS Avtar Khangure QC

Head of Chambers	Avtar Khangure QC
Chief Clerk	Joe Wilson
Tenants	178

55 Temple Row, Birmingham, B2 5LS
Tel (0121) 246 7000 **Fax** (0121) 246 7001 **DX** 723240 BIRMINGHAM 56
Email jwilson@st-philips.com **Website** www.st-philips.com

41 Park Square, Leeds, LS1 2NP

9 Gower Street, London, WC1E 6HB
Tel (020) 7467 9444 **Fax** (020) 7467 9441 **DX** 2105 EUSTON

MEMBERS

Mr Avtar Khangure QC (1985) (QC-2003) †
Mr David Crigman QC (1969) (QC-1989) †
Mr Stephen Linehan QC (1970) (QC-1993) † ^
Mr Timothy Raggatt QC (1972) (QC-1993) ^
Mr John Randall QC (1978) (QC-1995) † ++
Mr Christopher Millington QC (1976) (QC-2001) † ^
Mr Peter Haynes QC (1983) (QC-2008)
Mr Mohammed Zaman QC (1985) (QC-2009)
Mr Kevin Hegarty QC (1982) (QC-2010) † ^
Mr Andrew Lockhart QC (1991) (QC-2010) † ^
Mr Francis Laird QC (1986) (QC-2011) †
Mr Richard Atkins QC (1989) (QC-2011) † ^
Mr Alistair MacDonald QC (1995) (QC-2011) †
Mr Andrew Smith QC (1997) (QC-2012) † ^
Mr Edward Pepperall QC (1989) (QC-2013) †
Miss Kristina Montgomery QC (1993) (QC-2013) † ^
Mr Jonas Hankin QC (1994) (QC-2013)
Miss Elizabeth McGrath QC (1987) (QC-2014)
Mr Michael Garrett (1967) ^
Mr Malcolm Morse (1967) †
Mr Robert Hodgkinson (1968)
Mr Douglas Readings (1972) †
Ms Clare Dillon (1974) ^
Mr James Quirke (1974) ^
Mr Guy Spollon (1976)
Mr Andrew Neaves (1977)
Mr Giles Harrison-Hall (1977) ^
Mr Bernard Linnemann (1980)
Miss Martine Kushner (1980) †
Mr Simon Clegg (1980) ^
Mr Stephen Thomas (1980) †
Mr Makhan Shoker (1981)
Mr Barry Berlin (1981) †
Mr Stephen Eyre (1981) †
Miss Nergis-Anne Mathew (1981) ^
Mr Paul Mytton (1982) ^
Mr Petar Starcevic (1983) ^
Mr John Evans (1983)
Mr Lawrence Messling (1983) ^
Mr John Edwards (1983) †
Dr Mirza Ahmad (1984) ^
Mr Thomas Rochford (1984) †
Mr David Stockill (1985) ^
Mr Andrew Jackson (1986) ^
Mr Christopher Adams (1986) † ++
Mr Nicolas Cartwright (1986) † +++ ^
Mr Simon Ward (1986) †
Mr Aubrey Craig (1987) ^
Mr Dorian Day (1987) ^
Miss Blondel Thompson (1987) ^
Mr Jonathan Salmon (1987) +++ ^
Mr Conrad Rumney (1988)
Mr Andrew Maguire (1988) ^
Miss Sarah Buxton (1988) ^
Miss Sandra Bristoll (1989) †
Miss Alison Cook (1989) ^
Miss Sarah Harrison (1989)
Mr Amarjit Rai (1989) ^
Mr Mark Calway (1989) ^
Mr Simon Davis (1990) ^
Mr Michael George (1990) ^
Miss Sophie Garner (1990) ^
Miss Vanessa Meachin (1990) † ^
Mr Edmund Beever (1990)
Mr James Puzey (1990) ^
Mr Sean Kelly (1990) ^
Miss Sarah George (1991) ^ **
Mr Glyn Samuel (1991)
Mr Jonathan Gidney (1991) ^
Mr Robin Lewis (1991) ^
Ms Susan Todd (1991) ^
Mr Matthew Barnes (1992)
Miss Julie Moseley (1992)
Mr William Baker (1992)
Miss Julie Sparrow (1992) ^
Miss Heidi Kubik (1993) ^
Mr Lee Marklew (1993)
Mr Stefan Kolodynski (1993)
Mr Anthony Verduyn (1993) † ^
Mr Anthony Johnston (1993)
Mr Tariq Sadiq (1993) ^
Mr David Maxwell (1994) **
Mr Angus Burden (1994) ^
Mrs Elizabeth Walker (1994) †
Mr Patrick Wainwright (1994)
Mr Nicholas Smith (1994) ^
Mr Andrew Charman (1994) ^
Miss Rosalyn Carter (1994) †
Miss Jacqueline Humphreys (1994) ^
Mr Stuart Roberts (1994) ^
Miss Marisa Lloyd (1994) ^
Mr James Dunstan (1995) ^
Miss Carolyn Jones (1995)
Mr Darron Whitehead (1995) ^
Mr Gregory Pipe (1995)
Mr John Brennan (1996)
Miss Naomi Gilchrist (1996) ^
Mr Timothy Green (1996) † ^
Miss Louise McCabe (1996) ^ +++
Mr Simon Phillips (1996)
Mr Shane Crawford (1996) ^
Mr James Morgan (1996) †
Mr David Warner (1996) ^
Mr Huw Jones (1997)
Miss Emma Kelly (1997) ^ +++
Miss Huma Ali (1997)
Miss Rachel Rowley (1997) ^
Miss Elizabeth Hodgetts (1998) ^
Miss Lucianne Allen (1998)
Miss Raj Punia (1999) ^
Miss Heledd Williams (1999)
Miss Barbara Caulfield (1999) ^
Mr Richard Adams (1999) ^
Miss Leisha Bond (1999) ^
Mr Shakil Najib (1999) ^
Mr Anthony Edwards (1999) ^
Miss Poonam Bhari (1999) ^
Miss Kate Iliffe (2000)
Miss Jane Sarginson (2000)
Mr Zaheer Afzal (2000) ^
Miss Jennifer Josephs (2000) ^
Mr Benedict Mills (2000) ^
Mr Ian Speed (2000)
Mr Andrew Evans (2000) ^
Mr Jonathan Nosworthy (2000) ^
Mr Nicholas Howell-Jones (2000) ^
Mr Stephen Abberley (2000)
Mr Tom Walkling (2001)
Miss Rebecca Franklin (2001) ^
Mr David Griffiths (2001) ^
Miss Elizabeth Richards (2001) ^
Mr Sean O'Brien (2001) ^
Mr David Munro (2001) ^
Mr Paul J Dean (2001) ^
Mr William Buck (2001)
Miss Yolanda Pemberton (2002) ^
Mr Matthew Weaver (2002)
Mr James Tindal (2002) † +++ **
Mr Christopher Watson (2003)
Ms Naomi Candlin (2003) ^
Mr Colin Baran (2003) ^
Mr Peter Cherry (2003)
Miss Davinia Riley (2004) ^
Miss Victoria Edmonds (2004) ^
Mr Marc Brown (2004)
Miss Amrisha Parathalingam (2004) ^
Ms Suzanne Coleclough (2005) ^
Mr Nicholas Brown (2005)
Mr Bruce Frew (2005) ^
Mr Ben Williams (2006) ^
Mr Jonathan Barker (2006) ^
Miss Rosa Dickinson (2006)
Mr Jonathan Meichen (2006) ^

St Philips
BARRISTERS

ST PHILIPS CHAMBERS Avtar Khangure QC (continued)

Mr Amit Gupta (2006) ^
Miss Alice Winstanley (2006) ^
Miss Lydia Pemberton (2006)
Mr Ali-Reza Tabari (2006) ^
Mr Dominic Crossley (2006)
Miss Debbie Collins (2007) ^
Miss Hannah Bush (2007)
Mr Iqbal Mohammed (2007) ^
Miss Helen Gardiner (2007) ^
Mr Carl Garvie (2008) ^
Miss Lucie French (2008) ^
Mr Robert Mundy (2008)
Mr Jack Redmond (2009)
Mr Joseph Millington (2009)
Miss Kate Rogers (2009)
Mr Jonathan Gale (2009)
Miss Kathryn Vernon-Asimeng (2009)
Mr James Bruce (2010) ^
Miss Anna Stubley (2010)
Mr Dominic Roberts (2011)
Mr Mohammad Hafeez (2011)
Mr Andrew Burrow (2011)
Miss Hannah Tildesley (2012) ^
Miss Natasha Partos (2012) ^
Miss Jessica Brooke (2012)

† Recorder ++ Deputy High Court Judge +++ Deputy District Judge ** P/T Employment Tribunal Judge ^ Public Access

THE CHAMBERS St Philips is widely recognised as one of the most modern and progressive chambers in the UK. This multi-award winning set continues to break the mould, providing a high quality, personalised service, with the strength and the efficiency of a large set. St Philips consistently sets benchmarks for others to follow.
St Philips has recently expanded with the opening of two new offices in Leeds and London. This strategic move underlines the commitment to expand upon the first-class service it is renowned for, reinforcing its objective to make its exceptional team of barristers the first choice for clients nationally and internationally. Chambers serves a range of clients including international companies, local authorities, sporting authorities, trade unions, public bodies and regulators. Members of Chambers also accept instructions under the Direct Access rules.
St Philips attributes its continued success to a forward-thinking and flexible strategy coupled with innovation. Chambers has a reputation for being friendly and approachable whilst providing clients with a bespoke, professional service and a commercially minded approach. The dedicated clerks, led by Chief Clerk, Joe Wilson, are highly experienced and provide a personalised and professional service, as acknowledged in various legal directories. St Philips also has the benefit of in-house teams of support staff in IT, HR, marketing, finance and business development.

WORK UNDERTAKEN St Philips offers a specialist service in administrative law, ADR, arbitration (domestic and international), banking, clinical negligence, commercial, construction, criminal, employment, family, fraud (civil and criminal), immigration, insolvency, intellectual property, personal injury, property, public, regulatory, trusts and wills and probate.
St Philips Commercial Group has a reputation of providing excellence across the full spectrum of commercial, property and private client work. It offers specialist practice teams in Banking and Financial Services, Commercial Fraud, Company, Insolvency, Intellectual Property, Landlord and Tenant, Partnership, Professional Liability, Property, Technology and Construction, and Wills, Trusts and Probate.
St Philips Employment Group offers a truly nationwide service with members providing advice, drafting and advocacy in Tribunals, County Courts, the High Court and the EAT. Members have particular expertise in cases with issues of discrimination, religion and belief and in conducting complex group claims.
St Philips Personal Injury Group acts for claimants and defendants and offers particular expertise in cases of fatal accidents, catastrophic injuries, industrial disease (including stress), fraud and allegations of fraud and travel and holiday claims.
St Philips Clinical Negligence Group has gained a reputation for providing first class legal advice and attracts work from nationally recognised leading firms in this field. The team has particular expertise in the areas of birth injury, cosmetic surgery, hospital acquired infections, Coroners' inquests, maximum severity spinal injury and amputations, product liability, multi-party actions, human rights claims, dental claims and negligence in general practice.
St Philips Family Group is one of the largest in the country, having a leading reputation nationally for providing high quality specialist advice and representation across four key areas:
The Financial Remedy Team has expertise in all aspects of financial work arising from divorce or separation, including same sex relationships.
The Care and Adoption Team has expertise in the full range of public law Children Act proceedings acting for local authorities, parents and children. Members have appellate experience in the High Court and Court of Appeal, and extensive experience in the judicial review of local authority decisions.
The Children Team has experience and expertise in all aspects of private law Children Act proceedings, including cases involving domestic abuse, residence/contact disputes, international child abduction and cases in which the child is separately represented.
The Court of Protection Team offers barristers who have longstanding experience of dealing with cases involving issues of incapacity, acting for the Official Solicitor or in matters arising under the Mental Health Acts and Human Rights Act 1998.
St Philips Criminal Group offers unrivalled strength from junior through to silk. Members prosecute and defend in equal measure all aspects of serious crime across the country, including murder, corporate manslaughter, serious sexual offences, white collar fraud and large scale drug conspiracies. Members appear on the preferred lists for the Attorney General, Crown Prosecution Services, Organised Crime Divisions and key national defence firms.
St Philips Regulatory Group defends and prosecutes on behalf of a wide range of commercial clients and regulatory bodies throughout the UK. Matters include fatal accidents, corporate manslaughter, trading standards, environmental regulation, VAT and revenue appeals, health and safety, police powers, benefit fraud, licensing and inquests. In addition, several members sit on a variety of disciplinary bodies such as the RFU, ASA, BDO, The Sports Resolutions Disputes Panel, the GMC and the GDC, including one barrister who is an appointed arbitrator for the Court of Arbitration for Sport.

CROWN OFFICE ROW Philip Havers QC

Head of Chambers	Philip Havers QC
Chambers Director	Bob Wilson
Senior Clerk (Brighton)	David Bingham
Tenants	44

119 Church Street, Brighton, BN1 1UD
Tel (01273) 625625 **Fax** (01273) 698888 **DX** 36670 Brighton 2
Email clerks@1cor.com **Website** www.1cor.com

MEMBERS

Philip Havers QC (1974) (QC-1995)
James King-Smith (1980) ^
Paul Ashwell (1977)
Roger Booth (1966) ^
Christopher Morris-Coole (1974)
Karen McLaughlin (1982)
Neville Stevenson-Watt (1985) ^
Adam Smith (1987) ^
Timothy Bergin (1987) ^
Aviva Le Prevost (1990) ^
Christopher Rice (1991) ^
Jules Grant (1991)
Jeremy Cave (1992)
Simon Sinnatt (1993) ^
Nigel Taylor (1993) ^
^ Public/ Direct Access

Luisa Morelli (1993)
Rowan Jenkins (1994) ^
Christine Henson (1994) ^
Susan Healey (1995) ^
Rachael Claridge (1996) ^
Jacqueline Roach (1996)
Pegah Sharghy (1998) ^
Camilla Wells (1998) ^
Ghulam Hussain (1998) ^
Jane Peckham (1999) ^
Stuart Wright (2000) ^
Leo Cogin (2000)
Francesca Lewington (2001) ^
Anita Mehta (2002) ^
Gavin Howe (2003) ^
Lynn McFadyen (2003) ^

Richard Ager (2004) ^
Eleanor Battie (2004) ^
Hala Mustafa (2004) ^
Daniel Miller (2005) ^
Samantha Knott (2005)
Matthew Heywood (2006) ^
Lauren Godfrey (2007) ^
Charlotte John (2008) ^
Bruce Tregoning (2008) ^
Clare Ciborowska (2009) ^
Denise Saunders (2008) ^
Michael Walker (2008)
Catriona Murdoch (2009)
David Lewis-Hall (2010)

THE CHAMBERS Chambers have been in Brighton for over 40 years as an Annexe of 1 Crown Office Row in London. Chambers' modern premises are only a few minutes' walk away from the Brighton County and Magistrates' Courts. Conference, library and seminar facilities are excellent.

WORK UNDERTAKEN Chambers undertake all types of general common law work – civil, criminal and family. Particular expertise can be offered in all types of family proceedings, prosecuting and defending general and regulatory crime, commercial, property (including landlord and tenant and housing), probate and trusts of land, personal injury, employment, professional negligence and licensing. Several Members provide expert dispute resolution services and most accept work from lay clients direct through the Bar's Public Access scheme.

RECRUITMENT Up to two pupils are taken annually with an annual award of £19,000 each. This is split between an award in the first six months (£9500) and guaranteed £9500 of earnings for the second six. Applications should be made by letter together with a full CV addressed to Chambers (email: brightonpupillage@1cor.com).

1COR
CROWN OFFICE ROW
BRIGHTON

ALBION CHAMBERS Michael Fitton QC

Albion Chambers, Broad St, Bristol, BS1 1DR
Tel (0117) 927 2144 **Fax** (0117) 926 2569 **DX** 7822
Email clerks@albionchambers.co.uk **Website** www.albionchambers.co.uk

Head of Chambers	Michael Fitton QC
Chambers' Director	Paul Fletcher
Senior Clerk (Criminal)	Bonnie Colbeck
Senior Clerk (Civil/Family)	Michael Harding
Junior Clerk (Criminal)	Nicholas Jeanes
Junior Clerk (Civil/Family)	Julie Hathway
Junior Clerk	Ken Duthie
Tenants	61

MEMBERS

Michael Fitton QC (1991) (QC-2006) +
Ignatius Hughes QC (1986) (QC-2009) + ^
Adam Vaitilingam QC (1987) (QC-2010) + ^
Nkumbe Ekaney QC (1990) (QC-2011)
Claire Wills-Goldingham QC (1988) (QC-2012) ^
Charles Hyde QC (1998) (QC-2006) +
Christopher Jervis (1966)
Timothy Hills (1968) ^
Nicholas O'Brien (1968)
Louise Price (1972) ^
Paul Grumbar (1974) +
Nicholas Fridd (1975) ^
Martin Steen (1976)
Robert Duval (1979)
John Geraint Norris (1980)
Stephen Mooney (1987) ^
Don Tait (1987)
Fiona Elder (1988) ^
Deborah Dinan-Hayward (1988) ^
Virginia Cornwall (1990) ^
Claire Rowsell (1991)
Simon Burns (1992)
Nicholas Sproull (1992) ^
Paul Cook (1992) ^
Alan Fuller (1993) ^
Edward Burgess (1993) +
Jonathan Stanniland (1993)
Elizabeth Cunningham (1995) ^
Jason Taylor (1995) ^
Giles Nelson (1995)
Adrian Posta (1996) ^
Daniel Leafe (1996)
Kirsty Real (1996) ^
Kannan Siva (1996)
Kate Brunner (1997) ^
Hannah Wiltshire (1998)
Charlotte Pitts (1999) ^
Sarah Regan (2000)
David Chidgey (2000) ^
Linsey Knowles (2000) ^
Richard Shepherd (2001) ^
David Cotterell (2001) ^
James Cranfield (2002)
Stephen Roberts (2002)
Fiona Farquhar (2002)
Kate Goldie (2004) ^
Benjamin Jenkins (2004)
Joanna Lucas (2004)
Gemma Borkowski (2005) ^
Anna Midgley (2005) ^
Monisha Khandker (2005)
William Heckscher (2006)
Derek Perry (2006)
Alice Darian (2006)
Edward Hetherington (2006)
Stuart Fuller (2007)
Simon Emslie (2007) ^
Philip Baggley (2009)
Emily Brazenall (2009)
Andrew Thornhill QC (1969) (QC-1985) *
Paul Dunkels QC (1972) (QC-1993) *
Simon Mehigan QC (1980) (QC-1998) *
Kate Branigan (1985) (QC-2006) *
Erinna Foley-Fisher (2011)
Kevin Farquharson (2011)

+ Recorder * Door Tenant ^ Public/ Direct Access

THE CHAMBERS Albion Chambers is a long-established set with an excellent reputation for integrity, approachability and the highest standards of advice and advocacy.

The set's principal areas of expertise are within crime, regulatory (including Health and Safety), matrimonial finance, children, employment and disciplinary, inquests, probate and personal injury.

GUILDHALL CHAMBERS Peter Blair QC

Head of Chambers	Peter Blair QC
Chief Executive	Jeremy Sweetland
Principal Civil Clerk	Justin Emmett
Principal Crime Clerk	Lucy Northeast
Crime Clerks	Grant Bidwell
	Elena Brake
Civil Clerks	Mike Norton
	Chris Checketts
	Wendy Shaw
	Charlie Ellis
	Maggie Pearce
	Heather Bidwell
Tenants	79

Guildhall Chambers, 23 Broad Street, Bristol, BS1 2HG
Tel (0117) 930 9000 **Fax** (0117) 930 3800 **DX** 7823 Bristol
Email info@guildhallchambers.co.uk **Website** www.guildhallchambers.co.uk

MEMBERS

Peter Blair QC (1983) (QC-2006) + ^
Adrian Palmer QC (1972) (QC-1992) + *
Stephen Davies QC (1983) (QC-2000)
Richard Smith QC (1986) (QC-2001) +
Andrew Langdon QC (1986) (QC-2006) + ^
Christopher Quinlan QC (1992) (QC-2011)+ ^
John Whitting QC (1991) (QC-2011) ++
Ian Dixey (1984) ^
Kerry Barker (1972) ^
George Newsom (1973) ^
Adam Chippindall (1975) +
Rosaleen Collins (1996) +
Ian Fenny (1978) ^
Malcolm Warner (1979)
James Townsend (1980) +
William Batstone (1982) ^
John Virgo (1983)
Christopher Brockman (1985) ^
Susan Cavender (2004) ^
Neil Levy (1986) ^
Raj Sahonte (1986) ^
Ray Tully (1987) ^
Nicolas Gerasimidis (1988) + ^
Jeremy Bamford (1989)
Paul French (1989) ^
David Scutt (1989)
Nicholas Smith (1990)
Charles Thomas (1990)
Stephen Dent (1991) ^
Selena Plowden (1991)
Julian Benson (1991)
Anthony Reddiford (1991)
John Snell (1991)
Brendon Moorhouse (1992) ^
Matthew Wales (1993) °° ^
Gerard McMeel (1993)
Mark Worsley (1994) ^
Gabriel Farmer (1994)
Nicholas Briggs (1994)
Richard Ascroft (1995) ^
Ramin Pakrooh (1996)
Ewan Paton (1996) ^
Anna Vigars (1996) +
Debbie Grennan (1997)
Rupert Lowe (1998) + ^
Lucy Walker (2008)
Oliver Moore (2005)
Hugh Sims (1999) ^
Julian Allsop (1999)
Katherine Gibb (1999)
Matthew Porter-Bryant (1999) °° ^
Timothy Walsh (2000) ^
Robert Sowersby (2000)
Tara Wolfe (2000)
Pushpanjali Gohil (2000)
Martin Lanchester (2001) ^
James Bennett (2002)
Stefan Ramel (2002)
Tom Panton (2002)
Ross Fentem (2003) ^
Douglas Leach (2003)
Abigail Stamp (2004)
Allan Roberts (2004)
James Haskell (2004)
Daisy Brown (2006)
Mary Cowe (2006)
Gabriel Beeby (2006)
Michael Selway (2007)
Daniel Neill (2008)
Holly Doyle (2008)
Samuel Jones (2008) ^
James Wibberley (2009) ^
Simon Passfield (2009)
Sophie Holme (2009)
Oliver Mitchell (2009)
Caighli Taylor (2010)
Gregory Gordon (2010)
Suzanne Staunton (2010)
Matthew Brown (2011)
Jay Jagasia (2012)

+ Recorder * Deputy High Court Judge ++ Door Tenant °° Deputy District Judge ^ Public/ Direct Access

WORK UNDERTAKEN

Crime: One of the foremost criminal sets in the country with specialist expertise in sexual offences and child abuse, major public order cases, civil liberties and all types of appeal, as well as homicide, violence, drugs and vehicle crime.
Commercial Litigation: All aspects of commercial dispute resolution work in Court, arbitrations, adjudications and other ADR procedures.
Banking & Financial Services: Mortgages and charges, guarantees and indemnities, other third party securities, issues relating to the Consumer Credit Act, receiverships and retail banking transactions.
Professional Negligence & Indemnity: Expertise in all areas of professional liability acting for defendants and claimants in respect of negligence, breach of contract, breach of fiduciary duty and breach of trust.
Company Law: Key areas of expertise include the interpretation and dispute resolution of commercial contracts, partnership and joint ventures, shareholder agreements, the allotment and transfer of shares, directors' duties, shareholder disputes, derivative claims, just and equitable windings up.
Technology & Construction: The full range of technology and construction disputes, with familiarity with the workings and practices of the Technology and Construction Court.
Employment & Discrimination: Broad range of employment and discrimination expertise including unfair, constructive and wrongful dismissal; contractual disputes; actionable discrimination; TUPE; and many more.
Insolvency: All aspects of insolvency and company law, including corporate, partnership and personal insolvency, corporate and partnership break-up, CDDA etc.
Property & Estates: Full range of chancery work, including real property, landlord and tenant, agriculture, trusts, wills, estates and the Court of Protection.
Personal Injury: Work ranges from industrial and workplace accidents to fatalities and road traffic accidents with particular experience of acting for insurers in complex group claims.
Clinical Negligence: All aspects of litigation from minor to catastrophic claims acting for public and privately funded claimants, the NHSLA, NWSSP, Legal and Risk Services, Medical Defence organisations, and commercial providers of care.
Administrative & Public Law: Specialists who act for both claimants and defendants in significant appeals, judicial review proceedings, and statutory challenges with expertise in immigration, inquests, licensing, local government and in the Court of Protection.
Regulatory & Discipline: All aspects of professional disciplinary proceedings and regulation with specific experts in environment, financial services, fraud, health and safety, inquests and licensing.
Other: Specialist expertise in Sports Law and Costs & Litigation Funding.

Guildhall CHAMBERS

NO5 CHAMBERS Paul Bleasdale QC

38 Queen Square, Bristol, BS1 4QS
Tel 0845 210 5555 **Fax** (0117) 917 8501 **DX** 7838 Bristol
Email info@no5.com **Website** www.No5.com

Head of Chambers	Paul Bleasdale QC
Deputy Heads	Rex Tedd QC
	Ian Dove QC
Practice Director	Tony McDaid
Tenants	246

THE CHAMBERS No5 Chambers is a national set offering a comprehensive across the board service. Throughout its 100-year history, No5 Chambers has developed a reputation for breaking new ground and continues to be regarded as a progressive and forward-thinking set, maintaining its success in traditional sectors of law whilst offering specialist advice and representation at the cutting edge of newly evolving areas. Having grown to over 240 barristers including 26 silks, No5 Chambers provides a truly nationwide service from its offices in Birmingham, London, Bristol and the East Midlands.
In recent years chambers has made significant inroads into the South West and Wales from its office in Bristol whilst its London office continues to go from strength to strength, housing more than 50 tenants. Chambers continues to attract high quality work in all disciplines, combining excellent service standards with a progressive, modern and flexible approach to clients' needs. For further information and a full list of tenants please see the Birmingham entry or visit www.No5.com.

No5 CHAMBERS

OLD SQUARE CHAMBERS Nigel Cooksley QC & Jane McNeill QC

3 Orchard Court, St Augustine's Yard, Bristol BS1 5DP
Tel (0117) 930 5100 **Fax** (0117) 927 3478 **DX** 78229 Bristol
Email clerks@oldsquare.co.uk **Website** www.oldsquare.co.uk

Head of Chambers	Nigel Cooksley QC
	Jane McNeill QC
Senior Clerk	William Meade
Tenants	75

THE CHAMBERS This set remains the leading destination for employment law advice on the Western Circuit. Its members are regularly instructed in the Supreme Court, the ECJ and the ECHR and Old Square Chambers is recognised for its strong offering across the gamut of employment, personal injury and discrimination law.
Also at: 10-11 Bedford Row, London WC1R 4BU DX: 1046 Chancery Lane/London Tel: (020) 7269 0300 Fax: (020) 7405 1387. For further information and a list of tenants please see the London entry.

WORK UNDERTAKEN Employment law, personal injury, clinical negligence, product liability, health and safety, professional discipline and environmental law (see London entry for more details).

OLD SQUARE CHAMBERS

QUEEN SQUARE CHAMBERS Christopher Taylor

Queen Square Chambers, 56 Queen Square, Bristol, BS1 4PR
Tel (0117) 921 1966 **Fax** (0117) 927 6493 **DX** 7870 Bristol
Email civil@qs-c.co.uk / crime@qs-c.co.uk **Website** www.queensquarechambers.co.uk

Heads of Chambers	Christopher Taylor
Chief Executive	Steve Freeman
Head Clerk	James Dowse
Administrator	John Dummer
Tenants	46
Door Tenants	4

THE CHAMBERS Queen Square is structured with dedicated, specialist teams across several disciplines. A pragmatic but thorough approach to all areas of work undertaken is reflected in the close, team-working relationships the set enjoys with those instructing. Approachable, friendly and reliable, the set prides itself on its legal excellence which it combines with a competitive level of fees and first rate service standards, always endeavouring to work closely with those instructing to achieve the best possible outcome for their clients.

WORK UNDERTAKEN

Employment & Education: Regularly appearing in cases in almost every tribunal across the country, the team has a fairly even spread of Claimant and Respondent work. Instructed on behalf NHS Trusts, local authorities, trades union and leading companies the team also benefit from Panel status with several leading insurers. Work undertaken incorporates all areas of discrimination; equal pay claims; breach of contract; constructive dismissal; restrictive covenants; TUPE; unfair dismissal; wages claims; whistleblowing; wrongful dismissal; sports related issues. Education law cases. Members are fully conversant with the CPR and are able to undertake cases arising in that jurisdiction relating to occupational stress and bullying.

Family: Ancillary relief, including pensions and dissipation of assets; all aspects of care, adoption and supervision work. Contact and residence; injunctions and committals; child abduction; inheritance, cohabitees/TOLATA. Chambers also has expertise in cases involving mental health issues and family related crime (murder/infanticide, rape, sexual and physical abuse and paedophilia). Members of the Family Team are regularly instructed by several local authorities and are familiar with the particular demands involved.

Clinical Negligence: With extensive experience in all aspects of this challenging specialisation members undertake cases involving obstetrics, cardiology and orthopaedic claims as well as dental negligence.

Personal Injury: Catastrophic injury claims (particularly those involving brain and spinal injury); multiparty actions; fatal accident claims; asbestos and industrial related diseases; industrial accidents; occupier's liability; product liability; Animals Act claims; claims against the MOD.; RTA; CICA; 'trippers and slippers'.

Commercial/Chancery: Property related matters (including all areas of landlord and tenant and trusts of land); commercial disputes; contentious probate and Inheritance Act claims; insolvency; insurance and financial services; judicial review; partnership and professional negligence. Members accept instructions in cases involving arbitration and mediation.

Regulatory Law: All aspects of regulatory work including health and safety; maritime prosecutions; trading standards; prosecutions or disciplinary hearings relating to nursing homes; professional misconduct enquiries; police disciplinary hearings; Inquests; breaches of financial regulations etc.; and appeals and judicial review arising from Tribunal decisions.

Housing: Members represent both local authorities and individuals in matters including possession, homelessness, demoted tenancies, Section 204 Housing appeals and ASBOs, whether as part of possession proceedings or free-standing. Members have also represented the local authority in housing benefit appeals.

Licensing: Members of the department are fully conversant with the substantive and procedural issues involved and pride themselves on their practical and effective advice and representation provided throughout the licensing process.

Crime: Major fraud (including white collar fraud); internet crime; drugs importation and distribution; murder; rape and other serious, sexual offences; money laundering; corruption; confiscation and forfeiture; and the full range of indictable offences and appeals by way of case stated and judicial review.

QUEEN SQUARE CHAMBERS

ST JOHN'S CHAMBERS Richard Stead

101 Victoria Street, Bristol, BS1 6PU
Tel (0117) 923 4700 **Fax** (0117) 929 4821 **DX** 743350 Bristol 36
Email clerks@stjohnschambers.co.uk **Website** www.stjohnschambers.co.uk

Head of Chambers	Richard Stead
Chief Executive	Derek Jenkins
Practice Manager (Commercial/Chancery)	Robert Bocock
Practice Manager (Family)	Luke Hodgson
Practice Manager (Personal Injury & Clinical Negligence)	Annette Bushell
Office Manager	Isabelle Mills
Tenants	81

MEMBERS

Christopher Sharp QC (1975) (QC-1999) + ^
Christopher Wilson-Smith QC (1965) (QC-1986) ° ^
Robin Tolson QC (1980) (QC-2001) ^
Susan Jacklin QC (1980) (QC-2006) + ° ^
Leslie Blohm QC (1982) (QC-2006) +
Frances Judd QC (1984) (QC-2006) °
Suzanne Ornsby QC (1986) (QC-2012) °
Kathryn Skellorn QC (1993) (QC-2014)
David Fletcher (1971) ^
Ian Bullock (1975)
Timothy Grice (1975) +
Sheelagh Corfield (1975)
Kamala Das (1975) ^
Tim Higginson (1977) °
Richard Mawhinney (1977) °
Richard Stead (1979) + ^
Robin Neill (1979)
Charles Auld (1980)
Catriona Duthie (1981)
John Blackmore (1983) ^
Peter Wadsley (1984)
Susan Hunter (1985) ^
Willian Goodwin (1986) °
Glyn Edwards (1987)
Martha Maher (1987) ^
Simon Morgan (1988) **
Louise O'Neill (1989) ** ^
Guy Adams (1989) ^
Derek O'Sullivan (1990) °
Tom Leeper (1991) ^
John Sharples (1992) ^
Dianne Martin (1992) ^
Prof. Roy Light (1992) ^
Elizabeth Harris (1992)
Andrew McLaughlin (1993) ^
Adrian Maxwell (1993) ** ^
Nicholas Miller (1994)
Andrew Marsden (1994) ^
Jacqueline Humphreys (1994) °
Sarah Phillimore (1994) ^
David Regan (1994) ^
John FH Dickinson (1995) ^
Judi Evans (1996) ^
Matthew White (1997) ^
Kambiz Moradifar (1998) ^
Emma Zeb (1998) ^
Julian Horne (1998)
Alex Troup (1998) ^
Abigail Bond (1999)
Carol Mashembo (1999) ^
Delia Thornton (1999)
Vanessa McKinlay (2000)
Zahid Hussain (2001)
Rachel Russell (2001) ^
Anna Symington (2002)
Lucy Reed (2002) ^
James Pearce-Smith (2002)
Julia Belyavin (2003) ^
Zoë Saunders (2003) ^
Rebecca Taylor (2003) ^
Christopher Jones (2004)
Darren Lewis (2004) ^
Andrew Commins (2004) ^
George Rowell (2004) ^
Jeremy Phillips (2004) °
Jody Atkinson (2005) ^
Richard Gold (2006) ^
Sarah Knapton (2007) °
Paul Lewis (2007) °
Charles Coventry (2007)
Andrew Kearney (2007)
Ben Handy (2008)
Katie Hooper (2008) °
Patrick West (2009)
Michael Clarke (2009)
Oliver Wooding (2009)
Claire Leonard (2009)
Richard Norman (2009)
Nicholas Pointon (2010)
Jessica Wood (2010) ^
Charlie Newington-Bridges (2011)

+ Recorder ++ Associate Member and Deputy High Court Judge ** Deputy District Judge °Associate Member ^ Public/Direct Access

THE CHAMBERS St John's Chambers is one of the largest barristers' sets in the South West, with over 80 members including eight silks, specialising in all major areas of law.
Chambers is recognised nationally as providing first class legal advice and representation in the six core practice groups, commercial and chancery (which incorporates the following three main areas of law: property, wills, trusts and tax, and commercial), personal injury, family, public and administrative law, clinical negligence and employment. Chambers represent regional and national law firms, acting for and advising prominent businesses, private individuals, local and public authorities.
Chambers also provides advice and representation under the public access scheme to members of the public; planning consultants; managing directors and doctors.
The aim is to give clients an exemplary service with barristers providing an accurate and timely turnaround of work. Through chambers' highly capable team of clerks, clients receive an approachable and efficient service ensuring the right barrister is instructed for the relevant case.

St John's
CHAMBERS

Criminal Defence Service
Community Legal Service

Quality Mark - Legal Services Accredited Chambers

CIVITAS LAW

Senior Clerk	Andrea Mclean
Diary Clerks	Alyson Hartington-Clark Rhian Smith
Tenants	21
Door Tenants	2

Global Reach, Celtic Gateway, Cardiff Bay, Cardiff, CF11 0SN
Tel 0845 0713 007 Fax 0845 0713 008 DX 50750 Cardiff 2
Email clerks@civitaslaw.com Website www.civitaslaw.com

MEMBERS

Bryan Thomas (1978) ^
Jonathan Walters (1984) ^
Theodore Huckle QC (1985) (QC-2011)
Graham Walters (1986) ^
Nicholas David Jones (1987)
Mair Coombes Davies (1988) ^
Robert O'Leary (1990) ^
Michael Brace (1991)
Gareth Jones (1991) ^
Anthony Vines (1993) ^
Andrew Arentsen (1995) ^
Joanne Williams (1999) ^
Christopher Howells (1999) ^
Richard Cole (2000) ^
Simon Hughes (2003)
Nicklaus Thomas-Symonds (2004) ^
Mona Bayoumi (2004) ^
Victoria Hillier (2005) ^
Cathrine Grubb (2007) ^
Kate Parker (2010)
Owain Rhys James (2011)
Keith Bush QC (1977) (QC-2014) *
Rebecca Mansell (2005) *

^ Public/Direct Access * Door Tenant

THE CHAMBERS Civitas Law is an award-winning, leading specialist Civil and Public law barristers' chambers serving clients across Wales and England. It believes clients are best served by a set of highly specialist lawyers offering excellence and innovation in advisory work, drafting, mediation and advocacy. With the support of its dedicated, experienced and highly responsive Clerks and Client Support teams, barristers are able to provide a full range of counsel services in personal injuries and clinical negligence; employment; public, planning and regulatory; chancery, business consumer; and ADR matters. The wide range of experience within each group allows them to work successfully with clients from small track cases to a complex appeal. The set continues to develop its reputation by attracting the best of the Bar and aims to provide a cutting edge service whilst maintaining traditions of independence and integrity. The set works closely with its professional clients to ensure that chambers' services are tailored to their unique requirements and business objectives. Among its 21 members are barristers who write or contribute to leading practitioner texts and publications, act as mediators and arbitrators and are appointed as Treasury Counsel, to the Attorney General's Panel and as counsel to the Welsh Government and National Assembly for Wales. Civitas Law is also the chambers for the private practice of the Counsel General for Wales, Theo Huckle QC. Civitas Law has set itself for the highest standards in the delivery of services to its clients; that of excellence. The set aims to be professional and approachable and to provide legal advice which is clear and easily understood by lay clients.

WORK UNDERTAKEN Personal injuries and clinical negligence; chancery, business and consumer law; employment; public law, planning and regulatory; ADR.

CIVITAS LAW

THIRTY PARK PLACE Jonathan Furness QC

Head of Chambers	Jonathan Furness QC
Senior Clerk	Phillip Griffiths

Thirty Park Place, Cardiff, CF10 3BS
Tel: (02920) 398421 **Fax:** (02920) 398725 **DX:** 50756 CARDIFF 2
Emails: family@30parkplace.co.uk civil@30parkplace.co.uk crime@30parkplace.co.uk
Website: www.30parkplace.co.uk

MEMBERS

Jonathan Furness QC (1979) (QC-2003)
Malcolm Bishop QC (1968) (QC-1994)
James Tillyard QC (1978) (QC-2002)
Lloyd Williams QC (1981) (QC-2006)
Ruth Henke QC (1987) (QC-2006)
Rhodri Williams QC (1987) (QC-2010)
Michael Mather-Lees QC (1981) (QC-2012)
Charles Parsley (1973)
J Meirion Davies (1975)
Paul Hartley-Davies (1977)
Marian Lewis (1977)
Mark Allen (1981)
Andrew Taylor (1984)
D Huw Evans (1985)
Stephen Jeary (1987)
Robert Harrison (1988)
Tracey Lloyd-Nesling (1988)
Catherine Heyworth (1991)
Michelle Withers (1991)
Gareth Jonathan-Jones (1991)
Catrin John (1992)
Kate Hughes (1992)
Eugene Egan (1993)
Stephen Thomas (1993)
Elizabeth McGahey (1994)
Caroline Rees (1994)
Juliet Gibbon (1994)
Jane Foulser McFarlane (1994)
Hywel Hughes (1995)
Andrew Jones (1996)
Rhys Taylor (1996)
Carl Harrison (1997)
Harriet Edmondson (1997)
David Hughes (1997)
Colin Douglas (1998)
Ben Davies (1999)
Sarah Waters (1999)
Claire Pickthall (1999)
Nigel Fryer (1999)
Natalie Sandercock (2000)
Angharad Davies (2000)
Rhian Kirby (2000)
Andrew Morse (2000)
Stuart McLeesse (2000)
Katy Morgan (2002)
Byron Broadstock (2002)
Jeffrey Jones (2003)
Rebecca Harrington (2004)
Andrew Joseph (2004)
Claire Williams (2004)
Oliver Manley (2005)
Luke Garrett (2005)
Max Davies (2005)
Emma Sutton (2006)
Mikhael Puar (2006)
Hoa Dieu (2006)
Christian J Howells (2007)
Rebecca Stickler (2007)
Nathan Jones (2008)
Rhian Jones (2008)
Joe Al-Khayat (2008)
Olivia Pike (2008)
Rhys Evans (2008)
Gareth Duncan (2010)
Lowri Wynn Morgan (2010)

THE CHAMBERS Thirty Park Place is one of the largest chambers in Wales. Its members are very much in demand, providing a highly skilled, specialist and professional service at all levels in civil, criminal and family law.

Thirty Park Place
CHAMBERS

AMPERSAND

Parliament House, Parliament Square, Edinburgh, EH1 1RF
Tel (0131) 260 5674 Fax (0131) 225 3642 DX ED 549302 EDINBURGH 36
Email clerks@ampersandstable.com Website www.ampersandadvocates.com

Set Director	Geoffrey Mitchell QC
Clerk	Alan Moffat (0131) 260 5710
Deputies	Jennifer Dunn (0131) 260 5614
	Cheryl Stevens (0131) 260 5660
	Louise Millar (0131) 260 5616
Tenants	57

MEMBERS

Hugh Campbell QC (1969) (QC-1983)
Christopher Haddow QC (1971) (QC-1985)
Malcolm Thomson QC (1974) (QC-1987)
Ian Forrester QC (1972) (QC-1988)
Malcolm Scott QC (1978) (QC-1991)
Aidan O'Neill QC (1987) (QC-1999)
Robert Howie QC (1986) (QC-2000)
David Sellar QC (1995) (QC-2000)
Maria Maguire QC (1987) (QC-2002)
Simon Di Rollo QC (1987) (QC-2002)
Alan Dewar QC (1989) (QC-2002)
Ronnie Clancy QC (1990) (QC-2002)
David Stephenson QC (1991) (QC-2009)
Alastair Kinroy QC (1987) (QC-2005)
Ailsa Wilson QC (1993) (QC-2007)
Dorothy Bain QC (1994) (QC-2007)
Ailsa Carmichael QC (1993) (QC-2008)
Graham Primrose QC (1993) (QC-2008)
Geoffrey Mitchell QC (1992) (QC-2009)
Simon Bowie QC (1995) (QC-2009)
Craig Sandison QC (1996) (QC-2009)
Robert Weir QC (1995) (QC-2010)
Eugene Creally (1993) (QC-2011)
Mark Fitzpatrick (1985)
Archie MacSporran (1992)
Brian Fitzpatrick (1993)
Louise Milligan (1993)
Eoghainn Maclean (1995)
Lisa Henderson (1995)
Stephen Bell (1996)
Lauren Sutherland (1996)
Phil Stuart (1996)
Christian Marney (1998)
Douglas Ross (1998)
Una Doherty (1999)
Euan Mackenzie (1999)
Vinit Khurana (1999)
Laurence Kennedy (2000)
Susanne Tanner (2000)
Marcus McKay (2000)
Fiona Lake (2002)
Graeme I Hawkes (2003)
Michael Stuart (2003)
Isla Davie (2004)
Jamie Dawson (2004)
Jane Munro (2005)
Catherine Devaney (2006)
James McConnell (2006)
Graham Maciver (2007)
Roderick Campbell (2008)
Catherine MacColl (2008)
Laura-Anne van der Westhuizen (2009)
Paul Reid (2011)
Usman Tariq (2011)
Russell Bradley (2012)
Jennifer Nicholson (2013)
Ross Anderson (2013)

THE CHAMBERS Ampersand is considered to be one of the leading sets in Scotland, providing the full range of services offered by the Scottish Bar, both in contentious and non-contentious work, including advocacy, advice and related written work. Amongst its members are some of the Scottish Bar's most highly rated and successful counsel and QCs. Established in 1981 the stable presently has 57 members, including 23 QCs.

WORK UNDERTAKEN Ampersand has core strengths in the fields of commercial law, public law and human rights, planning and environment law and reparation work.
Commercial Law: There is particular expertise in relation to corporate law, construction and engineering litigation, contractual disputes, commercial property issues, intellectual property and insolvency.
Public Law & Human Rights: The work of the stable is extensive, with members acting both for and against central government agencies, the Scottish Government, local authorities and regulatory bodies. Members of the stable have been instructed in many of the leading cases arising out of devolution and the incorporation into law of the European Convention on Human Rights. The stable also has acknowledged expertise in the substantive law of the European Union.
Planning & Environmental Law: The set's membership includes several of Scotland's leading planning counsel acting in public inquires and advising in relation to environmental issues, such as renewable energy developments and flood prevention schemes, as well as transport and retail developments.
Personal Injury & Negligence Claims: In the context of personal injury work, Ampersand has a considerable depth of experience, acting both for claimants and those defending claims. Ampersand also has a number of practitioners with skill in the medical and professional negligence field. Members of the stable are regularly instructed in health and safety prosecutions and Fatal Accident Inquiries.

INTERNATIONAL The work of Ampersand includes advice and advocacy in relation to cross-border and international issues and disputes. Amongst Ampersand's membership are dual-qualified counsel in English law, as well as European Union law.

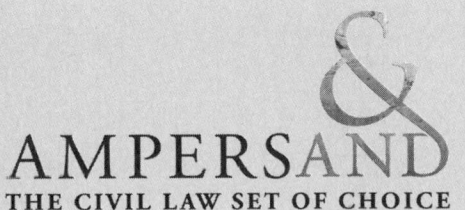

ARNOT MANDERSON

Advocates Library, Parliament House, Edinburgh, EH1 1RF **DX** ED549302 Edinburgh 36
Tel (0131) 260 5824 **Fax** (0131) 225 3642
Website www.amadvoactes.co.uk

Stable Director	Gerald Hanretty QC
Practice Managers	Elizabeth Manderson, (0131) 260 5699 elizabethmanderson@arnotmanderson.co.uk Andrew Sutherland, (0131) 260 5824 andrewsutherland@arnotmanderson.co.uk
Deputies	Catriona Downie, (0131) 260 5713 catrionadownie@arnotmanderson.co.uk Dawn Teitsma, (0131) 260 5655 dawnteitsma@arnotmanderson.co.uk Anne Webster, (0131) 260 5817 annewebster@arnotmanderson.co.uk

THE CHAMBERS Arnot Manderson Advocates is the largest Full Service Stable at the Scottish Bar. The Stable contains 67 Counsel, including 17 Queen's Counsel and also has a number of dual qualified members of the Scottish and English Bar. There are two Advocates Clerks and three Deputy Clerks who organise and support the work of the Advocates within the stable.

Arnot Manderson Advocates are able to provide the services of Advocates with experience in all areas of litigation and advisory work. Members provide an unparalleled depth of experience across the civil and criminal business of the Scottish Courts and beyond with Counsel regularly instructed in the Sheriff Courts, Court of Session, Court of Appeal and the UK Supreme Courts. .

The aim of the Stable is to provide Solicitors and other organisations with a source of first class legal expertise which can provide a solution to their litigation and dispute resolution needs. The Stable is committed to maintaining the highest standards of legal work, whilst continuing the very best traditions of the Bar in Scotland.

ARNOT MANDERSON
ADVOCATES

AXIOM ADVOCATES

Set Director	Jonathan Lake QC
Practice Manager	Lesley Flynn (0131) 260 5651
Deputies	Catriona Still (0131) 260 5653
	Scott Gray (0131) 260 5692
	Veronica Darling (0131) 260 5652
Tenants	44

Advocates Library, Parliament House, Edinburgh, EH1 1RF
Tel (0131) 226 2881 **Fax** (0131) 225 3642 **DX** ED 549302 EDINBURGH 36 LP:LP3 EDINBURGH 10
Website www.axiomadvocates.com

MEMBERS

Rt Honorable Lord Hamilton (1968) (QC-1982)
James McNeill QC (1978) (QC-1991)
Heriot Currie QC (1979) (QC-1992)
Richard Keen QC (1980) (QC-1993)
Lord (Neil) Davidson of Glen Clova QC (1979) (QC-1993)
Gerry Moynihan QC (1985) (QC-1997)
Iain Ferguson QC (1987) (QC-2000)
David Johnston QC (1992) (QC-2005)
James Wolffe QC (1992) (QC-2007) ++
Alistair Clark QC (1994) (QC-2007)
Ruth Crawford QC (1993) (QC-2008)
Jonathan Lake QC (1994) (QC-2008)
James Mure QC (1995) (QC-2009)
Roddy Dunlop QC (1998) (QC-2010)
Julian Ghosh QC (1999) (QC-2010)
Mark Lindsay QC (1996) (QC-2011)
Lorna Drummond QC (1998) (QC-2011)
Anna Poole QC (1998) (QC-2012)
Sean S Smith QC (1999) (QC-2012)
Alastair Duncan QC (1999) (QC-2012)
Kenneth McBrearty QC (2000) (QC-2013)
Garry Borland (2000)
Roisin Higgins (2000)
Gavin Walker (2003)
Morag Ross (2003)
Jonathan Barne (2003)
Almira Delibegović-Broome (2003)
David Thomson (2004)
Martin H Richardson (2004)
Paul O'Brien (2004)
Christopher Wilson (2005)
Euan Duthie (2006)
John MacGregor (2007)
Miranda Hamilton (2007)
Alasdair McKenzie (2009)
Helen Watts (2009)
Susan Ower (2009)
Chris Paterson (2010)
Dan Byrne (2010)
Ross McClelland (2011)
Jonathan Broome (2012)
Lesley Irvine (2012)
Elisabeth Roxburgh (2013)
Ewen Campbell (2013)

++ Dean of Faculty

THE CHAMBERS Axiom Advocates is a set specialising in commercial and public law. It has a firmly established reputation for high quality advice and advocacy. Unlike the traditional Scottish 'stables' of counsel, Axiom's membership has been selected on merit. The set contains many of the most highly-rated senior and junior counsel at the Scottish Bar. Many senior and junior counsel within the set are regarded as the foremost or leading, counsel in their chosen spheres. Its members have consistently appeared in the most significant cases in Scotland in recent years.

WORK UNDERTAKEN The set is particularly strong in commercial law at the Scottish Bar. The work undertaken encompasses almost all aspects of commerce and finance. In particular, Axiom offers specialists in commercial contracts, construction, corporate finance, energy, insolvency, intellectual property, media and entertainment, planning, property, professional negligence and sports law. In the public law, human rights and regulatory fields, the set has an unrivalled concentration of talent at the Scottish Bar. Several members have appointments as standing junior counsel to the Scottish Government and the UK government. Its members have acted in many ground breaking decisions in the areas of public law and human rights, particularly arising out of devolution and the incorporation into Scots law of the European Convention on Human Rights. Members are also regularly instructed in arbitrations, adjudications, disciplinary hearings, planning inquiries and appeals, and in relation to mediations.

INTERNATIONAL The work of the set includes advice and advocacy in relation to cross-border and international issues and disputes.

COMPASS CHAMBERS

Parliament House, Edinburgh, EH1 1RF
Tel (0131) 260 5648 **Fax** (0131) 225 3642 **DX** ED 549302 EDINBURGH 36 LP 3, EDINBURGH 10
Email info@compasschambers.com **Website** www.compasschambers.com

Set Director	Peter Gray QC
Senior Clerk	Gavin Herd (0131) 260 5648
Clerks	Grace Moran (0131) 260 5696
	Kiera Johnston (0131) 260 5657
	Lesley Hogg (0131) 260 5661
Tenants	47

MEMBERS

Ian Mackay QC (1980) (QC-1993)
Susan O'Brien QC (1987) (QC-1998)
Rory Anderson QC (1989) (QC-2000)
Marion Caldwell QC (1986) (QC-2000)
Andrew Smith QC (1988) (QC-2002)
Mark Stewart QC (1988) (QC-2005)
Peter Gray QC (1992) (QC-2002)
Lesley Shand QC (1990) (QC-2005)
Geoff Clarke QC (1994) (QC-2008)
Murdo MacLeod QC (1994) (QC-2008)
Angela Grahame QC (1995) (QC-2009)
Robert Milligan QC (1995) (QC-2009)
David Sheldon QC (1998) (QC-2013)
Peter Milligan (1992)
Preston Lloyd (1996)
Malcolm McGregor (1998)
Barry Divers (1999)
Sandy Forsyth (1999)
Gordon Lamont (1999)
Jan McCall (1999)
Kay Springham (1999)
Astrid Smart (1999)
Kenneth Christine (2000)
Steve Love (2001)
Steve Laing (2002)
Calum Wilson (2002)
David McNaughtan (2003)
Graeme Middleton (2003)
Claire Mitchell (2003)
Susan Duff (2003)
James Hastie (2004)
Amber Galbraith (2005)
Barry Smith (2005)
Derek Reekie (2005)
Robin Cleland (2005)
Yvonne Waugh (2006)
Louis Moll (2006)
Richard Pugh (2008)
Craig Murray (2008)
Richard Henderson (2009)
Gavin Thornley (2009)
Emma Toner (2009)
Jillian Martin-Brown (2010)
Charles Lugton (2012)
Clare Connelly (2013)
Barney Ross (2013)
Kate Bennett (2014)

THE CHAMBERS Compass Chambers is a recognised centre of excellence in reparation, professional negligence and regulatory crime litigation. Compass Chambers' ethos is simple: to demonstrate excellence at all times, working together with clients to achieve the best possible outcome, always. Chambers' membership, based exclusively on merit, embraces this ethos which is central to their outstanding reputation. Members include some of the most well instructed, and highly regarded counsel at the Scottish Bar and, as a result, have considerable experience in all Scottish courts from the Sheriff Court to the UK Supreme Court. Many of the chambers' members are on the panels of several leading insurers, publishers and disciplinary bodies.
An essential part of the Compass ethos is to seek to give added value at all times. To that end, Compass hosts regular conferences across the country at which the most recent developments in their respective core areas are presented to a wide audience.
As an organisation, Compass is at the forefront of innovating in the way in which counsel interact with agents and clients, and aims to offer a commercially sensitive, comprehensive and cost-effective service.

WORK UNDERTAKEN

Reparation: In the reparation field members of Compass specialise in personal injury, property damage, insurance law and fatal accident inquiries.

Regulatory Crime: In the field of regulatory crime, members specialise in the defence of the allegations brought under health and safety, environmental, corporate financial and road traffic legislation, and also appear regularly in fatal accident inquiries; in particular those relating to fatalities in the workplace.

Professional Negligence: In the field of professional negligence, members specialise in clinical negligence, solicitors negligence, property related actions and financial services actions.

In addition to its core strength, Compass includes specialists in contract and commercial litigation, public inquiries and judicial review proceedings within its membership.

Compass Chambers

TERRA FIRMA CHAMBERS

Parliament House, High Street, Edinburgh, EH1 1RF
Tel (0131) 260 5830 **Fax** (0131) 225 3642 **DX** 549302 Edinburgh 36
Website www.terrafirmachambers.com

Practice Manager	Emma Potter
Deputy Clerk	Andrew Veitch
Deputy Clerk	Tracy Whitelaw
Tenants	47

MEMBERS

Sir Menzies Campbell MP QC (1968) (QC-1982)
Roy Martin QC (1976) (QC-1988)
Stuart Gale QC (1980) (QC-1993)
J Gordon Reid QC (1980) (QC-1993)
Gordon Steele QC (1981) (QC-1996)
Scott Brady QC (1987) (QC-2000)
The Rt Hon Dame Elish Angiolini QC (2008) (QC-2001)
Peter Ferguson QC (1985) (QC-2005)
Douglas Armstrong QC (1990) (QC-2005)
Steven Stuart QC (1979) (QC-2008)
Roderick Thomson QC (1990) (QC-2008)
Alan Summers QC (1994) (QC-2008)
James Findlay QC (1984) (QC-2008) (England & Wales-1984) (Scotland-2008)
Andrew Bowen QC (1997) (QC-2012)
Colin MacKenzie (1982)
Derek Francis (1985)
Anthony MacIver (1986)
Robert Skinner (1987)
Peter Grant-Hutchison (1988)
Neil Beynon (1990)
Robert Sutherland (1992)
Nicholas Holroyd (1992)
David Bartos (1993)
Iain Maclean (1994)
Neil Kinnear (1994)
Maurice O'Carroll (1995)
William Frain-Bell (1999)
David Parratt (1999)
Steven Walker (1999)
Scott Blair (2000)
Luise Locke (2000)
David Logan (2000)
Fred Mackintosh (2000)
Stephen Govier (2001)
Philip J D Simpson (2001)
Stephen O'Rourke (2002)
Roddy McIlvride (2005)
Alasdair J Burnet (2006)
Gordon Watt (2007)
Julius Komorowski (2008)
John McKendrick (2008)
Graham Dunlop (2009)
Stephen Winter (2011)
Mark Mohammed (2011)
Dennis Edwards (2012)
Denis Garrity (2014)
Alasdair Sutherland (2014)

THE CHAMBERS Terra Firma Chambers was established in January 2008 with the purpose of providing specialised services in the areas of property, planning, commercial and administrative public law. It was quickly recognised as a leading set with members ranked in each of its core practice areas in either Scotland or England. It has also established an enviable reputation for the service provided by its members and clerks. The current Advocate General for Scotland was formerly a member and it has attracted the previous Lord Advocate for Scotland as a member after she left office in 2011. The chambers contains 47 counsel, including 14 Queen's Counsel. It has the largest number of dual qualified members of the Scottish and English Bars of any Scottish set, with several members in leading chambers at the English Bar. It also has more specialist arbitration advocates (and more arbitration academics) than any other set at the Scottish Bar, including one of the first specially accredited commercial arbitrators by the CEPMLP at Dundee University. Several members hold appointments as part-time sheriffs or part-time tribunal judges. Members of chambers accept instructions under the Faculty of Advocates Direct Access Rules.

WORK UNDERTAKEN The members of Terra Firma Chambers carry out the whole gamut of work related to property, planning, commercial and administrative law. Because many of the areas of law in which members specialise are also regulated by the European Union and the Human Rights Act 1988, members are also well placed to advise on the EU and ECHR aspects of any issue.
Property: Access rights, agriculture and crofting, boundary disputes, charities, commercial property, common good, conveyancing, executries and succession, housing, intellectual property, landlord and tenant, pensions, professional negligence, regulatory enforcement and liability, servitudes and wayleaves, taxation and estate planning, trusts and judicial factors, unjustified enrichment, valuation and rating, wills.
Planning: Conservation, compulsory purchase and compensation, contaminated land, drainage and flood prevention, environmental (civil and criminal) regulation, housing, industrial, infrastructure development, leisure, minerals, nuisance, planning, pollution prevention and control, renewable energy, retail, roads, sewage, telecommunications, waste.
Commercial: Bankruptcy and diligence, building and construction, contracts, commercial arbitration and dispute resolution, discrimination, employment, energy, health and safety, insolvency, intellectual property, partnership, professional negligence, public procurement, regulatory liability, restrictive covenants, roads and transport, taxation, valuation and rating. Members act as advocates, mediators and arbitrators within Scotland, England and internationally.
Administrative & Public Law: Charities, community care, constitutional law, election law, freedom of information, human rights, judicial review, licensing, local government, professional and disciplinary proceedings, public procurement, regulatory enforcement and liability, statutory appeals and review, valuation and rating, welfare law. Members regularly appear before courts, tribunals, inquiries, hearings and local authority committees.

tf terra firma CHAMBERS

WESTWATER ADVOCATES

Faculty of Advocates, Parliament House, Parliament Square, Edinburgh, EH1 1RF
Tel (0131) 260 5700 **Fax** (0131) 225 3642 **DX** 549302 Edinburgh 36 LP LP3, EDINBURGH 10
Email sheila.westwater@westwateradvocates.com **Website** www.westwateradvocates.com

Stable Director	Calum H S MacNeill QC (0131) 226 5071
Advocates Clerk	Sheila Westwater
Deputy Clerks	Christina Ballantyne
	Jane Morrison
Tenants	50

MEMBERS

James A Peoples QC (1979) (QC-1994)
Andrew Hajducki QC (1979) (QC-1994)
Sir Crispin Agnew of Lochnaw Bt QC (1982) (QC-1995)
James Campbell QC (1984) (QC-1997)
Gilmour Ivey QC (1985) (QC-1999)
Nick Ellis QC (1990) (QC-2002)
Calum H S MacNeill QC (1992) (QC-2007)
Janys M Scott QC (1992) (QC-2007)
Douglas Fairley QC (1999) (QC 2012)
Gillian Wade QC (1998) (QC 2013)
Desmond Cheyne (1986)
Gail Joughin (1989)
Maggie Hughes (1991)
Charlotte Coutts (1991)
Ian Sharpe (1992)
Isabella Ennis (1993)
John Speir (1993)
Gordon Lindhorst (1995)
Andrew MacMillan (1995)
Margaret Hodge (1996)
Robert Hayhow (1997)
Greg Cunningham (1997)
Charles Cowie (1998)
Bryan Heaney (1999)
Iain N J Artis (1999)
Jonathan Brown (2000)
Greg Sanders (2001)
Gavin Anderson (2001)
Mary Loudon (2002)
Laura Wray (2003)
Heather Carmichael (2004)
Lynda J Brabender (2005)
Ruth Innes (2005)
Donald Cameron (2005)
Juliette Casey (2006)
Adrian Stalker (2007)
Alice Stobart (2007)
Kirsty Malcolm (2007)
Ken Revie (2008)
David Hay (2008)
Alison M Wild (2008)
Colin Edward (2010)
Kenneth McGuire (2010)
Julianna F Cartwright (2011)
Neil MacDougall (2011)
Scott McAlpine (2012)
Paul McNairney (2013)
Mary Sharpe (2013)
David Anderson (2014)
Rachel Shewan (2014)

THE CHAMBERS Westwater Advocates is one of Scotland's longest established and largest multi-disciplinary stables, with 50 Advocate members including 10 silks. Sheila Westwater has been the clerk since 1991 and is assisted by Christina Ballantyne and Jane Morrison. The clerks provide excellent service, advising on the availability and suitability of advocates for particular work and willing to agree fees in advance.

WORK UNDERTAKEN At all levels of seniority, the stable offers advocates whose experience includes personal injury, professional (including medical) negligence, contract, commercial, construction, insolvency, financial provision on divorce, co-habitation and all aspects of public and private child law, employment, licensing, agricultural, land, media, judicial review and criminal law.

Westwater Advocates

ENTERPRISE CHAMBERS Zia Bhaloo QC

Head of Chambers	Zia Bhaloo QC
Senior Clerk	Antony Armstrong (London)
Clerks	Joanne Caunt
	Ellen Cockcroft
Tenants	37

43 Park Square, Leeds, LS1 2NP
Tel (0113) 246 0391 **Fax** (0113) 242 4802 **DX** 26448 Leeds Park Square
Email leeds@enterprisechambers.com **Website** www.enterprisechambers.com

For a full list of members please see the London entry. For further information about the set please visit the chambers' website.

Enterprise Chambers
London Leeds Newcastle

EXCHANGE CHAMBERS Bill Braithwaite QC

Oxford House, Oxford Row, Leeds, LS1 3BE
Tel (0113) 203 1970 **Fax** (0113) 345 3326 **DX** 26406 Leeds Park Square
Email info@exchangechambers.co.uk **Website** www.exchangechambers.co.uk

Head of Chambers	Bill Braithwaite QC
Chambers Director	Tom Handley
Practice Manager	Roy Finney
Senior Clerk	Ian Spencer
Clerks	Katie Heald
	Nicole Haigh
Tenants	155

MEMBERS

Bill Braithwaite QC (1970) (QC-1992)
Anthony Elleray QC (1977) (QC-1993)
Edward Bartley Jones QC (1975) (QC-1997) +
Gerard Martin QC (1978) (QC-2000) +
Mark Cawson QC (1982) (QC-2001)
John Richard Jones QC (1981) (QC-2002) +
Gordon Cole QC (1974) (QC-2006)
Tania Griffiths QC (1982) (QC-2006) +
William Waldron QC (1986) (QC-2006) +
Brian Cummings QC (1988) (QC-2008) +
Stephen Meadowcraft QC (1973) (QC-2007)
Amanda Yip QC (1991) (QC-2011)+
Simon Medland QC (1991) (QC-2011)
Ben Myers QC(1994) (QC-2014)
Chris Tehrani QC (1990) (QC-2004)
Michael Scholes (1996)
Simon Earlam (1975) +
Eric Lamb (1975) +
Judith Fordham (1991)
Digby Jess (1978)
Anthony Goff (1978)
Karen Troy (1981)
Ian Harris (1990) +
Paul Kirtley (1982) +
Karen Gregory (1985)
Roger Hillman (1983)
Neil Cadwallader (1984) +
Wayne Jackson (1984)
Paul Taylor (1985)
Paul Clark (1994)
William Hanbury (1985)
Simon Berkson (1986) +
Guy Vickers (1986)
David Knifton (1986) +
Sara Dodd (1987) +
Mark Mulrooney (1988)
Louis Browne (1988) +
Ian Foster (1988)
Tina Landale (1988) +
Rebecca Clark (1989)
Catherine Howells (1989) +
Michael Wood (1989)
Simon Vaughan (1989)
Mark Rhind (1989) +
Christopher Stables (1990)
Julie Case (1990)
Christopher Cook (1990)
Michael Lavery (1990)
David Potter (1990)
Jason MacAdam (1990)
Robert Golinski (1990)
David Toal (1990)
Paul Timothy Evans (1992)
Giles Maynard-Connor (1992)
Rachael Woods (1992)
Mark Ainsworth (1992) +
Kevin Naylor (1992)
Gregory Hoare (1992)
Oliver Jarvis (1992)
Amanda Johnson (1992)
Steven Crossley (1992)
John Wyn Williams (1992)
Charlotte Kenny (1993)
Robert Dudley (1993)
Robert Wyn Jones (1993)
Stephen Connolly (1992)
Alison Graham-Wells (1992)
Alario Bassano (1993)
Andrew Jebb (1993) +
Sarah Barlow (1993)
Nicholas Johnson (1994)
Kim Whittlestone (1994)
Louise Whaites (1994)
Damian Nolan (1994)
Richard Littler (1994)
Bruce Walker (1994)
Ceri Widdett (1994)
Michael Maher (1995)
Lisa Linklater (1995)
Mark Smith (1995)
Philip Parry (1995)
Claire Gourley (1996)
Scott Redpath (1996)
Jayne Acton (1996)
Sheren Guirguis (1996)
Andrew Smith (1996)
Imran Shafi (1996)
Ashley Serr (1996)
Pankaj Madan (1997)
Kevin Slack (1997)
Adrian Farrow (1997)
Louise Metcalf (1997)
Mark Stephenson (1997)
Steven Fennell (2014)
Jonathan French (1997)
Jon Close (1997)
David Fearon (2013)
Paul Burns (1998)
Sarah O'Brien (1998)
Katharine Titchmarsh (1998)
Nicholas Walker (1998)
Siân Jones (1998)
Neil Smart (1998)
David Bentley (1998)
Nigel Edwards (1999)
Daniel Travers (1999)
Jonathan Clarke (1999)
David Mohyuddin (1999)
Christopher Barnes (1999)
Martine Snowdon (2000)
Jonathan Rogers (2000)
Andrew Vinson (2000)
Andrew Ward (2000)
Nicola Daley (2000)
Laura Jane Gooding (2001)
Joshua Shields (2000)
David Temkin (2000)
Stephen Grattage (2000)
Paul Hodgkinson (2002)
Caroline Gee (2003)
Charlotte Atherton (2003)
Christian Taylor (2003)
Stephen McNally (2003)
Sarah Johnston (2003)
Sara Sutherland (2004)
Andrew Petterson (2004)
Esther Lin (2007)
Emma Bennett (2004)
Catherine Knowles (2004)
Alex Menary (2004)
Andrew Wastall (2005)
Kerron Rohrer (2005)
Carly Sandbach (2006)
Chris Gutteridge (2006)
Richard Tetlow (2006)
David Birrell (2006)
Alfred Weiss (2006)
Natalia Cornwall (2007)
Gareth Shires (2007)
Jonathan Lowe (2008)
Victoria Smith-Swain (2008)
Simon Whitfield (2009)
Chris Royle (2009)
Lee Speakman (2010)
Huw Edwards (2009)
Chris Allen (2012)
Ian Tucker (2010)
John Waiting (2010)
Stuart McCracken (2011)
Lisa Feng (2011)
Sarah Griffin (2011)
Simon Lewis (2012)
Peter Dixon (2013)
Holly Betke (2013)
Beth Harvey-Smith (2011)
John Charles Rees QC (1972) (QC-1991) *
Jonathan Turner QC (1974) (QC-2003) *
Nicholas Francis QC (1981) (QC-2002)
Daffydd Enoch QC (QC-2010)
Cairns Nelson QC (QC-2010)
Rhodri Williams QC (1987) (QC-2010)
Eleanor Laws QC (1990) (QC-2011)
Alun James (1986) *
John J McCarroll (1988) *
Andrew Maguire (1988)
Simon Fox (1994) *
Nancy Dooher (1997) *
Adam Chichester-Clark (2000) *

+ Recorder * Door Tenant

EXCHANGE CHAMBERS

EXCHANGE CHAMBERS Bill Braithwaite QC (continued)

THE CHAMBERS Exchange Chambers is an award-winning set of barristers' chambers based in Manchester, Liverpool and Leeds. Priding itself on service, Exchange Chambers' ongoing expansion strategy is based on attracting outstanding barristers and outstanding work.

WORK UNDERTAKEN The set has a proven track record in all major areas of law. There are over 150 members, including 14 silks and 30 trained mediators.
A record 57 members are ranked as leaders in their field by Chambers UK.
Crime: The team boasts 8 silks and over 60 juniors who have gained an outstanding reputation for prosecuting and defending all forms of criminal cases.
Personal Injury: Led by Personal Injury Barrister of the Year, Bill Braithwaite QC, the department has a wealth of expertise. Chambers has 4 other silks covering the areas of claimant / defendant personal injury, clinical negligence and industrial disease supported by over 40 juniors.
Commercial: The set is widely acclaimed for its complete range of commercial, insolvency and chancery services including property, planning and construction and has 3 silks and 39 juniors.
Family: The vast expertise of the family team covers not only complex situations of very high value but also lower value cases which can be equally as difficult.
Local Government & Social Housing: Members advise and represent local authorities and registered social housing providers across the country and frequently appear in high profile test litigation.
Civil: The team offers a full range of services in a number of specialist areas, including public law / judicial review, local authority litigation, housing management, landlord and tenant and anti-social behaviour litigation.
Employment: The team includes a silk and 16 juniors covering the full spectrum of employment law.
Regulatory: The team provides specialist advice and representation across a range of regulatory practice areas including Health and Safety, Inquests, Medical / Healthcare, Police Misconduct and Sports Discipline.
Inquests: With 3 team members sitting as Assistant Deputy Coroners, the set has a strong reputation throughout the UK.

KINGS CHAMBERS Nicholas Braslavsky QC

5 Park Square East, Leeds, LS1 2NE **DX** 713113 (Leeds PK SQ)

36 Young Street, Manchester, M3 3FT **DX** 718188 (MCH3)

Embassy House, 60 Church Street, Birmingham, B3 2DJ **DX** 13023 (Birmingham)

Tel 0845 034 3444 **Fax** 0845 034 3445
Email clerks@kingschambers.com **Website** www.kingschambers.com

Chambers Director	Debra Andres
Senior Clerks	William Brown
	Colin Griffin
	Stephen Loxton
Clerks	Andrew Reeves
	Rory Davis
	Gary Young
	Paul Clarke
	Harry Young
	Mark Ronson
	Scott Leach
	Aaron Smith
	Gary Smith
	Jake Brooke

MEMBERS

Dr Nicholas Braslavsky QC (1983) (QC-1999)
Mr Stephen J Sauvain QC (1997) (QC-1995)
Mr Vincent Fraser QC (1981) (QC-2001)
Mr Paul Chaisty QC (1982) (QC-2001)
Mr Richard Clayton QC (1977) (QC-2002)
Mr David Manley QC (1981) (QC-2003)
Ms Lesley Anderson QC (1989) (QC-2006)
Mr Anthony Crean QC (1987) (QC-2006)
Mr David Casement QC (1992) (QC-2008)
Mr Michael Rawlinson QC (1991) (QC-2009)
Mr Paul Tucker QC (1990) (QC-2010)
Mr Nigel Poole QC (1989) (QC 2012)
Reverend Eric Owen (1969)
Mr Jeffrey Terry (1976)
Mr Roger Lancaster (2002)
Mr Alan Evans (1978)
Mr Shokat Khan (1979)
Mr John Barrett (1982)
Mr Neil Berragan (1982)
Mr Mark Halliwell (1985)
Mr Gary Grant (1985)
Mr Simon Hilton (1987)
Mr Nigel Clayton (1987)
Miss Ruth Stockley (1988)
Miss Fiona Ashworth (1998)
Mr Andrew Singer (1990)
Mr Paul Johnson (2006)
Mr Simon Burrows (1990)
Mr Matthew Smith (1991)
Mr Andrew Grantham (1991)
Mr Martin Carter (1992)
Mr Wilson Horne (1992)
Miss Lucy Powis (1992)
Mr Mark Harper (1993)
Miss Sarah Pritchard (1993)
Mr Richard Lander (1993)
Mr Ian Ponter (1993)
Mr Michael Ditchfield (1993)
Miss Sarah Clover (1993)
Mr James Boyd (1994)
Miss Kelly Pennifer (1994)
Mr Andrew Latimer (1995)
Mr Gavin McBride (1996)
Mr Jeremy Roussak (1996)
Mr Louis Doyle (1996)
Mr Jonathan Easton (1996)
Mr Adam Fullwood (1996)
Mr Simon Plaut (1997)
Mr Colin Bourne (1997)
Dr Mark Friston (1997)
Mr Simon Young (1998)
Mr Stephen Maguire (2007)
Mr Giles Cannock (1998)
Professor Andrew McGee (1998)
Mr Matthew Hall (1999)
Miss Helen Mulholland (1999)
Mr Martin Budworth (1999)
Miss Tina Ranales-Cotos (1999)
Mr Brian Griffiths (1999)
Miss Eleanor Temple (2000)
Mrs Lisa Walmisley (2000)
Mr Paul Lakin (2000)
Miss Claire Jackson (2002)
Mr Paul Hughes (2001)
Mr Ben Williams (2001)
Mr Geraint Wheatley (2001)
Miss Claire Steward (2002)
Mr Craig Ralph (2002)
Mr Michael Rudd (2002)
Mr John Hunter (2002)
Mr Sam Karim (2002)
Miss Emily Duckworth (2003)
Miss Michelle Mayoh (2003)
Miss Sarah Lawrenson (2003)
Miss Sarah Reid (2004)
Miss Francesca Gardner (2004)
Miss Rachel Galloway (2004)
Miss Sophie Allan (2004)
Mr Paras Gorasia (2005)
Miss Charlotte Law (2005)
Mr Ben Harding (2005)
Miss Cheryl Dainty (2006)
Mr Richard Livingston (2006)
Mr Johnny Ward (2007)
Dr Nathan Smith (2007)
Miss Gemma Lieberman (2007)
Mr Kevin Latham (2007)
Mr Stephen McNamara (2008)
Mr Anthony Gill (2008)
Miss Eleanor d'Arcy (2008)
Miss Anna Macey (2008)
Mrs Laura Daniels (2009)
Miss Ruth Taylor (2010)
Mr Jonathan Wright (2010)
Mr Aidan Reay (2011)
Mr Freddie Humphries (2011)
Miss Erica Bedford (2012)
Mr Clive Freedman QC (1978) (QC-1997) *
Mr Marcus F Daly SC (1987) (SC-1999) *
Mr Colm o'hOisin SC (1998) (SC-2005) *
Mr Colin Crawford (1997) *
Mr James Henderson (1997) *
Mr Leo Charalambides (1998) *
Professor Andrew Keay (2010) *
David Gilliland QC (1964) (QC-1984) +

* Associates + Arbitrator

THE CHAMBERS Kings Chambers is ranked one of the country's leading sets. It provides barristers with the highest reputation for advocacy, knowledge and standards to service.
This is a large specialist set with a national reputation practising from Manchester, Leeds and Birmingham in several practice areas: predominantly chancery and commercial law; planning and environmental law, personal injury and clinical negligence, costs, employment, sports law, mediation, arbitration and public law.

WORK UNDERTAKEN
Planning: Kings Chambers is one of the largest planning and environmental chambers, with members appearing before a wide range of dedicated tribunals and inquiries. Chambers acts in all aspects of town and country planning and environmental law (including waste disposal and management), compulsory purchase compensation and highways.
Public Law: The public law group practises extensively in the Administrative Court, sitting in London and the regions. The group encompasses the range of public law work in community care, education, housing,

K KINGS CHAMBERS

KINGS CHAMBERS Nicholas Braslavsky QC (continued)

mental health, immigration, licensing, local government and social security matters. Members advise and appear before courts at all levels.

Chancery & Commercial: The chancery and commercial group has extensive experience in litigation (including agency, contracts, sale of goods, restraint of trade and restrictive covenants, corporate law); corporate and personal insolvency (including winding up, administration, administrative receivership and tracing assets), banking and professional negligence. Residential and commercial landlord and tenant work (including renewals, rent review, possession claims, arbitrations), partnership and all aspects of property and conveyancing. Chambers also undertakes trusts and probate work and has members specialising in construction disputes, intellectual property and taxation.

Personal Injury: All aspects of personal injury, including work-related diseases and injuries, sporting injuries, clinical negligence and all aspects of civil liability, contracts, negligence, nuisance, breach of statutory duty, health and safety are undertaken.

Employment: The employment team covers the entire spectrum of employment law and has particular strengths in race, sex, equal pay and disability discrimination.

Sports Law: The sports law team have been involved in some of the most substantial and high profile sports cases nationally in recent years involving, commercial dispute resolution, disciplinary and regulatory proceedings, anti-doping rules, employment issues, sports-related personal injury, breach of confidentiality and privacy, wealth management issues, intellectual property including image rights, trademark infringement and breach of copyright.

Costs: There is a specialist and dedicated costs team, practising exclusively in costs law, disputes and litigation funding.

Mediation: Mediation is an important part of the litigation process. The team comprises accredited mediators at various levels and with expertise in differing areas of law.

Arbitration: Kings Arbitration provides a panel of arbitrators and a panel of arbitration counsel based in the UK and Ireland operating in both domestic and international arbitrations.

PARKLANE PLOWDEN Andrew Axon

19 Westgate, Leeds, LS1 2RD
Tel (0844) 499 5678 **Fax** (0113) 200 1018 **DX** 26404 LEEDS
Email clerks@parklaneplowden.co.uk **Website** www.parklaneplowden.co.uk

Head of Chambers	Andrew Axon
Chambers Director	Neil Douglas
Senior Clerks	Michael Stubbs
	Andy Gray
	Mark Williams (Senior Family Clerk)
Clerks	Laura Storr
	Louise Pearce
	Stephanie Hunt
	Emma Rogers
Tenants	81 plus 2 door tenants

MEMBERS

Andrew Axon (1992)
David Wilby QC (1974) (QC-1998) ±
Stuart Brown QC (1974) (QC 1998) + ±
Tim Hirst (1970) +
David Reade QC (1983) (QC 2006) *
Jo Delahunty QC (1986) (QC-2006) * [A]
Howard Elgot (1974) [A]
Robert Sherman (1977)
Elizabeth O'Hare (1980) [A]
Christopher Williams (1981) +
Lindy Armitage (1985) +
Paul Brook (1986) [A]
David de Jehan (1988) [A]
Joanne Astbury (1989) +
Roger Cooper (1989) [A]
Michael James (1989) [A]
Hari Menon (1989) [A]
Craig Moore (1989)
Seamus Sweeney (1989) [A]
Kerry Cox (1990) [A]
Richard Copnall (1990)
Andrew Crouch (1990)
Alex Foster (1990) **
Jonathan Godfrey (1990)
Claire Lindsay (1991) **
Kaiser Nazir (1991) [A]
Guy Swiffen (1991)
Elizabeth Hodgson (1993) [A]
James Murphy (1993) + [A]
Julia Nelson (1993) [A]
Steven Turner (1993) [A]
Corin Furness (1994)
Dornier Whittaker (1994) [A]
Sara Anning (1995) [A]
Stephen Friday (1996)
Alan Weir (1996) [A]
Dominic Bayne (1996) [A]
Adrian Maitra (1997)
Kirti Jeram (1996) [A]
Zira Hussain (1997) [A]
Oliver Longstaff (1999) *
Tom Nossiter (1999)
Simon Stevenson (1999) [A]
Nicola Twine (1999) [A]
Simon Stevenson (1999) [A]
Elizabeth Jones (2000) [A]
Jane Semple (2000)
Alex Taylor (2000) [A]
Claire Millns (2001) [A]
Ian Pennock (2001) [A]
Andrew Sugarman (2001) [A]
Katherine Goss (2002)
Andrew Scott (2002) [A]
Catherine Souter (2002)
Mark Thomas (2003) [A]
Sarah Brewis (2003)
Stuart Jamieson (2003)
Lynn McFadyen (2003) *
Roger Quickfall (2003) [A]
Farzani Tai (2003) [A]
Philip Booth (2004) *
Razif Azmi (2005) [A]
Leila Benyounes (2005)
Victoria Logue (2005)
Andrew Webster (2005)
John Jackson (2006) *
Lucy Bairstow (2006) [A]
Tim Wilkinson (2006) [A]
Georgina Nolan (2006)
Susan Shakespeare (2007) ***
Duncan Maxwell-Stewart (2007) [A]
Natalia Levine (2007)
Gemma Meredith Davies (2007)
Bryony Clayton (2008)
Hylton Armstrong (2008)
Anna Clarke (2009) [A]
Gareth Price (2009)
Jim Hester (2010)
Simon Wilkinson (2010) [A]
Fay Collinson (2011) [A]
Paul Sangha (2012)
Sabrina Polak (2012)
Richard Ryan (2014) (former solicitor

+ Recorder ± Deputy High Court Judge ** Deputy District Judge ° Former Solicitor *** Deputy District Judge Former Solicitor * Door Tenant [A] Public/Direct Access

THE CHAMBERS As one of the largest sets in the North of England formed on 1st October 2007 following the merger of Park Lane Chambers (Leeds) and Plowden Chambers (Newcastle). It is now one of the stand out civil sets based on the North East Circuit offering strength and depth across a comprehensive range of professional services specialising in eight key practice areas: personal injury; clinical negligence and healthcare; family; employment; chancery and commercial; court of protection; insurance (credit hire and motor fraud); and litigation costs and funding.

The barristers have a reputation for being client focussed, approachable, innovative and commercially minded and have proven themselves to be strong adversaries.

Chambers' reputation as the North East's Leading set has been recognised by many legal publications. Mediation and Public Access are readily available.

Chambers operates an open communications policy using the latest digital technology. This affords its clients full access to members of chambers.

This illustrates that client care is at the forefront of its quality policy. Excellence is demonstrated by unsolicited testimonials in professional guides and continued growth in Chambers' client base.
Value for money is assured as fees for each case can be assessed individually and are based upon the complexity and value of the case, seniority of counsel and time spent in preparation. Fees can be agreed at the outset with one of Chambers' clerks.

WORK UNDERTAKEN

- Personal injury
- Clinical negligence and healthcare
- Employment
- Family
- Chancery and commercial

PARKLANE
PLOWDEN
CHAMBERS

PARKLANE PLOWDEN Andrew Axon (continued)

- Insurance
- Court of Protection
- Litigation funding

RECRUITMENT Chambers is committed to recruiting candidates of the highest calibre. In return it provides a well-structured, stimulating and varied pupillage in a friendly, supportive environment. Pupillage includes an opportunity to sit with judges (ex-members of chambers) at all levels.
Chamber's pupil supervisors are dedicated to providing quality tuition. They regard pupils as the future of Chambers and place great importance on their role. Their aim is to nurture your professional and personal relationships to assist you with pupils' future career at the Bar.

SOVEREIGN CHAMBERS Andrew Lewis QC

46 Park Place, Leeds, LS1 2RY
Tel (0113) 245 1841 **Fax** (0113) 242 0194 **DX** 26408 Leeds Park Square
Email clerks@sovereignchambers.co.uk **Website** www.sovereignchambers.co.uk

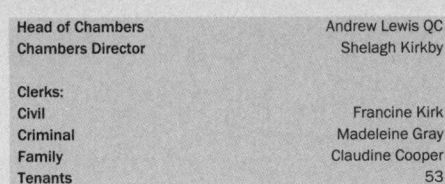

Head of Chambers	Andrew Lewis QC
Chambers Director	Shelagh Kirkby
Clerks:	
Civil	Francine Kirk
Criminal	Madeleine Gray
Family	Claudine Cooper
Tenants	53

THE CHAMBERS Sovereign Chambers is a long established common law set, known as friendly and approachable. They operate at all levels in the civil, criminal and family courts across the North Eastern Circuit and nationwide. Members of the team also sit as Deputy High Court Judges, Recorders and Deputy District Judges. A regular CPD accredited seminar programme is provided.

WORK UNDERTAKEN Civil (commercial, employment, insurance fraud and PI), crime, family (children, money and inheritance), regulatory and disciplinary.

INTERNATIONAL LANGUAGES SPOKEN: Chinese (Mandarin); French; German; Hebrew; Italian; Punjabi; Spanish; Urdu.

SovereignChambers

NO5 CHAMBERS Paul Bleasdale QC

5 Museum Square, Leicester, Leicestershire, LE1 6UF
Tel (0845) 210 5555 **Fax** (0116) 216 7607 **DX** 17004 Leicester 2
Email info@no5.com **Website** www.No5.com

Head of Chambers	Paul Bleasdale QC
Deputy Heads	Rex Tedd QC
	Ian Dove QC
Practice Director	Tony McDaid
Tenants	246

THE CHAMBERS No5 Chambers is a national set offering a comprehensive across the board service. Throughout its 100-year history, No5 Chambers has developed a reputation for breaking new ground and continues to be regarded as a progressive and forward-thinking set, maintaining its success in traditional sectors of law whilst offering specialist advice and representation at the cutting edge of newly evolving areas. Having grown to over 240 barristers including 26 silks, No5 Chambers provides a truly nationwide service from its offices in Birmingham, London, Bristol and the East Midlands.

In recent years chambers has made significant inroads into the South West and Wales from its office in Bristol whilst its London office continues to go from strength to strength, housing more than 50 tenants. Chambers continues to attract high quality work in all disciplines, combining excellent service standards with a progressive, modern and flexible approach to clients' needs. For further information and a full list of tenants please see the Birmingham entry or visit www.No5.com.

EXCHANGE CHAMBERS Bill Braithwaite QC

One Derby Square, Liverpool, L2 9XX
Tel (0151) 236 7747 **Fax** (0151) 236 3433 **DX** 14207 Liverpool
Email info@exchangechambers.co.uk **Website** www.exchangechambers.co.uk

Head of Chambers	Bill Braithwaite QC
Clerks	Kate Masher
	Suzanne Dutch
	Denise Sheen
	Rachel Williams
	Sarah Rotherham
Chambers Director	Tom Handley
Practice Manager	Roy Finney
Senior Clerks	Ian Spencer
	Nick Buckley
Tenants	155

MEMBERS
Bill Braithwaite QC (1970) (QC-1992)
Anthony Elleray QC (1977) (QC-1993)
Edward Bartley Jones QC (1975) (QC-1997) +
Gerard Martin QC (1978) (QC-2000) +
Mark Cawson QC (1982) (QC-2001)
John Richard Jones QC (1981) (QC-2002) +
Gordon Cole QC (1974) (QC-2006)
Tania Griffiths QC (1982) (QC-2006) +
William Waldron QC (1986) (QC-2006) +
Brian Cummings QC (1988) (QC-2008) +
Stephen Meadowcraft QC (1973) (QC-2007)
Amanda Yip QC (1991) (QC-2011)+
Simon Medland QC (1991) (QC-2011)
Ben Myers QC(1994) (QC-2014)
Chris Tehrani QC (1990) (QC-2004)
Michael Scholes (1996)
Simon Earlam (1975) +
Eric Lamb (1975) +
Judith Fordham (1991)
Digby Jess (1978)
Anthony Goff (1978)
Karen Troy (1981)
Ian Harris (1990) +
Paul Kirtley (1982) +
Karen Gregory (1985)
Roger Hillman (1983)
Neil Cadwallader (1984) +
Wayne Jackson (1984)
Paul Taylor (1985)
Paul Clark (1994)
William Hanbury (1985)
Simon Berkson (1986) +
Guy Vickers (1986)
David Knifton (1986) +
Sara Dodd (1987) +
Mark Mulrooney (1988)
Louis Browne (1988) +
Ian Foster (1988)
Tina Landale (1988) +
Rebecca Clark (1989)
Catherine Howells (1989) +
Michael Wood (1989)
Simon Vaughan (1989)
Mark Rhind (1989) +
Christopher Stables (1990)
Julie Case (1990)
Christopher Cook (1990)
Michael Lavery (1990)
David Potter (1990)
Jason MacAdam (1990)
Robert Golinski (1990)
David Toal (1990)
Paul Timothy Evans (1992)
Giles Maynard-Connor (1992)
Rachael Woods (1992)
Mark Ainsworth (1992) +
Kevin Naylor (1992)
Gregory Hoare (1992)
Oliver Jarvis (1992)
Amanda Johnson (1992)
Steven Crossley (1992)
John Wyn Williams (1992)
Charlotte Kenny (1993)
Robert Dudley (1993)
Robert Wyn Jones (1993)
Stephen Connolly (1992)
Alison Graham-Wells (1992)
Alario Bassano (1993)
Andrew Jebb (1993) +
Sarah Barlow (1993)
Nicholas Johnson (1994)
Kim Whittlestone (1994)
Louise Whaites (1994)
Damian Nolan (1994)
Richard Littler (1994)
Bruce Walker (1994)
Ceri Widdett (1994)
Michael Maher (1995)
Lisa Linklater (1995)
Mark Smith (1995)
Philip Parry (1995)
Claire Gourley (1996)
Scott Redpath (1996)
Jayne Acton (1996)
Sheren Guirguis (1996)
Andrew Smith (1996)
Imran Shafi (1996)
Ashley Serr (1996)
Pankaj Madan (1997)
Kevin Slack (1997)
Adrian Farrow (1997)
Louise Metcalf (1997)
Mark Stephenson (1997)
Steven Fennell (2014)
Jonathan French (1997)
Jon Close (1997)
David Fearon (2013)
Paul Burns (1998)
Sarah O'Brien (1998)
Katharine Titchmarsh (1998)
Nicholas Walker (1998)
Siân Jones (1998)
Neil Smart (1998)
David Bentley (1998)
Nigel Edwards (1999)
Daniel Travers (1999)
Jonathan Clarke (1999)
David Mohyuddin (1999)
Christopher Barnes (1999)
Martine Snowdon (2000)
Jonathan Rogers (2000)
Andrew Vinson (2000)
Andrew Ward (2000)
Nicola Daley (2000)
Laura Jane Gooding (2001)
Joshua Shields (2000)
David Temkin (2000)
Stephen Grattage (2000)
Paul Hodgkinson (2002)
Caroline Gee (2003)
Charlotte Atherton (2003)
Christian Taylor (2003)
Stephen McNally (2003)
Sarah Johnston (2003)
Sara Sutherland (2004)
Andrew Petterson (2004)
Esther Lin (2007)
Emma Bennett (2004)
Catherine Knowles (2004)
Alex Menary (2004)
Andrew Wastall (2005)
Kerron Rohrer (2005)
Carly Sandbach (2006)
Chris Gutteridge (2006)
Richard Tetlow (2006)
David Birrell (2006)
Alfred Weiss (2006)
Natalia Cornwall (2007)
Gareth Shires (2007)
Jonathan Lowe (2008)
Victoria Smith-Swain (2008)
Simon Whitfield (2009)
Chris Royle (2009)
Lee Speakman (2010)
Huw Edwards (2009)
Chris Allen (2012)
Ian Tucker (2010)
John Waiting (2010)
Stuart McCracken (2011)
Lisa Feng (2011)
Sarah Griffin (2011)
Simon Lewis (2012)
Peter Dixon (2013)
Holly Betke (2013)
Beth Harvey-Smith (2011)
John Charles Rees QC (1972) (QC-1991) *
Jonathan Turner QC (1974) (QC-2003) *
Nicholas Francis QC (1981) (QC-2002)
Daffydd Enoch QC (QC-2010)
Cairns Nelson QC (QC-2010)
Rhodri Williams QC (1987) (QC-2010)
Eleanor Laws QC (1990) (QC-2011)
Alun James (1986) *
John J McCarroll (1988) *
Andrew Maguire (1988)
Simon Fox (1994) *
Nancy Dooher (1997) *
Adam Chichester-Clark (2000) *

+ Recorder * Door Tenant

EXCHANGE CHAMBERS

EXCHANGE CHAMBERS Bill Braithwaite QC (continued)

THE CHAMBERS Exchange Chambers is an award-winning set of barristers' chambers based in Manchester, Liverpool and Leeds. Priding itself on service, Exchange Chambers' ongoing expansion strategy is based on attracting outstanding barristers and outstanding work.

WORK UNDERTAKEN The set has a proven track record in all major areas of law. There are over 150 members, including 14 silks and 30 trained mediators.
A record 57 members are ranked as leaders in their field by Chambers UK.
Crime: The team boasts 8 silks and over 60 juniors who have gained an outstanding reputation for prosecuting and defending all forms of criminal cases.
Personal Injury: Led by Personal Injury Barrister of the Year, Bill Braithwaite QC, the department has a wealth of expertise. Chambers has 4 other silks covering the areas of claimant / defendant personal injury, clinical negligence and industrial disease supported by over 40 juniors.
Commercial: The set is widely acclaimed for its complete range of commercial, insolvency and chancery services including property, planning and construction and has 3 silks and 39 juniors.
Family: The vast expertise of the family team covers not only complex situations of very high value but also lower value cases which can be equally as difficult.
Local Government & Social Housing: Members advise and represent local authorities and registered social housing providers across the country and frequently appear in high profile test litigation.
Civil: The team offers a full range of services in a number of specialist areas, including public law / judicial review, local authority litigation, housing management, landlord and tenant and anti-social behaviour litigation.
Employment: The team includes a silk and 16 juniors covering the full spectrum of employment law.
Regulatory: The team provides specialist advice and representation across a range of regulatory practice areas including Health and Safety, Inquests, Medical / Healthcare, Police Misconduct and Sports Discipline.
Inquests: With 3 team members sitting as Assistant Deputy Coroners, the set has a strong reputation throughout the UK.

7 HARRINGTON ST CHAMBERS Richard Pratt QC

Head of Chambers	Richard Pratt QC
Senior Clerk	John Kilgallon
Tenants	104

7 Harrington Street, Liverpool, L2 9YH
Tel (0151) 242 0707 **Fax** (0151) 236 2800 DX 14221 Liverpool 1
Email clerks@7hs.co.uk **Website** www.7hs.co.uk

MEMBERS

Richard Pratt QC (1980) (QC-2006)
Iain Goldrein QC (1975) (QC-1997)
Stephen Riordan QC (1972) (QC-1992) +
Anthony Berry QC (1976) (QC-1994) *
Neil Flewitt QC (1981) (QC-2003)
Nicholas Johnson QC (1987) (QC-2006)
Nigel Power QC (1992) (QC-2010)
Ian Unsworth QC (1992) (QC-2010)
Paul Russell QC (1984) (QC-2011) *
Joel Donovan QC (1991) (QC-2011) *
Nigel Lawrence QC (1988) (QC-2014)
David Geey (1970)
Andrew McDonald (1971)
Gordon Bellis (1972)
Mary Compton-Rickett (1972)
Michael J Pickavance (1974)
Neville Biddle (1974)
James Rae (1976)
Kevin Grice (1977) *
Michael Davies (1979)
Julian Nutter (1979)
Arthur Gibson (1980)
Henry Riding (1981)
Grant Lazarus (1981)
Peter Gregory (1982)
James McKeon (1982)
Andrew Loveridge (1983)
James Byrne (1983)
Kevin Reade (1983)
Simon J Killeen (1984)
Jamil Khan (1986)
Stephen Knapp (1986)
Peter Kidd (1987)
Janet Reaney (1987)
Tim Kenward (1987)
Keith Sutton (1988)
Diarmuid Flood (1989)
Andrew Downie (1990)
Kate Symms (1990)
Christine Bispham (1991)
Tim Grover (1991)
Stephen Seed (1991)
Simon Driver (1991)
Trevor Parry-Jones (1992)
Susan Sherman (1993)
Ian Whitehurst (1994)
Helen Wrenn (1994)
Gary Reynolds (1994)
Gerald Jones (1995)
Clive Baker (1995)
Andrew Carney (1995) *
Jeremy Greenfield (1995)
Brendan Burke (1995)
Nicola Turner (1995)
Teresa Loftus (1995)
Malcolm Dutchman-Smith (1995) *
Joanna Mallon (1996)
David McLachlan (1996)
Steven Ball (1996)
Andrew Ford (1997)
Daniel Rogers (1997)
Kenneth Grant (1998)
Elizabeth Brennan (1998)
Neil Bisarya (1998)
Jacqueline Swain (1998)
Michael Jones (1999)
Nicola Miles (1999)
Lianne Naughton (1999)
Sarah Holt (1999)
Daniel Wood (2000)
William Ralston (2000) *
Phillip Tully (2000)
Mark Roberts (2001)
Sarah Langley (2001)
Frances Hertzog (2001)
Lisa Edmunds (2002)
Emma Freeman (2002)
Jonathan Duffy (2002)
Martin Reid (2003)
Paul Wright (2003)
Craig Fisher (2004)
Christopher Knagg (2005)
David Dunne (2005)
Barbara Webster (2005)
Victoria Roberts (2005)
Fraser Lindsay (2006)
Katherine O'Donohue (2006)
Brian Treadwell (2006)
Lianne Birkett (2006)
Tim Wilkinson (2006)
Julie Ashley (2007)
Sarah Watters (2007)
Danielle Paton (2007)
Peter Harthan (2007)
Stephanie Varle (2009)
John O'Leary (2010)
Gemma Thomas (2010)
Francesca Martin (2010)
Hannah Brookfield (2011)
Matthew Hooper (2012)
Greg Plunkett (2013)
Frank Dillon (2014)

+ Recorder * Door Tenant

THE CHAMBERS 7 Harrington Street is one of the largest sets of chambers in the country. It has a policy of excellence, innovation and expansion with expertise in all aspects of law. Chambers has earned its reputation through continued professional excellence and a commitment to working to the highest ethical standards. Currently there are 104 barristers, including 11 QCs. They are supported by a large and dedicated team of clerking and administrative staff who consistently provide clients with a high level of service. As holders of the Legal Services Quality Mark, the set offers quality assured service to members of the public who need legal information, advice and assistance. Chambers is firmly committed to equal opportunities, and it accepts instructions from anyone regardless of background or circumstances. It is located in the heart of the commercial and legal centre of Liverpool, only a short walk from the QEII Combined Courts centre and the Liverpool Civil and Family Courts. 7 Harrington Street has extensive state of the art conference and seminar facilities, including a video conferencing suite.

7 Harrington St
CHAMBERS

6-8 MILL STREET Stephen Hockman QC

6-8 Mill Street, Maidstone, ME15 6XH
Tel (01622) 688094/688095 **Fax** (01622) 688096 DX 51967 Maidstone 2
Email annexe@6pumpcourt.co.uk **Website** www.6pumpcourt.co.uk

Head of Chambers	Stephen Hockman QC
Senior Clerk	Richard Constable
Tenants	56

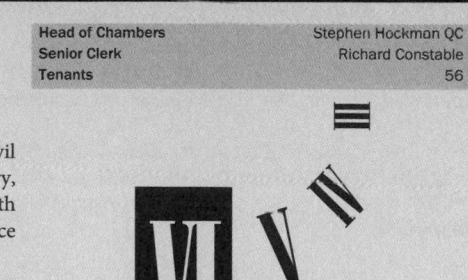

THE CHAMBERS A leading common law set in the south-east with particular specialist expertise in civil and commercial, criminal, employment, family, financial conduct, inquests and inquiries, personal injury, public, planning and environmental, and regulatory law. This combination of expertise ensures a depth and breadth of ability and experience, thoroughly combining a strong criminal and regulatory practice with a well-established reputation in planning and environmental, civil, employment and family work. With well-appointed offices in the heart of Kent, Chambers can meet the needs of clients throughout the county in an efficient, cost-effective and responsive manner.

WORK UNDERTAKEN Crime; civil and commercial; employment; family; financial conduct; inquests; personal injury; planning and environmental; public law; regulatory law.
Please see the London entry under 6 Pump Court for further details.

BYROM STREET CHAMBERS Raymond Machell QC

Head of Chambers	Raymond Machell QC
Senior Clerk	Terry Creathorn (Mrs)
Deputy Senior Clerk	Steve Price

12 Byrom Street, Manchester, M3 4PP
Tel (0161) 829 2100 **Fax** (0161) 829 2101 **DX** 718156 Manchester-3
Email clerks@byromstreet.com **Website** www.byromstreet.com

Crown Office Chambers, 2 Crown Office Row, London EC4Y 7HJ
Tel (020) 7797 8100 **Fax** (020) 7797 8101 **DX** 80 London Chancery Lane

MEMBERS

Raymond Machell QC (1973) (QC-1988)
Geoffrey Tattersall QC (1970) (QC-1992)
David Allan QC (1974) (QC-1995)
Winston Hunter QC (1985) (QC-2000)
Christopher Melton (1982) (QC-2001)
Simon Myerson QC (1986) (QC-2003)
James Rowley QC (1987) (QC-2006)
David Heaton QC (1983) (QC-2008)
Andrew Lewis QC (1985) (QC-2009)
Sally Hatfield QC (1988) (QC-2013)
Darryl Allen QC (1995) (QC-2014)
Richard Pearce (1985)
Mary Ruck (1993)
Peter Burns (1993)
Simon Kilvington (1995)
Benet Hytner
Dame Janet Smith

THE CHAMBERS Byrom Street Chambers is a forward-thinking set with traditional values, exclusively dedicated to the work of leading and senior junior counsel who have extensive expertise in high-value and complex cases. Chambers provides a highly individual and personalised service, focussing on clients' needs, combined with a friendly and open approach to clerking.

WORK UNDERTAKEN Chambers has a reputation for quality and service. Members offer advice and advocacy in a range of specialisations and can provide the depth of cover necessary to conduct litigation in the most complex of cases. They practise regularly in the fields of personal injury (with an emphasis on catastrophic cases, group and class actions, clinical negligence and disease litigation), health and safety, professional negligence, financial services, commercial, employment, human rights, mediation and civil fraud.
Sample cases include Dunhill v Burgin (SC 2014); Woodland v Essex CC (SC 2013); McDonald v Dept for Communities (COA 2013); Sienkiewicz and Willmore (SC 2011); R (on app of AB) v Oldham NHS and Direct Line (Admin); Huscroft v P&O Ferries (CA); Thompstone v Tameside (CA); Fairchild v Glenhaven (HoL); Sowden v Lodge (CA); Tomlinson v Congleton (HoL); RK&AK v Oldham NHS Trust (ECHR); Shipman Inquiry.

Byrom Street Chambers

DEANS COURT CHAMBERS Craig Sephton QC

24 St John Street, Manchester, M3 4DF
Tel (0161) 214 6000 **Fax** (0161) 214 6001 **DX** 718155 Manchester 3
Email clerks@deanscourt.co.uk **Website** www.deanscourt.co.uk

Head of Chambers	Craig Sephton QC
Senior Clerk	Matthew Gibbons
Tenants	84

MEMBERS

Craig Sephton QC (1981) (QC-2001)
Stephen Grime QC (1970) (QC-1987)
David Fish QC (1973) (QC-1997) ^
Tim Horlock (1981) (QC-1997)
Christopher Sokol QC (1977) (QC-2006)
Stuart Denney QC (1982) (QC-2008)^
Susan Grocott QC (1986) (QC-2008) ^
Mary O'Rourke QC (1981) (QC-2009)
Jane Cross QC (1982) (QC-2010)
Lewis Power QC (1990) (QC-2011)
Michael Hayton QC (1993) (QC-2013)
Peter Atherton (1975)
David Eccles (1976) MA (Cantab)
Timothy Ryder (1977)
Ruth Trippier (1978)
David Kenny (1982)
Hugh Davies (1982)
Timothy Trotman (1983)
Russell Davies (1983)
Glenn Campbell (1985)
Paul Humphries (1986)
Karen Brody (1986)
Christopher Hudson (1987)
Heather Hobson (1987)
Nicholas Grimshaw (1988)
Bansa Singh Hayer (1988)
Ciaran Rankin (1988)
Peter Smith (1988)
Jonathan Grace (1989)
Robin Kitching (1989) ^
Michael Smith (1989) MA, BCL
Julia Cheetham (1990)
Nicholas Courtney (1990)
Janet Ironfield (1992)
Timothy Edge (1992) ^
Alison Woodward (1992)
Fraser Livesey (1992) ^
Jonathan Butler (1992)
Mark Savill (1993) ^
Lisa Judge (1993) ^
Peter Horgan (1993) ^
Sebastian Clegg (1994)
Peter Rothery (1994) ^
Francesca Fothergill (1994)
Carolyn Bland (1995)
David Boyle (1996)
Simon McCann (1996) ^
Paul Higgins (1996)
Archna Dawar (1996)
Elizabeth Dudley-Jones (1997) ^
Sophie Cartwright (1998) ^
Richard Whitehall (1998)
Daniel Paul (1998)
Sasha Watkinson (1998)
Joanna Moody (1998)
Ross Olson (1999)
Pascale Hicks (1999)
Sarah J Booth (1999)
Virginia Hayton (1999) ^
Elizabeth Morton (1999)
Susan Deas (1999)
Joseph Hart (2000) ^
Ros Emsley-Smith (2001) ^
Anthony Singh (2001)
Robert McMaster (2001)
Zoe Earnshaw (2001) LLB
Alex Poole (2002)
Alex Taylor (2003) ^
William Tyler (2003)
Victoria Heyworth (2003)
Rebecca Gregg (2003)
Anna Bentley (2004)
Carly Walters (2004)
Jonathan Lally (2005) ^
Michelle Brown (2005) ^
Victoria Harrison (2006)
Rachel Greenwood (2008)
Jonathan King (2009)
Eliza Sharron (2009)
James Paterson (2010)
Nilufa Khanum (2009)
Simon Rowbotham (2011)
Emily Price (2012)
Junaid Dussani (2009)

^ Public/Direct Access

WORK UNDERTAKEN

Civil Litigation: Deans Court offers strength in depth, covering: the whole range of personal injury, including injuries of the utmost severity; class actions; industrial disease; fraudulent claims; road traffic and factory accidents; professional negligence, especially medical, lawyers, surveyors and architects; insurance, including coverage litigation, Road Traffic Act and Motor Insurers' Bureau; contractual disputes; sale of goods; consumer credit (including credit hire); product liability; arbitration (domestic and international); technology and construction; human rights and false imprisonment.

Chancery & Commercial: Includes commercial arbitration; banking; carriage of goods; civil fraud and tracing of assets; corporate and personal insolvency; company law (including shareholders' disputes and the protection of minority interest, directors' duties and disqualification); credit and leasing; financial services; injunctions and equitable remedies; insurance and reinsurance; intellectual property; landlord and tenant; mortgages; partnerships; pensions; probate; real property; sale of goods (domestic and international); trusts, settlements and wills.

Family: Finance: financial remedies on divorce/dissolution of civil partnership (including complex company structures, trust arrangements, offshore assets and freezing injunctions); cohabitation (including agreements, ToLATA and Schedule 1 provision for children); and family provision under the Inheritance (Provision for Family and Dependents) Act 1976. Children: members represent local authorities, parents, interveners and children in care and adoption cases (including death or serious injury to a child, fabricated and induced illness, and sexual abuse); difficult residence and contact disputes; international movement and abduction of children; and surrogacy. Members act in judicial review cases concerning social and health care.

Crime & Business Crime: Prosecution and defence work in: homicide and sexual offences; commercial fraud; conspiracy; drug importation and supply; Excise and Revenue offences; prosecutions under the Health and Safety at Work Act 1974 and other legislation; inquests; licensing; trademark and copyright; rail and transport; corporate manslaughter; trading standards; food safety; environmental prosecutions and DEFRA prosecutions.

Court of Protection & Community Care Law: Work includes: unlawful removal of adults from their home; deprivation of liberty cases; judicial review of decisions regarding provision of services; the use of the inherent jurisdiction for vulnerable adults; the conflicting roles of the Court of Protection and the Mental Health Act 1983; welfare decisions involving capacity; and property and affairs decisions (including financial abuse and ratification of gifts).

Professional Disciplinary & Regulatory: Specialist knowledge of law and procedure in Tribunals, particularly the Medical Practitioners Tribunal. Members represent various regulatory bodies (including the GMC) while also defending practitioners for the medical defence organisations; Chambers is appointed to the Medical Defence Union and Medical Protection Society Panels. Work before other disciplinary bodies includes the Nursing and Midwifery Council and NHS Foundation Trusts.

EXCHANGE CHAMBERS Bill Braithwaite QC

201 Deansgate, Manchester, M3 3NW
Tel (0161) 833 2722 **Fax** (0161) 833 2789 **DX** 14330 Manchester
Email info@exchangechambers.co.uk **Website** www.exchangechambers.co.uk

Head of Chambers	Bill Braithwaite QC
Clerks	David Haley
	Lynn Salter
	Leigh Daniels
	Ria Ashcroft
	Josh Finn
	Joe Mawson
Chambers Director	Tom Handley
Practice Manager	Roy Finney
Senior Clerk	Nick Buckley
Tenants	155

MEMBERS

Bill Braithwaite QC (1970) (QC-1992)
Anthony Elleray QC (1977) (QC-1993)
Edward Bartley Jones QC (1975) (QC-1997) +
Gerard Martin QC (1978) (QC-2000) +
Mark Cawson QC (1982) (QC-2001)
John Richard Jones QC (1981) (QC-2002) +
Gordon Cole QC (1974) (QC-2006)
Tania Griffiths QC (1982) (QC-2006) +
William Waldron QC (1986) (QC-2006) +
Brian Cummings QC (1988) (QC-2008) +
Stephen Meadowcraft QC (1973) (QC-2007)
Amanda Yip QC (1991) (QC-2011)+
Simon Medland QC (1991) (QC-2011)
Ben Myers QC(1994) (QC-2014)
Chris Tehrani QC (1990) (QC-2004)
Michael Scholes (1996)
Simon Earlam (1975) +
Eric Lamb (1975) +
Judith Fordham (1991)
Digby Jess (1978)
Anthony Goff (1978)
Karen Troy (1981)
Ian Harris (1990) +
Paul Kirtley (1982) +
Karen Gregory (1985)
Roger Hillman (1983)
Neil Cadwallader (1984) +
Wayne Jackson (1984)
Paul Taylor (1985)
Paul Clark (1994)
William Hanbury (1985)
Simon Berkson (1986) +
Guy Vickers (1986)
David Knifton (1986) +
Sara Dodd (1987) +
Mark Mulrooney (1988)
Louis Browne (1988) +
Ian Foster (1988)
Tina Landale (1988) +
Rebecca Clark (1989)
Catherine Howells (1989) +
Michael Wood (1989)
Simon Vaughan (1989)
Mark Rhind (1989) +
Christopher Stables (1990)
Julie Case (1990)
Christopher Cook (1990)
Michael Lavery (1990)
David Potter (1990)
Jason MacAdam (1990)
Robert Golinski (1990)
David Toal (1990)
Paul Timothy Evans (1992)
Giles Maynard-Connor (1992)
Rachael Woods (1992)
Mark Ainsworth (1992) +
Kevin Naylor (1992)
Gregory Hoare (1992)
Oliver Jarvis (1992)
Amanda Johnson (1992)
Steven Crossley (1992)
John Wyn Williams (1992)
Charlotte Kenny (1993)
Robert Dudley (1993)
Robert Wyn Jones (1993)
Stephen Connolly (1992)
Alison Graham-Wells (1992)
Alario Bassano (1993)
Andrew Jebb (1993) +
Sarah Barlow (1993)
Nicholas Johnson (1994)
Kim Whittlestone (1994)
Louise Whaites (1994)
Damian Nolan (1994)
Richard Littler (1994)
Bruce Walker (1994)
Ceri Widdett (1994)
Michael Maher (1995)
Lisa Linklater (1995)
Mark Smith (1995)
Philip Parry (1995)
Claire Gourley (1996)
Scott Redpath (1996)
Jayne Acton (1996)
Sheren Guirguis (1996)
Andrew Smith (1996)
Imran Shafi (1996)
Ashley Serr (1996)
Pankaj Madan (1997)
Kevin Slack (1997)
Adrian Farrow (1997)
Louise Metcalf (1997)
Mark Stephenson (1997)
Steven Fennell (2014)
Jonathan French (1997)
Jon Close (1997)
David Fearon (2013)
Paul Burns (1998)
Sarah O'Brien (1998)
Katharine Titchmarsh (1998)
Nicholas Walker (1998)
Siân Jones (1998)
Neil Smart (1998)
David Bentley (1998)
Nigel Edwards (1999)
Daniel Travers (1999)
Jonathan Clarke (1999)
David Mohyuddin (1999)
Christopher Barnes (1999)
Martine Snowdon (2000)
Jonathan Rogers (2000)
Andrew Vinson (2000)
Andrew Ward (2000)
Nicola Daley (2000)
Laura Jane Gooding (2001)
Joshua Shields (2000)
David Temkin (2000)
Stephen Grattage (2000)
Paul Hodgkinson (2002)
Caroline Gee (2003)
Charlotte Atherton (2003)
Christian Taylor (2003)
Stephen McNally (2003)
Sarah Johnston (2003)
Sara Sutherland (2004)
Andrew Petterson (2004)
Esther Lin (2007)
Emma Bennett (2004)
Catherine Knowles (2004)
Alex Menary (2004)
Andrew Wastall (2005)
Kerron Rohrer (2005)
Carly Sandbach (2006)
Chris Gutteridge (2006)
Richard Tetlow (2006)
David Birrell (2006)
Alfred Weiss (2006)
Natalia Cornwall (2007)
Gareth Shires (2007)
Jonathan Lowe (2008)
Victoria Smith-Swain (2008)
Simon Whitfield (2009)
Chris Royle (2009)
Lee Speakman (2010)
Huw Edwards (2009)
Chris Allen (2012)
Ian Tucker (2010)
John Waiting (2010)
Stuart McCracken (2011)
Lisa Feng (2011)
Sarah Griffin (2011)
Simon Lewis (2012)
Peter Dixon (2013)
Holly Betke (2013)
Beth Harvey-Smith (2011)
John Charles Rees QC (1972) (QC-1991) *
Jonathan Turner QC (1974) (QC-2003) *
Nicholas Francis QC (1981) (QC-2002)
Daffydd Enoch QC (QC-2010)
Cairns Nelson QC (QC-2010)
Rhodri Williams QC (1987) (QC-2010)
Eleanor Laws QC (1990) (QC-2011)
Alun James (1986) *
John J McCarroll (1988) *
Andrew Maguire (1988)
Simon Fox (1994) *
Nancy Dooher (1997) *
Adam Chichester-Clark (2000) *

+ Recorder * Door Tenant

EXCHANGE CHAMBERS

EXCHANGE CHAMBERS Bill Braithwaite QC (continued)

THE CHAMBERS Exchange Chambers is an award-winning set of barristers' chambers based in Manchester, Liverpool and Leeds. Priding itself on service, Exchange Chambers' ongoing expansion strategy is based on attracting outstanding barristers and outstanding work.

WORK UNDERTAKEN The set has a proven track record in all major areas of law. There are over 150 members, including 14 silks and 30 trained mediators.
A record 57 members are ranked as leaders in their field by Chambers UK.
Crime: The team boasts 8 silks and over 60 juniors who have gained an outstanding reputation for prosecuting and defending all forms of criminal cases.
Personal Injury: Led by Personal Injury Barrister of the Year, Bill Braithwaite QC, the department has a wealth of expertise. Chambers has 4 other silks covering the areas of claimant / defendant personal injury, clinical negligence and industrial disease supported by over 40 juniors.
Commercial: The set is widely acclaimed for its complete range of commercial, insolvency and chancery services including property, planning and construction and has 3 silks and 39 juniors.
Family: The vast expertise of the family team covers not only complex situations of very high value but also lower value cases which can be equally as difficult.
Local Government & Social Housing: Members advise and represent local authorities and registered social housing providers across the country and frequently appear in high profile test litigation.
Civil: The team offers a full range of services in a number of specialist areas, including public law / judicial review, local authority litigation, housing management, landlord and tenant and anti-social behaviour litigation.
Employment: The team includes a silk and 16 juniors covering the full spectrum of employment law.
Regulatory: The team provides specialist advice and representation across a range of regulatory practice areas including Health and Safety, Inquests, Medical / Healthcare, Police Misconduct and Sports Discipline.
Inquests: With 3 team members sitting as Assistant Deputy Coroners, the set has a strong reputation throughout the UK.

KENWORTHY'S CHAMBERS Frank Burns

Arlington House, Bloom Street, Salford, Manchester, M3 6AJ
Tel (0161) 832 4036 **Fax** (0161) 832 0370 **DX** 718200
Email maria@kenworthysbarristers.co.uk **Website** www.kenworthyschambers.co.uk

Head of Chambers	Frank Burns
Practice Manager	Maria Rushworth
Tenants	52

MEMBERS

Frank Burns (1971)
Benjamin Nolan QC (1971)
Robert Woodcock QC (1978)
Barry Grennan (1977) ^
John Marsh (1977) ^
William Donnelly (1981) ^
Patrick Cassidy (1982) ^
Roger Brown (1976) ^
Edmund Farrell (1981) ^
Anthony Morris (1986)
Gita Patel (1988) ^
Patrick Williamson (1989)
Amanda Flattery (1993) ^
Andrew Marrs (1995) ^
Geoff Whelan (1996)
Sami Rahman (1996)
Alison Mather (1997) ^
Barry Harwood-Gray (1998) ^
David Morton (1999)
Mark Asquith (1999)*
Rachel White (2000) ^
Sara Haque (2000) ^
Margaret McDonald (2000)
Shazia Khan (2000) ^
Denise Fitzpatrick (2000) ^
Sally Penni (2000) ^
Mark Schwenk (2001)
Joy Emmanuel (2001) ^
Sarah Johnson (2001) ^
Michael Smith (2001) ^
George Brown (2002) ^
Chudi Grant (2002) ^
Shysta Habib (2002) ^
Colin Buckle (2002) ^
Fung Sin (2003)
John Nicholson (2004)
Anisa Niaz (2004) ^
Janet Cragg (2005) ^
Martin Lugsdin (2005) ^
Alan Wilson (2005) ^
Julie-Anne Luck (2006)
Rebecca Pickering (2007)
Jonathan Robinshaw (2008) *
Carol Micah (2009) ^
Stephen Tettey (2010)
Peter Quegan (2010)
Simon Blakebrough (2011) ^
William Magill (2011)
Richard Lees (2011) ^
Kevin Lister (2012) ^
Paul IM Thurn (2012)
Joanne Carpanini (2009) P

^ Public/Direct Access P Pupil * Associate Tenant

Kenworthy's Chambers

THE CHAMBERS Kenworthy's Chambers is a progressive set that offers expert advice, experienced advocates and excellent service. Their barristers are well known for being approachable and pragmatic.

WORK UNDERTAKEN The set takes on a good blend of commercial and social justice work. It accepts work at all levels in crime, chancery, commercial, education, family, immigration, human rights, judicial review, prison law, police law, housing, health and safety, civil, employment, inquests, costs and personal injury.

Community Legal Service
Quality Mark - Legal Services Accredited Chambers

KINGS CHAMBERS Nicholas Braslavsky QC

36 Young Street, Manchester, M3 3FT **DX** 718188 (MCH3)

5 Park Square East, Leeds, LS1 2NE **DX** 713113 (Leeds PK SQ)

Embassy House, 60 Church Street, Birmingham, B3 2DJ **DX** 13023 (Birmingham)

Tel 0845 034 3444 **Fax** 0845 034 3445
Email: clerks@kingschambers.com **Website:** www.kingschambers.com

Chambers Director	Debra Andrés
Senior Clerks	William Brown
	Colin Griffin
	Stephen Loxton
Clerks	Gary Young
	Paul Clarke
	Harry Young
	Mark Ronson
	Scott Leach
	Aaron Smith
	Andrew Reeves
	Rory Davis
	Gary Smith
	Jake Brooke

MEMBERS

Dr Nicholas Braslavsky QC (1983) (QC-1999)
Mr Stephen J Sauvain QC (1997) (QC-1995)
Mr Vincent Fraser QC (1981) (QC-2001)
Mr Paul Chaisty QC (1982) (QC-2001)
Mr Richard Clayton QC (1977) (QC-2002)
Mr David Manley QC (1981) (QC-2003)
Ms Lesley Anderson QC (1989) (QC-2006)
Mr Anthony Crean QC (1987) (QC-2006)
Mr David Casement QC (1992) (QC-2008)
Mr Michael Rawlinson QC (1991) (QC-2009)
Mr Paul Tucker QC (1990) (QC-2010)
Mr Nigel Poole QC (1989) (QC-2012)
Reverend Eric Owen (1969)
Mr Jeffrey Terry (1976)
Mr Roger Lancaster (2002)
Mr Alan Evans (1978)
Mr Shokat Khan (1979)
Mr John Barrett (1982)
Mr Neil Berragan (1982)
Mr Mark Halliwell (1985)
Mr Gary Grant (1985)
Mr Simon Hilton (1987)
Mr Nigel Clayton (1987)
Miss Ruth Stockley (1988)
Miss Fiona Ashworth (1998)
Mr Andrew Singer (1990)
Mr Paul Johnson (2006)
Mr Simon Burrows (1990)
Mr Matthew Smith (1991)
Mr Andrew Grantham (1991)
Mr Martin Carter (1992)
Mr Wilson Horne (1992)
Miss Lucy Powis (1992)
Mr Mark Harper (1993)
Miss Sarah Pritchard (1993)
Mr Richard Lander (1993)
Mr Ian Ponter (1993)
Mr Michael Ditchfield (1993)
Miss Sarah Clover (1993)
Mr James Boyd (1994)
Miss Kelly Pennifer (1994)
Mr Andrew Latimer (1995)
Mr Gavin McBride (1996)
Mr Jeremy Roussak (1996)
Mr Louis Doyle (1996)
Mr Jonathan Easton (1996)
Mr Adam Fullwood (1996)
Mr Simon Plaut (1997)
Mr Colin Bourne (1997)
Dr Mark Friston (1997)
Mr Simon Young (1998)
Mr Stephen Maguire (2007)
Mr Giles Cannock (1998)
Professor Andrew McGee (1998)
Mr Matthew Hall (1999)
Miss Helen Mulholland (1999)
Mr Martin Budworth (1999)
Miss Tina Ranales-Cotos (1999)
Mr Brian Griffiths (1999)
Miss Eleanor Temple (2000)
Mrs Lisa Walmisley (2000)
Mr Paul Lakin (2000)
Miss Claire Jackson (2002)
Mr Paul Hughes (2001)
Mr Ben Williams (2001)
Mr Geraint Wheatley (2001)
Miss Claire Steward (2002)
Mr Craig Ralph (2002)
Mr Michael Rudd (2002)
Mr John Hunter (2002)
Mr Sam Karim (2002)
Miss Emily Duckworth (2003)
Miss Michelle Mayoh (2003)
Miss Sarah Lawrenson (2003)
Miss Sarah Reid (2004)
Miss Francesca Gardner (2004)
Miss Rachel Galloway (2004)
Miss Sophie Allan (2004)
Mr Paras Gorasia (2005)
Miss Charlotte Law (2005)
Mr Ben Harding (2005)
Miss Cheryl Dainty (2006)
Mr Richard Livingston (2006)
Mr Johnny Ward (2007)
Dr Nathan Smith (2007)
Miss Gemma Lieberman (2007)
Mr Kevin Latham (2007)
Mr Stephen McNamara (2008)
Mr Anthony Gill (2008)
Miss Eleanor d'Arcy (2008)
Miss Anna Macey (2008)
Mrs Laura Daniels (2009)
Miss Ruth Taylor (2010)
Mr Jonathan Wright (2010)
Mr Aidan Reay (2011)
Mr Freddie Humphries (2011)
Miss Erica Bedford (2012)
Mr Clive Freedman QC (1978) (QC-1997) *
Mr Marcus F Daly SC (1987) (SC-1999) *
Mr Colm o'hOisin SC (1998) (SC-2005) *
Mr Colin Crawford (1997) *
Mr James Henderson (1997) *
Mr Leo Charalambides (1998) *
Professor Andrew Keay (2010) *
David Gilliland QC (1964) (QC-1984) +

* Associates + Arbitrator

THE CHAMBERS Kings Chambers is ranked one of the country's leading sets. It provides barristers with the highest reputation for advocacy, knowledge and standards to service.
This is a large specialist set with a national reputation practising from Manchester, Leeds and Birmingham in several practice areas: predominantly chancery and commercial law; planning and environmental law, personal injury and clinical negligence, costs, employment, sports law, mediation, arbitration and public law.

WORK UNDERTAKEN
Planning: Kings Chambers is one of the largest planning and environmental chambers, with members appearing before a wide range of dedicated tribunals and inquiries. Chambers acts in all aspects of town and country planning and environmental law (including waste disposal and management), compulsory purchase compensation and highways.
Public Law: The public law group practises extensively in the Administrative Court, sitting in London and the regions. The group encompasses the range of public law work in community care, education, housing, mental health, immigration, licensing, local government and social security matters. Members advise and appear before

KINGS CHAMBERS

KINGS CHAMBERS Nicholas Braslavsky QC (continued)

courts at all levels.

Chancery & Commercial: The chancery and commercial group has extensive experience in litigation (including agency, contracts, sale of goods, restraint of trade and restrictive covenants, corporate law); corporate and personal insolvency (including winding up, administration, administrative receivership and tracing assets), banking and professional negligence. Residential and commercial landlord and tenant work (including renewals, rent review, possession claims, arbitrations), partnership and all aspects of property and conveyancing. Chambers also undertakes trusts and probate work and has members specialising in construction disputes, intellectual property and taxation.

Personal Injury: All aspects of personal injury, including work-related diseases and injuries, sporting injuries, clinical negligence and all aspects of civil liability, contracts, negligence, nuisance, breach of statutory duty, health and safety are undertaken.

Employment: The employment team covers the entire spectrum of employment law and has particular strengths in race, sex, equal pay and disability discrimination.

Sports Law: The sports law team have been involved in some of the most substantial and high profile sports cases nationally in recent years involving, commercial dispute resolution, disciplinary and regulatory proceedings, anti-doping rules, employment issues, sports-related personal injury, breach of confidentiality and privacy, wealth management issues, intellectual property including image rights, trademark infringement and breach of copyright.

Costs: There is a specialist and dedicated costs team, practising exclusively in costs law, disputes and litigation funding.

Mediation: Mediation is an important part of the litigation process. The team comprises accredited mediators at various levels and with expertise in differing areas of law.

Arbitration: Kings Arbitration provides a panel of arbitrators and a panel of arbitration counsel based in the UK and Ireland operating in both domestic and international arbitrations.

LINCOLN HOUSE CHAMBERS Alistair Webster QC

8th Floor, Tower 12, Spinningfields, 18 – 22 Bridge Street, Manchester, M3 3BZ
Tel (0161) 832 5701 **Fax** (0161) 832 0839 **DX** 14338 Manchester 1
Email info@lincolnhousechambers.com **Website** www.lincolnhousechambers.com

Heads of Chambers	Alistair Webster QC
Director of Clerking	David Wright
Clerks	David Gibbons
	Andrew McGuinness
	Ty Price
	Lucy Rock
	Richard Smith
	Matthew Tudor

MEMBERS

Alistair Webster QC (1976)
Guy Gozem QC (1972)
Mukhtar Hussain QC (1971)
Peter Wright QC (1981)
James Pickup QC (1976)
Paul Reid QC (1973)
Maura McGowan QC (1980)
Anthony Cross QC (1982)
Suzanne Goddard QC (1986)
Andrew Thomas QC (1989)
Simon Csoka QC (1991)
Katherine Blackwell QC (1982)
Christopher Daw QC (1993)
Jeremy Lasker (1976)
Andrew Nuttall (1978)
Philip Curran (1979)
Robert Elias (1979)
Ahmed Nadim (1982)
Elizabeth Nicholls (1984)
Charles Bloomer (1985)
Mark Stuart (1985)
Bernadette Baxter (1987)
Paul Lawton (1987)
Ian McMeekin (1987)
Kathryn Johnson (1989)
Hugh Barton (1989)
Neil Fryman (1989)
Rachel Smith (1990)
Ivan Bowley (1990)
Richard Simons (1991)
Mark Ford (1991)
Kevin Donnelly (1991)
Philip Boyd (1993)
Lisa Roberts (1993)
Neil Usher (1993)
Abigail Holt (1993)
Timothy Storrie (1993)
Peter Warne (1993)
Gerard Doran (1993)
Henry Blackshaw (1993)
Philip Holden (1994)
Ricky Holland (1994)
Martin Hackett (1995)
Mohammed Nawaz (1995)
Robert Kearney (1996)
Charlotte Holland (1996)
Shirlie Duckworth (1997)
Katherine Pierpoint (1998)
Louise Kitchin (1998)
Richard Dawson (2001)
Alexander Leach (2001)
Mark Friend (2002)
Richard English (2003)
Katie Jones (2003)
Austin Welch (2005)
Daniel Thomas (2005)
James Heyworth (2006)
Simon Gurney (2006)
Laura Barbour (2006)
Brendan O'Leary (2007)
Rachel Cooper (2007)
Louise Cowen (2010)
Leila Ghahhary (2010)

THE CHAMBERS LHC is a Manchester based set with a national reach and unrivalled reputation. LHC is recognised for its depth of ability across growing practice areas, but is particularly admired for its work in the defence and prosecution of serious crime, its professional disciplinary team and its industrial disease PI expertise. Now based at stylish new premises in the heart of the legal district, LHC has re-engineered itself to meet the demands of tomorrow's legal world. Major investment in IT allows for a modern system of document management, case administration and communication. Teams of counsel undertake a wide range of regulatory, professional disciplinary, civil and public law work. Many of its counsel receive work through Direct Access. Chambers has also launched LHC Private Client, a new service for clients who require greater access to counsel.

WORK UNDERTAKEN

Crime: Chambers' caseload has always reflected involvement in high profile cases, for example R v Shipman, Sally Clarke. Recent work includes R v Nigel Evans, R v Stuart Hall, the Stepping Hill Hospital murders, the Rochdale abuse cases and the Dale Cregan & others murders.
Fraud: In cases of business crime LHC counts on experience and a hard-won reputation for excellence. Cases include iSOFT, London City Bond, Operation Tandem and a host of renowned MTIC cases.
Regulatory: Chambers is recognised as a leading professional disciplinary set and are regularly involved in GMC, NMC and Police cases of note. Additionally LHC works in the following fields: VAT Tribunal, HSE, local authority work, Environment Agency cases, Election regulation, DEFRA regulation and trading standards.
Civil: LHC is well known for its experience in industrial disease work, such as British Coal respiratory disease, surface dust and phurnacite. LHC boasts an established and busy team dealing with PI and negligence cases.
Public: LHC often act for clients in public law challenges that rise from Chambers' regulatory and professional disciplinary work, or in its tribunal work. Examples include divisional court actions against judicial decisions, immigration, discrimination issues and search warrants, as well as many other areas.

LINCOLN
HOUSE
CHAMBERS

ST JOHNS BUILDINGS Sally Harrison QC

24a-28 St John Street, Manchester, M3 4DJ
Tel (0161) 214 1500 **Fax** (0161) 835 3929 **DX** 728861 Manchester 4
Email clerk@stjohnsbuildings.co.uk **Website** www.stjohnsbuildings.co.uk

Head of Chambers	Sally Harrison QC
Chief Executive	Chris Ronan
Head of Corporate Services	David Anderson
Head of Finance	Paula Blackshaw
Tenants	256

MEMBERS

Sally Harrison QC (1992) (QC-2010)
Michael Shorrock QC (1966) (QC-1988) *
Michael Redfern QC (1970) (QC-1993)
William Lowe QC (1972) (QC-1997)
Andrew O'Byrne QC (1978) (QC-2006)
David Berkley QC (1979) (QC-1999)
Kim Hollis QC (1979) (QC-2002)
Frances Heaton QC (1985) (QC-2012)
Jeffrey K Samuels QC (1988) (QC-2009)
Brendon Kelly QC (1988) (QC-2008)
Karl Rowley QC (1994) (QC 2013)
John Vater QC (1995) (QC-2012)
Graeme Wood (1968)
Mark Lamberty (1970)
Bernard Phillips (1970)
John Hedgecoe (1972)
Raymond Herman (1972)
Nicholas Neale (1972)
John McNeill (1974)
Eric Shannon (1974)
Stephen Bedford (1974)
Geoffrey Lowe (1975)
Philip Andrews (1977)
Charles Feeny (1977)
Antony Longworth (1978)
David Mercer (1980)
Andrew Long (1981)
Sonia Gal (1982)
David Garside (1982)
M Julian Holt (1982)
David L Bruce (1982)
Peter Harrison (1983)
Keith Harrison (1983)
Brian McKenna (1983)
Michael Slater (1983)
Julian Shaw (1984)
David Pickup (1984)
Julian Lloyd (1985)
Michael Kennedy (1985)
Diana Kloss (1986) *
Julian Taylor (1986)
Jonathan Dickinson (1986)
Timothy W Brennand (1987)
Jane Dagnall (1987)
Jane Walker (1987)
John Oates (1987)
Nicholas Price (1987)
Bunty L Batra (1988)
Simon Crabtree (1988)
Paula Davitt (1988)
Charles P Eastwood (1988)
Damian Sanders (1988)
Anne Britcliffe (1989)
Clare Grundy (1989)
Lisa Partington (1989)
Michael Blakey (1989)
Simon Holder (1989)
Joseph O'Brien (1989)
Paul O'Shea (1989)
Richard Carter (1990)
Jonathan Thompson (1990)
Deborah Gould (1990)
Ian Groom (1990)
Desmond Rosario (1990)
David Watson (1990)
Matthew E Mawdsley (1991)
Mark Roberts (1991)
Alastair Wright (1991)
Zia Chaudhry (1991)
Jonathan Taylor (1991)
Patricia Pratt (1991)
Magdalen Case (1992)
Andrew Green (1992)
Richard Norton (1992)
Kevin McNerney (1992)
Gaynor Lloyd (1992)
Alison Dorrell (1992)
Timothy Ashmole (1992)
Richard Orme (1993)
Ginnette Fitzharris (1993)
Alexander W Kloss (1993)
Joanna Rodikis (1993)
Guy AD Mathieson (1993)
Jason Searle (1993)
Myles Wilson (1993)
Benjamin William Jones (1993)
David Flood (1993)
John Gibson (1993)
Leona Harrison (1993)
David S Polglase (1993)
Dermot Hughes (1993)
Rachael Harrison (1993)
Shama Nijabat (1993)
Stuart Newton (1993)
Caroline Ford (1993)
Penelope Stanistreet (1993)
Nigel Booth (1994)
Mark Connor (1994)
Stephen Douglas (1994)
Daniel Frieze (1994)
Annette P Gumbs (1994)
Lisa Houghton (1994)
Robert McGinty (1994)
Steven Wild (1994)
Sara A Mann (1994)
John O Chukwuemeka (1994)
Megan Rhys (1994)
Craig Lowe (1994)
James Gatenby (1994)
Paul Treble (1994)
Justine Cole (1994)
Andrew Lawson (1995)
Pauline M McHugh (1995)
Ian Simkin (1995)
Gordon Stables (1995)
Siobhan Kelly (1995)
Olivia Weir (1995)
Pepin Aslett (1996)
Darrel Crilley (1996)
Samantha Hillas (1996)
Ghazan Mahmood (1997)
Simon Parry (1997)
Sarah V Spear (1997)
Remy Zentar (1997)
Simeon Evans (1997)
Zillah Williams (1997)
Lorraine Mensah (1997)
Douglas Denton (1997)
Ian Goldsack (1997)
Andrew Bailey (1997)
Alexandra Simmonds (1998)
Liam Murdin (1998)
David James (1998)
Kate Burnell (1998)
Matthew Stockwell (1998)
David C Taylor (1998)
Susan Edwards (1998)
Clare Thomas (1998)
Abigail Bennett (1998)
Susan Deas (1999)
John Ratledge (1999)
Linda Sweeney (1999)
Philip Astbury (1999)
Lara LJ Holsgrove (1999)
Andrew Lord (1999)
Yasmin Kauser (1999)
Philip Byrne (1999)
Sufiyan Rana (1999)
Lorraine Cavanagh (2000)
Natasha Leach (2000)
Kathryn Hayes (2000)
Jennifer Blewitt (2001)
Andrew Bridgman (2001)
Oliver King (2001)
David Pojur (2001)
Clare Porter-Phillips (2001)
Audrey Van der Haer (2001)
Sylvia Vir Singh (2001)
David Farley (2001)
Siraj I Ahmed (2001)
Andrew Wynne (2001)
Nichola Quinney (2001)
Laura Marshall (2001)
Paul Smith (2002)
James Malam (2002)
Christopher Moss (2002)
Richard Thyne (2002)
Wendy J Owen (2002)
Mark Senior (2002)
Jennifer Menzies (2002)
Louise McCloskey (2002)
Rebecca E Smith (2002)
Cheryl Mottram (2002)
Kashif Ali (2003)

ST JOHNS BUILDINGS
BARRISTERS CHAMBERS

Criminal Defence Service
Community Legal Service

QUALITY ASSURED FIRM ISO 9002 SGS

BAR MARK

ST JOHNS BUILDINGS Sally Harrison QC (continued)

Abigail Hudson (2003)
Benjamin Lawrence (2003)
Louise Quigley (2003)
Clodagh Maguire (2003)
Robert Akers (2003)
Timothy Connolly (2004)
William Poole (2004)
Philippa Waddell (2004)
Catherine Rimmer (2004)
Peta M Harrison (2004)
Ana Samuel (2004)
Helen Wilson (2004)
Douglas R Cooper (2004)
Rebecca Sutton (2004)
Joanne Jade Abraham (2004)
Abigail Hickinbottom (2004)
Louise Stanbury (2004)
Steven McGarry (2005)
Neil Christian (2005)
Lucy Marshall (2005)
Gareth Thompson (2005)
Debra White (2005)
Frances de Navarro (2005)
Shaun Spencer (2005)
Ben Kelly (2006)
Christopher Pare (2006)
Louise Rae (2006)
Steven Flynn (2006)
Julian Goode (2006)
Jennifer Scully (2006)
Rachael Rook (2006)
Helen Davey (2006)
Kate Morley (2006)
Henry Vanderpump (2007)
Hannah Wood (2007)
Neil Owen-Casey (2007)
Andrew Haggis (2007)
Nicole Erlen (2007)
Jessica Pemberton (2007)
Peter Gilmour (2007)
Philip Clemo (2007)
Simon Murray (2008)
Elisabeth Cooper (2008)
Elis Gomer (2008)
Cerys Williams (2008)
Simon N Maddison (2008)
Jonathan Bellamy (2008)
Hannah Walker (2008)
Laura England (2008)
Jamie Jenkins (2008)
Huw Edwards (2009)
David Baines (2009)
Laura Nash (2009)
Elliw Roberts (2009)
Daniel Metcalfe (2009)
Ginny Whiteley (2010)
Jessica Southcote-Want (2010)
Jane Crowley QC (1976) (QC-1998) *

* Door Tenant

THE CHAMBERS Also at:
Chester: 21 White Friars, Chester, CH1 1NZ Tel: 01244 323 070, Fax: 01244 342 930, DX: 19979 CHESTER
Liverpool: 38 Vernon Street, Liverpool, L2 2AY Tel: 0151 243 6000, Fax: 0151 243 6040, DX: 14227 LIVERPOOL
Preston: 16 Winckley Square, Preston, PR1 3JJ Tel: 01772 256100, Fax: 01772 256101, DX: 714582 Preston 14
Sheffield: 7 Leopold Street, Sheffield, S1 2GY Telephone: 0114 273 8951, Fax: 0114 276 0848 DX: 10565 Sheffield 1

THE CHAMBERS Service excellence is at the heart of everything St John's Buildings does. Chambers provides a client focussed advocacy service throughout England and Wales and to International clients. Working in partnership with clients, members of St John's Buildings embrace a team ethos, sharing experiences and knowledge to the clients' benefit. Chambers' approach includes agreeing fixed service standards, having a large and highly trained staff team and providing state of the art facilities in a number of city centre locations.

WORK UNDERTAKEN
St John's Buildings has a national reputation for the quality of its advocates. Each practice area has a large team of highly regarded experts, clerked by knowledgeable and friendly specialist clerks. The core practice groups are:
Clinical Negligence: Acting for claimants and defendants including medical negligence, claims arising out of cosmetic surgery, dental negligence, Government Inquiries and disciplinary tribunals.
Commercial & Chancery: Expert in banking, financial services, insolvency, partnership disputes, credit and securities, general commercial, property, planning and construction, intellectual property, IT, data protection, fraud, property, planning, waste management, mis-selling, professional negligence, Office-holder claims, sports law
Criminal: Covering all aspects and levels of complexity of criminal cases for both prosecution and defence.
Employment: specialists in all aspects of employment law, including all employment rights, both contentious and non-contentious.
Family: The team covers all areas of family work, including public and private law cases for local authorities, parents, grandparents and guardians, and all forms of financial provision cases, judicial review and removal from jurisdiction cases.
Personal Injury: Claimants and defendants from a wide range of individuals and organisations. With expertise in serious head and spinal injury cases, industrial diseases, fatal accidents, public and employers' liability, travel, stress and road traffic accidents.
Property & Private Client: Specialist barristers in boundary disputes, right to manage, easements, business tenancies, residential landlord and tenant, dilapidation, disrepair and service charge disputes.
Public & Administrative Law: Extensive knowledge of all aspects of public law, including mental health, Court of Protection, education, social services, housing, immigration, Judicial Review proceedings, public procurement, countryside law and FOI/data protection.
Regulatory: Chambers provides expertise in regulatory matters including cases involving the HSE, Environment Agency, Solicitors Regulatory Authority, GMC, General Dental Council, licensing, professional sports people, Police Disciplinary and Appeals Tribunals, OFSTED, Local Authorities, RSPCA and Inquests work.
ADR/Mediation: Dedicated mediation unit, with accredited mediators, including a Silk mediator. The unit delivers mediation and alternative dispute resolution services in commercial, PI, employment and family law.

9 ST JOHN STREET Charles Garside QC

9 St John Street, Manchester, M3 4DN
Tel (0161) 955 9000 **Fax** (0161) 955 9001 **DX** 14326
Email civilclerks@9sjs.com criminalclerks@9sjs.com **Website** www.9sjs.com

Head of Chambers	Charles Garside QC
Chambers Manager	Ruth Bailey
Senior Clerk (Civil)	Tony Morrissey
Senior Clerk (Crime)	Chris Swann
Team Leader Personal Injury & Insurance Fraud	Joe Gibson
Team Leader Employment & Commercial	Julie Lanza
Civil Clerks	Jane Slingsby
	Peadar McKinstry
	Matt Rigby
	Phillip Spencer
	Sam Roberts
Junior Criminal Clerks	Andrew Leech
	Anthony Brown

MEMBERS

Charles Garside QC (1971) (QC-1993) +
Roderick Carus QC (1971) (QC-1990) +
Stephen Lesley QC (1971) (QC-1993)
Nicholas Hinchliffe QC (1980) (QC-1999) +
Gerard McDermott QC (1987) ^ (QC-1999)
Geraint Jones QC (1976) (QC-2001)
Simon Jackson QC (1982) (QC-2003) +
Nicholas Clarke QC (1981) (QC-2006) +
Paul Gilroy QC (1985) ^ (QC-2006)
Christopher L P Kennedy QC (1989) ^ (QC-2010)
Mark Hill QC (1987) (QC-2011)
Terence Rigby (1971) +
Peter Cadwallader (1973)
Christine Riley (1974)
Paul McDonald (1975)
Nigel Grundy (1983) + ^
Alistair Bower (1986) ^
Carlo Breen (1987)
David Gilchrist (1987)
Mark Monaghan (1987)
Nicola Gatto (1987)
Thomas Fitzpatrick (1988)
Ian Little (1989)
Edward Morgan (1989)
Joanne Woodward (1989) ^
Joanne Barnett (1989) ^
Darren Preston (1991)
Christopher Scorah (1991)
Anthony Howard (1992)
Joanne Connolly (1992)
Karim Sabry (1992) ^
Graham Bailey (1993)
Rachel Wedderspoon (1993) ^
Kirsten Barry (1993) ^
Jaime Hamilton (1993)
James Fryer-Spedding (1994)
Michael Lemmy (1994)
Andrew Clark (1994) ^
Robert Darbyshire (1995)
Brian McCluggage (1995) ^
Stefan Brochwicz-Lewinski (1995)
Katie Nowell (1996)
Sara Lewis (1996)
Boyd Morwood (1996)
Gary Woodhall (1997)
Rachael Heppenstall (1997)
Kate Hollyoak (1997)
Vanessa Thomson (1997)
Kathrine Mallory (1998)
Jane Mabon (1998)
Assunta del Priore (1998) ^
Helen Redmond (1999)
Zoë Thompson (1999) ^
Lucinda Leeming (1999)
Matthew Haisley (1999)
Victoria Rigby (2000)
Rebecca Eeley (2001)
Alison Heyworth (2001)
Matthew Snarr (2001) ^
Dawn Thomas (2001)
Kirsty McKinlay (2001)
Russell Dickinson (2002)
Jonathan Savage (2003)
Louise Brandon (2003)
Thomas Gilbart (2003)
Joanna Vicary (2003)
Caroline Curry (2003)
Ian Denham (2003)
Benjamin Morris (2004)
Hannah Haines (2005)
Robert Smith (2005)
Laura D'Cruz (2006)
Rachael Levene (2006)
Lena Amartey (2008)
William Hamilton (2008)
Graham Robinson (2009)
Richard Price (2010)
Emma Greenhalgh (2010)
Alex Langhorn (2010)
Cath Cundy (2011)
Fiona Wise (2012)
Jasmine Skander (2012)
Adam Willoughby (2012)
Amy Smith (2013)

+ Recorder ^ Direct/Public Access

THE CHAMBERS In order to meet the increasing demand for specialist advice, chambers has established the following special interest groups: Commercial, Crime, Employment, Family, Insurance Fraud, Health and Safety, Travel Law and Personal Injury. Chambers is accredited by The Law Society for CPD purposes and is happy to provide seminars on a wide range of subjects either in-house or in chambers. If you are interested in this service, please contact Tony Morrissey (0161) 955 5176 (tony.morrissey@9sjs.com) or Chris Swann (0161) 955 5172 (chris.swann@9sjs.co.uk).

NINESTJOHNSTREET

18 ST JOHN STREET Peter Birkett QC

Head of Chambers	Peter Birkett QC
Senior Civil Clerk	John Hammond
Chambers Manager	Elizabeth Sheen
Tenants	75

18 St John Street, Manchester, M3 4EA
Tel (0161) 278 1800 **Fax** (0161) 278 8220 **DX** 728854 Manchester 4
Email clerks@18sjs.com **Website** www.18sjs.com

MEMBERS

Peter Birkett QC (1972) (QC-1989)
Raymond Wigglesworth QC (1974) (QC-1999)
Alastair Forrest (1972)
Paul Dockery (1973)
Paul O'Brien (1974)
Christopher Diamond (1975)
Christopher Limb (1975)
Nicholas Fewtrell (1977)
Mark Laprell (1979)
Michael Murray (1979)
Ian Huffer (1979)
Richard Vardon (1985)
Alexandra Stansby (1985)
Stephen J Murray (1986)
Yvonne Healing (1988)
Toby Sasse (1988)
Samantha Birtles (1989)
Elisabeth Tythcott (1989)
Fiona Holloran (1989)
Raquel Simpson (1990)
Jonathan Dale (1991)
Joy Booth (1992)
Michael Brady (1992)
Susan Harrison (1993)
Rachel Shenton (1993)
Paul Manasse (1995)
David Hoffman (1997)
Saul Brody (1996)
Andrew Moore (1996)
Adam Lodge (1996)
Rachel Faux (1997)
David Mackley (1997)
Richard Chapman (1998)
Kalsoom Maqsood (1999)
Jonathan Grierson (1999)
Wayne Goldstein (1999)
Sarah Kilvington (1999)
Kate Bramall (1999)
Andrea Markham (2000)
Lukhvinder Kaur (2000)
Ben Norman (2000)
Andrew Scott (2000)
Leonie Caplan (2001)
Soria Kajue (2001)
Nicholas Clarke (2001)
Sarah Donaldson (2003)
Laura Thomas (2003)
Philip De Berry (2003)
Rehana Begum (2004)
Simon Charles (2004)
Christopher McNall (2005)
Kate Henthorn (2005)
Saiqa Chaudhry (2005)
Vanessa Lau (2005)
Elizabeth Murray (2005)
Michael Wilkinson (2006)
Evonnie Chan (2006)
Danish Ameen (2006)
Jason Wells (2007)
Rupert Davies (2007)
Andrew Evans (2007)
Stuart Martin (2007)
Kane Simons (2007)
Oliver Caplan (2007)
Fergal Allen (2007)
Sandra Pope (2008)
Daniel Calder (2008)
Lisi Ke (2009)
George Matthews (2011)
Gemma McGungle (2011)
Lord Brennan QC (1967) (QC-1984) ++
Sally Bradley QC (1978) (QC-1999) ++
Roger Hedgeland (1972) ++
Malcolm McEwan (1976) ++
Laura Briggs (2001) ++
Hugh Rimmer (2003) ++
Francesca Dowse (2004) ++

++ Associate Member

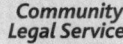

Criminal Defence Service
Community Legal Service
Quality Mark - Legal Services Accredited Chambers

THE CHAMBERS A general common law chambers with distinct civil, family, chancery and criminal departments, and expertise at all levels.

TRINITY CHAMBERS Toby Hedworth QC

Multi Media Exchange, 72-80 Corporation Road, Middlesbrough, TS1 2RF
Tel (01642) 247 569 **Fax** (01642) 249 897 **DX** 60537 (Middlesbrough)
Email info@trinitychambers.co.uk **Website** www.trinitychambers.co.uk

Head of Chambers	Mr Alan Toby Hedworth QC
Tenants	76

THE CHAMBERS 76 practitioners operating from Middlesbrough and Newcastle upon Tyne under the following specialist practice groups: agriculture, ADR, business, chancery, costs, crime, employment, family, immigration, judicial review, licensing, mental health and Court of Protection, PI & CN, planning and environment, regulatory.

INVESTOR IN PEOPLE

BAR MARK

ENTERPRISE CHAMBERS Zia Bhaloo QC

Head of Chambers	Zia Bhaloo QC
Senior Clerk	Antony Armstrong (London)
Clerk	Stephen Walker
Tenants	37

65 Quayside, Newcastle upon Tyne, NE1 3DE
Tel (0191) 222 3344 **Fax** (0191) 222 3340 **DX** 61134 Newcastle upon Tyne
Email newcastle@enterprisechambers.com **Website** www.enterprisechambers.com

For a full list of members please see the London entry. For further information about the set please visit the chambers' website.

Enterprise Chambers
London Leeds Newcastle

PARKLANE PLOWDEN Andrew Axon

Head of Chambers	Andrew Axon
Chambers Director	Neil Douglas
Senior Clerks	Michael Stubbs
	Andy Gray
	Mark Williams (Senior Family Clerk)
Clerks	Laura Storr
	Louise Pearce
	Stephanie Hunt
	Emma Rogers
Tenants	81 plus 2 door tenants

Lombard House, 4-8 Lombard Street, Newcastle upon Tyne, NE1 3AE
Tel (0844) 499 5678 **Fax** (0191) 221 2122 **DX** 61062 Newcastle
Email clerks@parklaneplowden.co.uk **Website** www.parklaneplowden.co.uk

See the entry under Parklane Plowden, Leeds for more information.

TRINITY CHAMBERS Toby Hedworth QC

Trinity Chambers, The Custom House, Quayside, Newcastle upon Tyne, NE1 3DE
Tel (0191) 232 1927 **Fax** (0191) 232 7975 **DX** 61185 (Newcastle)
Email info@trinitychambers.co.uk **Website** www.trinitychambers.co.uk

Head of Chambers	Mr Alan Toby Hedworth QC
Practice Director	Simon Stewart OBE
	Chris Lucarelli (Business Development)
Senior Clerk	Alison Dickason
Leaders Clerk	Richard Embley
Development Clerk	Kirsty Hart
Teesside Clerk	Chris Gibbin
Criminal Clerks	Peter Finkill
	David Knight
	Tracie Ruttor
Civil & Family Clerks	Liam Gorman
	Kirsty Hart
	Ken Mclafferty
	Steven Preen
Trinity Teesside	Fiona Bullock
Fees & Accounts	Alisa Charlton
	Rebecca Dixon
	David Robinson
Tenants	76

MEMBERS

Toby Hedworth QC (1975) (QC-1986)
Stephen Duffield (1969)
Christopher Knox (1974)
Anthony Hawks (1975)
David Callan (1979)
Phillip Engelman (1979)
John Wilkinson (1979)
Jacqueline Smart (1981)
James Richardson (1982)
Peter Walsh (1982)
Lesley McKenzie (1983)
Timothy Spain (1983)
John O'Sullivan (1984)
Fiona McCrae (1986)
Susan Taylor (1987)
Caroline Goodwin (1988)
Shaun Routledge (1988)
Carl Gumsley (1989)
Alan Inglis (1989)
Tim Gittins (1990)
Andrew Rutter (1990)
Nicola Shaw (1992)
Rachel Smith (1992)
Ros Scott Bell (1993)
Katherine Dunn (1993)
Justin Gray (1993)
Nicholas Stonor (1993)
Charles Holland (1994)
Jane Callan (1995)
Margaret Sweeting (1996)
Kevin Crawley (1998)
Kristian Mills (1998)
Yvonne Taylor (1998)
Fiona Walker (1998)
Asa Anderson (1998)
Nicola Allan (1999)
Simon Goldberg (1999)
Rachel Hedworth (1999)
James Kemp (1999)
Kossar Kitching (1999)
Elizabeth Mendoza (1999)
Michael Graham (1999)
Xanthe Craddock (2000)
Paul Currer (2000)
Angela Giovannini (2000)
Christopher Mitford (2001)
Ruth Phillips (2001)
Miriam Rasoul (2001)
Brian Mather (2002)
Joan Smith (2002)
Henry Stevens (2002)
Katherine Wood (2002)
Jane Foley (2002)
Tony Cornberg (2003)
Robert Spragg (2003)
Jamie Anderson (2004)
Claire Brissenden (2004)
Mike Hill (2004)
Antoine Tinnion (2004)
David Comb (2005)
Richard Stubbs (2005)
Will Byrne (2006)
Jamie Morgan (2006)
Rebecca Stokes-Herbst (2006)
Johanna Darby (2007)
James Marwick (2008)
Andrew Crammond (2008)
Thomas Pacey (2008)
Amanda Sehat (2009)
James McHugh (2010)
Laura Nagel (2012)
Stephen Duffy (2013)
Andrew Stafford QC (1980) (QC-2000) *
Francis FitzGibbon QC (1986) (QC-2010) *
Deveral Capps (1995) *

* Door Tenant

THE CHAMBERS Trinity Chambers, established in 1954, operating from Newcastle upon Tyne and Middlesbrough. Trinity Chambers abides by its equality and diversity policies, copies of which are available on request.

WORK UNDERTAKEN

Agriculture: Tenancies, Common Agricultural Policy, livestock, conservation, renewables.
ADR: Mediation and arbitration.
Business: Insolvency, company, partnership and commercial disputes, directors' duties, disqualifications.
Chancery: Probate, Inheritance Act, Trusts of Land, property disputes, housing, landlord and tenant.
Costs: Several members sit as Deputy District Judges, costs budgeting, appeals.
Crime: Instructed by prosecution and defence in often high profile cases of murder, manslaughter, POCA.
Employment: National reputation for equal pay, discrimination, whistleblowing, redundancy, TUPE.
Family & Matrimonial Finance: Care, adoption, honour violence, ancillary relief, TOLATA.
Immigration: Points based system, entry clearance, UK Border Agency, asylum and human rights issues.
Judicial Review: Procurement, regulatory, licensing and planning.
Licensing: Alcohol, taxis, premises, firearms, sex industry, gaming, betting and judicial review.
Mental Health & Court of Protection: Community care, deprivation of liberty, abuse, capacity.
Personal Injury & Clinical Negligence: Small claims, fast-track and multi-track matters, credit hire.
Planning & Environment: Inquiries, appeals, enforcement, Judicial review, environmental protection.
Regulatory: Fitness to practise NMC, HCPC, GMC, Trading Standards, health and safety, inquests.

TRINITY BARRISTERS

INVESTOR IN PEOPLE

BAR MARK

ROPEWALK CHAMBERS

24, The Ropewalk, Nottingham, NG1 5EF
Tel (0115) 947 2581 **Fax** (0115) 947 6532 **DX** 10060 Nottingham 17
Email clerks@ropewalk.co.uk **Website** www.ropewalk.co.uk

Head of Chambers	Patrick Limb QC
Senior Clerk	Tony Hill
Tenants	40

MEMBERS

Patrick Limb QC (1987) (QC – 2006) ^
Dominic Nolan QC (1985) (QC – 2006)
Graham Machin (1965)
Douglas Herbert (1973)
Stephen Beresford (1976)
Simon Gash (1977) ^
Jayne Adams (1982) ^
Soofi Din (1984) ^
Andrew Prestwich (1986)
Richard Seabrook (1987) ^
Toby Stewart (1989)
Philip Turton (1989)
Jonathan Mitchell (1992) ^
Jason Cox (1992)
Andrew McNamara (1992) ^
Deborah Davies (1993)
Richard Gregory (1993)
Ivan Cartwright (1993) ^
Andrew Hogan (1996) ^
Mark Diggle (1996) ^
Shilpa Shah (1998) ^
Clare Haddon (1999) ^
Christopher Lowe (2001)
Andrew Lyons (2002)
Edward James (2002) ^
Jan Alam (2003) ^
Jonathan Owen (2004) ^
Kate Herbert (2004) ^
Kam Jaspal (2005) ^
Rochelle Rong (2005)
Rachel Young (2006) ^
Georgina Cursham (2007) ^
Nicholas Robinson (2007)
Simon Buss (2007)
Daniel Wood (2008)
Philip Davy (2009)
Cassandra Williams (2010)
Philip Godfrey (2010)
Nikhil Arora (2011) ^
Tom Carter (2012) ^

THE CHAMBERS The set gives every case the care and attention it deserves.
You will receive more than just advice and representation from Ropewalk Chambers; you will secure consistently excellent oral and written advocacy, delivered with the highest levels of service and integrity.
Quality advocacy starts with thorough preparation. The set's attention to detail produces the level of understanding that promotes sound judgements and advice of the highest calibre. This gives the added value that will improve the prospects of achieving the best possible outcome for you and your clients.
Communication is at the heart of the service you will receive. You will find the barristers and clerks to be approachable and responsive. The set's assistance is accessible when you need it; and its people are always available to discuss your case outside of formal instruction.
Integrity is about more than just honesty. For Ropewalk Chambers, integrity also means giving the unwavering direction necessary to give your case stability and cohesion. To do that, its barristers make decisions, take responsibility for them and then stand by those decisions.
This is what you should expect of Ropewalk Chambers for every single case.

TYPES OF WORK UNDERTAKEN
Clinical Negligence, Commercial, Counter Fraud, Costs, Criminal Regulatory, Disease, Employment, Housing, Personal Injury, Planning and Environmental, Property and Chancery, Professional Discipline and Regulation, Public Sector and Not for Profit.

ST MARY'S FAMILY LAW CHAMBERS Vickie Hodges & Jason Reece

26-28 High Pavement, Nottingham, NG1 1HN
Tel (0115) 950 3503 **Fax** (0115) 958 3060 **DX** 10036 Nottingham
Email clerks@stmarysflc.co.uk **Website** www.stmarysflc.co.uk **Twitter** @stmarysflc

Heads of Chambers	Vickie Hodges Jason Reece
Senior Clerk	Scott Baldwin

ST. MARY'S CHAMBERS

THE CHAMBERS St Mary's Chambers became a specialist family law set in 1999. Through careful expansion chambers gradually grew from 12 members at its creation to the 30 members it has today.

WORK UNDERTAKEN The set's barristers provide expert advice and representation of the highest quality in all aspects of family law including: matrimonial finance and cohabitee disputes, public law care work, private law children and injunctive relief. Individual members also have expertise in Islamic law, Court of Protection, inquests and non-court dispute resolution.

HARCOURT CHAMBERS

Churchill House, 3 St. Aldates Courtyard, 38 St. Aldates, Oxford, OX1 1BN
Tel (0844) 561 7135 **Fax** (01865) 791585 **DX** 96453 Oxford 4
Email clerks@harcourtchambers.co.uk **Website** www.harcourtchambers.co.uk

Head of Chambers	Frances Judd QC
Chambers Director	Simon Boutwood
Practice Manager	Judith Partington
Tenants	45

MEMBERS

Frances Judd QC (1984) (QC-2006)
John Vater QC (1995) (QC-2012) ^
Nicholas Goodwin QC (1995) (QC-2014)
Roger Evans (1970) ^
June Rodgers (1971) ^
Benedict Sefi (1972) ^
Alicia Collinson (1982)
Matthew Brett (1987) ^
Sarah Gibbons (1987)
Fiona Hay (1989) ^
Sara Granshaw (1991)
Damian Garrido (1993) ^
Louise Potter (1993) ^
Aidan Vine (1995)
Douglas Allen (1995) ^
Simon Miller (1996)
Jonathan Sampson (1997)
Matthew Brookes-Baker (1998) ^
Cecilia Barrett (1998) ^
Oliver Wraight (1998)
Andrew Leong (1998) ^
Edward Kirkwood (1999)
Helen Little (1999)
Margaret Styles (2000) ^
Craig Jeakings (2000)
James Turner (2001)
Edward Devereux (2001)
Jason Green (2001) ^
Alex Forbes (2003) ^
Alison Williams (2004)
Elizabeth Tomlinson (2004)
Frances Harris (2005) ^
Kit Firbank (2005)
Mark Higgins (2005) *
Chloe Wilkins (2006)
Helen Wilkinson (2007)
Alex Perry (2007)
Sian Cox (2008) ^
Stephen Crispin (2008)
Mehvish Chaudhry (2008)
Emily Rayner (2009) ^
Gemma Bowes (2009)
David Marusza (2009) ^
Annie Sayers (2009)
Justine Ramsden (2010) ^
Maria Scott-Wittenborn (2012)
Anna Yarde (2012)

* Door Tenant ^ Public/Direct Access

THE CHAMBERS Harcourt Chambers is one of the leading family law sets in the country. It is recommended for both children law and family finance, and combines its expertise in family law with a strong reputation in civil litigation.Based in the Temple and in Oxford, it is home to well-known family silks Frances Judd QC, John Vater QC, Nick Goodwin QC and 42 junior barristers, many of whom are acknowledged as leading practitioners in their fields. Over the past decade, Harcourt Chambers has established itself as one of the very top 'across the range' family law sets. It has grown significantly in size and prominence and its members are regularly to be found in high- profile and leading cases at first instance and on appeal. Harcourt Chambers is particularly known for the high quality of its advocacy, advice and client care, for its genuine strength in depth and for its modern and approachable style.

HARCOURT CHAMBERS
LONDON OXFORD

INDEX OF SETS

London Band 3 p.108, Energy & Natural Resources: London Band 3 p.226, Insurance: London Band 1 p.315, International Arbitration: General Commercial & Insurance: London Band 2 p.328, Professional Negligence: London Band 4 p.420, Shipping & Commodities: London Band 2 p.465

12 King's Bench Walk
Profile: p.828
Overview(s): Personal Injury p.366
Table(s): Personal Injury: London Band 1 p.367

Kings Chambers
Profile: p.881, p.905, p.918
Table(s): Administrative & Public Law: Northern Band 1 p.39, Banking & Finance: Northern Band 1 p.57, Chancery: Northern Band 1 p.75, Civil Liberties & Human Rights: Northern Band 1 p.89, Clinical Negligence: Northern Band 2 p.103, Commercial Dispute Resolution: North Eastern Band 1 p.126, Northern Band 1 p.127, Company: Northern Band 1 p.140, Costs Litigation: Northern Band 1 p.162, Employment: Northern Band 3 p.221, Environment: Northern Band 1 p.235, Local Government: Northern Band 1 p.344, Partnership: Northern Band 1 p.361, Personal Injury: Northern Band 3 p.380, Planning: Northern Band 1 p.394, Real Estate Litigation: Northern Band 1 p.452, Restructuring/Insolvency: North Eastern Band 2 p.461, Northern Band 1 p.462

5 King's Bench Walk
Table(s): Crime: London Band 4 p.172

L

Landmark Chambers
Profile: p.829
Table(s): Administrative & Public Law: London Band 3 p.27, Agriculture & Rural Affairs: London Band 2 p.41, Civil Liberties & Human Rights: London Band 3 p.81, Environment: London Band 1 p.231, Immigration: London Band 3 p.297, Local Government: London Band 1 p.340, Planning: London Band 1 p.386, Real Estate Litigation: London Band 2 p.442

Lincoln House Chambers
Profile: p.920
Table(s): Crime: Northern Band 1 p.186

Littleton Chambers
Profile: p.830
Overview(s): Mediators p.812
Table(s): Employment: London Band 1 p.207

M

Maitland Chambers
Profile: p.831
Overview(s): Chancery p.58
Table(s): Agriculture & Rural Affairs: London Band 2 p.41, Chancery: Commercial: London Band 1 p.59, Traditional: London Band 3 p.67, Charities: London Band 2 p.79, Commercial Dispute Resolution: London Band 3 p.108, Company: London Band 3 p.135, Fraud: Civil: London Band 1 p.281, Offshore: London Band 1 p.353, Partnership: London Band 3 p.359, Professional Negligence: London Band 3 p.420, Real Estate Litigation: London Band 2 p.442, Restructuring/Insolvency: London Band 2 p.455

Matrix Chambers
Profile: p.832
Table(s): Administrative & Public Law: London Band 2 p.27, Civil Liberties & Human Rights: London Band 1 p.81, Crime: London Band 2 p.172, Data Protection: London Band 2 p.195, Defamation/Privacy: London Band 2 p.199, Education: London Band 2 p.203, Employment: London Band 2 p.207, Environment: London Band 2 p.231, Financial Crime: London Band 2 p.266, Immigration: London Band 2 p.297, Inquests & Public Inquiries: London Band 3 p.309, POCA Work & Asset Forfeiture: All Circuits Band 2 p.397, Police Law: Mainly Claimant: All Circuits Band 2 p.400, Public International Law: London Band 2 p.435

6-8 Mill Street
Profile: p.913

Monckton Chambers
Profile: p.833
Table(s): Administrative & Public Law: London Band 3 p.27, Competition Law: London Band 1 p.142, Data Protection: London Band 2 p.195, Environment: London Band 3 p.231, European Law: London Band 1 p.237, Public Procurement: London Band 1 p.439, Tax: Indirect Tax: London Band 1 p.485, Telecommunications: London Band 1 p.491

N

New Court Chambers
Profile: p.834
Table(s): Family/Matrimonial: Family: Children: London Band 3 p.245

New Park Court Chambers
Table(s): Crime: North Eastern Band 1 p.184, Professional Discipline: The Regions Band 2 p.417

Three New Square
Profile: p.834
Table(s): Intellectual Property: London Band 1 p.322

4 New Square
Profile: p.835
Overview(s): Professional Negligence p.419
Table(s): Construction: London Band 4 p.146, Costs Litigation: London Band 1 p.160, Insurance: London Band 3 p.315, Product Liability: London Band 2 p.406, Professional Discipline: London Band 3 p.410, Professional Negligence: London Band 1 p.420, Technology & Construction: London Band 2 p.427, Sport: London Band 2 p.478

8 New Square
Profile: p.836
Table(s): Information Technology: London Band 2 p.304, Intellectual Property: London Band 1 p.322, Media & Entertainment: London Band 1 p.345

New Square Chambers
Profile: p.837
Table(s): Agriculture & Rural Affairs: London Band 2 p.41, Chancery: Commercial: London Band 3 p.59, Traditional: London Band 2 p.67, Company: London Band 3 p.135, Offshore: London Band 2 p.353, Real Estate Litigation: London Band 4 p.442, Restructuring/Insolvency: London Band 3 p.455

11 New Square
Table(s): Tax: London Band 2 p.482

No5 Chambers
Profile: p.837, p.883, p.891, p.909
Table(s): Administrative & Public Law: Midlands Band 1 p.38, Chancery: Midlands Band 2 p.73, Clinical Negligence: Midlands Band 1 p.102, Commercial Dispute Resolution: Midlands Band 2 p., Company: Midlands Band 1 p.140, Construction: Midlands Band 1 p.153, Court of Protection: Health & Welfare: All Circuits Band 3 p.165, Crime: Midlands Band 1 p.181, Employment: Midlands Band 1 p.218, Environment: Midlands Band 1 p.235, Family/Matrimonial: Midlands Band 1 p.254, Health & Safety: Midlands Band 1 p.295, Immigration: Midlands Band 1 p.308, Personal Injury: Midlands Band 1 p.377, Planning: Midlands Band 1 p.393, Real Estate Litigation: Midlands Band 2 p.450

No.6 Barristers Chambers
Table(s): Crime: North Eastern Band 1 p.184

Number 8 Chambers
Table(s): Immigration: Midlands Band 1 p.308

O

Octagon House Chambers
Table(s): Crime: South Eastern Band 1 p.188

XXIV Old Buildings
Profile: p.838
Overview(s): Offshore p.352
Table(s): Aviation: London Band 2 p.46, Chancery: Commercial: London Band 2 p.59, Traditional: London Band 1 p.67, Company: London Band 3 p.135, Fraud: Civil: London Band 2 p.281, Offshore: London Band 1 p.353, Partnership: London Band 2 p.359, Professional Negligence: London Band 4 p.420, Restructuring/Insolvency: London Band 3 p.455

Ten Old Square
Profile: p.839
Table(s): Chancery: Traditional: London Band 2 p.67, Partnership: London Band 2 p.359

Old Square Chambers
Profile: p.840
Table(s): Employment: London Band 2 p.207, Western Band 1 p.223, Environment: London Band 3 p.231, Personal Injury: London Band 3 p.367, Western Band 1 p.384, Professional Discipline: London Band 4 p.410

One Paper Buildings
Profile: p.841
Table(s): Crime: South Eastern Band 1 p.188, Western Band 2 p.192

Outer Temple Chambers
Profile: p.842
Table(s): Clinical Negligence: London Band 2 p.92, Employment: London Band 3 p.207, Financial Crime: London Band 3 p.266, Financial Services: London Band 2 p.276, Health & Safety: London Band 2 p.291, Pensions: London Band 2 p.363, Personal Injury: London Band 1 p.367, Professional Discipline: London Band 2 p.410, Travel: International Personal Injury: London Band 2 p.495

P

4 Paper Buildings
Profile: p.843
Table(s): Family/Matrimonial: Family: Matrimonial Finance: London Band 2 p.244, Family: Children: London Band 1 p.244

5 Paper Buildings
Profile: p.844
Overview(s): Consumer Law p.155
Table(s): Consumer Law: London Band 3 p.156, Crime: London Band 4 p.172, Financial Crime: London Band 3 p.266

Five Paper
Profile: p.845
Table(s): Social Housing: London Band 2 p.471

9 Park Place
Table(s): Crime: Wales & Chester Band 1 p.191

Parklane Plowden
Profile: p.907, p.926
Table(s): Personal Injury: North Eastern Band 1 p.379

30 Park Place
Profile: p.895
Table(s): Crime: Wales & Chester Band 1 p.191, Family/Matrimonial: Wales & Chester Band 1 p.261, Personal Injury: Wales & Chester Band 2 p.383

3PB Barristers
Profile: p.846
Table(s): Clinical Negligence: Western Band 2 p.106, Commercial Dispute Resolution: South Eastern Band 1 p.129, Crime: Western Band 1 p.192, Employment: Western Band 2 p.223, POCA Work & Asset Forfeiture: All Circuits Band 2 p.397

1 Pump Court
Profile: p.848
Table(s): Immigration: London Band 3 p.297, Social Housing: London Band 3 p.471

4 Pump Court
Profile: p.849
Table(s): Commercial Dispute Resolution: London Band 3 p.108, Construction: London Band 2 p.146, Energy & Natural Resources: London Band 2 p.226, Information Technology: London Band 1 p.304, Insurance: London Band 4 p.315, International Arbitration: Construction/Engineering: London Band 2 p.333, Professional Negligence: London Band 2 p.420, Technology & Construction: London Band 1 p.427, Shipping & Commodities: London Band 4 p.465

6 Pump Court
Profile: p.850
Table(s): Environment: London Band 2 p.231, Health & Safety: London Band 1 p.291, Planning: London Band 4 p.386

Pump Court Chambers
Profile: p.851
Table(s): Crime: Western Band 2 p.192, Employment: Western Band 2 p.223, Family/Matrimonial: Western Band 1 p.262

Pump Court Tax Chambers
Profile: p.852
Table(s): Tax: London Band 1 p.482, Indirect Tax: London Band 1 p.485, Private Client: London Band 1 p.488

Q

QEB Hollis Whiteman
Profile: p.853
Table(s): Crime: London Band 1 p.172, Financial Crime: London Band 2 p.266, Professional Discipline: London Band 2 p.410

Quadrant Chambers
Profile: p.854

INDEX OF BARRISTERS

A

Antelme, Alexander
Table(s): Clinical Negligence: London New Silks p.92, Personal Injury: London New Silks p.367, Product Liability: London New Silks p.406, Property Damage: London New Silks p.433

Antrobus, Simon
Profile: p.536
Table(s): Consumer Law: London Band 1 p.156, Health & Safety: London Star individuals p.291, Inquests & Public Inquiries: London Band 3 p.309

Apps, Katherine
Profile: p.536
Table(s): Administrative & Public Law: London Band 4 p.28

Archer, Stephen
Table(s): Personal Injury: London Band 3 p.368

Arden, Andrew
Profile: p.537
Table(s): Local Government: London Band 2 p.340, Social Housing: London Star individuals p.471

Arden, Peter
Profile: p.537
Table(s): Chancery: Commercial: London Band 2 p.59, Company: London Band 2 p.135, Restructuring/Insolvency: London Band 1 p.455

Arentsen, Andrew
Profile: p.537
Table(s): Personal Injury: Wales & Chester (Bar) Band 2 p.383

Arkush, Jonathan
Profile: p.537
Table(s): Chancery: Traditional: London Band 4 p.67, Mediators: All Circuits Band 3 p.348

Arlidge, Anthony
Profile: p.537
Table(s): Crime: London Band 5 p.173

Armstrong, Dean
Profile: p.537
Table(s): Crime: London New Silks p.173, Financial Crime: London New Silks p.266

Armstrong, Douglas
Profile: p.537
Table(s): Planning & Environment: Scotland (Bar) Band 1 p.522

Armstrong, Nicholas
Table(s): Administrative & Public Law: London Band 2 p.28, Civil Liberties & Human Rights: London Band 4 p.82, Community Care: London Band 1 p.132, Education: London Band 3 p.203, Immigration: London Band 2 p.297

Arnfield, Robert
Profile: p.537
Table(s): Chancery: Traditional: London Band 4 p.67

Arnold, Mark
Profile: p.538
Table(s): Restructuring/Insolvency: London Band 5 p.455

Arnot, Lee
Profile: p.538
Table(s): Family: Children: London Band 3 p.245

Arshad, Farrhat
Table(s): Administrative & Public Law: Northern (Bar) Band 3 p.39, Civil Liberties & Human Rights: Northern (Bar) Band 2 p.89, Crime: Northern (Bar) Band 3 p.186

Artis, Iain N J
Profile: p.538
Table(s): Tax: Scotland (Bar) Band 2 p.527

Ascroft, Richard
Profile: p.538
Table(s): Commercial Dispute Resolution: Western (Bar) Band 2 p.130, Company: Western (Bar) Band 1 p.141, Restructuring/Insolvency: Western (Bar) Band 1 p.463

Ash, Brian
Table(s): Planning: London Band 2 p.386

Ashcroft, Michael
Table(s): Shipping & Commodities: London Band 1 p.465

Ashley, Neil
Table(s): Employment: South Eastern (Bar) Band 1 p.222

Ashley-Norman, Jonathan
Profile: p.538
Table(s): Financial Crime: London Band 1 p.267, Health & Safety: London Band 2 p.291, POCA Work & Asset Forfeiture: All Circuits Band 2 p.397

Ashraph, Sareta
Table(s): Crime: International Criminal Law: London p.175

Ashwell, Paul
Table(s): Commercial Dispute Resolution: South Eastern (Bar) Band 1 p.129

Ashworth, Fiona
Profile: p.538
Table(s): Personal Injury: Northern (Bar) Band 2 p.380

Ashworth, Lance
Profile: p.538
Table(s): Chancery: Commercial: London Band 4 p.59, Commercial Dispute Resolution: London Band 3 p.109

Assersohn, Oliver
Table(s): Financial Services: London Band 1 p.276

Astbury, Joanne
Table(s): Family/Matrimonial: North Eastern (Bar) Band 2 p.256

Aswani, Ravi
Profile: p.538
Table(s): Shipping & Commodities: London Band 2 p.465

Atchley, Richard
Table(s): Professional Discipline: London Band 5 p.411

Atherton, Peter
Profile: p.539
Table(s): Professional Discipline: The Regions Band 2 p.417

Atherton, Stephen
Table(s): Offshore: London Band 2 p.353, Restructuring/Insolvency: London Band 2 p.455

Atkins, Mike
Profile: p.539
Table(s): Health & Safety: London Band 3 p.291

Atkins, Richard
Profile: p.539
Table(s): Crime: Midlands (Bar) Band 2 p.181

Atkinson, Duncan
Profile: p.539
Table(s): Crime: London Band 1 p.174

Atkinson, Jody
Profile: p.539
Table(s): Family/Matrimonial: Western (Bar) Band 3 p.262

Atkinson, Timothy
Profile: p.539
Table(s): Defamation/Privacy: London Band 4 p.199

Atrill, Simon
Profile: p.539
Table(s): Banking & Finance: London Band 1 p.50, Commercial Dispute Resolution: London Band 5 p.110, Fraud: Civil: London Band 2 p.282

Auburn, Jonathan
Profile: p.539
Table(s): Administrative & Public Law: London Band 2 p.28, Community Care: London Band 1 p.132, Education: London Band 3 p.203, Local Government: London Band 3 p.340

Audland, William
Profile: p.540
Table(s): Personal Injury: London Band 1 p.368, Travel: International Personal Injury: London Band 2 p.495

Auld, Charles
Table(s): Chancery: Western (Bar) Band 1 p.77, Real Estate Litigation: Western (Bar) Band 2 p.453

Auld, Stephen
Table(s): Banking & Finance: London Band 1 p.49, Commercial Dispute Resolution: London Band 2 p.109, Fraud: Civil: London Band 4 p.281

Axon, Andrew
Table(s): Clinical Negligence: North Eastern (Bar) Band 1 p.103, Personal Injury: North Eastern (Bar) Band 1 p.379

Ayers, Guy
Table(s): Crime: South Eastern (Bar) Band 3 p.188

Aylett, Crispin
Table(s): Crime: London Band 1 p.173

Aylett, Ken
Table(s): Crime: London Band 5 p.174

Ayliffe, James
Table(s): Chancery: Commercial: London Band 2 p.59, Offshore: London Band 3 p.353, Professional Negligence: London Band 3 p.420, Real Estate Litigation: London Band 4 p.442

Ayling, Judith
Table(s): Costs Litigation: London Band 2 p.160, Personal Injury: London Band 2 p.368

Ayling, Tracy
Profile: p.540
Table(s): Crime: London Band 4 p.173

Aylott, Colin
Profile: p.540
Table(s): Crime: London Band 3 p.174, Financial Crime: London Band 3 p.267

Ayres, Andrew
Profile: p.540
Table(s): Banking & Finance: London Band 4 p.50

B

Baatz, Nicholas
Table(s): Construction: London Band 2 p.146, Information Technology: London Band 3 p.304, Professional Negligence: Technology & Construction: London Band 2 p.428

Bache, Nina
Profile: p.540
Table(s): Family/Matrimonial: Midlands (Bar) Band 2 p.254

Bacon, Francis
Profile: p.540
Table(s): Professional Negligence: London Band 2 p.421

Bacon, Kelyn
Table(s): Administrative & Public Law: London New Silks p.27, Competition Law: London New Silks p.142, European Law: London New Silks p.237, Intellectual Property: London New Silks p.322, Telecommunications: London New Silks p.491

Bacon, Nicholas
Profile: p.540
Table(s): Costs Litigation: London Band 1 p.160

Badenoch, James
Table(s): Clinical Negligence: London Band 1 p.92

Badger, Christopher
Profile: p.540
Table(s): Environment: London Band 2 p.231

Bagchi, Andrew
Profile: p.540
Table(s): Court of Protection: Health & Welfare: All Circuits Band 1 p.165, Family: Children: London Band 1 p.245

Bagley, Louisa
Profile: p.541
Table(s): Crime: Western (Bar) Band 3 p.192

Bagot, Charles
Profile: p.541
Table(s): Personal Injury: London Band 1 p.368

Bailey, David
Table(s): Competition Law: London Up-and-coming individuals p.142

Bailey, David
Table(s): Insurance: London Band 4 p.315, Shipping & Commodities: London Band 3 p.465

Bailey, James
Profile: p.541
Table(s): Chancery: Commercial: London Band 3 p.60, Company: London Band 3 p.135, Restructuring/Insolvency: London Band 4 p.455

Bailey-Harris, Rebecca
Table(s): Family: Matrimonial Finance: London Band 2 p.244

Bailin, Alex
Profile: p.541
Table(s): Administrative & Public Law: London Band 2 p.27, Civil Liberties & Human Rights: London Band 2 p.81, Crime: London Band 3 p.173, Defamation/Privacy: London Band 2 p.199, Financial Crime: London Band 2 p.266, Financial Crime: Corporates: London Band 2 p.266

Bain, Dorothy
Table(s): Personal Injury: Scotland (Bar) Band 2 p.520

Bain, Giles
Profile: p.541
Table(s): Family: Children: London Band 3 p.245

Bajwa, Ali Naseem
Table(s): Crime: London Band 2 p.173

Baker, Andrew
Table(s): Banking & Finance: London Band 2 p.49, Commercial Dispute Resolution: London Band 3 p.109, International Arbitration: General Commercial & Insurance: London Band 3 p.328, Shipping & Commodities: London Band 2 p.465

Baker, Caroline
Table(s): Family/Matrimonial: Midlands (Bar) Band 2 p.254

Baker, Christopher
Profile: p.541
Table(s): Local Government: London Band 2 p.340, Social Housing: London Band 1 p.471

Beattie, Kate
Table(s): Administrative & Public Law: London Up-and-coming individuals p.28, Inquests & Public Inquiries: London Up-and-coming individuals p.309

Beattie, Sharon
Table(s): Professional Discipline: The Regions Band 1 p.417

Bebb, Gordon
Table(s): Clinical Negligence: London Band 3 p.92, Professional Discipline: London Band 4 p.410

Beckley, John
Table(s): Social Housing: London Band 2 p.471

Bedford, Erica
Profile: p.546
Table(s): Costs Litigation: Northern (Bar) Up-and-coming individuals p.162

Bedford, Michael
Profile: p.546
Table(s): Planning: London Band 1 p.386

Bedworth, Georgia
Profile: p.546
Table(s): Chancery: Traditional: London Band 2 p.67, Court of Protection: Property & Affairs: All Circuits Band 3 p.169

Beeby, Gabriel
Table(s): Clinical Negligence: Western (Bar) Up-and-coming individuals p.106

Beecham, Sara
Profile: p.546
Table(s): Social Housing: London Band 2 p.471

Beer, Jason
Profile: p.547
Table(s): Administrative & Public Law: London Band 4 p.27, Inquests & Public Inquiries: London Band 1 p.309, Police Law: Mainly Defendant: All Circuits Band 1 p.402, Professional Discipline: London Band 4 p.410

Beever, Edmund
Profile: p.547
Table(s): Commercial Dispute Resolution: Midlands (Bar) Band 2 p.125, Employment: Midlands (Bar) Band 1 p.218

Beggs, John
Profile: p.547
Table(s): Inquests & Public Inquiries: London Band 1 p.309, Police Law: Mainly Defendant: All Circuits Star individuals p.402, Professional Discipline: London Band 1 p.410

Beglan, Wayne
Profile: p.547
Table(s): Local Government: London Band 4 p.340, Social Housing: London Band 2 p.471

Begley, Laura
Table(s): Clinical Negligence: London Band 3 p.93, Personal Injury: London Band 1 p.368

Belgrove, Sophie
Profile: p.547
Table(s): Employment: London Band 3 p.208

Bell, James
Table(s): Personal Injury: London Band 2 p.368

Bell, Laura
Profile: p.547
Table(s): Employment: London Up-and-coming individuals p.208

Beloff, Michael
Table(s): Administrative & Public Law: London Senior Statesmen p.27, Education: London Band 2 p.203, European Law: London Senior Statesmen p.237, Professional Discipline: London Band 4 p.410, Sport: London Band 3 p.478

Beltrami, Adrian
Table(s): Banking & Finance: London Band 1 p.49, Chancery: Commercial: London Band 1 p.59, Commercial Dispute Resolution: London Band 2 p.109, Fraud: Civil: London Band 2 p.281, Restructuring/Insolvency: London Band 4 p.455

Bennathan, Joel
Table(s): Crime: London Band 2 p.173

Bennett, Daniel
Table(s): Clinical Negligence: Western (Bar) Band 2 p.106, Personal Injury: London Band 3 p.368, Personal Injury: Industrial Disease: London p.368, Personal Injury: Western (Bar) Band 3 , Product Liability: London Band 3 p.406

Bennett, Emma
Table(s): Crime: Northern (Bar) Band 3 p.186

Bennett, James
Table(s): Crime: Western (Bar) Band 3 p.192, Health & Safety: Western (Bar) Band 2 p.296

Bennett, Jonathan
Table(s): Family: Children: London Band 2 p.245

Bennett, Lee
Table(s): Health & Safety: London Band 2 p.291

Bennett, Martyn
Table(s): Family/Matrimonial: Northern (Bar) Band 2 p.258

Bennett, Miles
Profile: p.547
Table(s): Consumer Law: London Band 1 p.156

Bennett, William
Table(s): Defamation/Privacy: London Band 1 p.199

Bennett-Jenkins, Sallie
Profile: p.547
Table(s): Crime: London Band 2 p.173

Benson, Jeremy
Profile: p.547
Table(s): Crime: London Band 4 p.173, Financial Crime: London Band 4 p.266

Benson, Julian
Table(s): Personal Injury: Western (Bar) Band 1

Bentham, Daniel
Profile: p.548
Table(s): Family: Matrimonial Finance: London Band 2 p.244

Bentley, David
Table(s): Crime: London Band 6 p.173

Bentley, Harry
Profile: p.548
Table(s): Financial Crime: London Up-and-coming individuals p.267

Beresford, Stephen
Profile: p.548
Table(s): Commercial Dispute Resolution: Midlands (Bar) Band 2 p.125

Bergin, Terence
Profile: p.548
Table(s): Information Technology: London Star individuals p.304

Berkeley, Iona
Profile: p.548
Table(s): Intellectual Property: London Band 3 p.322

Berkley, David
Table(s): Chancery: Northern (Bar) Band 2 p.75

Berkley, Michael
Table(s): Chancery: Western (Bar) Band 3 p.77

Berkson, Simon
Table(s): Crime: Northern (Bar) Band 2 p.186

Berlin, Barry
Profile: p.548
Table(s): Consumer Law: Midlands (Bar) Band 1 p.158, Environment: Midlands (Bar) Band 2 p.235, Health & Safety: Midlands (Bar) Band 2 p.295

Berman, Franklin
Table(s): Public International Law: London Senior Statesmen p.435

Berragan, Neil
Profile: p.548
Table(s): Chancery: Northern (Bar) Band 1 p.75, Commercial Dispute Resolution: Northern (Bar) Band 1 p.127, Partnership: Northern (Bar) Band 1 p.361, Restructuring/Insolvency: Northern (Bar) Band 1 p.462

Berridge, Alison
Profile: p.548
Table(s): Competition Law: London Band 3 p.142

Berry, Adrian
Table(s): Immigration: London Band 1 p.297, Social Housing: London Band 2 p.471

Berry, Anthony
Profile: p.548
Table(s): Crime: London Band 2 p.173

Berry, James
Profile: p.549
Table(s): Police Law: Mainly Defendant: All Circuits Band 2 p.402

Berry, Steven
Table(s): Commercial Dispute Resolution: London Band 3 p.109, Insurance: London Band 2 p.315, International Arbitration: General Commercial & Insurance: London Band 4 p.328, Shipping & Commodities: London Band 2 p.465

Bertram, Jonathan
Profile: p.549
Table(s): Clinical Negligence: London Band 4 p.93

Beswetherick, Anthony
Table(s): Restructuring/Insolvency: London Band 5 p.455

Bethlehem, Daniel
Table(s): Public International Law: London Band 1 p.435

Bex, Kate
Profile: p.549
Table(s): Crime: London Band 5 p.174, Professional Discipline: London Band 4 p.411

Bhaloo, Zia
Table(s): Chancery: Commercial: London Band 2 p.59, Real Estate Litigation: London Band 2 p.442, Social Housing: London Band 3 p.471

Bhogal, Kuljit
Profile: p.549
Table(s): Social Housing: London Band 3 p.471

Bhose, Ranjit
Profile: p.549
Table(s): Local Government: London Band 3 p.340, Real Estate Litigation: London Band 3 p.442, Social Housing: London Band 2 p.471

Bicarregui, Anna
Table(s): Education: London Band 3 p.203

Bickerdike, Roger
Table(s): Family/Matrimonial: North Eastern (Bar) Band 2 p.256

Bickerstaff, Jane
Profile: p.549
Table(s): Crime: London Band 5 p.173

Bickford Smith, James
Profile: p.549
Table(s): Employment: London Up-and-coming individuals p.208

Bickford-Smith, Stephen
Table(s): Real Estate Litigation: London Band 4 p.443

Bignell, Janet
Profile: p.550
Table(s): Real Estate Litigation: London Band 1 p.443

Bingham, Camilla
Table(s): Commercial Dispute Resolution: London Band 5 p.109

Birch, Elizabeth
Table(s): Mediators: All Circuits Band 4 p.348

Bird, Andrew
Profile: p.550
Table(s): POCA Work & Asset Forfeiture: All Circuits Star individuals p.397

Bird, Simon
Profile: p.550
Table(s): Planning: London Band 2 p.386

Birnbaum, Michael
Table(s): Crime: London Band 5 p.173

Birt, Simon
Table(s): Banking & Finance: London Band 2 p.50, Commercial Dispute Resolution: London Band 2 p.110

Birtles, Samantha
Profile: p.550
Table(s): Family/Matrimonial: Northern (Bar) Band 3 p.258

Bishop, Edward
Profile: p.550
Table(s): Clinical Negligence: London Band 2 p.92, Personal Injury: London Band 3 p.367, Police Law: Mainly Defendant: All Circuits Band 3 p.402

Bishop, Timothy
Table(s): Family: Matrimonial Finance: London Band 2 p.244

Black, Michael
Table(s): Construction: London Band 4 p.146, International Arbitration: General Commercial & Insurance: London Band 4 p.328, International Arbitration: Construction/Engineering: London Band 2 p.333, International Arbitration: Arbitrators: London Band 1 p.335, Offshore: London Band 2 p.353

Blackburn, Elizabeth
Profile: p.550
Table(s): Shipping & Commodities: London Band 2 p.465

Blackburn, John
Profile: p.550
Table(s): International Arbitration: Arbitrators: London Band 1 p.335

Blackett-Ord, Mark
Profile: p.550
Table(s): Partnership: London Band 2 p.359

Blackmore, Sally
Profile: p.550
Table(s): Social Housing: London Band 3 p.471

Blackwell, Kate
Table(s): Crime: Northern (Bar) Band 3 p.186

Blackwood, Andrew Guy
Table(s): Commercial Dispute Resolution: London New Silks p.109, Insurance: London New Silks p.315

Blackwood, Anneliese
Table(s): Competition Law: London Up-and-coming individuals p.142, Data Protection: London Up-and-coming individuals p.195

Blair, Bruce
Table(s): Family: Matrimonial Finance: London Band 2 p.244

Blair, Michael
Table(s): Financial Services: London Star Individuals p.276

Blair, Peter
Table(s): Financial Crime: The Regions Band 1 p.275

Blake, Andrew
Profile: p.551
Table(s): Employment: London Band 4 p.208

Blakeley, Richard
Table(s): Commercial Dispute Resolution: London Band 5 p.110, European Law: London Band 2 p.237

Blaker, Gary
Profile: p.551
Table(s): Real Estate Litigation: London Band 4 p.443

Blakesley, Patrick
Profile: p.551
Table(s): Personal Injury: London Band 1 p.368

Blanchard, Claire
Table(s): Commercial Dispute Resolution: London Band 5 p.109, Energy & Natural Resources: London Band 2 p.226, Insurance: London Band 3 p.315, Shipping & Commodities: London Band 3 p.465

Blaxland, Henry
Table(s): Crime: London Band 1 p.173

Blayney, David
Profile: p.551
Table(s): Banking & Finance: London Band 4 p.49, Chancery: Commercial: London Band 4 p.59, Commercial Dispute Resolution: London Band 4 p.109, Company: London Band 3 p.135, Partnership: London Band 3 p.359

Bleasdale, Marie-Claire
Table(s): Real Estate Litigation: London Band 3 p.443

Bleasdale, Paul
Table(s): Personal Injury: Midlands (Bar) Band 1 p.377

Bloch, Michael
Table(s): Intellectual Property: London Band 1 p.322, International Arbitration: General Commercial & Insurance: London Band 4 p.328

Bloch, Selwyn
Profile: p.551
Table(s): Employment: London Band 1 p.207

Block, Neil
Profile: p.551
Table(s): Clinical Negligence: London Band 1 p.92, Personal Injury: London Star Individuals p.367, Product Liability: London Band 2 p.406, Travel: International Personal Injury: London Band 3 p.495

Blohm, Leslie
Table(s): Administrative & Public Law: Western (Bar) Band 1 p.40, Agriculture & Rural Affairs: Western (Bar) Band 1 p.43, Chancery: Western (Bar) Band 1 p.77, Commercial Dispute Resolution: Western (Bar) Band 1 p.130, Real Estate Litigation: Western (Bar) Band 1 p.453

Bloom, Margaret
Table(s): Clinical Negligence: London Band 4 p.93

Blum, Doron
Table(s): Immigration: London Band 4 p.297

Blundell, David
Table(s): Administrative & Public Law: London Band 3 p.28, Immigration: London Band 3 p.297

Blunt, David
Profile: p.551
Table(s): Information Technology: London Band 2 p.304

Blunt, Oliver
Profile: p.551
Table(s): Crime: London Band 1 p.173

Boardman, Christopher
Table(s): Chancery: Commercial: London Band 4 p.60, Restructuring/Insolvency: London Band 2 p.455

Boase, Anna
Table(s): Commercial Dispute Resolution: London Band 2 p.110

Bodnar, Alexandra
Profile: p.552
Table(s): Construction: London Band 4 p.147

Bodnar, Andrew
Profile: p.552
Table(s): Financial Crime: London Band 1 p.267, POCA Work & Asset Forfeiture: All Circuits Band 1 p.397

Boeddinghaus, Hermann
Profile: p.552
Table(s): Chancery: Commercial: London Band 3 p.60

Bogan, Paul
Table(s): Crime: London Band 4 p.173, Financial Crime: London Band 3 p.266

Bompas, George
Table(s): Chancery: Commercial: London Band 1 p.59, Commercial Dispute Resolution: London Band 5 p.109, Company: London Band 1 p.135, Financial Services: London Band 2 p.276, Restructuring/Insolvency: London Band 3 p.455

Bond, Kelly
Table(s): Restructuring/Insolvency: North Eastern (Bar) Up-and-coming Individuals p.461

Bond, Leisha
Profile: p.552
Table(s): Family/Matrimonial: Midlands (Bar) Band 2 p.254

Bone, Lucy
Profile: p.552
Table(s): Employment: London Band 3 p.208

Bools, Michael
Table(s): Commercial Dispute Resolution: London Band 3 p.109, Energy & Natural Resources: London Band 3 p.226

Boon, Elizabeth
Profile: p.552
Table(s): Property Damage: London Up-and-coming Individuals p.433

Boon, Lucinda
Table(s): Police Law: Mainly Defendant: All Circuits Band 3 p.402

Booth, Alexander
Profile: p.552
Table(s): Planning: London Band 3 p.386

Booth, Richard
Table(s): Clinical Negligence: London Band 3 p.92, Professional Discipline: London Band 4 p.410

Borland, Garry
Profile: p.553
Table(s): Commercial Dispute Resolution: Scotland (Bar) Band 1 p.512, Construction: Scotland (Bar) Band 1 p.515, Restructuring/Insolvency: Scotland (Bar) Band 1 p.526

Borrelli, Michael
Profile: p.553
Table(s): Crime: London Band 2 p.173

Boswood, Anthony
Table(s): Banking & Finance: London Band 3 p.49, Energy & Natural Resources: London Band 4 p.226, Insurance: London Band 1 p.315, International Arbitration: Arbitrators: London Band 1 p.335

Bott, Charles
Profile: p.553
Table(s): Crime: London Band 3 p.173, Financial Crime: London Band 1 p.266

Boulding, Philip
Profile: p.553
Table(s): Construction: London Band 2 p.146, International Arbitration: Construction/Engineering: London Band 1 p.333

Boulton, Richard
Table(s): Commercial Dispute Resolution: London Band 4 p.109

Bourne, Charles
Profile: p.553
Table(s): Administrative & Public Law: London New Silks p.27, Immigration: London New Silks p.297

Bourne, Colin
Profile: p.553
Table(s): Employment: North Eastern (Bar) Band 2 p.220

Bourne, Ian
Profile: p.553
Table(s): Crime: London Band 4 p.173

Bovey, Mungo
Table(s): Administrative & Public Law: Scotland (Bar) Band 2 p.507, Civil Liberties & Human Rights: Scotland (Bar) Band 2 p.509

Bowcock, Samantha
Table(s): Family/Matrimonial: Northern (Bar) Band 2 p.258

Bowdery, Martin
Table(s): Construction: London Band 3 p.146, Professional Negligence: Technology & Construction: London Band 2 p.428

Bowen, James
Table(s): Social Housing: London Band 3 p.471

Bowen, Nicholas
Table(s): Education: London Band 2 p.203, Police Law: Mainly Claimant: All Circuits Band 2 p.400

Bowen, Paul
Table(s): Administrative & Public Law: London Band 4 p.27, Civil Liberties & Human Rights: London Band 2 p.81, Community Care: London Band 2 p.132, Court of Protection: Health & Welfare: All Circuits Band 1 p.165, Police Law: Mainly Claimant: All Circuits Band 2 p.400

Bowers, John
Table(s): Employment: London Star Individuals p.207

Bowers, Rupert
Table(s): Financial Crime: London Band 4 p.267

Bowes, Michael
Profile: p.553
Table(s): Financial Crime: London Band 2 p.266, Financial Crime: Corporates: London Band 2 p.266, Financial Services: London Band 3 p.276

Bowhill, Jessie
Profile: p.554
Table(s): Intellectual Property: London Band 4 p.322

Bowie, Simon
Table(s): Clinical Negligence: Scotland (Bar) Band 2 p.510

Bowley, Ivan
Table(s): Personal Injury: Industrial Disease: London p.368, Personal Injury: Northern (Bar) Band 1 p.380

Bowling, James
Profile: p.554
Table(s): Construction: London Band 2 p.147

Bowron, Margaret
Table(s): Clinical Negligence: London Band 1 p.92

Bowsher, Michael
Profile: p.554
Table(s): Construction: London Band 4 p.146, Public Procurement: London Star Individuals p.439

Boyce, William
Table(s): Crime: London Band 1 p.173, Financial Crime: London Band 2 p.266

Boyd, James
Table(s): Employment: Northern (Bar) Band 1 p.221

Boyd, Jessica
Table(s): Administrative & Public Law: London Band 4 p.28, Competition Law: London Band 3 p.142

Boyd, Kerstin
Profile: p.554
Table(s): Family: Matrimonial Finance: London Band 4 p.244

Boydell, Edward
Profile: p.554
Table(s): Family/Matrimonial: Western (Bar) Band 1 p.262

Boyle, Alan
Profile: p.554
Table(s): Chancery: Commercial: London Band 1 p.59, Chancery: Traditional: London Band 1 p.67, Commercial Dispute Resolution: London Band 3 p.109, Company: London Band 2 p.135, Fraud: Civil: London Band 2 p.281, Offshore: London Band 1 p.353, Trusts: London Band 1 p.498

Boyle, Alan
Table(s): Public International Law: London Band 2 p.435

Boyle, Christopher
Table(s): Planning: London Band 4 p.386

Boyle, Gerard
Profile: p.554
Table(s): Clinical Negligence: London Band 1 p.93, Police Law: Mainly Defendant: All Circuits Band 1 p.402, Professional Discipline: London Band 1 p.411

Boyle, Matthew
Profile: p.554
Table(s): Personal Injury: London Band 3 p.368

Brabender, Lynda J
Profile: p.554
Table(s): Family/Matrimonial: Scotland (Bar) Band 1 p.517

Brace, Michael
Profile: p.555
Table(s): Clinical Negligence: Wales & Chester (Bar) Band 1 p.105, Personal Injury: Industrial Disease: London p.368, Personal Injury: Wales & Chester (Bar) Band 1 p.383

Bradbury, Timothy
Table(s): Crime: Western (Bar) Band 3 p.192

Bradley, Ben
Table(s): Clinical Negligence: London Band 4 p.93, Travel: International Personal Injury: London Band 3 p.495

Bradley, Clodagh
Table(s): Clinical Negligence: London Band 2 p.93, Professional Discipline: London Band 2 p.411

Bradley, Matthew
Profile: p.555
Table(s): Product Liability: London Band 3 p.406

Bradley, Michael
Table(s): Family: Matrimonial Finance: London Band 3 p.244

Bradley, Phillip
Table(s): Crime: Midlands (Bar) Band 2 p.181

Bradly, David
Table(s): Professional Discipline: London Band 1 p.411

Brady, Jane
Profile: p.555
Table(s): Crime: South Eastern (Bar) Band 4 p.188

Braithwaite, Bill
Table(s): Personal Injury: Northern (Bar) Band 1 p.380

Braithwaite, Thomas
Profile: p.555
Table(s): Partnership: London Band 3 p.359, Real Estate Litigation: London Band 4 p.443

Brand, Rachel
Table(s): Crime: Midlands (Bar) Band 2 p.181

Brander, Ruth
Table(s): Civil Liberties & Human Rights: London Band 2 p.82, Police Law: Mainly Claimant: All Circuits Band 1 p.400

Brandon, Ben
Table(s): Extradition: London Band 1 p.240, Financial Crime: London Band 2 p.267

Brandon, Stephen
Profile: p.555
Table(s): Tax: London Band 2 p.482, Tax: Private Client: London Band 2 p.488

Brandreth, Benet
Table(s): Intellectual Property: London Band 2 p.322

Brannigan, Sean
Profile: p.555
Table(s): Construction: London Star individuals p.146, Energy & Natural Resources: London Band 2 p.226, International Arbitration: Construction/Engineering: London Band 2 p.333, Professional Negligence: London Band 3 p.420, Professional Negligence: Technology & Construction: London Band 1 p.428

Branston, Barnabas
Profile: p.555
Table(s): Police Law: Mainly Defendant: All Circuits Band 2 p.402

Braslavsky, Nicholas
Profile: p.555
Table(s): Clinical Negligence: Northern (Bar) Band 2 p.103, Personal Injury: Northern (Bar) Band 2 p.380

Brassington, Stephen
Profile: p.555
Table(s): Professional Discipline: London Band 1 p.411

Brazil, Dominic
Profile: p.555
Table(s): Family: Matrimonial Finance: London Band 2 p.244

Brealey, Mark
Table(s): Competition Law: London Band 1 p.142

Bredemear, Zachary
Profile: p.556
Table(s): Real Estate Litigation: London Band 4 p.443

Bremner, Jonathan
Profile: p.556
Table(s): Tax: London Band 2 p.482

Brennan, John
Profile: p.556
Table(s): Chancery: Midlands (Bar) Band 1 p.73, Commercial Dispute Resolution: Midlands (Bar) Band 1 p.125

Brennan, Timothy
Profile: p.556
Table(s): Employment: London Band 3 p.207, Tax: London Band 2 p.482

Brent, Richard
Table(s): Banking & Finance: London Band 2 p.50, Financial Services: London Band 2 p.276

Brenton, Timothy
Table(s): Energy & Natural Resources: London Band 3 p.226, Shipping & Commodities: London Band 1 p.465

Brereton, Joy
Table(s): Family: Children: London Band 3 p.245

Bretherton, Kerry
Table(s): Administrative & Public Law: London Band 4 p.28, Court of Protection: Health & Welfare: All Circuits Band 2 p.165, Social Housing: London Band 1 p.471

Brewer, Michelle
Table(s): Immigration: London Band 3 p.297

Bridge, Ian
Profile: p.556
Table(s): Financial Crime: The Regions Band 1 p.275

Bridgman, Andrew
Table(s): Clinical Negligence: Northern (Bar) Band 2 p.103

Brier, Jeremy
Table(s): Commercial Dispute Resolution: London Band 5 p.110

Briggs, John
Profile: p.556
Table(s): Restructuring/Insolvency: London Band 2 p.455

Briggs, Lucie
Table(s): Construction: London Band 4 p.147

Briggs, Nicholas
Table(s): Chancery: Western (Bar) Band 2 p.77, Commercial Dispute Resolution: Western (Bar) Band 1 p.130, Professional Negligence: Western (Bar) Band 2 p.431, Restructuring/Insolvency: Western (Bar) Band 2 p.463

Bright, Christopher
Profile: p.556
Table(s): Clinical Negligence: Midlands (Bar) Band 2 p.102, Personal Injury: Midlands (Bar) Band 2 p.377

Bright, David
Table(s): Crime: Midlands (Bar) Band 3 p.181

Bright, Robert
Table(s): International Arbitration: General Commercial & Insurance: London Band 3 p.328, Shipping & Commodities: London Band 2 p.465

Brightwell, James
Profile: p.556
Table(s): Chancery: Traditional: London Band 3 p.67, Offshore: London Band 1 p.353

Brimelow, Kirsty
Table(s): Crime: London Band 5 p.173

Brindle, Michael
Table(s): Banking & Finance: London Star individuals p.49, Commercial Dispute Resolution: London Star individuals p.109, Financial Services: London Star individuals p.276, Fraud: Civil: London Band 1 p.281, International Arbitration: General Commercial & Insurance: London Band 2 p.328, Professional Negligence: London Band 1 p.420

Brinsmead-Stockham, John
Table(s): Tax: Indirect Tax: London Band 3 p.486

Brisby, John
Table(s): Chancery: Commercial: London Band 2 p.59, Commercial Dispute Resolution: London Band 4 p.109, Company: London Band 2 p.135, Financial Services: London Band 3 p.276, Fraud: Civil: London Band 3 p.281, Restructuring/Insolvency: London Band 3 p.455

Bristoll, Sandra
Table(s): Commercial Dispute Resolution: Midlands (Bar) Band 2 p.125, Restructuring/Insolvency: Midlands (Bar) Band 2 p.461

Brittenden, Stuart
Profile: p.556
Table(s): Employment: London Band 3 p.208

Broach, Stephen
Table(s): Administrative & Public Law: London Band 3 p.28, Community Care: London Band 1 p.132, Education: London Band 4 p.203

Broadfoot, Samantha
Table(s): Administrative & Public Law: London Band 4 p.28

Brochwicz-Lewinski, Stefan
Table(s): Employment: Northern (Bar) Band 1 p.221

Brocklebank, James
Table(s): Commercial Dispute Resolution: London Band 3 p.110, Insurance: London Band 2 p.316, Professional Negligence: London Band 2 p.421

Brockman, Christopher
Table(s): Restructuring/Insolvency: Western (Bar) Band 1 p.463

Brodie, Graham
Table(s): Financial Crime: London Band 4 p.266, POCA Work & Asset Forfeiture: All Circuits Band 2 p.397

Brody, Karen
Table(s): Family/Matrimonial: Northern (Bar) Band 1 p.258

Bromley-Martin, Michael
Table(s): Crime: London Band 2 p.173, Licensing: London Band 2 p.337

Brompton, Michael
Profile: p.557
Table(s): Crime: London Band 6 p.173

Brook, David
Table(s): Employment: London Band 5 p.208

Brook Smith, Philip
Profile: p.557
Table(s): Product Liability: London Band 2 p.406

Brooke, David
Table(s): Crime: North Eastern (Bar) Band 2 p.184

Brooke-Smith, John
Table(s): Family/Matrimonial: South Eastern (Bar) Band 3 p.259

Brooks, Duncan
Profile: p.557
Table(s): Family: Matrimonial Finance: London Band 2 p.244, Family: Children: London Band 3 p.244

Brooks, Peter
Profile: p.557
Table(s): Personal Injury: Wales & Chester (Bar) Band 2 p.383

Broome, Jonathan
Table(s): Construction: Scotland (Bar) Band 2 p.515, Professional Negligence: Scotland (Bar) Band 2 p.523

Brown, Anne
Profile: p.557
Table(s): Crime: Western (Bar) Band 3 p.192

Brown, Catherine
Profile: p.557
Table(s): Personal Injury: London Band 2 p.368

Brown, Christopher
Profile: p.557
Table(s): Competition Law: London Band 3 p.142

Brown, Daisy
Table(s): Restructuring/Insolvency: Western (Bar) Band 2 p.463

Brown, Damian
Table(s): Employment: London Band 3 p.207, Sport: London Band 5 p.478

Brown, Edward
Table(s): Commercial Dispute Resolution: London Band 4 p.110, Employment: London Band 3 p.208, Tax: Indirect Tax: London Band 3 p.486

Brown, Edward
Profile: p.557
Table(s): Crime: London Band 2 p.173

Brown, Emma
Profile: p.557
Table(s): Clinical Negligence: Midlands (Bar) Band 2 p.102

Brown, Geoffrey
Table(s): Personal Injury: London Band 1 p.368, Property Damage: London Band 1 p.433

Brown, George
Table(s): Immigration: Northern (Bar) Band 2 p.309

Brown, Hannah
Table(s): Banking & Finance: London Band 3 p.50

Brown, James
Table(s): Family/Matrimonial: North Eastern (Bar) Band 3 p.256

Brown, Jonathan
Table(s): Commercial Dispute Resolution: Scotland (Bar) Band 2 p.512, Professional Discipline: Scotland (Bar) Band 2 p.523

Brown, Marc
Profile: p.558
Table(s): Commercial Dispute Resolution: Midlands (Bar) Band 2 p.125, Restructuring/Insolvency: Midlands (Bar) Band 2 p.461

Brown, Nick
Table(s): Police Law: Mainly Claimant: All Circuits Band 2 p.400

Brown, Paul
Table(s): Administrative & Public Law: London Band 4 p.27, Local Government: London Band 4 p.340, Planning: London Band 2 p.386

Brown, Robert
Profile: p.558
Table(s): Social Housing: London Up-and-coming individuals p.471

Brown, Simon J
Table(s): Costs Litigation: London Band 3 p.160

Brown, Stephanie
Table(s): Family/Matrimonial: Midlands (Bar) Band 1 p.254

Brown, Stuart
Table(s): Clinical Negligence: North Eastern (Bar) Band 1 p.103, Clinical Negligence: Northern (Bar) Band 1 p.103, Personal Injury: North Eastern (Bar) Senior Statesmen p.379

Brown, Thomas
Profile: p.558
Table(s): Employment: London Band 5 p.208

Brown, Tim
Profile: p.558
Table(s): **Tax: Indirect Tax:** London **Band 3** p.486

Brownbill, David
Table(s): **Chancery: Commercial:** London **Band 2** p.59, **Chancery: Traditional:** London **Band 1** p.67, **Offshore:** London **Band 2** p.353, **Trusts:** London **Band 1** p.498

Browne, Benjamin
Profile: p.558
Table(s): **Clinical Negligence:** London **Band 1** p.92, **Personal Injury:** London **Band 1** p.367, **Travel: International Personal Injury:** London **Band 2** p.495

Browne, Desmond
Table(s): **Defamation/Privacy:** London **Band 1** p.199

Browne, Simon P
Table(s): **Costs Litigation:** London **Band 2** p.160, **Personal Injury:** London **Band 3** p.367

Browne-Wilkinson, Simon
Profile: p.558
Table(s): **Fraud: Civil:** London **Band 2** p.281

Brownhill, Joanna
Profile: p.558
Table(s): **Social Housing:** London **Band 3** p.471

Bruce, Andrew
Profile: p.558
Table(s): **Real Estate Litigation:** London **Band 2** p.443

Brunner, Kate
Table(s): **Crime:** Western (Bar) **Band 1** p.192

Brunning, Matthew
Profile: p.559
Table(s): **Personal Injury:** Midlands (Bar) **Band 2** p.377

Bryan, Robert
Profile: p.559
Table(s): **Crime:** Western (Bar) **Band 3** p.192

Bryan, Simon
Table(s): **Energy & Natural Resources:** London **Band 2** p.226, **Insurance:** London **Band 3** p.315, **Shipping & Commodities:** London **Band 3** p.465

Bryant, Judith
Table(s): **Chancery: Traditional:** London **Band 2** p.67

Bryant, Keith
Table(s): **Employment:** London **Band 4** p.207, **Pensions:** London **Band 3** p.363

Bryant-Heron, Mark
Profile: p.559
Table(s): **Crime:** London **New Silks** p.173

Bryce, Joseph
Table(s): **Immigration:** Scotland (Bar) **Band 1** p.518

Brynmor Thomas, David
Profile: p.559
Table(s): **International Arbitration: Arbitrators:** London **Band 1** p.335

Buchanan, James
Profile: p.559
Table(s): **Crime:** London **Band 3** p.174, **Health & Safety:** London **Band 3** p.291

Buck, William
Profile: p.559
Table(s): **Commercial Dispute Resolution:** North Eastern (Bar) **Band 3** p.126

Buckett, Edwin
Profile: p.559
Table(s): **Police Law: Mainly Defendant:** All Circuits **Band 2** p.402

Buckingham, Paul
Profile: p.560
Table(s): **Construction:** London **Band 3** p.147, **Energy & Natural Resources:** London **Band 2** p.226, **International Arbitration: Construction/Engineering:** London **Band 2** p.333

Buckingham, Stewart
Table(s): **Shipping & Commodities:** London **Band 2** p.465

Buckpitt, Michael
Profile: p.560
Table(s): **Real Estate Litigation:** London **Band 2** p.443

Budden, Rosemary
Profile: p.560
Table(s): **Family: Matrimonial Finance:** London **Band 4** p.244

Budworth, Martin
Table(s): **Sport:** The Regions **Band 1** p.480

Buehrlen, Veronique
Profile: p.560
Table(s): **Energy & Natural Resources:** London **Band 4** p.226, **International Arbitration: Construction/Engineering:** London **Band 2** p.333

Buley, Tim
Table(s): **Administrative & Public Law:** London **Band 2** p.28, **Civil Liberties & Human Rights:** London **Band 1** p.82, **Community Care:** London **Band 1** p.132, **Immigration:** London **Band 1** p.297

Bundell, Katharine
Table(s): **Family/Matrimonial:** South Eastern (Bar) **Band 3** p.259

Bunting, Jude
Table(s): **Administrative & Public Law:** London **Band 4** p.28, **Civil Liberties & Human Rights:** London **Band 2** p.82, **Police Law: Mainly Claimant:** All Circuits **Band 2** p.400

Bunyan, Angus
Profile: p.560
Table(s): **Crime:** London **Band 6** p.174

Burden, Angus
Profile: p.560
Table(s): **Chancery:** Midlands (Bar) **Band 1** p.73

Burgess, Edward
Table(s): **Crime:** Western (Bar) **Band 1** p.192

Burgher, Benjimin
Profile: p.560
Table(s): **Employment:** London **Band 5** p.208

Burke, Trevor
Profile: p.560
Table(s): **Crime:** London **Band 1** p.173, **Financial Crime:** London **Band 2** p.266

Burkill, Guy
Profile: p.561
Table(s): **Intellectual Property:** London **Band 1** p.322

Burles, David
Profile: p.561
Table(s): **Family: Matrimonial Finance:** London **Band 2** p.244

Burnet, Alasdair J
Profile: p.561
Table(s): **Planning & Environment:** Scotland (Bar) **Band 1** p.522

Burnham, Ulele
Table(s): **Court of Protection: Health & Welfare:** All Circuits **Band 2** p.165

Burns, Andrew
Profile: p.561
Table(s): **Employment:** London **Band 1** p.208, **Insurance:** London **Band 3** p.316

Burns, Paul
Profile: p.561
Table(s): **Local Government:** Northern (Bar) **Band 1** p.344, **Social Housing:** Northern (Bar) **Band 1** p.476

Burns, Peter
Table(s): **Personal Injury:** Northern (Bar) **Band 1** p.380

Burroughs, Nigel
Profile: p.561
Table(s): **Pensions:** London **Band 3** p.363

Burrows, Michael
Profile: p.561
Table(s): **Crime:** Midlands (Bar) **Band 3** p.181

Burrows, Simon
Profile: p.561
Table(s): **Administrative & Public Law:** Northern (Bar) **Band 2** p.39, **Court of Protection: Health & Welfare:** All Circuits **Band 1** p.165

Burton, Frank
Profile: p.562
Table(s): **Clinical Negligence:** London **Band 2** p.92, **Personal Injury:** London **Star individuals** p.367, **Personal Injury: Industrial Disease:** London p.367

Burton, James
Table(s): **Environment:** London **Band 3** p.231, **Planning:** London **Band 3** p.386

Burton, Jamie
Table(s): **Administrative & Public Law:** London **Band 4** p.28, **Social Housing:** London **Band 1** p.471

Burton, Paul
Profile: p.562
Table(s): **Restructuring/Insolvency:** London **Band 5** p.455

Busch, Lisa
Table(s): **Administrative & Public Law:** London **Band 3** p.28, **Environment:** London **Band 3** p.231, **Local Government:** London **Band 2** p.340, **Planning:** London **Band 4** p.386

Busuttil, Godwin
Profile: p.562
Table(s): **Defamation/Privacy:** London **Band 2** p.199

Butcher, Christopher
Table(s): **Banking & Finance:** London **Band 4** p.49, **Commercial Dispute Resolution:** London **Band 2** p.109, **Insurance:** London **Band 1** p.315, **International Arbitration: General Commercial & Insurance:** London **Band 4** p.328, **Professional Negligence:** London **Band 2** p.420, **Shipping & Commodities:** London **Band 3** p.465

Butler, Andrew
Profile: p.562
Table(s): **Real Estate Litigation:** London **Band 4** p.443

Butler, Jonathan
Table(s): **Civil Liberties & Human Rights:** Northern (Bar) **Band 2** p.89

Butler, Michelle
Profile: p.562
Table(s): **Crime: International Criminal Law:** London p.175

Butler, Rupert
Table(s): **Sport:** London **Band 5** p.478

Butler-Cole, Victoria
Table(s): **Administrative & Public Law:** London **Band 4** p.28, **Community Care:** London **Band 2** p.132, **Court of Protection: Health & Welfare:** All Circuits **Band 1** p.165

Butt, Matthew
Profile: p.562
Table(s): **Crime:** London **Band 3** p.174, **Extradition:** London **Band 3** p.240, **Inquests & Public Inquiries:** London **Band 3** p.309, **Licensing:** London **Band 2** p.337, **Professional Discipline:** London **Band 4** p.411

Buttler, Chris
Table(s): **Administrative & Public Law:** London **Band 2** p.28, **Civil Liberties & Human Rights:** London **Band 3** p.82, **Community Care:** London **Band 1** p.132, **Court of Protection: Health & Welfare:** All Circuits **Band 2** p.165

Byam-Cook, Henry
Table(s): **International Arbitration: General Commercial & Insurance:** London **Band 2** p.328, **Shipping & Commodities:** London **Band 3** p.465

Byles, Andrew
Table(s): **Social Housing:** Northern (Bar) **Band 2** p.476

Byrne, Daniel
Table(s): **Administrative & Public Law:** Scotland (Bar) **Up-and-coming individuals** p.507, **Civil Liberties & Human Rights:** Scotland (Bar) **Up-and-coming individuals** p.509, **Immigration:** Scotland (Bar) **Up-and-coming individuals** p.518

Byrne, Garrett
Profile: p.562
Table(s): **Environment:** London **Band 3** p.231

Byrnes, Aisling
Table(s): **Crime:** London **Band 1** p.174

C

Caddick, Nicholas
Table(s): **Chancery: Commercial:** London **Band 4** p.59

Cade Davies, Lynsey
Profile: p.562
Table(s): **Family: Matrimonial Finance:** London **Band 4** p.244

Cadwallader, Neil
Table(s): **Partnership:** Northern (Bar) **Band 2** p.361

Cahill, Jeremy
Table(s): **Environment:** Midlands (Bar) **Band 1** p.235, **Planning:** Midlands (Bar) **Band 1** p.393

Caldecott, Andrew
Profile: p.562
Table(s): **Data Protection:** London **Band 1** p.195, **Defamation/Privacy:** London **Star individuals** p.199

Caldwell, Marion
Table(s): **Clinical Negligence:** Scotland (Bar) **Band 1** p.510, **Personal Injury:** Scotland (Bar) **Band 1** p.520

Caldwell, Peter
Profile: p.563
Table(s): **Extradition:** London **Band 1** p.240, **Financial Crime:** London **Band 4** p.267

Calhaem, Simon
Profile: p.563
Table(s): **Family: Matrimonial Finance:** London **Band 3** p.244

Callaghan, Catherine
Table(s): **Administrative & Public Law:** London **Band 3** p.28, **Employment:** London **Band 3** p.208, **Professional Discipline:** London **Band 4** p.411

Callan, Jane
Profile: p.563
Table(s): **Employment:** North Eastern (Bar) **Band 1** p.220

Chamberlain, Martin
Table(s): Administrative & Public Law: London Band 1 p.27, Civil Liberties & Human Rights: London Band 2 p.81, Environment: London Band 3 p.231, European Law: London Band 2 p.237

Chamberlayne, Patrick
Profile: p.568
Table(s): Family: Matrimonial Finance: London Band 1 p.244

Chambers, Gaynor
Profile: p.568
Table(s): Construction: London Band 3 p.147, Energy & Natural Resources: London Band 3 p.226

Chambers, Jonathan
Table(s): Aviation: London Band 2 p.47

Chan, Susan
Table(s): Employment: London Band 5 p.208

Chandler, Alexander
Profile: p.568
Table(s): Family: Matrimonial Finance: London Band 3 p.244

Chandran, Parosha
Table(s): Civil Liberties & Human Rights: London Band 4 p.82, Immigration: London Band 2 p.297

Chapman, Graham
Profile: p.568
Table(s): Construction: London New Silks p.146, Professional Negligence: London New Silks p.420

Chapman, Jeffrey
Profile: p.568
Table(s): Banking & Finance: London Band 3 p.49, Commercial Dispute Resolution: London Band 4 p.109, Fraud: Civil: London Band 3 p.281

Chapman, John
Profile: p.569
Table(s): Family/Matrimonial: Western (Bar) Band 3 p.262

Chapman, Matthew
Profile: p.569
Table(s): Personal Injury: London Band 3 p.368

Chapman, Nicholas
Profile: p.569
Table(s): Family: Matrimonial Finance: London Band 4 p.244

Chapman, Rebecca
Table(s): Immigration: London Band 1 p.297

Chapman, Richard
Profile: p.569
Table(s): Commercial Dispute Resolution: Northern (Bar) Band 2 p.127

Chapman, Vivian R
Profile: p.569
Table(s): Agriculture & Rural Affairs: London Band 2 p.41

Chapple, Malcolm
Profile: p.569
Table(s): Intellectual Property: London Band 4 p.322, Telecommunications: London Band 2 p.491

Charalambides, Leo
Table(s): Licensing: London Band 2 p.337

Charbit, Valerie
Profile: p.569
Table(s): Crime: London Band 5 p.174

Charles, Henry
Profile: p.570
Table(s): Clinical Negligence: London Band 4 p.93, Personal Injury: London Band 1 p.368

Charlton, Alex
Table(s): Information Technology: London Band 1 p.304, Telecommunications: London Band 3 p.491

Charlwood, Spike
Profile: p.570
Table(s): Professional Negligence: London Star individuals p.421

Charman, Andrew
Profile: p.
Table(s): Chancery: Midlands (Bar) Band 2 p.73, Commercial Dispute Resolution: Midlands (Bar) Band 1 p.125

Chataway, Ben
Table(s): Social Housing: London Band 3 p.471

Chawla, Mukul
Profile: p.570
Table(s): Crime: London Band 1 p.173, Financial Crime: London Band 1 p.266

Checa-Dover, Olivia
Table(s): Family/Matrimonial: North Eastern (Bar) Up-and-coming individuals p.256

Cheema, Bobbie
Profile: p.570
Table(s): Crime: London Band 6 p.173

Cheetham, Simon
Profile: p.570
Table(s): Employment: London Band 2 p.208

Chelvan, S
Profile: p.570
Table(s): Immigration: London Band 2 p.297

Cheng, Serena
Profile: p.570
Table(s): Construction: London Band 3 p.147

Chennells, Mark
Table(s): Construction: London Band 2 p.147, International Arbitration: Construction/Engineering: London Band 2 p.333

Chern, Cyril
Profile: p.570
Table(s): Construction: London Band 3 p.147, International Arbitration: Construction/Engineering: London Band 2 p.333

Cherrill, Beverly
Table(s): Crime: South Eastern (Bar) Band 2 p.188

Cherry, Joanna
Profile: p.570
Table(s): Clinical Negligence: Scotland (Bar) Band 2 p.510

Child, Andrew J
Profile: p.571
Table(s): Chancery: Traditional: London Band 2 p.67, Offshore: London Band 2 p.353, Trusts: London Band 1 p.498

Child, John
Table(s): Chancery: Traditional: London Band 4 p.67

Chinn, Antony
Profile: p.571
Table(s): Crime: London Band 6 p.173

Chippindall, Adam
Table(s): Personal Injury: Western (Bar) Band 3

Chirico, David
Table(s): Immigration: London Band 1 p.297

Chisholm, Malcolm
Profile: p.571
Table(s): Court of Protection: Health & Welfare: All Circuits Band 1 p.165

Chivers, David
Profile: p.571
Table(s): Commercial Dispute Resolution: London Band 4 p.109, Company: London Star individuals p.135, Restructuring/Insolvency: London Band 2 p.455

Choo Choy, Alain
Table(s): Banking & Finance: London Band 2 p.49, Commercial Dispute Resolution: London Band 2 p.109, Energy & Natural Resources: London Band 2 p.226, Fraud: Civil: London Band 2 p.281, International Arbitration: General Commercial & Insurance: London Band 4 p.328

Choongh, Satnam
Profile: p.571
Table(s): Planning: Midlands (Bar) Band 2 p.393

Chorfi, Camilla
Profile: p.571
Table(s): Real Estate Litigation: London Band 4 p.443

Choudhury, Akhlaq
Profile: p.571
Table(s): Data Protection: London Band 4 p.195, Employment: London Band 2 p.208

Christie, Aidan
Profile: p.571
Table(s): Insurance: London Band 2 p.315, Professional Negligence: London Band 3 p.420

Christie, Richard
Profile: p.571
Table(s): Crime: London Band 3 p.173, Crime: South Eastern (Bar) Band 2 p.188

Christine, Kenneth
Table(s): Personal Injury: Scotland (Bar) Band 2 p.520

Christopher, Julian
Profile: p.572
Table(s): Crime: London Band 3 p.173, Financial Crime: London Band 4 p.266

Chudleigh, Louise
Profile: p.572
Table(s): Employment: London Band 3 p.208

Ciumei, Charles
Table(s): Employment: London New Silks p.207

Clancy, Ronald
Table(s): Clinical Negligence: Scotland (Bar) Band 2 p.510, Commercial Dispute Resolution: Scotland (Bar) Band 2 p.512, Media Law: Scotland (Bar) Band 1 p.519, Personal Injury: Scotland (Bar) Band 1 p.520

Clare, Allison
Profile: p.572
Table(s): Financial Crime: London Band 1 p.267

Clare, Michael
Table(s): Crime: South Eastern (Bar) Band 1 p.188

Clargo, John
Table(s): Commercial Dispute Resolution: South Eastern (Bar) Band 1 p.129

Claridge, Rachael
Table(s): Family/Matrimonial: South Eastern (Bar) Band 3 p.259

Clark, Alistair
Table(s): Administrative & Public Law: Scotland (Bar) Band 2 p.507, Commercial Dispute Resolution: Scotland (Bar) Band 1 p.512, Media Law: Scotland (Bar) Band 1 p.519, Public Procurement: Scotland (Bar) Band 1 p.525

Clark, Marie H
Table(s): Family/Matrimonial: Scotland (Bar) Band 2 p.517

Clark, Wayne
Table(s): Real Estate Litigation: London Band 1 p.443

Clarke, Andrew
Profile: p.572
Table(s): Employment: London Band 1 p.207

Clarke, Elizabeth
Profile: p.572
Table(s): Family: Matrimonial Finance: London Star individuals p.244

Clarke, Geoff
Profile: p.572
Table(s): Personal Injury: Scotland (Bar) Band 2 p.520

Clarke, Gerard
Table(s): Employment: London Band 3 p.208

Clarke, Ian
Profile: p.572
Table(s): Real Estate Litigation: London Band 4 p.443

Clarke, Patrick
Profile: p.573
Table(s): Construction: London Band 3 p.147

Clarke, Sarah
Profile: p.573
Table(s): Financial Crime: London Band 3 p.267, Financial Services: London Band 3 p.276

Clarkson, Patrick
Table(s): Planning: London Band 1 p.386

Clay, Jonathan
Table(s): Planning: London Band 4 p.386

Clay, Robert
Profile: p.573
Table(s): Construction: London Band 3 p.147

Clayton, Richard
Profile: p.573
Table(s): Administrative & Public Law: London Band 3 p.27, Civil Liberties & Human Rights: London Band 3 p.81, Local Government: London Band 4 p.340

Clayton, Richard
Profile: p.573
Table(s): Administrative & Public Law: Midlands (Bar) Band 1 p.38, Civil Liberties & Human Rights: Midlands (Bar) Band 1 p.89

Clee, Christopher
Table(s): Crime: Wales & Chester (Bar) Band 2 p.191

Clegg, Richard
Profile: p.573
Table(s): Real Estate Litigation: London Band 4 p.443

Clegg, Simon
Profile: p.573
Table(s): Commercial Dispute Resolution: Midlands (Bar) Band 1 p.125

Clegg, William
Profile: p.573
Table(s): Crime: London Band 1 p.173, Financial Crime: London Band 2 p.266, Financial Crime: Corporates: London Band 2 p.266

Clemens, Adam
Table(s): Police Law: Mainly Defendant: All Circuits Band 3 p.402

Clement, Joanne
Profile: p.574
Table(s): Administrative & Public Law: London Band 3 p.28, Civil Liberties & Human Rights: London Band 4 p.82, Community Care: London Band 2 p.132, Education: London Band 3 p.203, Local Government: London Band 3 p.340

Clifford, James
Profile: p.574
Table(s): Pensions: London Band 2 p.363

Corre, Neil
Table(s): Crime: London Band 6 p.174

Corsellis, Nicholas
Profile: p.578
Table(s): Crime: London Band 3 p.174

Cory-Wright, Charles
Table(s): Administrative & Public Law: London Band 3 p.27, Personal Injury: London Band 1 p.367

Cosgrove, Thomas
Profile: p.579
Table(s): Planning: London Band 2 p.386, Professional Discipline: London Band 5 p.411

Cottage, Rosina
Profile: p.579
Table(s): Crime: London Band 3 p.173

Cotter, Mark
Profile: p.579
Table(s): Crime: London Band 5 p.174

Cottle, Stephen
Table(s): Social Housing: London Band 3 p.471

Coughlan, John
Profile: p.579
Table(s): Clinical Negligence: Midlands (Bar) Band 2 p.102, Personal Injury: Midlands (Bar) Band 2 p.377

Counsell, James
Table(s): Professional Discipline: London Band 2 p.411

Cousins, Jeremy
Profile: p.579
Table(s): Banking & Finance: London Band 4 p.49, Chancery: Commercial: London Band 3 p.59, Professional Negligence: London Band 3 p.420

Coventry, Charles
Table(s): Clinical Negligence: Western (Bar) Up-and-coming individuals p.106

Cover, Martha
Profile: p.579
Table(s): Family: Children: London Band 1 p.245

Cowan, Peter
Table(s): Personal Injury: Industrial Disease: London p.368, Personal Injury: Northern (Bar) Band 1 p.380

Cowen, Gary
Table(s): Real Estate Litigation: London Band 2 p.443

Cowton, Catherine
Profile: p.579
Table(s): Family: Matrimonial Finance: London Band 1 p.244

Cox, Jason
Profile: p.579
Table(s): Clinical Negligence: Midlands (Bar) Band 2 p.102, Personal Injury: Midlands (Bar) Band 2 p.377

Cox, Raymond
Profile: p.580
Table(s): Banking & Finance: London Band 2 p.49, Insurance: London Band 4 p.315

Cox, Tamsin
Table(s): Real Estate Litigation: London Band 5 p.443

Cragg, Stephen
Table(s): Administrative & Public Law: London Band 4 p.27, Civil Liberties & Human Rights: London Band 4 p.81, Community Care: London Band 2 p.132, Police Law: Mainly Claimant: All Circuits Band 2 p.400

Craig, Aubrey
Profile: p.580
Table(s): Intellectual Property: The Regions Band 1 p.327

Craig, David
Table(s): Employment: London Star individuals p.208

Craig, Nicholas
Profile: p.580
Table(s): Commercial Dispute Resolution: London Band 4 p.110, Insurance: London Band 2 p.316, Shipping & Commodities: London Band 3 p.465

Crail, Ross
Profile: p.580
Table(s): Agriculture & Rural Affairs: London Band 1 p.41, Real Estate Litigation: London Band 4 p.443

Crampin, Peter
Profile: p.580
Table(s): Chancery: Traditional: London Band 3 p.67, Charities: London Band 1 p.79, Real Estate Litigation: London Band 4 p.442

Crane, Michael
Table(s): Aviation: London Star individuals p.47, Commercial Dispute Resolution: London Band 2 p.109, Insurance: London Band 1 p.315, International Arbitration: General Commercial & Insurance: London Band 2 p.328, Travel: Regulatory & Commercial: London Band 1 p.495

Crangle, Thomas
Profile: p.580
Table(s): Construction: London Band 4 p.147

Crapper, Sadie
Profile: p.580
Table(s): Motor Insurance Fraud: All Circuits Band 1 p.350, Personal Injury: London Band 3 p.368

Crasnow, Rachel
Profile: p.580
Table(s): Employment: London Band 1 p.208

Craven, Edward
Profile: p.580
Table(s): Defamation/Privacy: London Up-and-coming individuals p.199

Crawford, Colin
Table(s): Local Government: Northern (Bar) Band 2 p.344

Crawford, Grant
Profile: p.580
Table(s): Chancery: Traditional: London Band 3 p.67

Crawford, James R
Table(s): International Arbitration: General Commercial & Insurance: London Band 3 p.328, Public International Law: London Star individuals p.435

Crawford, Ruth
Profile: p.580
Table(s): Administrative & Public Law: Scotland (Bar) Band 2 p.507, Planning & Environment: Scotland (Bar) Band 2 p.522

Crawshaw, Simon
Profile: p.581
Table(s): Construction: London Up-and-coming individuals p.147

Cray, Timothy
Table(s): Crime: London Band 3 p.174

Crean, Anthony
Profile: p.581
Table(s): Planning: Midlands (Bar) Band 1 p.393, Planning: Northern (Bar) Band 1 p.394

Criddle, Betsan
Profile: p.581
Table(s): Employment: London Band 5 p.208

Cridland, Simon
Profile: p.581
Table(s): Clinical Negligence: London Band 3 p.93, Professional Discipline: London Band 3 p.411

Crigman, David
Profile: p.581
Table(s): Crime: Midlands (Bar) Star individuals p.181

Croall, Simon
Table(s): Information Technology: London Band 3 p.304, Shipping & Commodities: London Band 2 p.465

Cronin, Kathryn
Table(s): Immigration: London Band 1 p.297

Cross, James
Profile: p.581
Table(s): Construction: London Band 3 p.146, Professional Negligence: London Band 4 p.420, Professional Negligence: Technology & Construction: London Band 2 p.428, Property Damage: London Band 2 p.433

Cross, Jane
Table(s): Family/Matrimonial: Northern (Bar) Band 2 p.258

Cross, Tom
Profile: p.581
Table(s): Data Protection: London Band 4 p.195, Education: London Band 4 p.203, Employment: London Band 5 p.208

Crossley, Dominic
Table(s): Chancery: North Eastern (Bar) Up-and-coming individuals p.74

Crow, Charles
Profile: p.581
Table(s): Employment: Midlands (Bar) Band 2 p.218

Crow, Jonathan
Profile: p.582
Table(s): Administrative & Public Law: London Band 1 p.27, Banking & Finance: London Band 3 p.49, Chancery: Commercial: London Star individuals p.59, Commercial Dispute Resolution: London Band 1 p.109, Company: London Star individuals p.135, Financial Services: London Band 2 p.276, Fraud: Civil: London Band 4 p.281, Offshore: London Band 1 p.353, Restructuring/Insolvency: London Band 2 p.455, Telecommunications: London Band 3 p.491

Crowe, Cameron
Profile: p.582
Table(s): Consumer Law: London Band 3 p.156

Crowley, Daniel
Table(s): Property Damage: London Band 1 p.433

Crowley, Jane
Profile: p.582
Table(s): Family: Children: London Band 3 p.245

Crowley, Jane
Table(s): Family/Matrimonial: Wales & Chester (Bar) Band 2 p.261

Crowther, Sarah
Table(s): Civil Liberties & Human Rights: London Band 4 p.82, Travel: International Personal Injury: London Band 1 p.495

Croxford, Ian
Table(s): Chancery: Commercial: London Band 2 p.59, Commercial Dispute Resolution: London Band 3 p.109, Fraud: Civil: London Band 2 p.281, Professional Negligence: London Band 2 p.420

Croxford, Thomas
Table(s): Employment: London Band 1 p.208

Crystal, Jonathan
Table(s): Sport: London Band 2 p.478

Crystal, Michael
Table(s): Restructuring/Insolvency: London Band 3 p.455

Csoka, Simon
Table(s): Financial Crime: The Regions Band 1 p.275

Cudby, Markanza
Table(s): Family: Children: London Band 2 p.245

Cuddigan, Hugo
Table(s): Intellectual Property: London Band 1 p.322, Media & Entertainment: London Band 3 p.345

Cullen, Edmund
Profile: p.582
Table(s): Chancery: Commercial: London Band 4 p.59, Commercial Dispute Resolution: London Band 5 p.109, Intellectual Property: London Band 3 p.322, Media & Entertainment: London Band 1 p.345, Professional Negligence: London Band 4 p.420

Cullen, Felicity
Table(s): Tax: London Band 3 p.482

Cullen, Grace
Table(s): Employment: South Eastern (Bar) Up-and-coming individuals p.222

Cumberland, Melanie
Table(s): Administrative & Public Law: London Band 4 p.28, Crime: London Band 5 p.174, Extradition: London Band 2 p.240

Cumming, Edward
Table(s): Aviation: London Band 3 p.47, Chancery: Traditional: London Band 3 p.67, Commercial Dispute Resolution: London Band 4 p.110, Company: London Band 3 p.135, Offshore: London Band 3 p.353

Cunningham, Elizabeth
Table(s): Employment: Western (Bar) Band 2 p.223

Cunningham, Greg
Table(s): Pensions: Scotland (Bar) Band 1 p.520

Cunningham, Mark
Profile: p.582
Table(s): Chancery: Commercial: London Band 4 p.59

Cunningham, Naomi
Table(s): Employment: London Band 5 p.208

Curl, Joseph
Table(s): Restructuring/Insolvency: London Band 4 p.455

Curran, Philip
Table(s): Crime: Northern (Bar) Band 1 p.186

Currie, Fergus
Table(s): Employment: Western (Bar) Band 3 p.223

Currie, Heriot
Table(s): Commercial Dispute Resolution: Scotland (Bar) Band 1 p.512, Company: Scotland (Bar) Band 2 p.515, Construction: Scotland (Bar) Band 1 p.515, Intellectual Property: Scotland (Bar) Band 1 p.519, Tax: Scotland (Bar) Band 2 p.527

Curtis, Michael
Table(s): Construction: London Band 4 p.146

Cusworth, Nicholas
Table(s): Family: Matrimonial Finance: London Band 1 p.244

Cutress, James
Profile: p.582
Table(s): Aviation: London Band 2 p.47, Banking & Finance: London Band 3 p.50, Commercial Dispute Resolution: London Band 3 p.110, Insurance: London Band 2 p.316, Professional Negligence: London Band 4 p.421

Barristers index

D

Delaney, Joe
Table(s): Intellectual Property: London Band 3 p.322

Delibegović-Broome, Almira
Table(s): Commercial Dispute Resolution: Scotland (Bar) Band 1 p.512, Restructuring/Insolvency: Scotland (Bar) Band 1 p.526

Demachkie, Jamal
Table(s): Real Estate Litigation: London Band 4 p.443

Demetriou, Marie
Table(s): Administrative & Public Law: London Band 4 p.27, Civil Liberties & Human Rights: London Band 3 p.81, Competition Law: London Band 2 p.142, European Law: London Band 2 p.237, Telecommunications: London Band 3 p.491

Dempster, Jennifer
Profile: p.586
Table(s): Crime: London Band 1 p.174

Denehan, Edward
Table(s): Real Estate Litigation: London Band 2 p.443

Denholm, Graham
Table(s): Immigration: London Band 2 p.297

Denison, Simon
Profile: p.587
Table(s): Crime: London Band 3 p.173

Denney, Stuart
Table(s): Crime: Northern (Bar) Band 2 p.186, Health & Safety: Northern (Bar) Band 2 p.296

Dennis, Mark
Table(s): Crime: London Band 1 p.173

Dennis, Rebecca
Table(s): Clinical Negligence: Western (Bar) Band 2 p.106, Personal Injury: Western (Bar) Band 3

Dennison, Stephen
Profile: p.587
Table(s): Construction: London Band 1 p.146, Energy & Natural Resources: London Band 2 p.226, International Arbitration: Construction/Engineering: London Band 1 p.333, Professional Negligence: Technology & Construction: London Band 2 p.428

Dennys, Nicholas
Table(s): Construction: London Band 1 p.146, Energy & Natural Resources: London Band 3 p.226, Information Technology: London Band 2 p.304, International Arbitration: Construction/Engineering: London Band 2 p.333, Professional Negligence: Technology & Construction: London Band 2 p.428

Denton-Cox, Gregory
Profile: p.587
Table(s): Chancery: Commercial: London Band 1 p.60, Company: London Band 2 p.135, Fraud: Civil: London Band 3 p.282

Denyer-Green, Barry
Profile: p.587
Table(s): Real Estate Litigation: London Band 4 p.443

Devaney, Catherine
Table(s): Clinical Negligence: Scotland (Bar) Up-and-coming individuals p.510

Devereux, Edward
Table(s): Family: Children: London Band 2 p.245

Devonshire, Simon
Profile: p.587
Table(s): Employment: London Band 3 p.207

Dew, Richard
Profile: p.587
Table(s): Chancery: Traditional: London Band 2 p.67

Dhar, Siddharth
Table(s): International Arbitration: General Commercial & Insurance: London Band 2 p.328

Dhillon, Jasbir
Table(s): Banking & Finance: London Band 4 p.49, Commercial Dispute Resolution: London Band 5 p.109

Di Rollo, Simon
Table(s): Personal Injury: Scotland (Bar) Band 2 p.520

Dias, Dexter
Table(s): Inquests & Public Inquiries: London Band 3 p.309

Dicker, Robin
Profile: p.588
Table(s): Banking & Finance: London Star individuals p.49, Chancery: Commercial: London Band 1 p.59, Commercial Dispute Resolution: London Band 2 p.109, Company: London Band 1 p.135, Offshore: London Band 1 p.353, Restructuring/Insolvency: London Star individuals p.455

Dickinson, John FH
Profile: p.588
Table(s): Chancery: Western (Bar) Band 2 p.77, Commercial Dispute Resolution: Western (Bar) Band 1 p.130, Company: Western (Bar) Band 2 p.141, Professional Negligence: Western (Bar) Band 2 p.431

Dignum, Marcus
Profile: p.588
Table(s): Personal Injury: London Band 2 p.368

Dilnot, Anna
Table(s): Commercial Dispute Resolution: London Band 3 p.110, Fraud: Civil: London Band 3 p.282

Dilworth, Noel
Profile: p.588
Table(s): Product Liability: London Band 2 p.406

Dinan-Hayward, Deborah
Table(s): Family/Matrimonial: Western (Bar) Band 1 p.262

Dineen, Maria
Profile: p.588
Table(s): Crime: London Band 3 p.174

Dinkin, Anthony
Table(s): Planning: London Band 5 p.386

Ditchfield, Michael
Table(s): Personal Injury: North Eastern (Bar) Band 2 p.379

Diwan, Ricky
Table(s): Commercial Dispute Resolution: London Band 5 p.110, International Arbitration: General Commercial & Insurance: London Band 1 p.328

Dixey, Ian
Table(s): Health & Safety: Western (Bar) Band 1 p.296

Dixey, Jonathan
Profile: p.588
Table(s): Police Law: Mainly Defendant: All Circuits Up-and-coming individuals p.402

Dixon, Clare
Profile: p.588
Table(s): Professional Negligence: London Band 4 p.421

Dixon, David S
Table(s): Crime: North Eastern (Bar) Band 2 p.184

Dixon, Emma
Table(s): Administrative & Public Law: London Band 4 p.28, Environment: London Band 1 p.231

Dixon, Ralph
Table(s): Family/Matrimonial: Western (Bar) Band 2 p.262

Dixon, Rod
Table(s): Crime: International Criminal Law: London p.175

Dixon, Rodney
Table(s): Public International Law: London New Silks p.435

Dobbie, Olivia-Faith
Profile: p.588
Table(s): Employment: London Band 5 p.208

Dobbin, Clair
Profile: p.589
Table(s): Administrative & Public Law: London Band 3 p.28, Extradition: London Band 1 p.240, Inquests & Public Inquiries: London Band 1 p.309, Professional Discipline: London Band 5 p.411

Dobie, Lisa
Profile: p.589
Table(s): Clinical Negligence: London Up-and-coming individuals p.93, Police Law: Mainly Defendant: All Circuits Up-and-coming individuals p.402

Dobson, Catherine
Table(s): Court of Protection: Health & Welfare: All Circuits Up-and-coming individuals p.165

Doctor, Brian
Profile: p.589
Table(s): Commercial Dispute Resolution: London Band 5 p.109

Doerries, Chantal-Aimée
Profile: p.589
Table(s): Construction: London Band 2 p.146, Energy & Natural Resources: London Band 2 p.226, International Arbitration: Construction/Engineering: London Band 2 p.333, Professional Negligence: Technology & Construction: London Band 2 p.428

Doherty, Bernard
Table(s): Personal Injury: London Band 1 p.368, Travel: International Personal Injury: London Band 1 p.495

Dohmann, Barbara
Table(s): Banking & Finance: London Band 3 p.49, Commercial Dispute Resolution: London Band 4 p.109, Financial Services: London Band 2 p.276, Fraud: Civil: London Band 2 p.281, Offshore: London Band 3 p.353

Dolan, Bridget
Profile: p.589
Table(s): Clinical Negligence: London Band 3 p.93, Court of Protection: Health & Welfare: All Circuits Band 1 p.165

Domenge, Victoria
Profile: p.589
Table(s): Family: Matrimonial Finance: London Band 4 p.244

Donnellan, Christopher
Profile: p.589
Table(s): Crime: Midlands (Bar) Band 3 p.181

Donnelly, Kathleen
Profile: p.589
Table(s): Employment: London Band 5 p.208

Donnelly, Kevin
Table(s): Health & Safety: Northern (Bar) Band 2 p.296

Donnelly, Lewis
Table(s): Family/Matrimonial: North Eastern (Bar) Up-and-coming individuals p.256

Donovan, Joel
Table(s): Clinical Negligence: London Band 2 p.92, Personal Injury: London Band 2 p.367

Donovan, Scott
Table(s): Clinical Negligence: Northern (Bar) Band 2 p.103

Dougherty, Charles
Profile: p.589
Table(s): Commercial Dispute Resolution: London Band 5 p.109, Fraud: Civil: London Band 3 p.281, Insurance: London Band 4 p.315, Product Liability: London Band 2 p.406, Professional Negligence: London Band 3 p.420, Travel: International Personal Injury: London Band 3 p.495

Dougherty, Nigel
Profile: p.589
Table(s): Company: London Band 2 p.135

Douglas, Colin
Table(s): Family/Matrimonial: Wales & Chester (Bar) Band 2 p.261

Douglas, Michael
Profile: p.589
Table(s): Commercial Dispute Resolution: London Band 4 p.109, Information Technology: London Band 2 p.304, Professional Negligence: London Band 2 p.420, Professional Negligence: Technology & Construction: London Band 1 p.428

Douglas, Zachary
Profile: p.590
Table(s): International Arbitration: General Commercial & Insurance: London Band 1 p.328, Public International Law: London Band 1 p.435

Douglas-Jones, Ben
Profile: p.590
Table(s): Consumer Law: London Band 2 p.156, Financial Crime: London Band 3 p.267

Dovar, Daniel
Profile: p.590
Table(s): Real Estate Litigation: London Band 4 p.443

Dove, Ian
Table(s): Administrative & Public Law: Midlands (Bar) Band 1 p.38, Planning: London Band 2 p.386, Planning: Midlands (Bar) Band 1 p.393

Dowdalls, Catherine
Table(s): Family/Matrimonial: Scotland (Bar) Band 1 p.517

Dowding, Nicholas
Profile: p.590
Table(s): Real Estate Litigation: London Star individuals p.442

Dowley, Dominic
Profile: p.590
Table(s): Chancery: Commercial: London Band 3 p.59, Fraud: Civil: London Band 3 p.281

Downes, Paul
Table(s): Banking & Finance: London Band 3 p.49, Commercial Dispute Resolution: London Band 4 p.109

Doyle, Holly
Table(s): Restructuring/Insolvency: Western (Bar) Band 2 p.463

Doyle, Louis
Profile: p.590
Table(s): Chancery: Northern (Bar) Band 2 p.75, Restructuring/Insolvency: Northern (Bar) Band 1 p.462

Doyle, Peter
Table(s): Financial Crime: London Band 3 p.266

Drabble, Richard
Table(s): Administrative & Public Law: London Band 1 p.27, Civil Liberties & Human Rights: London Band 2 p.81, Costs Litigation: London Band 3 p.160, Environment: London Band 1 p.231, Local Government: London Band 1 p.340, Planning: London Band 3 p.386, Social Housing: London Band 1 p.471

E

F

Faulks, Edward
Profile: p.599
Table(s): **Clinical Negligence:** London **Band 1** p.92, **Local Government:** London **Band 3** p.340, **Personal Injury:** London **Band 1** p.367

Fealy, Michael
Table(s): **Commercial Dispute Resolution:** London **New Silks** p.109, **Energy & Natural Resources:** London **New Silks** p.226

Fear-Davies, Harriet
Table(s): **Employment:** Western (Bar) **Up-and-coming individuals** p.223

Featherby, William
Profile: p.599
Table(s): **Motor Insurance Fraud:** All Circuits **Band 2** p.350, **Personal Injury:** London **Band 2** p.367

Feehan, Frank
Table(s): **Family: Children:** London **Band 1** p.245

Feeny, Charles
Table(s): **Clinical Negligence:** Northern (Bar) **Band 1** p.103, **Personal Injury: Industrial Disease:** London p.368, **Personal Injury:** Northern (Bar) **Star individuals** p.380

Feest, Adam
Table(s): **Crime:** Western (Bar) **Band 2** p.192

Feldschreiber, Peter
Profile: p.599
Table(s): **Product Liability:** London **Band 2** p.406

Felstead, Christopher
Table(s): **Family/Matrimonial:** Wales & Chester (Bar) **Band 2** p.261

Feltham, Piers
Profile: p.599
Table(s): **Chancery: Traditional:** London **Band 2** p.67, **Court of Protection: Property & Affairs:** All Circuits **Band 1** p.169

Fenhalls, Mark
Table(s): **Crime:** London **New Silks** p.173, **Financial Crime:** London **New Silks** p.266

Fenn, Andrew
Profile: p.599
Table(s): **Construction:** London **Band 4** p.147

Fentem, Ross
Table(s): **Banking & Finance:** Western (Bar) **Band 1** p.57, **Commercial Dispute Resolution:** Western (Bar) **Band 2** p.130

Fenton, Adam
Table(s): **Insurance:** London **Band 3** p.315

Fenwick, Justin
Profile: p.599
Table(s): **Commercial Dispute Resolution:** London **Band 3** p.109, **Construction:** London **Band 3** p.146, **Fraud: Civil:** London **Band 4** p.281, **Insurance:** London **Band 3** p.315, **Offshore:** London **Band 3** p.353, **Product Liability:** London **Band 3** p.406, **Professional Negligence:** London **Star individuals** p.420

Ferguson, Craig
Profile: p.599
Table(s): **Crime:** London **Band 1** p.174, **Financial Crime:** London **Band 2** p.267, **Health & Safety:** London **Band 3** p.291, **Professional Discipline:** London **Band 1** p.411

Ferguson, Eva
Profile: p.599
Table(s): **Professional Negligence:** London **Band 4** p.421

Ferguson, Iain
Table(s): **Clinical Negligence:** Scotland (Bar) **Band 1** p.510, **Professional Negligence:** Scotland (Bar) **Band 1** p.523

Ferguson, Stephen Michael
Table(s): **Crime:** London **Band 6** p.174, **Financial Crime:** London **Band 2** p.267

Fernyhough, Richard
Profile: p.600
Table(s): **Construction:** London **Band 2** p.146, **International Arbitration: Arbitrators:** London **Band 1** p.335

Ferrier, Susan
Table(s): **Crime:** Wales & Chester (Bar) **Band 1** p.191

Ferris, Shaun
Profile: p.600
Table(s): **Personal Injury:** London **Band 3** p.368

Fetherstonhaugh, Guy
Profile: p.600
Table(s): **Real Estate Litigation:** London **Band 1** p.442

Field, Julian
Table(s): **Property Damage:** London **Band 2** p.433

Fieldsend, James
Profile: p.600
Table(s): **Real Estate Litigation:** London **Band 2** p.443

Finch, Nadine
Table(s): **Civil Liberties & Human Rights:** London **Band 3** p.82, **Immigration:** London **Band 2** p.297

Findlay, James
Profile: p.600
Table(s): **Environment:** London **Band 3** p.231, **Licensing:** London **Band 2** p.337, **Local Government:** London **Band 3** p.340, **Planning:** London **Band 5** p.386

Findlay, James
Profile: p.600
Table(s): **Administrative & Public Law:** Scotland (Bar) **Band 2** p.507, **Planning & Environment:** Scotland (Bar) **Band 2** p.522

Finnigan, Peter
Table(s): **Financial Crime:** London **Band 3** p.266

Finucane, Brendan
Table(s): **Professional Discipline:** London **Band 4** p.410

Firth, Matthew
Profile: p.600
Table(s): **Family: Matrimonial Finance:** London **Band 3** p.244

Fish, David
Table(s): **Crime:** Northern (Bar) **Band 3** p.186

Fisher, Andrew
Table(s): **Crime:** Midlands (Bar) **Band 2** p.181

Fisher, David
Table(s): **Crime:** London **Band 2** p.173

Fisher, Jonathan
Profile: p.600
Table(s): **Financial Crime:** London **Band 1** p.266, **Financial Services:** London **Band 3** p.276, **POCA Work & Asset Forfeiture:** All Circuits **Band 2** p.397, **Tax:** London **Band 3** p.482

Fisher, Richard
Profile: p.600
Table(s): **Chancery: Commercial:** London **Band 3** p.60, **Restructuring/Insolvency:** London **Band 1** p.455

Fisher, Richard
Table(s): **Crime:** London **Band 4** p.174, **POCA Work & Asset Forfeiture:** All Circuits **Band 2** p.397

Fitton, Michael
Table(s): **Crime:** Western (Bar) **Band 1** p.192

FitzGerald, Ben
Profile: p.600
Table(s): **Crime:** London **Band 3** p.174

Fitzgerald, Edward
Table(s): **Administrative & Public Law:** London **Band 1** p.27, **Civil Liberties & Human Rights:** London **Star individuals** p.81, **Crime:** London **Star individuals** p.173, **Extradition:** London **Star individuals** p.240

Fitzgerald, Elizabeth
Table(s): **Real Estate Litigation:** London **Band 3** p.443

FitzGerald, Susanna
Table(s): **Licensing:** London **Band 1** p.337

FitzGibbon, Francis
Table(s): **Crime:** London **Band 4** p.173

Fitzpatrick, Brian
Table(s): **Personal Injury:** Scotland (Bar) **Band 2** p.520

Fitzpatrick, Edward
Table(s): **Social Housing:** London **Band 2** p.471

Fitzpatrick, Francis
Table(s): **Tax:** London **Band 1** p.482

Flanagan, Hugh
Profile: p.601
Table(s): **Planning:** London **Up-and-coming individuals** p.386

Flanagan, Julia
Profile: p.601
Table(s): **Crime:** London **Band 4** p.174

Flenley, William
Profile: p.601
Table(s): **Professional Negligence:** London **Band 2** p.420

Flesch, Michael
Table(s): **Tax:** London **Band 1** p.482, **Tax: Private Client:** London **Band 2** p.488

Fletcher, Andrew
Table(s): **Commercial Dispute Resolution:** London **Band 5** p.109

Fletcher, James
Profile: p.601
Table(s): **POCA Work & Asset Forfeiture:** All Circuits **Band 1** p.397

Fletcher, Stephen
Profile: p.601
Table(s): **Real Estate Litigation:** North Eastern (Bar) **Band 2** p.451

Flint, Charles
Table(s): **Financial Services:** London **Star individuals** p.276, **Mediators:** All Circuits **Band 4** p.348, **Professional Discipline:** London **Band 2** p.410

Flynn, James
Table(s): **Competition Law:** London **Band 1** p.142

Flynn, Vernon
Table(s): **Commercial Dispute Resolution:** London **Band 2** p.109, **International Arbitration: General Commercial & Insurance:** London **Band 2** p.328, **Offshore:** London **Band 3** p.353, **Shipping & Commodities:** London **Band 3** p.465

Fodder, Martin
Profile: p.601
Table(s): **Employment:** London **Band 4** p.208

Forbes Smith, Henry
Table(s): **Banking & Finance:** London **Band 4** p.50

Ford, Charlotte
Profile: p.601
Table(s): **Chancery: Traditional:** London **Up-and-coming individuals** p.67

Ford, Jeremy
Profile: p.601
Table(s): **Personal Injury:** London **Band 2** p.368

Ford, Michael
Table(s): **Employment:** London **Band 4** p.207, **Employment:** Western (Bar) **Band 1** p.223

Ford, Sarah
Table(s): **Competition Law:** London **Band 2** p.142, **Telecommunications:** London **Band 3** p.491

Ford, Steven
Table(s): **Personal Injury:** London **Band 3** p.367

Forde, Martin
Table(s): **Clinical Negligence:** London **Band 2** p.92, **Professional Discipline:** London **Band 1** p.410

Fordham, Judith
Table(s): **Family/Matrimonial:** Northern (Bar) **Band 1** p.258

Fordham, Michael
Table(s): **Administrative & Public Law:** London **Star individuals** p.27, **Civil Liberties & Human Rights:** London **Star individuals** p.81, **Environment:** London **Band 2** p.231, **European Law:** London **Band 2** p.237, **Immigration:** London **Star individuals** p.297

Forgan, Hugh
Table(s): **Crime:** London **Band 6** p.174

Forlin, Gerard
Profile: p.601
Table(s): **Health & Safety:** London **Band 3** p.291

Formby, Emily
Profile: p.602
Table(s): **Clinical Negligence:** London **Band 2** p.93, **Personal Injury:** London **Band 3** p.368

Forrest, Alastair
Table(s): **Clinical Negligence:** Northern (Bar) **Band 1** p.103

Forsdick, David
Table(s): **Administrative & Public Law:** London **New Silks** p.27, **Environment:** London **New Silks** p.231, **Local Government:** London **New Silks** p.340, **Planning:** London **New Silks** p.386

Forshall, Isabella
Table(s): **Crime:** London **Band 3** p.173

Forshaw, Sarah
Table(s): **Crime:** London **Band 3** p.173

Forshaw, Simon
Profile: p.602
Table(s): **Employment:** London **Band 2** p.208

Forster, Sarah
Table(s): **Family: Children:** London **Band 2** p.245

Forster, Tom
Profile: p.602
Table(s): **Crime:** London **Band 2** p.174, **Financial Crime:** London **Band 1** p.267

Forsyth, Sandy
Profile: p.602
Table(s): **Clinical Negligence:** Scotland (Bar) **Band 3** p.510

Forte, Timothy
Profile: p.602
Table(s): **Crime:** London **Band 4** p.174

Fortson, Rudi
Table(s): **Crime:** London **Band 5** p.173, **Financial Crime:** London **Band 4** p.266

Fortt, Russell
Table(s): **Police Law: Mainly Defendant:** All Circuits **Band 3** p.402

Fortune, Malcolm
Table(s): **Professional Discipline:** London **Band 4** p.411

Foskett, Rosanna
Profile: p.602
Table(s): Chancery: Commercial: London Band 4 p.60

Foster, Alison
Table(s): Administrative & Public Law: London Band 3 p.27, Professional Discipline: London Band 1 p.410, Tax: Indirect Tax: London Band 2 p.486

Foster, Catherine
Profile: p.602
Table(s): Personal Injury: London Band 1 p.368, Personal Injury: Industrial Disease: London p.368

Foster, Charles
Profile: p.603
Table(s): Clinical Negligence: London Band 4 p.93, Professional Discipline: London Band 1 p.411

Foster, Ian
Table(s): Real Estate Litigation: Northern (Bar) Band 3 p.452

Fothergill, Francesca
Table(s): Family/Matrimonial: Northern (Bar) Band 2 p.258

Fottrell, Deirdre
Profile: p.603
Table(s): Family: Children: London Band 2 p.245

Fox, Nicola
Profile: p.603
Table(s): Family: Matrimonial Finance: London Band 4 p.244, Family: Children: London Band 2 p.244

Fox, Simon
Table(s): Clinical Negligence: Midlands (Bar) Band 1 p.102, Clinical Negligence: Western (Bar) Star individuals p.106

Foxton, David
Table(s): Banking & Finance: London Band 1 p.49, Commercial Dispute Resolution: London Band 1 p.109, Energy & Natural Resources: London Band 1 p.226, Insurance: London Band 1 p.315, International Arbitration: General Commercial & Insurance: London Band 1 p.328

Foy, John
Profile: p.603
Table(s): Personal Injury: London Band 2 p.367

Francis, Andrew
Profile: p.603
Table(s): Real Estate Litigation: London Band 2 p.443

Francis, Derek
Profile: p.603
Table(s): Tax: Scotland (Bar) Band 2 p.527

Francis, Edward
Table(s): Chancery: Commercial: London Band 2 p.60, Real Estate Litigation: London Band 5 p.443

Francis, Nicholas
Profile: p.603
Table(s): Family: Matrimonial Finance: London Band 1 p.244

Francis, Robert
Profile: p.603
Table(s): Clinical Negligence: London Band 1 p.92, Inquests & Public Inquiries: London Band 3 p.309, Professional Discipline: London Band 2 p.410

Franklin, Kim
Table(s): Construction: London Band 3 p.147

Fransman, Laurie
Table(s): Immigration: London Star individuals p.297

Fraser, Orlando
Table(s): Fraud: Civil: London New Silks p.281

Fraser, Peter D
Profile: p.603
Table(s): Construction: London Band 2 p.146, Professional Negligence: Technology & Construction: London Band 2 p.428

Fraser, Vincent
Profile: p.604
Table(s): Environment: Northern (Bar) Band 1 p.235, Local Government: Northern (Bar) Band 2 p.344, Planning: Northern (Bar) Band 1 p.394

Fraser Butlin, Sarah
Profile: p.604
Table(s): Employment: London Up-and-coming individuals p.208

Fraser-Urquhart, Andrew
Profile: p.604
Table(s): Planning: London Band 4 p.386

Frazer, Lucy
Table(s): Restructuring/Insolvency: London Band 5 p.455

Freedman, Clive
Table(s): Commercial Dispute Resolution: London Band 3 p.109, Fraud: Civil: London Band 2 p.281

Freedman, Clive
Profile: p.604
Table(s): Information Technology: London Band 2 p.304

Freeman, Lisa
Table(s): POCA Work & Asset Forfeiture: All Circuits Band 3 p.397

Freeman, Peter
Table(s): Personal Injury: London Band 1 p.368

French, Paul
Table(s): Restructuring/Insolvency: Western (Bar) Band 1 p.463

Friday, Stephen
Table(s): Personal Injury: North Eastern (Bar) Band 1 p.379

Friedman, Bobby
Table(s): Pensions: London Up-and-coming individuals p.363

Friedman, Danny
Profile: p.604
Table(s): Administrative & Public Law: London Band 4 p.27, Civil Liberties & Human Rights: London Band 2 p.81, Crime: London Band 3 p.173, Inquests & Public Inquiries: London Band 3 p.309

Friedman, David
Profile: p.604
Table(s): Construction: London Band 2 p.146, Professional Negligence: Technology & Construction: London Band 2 p.428

Friel, John
Profile: p.604
Table(s): Education: London Band 2 p.203

Friel, Michele
Table(s): Family/Matrimonial: Midlands (Bar) Band 1 p.254

Fripp, Eric
Table(s): Immigration: London Band 2 p.297

Friston, Mark
Table(s): Costs Litigation: Northern (Bar) Band 1 p.162

Fryer-Spedding, James
Profile: p.604
Table(s): Chancery: Northern (Bar) Band 2 p.75, Commercial Dispute Resolution: Northern (Bar) Band 2 p.127

Fullwood, Adam
Profile: p.604
Table(s): Administrative & Public Law: Northern (Bar) Band 1 p.39, Civil Liberties & Human Rights: Northern (Bar) Band 2 p.89, Court of Protection: Health & Welfare: All Circuits Band 2 p.165, Social Housing: Northern (Bar) Band 1 p.476

Furber, John
Table(s): Real Estate Litigation: London Band 3 p.442

Furlong, Richard
Profile: p.605
Table(s): Financial Crime: London Band 2 p.267

Furness, Corin
Table(s): Motor Insurance Fraud: All Circuits Band 2 p.350, Personal Injury: North Eastern (Bar) Band 2 p.379

Furness, Jonathan
Table(s): Family/Matrimonial: Wales & Chester (Bar) Band 1 p.261

Furness, Michael
Table(s): Chancery: Traditional: London Band 2 p.67, Charities: London Band 2 p.79, Offshore: London Band 3 p.353, Pensions: London Band 1 p.363, Tax: London Band 2 p.482

Furniss, Richard
Table(s): Clinical Negligence: London Band 1 p.93, Personal Injury: London Band 3 p.368

Furst, Stephen
Profile: p.605
Table(s): Construction: London Band 1 p.146, International Arbitration: Construction/Engineering: London Band 2 p.333, International Arbitration: Arbitrators: London Band 1 p.335

G

Gaisman, Jonathan
Table(s): Commercial Dispute Resolution: London Star individuals p.109, Insurance: London Band 1 p.315, International Arbitration: General Commercial & Insurance: London Band 4 p.328, Professional Negligence: London Band 1 p.420

Gaitskell, Robert
Profile: p.605
Table(s): International Arbitration: Arbitrators: London Band 1 p.335

Galbraith, Amber
Profile: p.605
Table(s): Personal Injury: Scotland (Bar) Band 1 p.520

Galbraith-Marten, Jason
Profile: p.605
Table(s): Employment: London New Silks p.207

Gallacher, Kirsty
Profile: p.605
Table(s): Family/Matrimonial: Midlands (Bar) Up-and-coming individuals p.254

Gallafent, Kate
Table(s): Administrative & Public Law: London New Silks p.27, Civil Liberties & Human Rights: London New Silks p.81, Data Protection: London New Silks p.195, Employment: London New Silks p.207, Professional Discipline: London New Silks p.410, Sport: London New Silks p.478

Gallagher, Caoilfhionn
Table(s): Administrative & Public Law: London Band 2 p.28, Civil Liberties & Human Rights: London Band 2 p.82, Community Care: London Band 2 p.132, Inquests & Public Inquiries: London Band 2 p.309, Police Law: Mainly Claimant: All Circuits Band 2 p.400

Gallivan, Terence
Profile: p.605
Table(s): Social Housing: London Band 2 p.471

Galloway, Malcolm
Table(s): Environment: London Band 3 p.231, Health & Safety: London Band 3 p.291

Galvin, Kieran
Profile: p.605
Table(s): Crime: London Band 5 p.174

Gammie, Malcolm
Table(s): Tax: London Band 1 p.482

Gannon, Kevin
Table(s): Social Housing: London Band 3 p.471

Garcha, Gurdeep
Table(s): Crime: Midlands (Bar) Band 3 p.181

Gardiner, Bruce
Table(s): Employment: London Band 4 p.208

Gardiner, John
Table(s): Tax: London Star individuals p.482

Gardiner, Sebastian
Table(s): Crime: London Band 5 p.174

Gardner, Alan
Table(s): Crime: South Eastern (Bar) Band 4 p.188

Gardner, Piers
Table(s): Civil Liberties & Human Rights: London Band 4 p.82

Garlick, Paul
Profile: p.606
Table(s): Extradition: London Band 2 p.240

Garnham, Clare
Table(s): Family/Matrimonial: North Eastern (Bar) Up-and-coming individuals p.256

Garnham, Neil
Profile: p.606
Table(s): Administrative & Public Law: London Band 2 p.27, Inquests & Public Inquiries: London Star individuals p.309

Garnier, Edward
Profile: p.606
Table(s): Defamation/Privacy: London Band 2 p.199

Garrett, Lucy
Profile: p.606
Table(s): Construction: London Band 2 p.147, International Arbitration: Construction/Engineering: London Band 2 p.333, Professional Negligence: Technology & Construction: London Band 3 p.428

Garvie, Carl
Table(s): Commercial Dispute Resolution: Midlands (Bar) Band 2 p.125

Gask, Alex
Table(s): Civil Liberties & Human Rights: London Band 4 p.82, Police Law: Mainly Claimant: All Circuits Band 2 p.400

Gatty, Daniel
Profile: p.606
Table(s): Real Estate Litigation: London Band 4 p.443

Gaunt, Jonathan
Profile: p.606
Table(s): Agriculture & Rural Affairs: London Band 3 p.41, Real Estate Litigation: London Band 1 p.442

Gavaghan, Jonathan
Profile: p.606
Table(s): Chancery: Commercial: London Band 4 p.60, Partnership: London Band 1 p.359

Geddes, Gillian
Table(s): Family: Children: London Band 4 p.245

Gee, Caroline
Table(s): Family/Matrimonial: Northern (Bar) Band 3 p.258

Gee, Steven
Table(s): Commercial Dispute Resolution: London Band 4 p.109, Fraud: Civil: London Band 3 p.281, International Arbitration: General Commercial & Insurance: London Band 4 p.328, Shipping & Commodities: London Band 4 p.465

Gee, Toby
Table(s): Product Liability: London Band 3 p.406

Geekie, Charles
Profile: p.607
Table(s): Family: Children: London Band 1 p.245

Genn, Yvette
Table(s): Employment: London Band 5 p.208

Gentleman, Tom
Table(s): Chancery: Commercial: London Up-and-coming individuals p.60

George, Andrew
Table(s): Commercial Dispute Resolution: London Band 2 p.110, Financial Services: London Band 1 p.276, Fraud: Civil: London Band 4 p.282

George, Charles
Table(s): Agriculture & Rural Affairs: London Band 2 p.41, Local Government: London Band 2 p.340, Planning: London Senior Statesmen p.386

George, Dean
Table(s): Crime: London Band 4 p.174, Financial Crime: London Band 4 p.267

George, Mark
Table(s): Crime: Northern (Bar) Band 3 p.186

George, Sarah
Profile: p.607
Table(s): Employment: Midlands (Bar) Band 2 p.218

Gerasimidis, Nicolas
Table(s): Crime: Western (Bar) Band 2 p.192

Gerry, Alison
Table(s): Civil Liberties & Human Rights: London Band 2 p.82, Inquests & Public Inquiries: London Band 3 p.309, Police Law: Mainly Claimant: All Circuits Band 2 p.400

Gerry, Felicity
Table(s): Crime: Midlands (Bar) New Silks p.181, Crime: South Eastern (Bar) New Silks p.188

Ghaffar, Arshad
Table(s): Aviation: London Band 3 p.47

Ghaly, Karim
Profile: p.607
Table(s): Construction: London Band 2 p.147, International Arbitration: Construction/Engineering: London Band 1 p.333

Ghosh, Julian
Profile: p.607
Table(s): Tax: London Band 1 p.482, Tax: Indirect Tax: London Band 2 p.486, Tax: Private Client: London Band 2 p.488

Ghosh, Julian
Table(s): Tax: Scotland (Bar) Star individuals p.527

Gibaud, Catherine
Table(s): Banking & Finance: London New Silks p.49

Gibb, Katherine
Table(s): Restructuring/Insolvency: Western (Bar) Band 2 p.463

Gibbon, Michael
Profile: p.607
Table(s): Chancery: Commercial: London Band 3 p.59, Company: London Band 2 p.135, Restructuring/Insolvency: London Band 4 p.455, Tax: London Band 3 p.482

Gibbons, Ellodie
Profile: p.607
Table(s): Real Estate Litigation: London Band 4 p.443

Gibbons, Sarah
Table(s): Family/Matrimonial: South Eastern (Bar) Band 2 p.259

Gibbs, Georgina
Profile: p.607
Table(s): Crime: South Eastern (Bar) Band 3 p.188

Gibbs, Patrick
Profile: p.607
Table(s): Crime: London Star individuals p.173, Financial Crime: London Star individuals p.266, Financial Crime: Corporates: London Band 1 p.266, Inquests & Public Inquiries: London Band 1 p.309, Professional Discipline: London Band 2 p.410

Gibson, Charles
Profile: p.607
Table(s): Environment: London Band 2 p.231, Health & Safety: London Band 3 p.291, Product Liability: London Star individuals p.406

Gibson, Christopher
Table(s): Clinical Negligence: London Band 1 p.92

Gibson, Nicholas
Table(s): Competition Law: London Up-and-coming individuals p.142, Telecommunications: London Up-and-coming individuals p.491

Gidney, Jonathan
Profile: p.608
Table(s): Employment: Midlands (Bar) Band 2 p.218

Giffin, Nigel
Table(s): Administrative & Public Law: London Band 1 p.27, Civil Liberties & Human Rights: London Band 2 p.81, Community Care: London Band 1 p.132, Education: London Band 1 p.203, Inquests & Public Inquiries: London Band 2 p.309, Local Government: London Star individuals p.340, Public Procurement: London Star individuals p.439

Gilchrist, David
Table(s): Chancery: Northern (Bar) Band 3 p.75, Commercial Dispute Resolution: Northern (Bar) Band 3 p.127

Gilchrist, Naomi
Profile: p.608
Table(s): Crime: Midlands (Bar) Band 2 p.181, Health & Safety: Midlands (Bar) Band 2 p.295

Gilead, Beryl
Table(s): Family/Matrimonial: Midlands (Bar) Band 2 p.254

Gillett, Emily
Profile: p.608
Table(s): Chancery: Commercial: London Band 4 p.60, Fraud: Civil: London Band 4 p.282

Gillies, Jennie
Profile: p.608
Table(s): Construction: London Band 3 p.147

Gillis, Richard
Profile: p.608
Table(s): Commercial Dispute Resolution: London Band 4 p.109, Fraud: Civil: London Band 3 p.281, Restructuring/Insolvency: London Band 5 p.455

Gillyon, Philip
Profile: p.608
Table(s): Company: London Band 2 p.135

Gilroy, Paul
Profile: p.608
Table(s): Employment: Northern (Bar) Band 1 p.221, Sport: The Regions Band 2 p.480

Giovannetti, Lisa
Table(s): Administrative & Public Law: London Band 4 p.27, Immigration: London Band 1 p.297

Girolami, Paul
Profile: p.608
Table(s): Chancery: Commercial: London Band 1 p.59, Commercial Dispute Resolution: London Band 3 p.109, Company: London Band 1 p.135, Fraud: Civil: London Band 1 p.281, Offshore: London Band 1 p.353, Restructuring/Insolvency: London Band 2 p.455

Glancy, Robert
Profile: p.609
Table(s): Clinical Negligence: London Band 1 p.92, Personal Injury: London Band 1 p.367

Glaser, Michael
Profile: p.609
Table(s): Family: Matrimonial Finance: London Band 1 p.244, Family: Children: London Band 3 p.244

Glasgow, Edwin
Table(s): Mediators: All Circuits Band 2 p.348

Glasgow, Oliver
Profile: p.609
Table(s): Crime: London Band 1 p.174

Glassbrook, Alex
Profile: p.609
Table(s): Consumer Law: London Band 3 p.156, Motor Insurance Fraud: All Circuits Band 2 p.350

Glasson, Jonathan
Profile: p.609
Table(s): Inquests & Public Inquiries: London Band 3 p.309, Product Liability: London Band 3 p.406

Gledhill, Andreas
Table(s): Restructuring/Insolvency: London Band 2 p.455

Gledhill, Orlando
Profile: p.609
Table(s): Commercial Dispute Resolution: London Band 2 p.110, Energy & Natural Resources: London Band 2 p.226, Fraud: Civil: London Band 3 p.282

Glen, David
Profile: p.609
Table(s): Data Protection: London Band 4 p.195, Defamation/Privacy: London Band 2 p.199

Glen, Ian
Table(s): Crime: London Band 5 p.173

Glenser, Peter
Profile: p.609
Table(s): Licensing: London Band 2 p.337

Glick, Ian
Table(s): Banking & Finance: London Band 2 p.49, Commercial Dispute Resolution: London Band 4 p.109, Energy & Natural Resources: London Band 1 p.226, International Arbitration: Arbitrators: London Band 1 p.335

Glover, Richard
Table(s): Local Government: London Band 2 p.340, Planning: London Band 3 p.386

Glover, Stephen J
Table(s): Family/Matrimonial: North Eastern (Bar) Band 3 p.256

Glyn, Caspar
Profile: p.610
Table(s): Employment: London Band 2 p.207, Sport: London Band 5 p.478

Glynn, Joanna
Table(s): Professional Discipline: London Band 1 p.410

Glynn, Stephen
Profile: p.610
Table(s): Personal Injury: London Band 2 p.368, Personal Injury: Industrial Disease: London p.368

Goatley, Peter
Table(s): Planning: Midlands (Bar) Band 1 p.393

Goddard, Andrew
Profile: p.610
Table(s): Construction: London Band 3 p.146, International Arbitration: Construction/Engineering: London Band 2 p.333

Goddard, Katherine L
Table(s): Crime: North Eastern (Bar) Band 2 p.184

Goddard, Suzanne
Table(s): Crime: Northern (Bar) Band 2 p.186

Godfrey, Christopher
Table(s): Family/Matrimonial: Western (Bar) Band 3 p.262

Godfrey, Hannah
Profile: p.610
Table(s): Clinical Negligence: London Band 4 p.93

Godfrey, Howard
Table(s): Crime: London Band 4 p.173

Godfrey, Lauren
Table(s): Commercial Dispute Resolution: South Eastern (Bar) Up-and-coming individuals p.129, Employment: South Eastern (Bar) Up-and-coming individuals p.222

Gohil, Pushpanjali
Table(s): Crime: Western (Bar) Band 3 p.192

Gokani, Rachna
Table(s): Financial Crime: London Up-and-coming individuals p.267

Goldberg, David
Table(s): Tax: London Star individuals p.482

Goldberg, Jonathan
Profile: p.610
Table(s): Crime: London Band 6 p.173

Goldberg, Simon
Profile: p.610
Table(s): Chancery: North Eastern (Bar) Band 3 p.74, Commercial Dispute Resolution: North Eastern (Bar) Band 2 p.126, Employment: North Eastern (Bar) Band 2 p.220

Goldring, Jenny
Profile: p.610
Table(s): Crime: London Band 5 p.174

Goldring, Jeremy
Table(s): Banking & Finance: London Band 3 p.49, Chancery: Commercial: London Band 4 p.59, Commercial Dispute Resolution: London Band 5 p.109, Company: London Band 3 p.135, Restructuring/Insolvency: London Band 5 p.455

Goldsack, Ian
Table(s): Crime: North Eastern (Bar) Band 2 p.184

Goldsmith, Jamie
Profile: p.610
Table(s): Commercial Dispute Resolution: London Band 1 p.110

Goldsmith, Joseph
Profile: p.611
Table(s): Chancery: Traditional: London Band 2 p.67, Court of Protection: Property & Affairs: All Circuits Band 1 p.169, Pensions: London Band 2 p.363

Goldstone, David
Table(s): **Shipping & Commodities:** London **Band 1** p.465

Gollancz, David
Profile: p.611
Table(s): **Public Procurement:** London **Band 2** p.439

Gollop, Katharine
Profile: p.611
Table(s): **Clinical Negligence:** London **Band 2** p.93, **Professional Discipline:** London **Band 3** p.411

Goodall, Emma
Table(s): **Crime:** London **Band 6** p.174

Goodall, Patrick
Profile: p.611
Table(s): **Banking & Finance:** London **New Silks** p.49, **Commercial Dispute Resolution:** London **New Silks** p.109, **Fraud: Civil:** London **New Silks** p.281, **Insurance:** London **New Silks** p.315, **Professional Negligence:** London **New Silks** p.420

Goodall, Rachael
Table(s): **Family/Matrimonial:** Western (Bar) **Band 2** p.262

Goodfellow, Giles W J
Profile: p.611
Table(s): **Tax:** London **Band 2** p.482

Goodison, Adam
Profile: p.611
Table(s): **Restructuring/Insolvency:** London **Band 3** p.455

Goodman, Alex
Table(s): **Immigration:** London **Band 2** p.297, **Planning:** London **Band 5** p.386

Goodwin, Deirdre
Profile: p.611
Table(s): **Clinical Negligence:** London **Band 3** p.93

Goodwin, Nicholas
Table(s): **Family: Children:** London **New Silks** p.245, **Family/Matrimonial:** South Eastern (Bar) **New Silks** p.259

Goodwin-Gill, Guy
Table(s): **Public International Law:** London **Band 2** p.435

Goolamali, Nina
Profile: p.611
Table(s): **Personal Injury:** London **Band 2** p.368

Gorasia, Paras
Profile: p.612
Table(s): **Employment:** Northern (Bar) **Band 2** p.221

Gordon, Richard
Table(s): **Administrative & Public Law:** London **Band 1** p.27, **Civil Liberties & Human Rights:** London **Band 3** p.81, **Environment:** London **Band 2** p.231

Gore, Andrew
Table(s): **Agriculture & Rural Affairs:** South Eastern (Bar) **Band 2** p.43

Gorton, Simon
Table(s): **Employment:** Northern (Bar) **Band 2** p.221

Gott, Paul
Profile: p.612
Table(s): **Employment:** London **Band 4** p.207

Gottlieb, David
Profile: p.612
Table(s): **Crime:** London **Band 6** p.174

Goudie, James
Profile: p.612
Table(s): **Administrative & Public Law:** London **Band 2** p.27, **Education:** London **Band 2** p.203, **Employment:** London **Band 3** p.207, **Local Government:** London **Band 1** p.340, **Public Procurement:** London **Band 1** p.439

Goudie, Martin
Profile: p.612
Table(s): **Crime:** London **Band 6** p.174

Gough, Karen
Profile: p.612
Table(s): **Construction:** London **Band 4** p.147

Goulding, Jonathan
Profile: p.612
Table(s): **Consumer Law:** London **Band 1** p.156

Goulding, Paul
Table(s): **Employment:** London **Star individuals** p.207, **Sport:** London **Band 5** p.478

Gourgey, Alan
Profile: p.612
Table(s): **Chancery: Commercial:** London **Band 2** p.59, **Commercial Dispute Resolution:** London **Band 2** p.109, **Fraud: Civil:** London **Band 3** p.281, **Information Technology:** London **Band 3** p.304

Gouriet, Gerald
Profile: p.613
Table(s): **Licensing:** London **Star individuals** p.337

Gowen, Matthew
Profile: p.613
Table(s): **Crime:** South Eastern (Bar) **Band 4** p.188

Gower, Helen
Table(s): **Employment:** Western (Bar) **Band 3** p.223

Goy, David
Table(s): **Tax:** London **Band 1** p.482, **Tax: Indirect Tax:** London **Band 3** p.486

Gozem, Guy
Table(s): **Financial Crime:** The Regions **Band 1** p.275

Grabiner, Anthony
Table(s): **Banking & Finance:** London **Star individuals** p.49, **Commercial Dispute Resolution:** London **Star individuals** p.109, **Energy & Natural Resources:** London **Band 1** p.226, **Fraud: Civil:** London **Band 2** p.281

Grace, Jonathan
Table(s): **Personal Injury:** Northern (Bar) **Band 1** p.380

Graham, Charles
Profile: p.613
Table(s): **Commercial Dispute Resolution:** London **Band 4** p.109

Graham, Gareth
Table(s): **Employment:** Western (Bar) **Up-and-coming individuals** p.223

Graham, Thomas
Profile: p.613
Table(s): **Chancery: Commercial:** London **Band 4** p.60

Graham Paul, Annabel
Profile: p.613
Table(s): **Planning:** London **Up-and-coming individuals** p.386

Grahame, Angela
Profile: p.613
Table(s): **Personal Injury:** Scotland (Bar) **Band 2** p.520

Grandison, Myles
Profile: p.613
Table(s): **Extradition:** London **Band 3** p.240

Grange, Kate
Table(s): **Administrative & Public Law:** London **Band 3** p.28, **Construction:** London **Band 2** p.147

Grant, Chudi
Table(s): **Crime:** Northern (Bar) **Band 3** p.186

Grant, David E
Table(s): **Pensions:** London **Band 2** p.363

Grant, Edward
Table(s): **Planning:** London **Band 5** p.386

Grant, Gary
Profile: p.613
Table(s): **Licensing:** London **Band 1** p.337

Grant, Marcus
Profile: p.614
Table(s): **Motor Insurance Fraud:** All Circuits **Band 1** p.350, **Personal Injury:** London **Band 1** p.368

Grant, Thomas
Table(s): **Chancery: Commercial:** London **Band 4** p.59, **Professional Negligence:** London **Band 4** p.420, **Real Estate Litigation:** London **Band 4** p.442

Grant-Hutchison, Peter
Profile: p.614
Table(s): **Employment:** Scotland (Bar) **Band 2** p.516

Grantham, Andrew
Profile: p.614
Table(s): **Chancery:** Northern (Bar) **Band 2** p.75, **Commercial Dispute Resolution:** Northern (Bar) **Band 2** p.127

Gration, Michael
Table(s): **Family: Children:** London **Band 3** p.245

Grattage, Stephen
Table(s): **Crime:** Northern (Bar) **Band 3** p.186, **Financial Crime:** The Regions **Band 1** p.275

Gray, Jennifer
Table(s): **Crime:** South Eastern (Bar) **Band 4** p.188

Gray, Justin
Profile: p.614
Table(s): **Family/Matrimonial:** North Eastern (Bar) **Band 3** p.256

Gray, Margaret
Table(s): **Public Procurement:** London **Band 3** p.439

Gray, Nichola
Table(s): **Family: Matrimonial Finance:** London **Band 1** p.244

Gray, Peter
Profile: p.614
Table(s): **Health & Safety:** Scotland (Bar) **Star individuals** p.518

Greaney, Nicola
Profile: p.614
Table(s): **Community Care:** London **Band 2** p.132, **Court of Protection: Health & Welfare:** All Circuits **Band 1** p.165, **Professional Discipline:** London **Band 4** p.411

Greaney, Paul
Profile: p.614
Table(s): **Crime:** North Eastern (Bar) **Band 1** p.184, **Sport:** The Regions **Band 2** p.480

Greatorex, Paul
Profile: p.614
Table(s): **Court of Protection: Health & Welfare:** All Circuits **Band 2** p.165, **Education:** London **Band 3** p.203, **Local Government:** London **Band 4** p.340

Green, Alison
Profile: p.615
Table(s): **Insurance:** London **Band 4** p.316

Green, Andrew
Table(s): **Financial Services:** London **Band 2** p.276, **Insurance:** London **Band 3** p.315, **International Arbitration: General Commercial & Insurance:** London **Band 3** p.328, **Media & Entertainment:** London **Band 3** p.345, **Sport:** London **Band 4** p.478

Green, Brian
Table(s): **Chancery: Traditional:** London **Star individuals** p.67, **Offshore:** London **Band 1** p.353, **Pensions:** London **Star individuals** p.363, **Trusts:** London **Band 1** p.498

Green, David
Profile: p.615
Table(s): **Chancery:** Northern (Bar) **Band 3** p.75, **Real Estate Litigation:** Northern (Bar) **Band 2** p.452

Green, Doré
Profile: p.615
Table(s): **Property Damage:** London **Band 2** p.433

Green, Michael
Profile: p.615
Table(s): **Company:** London **Band 2** p.135, **Tax:** London **Band 3** p.482

Green, Patrick
Profile: p.615
Table(s): **Employment:** London **Band 4** p.207

Green, Robin
Profile: p.615
Table(s): **Local Government:** London **Band 4** p.340, **Planning:** London **Band 4** p.386

Green, Timothy
Table(s): **Environment:** Midlands (Bar) **Band 2** p.235, **Health & Safety:** Midlands (Bar) **Band 2** p.295, **POCA Work & Asset Forfeiture:** All Circuits **Band 3** p.397

Greenhalgh, Emma
Table(s): **Family/Matrimonial:** Northern (Bar) **Up-and-coming individuals** p.258

Greenhalgh, Jane
Profile: p.615
Table(s): **Crime:** Northern (Bar) **Band 3** p.186

Greenhill, Julian
Table(s): **Real Estate Litigation:** London **Band 2** p.443

Greenwood, Paul
Table(s): **Chancery: Commercial:** London **Band 2** p.60, **Company:** London **Band 2** p.135

Gregory, Julian
Table(s): **Competition Law:** London **Band 2** p.142

Gregory, Karen
Table(s): **Family/Matrimonial:** Northern (Bar) **Band 3** p.258

Gregory, Peter
Table(s): **Personal Injury:** Northern (Bar) **Band 2** p.380

Gregory, Richard
Table(s): **Personal Injury:** London **Band 3** p.368

Gregory, Richard
Table(s): **Personal Injury:** Midlands (Bar) **Band 2** p.377

Grennan, Barry
Table(s): **Crime:** Northern (Bar) **Band 1** p.186

Grennan, Debbie
Table(s): **Employment:** Western (Bar) **Band 1** p.223

Grey, Eleanor
Table(s): **Data Protection:** London **Band 1** p.195, **Inquests & Public Inquiries:** London **Band 1** p.309, **Professional Discipline:** London **Band 4** p.410

Grey, Robert
Table(s): **Crime:** Western (Bar) **Band 3** p.192

Grey, Siobhan
Table(s): Financial Crime: London Band 2 p.267

Grice, Timothy
Table(s): Clinical Negligence: Western (Bar) Band 1 p.106, Personal Injury: Western (Bar) Band 1

Grief, Alison
Table(s): Family: Children: London Band 2 p.245

Grieves, Edward
Table(s): Civil Liberties & Human Rights: London Band 4 p.82

Griffin, Lynn
Table(s): Professional Discipline: London Band 2 p.411

Griffin, Margaret
Table(s): Chancery: North Eastern (Bar) Band 2 p.74, Real Estate Litigation: North Eastern (Bar) Band 2 p.451

Griffin, Nicholas
Profile: p.615
Table(s): Inquests & Public Inquiries: London Band 2 p.309

Griffiths, Ben
Table(s): Company: London Band 2 p.135, Restructuring/Insolvency: London Band 3 p.455

Griffiths, Courtenay
Table(s): Crime: London Band 1 p.173, Crime: International Criminal Law: London p.173, Financial Crime: London Band 4 p.266

Griffiths, Martin
Table(s): Employment: London Band 2 p.207

Griffiths, Peter
Table(s): Chancery: Commercial: London Band 3 p.60, Company: London Band 3 p.135

Griffiths, Peter
Profile: p.615
Table(s): Financial Crime: London Band 4 p.266

Griffiths, Roger
Table(s): Crime: Wales & Chester (Bar) Band 2 p.191

Grime, Stephen
Table(s): Clinical Negligence: Northern (Bar) Band 1 p.103, Personal Injury: Northern (Bar) Band 1 p.380

Grocott, Susan
Table(s): Family/Matrimonial: Northern (Bar) Band 2 p.258

Grodzinski, Sam
Table(s): Administrative & Public Law: London Band 3 p.27, Civil Liberties & Human Rights: London Band 2 p.81, Education: London Band 2 p.203, Local Government: London Band 4 p.340, Tax: Indirect Tax: London Band 2 p.486

Ground, Richard
Profile: p.616
Table(s): Planning: London Band 2 p.386

Groves, Hugo
Table(s): Chancery: North Eastern (Bar) Band 2 p.74, Commercial Dispute Resolution: North Eastern (Bar) Band 1 p.126, Restructuring/Insolvency: North Eastern (Bar) Band 1 p.461

Groves, Hugo
Table(s): Restructuring/Insolvency: London Band 4 p.455

Grubeck, Nikolaus
Table(s): Administrative & Public Law: London Up-and-coming individuals p.28

Gruder, Jeffrey
Table(s): Banking & Finance: London Band 4 p.49, Commercial Dispute Resolution: London Band 5 p.109, International Arbitration: General Commercial & Insurance: London Band 3 p.328

Grundy, Nicholas
Profile: p.616
Table(s): Social Housing: London Band 2 p.471

Grundy, Nigel
Table(s): Employment: Northern (Bar) Band 2 p.221, Professional Discipline: The Regions Band 2 p.417

Grundy, Philip
Table(s): Personal Injury: Northern (Bar) Band 1 p.380

Grunwald, Henry
Profile: p.616
Table(s): Crime: London Band 4 p.173

Guest, Peter
Profile: p.616
Table(s): Financial Crime: London Band 2 p.267

Guha, Anita
Table(s): Family: Children: London Band 3 p.245

Guirguis, Sheren
Table(s): Family/Matrimonial: Northern (Bar) Band 2 p.258

Gumbel, Elizabeth-Anne
Table(s): Clinical Negligence: London Band 1 p.92, Personal Injury: London Star individuals p.367

Gumbs, Annette P
Table(s): Employment: Northern (Bar) Band 1 p.221

Gun Cuninghame, Julian
Profile: p.616
Table(s): Consumer Law: London Band 3 p.156

Gunaratna, Kavan
Table(s): Chancery: Commercial: London Band 3 p.60, Real Estate Litigation: London Band 4 p.443

Gunning, Alexander
Profile: p.616
Table(s): Commercial Dispute Resolution: London Band 5 p.109, Energy & Natural Resources: London Band 4 p.226, International Arbitration: General Commercial & Insurance: London Band 3 p.328, International Arbitration: Construction/Engineering: London Band 2 p.333, Shipping & Commodities: London Band 4 p.465

Gupta, Mamta
Profile: p.616
Table(s): Clinical Negligence: Midlands (Bar) Up-and-coming individuals p.102

Gupta, Teertha
Table(s): Family: Children: London Band 1 p.245

Guthrie, Cara
Table(s): Clinical Negligence: London Band 1 p.93

Guthrie, James
Table(s): Administrative & Public Law: London Band 4 p.27

H

Habboo, Camille
Profile: p.616
Table(s): Family: Children: London Band 3 p.245

Hacker, Richard
Table(s): Offshore: London Band 2 p.353

Hackett, Philip
Profile: p.616
Table(s): Financial Crime: London Band 2 p.266

Hadley, Richard
Table(s): Family/Matrimonial: Midlands (Bar) Band 2 p.254

Hagen, Dakis
Profile: p.616
Table(s): Chancery: Commercial: London Band 2 p.60, Chancery: Traditional: London Band 3 p.67, Offshore: London Band 1 p.353, Trusts: London Band 1 p.498

Haggan, Nicholas
Table(s): Health & Safety: Western (Bar) Band 1 p.296

Haines, David
Table(s): Personal Injury: Western (Bar) Band 3

Hajducki, Andrew
Table(s): Personal Injury: Scotland (Bar) Band 1 p.520

Hajimitsis, Anthony
Table(s): Family/Matrimonial: North Eastern (Bar) Band 1 p.256

Hale, Charles
Table(s): Family: Matrimonial Finance: London Band 3 p.244, Family: Children: London Band 3 p.244

Hales, Sally-Ann
Profile: p.617
Table(s): Financial Crime: London Band 4 p.266

Halkerston, Graeme
Table(s): Chancery: Commercial: London Band 3 p.60

Hall, Andrew
Table(s): Crime: London Band 3 p.173

Hall, Chris
Table(s): Intellectual Property: London Up-and-coming individuals p.322

Hall, Jeremy
Table(s): Family/Matrimonial: South Eastern (Bar) Band 3 p.259

Hall, Jonathan
Table(s): Administrative & Public Law: London New Silks p.27, POCA Work & Asset Forfeiture: All Circuits New Silks p.397

Hall, Matthew
Profile: p.617
Table(s): Real Estate Litigation: Northern (Bar) Band 2 p.452

Hall, Melanie
Profile: p.617
Table(s): Tax: Indirect Tax: London Band 1 p.486

Hall Taylor, Alex
Profile: p.617
Table(s): Chancery: Commercial: London Band 4 p.60, Financial Services: London Band 3 p.276, Fraud: Civil: London Band 4 p.282, Professional Negligence: London Band 2 p.421

Hallam, Jacob
Profile: p.617
Table(s): Crime: London Band 3 p.174

Halliday, Patrick
Profile: p.617
Table(s): Employment: London Band 4 p.208

Hallissey, Caroline
Table(s): Clinical Negligence: London Band 1 p.93

Halliwell, Mark
Profile: p.617
Table(s): Chancery: Northern (Bar) Band 2 p.75, Commercial Dispute Resolution: Northern (Bar) Band 3 p.127, Real Estate Litigation: Northern (Bar) Band 3 p.452

Halpern, David
Profile: p.617
Table(s): Professional Negligence: London Band 2 p.420, Real Estate Litigation: London Band 4 p.442

Ham, Robert
Table(s): Chancery: Traditional: London Band 1 p.67, Offshore: London Band 2 p.353, Pensions: London Band 2 p.363, Trusts: London Band 1 p.498

Hamblin, Nicholas
Table(s): Crime: South Eastern (Bar) Band 2 p.188

Hamer, Kenneth
Profile: p.618
Table(s): Professional Discipline: London Band 3 p.411

Hames, Christopher
Table(s): Family: Children: London Band 2 p.245

Hamill, Hugh
Profile: p.618
Table(s): Personal Injury: London Band 2 p.368

Hamilton, Duncan
Profile: p.618
Table(s): Media Law: Scotland (Bar) Band 1 p.519

Hamilton, Penny
Profile: p.618
Table(s): Tax: Indirect Tax: London Band 1 p.486

Hammond, Sean
Profile: p.618
Table(s): Financial Crime: London Band 4 p.267

Hancock, Christopher
Table(s): Energy & Natural Resources: London Band 3 p.226, Insurance: London Band 1 p.315, Shipping & Commodities: London Band 2 p.465

Hancock, Maria
Table(s): Family/Matrimonial: South Eastern (Bar) Band 3 p.259

Hand, Jonathan
Table(s): Clinical Negligence: London Band 3 p.93

Handyside, Richard
Profile: p.618
Table(s): Banking & Finance: London Band 1 p.49, Commercial Dispute Resolution: London Band 2 p.109

Hanif, Saima
Profile: p.618
Table(s): Financial Services: London Band 3 p.276, Professional Discipline: London Band 5 p.411

Hankin, Jonas
Table(s): Crime: Midlands (Bar) Band 3 p.181

Hanna, Ronan
Profile: p.618
Table(s): Construction: London Band 4 p.147, Energy & Natural Resources: London Band 4 p.226, Professional Negligence: Technology & Construction: London Band 3 p.428

Hannaford, Sarah
Profile: p.618
Table(s): Construction: London Band 4 p.146, Public Procurement: London Star individuals p.439

Hannam, Timothy
Table(s): Crime: Midlands (Bar) Band 2 p.181, POCA Work & Asset Forfeiture: All Circuits Band 3 p.397

Hannett, Sarah
Table(s): Administrative & Public Law: London Band 4 p.28, Community Care: London Band 3 p.132, Education: London Band 2 p.203, Local Government: London Band 4 p.340, Planning: London Band 5 p.386

Hanretty, Gerald
Table(s): Personal Injury: Scotland (Bar) Band 1 p.520, Professional Negligence: Scotland (Bar) Band 1 p.523

Hapgood, Mark
Table(s): Banking & Finance: London Star Individuals p.49, Commercial Dispute Resolution: London Band 1 p.109, Offshore: London Band 3 p.353

Haque, Muhammed
Profile: p.619
Table(s): Personal Injury: London Band 3 p.368

Harbage, William
Profile: p.619
Table(s): Crime: London Band 4 p.173, Crime: Midlands (Bar) Band 3 p.181

Harbottle, Gwilym
Table(s): Intellectual Property: London Band 3 p.322, Media & Entertainment: London Band 2 p.345

Harding, Ben
Profile: p.619
Table(s): Commercial Dispute Resolution: Northern (Bar) Up-and-coming Individuals p.127

Harding, Jack
Profile: p.619
Table(s): Travel: International Personal Injury: London Band 2 p.495

Harding, Richard
Profile: p.619
Table(s): Construction: London Band 2 p.146, International Arbitration: Construction/Engineering: London Band 1 p.333

Hardman, Alasdair
Table(s): Employment: Scotland (Bar) Band 1 p.516

Hardwick, Matthew
Table(s): Banking & Finance: London New Silks p.49, Commercial Dispute Resolution: London New Silks p.109, Restructuring/Insolvency: London New Silks p.455

Hardy, Amanda
Profile: p.619
Table(s): Tax: Private Client: London Band 3 p.488

Hardy, John
Profile: p.619
Table(s): Extradition: London Band 2 p.240

Hare, Ivan
Table(s): Employment: London Band 4 p.208, Police Law: Mainly Defendant: All Circuits Band 3 p.402, Professional Discipline: London Band 2 p.411

Haren, Sarah
Profile: p.619
Table(s): Chancery: Traditional: London Band 4 p.67, Court of Protection: Property & Affairs: All Circuits Band 2 p.169

Hargan, James
Table(s): Family/Matrimonial: North Eastern (Bar) Band 3 p.256

Hargreaves, Simon
Profile: p.620
Table(s): Construction: London Band 2 p.146, Professional Negligence: Technology & Construction: London Band 3 p.428

Harper, Mark
Profile: p.620
Table(s): Banking & Finance: Northern (Bar) Band 1 p.57, Chancery: Northern (Bar) Band 1 p.75, Commercial Dispute Resolution: Northern (Bar) Band 1 p.127, Partnership: Northern (Bar) Band 1 p.361

Harpum, Charles
Profile: p.620
Table(s): Real Estate Litigation: London Band 2 p.443

Harries, Mark
Profile: p.620
Table(s): Crime: London Band 4 p.174, Financial Crime: London Band 2 p.267

Harrington, Patrick
Table(s): Crime: Wales & Chester (Bar) Band 1 p.191, Financial Crime: The Regions Band 1 p.275

Harris, Bethan
Table(s): Court of Protection: Health & Welfare: All Circuits Band 3 p.165, Social Housing: London Band 2 p.471

Harris, Caroline
Profile: p.620
Table(s): Crime: South Eastern (Bar) Up-and-coming individuals p.188

Harris, Christopher
Profile: p.620
Table(s): Commercial Dispute Resolution: London Band 5 p.110, Energy & Natural Resources: London Band 4 p.226, International Arbitration: General Commercial & Insurance: London Band 1 p.328

Harris, Ian
Table(s): Crime: Northern (Bar) Band 2 p.186

Harris, Lucinda
Profile: p.620
Table(s): Employment: London Band 4 p.208

Harris, Luke
Profile: p.620
Table(s): Art and Cultural Property Law : London Band 1 p.45

Harris, Mark
Table(s): Environment: London Band 1 p.231, Health & Safety: London Band 1 p.291

Harris, Miles
Profile: p.620
Table(s): Professional Negligence: London Band 4 p.421

Harris, Paul
Table(s): Competition Law: London Band 2 p.142, Sport: London Band 1 p.478

Harris, Rebecca
Profile: p.621
Table(s): Professional Discipline: London Band 4 p.411

Harris, Roger
Table(s): Clinical Negligence: London Band 4 p.93, Personal Injury: London Band 2 p.368

Harris, Russell
Table(s): Planning: London Band 1 p.386

Harrison, Caroline
Profile: p.621
Table(s): Clinical Negligence: London Band 3 p.92

Harrison, Christopher
Profile: p.621
Table(s): Chancery: Commercial: London Band 2 p.60, Company: London Band 2 p.135, Fraud: Civil: London Band 2 p.282

Harrison, Keith
Table(s): Crime: Northern (Bar) Band 2 p.186

Harrison, Nicholas
Profile: p.621
Table(s): Chancery: Commercial: London Band 4 p.60, Fraud: Civil: London Band 2 p.282, Offshore: London Band 1 p.353

Harrison, Peter
Table(s): Personal Injury: Northern (Bar) Band 2 p.380

Harrison, Philomena
Profile: p.621
Table(s): Real Estate Litigation: London Band 4 p.443

Harrison, Richard
Profile: p.621
Table(s): Family: Matrimonial Finance: London Band 2 p.244, Family: Children: London Band 2 p.244

Harrison, Richard
Profile: p.621
Table(s): Insurance: London Band 3 p.316

Harrison, Robert
Table(s): Personal Injury: Wales & Chester (Bar) Band 2 p.383

Harrison, Sally
Table(s): Family/Matrimonial: Northern (Bar) Band 1 p.258

Harrison, Sarah
Profile: p.621
Table(s): Chancery: North Eastern (Bar) Band 1 p.74

Harrison, Stephanie
Table(s): Administrative & Public Law: London Band 4 p.27, Civil Liberties & Human Rights: London Band 4 p.81, Immigration: London Band 2 p.297

Harrop Griffiths, Hilton
Table(s): Administrative & Public Law: London Band 3 p.28

Harrop-Griffiths, Hilton
Table(s): Community Care: London Band 1 p.132, Local Government: London Band 3 p.340

Harry, Timothy
Profile: p.621
Table(s): Real Estate Litigation: London Band 2 p.443

Hart, David
Table(s): Clinical Negligence: London Band 3 p.92, Environment: London Band 1 p.231

Hart, Joseph
Profile: p.622
Table(s): Crime: Northern (Bar) Band 3 p.186, Environment: Northern (Bar) Band 1 p.235

Hartley, Richard
Table(s): Personal Injury: Northern (Bar) Band 1 p.380

Harvey, Michael
Table(s): Insurance: London Band 4 p.315, Professional Negligence: London Band 2 p.420

Harvey, Richard
Table(s): Crime: International Criminal Law: London p.175

Harwood, Richard
Profile: p.622
Table(s): Environment: London Band 3 p.231, Local Government: London Band 3 p.340, Planning: London Band 4 p.386

Haskell, James
Table(s): Crime: Western (Bar) Band 3 p.192

Hatfield, Sally
Table(s): Clinical Negligence: Northern (Bar) Band 1 p.103

Hattan, Simon
Profile: p.622
Table(s): Banking & Finance: London Band 3 p.50, Chancery: Commercial: London Band 3 p.60, Financial Services: London Band 1 p.276, Fraud: Civil: London Band 3 p.282

Haughey, Caroline
Profile: p.622
Table(s): Crime: London Band 5 p.174

Havers, Philip
Table(s): Administrative & Public Law: London Band 1 p.27, Civil Liberties & Human Rights: London Band 2 p.81, Clinical Negligence: London Band 1 p.92, Professional Discipline: London Band 3 p.410

Hawes, Neil
Profile: p.622
Table(s): Financial Crime: London Band 3 p.267

Hawkes, Malcolm
Table(s): Extradition: London Up-and-coming individuals p.240

Hay, David
Profile: p.622
Table(s): Employment: Scotland (Bar) Band 3 p.516

Hay, Deborah
Table(s): Education: London Band 3 p.203

Hay, Fiona
Table(s): Family/Matrimonial: South Eastern (Bar) Band 1 p.259

Haycroft, Anthony
Table(s): Professional Discipline: London Band 1 p.411

Haydon, Alec
Table(s): Commercial Dispute Resolution: London Band 3 p.110, Fraud: Civil: London Band 2 p.282

Hayes, John
Table(s): Family/Matrimonial: North Eastern (Bar) Band 2 p.256

Hayhow, Robert
Table(s): Family/Matrimonial: Scotland (Bar) Band 2 p.517

Hayman, George
Profile: p.622
Table(s): Chancery: Commercial: London Band 4 p.60, Fraud: Civil: London Band 3 p.282

Haynes, Matthew
Profile: p.622
Table(s): Family/Matrimonial: Midlands (Bar) Band 2 p.254

Haynes, Peter
Table(s): Crime: International Criminal Law: London p.175

Hays, William
Profile: p.623
Table(s): POCA Work & Asset Forfeiture: All Circuits Up-and-coming individuals p.397

Haywood, Janet
Table(s): Family/Matrimonial: South Eastern (Bar) Band 3 p.259

Haywood, Jennifer
Profile: p.623
Table(s): Partnership: London Band 2 p.359

Haywood, Marcus
Table(s): Restructuring/Insolvency: London Band 3 p.455

Haywood, Philip
Table(s): Immigration: London Band 2 p.297

Head, David
Table(s): Commercial Dispute Resolution: London Band 4 p.110, Fraud: Civil: London Band 3 p.282, Professional Negligence: London Band 4 p.421

Head, Peter
Profile: p.623
Table(s): Chancery: Commercial: London Band 4 p.60

Heal, Madeleine
Profile: p.623
Table(s): Intellectual Property: London Band 4 p.322

Heald, Jeremy
Table(s): Intellectual Property: London Up-and-coming individuals p.322

Healey, Greville
Table(s): Agriculture & Rural Affairs: London Band 2 p.41, Real Estate Litigation: London Band 2 p.443

Healy, Alexandra
Profile: p.623
Table(s): Crime: London Band 3 p.173

Healy, Sandra
Profile: p.623
Table(s): Energy & Natural Resources: London Band 4 p.226, Shipping & Commodities: London Band 4 p.465

Healy, Siobán
Table(s): Insurance: London Band 3 p.315, International Arbitration: General Commercial & Insurance: London Band 4 p.328, Shipping & Commodities: London Band 2 p.465

Hearnden, Alexis
Table(s): Court of Protection: Health & Welfare: All Circuits Band 3 p.165, Professional Discipline: London Band 5 p.411

Heath, Duncan
Table(s): Chancery: North Eastern (Bar) Up-and-coming individuals p.74

Heather, Christopher
Profile: p.623
Table(s): Real Estate Litigation: London Band 2 p.443

Heaton, David
Table(s): Clinical Negligence: Northern (Bar) Band 1 p.103, Personal Injury: Northern (Bar) Band 1 p.380

Heaton, Frances
Table(s): Family/Matrimonial: Northern (Bar) Band 2 p.258

Heaton, Laura
Profile: p.624
Table(s): Family: Matrimonial Finance: London Band 2 p.244

Heaven, Kirsten
Table(s): Inquests & Public Inquiries: London Up-and-coming individuals p.309, Police Law: Mainly Claimant: All Circuits Up-and-coming individuals p.400

Hedworth, Toby
Profile: p.624
Table(s): Crime: North Eastern (Bar) Band 2 p.184

Heeley, Michelle
Table(s): Crime: Midlands (Bar) Band 3 p.181

Heer, Deanna
Profile: p.624
Table(s): Crime: London Band 5 p.174, Health & Safety: London Band 2 p.291

Heilbron, Hilary
Table(s): International Arbitration: Arbitrators: London Band 1 p.335

Heller, Richard
Table(s): Consumer Law: London Band 2 p.156

Helme, Ian
Profile: p.624
Table(s): Defamation/Privacy: London Band 2 p.199

Helme, Ned
Table(s): Planning: London Up-and-coming individuals p.386

Helmore, Katie
Table(s): Real Estate Litigation: London Up-and-coming individuals p.443

Hemingway, Sarah
Table(s): Civil Liberties & Human Rights: London Band 4 p.82, Police Law: Mainly Claimant: All Circuits Band 2 p.400

Henderson, James
Profile: p.624
Table(s): Tax: London Band 2 p.482, Tax: Indirect Tax: London Band 3 p.486

Henderson, Lisa
Table(s): Clinical Negligence: Scotland (Bar) Band 1 p.510, Personal Injury: Scotland (Bar) Band 2 p.520

Henderson, Mark
Table(s): Immigration: London Band 1 p.297

Henderson, Neil
Profile: p.624
Table(s): Shipping & Commodities: London Up-and-coming individuals p.465

Henderson, Simon
Profile: p.624
Table(s): Construction: London Band 1 p.147, Information Technology: London Band 1 p.304, Professional Negligence: Technology & Construction: London Band 2 p.428

Henderson, William
Profile: p.624
Table(s): Chancery: Traditional: London Star individuals p.67, Charities: London Band 1 p.79, Trusts: London Band 1 p.498

Hendy, John
Profile: p.624
Table(s): Employment: London Band 1 p.207, Professional Discipline: London Band 4 p.410

Henke, Ruth
Table(s): Administrative & Public Law: Wales & Chester (Bar) Band 2 p.40, Family/Matrimonial: Wales & Chester (Bar) Band 2 p.261

Henley, Christopher
Profile: p.624
Table(s): Crime: London Band 4 p.174

Henry, Annette
Profile: p.625
Table(s): Crime: London New Silks p.173, Financial Crime: London New Silks p.266

Henry, Edward
Profile: p.625
Table(s): Crime: London Band 3 p.174

Henshaw, Andrew
Table(s): Banking & Finance: London Band 4 p.49, Commercial Dispute Resolution: London Band 5 p.109

Henton, Paul
Profile: p.625
Table(s): Aviation: London Band 3 p.47

Heppenstall, Rachael
Table(s): Family/Matrimonial: Northern (Bar) Band 3 p.258

Heppinstall, Adam
Profile: p.625
Table(s): Professional Discipline: London Band 4 p.411

Herberg, Javan
Table(s): Administrative & Public Law: London Band 2 p.27, Financial Services: London Band 1 p.276, Professional Discipline: London Band 3 p.410, Public Procurement: London Band 3 p.439, Telecommunications: London Band 2 p.491

Herbert, Douglas
Profile: p.625
Table(s): Personal Injury: Midlands (Bar) Band 2 p.377

Herbert, Mark
Profile: p.625
Table(s): Chancery: Traditional: London Band 1 p.67, Charities: London Band 2 p.79, Trusts: London Band 1 p.498

Hermer, Richard
Table(s): Administrative & Public Law: London Band 4 p.27, Civil Liberties & Human Rights: London Band 2 p.81, Environment: London Band 2 p.231, Personal Injury: London Band 2 p.367, Police Law: Mainly Claimant: All Circuits Band 2 p.400, Public International Law: London Band 3 p.435

Heslop, Martin S
Profile: p.625
Table(s): Crime: London Band 3 p.173, Licensing: London Band 3 p.337

Hewitt, Alison
Profile: p.625
Table(s): Inquests & Public Inquiries: London Band 2 p.309

Hewson, Barbara
Table(s): Court of Protection: Health & Welfare: All Circuits Band 1 p.165

Heywood, Mark
Table(s): Crime: London Band 1 p.173

Heywood, Mark
Profile: p.626
Table(s): Crime: Midlands (Bar) Band 3 p.181

Heywood, Michael
Table(s): Agriculture & Rural Affairs: London Band 3 p.41

Heyworth, Catherine Louise
Table(s): Family/Matrimonial: Wales & Chester (Bar) Band 2 p.261

Hibbert, William
Profile: p.626
Table(s): Consumer Law: London Band 1 p.156

Hickey, Alexander
Profile: p.626
Table(s): Construction: London Band 1 p.147, Energy & Natural Resources: London Band 2 p.226, International Arbitration: Construction/Engineering: London Band 2 p.333, Professional Negligence: Technology & Construction: London Band 2 p.428

Hickman, Tom
Table(s): Administrative & Public Law: London Band 1 p.28, Civil Liberties & Human Rights: London Band 1 p.82, Media & Entertainment: London Band 3 p.345, Sport: London Band 5 p.478

Hicks, Edward
Profile: p.626
Table(s): Real Estate Litigation: London Band 5 p.443

Hicks, Martin
Profile: p.626
Table(s): Crime: London Band 2 p.173, Financial Crime: London Band 3 p.266

Hicks, Michael
Table(s): Information Technology: London Band 2 p.304, Intellectual Property: London Band 1 p.322, Media & Entertainment: London Band 2 p.345

Hicks, William
Table(s): Planning: London Band 2 p.386

Higgins, Gabrielle
Table(s): Real Estate Litigation: London Band 3 p.443

Higgins, Gillian
Profile: p.626
Table(s): Crime: International Criminal Law: London p.175

Higgins, Nichola
Profile: p.626
Table(s): Crime: London Band 5 p.174

Higgins, Paul
Table(s): Motor Insurance Fraud: All Circuits Band 1 p.350

Higgins, Roisin
Profile: p.626
Table(s): Commercial Dispute Resolution: Scotland (Bar) Band 2 p.512, Intellectual Property: Scotland (Bar) Band 1 p.519

Higgo, Justin
Profile: p.627
Table(s): Chancery: Commercial: London Band 2 p.60, Commercial Dispute Resolution: London Band 3 p.110, Fraud: Civil: London Band 1 p.282

Higgs, Jonathan
Table(s): Crime: London Band 5 p.173

Hignett, Richard
Table(s): Employment: Midlands (Bar) Band 1 p.218

Hill, Henrietta
Table(s): Administrative & Public Law: London Band 2 p.28, Civil Liberties & Human Rights: London Band 2 p.82, Employment: London Band 3 p.208, Inquests & Public Inquiries: London Band 1 p.309, Police Law: Mainly Claimant: All Circuits Band 1 p.400

Hill, Jonathan
Profile: p.627
Table(s): Intellectual Property: London Band 4 p.322

Hill, Mark
Profile: p.627
Table(s): Civil Liberties & Human Rights: London Band 4 p.81

Hill, Matthew
Table(s): Clinical Negligence: London Band 4 p.93, Inquests & Public Inquiries: London Band 1 p.309

Hill, Max
Profile: p.627
Table(s): Crime: London Band 2 p.173

Hill, Michael
Profile: p.627
Table(s): Clinical Negligence: North Eastern (Bar) Band 2 p.103

Hill, Miranda
Table(s): Crime: London Band 2 p.174, Financial Crime: London Band 1 p.267, Financial Crime: Corporates: London Band 1 p.267

Hill, Raymond
Table(s): Tax: Indirect Tax: London Band 2 p.486

Hill, Rebecca
Profile: p.627
Table(s): Extradition: London Band 2 p.240

Hill, Richard G
Table(s): Banking & Finance: London Band 3 p.49, Chancery: Commercial: London Band 3 p.59, Commercial Dispute Resolution: London Band 4 p.109, Company: London Band 2 p.135, Fraud: Civil: London Band 3 p.281, Restructuring/Insolvency: London Band 3 p.455

Hill, Rina-Marie
Table(s): Crime: London Band 6 p.174

Hill, Thomas
Profile: p.627
Table(s): Planning: London Band 2 p.386

Hill, Timothy
Profile: p.627
Table(s): Shipping & Commodities: London Band 2 p.465

Hill-Smith, Alexander
Profile: p.628
Table(s): Chancery: Traditional: London Band 4 p.67

Hillas, Samantha
Table(s): Family/Matrimonial: Northern (Bar) Band 3 p.258

Hilliard, Emma
Table(s): Aviation: London Band 3 p.47

Hilliard, Jonathan
Table(s): Chancery: Traditional: London Band 2 p.67, Offshore: London Band 2 p.353, Pensions: London Band 1 p.363

Hilliard, Lexa
Table(s): Chancery: Commercial: London Band 3 p.59, Company: London Band 2 p.135, Restructuring/Insolvency: London Band 2 p.455

Hillier, Nicolas
Profile: p.628
Table(s): Personal Injury: London Band 1 p.368

Hillier, Victoria
Profile: p.628
Table(s): Administrative & Public Law: Wales & Chester (Bar) Band 2 p.40

Hillman, Gerard
Profile: p.628
Table(s): Financial Crime: London Band 4 p.267

Himsworth, Emma
Table(s): Intellectual Property: London Band 3 p.322

Hinchliffe, Nicholas
Table(s): Personal Injury: Northern (Bar) Band 2 p.380

Hinchliffe, Thomas
Profile: p.628
Table(s): Intellectual Property: London Star individuals p.322

Hines, James
Profile: p.628
Table(s): Crime: London Band 1 p.174, Extradition: London Band 2 p.240, Financial Crime: London Band 1 p.267

Hinks, Frank
Profile: p.628
Table(s): Chancery: Traditional: London Band 1 p.67, Offshore: London Band 2 p.353, Trusts: London Band 1 p.498

Hinks, Philip
Table(s): Restructuring/Insolvency: London Up-and-coming individuals p.455

Hiorns, Roger
Table(s): Personal Injury: London Band 3 p.368, Personal Injury: Industrial Disease: London p.368

Hirst, David
Table(s): Defamation/Privacy: London Band 4 p.199

Hirst, Jonathan
Table(s): Commercial Dispute Resolution: London Band 2 p.109, Insurance: London Band 2 p.315, International Arbitration: Arbitrators: London Band 1 p.335

Hirst, Karl
Table(s): Clinical Negligence: Midlands (Bar) Band 2 p.102, Personal Injury: Midlands (Bar) Band 2 p.377

Hirst, Leonie
Table(s): Civil Liberties & Human Rights: London Band 4 p.82, Community Care: London Band 3 p.132, Court of Protection: Health & Welfare: All Circuits Band 2 p.165, Immigration: London Band 4 p.297

Hislop, David
Table(s): Crime: London Band 4 p.173

Hitchcock, Patricia
Profile: p.628
Table(s): Clinical Negligence: London Band 2 p.92, Personal Injury: London Band 3 p.367

Hitchcock, Richard
Table(s): Pensions: London New Silks p.363

Hitchmough, Andrew
Table(s): Tax: Indirect Tax: London Band 2 p.486

Hobbs, Geoffrey
Table(s): Intellectual Property: London Star individuals p.322

Hobcraft, Gemma
Table(s): Extradition: London Band 3 p.240, Professional Discipline: London Band 4 p.411

Hobson, Fred
Table(s): Commercial Dispute Resolution: London Band 5 p.110

Hobson, John
Table(s): Planning: London Band 3 p.386

Hobson, John S
Table(s): Social Housing: Northern (Bar) Band 2 p.476

Hochberg, Daniel
Table(s): Chancery: Traditional: London Band 4 p.67, Offshore: London Band 2 p.353

Hochhauser, Andrew
Table(s): Commercial Dispute Resolution: London Band 3 p.109, Employment: London Star individuals p.207

Hockman, Stephen
Profile: p.629
Table(s): Environment: London Band 1 p.231, Health & Safety: London Band 3 p.291, Local Government: London Band 3 p.340

Hockton, Andrew
Profile: p.629
Table(s): Clinical Negligence: London Band 4 p.93, Professional Discipline: London Band 1 p.411

Hodge, Margaret
Table(s): Clinical Negligence: Scotland (Bar) Band 2 p.510

Hodgetts, Elizabeth
Profile: p.629
Table(s): Employment: Midlands (Bar) Band 2 p.218

Hodgetts, Glen
Table(s): Immigration: London Band 3 p.297

Hodgson, Jane
Profile: p.629
Table(s): Social Housing: London Band 3 p.471

Hodgson, Martin
Table(s): Social Housing: London Band 3 p.471

Hodivala, Jamas
Profile: p.629
Table(s): Professional Discipline: London Band 4 p.411

Hoffmann, Lord
Table(s): International Arbitration: Arbitrators: London Star individuals p.335

Hofmeyr, Stephen
Table(s): Insurance: London Band 3 p.315, Shipping & Commodities: London Band 4 p.465

Hogan, Andrew
Table(s): Costs Litigation: Midlands (Bar) Band 1 p.162

Hogarth, Andrew
Profile: p.629
Table(s): Personal Injury: London Band 2 p.367

Holbech, Charles
Profile: p.629
Table(s): Chancery: Traditional: London Band 4 p.67

Holbrook, Jon
Profile: p.629
Table(s): Social Housing: London Band 1 p.471

Holdcroft, Matthew
Profile: p.629
Table(s): Police Law: Mainly Defendant: All Circuits Band 2 p.402, Professional Discipline: London Band 5 p.411

Holden, Andrew
Table(s): Chancery: Traditional: London Band 4 p.67, Offshore: London Band 3 p.353

Holgate, David
Table(s): Local Government: London Band 3 p.340, Planning: London Band 1 p.386

Holl-Allen, Jonathan
Profile: p.629
Table(s): Clinical Negligence: London Band 2 p.93, Professional Discipline: London Band 1 p.411

Holland, Charles
Profile: p.630
Table(s): Commercial Dispute Resolution: North Eastern (Bar) Band 3 p.126, Licensing: North Eastern (Bar) Band 1 p.339

Holland, David
Table(s): Costs Litigation: London Band 3 p.160, Real Estate Litigation: London Band 2 p.442

Holland, Jordan
Profile: p.630
Table(s): Court of Protection: Property & Affairs: All Circuits Up-and-coming individuals p.169

Holland, Katharine
Table(s): Real Estate Litigation: London Band 2 p.442

Hollander, Charles
Table(s): Commercial Dispute Resolution: London Band 1 p.109, Energy & Natural Resources: London Band 4 p.226, Professional Negligence: London Band 2 p.420, Sport: London Band 4 p.478

Hollington, Robin
Profile: p.630
Table(s): Company: London Star individuals p.135, Offshore: London Band 2 p.353, Restructuring/Insolvency: London Band 3 p.455

Hollingworth, Guy
Table(s): Intellectual Property: London Band 1 p.322

Holloway, Orlando
Table(s): Employment: London Up-and-coming individuals p.208

Holme, Sophie
Table(s): Clinical Negligence: Western (Bar) Up-and-coming individuals p.106

Holmes, Elisa
Table(s): Public Procurement: London Band 3 p.439

Holmes, Josh
Profile: p.630
Table(s): Competition Law: London Star individuals p.142, European Law: London Band 2 p.237, Telecommunications: London Band 1 p.491

Holmes, Justin
Table(s): Chancery: Traditional: London Band 3 p.67, Court of Protection: Property & Affairs: All Circuits Band 1 p.169

Holmes, Michael
Table(s): Insurance: London Band 4 p.316, International Arbitration: General Commercial & Insurance: London Band 2 p.328, Shipping & Commodities: London Band 3 p.465

Holtham den Besten, Ruth
Profile: p.630
Table(s): Chancery: Commercial: London Band 4 p.60, Commercial Dispute Resolution: London Band 4 p.110, Company: London Band 3 p.135, Fraud: Civil: London Band 3 p.282

Holwill, Derek
Profile: p.630
Table(s): Clinical Negligence: London Band 4 p.93, Professional Negligence: London Band 1 p.421

Honey, Richard
Profile: p.630
Table(s): Agriculture & Rural Affairs: London Band 3 p.41, Environment: London Band 3 p.231, Local Government: London Band 4 p.340, Planning: London Band 3 p.386

Hood, Nigel
Profile: p.630
Table(s): Chancery: Commercial: London Band 4 p.60, Fraud: Civil: London Band 3 p.282

Hooper, Ben
Profile: p.630
Table(s): Administrative & Public Law: London Band 1 p.28, Civil Liberties & Human Rights: London Band 2 p.82, Data Protection: London Band 1 p.106

Hooper, David
Table(s): Crime: International Criminal Law: London p.175

Hopkins, Adrian
Profile: p.631
Table(s): Clinical Negligence: London Band 1 p.92, Professional Discipline: London Band 1 p.410

Hopkins, Paul
Table(s): Family/Matrimonial: Wales & Chester (Bar) Band 2 p.261

Hopkins, Philippa
Table(s): Shipping & Commodities: London Band 3 p.465

Hopkins, Robin
Profile: p.631
Table(s): Data Protection: London Band 1 p.195

Hopper, Stephen
Profile: p.631
Table(s): Financial Crime: London Band 4 p.267

Horan, Stephen
Table(s): Company: London Band 2 p.135

Horder, Tom
Table(s): Crime: Western (Bar) Up-and-coming individuals p.192

Horlick, Fiona
Table(s): Crime: London Band 5 p.174, Professional Discipline: London Band 2 p.411

Horlock, Timothy
Table(s): Health & Safety: Northern (Bar) Band 1 p.296, Personal Injury: Northern (Bar) Band 1 p.380

Horne, James
Table(s): Crime: North Eastern (Bar) Band 3 p.184

Horne, Michael
Profile: p.631
Table(s): Clinical Negligence: London Band 1 p.93

Horne, Wilson
Profile: p.631
Table(s): Real Estate Litigation: Northern (Bar) Band 1 p.452

Hornett, Stuart
Profile: p.631
Table(s): Chancery: Commercial: London Band 4 p.60, Real Estate Litigation: London Band 2 p.443

Horstead, Sean
Table(s): Inquests & Public Inquiries: London Band 3 p.309

Horton, Matthew
Table(s): Planning: London Band 4 p.386

Horwell, Richard
Table(s): Crime: London Band 1 p.173, Financial Crime: London Band 4 p.266, Inquests & Public Inquiries: London Band 2 p.309

Hosking, Ruth
Table(s): Shipping & Commodities: London Band 4 p.465

Hoskins, Mark
Table(s): Administrative & Public Law: London Band 3 p.27, Competition Law: London Band 1 p.142, European Law: London Band 2 p.237

Hossain, Ahmed
Table(s): Crime: London Band 6 p.174

Hossain, Sa'ad
Table(s): Commercial Dispute Resolution: London Band 4 p.109, Energy & Natural Resources: London Band 4 p.226, International Arbitration: General Commercial & Insurance: London Band 3 p.328

Hotten, Christopher
Table(s): Crime: Midlands (Bar) Band 2 p.181

Hough, Christopher
Table(s): Clinical Negligence: London Band 2 p.93

Hough, Jonathan
Profile: p.631
Table(s): Consumer Law: London New Silks p.156, Inquests & Public Inquiries: London New Silks p.309, Insurance: London New Silks p.315

Houseman, Stephen
Table(s): Commercial Dispute Resolution: London Band 5 p.109, Insurance: London Band 4 p.315

Howard, Anneli
Table(s): Competition Law: London Band 2 p.142, Telecommunications: London Band 2 p.491

Howard, Charles
Table(s): Family: Matrimonial Finance: London Band 1 p.244, Family: Children: London Band 2 p.244

Howard, Mark
Table(s): Banking & Finance: London Star individuals p.49, Commercial Dispute Resolution: London Star individuals p.109, Competition Law: London Band 2 p.142, Energy & Natural Resources: London Band 1 p.226, Fraud: Civil: London Band 1 p.281, Insurance: London Band 2 p.315, International Arbitration: General Commercial & Insurance: London Band 2 p.328, Offshore: London Band 3 p.353, Professional Negligence: London Band 1 p.420

Howard, Nicola
Table(s): Crime: London Band 4 p.174, Financial Crime: London Band 2 p.267

Howarth, Simon
Profile: p.631
Table(s): Professional Negligence: London Band 3 p.421

Howd, Stephen
Table(s): Chancery: North Eastern (Bar) Band 2 p.74, Real Estate Litigation: North Eastern (Bar) Band 1 p.451

Howe, Martin
Profile: p.631
Table(s): Information Technology: London Band 1 p.304, Intellectual Property: London Band 2 p.322, Media & Entertainment: London Band 3 p.345

Howe, Robert
Table(s): Commercial Dispute Resolution: London Band 3 p.109, Employment: London Band 4 p.207, Fraud: Civil: London Band 4 p.281, Media & Entertainment: London Band 1 p.345, Sport: London Band 4 p.478

Howe, Timothy
Profile: p.632
Table(s): Banking & Finance: London Band 2 p.49, Commercial Dispute Resolution: London Band 3 p.109, Energy & Natural Resources: London Band 4 p.226, Fraud: Civil: London Band 4 p.281, Insurance: London Band 3 p.315, International Arbitration: General Commercial & Insurance: London Band 4 p.328, Professional Negligence: London Band 3 p.420, Telecommunications: London Band 3 p.491

Howell, John
Table(s): Administrative & Public Law: London Band 1 p.27, Civil Liberties & Human Rights: London Band 1 p.81, Community Care: London Band 1 p.132, Environment: London Band 1 p.231, Local Government: London Star individuals p.340, Public Procurement: London Band 1 p.439

Howell Williams, Craig
Profile: p.632
Table(s): Planning: London Band 3 p.386

Howells, Catherine
Table(s): Personal Injury: Northern (Bar) Band 2 p.380

Howells, Chris
Profile: p.632
Table(s): Employment: Wales & Chester (Bar) Band 2 p.223

Howells, James
Profile: p.632
Table(s): Construction: London New Silks p.146, Energy & Natural Resources: London New Silks p.226, Information Technology: London New Silks p.304, International Arbitration: Construction/Engineering: London New Silks p.333

Howells, Katherine
Profile: p.632
Table(s): Travel: International Personal Injury: London Band 3 p.495, Travel: Regulatory & Commercial: London Band 3 p.495

Howie, Robert
Table(s): Commercial Dispute Resolution: Scotland (Bar) Band 1 p.512, Construction: Scotland (Bar) Band 1 p.515, Professional Negligence: Scotland (Bar) Band 2 p.523, Restructuring/Insolvency: Scotland (Bar) Band 1 p.526

Howker, David
Table(s): Crime: London Band 2 p.173, Financial Crime: The Regions Band 1 p.275

Howlin, Michael P
Table(s): Commercial Dispute Resolution: Scotland (Bar) Band 3 p.512, Company: Scotland (Bar) Band 2 p.515, Restructuring/Insolvency: Scotland (Bar) Band 1 p.526

Hoyal, Jane
Table(s): Family: Children: London Band 4 p.245

Hubbard, Daniel
Table(s): Commercial Dispute Resolution: London Band 5 p.110

Hubbard, Mark
Profile: p.632
Table(s): Chancery: Traditional: London Band 2 p.67, Fraud: Civil: London Band 2 p.282, Offshore: London Band 3 p.353

Hubble, Ben
Profile: p.632
Table(s): Insurance: London Band 4 p.315, Offshore: London Band 3 p.353, Professional Discipline: London Band 2 p.410, Professional Negligence: London Band 1 p.420

Huckle, Theodore
Profile: p.632
Table(s): Clinical Negligence: Wales & Chester (Bar) Band 1 p.105, Personal Injury: Industrial Disease: London p.368, Personal Injury: Wales & Chester (Bar) Band 1 p.383

Hudson, Anthony
Table(s): Defamation/Privacy: London Band 1 p.199

Hugh-Jones, George
Profile: p.633
Table(s): Professional Discipline: London Band 2 p.410

Hughes, Adrian
Table(s): Construction: London Band 3 p.146, International Arbitration: Construction/Engineering: London Band 2 p.333

Hughes, David
Profile: p.633
Table(s): Crime: London Band 2 p.174

Hughes, Gwydion
Profile: p.633
Table(s): Chancery: Wales & Chester (Bar) Band 1 p.77, Commercial Dispute Resolution: Wales & Chester (Bar) Band 2 p.129

Hughes, Ignatius
Table(s): Crime: Western (Bar) Band 3 p.192

Hughes, Jessica
Table(s): Chancery: Commercial: London Band 4 p.60, Chancery: Traditional: London Band 3 p.67

Hughes, Paul
Profile: p.633
Table(s): Costs Litigation: Northern (Bar) Band 1 p.162

Hughes, Ruth
Profile: p.633
Table(s): Court of Protection: Property & Affairs: All Circuits Band 2 p.169

Hughes, Simon
Profile: p.633
Table(s): Construction: London Band 4 p.146

Hughes, William
Profile: p.633
Table(s): Crime: London Band 5 p.173

Humphreys, Richard
Table(s): Planning: London Band 4 p.386

Humphries, Michael
Profile: p.633
Table(s): Planning: London Star individuals p.386

Humphryes, Jane
Profile: p.633
Table(s): Crime: London Band 3 p.173

Hunjan, Satinder
Table(s): Clinical Negligence: Midlands (Bar) Band 1 p.102, Personal Injury: Midlands (Bar) Band 1 p.377

Hunter, Andrew
Table(s): Commercial Dispute Resolution: London Band 4 p.109, Financial Services: London Band 3 p.276, Fraud: Civil: London Band 3 p.281, Insurance: London Band 3 p.315, International Arbitration: General Commercial & Insurance: London Band 4 p.328, Media & Entertainment: London Band 3 p.345, Sport: London Band 3 p.478

Hunter, John
Profile: p.634
Table(s): Administrative & Public Law: Northern (Bar) Band 3 p.39, Planning: Northern (Bar) Band 2 p.394

Hunter, Robert
Profile: p.634
Table(s): Personal Injury: London Band 3 p.368

Hunter, Susan
Table(s): Family/Matrimonial: Western (Bar) Band 2 p.262

Hunter, Timothy
Table(s): Crime: London Band 4 p.174

Hunter, Winston
Profile: p.634
Table(s): Clinical Negligence: Northern (Bar) Band 2 p.103, Personal Injury: Northern (Bar) Star individuals p.380

Huntley, Clare
Profile: p.634
Table(s): Crime: London Band 5 p.174

Hurst, Andrew
Profile: p.634
Table(s): Professional Discipline: London Band 2 p.411

Husain, Raza
Table(s): Administrative & Public Law: London Band 2 p.27, Civil Liberties & Human Rights: London Band 1 p.81, Immigration: London Star individuals p.297

Hussain, Gul Nawaz Mahboob
Table(s): Crime: North Eastern (Bar) Band 2 p.184

Hussain, Riaz
Profile: p.634
Table(s): Construction: London Band 2 p.147, International Arbitration: Construction/Engineering: London Band 2 p.333, Professional Negligence: Technology & Construction: London Band 3 p.428

Hussain, Tasaddat
Profile: p.634
Table(s): Administrative & Public Law: North Eastern (Bar) Band 1 p.39

Hussey, Ann
Table(s): Family: Matrimonial Finance: London Band 3 p.244

Hutchings, Martin
Profile: p.634
Table(s): Real Estate Litigation: London Band 3 p.442

Hutchings, Matthew
Table(s): Local Government: London Band 2 p.340, Social Housing: London Band 1 p.471

Hutchinson, Colin
Table(s): Police Law: Mainly Claimant: All Circuits Band 2 p.400

Hutton, Alexander
Profile: p.635
Table(s): Clinical Negligence: London Band 2 p.92, Costs Litigation: London Band 2 p.160, Professional Discipline: London Band 3 p.410

Hutton, Caroline
Table(s): Agriculture & Rural Affairs: London Band 1 p.41, Real Estate Litigation: London Band 3 p.443

Hutton, Louise
Profile: p.635
Table(s): Banking & Finance: London Band 4 p.50, Chancery: Commercial: London Band 1 p.60, Fraud: Civil: London Band 1 p.282

Hyam, Jeremy
Table(s): Administrative & Public Law: London Band 2 p.28, Civil Liberties & Human Rights: London Band 3 p.82, Clinical Negligence: London Band 2 p.93, Environment: London Band 2 p.231, Professional Discipline: London Band 4 p.411

Hyams, Oliver
Profile: p.635
Table(s): Education: London Band 2 p.203

Hyde, Charles
Table(s): Family: Matrimonial Finance: London Band 2 p.244, Family: Children: London Band 4 p.244

Hynes, Paul
Table(s): Crime: London Band 5 p.173

I

I'Anson Banks, Roderick
Profile: p.635
Table(s): Partnership: London Star individuals p.359

Ife, Linden
Table(s): Chancery: Commercial: London Band 3 p.60, Commercial Dispute Resolution: London Band 4 p.110, Company: London Band 3 p.135, Restructuring/Insolvency: London Band 3 p.455

Ilyas, Shaiba
Table(s): Real Estate Litigation: London Band 5 p.443

Innes, Ruth
Profile: p.635
Table(s): Family/Matrimonial: Scotland (Bar) Star individuals p.517

Irving, Gillian
Table(s): Family/Matrimonial: Northern (Bar) Band 2 p.258

Irwin, Gavin
Profile: p.635
Table(s): Financial Crime: London Band 3 p.267, POCA Work & Asset Forfeiture: All Circuits Band 3 p.397

Isaac, Nicholas
Profile: p.635
Table(s): Real Estate Litigation: London Band 4 p.443

Isaac, Sebastian
Table(s): Banking & Finance: London Band 4 p.50, Commercial Dispute Resolution: London Band 3 p.110

Isaacs, Barry
Profile: p.635
Table(s): Restructuring/Insolvency: London Band 3 p.455

Isaacs, Elizabeth
Profile: p.636
Table(s): Family/Matrimonial: Midlands (Bar) Band 2 p.254

Isaacs, Paul
Profile: p.636
Table(s): Family/Matrimonial: North Eastern (Bar) Band 1 p.256

Isherwood, John
Table(s): Personal Injury: Western (Bar) Band 2

Islam-Chowdhury, Mugni
Table(s): Employment: Midlands (Bar) Band 2 p.218

Iten, Corinne
Profile: p.636
Table(s): Family/Matrimonial: Western (Bar) Up-and-coming individuals p.262

Ivey, Gilmour
Table(s): Personal Injury: Scotland (Bar) Band 2 p.520

Ivill, Scott
Profile: p.636
Table(s): Crime: London Band 5 p.174

J

Jack, David
Table(s): Family/Matrimonial: Scotland (Bar) Band 1 p.517

Jacklin, Susan
Profile: p.636
Table(s): Family/Matrimonial: Western (Bar) Band 1 p.262

Jackson, Andrew
Profile: p.636
Table(s): Crime: Midlands (Bar) Band 1 p.181

Jackson, Claire
Profile: p.636
Table(s): Restructuring/Insolvency: North Eastern (Bar) Band 1 p.461

Jackson, David
Profile: p.636
Table(s): Crime: Midlands (Bar) Band 3 p.181

Jackson, Fiona
Table(s): POCA Work & Asset Forfeiture: All Circuits Band 2 p.397

Jackson, Hugh
Profile: p.636
Table(s): Commercial Dispute Resolution: London Band 5 p.110, Professional Negligence: London Band 3 p.421

Jackson, Judith
Profile: p.636
Table(s): Real Estate Litigation: London Band 4 p.442

Jackson, Matthew
Profile: p.637
Table(s): Clinical Negligence: London Band 1 p.93, Professional Negligence: London Band 4 p.421

Jackson, Rosemary
Profile: p.637
Table(s): Mediators: All Circuits Band 2 p.348

Jacobs, Nigel
Table(s): Shipping & Commodities: London Band 2 p.465

Jacobs, Richard
Table(s): Commercial Dispute Resolution: London Band 3 p.109, Insurance: London Band 2 p.315, International Arbitration: General Commercial & Insurance: London Band 4 p.328, International Arbitration: Arbitrators: London Band 1 p.335

Jaffa, Ronald
Table(s): Crime: London Band 4 p.174

Jafferjee, Aftab
Table(s): Crime: London Band 1 p.173

Jaffey, Ben
Table(s): Administrative & Public Law: London Star individuals p.28, Civil Liberties & Human Rights: London Star individuals p.82, Financial Services: London Band 1 p.276

Jagadesham, Vijay
Table(s): Administrative & Public Law: Northern (Bar) Band 2 p.39, Civil Liberties & Human Rights: Northern (Bar) Band 2 p.89, Immigration: Northern (Bar) Band 2 p.309

Jamal, Isabel
Profile: p.637
Table(s): Intellectual Property: London Band 4 p.322

James, Alun
Profile: p.637
Table(s): Tax: London Band 2 p.482

James, Christopher
Table(s): Family/Matrimonial: Midlands (Bar) Band 1 p.254

James, Grahame
Profile: p.637
Table(s): Crime: London Band 6 p.174

James, Ian
Table(s): Crime: South Eastern (Bar) Band 2 p.188

James, Mark
Table(s): Costs Litigation: London Band 3 p.160

James, Rhodri
Table(s): Crime: South Eastern (Bar) Band 4 p.188

Janusz, Pierre
Table(s): Travel: International Personal Injury: London Band 2 p.495

Jarmain, Stephen
Profile: p.637
Table(s): Family: Children: London Band 2 p.245

Jarman, Mark
Table(s): Family: Children: London Band 3 p.245

Jarron, Stephanie
Table(s): Real Estate Litigation: North Eastern (Bar) Band 2 p.451

Jarvis, John
Table(s): Commercial Dispute Resolution: London Band 5 p.109

Jarvis, Malcolm
Table(s): Energy & Natural Resources: London Band 4 p.226

Jarvis, Paul
Table(s): Crime: London Band 3 p.174, POCA Work & Asset Forfeiture: All Circuits Band 2 p.397

Jeans, Christopher
Profile: p.637
Table(s): Employment: London Star individuals p.207, Sport: London Band 5 p.478

Jeary, Stephen
Table(s): Crime: Wales & Chester (Bar) Band 3 p.191

Jeavons, Anne
Table(s): Chancery: Commercial: London Band 4 p.60, Commercial Dispute Resolution: London Band 5 p.110

Jebb, Andrew
Table(s): Financial Crime: The Regions Band 1 p.275

Jefferies, Andrew
Table(s): Crime: London Band 4 p.173

Jefferies, Thomas
Table(s): Real Estate Litigation: London Band 3 p.443

Jefferson, Helen
Table(s): Family: Children: London Band 4 p.245

Jefford, Nerys
Profile: p.637
Table(s): Construction: London Band 4 p.146

Jeffreys, Alan
Table(s): Personal Injury: London Band 1 p.367

Jegarajah, Shivani
Table(s): Immigration: London Band 3 p.297

Jelf, Simon
Profile: p.638
Table(s): Partnership: London Band 1 p.359

Jenkins, Alan
Profile: p.638
Table(s): Professional Discipline: London Band 1 p.411

Jenkins, Catherine
Profile: p.638
Table(s): Family: Children: London Band 3 p.245

Jenkins, Rowan
Table(s): Crime: South Eastern (Bar) Band 3 p.188

Jeram, Kirti
Table(s): Employment: North Eastern (Bar) Band 2 p.220

Jeremy, David
Table(s): Crime: London Band 4 p.173

Jerman, Anthony
Table(s): Family: Children: London Band 2 p.245

Jerram, Harriet
Table(s): Clinical Negligence: London Band 3 p.93

Jewell, Matthew
Profile: p.638
Table(s): Crime: Western (Bar) Band 2 p.192

Jinadu, Abdul
Profile: p.638
Table(s): Construction: London Band 4 p.147

Jobling, Ian
Table(s): Crime: London Band 5 p.174

John, Benjamin
Profile: p.638
Table(s): Chancery: Commercial: London Band 3 p.60, Commercial Dispute Resolution: London Band 4 p.110, Fraud: Civil: London Band 4 p.282

John, Catrin
Table(s): Family/Matrimonial: Wales & Chester (Bar) Band 2 p.261

John, Laura
Table(s): Banking & Finance: London Band 2 p.50, Commercial Dispute Resolution: London Band 3 p.110, Fraud: Civil: London Band 3 p.282

John, Laura Elizabeth
Profile: p.638
Table(s): Competition Law: London Up-and-coming individuals p.142, Data Protection: London Band 4 p.195

Johns, Alan
Profile: p.638
Table(s): Real Estate Litigation: London Band 1 p.443

Johnson, Edwin
Profile: p.638
Table(s): Real Estate Litigation: London Band 1 p.442

Johnson, Jeremy
Profile: p.639
Table(s): Administrative & Public Law: London Band 3 p.27, Inquests & Public Inquiries: London Band 2 p.309, Immigration: London Band 3 p.297, Police Law: Mainly Defendant: All Circuits Band 1 p.402

Johnson, Laura
Profile: p.639
Table(s): Clinical Negligence: London Band 3 p.93, Personal Injury: London Band 2 p.368, Police Law: Mainly Defendant: All Circuits Band 2 p.402

Johnson, Lindsay
Table(s): Social Housing: London Band 2 p.471

Johnson, Nicholas
Table(s): Crime: Northern (Bar) Band 3 p.186

Johnson, Nicholas
Table(s): Financial Crime: The Regions Band 1 p.275

Johnson, Paul
Profile: p.639
Table(s): Mediators: All Circuits Band 2 p.348

Johnson, Zoe
Profile: p.639
Table(s): Crime: London Band 4 p.173, Professional Discipline: London Band 2 p.410

Johnston, Christopher
Profile: p.639
Table(s): Clinical Negligence: London Band 2 p.92, Court of Protection: Health & Welfare: All Circuits Band 2 p.165, Product Liability: London Band 2 p.406

Johnston, Connor
Table(s): Social Housing: London Up-and-coming individuals p.471

Johnston, David
Table(s): Administrative & Public Law: Scotland (Bar) Band 1 p.507

Johnston, Justine
Table(s): Family: Children: London Band 1 p.245

Jolliffe, Victoria
Table(s): Defamation/Privacy: London Band 3 p.199

Jolly, Schona
Profile: p.639
Table(s): Employment: London Band 3 p.208

Jones, Alun
Table(s): Crime: London Band 6 p.173, Extradition: London Band 1 p.240

Jones, Charlotte
Profile: p.639
Table(s): Clinical Negligence: London Band 1 p.93

Jones, Christopher
Table(s): Chancery: Western (Bar) Band 2 p.77, Real Estate Litigation: Western (Bar) Band 2 p.453

Jones, David
Table(s): Immigration: London Band 3 p.297

Jones, Elizabeth
Profile: p.639
Table(s): Chancery: Commercial: London Band 2 p.59, Commercial Dispute Resolution: London Band 5 p.109, Media & Entertainment: London Band 3 p.345, Mediators: All Circuits Band 3 p.348, Offshore: London Band 2 p.353

Jones, Emyr
Table(s): Chancery: Wales & Chester (Bar) Band 2 p.77, Commercial Dispute Resolution: Wales & Chester (Bar) Band 1 p.129

Jones, Gillian
Profile: p.640
Table(s): Crime: London Band 2 p.174, Financial Crime: London Band 2 p.267

Jones, Gregory
Table(s): Environment: London Band 2 p.231, Planning: London Band 3 p.386

Jones, Jennifer
Profile: p.640
Table(s): Construction: London Band 4 p.147

Jones, John
Table(s): Crime: International Criminal Law: London p.175, Extradition: London Band 2 p.240

Jones, John Richard
Profile: p.640
Table(s): Financial Crime: London Band 3 p.266

Jones, Jonathan
Profile: p.640
Table(s): Clinical Negligence: Midlands (Bar) Band 2 p.102, Personal Injury: Midlands (Bar) Band 2 p.377

Jones, Maggie
Table(s): Family: Children: London Band 3 p.245

Jones, Mark
Profile: p.640
Table(s): Shipping & Commodities: London Band 3 p.465

Jones, Michael
Table(s): Personal Injury: Northern (Bar) Band 2 p.380

Jones, Michael
Table(s): Tax: London Band 2 p.482

Jones, Nicholas David
Profile: p.640
Table(s): Clinical Negligence: Wales & Chester (Bar) Band 1 p.105, Personal Injury: Wales & Chester (Bar) Band 1 p.383

Jones, Nigel
Profile: p.641
Table(s): Construction: London Band 4 p.146, Insurance: London Band 4 p.315, Professional Negligence: London Band 3 p.420

Jones, Oliver
Table(s): Commercial Dispute Resolution: London Band 4 p.110

Jones, Philip
Profile: p.641
Table(s): Chancery: Commercial: London Band 1 p.59, Commercial Dispute Resolution: London Band 2 p.109, Company: London Band 2 p.135, Fraud: Civil: London Band 2 p.281, Partnership: London Band 1 p.359, Professional Negligence: London Band 2 p.420, Restructuring/Insolvency: London Band 2 p.455, Tax: London Band 2 p.482

Jones, Rhiannon
Table(s): Personal Injury: London Band 3 p.368

Jones, Richard
Table(s): Commercial Dispute Resolution: Midlands (Bar) Band 2 p.125

Jones, Richard
Profile: p.641
Table(s): Family: Children: London Band 4 p.245

Jones, Rupert
Table(s): POCA Work & Asset Forfeiture: All Circuits Band 1 p.397

Jones, Samuel
Table(s): Crime: Western (Bar) Up-and-coming individuals p.192, Health & Safety: Western (Bar) Up-and-coming individuals p.296

Jones, Sarah
Table(s): Crime: Western (Bar) Band 3 p.192

Jones, Seán
Profile: p.641
Table(s): Employment: London Band 2 p.207, Sport: London Band 5 p.478

Jones, Susannah
Table(s): Shipping & Commodities: London Band 3 p.465

Jones, Timothy
Profile: p.641
Table(s): Planning: Midlands (Bar) Band 2 p.393

Jones, Tristan
Table(s): Administrative & Public Law: London Band 4 p.28, Competition Law: London Band 3 p.142, Professional Discipline: London Band 5 p.411, Telecommunications: London Band 3 p.491

Jones, Victoria
Table(s): Intellectual Property: The Regions Band 1 p.327

Jordan, Ruth
Profile: p.641
Table(s): Restructuring/Insolvency: London Band 5 p.455

Jorro, Peter
Table(s): Immigration: London Band 2 p.297

Jory, Hugh
Table(s): Chancery: North Eastern (Bar) New Silks p.74, Commercial Dispute Resolution: North Eastern (Bar) New Silks p.126, Restructuring/Insolvency: North Eastern (Bar) New Silks p.461

Jory, Richard
Profile: p.641
Table(s): Crime: London Band 5 p.173

Joseph, David
Table(s): International Arbitration: General Commercial & Insurance: London Band 1 p.328

Joseph, Paul
Profile: p.641
Table(s): Commercial Dispute Resolution: Midlands (Bar) Band 2 p.125

Joughin, Gail
Table(s): Agriculture & Rural Affairs: Scotland (Bar) Band 3 p.509

Jourdan, Stephen
Profile: p.641
Table(s): Agriculture & Rural Affairs: London Band 1 p.41, Real Estate Litigation: London Band 1 p.442

Jowell, Daniel
Table(s): Commercial Dispute Resolution: London Band 3 p.109, Competition Law: London Band 2 p.142, Energy & Natural Resources: London Band 3 p.226, European Law: London Band 2 p.237, Tax: London Band 3 p.482

Joyce, Peter
Table(s): Crime: Midlands (Bar) Band 1 p.181

Jubb, Brian
Table(s): Family: Children: London Band 4 p.245

Judd, Frances
Table(s): Family/Matrimonial: South Eastern (Bar) Band 1 p.259

Judge, Lisa
Table(s): Crime: Northern (Bar) Band 3 p.186, Health & Safety: Northern (Bar) Band 1 p.296

K

Kalfon, Olivier
Table(s): Chancery: Commercial: London Band 4 p.60, Real Estate Litigation: London Band 3 p.443, Restructuring/Insolvency: London Band 2 p.455

Kallipetis, Michel
Table(s): Mediators: All Circuits Band 1 p.348

Kamlish, Stephen
Table(s): Crime: London Band 1 p.173

Kamm, Rachel
Profile: p.641
Table(s): Data Protection: London Band 4 p.195, Education: London Band 4 p.203

Kane, Adam
Profile: p.642
Table(s): Financial Crime: London Band 2 p.267

Kapila, Rachel
Profile: p.642
Table(s): Extradition: London Band 3 p.240, Licensing: London Band 3 p.337

Karas, Jonathan
Profile: p.642
Table(s): Agriculture & Rural Affairs: London Band 3 p.41, Planning: London Band 4 p.386, Real Estate Litigation: London Band 1 p.442

Karia, Chirag
Profile: p.642
Table(s): Shipping & Commodities: London Band 4 p.465

Karim, Sam
Profile: p.642
Table(s): Administrative & Public Law: Northern (Bar) Band 2 p.39, Civil Liberties & Human Rights: Northern (Bar) Band 2 p.89, Court of Protection: Health & Welfare: All Circuits Band 3 p.165

Kark, Tom
Table(s): Financial Crime: London Band 4 p.266, Inquests & Public Inquiries: London Band 3 p.309, Professional Discipline: London Band 1 p.410

Katkowski, Christopher
Table(s): Planning: London Star individuals p.386

Kaufmann, Phillippa
Table(s): Administrative & Public Law: London Band 1 p.27, Civil Liberties & Human Rights: London Band 1 p.81, Police Law: Mainly Claimant: All Circuits Star individuals p.400

Kay, Dominic
Profile: p.642
Table(s): Health & Safety: London Band 1 p.291

Kay, Steven
Profile: p.642
Table(s): Crime: International Criminal Law: London p.175

Kealey, Gavin
Table(s): Aviation: London Band 2 p.47, Commercial Dispute Resolution: London Band 3 p.109, Insurance: London Band 1 p.315, International Arbitration: General Commercial & Insurance: London Band 1 p.328

Kearney, Andrew
Table(s): Construction: Western (Bar) Band 1 p.154

Kee, Peter
Profile: p.643
Table(s): Local Government: South Eastern (Bar) Band 1 p.344

Keegan, Leslie
Table(s): Clinical Negligence: London Band 3 p.93

Keeling, Adrian
Profile: p.643
Table(s): Crime: Midlands (Bar) Band 2 p.181, Police Law: Mainly Defendant: All Circuits Band 3 p.402, Professional Discipline: The Regions Band 1 p.417

Keen, Graeme
Table(s): Planning: London Band 4 p.386

Keen, Richard
Table(s): Administrative & Public Law: Scotland (Bar) Band 1 p.507, Commercial Dispute Resolution: Scotland (Bar) Star individuals p.512, Company: Scotland (Bar) Band 1 p.515, Construction: Scotland (Bar) Band 1 p.515

Keen, Spencer
Table(s): Employment: Western (Bar) Band 2 p.223

Kefford, Anthony
Table(s): Family/Matrimonial: South Eastern (Bar) Band 2 p.259

Keith, Benjamin
Profile: p.643
Table(s): Extradition: London Band 2 p.240

Keith, Hugo
Profile: p.643
Table(s): Administrative & Public Law: London Band 2 p.27, Crime: London Band 1 p.173, Extradition: London Star individuals p.240, Financial Crime: London Band 1 p.266, Financial Crime: Corporates: London Band 2 p.266, Inquests & Public Inquiries: London Band 2 p.309

Keleher, Paul
Table(s): Crime: London Band 3 p.173

Kellar, Robert
Table(s): Personal Injury: London Band 3 p.368

Keller, Ciaran
Profile: p.643
Table(s): Chancery: Commercial: London Band 3 p.60, Commercial Dispute Resolution: London Band 3 p.110, Real Estate Litigation: London Band 5 p.443

Kelly, Brendan
Profile: p.643
Table(s): Crime: London Band 2 p.173, Financial Crime: London Band 2 p.266

Kelly, Emma
Profile: p.643
Table(s): Real Estate Litigation: Midlands (Bar) Band 3 p.450

Kelly, Geoffrey
Profile: p.643
Table(s): Family/Matrimonial: Western (Bar) Band 3 p.262

Kelly, Mark
Profile: p.644
Table(s): Financial Crime: The Regions Band 1 p.275

Kelly, Sean
Profile: p.644
Table(s): Chancery: North Eastern (Bar) Band 2 p.74

Kelsey, Katherine
Profile: p.644
Table(s): Family: Matrimonial Finance: London Band 2 p.244, Family: Children: London Band 3 p.244

Kelsey-Fry, John
Profile: p.644
Table(s): Crime: London Star individuals p.173, Financial Crime: London Star individuals p.266, Financial Crime: Corporates: London Band 1 p.266

Kember, Richard
Profile: p.644
Table(s): Chancery: Wales & Chester (Bar) Band 2 p.77

Kemp, Christopher
Table(s): Clinical Negligence: London Band 2 p.93, Personal Injury: London Band 3 p.368

Kemp, Edward
Profile: p.644
Table(s): Employment: London Band 5 p.208

Kempster, Toby
Table(s): Employment: Western (Bar) Band 2 p.223, Personal Injury: Western (Bar) Band 2

Kendal, Timothy
Table(s): Crime: London Band 3 p.174, Financial Crime: London Band 1 p.267

Kendrick, Dominic
Table(s): Energy & Natural Resources: London Band 4 p.226, Insurance: London Band 1 p.315, International Arbitration: General Commercial & Insurance: London Band 4 p.328, Shipping & Commodities: London Band 2 p.465

Kendrick, Julia
Profile: p.644
Table(s): Health & Safety: London Up-and-coming individuals p.291

Kennedy, Andrew
Table(s): Clinical Negligence: London Band 1 p.93, Professional Discipline: London Band 1 p.411

Kennedy, Christopher
Table(s): Health & Safety: Northern (Bar) Band 2 p.296, Motor Insurance Fraud: All Circuits Band 1 p.350, Personal Injury: Northern (Bar) Band 1 p.380

Kennedy, Stuart
Table(s): Construction: London Band 4 p.147, International Arbitration: Construction/Engineering: London Band 2 p.333

Kennelly, Brian
Table(s): Administrative & Public Law: London Band 3 p.28, Competition Law: London Star individuals p.142, European Law: London Band 1 p.237, Sport: London Band 3 p.478, Telecommunications: London Band 1 p.491

Kenny, Christian
Table(s): Family: Matrimonial Finance: London Band 4 p.244

Kenny, Julian
Table(s): Banking & Finance: London Band 3 p.50, Shipping & Commodities: London Band 1 p.465

Kenny, Stephen
Table(s): Shipping & Commodities: London Band 4 p.465

Kent, Alan
Table(s): Crime: London Band 3 p.173

Kent, Michael
Profile: p.644
Table(s): Personal Injury: London Band 2 p.367, Personal Injury: Industrial Disease: London p.367

Kenyon, Flavia
Profile: p.645
Table(s): Crime: London Band 5 p.174

Ker-Reid, John
Table(s): Family/Matrimonial: Western (Bar) Band 3 p.262

Kerr, Simon
Table(s): Insurance: London Band 2 p.316

Kerr, Tim
Profile: p.645
Table(s): Education: London Band 2 p.203, Public Procurement: London Band 3 p.439, Sport: London Band 3 p.478

Kershen, Lawrence
Table(s): Mediators: All Circuits Band 2 p.348

Kessler, James
Profile: p.645
Table(s): Charities: London Band 2 p.79, Tax: Private Client: London Band 1 p.488

Key, Paul
Table(s): Commercial Dispute Resolution: London Band 5 p.109, International Arbitration: General Commercial & Insurance: London Band 4 p.328, Tax: Indirect Tax: London Band 3 p.486

Khalil, Karim
Profile: p.645
Table(s): Crime: South Eastern (Bar) Band 1 p.188

Khalique, Nageena
Table(s): Administrative & Public Law: Midlands (Bar) Band 1 p.38, Civil Liberties & Human Rights: Midlands (Bar) Band 1 p.89, Clinical Negligence: Midlands (Bar) Band 2 p.102, Court of Protection: Health & Welfare: All Circuits Band 1 p.165

Khan, Ashraf
Profile: p.645
Table(s): Crime: London Band 4 p.174, Financial Crime: London Band 4 p.267

Khan, Farhaz
Table(s): Banking & Finance: London Band 3 p.50, Chancery: Commercial: London Band 4 p.60, Financial Services: London Band 2 p.276, Pensions: London Band 2 p.363

Khan, Hassan
Table(s): Family: Children: London Band 4 p.245

Khan, Judy
Table(s): Crime: London Band 2 p.173

Khan, Karim
Table(s): Crime: International Criminal Law: London p.175

Khan, Shazia
Table(s): Immigration: Northern (Bar) Band 2 p.309

Khan, Tahir
Table(s): Crime: North Eastern (Bar) Band 3 p.184

Khan, Zarif
Profile: p.645
Table(s): Crime: London Band 4 p.174

Khangure, Avtar
Table(s): Commercial Dispute Resolution: Midlands (Bar) Band 1 p.125, Company: Midlands (Bar) Band 1 p.140, Restructuring/Insolvency: Midlands (Bar) Band 1 p.461

Khayum, Zulfikar
Profile: p.645
Table(s): Construction: London Band 4 p.147

Khubber, Ranjiv
Table(s): Immigration: London Band 1 p.297

Khurana, Vinit
Table(s): Clinical Negligence: Scotland (Bar) Band 3 p.510

Khurshid, Jawdat
Table(s): Insurance: London Band 2 p.316

Kiai, Gilda
Table(s): Immigration: London Band 4 p.297

Kibling, Thomas
Table(s): Employment: London Band 1 p.208

Kilcoyne, Paul
Profile: p.645
Table(s): Personal Injury: London Band 3 p.368

Killalea, Stephen
Profile: p.646
Table(s): Health & Safety: London Band 1 p.291, Personal Injury: London Band 1 p.367, Travel: International Personal Injury: London Band 3 p.495

Kilroy, Charlotte
Table(s): Civil Liberties & Human Rights: London Band 3 p.82, Immigration: London Band 3 p.297

Kilvington, Simon
Profile: p.646
Table(s): Personal Injury: Northern (Bar) Band 1 p.380

Kimbell, John
Table(s): Aviation: London Band 1 p.47, Shipping & Commodities: London Band 3 p.465, Travel: Regulatory & Commercial: London Band 2 p.495

Kimblin, Richard
Profile: p.646
Table(s): Environment: Midlands (Bar) Band 1 p.235, Planning: Midlands (Bar) Band 1 p.393

Kimmins, Charles
Table(s): Banking & Finance: London Band 4 p.49, Commercial Dispute Resolution: London Band 5 p.109, International Arbitration: General Commercial & Insurance: London Band 2 p.328, Shipping & Commodities: London Band 2 p.465

King, Edmund
Table(s): Banking & Finance: London Band 1 p.50, Chancery: Commercial: London Band 2 p.60, Commercial Dispute Resolution: London Band 3 p.110, Fraud: Civil: London Band 3 p.282, Shipping & Commodities: London Band 3 p.465, Tax: Indirect Tax: London Band 3 p.486

King, Henry
Profile: p.646
Table(s): Banking & Finance: London Band 2 p.50, Financial Services: London Band 3 p.276

King, Michael
Table(s): Chancery: Traditional: London Band 1 p.67, Charities: London Band 2 p.79, Mediators: All Circuits Band 4 p.348, Partnership: London Band 2 p.359

King, Neil
Table(s): Planning: London Band 1 p.386

King, Samantha
Table(s): Family: Children: London Band 1 p.245

King, Simon
Table(s): Clinical Negligence: London Band 4 p.93, Personal Injury: London Band 2 p.368

King-Smith, James
Table(s): Family/Matrimonial: South Eastern (Bar) Band 3 p.259

Kingscote, Geoffrey
Table(s): Family: Matrimonial Finance: London Band 1 p.244

Kingston, Martin
Table(s): Planning: London Band 1 p.386, Planning: Midlands (Bar) Star individuals p.393

Kinnear, Jonathan S
Profile: p.646
Table(s): Financial Crime: London Band 4 p.266

Kinnier, Andrew
Profile: p.646
Table(s): Local Government: London Band 4 p.340, Product Liability: London Band 2 p.406, Public Procurement: London Band 3 p.439

Kinsky, Cyril
Table(s): Commercial Dispute Resolution: London Band 3 p.109, Professional Negligence: London Band 4 p.420

Kinsler, Marie Louise
Table(s): Travel: International Personal Injury: London Band 1 p.495

Kirby, PJ
Profile: p.646
Table(s): Commercial Dispute Resolution: London Band 5 p.109, Costs Litigation: London Band 3 p.160

Kirk, Anthony
Profile: p.646
Table(s): Family: Children: London Band 3 p.245

Kirk, Jonathan
Profile: p.646
Table(s): Consumer Law: London Band 1 p.156

Kirtley, Paul
Table(s): Employment: North Eastern (Bar) Band 3 p.220

Kisser, Amy
Profile: p.647
Table(s): Family: Matrimonial Finance: London Up-and-coming individuals p.244

Kissin, Clare
Profile: p.647
Table(s): Defamation/Privacy: London Up-and-coming individuals p.199

Kitchener, Neil
Table(s): Banking & Finance: London Band 3 p.49, Commercial Dispute Resolution: London Band 2 p.109, Fraud: Civil: London Band 2 p.281

Kitching, Robin
Table(s): Professional Discipline: The Regions Band 1 p.417

Kitson, Justin
Profile: p.647
Table(s): Real Estate Litigation: London Band 3 p.443

Klein, Jonathan
Table(s): Chancery: North Eastern (Bar) Band 1 p.74, Commercial Dispute Resolution: North Eastern (Bar) Band 2 p.126, Real Estate Litigation: North Eastern (Bar) Band 1 p.451

Kloss, Alexander W
Table(s): Family/Matrimonial: Northern (Bar) Band 2 p.258

Knafler, Stephen
Table(s): Administrative & Public Law: London Band 3 p.27, Civil Liberties & Human Rights: London Band 3 p.81, Community Care: London Band 1 p.132, Immigration: London Band 1 p.297, Local Government: London Band 3 p.340, Social Housing: London Band 1 p.471

Knifton, David
Table(s): Personal Injury: Northern (Bar) Band 2 p.380

Knight, Christopher
Profile: p.647
Table(s): Administrative & Public Law: London Up-and-coming individuals p.28, Data Protection: London Up-and-coming individuals p.195

Knight, Heidi
Profile: p.647
Table(s): Clinical Negligence: London Band 4 p.93, Product Liability: London Band 3 p.406

Knights, Samantha
Table(s): Civil Liberties & Human Rights: London Band 3 p.82, Immigration: London Band 2 p.297

Knorr, Michelle
Table(s): Immigration: London Up-and-coming individuals p.297

Knott, James
Table(s): Company: London Band 3 p.135

Knowles, Julian
Table(s): Crime: London Band 3 p.173, Extradition: London Band 2 p.240, Financial Crime: London Band 2 p.266

Knowles CBE, Robin
Table(s): Banking & Finance: London Band 4 p.49, Company: London Band 3 p.135, Restructuring/Insolvency: London Band 3 p.455

Knox, Christopher
Profile: p.647
Table(s): Crime: North Eastern (Bar) Band 1 p.184, Family/Matrimonial: North Eastern (Bar) Band 2 p.256

Knox, Peter
Table(s): Administrative & Public Law: London Band 4 p.27

Kohli, Ryan
Profile: p.647
Table(s): Planning: London Band 5 p.386, Social Housing: London Band 2 p.471

Kokelaar, Sebastian
Table(s): Real Estate Litigation: London Band 5 p.443

Kolinsky, Daniel
Profile: p.648
Table(s): Administrative & Public Law: London Band 3 p.28, Local Government: London Band 1 p.340, Planning: London Band 3 p.386

Kolvin, Philip
Profile: p.648
Table(s): Licensing: London Band 1 p.337

Komorowski, Julius
Profile: p.648
Table(s): Civil Liberties & Human Rights: Scotland (Bar) Up-and-coming individuals p.509

Korn, Adam
Table(s): Clinical Negligence: London Band 2 p.93, Product Liability: London Band 2 p.406

Korn, Anthony
Profile: p.648
Table(s): Employment: Midlands (Bar) Band 2 p.218

Kovalevsky, Richard
Profile: p.648
Table(s): Crime: London Band 4 p.173, Financial Crime: London Band 2 p.266, Financial Crime: Corporates: London Band 2 p.266

Kovats, Steven
Table(s): Administrative & Public Law: London Band 4 p.27, Immigration: London Band 3 p.297

Kramer, Adam
Profile: p.648
Table(s): Banking & Finance: London Band 3 p.50, Commercial Dispute Resolution: London Band 3 p.110, Energy & Natural Resources: London Band 3 p.226, Fraud: Civil: London Band 3 p.282, Insurance: London Band 3 p.316

Kreisberger, Ronit
Profile: p.648
Table(s): Competition Law: London Band 1 p.142

Kremen, Philip
Profile: p.648
Table(s): Real Estate Litigation: London Band 5 p.443

Krolick, Ivan
Table(s): Crime: South Eastern (Bar) Band 4 p.188, POCA Work & Asset Forfeiture: All Circuits Band 3 p.397

Kubik, Heidi
Profile: p.648
Table(s): Crime: Midlands (Bar) Band 3 p.181

Kulkarni, Yash
Table(s): Information Technology: London Band 3 p.304

Kverndal, Simon
Table(s): Shipping & Commodities: London Band 3 p.465

Kynoch, Duncan
Profile: p.649
Table(s): Chancery: Commercial: London Band 4 p.60

Kyriakides, Tina
Table(s): Company: London Band 3 p.135, Restructuring/Insolvency: London Band 3 p.455

L

Laddie, James
Table(s): Employment: London Band 1 p.207, Police Law: Mainly Claimant: All Circuits Band 2 p.400

Ladenburg, Guy
Profile: p.649
Table(s): Crime: London Band 6 p.174, Professional Discipline: London Band 5 p.411

Laidlaw, Jonathan
Profile: p.649
Table(s): Crime: London Star individuals p.173, Financial Crime: London Band 3 p.266, Health & Safety: London Band 2 p.291

Laird, Francis
Profile: p.649
Table(s): Crime: Midlands (Bar) Band 3 p.181

Lake, Fiona
Table(s): Clinical Negligence: Scotland (Bar) Band 2 p.510

Lake, Jonathan C
Table(s): Commercial Dispute Resolution: Scotland (Bar) Band 2 p.512, Intellectual Property: Scotland (Bar) Band 1 p.519, Professional Negligence: Scotland (Bar) Band 2 p.523

Lakha, Abbas
Profile: p.649
Table(s): Crime: London Band 1 p.173

Lakin, Tracy
Profile: p.649
Table(s): Family/Matrimonial: Midlands (Bar) Band 2 p.254

Lamb, Jeffrey
Table(s): Crime: South Eastern (Bar) Band 2 p.188

Lamb, Maria
Profile: p.649
Table(s): Crime: Western (Bar) Band 2 p.192

Lambert, Christina
Table(s): Clinical Negligence: London Band 1 p.92, Inquests & Public Inquiries: London Band 1 p.309, Professional Discipline: London Band 1 p.410

Lambert, Jane
Table(s): Intellectual Property: The Regions Band 1 p.327

Lambert, Nigel
Profile: p.649
Table(s): Crime: London Band 4 p.173

Lambert, Sarah
Profile: p.650
Table(s): Clinical Negligence: London Band 2 p.93, Costs Litigation: London Band 4 p.160

Lambis, Marios
Table(s): Professional Discipline: London Band 1 p.411

Lamont, Calum
Profile: p.650
Table(s): Construction: London Band 2 p.147, International Arbitration: Construction/Engineering: London Band 2 p.333, Public Procurement: London Band 2 p.439

Lamont, Camilla
Table(s): Real Estate Litigation: London Band 2 p.443

Lamont, Gordon
Table(s): Personal Injury: Scotland (Bar) Band 1 p.520

Lancaster, Roger
Profile: p.650
Table(s): Planning: Northern (Bar) Band 1 p.394

Landau, Toby
Table(s): International Arbitration: General Commercial & Insurance: London Star individuals p.328, International Arbitration: Arbitrators: London Band 1 p.335, Public International Law: London Band 2 p.435

Lander, Richard
Profile: p.650
Table(s): Real Estate Litigation: Northern (Bar) Band 1 p.452

Lane, Andrew
Profile: p.650
Table(s): Social Housing: London Band 1 p.471

Lane, Lindsay
Profile: p.650
Table(s): Intellectual Property: London Band 2 p.322, Media & Entertainment: London Band 2 p.345

Laney, Anna
Table(s): Construction: London Band 3 p.147, International Arbitration: Construction/Engineering: London Band 2 p.333

Langdale, Adrian
Table(s): Crime: Midlands (Bar) Band 2 p.181

Langdale, Rachel
Profile: p.650
Table(s): Family: Children: London Band 2 p.245

Langdale, Timothy
Profile: p.650
Table(s): Crime: London Band 1 p.173, Financial Crime: London Star individuals p.266, Financial Crime: Corporates: London Band 1 p.266

Langdon, Andrew
Table(s): Crime: Western (Bar) Star individuals p.192, Health & Safety: Western (Bar) Band 1 p.296

Langley, Charles
Profile: p.650
Table(s): Crime: London Band 6 p.174

Langley, Sir Gordon
Table(s): International Arbitration: Arbitrators: London Band 1 p.335

Langlois, Nicole
Table(s): Offshore: London Band 2 p.353

Langridge, Niki
Profile: p.651
Table(s): Family: Matrimonial Finance: London Band 4 p.244, Family: Children: London Band 4 p.244

Laprell, Mark
Profile: p.651
Table(s): Personal Injury: Northern (Bar) Band 2 p.380

Larkin, Sean
Profile: p.651
Table(s): Crime: London Band 3 p.173, Financial Crime: London Band 2 p.266, Professional Discipline: London Band 2 p.410

Lascelles, David
Profile: p.651
Table(s): Commercial Dispute Resolution: London Band 4 p.110, Company: London Band 3 p.135

Lask, Ben
Table(s): Competition Law: London Band 2 p.142, Data Protection: London Band 4 p.195, Telecommunications: London Band 3 p.491

Lasok, Paul
Profile: p.651
Table(s): Competition Law: London Band 2 p.142, European Law: London Band 1 p.237, Public Procurement: London Band 1 p.439, Tax: Indirect Tax: London Band 1 p.486

Latham, Kevin
Profile: p.651
Table(s): Costs Litigation: Northern (Bar) Band 2 p.162

Latham, Richard
Table(s): Crime: London Band 2 p.173, Financial Crime: London Band 2 p.266

Latimer, Andrew
Profile: p.651
Table(s): Chancery: Northern (Bar) Band 1 p.75, Commercial Dispute Resolution: North Eastern (Bar) Band 1 p.126

Latimer-Sayer, William
Table(s): Clinical Negligence: London Band 1 p.93, Personal Injury: London Star individuals p.368

Lattimer, Justine
Profile: p.651
Table(s): Court of Protection: Health & Welfare: All Circuits Band 3 p.165

Laughland, James
Profile: p.651
Table(s): Costs Litigation: London Band 3 p.160, Motor Insurance Fraud: All Circuits Band 1 p.350, Personal Injury: London Band 2 p.368

Laughton, Victoria
Table(s): Immigration: London Band 4 p.297

Laurence, George
Profile: p.652
Table(s): Agriculture & Rural Affairs: London Band 1 p.41, Chancery: Traditional: London Band 2 p.67, Real Estate Litigation: London Band 3 p.442

Lauterpacht, Elihu
Table(s): Public International Law: London Senior Statesmen p.435

Lavender, Nicholas
Profile: p.652
Table(s): Banking & Finance: London Band 3 p.49, Commercial Dispute Resolution: London Band 4 p.109

Lavery, Michael
Table(s): Crime: Northern (Bar) Band 3 p.186

Lavy, Matthew
Profile: p.652
Table(s): Information Technology: London Band 1 p.304, Telecommunications: London Band 3 p.491

Law, Charlotte
Profile: p.652
Table(s): Clinical Negligence: Northern (Bar) Up-and-coming individuals p.103

Law, Helen
Table(s): Civil Liberties & Human Rights: London Band 4 p.82, Police Law: Mainly Claimant: All Circuits Band 2 p.400

Lawrence, Anne
Profile: p.652
Table(s): Education: London Band 4 p.203

Lawrence, Heather
Table(s): Intellectual Property: London Band 4 p.322

Lawrence, Nigel
Table(s): Health & Safety: Northern (Bar) Band 2 p.296

Lawrence, Patrick
Profile: p.652
Table(s): Professional Discipline: London Band 3 p.410, Professional Negligence: London Band 1 p.420

Lawrie, Ian
Table(s): Crime: Western (Bar) Band 3 p.192, Environment: Western (Bar) Band 1 p.236, Health & Safety: London Band 3 p.291

Laws, Eleanor
Profile: p.652
Table(s): Crime: London Band 3 p.173, Crime: South Eastern (Bar) Band 2 p.188

Laws, Simon
Table(s): Crime: Western (Bar) Band 2 p.192

Lawson, Daniel
Profile: p.652
Table(s): Personal Injury: London Band 1 p.368

Lawson, David
Table(s): Education: London Band 1 p.203, Local Government: London Band 4 p.340

Lawson, Robert
Profile: p.653
Table(s): Aviation: London Band 1 p.47, Product Liability: London Band 3 p.406, Travel: Regulatory & Commercial: London Band 1 p.495

Lawton, Paul A
Table(s): Financial Crime: The Regions Band 1 p.275

Lazarides, Marcus
Profile: p.653
Table(s): Family: Matrimonial Finance: London Band 2 p.244, Family: Children: London Band 4 p.244

Lazarus, Michael
Table(s): Banking & Finance: London Band 3 p.50, Commercial Dispute Resolution: London Band 1 p.110, Fraud: Civil: London Band 3 p.282, Information Technology: London Star individuals p.304, Telecommunications: London Band 2 p.491

Lazarus, Robert
Table(s): Professional Discipline: London Up-and-coming individuals p.411

Lazur, Thomas
Profile: p.653
Table(s): Construction: London Band 4 p.147, Energy & Natural Resources: London Band 3 p.226

Le Fevre, Sarah
Profile: p.653
Table(s): Health & Safety: London Band 3 p.291, Licensing: London Band 1 p.337

Le Grice, Valentine
Table(s): Family: Matrimonial Finance: London Band 3 p.244

Le Poidevin, Nicholas
Profile: p.653
Table(s): Chancery: Traditional: London Band 2 p.67, Offshore: London Band 1 p.353, Trusts: London Band 1 p.498

Leabeater, James
Profile: p.653
Table(s): Construction: London Band 2 p.147, Energy & Natural Resources: London Band 4 p.226, Professional Negligence: Technology & Construction: London Band 3 p.428, Shipping & Commodities: London Band 3 p.465

Leach, Douglas
Table(s): Employment: Western (Bar) Band 3 p.223

Leach, Robin
Table(s): Sport: The Regions Band 1 p.480

Leader, Lucy
Table(s): Family/Matrimonial: Wales & Chester (Bar) Band 2 p.261

Leafe, Daniel
Table(s): Family/Matrimonial: Western (Bar) Band 1 p.262

Leahy, Blair
Table(s): Restructuring/Insolvency: London Band 3 p.455

Learmonth, Alexander
Profile: p.653
Table(s): Chancery: Traditional: London Band 2 p.67

Leaver, Peter
Table(s): International Arbitration: Arbitrators: London Band 1 p.335

Ledward, Jocelyn
Table(s): Crime: London Band 2 p.174

Lee, Jonathan
Profile: p.653
Table(s): Construction: London Band 3 p.147

Lee, Krista
Profile: p.653
Table(s): Construction: London Band 4 p.147

Lee, Michael
Profile: p.654
Table(s): Employment: London Up-and-coming individuals p.208

Lee, Sarah
Table(s): Competition Law: London Band 3 p.142, Telecommunications: London Band 3 p.491

Lee, Taryn
Table(s): Family/Matrimonial: North Eastern (Bar) Band 1 p.256

Leech, Stewart
Profile: p.654
Table(s): Family: Matrimonial Finance: London Band 1 p.244

Leek, Samantha
Profile: p.654
Table(s): Inquests & Public Inquiries: London Band 3 p.309, Police Law: Mainly Defendant: All Circuits Band 2 p.402

Leeper, Tom
Table(s): Clinical Negligence: Western (Bar) Band 1 p.106

Legard, Edward
Profile: p.654
Table(s): Employment: North Eastern (Bar) Band 2 p.220

Legge, Henry
Profile: p.654
Table(s): Art and Cultural Property Law : London Band 1 p.45, Chancery: Traditional: London Band 2 p.67, Offshore: London Band 3 p.353, Pensions: London Band 3 p.363

Leighton Williams, John
Table(s): Personal Injury: London Band 2 p.367

Leiper, Richard
Profile: p.654
Table(s): Employment: London Star individuals p.208

Lemer, David
Table(s): Immigration: London Band 4 p.297

Lemmy, Michael
Table(s): Personal Injury: Northern (Bar) Band 2 p.380

Lemon, Jane
Profile: p.654
Table(s): Construction: London Band 2 p.147, Energy & Natural Resources: London Band 4 p.226, International Arbitration: Construction/ Engineering: London Band 2 p.333, Professional Negligence: Technology & Construction: London Band 3 p.428

Lemos, Marika
Profile: p.654
Table(s): Tax: London Band 2 p.482, Tax: Private Client: London Band 2 p.488

Lennon, John
Table(s): Financial Crime: London Band 3 p.267

Lennon, Jonathan
Table(s): Financial Crime: London Band 2 p.267, POCA Work & Asset Forfeiture: All Circuits Band 2 p.397

Leonard, James
Table(s): Health & Safety: London Band 3 p.291, Professional Discipline: London Band 1 p.411

Lester, Maya
Table(s): Administrative & Public Law: London Band 2 p.28, Civil Liberties & Human Rights: London Band 3 p.82, Competition Law: London Band 1 p.142, European Law: London Band 1 p.237, Public International Law: London Band 3 p.435

Lester of Herne Hill, Anthony
Table(s): Administrative & Public Law: London Senior Statesmen p.27, Civil Liberties & Human Rights: London Senior Statesmen p.81

Letman, Paul
Table(s): Real Estate Litigation: London Band 3 p.443

Levene, Simon
Profile: p.655
Table(s): Personal Injury: London Band 3 p.368, Personal Injury: Industrial Disease: London p.368

Levey, Edward
Table(s): Commercial Dispute Resolution: London Band 3 p.110

Levinson, Jemma
Table(s): Crime: London Band 6 p.174

Levinson, Justin
Table(s): Personal Injury: London Band 1 p.368

Levy, Jacob
Profile: p.655
Table(s): Clinical Negligence: London New Silks p.92, Personal Injury: London New Silks p.367

Levy, Juliette
Profile: p.655
Table(s): Chancery: Commercial: London Band 3 p.60, Telecommunications: London Band 2 p.491

Levy, Neil
Profile: p.655
Table(s): Banking & Finance: Western (Bar) Band 1 p.57, Commercial Dispute Resolution: Western (Bar) Band 1 p.130, Restructuring/ Insolvency: Western (Bar) Band 2 p.463

Levy, Robert
Table(s): Chancery: Commercial: London Band 4 p.59, Commercial Dispute Resolution: London Band 5 p.109, Fraud: Civil: London Band 4 p.281, Offshore: London Band 3 p.353

Lew, Julian D. M.
Table(s): International Arbitration: Arbitrators: London Band 1 p.335

Lewers, Nigel
Profile: p.655
Table(s): Personal Injury: London Band 1 p.368

Lewis, Adam
Table(s): Public Procurement: London Band 2 p.439, Sport: London Star individuals p.478

Lewis, Andrew
Table(s): Personal Injury: North Eastern (Bar) Band 1 p.379

Lewis, Anya
Table(s): Crime: London Band 5 p.174

Lewis, Christopher
Profile: p.655
Table(s): Construction: London Band 1 p.147, Energy & Natural Resources: London Band 1 p.226, Information Technology: London Band 3 p.304, International Arbitration: Construction/ Engineering: London Band 1 p.333

Lewis, David
Table(s): Commercial Dispute Resolution: London New Silks p.109, International Arbitration: General Commercial & Insurance: London New Silks p.328, Shipping & Commodities: London New Silks p.465

Lewis, David
Profile: p.655
Table(s): Commercial Dispute Resolution: London Band 5 p.110

Lewis, Gwion
Table(s): Administrative & Public Law: London Up-and-coming individuals p.28

Lewis, James
Table(s): Crime: London Band 1 p.173, Extradition: London Band 1 p.240, Financial Crime: London Band 3 p.266

Lewis, Jeremy
Table(s): Employment: London Band 3 p.208

Lewis, Jonathan
Profile: p.655
Table(s): Construction: London Band 3 p.147

Lewis, Marian
Table(s): Crime: Wales & Chester (Bar) Band 1 p.191

Lewis, Meyric
Profile: p.655
Table(s): Planning: London Band 3 p.386

Lewis, Patrick
Table(s): Immigration: London Band 2 p.297

Lewis, Paul
Profile: p.655
Table(s): Crime: Wales & Chester (Bar) Band 2 p.191

Lewison, Josh
Profile: p.656
Table(s): Charities: London Band 3 p.79

Ley-Morgan, Mark
Profile: p.656
Table(s): Police Law: Mainly Defendant: All Circuits Band 1 p.402, Professional Discipline: London Band 3 p.411

Lickley, Nigel
Table(s): Crime: Western (Bar) Band 1 p.192

Liddell, Richard
Profile: p.656
Table(s): Professional Negligence: London Band 3 p.421, Sport: London Band 3 p.478

Liddiard, Martin
Table(s): Crime: Midlands (Bar) Band 2 p.181, POCA Work & Asset Forfeiture: All Circuits Band 3 p.397

Lidington, Gary
Profile: p.656
Table(s): Commercial Dispute Resolution: London Band 5 p.110, Real Estate Litigation: London Band 5 p.443

Lieven, Nathalie
Table(s): Administrative & Public Law: London Band 1 p.27, Civil Liberties & Human Rights: London Band 1 p.81, Environment: London Band 1 p.231, Local Government: London Band 1 p.340, Planning: London Band 1 p.386, Social Housing: London Band 2 p.471

Light, Roy
Table(s): Licensing: Western (Bar) Band 1 p.339

Lightfoot, Jeremy
Profile: p.656
Table(s): Shipping & Commodities: London Band 4 p.465

Lightman, Daniel
Profile: p.656
Table(s): Chancery: Commercial: London Band 2 p.60, Commercial Dispute Resolution: London Band 2 p.110, Company: London Band 1 p.135, Restructuring/Insolvency: London Band 2 p.455

Limb, Christopher
Profile: p.656
Table(s): Clinical Negligence: Northern (Bar) Band 2 p.103

Limb, Patrick
Profile: p.656
Table(s): Personal Injury: Industrial Disease: London p.368, Personal Injury: Midlands (Bar) Band 1 p.377

Linden, Thomas
Table(s): Employment: London Star individuals p.207

Lindop, Sarah
Table(s): Crime: South Eastern (Bar) Band 4 p.188

Lindsay, Alistair
Table(s): Competition Law: London Band 2 p.142

Lindsay, Mark
Table(s): Administrative & Public Law: Scotland (Bar) Band 1 p.507, Civil Liberties & Human Rights: Scotland (Bar) Band 3 p.509, Commercial Dispute Resolution: Scotland (Bar) Band 2 p.512, Immigration: Scotland (Bar) Band 1 p.518, Professional Discipline: Scotland (Bar) Band 1 p.523

Linford, Robert
Table(s): Crime: Western (Bar) Band 3 p.192

Ling, Naomi
Table(s): Employment: London Band 4 p.208, Pensions: London Band 3 p.363

Linklater, Lisa
Table(s): Restructuring/Insolvency: Northern (Bar) Band 3 p.462

Lintott, David
Profile: p.656
Table(s): Social Housing: London Band 3 p.471

Lissack, Richard
Profile: p.657
Table(s): Financial Crime: London Band 2 p.266, Financial Crime: Corporates: London Band 2 p.266, Financial Services: London Star individuals p.276, Health & Safety: London Star individuals p.291, Inquests & Public Inquiries: London Band 2 p.309

Lister, Caroline
Table(s): Family: Matrimonial Finance: London Band 4 p.244, Family: Children: London Band 2 p.244

Lithman, Nigel
Table(s): Crime: London Band 2 p.173

Little, Ian
Table(s): Personal Injury: Northern (Bar) Band 2 p.380

Little, Tom
Profile: p.657
Table(s): Crime: London Band 2 p.174, Financial Crime: London Band 2 p.267

Litton, John
Table(s): Planning: London Band 4 p.386

Livesey, Bernard
Profile: p.657
Table(s): Professional Negligence: London Band 4 p.420

Livesey, Kate
Profile: p.657
Table(s): Construction: London Band 2 p.147, Professional Negligence: London Star individuals p.421

Lloyd, Ben
Table(s): Crime: London Band 4 p.174, Extradition: London Band 1 p.240

Lloyd, Preston
Table(s): Personal Injury: Scotland (Bar) Band 1 p.520

Lloyd, Trefor
Table(s): Agriculture & Rural Affairs: Wales & Chester (Bar) Band 1 p.43

Lloyd-Jones, John
Profile: p.657
Table(s): Crime: Midlands (Bar) Band 3 p.181

Lock, David
Table(s): Court of Protection: Health & Welfare: All Circuits Band 2 p.165

Lockey, John
Table(s): Commercial Dispute Resolution: London Band 5 p.109, Insurance: London Band 1 p.315

Lockhart, Andrew
Table(s): Crime: Midlands (Bar) Band 3 p.181

Lockhart-Mummery, Christopher
Table(s): Planning: London Band 1 p.386

Lodder, Peter
Table(s): Crime: London Band 2 p.173, Financial Crime: London Band 3 p.266

Lofthouse, Simon
Profile: p.658
Table(s): Construction: London Band 4 p.146, International Arbitration: Construction/Engineering: London Band 2 p.333, Professional Negligence: Technology & Construction: London Band 2 p.428

Lomas, Mark
Table(s): Clinical Negligence: Western (Bar) Band 2 p.106, Personal Injury: Western (Bar) Band 2

Lomas, Mark
Table(s): Mediators: All Circuits Band 1 p.348

Lomnicka, Eva
Profile: p.658
Table(s): Consumer Law: London Band 1 p.156, Financial Services: London Band 2 p.276

Longstaff, Benjamin
Table(s): Intellectual Property: London Up-and-coming individuals p.322

Lopez, Juan
Table(s): Licensing: London Band 3 p.337

Lopez, Paul
Table(s): Court of Protection: Health & Welfare: All Circuits Band 2 p.165, Family/Matrimonial: Midlands (Bar) Band 1 p.254

Lord, David W
Profile: p.658
Table(s): Insurance: London Band 3 p.315, Offshore: London Band 2 p.353

Lord, Richard
Table(s): Shipping & Commodities: London Band 3 p.465

Lord, Tim
Table(s): Banking & Finance: London Band 1 p.49, Commercial Dispute Resolution: London Band 2 p.109, Professional Negligence: London Band 3 p.420

Loudon, Mary
Table(s): Family/Matrimonial: Scotland (Bar) Band 2 p.517

Love, Sarah
Table(s): Administrative & Public Law: London Band 4 p.28, Competition Law: London Band 3 p.142

Love, Steve
Profile: p.658
Table(s): Personal Injury: Scotland (Bar) Band 1 p.520

Loveday, Mark
Profile: p.658
Table(s): Real Estate Litigation: London Band 5 p.443

Lovell-Pank, Dorian
Table(s): Crime: London Band 3 p.173

Lowe, Mark
Table(s): Local Government: London Band 3 p.340, Planning: London Band 1 p.386

Lowe, Rupert
Table(s): Crime: Western (Bar) Band 2 p.192, Health & Safety: Western (Bar) Band 2 p.296

Lowe, Thomas
Table(s): Offshore: London Band 3 p.353

Lowe, Vaughan
Table(s): Public International Law: London Star individuals p.435

Lowenstein, Paul
Table(s): Commercial Dispute Resolution: London Band 3 p.109, Telecommunications: London Band 2 p.491

Lownds, Peter
Profile: p.658
Table(s): Crime: London Band 3 p.174

Luba, Jan
Table(s): Administrative & Public Law: London Band 2 p.27, Social Housing: London Star individuals p.471

Lucking, Adrienne
Profile: p.658
Table(s): Crime: Midlands (Bar) New Silks p.181

Luh, Shu Shin
Table(s): Administrative & Public Law: London Band 4 p.28, Community Care: London Band 2 p.132, Education: London Band 4 p.203

Lumsdon, Kate
Table(s): Crime: London Band 3 p.174

Lydiard, Andrew
Table(s): Aviation: London Band 2 p.47, Insurance: London Band 3 p.315

Lykiardopoulos, Andrew
Profile: p.658
Table(s): Intellectual Property: London New Silks p.322

Lynagh, Richard
Table(s): Personal Injury: London Band 1 p.367

Lynch, Adrian
Profile: p.659
Table(s): Employment: London Band 3 p.207

Lynch, Ben
Profile: p.659
Table(s): Commercial Dispute Resolution: London Band 5 p.110, Insurance: London Band 2 p.316, Professional Negligence: London Band 4 p.421, Telecommunications: London Band 3 p.491

Lynch, Jerome
Profile: p.659
Table(s): Crime: London Band 5 p.173

Lyness, Scott
Table(s): Planning: London Band 1 p.386

Lyon, Stephen
Table(s): Family: Matrimonial Finance: London Band 4 p.244

Lyons, Timothy
Profile: p.659
Table(s): Tax: Indirect Tax: London Band 2 p.486

M

Mabb, David
Table(s): Company: London Band 1 p.135

Mably, Louis
Table(s): Administrative & Public Law: London Band 4 p.28, Crime: London Band 2 p.174

Monkcom, Stephen
Table(s): Licensing: London Band 3 p.337

Monnington, Bruce
Table(s): Agriculture & Rural Affairs: South Eastern (Bar) Band 1 p.43

Montagu-Smith, Tom
Table(s): Construction: London Band 3 p.147

Montgomery, Clare
Table(s): Administrative & Public Law: London Band 2 p.27, Civil Liberties & Human Rights: London Band 2 p.81, Crime: London Star individuals p.173, Extradition: London Star individuals p.240, Financial Crime: London Star individuals p.266, Financial Crime: Corporates: London Band 1 p.266, Fraud: Civil: London Band 1 p.281, POCA Work & Asset Forfeiture: All Circuits Band 2 p.397

Montgomery, Kristina
Table(s): Crime: Midlands (Bar) Band 3 p.181

Monty, Simon
Profile: p.675
Table(s): Professional Discipline: London Band 4 p.410

Moody, Neil
Table(s): Insurance: London Band 3 p.315, Product Liability: London Band 3 p.406, Professional Negligence: Technology & Construction: London Band 2 p.428, Property Damage: London Band 1 p.433

Moody-Stuart, Thomas
Profile: p.675
Table(s): Information Technology: London Band 3 p.304, Intellectual Property: London Band 1 p.322, Media & Entertainment: London Band 2 p.345

Moollan, Salim
Table(s): International Arbitration: General Commercial & Insurance: London Band 2 p.328

Moon, Angus
Profile: p.675
Table(s): Clinical Negligence: London Band 1 p.92, Professional Discipline: London Band 1 p.410

Mooney, Giles
Profile: p.675
Table(s): Personal Injury: London Band 3 p.368

Mooney, Stephen
Table(s): Crime: Western (Bar) Band 1 p.192

Moore, Craig
Table(s): Sport: The Regions Band 2 p.480

Moore, Martin
Profile: p.675
Table(s): Company: London Star individuals p.135

Moore, Miranda
Profile: p.676
Table(s): Crime: London Band 2 p.173

Moore, Oliver
Table(s): Costs Litigation: Western (Bar) Band 1 p.163

Moorhouse, Brendon
Table(s): Environment: Western (Bar) Band 1 p.236

Moran, Andrew
Profile: p.676
Table(s): Fraud: Civil: London Band 4 p.282

Moran, Vincent
Profile: p.676
Table(s): Construction: London Band 3 p.146, Energy & Natural Resources: London Band 4 p.226, International Arbitration: Construction/Engineering: London Band 2 p.333, Professional Negligence: Technology & Construction: London Band 3 p.428

Morgan, Alison
Table(s): Crime: London Band 1 p.174

Morgan, Charles
Table(s): Environment: North Eastern (Bar) Band 1 p.235

Morgan, Edward
Table(s): Employment: Northern (Bar) Band 1 p.221

Morgan, Gemma
Table(s): Commercial Dispute Resolution: London Band 5 p.110, Shipping & Commodities: London Band 4 p.465

Morgan, James
Profile: p.676
Table(s): Chancery: Midlands (Bar) Band 1 p.73, Commercial Dispute Resolution: Midlands (Bar) Band 1 p.125, Restructuring/Insolvency: Midlands (Bar) Band 1 p.461

Morgan, Jamie
Profile: p.676
Table(s): Employment: North Eastern (Bar) Band 3 p.220

Morgan, Richard
Profile: p.676
Table(s): Commercial Dispute Resolution: London Band 5 p.109, Fraud: Civil: London Band 3 p.281

Morgan, Sarah
Profile: p.676
Table(s): Family: Children: London Band 2 p.245

Morgan, Simon
Table(s): Crime: Western (Bar) Band 1 p.192, Health & Safety: Western (Bar) Band 2 p.290

Morgan, Stephen
Table(s): Planning: London Band 3 p.386

Morgans, John
Table(s): Crime: South Eastern (Bar) Band 2 p.188

Moriarty, Stephen
Profile: p.676
Table(s): Aviation: London Band 2 p.47, Commercial Dispute Resolution: London Band 4 p.109, Insurance: London Band 2 p.315, Professional Negligence: London Band 3 p.420

Morley, Stephen
Profile: p.677
Table(s): Police Law: Mainly Defendant: All Circuits Band 2 p.402

Morrell, Roxanne
Profile: p.677
Table(s): Crime: London Band 5 p.174

Morris, Anna
Table(s): Civil Liberties & Human Rights: London Band 4 p.82, Police Law: Mainly Claimant: All Circuits Band 2 p.400

Morris, David
Table(s): Professional Discipline: London Band 1 p.411

Morris, Fenella
Table(s): Administrative & Public Law: London Band 3 p.27, Civil Liberties & Human Rights: London Band 4 p.81, Community Care: London Band 2 p.132, Court of Protection: Health & Welfare: All Circuits Band 1 p.165, Education: London Band 3 p.203, Local Government: London Band 3 p.340, Professional Discipline: London Band 4 p.410

Morris, Stephen
Table(s): Competition Law: London Band 1 p.142

Morrison, Craig
Table(s): Banking & Finance: London Band 4 p.50

Morrison, Matthew
Profile: p.677
Table(s): Fraud: Civil: London Band 4 p.282

Morse, Malcolm
Profile: p.677
Table(s): Crime: Midlands (Bar) Band 3 p.181

Morshead, Timothy
Table(s): Agriculture & Rural Affairs: London Band 3 p.41, Real Estate Litigation: London Band 2 p.442

Mort, Justin
Profile: p.677
Table(s): Construction: London New Silks p.146, Energy & Natural Resources: London New Silks p.226

Mortimer, Sophie
Profile: p.677
Table(s): Clinical Negligence: London Band 4 p.93, Police Law: Mainly Defendant: All Circuits Band 3 p.402

Mortimore, Simon
Profile: p.677
Table(s): Restructuring/Insolvency: London Band 3 p.455

Morton, Keith
Profile: p.677
Table(s): Health & Safety: London Band 2 p.291, Inquests & Public Inquiries: London Band 2 p.309

Moser, Philip
Profile: p.677
Table(s): European Law: London Band 2 p.237, Public Procurement: London Band 2 p.439, Tax: Indirect Tax: London Band 3 p.486

Moses, Stephen
Profile: p.677
Table(s): Crime: London Band 3 p.174

Moss, Gabriel
Table(s): Chancery: Commercial: London Band 1 p.59, Company: London Band 2 p.135, Restructuring/Insolvency: London Star individuals p.455

Moss, Joanne
Table(s): Agriculture & Rural Affairs: London Band 1 p.41

Moss, Jonathan
Table(s): Intellectual Property: London Up-and-coming individuals p.322

Moss, Nicholas
Table(s): Inquests & Public Inquiries: London Band 2 p.309

Motraghi, Nadia
Profile: p.678
Table(s): Employment: London Band 4 p.208

Mott, Philip
Table(s): Crime: Western (Bar) Band 3 p.192

Mott, Richard
Profile: p.678
Table(s): Banking & Finance: London Band 4 p.50, Commercial Dispute Resolution: London Band 4 p.110

Mould, Timothy
Table(s): Local Government: London Band 3 p.340, Planning: London Band 1 p.386

Moules, Richard
Table(s): Planning: London Band 5 p.386

Moulson, Peter
Table(s): Crime: North Eastern (Bar) Band 2 p.184

Mountfield, Helen
Profile: p.678
Table(s): Administrative & Public Law: London Band 2 p.27, Civil Liberties & Human Rights: London Band 2 p.81, Education: London Band 1 p.203, Employment: London Band 4 p.207, Local Government: London Band 4 p.340

Mountford, Tom
Table(s): Sport: London Up-and-coming individuals p.478

Moverley Smith, Stephen
Table(s): Chancery: Commercial: London Band 3 p.59, Company: London Band 2 p.135, Fraud: Civil: London Band 3 p.281, Offshore: London Band 1 p.353, Restructuring/Insolvency: London Band 4 p.455

Mowschenson, Terence
Table(s): Chancery: Commercial: London Band 1 p.59, Commercial Dispute Resolution: London Band 5 p.109, Company: London Band 1 p.135, Offshore: London Band 2 p.353

Moxon Browne, Robert
Profile: p.678
Table(s): Insurance: London Band 4 p.315, Professional Negligence: London Band 4 p.420, Property Damage: London Band 1 p.433

Moynihan, Gerry
Table(s): Administrative & Public Law: Scotland (Bar) Band 1 p.507, Commercial Dispute Resolution: Scotland (Bar) Band 1 p.512

Moys, Clive
Table(s): Planning: London Band 5 p.386

Muir, Nicola
Profile: p.678
Table(s): Real Estate Litigation: London Band 3 p.443

Mulcahy, Jane
Table(s): Employment: London New Silks p.207, Sport: London New Silks p.478

Mulcahy, Leigh-Ann
Profile: p.678
Table(s): Insurance: London Band 4 p.315, Product Liability: London Band 2 p.406, Professional Negligence: London Band 4 p.420

Mulholland, Helen
Profile: p.679
Table(s): Clinical Negligence: Northern (Bar) Band 2 p.103

Mullen, Jayne
Profile: p.679
Table(s): Family/Matrimonial: Midlands (Bar) Band 1 p.254

Mullen, Mark
Table(s): Charities: London Band 2 p.79, Court of Protection: Property & Affairs: All Circuits Band 1 p.169

Mullins, Mark
Table(s): Court of Protection: Health & Welfare: All Circuits Band 3 p.165

Mullis, Roger
Table(s): Chancery: Traditional: London Band 3 p.67

Muman, Tony
Table(s): Immigration: Midlands (Bar) Band 2 p.302

Mumford, David
Profile: p.679
Table(s): Banking & Finance: London Band 1 p.50, Chancery: Commercial: London Star individuals p.60, Commercial Dispute Resolution: London Band 1 p.110, Company: London Band 2 p.135, Fraud: Civil: London Band 1 p.282, Offshore: London Band 2 p.353, Partnership: London Band 3 p.359

Smith, Andrew
Table(s): Clinical Negligence: Scotland (Bar) Band 1 p.510, Personal Injury: Scotland (Bar) Band 2 p.520

Smith, Barry
Profile: p.723
Table(s): Health & Safety: Scotland (Bar) Band 1 p.518

Smith, Christopher
Table(s): Shipping & Commodities: London Band 3 p.465

Smith, Christopher M
Table(s): Shipping & Commodities: London Band 2 p.465

Smith, Howard
Table(s): Court of Protection: Property & Affairs: All Circuits Band 2 p.169

Smith, Ian
Profile: p.723
Table(s): Fraud: Civil: London Band 3 p.282, POCA Work & Asset Forfeiture: All Circuits Band 1 p.397

Smith, Jamie
Profile: p.723
Table(s): Professional Negligence: London Star individuals p.421

Smith, Jane
Table(s): Administrative & Public Law: Scotland (Bar) Band 2 p.507, Commercial Dispute Resolution: Scotland (Bar) Band 3 p.512

Smith, Joan
Profile: p.723
Table(s): Licensing: North Eastern (Bar) Band 2 p.339

Smith, Joanna
Table(s): Chancery: Commercial: London Band 4 p.59, Construction: London Band 3 p.146, Professional Negligence: London Band 2 p.420

Smith, Joel
Profile: p.723
Table(s): Extradition: London Band 2 p.240

Smith, Julia
Profile: p.723
Table(s): Consumer Law: London Band 1 p.156, Financial Services: London Band 3 p.276

Smith, Julian
Table(s): Crime: North Eastern (Bar) Band 3 p.184

Smith, Kassie
Table(s): Competition Law: London Band 2 p.142, Environment: London Band 3 p.231, European Law: London Band 2 p.237, Telecommunications: London Band 3 p.491

Smith, Kerry
Table(s): Employment: Northern (Bar) Band 2 p.221

Smith, Leonard
Profile: p.724
Table(s): Financial Crime: London Band 3 p.266

Smith, Marion
Table(s): Construction: London Band 3 p.147

Smith, Matthew
Profile: p.724
Table(s): Charities: London Band 1 p.79

Smith, Matthew
Profile: p.724
Table(s): Costs Litigation: Northern (Bar) Band 2 p.162

Smith, Michael
Table(s): Clinical Negligence: Northern (Bar) Band 2 p.103

Smith, Nicholas G
Table(s): Employment: Western (Bar) Band 1 p.223

Smith, Peter
Table(s): Charities: London Band 3 p.79

Smith, Peter
Table(s): Health & Safety: Northern (Bar) Band 2 p.296

Smith, Richard
Table(s): Crime: Western (Bar) Star individuals p.192, Sport: The Regions Band 1 p.480

Smith, Robert
Table(s): Crime: North Eastern (Bar) Star individuals p.184, Health & Safety: North Eastern (Bar) Band 1 p.295

Smith, Sally
Table(s): Clinical Negligence: London Band 3 p.92, Inquests & Public Inquiries: London Band 3 p.309

Smith, Shaun
Table(s): Crime: Midlands (Bar) Band 2 p.181

Smith, Stephanie
Profile: p.724
Table(s): Social Housing: London Up-and-coming individuals p.471

Smith, Stephen
Profile: p.724
Table(s): Chancery: Commercial: London Band 1 p.59, Commercial Dispute Resolution: London Band 1 p.109, Fraud: Civil: London Band 1 p.281, Offshore: London Band 2 p.353

Smith, Tom
Profile: p.724
Table(s): Banking & Finance: London New Silks p.49, Chancery: Commercial: London New Silks p.59, Commercial Dispute Resolution: London New Silks p.109, Company: London New Silks p.135, Restructuring/Insolvency: London New Silks p.455

Smith, Tyrone
Table(s): Crime: London New Silks p.173

Smitten, Ben
Table(s): Crime: London Band 3 p.174

Smouha, Joe
Table(s): Art and Cultural Property Law : London Band 2 p.45, Banking & Finance: London Band 2 p.49, Commercial Dispute Resolution: London Band 1 p.109, Fraud: Civil: London Band 1 p.281, International Arbitration: General Commercial & Insurance: London Band 1 p.328, International Arbitration: Arbitrators: London Band 1 p.335

Snarr, Matthew
Table(s): Employment: Northern (Bar) Band 2 p.221, Health & Safety: Northern (Bar) Band 2 p.296, Motor Insurance Fraud: All Circuits Band 2 p.350, Personal Injury: Northern (Bar) Band 2 p.380

Snell, John
Table(s): Clinical Negligence: Western (Bar) Band 1 p.106, Personal Injury: Western (Bar) Band 1

Snowden, Richard
Table(s): Banking & Finance: London Band 2 p.49, Commercial Dispute Resolution: London Band 3 p.109, Company: London Star individuals p.135, Offshore: London Band 3 p.353, Restructuring/Insolvency: London Star individuals p.455

Snowden, Steven
Profile: p.724
Table(s): Personal Injury: London Band 1 p.368, Personal Injury: Industrial Disease: London p.368

Soares, Patrick
Profile: p.724
Table(s): Tax: London Band 2 p.482, Tax: Indirect Tax: London Band 3 p.486, Tax: Private Client: London Band 2 p.488

Soertsz, Lauren
Table(s): Crime: London Band 4 p.174

Solley, Stephen
Profile: p.725
Table(s): Crime: London Band 5 p.173

Solomon, Adam
Table(s): Employment: London Band 2 p.208

Soole, Michael
Profile: p.725
Table(s): Construction: London Band 2 p.146, Professional Negligence: Technology & Construction: London Band 3 p.428

Souter, Catherine
Table(s): Personal Injury: North Eastern (Bar) Band 2 p.379

Southern, David
Profile: p.725
Table(s): Tax: Indirect Tax: London New Silks p.486

Southern, Richard
Table(s): Shipping & Commodities: London Band 2 p.465

Southey, Hugh
Profile: p.725
Table(s): Administrative & Public Law: London Band 4 p.27, Civil Liberties & Human Rights: London Band 2 p.81, Immigration: London Band 1 p.297, Police Law: Mainly Claimant: All Circuits Band 1 p.400

Southgate, Jonathan
Profile: p.725
Table(s): Family: Matrimonial Finance: London Band 3 p.244

Sowersby, Robert
Table(s): Clinical Negligence: Western (Bar) Band 1 p.106

Spain, Timothy
Profile: p.725
Table(s): Family/Matrimonial: North Eastern (Bar) Band 2 p.256

Spalton, George
Profile: p.725
Table(s): Commercial Dispute Resolution: London Band 5 p.110, International Arbitration: General Commercial & Insurance: London Band 3 p.328, Professional Discipline: London Band 5 p.411, Professional Negligence: London Band 4 p.421

Sparks, Paula
Table(s): Clinical Negligence: London Band 2 p.93

Speaight, Anthony
Profile: p.725
Table(s): Construction: London Band 3 p.146

Spearman, Richard
Profile: p.726
Table(s): Data Protection: London Band 1 p.195, Defamation/Privacy: London Band 1 p.199, Media & Entertainment: London Band 1 p.345

Speck, Adrian
Profile: p.726
Table(s): Information Technology: London Band 3 p.304, Intellectual Property: London Band 2 p.322, Media & Entertainment: London Band 3 p.345

Speir, John
Profile: p.726
Table(s): Family/Matrimonial: Scotland (Bar) Band 1 p.517

Speker, Adam
Table(s): Defamation/Privacy: London Band 1 p.199

Spence, Simon
Profile: p.726
Table(s): Crime: South Eastern (Bar) Band 3 p.188

Spence, Stephen
Profile: p.726
Table(s): Crime: South Eastern (Bar) Band 3 p.188

Spencer, Andrew
Profile: p.726
Table(s): Professional Negligence: London Band 4 p.421

Spencer, Martin
Profile: p.726
Table(s): Clinical Negligence: London Band 1 p.92

Spencer, Michael
Table(s): Product Liability: London Band 2 p.406

Spencer, Paul
Profile: p.726
Table(s): Professional Discipline: London Band 4 p.411

Spencer, Timothy
Table(s): Crime: London Band 2 p.173, Crime: Midlands (Bar) Band 2 p.181

Spens, David
Table(s): Crime: London Band 2 p.173

Spink, Andrew
Table(s): Pensions: London Band 1 p.363

Spinks, Roderick
Table(s): Family/Matrimonial: South Eastern (Bar) Band 3 p.259

Spiro, Dafna
Table(s): Crime: London Band 6 p.174

Spitz, Derek
Table(s): Competition Law: London Band 3 p.142

Sprinz, Lucy
Profile: p.726
Table(s): Family: Children: London Up-and-coming individuals p.245

Sproull, Nicholas
Table(s): Family/Matrimonial: Western (Bar) Band 1 p.262

Spurrier, Martha
Table(s): Inquests & Public Inquiries: London Up-and-coming individuals p.309

Squires, Daniel
Table(s): Administrative & Public Law: London Band 1 p.28, Civil Liberties & Human Rights: London Star individuals p.82, Education: London Band 2 p.203

St Quintin, Thomas
Table(s): Intellectual Property: London Band 3 p.322, Media & Entertainment: London Band 3 p.345

St Ville, James
Profile: p.727
Table(s): Information Technology: London Band 3 p.304, Intellectual Property: London Band 3 p.322

Stacey, Dan
Profile: p.727
Table(s): Costs Litigation: London Band 4 p.160

Stacey, Myriam
Table(s): Real Estate Litigation: London Band 1 p.443

Staff, Marcus
Table(s): Chancery: Commercial: London Band 3 p.60

Stagg, Paul
Profile: p.727
Table(s): Personal Injury: London Band 3 p.368, Police Law: Mainly Defendant: All Circuits Band 2 p.402

Stallworthy, Nicolas
Table(s): Chancery: Commercial: London Band 3 p.59, Pensions: London Band 1 p.363

Stamp, Abigail
Table(s): Clinical Negligence: Western (Bar) Band 2 p.106

Stanage, Nick
Table(s): Civil Liberties & Human Rights: Northern (Bar) Band 1 p.89, Immigration: Northern (Bar) Band 1 p.303, Police Law: Mainly Claimant: All Circuits Band 2 p.400

Stanbury, Matthew
Table(s): Administrative & Public Law: Northern (Bar) Band 2 p.39, Civil Liberties & Human Rights: Northern (Bar) Band 2 p.89

Stancombe, Barry
Table(s): POCA Work & Asset Forfeiture: All Circuits Band 2 p.397

Stanistreet, Penelope
Table(s): Family/Matrimonial: North Eastern (Bar) Band 3 p.256

Stanley, Clare
Table(s): Professional Negligence: London Band 4 p.421

Stanley, Paul
Table(s): Commercial Dispute Resolution: London Band 3 p.109, Fraud: Civil: London Band 3 p.281, Insurance: London Band 2 p.315

Stanfield, Piers
Profile: p.727
Table(s): Construction: London Band 3 p.146

Stark, James
Table(s): Social Housing: Northern (Bar) Band 1 p.476

Starks, Nicholas
Profile: p.727
Table(s): Family/Matrimonial: Midlands (Bar) Band 1 p.254

Start, Angharad
Table(s): Restructuring/Insolvency: London Band 5 p.455

Starte, Harvey
Profile: p.727
Table(s): Defamation/Privacy: London Band 3 p.199

Staunton, Ulick
Table(s): Chancery: Commercial: London Band 3 p.60, Chancery: Traditional: London Band 3 p.67, Commercial Dispute Resolution: London Band 4 p.110, Court of Protection: Property & Affairs: All Circuits Band 3 p.169

Stead, Richard
Table(s): Commercial Dispute Resolution: Western (Bar) Band 2 p.130, Construction: Western (Bar) Band 2 p.154, Personal Injury: Western (Bar) Band 1

Steel, John
Profile: p.727
Table(s): Aviation: London Band 3 p.47, Planning: London Band 2 p.386

Steele, Gordon
Profile: p.727
Table(s): Planning & Environment: Scotland (Bar) Band 2 p.522

Steele, Iain
Table(s): Administrative & Public Law: London Band 4 p.28, Civil Liberties & Human Rights: London Band 3 p.82

Stein, Sam
Table(s): Crime: London Band 4 p.173

Steinberg, Harry
Profile: p.727
Table(s): Personal Injury: London Band 1 p.368, Personal Injury: Industrial Disease: London p.368

Steinert, Jonathan
Profile: p.727
Table(s): Real Estate Litigation: London Band 3 p.443

Steinfeld, Alan
Table(s): Chancery: Commercial: London Band 1 p.59, Chancery: Traditional: London Band 1 p.67, Commercial Dispute Resolution: London Band 2 p.109, Company: London Band 1 p.135, Fraud: Civil: London Band 2 p.281, Offshore: London Band 1 p.353, Partnership: London Band 2 p.359, Pensions: London Band 3 p.363, Professional Negligence: London Band 2 p.420, Restructuring/Insolvency: London Band 4 p.455, Trusts: London Band 1 p.498

Stephens, Andrew
Table(s): Crime: South Eastern (Bar) Band 3 p.188

Stephens, Jessica
Profile: p.728
Table(s): Construction: London Band 3 p.147

Stephens, John
Table(s): Chancery: Commercial: London Band 3 p.60, Commercial Dispute Resolution: London Band 5 p.110, Pensions: London Band 4 p.363

Stephenson, Christopher
Profile: p.728
Table(s): Clinical Negligence: London Band 3 p.93, Personal Injury: London Band 2 p.368

Stephenson, David
Table(s): Clinical Negligence: Scotland (Bar) Band 2 p.510

Stern, David
Profile: p.728
Table(s): Financial Crime: London Band 4 p.267

Stern, Ian
Table(s): Crime: London Band 3 p.173, Professional Discipline: London Band 1 p.410

Sternberg, Daniel
Profile: p.728
Table(s): Extradition: London Band 3 p.240

Sternberg, Michael
Table(s): Family: Matrimonial Finance: London Band 3 p.244, Family: Children: London Band 3 p.244

Stevens, Andrew
Profile: p.728
Table(s): Shipping & Commodities: London Up-and-coming individuals p.465

Stevens, Howard
Table(s): Personal Injury: London Band 3 p.367, Travel: International Personal Injury: London Band 2 p.495

Stevens-Hoare, Brie
Table(s): Real Estate Litigation: London Band 4 p.442

Steward, Claire
Profile: p.728
Table(s): Clinical Negligence: Northern (Bar) Band 2 p.103

Stewart, Roger
Profile: p.728
Table(s): Construction: London Band 2 p.146, Insurance: London Band 3 p.315, International Arbitration: General Commercial & Insurance: London Band 3 p.328, Professional Negligence: London Star individuals p.420, Professional Negligence: Technology & Construction: London Band 1 p.428

Stewart, Toby
Table(s): Personal Injury: Midlands (Bar) Band 2 p.377

Stewart Smith, Rodney
Profile: p.728
Table(s): Chancery: Traditional: London Band 4 p.67

Steyn, Karen
Profile: p.728
Table(s): Administrative & Public Law: London New Silks p.27, Civil Liberties & Human Rights: London New Silks p.81, Data Protection: London New Silks p.195, Local Government: London New Silks p.340

Stickler, Rebecca
Table(s): Administrative & Public Law: Wales & Chester (Bar) Up-and-coming individuals p.40

Stilitz, Daniel
Profile: p.729
Table(s): Administrative & Public Law: London Band 2 p.27, Employment: London Band 2 p.207

Stinchcombe, Paul
Table(s): Planning: London Band 2 p.386

Stoate, Tom
Table(s): Inquests & Public Inquiries: London Up-and-coming individuals p.309

Stobart, Alice
Table(s): Employment: Scotland (Bar) Band 2 p.516

Stockill, David
Table(s): Chancery: Midlands (Bar) Band 2 p.73

Stockley, Ruth
Profile: p.729
Table(s): Environment: Northern (Bar) Band 1 p.235, Planning: Northern (Bar) Band 2 p.394

Stockwell, Matthew
Table(s): Administrative & Public Law: Northern (Bar) Band 3 p.39, Court of Protection: Health & Welfare: All Circuits Band 3 p.165, Personal Injury: Northern (Bar) Band 2 p.380

Stokes, Mary
Profile: p.729
Table(s): Company: London Band 2 p.135

Stone, Christopher
Profile: p.729
Table(s): Employment: London Up-and-coming individuals p.208, Tax: London Up-and-coming individuals p.482

Stone, Judy
Profile: p.729
Table(s): Employment: London Band 3 p.208

Stone, Kate
Table(s): Administrative & Public Law: Northern (Bar) Band 2 p.39

Stone, Lucy
Profile: p.729
Table(s): Family: Matrimonial Finance: London Band 1 p.244

Stone, Sally
Profile: p.729
Table(s): Family: Children: London Band 4 p.245

Stonefrost, Hilary
Table(s): Company: London Band 2 p.135, Restructuring/Insolvency: London Band 2 p.455

Stoner, Christopher
Profile: p.729
Table(s): Real Estate Litigation: London Band 3 p.442, Sport: London Band 5 p.478

Stonor, Nicholas
Profile: p.729
Table(s): Family/Matrimonial: North Eastern (Bar) Band 3 p.256

Storey, Jeremy
Profile: p.730
Table(s): Information Technology: London Band 1 p.304

Storey, Paul
Profile: p.730
Table(s): Family: Children: London Band 1 p.245

Storey, Tom
Table(s): Crime: North Eastern (Bar) Band 2 p.184

Stout, Holly
Profile: p.730
Table(s): Data Protection: London Band 2 p.195, Education: London Band 1 p.203, Employment: London Band 4 p.208

Strachan, James
Table(s): Administrative & Public Law: London Band 4 p.27, Civil Liberties & Human Rights: London Band 4 p.81, Environment: London Band 3 p.231, Local Government: London Band 3 p.340, Planning: London Band 3 p.386

Straker, Timothy
Profile: p.730
Table(s): Environment: London Band 3 p.231, Local Government: London Band 1 p.340, Planning: London Band 3 p.386

Stratford, Jemima
Table(s): Administrative & Public Law: London Band 3 p.27, Civil Liberties & Human Rights: London Band 4 p.81, Competition Law: London Band 2 p.142, European Law: London Band 1 p.237

Straw, Adam
Table(s): Administrative & Public Law: London Band 1 p.28, Civil Liberties & Human Rights: London Band 2 p.82, Inquests & Public Inquiries: London Band 1 p.309, Police Law: Mainly Claimant: All Circuits Band 2 p.400

Streatfeild-James, David
Table(s): Construction: London Star individuals p.146, Energy & Natural Resources: London Band 1 p.226, Information Technology: London Band 1 p.304, International Arbitration: Construction/Engineering: London Band 1 p.333, Professional Negligence: Technology & Construction: London Band 1 p.428

Street, Amy
Profile: p.730
Table(s): Administrative & Public Law: London Band 4 p.28, Court of Protection: Health & Welfare: All Circuits Band 1 p.165

Strong, Benjamin
Profile: p.730
Table(s): Banking & Finance: London New Silks p.49, Commercial Dispute Resolution: London New Silks p.109, Financial Services: London New Silks p.276

Strudwick, Linda
Profile: p.730
Table(s): Crime: London Band 3 p.174

Stuart, Damian
Profile: p.730
Table(s): Family: Children: London Up-and-coming individuals p.245

Stuart, Philip
Table(s): Professional Discipline: Scotland (Bar) Band 2 p.523

Stubbs, Andrew
Table(s): Crime: North Eastern (Bar) Band 3 p.184

Stubbs, Rebecca
Profile: p.730
Table(s): Company: London Band 2 p.135, Restructuring/Insolvency: London Band 4 p.455

Stubbs, Richard
Profile: p.731
Table(s): **Employment**: North Eastern (Bar) **Band 2** p.220

Studd, Anne
Profile: p.731
Table(s): **Police Law: Mainly Defendant**: All Circuits **Band 2** p.402

Studer, Mark
Profile: p.731
Table(s): **Chancery: Traditional**: London **Band 2** p.67, **Charities**: London **Band 2** p.79

Sturman, Jim
Profile: p.731
Table(s): **Crime**: London **Band 1** p.173, **Financial Crime**: London **Band 1** p.266, **Financial Crime: Corporates**: London **Band 2** p.266, **Health & Safety**: London **Band 2** p.291, **Sport**: London **Band 1** p.478

Sturrock, John
Table(s): **Mediators**: All Circuits **Band 2** p.348

Sugarman, Andrew
Table(s): **Employment**: North Eastern (Bar) **Band 1** p.220

Sullivan, James
Profile: p.731
Table(s): **Personal Injury**: London **Up-and-coming individuals** p.368

Sullivan, Lisa
Profile: p.731
Table(s): **Clinical Negligence**: London **Band 2** p.93

Summers, Alan A.
Profile: p.732
Table(s): **Restructuring/Insolvency**: Scotland (Bar) **Band 2** p.526

Summers, Ben
Profile: p.732
Table(s): **Financial Crime**: London **Band 2** p.267, **Financial Crime: Corporates**: London **Band 2** p.267

Summers, Gary
Table(s): **Financial Crime**: London **Band 2** p.267

Summers, Mark
Profile: p.732
Table(s): **Crime**: London **New Silks** p.173, **Extradition**: London **New Silks** p.240

Sumnall, Charlene
Profile: p.732
Table(s): **Consumer Law**: London **Band 3** p.156

Sumner, Emma
Table(s): **Family: Matrimonial Finance**: London **Band 2** p.244

Susman, Peter
Profile: p.732
Table(s): **Information Technology**: London **Band 2** p.304

Sutcliffe, Andrew
Table(s): **Banking & Finance**: London **Band 2** p.49, **Commercial Dispute Resolution**: London **Band 3** p.109, **Fraud: Civil**: London **Band 3** p.281, **Media & Entertainment**: London **Band 2** p.345

Suterwalla, Azeem
Profile: p.732
Table(s): **Administrative & Public Law**: London **Band 3** p.28, **Civil Liberties & Human Rights**: London **Band 4** p.82, **Community Care**: London **Band 2** p.132

Sutherland, Jessica
Table(s): **Insurance**: London **Band 3** p.316, **Shipping & Commodities**: London **Band 4** p.465

Sutherland, Lauren
Table(s): **Clinical Negligence**: Scotland (Bar) **Band 1** p.510

Sutherland, Robert
Profile: p.732
Table(s): **Agriculture & Rural Affairs**: Scotland (Bar) **Band 1** p.509

Sutton, David
Table(s): **International Arbitration: Arbitrators**: London **Band 1** p.335

Sutton, Emma
Table(s): **Family/Matrimonial**: Wales & Chester (Bar) **Up-and-coming individuals** p.261

Sutton, Mark
Table(s): **Employment**: London **Band 3** p.207, **Professional Discipline**: London **Band 2** p.410

Swain, Jon
Profile: p.732
Table(s): **Crime**: London **Band 4** p.174

Swainston, Michael
Table(s): **Commercial Dispute Resolution**: London **Band 4** p.109, **Fraud: Civil**: London **Band 3** p.281, **Insurance**: London **Band 3** p.315, **International Arbitration: General Commercial & Insurance**: London **Band 4** p.328

Sweeney, Seamus
Table(s): **Employment**: North Eastern (Bar) **Star individuals** p.220

Sweet, Louise
Profile: p.732
Table(s): **Crime**: London **Band 6** p.174

Sweeting, Derek
Table(s): **Clinical Negligence**: London **Band 2** p.92

Swiffen, Guy
Table(s): **Family/Matrimonial**: North Eastern (Bar) **Band 2** p.256

Swift, Jonathan
Profile: p.733
Table(s): **Administrative & Public Law**: London **Band 2** p.27, **Civil Liberties & Human Rights**: London **Band 2** p.81, **Data Protection**: London **Band 2** p.195, **European Law**: London **Band 2** p.237

Swift, Malcolm
Profile: p.733
Table(s): **Crime**: London **Band 4** p.173

Swift, Malcolm
Table(s): **Crime**: North Eastern (Bar) **Band 1** p.184

Sykes, Laurent
Table(s): **Tax**: London **Band 1** p.482

Symes, Mark
Table(s): **Immigration**: London **Band 2** p.297

Symington, Anna
Table(s): **Motor Insurance Fraud**: All Circuits **Band 2** p.350, **Personal Injury**: Western (Bar) **Band 2**

Symons, Christopher
Table(s): **Commercial Dispute Resolution**: London **Band 5** p.109, **Insurance**: London **Band 2** p.315, **International Arbitration: Arbitrators**: London **Band 1** p.335, **Professional Negligence**: London **Band 2** p.420

T

Tabachnik, Andrew
Table(s): **Employment**: London **Band 4** p.208, **Planning**: London **Band 4** p.386, **Professional Discipline**: London **Band 2** p.411

Tackaberry, John
Table(s): **International Arbitration: Arbitrators**: London **Band 1** p.335

Tager, Romie
Profile: p.733
Table(s): **Chancery: Commercial**: London **Band 2** p.59, **Commercial Dispute Resolution**: London **Band 3** p.109, **Real Estate Litigation**: London **Band 3** p.442

Taggart, Nicholas
Table(s): **Real Estate Litigation**: London **Band 1** p.443

Tahir, Perican
Profile: p.733
Table(s): **Family/Matrimonial**: South Eastern (Bar) **Band 2** p.259

Tait, Andrew
Table(s): **Planning**: London **Band 3** p.386

Tait, Arabella
Table(s): **Clinical Negligence**: Scotland (Bar) **Band 2** p.510, **Personal Injury**: Scotland (Bar) **Band 2** p.520

Takatsuki, Yuli
Table(s): **Defamation/Privacy**: London **Up-and-coming individuals** p.199, **Media & Entertainment**: London **Up-and-coming individuals** p.345

Talbot, Kennedy
Table(s): **POCA Work & Asset Forfeiture**: All Circuits **Star individuals** p.397

Talbot Rice, Elspeth
Table(s): **Chancery: Traditional**: London **Band 1** p.67, **Commercial Dispute Resolution**: London **Band 4** p.109, **Fraud: Civil**: London **Band 4** p.281, **Offshore**: London **Band 1** p.353, **Partnership**: London **Band 2** p.359, **Trusts**: London **Band 1** p.498

Tam, Robin
Profile: p.733
Table(s): **Administrative & Public Law**: London **Band 2** p.27, **Inquests & Public Inquiries**: London **Band 2** p.309, **Immigration**: London **Band 1** p.297

Tambling, Richard
Profile: p.733
Table(s): **Family: Matrimonial Finance**: London **Band 4** p.244

Tamlyn, Lloyd
Table(s): **Restructuring/Insolvency**: London **Band 1** p.455

Tampakopoulos, Alex
Profile: p.733
Table(s): **Inquests & Public Inquiries**: London **Up-and-coming individuals** p.309

Tan, Charlotte
Table(s): **Insurance**: London **Band 4** p.316

Tanchel, Vivienne
Profile: p.734
Table(s): **Crime**: London **Band 6** p.174, **Financial Crime**: London **Band 3** p.267

Tanney, Anthony
Profile: p.734
Table(s): **Real Estate Litigation**: London **Band 2** p.443

Tappin, Michael
Profile: p.734
Table(s): **Intellectual Property**: London **Band 1** p.322

Tapsell, Paul
Profile: p.734
Table(s): **Local Government**: South Eastern (Bar) **Band 1** p.344

Taskis, Catherine
Profile: p.
Table(s): **Agriculture & Rural Affairs**: London **Band 2** p.41, **Real Estate Litigation**: London **Band 3** p.443

Tattersall, Simon
Table(s): **Family/Matrimonial**: South Eastern (Bar) **Band 1** p.259

Tatton-Brown, Daniel
Table(s): **Employment**: London **Band 2** p.208

Taube, Simon
Profile: p.734
Table(s): **Chancery: Traditional**: London **Star individuals** p.67, **Charities**: London **Band 1** p.79, **Offshore**: London **Band 1** p.353, **Trusts**: London **Band 1** p.498

Tavares, Nathan
Table(s): **Clinical Negligence**: London **Band 4** p.93, **Personal Injury**: London **Band 2** p.368

Taverner, Marcus
Profile: p.734
Table(s): **Construction**: London **Star individuals** p.146, **Energy & Natural Resources**: London **Band 3** p.226, **International Arbitration: Construction/Engineering**: London **Band 1** p.333, **Professional Negligence: Technology & Construction**: London **Band 1** p.428

Taylor, Christopher
Profile: p.734
Table(s): **Personal Injury**: Western (Bar) **Band 2**

Taylor, David
Table(s): **Chancery**: Midlands (Bar) **Band 1** p.73, **Commercial Dispute Resolution**: Midlands (Bar) **Band 1** p.125, **Real Estate Litigation**: Midlands (Bar) **Band 2** p.450

Taylor, John
Profile: p.734
Table(s): **Aviation**: London **Band 3** p.47, **Banking & Finance**: London **Band 4** p.49, **Commercial Dispute Resolution**: London **Band 5** p.109

Taylor, Martin
Profile: p.735
Table(s): **Crime**: London **Band 6** p.174

Taylor, Michael
Profile: p.735
Table(s): **Information Technology**: London **Band 3** p.304

Taylor, Paul
Table(s): **Crime**: London **Band 3** p.174

Taylor, Rebecca
Table(s): **Construction**: London **Band 4** p.147

Taylor, Rebecca
Table(s): **Construction**: Western (Bar) **Band 2** p.154

Taylor, Reuben
Table(s): **Planning**: London **New Silks** p.386

Taylor, Rhys
Table(s): **Family/Matrimonial**: Wales & Chester (Bar) **Band 1** p.261

Taylor, Simon
Table(s): **Crime**: South Eastern (Bar) **Band 3** p.188

Taylor, Simon
Profile: p.735
Table(s): **Public Procurement**: London **Band 3** p.439

Taylor, Simon W
Profile: p.735
Table(s): **Clinical Negligence**: London **Band 1** p.92

Teacher, Petra
Profile: p.735
Table(s): **Family: Matrimonial Finance**: London **Band 4** p.244

Tedd, Rex
Table(s): **Crime**: Midlands (Bar) **Band 2** p.181, **Health & Safety**: Midlands (Bar) **Band 1** p.295

Temmink, Robert-Jan
Table(s): **Commercial Dispute Resolution**: London **Band 4** p.110

Temple, Eleanor
Profile: p.735
Table(s): Banking & Finance: Northern (Bar) Band 1 p.57, Chancery: Northern (Bar) Band 2 p.75, Commercial Dispute Resolution: North Eastern (Bar) Band 2 p.126, Restructuring/Insolvency: North Eastern (Bar) Band 1 p.461

Tennet, Michael
Table(s): Pensions: London Band 1 p.363

ter Haar, Roger
Table(s): Commercial Dispute Resolution: London Band 5 p.109, Construction: London Band 1 p.146, Energy & Natural Resources: London Band 3 p.226, Insurance: London Band 4 p.315, International Arbitration: Construction/Engineering: London Band 1 p.333, Professional Negligence: Technology & Construction: London Band 1 p.428, Property Damage: London Band 2 p.433

Terry, Jeffrey
Profile: p.735
Table(s): Chancery: Northern (Bar) Band 2 p.75, Commercial Dispute Resolution: Northern (Bar) Band 2 p.127

Tether, Melanie
Profile: p.735
Table(s): Employment: London Band 4 p.208, Employment: Western (Bar) Band 2 p.223

Thacker, James
Profile: p.735
Table(s): Financial Crime: London Band 4 p.267

Thacker, Rajeev
Table(s): Police Law: Mainly Claimant: All Circuits Band 2 p.400

Thackray, John
Table(s): Crime: North Eastern (Bar) Band 1 p.184

Thanki, Bankim
Profile: p.735
Table(s): Aviation: London Band 1 p.47, Banking & Finance: London Band 1 p.49, Commercial Dispute Resolution: London Band 1 p.109, Financial Services: London Band 2 p.276, Fraud: Civil: London Band 1 p.281, Insurance: London Band 2 p.315, International Arbitration: General Commercial & Insurance: London Band 2 p.328, Offshore: London Band 2 p.353, Professional Negligence: London Band 2 p.420, Travel: Regulatory & Commercial: London Band 2 p.495

Thom, James
Profile: p.736
Table(s): Offshore: London Band 3 p.353

Thomas, Bryan
Profile: p.736
Table(s): Clinical Negligence: Wales & Chester (Bar) Band 1 p.105, Personal Injury: Wales & Chester (Bar) Band 1 p.383

Thomas, David
Profile: p.736
Table(s): Construction: London Band 1 p.146, International Arbitration: Construction/Engineering: London Band 2 p.333

Thomas, George
Profile: p.736
Table(s): Police Law: Mainly Defendant: All Circuits Band 2 p.402

Thomas, Leslie
Table(s): Civil Liberties & Human Rights: London New Silks p.81, Inquests & Public Inquiries: London New Silks p.309, Police Law: Mainly Claimant: All Circuits New Silks p.400

Thomas, Megan
Table(s): Planning: London Band 5 p.386

Thomas, Michael
Table(s): Tax: London Band 1 p.482, Tax: Indirect Tax: London Band 2 p.486

Thomas, Nigel
Profile: p.736
Table(s): Agriculture & Rural Affairs: London Band 1 p.41, Chancery: Traditional: London Band 4 p.67

Thomas, Owain
Table(s): Clinical Negligence: London Band 2 p.93, Inquests & Public Inquiries: London Band 3 p.309, Professional Discipline: London Band 3 p.411, Tax: Indirect Tax: London Band 1 p.486

Thomas, Owen
Table(s): Family/Matrimonial: Wales & Chester (Bar) Band 1 p.261

Thomas, Richard
Table(s): Crime: London Band 4 p.174

Thomas, Robert
Table(s): Shipping & Commodities: London Band 3 p.465

Thomas, Roger
Profile: p.736
Table(s): Tax: London New Silks p.482, Tax: Indirect Tax: London New Silks p.486

Thomas-Symonds, Nicklaus
Profile: p.736
Table(s): Chancery: Wales & Chester (Bar) Band 2 p.77, Commercial Dispute Resolution: Wales & Chester (Bar) Band 2 p.129

Thompson, Andrew
Profile: p.736
Table(s): Company: London New Silks p.135

Thompson, Andrew
Profile: p.736
Table(s): Crime: South Eastern (Bar) Band 2 p.188

Thompson, Collingwood
Table(s): Financial Crime: London Band 1 p.266

Thompson, James
Profile: p.737
Table(s): Construction: London Up-and-coming individuals p.147

Thompson, Patrick
Table(s): Crime: Northern (Bar) Band 2 p.186

Thompson, Rhodri
Profile: p.737
Table(s): Competition Law: London Band 1 p.142, European Law: London Band 1 p.237, Telecommunications: London Band 3 p.491

Thompson, Steven
Table(s): Aviation: London Band 2 p.47, Fraud: Civil: London Band 2 p.282, Restructuring/Insolvency: London Band 5 p.455

Thomson, David
Profile: p.737
Table(s): Clinical Negligence: London Band 3 p.93

Thomson, David
Profile: p.737
Table(s): Commercial Dispute Resolution: Scotland (Bar) Band 3 p.512, Company: Scotland (Bar) Band 1 p.515, Real Estate Litigation: Scotland (Bar) Band 1 p.525, Restructuring/Insolvency: Scotland (Bar) Band 1 p.526

Thomson, Malcolm
Table(s): Administrative & Public Law: Scotland (Bar) Band 2 p.507, Planning & Environment: Scotland (Bar) Band 1 p.522

Thomson, Roderick
Table(s): Tax: Scotland (Bar) Band 2 p.527

Thornhill, Andrew
Profile: p.737
Table(s): Tax: London Band 1 p.482

Thornley, Hannah
Profile: p.737
Table(s): Restructuring/Insolvency: London Band 5 p.455

Thornton, Andrew
Profile: p.737
Table(s): Company: London Star individuals p.135

Thornton, Justine
Table(s): Environment: London Band 1 p.231

Thorogood, Bernard
Profile: p.737
Table(s): Consumer Law: Midlands (Bar) Band 2 p.158, Health & Safety: Midlands (Bar) Band 1 p.295

Thorpe, Alexander
Profile: p.737
Table(s): Family: Matrimonial Finance: London Band 3 p.244

Thwaites, Ronald
Profile: p.738
Table(s): Defamation/Privacy: London Band 2 p.199, Inquests & Public Inquiries: London Band 3 p.309

Tibbitts, Simon
Table(s): Employment: Western (Bar) Up-and-coming individuals p.223

Tidmarsh, Christopher
Profile: p.738
Table(s): Chancery: Traditional: London Band 2 p.67, Pensions: London Band 3 p.363

Tillyard, James
Table(s): Family/Matrimonial: Wales & Chester (Bar) Band 1 p.261

Tindal, Jim
Profile: p.738
Table(s): Civil Liberties & Human Rights: Midlands (Bar) Band 1 p.89, Employment: Midlands (Bar) Band 2 p.218

Tindall, Paul
Table(s): Restructuring/Insolvency: Northern (Bar) Band 3 p.462

Tipples, Amanda
Profile: p.738
Table(s): Chancery: Commercial: London Band 3 p.59, Charities: London Band 2 p.79, Partnership: London Band 2 p.359, Real Estate Litigation: London Band 4 p.442

Toal, Ronan
Table(s): Immigration: London Band 1 p.297

Tod, Jonathan
Profile: p.738
Table(s): Family: Matrimonial Finance: London Band 2 p.244, Family: Children: London Band 2 p.244

Todd, James
Table(s): Personal Injury: London Band 1 p.368, Personal Injury: Industrial Disease: London p.368

Todd, Martin
Table(s): Family/Matrimonial: North Eastern (Bar) Band 3 p.256

Todd, Michael
Profile: p.738
Table(s): Company: London Star individuals p.135, Offshore: London Band 3 p.353

Todd, Richard
Table(s): Family: Matrimonial Finance: London Band 1 p.244

Tolaney, Sonia
Table(s): Banking & Finance: London Band 1 p.49, Chancery: Commercial: London Band 2 p.59, Commercial Dispute Resolution: London Band 2 p.109, Fraud: Civil: London Band 2 p.281, Restructuring/Insolvency: London Band 3 p.455

Toledano, Daniel
Table(s): Banking & Finance: London Band 1 p.49, Commercial Dispute Resolution: London Band 2 p.109, Energy & Natural Resources: London Band 1 p.226, Fraud: Civil: London Band 2 p.281, International Arbitration: General Commercial & Insurance: London Band 3 p.328

Tolley, Adam
Profile: p.738
Table(s): Employment: London New Silks p.207

Tolson, Robin
Table(s): Family/Matrimonial: Western (Bar) Band 3 p.262

Tomlinson, Hugh
Table(s): Data Protection: London Band 1 p.195, Defamation/Privacy: London Band 1 p.199, Police Law: Mainly Claimant: All Circuits Band 2 p.400

Toms, Nick
Table(s): Employment: London Band 5 p.208

Toms, Paul
Table(s): Shipping & Commodities: London Band 4 p.465

Tomson, Alastair
Table(s): Company: London Band 3 p.135

Toney, Rachel
Profile: p.738
Table(s): Shipping & Commodities: London Band 4 p.465

Toogood, Claire
Profile: p.739
Table(s): Clinical Negligence: London Band 3 p.93

Topping, Caroline
Table(s): Family/Matrimonial: South Eastern (Bar) Band 3 p.259

Toube, Felicity
Profile: p.739
Table(s): Chancery: Commercial: London Band 4 p.59, Company: London Band 3 p.135, Restructuring/Insolvency: London Band 2 p.455

Townend, Samuel
Profile: p.739
Table(s): Construction: London Band 3 p.147

Townsend, Harriet
Profile: p.739
Table(s): Planning: London Band 5 p.386

Townsend, James
Table(s): Clinical Negligence: Western (Bar) Band 1 p.106

Tozer, Stephanie
Profile: p.739
Table(s): Real Estate Litigation: London Band 1 p.443

Tozzi, Nigel
Profile: p.739
Table(s): Commercial Dispute Resolution: London Band 2 p.109, Energy & Natural Resources: London Band 3 p.226, Information Technology: London Band 2 p.304, Insurance: London Band 4 p.315, International Arbitration: General Commercial & Insurance: London Band 2 p.328, Professional Negligence: London Band 1 p.420, Shipping & Commodities: London Band 4 p.465

Trace, Anthony
Profile: p.739
Table(s): Chancery: Commercial: London Band 1 p.59, Commercial Dispute Resolution: London Band 2 p.109, Company: London Band 2 p.135, Fraud: Civil: London Band 1 p.281, Offshore: London Band 3 p.353, Professional Negligence: London Band 3 p.420, Real Estate Litigation: London Band 4 p.442, Restructuring/Insolvency: London Band 4 p.455

Tracy Forster, Jane
Profile: p.740
Table(s): **Clinical Negligence:** London **Band 1** p.93

Travers, David
Profile: p.740
Table(s): **Consumer Law:** London **Band 1** p.156, **Environment:** London **Band 2** p.231, **Health & Safety:** London **Band 1** p.291

Tregear, Francis
Table(s): **Banking & Finance:** London **Band 4** p.49, **Chancery: Traditional:** London **Band 3** p.67, **Commercial Dispute Resolution:** London **Band 5** p.109, **Company:** London **Band 2** p.135, **Offshore:** London **Band 3** p.353, **Professional Negligence:** London **Band 4** p.420

Trembath, Graham
Profile: p.740
Table(s): **Crime:** London **Band 2** p.173

Trevelyan Thomas, Adrian
Table(s): **Planning:** London **Band 5** p.386

Treverton-Jones, Gregory
Table(s): **Professional Discipline:** London **Band 1** p.410

Tridimas, Takis
Table(s): **European Law:** London **Band 2** p.237

Trigger, Simon
Profile: p.740
Table(s): **Professional Negligence:** London **Band 4** p.421

Tritton, Guy
Table(s): **Intellectual Property:** London **Band 2** p.322

Trollope, Andrew
Profile: p.740
Table(s): **Crime:** London **Band 3** p.173, **Financial Crime:** London **Band 2** p.266

Troman, Carl
Profile: p.740
Table(s): **Professional Negligence:** London **Band 3** p.421

Tromans, Stephen
Table(s): **Energy & Natural Resources:** London **Band 3** p.226, **Environment:** London **Star individuals** p.231, **Planning:** London **Band 3** p.386

Trompeter, Nicholas
Profile: p.740
Table(s): **Chancery: Commercial:** London **Band 4** p.60, **Real Estate Litigation:** London **Band 4** p.443

Trotter, Helen
Profile: p.740
Table(s): **Employment:** Northern (Bar) **Up-and-coming individuals** p.221

Troup, Alex
Table(s): **Chancery:** Western (Bar) **Band 1** p.77, **Commercial Dispute Resolution:** Western (Bar) **Band 2** p.130

Trowell, Stephen
Table(s): **Family: Matrimonial Finance:** London **Band 1** p.244

Trower, William
Table(s): **Banking & Finance:** London **Band 4** p.49, **Company:** London **Band 1** p.135, **Restructuring/Insolvency:** London **Star individuals** p.455

Trowler, Rebecca
Profile: p.741
Table(s): **Crime:** London **Band 3** p.173

Trusted, Harry
Table(s): **Clinical Negligence:** London **Band 2** p.93, **Personal Injury:** London **Band 2** p.368

Tselentis, Michael
Table(s): **Energy & Natural Resources:** London **Band 2** p.226

Tuck, Rebecca
Profile: p.741
Table(s): **Employment:** London **Band 3** p.208

Tucker, Lynton
Profile: p.741
Table(s): **Chancery: Traditional:** London **Star individuals** p.67, **Offshore:** London **Band 1** p.353, **Trusts:** London **Band 1** p.498

Tucker, Paul
Profile: p.741
Table(s): **Planning:** Northern (Bar) **Band 1** p.394

Tuckey, Simon
Table(s): **International Arbitration: Arbitrators:** London **Band 1** p.335

Tueje, Patricia
Table(s): **Social Housing:** London **Band 3** p.471

Tughan, John
Table(s): **Family: Children:** London **Band 3** p.245

Tully, Ray
Table(s): **Crime:** Western (Bar) **Band 1** p.192

Turner, Adam
Table(s): **Shipping & Commodities:** London **Up-and-coming individuals** p.465

Turner, David
Table(s): **Product Liability:** London **Band 3** p.406, **Professional Negligence:** London **Band 3** p.420

Turner, James
Table(s): **Family: Matrimonial Finance:** London **Band 1** p.244, **Family: Children:** London **Band 2** p.244

Turner, James M
Profile: p.741
Table(s): **Shipping & Commodities:** London **Band 4** p.465

Turner, Jon
Profile: p.741
Table(s): **Administrative & Public Law:** London **Band 3** p.27, **Competition Law:** London **Star individuals** p.142, **Environment:** London **Band 2** p.231, **European Law:** London **Band 2** p.237, **Telecommunications:** London **Band 1** p.491

Turner, Jonathan
Profile: p.741
Table(s): **Crime:** London **Band 4** p.173

Turner, Justin
Profile: p.741
Table(s): **Intellectual Property:** London **Band 2** p.322

Turner, Michael
Table(s): **Crime:** London **Band 2** p.173

Turner, Steven
Table(s): **Personal Injury:** North Eastern (Bar) **Band 2** p.379, **Sport:** The Regions **Band 1** p.480

Turney, Richard
Table(s): **Planning:** London **Up-and-coming individuals** p.386

Turton, Philip
Profile: p.741
Table(s): **Personal Injury:** Midlands (Bar) **Band 2** p.377

Tweedy, Laura
Profile: p.741
Table(s): **Social Housing:** London **Band 3** p.471

Twigger, Andrew M
Profile: p.742
Table(s): **Banking & Finance:** London **Band 4** p.49, **Chancery: Commercial:** London **Band 2** p.59, **Commercial Dispute Resolution:** London **Band 5** p.109

Tyack, David
Profile: p.742
Table(s): **Clinical Negligence:** Midlands (Bar) **Band 2** p.102

Tyler, William
Profile: p.742
Table(s): **Family: Children:** London **Band 4** p.245

Tyson, Richard
Table(s): **Professional Discipline:** The Regions **Band 2** p.417

Tyzack, William
Profile: p.742
Table(s): **Family: Matrimonial Finance:** London **Up-and-coming individuals** p.244, **Family: Children:** London **Up-and-coming individuals** p.244

U

Uberoi, Michael
Table(s): **Inquests & Public Inquiries:** London **Band 3** p.309, **Professional Discipline:** London **Band 5** p.411

Uff, John
Profile: p.742
Table(s): **International Arbitration: Arbitrators:** London **Band 1** p.335

Ullstein, Augustus
Table(s): **Personal Injury:** London **Band 3** p.367

Underwood, Dean
Profile: p.742
Table(s): **Social Housing:** London **Band 1** p.471

Unsworth, Ian
Table(s): **Crime:** Northern (Bar) **Band 2** p.186, **Sport:** The Regions **Band 2** p.480

Upton, Rebecca
Table(s): **Crime:** South Eastern (Bar) **Band 2** p.188

Upton, William
Table(s): **Environment:** London **Band 2** p.231, **Planning:** London **Band 4** p.386

Urell, Kate
Profile: p.742
Table(s): **Consumer Law:** London **Band 2** p.156

Utley, Charles
Table(s): **Clinical Negligence:** London **Band 2** p.93

V

Valentin, Ben
Profile: p.742
Table(s): **Banking & Finance:** London **Band 1** p.50, **Commercial Dispute Resolution:** London **Band 2** p.110, **Fraud: Civil:** London **Band 2** p.282, **International Arbitration: General Commercial & Insurance:** London **Band 2** p.328

Vallat, Richard
Profile: p.743
Table(s): **Tax:** London **Band 1** p.482, **Tax: Private Client:** London **Band 2** p.488

Van der Zwart, Mark
Table(s): **Crime:** Midlands (Bar) **Band 3** p.181

Vanhegan, Mark
Table(s): **Information Technology:** London **Band 2** p.304, **Intellectual Property:** London **Band 1** p.322

Vanhegan, Toby B
Table(s): **Social Housing:** London **Band 2** p.471

Vassall-Adams, Guy
Table(s): **Defamation/Privacy:** London **Band 2** p.199

Vater, John
Table(s): **Family/Matrimonial:** South Eastern (Bar) **Band 1** p.259

Vaughan, David
Table(s): **Competition Law:** London **Senior Statesmen** p.142, **European Law:** London **Senior Statesmen** p.237

Vaughan, Kieran
Table(s): **Crime:** London **Band 3** p.173

Vaughan Jones, Sarah
Profile: p.743
Table(s): **Clinical Negligence:** London **Band 1** p.92

Vavrecka, David
Profile: p.743
Table(s): **Family: Children:** London **Band 3** p.245

Veeder, V V
Table(s): **International Arbitration: Arbitrators:** London **Band 1** p.335

Venables, Robert
Table(s): **Tax:** London **Band 3** p.482

Ventham, Charlotte
Profile: p.743
Table(s): **Police Law: Mainly Defendant:** All Circuits **Band 3** p.402

Verdan, Alex
Table(s): **Family: Children:** London **Star individuals** p.245

Verdirame, Guglielmo
Table(s): **Public International Law:** London **Band 2** p.435

Verduyn, Anthony
Profile: p.743
Table(s): **Real Estate Litigation:** Midlands (Bar) **Band 1** p.450

Vernon, Robert
Profile: p.743
Table(s): **Employment:** Wales & Chester (Bar) **Band 3** p.223

Vickers, Rachel
Table(s): **Clinical Negligence:** London **Band 2** p.93

Vigars, Anna
Table(s): **Crime:** Western (Bar) **Band 3** p.192, **Health & Safety:** Western (Bar) **Band 2** p.296

Village, Peter
Table(s): **Planning:** London **Band 1** p.386

Vinall, Mark
Table(s): **Commercial Dispute Resolution:** London **Band 5** p.110, **Media & Entertainment:** London **Band 2** p.345

Vincent, Patrick
Profile: p.743
Table(s): **Personal Injury:** London **Band 2** p.368

Vindis, Tara
Profile: p.743
Table(s): **Family: Children:** London **Band 4** p.245

Vine, Aidan
Table(s): **Family/Matrimonial:** South Eastern (Bar) **Band 3** p.259

Vineall, Nicholas
Profile: p.743
Table(s): **Energy & Natural Resources:** London **Band 4** p.226, **Financial Services:** London **Band 1** p.276, **Fraud: Civil:** London **Band 4** p.281, **Shipping & Commodities:** London **Band 4** p.465

Vines, Anthony
Profile: p.744
Table(s): Commercial Dispute Resolution: Wales & Chester (Bar) Band 1 p.129, Employment: Wales & Chester (Bar) Band 3 p.223

Vinson, Andrew
Table(s): Chancery: Northern (Bar) Band 2 p.75

Vinson, Andrew
Table(s): Commercial Dispute Resolution: Northern (Bar) Band 2 p.127

Virgo, John
Table(s): Commercial Dispute Resolution: Western (Bar) Band 1 p.130, Professional Negligence: Western (Bar) Band 1 p.431

Vokes, Stephen
Profile: p.744
Table(s): Immigration: Midlands (Bar) Band 2 p.302

von Wachter, Victoria
Profile: p.744
Table(s): Employment: London Band 5 p.208

Vullo, Stephen
Table(s): Crime: London New Silks p.173

W

Wagner, Adam
Table(s): Civil Liberties & Human Rights: London Band 3 p.82

Wagstaffe, Christopher
Profile: p.744
Table(s): Family: Matrimonial Finance: London Band 2 p.244

Waite, John-Paul
Table(s): Immigration: London Band 3 p.297

Waite, Jonathan
Table(s): Product Liability: London Band 1 p.406, Property Damage: London Band 2 p.433

Wakefield, Victoria
Table(s): Administrative & Public Law: London Band 3 p.28, Competition Law: London Band 3 p.142, European Law: London Band 2 p.237, Inquests & Public Inquiries: London Band 1 p.309

Wakerley, Paul
Table(s): Crime: London Band 4 p.174

Wald, Richard
Table(s): Environment: London Band 1 p.231, Planning: London Band 3 p.386

Walder, Aaron
Table(s): Real Estate Litigation: London Band 5 p.443

Waldron, William
Table(s): Personal Injury: Northern (Bar) Band 1 p.380, Police Law: Mainly Defendant: All Circuits Band 2 p.402

Wales, Andrew
Table(s): Professional Negligence: London Band 4 p.420

Wales, Matthew
Table(s): Chancery: Western (Bar) Band 1 p.77, Real Estate Litigation: Western (Bar) Band 2 p.453

Walford, Philip
Profile: p.744
Table(s): Tax: London Band 2 p.482

Walker, Adam
Profile: p.744
Table(s): Clinical Negligence: London Band 4 p.93

Walker, Amelia
Profile: p.744
Table(s): Education: London Band 4 p.203

Walker, Andrew
Profile: p.744
Table(s): Real Estate Litigation: London Band 2 p.442

Walker, Bruce
Table(s): Chancery: North Eastern (Bar) Band 3 p.74, Real Estate Litigation: Northern (Bar) Band 3 p.452

Walker, Christopher
Table(s): Personal Injury: London Band 3 p.368, Personal Injury: Western (Bar) Band 1

Walker, Damien
Table(s): International Arbitration: General Commercial & Insurance: London Band 3 p.328

Walker, Elizabeth
Profile: p.745
Table(s): Family/Matrimonial: Midlands (Bar) Band 1 p.254

Walker, Gavin
Table(s): Commercial Dispute Resolution: Scotland (Bar) Band 3 p.512, Construction: Scotland (Bar) Band 2 p.515, Intellectual Property: Scotland (Bar) Band 2 p.519, Professional Negligence: Scotland (Bar) Band 2 p.523

Walker, Ronald
Profile: p.745
Table(s): Personal Injury: London Band 1 p.367, Personal Injury: Industrial Disease: London p.367

Walker, Steven
Profile: p.745
Table(s): Construction: London Band 3 p.146, Energy & Natural Resources: London Band 3 p.226

Walker, Steven
Profile: p.745
Table(s): International Arbitration: Construction/Engineering: London Band 2 p.333

Wall, Mark
Table(s): Crime: Midlands (Bar) Band 1 p.181

Wallace, Sam
Profile: p.745
Table(s): Family: Children: London Band 4 p.245

Waller, Richard
Table(s): Insurance: London Band 3 p.315, International Arbitration: General Commercial & Insurance: London Band 4 p.328, Shipping & Commodities: London Band 2 p.465

Walmisley, Lisa
Profile: p.745
Table(s): Restructuring/Insolvency: Northern (Bar) Band 1 p.462

Walmsley, James
Table(s): Pensions: London Band 2 p.363

Walsh, David
Table(s): Shipping & Commodities: London Up-and-coming individuals p.465

Walsh, John
Table(s): Immigration: London Band 2 p.297

Walsh, Stephen
Profile: p.745
Table(s): Health & Safety: London Band 3 p.291, Licensing: London Star individuals p.337

Walsh, Timothy
Profile: p.745
Table(s): Real Estate Litigation: Western (Bar) Band 2 p.453

Walters, Graham
Profile: p.745
Table(s): Administrative & Public Law: Wales & Chester (Bar) Band 1 p.40, Chancery: Wales & Chester (Bar) Band 1 p.77, Commercial Dispute Resolution: Wales & Chester (Bar) Band 1 p.129

Walters, Jonathan
Table(s): Employment: Wales & Chester (Bar) Band 1 p.223

Walton, Alastair
Profile: p.745
Table(s): Chancery: Commercial: London Band 3 p.60

Walton, Robert
Table(s): Planning: London Band 3 p.386

Wan Daud, Malek
Table(s): Family: Children: London Band 4 p.245

Ward, Alexandra
Profile: p.746
Table(s): Crime: London Band 3 p.174

Ward, Annie
Table(s): Family/Matrimonial: Western (Bar) Band 3 p.262

Ward, Galina
Table(s): Education: London Band 3 p.203, Immigration: London Band 4 p.297, Real Estate Litigation: London Band 4 p.443

Ward, Henry
Profile: p.746
Table(s): Intellectual Property: London Band 2 p.322

Ward, Tim
Profile: p.746
Table(s): Administrative & Public Law: London Band 2 p.27, Competition Law: London Band 1 p.142, European Law: London Band 1 p.237, Telecommunications: London Band 2 p.491

Wardell, John
Table(s): Chancery: Commercial: London Band 2 p.59, Commercial Dispute Resolution: London Band 4 p.109, Fraud: Civil: London Band 2 p.281, Professional Negligence: London Band 2 p.420

Warner, David
Profile: p.746
Table(s): Real Estate Litigation: Midlands (Bar) Band 3 p.450

Warner, Malcolm
Table(s): Partnership: Western (Bar) Band 2 p.362

Warnock, Andrew
Profile: p.746
Table(s): Education: London Band 3 p.203, Local Government: London Band 3 p.340, Personal Injury: London Band 2 p.367, Police Law: Mainly Defendant: All Circuits Band 2 p.402, Professional Negligence: London Band 4 p.420

Warnock-Smith, Shân
Profile: p.746
Table(s): Chancery: Traditional: London Band 1 p.67, Charities: London Band 2 p.79, Offshore: London Band 1 p.353, Trusts: London Band 1 p.498

Warren, Rupert
Table(s): Planning: London Band 3 p.386

Warrington, John
Profile: p.746
Table(s): Crime: London Band 6 p.174

Warshaw, Justin
Table(s): Family: Matrimonial Finance: London Band 1 p.244

Warwick, Mark
Profile: p.747
Table(s): Real Estate Litigation: London Band 4 p.442

Wass, Sasha
Table(s): Crime: London Band 2 p.173, Financial Crime: London Band 3 p.266

Waterman, Adrian
Table(s): Crime: London Band 6 p.173

Waters, Andrew
Table(s): Police Law: Mainly Defendant: All Circuits Band 1 p.402

Waters, Julian
Profile: p.747
Table(s): Personal Injury: London Band 3 p.368

Waters, Malcolm
Profile: p.747
Table(s): Banking & Finance: London Band 2 p.49, Consumer Law: London Band 1 p.156

Waters, Sarah
Table(s): Crime: Wales & Chester (Bar) Band 3 p.191

Watkin, Toby
Table(s): Real Estate Litigation: London Band 4 p.443

Watkins, Aaron
Table(s): Extradition: London Band 2 p.240

Watkins, Michael
Table(s): Energy & Natural Resources: London Up-and-coming individuals p.226

Watson, Ben
Profile: p.747
Table(s): Administrative & Public Law: London Band 3 p.28, Civil Liberties & Human Rights: London Band 4 p.82, Extradition: London Band 1 p.240

Watson, Claire
Profile: p.747
Table(s): Professional Discipline: London Band 2 p.411

Watson, Duncan
Profile: p.747
Table(s): Family/Matrimonial: South Eastern (Bar) Band 3 p.259

Watson, Graham
Table(s): Employment: Western (Bar) Band 3 p.223

Watson, James
Profile: p.747
Table(s): Clinical Negligence: London Band 1 p.92, Police Law: Mainly Defendant: All Circuits Band 3 p.402

Watson, Mark
Table(s): Consumer Law: London Band 1 p.156, Environment: London Band 2 p.231, Health & Safety: London Band 1 p.291

Watt-Pringle, Jonathan
Profile: p.747
Table(s): Health & Safety: London Band 3 p.291, Personal Injury: London Band 2 p.367

Watthey, James
Profile: p.747
Table(s): Shipping & Commodities: London Band 4 p.465

Waugh, Andrew
Profile: p.747
Table(s): Intellectual Property: London Band 1 p.322

Way, Ian
Table(s): Crime: Midlands (Bar) Band 1 p.181

Way, Patrick
Profile: p.748
Table(s): Tax: London Band 3 p.482

Weale, James
Profile: p.748
Table(s): Chancery: Commercial: London Band 3 p.60

Weatherby, Pete
Table(s): Administrative & Public Law: Northern (Bar) Band 1 p.39, Civil Liberties & Human Rights: Northern (Bar) Band 1 p.89, Crime: Northern (Bar) Band 3 p.186

Weatherill, Bernard
Table(s): Chancery: Commercial: London Band 3 p.59

Weaver, Elizabeth
Table(s): Chancery: Traditional: London Band 2 p.67, Offshore: London Band 3 p.353, Professional Negligence: London Band 3 p.421

Weaver, Matthew
Profile: p.748
Table(s): Restructuring/Insolvency: Midlands (Bar) Band 2 p.461

Webb, Geraint
Profile: p.748
Table(s): Insurance: London Band 4 p.315, International Arbitration: General Commercial & Insurance: London Band 4 p.328, Local Government: London Band 4 p.340, Product Liability: London Band 2 p.406, Property Damage: London Band 3 p.433

Webb, William
Profile: p.748
Table(s): Construction: London Band 3 p.147

Webster, Alistair
Table(s): Financial Crime: London Band 4 p.266

Webster, Alistair
Table(s): Financial Crime: The Regions Band 1 p.275

Webster, Andrew G
Table(s): Administrative & Public Law: Scotland (Bar) Band 1 p.507, Civil Liberties & Human Rights: Scotland (Bar) Band 1 p.509

Webster, Simon
Table(s): Family: Matrimonial Finance: London Band 1 p.244

Weddell, Geoffrey
Profile: p.748
Table(s): Police Law: Mainly Defendant: All Circuits Band 2 p.402

Wedderspoon, Rachel
Table(s): Employment: Northern (Bar) Band 1 p.221

Weekes, Mark
Table(s): Crime: London Band 5 p.174, Extradition: London Band 3 p.240

Weekes, Robert
Table(s): Commercial Dispute Resolution: London Band 3 p.110, Fraud: Civil: London Band 3 p.282

Weekes, Tom
Table(s): Real Estate Litigation: London Band 2 p.443

Weeks, Janet
Profile: p.748
Table(s): Financial Crime: London Band 4 p.267

Weereratne, Aswini
Table(s): Civil Liberties & Human Rights: London Band 4 p.82, Court of Protection: Health & Welfare: All Circuits Band 1 p.165

Weetman, Gareth
Profile: p.748
Table(s): Crime: Midlands (Bar) Band 3 p.181

Weir, Robert
Profile: p.748
Table(s): Clinical Negligence: London Band 1 p.92, Personal Injury: London Star individuals p.367, Travel: International Personal Injury: London Band 1 p.495

Weir, Robert
Table(s): Commercial Dispute Resolution: Scotland (Bar) Band 3 p.512

Weisselberg, Tom
Table(s): Commercial Dispute Resolution: London New Silks p.109, Fraud: Civil: London New Silks p.281, Intellectual Property: London New Silks p.322, Media & Entertainment: London New Silks p.345

Weitzman, Adam
Table(s): Clinical Negligence: London Band 3 p.93, Personal Injury: London Band 2 p.368

Weitzman, Tom
Table(s): Insurance: London Band 2 p.315, Professional Negligence: London Band 1 p.420

Welfare, Damien
Profile: p.748
Table(s): Data Protection: London Band 4 p.195

Wells, Colin
Profile: p.749
Table(s): Financial Crime: London Band 3 p.267

Wells, Graham
Table(s): Police Law: Mainly Defendant: All Circuits Band 2 p.402

Wells, Jason
Profile: p.749
Table(s): Clinical Negligence: Northern (Bar) Up-and-coming individuals p.103

Wells, Nathan
Profile: p.749
Table(s): Chancery: Traditional: London Band 4 p.67

West, Colin
Table(s): Commercial Dispute Resolution: London Band 4 p.110

West, Ewan
Table(s): Public Procurement: London Band 2 p.439

West, Mark
Profile: p.749
Table(s): Chancery: Traditional: London Band 3 p.67, Real Estate Litigation: London Band 3 p.443

Westaway, Ned
Table(s): Environment: London Up-and-coming individuals p.231, Planning: London Up-and-coming individuals p.386

Westcott, David
Table(s): Clinical Negligence: London Band 1 p.92, Personal Injury: London Band 1 p.367

Westcott, Mary
Table(s): Extradition: London Band 3 p.240

Westgate, Martin
Table(s): Administrative & Public Law: London Band 3 p.27, Civil Liberties & Human Rights: London Band 3 p.81, Local Government: London Band 3 p.340, Social Housing: London Band 2 p.471

Westmoreland Smith, Mark
Table(s): Planning: London Band 5 p.386

Weston, Amanda
Table(s): Civil Liberties & Human Rights: London Band 3 p.82, Court of Protection: Health & Welfare: All Circuits Band 2 p.165, Immigration: London Band 2 p.297

Weston, Jeremy
Profile: p.749
Table(s): Family/Matrimonial: Midlands (Bar) Band 1 p.254

Weston, Louis
Table(s): Clinical Negligence: Western (Bar) Band 2 p.106, Sport: London Band 2 p.478

Westwood, Andrew
Profile: p.749
Table(s): Charities: London Band 2 p.79

Whale, Stephen
Profile: p.749
Table(s): Licensing: London Band 3 p.337, Planning: London Band 3 p.386

Wheater, Michael
Profile: p.750
Table(s): Construction: London Band 3 p.147

Wheatley, Geraint
Profile: p.750
Table(s): Real Estate Litigation: Northern (Bar) Band 3 p.452

Wheeler, Andrew
Table(s): Financial Crime: London Band 3 p.267

Wheeler, Marina
Table(s): Administrative & Public Law: London Band 4 p.28

Whipple, Philippa
Table(s): Clinical Negligence: London Band 2 p.92, Inquests & Public Inquiries: London Band 2 p.309, Tax: Indirect Tax: London Band 1 p.486

Whitaker, Stephen
Table(s): Partnership: Midlands (Bar) Band 1 p.361

Whitcombe, Mark
Table(s): Employment: Western (Bar) Band 3 p.223

White, Andrew
Profile: p.750
Table(s): Construction: London Star individuals p.146, Energy & Natural Resources: London Band 1 p.226, International Arbitration: General Commercial & Insurance: London Band 4 p.328, International Arbitration: Construction/Engineering: London Band 1 p.333, Professional Negligence: Technology & Construction: London Band 1 p.428

White, Antony
Profile: p.750
Table(s): Commercial Dispute Resolution: London Band 4 p.109, Data Protection: London Band 3 p.195, Defamation/Privacy: London Band 1 p.199, Employment: London Band 2 p.207

White, Gemma
Table(s): Education: London Band 4 p.203

White, Jeremy
Profile: p.750
Table(s): Tax: Indirect Tax: London Band 2 p.486

White, Matthew
Table(s): Employment: Western (Bar) Band 2 p.223, Personal Injury: Western (Bar) Band 2

White, Robin
Profile: p.750
Table(s): Employment: London Band 4 p.208

White, Sasha
Table(s): Planning: London Band 4 p.386

Whitehall, Mark
Table(s): Family/Matrimonial: Western (Bar) Band 2 p.262

Whitehall, Richard
Table(s): Personal Injury: Northern (Bar) Band 1 p.380

Whitehead, Thomas
Profile: p.751
Table(s): Shipping & Commodities: London Band 3 p.465

Whitehouse, Christopher
Profile: p.751
Table(s): Chancery: Traditional: London Band 1 p.67, Tax: Private Client: London Band 1 p.488

Whitehouse, Sarah
Profile: p.751
Table(s): Crime: London New Silks p.173

Whitehurst, Ian
Table(s): Crime: Northern (Bar) Band 3 p.186, Financial Crime: The Regions Band 1 p.275

Whitelaw, Francesca
Profile: p.751
Table(s): Professional Discipline: London Band 5 p.411

Whiteman, Peter
Table(s): Tax: London Band 3 p.482

Whitfield, Jonathan
Table(s): Crime: London Band 6 p.173

Whittaker, David
Profile: p.751
Table(s): Crime: London Band 2 p.174, Financial Crime: London Band 2 p.267

Whittam, Richard
Table(s): Crime: London Band 1 p.173

Whitting, John
Profile: p.751
Table(s): Clinical Negligence: London Band 2 p.92

Whyte, Anne
Table(s): Police Law: Mainly Defendant: All Circuits Band 3 p.402

Whyte, James
Profile: p.751
Table(s): Intellectual Property: London Band 2 p.322

Wicks, Joanne
Table(s): Real Estate Litigation: London Band 1 p.442

Widdett, Ceri
Table(s): Employment: North Eastern (Bar) Band 3 p.220

Wignall, Gordon
Table(s): Costs Litigation: London Band 4 p.160

Wignall, Gordon
Table(s): Environment: Midlands (Bar) Band 2 p.235

Wijeyaratne, Asela
Table(s): Travel: International Personal Injury: London Band 3 p.495

Wilby, David
Table(s): Clinical Negligence: North Eastern (Bar) Band 2 p.103

Wilcock, Peter
Table(s): Crime: London Band 5 p.173

Wild, Alison
Profile: p.751
Table(s): Family/Matrimonial: Scotland (Bar) Band 2 p.517

Wilding, Lisa
Profile: p.751
Table(s): Crime: London New Silks p.173

Wilken, Sean
Table(s): Construction: London Band 3 p.146, Energy & Natural Resources: London Band 4 p.226, International Arbitration: Construction/Engineering: London Band 2 p.333

Wilkins, Susan
Table(s): Family: Matrimonial Finance: London Band 4 p.244

Wilkinson, Kate
Profile: p.752
Table(s): Crime: London Band 5 p.174

Wilkinson, Nicholas
Table(s): Family: Matrimonial Finance: London Band 4 p.244

Wilkinson, Richard
Profile: p.752
Table(s): Costs Litigation: London Band 4 p.160, Personal Injury: London Band 2 p.368

Willan, James
Table(s): Commercial Dispute Resolution: London Band 2 p.110, Fraud: Civil: London Band 3 p.282, International Arbitration: General Commercial & Insurance: London Band 2 p.328

Willcocks, Hannah
Table(s): Financial Crime: London Band 4 p.267

Willems, Marc
Table(s): Personal Injury: Northern (Bar) Band 1 p.380

Willers, Marc
Table(s): Planning: London New Silks p.386

Willetts, Glenn
Table(s): Commercial Dispute Resolution: Midlands (Bar) Band 2 p.125

Williams, A John
Profile: p.752
Table(s): Personal Injury: London Band 2 p.368

Williams, Anne
Table(s): Planning: London Band 5 p.386

Williams, Ben
Profile: p.752
Table(s): Licensing: Midlands (Bar) Band 1 p.339

Williams, Benjamin
Table(s): Consumer Law: London Band 2 p.156, Costs Litigation: London Band 1 p.160

Williams, Christopher
Table(s): Personal Injury: North Eastern (Bar) Band 2 p.379

Williams, Claire
Table(s): Family/Matrimonial: Wales & Chester (Bar) Up-and-coming individuals p.261

Williams, David
Table(s): Family: Children: London Band 2 p.245

Williams, Ed
Profile: p.752
Table(s): Employment: London Band 5 p.208

Williams, Felicity
Table(s): Community Care: London Band 3 p.132

Williams, Geoffrey
Profile: p.752
Table(s): Professional Discipline: London Band 2 p.410

Williams, Guy
Table(s): Planning: London Band 3 p.386

Williams, Heather
Table(s): Civil Liberties & Human Rights: London Band 1 p.81, Employment: London Band 3 p.207, Police Law: Mainly Claimant: All Circuits Band 1 p.400

Williams, Joanne
Profile: p.752
Table(s): Personal Injury: Wales & Chester (Bar) Band 2 p.383

Williams, Lloyd
Table(s): Personal Injury: Wales & Chester (Bar) Band 1 p.383

Williams, Rhodri
Table(s): Administrative & Public Law: Wales & Chester (Bar) Band 1 p.40

Williams, Rhodri
Profile: p.752
Table(s): Data Protection: London Band 4 p.195, Local Government: London Band 4 p.340, Public Procurement: London Band 2 p.439

Williams, Rob
Table(s): Competition Law: London Band 3 p.142, Public Procurement: London Band 1 p.439

Williams, Simon
Profile: p.752
Table(s): Real Estate Litigation: London Band 4 p.443

Williams, Vincent
Table(s): Police Law: Mainly Defendant: All Circuits Band 2 p.402

Williamson, Adrian
Profile: p.753
Table(s): Construction: London Band 1 p.146, Professional Negligence: Technology & Construction: London Band 1 p.428

Williamson, Alisdair
Profile: p.753
Table(s): Crime: London Band 1 p.174

Williamson, Nicholas
Table(s): Family/Matrimonial: Western (Bar) Up-and-coming individuals p.262

Williamson, Oliver
Profile: p.753
Table(s): Police Law: Mainly Defendant: All Circuits Up-and-coming individuals p.402

Willis, Tony
Table(s): Mediators: All Circuits Band 1 p.348

Willock, Gary
Table(s): Social Housing: Northern (Bar) Up-and-coming individuals p.476

Wills, Jonathan
Table(s): Planning: London Up-and-coming individuals p.386

Wills-Goldingham, Claire
Table(s): Family/Matrimonial: Western (Bar) Band 2 p.262

Willson, William
Profile: p.753
Table(s): Restructuring/Insolvency: London Up-and-coming individuals p.455

Wilmot-Smith, Richard
Table(s): Construction: London Band 1 p.146, Energy & Natural Resources: London Band 4 p.226, Professional Negligence: Technology & Construction: London Band 1 p.428

Wilson, Ailsa
Table(s): Planning & Environment: Scotland (Bar) Band 1 p.522

Wilson, Alastair
Table(s): Intellectual Property: London Band 2 p.322

Wilson, Elizabeth
Profile: p.753
Table(s): Tax: Private Client: London Band 1 p.488

Wilson, Ian
Table(s): Banking & Finance: London Band 3 p.50

Wilson, John
Table(s): Family: Matrimonial Finance: London Band 2 p.244

Wilson, Julian
Profile: p.753
Table(s): Employment: London Band 5 p.208

Wilson, Kate
Table(s): Defamation/Privacy: London Band 3 p.199

Wilson, Paul
Table(s): Employment: North Eastern (Bar) Band 3 p.220

Wilson, Peter J
Table(s): Motor Insurance Fraud: All Circuits Band 1 p.350

Wilson, Richard
Profile: p.753
Table(s): Chancery: Traditional: London Band 1 p.67, Offshore: London Band 1 p.353, Trusts: London Band 1 p.498

Wilson-Smith, Christopher
Profile: p.753
Table(s): Clinical Negligence: London Band 2 p.92, Personal Injury: London Band 2 p.367

Wilton, Simon
Profile: p.754
Table(s): Professional Negligence: London Band 2 p.421

Windle, Victoria
Table(s): Employment: London Band 3 p.208

Windsor, Emily
Table(s): Agriculture & Rural Affairs: London Band 1 p.41, Real Estate Litigation: London Band 2 p.443

Winfield, Joshua
Table(s): Charities: London Band 3 p.79

Winser, Crispin
Profile: p.754
Table(s): Construction: London Band 3 p.147

Winston, Naomi
Profile: p.754
Table(s): Partnership: London Up-and-coming individuals p.359

Winstone, Hilary
Profile: p.754
Table(s): Employment: London Band 5 p.208, Employment: Western (Bar) Band 2 p.223

Winter, Alexander
Profile: p.754
Table(s): Chancery: Commercial: London Band 2 p.60, Fraud: Civil: London Band 2 p.282

Winter, Ian
Profile: p.754
Table(s): Crime: London Star individuals p.173, Financial Crime: London Star individuals p.266, Financial Crime: Corporates: London Band 1 p.266, Professional Discipline: London Band 4 p.410

Winter, Stephen
Profile: p.755
Table(s): Immigration: Scotland (Bar) Band 1 p.518

Wise, Ian
Table(s): Administrative & Public Law: London Band 4 p.27, Civil Liberties & Human Rights: London Band 4 p.81, Community Care: London Band 2 p.132, Education: London Band 3 p.203, Local Government: London Band 4 p.340

Wiseman, Naomi
Profile: p.755
Table(s): Family: Matrimonial Finance: London Up-and-coming individuals p.244, Family: Children: London Up-and-coming individuals p.244

Witcomb, Henry
Table(s): Clinical Negligence: London Star individuals p.93, Personal Injury: London Band 1 p.368

Wolanski, Adam
Table(s): Defamation/Privacy: London Band 1 p.199

Wolfe, David
Profile: p.755
Table(s): Administrative & Public Law: London Band 3 p.27, Civil Liberties & Human Rights: London Band 3 p.81, Community Care: London Band 2 p.132, Education: London Band 2 p.203, Environment: London Band 3 p.231

Wolfe, Georgina
Profile: p.755
Table(s): Police Law: Mainly Defendant: All Circuits Band 3 p.402

Wolffe, James
Profile: p.755
Table(s): Administrative & Public Law: Scotland (Bar) Band 1 p.507, Commercial Dispute Resolution: Scotland (Bar) Band 1 p.512, Construction: Scotland (Bar) Band 2 p.515

Wolfson, David
Table(s): Banking & Finance: London Band 1 p.49, Commercial Dispute Resolution: London Band 2 p.109, Energy & Natural Resources: London Band 4 p.226, International Arbitration: General Commercial & Insurance: London Band 3 p.328

Wolkind, Michael
Table(s): Crime: London Band 2 p.173

Wong, Natasha
Profile: p.755
Table(s): Financial Crime: London Band 2 p.267

Wonnacott, Mark
Table(s): Agriculture & Rural Affairs: London Band 3 p.41, Real Estate Litigation: London Band 3 p.442

Wood, Benjamin
Profile: p.755
Table(s): Professional Negligence: London Up-and-coming individuals p.421

Wood, Catherine
Table(s): Family: Children: London Band 1 p.245

Wood, Emily
Table(s): Commercial Dispute Resolution: London Band 5 p.110, International Arbitration: General Commercial & Insurance: London Band 2 p.328

Wood, James
Table(s): Crime: London Band 1 p.173

Wood, Martin
Table(s): Family/Matrimonial: North Eastern (Bar) Band 1 p.256

Wood, Michael
Table(s): Public International Law: London Band 1 p.435

Wood, William
Table(s): Mediators: All Circuits Band 1 p.348

Woodcock, Robert
Table(s): Crime: North Eastern (Bar) Band 3 p.184

Woodham, Samantha
Profile: p.755
Table(s): Family: Matrimonial Finance: London Band 4 p.244

Woodhouse, Charles
Profile: p.755
Table(s): Personal Injury: London Band 2 p.368, Personal Injury: Western (Bar) Band 2

Woodward, Alison
Table(s): Family/Matrimonial: Northern (Bar) Band 3 p.258

Woodward, Joanne
Table(s): Employment: Northern (Bar) Band 1 p.221

Woodward-Carlton, Damian
Table(s): **Family: Children:** London **Band 3** p.245

Woolf, Eliot
Profile: p.756
Table(s): **Clinical Negligence:** London **Band 1** p.93, **Personal Injury:** London **Band 1** p.368, **Personal Injury: Industrial Disease:** London p.368, **Travel: International Personal Injury:** London **Band 1** p.495

Woolf, Jeremy
Profile: p.756
Table(s): **Tax:** London **Band 2** p.482

Woolfe, Philip
Profile: p.756
Table(s): **Competition Law:** London **Band 3** p.142, **Telecommunications:** London **Band 2** p.491

Wordsworth, Samuel
Table(s): **International Arbitration: General Commercial & Insurance:** London **Band 4** p.328, **Public International Law:** London **Band 2** p.435

Wormald, Richard
Table(s): **Crime:** London **Band 2** p.174, **Financial Crime:** London **Band 3** p.267

Worsley, Mark
Table(s): **Crime:** Western (Bar) **Band 3** p.192

Worthington, Stephen
Profile: p.756
Table(s): **Personal Injury:** London **Band 1** p.367

Wraight, William
Profile: p.756
Table(s): **Clinical Negligence:** London **Up-and-coming individuals** p.93

Wray, Laura
Profile: p.756
Table(s): **Personal Injury:** Scotland (Bar) **Band 2** p.520

Wright, Alastair
Table(s): **Clinical Negligence:** Northern (Bar) **Band 2** p.103

Wright, Alexander
Profile: p.756
Table(s): **Shipping & Commodities:** London **Band 3** p.465

Wright, Peter
Profile: p.756
Table(s): **Crime:** London **Band 1** p.173

Wright, Peter
Table(s): **Crime:** Northern (Bar) **Band 1** p.186

Wright, Richard
Table(s): **Crime:** North Eastern (Bar) **Band 2** p.184

Wright, Stuart
Table(s): **Commercial Dispute Resolution:** South Eastern (Bar) **Band 2** p.129

Wyand, Roger
Table(s): **Intellectual Property:** London **Band 1** p.322

Wyatt, Derrick
Table(s): **European Law:** London **Band 2** p.237

Wyeth, Stephen
Table(s): **Employment:** Western (Bar) **Up-and-coming individuals** p.223

Wygas, Luke
Profile: p.756
Table(s): **Commercial Dispute Resolution:** London **Band 5** p.110, **Professional Negligence:** London **Band 4** p.421

Wyles, Lucy
Table(s): **Travel: International Personal Injury:** London **Band 2** p.495

Wynn, Toby
Table(s): **Police Law: Mainly Defendant:** All Circuits **Band 2** p.402

Wynne, Ashley
Table(s): **Family/Matrimonial:** Midlands (Bar) **Band 1** p.254

Wynne, James
Profile: p.756
Table(s): **Employment:** London **Band 5** p.208

Wynter, Colin
Table(s): **Insurance:** London **Band 2** p.315

Y

Yang, Zizhen
Profile: p.757
Table(s): **Tax:** London **Band 3** p.482

Yates, David
Profile: p.757
Table(s): **Professional Negligence:** London **Band 4** p.421, **Tax:** London **Band 2** p.482

Yates, Katrina
Table(s): **Real Estate Litigation:** London **Band 5** p.443

Yates, Nicholas
Profile: p.757
Table(s): **Family: Matrimonial Finance:** London **Band 2** p.244

Yeginsu, Can
Profile: p.757
Table(s): **Administrative & Public Law:** London **Band 4** p.28

Yeo, Colin
Profile: p.757
Table(s): **Immigration:** London **Band 3** p.297

Yeo, Nicholas
Table(s): **Crime:** London **Band 3** p.174, **Financial Crime:** London **Band 3** p.267, **POCA Work & Asset Forfeiture:** All Circuits **Band 3** p.397

Yeo, Nik
Profile: p.757
Table(s): **Banking & Finance:** London **Band 4** p.50, **International Arbitration: General Commercial & Insurance:** London **Band 2** p.328, **Professional Negligence:** London **Band 2** p.421

Yip, Amanda
Table(s): **Clinical Negligence:** Northern (Bar) **Band 2** p.103, **Personal Injury:** Northern (Bar) **Band 1** p.380

Young, Andrew
Table(s): **Travel: International Personal Injury:** London **Band 2** p.495

Young, Andrew R W
Profile: p.757
Table(s): **Clinical Negligence:** Scotland (Bar) **Band 2** p.510, **Commercial Dispute Resolution:** Scotland (Bar) **Band 2** p.512, **Personal Injury:** Scotland (Bar) **Band 2** p.520, **Professional Negligence:** Scotland (Bar) **Band 1** p.523, **Tax:** Scotland (Bar) **Band 2** p.527

Young, Christopher
Table(s): **Planning:** Midlands (Bar) **Band 1** p.393

Young, David
Profile: p.757
Table(s): **Crime: International Criminal Law:** London p.175

Young, Timothy
Table(s): **Shipping & Commodities:** London **Band 1** p.465

Z

Zacaroli, Antony
Table(s): **Banking & Finance:** London **Star individuals** p.49, **Chancery: Commercial:** London **Band 1** p.59, **Commercial Dispute Resolution:** London **Band 1** p.109, **Company:** London **Band 1** p.135, **Financial Services:** London **Band 1** p.276, **Restructuring/Insolvency:** London **Star individuals** p.455

Zahir, Hossein
Table(s): **Crime:** London **Up-and-coming individuals** p.174

Zaman, Mohammed
Table(s): **Commercial Dispute Resolution:** Midlands (Bar) **Band 1** p.125

Zeb, Emma
Table(s): **Clinical Negligence:** Western (Bar) **Band 2** p.106, **Personal Injury:** Western (Bar) **Band 3**

Zelin, Geoffrey
Table(s): **Company:** London **Band 3** p.135, **Restructuring/Insolvency:** London **Band 3** p.455

Zellick, Adam
Profile: p.758
Table(s): **Aviation:** London **Band 3** p.47, **Banking & Finance:** London **Band 2** p.50, **Commercial Dispute Resolution:** London **Band 3** p.110, **Fraud: Civil:** London **Band 3** p.282

Zwart, Christiaan
Profile: p.758
Table(s): **Planning:** London **Band 5** p.386